Introductory Statistics

SENIOR CONTRIBUTING AUTHORS
BARBARA ILLOWSKY, DE ANZA COLLEGE
SUSAN DEAN, DE ANZA COLLEGE

ISBN: 978-1-50669-823-6

OpenStax
Rice University
6100 Main Street MS-375
Houston, Texas 77005

To learn more about OpenStax, visit https://openstax.org.
Individual print copies and bulk orders can be purchased through our website.

HARDCOVER BOOK ISBN-13	978-1-938168-20-8
PAPERBACK BOOK ISBN-13	978-1-947172-84-5
B&W PAPERBACK BOOK ISBN-13	978-1-50669-823-6
DIGITAL VERSION ISBN-13	978-1-947172-05-0
ENHANCED TEXTBOOK ISBN-13	978-1-938168-29-1
Revision Number	ST-2013-002(03/18)-LC
Original Publication Year	2013

Printed by

XanEdu

4750 Venture Drive, Suite 400
Ann Arbor, MI 48108
800-562-2147
www.xanedu.com

OPENSTAX

OpenStax provides free, peer-reviewed, openly licensed textbooks for introductory college and Advanced Placement® courses and low-cost, personalized courseware that helps students learn. A nonprofit ed tech initiative based at Rice University, we're committed to helping students access the tools they need to complete their courses and meet their educational goals.

RICE UNIVERSITY

OpenStax, OpenStax CNX, and OpenStax Tutor are initiatives of Rice University. As a leading research university with a distinctive commitment to undergraduate education, Rice University aspires to path-breaking research, unsurpassed teaching, and contributions to the betterment of our world. It seeks to fulfill this mission by cultivating a diverse community of learning and discovery that produces leaders across the spectrum of human endeavor.

FOUNDATION SUPPORT

OpenStax is grateful for the tremendous support of our sponsors. Without their strong engagement, the goal of free access to high-quality textbooks would remain just a dream.

Laura and John Arnold Foundation (LJAF) actively seeks opportunities to invest in organizations and thought leaders that have a sincere interest in implementing fundamental changes that not only yield immediate gains, but also repair broken systems for future generations. LJAF currently focuses its strategic investments on education, criminal justice, research integrity, and public accountability.

The William and Flora Hewlett Foundation has been making grants since 1967 to help solve social and environmental problems at home and around the world. The Foundation concentrates its resources on activities in education, the environment, global development and population, performing arts, and philanthropy, and makes grants to support disadvantaged communities in the San Francisco Bay Area.

Calvin K. Kazanjian was the founder and president of Peter Paul (Almond Joy), Inc. He firmly believed that the more people understood about basic economics the happier and more prosperous they would be. Accordingly, he established the Calvin K. Kazanjian Economics Foundation Inc, in 1949 as a philanthropic, nonpolitical educational organization to support efforts that enhanced economic understanding.

Guided by the belief that every life has equal value, the Bill & Melinda Gates Foundation works to help all people lead healthy, productive lives. In developing countries, it focuses on improving people's health with vaccines and other life-saving tools and giving them the chance to lift themselves out of hunger and extreme poverty. In the United States, it seeks to significantly improve education so that all young people have the opportunity to reach their full potential. Based in Seattle, Washington, the foundation is led by CEO Jeff Raikes and Co-chair William H. Gates Sr., under the direction of Bill and Melinda Gates and Warren Buffett.

The Maxfield Foundation supports projects with potential for high impact in science, education, sustainability, and other areas of social importance.

Our mission at The Michelson 20MM Foundation is to grow access and success by eliminating unnecessary hurdles to affordability. We support the creation, sharing, and proliferation of more effective, more affordable educational content by leveraging disruptive technologies, open educational resources, and new models for collaboration between for-profit, nonprofit, and public entities.

The Bill and Stephanie Sick Fund supports innovative projects in the areas of Education, Art, Science and Engineering.

Table of Contents

Preface 1
Chapter 1: Sampling and Data 5
  1.1 Definitions of Statistics, Probability, and Key Terms 5
  1.2 Data, Sampling, and Variation in Data and Sampling 10
  1.3 Frequency, Frequency Tables, and Levels of Measurement 26
  1.4 Experimental Design and Ethics 35
  1.5 Data Collection Experiment 39
  1.6 Sampling Experiment 41
Chapter 2: Descriptive Statistics 67
  2.1 Stem-and-Leaf Graphs (Stemplots), Line Graphs, and Bar Graphs 68
  2.2 Histograms, Frequency Polygons, and Time Series Graphs 77
  2.3 Measures of the Location of the Data 87
  2.4 Box Plots 96
  2.5 Measures of the Center of the Data 100
  2.6 Skewness and the Mean, Median, and Mode 106
  2.7 Measures of the Spread of the Data 110
  2.8 Descriptive Statistics 120
Chapter 3: Probability Topics 175
  3.1 Terminology 176
  3.2 Independent and Mutually Exclusive Events 181
  3.3 Two Basic Rules of Probability 188
  3.4 Contingency Tables 193
  3.5 Tree and Venn Diagrams 199
  3.6 Probability Topics 209
Chapter 4: Discrete Random Variables 243
  4.1 Probability Distribution Function (PDF) for a Discrete Random Variable 244
  4.2 Mean or Expected Value and Standard Deviation 247
  4.3 Binomial Distribution 253
  4.4 Geometric Distribution 259
  4.5 Hypergeometric Distribution 263
  4.6 Poisson Distribution 266
  4.7 Discrete Distribution (Playing Card Experiment) 271
  4.8 Discrete Distribution (Lucky Dice Experiment) 274
Chapter 5: Continuous Random Variables 311
  5.1 Continuous Probability Functions 313
  5.2 The Uniform Distribution 316
  5.3 The Exponential Distribution 326
  5.4 Continuous Distribution 338
Chapter 6: The Normal Distribution 365
  6.1 The Standard Normal Distribution 366
  6.2 Using the Normal Distribution 371
  6.3 Normal Distribution (Lap Times) 379
  6.4 Normal Distribution (Pinkie Length) 381
Chapter 7: The Central Limit Theorem 399
  7.1 The Central Limit Theorem for Sample Means (Averages) 400
  7.2 The Central Limit Theorem for Sums 405
  7.3 Using the Central Limit Theorem 408
  7.4 Central Limit Theorem (Pocket Change) 417
  7.5 Central Limit Theorem (Cookie Recipes) 420
Chapter 8: Confidence Intervals 443
  8.1 A Single Population Mean using the Normal Distribution 445
  8.2 A Single Population Mean using the Student t Distribution 456
  8.3 A Population Proportion 460
  8.4 Confidence Interval (Home Costs) 467
  8.5 Confidence Interval (Place of Birth) 469
  8.6 Confidence Interval (Women's Heights) 471
Chapter 9: Hypothesis Testing with One Sample 505

9.1 Null and Alternative Hypotheses 506
9.2 Outcomes and the Type I and Type II Errors 508
9.3 Distribution Needed for Hypothesis Testing 510
9.4 Rare Events, the Sample, Decision and Conclusion 511
9.5 Additional Information and Full Hypothesis Test Examples 514
9.6 Hypothesis Testing of a Single Mean and Single Proportion 530
Chapter 10: Hypothesis Testing with Two Samples **567**
10.1 Two Population Means with Unknown Standard Deviations 568
10.2 Two Population Means with Known Standard Deviations 576
10.3 Comparing Two Independent Population Proportions 579
10.4 Matched or Paired Samples 584
10.5 Hypothesis Testing for Two Means and Two Proportions 590
Chapter 11: The Chi-Square Distribution **621**
11.1 Facts About the Chi-Square Distribution 622
11.2 Goodness-of-Fit Test 623
11.3 Test of Independence 633
11.4 Test for Homogeneity 638
11.5 Comparison of the Chi-Square Tests 641
11.6 Test of a Single Variance 641
11.7 Lab 1: Chi-Square Goodness-of-Fit 644
11.8 Lab 2: Chi-Square Test of Independence 648
Chapter 12: Linear Regression and Correlation **679**
12.1 Linear Equations 680
12.2 Scatter Plots 682
12.3 The Regression Equation 685
12.4 Testing the Significance of the Correlation Coefficient 691
12.5 Prediction 696
12.6 Outliers 697
12.7 Regression (Distance from School) 704
12.8 Regression (Textbook Cost) 706
12.9 Regression (Fuel Efficiency) 708
Chapter 13: F Distribution and One-Way ANOVA **743**
13.1 One-Way ANOVA 744
13.2 The F Distribution and the F-Ratio 745
13.3 Facts About the F Distribution 749
13.4 Test of Two Variances 756
13.5 Lab: One-Way ANOVA 759
Appendix A: Review Exercises (Ch 3-13) **785**
Appendix B: Practice Tests (1-4) and Final Exams **813**
Appendix C: Data Sets **869**
Appendix D: Group and Partner Projects **873**
Appendix E: Solution Sheets **879**
Appendix F: Mathematical Phrases, Symbols, and Formulas **883**
Appendix G: Notes for the TI-83, 83+, 84, 84+ Calculators **889**
Appendix H: Tables **901**
Index **903**

PREFACE

Welcome to *Introductory Statistics*, an OpenStax resource. This textbook was written to increase student access to high-quality learning materials, maintaining highest standards of academic rigor at little to no cost.

The foundation of this textbook is *Collaborative Statistics*, by Barbara Illowsky and Susan Dean. Additional topics, examples, and innovations in terminology and practical applications have been added, all with a goal of increasing relevance and accessibility for students.

About OpenStax

OpenStax is a nonprofit based at Rice University, and it's our mission to improve student access to education. Our first openly licensed college textbook was published in 2012, and our library has since scaled to over 25 books for college and AP® courses used by hundreds of thousands of students. OpenStax Tutor, our low-cost personalized learning tool, is being used in college courses throughout the country. Through our partnerships with philanthropic foundations and our alliance with other educational resource organizations, OpenStax is breaking down the most common barriers to learning and empowering students and instructors to succeed.

About OpenStax's resources
Customization

Introductory Statistics is licensed under a Creative Commons Attribution 4.0 International (CC BY) license, which means that you can distribute, remix, and build upon the content, as long as you provide attribution to OpenStax and its content contributors.

Because our books are openly licensed, you are free to use the entire book or pick and choose the sections that are most relevant to the needs of your course. Feel free to remix the content by assigning your students certain chapters and sections in your syllabus, in the order that you prefer. You can even provide a direct link in your syllabus to the sections in the web view of your book.

Instructors also have the option of creating a customized version of their OpenStax book. The custom version can be made available to students in low-cost print or digital form through their campus bookstore. Visit your book page on OpenStax.org for more information.

Errata

All OpenStax textbooks undergo a rigorous review process. However, like any professional-grade textbook, errors sometimes occur. Since our books are web based, we can make updates periodically when deemed pedagogically necessary. If you have a correction to suggest, submit it through the link on your book page on OpenStax.org. Subject matter experts review all errata suggestions. OpenStax is committed to remaining transparent about all updates, so you will also find a list of past errata changes on your book page on OpenStax.org.

Format

You can access this textbook for free in web view or PDF through OpenStax.org, and in low-cost print and iBooks editions.

Coverage and scope

Chapter 1 Sampling and Data
Chapter 2 Descriptive Statistics
Chapter 3 Probability Topics
Chapter 4 Discrete Random Variables
Chapter 5 Continuous Random Variables
Chapter 6 The Normal Distribution
Chapter 7 The Central Limit Theorem
Chapter 8 Confidence Intervals
Chapter 9 Hypothesis Testing with One Sample
Chapter 10 Hypothesis Testing with Two Samples
Chapter 11 The Chi-Square Distribution
Chapter 12 Linear Regression and Correlation
Chapter 13 F Distribution and One-Way ANOVA

Alternate sequencing

Introductory Statistics was conceived and written to fit a particular topical sequence, but it can be used flexibly to accommodate other course structures. One such potential structure, which fits reasonably well with the textbook content, is provided below. Please consider, however, that the chapters were not written to be completely independent, and that the proposed alternate sequence should be carefully considered for student preparation and textual consistency.

Chapter 1 Sampling and Data
Chapter 2 Descriptive Statistics
Chapter 12 Linear Regression and Correlation
Chapter 3 Probability Topics
Chapter 4 Discrete Random Variables
Chapter 5 Continuous Random Variables
Chapter 6 The Normal Distribution
Chapter 7 The Central Limit Theorem
Chapter 8 Confidence Intervals
Chapter 9 Hypothesis Testing with One Sample
Chapter 10 Hypothesis Testing with Two Samples
Chapter 11 The Chi-Square Distribution
Chapter 13 F Distribution and One-Way ANOVA

Pedagogical foundation and features

- **Examples** are placed strategically throughout the text to show students the step-by-step process of interpreting and solving statistical problems. To keep the text relevant for students, the examples are drawn from a broad spectrum of practical topics, including examples about college life and learning, health and medicine, retail and business, and sports and entertainment.

- **Try It** practice problems immediately follow many examples and give students the opportunity to practice as they read the text. **They are usually based on practical and familiar topics, like the Examples themselves**.

- **Collaborative Exercises** provide an in-class scenario for students to work together to explore presented concepts.

- **Using the TI-83, 83+, 84, 84+ Calculator** shows students step-by-step instructions to input problems into their calculator.

- **The Technology Icon** indicates where the use of a TI calculator or computer software is recommended.

- **Practice, Homework, and Bringing It Together** problems give the students problems at various degrees of difficulty while also including real-world scenarios to engage students.

Statistics labs

These innovative activities were developed by Barbara Illowsky and Susan Dean in order to offer students the experience of designing, implementing, and interpreting statistical analyses. They are drawn from actual experiments and data-gathering processes and offer a unique hands-on and collaborative experience. The labs provide a foundation for further learning and classroom interaction that will produce a meaningful application of statistics.

Statistics Labs appear at the end of each chapter and begin with student learning outcomes, general estimates for time on task, and any global implementation notes. Students are then provided with step-by-step guidance, including sample data tables and calculation prompts. The detailed assistance will help the students successfully apply the concepts in the text and lay the groundwork for future collaborative or individual work.

Additional resources
Student and instructor resources

We've compiled additional resources for both students and instructors, including Getting Started Guides, an instructor solution manual, and PowerPoint slides. Instructor resources require a verified instructor account, which you can apply for when you log in or create your account on OpenStax.org. Take advantage of these resources to supplement your OpenStax book.

Community Hubs

OpenStax partners with the Institute for the Study of Knowledge Management in Education (ISKME) to offer Community Hubs on OER Commons – a platform for instructors to share community-created resources that support OpenStax books, free of charge. Through our Community Hubs, instructors can upload their own materials or download resources to use in their own courses, including additional ancillaries, teaching material, multimedia, and relevant course content. We encourage instructors to join the hubs for the subjects most relevant to your teaching and research as an opportunity both to enrich your courses and to engage with other faculty.

To reach the Community Hubs, visit **www.oercommons.org/hubs/OpenStax**.

Partner resources

OpenStax Partners are our allies in the mission to make high-quality learning materials affordable and accessible to students and instructors everywhere. Their tools integrate seamlessly with our OpenStax titles at a low cost. To access the partner resources for your text, visit your book page on OpenStax.org.

About the authors
Senior contributing authors

Barbara Illowsky, De Anza College
Susan Dean, De Anza College

Contributing authors

Birgit Aquilonius, West Valley College
Charles Ashbacher, Upper Iowa University, Cedar Rapids
Abraham Biggs, Broward Community College
Daniel Birmajer, Nazareth College
Roberta Bloom, De Anza College
Bryan Blount, Kentucky Wesleyan College
Ernest Bonat, Portland Community College
Sarah Boslaugh, Kennesaw State University
David Bosworth, Hutchinson Community College
Sheri Boyd, Rollins College
George Bratton, University of Central Arkansas
Jing Chang, College of Saint Mary
Laurel Chiappetta, University of Pittsburgh
Lenore Desilets, De Anza College
Matthew Einsohn, Prescott College
Ann Flanigan, Kapiolani Community College
David French, Tidewater Community College
Mo Geraghty, De Anza College
Larry Green, Lake Tahoe Community College
Michael Greenwich, College of Southern Nevada
Inna Grushko, De Anza College
Valier Hauber, De Anza College
Janice Hector, De Anza College
Jim Helmreich, Marist College
Robert Henderson, Stephen F. Austin State University
Mel Jacobsen, Snow College
Mary Jo Kane, De Anza College
Lynette Kenyon, Collin County Community College
Charles Klein, De Anza College
Alexander Kolovos
Sheldon Lee, Viterbo University
Sara Lenhart, Christopher Newport University
Wendy Lightheart, Lane Community College
Vladimir Logvenenko, De Anza College
Jim Lucas, De Anza College
Lisa Markus, De Anza College
Miriam Masullo, SUNY Purchase
Diane Mathios, De Anza College
Robert McDevitt, Germanna Community College
Mark Mills, Central College
Cindy Moss, Skyline College
Nydia Nelson, St. Petersburg College
Benjamin Ngwudike, Jackson State University
Jonathan Oaks, Macomb Community College

Carol Olmstead, De Anza College
Adam Pennell, Greensboro College
Kathy Plum, De Anza College
Lisa Rosenberg, Elon University
Sudipta Roy, Kankakee Community College
Javier Rueda, De Anza College
Yvonne Sandoval, Pima Community College
Rupinder Sekhon, De Anza College
Travis Short, St. Petersburg College
Frank Snow, De Anza College
Abdulhamid Sukar, Cameron University
Jeffery Taub, Maine Maritime Academy
Mary Teegarden, San Diego Mesa College
John Thomas, College of Lake County
Philip J. Verrecchia, York College of Pennsylvania
Dennis Walsh, Middle Tennessee State University
Cheryl Wartman, University of Prince Edward Island
Carol Weideman, St. Petersburg College
Andrew Wiesner, Pennsylvania State University

1 | SAMPLING AND DATA

Figure 1.1 We encounter statistics in our daily lives more often than we probably realize and from many different sources, like the news. (credit: David Sim)

Introduction

Chapter Objectives
By the end of this chapter, the student should be able to: • Recognize and differentiate between key terms. • Apply various types of sampling methods to data collection. • Create and interpret frequency tables.

You are probably asking yourself the question, "When and where will I use statistics?" If you read any newspaper, watch television, or use the Internet, you will see statistical information. There are statistics about crime, sports, education, politics, and real estate. Typically, when you read a newspaper article or watch a television news program, you are given sample information. With this information, you may make a decision about the correctness of a statement, claim, or "fact." Statistical methods can help you make the "best educated guess."

Since you will undoubtedly be given statistical information at some point in your life, you need to know some techniques for analyzing the information thoughtfully. Think about buying a house or managing a budget. Think about your chosen profession. The fields of economics, business, psychology, education, biology, law, computer science, police science, and early childhood development require at least one course in statistics.

Included in this chapter are the basic ideas and words of probability and statistics. You will soon understand that statistics and probability work together. You will also learn how data are gathered and what "good" data can be distinguished from "bad."

1.1 | Definitions of Statistics, Probability, and Key Terms

The science of **statistics** deals with the collection, analysis, interpretation, and presentation of **data**. We see and use data in our everyday lives.

Collaborative Exercise

In your classroom, try this exercise. Have class members write down the average time (in hours, to the nearest half-hour) they sleep per night. Your instructor will record the data. Then create a simple graph (called a **dot plot**) of the data. A dot plot consists of a number line and dots (or points) positioned above the number line. For example, consider the following data:

5; 5.5; 6; 6; 6; 6.5; 6.5; 6.5; 6.5; 7; 7; 8; 8; 9

The dot plot for this data would be as follows:

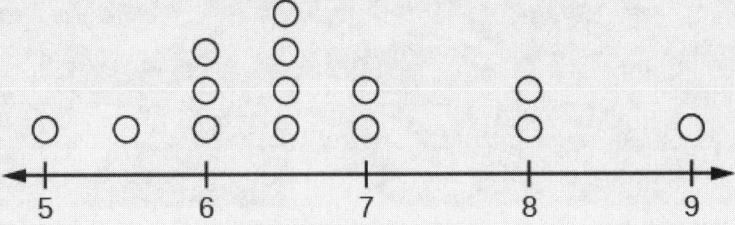

Frequency of Average Time (in Hours) Spent Sleeping per Night

Figure 1.2

Does your dot plot look the same as or different from the example? Why? If you did the same example in an English class with the same number of students, do you think the results would be the same? Why or why not?

Where do your data appear to cluster? How might you interpret the clustering?

The questions above ask you to analyze and interpret your data. With this example, you have begun your study of statistics.

In this course, you will learn how to organize and summarize data. Organizing and summarizing data is called **descriptive statistics**. Two ways to summarize data are by graphing and by using numbers (for example, finding an average). After you have studied probability and probability distributions, you will use formal methods for drawing conclusions from "good" data. The formal methods are called **inferential statistics**. Statistical inference uses probability to determine how confident we can be that our conclusions are correct.

Effective interpretation of data (inference) is based on good procedures for producing data and thoughtful examination of the data. You will encounter what will seem to be too many mathematical formulas for interpreting data. The goal of statistics is not to perform numerous calculations using the formulas, but to gain an understanding of your data. The calculations can be done using a calculator or a computer. The understanding must come from you. If you can thoroughly grasp the basics of statistics, you can be more confident in the decisions you make in life.

Probability

Probability is a mathematical tool used to study randomness. It deals with the chance (the likelihood) of an event occurring. For example, if you toss a **fair** coin four times, the outcomes may not be two heads and two tails. However, if you toss the same coin 4,000 times, the outcomes will be close to half heads and half tails. The expected theoretical probability of heads in any one toss is $\frac{1}{2}$ or 0.5. Even though the outcomes of a few repetitions are uncertain, there is a regular pattern of outcomes when there are many repetitions. After reading about the English statistician Karl **Pearson** who tossed a coin 24,000 times with a result of 12,012 heads, one of the authors tossed a coin 2,000 times. The results were 996 heads. The fraction $\frac{996}{2000}$ is equal to 0.498 which is very close to 0.5, the expected probability.

The theory of probability began with the study of games of chance such as poker. Predictions take the form of probabilities. To predict the likelihood of an earthquake, of rain, or whether you will get an A in this course, we use probabilities. Doctors use probability to determine the chance of a vaccination causing the disease the vaccination is supposed to prevent. A stockbroker uses probability to determine the rate of return on a client's investments. You might use probability to decide to buy a lottery ticket or not. In your study of statistics, you will use the power of mathematics through probability calculations to analyze and interpret your data.

Key Terms

In statistics, we generally want to study a **population**. You can think of a population as a collection of persons, things, or objects under study. To study the population, we select a **sample**. The idea of **sampling** is to select a portion (or subset) of the larger population and study that portion (the sample) to gain information about the population. Data are the result of sampling from a population.

Because it takes a lot of time and money to examine an entire population, sampling is a very practical technique. If you wished to compute the overall grade point average at your school, it would make sense to select a sample of students who attend the school. The data collected from the sample would be the students' grade point averages. In presidential elections, opinion poll samples of 1,000–2,000 people are taken. The opinion poll is supposed to represent the views of the people in the entire country. Manufacturers of canned carbonated drinks take samples to determine if a 16 ounce can contains 16 ounces of carbonated drink.

From the sample data, we can calculate a statistic. A **statistic** is a number that represents a property of the sample. For example, if we consider one math class to be a sample of the population of all math classes, then the average number of points earned by students in that one math class at the end of the term is an example of a statistic. The statistic is an estimate of a population parameter. A **parameter** is a numerical characteristic of the whole population that can be estimated by a statistic. Since we considered all math classes to be the population, then the average number of points earned per student over all the math classes is an example of a parameter.

One of the main concerns in the field of statistics is how accurately a statistic estimates a parameter. The accuracy really depends on how well the sample represents the population. The sample must contain the characteristics of the population in order to be a **representative sample**. We are interested in both the sample statistic and the population parameter in inferential statistics. In a later chapter, we will use the sample statistic to test the validity of the established population parameter.

A **variable**, usually notated by capital letters such as X and Y, is a characteristic or measurement that can be determined for each member of a population. Variables may be **numerical** or **categorical**. **Numerical variables** take on values with equal units such as weight in pounds and time in hours. **Categorical variables** place the person or thing into a category. If we let X equal the number of points earned by one math student at the end of a term, then X is a numerical variable. If we let Y be a person's party affiliation, then some examples of Y include Republican, Democrat, and Independent. Y is a categorical variable. We could do some math with values of X (calculate the average number of points earned, for example), but it makes no sense to do math with values of Y (calculating an average party affiliation makes no sense).

Data are the actual values of the variable. They may be numbers or they may be words. **Datum** is a single value.

Two words that come up often in statistics are **mean** and **proportion**. If you were to take three exams in your math classes and obtain scores of 86, 75, and 92, you would calculate your mean score by adding the three exam scores and dividing by three (your mean score would be 84.3 to one decimal place). If, in your math class, there are 40 students and 22 are men and 18 are women, then the proportion of men students is $\frac{22}{40}$ and the proportion of women students is $\frac{18}{40}$. Mean and proportion are discussed in more detail in later chapters.

NOTE

The words "**mean**" and "**average**" are often used interchangeably. The substitution of one word for the other is common practice. The technical term is "arithmetic mean," and "average" is technically a center location. However, in practice among non-statisticians, "average" is commonly accepted for "arithmetic mean."

Example 1.1

Determine what the key terms refer to in the following study. We want to know the average (mean) amount of money first year college students spend at ABC College on school supplies that do not include books. We randomly surveyed 100 first year students at the college. Three of those students spent $150, $200, and $225, respectively.

Solution 1.1

The **population** is all first year students attending ABC College this term.

The **sample** could be all students enrolled in one section of a beginning statistics course at ABC College (although this sample may not represent the entire population).

The **parameter** is the average (mean) amount of money spent (excluding books) by first year college students at ABC College this term.

The **statistic** is the average (mean) amount of money spent (excluding books) by first year college students in the sample.

The **variable** could be the amount of money spent (excluding books) by one first year student. Let X = the amount of money spent (excluding books) by one first year student attending ABC College.

The **data** are the dollar amounts spent by the first year students. Examples of the data are $150, $200, and $225.

Try It Σ

1.1 Determine what the key terms refer to in the following study. We want to know the average (mean) amount of money spent on school uniforms each year by families with children at Knoll Academy. We randomly survey 100 families with children in the school. Three of the families spent $65, $75, and $95, respectively.

Example 1.2

Determine what the key terms refer to in the following study.

A study was conducted at a local college to analyze the average cumulative GPA's of students who graduated last year. Fill in the letter of the phrase that best describes each of the items below.

1. Population_____   2. Statistic _____   3. Parameter _____   4. Sample _____   5. Variable _____   6. Data _____

a) all students who attended the college last year
b) the cumulative GPA of one student who graduated from the college last year
c) 3.65, 2.80, 1.50, 3.90
d) a group of students who graduated from the college last year, randomly selected
e) the average cumulative GPA of students who graduated from the college last year
f) all students who graduated from the college last year
g) the average cumulative GPA of students in the study who graduated from the college last year

Solution 1.2
1. f; 2. g; 3. e; 4. d; 5. b; 6. c

Example 1.3

Determine what the key terms refer to in the following study.

As part of a study designed to test the safety of automobiles, the National Transportation Safety Board collected and reviewed data about the effects of an automobile crash on test dummies. Here is the criterion they used:

Speed at which Cars Crashed	Location of "drive" (i.e. dummies)
35 miles/hour	Front Seat

Table 1.1

Cars with dummies in the front seats were crashed into a wall at a speed of 35 miles per hour. We want to know the proportion of dummies in the driver's seat that would have had head injuries, if they had been actual drivers. We start with a simple random sample of 75 cars.

Solution 1.3

The **population** is all cars containing dummies in the front seat.

The **sample** is the 75 cars, selected by a simple random sample.

The **parameter** is the proportion of driver dummies (if they had been real people) who would have suffered head injuries in the population.

The **statistic** is proportion of driver dummies (if they had been real people) who would have suffered head injuries in the sample.

The **variable** X = the number of driver dummies (if they had been real people) who would have suffered head injuries.

The **data** are either: yes, had head injury, or no, did not.

Example 1.4

Determine what the key terms refer to in the following study.

An insurance company would like to determine the proportion of all medical doctors who have been involved in one or more malpractice lawsuits. The company selects 500 doctors at random from a professional directory and determines the number in the sample who have been involved in a malpractice lawsuit.

Solution 1.4

The **population** is all medical doctors listed in the professional directory.

The **parameter** is the proportion of medical doctors who have been involved in one or more malpractice suits in the population.

The **sample** is the 500 doctors selected at random from the professional directory.

The **statistic** is the proportion of medical doctors who have been involved in one or more malpractice suits in the sample.

The **variable** X = the number of medical doctors who have been involved in one or more malpractice suits.

The **data** are either: yes, was involved in one or more malpractice lawsuits, or no, was not.

Collaborative Exercise

Do the following exercise collaboratively with up to four people per group. Find a population, a sample, the parameter, the statistic, a variable, and data for the following study: You want to determine the average (mean) number of glasses of milk college students drink per day. Suppose yesterday, in your English class, you asked five students how many glasses of milk they drank the day before. The answers were 1, 0, 1, 3, and 4 glasses of milk.

1.2 | Data, Sampling, and Variation in Data and Sampling

Data may come from a population or from a sample. Lowercase letters like x or y generally are used to represent data values. Most data can be put into the following categories:

- Qualitative
- Quantitative

Qualitative data are the result of categorizing or describing attributes of a population. Qualitative data are also often called **categorical data**. Hair color, blood type, ethnic group, the car a person drives, and the street a person lives on are examples of qualitative data. Qualitative data are generally described by words or letters. For instance, hair color might be black, dark brown, light brown, blonde, gray, or red. Blood type might be AB+, O-, or B+. Researchers often prefer to use quantitative data over qualitative data because it lends itself more easily to mathematical analysis. For example, it does not make sense to find an average hair color or blood type.

Quantitative data are always numbers. Quantitative data are the result of **counting** or **measuring** attributes of a population. Amount of money, pulse rate, weight, number of people living in your town, and number of students who take statistics are examples of quantitative data. Quantitative data may be either **discrete** or **continuous**.

All data that are the result of counting are called **quantitative discrete data**. These data take on only certain numerical values. If you count the number of phone calls you receive for each day of the week, you might get values such as zero, one, two, or three.

Data that are not only made up of counting numbers, but that may include fractions, decimals, or irrational numbers, are called **quantitative continuous data**. Continuous data are often the results of measurements like lengths, weights, or times. A list of the lengths in minutes for all the phone calls that you make in a week, with numbers like 2.4, 7.5, or 11.0, would be quantitative continuous data.

Example 1.5 Data Sample of Quantitative Discrete Data

The data are the number of books students carry in their backpacks. You sample five students. Two students carry three books, one student carries four books, one student carries two books, and one student carries one book. The numbers of books (three, four, two, and one) are the quantitative discrete data.

Try It Σ

1.5 The data are the number of machines in a gym. You sample five gyms. One gym has 12 machines, one gym has 15 machines, one gym has ten machines, one gym has 22 machines, and the other gym has 20 machines. What type of data is this?

Example 1.6 Data Sample of Quantitative Continuous Data

The data are the weights of backpacks with books in them. You sample the same five students. The weights (in pounds) of their backpacks are 6.2, 7, 6.8, 9.1, 4.3. Notice that backpacks carrying three books can have different weights. Weights are quantitative continuous data.

Try It Σ

1.6 The data are the areas of lawns in square feet. You sample five houses. The areas of the lawns are 144 sq. feet, 160 sq. feet, 190 sq. feet, 180 sq. feet, and 210 sq. feet. What type of data is this?

Example 1.7

You go to the supermarket and purchase three cans of soup (19 ounces tomato bisque, 14.1 ounces lentil, and 19 ounces Italian wedding), two packages of nuts (walnuts and peanuts), four different kinds of vegetable (broccoli, cauliflower, spinach, and carrots), and two desserts (16 ounces pistachio ice cream and 32 ounces chocolate chip cookies).

Name data sets that are quantitative discrete, quantitative continuous, and qualitative.

Solution 1.7

One Possible Solution:

- The three cans of soup, two packages of nuts, four kinds of vegetables and two desserts are quantitative discrete data because you count them.

- The weights of the soups (19 ounces, 14.1 ounces, 19 ounces) are quantitative continuous data because you measure weights as precisely as possible.

- Types of soups, nuts, vegetables and desserts are qualitative data because they are categorical.

Try to identify additional data sets in this example.

Example 1.8

The data are the colors of backpacks. Again, you sample the same five students. One student has a red backpack, two students have black backpacks, one student has a green backpack, and one student has a gray backpack. The colors red, black, black, green, and gray are qualitative data.

Try It Σ

1.8 The data are the colors of houses. You sample five houses. The colors of the houses are white, yellow, white, red, and white. What type of data is this?

NOTE

You may collect data as numbers and report it categorically. For example, the quiz scores for each student are recorded throughout the term. At the end of the term, the quiz scores are reported as A, B, C, D, or F.

Example 1.9

Work collaboratively to determine the correct data type (quantitative or qualitative). Indicate whether quantitative data are continuous or discrete. Hint: Data that are discrete often start with the words "the number of."

a. the number of pairs of shoes you own

b. the type of car you drive

c. the distance it is from your home to the nearest grocery store

d. the number of classes you take per school year.

e. the type of calculator you use

f. weights of sumo wrestlers

g. number of correct answers on a quiz

h. IQ scores (This may cause some discussion.)

Solution 1.9

Items a, d, and g are quantitative discrete; items c, f, and h are quantitative continuous; items b and e are qualitative, or categorical.

1.9 Determine the correct data type (quantitative or qualitative) for the number of cars in a parking lot. Indicate whether quantitative data are continuous or discrete.

Example 1.10

A statistics professor collects information about the classification of her students as freshmen, sophomores, juniors, or seniors. The data she collects are summarized in the pie chart **Figure 1.2**. What type of data does this graph show?

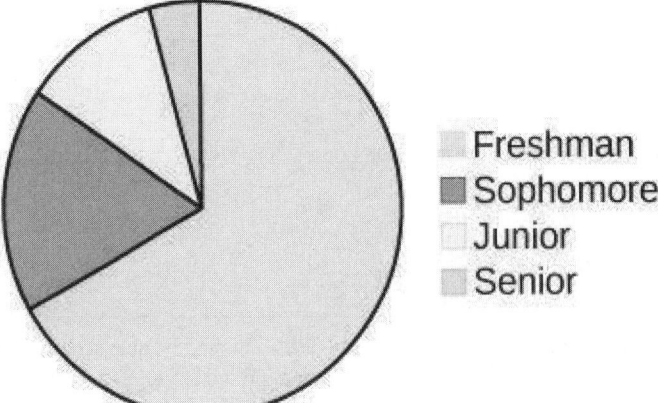

Figure 1.3

Solution 1.10
This pie chart shows the students in each year, which is **qualitative (or categorical) data**.

Try It Σ

1.10 The registrar at State University keeps records of the number of credit hours students complete each semester. The data he collects are summarized in the histogram. The class boundaries are 10 to less than 13, 13 to less than 16, 16 to less than 19, 19 to less than 22, and 22 to less than 25.

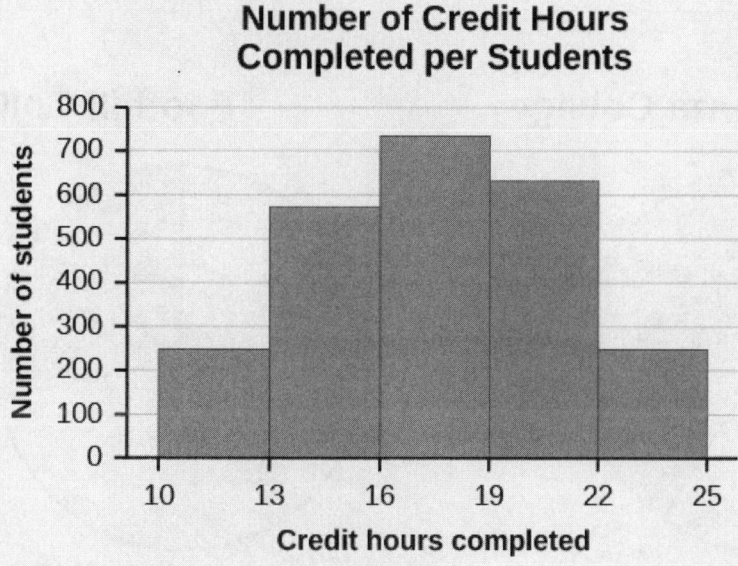

Figure 1.4

What type of data does this graph show?

Qualitative Data Discussion

Below are tables comparing the number of part-time and full-time students at De Anza College and Foothill College enrolled for the spring 2010 quarter. The tables display counts (frequencies) and percentages or proportions (relative frequencies). The percent columns make comparing the same categories in the colleges easier. Displaying percentages along with the numbers is often helpful, but it is particularly important when comparing sets of data that do not have the same totals, such as the total enrollments for both colleges in this example. Notice how much larger the percentage for part-time students at Foothill College is compared to De Anza College.

De Anza College				Foothill College		
	Number	Percent			Number	Percent
Full-time	9,200	40.9%		Full-time	4,059	28.6%
Part-time	13,296	59.1%		Part-time	10,124	71.4%
Total	22,496	100%		Total	14,183	100%

Table 1.2 Fall Term 2007 (Census day)

Tables are a good way of organizing and displaying data. But graphs can be even more helpful in understanding the data. There are no strict rules concerning which graphs to use. Two graphs that are used to display qualitative data are pie charts and bar graphs.

In a **pie chart**, categories of data are represented by wedges in a circle and are proportional in size to the percent of individuals in each category.

In a **bar graph**, the length of the bar for each category is proportional to the number or percent of individuals in each category. Bars may be vertical or horizontal.

A **Pareto chart** consists of bars that are sorted into order by category size (largest to smallest).

Look at **Figure 1.5** and **Figure 1.6** and determine which graph (pie or bar) you think displays the comparisons better.

It is a good idea to look at a variety of graphs to see which is the most helpful in displaying the data. We might make different choices of what we think is the "best" graph depending on the data and the context. Our choice also depends on what we are using the data for.

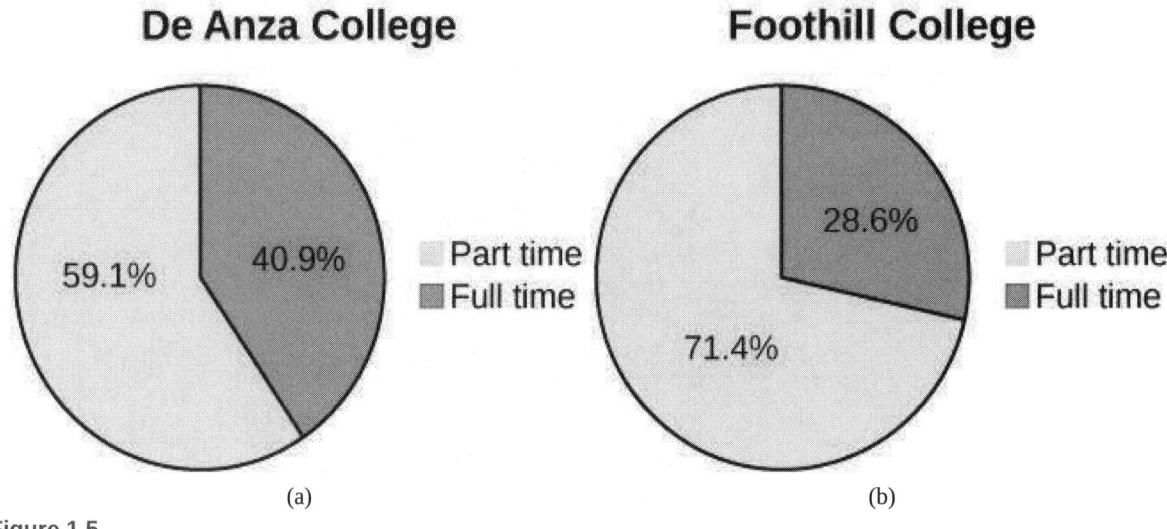

Figure 1.5

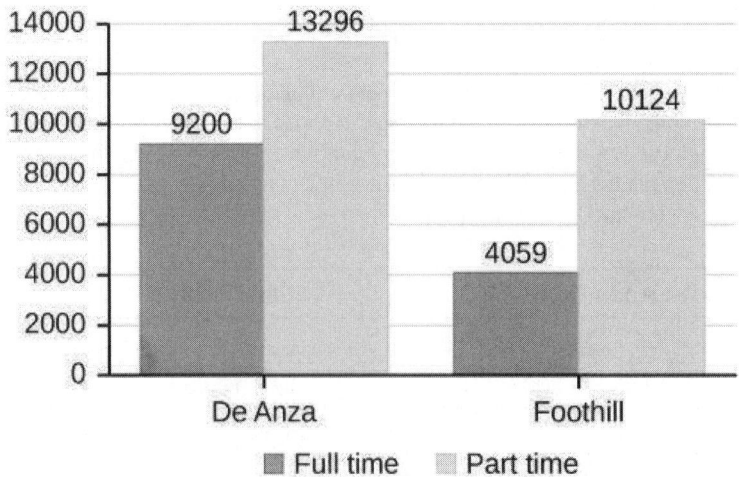

Figure 1.6

Percentages That Add to More (or Less) Than 100%

Sometimes percentages add up to be more than 100% (or less than 100%). In the graph, the percentages add to more than 100% because students can be in more than one category. A bar graph is appropriate to compare the relative size of the categories. A pie chart cannot be used. It also could not be used if the percentages added to less than 100%.

Characteristic/Category	Percent
Full-Time Students	40.9%
Students who intend to transfer to a 4-year educational institution	48.6%
Students under age 25	61.0%
TOTAL	150.5%

Table 1.3 De Anza College Spring 2010

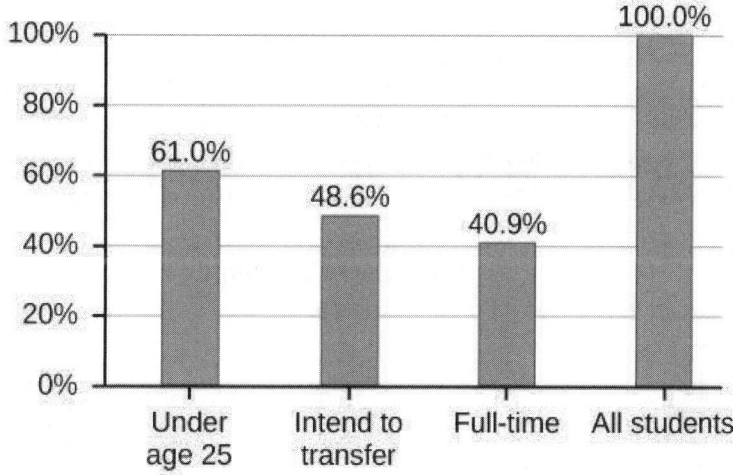

Figure 1.7

Omitting Categories/Missing Data

The table displays Ethnicity of Students but is missing the "Other/Unknown" category. This category contains people who did not feel they fit into any of the ethnicity categories or declined to respond. Notice that the frequencies do not add up to the total number of students. In this situation, create a bar graph and not a pie chart.

	Frequency	Percent
Asian	8,794	36.1%
Black	1,412	5.8%
Filipino	1,298	5.3%
Hispanic	4,180	17.1%
Native American	146	0.6%
Pacific Islander	236	1.0%
White	5,978	24.5%
TOTAL	22,044 out of 24,382	90.4% out of 100%

Table 1.4 Ethnicity of Students at De Anza College Fall Term 2007 (Census Day)

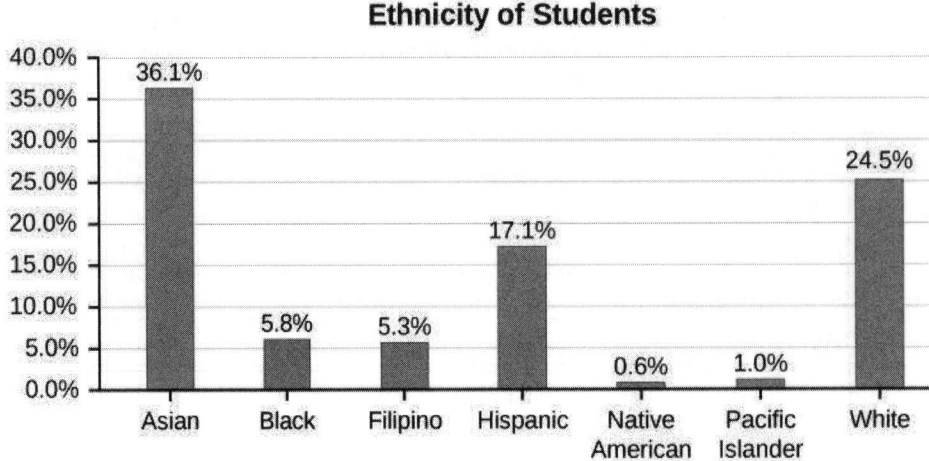

Figure 1.8

The following graph is the same as the previous graph but the "Other/Unknown" percent (9.6%) has been included. The "Other/Unknown" category is large compared to some of the other categories (Native American, 0.6%, Pacific Islander 1.0%). This is important to know when we think about what the data are telling us.

This particular bar graph in **Figure 1.9** can be difficult to understand visually. The graph in **Figure 1.10** is a Pareto chart. The Pareto chart has the bars sorted from largest to smallest and is easier to read and interpret.

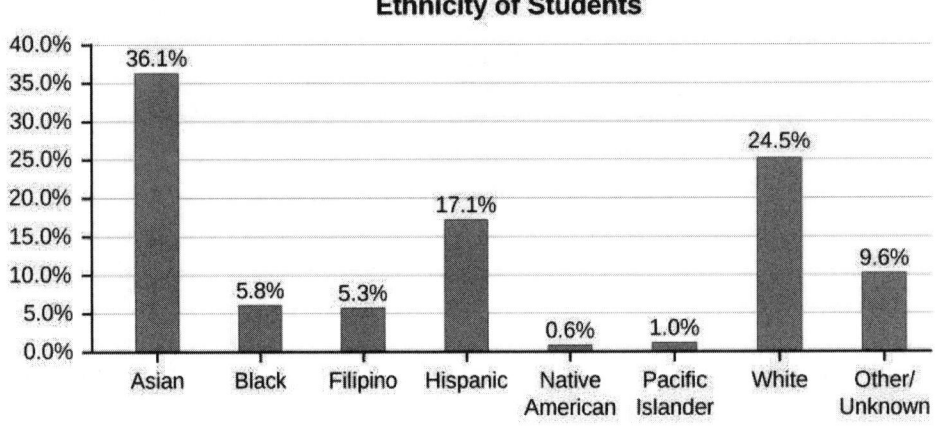

Figure 1.9 Bar Graph with Other/Unknown Category

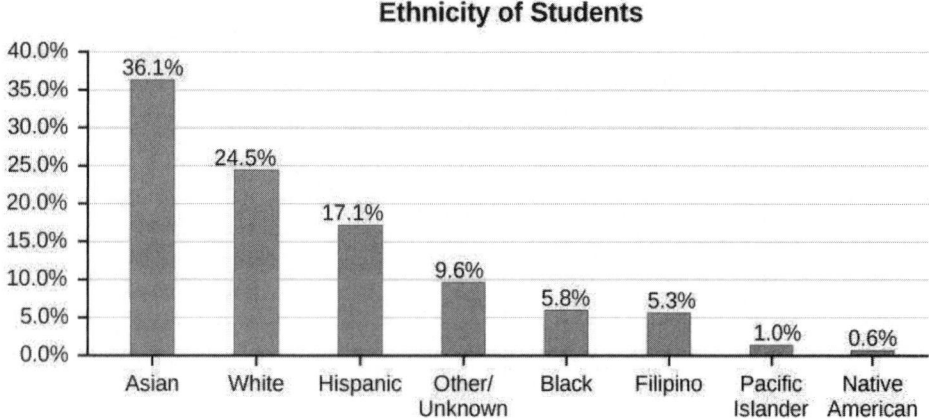

Figure 1.10 Pareto Chart With Bars Sorted by Size

Pie Charts: No Missing Data

The following pie charts have the "Other/Unknown" category included (since the percentages must add to 100%). The chart in **Figure 1.11b** is organized by the size of each wedge, which makes it a more visually informative graph than the unsorted, alphabetical graph in **Figure 1.11a**.

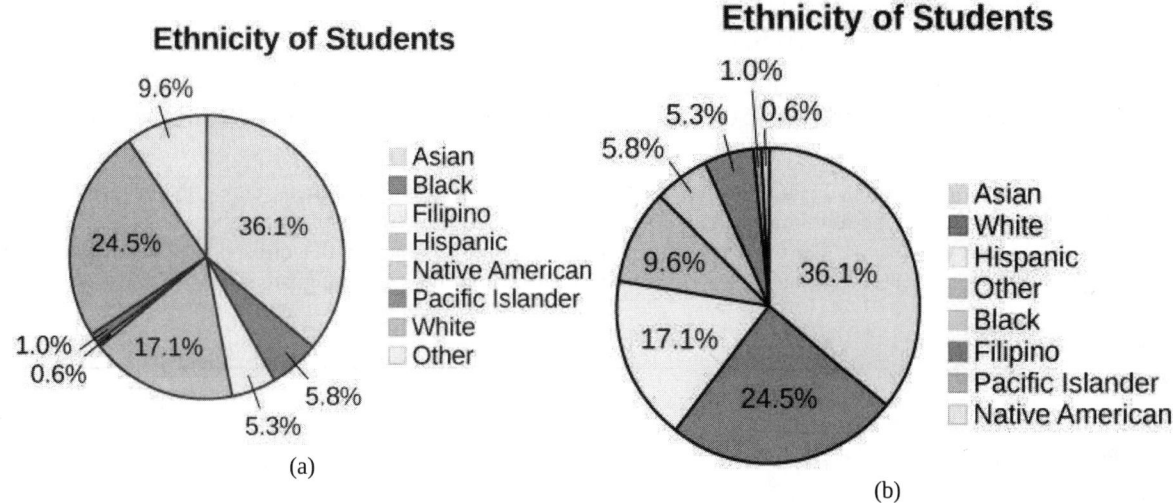

Figure 1.11

Sampling

Gathering information about an entire population often costs too much or is virtually impossible. Instead, we use a sample of the population. **A sample should have the same characteristics as the population it is representing.** Most statisticians use various methods of random sampling in an attempt to achieve this goal. This section will describe a few of the most common methods. There are several different methods of **random sampling**. In each form of random sampling, each member of a population initially has an equal chance of being selected for the sample. Each method has pros and cons. The easiest method to describe is called a **simple random sample**. Any group of n individuals is equally likely to be chosen as any other group of n individuals if the simple random sampling technique is used. In other words, each sample of the same size has an equal chance of being selected. For example, suppose Lisa wants to form a four-person study group (herself and three other people) from her pre-calculus class, which has 31 members not including Lisa. To choose a simple random sample of size three from the other members of her class, Lisa could put all 31 names in a hat, shake the hat, close her eyes, and pick out three names. A more technological way is for Lisa to first list the last names of the members of her class together with a two-digit number, as in **Table 1.5**:

ID	Name	ID	Name	ID	Name
00	Anselmo	11	King	21	Roquero
01	Bautista	12	Legeny	22	Roth
02	Bayani	13	Lundquist	23	Rowell
03	Cheng	14	Macierz	24	Salangsang
04	Cuarismo	15	Motogawa	25	Slade
05	Cuningham	16	Okimoto	26	Stratcher
06	Fontecha	17	Patel	27	Tallai
07	Hong	18	Price	28	Tran
08	Hoobler	19	Quizon	29	Wai
09	Jiao	20	Reyes	30	Wood
10	Khan				

Table 1.5 Class Roster

Lisa can use a table of random numbers (found in many statistics books and mathematical handbooks), a calculator, or a computer to generate random numbers. For this example, suppose Lisa chooses to generate random numbers from a calculator. The numbers generated are as follows:

0.94360; 0.99832; 0.14669; 0.51470; 0.40581; 0.73381; 0.04399

Lisa reads two-digit groups until she has chosen three class members (that is, she reads 0.94360 as the groups 94, 43, 36, 60). Each random number may only contribute one class member. If she needed to, Lisa could have generated more random numbers.

The random numbers 0.94360 and 0.99832 do not contain appropriate two digit numbers. However the third random number, 0.14669, contains 14 (the fourth random number also contains 14), the fifth random number contains 05, and the seventh random number contains 04. The two-digit number 14 corresponds to Macierz, 05 corresponds to Cuningham, and 04 corresponds to Cuarismo. Besides herself, Lisa's group will consist of Marcierz, Cuningham, and Cuarismo.

 Using the TI-83, 83+, 84, 84+ Calculator

To generate random numbers:

- Press MATH.
- Arrow over to PRB.
- Press 5:randInt(. Enter 0, 30).
- Press ENTER for the first random number.
- Press ENTER two more times for the other 2 random numbers. If there is a repeat press ENTER again.

Note: randInt(0, 30, 3) will generate 3 random numbers.

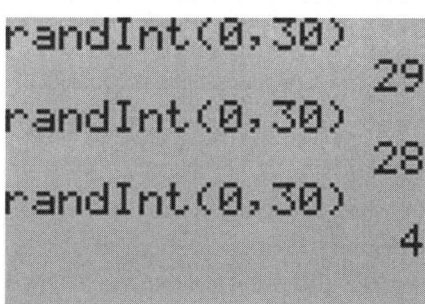

Figure 1.12

Besides simple random sampling, there are other forms of sampling that involve a chance process for getting the sample. **Other well-known random sampling methods are the stratified sample, the cluster sample, and the systematic sample.**

To choose a **stratified sample**, divide the population into groups called strata and then take a **proportionate** number from each stratum. For example, you could stratify (group) your college population by department and then choose a proportionate simple random sample from each stratum (each department) to get a stratified random sample. To choose a simple random sample from each department, number each member of the first department, number each member of the second department, and do the same for the remaining departments. Then use simple random sampling to choose proportionate numbers from the first department and do the same for each of the remaining departments. Those numbers picked from the first department, picked from the second department, and so on represent the members who make up the stratified sample.

To choose a **cluster sample**, divide the population into clusters (groups) and then randomly select some of the clusters. All the members from these clusters are in the cluster sample. For example, if you randomly sample four departments from your college population, the four departments make up the cluster sample. Divide your college faculty by department. The departments are the clusters. Number each department, and then choose four different numbers using simple random sampling. All members of the four departments with those numbers are the cluster sample.

To choose a **systematic sample**, randomly select a starting point and take every n^{th} piece of data from a listing of the population. For example, suppose you have to do a phone survey. Your phone book contains 20,000 residence listings. You must choose 400 names for the sample. Number the population 1–20,000 and then use a simple random sample to pick a number that represents the first name in the sample. Then choose every fiftieth name thereafter until you have a total of 400 names (you might have to go back to the beginning of your phone list). Systematic sampling is frequently chosen because it is a simple method.

A type of sampling that is non-random is convenience sampling. **Convenience sampling** involves using results that are readily available. For example, a computer software store conducts a marketing study by interviewing potential customers who happen to be in the store browsing through the available software. The results of convenience sampling may be very good in some cases and highly biased (favor certain outcomes) in others.

Sampling data should be done very carefully. Collecting data carelessly can have devastating results. Surveys mailed to households and then returned may be very biased (they may favor a certain group). It is better for the person conducting the survey to select the sample respondents.

True random sampling is done **with replacement**. That is, once a member is picked, that member goes back into the population and thus may be chosen more than once. However for practical reasons, in most populations, simple random sampling is done **without replacement**. Surveys are typically done without replacement. That is, a member of the population may be chosen only once. Most samples are taken from large populations and the sample tends to be small in comparison to the population. Since this is the case, sampling without replacement is approximately the same as sampling with replacement because the chance of picking the same individual more than once with replacement is very low.

In a college population of 10,000 people, suppose you want to pick a sample of 1,000 randomly for a survey. **For any particular sample of 1,000**, if you are sampling **with replacement**,

- the chance of picking the first person is 1,000 out of 10,000 (0.1000);

- the chance of picking a different second person for this sample is 999 out of 10,000 (0.0999);

- the chance of picking the same person again is 1 out of 10,000 (very low).

If you are sampling **without replacement**,

- the chance of picking the first person for any particular sample is 1000 out of 10,000 (0.1000);
- the chance of picking a different second person is 999 out of 9,999 (0.0999);
- you do not replace the first person before picking the next person.

Compare the fractions 999/10,000 and 999/9,999. For accuracy, carry the decimal answers to four decimal places. To four decimal places, these numbers are equivalent (0.0999).

Sampling without replacement instead of sampling with replacement becomes a mathematical issue only when the population is small. For example, if the population is 25 people, the sample is ten, and you are sampling **with replacement for any particular sample**, then the chance of picking the first person is ten out of 25, and the chance of picking a different second person is nine out of 25 (you replace the first person).

If you sample **without replacement**, then the chance of picking the first person is ten out of 25, and then the chance of picking the second person (who is different) is nine out of 24 (you do not replace the first person).

Compare the fractions 9/25 and 9/24. To four decimal places, 9/25 = 0.3600 and 9/24 = 0.3750. To four decimal places, these numbers are not equivalent.

When you analyze data, it is important to be aware of **sampling errors** and nonsampling errors. The actual process of sampling causes sampling errors. For example, the sample may not be large enough. Factors not related to the sampling process cause **nonsampling errors**. A defective counting device can cause a nonsampling error.

In reality, a sample will never be exactly representative of the population so there will always be some sampling error. As a rule, the larger the sample, the smaller the sampling error.

In statistics, **a sampling bias** is created when a sample is collected from a population and some members of the population are not as likely to be chosen as others (remember, each member of the population should have an equally likely chance of being chosen). When a sampling bias happens, there can be incorrect conclusions drawn about the population that is being studied.

Critical Evaluation

We need to evaluate the statistical studies we read about critically and analyze them before accepting the results of the studies. Common problems to be aware of include

- Problems with samples: A sample must be representative of the population. A sample that is not representative of the population is biased. Biased samples that are not representative of the population give results that are inaccurate and not valid.
- Self-selected samples: Responses only by people who choose to respond, such as call-in surveys, are often unreliable.
- Sample size issues: Samples that are too small may be unreliable. Larger samples are better, if possible. In some situations, having small samples is unavoidable and can still be used to draw conclusions. Examples: crash testing cars or medical testing for rare conditions
- Undue influence: collecting data or asking questions in a way that influences the response
- Non-response or refusal of subject to participate: The collected responses may no longer be representative of the population. Often, people with strong positive or negative opinions may answer surveys, which can affect the results.
- Causality: A relationship between two variables does not mean that one causes the other to occur. They may be related (correlated) because of their relationship through a different variable.
- Self-funded or self-interest studies: A study performed by a person or organization in order to support their claim. Is the study impartial? Read the study carefully to evaluate the work. Do not automatically assume that the study is good, but do not automatically assume the study is bad either. Evaluate it on its merits and the work done.
- Misleading use of data: improperly displayed graphs, incomplete data, or lack of context
- Confounding: When the effects of multiple factors on a response cannot be separated. Confounding makes it difficult or impossible to draw valid conclusions about the effect of each factor.

COLLABORATIVE EXERCISE

As a class, determine whether or not the following samples are representative. If they are not, discuss the reasons.

1. To find the average GPA of all students in a university, use all honor students at the university as the sample.

2. To find out the most popular cereal among young people under the age of ten, stand outside a large supermarket for three hours and speak to every twentieth child under age ten who enters the supermarket.

3. To find the average annual income of all adults in the United States, sample U.S. congressmen. Create a cluster sample by considering each state as a stratum (group). By using simple random sampling, select states to be part of the cluster. Then survey every U.S. congressman in the cluster.

4. To determine the proportion of people taking public transportation to work, survey 20 people in New York City. Conduct the survey by sitting in Central Park on a bench and interviewing every person who sits next to you.

5. To determine the average cost of a two-day stay in a hospital in Massachusetts, survey 100 hospitals across the state using simple random sampling.

Example 1.11

A study is done to determine the average tuition that San Jose State undergraduate students pay per semester. Each student in the following samples is asked how much tuition he or she paid for the Fall semester. What is the type of sampling in each case?

a. A sample of 100 undergraduate San Jose State students is taken by organizing the students' names by classification (freshman, sophomore, junior, or senior), and then selecting 25 students from each.

b. A random number generator is used to select a student from the alphabetical listing of all undergraduate students in the Fall semester. Starting with that student, every 50th student is chosen until 75 students are included in the sample.

c. A completely random method is used to select 75 students. Each undergraduate student in the fall semester has the same probability of being chosen at any stage of the sampling process.

d. The freshman, sophomore, junior, and senior years are numbered one, two, three, and four, respectively. A random number generator is used to pick two of those years. All students in those two years are in the sample.

e. An administrative assistant is asked to stand in front of the library one Wednesday and to ask the first 100 undergraduate students he encounters what they paid for tuition the Fall semester. Those 100 students are the sample.

Solution 1.11
a. stratified; b. systematic; c. simple random; d. cluster; e. convenience

1.11 You are going to use the random number generator to generate different types of samples from the data.

This table displays six sets of quiz scores (each quiz counts 10 points) for an elementary statistics class.

#1	#2	#3	#4	#5	#6
5	7	10	9	8	3
10	5	9	8	7	6
9	10	8	6	7	9
9	10	10	9	8	9
7	8	9	5	7	4
9	9	9	10	8	7
7	7	10	9	8	8
8	8	9	10	8	8
9	7	8	7	7	8
8	8	10	9	8	7

Table 1.6

Instructions: Use the Random Number Generator to pick samples.

1. Create a stratified sample by column. Pick three quiz scores randomly from each column.
   - Number each row one through ten.
   - On your calculator, press Math and arrow over to PRB.
   - For column 1, Press 5:randInt(and enter 1,10). Press ENTER. Record the number. Press ENTER 2 more times (even the repeats). Record these numbers. Record the three quiz scores in column one that correspond to these three numbers.
   - Repeat for columns two through six.
   - These 18 quiz scores are a stratified sample.

2. Create a cluster sample by picking two of the columns. Use the column numbers: one through six.
   - Press MATH and arrow over to PRB.
   - Press 5:randInt(and enter 1,6). Press ENTER. Record the number. Press ENTER and record that number.
   - The two numbers are for two of the columns.
   - The quiz scores (20 of them) in these 2 columns are the cluster sample.

3. Create a simple random sample of 15 quiz scores.
   - Use the numbering one through 60.
   - Press MATH. Arrow over to PRB. Press 5:randInt(and enter 1, 60).
   - Press ENTER 15 times and record the numbers.
   - Record the quiz scores that correspond to these numbers.
   - These 15 quiz scores are the systematic sample.

4. Create a systematic sample of 12 quiz scores.
   - Use the numbering one through 60.

- ◦ Press MATH. Arrow over to PRB. Press 5:randInt(and enter 1, 60).
- ◦ Press ENTER. Record the number and the first quiz score. From that number, count ten quiz scores and record that quiz score. Keep counting ten quiz scores and recording the quiz score until you have a sample of 12 quiz scores. You may wrap around (go back to the beginning).

Example 1.12

Determine the type of sampling used (simple random, stratified, systematic, cluster, or convenience).

a. A soccer coach selects six players from a group of boys aged eight to ten, seven players from a group of boys aged 11 to 12, and three players from a group of boys aged 13 to 14 to form a recreational soccer team.

b. A pollster interviews all human resource personnel in five different high tech companies.

c. A high school educational researcher interviews 50 high school female teachers and 50 high school male teachers.

d. A medical researcher interviews every third cancer patient from a list of cancer patients at a local hospital.

e. A high school counselor uses a computer to generate 50 random numbers and then picks students whose names correspond to the numbers.

f. A student interviews classmates in his algebra class to determine how many pairs of jeans a student owns, on the average.

Solution 1.12
a. stratified; b. cluster; c. stratified; d. systematic; e. simple random; f.convenience

1.12 Determine the type of sampling used (simple random, stratified, systematic, cluster, or convenience).

A high school principal polls 50 freshmen, 50 sophomores, 50 juniors, and 50 seniors regarding policy changes for after school activities.

If we were to examine two samples representing the same population, even if we used random sampling methods for the samples, they would not be exactly the same. Just as there is variation in data, there is variation in samples. As you become accustomed to sampling, the variability will begin to seem natural.

Example 1.13

Suppose ABC College has 10,000 part-time students (the population). We are interested in the average amount of money a part-time student spends on books in the fall term. Asking all 10,000 students is an almost impossible task.

Suppose we take two different samples.

First, we use convenience sampling and survey ten students from a first term organic chemistry class. Many of these students are taking first term calculus in addition to the organic chemistry class. The amount of money they spend on books is as follows:

$128; $87; $173; $116; $130; $204; $147; $189; $93; $153

The second sample is taken using a list of senior citizens who take P.E. classes and taking every fifth senior citizen on the list, for a total of ten senior citizens. They spend:

$50; $40; $36; $15; $50; $100; $40; $53; $22; $22

It is unlikely that any student is in both samples.

a. Do you think that either of these samples is representative of (or is characteristic of) the entire 10,000 part-time student population?

Solution 1.13

a. No. The first sample probably consists of science-oriented students. Besides the chemistry course, some of them are also taking first-term calculus. Books for these classes tend to be expensive. Most of these students are, more than likely, paying more than the average part-time student for their books. The second sample is a group of senior citizens who are, more than likely, taking courses for health and interest. The amount of money they spend on books is probably much less than the average parttime student. Both samples are biased. Also, in both cases, not all students have a chance to be in either sample.

b. Since these samples are not representative of the entire population, is it wise to use the results to describe the entire population?

Solution 1.13

b. No. For these samples, each member of the population did not have an equally likely chance of being chosen.

Now, suppose we take a third sample. We choose ten different part-time students from the disciplines of chemistry, math, English, psychology, sociology, history, nursing, physical education, art, and early childhood development. (We assume that these are the only disciplines in which part-time students at ABC College are enrolled and that an equal number of part-time students are enrolled in each of the disciplines.) Each student is chosen using simple random sampling. Using a calculator, random numbers are generated and a student from a particular discipline is selected if he or she has a corresponding number. The students spend the following amounts:

$180; $50; $150; $85; $260; $75; $180; $200; $200; $150

c. Is the sample biased?

Solution 1.13

c. The sample is unbiased, but a larger sample would be recommended to increase the likelihood that the sample will be close to representative of the population. However, for a biased sampling technique, even a large sample runs the risk of not being representative of the population.

Students often ask if it is "good enough" to take a sample, instead of surveying the entire population. If the survey is done well, the answer is yes.

1.13 A local radio station has a fan base of 20,000 listeners. The station wants to know if its audience would prefer more music or more talk shows. Asking all 20,000 listeners is an almost impossible task.

The station uses convenience sampling and surveys the first 200 people they meet at one of the station's music concert events. 24 people said they'd prefer more talk shows, and 176 people said they'd prefer more music.

Do you think that this sample is representative of (or is characteristic of) the entire 20,000 listener population?

Variation in Data

Variation is present in any set of data. For example, 16-ounce cans of beverage may contain more or less than 16 ounces of liquid. In one study, eight 16 ounce cans were measured and produced the following amount (in ounces) of beverage:

15.8; 16.1; 15.2; 14.8; 15.8; 15.9; 16.0; 15.5

Measurements of the amount of beverage in a 16-ounce can may vary because different people make the measurements or because the exact amount, 16 ounces of liquid, was not put into the cans. Manufacturers regularly run tests to determine if the amount of beverage in a 16-ounce can falls within the desired range.

Be aware that as you take data, your data may vary somewhat from the data someone else is taking for the same purpose. This is completely natural. However, if two or more of you are taking the same data and get very different results, it is time for you and the others to reevaluate your data-taking methods and your accuracy.

Variation in Samples

It was mentioned previously that two or more **samples** from the same **population**, taken randomly, and having close to the same characteristics of the population will likely be different from each other. Suppose Doreen and Jung both decide to study the average amount of time students at their college sleep each night. Doreen and Jung each take samples of 500 students. Doreen uses systematic sampling and Jung uses cluster sampling. Doreen's sample will be different from Jung's sample. Even if Doreen and Jung used the same sampling method, in all likelihood their samples would be different. Neither would be wrong, however.

Think about what contributes to making Doreen's and Jung's samples different.

If Doreen and Jung took larger samples (i.e. the number of data values is increased), their sample results (the average amount of time a student sleeps) might be closer to the actual population average. But still, their samples would be, in all likelihood, different from each other. This **variability in samples** cannot be stressed enough.

Size of a Sample

The size of a sample (often called the number of observations) is important. The examples you have seen in this book so far have been small. Samples of only a few hundred observations, or even smaller, are sufficient for many purposes. In polling, samples that are from 1,200 to 1,500 observations are considered large enough and good enough if the survey is random and is well done. You will learn why when you study confidence intervals.

Be aware that many large samples are biased. For example, call-in surveys are invariably biased, because people choose to respond or not.

Collaborative Exercise

Divide into groups of two, three, or four. Your instructor will give each group one six-sided die. Try this experiment twice. Roll one fair die (six-sided) 20 times. Record the number of ones, twos, threes, fours, fives, and sixes you get in **Table 1.7** and **Table 1.8** ("frequency" is the number of times a particular face of the die occurs):

Face on Die	Frequency
1	
2	
3	
4	
5	
6	

Table 1.7 First Experiment (20 rolls)

Face on Die	Frequency
1	
2	
3	
4	
5	
6	

Table 1.8 Second Experiment (20 rolls)

Did the two experiments have the same results? Probably not. If you did the experiment a third time, do you expect the results to be identical to the first or second experiment? Why or why not?

Which experiment had the correct results? They both did. The job of the statistician is to see through the variability and draw appropriate conclusions.

1.3 | Frequency, Frequency Tables, and Levels of Measurement

Once you have a set of data, you will need to organize it so that you can analyze how frequently each datum occurs in the set. However, when calculating the frequency, you may need to round your answers so that they are as precise as possible.

Answers and Rounding Off

A simple way to round off answers is to carry your final answer one more decimal place than was present in the original data. Round off only the final answer. Do not round off any intermediate results, if possible. If it becomes necessary to round off intermediate results, carry them to at least twice as many decimal places as the final answer. For example, the average of the three quiz scores four, six, and nine is 6.3, rounded off to the nearest tenth, because the data are whole numbers. Most answers will be rounded off in this manner.

It is not necessary to reduce most fractions in this course. Especially in **Probability Topics**, the chapter on probability, it is more helpful to leave an answer as an unreduced fraction.

Levels of Measurement

The way a set of data is measured is called its **level of measurement**. Correct statistical procedures depend on a researcher being familiar with levels of measurement. Not every statistical operation can be used with every set of data. Data can be classified into four levels of measurement. They are (from lowest to highest level):

- **Nominal scale level**
- **Ordinal scale level**
- **Interval scale level**
- **Ratio scale level**

Data that is measured using a **nominal scale** is **qualitative(categorical)**. Categories, colors, names, labels and favorite foods along with yes or no responses are examples of nominal level data. Nominal scale data are not ordered. For example, trying to classify people according to their favorite food does not make any sense. Putting pizza first and sushi second is not meaningful.

Smartphone companies are another example of nominal scale data. The data are the names of the companies that make smartphones, but there is no agreed upon order of these brands, even though people may have personal preferences. Nominal scale data cannot be used in calculations.

Data that is measured using an **ordinal scale** is similar to nominal scale data but there is a big difference. The ordinal scale data can be ordered. An example of ordinal scale data is a list of the top five national parks in the United States. The top five national parks in the United States can be ranked from one to five but we cannot measure differences between the data.

Another example of using the ordinal scale is a cruise survey where the responses to questions about the cruise are "excellent," "good," "satisfactory," and "unsatisfactory." These responses are ordered from the most desired response to the least desired. But the differences between two pieces of data cannot be measured. Like the nominal scale data, ordinal scale data cannot be used in calculations.

Data that is measured using the **interval scale** is similar to ordinal level data because it has a definite ordering but there is a difference between data. The differences between interval scale data can be measured though the data does not have a starting point.

Temperature scales like Celsius (C) and Fahrenheit (F) are measured by using the interval scale. In both temperature measurements, 40° is equal to 100° minus 60°. Differences make sense. But 0 degrees does not because, in both scales, 0 is not the absolute lowest temperature. Temperatures like -10° F and -15° C exist and are colder than 0.

Interval level data can be used in calculations, but one type of comparison cannot be done. 80° C is not four times as hot as 20° C (nor is 80° F four times as hot as 20° F). There is no meaning to the ratio of 80 to 20 (or four to one).

Data that is measured using the **ratio scale** takes care of the ratio problem and gives you the most information. Ratio scale data is like interval scale data, but it has a 0 point and ratios can be calculated. For example, four multiple choice statistics final exam scores are 80, 68, 20 and 92 (out of a possible 100 points). The exams are machine-graded.

The data can be put in order from lowest to highest: 20, 68, 80, 92.

The differences between the data have meaning. The score 92 is more than the score 68 by 24 points. Ratios can be calculated. The smallest score is 0. So 80 is four times 20. The score of 80 is four times better than the score of 20.

Frequency

Twenty students were asked how many hours they worked per day. Their responses, in hours, are as follows: 5; 6; 3; 3; 2; 4; 7; 5; 2; 3; 5; 6; 5; 4; 4; 3; 5; 2; 5; 3.

Table 1.9 lists the different data values in ascending order and their frequencies.

DATA VALUE	FREQUENCY
2	3

Table 1.9 Frequency Table of Student Work Hours

DATA VALUE	FREQUENCY
3	5
4	3
5	6
6	2
7	1

Table 1.9 Frequency Table of Student Work Hours

A **frequency** is the number of times a value of the data occurs. According to **Table 1.9**, there are three students who work two hours, five students who work three hours, and so on. The sum of the values in the frequency column, 20, represents the total number of students included in the sample.

A **relative frequency** is the ratio (fraction or proportion) of the number of times a value of the data occurs in the set of all outcomes to the total number of outcomes. To find the relative frequencies, divide each frequency by the total number of students in the sample–in this case, 20. Relative frequencies can be written as fractions, percents, or decimals.

DATA VALUE	FREQUENCY	RELATIVE FREQUENCY
2	3	$\frac{3}{20}$ or 0.15
3	5	$\frac{5}{20}$ or 0.25
4	3	$\frac{3}{20}$ or 0.15
5	6	$\frac{6}{20}$ or 0.30
6	2	$\frac{2}{20}$ or 0.10
7	1	$\frac{1}{20}$ or 0.05

Table 1.10 Frequency Table of Student Work Hours with Relative Frequencies

The sum of the values in the relative frequency column of **Table 1.10** is $\frac{20}{20}$, or 1.

Cumulative relative frequency is the accumulation of the previous relative frequencies. To find the cumulative relative frequencies, add all the previous relative frequencies to the relative frequency for the current row, as shown in **Table 1.11**.

DATA VALUE	FREQUENCY	RELATIVE FREQUENCY	CUMULATIVE RELATIVE FREQUENCY
2	3	$\frac{3}{20}$ or 0.15	0.15
3	5	$\frac{5}{20}$ or 0.25	0.15 + 0.25 = 0.40

Table 1.11 Frequency Table of Student Work Hours with Relative and Cumulative Relative Frequencies

DATA VALUE	FREQUENCY	RELATIVE FREQUENCY	CUMULATIVE RELATIVE FREQUENCY
4	3	$\frac{3}{20}$ or 0.15	0.40 + 0.15 = 0.55
5	6	$\frac{6}{20}$ or 0.30	0.55 + 0.30 = 0.85
6	2	$\frac{2}{20}$ or 0.10	0.85 + 0.10 = 0.95
7	1	$\frac{1}{20}$ or 0.05	0.95 + 0.05 = 1.00

Table 1.11 Frequency Table of Student Work Hours with Relative and Cumulative Relative Frequencies

The last entry of the cumulative relative frequency column is one, indicating that one hundred percent of the data has been accumulated.

NOTE

Because of rounding, the relative frequency column may not always sum to one, and the last entry in the cumulative relative frequency column may not be one. However, they each should be close to one.

Table 1.12 represents the heights, in inches, of a sample of 100 male semiprofessional soccer players.

HEIGHTS (INCHES)	FREQUENCY	RELATIVE FREQUENCY	CUMULATIVE RELATIVE FREQUENCY
59.95–61.95	5	$\frac{5}{100}$ = 0.05	0.05
61.95–63.95	3	$\frac{3}{100}$ = 0.03	0.05 + 0.03 = 0.08
63.95–65.95	15	$\frac{15}{100}$ = 0.15	0.08 + 0.15 = 0.23
65.95–67.95	40	$\frac{40}{100}$ = 0.40	0.23 + 0.40 = 0.63
67.95–69.95	17	$\frac{17}{100}$ = 0.17	0.63 + 0.17 = 0.80
69.95–71.95	12	$\frac{12}{100}$ = 0.12	0.80 + 0.12 = 0.92
71.95–73.95	7	$\frac{7}{100}$ = 0.07	0.92 + 0.07 = 0.99
73.95–75.95	1	$\frac{1}{100}$ = 0.01	0.99 + 0.01 = 1.00
	Total = 100	Total = 1.00	

Table 1.12 Frequency Table of Soccer Player Height

The data in this table have been **grouped** into the following intervals:

- 59.95 to 61.95 inches

- 61.95 to 63.95 inches
- 63.95 to 65.95 inches
- 65.95 to 67.95 inches
- 67.95 to 69.95 inches
- 69.95 to 71.95 inches
- 71.95 to 73.95 inches
- 73.95 to 75.95 inches

NOTE

This example is used again in **Descriptive Statistics**, where the method used to compute the intervals will be explained.

In this sample, there are **five** players whose heights fall within the interval 59.95–61.95 inches, **three** players whose heights fall within the interval 61.95–63.95 inches, **15** players whose heights fall within the interval 63.95–65.95 inches, **40** players whose heights fall within the interval 65.95–67.95 inches, **17** players whose heights fall within the interval 67.95–69.95 inches, **12** players whose heights fall within the interval 69.95–71.95, **seven** players whose heights fall within the interval 71.95–73.95, and **one** player whose heights fall within the interval 73.95–75.95. All heights fall between the endpoints of an interval and not at the endpoints.

Example 1.14

From **Table 1.12**, find the percentage of heights that are less than 65.95 inches.

Solution 1.14

If you look at the first, second, and third rows, the heights are all less than 65.95 inches. There are 5 + 3 + 15 = 23 players whose heights are less than 65.95 inches. The percentage of heights less than 65.95 inches is then $\frac{23}{100}$ or 23%. This percentage is the cumulative relative frequency entry in the third row.

Try It

1.14 Table 1.13 shows the amount, in inches, of annual rainfall in a sample of towns.

Rainfall (Inches)	Frequency	Relative Frequency	Cumulative Relative Frequency
2.95–4.97	6	$\frac{6}{50}$ = 0.12	0.12
4.97–6.99	7	$\frac{7}{50}$ = 0.14	0.12 + 0.14 = 0.26
6.99–9.01	15	$\frac{15}{50}$ = 0.30	0.26 + 0.30 = 0.56
9.01–11.03	8	$\frac{8}{50}$ = 0.16	0.56 + 0.16 = 0.72
11.03–13.05	9	$\frac{9}{50}$ = 0.18	0.72 + 0.18 = 0.90

Table 1.13

Rainfall (Inches)	Frequency	Relative Frequency	Cumulative Relative Frequency
13.05–15.07	5	$\frac{5}{50}$ = 0.10	0.90 + 0.10 = 1.00
	Total = 50	Total = 1.00	

Table 1.13

From **Table 1.13**, find the percentage of rainfall that is less than 9.01 inches.

Example 1.15

From **Table 1.12**, find the percentage of heights that fall between 61.95 and 65.95 inches.

Solution 1.15
Add the relative frequencies in the second and third rows: 0.03 + 0.15 = 0.18 or 18%.

1.15 From **Table 1.13**, find the percentage of rainfall that is between 6.99 and 13.05 inches.

Example 1.16

Use the heights of the 100 male semiprofessional soccer players in **Table 1.12**. Fill in the blanks and check your answers.

   a. The percentage of heights that are from 67.95 to 71.95 inches is: ____.

   b. The percentage of heights that are from 67.95 to 73.95 inches is: ____.

   c. The percentage of heights that are more than 65.95 inches is: ____.

   d. The number of players in the sample who are between 61.95 and 71.95 inches tall is: ____.

   e. What kind of data are the heights?

   f. Describe how you could gather this data (the heights) so that the data are characteristic of all male semiprofessional soccer players.

Remember, you **count frequencies**. To find the relative frequency, divide the frequency by the total number of data values. To find the cumulative relative frequency, add all of the previous relative frequencies to the relative frequency for the current row.

Solution 1.16
   a. 29%

   b. 36%

   c. 77%

   d. 87

   e. quantitative continuous

   f. get rosters from each team and choose a simple random sample from each

Try It Σ

1.16 From **Table 1.13**, find the number of towns that have rainfall between 2.95 and 9.01 inches.

Collaborative Exercise

In your class, have someone conduct a survey of the number of siblings (brothers and sisters) each student has. Create a frequency table. Add to it a relative frequency column and a cumulative relative frequency column. Answer the following questions:

1. What percentage of the students in your class have no siblings?

2. What percentage of the students have from one to three siblings?

3. What percentage of the students have fewer than three siblings?

Example 1.17

Nineteen people were asked how many miles, to the nearest mile, they commute to work each day. The data are as follows: 2; 5; 7; 3; 2; 10; 18; 15; 20; 7; 10; 18; 5; 12; 13; 12; 4; 5; 10. **Table 1.14** was produced:

DATA	FREQUENCY	RELATIVE FREQUENCY	CUMULATIVE RELATIVE FREQUENCY
3	3	$\frac{3}{19}$	0.1579
4	1	$\frac{1}{19}$	0.2105
5	3	$\frac{3}{19}$	0.1579
7	2	$\frac{2}{19}$	0.2632
10	3	$\frac{4}{19}$	0.4737
12	2	$\frac{2}{19}$	0.7895
13	1	$\frac{1}{19}$	0.8421
15	1	$\frac{1}{19}$	0.8948
18	1	$\frac{1}{19}$	0.9474
20	1	$\frac{1}{19}$	1.0000

Table 1.14 Frequency of Commuting Distances

a. Is the table correct? If it is not correct, what is wrong?

b. True or False: Three percent of the people surveyed commute three miles. If the statement is not correct, what should it be? If the table is incorrect, make the corrections.

c. What fraction of the people surveyed commute five or seven miles?

d. What fraction of the people surveyed commute 12 miles or more? Less than 12 miles? Between five and 13 miles (not including five and 13 miles)?

Solution 1.17

a. No. The frequency column sums to 18, not 19. Not all cumulative relative frequencies are correct.

b. False. The frequency for three miles should be one; for two miles (left out), two. The cumulative relative frequency column should read: 0.1052, 0.1579, 0.2105, 0.3684, 0.4737, 0.6316, 0.7368, 0.7895, 0.8421, 0.9474, 1.0000.

c. $\frac{5}{19}$

d. $\frac{7}{19}$, $\frac{12}{19}$, $\frac{7}{19}$

1.17 **Table** 1.13 represents the amount, in inches, of annual rainfall in a sample of towns. What fraction of towns surveyed get between 11.03 and 13.05 inches of rainfall each year?

Example 1.18

Table 1.15 contains the total number of deaths worldwide as a result of earthquakes for the period from 2000 to 2012.

Year	Total Number of Deaths
2000	231
2001	21,357
2002	11,685
2003	33,819
2004	228,802
2005	88,003
2006	6,605
2007	712
2008	88,011
2009	1,790
2010	320,120
2011	21,953
2012	768
Total	823,856

Table 1.15

Answer the following questions.

   a. What is the frequency of deaths measured from 2006 through 2009?

   b. What percentage of deaths occurred after 2009?

   c. What is the relative frequency of deaths that occurred in 2003 or earlier?

   d. What is the percentage of deaths that occurred in 2004?

   e. What kind of data are the numbers of deaths?

   f. The Richter scale is used to quantify the energy produced by an earthquake. Examples of Richter scale numbers are 2.3, 4.0, 6.1, and 7.0. What kind of data are these numbers?

Solution 1.18

   a. 97,118 (11.8%)

   b. 41.6%

   c. 67,092/823,356 or 0.081 or 8.1 %

   d. 27.8%

e. Quantitative discrete

f. Quantitative continuous

1.18 Table 1.16 contains the total number of fatal motor vehicle traffic crashes in the United States for the period from 1994 to 2011.

Year	Total Number of Crashes	Year	Total Number of Crashes
1994	36,254	2004	38,444
1995	37,241	2005	39,252
1996	37,494	2006	38,648
1997	37,324	2007	37,435
1998	37,107	2008	34,172
1999	37,140	2009	30,862
2000	37,526	2010	30,296
2001	37,862	2011	29,757
2002	38,491	Total	653,782
2003	38,477		

Table 1.16

Answer the following questions.

a. What is the frequency of deaths measured from 2000 through 2004?

b. What percentage of deaths occurred after 2006?

c. What is the relative frequency of deaths that occurred in 2000 or before?

d. What is the percentage of deaths that occurred in 2011?

e. What is the cumulative relative frequency for 2006? Explain what this number tells you about the data.

1.4 | Experimental Design and Ethics

Does aspirin reduce the risk of heart attacks? Is one brand of fertilizer more effective at growing roses than another? Is fatigue as dangerous to a driver as the influence of alcohol? Questions like these are answered using randomized experiments. In this module, you will learn important aspects of experimental design. Proper study design ensures the production of reliable, accurate data.

The purpose of an experiment is to investigate the relationship between two variables. When one variable causes change in another, we call the first variable the **explanatory variable**. The affected variable is called the **response variable**. In a randomized experiment, the researcher manipulates values of the explanatory variable and measures the resulting changes in the response variable. The different values of the explanatory variable are called **treatments**. An **experimental unit** is a single object or individual to be measured.

You want to investigate the effectiveness of vitamin E in preventing disease. You recruit a group of subjects and ask them if they regularly take vitamin E. You notice that the subjects who take vitamin E exhibit better health on average than those who do not. Does this prove that vitamin E is effective in disease prevention? It does not. There are many differences between the two groups compared in addition to vitamin E consumption. People who take vitamin E regularly often take other steps to improve their health: exercise, diet, other vitamin supplements, choosing not to smoke. Any one of these factors could be influencing health. As described, this study does not prove that vitamin E is the key to disease prevention.

Additional variables that can cloud a study are called **lurking variables**. In order to prove that the explanatory variable is causing a change in the response variable, it is necessary to isolate the explanatory variable. The researcher must design her experiment in such a way that there is only one difference between groups being compared: the planned treatments. This is accomplished by the **random assignment** of experimental units to treatment groups. When subjects are assigned treatments randomly, all of the potential lurking variables are spread equally among the groups. At this point the only difference between groups is the one imposed by the researcher. Different outcomes measured in the response variable, therefore, must be a direct result of the different treatments. In this way, an experiment can prove a cause-and-effect connection between the explanatory and response variables.

The power of suggestion can have an important influence on the outcome of an experiment. Studies have shown that the expectation of the study participant can be as important as the actual medication. In one study of performance-enhancing drugs, researchers noted:

Results showed that believing one had taken the substance resulted in [performance] times almost as fast as those associated with consuming the drug itself. In contrast, taking the drug without knowledge yielded no significant performance increment.[1]

When participation in a study prompts a physical response from a participant, it is difficult to isolate the effects of the explanatory variable. To counter the power of suggestion, researchers set aside one treatment group as a **control group**. This group is given a **placebo** treatment–a treatment that cannot influence the response variable. The control group helps researchers balance the effects of being in an experiment with the effects of the active treatments. Of course, if you are participating in a study and you know that you are receiving a pill which contains no actual medication, then the power of suggestion is no longer a factor. **Blinding** in a randomized experiment preserves the power of suggestion. When a person involved in a research study is blinded, he does not know who is receiving the active treatment(s) and who is receiving the placebo treatment. A **double-blind experiment** is one in which both the subjects and the researchers involved with the subjects are blinded.

Example 1.19

Researchers want to investigate whether taking aspirin regularly reduces the risk of heart attack. Four hundred men between the ages of 50 and 84 are recruited as participants. The men are divided randomly into two groups: one group will take aspirin, and the other group will take a placebo. Each man takes one pill each day for three years, but he does not know whether he is taking aspirin or the placebo. At the end of the study, researchers count the number of men in each group who have had heart attacks.

Identify the following values for this study: population, sample, experimental units, explanatory variable, response variable, treatments.

Solution 1.19
The *population* is men aged 50 to 84.
The *sample* is the 400 men who participated.
The *experimental units* are the individual men in the study.
The *explanatory variable* is oral medication.
The *treatments* are aspirin and a placebo.
The *response variable* is whether a subject had a heart attack.

Example 1.20

The Smell & Taste Treatment and Research Foundation conducted a study to investigate whether smell can affect learning. Subjects completed mazes multiple times while wearing masks. They completed the pencil and paper mazes three times wearing floral-scented masks, and three times with unscented masks. Participants were

---

1. McClung, M. Collins, D. "Because I know it will!": placebo effects of an ergogenic aid on athletic performance. Journal of Sport & Exercise Psychology. 2007 Jun. 29(3):382-94. Web. April 30, 2013.

assigned at random to wear the floral mask during the first three trials or during the last three trials. For each trial, researchers recorded the time it took to complete the maze and the subject's impression of the mask's scent: positive, negative, or neutral.

a. Describe the explanatory and response variables in this study.

b. What are the treatments?

c. Identify any lurking variables that could interfere with this study.

d. Is it possible to use blinding in this study?

Solution 1.20

a. The explanatory variable is scent, and the response variable is the time it takes to complete the maze.

b. There are two treatments: a floral-scented mask and an unscented mask.

c. All subjects experienced both treatments. The order of treatments was randomly assigned so there were no differences between the treatment groups. Random assignment eliminates the problem of lurking variables.

d. Subjects will clearly know whether they can smell flowers or not, so subjects cannot be blinded in this study. Researchers timing the mazes can be blinded, though. The researcher who is observing a subject will not know which mask is being worn.

Example 1.21

A researcher wants to study the effects of birth order on personality. Explain why this study could not be conducted as a randomized experiment. What is the main problem in a study that cannot be designed as a randomized experiment?

Solution 1.21

The explanatory variable is birth order. You cannot randomly assign a person's birth order. Random assignment eliminates the impact of lurking variables. When you cannot assign subjects to treatment groups at random, there will be differences between the groups other than the explanatory variable.

1.21 You are concerned about the effects of texting on driving performance. Design a study to test the response time of drivers while texting and while driving only. How many seconds does it take for a driver to respond when a leading car hits the brakes?

a. Describe the explanatory and response variables in the study.

b. What are the treatments?

c. What should you consider when selecting participants?

d. Your research partner wants to divide participants randomly into two groups: one to drive without distraction and one to text and drive simultaneously. Is this a good idea? Why or why not?

e. Identify any lurking variables that could interfere with this study.

f. How can blinding be used in this study?

Ethics

The widespread misuse and misrepresentation of statistical information often gives the field a bad name. Some say that "numbers don't lie," but the people who use numbers to support their claims often do.

A recent investigation of famous social psychologist, Diederik Stapel, has led to the retraction of his articles from some of the world's top journals including *Journal of Experimental Social Psychology, Social Psychology, Basic and Applied Social Psychology, British Journal of Social Psychology,* and the magazine *Science.* Diederik Stapel is a former professor at Tilburg University in the Netherlands. Over the past two years, an extensive investigation involving three universities where Stapel has worked concluded that the psychologist is guilty of fraud on a colossal scale. Falsified data taints over 55 papers he authored and 10 Ph.D. dissertations that he supervised.

Stapel did not deny that his deceit was driven by ambition. But it was more complicated than that, he told me. He insisted that he loved social psychology but had been frustrated by the messiness of experimental data, which rarely led to clear conclusions. His lifelong obsession with elegance and order, he said, led him to concoct sexy results that journals found attractive. "It was a quest for aesthetics, for beauty—instead of the truth," he said. He described his behavior as an addiction that drove him to carry out acts of increasingly daring fraud, like a junkie seeking a bigger and better high.[2]

The committee investigating Stapel concluded that he is guilty of several practices including:

- creating datasets, which largely confirmed the prior expectations,

- altering data in existing datasets,

- changing measuring instruments without reporting the change, and

- misrepresenting the number of experimental subjects.

Clearly, it is never acceptable to falsify data the way this researcher did. Sometimes, however, violations of ethics are not as easy to spot.

Researchers have a responsibility to verify that proper methods are being followed. The report describing the investigation of Stapel's fraud states that, "statistical flaws frequently revealed a lack of familiarity with elementary statistics."[3] Many of Stapel's co-authors should have spotted irregularities in his data. Unfortunately, they did not know very much about statistical analysis, and they simply trusted that he was collecting and reporting data properly.

Many types of statistical fraud are difficult to spot. Some researchers simply stop collecting data once they have just enough to prove what they had hoped to prove. They don't want to take the chance that a more extensive study would complicate their lives by producing data contradicting their hypothesis.

Professional organizations, like the American Statistical Association, clearly define expectations for researchers. There are even laws in the federal code about the use of research data.

When a statistical study uses human participants, as in medical studies, both ethics and the law dictate that researchers should be mindful of the safety of their research subjects. The U.S. Department of Health and Human Services oversees federal regulations of research studies with the aim of protecting participants. When a university or other research institution engages in research, it must ensure the safety of all human subjects. For this reason, research institutions establish oversight committees known as **Institutional Review Boards (IRB)**. All planned studies must be approved in advance by the IRB. Key protections that are mandated by law include the following:

- Risks to participants must be minimized and reasonable with respect to projected benefits.

- Participants must give **informed consent**. This means that the risks of participation must be clearly explained to the subjects of the study. Subjects must consent in writing, and researchers are required to keep documentation of their consent.

- Data collected from individuals must be guarded carefully to protect their privacy.

These ideas may seem fundamental, but they can be very difficult to verify in practice. Is removing a participant's name from the data record sufficient to protect privacy? Perhaps the person's identity could be discovered from the data that remains. What happens if the study does not proceed as planned and risks arise that were not anticipated? When is informed consent really necessary? Suppose your doctor wants a blood sample to check your cholesterol level. Once the sample has been tested, you expect the lab to dispose of the remaining blood. At that point the blood becomes biological waste. Does a researcher have the right to take it for use in a study?

It is important that students of statistics take time to consider the ethical questions that arise in statistical studies. How prevalent is fraud in statistical studies? You might be surprised—and disappointed. There is a **website (http://www.retractionwatch.com)** dedicated to cataloging retractions of study articles that have been proven

2.   Yudhijit Bhattacharjee, "The Mind of a Con Man," *Magazine, New York Times, April 26, 2013.* Available online at: *http://www.nytimes.com/2013/04/28/magazine/diederik-stapels-audacious-academic-fraud.html?src=dayp&_r=2& (accessed May 1, 2013).*

3.   "Flawed Science: The Fraudulent Research Practices of Social Psychologist Diederik Stapel," Tillburg University, November 28, 2012, http://www.tilburguniversity.edu/upload/064a10cd-bce5-4385-b9ff-05b840caeae6_120695_Rapp_nov_2012_UK_web.pdf (accessed May 1, 2013).

fraudulent. A quick glance will show that the misuse of statistics is a bigger problem than most people realize.

Vigilance against fraud requires knowledge. Learning the basic theory of statistics will empower you to analyze statistical studies critically.

Example 1.22

Describe the unethical behavior in each example and describe how it could impact the reliability of the resulting data. Explain how the problem should be corrected.

A researcher is collecting data in a community.

a. She selects a block where she is comfortable walking because she knows many of the people living on the street.

b. No one seems to be home at four houses on her route. She does not record the addresses and does not return at a later time to try to find residents at home.

c. She skips four houses on her route because she is running late for an appointment. When she gets home, she fills in the forms by selecting random answers from other residents in the neighborhood.

Solution 1.22

a. By selecting a convenient sample, the researcher is intentionally selecting a sample that could be biased. Claiming that this sample represents the community is misleading. The researcher needs to select areas in the community at random.

b. Intentionally omitting relevant data will create bias in the sample. Suppose the researcher is gathering information about jobs and child care. By ignoring people who are not home, she may be missing data from working families that are relevant to her study. She needs to make every effort to interview all members of the target sample.

c. It is never acceptable to fake data. Even though the responses she uses are "real" responses provided by other participants, the duplication is fraudulent and can create bias in the data. She needs to work diligently to interview everyone on her route.

Try It Σ

1.22 Describe the unethical behavior, if any, in each example and describe how it could impact the reliability of the resulting data. Explain how the problem should be corrected.

A study is commissioned to determine the favorite brand of fruit juice among teens in California.

a. The survey is commissioned by the seller of a popular brand of apple juice.

b. There are only two types of juice included in the study: apple juice and cranberry juice.

c. Researchers allow participants to see the brand of juice as samples are poured for a taste test.

d. Twenty-five percent of participants prefer Brand X, 33% prefer Brand Y and 42% have no preference between the two brands. Brand X references the study in a commercial saying "Most teens like Brand X as much as or more than Brand Y."

1.5 | Data Collection Experiment

Stats Lab

1.1 Data Collection Experiment

Class Time:

Names:

Student Learning Outcomes

- The student will demonstrate the systematic sampling technique.
- The student will construct relative frequency tables.
- The student will interpret results and their differences from different data groupings.

Movie Survey

Ask five classmates from a different class how many movies they saw at the theater last month. Do not include rented movies.

1. Record the data.

2. In class, randomly pick one person. On the class list, mark that person's name. Move down four names on the class list. Mark that person's name. Continue doing this until you have marked 12 names. You may need to go back to the start of the list. For each marked name record the five data values. You now have a total of 60 data values.

3. For each name marked, record the data.

Table 1.17

Order the Data

Complete the two relative frequency tables below using your class data.

Number of Movies	Frequency	Relative Frequency	Cumulative Relative Frequency
0			
1			
2			
3			
4			
5			
6			

Number of Movies	Frequency	Relative Frequency	Cumulative Relative Frequency
7+			

Table 1.18 Frequency of Number of Movies Viewed

Number of Movies	Frequency	Relative Frequency	Cumulative Relative Frequency
0–1			
2–3			
4–5			
6–7+			

Table 1.19 Frequency of Number of Movies Viewed

1. Using the tables, find the percent of data that is at most two. Which table did you use and why?
2. Using the tables, find the percent of data that is at most three. Which table did you use and why?
3. Using the tables, find the percent of data that is more than two. Which table did you use and why?
4. Using the tables, find the percent of data that is more than three. Which table did you use and why?

Discussion Questions

1. Is one of the tables "more correct" than the other? Why or why not?
2. In general, how could you group the data differently? Are there any advantages to either way of grouping the data?
3. Why did you switch between tables, if you did, when answering the question above?

1.6 | Sampling Experiment

Stats Lab

1.2 Sampling Experiment

Class Time:

Names:

Student Learning Outcomes

- The student will demonstrate the simple random, systematic, stratified, and cluster sampling techniques.
- The student will explain the details of each procedure used.

In this lab, you will be asked to pick several random samples of restaurants. In each case, describe your procedure briefly, including how you might have used the random number generator, and then list the restaurants in the sample you obtained.

NOTE

The following section contains restaurants stratified by city into columns and grouped horizontally by entree cost (clusters).

Restaurants Stratified by City and Entree Cost

Entree Cost	Under $10	$10 to under $15	$15 to under $20	Over $20
San Jose	El Abuelo Taq, Pasta Mia, Emma's Express, Bamboo Hut	Emperor's Guard, Creekside Inn	Agenda, Gervais, Miro's	Blake's, Eulipia, Hayes Mansion, Germania
Palo Alto	Senor Taco, Olive Garden, Taxi's	Ming's, P.A. Joe's, Stickney's	Scott's Seafood, Poolside Grill, Fish Market	Sundance Mine, Maddalena's, Spago's
Los Gatos	Mary's Patio, Mount Everest, Sweet Pea's, Andele Taqueria	Lindsey's, Willow Street	Toll House	Charter House, La Maison Du Cafe
Mountain View	Maharaja, New Ma's, Thai-Rific, Garden Fresh	Amber Indian, La Fiesta, Fiesta del Mar, Dawit	Austin's, Shiva's, Mazeh	Le Petit Bistro
Cupertino	Hobees, Hung Fu, Samrat, Panda Express	Santa Barb. Grill, Mand. Gourmet, Bombay Oven, Kathmandu West	Fontana's, Blue Pheasant	Hamasushi, Helios
Sunnyvale	Chekijababi, Taj India, Full Throttle, Tia Juana, Lemon Grass	Pacific Fresh, Charley Brown's, Cafe Cameroon, Faz, Aruba's	Lion & Compass, The Palace, Beau Sejour	
Santa Clara	Rangoli, Armadillo Willy's, Thai Pepper, Pasand	Arthur's, Katie's Cafe, Pedro's, La Galleria	Birk's, Truya Sushi, Valley Plaza	Lakeside, Mariani's

Table 1.20 Restaurants Used in Sample

A Simple Random Sample

Pick a **simple random sample** of 15 restaurants.

1. Describe your procedure.
2. Complete the table with your sample.

1. _____	6. _____	11. _____
2. _____	7. _____	12. _____
3. _____	8. _____	13. _____
4. _____	9. _____	14. _____
5. _____	10. _____	15. _____

Table 1.21

A Systematic Sample

Pick a **systematic sample** of 15 restaurants.

1. Describe your procedure.
2. Complete the table with your sample.

1. _____	6. _____	11. _____
2. _____	7. _____	12. _____
3. _____	8. _____	13. _____
4. _____	9. _____	14. _____
5. _____	10. _____	15. _____

Table 1.22

A Stratified Sample

Pick a **stratified sample**, by city, of 20 restaurants. Use 25% of the restaurants from each stratum. Round to the nearest whole number.

1. Describe your procedure.
2. Complete the table with your sample.

1. _____	6. _____	11. _____	16. _____
2. _____	7. _____	12. _____	17. _____
3. _____	8. _____	13. _____	18. _____
4. _____	9. _____	14. _____	19. _____
5. _____	10. _____	15. _____	20. _____

Table 1.23

A Stratified Sample

Pick a **stratified sample**, by entree cost, of 21 restaurants. Use 25% of the restaurants from each stratum. Round to the nearest whole number.

1. Describe your procedure.

2. Complete the table with your sample.

1. _____	6. _____	11. _____	16. _____
2. _____	7. _____	12. _____	17. _____
3. _____	8. _____	13. _____	18. _____
4. _____	9. _____	14. _____	19. _____
5. _____	10. _____	15. _____	20. _____
			21. _____

Table 1.24

A Cluster Sample

Pick a **cluster sample** of restaurants from two cities. The number of restaurants will vary.

1. Describe your procedure.

2. Complete the table with your sample.

1. _____	6. _____	11. _____	16. _____	21. _____
2. _____	7. _____	12. _____	17. _____	22. _____
3. _____	8. _____	13. _____	18. _____	23. _____
4. _____	9. _____	14. _____	19. _____	24. _____
5. _____	10. _____	15. _____	20. _____	25. _____

Table 1.25

KEY TERMS

Average also called mean; a number that describes the central tendency of the data

Blinding not telling participants which treatment a subject is receiving

Categorical Variable variables that take on values that are names or labels

Cluster Sampling a method for selecting a random sample and dividing the population into groups (clusters); use simple random sampling to select a set of clusters. Every individual in the chosen clusters is included in the sample.

Continuous Random Variable a random variable (RV) whose outcomes are measured; the height of trees in the forest is a continuous RV.

Control Group a group in a randomized experiment that receives an inactive treatment but is otherwise managed exactly as the other groups

Convenience Sampling a nonrandom method of selecting a sample; this method selects individuals that are easily accessible and may result in biased data.

Cumulative Relative Frequency The term applies to an ordered set of observations from smallest to largest. The cumulative relative frequency is the sum of the relative frequencies for all values that are less than or equal to the given value.

Data a set of observations (a set of possible outcomes); most data can be put into two groups: **qualitative** (an attribute whose value is indicated by a label) or **quantitative** (an attribute whose value is indicated by a number). Quantitative data can be separated into two subgroups: **discrete** and **continuous**. Data is discrete if it is the result of counting (such as the number of students of a given ethnic group in a class or the number of books on a shelf). Data is continuous if it is the result of measuring (such as distance traveled or weight of luggage)

Discrete Random Variable a random variable (RV) whose outcomes are counted

Double-blinding the act of blinding both the subjects of an experiment and the researchers who work with the subjects

Experimental Unit any individual or object to be measured

Explanatory Variable the independent variable in an experiment; the value controlled by researchers

Frequency the number of times a value of the data occurs

Informed Consent Any human subject in a research study must be cognizant of any risks or costs associated with the study. The subject has the right to know the nature of the treatments included in the study, their potential risks, and their potential benefits. Consent must be given freely by an informed, fit participant.

Institutional Review Board a committee tasked with oversight of research programs that involve human subjects

Lurking Variable a variable that has an effect on a study even though it is neither an explanatory variable nor a response variable

Nonsampling Error an issue that affects the reliability of sampling data other than natural variation; it includes a variety of human errors including poor study design, biased sampling methods, inaccurate information provided by study participants, data entry errors, and poor analysis.

Numerical Variable variables that take on values that are indicated by numbers

Parameter a number that is used to represent a population characteristic and that generally cannot be determined easily

Placebo an inactive treatment that has no real effect on the explanatory variable

Population all individuals, objects, or measurements whose properties are being studied

Probability a number between zero and one, inclusive, that gives the likelihood that a specific event will occur

Proportion the number of successes divided by the total number in the sample

Qualitative Data See **Data**.

Quantitative Data See **Data**.

Random Assignment the act of organizing experimental units into treatment groups using random methods

Random Sampling a method of selecting a sample that gives every member of the population an equal chance of being selected.

Relative Frequency the ratio of the number of times a value of the data occurs in the set of all outcomes to the number of all outcomes to the total number of outcomes

Representative Sample a subset of the population that has the same characteristics as the population

Response Variable the dependent variable in an experiment; the value that is measured for change at the end of an experiment

Sample a subset of the population studied

Sampling Bias not all members of the population are equally likely to be selected

Sampling Error the natural variation that results from selecting a sample to represent a larger population; this variation decreases as the sample size increases, so selecting larger samples reduces sampling error.

Sampling with Replacement Once a member of the population is selected for inclusion in a sample, that member is returned to the population for the selection of the next individual.

Sampling without Replacement A member of the population may be chosen for inclusion in a sample only once. If chosen, the member is not returned to the population before the next selection.

Simple Random Sampling a straightforward method for selecting a random sample; give each member of the population a number. Use a random number generator to select a set of labels. These randomly selected labels identify the members of your sample.

Statistic a numerical characteristic of the sample; a statistic estimates the corresponding population parameter.

Stratified Sampling a method for selecting a random sample used to ensure that subgroups of the population are represented adequately; divide the population into groups (strata). Use simple random sampling to identify a proportionate number of individuals from each stratum.

Systematic Sampling a method for selecting a random sample; list the members of the population. Use simple random sampling to select a starting point in the population. Let k = (number of individuals in the population)/(number of individuals needed in the sample). Choose every kth individual in the list starting with the one that was randomly selected. If necessary, return to the beginning of the population list to complete your sample.

Treatments different values or components of the explanatory variable applied in an experiment

Variable a characteristic of interest for each person or object in a population

CHAPTER REVIEW

1.1 Definitions of Statistics, Probability, and Key Terms

The mathematical theory of statistics is easier to learn when you know the language. This module presents important terms that will be used throughout the text.

1.2 Data, Sampling, and Variation in Data and Sampling

Data are individual items of information that come from a population or sample. Data may be classified as qualitative(categorical), quantitative continuous, or quantitative discrete.

Because it is not practical to measure the entire population in a study, researchers use samples to represent the population. A random sample is a representative group from the population chosen by using a method that gives each individual in the population an equal chance of being included in the sample. Random sampling methods include simple random sampling, stratified sampling, cluster sampling, and systematic sampling. Convenience sampling is a nonrandom method of choosing a sample that often produces biased data.

Samples that contain different individuals result in different data. This is true even when the samples are well-chosen and representative of the population. When properly selected, larger samples model the population more closely than smaller samples. There are many different potential problems that can affect the reliability of a sample. Statistical data needs to be critically analyzed, not simply accepted.

1.3 Frequency, Frequency Tables, and Levels of Measurement

Some calculations generate numbers that are artificially precise. It is not necessary to report a value to eight decimal places when the measures that generated that value were only accurate to the nearest tenth. Round off your final answer to one more decimal place than was present in the original data. This means that if you have data measured to the nearest tenth of a unit, report the final statistic to the nearest hundredth.

In addition to rounding your answers, you can measure your data using the following four levels of measurement.

- **Nominal scale level:** data that cannot be ordered nor can it be used in calculations

- **Ordinal scale level:** data that can be ordered; the differences cannot be measured

- **Interval scale level:** data with a definite ordering but no starting point; the differences can be measured, but there is no such thing as a ratio.

- **Ratio scale level:** data with a starting point that can be ordered; the differences have meaning and ratios can be calculated.

When organizing data, it is important to know how many times a value appears. How many statistics students study five hours or more for an exam? What percent of families on our block own two pets? Frequency, relative frequency, and cumulative relative frequency are measures that answer questions like these.

1.4 Experimental Design and Ethics

A poorly designed study will not produce reliable data. There are certain key components that must be included in every experiment. To eliminate lurking variables, subjects must be assigned randomly to different treatment groups. One of the groups must act as a control group, demonstrating what happens when the active treatment is not applied. Participants in the control group receive a placebo treatment that looks exactly like the active treatments but cannot influence the response variable. To preserve the integrity of the placebo, both researchers and subjects may be blinded. When a study is designed properly, the only difference between treatment groups is the one imposed by the researcher. Therefore, when groups respond differently to different treatments, the difference must be due to the influence of the explanatory variable.

"An ethics problem arises when you are considering an action that benefits you or some cause you support, hurts or reduces benefits to others, and violates some rule."[4] Ethical violations in statistics are not always easy to spot. Professional associations and federal agencies post guidelines for proper conduct. It is important that you learn basic statistical procedures so that you can recognize proper data analysis.

PRACTICE

1.1 Definitions of Statistics, Probability, and Key Terms

Use the following information to answer the next five exercises. Studies are often done by pharmaceutical companies to determine the effectiveness of a treatment program. Suppose that a new AIDS antibody drug is currently under study. It is given to patients once the AIDS symptoms have revealed themselves. Of interest is the average (mean) length of time in months patients live once they start the treatment. Two researchers each follow a different set of 40 patients with AIDS from the start of treatment until their deaths. The following data (in months) are collected.

---

4. Andrew Gelman, "Open Data and Open Methods," Ethics and Statistics, http://www.stat.columbia.edu/~gelman/research/published/ChanceEthics1.pdf (accessed May 1, 2013).

Researcher A:

3; 4; 11; 15; 16; 17; 22; 44; 37; 16; 14; 24; 25; 15; 26; 27; 33; 29; 35; 44; 13; 21; 22; 10; 12; 8; 40; 32; 26; 27; 31; 34; 29; 17; 8; 24; 18; 47; 33; 34

Researcher B:

3; 14; 11; 5; 16; 17; 28; 41; 31; 18; 14; 14; 26; 25; 21; 22; 31; 2; 35; 44; 23; 21; 21; 16; 12; 18; 41; 22; 16; 25; 33; 34; 29; 13; 18; 24; 23; 42; 33; 29

Determine what the key terms refer to in the example for Researcher A.

1. population

2. sample

3. parameter

4. statistic

5. variable

1.2 Data, Sampling, and Variation in Data and Sampling

6. "Number of times per week" is what type of data?

a. qualitative(categorical); b. quantitative discrete; c. quantitative continuous

Use the following information to answer the next four exercises: A study was done to determine the age, number of times per week, and the duration (amount of time) of residents using a local park in San Antonio, Texas. The first house in the neighborhood around the park was selected randomly, and then the resident of every eighth house in the neighborhood around the park was interviewed.

7. The sampling method was

a. simple random; b. systematic; c. stratified; d. cluster

8. "Duration (amount of time)" is what type of data?

a. qualitative(categorical); b. quantitative discrete; c. quantitative continuous

9. The colors of the houses around the park are what kind of data?

a. qualitative(categorical); b. quantitative discrete; c. quantitative continuous

10. The population is _____

11. Table 1.26 contains the total number of deaths worldwide as a result of earthquakes from 2000 to 2012.

Year	Total Number of Deaths
2000	231
2001	21,357
2002	11,685
2003	33,819
2004	228,802
2005	88,003
2006	6,605
2007	712
2008	88,011
2009	1,790
2010	320,120
2011	21,953
2012	768
Total	**823,856**

Table 1.26

Use **Table 1.26** to answer the following questions.

    a.   What is the proportion of deaths between 2007 and 2012?
    b.   What percent of deaths occurred before 2001?
    c.   What is the percent of deaths that occurred in 2003 or after 2010?
    d.   What is the fraction of deaths that happened before 2012?
    e.   What kind of data is the number of deaths?
    f.   Earthquakes are quantified according to the amount of energy they produce (examples are 2.1, 5.0, 6.7). What type of data is that?
    g.   What contributed to the large number of deaths in 2010? In 2004? Explain.

For the following four exercises, determine the type of sampling used (simple random, stratified, systematic, cluster, or convenience).

12. A group of test subjects is divided into twelve groups; then four of the groups are chosen at random.

13. A market researcher polls every tenth person who walks into a store.

14. The first 50 people who walk into a sporting event are polled on their television preferences.

15. A computer generates 100 random numbers, and 100 people whose names correspond with the numbers on the list are chosen.

Use the following information to answer the next seven exercises: Studies are often done by pharmaceutical companies to determine the effectiveness of a treatment program. Suppose that a new AIDS antibody drug is currently under study. It is given to patients once the AIDS symptoms have revealed themselves. Of interest is the average (mean) length of time in months patients live once starting the treatment. Two researchers each follow a different set of 40 AIDS patients from the start of treatment until their deaths. The following data (in months) are collected.

Researcher A: 3; 4; 11; 15; 16; 17; 22; 44; 37; 16; 14; 24; 25; 15; 26; 27; 33; 29; 35; 44; 13; 21; 22; 10; 12; 8; 40; 32; 26; 27; 31; 34; 29; 17; 8; 24; 18; 47; 33; 34

Researcher B: 3; 14; 11; 5; 16; 17; 28; 41; 31; 18; 14; 14; 26; 25; 21; 22; 31; 2; 35; 44; 23; 21; 21; 16; 12; 18; 41; 22; 16; 25; 33; 34; 29; 13; 18; 24; 23; 42; 33; 29

16. Complete the tables using the data provided:

Survival Length (in months)	Frequency	Relative Frequency	Cumulative Relative Frequency
0.5–6.5			
6.5–12.5			
12.5–18.5			
18.5–24.5			
24.5–30.5			
30.5–36.5			
36.5–42.5			
42.5–48.5			

Table 1.27 Researcher A

Survival Length (in months)	Frequency	Relative Frequency	Cumulative Relative Frequency
0.5–6.5			
6.5–12.5			
12.5–18.5			
18.5–24.5			
24.5–30.5			
30.5–36.5			
36.5-45.5			

Table 1.28 Researcher B

17. Determine what the key term *data* refers to in the above example for Researcher A.

18. List two reasons why the data may differ.

19. Can you tell if one researcher is correct and the other one is incorrect? Why?

20. Would you expect the data to be identical? Why or why not?

21. Suggest at least two methods the researchers might use to gather random data.

22. Suppose that the first researcher conducted his survey by randomly choosing one state in the nation and then randomly picking 40 patients from that state. What sampling method would that researcher have used?

23. Suppose that the second researcher conducted his survey by choosing 40 patients he knew. What sampling method would that researcher have used? What concerns would you have about this data set, based upon the data collection method?

Use the following data to answer the next five exercises: Two researchers are gathering data on hours of video games played by school-aged children and young adults. They each randomly sample different groups of 150 students from the same school. They collect the following data.

Hours Played per Week	Frequency	Relative Frequency	Cumulative Relative Frequency
0–2	26	0.17	0.17

Table 1.29 Researcher A

Hours Played per Week	Frequency	Relative Frequency	Cumulative Relative Frequency
2–4	30	0.20	0.37
4–6	49	0.33	0.70
6–8	25	0.17	0.87
8–10	12	0.08	0.95
10–12	8	0.05	1

Table 1.29 Researcher A

Hours Played per Week	Frequency	Relative Frequency	Cumulative Relative Frequency
0–2	48	0.32	0.32
2–4	51	0.34	0.66
4–6	24	0.16	0.82
6–8	12	0.08	0.90
8–10	11	0.07	0.97
10–12	4	0.03	1

Table 1.30 Researcher B

24. Give a reason why the data may differ.

25. Would the sample size be large enough if the population is the students in the school?

26. Would the sample size be large enough if the population is school-aged children and young adults in the United States?

27. Researcher A concludes that most students play video games between four and six hours each week. Researcher B concludes that most students play video games between two and four hours each week. Who is correct?

28. As part of a way to reward students for participating in the survey, the researchers gave each student a gift card to a video game store. Would this affect the data if students knew about the award before the study?

Use the following data to answer the next five exercises: A pair of studies was performed to measure the effectiveness of a new software program designed to help stroke patients regain their problem-solving skills. Patients were asked to use the software program twice a day, once in the morning and once in the evening. The studies observed 200 stroke patients recovering over a period of several weeks. The first study collected the data in **Table 1.31**. The second study collected the data in **Table 1.32**.

Group	Showed improvement	No improvement	Deterioration
Used program	142	43	15
Did not use program	72	110	18

Table 1.31

Group	Showed improvement	No improvement	Deterioration
Used program	105	74	19
Did not use program	89	99	12

Table 1.32

29. Given what you know, which study is correct?

30. The first study was performed by the company that designed the software program. The second study was performed by the American Medical Association. Which study is more reliable?

31. Both groups that performed the study concluded that the software works. Is this accurate?

32. The company takes the two studies as proof that their software causes mental improvement in stroke patients. Is this a fair statement?

33. Patients who used the software were also a part of an exercise program whereas patients who did not use the software were not. Does this change the validity of the conclusions from **Exercise 1.31**?

34. Is a sample size of 1,000 a reliable measure for a population of 5,000?

35. Is a sample of 500 volunteers a reliable measure for a population of 2,500?

36. A question on a survey reads: "Do you prefer the delicious taste of Brand X or the taste of Brand Y?" Is this a fair question?

37. Is a sample size of two representative of a population of five?

38. Is it possible for two experiments to be well run with similar sample sizes to get different data?

1.3 Frequency, Frequency Tables, and Levels of Measurement

39. What type of measure scale is being used? Nominal, ordinal, interval or ratio.
  a. High school soccer players classified by their athletic ability: Superior, Average, Above average
  b. Baking temperatures for various main dishes: 350, 400, 325, 250, 300
  c. The colors of crayons in a 24-crayon box
  d. Social security numbers
  e. Incomes measured in dollars
  f. A satisfaction survey of a social website by number: 1 = very satisfied, 2 = somewhat satisfied, 3 = not satisfied
  g. Political outlook: extreme left, left-of-center, right-of-center, extreme right
  h. Time of day on an analog watch
  i. The distance in miles to the closest grocery store
  j. The dates 1066, 1492, 1644, 1947, and 1944
  k. The heights of 21–65 year-old women
  l. Common letter grades: A, B, C, D, and F

1.4 Experimental Design and Ethics

40. Design an experiment. Identify the explanatory and response variables. Describe the population being studied and the experimental units. Explain the treatments that will be used and how they will be assigned to the experimental units. Describe how blinding and placebos may be used to counter the power of suggestion.

41. Discuss potential violations of the rule requiring informed consent.
  a. Inmates in a correctional facility are offered good behavior credit in return for participation in a study.
  b. A research study is designed to investigate a new children's allergy medication.
  c. Participants in a study are told that the new medication being tested is highly promising, but they are not told that only a small portion of participants will receive the new medication. Others will receive placebo treatments and traditional treatments.

HOMEWORK

1.1 Definitions of Statistics, Probability, and Key Terms

For each of the following eight exercises, identify: a. the population, b. the sample, c. the parameter, d. the statistic, e. the variable, and f. the data. Give examples where appropriate.

42. A fitness center is interested in the mean amount of time a client exercises in the center each week.

43. Ski resorts are interested in the mean age that children take their first ski and snowboard lessons. They need this information to plan their ski classes optimally.

44. A cardiologist is interested in the mean recovery period of her patients who have had heart attacks.

45. Insurance companies are interested in the mean health costs each year of their clients, so that they can determine the costs of health insurance.

46. A politician is interested in the proportion of voters in his district who think he is doing a good job.

47. A marriage counselor is interested in the proportion of clients she counsels who stay married.

48. Political pollsters may be interested in the proportion of people who will vote for a particular cause.

49. A marketing company is interested in the proportion of people who will buy a particular product.

Use the following information to answer the next three exercises: A Lake Tahoe Community College instructor is interested in the mean number of days Lake Tahoe Community College math students are absent from class during a quarter.

50. What is the population she is interested in?
   a.   all Lake Tahoe Community College students
   b.   all Lake Tahoe Community College English students
   c.   all Lake Tahoe Community College students in her classes
   d.   all Lake Tahoe Community College math students

51. Consider the following:

X = number of days a Lake Tahoe Community College math student is absent

In this case, X is an example of a:

   a.   variable.
   b.   population.
   c.   statistic.
   d.   data.

52. The instructor's sample produces a mean number of days absent of 3.5 days. This value is an example of a:
   a.   parameter.
   b.   data.
   c.   statistic.
   d.   variable.

1.2 Data, Sampling, and Variation in Data and Sampling

For the following exercises, identify the type of data that would be used to describe a response (quantitative discrete, quantitative continuous, or qualitative), and give an example of the data.

53. number of tickets sold to a concert

54. percent of body fat

55. favorite baseball team

56. time in line to buy groceries

57. number of students enrolled at Evergreen Valley College

58. most-watched television show

59. brand of toothpaste

60. distance to the closest movie theatre

61. age of executives in Fortune 500 companies

62. number of competing computer spreadsheet software packages

Use the following information to answer the next two exercises: A study was done to determine the age, number of times per week, and the duration (amount of time) of resident use of a local park in San Jose. The first house in the neighborhood around the park was selected randomly and then every 8th house in the neighborhood around the park was interviewed.

63. "Number of times per week" is what type of data?
   a. qualitative
   b. quantitative discrete
   c. quantitative continuous

64. "Duration (amount of time)" is what type of data?
   a. qualitative
   b. quantitative discrete
   c. quantitative continuous

65. Airline companies are interested in the consistency of the number of babies on each flight, so that they have adequate safety equipment. Suppose an airline conducts a survey. Over Thanksgiving weekend, it surveys six flights from Boston to Salt Lake City to determine the number of babies on the flights. It determines the amount of safety equipment needed by the result of that study.
   a. Using complete sentences, list three things wrong with the way the survey was conducted.
   b. Using complete sentences, list three ways that you would improve the survey if it were to be repeated.

66. Suppose you want to determine the mean number of students per statistics class in your state. Describe a possible sampling method in three to five complete sentences. Make the description detailed.

67. Suppose you want to determine the mean number of cans of soda drunk each month by students in their twenties at your school. Describe a possible sampling method in three to five complete sentences. Make the description detailed.

68. List some practical difficulties involved in getting accurate results from a telephone survey.

69. List some practical difficulties involved in getting accurate results from a mailed survey.

70. With your classmates, brainstorm some ways you could overcome these problems if you needed to conduct a phone or mail survey.

71. The instructor takes her sample by gathering data on five randomly selected students from each Lake Tahoe Community College math class. The type of sampling she used is
   a. cluster sampling
   b. stratified sampling
   c. simple random sampling
   d. convenience sampling

72. A study was done to determine the age, number of times per week, and the duration (amount of time) of residents using a local park in San Jose. The first house in the neighborhood around the park was selected randomly and then every eighth house in the neighborhood around the park was interviewed. The sampling method was:
   a. simple random
   b. systematic
   c. stratified
   d. cluster

73. Name the sampling method used in each of the following situations:
   a. A woman in the airport is handing out questionnaires to travelers asking them to evaluate the airport's service. She does not ask travelers who are hurrying through the airport with their hands full of luggage, but instead asks all travelers who are sitting near gates and not taking naps while they wait.
   b. A teacher wants to know if her students are doing homework, so she randomly selects rows two and five and then calls on all students in row two and all students in row five to present the solutions to homework problems to the class.
   c. The marketing manager for an electronics chain store wants information about the ages of its customers. Over the next two weeks, at each store location, 100 randomly selected customers are given questionnaires to fill out asking for information about age, as well as about other variables of interest.
   d. The librarian at a public library wants to determine what proportion of the library users are children. The librarian has a tally sheet on which she marks whether books are checked out by an adult or a child. She records this data for every fourth patron who checks out books.
   e. A political party wants to know the reaction of voters to a debate between the candidates. The day after the debate, the party's polling staff calls 1,200 randomly selected phone numbers. If a registered voter answers the phone or is available to come to the phone, that registered voter is asked whom he or she intends to vote for and whether the debate changed his or her opinion of the candidates.

74. A "random survey" was conducted of 3,274 people of the "microprocessor generation" (people born since 1971, the year the microprocessor was invented). It was reported that 48% of those individuals surveyed stated that if they had $2,000 to spend, they would use it for computer equipment. Also, 66% of those surveyed considered themselves relatively savvy computer users.

    a. Do you consider the sample size large enough for a study of this type? Why or why not?

    b. Based on your "gut feeling," do you believe the percents accurately reflect the U.S. population for those individuals born since 1971? If not, do you think the percents of the population are actually higher or lower than the sample statistics? Why?

       Additional information: The survey, reported by Intel Corporation, was filled out by individuals who visited the Los Angeles Convention Center to see the Smithsonian Institute's road show called "America's Smithsonian."

    c. With this additional information, do you feel that all demographic and ethnic groups were equally represented at the event? Why or why not?

    d. With the additional information, comment on how accurately you think the sample statistics reflect the population parameters.

75. The Well-Being Index is a survey that follows trends of U.S. residents on a regular basis. There are six areas of health and wellness covered in the survey: Life Evaluation, Emotional Health, Physical Health, Healthy Behavior, Work Environment, and Basic Access. Some of the questions used to measure the Index are listed below.

Identify the type of data obtained from each question used in this survey: qualitative, quantitative discrete, or quantitative continuous.

    a. Do you have any health problems that prevent you from doing any of the things people your age can normally do?

    b. During the past 30 days, for about how many days did poor health keep you from doing your usual activities?

    c. In the last seven days, on how many days did you exercise for 30 minutes or more?

    d. Do you have health insurance coverage?

76. In advance of the 1936 Presidential Election, a magazine titled Literary Digest released the results of an opinion poll predicting that the republican candidate Alf Landon would win by a large margin. The magazine sent post cards to approximately 10,000,000 prospective voters. These prospective voters were selected from the subscription list of the magazine, from automobile registration lists, from phone lists, and from club membership lists. Approximately 2,300,000 people returned the postcards.

    a. Think about the state of the United States in 1936. Explain why a sample chosen from magazine subscription lists, automobile registration lists, phone books, and club membership lists was not representative of the population of the United States at that time.

    b. What effect does the low response rate have on the reliability of the sample?

    c. Are these problems examples of sampling error or nonsampling error?

    d. During the same year, George Gallup conducted his own poll of 30,000 prospective voters. These researchers used a method they called "quota sampling" to obtain survey answers from specific subsets of the population. Quota sampling is an example of which sampling method described in this module?

77. Crime-related and demographic statistics for 47 US states in 1960 were collected from government agencies, including the FBI's *Uniform Crime Report*. One analysis of this data found a strong connection between education and crime indicating that higher levels of education in a community correspond to higher crime rates.

Which of the potential problems with samples discussed in **Section 1.2** could explain this connection?

78. YouPolls is a website that allows anyone to create and respond to polls. One question posted April 15 asks:

"Do you feel happy paying your taxes when members of the Obama administration are allowed to ignore their tax liabilities?"[5]

As of April 25, 11 people responded to this question. Each participant answered "NO!"

Which of the potential problems with samples discussed in this module could explain this connection?

---

5. lastbaldeagle. 2013. On Tax Day, House to Call for Firing Federal Workers Who Owe Back Taxes. Opinion poll posted online at: http://www.youpolls.com/details.aspx?id=12328 (accessed May 1, 2013).

79. A scholarly article about response rates begins with the following quote:

"Declining contact and cooperation rates in random digit dial (RDD) national telephone surveys raise serious concerns about the validity of estimates drawn from such research."[6]

The Pew Research Center for People and the Press admits:

"The percentage of people we interview – out of all we try to interview – has been declining over the past decade or more."[7]

    a. What are some reasons for the decline in response rate over the past decade?
    b. Explain why researchers are concerned with the impact of the declining response rate on public opinion polls.

1.3 Frequency, Frequency Tables, and Levels of Measurement

80. Fifty part-time students were asked how many courses they were taking this term. The (incomplete) results are shown below:

# of Courses	Frequency	Relative Frequency	Cumulative Relative Frequency
1	30	0.6	
2	15		
3			

Table 1.33 Part-time Student Course Loads

    a. Fill in the blanks in **Table 1.33**.
    b. What percent of students take exactly two courses?
    c. What percent of students take one or two courses?

81. Sixty adults with gum disease were asked the number of times per week they used to floss before their diagnosis. The (incomplete) results are shown in **Table 1.34**.

# Flossing per Week	Frequency	Relative Frequency	Cumulative Relative Freq.
0	27	0.4500	
1	18		
3			0.9333
6	3	0.0500	
7	1	0.0167	

Table 1.34 Flossing Frequency for Adults with Gum Disease

    a. Fill in the blanks in **Table 1.34**.
    b. What percent of adults flossed six times per week?
    c. What percent flossed at most three times per week?

6. Scott Keeter et al., "Gauging the Impact of Growing Nonresponse on Estimates from a National RDD Telephone Survey," Public Opinion Quarterly 70 no. 5 (2006), http://poq.oxfordjournals.org/content/70/5/759.full (http://poq.oxfordjournals.org/content/70/5/759.full) (accessed May 1, 2013).

7. Frequently Asked Questions, Pew Research Center for the People & the Press, http://www.people-press.org/methodology/frequently-asked-questions/#dont-you-have-trouble-getting-people-to-answer-your-polls (accessed May 1, 2013).

82. Nineteen immigrants to the U.S were asked how many years, to the nearest year, they have lived in the U.S. The data are as follows: 2; 5; 7; 2; 2; 10; 20; 15; 0; 7; 0; 20; 5; 12; 15; 12; 4; 5; 10.

Table 1.35 was produced.

Data	Frequency	Relative Frequency	Cumulative Relative Frequency
0	2	$\frac{2}{19}$	0.1053
2	3	$\frac{3}{19}$	0.2632
4	1	$\frac{1}{19}$	0.3158
5	3	$\frac{3}{19}$	0.4737
7	2	$\frac{2}{19}$	0.5789
10	2	$\frac{2}{19}$	0.6842
12	2	$\frac{2}{19}$	0.7895
15	1	$\frac{1}{19}$	0.8421
20	1	$\frac{1}{19}$	1.0000

Table 1.35 Frequency of Immigrant Survey Responses

a. Fix the errors in **Table 1.35**. Also, explain how someone might have arrived at the incorrect number(s).
b. Explain what is wrong with this statement: "47 percent of the people surveyed have lived in the U.S. for 5 years."
c. Fix the statement in **b** to make it correct.
d. What fraction of the people surveyed have lived in the U.S. five or seven years?
e. What fraction of the people surveyed have lived in the U.S. at most 12 years?
f. What fraction of the people surveyed have lived in the U.S. fewer than 12 years?
g. What fraction of the people surveyed have lived in the U.S. from five to 20 years, inclusive?

83. How much time does it take to travel to work? **Table 1.36** shows the mean commute time by state for workers at least 16 years old who are not working at home. Find the mean travel time, and round off the answer properly.

24.0	24.3	25.9	18.9	27.5	17.9	21.8	20.9	16.7	27.3
18.2	24.7	20.0	22.6	23.9	18.0	31.4	22.3	24.0	25.5
24.7	24.6	28.1	24.9	22.6	23.6	23.4	25.7	24.8	25.5
21.2	25.7	23.1	23.0	23.9	26.0	16.3	23.1	21.4	21.5
27.0	27.0	18.6	31.7	23.3	30.1	22.9	23.3	21.7	18.6

Table 1.36

84. *Forbes* magazine published data on the best small firms in 2012. These were firms which had been publicly traded for at least a year, have a stock price of at least $5 per share, and have reported annual revenue between $5 million and $1 billion. **Table 1.37** shows the ages of the chief executive officers for the first 60 ranked firms.

Age	Frequency	Relative Frequency	Cumulative Relative Frequency
40–44	3		
45–49	11		
50–54	13		
55–59	16		
60–64	10		
65–69	6		
70–74	1		

Table 1.37

a. What is the frequency for CEO ages between 54 and 65?
b. What percentage of CEOs are 65 years or older?
c. What is the relative frequency of ages under 50?
d. What is the cumulative relative frequency for CEOs younger than 55?
e. Which graph shows the relative frequency and which shows the cumulative relative frequency?

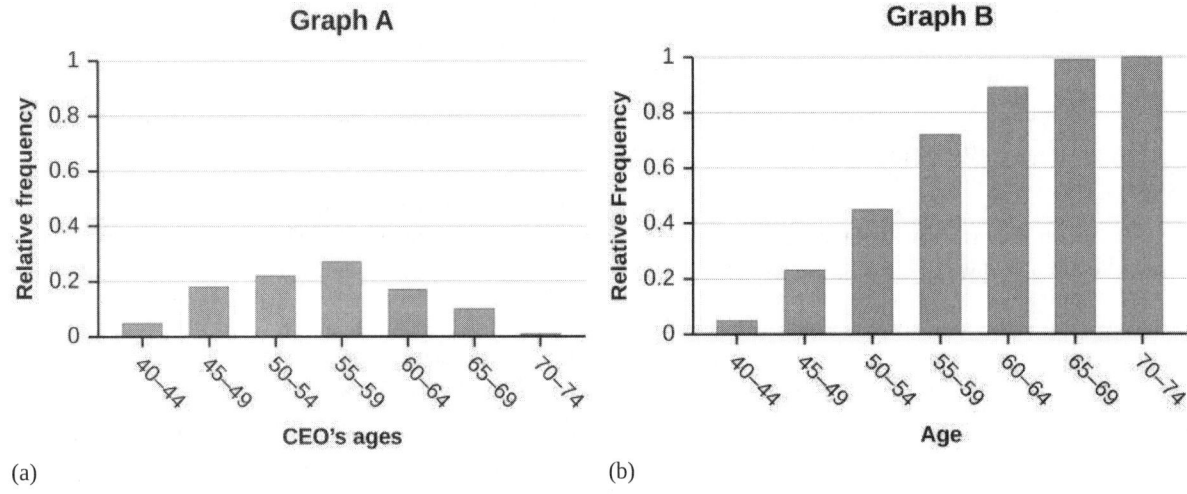

(a)   (b)

Figure 1.13

Use the following information to answer the next two exercises: **Table 1.38** contains data on hurricanes that have made direct hits on the U.S. Between 1851 and 2004. A hurricane is given a strength category rating based on the minimum wind speed generated by the storm.

Category	Number of Direct Hits	Relative Frequency	Cumulative Frequency
1	109	0.3993	0.3993
2	72	0.2637	0.6630
3	71	0.2601	
	Total = 273		

Table 1.38 Frequency of Hurricane Direct Hits

Category	Number of Direct Hits	Relative Frequency	Cumulative Frequency
4	18		0.9890
5	3	0.0110	1.0000
	Total = 273		

Table 1.38 Frequency of Hurricane Direct Hits

85. What is the relative frequency of direct hits that were category 4 hurricanes?
- a. 0.0768
- b. 0.0659
- c. 0.2601
- d. Not enough information to calculate

86. What is the relative frequency of direct hits that were AT MOST a category 3 storm?
- a. 0.3480
- b. 0.9231
- c. 0.2601
- d. 0.3370

1.4 Experimental Design and Ethics

87. How does sleep deprivation affect your ability to drive? A recent study measured the effects on 19 professional drivers. Each driver participated in two experimental sessions: one after normal sleep and one after 27 hours of total sleep deprivation. The treatments were assigned in random order. In each session, performance was measured on a variety of tasks including a driving simulation.

Use key terms from this module to describe the design of this experiment.

88. An advertisement for Acme Investments displays the two graphs in **Figure 1.14** to show the value of Acme's product in comparison with the Other Guy's product. Describe the potentially misleading visual effect of these comparison graphs. How can this be corrected?

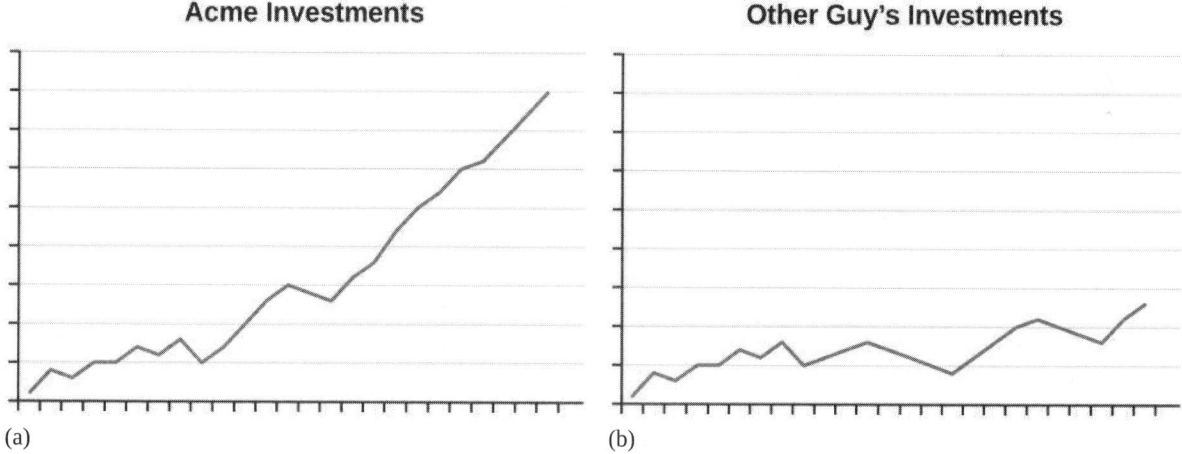

(a)   (b)

Figure 1.14 As the graphs show, Acme consistently outperforms the Other Guys!

89. The graph in **Figure 1.15** shows the number of complaints for six different airlines as reported to the US Department of Transportation in February 2013. Alaska, Pinnacle, and Airtran Airlines have far fewer complaints reported than American, Delta, and United. Can we conclude that American, Delta, and United are the worst airline carriers since they have the most complaints?

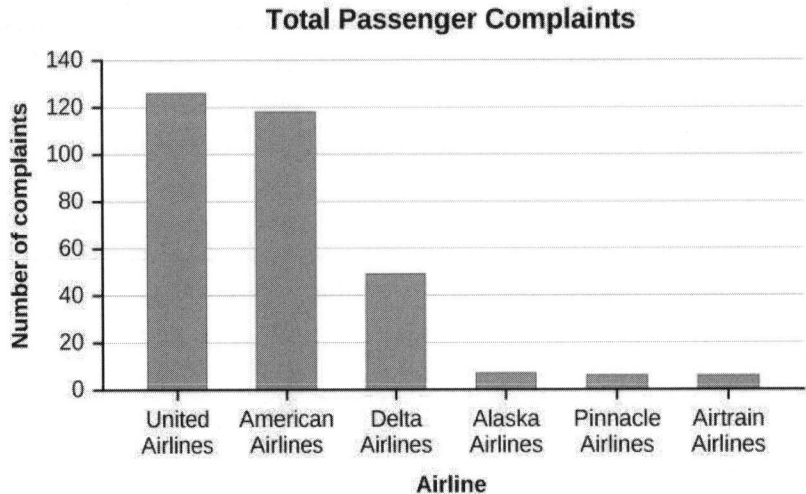

Figure 1.15

BRINGING IT TOGETHER: HOMEWORK

90. Seven hundred and seventy-one distance learning students at Long Beach City College responded to surveys in the 2010-11 academic year. Highlights of the summary report are listed in **Table 1.39**.

Have computer at home	96%
Unable to come to campus for classes	65%
Age 41 or over	24%
Would like LBCC to offer more DL courses	95%
Took DL classes due to a disability	17%
Live at least 16 miles from campus	13%
Took DL courses to fulfill transfer requirements	71%

Table 1.39 LBCC Distance Learning Survey Results

a. What percent of the students surveyed do not have a computer at home?
b. About how many students in the survey live at least 16 miles from campus?
c. If the same survey were done at Great Basin College in Elko, Nevada, do you think the percentages would be the same? Why?

91. Several online textbook retailers advertise that they have lower prices than on-campus bookstores. However, an important factor is whether the Internet retailers actually have the textbooks that students need in stock. Students need to be able to get textbooks promptly at the beginning of the college term. If the book is not available, then a student would not be able to get the textbook at all, or might get a delayed delivery if the book is back ordered.

A college newspaper reporter is investigating textbook availability at online retailers. He decides to investigate one textbook for each of the following seven subjects: calculus, biology, chemistry, physics, statistics, geology, and general engineering. He consults textbook industry sales data and selects the most popular nationally used textbook in each of these subjects. He visits websites for a random sample of major online textbook sellers and looks up each of these seven textbooks to see if they are available in stock for quick delivery through these retailers. Based on his investigation, he writes an article in which he draws conclusions about the overall availability of all college textbooks through online textbook retailers.

Write an analysis of his study that addresses the following issues: Is his sample representative of the population of all college textbooks? Explain why or why not. Describe some possible sources of bias in this study, and how it might affect the results of the study. Give some suggestions about what could be done to improve the study.

REFERENCES

1.1 Definitions of Statistics, Probability, and Key Terms

The Data and Story Library, http://lib.stat.cmu.edu/DASL/Stories/CrashTestDummies.html (accessed May 1, 2013).

1.2 Data, Sampling, and Variation in Data and Sampling

Gallup-Healthways Well-Being Index. http://www.well-beingindex.com/default.asp (accessed May 1, 2013).

Gallup-Healthways Well-Being Index. http://www.well-beingindex.com/methodology.asp (accessed May 1, 2013).

Gallup-Healthways Well-Being Index. http://www.gallup.com/poll/146822/gallup-healthways-index-questions.aspx (accessed May 1, 2013).

Data from http://www.bookofodds.com/Relationships-Society/Articles/A0374-How-George-Gallup-Picked-the-President

Dominic Lusinchi, "'President' Landon and the 1936 *Literary Digest* Poll: Were Automobile and Telephone Owners to Blame?" Social Science History 36, no. 1: 23-54 (2012), http://ssh.dukejournals.org/content/36/1/23.abstract (accessed May 1, 2013).

"The Literary Digest Poll," Virtual Laboratories in Probability and Statistics http://www.math.uah.edu/stat/data/LiteraryDigest.html (accessed May 1, 2013).

"Gallup Presidential Election Trial-Heat Trends, 1936–2008," Gallup Politics http://www.gallup.com/poll/110548/gallup-presidential-election-trialheat-trends-19362004.aspx#4 (accessed May 1, 2013).

The Data and Story Library, http://lib.stat.cmu.edu/DASL/Datafiles/USCrime.html (accessed May 1, 2013).

LBCC Distance Learning (DL) program data in 2010-2011, http://de.lbcc.edu/reports/2010-11/future/highlights.html#focus (accessed May 1, 2013).

Data from San Jose Mercury News

1.3 Frequency, Frequency Tables, and Levels of Measurement

"State & County QuickFacts," U.S. Census Bureau. http://quickfacts.census.gov/qfd/download_data.html (accessed May 1, 2013).

"State & County QuickFacts: Quick, easy access to facts about people, business, and geography," U.S. Census Bureau. http://quickfacts.census.gov/qfd/index.html (accessed May 1, 2013).

"Table 5: Direct hits by mainland United States Hurricanes (1851-2004)," National Hurricane Center, http://www.nhc.noaa.gov/gifs/table5.gif (accessed May 1, 2013).

"Levels of Measurement," http://infinity.cos.edu/faculty/woodbury/stats/tutorial/Data_Levels.htm (accessed May 1, 2013).

Courtney Taylor, "Levels of Measurement," about.com, http://statistics.about.com/od/HelpandTutorials/a/Levels-Of-Measurement.htm (accessed May 1, 2013).

David Lane. "Levels of Measurement," Connexions, http://cnx.org/content/m10809/latest/ (accessed May 1, 2013).

1.4 Experimental Design and Ethics

"Vitamin E and Health," Nutrition Source, Harvard School of Public Health, http://www.hsph.harvard.edu/nutritionsource/vitamin-e/ (accessed May 1, 2013).

Stan Reents. "Don't Underestimate the Power of Suggestion," athleteinme.com, http://www.athleteinme.com/ArticleView.aspx?id=1053 (accessed May 1, 2013).

Ankita Mehta. "Daily Dose of Aspiring Helps Reduce Heart Attacks: Study," International Business Times, July 21, 2011. Also available online at http://www.ibtimes.com/daily-dose-aspirin-helps-reduce-heart-attacks-study-300443 (accessed May 1, 2013).

The Data and Story Library, http://lib.stat.cmu.edu/DASL/Stories/ScentsandLearning.html (accessed May 1, 2013).

M.L. Jacskon et al., "Cognitive Components of Simulated Driving Performance: Sleep Loss effect and Predictors," Accident Analysis and Prevention Journal, Jan no. 50 (2013), http://www.ncbi.nlm.nih.gov/pubmed/22721550 (accessed May 1, 2013).

"Earthquake Information by Year," U.S. Geological Survey. http://earthquake.usgs.gov/earthquakes/eqarchives/year/ (accessed May 1, 2013).

"Fatality Analysis Report Systems (FARS) Encyclopedia," National Highway Traffic and Safety Administration. http://www-fars.nhtsa.dot.gov/Main/index.aspx (accessed May 1, 2013).

Data from www.businessweek.com (accessed May 1, 2013).

Data from www.forbes.com (accessed May 1, 2013).

"America's Best Small Companies," http://www.forbes.com/best-small-companies/list/ (accessed May 1, 2013).

U.S. Department of Health and Human Services, Code of Federal Regulations Title 45 Public Welfare Department of Health and Human Services Part 46 Protection of Human Subjects revised January 15, 2009. Section 46.111:Criteria for IRB Approval of Research.

"April 2013 Air Travel Consumer Report," U.S. Department of Transportation, April 11 (2013), http://www.dot.gov/airconsumer/april-2013-air-travel-consumer-report (accessed May 1, 2013).

Lori Alden, "Statistics can be Misleading," econoclass.com, http://www.econoclass.com/misleadingstats.html (accessed May 1, 2013).

Maria de los A. Medina, "Ethics in Statistics," Based on "Building an Ethics Module for Business, Science, and Engineering Students" by Jose A. Cruz-Cruz and William Frey, Connexions, http://cnx.org/content/m15555/latest/ (accessed May 1, 2013).

SOLUTIONS

1 AIDS patients.

3 The average length of time (in months) AIDS patients live after treatment.

5 X = the length of time (in months) AIDS patients live after treatment

7 b

9 a

11
  a. 0.5242
  b. 0.03%
  c. 6.86%

d. $\dfrac{823{,}088}{823{,}856}$

e. quantitative discrete

f. quantitative continuous

g. In both years, underwater earthquakes produced massive tsunamis.

13 systematic

15 simple random

17 values for *X*, such as 3, 4, 11, and so on

19 No, we do not have enough information to make such a claim.

21 Take a simple random sample from each group. One way is by assigning a number to each patient and using a random number generator to randomly select patients.

23 This would be convenience sampling and is not random.

25 Yes, the sample size of 150 would be large enough to reflect a population of one school.

27 Even though the specific data support each researcher's conclusions, the different results suggest that more data need to be collected before the researchers can reach a conclusion.

29 There is not enough information given to judge if either one is correct or incorrect.

31 The software program seems to work because the second study shows that more patients improve while using the software than not. Even though the difference is not as large as that in the first study, the results from the second study are likely more reliable and still show improvement.

33 Yes, because we cannot tell if the improvement was due to the software or the exercise; the data is confounded, and a reliable conclusion cannot be drawn. New studies should be performed.

35 No, even though the sample is large enough, the fact that the sample consists of volunteers makes it a self-selected sample, which is not reliable.

37 No, even though the sample is a large portion of the population, two responses are not enough to justify any conclusions. Because the population is so small, it would be better to include everyone in the population to get the most accurate data.

39
a. ordinal

b. interval

c. nominal

d. nominal

e. ratio

f. ordinal

g. nominal

h. interval

i. ratio

j. interval

k. ratio

l. ordinal

41
a. Inmates may not feel comfortable refusing participation, or may feel obligated to take advantage of the promised benefits. They may not feel truly free to refuse participation.

b. Parents can provide consent on behalf of their children, but children are not competent to provide consent for themselves.

c. All risks and benefits must be clearly outlined. Study participants must be informed of relevant aspects of the study in order to give appropriate consent.

43
a. all children who take ski or snowboard lessons

b. a group of these children

c. the population mean age of children who take their first snowboard lesson

d. the sample mean age of children who take their first snowboard lesson

e. X = the age of one child who takes his or her first ski or snowboard lesson

f. values for X, such as 3, 7, and so on

45
a. the clients of the insurance companies

b. a group of the clients

c. the mean health costs of the clients

d. the mean health costs of the sample

e. X = the health costs of one client

f. values for X, such as 34, 9, 82, and so on

47
a. all the clients of this counselor

b. a group of clients of this marriage counselor

c. the proportion of all her clients who stay married

d. the proportion of the sample of the counselor's clients who stay married

e. X = the number of couples who stay married

f. yes, no

49
a. all people (maybe in a certain geographic area, such as the United States)

b. a group of the people

c. the proportion of all people who will buy the product

d. the proportion of the sample who will buy the product

e. X = the number of people who will buy it

f. buy, not buy

51 a

53 quantitative discrete, 150

55 qualitative, Oakland A's

57 quantitative discrete, 11,234 students

59 qualitative, Crest

61 quantitative continuous, 47.3 years

63 b

65
a. The survey was conducted using six similar flights.
The survey would not be a true representation of the entire population of air travelers.
Conducting the survey on a holiday weekend will not produce representative results.

b. Conduct the survey during different times of the year.
Conduct the survey using flights to and from various locations.
Conduct the survey on different days of the week.

67 Answers will vary. Sample Answer: You could use a systematic sampling method. Stop the tenth person as they leave one of the buildings on campus at 9:50 in the morning. Then stop the tenth person as they leave a different building on campus at 1:50 in the afternoon.

69 Answers will vary. Sample Answer: Many people will not respond to mail surveys. If they do respond to the surveys, you can't be sure who is responding. In addition, mailing lists can be incomplete.

71 b

73 convenience; cluster; stratified ; systematic; simple random

75

a. qualitative

b. quantitative discrete

c. quantitative discrete

d. qualitative

77 Causality: The fact that two variables are related does not guarantee that one variable is influencing the other. We cannot assume that crime rate impacts education level or that education level impacts crime rate. Confounding: There are many factors that define a community other than education level and crime rate. Communities with high crime rates and high education levels may have other lurking variables that distinguish them from communities with lower crime rates and lower education levels. Because we cannot isolate these variables of interest, we cannot draw valid conclusions about the connection between education and crime. Possible lurking variables include police expenditures, unemployment levels, region, average age, and size.

79

a. Possible reasons: increased use of caller id, decreased use of landlines, increased use of private numbers, voice mail, privacy managers, hectic nature of personal schedules, decreased willingness to be interviewed

b. When a large number of people refuse to participate, then the sample may not have the same characteristics of the population. Perhaps the majority of people willing to participate are doing so because they feel strongly about the subject of the survey.

81

a.

# Flossing per Week	Frequency	Relative Frequency	Cumulative Relative Frequency
0	27	0.4500	0.4500
1	18	0.3000	0.7500
3	11	0.1833	0.9333
6	3	0.0500	0.9833
7	1	0.0167	1

Table 1.40

b. 5.00%

c. 93.33%

83 The sum of the travel times is 1,173.1. Divide the sum by 50 to calculate the mean value: 23.462. Because each state's travel time was measured to the nearest tenth, round this calculation to the nearest hundredth: 23.46.

85 b

87 Explanatory variable: amount of sleep

Response variable: performance measured in assigned tasks

Treatments: normal sleep and 27 hours of total sleep deprivation

Experimental Units: 19 professional drivers

Lurking variables: none – all drivers participated in both treatments

Random assignment: treatments were assigned in random order; this eliminated the effect of any "learning" that may take place during the first experimental session

Control/Placebo: completing the experimental session under normal sleep conditions

Blinding: researchers evaluating subjects' performance must not know which treatment is being applied at the time

89 You cannot assume that the numbers of complaints reflect the quality of the airlines. The airlines shown with the greatest number of complaints are the ones with the most passengers. You must consider the appropriateness of methods for presenting data; in this case displaying totals is misleading.

91 Answers will vary. Sample answer: The sample is not representative of the population of all college textbooks. Two reasons why it is not representative are that he only sampled seven subjects and he only investigated one textbook in each subject. There are several possible sources of bias in the study. The seven subjects that he investigated are all in mathematics and the sciences; there are many subjects in the humanities, social sciences, and other subject areas, (for example: literature, art, history, psychology, sociology, business) that he did not investigate at all. It may be that different subject areas exhibit different patterns of textbook availability, but his sample would not detect such results. He also looked only at the most popular textbook in each of the subjects he investigated. The availability of the most popular textbooks may differ from the availability of other textbooks in one of two ways:

- the most popular textbooks may be more readily available online, because more new copies are printed, and more students nationwide are selling back their used copies OR

- the most popular textbooks may be harder to find available online, because more student demand exhausts the supply more quickly.

In reality, many college students do not use the most popular textbook in their subject, and this study gives no useful information about the situation for those less popular textbooks. He could improve this study by:

- expanding the selection of subjects he investigates so that it is more representative of all subjects studied by college students, and

- expanding the selection of textbooks he investigates within each subject to include a mixed representation of both the most popular and less popular textbooks.

2 | DESCRIPTIVE STATISTICS

Figure 2.1 When you have large amounts of data, you will need to organize it in a way that makes sense. These ballots from an election are rolled together with similar ballots to keep them organized. (credit: William Greeson)

Introduction

<table>
<tr><td>Chapter Objectives</td></tr>
</table>

By the end of this chapter, the student should be able to:

- Display data graphically and interpret graphs: stemplots, histograms, and box plots.
- Recognize, describe, and calculate the measures of location of data: quartiles and percentiles.
- Recognize, describe, and calculate the measures of the center of data: mean, median, and mode.
- Recognize, describe, and calculate the measures of the spread of data: variance, standard deviation, and range.

Once you have collected data, what will you do with it? Data can be described and presented in many different formats. For example, suppose you are interested in buying a house in a particular area. You may have no clue about the house prices, so you might ask your real estate agent to give you a sample data set of prices. Looking at all the prices in the sample often is overwhelming. A better way might be to look at the median price and the variation of prices. The median and variation are just two ways that you will learn to describe data. Your agent might also provide you with a graph of the data.

In this chapter, you will study numerical and graphical ways to describe and display your data. This area of statistics is called **"Descriptive Statistics."** You will learn how to calculate, and even more importantly, how to interpret these measurements and graphs.

A statistical graph is a tool that helps you learn about the shape or distribution of a sample or a population. A graph can be a more effective way of presenting data than a mass of numbers because we can see where data clusters and where there are only a few data values. Newspapers and the Internet use graphs to show trends and to enable readers to compare facts and figures quickly. Statisticians often graph data first to get a picture of the data. Then, more formal tools may be applied.

Some of the types of graphs that are used to summarize and organize data are the dot plot, the bar graph, the histogram, the stem-and-leaf plot, the frequency polygon (a type of broken line graph), the pie chart, and the box plot. In this chapter, we will briefly look at stem-and-leaf plots, line graphs, and bar graphs, as well as frequency polygons, and time series graphs. Our emphasis will be on histograms and box plots.

NOTE

This book contains instructions for constructing a histogram and a box plot for the TI-83+ and TI-84 calculators. The **Texas Instruments (TI) website (http://education.ti.com/educationportal/sites/US/sectionHome/ support.html)** provides additional instructions for using these calculators.

2.1 | Stem-and-Leaf Graphs (Stemplots), Line Graphs, and Bar Graphs

One simple graph, the **stem-and-leaf graph** or **stemplot**, comes from the field of exploratory data analysis. It is a good choice when the data sets are small. To create the plot, divide each observation of data into a stem and a leaf. The leaf consists of a **final significant digit**. For example, 23 has stem two and leaf three. The number 432 has stem 43 and leaf two. Likewise, the number 5,432 has stem 543 and leaf two. The decimal 9.3 has stem nine and leaf three. Write the stems in a vertical line from smallest to largest. Draw a vertical line to the right of the stems. Then write the leaves in increasing order next to their corresponding stem.

Example 2.1

For Susan Dean's spring pre-calculus class, scores for the first exam were as follows (smallest to largest):
33; 42; 49; 49; 53; 55; 55; 61; 63; 67; 68; 68; 69; 69; 72; 73; 74; 78; 80; 83; 88; 88; 88; 90; 92; 94; 94; 94; 94; 96; 100

Stem	Leaf
3	3
4	2 9 9
5	3 5 5
6	1 3 7 8 8 9 9
7	2 3 4 8
8	0 3 8 8 8
9	0 2 4 4 4 4 6
10	0

Table 2.1 Stem-and-Leaf Graph

The stemplot shows that most scores fell in the 60s, 70s, 80s, and 90s. Eight out of the 31 scores or approximately

26% $\left(\frac{8}{31}\right)$ were in the 90s or 100, a fairly high number of As.

Try It Σ

2.1 For the Park City basketball team, scores for the last 30 games were as follows (smallest to largest):
32; 32; 33; 34; 38; 40; 42; 42; 43; 44; 46; 47; 47; 48; 48; 48; 49; 50; 50; 51; 52; 52; 52; 53; 54; 56; 57; 57; 60; 61
Construct a stem plot for the data.

The stemplot is a quick way to graph data and gives an exact picture of the data. You want to look for an overall pattern and any outliers. An **outlier** is an observation of data that does not fit the rest of the data. It is sometimes called an **extreme value.** When you graph an outlier, it will appear not to fit the pattern of the graph. Some outliers are due to mistakes (for example, writing down 50 instead of 500) while others may indicate that something unusual is happening. It takes some background information to explain outliers, so we will cover them in more detail later.

Example 2.2

The data are the distances (in kilometers) from a home to local supermarkets. Create a stemplot using the data:
1.1; 1.5; 2.3; 2.5; 2.7; 3.2; 3.3; 3.3; 3.5; 3.8; 4.0; 4.2; 4.5; 4.5; 4.7; 4.8; 5.5; 5.6; 6.5; 6.7; 12.3

Do the data seem to have any concentration of values?

NOTE

The leaves are to the right of the decimal.

Solution 2.2

The value 12.3 may be an outlier. Values appear to concentrate at three and four kilometers.

Stem	Leaf
1	1 5
2	3 5 7
3	2 3 3 5 8
4	0 2 5 5 7 8
5	5 6
6	5 7
7	
8	
9	
10	
11	
12	3

Table 2.2

Try It Σ

2.2 The following data show the distances (in miles) from the homes of off-campus statistics students to the college. Create a stem plot using the data and identify any outliers:

0.5; 0.7; 1.1; 1.2; 1.2; 1.3; 1.3; 1.5; 1.5; 1.7; 1.7; 1.8; 1.9; 2.0; 2.2; 2.5; 2.6; 2.8; 2.8; 2.8; 3.5; 3.8; 4.4; 4.8; 4.9; 5.2; 5.5; 5.7; 5.8; 8.0

Example 2.3

A **side-by-side stem-and-leaf plot** allows a comparison of the two data sets in two columns. In a side-by-side stem-and-leaf plot, two sets of leaves share the same stem. The leaves are to the left and the right of the stems. **Table 2.4** and **Table 2.5** show the ages of presidents at their inauguration and at their death. Construct a side-by-side stem-and-leaf plot using this data.

Solution 2.3

Ages at Inauguration		Ages at Death
9 9 8 7 7 7 6 3 2	4	6 9
8 7 7 7 7 6 6 6 5 5 5 5 4 4 4 4 4 2 2 1 1 1 1 1 1 0	5	3 6 6 7 7 8
9 8 5 4 4 2 1 1 1 0	6	0 0 3 3 4 4 5 6 7 7 7 8
	7	0 0 1 1 1 4 7 8 8 9
	8	0 1 3 5 8
	9	0 0 3 3

Table 2.3

President	Age	President	Age	President	Age
Washington	57	Lincoln	52	Hoover	54
J. Adams	61	A. Johnson	56	F. Roosevelt	51
Jefferson	57	Grant	46	Truman	60
Madison	57	Hayes	54	Eisenhower	62
Monroe	58	Garfield	49	Kennedy	43
J. Q. Adams	57	Arthur	51	L. Johnson	55
Jackson	61	Cleveland	47	Nixon	56
Van Buren	54	B. Harrison	55	Ford	61
W. H. Harrison	68	Cleveland	55	Carter	52
Tyler	51	McKinley	54	Reagan	69
Polk	49	T. Roosevelt	42	G.H.W. Bush	64
Taylor	64	Taft	51	Clinton	47
Fillmore	50	Wilson	56	G. W. Bush	54
Pierce	48	Harding	55	Obama	47
Buchanan	65	Coolidge	51		

Table 2.4 Presidential Ages at Inauguration

President	Age	President	Age	President	Age
Washington	67	Lincoln	56	Hoover	90
J. Adams	90	A. Johnson	66	F. Roosevelt	63
Jefferson	83	Grant	63	Truman	88
Madison	85	Hayes	70	Eisenhower	78
Monroe	73	Garfield	49	Kennedy	46

Table 2.5 Presidential Age at Death

President	Age	President	Age	President	Age
J. Q. Adams	80	Arthur	56	L. Johnson	64
Jackson	78	Cleveland	71	Nixon	81
Van Buren	79	B. Harrison	67	Ford	93
W. H. Harrison	68	Cleveland	71	Reagan	93
Tyler	71	McKinley	58		
Polk	53	T. Roosevelt	60		
Taylor	65	Taft	72		
Fillmore	74	Wilson	67		
Pierce	64	Harding	57		
Buchanan	77	Coolidge	60		

Table 2.5 Presidential Age at Death

2.3 The table shows the number of wins and losses the Atlanta Hawks have had in 42 seasons. Create a side-by-side stem-and-leaf plot of these wins and losses.

Losses	Wins	Year	Losses	Wins	Year
34	48	1968–1969	41	41	1989–1990
34	48	1969–1970	39	43	1990–1991
46	36	1970–1971	44	38	1991–1992
46	36	1971–1972	39	43	1992–1993
36	46	1972–1973	25	57	1993–1994
47	35	1973–1974	40	42	1994–1995
51	31	1974–1975	36	46	1995–1996
53	29	1975–1976	26	56	1996–1997
51	31	1976–1977	32	50	1997–1998
41	41	1977–1978	19	31	1998–1999
36	46	1978–1979	54	28	1999–2000
32	50	1979–1980	57	25	2000–2001
51	31	1980–1981	49	33	2001–2002
40	42	1981–1982	47	35	2002–2003
39	43	1982–1983	54	28	2003–2004
42	40	1983–1984	69	13	2004–2005
48	34	1984–1985	56	26	2005–2006
32	50	1985–1986	52	30	2006–2007

Table 2.6

Losses	Wins	Year	Losses	Wins	Year
25	57	1986–1987	45	37	2007–2008
32	50	1987–1988	35	47	2008–2009
30	52	1988–1989	29	53	2009–2010

Table 2.6

Another type of graph that is useful for specific data values is a **line graph**. In the particular line graph shown in **Example 2.4**, the *x*-axis (horizontal axis) consists of **data values** and the *y*-axis (vertical axis) consists of **frequency points**. The frequency points are connected using line segments.

Example 2.4

In a survey, 40 mothers were asked how many times per week a teenager must be reminded to do his or her chores. The results are shown in **Table 2.7** and in **Figure 2.2**.

Number of times teenager is reminded	Frequency
0	2
1	5
2	8
3	14
4	7
5	4

Table 2.7

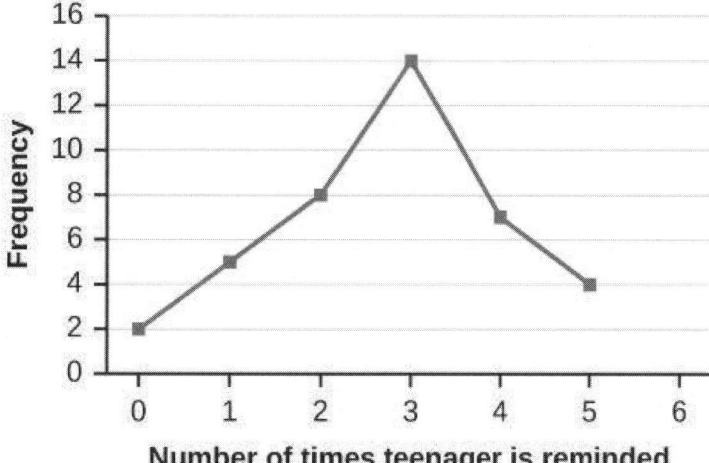

Figure 2.2

2.4 In a survey, 40 people were asked how many times per year they had their car in the shop for repairs. The results are shown in **Table 2.8**. Construct a line graph.

Number of times in shop	Frequency
0	7
1	10
2	14
3	9

Table 2.8

Bar graphs consist of bars that are separated from each other. The bars can be rectangles or they can be rectangular boxes (used in three-dimensional plots), and they can be vertical or horizontal. The **bar graph** shown in **Example 2.5** has age groups represented on the *x*-axis and proportions on the *y*-axis.

Example 2.5

By the end of 2011, Facebook had over 146 million users in the United States. **Table 2.8** shows three age groups, the number of users in each age group, and the proportion (%) of users in each age group. Construct a bar graph using this data.

Age groups	Number of Facebook users	Proportion (%) of Facebook users
13–25	65,082,280	45%
26–44	53,300,200	36%
45–64	27,885,100	19%

Table 2.9

Solution 2.5

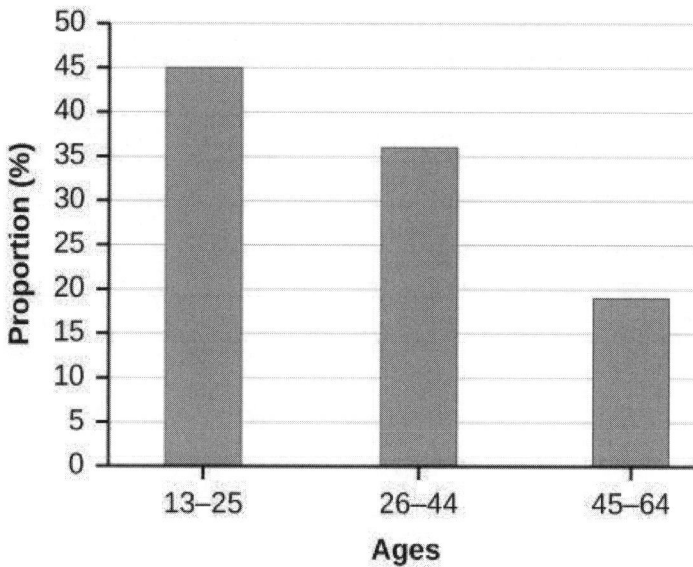

Figure 2.3

Try It ∑

2.5 The population in Park City is made up of children, working-age adults, and retirees. **Table 2.10** shows the three age groups, the number of people in the town from each age group, and the proportion (%) of people in each age group. Construct a bar graph showing the proportions.

Age groups	Number of people	Proportion of population
Children	67,059	19%
Working-age adults	152,198	43%
Retirees	131,662	38%

Table 2.10

Example 2.6

The columns in **Table 2.10** contain: the race or ethnicity of students in U.S. Public Schools for the class of 2011, percentages for the Advanced Placement examine population for that class, and percentages for the overall student population. Create a bar graph with the student race or ethnicity (qualitative data) on the *x*-axis, and the Advanced Placement examinee population percentages on the *y*-axis.

Race/Ethnicity	AP Examinee Population	Overall Student Population
1 = Asian, Asian American or Pacific Islander	10.3%	5.7%
2 = Black or African American	9.0%	14.7%
3 = Hispanic or Latino	17.0%	17.6%
4 = American Indian or Alaska Native	0.6%	1.1%
5 = White	57.1%	59.2%
6 = Not reported/other	6.0%	1.7%

Table 2.11

Solution 2.6

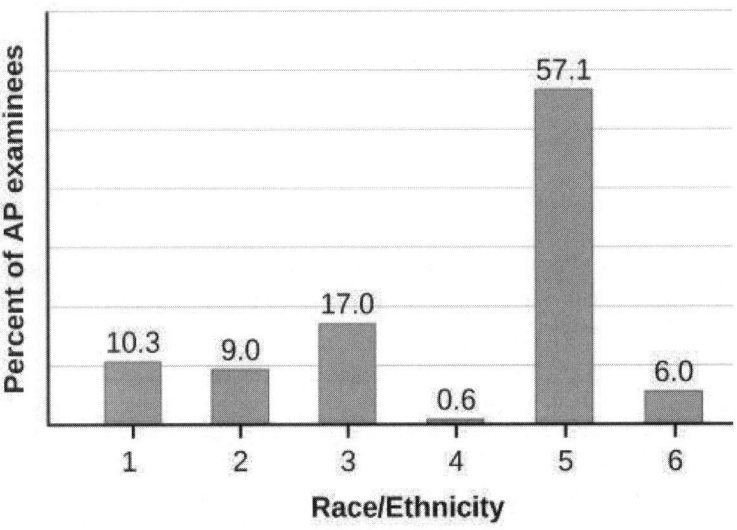

Figure 2.4

2.6 Park city is broken down into six voting districts. The table shows the percent of the total registered voter population that lives in each district as well as the percent total of the entire population that lives in each district. Construct a bar graph that shows the registered voter population by district.

District	Registered voter population	Overall city population
1	15.5%	19.4%
2	12.2%	15.6%

Table 2.12

District	Registered voter population	Overall city population
3	9.8%	9.0%
4	17.4%	18.5%
5	22.8%	20.7%
6	22.3%	16.8%

Table 2.12

2.2 | Histograms, Frequency Polygons, and Time Series Graphs

For most of the work you do in this book, you will use a histogram to display the data. One advantage of a histogram is that it can readily display large data sets. A rule of thumb is to use a histogram when the data set consists of 100 values or more.

A **histogram** consists of contiguous (adjoining) boxes. It has both a horizontal axis and a vertical axis. The horizontal axis is labeled with what the data represents (for instance, distance from your home to school). The vertical axis is labeled either **frequency** or **relative frequency** (or percent frequency or probability). The graph will have the same shape with either label. The histogram (like the stemplot) can give you the shape of the data, the center, and the spread of the data.

The relative frequency is equal to the frequency for an observed value of the data divided by the total number of data values in the sample. (Remember, frequency is defined as the number of times an answer occurs.) If:

- f = frequency
- n = total number of data values (or the sum of the individual frequencies), and
- RF = relative frequency,

then:

$$RF = \frac{f}{n}$$

For example, if three students in Mr. Ahab's English class of 40 students received from 90% to 100%, then, f = 3, n = 40, and $RF = \frac{f}{n} = \frac{3}{40}$ = 0.075. 7.5% of the students received 90–100%. 90–100% are quantitative measures.

To construct a histogram, first decide how many **bars** or **intervals**, also called classes, represent the data. Many histograms consist of five to 15 bars or classes for clarity. The number of bars needs to be chosen. Choose a starting point for the first interval to be less than the smallest data value. A **convenient starting point** is a lower value carried out to one more decimal place than the value with the most decimal places. For example, if the value with the most decimal places is 6.1 and this is the smallest value, a convenient starting point is 6.05 (6.1 – 0.05 = 6.05). We say that 6.05 has more precision. If the value with the most decimal places is 2.23 and the lowest value is 1.5, a convenient starting point is 1.495 (1.5 – 0.005 = 1.495). If the value with the most decimal places is 3.234 and the lowest value is 1.0, a convenient starting point is 0.9995 (1.0 – 0.0005 = 0.9995). If all the data happen to be integers and the smallest value is two, then a convenient starting point is 1.5 (2 – 0.5 = 1.5). Also, when the starting point and other boundaries are carried to one additional decimal place, no data value will fall on a boundary. The next two examples go into detail about how to construct a histogram using continuous data and how to create a histogram using discrete data.

Example 2.7

The following data are the heights (in inches to the nearest half inch) of 100 male semiprofessional soccer players. The heights are **continuous** data, since height is measured.
60; 60.5; 61; 61; 61.5

63.5; 63.5; 63.5

64; 64; 64; 64; 64; 64; 64; 64.5; 64.5; 64.5; 64.5; 64.5; 64.5; 64.5; 64.5

66; 66; 66; 66; 66; 66; 66; 66; 66; 66; 66.5; 66.5; 66.5; 66.5; 66.5; 66.5; 66.5; 66.5; 66.5; 66.5; 66.5; 67; 67; 67; 67; 67; 67; 67; 67; 67; 67; 67; 67; 67; 67.5; 67.5; 67.5; 67.5; 67.5; 67.5; 67.5

68; 68; 69; 69; 69; 69; 69; 69; 69; 69; 69; 69.5; 69.5; 69.5; 69.5; 69.5

70; 70; 70; 70; 70; 70; 70.5; 70.5; 70.5; 71; 71; 71

72; 72; 72; 72.5; 72.5; 73; 73.5

74

The smallest data value is 60. Since the data with the most decimal places has one decimal (for instance, 61.5), we want our starting point to have two decimal places. Since the numbers 0.5, 0.05, 0.005, etc. are convenient numbers, use 0.05 and subtract it from 60, the smallest value, for the convenient starting point.

$60 - 0.05 = 59.95$ which is more precise than, say, 61.5 by one decimal place. The starting point is, then, 59.95.

The largest value is 74, so $74 + 0.05 = 74.05$ is the ending value.

Next, calculate the width of each bar or class interval. To calculate this width, subtract the starting point from the ending value and divide by the number of bars (you must choose the number of bars you desire). Suppose you choose eight bars.

$$\frac{74.05 - 59.95}{8} = 1.76$$

NOTE

We will round up to two and make each bar or class interval two units wide. Rounding up to two is one way to prevent a value from falling on a boundary. Rounding to the next number is often necessary even if it goes against the standard rules of rounding. For this example, using 1.76 as the width would also work. A guideline that is followed by some for the number of bars or class intervals is to take the square root of the number of data values and then round to the nearest whole number, if necessary. For example, if there are 150 values of data, take the square root of 150 and round to 12 bars or intervals.

The boundaries are:

- 59.95

- $59.95 + 2 = 61.95$

- $61.95 + 2 = 63.95$

- $63.95 + 2 = 65.95$

- $65.95 + 2 = 67.95$

- $67.95 + 2 = 69.95$

- $69.95 + 2 = 71.95$

- $71.95 + 2 = 73.95$

- $73.95 + 2 = 75.95$

The heights 60 through 61.5 inches are in the interval 59.95–61.95. The heights that are 63.5 are in the interval 61.95–63.95. The heights that are 64 through 64.5 are in the interval 63.95–65.95. The heights 66 through 67.5 are in the interval 65.95–67.95. The heights 68 through 69.5 are in the interval 67.95–69.95. The heights 70 through 71 are in the interval 69.95–71.95. The heights 72 through 73.5 are in the interval 71.95–73.95. The height 74 is in the interval 73.95–75.95.

The following histogram displays the heights on the *x*-axis and relative frequency on the *y*-axis.

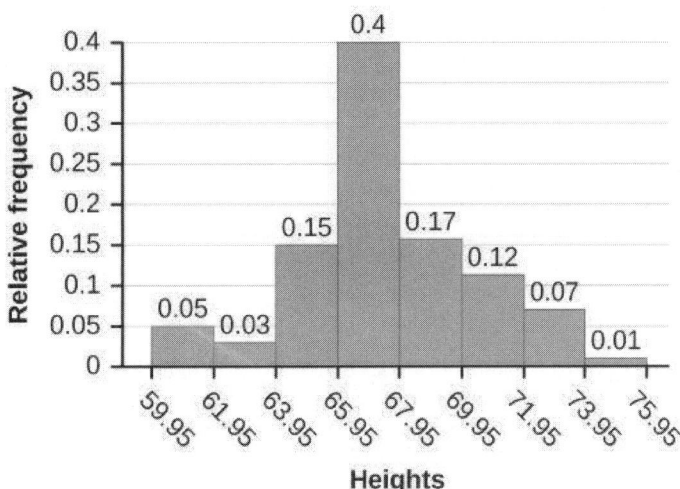

Figure 2.5

2.7 The following data are the shoe sizes of 50 male students. The sizes are continuous data since shoe size is measured. Construct a histogram and calculate the width of each bar or class interval. Suppose you choose six bars.

9; 9; 9.5; 9.5; 10; 10; 10; 10; 10; 10; 10.5; 10.5; 10.5; 10.5; 10.5; 10.5; 10.5; 10.5

11; 11; 11; 11; 11; 11; 11; 11; 11; 11; 11; 11; 11; 11.5; 11.5; 11.5; 11.5; 11.5; 11.5; 11.5

12; 12; 12; 12; 12; 12; 12; 12.5; 12.5; 12.5; 12.5; 14

Example 2.8

Create a histogram for the following data: the number of books bought by 50 part-time college students at ABC College.the number of books bought by 50 part-time college students at ABC College. The number of books is **discrete data**, since books are counted.

1; 1; 1; 1; 1; 1; 1; 1; 1; 1; 1

2; 2; 2; 2; 2; 2; 2; 2; 2; 2

3; 3; 3; 3; 3; 3; 3; 3; 3; 3; 3; 3; 3; 3; 3; 3

4; 4; 4; 4; 4; 4

5; 5; 5; 5; 5

6; 6

Eleven students buy one book. Ten students buy two books. Sixteen students buy three books. Six students buy four books. Five students buy five books. Two students buy six books.

Because the data are integers, subtract 0.5 from 1, the smallest data value and add 0.5 to 6, the largest data value. Then the starting point is 0.5 and the ending value is 6.5.

Next, calculate the width of each bar or class interval. If the data are discrete and there are not too many different values, a width that places the data values in the middle of the bar or class interval is the most convenient. Since the data consist of the numbers 1, 2, 3, 4, 5, 6, and the starting point is 0.5, a width of one places the 1 in the middle of the interval from 0.5 to 1.5, the 2 in the middle of the interval from 1.5 to 2.5, the 3 in the middle of the interval from 2.5 to 3.5, the 4 in the middle of the interval from _____ to _____, the 5 in the middle of the interval from _____ to _____, and the _____ in the middle of the interval from _____ to _____ .

Solution 2.8

- 3.5 to 4.5

- 4.5 to 5.5

- 6

- 5.5 to 6.5

Calculate the number of bars as follows:

$$\frac{6.5 - 0.5}{\text{number of bars}} = 1$$

where 1 is the width of a bar. Therefore, bars = 6.

The following histogram displays the number of books on the *x*-axis and the frequency on the *y*-axis.

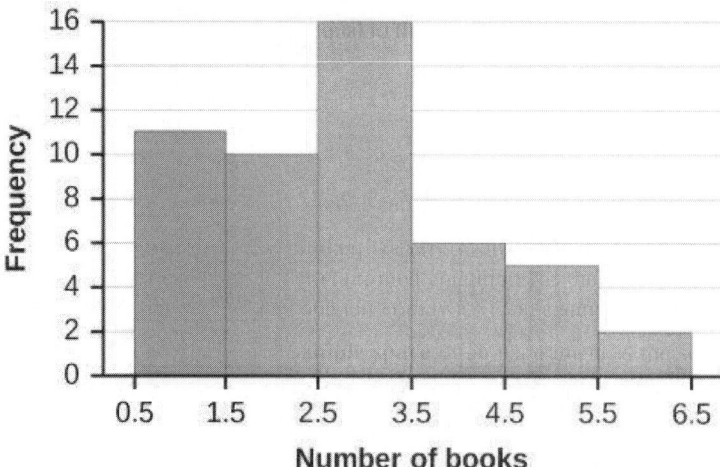

Figure 2.6

 Using the TI-83, 83+, 84, 84+ Calculator

Go to **Appendix G**. There are calculator instructions for entering data and for creating a customized histogram. Create the histogram for **Example 2.8**.

- Press Y=. Press CLEAR to delete any equations.

- Press STAT 1:EDIT. If L1 has data in it, arrow up into the name L1, press CLEAR and then arrow down. If necessary, do the same for L2.

- Into L1, enter 1, 2, 3, 4, 5, 6.

- Into L2, enter 11, 10, 16, 6, 5, 2.

- Press WINDOW. Set Xmin = .5, Xmax = 6.5, Xscl = (6.5 − .5)/6, Ymin = −1, Ymax = 20, Yscl = 1, Xres = 1.

- Press 2nd Y=. Start by pressing 4:Plotsoff ENTER.

- Press 2nd Y=. Press 1:Plot1. Press ENTER. Arrow down to TYPE. Arrow to the 3rd picture (histogram). Press ENTER.

- Arrow down to Xlist: Enter L1 (2nd 1). Arrow down to Freq. Enter L2 (2nd 2).

- Press GRAPH.

- Use the TRACE key and the arrow keys to examine the histogram.

Try It Σ

2.8 The following data are the number of sports played by 50 student athletes. The number of sports is discrete data since sports are counted.

1; 1; 1; 1; 1; 1; 1; 1; 1; 1; 1; 1; 1; 1; 1; 1; 1; 1; 1; 1
2; 2; 2; 2; 2; 2; 2; 2; 2; 2; 2; 2; 2; 2; 2; 2; 2; 2; 2; 2; 2; 2
3; 3; 3; 3; 3; 3; 3; 3
20 student athletes play one sport. 22 student athletes play two sports. Eight student athletes play three sports.

Fill in the blanks for the following sentence. Since the data consist of the numbers 1, 2, 3, and the starting point is 0.5, a width of one places the 1 in the middle of the interval 0.5 to _____, the 2 in the middle of the interval from _____ to _____, and the 3 in the middle of the interval from _____ to _____.

Example 2.9

Using this data set, construct a histogram.

Number of Hours My Classmates Spent Playing Video Games on Weekends				
9.95	10	2.25	16.75	0
19.5	22.5	7.5	15	12.75
5.5	11	10	20.75	17.5
23	21.9	24	23.75	18
20	15	22.9	18.8	20.5

Table 2.13

Solution 2.9

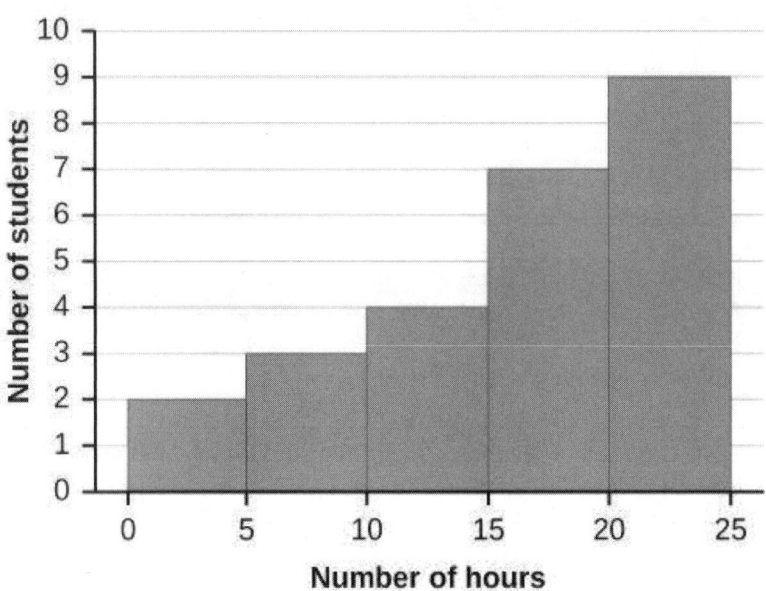

Figure 2.7

Some values in this data set fall on boundaries for the class intervals. A value is counted in a class interval if it falls on the left boundary, but not if it falls on the right boundary. Different researchers may set up histograms for the same data in different ways. There is more than one correct way to set up a histogram.

Try It Σ

2.9 The following data represent the number of employees at various restaurants in New York City. Using this data, create a histogram.

22; 35; 15; 26; 40; 28; 18; 20; 25; 34; 39; 42; 24; 22; 19; 27; 22; 34; 40; 20; 38; and 28
Use 10–19 as the first interval.

Collaborative Exercise

Count the money (bills and change) in your pocket or purse. Your instructor will record the amounts. As a class, construct a histogram displaying the data. Discuss how many intervals you think is appropriate. You may want to experiment with the number of intervals.

Frequency Polygons

Frequency polygons are analogous to line graphs, and just as line graphs make continuous data visually easy to interpret, so too do frequency polygons.

To construct a frequency polygon, first examine the data and decide on the number of intervals, or class intervals, to use on the *x*-axis and *y*-axis. After choosing the appropriate ranges, begin plotting the data points. After all the points are plotted, draw line segments to connect them.

Example 2.10

A frequency polygon was constructed from the frequency table below.

Frequency Distribution for Calculus Final Test Scores			
Lower Bound	**Upper Bound**	**Frequency**	**Cumulative Frequency**
49.5	59.5	5	5
59.5	69.5	10	15
69.5	79.5	30	45
79.5	89.5	40	85
89.5	99.5	15	100

Table 2.14

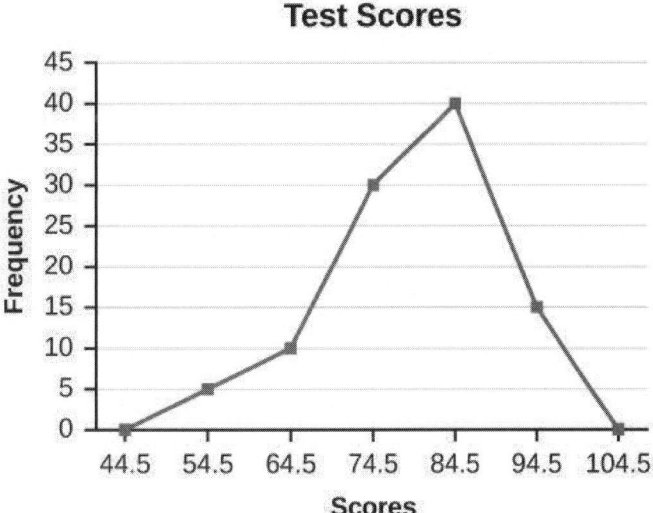

Figure 2.8

The first label on the *x*-axis is 44.5. This represents an interval extending from 39.5 to 49.5. Since the lowest test score is 54.5, this interval is used only to allow the graph to touch the *x*-axis. The point labeled 54.5 represents the next interval, or the first "real" interval from the table, and contains five scores. This reasoning is followed for each of the remaining intervals with the point 104.5 representing the interval from 99.5 to 109.5. Again, this interval contains no data and is only used so that the graph will touch the *x*-axis. Looking at the graph, we say that this distribution is skewed because one side of the graph does not mirror the other side.

Try It Σ

2.10 Construct a frequency polygon of U.S. Presidents' ages at inauguration shown in **Table 2.15**.

Age at Inauguration	Frequency
41.5–46.5	4
46.5–51.5	11
51.5–56.5	14
56.5–61.5	9
61.5–66.5	4
66.5–71.5	2

Table 2.15

Frequency polygons are useful for comparing distributions. This is achieved by overlaying the frequency polygons drawn for different data sets.

Example 2.11

We will construct an overlay frequency polygon comparing the scores from **Example 2.10** with the students' final numeric grade.

Frequency Distribution for Calculus Final Test Scores			
Lower Bound	**Upper Bound**	**Frequency**	**Cumulative Frequency**
49.5	59.5	5	5
59.5	69.5	10	15
69.5	79.5	30	45
79.5	89.5	40	85
89.5	99.5	15	100

Table 2.16

Frequency Distribution for Calculus Final Grades			
Lower Bound	**Upper Bound**	**Frequency**	**Cumulative Frequency**
49.5	59.5	10	10
59.5	69.5	10	20
69.5	79.5	30	50
79.5	89.5	45	95
89.5	99.5	5	100

Table 2.17

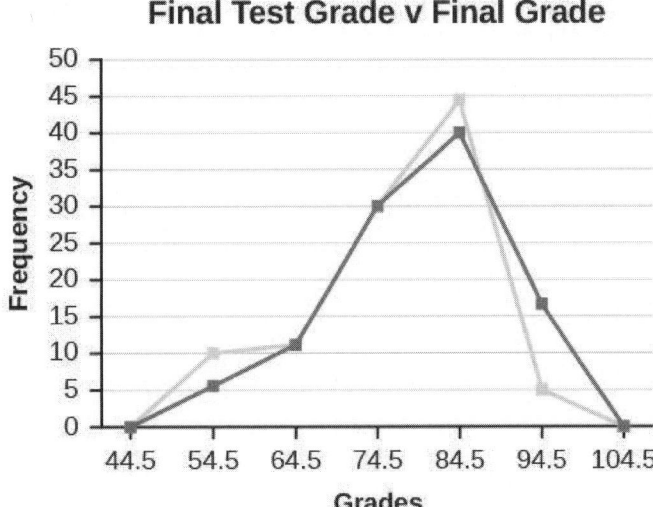

Figure 2.9

Suppose that we want to study the temperature range of a region for an entire month. Every day at noon we note the temperature and write this down in a log. A variety of statistical studies could be done with this data. We could find the mean or the median temperature for the month. We could construct a histogram displaying the number of days that temperatures reach a certain range of values. However, all of these methods ignore a portion of the data that we have collected.

One feature of the data that we may want to consider is that of time. Since each date is paired with the temperature reading for the day, we don't have to think of the data as being random. We can instead use the times given to impose a chronological order on the data. A graph that recognizes this ordering and displays the changing temperature as the month progresses is called a time series graph.

Constructing a Time Series Graph

To construct a time series graph, we must look at both pieces of our **paired data set**. We start with a standard Cartesian coordinate system. The horizontal axis is used to plot the date or time increments, and the vertical axis is used to plot the values of the variable that we are measuring. By doing this, we make each point on the graph correspond to a date and a measured quantity. The points on the graph are typically connected by straight lines in the order in which they occur.

Example 2.12

The following data shows the Annual Consumer Price Index, each month, for ten years. Construct a time series graph for the Annual Consumer Price Index data only.

Year	Jan	Feb	Mar	Apr	May	Jun	Jul
2003	181.7	183.1	184.2	183.8	183.5	183.7	183.9
2004	185.2	186.2	187.4	188.0	189.1	189.7	189.4
2005	190.7	191.8	193.3	194.6	194.4	194.5	195.4
2006	198.3	198.7	199.8	201.5	202.5	202.9	203.5
2007	202.416	203.499	205.352	206.686	207.949	208.352	208.299
2008	211.080	211.693	213.528	214.823	216.632	218.815	219.964
2009	211.143	212.193	212.709	213.240	213.856	215.693	215.351
2010	216.687	216.741	217.631	218.009	218.178	217.965	218.011
2011	220.223	221.309	223.467	224.906	225.964	225.722	225.922
2012	226.665	227.663	229.392	230.085	229.815	229.478	229.104

Table 2.18

Year	Aug	Sep	Oct	Nov	Dec	Annual
2003	184.6	185.2	185.0	184.5	184.3	184.0
2004	189.5	189.9	190.9	191.0	190.3	188.9
2005	196.4	198.8	199.2	197.6	196.8	195.3
2006	203.9	202.9	201.8	201.5	201.8	201.6
2007	207.917	208.490	208.936	210.177	210.036	207.342
2008	219.086	218.783	216.573	212.425	210.228	215.303
2009	215.834	215.969	216.177	216.330	215.949	214.537
2010	218.312	218.439	218.711	218.803	219.179	218.056
2011	226.545	226.889	226.421	226.230	225.672	224.939
2012	230.379	231.407	231.317	230.221	229.601	229.594

Table 2.19

Solution 2.12

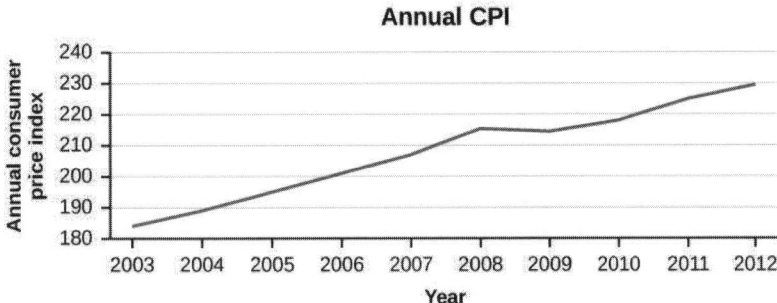

Figure 2.10

Try It Σ

2.12 The following table is a portion of a data set from www.worldbank.org. Use the table to construct a time series graph for CO_2 emissions for the United States.

CO2 Emissions			
	Ukraine	**United Kingdom**	**United States**
2003	352,259	540,640	5,681,664
2004	343,121	540,409	5,790,761
2005	339,029	541,990	5,826,394
2006	327,797	542,045	5,737,615
2007	328,357	528,631	5,828,697
2008	323,657	522,247	5,656,839
2009	272,176	474,579	5,299,563

Table 2.20

Uses of a Time Series Graph

Time series graphs are important tools in various applications of statistics. When recording values of the same variable over an extended period of time, sometimes it is difficult to discern any trend or pattern. However, once the same data points are displayed graphically, some features jump out. Time series graphs make trends easy to spot.

2.3 | Measures of the Location of the Data

The common measures of location are **quartiles** and **percentiles**

Quartiles are special percentiles. The first quartile, Q_1, is the same as the 25th percentile, and the third quartile, Q_3, is the same as the 75th percentile. The median, M, is called both the second quartile and the 50th percentile.

To calculate quartiles and percentiles, the data must be ordered from smallest to largest. Quartiles divide ordered data into quarters. Percentiles divide ordered data into hundredths. To score in the 90th percentile of an exam does not mean, necessarily, that you received 90% on a test. It means that 90% of test scores are the same or less than your score and 10% of the test scores are the same or greater than your test score.

Percentiles are useful for comparing values. For this reason, universities and colleges use percentiles extensively. One instance in which colleges and universities use percentiles is when SAT results are used to determine a minimum testing score that will be used as an acceptance factor. For example, suppose Duke accepts SAT scores at or above the 75th percentile. That translates into a score of at least 1220.

Percentiles are mostly used with very large populations. Therefore, if you were to say that 90% of the test scores are less (and not the same or less) than your score, it would be acceptable because removing one particular data value is not significant.

The **median** is a number that measures the "center" of the data. You can think of the median as the "middle value," but it does not actually have to be one of the observed values. It is a number that separates ordered data into halves. Half the values are the same number or smaller than the median, and half the values are the same number or larger. For example, consider the following data.
1; 11.5; 6; 7.2; 4; 8; 9; 10; 6.8; 8.3; 2; 2; 10; 1
Ordered from smallest to largest:
1; 1; 2; 2; 4; 6; 6.8; 7.2; 8; 8.3; 9; 10; 10; 11.5

Since there are 14 observations, the median is between the seventh value, 6.8, and the eighth value, 7.2. To find the median, add the two values together and divide by two.

$$\frac{6.8 + 7.2}{2} = 7$$

The median is seven. Half of the values are smaller than seven and half of the values are larger than seven.

Quartiles are numbers that separate the data into quarters. Quartiles may or may not be part of the data. To find the quartiles, first find the median or second quartile. The first quartile, Q_1, is the middle value of the lower half of the data, and the third quartile, Q_3, is the middle value, or median, of the upper half of the data. To get the idea, consider the same data set:
1; 1; 2; 2; 4; 6; 6.8; 7.2; 8; 8.3; 9; 10; 10; 11.5

The median or **second quartile** is seven. The lower half of the data are 1, 1, 2, 2, 4, 6, 6.8. The middle value of the lower half is two.
1; 1; 2; 2; 4; 6; 6.8

The number two, which is part of the data, is the **first quartile**. One-fourth of the entire sets of values are the same as or less than two and three-fourths of the values are more than two.

The upper half of the data is 7.2, 8, 8.3, 9, 10, 10, 11.5. The middle value of the upper half is nine.

The **third quartile**, Q_3, is nine. Three-fourths (75%) of the ordered data set are less than nine. One-fourth (25%) of the ordered data set are greater than nine. The third quartile is part of the data set in this example.

The **interquartile range** is a number that indicates the spread of the middle half or the middle 50% of the data. It is the difference between the third quartile (Q_3) and the first quartile (Q_1).

$IQR = Q_3 - Q_1$

The IQR can help to determine potential **outliers**. **A value is suspected to be a potential outlier if it is less than (1.5)(IQR) below the first quartile or more than (1.5)(IQR) above the third quartile**. Potential outliers always require further investigation.

NOTE

A potential outlier is a data point that is significantly different from the other data points. These special data points may be errors or some kind of abnormality or they may be a key to understanding the data.

Example 2.13

For the following 13 real estate prices, calculate the IQR and determine if any prices are potential outliers. Prices are in dollars.
389,950; 230,500; 158,000; 479,000; 639,000; 114,950; 5,500,000; 387,000; 659,000; 529,000; 575,000; 488,800; 1,095,000

Solution 2.13

Order the data from smallest to largest.
114,950; 158,000; 230,500; 387,000; 389,950; 479,000; 488,800; 529,000; 575,000; 639,000; 659,000; 1,095,000; 5,500,000

$M = 488,800$

$Q_1 = \dfrac{230,500 + 387,000}{2} = 308,750$

$Q_3 = \dfrac{639,000 + 659,000}{2} = 649,000$

$IQR = 649,000 - 308,750 = 340,250$

$(1.5)(IQR) = (1.5)(340,250) = 510,375$

$Q_1 - (1.5)(IQR) = 308,750 - 510,375 = -201,625$

$Q_3 + (1.5)(IQR) = 649,000 + 510,375 = 1,159,375$

No house price is less than –201,625. However, 5,500,000 is more than 1,159,375. Therefore, 5,500,000 is a potential **outlier**.

Try It Σ

2.13 For the following 11 salaries, calculate the *IQR* and determine if any salaries are outliers. The salaries are in dollars.

$33,000; $64,500; $28,000; $54,000; $72,000; $68,500; $69,000; $42,000; $54,000; $120,000; $40,500

Example 2.14

For the two data sets in the **test scores example**, find the following:

a. The interquartile range. Compare the two interquartile ranges.

b. Any outliers in either set.

Solution 2.14

The five number summary for the day and night classes is

	Minimum	Q_1	Median	Q_3	Maximum
Day	32	56	74.5	82.5	99
Night	25.5	78	81	89	98

Table 2.21

a. The IQR for the day group is $Q_3 - Q_1 = 82.5 - 56 = 26.5$
The IQR for the night group is $Q_3 - Q_1 = 89 - 78 = 11$

The interquartile range (the spread or variability) for the day class is larger than the night class *IQR*. This suggests more variation will be found in the day class's class test scores.

b. Day class outliers are found using the IQR times 1.5 rule. So,
$Q_1 - IQR(1.5) = 56 - 26.5(1.5) = 16.25$

$Q_3 + IQR(1.5) = 82.5 + 26.5(1.5) = 122.25$

Since the minimum and maximum values for the day class are greater than 16.25 and less than 122.25, there are no outliers.

Night class outliers are calculated as:

$Q_1 - IQR\ (1.5) = 78 - 11(1.5) = 61.5$

$Q_3 + IQR(1.5) = 89 + 11(1.5) = 105.5$

For this class, any test score less than 61.5 is an outlier. Therefore, the scores of 45 and 25.5 are outliers. Since no test score is greater than 105.5, there is no upper end outlier.

2.14 Find the interquartile range for the following two data sets and compare them.

Test Scores for Class *A*
69; 96; 81; 79; 65; 76; 83; 99; 89; 67; 90; 77; 85; 98; 66; 91; 77; 69; 80; 94
Test Scores for Class *B*
90; 72; 80; 92; 90; 97; 92; 75; 79; 68; 70; 80; 99; 95; 78; 73; 71; 68; 95; 100

Example 2.15

Fifty statistics students were asked how much sleep they get per school night (rounded to the nearest hour). The results were:

AMOUNT OF SLEEP PER SCHOOL NIGHT (HOURS)	FREQUENCY	RELATIVE FREQUENCY	CUMULATIVE RELATIVE FREQUENCY
4	2	0.04	0.04
5	5	0.10	0.14
6	7	0.14	0.28
7	12	0.24	0.52
8	14	0.28	0.80
9	7	0.14	0.94
10	3	0.06	1.00

Table 2.22

Find the 28th percentile. Notice the 0.28 in the "cumulative relative frequency" column. Twenty-eight percent of 50 data values is 14 values. There are 14 values less than the 28th percentile. They include the two 4s, the five 5s, and the seven 6s. The 28th percentile is between the last six and the first seven. **The 28th percentile is 6.5.**

Find the median. Look again at the "cumulative relative frequency" column and find 0.52. The median is the 50th percentile or the second quartile. 50% of 50 is 25. There are 25 values less than the median. They include the two 4s, the five 5s, the seven 6s, and eleven of the 7s. The median or 50th percentile is between the 25th, or seven, and 26th, or seven, values. **The median is seven.**

Find the third quartile. The third quartile is the same as the 75th percentile. You can "eyeball" this answer. If you look at the "cumulative relative frequency" column, you find 0.52 and 0.80. When you have all the fours, fives, sixes and sevens, you have 52% of the data. When you include all the 8s, you have 80% of the data. **The 75th percentile, then, must be an eight**. Another way to look at the problem is to find 75% of 50, which is 37.5, and round up to 38. The third quartile, Q_3, is the 38th value, which is an eight. You can check this answer by counting the values. (There are 37 values below the third quartile and 12 values above.)

Try It Σ

2.15 Forty bus drivers were asked how many hours they spend each day running their routes (rounded to the nearest hour). Find the 65th percentile.

Amount of time spent on route (hours)	Frequency	Relative Frequency	Cumulative Relative Frequency
2	12	0.30	0.30
3	14	0.35	0.65
4	10	0.25	0.90
5	4	0.10	1.00

Table 2.23

Example 2.16

Using **Table 2.22**:

a. Find the 80th percentile.

b. Find the 90th percentile.

c. Find the first quartile. What is another name for the first quartile?

Solution 2.16

Using the data from the frequency table, we have:

a. The 80th percentile is between the last eight and the first nine in the table (between the 40th and 41st values). Therefore, we need to take the mean of the 40th an 41st values. The 80th percentile $= \frac{8+9}{2} = 8.5$

b. The 90th percentile will be the 45th data value (location is 0.90(50) = 45) and the 45th data value is nine.

c. Q_1 is also the 25th percentile. The 25th percentile location calculation: $P_{25} = 0.25(50) = 12.5 \approx 13$ the 13th data value. Thus, the 25th percentile is six.

Try It Σ

2.16 Refer to the **Table 2.23**. Find the third quartile. What is another name for the third quartile?

Collaborative Exercise

Your instructor or a member of the class will ask everyone in class how many sweaters they own. Answer the following questions:

1. How many students were surveyed?

2. What kind of sampling did you do?

3. Construct two different histograms. For each, starting value = _____ ending value = ____.

4. Find the median, first quartile, and third quartile.

5. Construct a table of the data to find the following:

   a. the 10th percentile

   b. the 70th percentile

   c. the percent of students who own less than four sweaters

A Formula for Finding the *k*th Percentile

If you were to do a little research, you would find several formulas for calculating the kth percentile. Here is one of them.

k = the kth percentile. It may or may not be part of the data.

i = the index (ranking or position of a data value)

n = the total number of data

- Order the data from smallest to largest.

- Calculate $i = \frac{k}{100}(n + 1)$

- If i is an integer, then the kth percentile is the data value in the ith position in the ordered set of data.

- If i is not an integer, then round i up and round i down to the nearest integers. Average the two data values in these two positions in the ordered data set. This is easier to understand in an example.

Example 2.17

Listed are 29 ages for Academy Award winning best actors *in order from smallest to largest.*
18; 21; 22; 25; 26; 27; 29; 30; 31; 33; 36; 37; 41; 42; 47; 52; 55; 57; 58; 62; 64; 67; 69; 71; 72; 73; 74; 76; 77

a. Find the 70th percentile.

b. Find the 83rd percentile.

Solution 2.17

a. $k = 70$
   i = the index
   $n = 29$
   $i = \frac{k}{100}(n + 1) = (\frac{70}{100})(29 + 1) = 21$. Twenty-one is an integer, and the data value in the 21st position in the ordered data set is 64. The 70th percentile is 64 years.

b. $k = 83$rd percentile
   i = the index

$n = 29$

$i = \dfrac{k}{100}(n + 1) =)\dfrac{83}{100})(29 + 1) = 24.9$, which is NOT an integer. Round it down to 24 and up to 25. The age in the 24th position is 71 and the age in the 25th position is 72. Average 71 and 72. The 83rd percentile is 71.5 years.

Try It Σ

2.17 Listed are 29 ages for Academy Award winning best actors *in order from smallest to largest.*

18; 21; 22; 25; 26; 27; 29; 30; 31; 33; 36; 37; 41; 42; 47; 52; 55; 57; 58; 62; 64; 67; 69; 71; 72; 73; 74; 76; 77
Calculate the 20th percentile and the 55th percentile.

NOTE

 You can calculate percentiles using calculators and computers. There are a variety of online calculators.

A Formula for Finding the Percentile of a Value in a Data Set

- Order the data from smallest to largest.
- x = the number of data values counting from the bottom of the data list up to but not including the data value for which you want to find the percentile.
- y = the number of data values equal to the data value for which you want to find the percentile.
- n = the total number of data.
- Calculate $\dfrac{x + 0.5y}{n}(100)$. Then round to the nearest integer.

Example 2.18

Listed are 29 ages for Academy Award winning best actors *in order from smallest to largest.*
18; 21; 22; 25; 26; 27; 29; 30; 31; 33; 36; 37; 41; 42; 47; 52; 55; 57; 58; 62; 64; 67; 69; 71; 72; 73; 74; 76; 77

a. Find the percentile for 58.
b. Find the percentile for 25.

Solution 2.18

a. Counting from the bottom of the list, there are 18 data values less than 58. There is one value of 58.
   $x = 18$ and $y = 1$. $\dfrac{x + 0.5y}{n}(100) = \dfrac{18 + 0.5(1)}{29}(100) = 63.80$. 58 is the 64th percentile.

b. Counting from the bottom of the list, there are three data values less than 25. There is one value of 25.
   $x = 3$ and $y = 1$. $\dfrac{x + 0.5y}{n}(100) = \dfrac{3 + 0.5(1)}{29}(100) = 12.07$. Twenty-five is the 12th percentile.

2.18 Listed are 30 ages for Academy Award winning best actors <u>in order from smallest to largest.</u>

18; 21; 22; 25; 26; 27; 29; 30; 31; 31; 33; 36; 37; 41; 42; 47; 52; 55; 57; 58; 62; 64; 67; 69; 71; 72; 73; 74; 76; 77
Find the percentiles for 47 and 31.

Interpreting Percentiles, Quartiles, and Median

A percentile indicates the relative standing of a data value when data are sorted into numerical order from smallest to largest. Percentages of data values are less than or equal to the pth percentile. For example, 15% of data values are less than or equal to the 15th percentile.

- Low percentiles always correspond to lower data values.

- High percentiles always correspond to higher data values.

A percentile may or may not correspond to a value judgment about whether it is "good" or "bad." The interpretation of whether a certain percentile is "good" or "bad" depends on the context of the situation to which the data applies. In some situations, a low percentile would be considered "good;" in other contexts a high percentile might be considered "good". In many situations, there is no value judgment that applies.

Understanding how to interpret percentiles properly is important not only when describing data, but also when calculating probabilities in later chapters of this text.

NOTE

When writing the interpretation of a percentile in the context of the given data, the sentence should contain the following information.

- information about the context of the situation being considered

- the data value (value of the variable) that represents the percentile

- the percent of individuals or items with data values below the percentile

- the percent of individuals or items with data values above the percentile.

Example 2.19

On a timed math test, the first quartile for time it took to finish the exam was 35 minutes. Interpret the first quartile in the context of this situation.

Solution 2.19
- Twenty-five percent of students finished the exam in 35 minutes or less.

- Seventy-five percent of students finished the exam in 35 minutes or more.

- A low percentile could be considered good, as finishing more quickly on a timed exam is desirable. (If you take too long, you might not be able to finish.)

2.19 For the 100-meter dash, the third quartile for times for finishing the race was 11.5 seconds. Interpret the third quartile in the context of the situation.

Example 2.20

On a 20 question math test, the 70th percentile for number of correct answers was 16. Interpret the 70th percentile in the context of this situation.

Solution 2.20

- Seventy percent of students answered 16 or fewer questions correctly.

- Thirty percent of students answered 16 or more questions correctly.

- A higher percentile could be considered good, as answering more questions correctly is desirable.

2.20 On a 60 point written assignment, the 80th percentile for the number of points earned was 49. Interpret the 80th percentile in the context of this situation.

Example 2.21

At a community college, it was found that the 30th percentile of credit units that students are enrolled for is seven units. Interpret the 30th percentile in the context of this situation.

Solution 2.21

- Thirty percent of students are enrolled in seven or fewer credit units.

- Seventy percent of students are enrolled in seven or more credit units.

- In this example, there is no "good" or "bad" value judgment associated with a higher or lower percentile. Students attend community college for varied reasons and needs, and their course load varies according to their needs.

2.21 During a season, the 40th percentile for points scored per player in a game is eight. Interpret the 40th percentile in the context of this situation.

Example 2.22

Sharpe Middle School is applying for a grant that will be used to add fitness equipment to the gym. The principal surveyed 15 anonymous students to determine how many minutes a day the students spend exercising. The results from the 15 anonymous students are shown.

0 minutes; 40 minutes; 60 minutes; 30 minutes; 60 minutes

10 minutes; 45 minutes; 30 minutes; 300 minutes; 90 minutes;

30 minutes; 120 minutes; 60 minutes; 0 minutes; 20 minutes

Determine the following five values.

Min = 0

$Q_1 = 20$

Med = 40

Q_3 = 60

Max = 300

If you were the principal, would you be justified in purchasing new fitness equipment? Since 75% of the students exercise for 60 minutes or less daily, and since the *IQR* is 40 minutes (60 − 20 = 40), we know that half of the students surveyed exercise between 20 minutes and 60 minutes daily. This seems a reasonable amount of time spent exercising, so the principal would be justified in purchasing the new equipment.

However, the principal needs to be careful. The value 300 appears to be a potential outlier.

Q_3 + 1.5(*IQR*) = 60 + (1.5)(40) = 120.

The value 300 is greater than 120 so it is a potential outlier. If we delete it and calculate the five values, we get the following values:

Min = 0

Q_1 = 20

Q_3 = 60

Max = 120

We still have 75% of the students exercising for 60 minutes or less daily and half of the students exercising between 20 and 60 minutes a day. However, 15 students is a small sample and the principal should survey more students to be sure of his survey results.

2.4 | Box Plots

Box plots (also called **box-and-whisker plots** or **box-whisker plots**) give a good graphical image of the concentration of the data. They also show how far the extreme values are from most of the data. A box plot is constructed from five values: the minimum value, the first quartile, the median, the third quartile, and the maximum value. We use these values to compare how close other data values are to them.

To construct a box plot, use a horizontal or vertical number line and a rectangular box. The smallest and largest data values label the endpoints of the axis. The first quartile marks one end of the box and the third quartile marks the other end of the box. Approximately **the middle 50 percent of the data fall inside the box.** The "whiskers" extend from the ends of the box to the smallest and largest data values. The median or second quartile can be between the first and third quartiles, or it can be one, or the other, or both. The box plot gives a good, quick picture of the data.

NOTE

You may encounter box-and-whisker plots that have dots marking outlier values. In those cases, the whiskers are not extending to the minimum and maximum values.

Consider, again, this dataset.

1; 1; 2; 2; 4; 6; 6.8; 7.2; 8; 8.3; 9; 10; 10; 11.5

The first quartile is two, the median is seven, and the third quartile is nine. The smallest value is one, and the largest value is 11.5. The following image shows the constructed box plot.

NOTE

See the calculator instructions on the **TI web site (http://education.ti.com/educationportal/sites/US/ sectionHome/support.html)** or in the appendix.

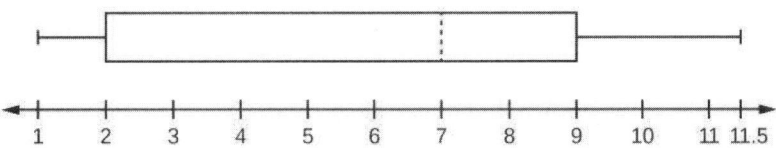

Figure 2.11

The two whiskers extend from the first quartile to the smallest value and from the third quartile to the largest value. The median is shown with a dashed line.

NOTE
___

It is important to start a box plot with a **scaled number line**. Otherwise the box plot may not be useful.

Example 2.23

The following data are the heights of 40 students in a statistics class.

59; 60; 61; 62; 62; 63; 63; 64; 64; 64; 65; 65; 65; 65; 65; 65; 65; 65; 65; 66; 66; 67; 67; 68; 68; 69; 70; 70; 70; 70; 70; 71; 71; 72; 72; 73; 74; 74; 75; 77

Construct a box plot with the following properties; the calculator intructions for the minimum and maximum values as well as the quartiles follow the example.

- Minimum value = 59

- Maximum value = 77

- Q1: First quartile = 64.5

- Q2: Second quartile or median= 66

- Q3: Third quartile = 70

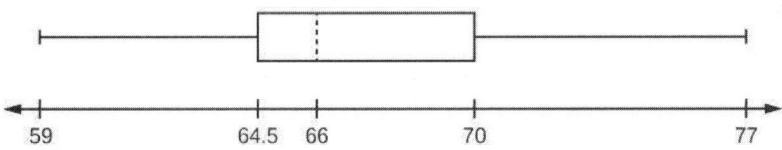

Figure 2.12

a. Each quarter has approximately 25% of the data.

b. The spreads of the four quarters are 64.5 – 59 = 5.5 (first quarter), 66 – 64.5 = 1.5 (second quarter), 70 – 66 = 4 (third quarter), and 77 – 70 = 7 (fourth quarter). So, the second quarter has the smallest spread and the fourth quarter has the largest spread.

c. Range = maximum value – the minimum value = 77 – 59 = 18

d. Interquartile Range: $IQR = Q3 - Q1 = 70 - 64.5 = 5.5$.

e. The interval 59–65 has more than 25% of the data so it has more data in it than the interval 66 through 70 which has 25% of the data.

f. The middle 50% (middle half) of the data has a range of 5.5 inches.

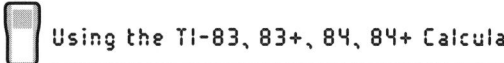 Using the TI-83, 83+, 84, 84+ Calculator

To find the minimum, maximum, and quartiles:

Enter data into the list editor (Pres STAT 1:EDIT). If you need to clear the list, arrow up to the name L1, press CLEAR, and then arrow down.

Put the data values into the list L1.

Press STAT and arrow to CALC. Press 1:1-VarStats. Enter L1.

Press ENTER.

Use the down and up arrow keys to scroll.

Smallest value = 59.

Largest value = 77.

Q_1: First quartile = 64.5.

Q_2: Second quartile or median = 66.

Q_3: Third quartile = 70.

To construct the box plot:

Press 4:Plotsoff. Press ENTER.

Arrow down and then use the right arrow key to go to the fifth picture, which is the box plot. Press ENTER.

Arrow down to Xlist: Press 2nd 1 for L1

Arrow down to Freq: Press ALPHA. Press 1.

Press Zoom. Press 9: ZoomStat.

Press TRACE, and use the arrow keys to examine the box plot.

 Try It ∑

2.23 The following data are the number of pages in 40 books on a shelf. Construct a box plot using a graphing calculator, and state the interquartile range.

136; 140; 178; 190; 205; 215; 217; 218; 232; 234; 240; 255; 270; 275; 290; 301; 303; 315; 317; 318; 326; 333; 343; 349; 360; 369; 377; 388; 391; 392; 398; 400; 402; 405; 408; 422; 429; 450; 475; 512

For some sets of data, some of the largest value, smallest value, first quartile, median, and third quartile may be the same. For instance, you might have a data set in which the median and the third quartile are the same. In this case, the diagram would not have a dotted line inside the box displaying the median. The right side of the box would display both the third quartile and the median. For example, if the smallest value and the first quartile were both one, the median and the third quartile were both five, and the largest value was seven, the box plot would look like:

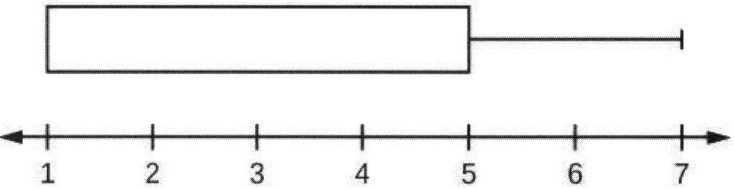

Figure 2.13

In this case, at least 25% of the values are equal to one. Twenty-five percent of the values are between one and five, inclusive. At least 25% of the values are equal to five. The top 25% of the values fall between five and seven, inclusive.

Example 2.24

Test scores for a college statistics class held during the day are:

99; 56; 78; 55.5; 32; 90; 80; 81; 56; 59; 45; 77; 84.5; 84; 70; 72; 68; 32; 79; 90

Test scores for a college statistics class held during the evening are:

98; 78; 68; 83; 81; 89; 88; 76; 65; 45; 98; 90; 80; 84.5; 85; 79; 78; 98; 90; 79; 81; 25.5

a. Find the smallest and largest values, the median, and the first and third quartile for the day class.

b. Find the smallest and largest values, the median, and the first and third quartile for the night class.

c. For each data set, what percentage of the data is between the smallest value and the first quartile? the first quartile and the median? the median and the third quartile? the third quartile and the largest value? What percentage of the data is between the first quartile and the largest value?

d. Create a box plot for each set of data. Use one number line for both box plots.

e. Which box plot has the widest spread for the middle 50% of the data (the data between the first and third quartiles)? What does this mean for that set of data in comparison to the other set of data?

Solution 2.24

a. Min = 32
$Q_1 = 56$
$M = 74.5$
$Q_3 = 82.5$
Max = 99

b. Min = 25.5
$Q_1 = 78$
$M = 81$
$Q_3 = 89$
Max = 98

c. Day class: There are six data values ranging from 32 to 56: 30%. There are six data values ranging from 56 to 74.5: 30%. There are five data values ranging from 74.5 to 82.5: 25%. There are five data values ranging from 82.5 to 99: 25%. There are 16 data values between the first quartile, 56, and the largest value, 99: 75%. Night class:

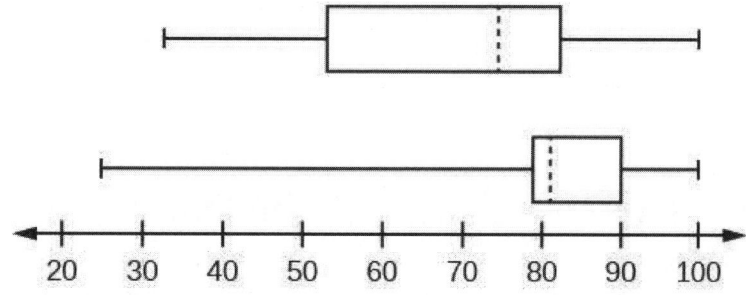

d.

Figure 2.14

e. The first data set has the wider spread for the middle 50% of the data. The IQR for the first data set is greater than the IQR for the second set. This means that there is more variability in the middle 50% of the first data set.

2.24 The following data set shows the heights in inches for the boys in a class of 40 students.

66; 66; 67; 67; 68; 68; 68; 68; 68; 69; 69; 69; 70; 71; 72; 72; 72; 73; 73; 74
The following data set shows the heights in inches for the girls in a class of 40 students.
61; 61; 62; 62; 63; 63; 63; 65; 65; 65; 66; 66; 66; 67; 68; 68; 68; 69; 69; 69
Construct a box plot using a graphing calculator for each data set, and state which box plot has the wider spread for the middle 50% of the data.

Example 2.25

Graph a box-and-whisker plot for the data values shown.

10; 10; 10; 15; 35; 75; 90; 95; 100; 175; 420; 490; 515; 515; 790

The five numbers used to create a box-and-whisker plot are:

Min: 10
Q_1: 15
Med: 95
Q_3: 490
Max: 790

The following graph shows the box-and-whisker plot.

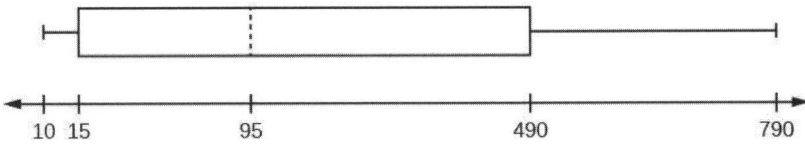

Figure 2.15

2.25 Follow the steps you used to graph a box-and-whisker plot for the data values shown.

0; 5; 5; 15; 30; 30; 45; 50; 50; 60; 75; 110; 140; 240; 330

2.5 | Measures of the Center of the Data

The "center" of a data set is also a way of describing location. The two most widely used measures of the "center" of the data are the **mean** (average) and the **median**. To calculate the **mean weight** of 50 people, add the 50 weights together and divide by 50. To find the **median weight** of the 50 people, order the data and find the number that splits the data into two equal parts. The median is generally a better measure of the center when there are extreme values or outliers because it is not affected by the precise numerical values of the outliers. The mean is the most common measure of the center.

NOTE

The words "mean" and "average" are often used interchangeably. The substitution of one word for the other is common practice. The technical term is "arithmetic mean" and "average" is technically a center location. However, in practice among non-statisticians, "average" is commonly accepted for "arithmetic mean."

When each value in the data set is not unique, the mean can be calculated by multiplying each distinct value by its frequency and then dividing the sum by the total number of data values. The letter used to represent the **sample mean** is an *x* with a bar over it (pronounced "*x* bar"): $\bar{x}$.

The Greek letter μ (pronounced "mew") represents the **population mean**. One of the requirements for the **sample mean** to be a good estimate of the **population mean** is for the sample taken to be truly random.

To see that both ways of calculating the mean are the same, consider the sample:
1; 1; 1; 2; 2; 3; 4; 4; 4; 4; 4

$$\bar{x} = \frac{1+1+1+2+2+3+4+4+4+4+4}{11} = 2.7$$

$$\bar{x} = \frac{3(1) + 2(2) + 1(3) + 5(4)}{11} = 2.7$$

In the second calculation, the frequencies are 3, 2, 1, and 5.

You can quickly find the location of the median by using the expression $\frac{n+1}{2}$.

The letter *n* is the total number of data values in the sample. If *n* is an odd number, the median is the middle value of the ordered data (ordered smallest to largest). If *n* is an even number, the median is equal to the two middle values added together and divided by two after the data has been ordered. For example, if the total number of data values is 97, then $\frac{n+1}{2} = \frac{97+1}{2} = 49$. The median is the 49th value in the ordered data. If the total number of data values is 100, then $\frac{n+1}{2} = \frac{100+1}{2} = 50.5$. The median occurs midway between the 50th and 51st values. The location of the median and the value of the median are **not** the same. The upper case letter *M* is often used to represent the median. The next example illustrates the location of the median and the value of the median.

Example 2.26

AIDS data indicating the number of months a patient with AIDS lives after taking a new antibody drug are as follows (smallest to largest):
3; 4; 8; 8; 10; 11; 12; 13; 14; 15; 15; 16; 16; 17; 17; 18; 21; 22; 22; 24; 24; 25; 26; 26; 27; 27; 29; 29; 31; 32; 33; 33; 34; 34; 35; 37; 40; 44; 44; 47;
Calculate the mean and the median.

Solution 2.26

The calculation for the mean is:

$$\bar{x} = \frac{[3 + 4 + (8)(2) + 10 + 11 + 12 + 13 + 14 + (15)(2) + (16)(2) + ... + 35 + 37 + 40 + (44)(2) + 47]}{40} = 23.6$$

To find the median, *M*, first use the formula for the location. The location is:
$$\frac{n+1}{2} = \frac{40+1}{2} = 20.5$$

Starting at the smallest value, the median is located between the 20th and 21st values (the two 24s):
3; 4; 8; 8; 10; 11; 12; 13; 14; 15; 15; 16; 16; 17; 17; 18; 21; 22; 22; 24; 24; 25; 26; 26; 27; 27; 29; 29; 31; 32; 33; 33; 34; 34; 35; 37; 40; 44; 44; 47;

$$M = \frac{24 + 24}{2} = 24$$

Using the TI-83, 83+, 84, 84+ Calculator

To find the mean and the median:

Clear list L1. Pres STAT 4:ClrList. Enter 2nd 1 for list L1. Press ENTER.

Enter data into the list editor. Press STAT 1:EDIT.

Put the data values into list L1.

Press STAT and arrow to CALC. Press 1:1-VarStats. Press 2nd 1 for L1 and then ENTER.

Press the down and up arrow keys to scroll.

$\bar{x} = 23.6, M = 24$

2.26 The following data show the number of months patients typically wait on a transplant list before getting surgery. The data are ordered from smallest to largest. Calculate the mean and median.

3; 4; 5; 7; 7; 7; 7; 8; 8; 9; 9; 10; 10; 10; 10; 10; 11; 12; 12; 13; 14; 14; 15; 15; 17; 17; 18; 19; 19; 19; 21; 21; 22; 22; 23; 24; 24; 24; 24

Example 2.27

Suppose that in a small town of 50 people, one person earns $5,000,000 per year and the other 49 each earn $30,000. Which is the better measure of the "center": the mean or the median?

Solution 2.27

$$\bar{x} = \frac{5,000,000 + 49(30,000)}{50} = 129,400$$

$M = 30,000$

(There are 49 people who earn $30,000 and one person who earns $5,000,000.)

The median is a better measure of the "center" than the mean because 49 of the values are 30,000 and one is 5,000,000. The 5,000,000 is an outlier. The 30,000 gives us a better sense of the middle of the data.

2.27 In a sample of 60 households, one house is worth $2,500,000. Half of the rest are worth $280,000, and all the others are worth $315,000. Which is the better measure of the "center": the mean or the median?

Another measure of the center is the mode. The **mode** is the most frequent value. There can be more than one mode in a data set as long as those values have the same frequency and that frequency is the highest. A data set with two modes is called bimodal.

Example 2.28

Statistics exam scores for 20 students are as follows:

50; 53; 59; 59; 63; 63; 72; 72; 72; 72; 72; 76; 78; 81; 83; 84; 84; 84; 90; 93

Find the mode.

Solution 2.28
The most frequent score is 72, which occurs five times. Mode = 72.

2.28 The number of books checked out from the library from 25 students are as follows:

0; 0; 0; 1; 2; 3; 3; 4; 4; 5; 5; 7; 7; 7; 7; 8; 8; 8; 9; 10; 10; 11; 11; 12; 12
Find the mode.

Example 2.29

Five real estate exam scores are 430, 430, 480, 480, 495. The data set is bimodal because the scores 430 and 480 each occur twice.

When is the mode the best measure of the "center"? Consider a weight loss program that advertises a mean weight loss of six pounds the first week of the program. The mode might indicate that most people lose two pounds the first week, making the program less appealing.

> **NOTE**
>
> The mode can be calculated for qualitative data as well as for quantitative data. For example, if the data set is: red, red, red, green, green, yellow, purple, black, blue, the mode is red.

Statistical software will easily calculate the mean, the median, and the mode. Some graphing calculators can also make these calculations. In the real world, people make these calculations using software.

2.29 Five credit scores are 680, 680, 700, 720, 720. The data set is bimodal because the scores 680 and 720 each occur twice. Consider the annual earnings of workers at a factory. The mode is $25,000 and occurs 150 times out of 301. The median is $50,000 and the mean is $47,500. What would be the best measure of the "center"?

The Law of Large Numbers and the Mean

The Law of Large Numbers says that if you take samples of larger and larger size from any population, then the mean $\bar{x}$ of the sample is very likely to get closer and closer to μ. This is discussed in more detail later in the text.

Sampling Distributions and Statistic of a Sampling Distribution

You can think of a **sampling distribution** as a **relative frequency distribution** with a great many samples. (See **Sampling and Data** for a review of relative frequency). Suppose thirty randomly selected students were asked the number of movies they watched the previous week. The results are in the **relative frequency table** shown below.

# of movies	Relative Frequency
0	$\frac{5}{30}$
1	$\frac{15}{30}$
2	$\frac{6}{30}$
3	$\frac{3}{30}$
4	$\frac{1}{30}$

Table 2.24

If you let the number of samples get very large (say, 300 million or more), the relative frequency table becomes a relative frequency distribution.

A **statistic** is a number calculated from a sample. Statistic examples include the mean, the median and the mode as well as others. The sample mean $\bar{x}$ is an example of a statistic which estimates the population mean μ.

Calculating the Mean of Grouped Frequency Tables

When only grouped data is available, you do not know the individual data values (we only know intervals and interval frequencies); therefore, you cannot compute an exact mean for the data set. What we must do is estimate the actual mean by calculating the mean of a frequency table. A frequency table is a data representation in which grouped data is displayed along with the corresponding frequencies. To calculate the mean from a grouped frequency table we can apply the basic definition of mean: $mean = \frac{data\ sum}{number\ of\ data\ values}$ We simply need to modify the definition to fit within the restrictions of a frequency table.

Since we do not know the individual data values we can instead find the midpoint of each interval. The midpoint is $\frac{lower\ boundary + upper\ boundary}{2}$. We can now modify the mean definition to be

$$Mean\ of\ Frequency\ Table = \frac{\sum fm}{\sum f}$$ where f = the frequency of the interval and m = the midpoint of the interval.

Example 2.30

A frequency table displaying professor Blount's last statistic test is shown. Find the best estimate of the class mean.

Grade Interval	Number of Students
50–56.5	1
56.5–62.5	0
62.5–68.5	4
68.5–74.5	4
74.5–80.5	2
80.5–86.5	3
86.5–92.5	4
92.5–98.5	1

Table 2.25

Solution 2.30

- Find the midpoints for all intervals

Grade Interval	Midpoint
50–56.5	53.25
56.5–62.5	59.5
62.5–68.5	65.5
68.5–74.5	71.5
74.5–80.5	77.5
80.5–86.5	83.5
86.5–92.5	89.5
92.5–98.5	95.5

Table 2.26

- Calculate the sum of the product of each interval frequency and midpoint. $\sum fm$

$$53.25(1) + 59.5(0) + 65.5(4) + 71.5(4) + 77.5(2) + 83.5(3) + 89.5(4) + 95.5(1) = 1460.25$$

- $\mu = \dfrac{\sum fm}{\sum f} = \dfrac{1460.25}{19} = 76.86$

2.30 Maris conducted a study on the effect that playing video games has on memory recall. As part of her study, she compiled the following data:

Hours Teenagers Spend on Video Games	Number of Teenagers
0–3.5	3
3.5–7.5	7
7.5–11.5	12
11.5–15.5	7
15.5–19.5	9

Table 2.27

What is the best estimate for the mean number of hours spent playing video games?

2.6 | Skewness and the Mean, Median, and Mode

Consider the following data set.
4; 5; 6; 6; 6; 7; 7; 7; 7; 7; 7; 8; 8; 8; 9; 10

This data set can be represented by following histogram. Each interval has width one, and each value is located in the middle of an interval.

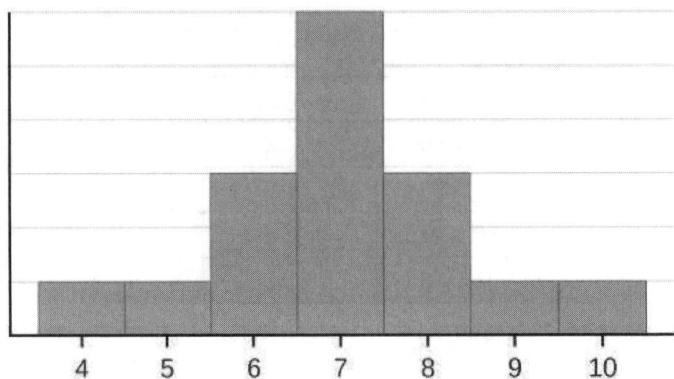

Figure 2.16

The histogram displays a **symmetrical** distribution of data. A distribution is symmetrical if a vertical line can be drawn at some point in the histogram such that the shape to the left and the right of the vertical line are mirror images of each other. The mean, the median, and the mode are each seven for these data. **In a perfectly symmetrical distribution, the mean and the median are the same.** This example has one mode (unimodal), and the mode is the same as the mean and median. In a symmetrical distribution that has two modes (bimodal), the two modes would be different from the mean and median.

The histogram for the data: 4; 5; 6; 6; 6; 7; 7; 7; 7; 8 is not symmetrical. The right-hand side seems "chopped off" compared to the left side. A distribution of this type is called **skewed to the left** because it is pulled out to the left.

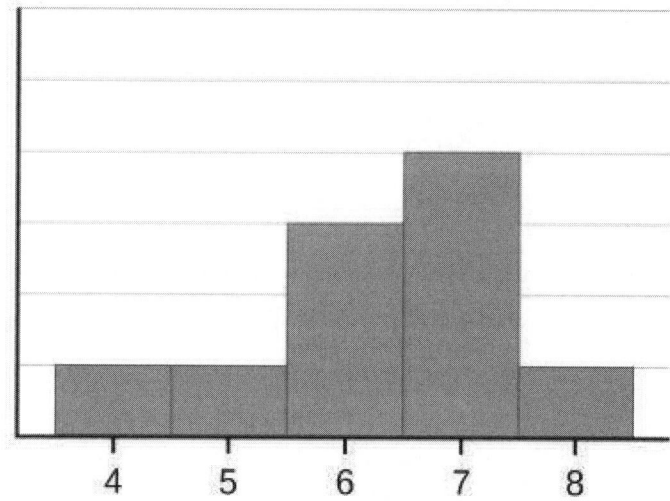

Figure 2.17

The mean is 6.3, the median is 6.5, and the mode is seven. **Notice that the mean is less than the median, and they are both less than the mode.** The mean and the median both reflect the skewing, but the mean reflects it more so.

The histogram for the data: 6; 7; 7; 7; 7; 8; 8; 8; 9; 10, is also not symmetrical. It is **skewed to the right**.

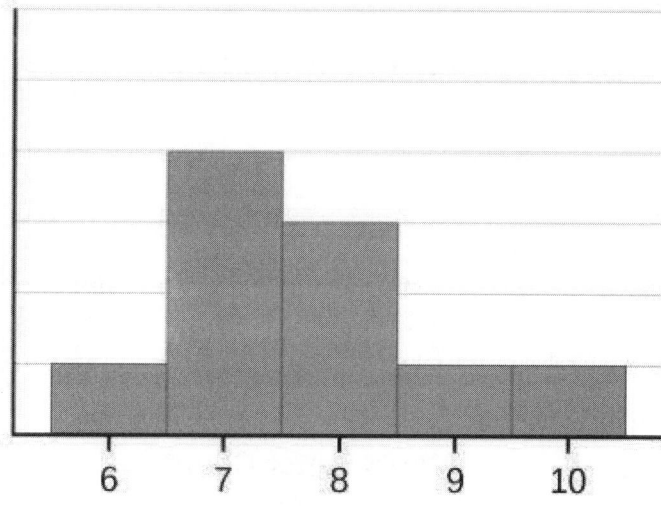

Figure 2.18

The mean is 7.7, the median is 7.5, and the mode is seven. Of the three statistics, **the mean is the largest, while the mode is the smallest**. Again, the mean reflects the skewing the most.

To summarize, generally if the distribution of data is skewed to the left, the mean is less than the median, which is often less than the mode. If the distribution of data is skewed to the right, the mode is often less than the median, which is less than the mean.

Skewness and symmetry become important when we discuss probability distributions in later chapters.

Example 2.31

Statistics are used to compare and sometimes identify authors. The following lists shows a simple random sample that compares the letter counts for three authors.

Terry: 7; 9; 3; 3; 3; 4; 1; 3; 2; 2

Davis: 3; 3; 3; 4; 1; 4; 3; 2; 3; 1

Maris: 2; 3; 4; 4; 4; 6; 6; 6; 8; 3

    a. Make a dot plot for the three authors and compare the shapes.

    b. Calculate the mean for each.

    c. Calculate the median for each.

    d. Describe any pattern you notice between the shape and the measures of center.

Solution 2.31

a.

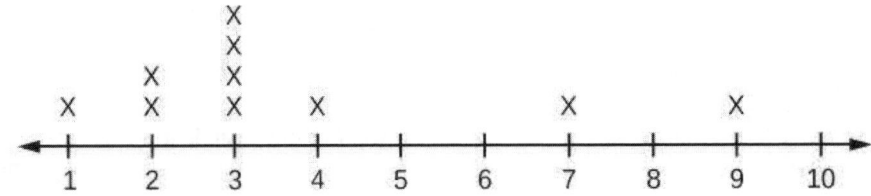

Figure 2.19 Terry's distribution has a right (positive) skew.

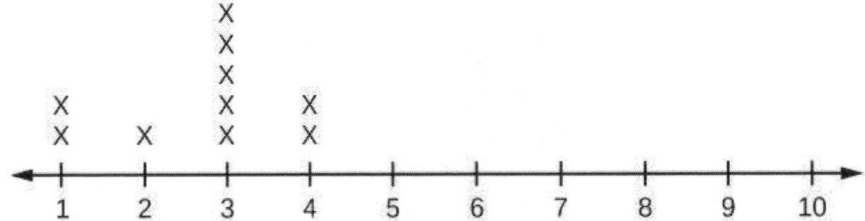

Figure 2.20 Davis' distribution has a left (negative) skew

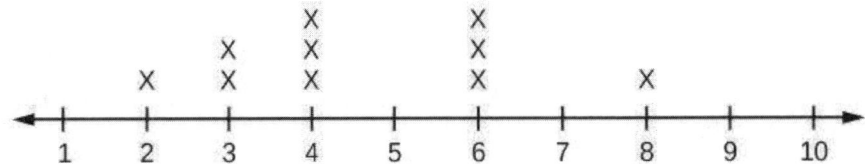

Figure 2.21 Maris' distribution is symmetrically shaped.

    b. Terry's mean is 3.7, Davis' mean is 2.7, Maris' mean is 4.6.

    c. Terry's median is three, Davis' median is three. Maris' median is four.

    d. It appears that the median is always closest to the high point (the mode), while the mean tends to be farther out on the tail. In a symmetrical distribution, the mean and the median are both centrally located close to the high point of the distribution.

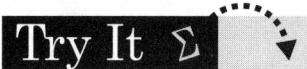

2.31 Discuss the mean, median, and mode for each of the following problems. Is there a pattern between the shape and measure of the center?

a.

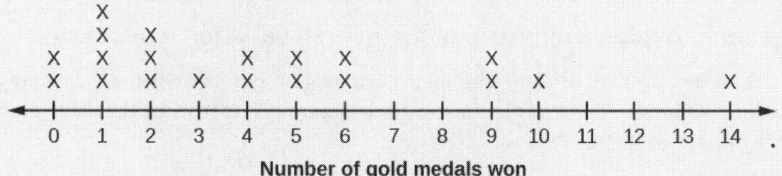

2010 Winter Olympics Gold Medal Wins by Top 20 Medal-Winning Countries

Figure 2.22

b.

The Ages Former U.S Presidents Died	
4	6 9
5	3 6 7 7 7 8
6	0 0 3 3 4 4 5 6 7 7 7 8
7	0 1 1 2 3 4 7 8 8 9
8	0 1 3 5 8
9	0 0 3 3
Key: 8|0 means 80.	

Table 2.28

c.

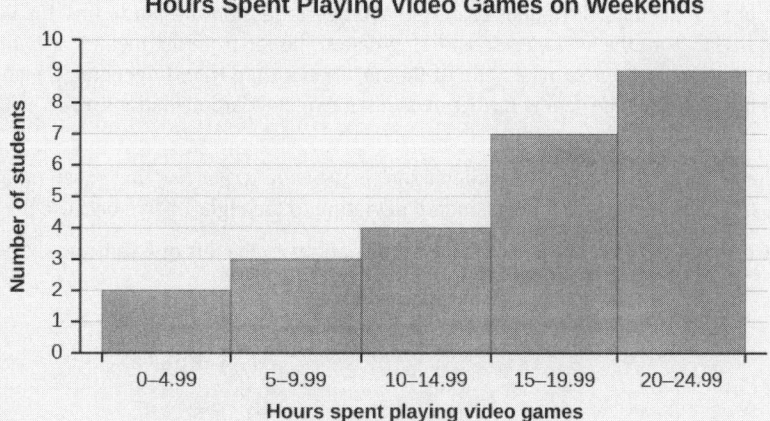

Figure 2.23

2.7 | Measures of the Spread of the Data

An important characteristic of any set of data is the variation in the data. In some data sets, the data values are concentrated closely near the mean; in other data sets, the data values are more widely spread out from the mean. The most common measure of variation, or spread, is the standard deviation. The **standard deviation** is a number that measures how far data values are from their mean.

The standard deviation

- provides a numerical measure of the overall amount of variation in a data set, and

- can be used to determine whether a particular data value is close to or far from the mean.

The standard deviation provides a measure of the overall variation in a data set

The standard deviation is always positive or zero. The standard deviation is small when the data are all concentrated close to the mean, exhibiting little variation or spread. The standard deviation is larger when the data values are more spread out from the mean, exhibiting more variation.

Suppose that we are studying the amount of time customers wait in line at the checkout at supermarket *A* and supermarket *B*. the average wait time at both supermarkets is five minutes. At supermarket *A*, the standard deviation for the wait time is two minutes; at supermarket *B* the standard deviation for the wait time is four minutes.

Because supermarket *B* has a higher standard deviation, we know that there is more variation in the wait times at supermarket *B*. Overall, wait times at supermarket *B* are more spread out from the average; wait times at supermarket *A* are more concentrated near the average.

The standard deviation can be used to determine whether a data value is close to or far from the mean.

Suppose that Rosa and Binh both shop at supermarket *A*. Rosa waits at the checkout counter for seven minutes and Binh waits for one minute. At supermarket *A*, the mean waiting time is five minutes and the standard deviation is two minutes. The standard deviation can be used to determine whether a data value is close to or far from the mean.

Rosa waits for seven minutes:

- Seven is two minutes longer than the average of five; two minutes is equal to one standard deviation.

- Rosa's wait time of seven minutes is **two minutes longer than the average** of five minutes.

- Rosa's wait time of seven minutes is **one standard deviation above the average** of five minutes.

Binh waits for one minute.

- One is four minutes less than the average of five; four minutes is equal to two standard deviations.

- Binh's wait time of one minute is **four minutes less than the average** of five minutes.

- Binh's wait time of one minute is **two standard deviations below the average** of five minutes.

- A data value that is two standard deviations from the average is just on the borderline for what many statisticians would consider to be far from the average. Considering data to be far from the mean if it is more than two standard deviations away is more of an approximate "rule of thumb" than a rigid rule. In general, the shape of the distribution of the data affects how much of the data is further away than two standard deviations. (You will learn more about this in later chapters.)

The number line may help you understand standard deviation. If we were to put five and seven on a number line, seven is to the right of five. We say, then, that seven is **one** standard deviation to the **right** of five because 5 + (1)(2) = 7.

If one were also part of the data set, then one is **two** standard deviations to the **left** of five because 5 + (−2)(2) = 1.

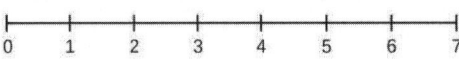

Figure 2.24

- In general, a **value = mean + (#ofSTDEV)(standard deviation)**

- where #ofSTDEVs = the number of standard deviations

- #ofSTDEV does not need to be an integer

- One is **two standard deviations less than the mean** of five because: $1 = 5 + (-2)(2)$.

The equation **value = mean + (#ofSTDEVs)(standard deviation)** can be expressed for a sample and for a population.

- **sample:** $x = \bar{x} + (\# \, of STDEV)(s)$

- **Population:** $x = \mu + (\# \, of STDEV)(\sigma)$

The lower case letter s represents the sample standard deviation and the Greek letter σ (sigma, lower case) represents the population standard deviation.

The symbol $\bar{x}$ is the sample mean and the Greek symbol μ is the population mean.

Calculating the Standard Deviation

If x is a number, then the difference "x – mean" is called its **deviation**. In a data set, there are as many deviations as there are items in the data set. The deviations are used to calculate the standard deviation. If the numbers belong to a population, in symbols a deviation is $x - \mu$. For sample data, in symbols a deviation is $x - \bar{x}$.

The procedure to calculate the standard deviation depends on whether the numbers are the entire population or are data from a sample. The calculations are similar, but not identical. Therefore the symbol used to represent the standard deviation depends on whether it is calculated from a population or a sample. The lower case letter s represents the sample standard deviation and the Greek letter σ (sigma, lower case) represents the population standard deviation. If the sample has the same characteristics as the population, then s should be a good estimate of σ.

To calculate the standard deviation, we need to calculate the variance first. The **variance** is the **average of the squares of the deviations** (the $x - \bar{x}$ values for a sample, or the $x - \mu$ values for a population). The symbol σ^2 represents the population variance; the population standard deviation σ is the square root of the population variance. The symbol s^2 represents the sample variance; the sample standard deviation s is the square root of the sample variance. You can think of the standard deviation as a special average of the deviations.

If the numbers come from a census of the entire **population** and not a sample, when we calculate the average of the squared deviations to find the variance, we divide by N, the number of items in the population. If the data are from a **sample** rather than a population, when we calculate the average of the squared deviations, we divide by $n - 1$, one less than the number of items in the sample.

Formulas for the Sample Standard Deviation

- $s = \sqrt{\dfrac{\Sigma(x - \bar{x})^2}{n - 1}}$ or $s = \sqrt{\dfrac{\Sigma f(x - \bar{x})^2}{n - 1}}$

- For the sample standard deviation, the denominator is $n - 1$, that is the sample size MINUS 1.

Formulas for the Population Standard Deviation

- $\sigma = \sqrt{\dfrac{\Sigma(x - \mu)^2}{N}}$ or $\sigma = \sqrt{\dfrac{\Sigma f(x - \mu)^2}{N}}$

- For the population standard deviation, the denominator is N, the number of items in the population.

In these formulas, f represents the frequency with which a value appears. For example, if a value appears once, f is one. If a value appears three times in the data set or population, f is three.

Sampling Variability of a Statistic

The statistic of a sampling distribution was discussed in **Descriptive Statistics: Measuring the Center of the Data**. How much the statistic varies from one sample to another is known as the **sampling variability of a statistic**. You typically measure the sampling variability of a statistic by its standard error. The **standard error of the mean** is an example of a standard error. It is a special standard deviation and is known as the standard deviation of the sampling distribution of the mean. You will cover the standard error of the mean in the chapter **The Central Limit Theorem** (not now). The notation for the standard error of the mean is $\frac{\sigma}{\sqrt{n}}$ where σ is the standard deviation of the population and n is the size of the sample.

NOTE

👉 **In practice, USE A CALCULATOR OR COMPUTER SOFTWARE TO CALCULATE THE STANDARD DEVIATION. If you are using a TI-83, 83+, 84+ calculator, you need to select the appropriate standard deviation** σ_x **or** s_x **from the summary statistics.** We will concentrate on using and interpreting the information that the standard deviation gives us. However you should study the following step-by-step example to help you understand how the standard deviation measures variation from the mean. (The calculator instructions appear at the end of this example.)

Example 2.32

In a fifth grade class, the teacher was interested in the average age and the sample standard deviation of the ages of her students. The following data are the ages for a SAMPLE of $n = 20$ fifth grade students. The ages are rounded to the nearest half year:

9; 9.5; 9.5; 10; 10; 10; 10; 10.5; 10.5; 10.5; 10.5; 11; 11; 11; 11; 11; 11; 11.5; 11.5; 11.5;

$$\bar{x} = \frac{9 + 9.5(2) + 10(4) + 10.5(4) + 11(6) + 11.5(3)}{20} = 10.525$$

The average age is 10.53 years, rounded to two places.

The variance may be calculated by using a table. Then the standard deviation is calculated by taking the square root of the variance. We will explain the parts of the table after calculating s.

Data	Freq.	Deviations	*Deviations*^{2}	(Freq.)(*Deviations*^{2})
x	f	$(x - \bar{x})$	$(x - \bar{x})^2$	$(f)(x - \bar{x})^2$
9	1	$9 - 10.525 = -1.525$	$(-1.525)^2 = 2.325625$	$1 \times 2.325625 = 2.325625$
9.5	2	$9.5 - 10.525 = -1.025$	$(-1.025)^2 = 1.050625$	$2 \times 1.050625 = 2.101250$
10	4	$10 - 10.525 = -0.525$	$(-0.525)^2 = 0.275625$	$4 \times 0.275625 = 1.1025$
10.5	4	$10.5 - 10.525 = -0.025$	$(-0.025)^2 = 0.000625$	$4 \times 0.000625 = 0.0025$
11	6	$11 - 10.525 = 0.475$	$(0.475)^2 = 0.225625$	$6 \times 0.225625 = 1.35375$
11.5	3	$11.5 - 10.525 = 0.975$	$(0.975)^2 = 0.950625$	$3 \times 0.950625 = 2.851875$
				The total is 9.7375

Table 2.29

The sample variance, s^2, is equal to the sum of the last column (9.7375) divided by the total number of data values minus one (20 – 1):

$$s^2 = \frac{9.7375}{20 - 1} = 0.5125$$

The **sample standard deviation** s is equal to the square root of the sample variance:

$s = \sqrt{0.5125} = 0.715891$, which is rounded to two decimal places, $s = 0.72$.

Typically, you do the calculation for the standard deviation on your calculator or computer. The intermediate results are not rounded. This is done for accuracy.

- For the following problems, recall that **value = mean + (#ofSTDEVs)(standard deviation)**. Verify the mean and standard deviation or a calculator or computer.

- For a sample: $x = \bar{x} + (\#ofSTDEVs)(s)$

- For a population: $x = \mu + (\#ofSTDEVs)(\sigma)$

- For this example, use $x = \bar{x} + (\#ofSTDEVs)(s)$ because the data is from a sample

a. Verify the mean and standard deviation on your calculator or computer.

b. Find the value that is one standard deviation above the mean. Find ($\bar{x} + 1s$).

c. Find the value that is two standard deviations below the mean. Find ($\bar{x} - 2s$).

d. Find the values that are 1.5 standard deviations **from** (below and above) the mean.

Solution 2.32

a. ◦ Clear lists L1 and L2. Press STAT 4:ClrList. Enter 2nd 1 for L1, the comma (,), and 2nd 2 for L2.

   ◦ Enter data into the list editor. Press STAT 1:EDIT. If necessary, clear the lists by arrowing up into the name. Press CLEAR and arrow down.

   ◦ Put the data values (9, 9.5, 10, 10.5, 11, 11.5) into list L1 and the frequencies (1, 2, 4, 4, 6, 3) into list L2. Use the arrow keys to move around.

   ◦ Press STAT and arrow to CALC. Press 1:1-VarStats and enter L1 (2nd 1), L2 (2nd 2). Do not forget the comma. Press ENTER.

   ◦ $\bar{x} = 10.525$

   ◦ Use Sx because this is sample data (not a population): Sx=0.715891

b. ($\bar{x} + 1s$) = 10.53 + (1)(0.72) = 11.25

c. ($\bar{x} - 2s$) = 10.53 − (2)(0.72) = 9.09

d. ◦ ($\bar{x} - 1.5s$) = 10.53 − (1.5)(0.72) = 9.45

   ◦ ($\bar{x} + 1.5s$) = 10.53 + (1.5)(0.72) = 11.61

☞ **2.32** On a baseball team, the ages of each of the players are as follows:

21; 21; 22; 23; 24; 24; 25; 25; 28; 29; 29; 31; 32; 33; 33; 34; 35; 36; 36; 36; 36; 38; 38; 38; 40

Use your calculator or computer to find the mean and standard deviation. Then find the value that is two standard deviations above the mean.

Explanation of the standard deviation calculation shown in the table

The deviations show how spread out the data are about the mean. The data value 11.5 is farther from the mean than is the data value 11 which is indicated by the deviations 0.97 and 0.47. A positive deviation occurs when the data value is greater than the mean, whereas a negative deviation occurs when the data value is less than the mean. The deviation is −1.525 for the data value nine. **If you add the deviations, the sum is always zero.** (For **Example 2.32**, there are $n = 20$ deviations.) So you cannot simply add the deviations to get the spread of the data. By squaring the deviations, you make them positive numbers, and the sum will also be positive. The variance, then, is the average squared deviation.

The variance is a squared measure and does not have the same units as the data. Taking the square root solves the problem. The standard deviation measures the spread in the same units as the data.

Notice that instead of dividing by $n = 20$, the calculation divided by $n − 1 = 20 − 1 = 19$ because the data is a sample.

For the **sample** variance, we divide by the sample size minus one ($n - 1$). Why not divide by n? The answer has to do with the population variance. **The sample variance is an estimate of the population variance.** Based on the theoretical mathematics that lies behind these calculations, dividing by ($n - 1$) gives a better estimate of the population variance.

NOTE

☞ Your concentration should be on what the standard deviation tells us about the data. The standard deviation is a number which measures how far the data are spread from the mean. Let a calculator or computer do the arithmetic.

The standard deviation, s or σ, is either zero or larger than zero. Describing the data with reference to the spread is called "variability". The variability in data depends upon the method by which the outcomes are obtained; for example, by measuring or by random sampling. When the standard deviation is zero, there is no spread; that is, the all the data values are equal to each other. The standard deviation is small when the data are all concentrated close to the mean, and is larger when the data values show more variation from the mean. When the standard deviation is a lot larger than zero, the data values are very spread out about the mean; outliers can make s or σ very large.

The standard deviation, when first presented, can seem unclear. By graphing your data, you can get a better "feel" for the deviations and the standard deviation. You will find that in symmetrical distributions, the standard deviation can be very helpful but in skewed distributions, the standard deviation may not be much help. The reason is that the two sides of a skewed distribution have different spreads. In a skewed distribution, it is better to look at the first quartile, the median, the third quartile, the smallest value, and the largest value. Because numbers can be confusing, **always graph your data**. Display your data in a histogram or a box plot.

Example 2.33

Use the following data (first exam scores) from Susan Dean's spring pre-calculus class:

33; 42; 49; 49; 53; 55; 55; 61; 63; 67; 68; 68; 69; 69; 72; 73; 74; 78; 80; 83; 88; 88; 88; 90; 92; 94; 94; 94; 94; 96; 100

a. Create a chart containing the data, frequencies, relative frequencies, and cumulative relative frequencies to three decimal places.

b. Calculate the following to one decimal place using a TI-83+ or TI-84 calculator:

    i. The sample mean

    ii. The sample standard deviation

    iii. The median

    iv. The first quartile

    v. The third quartile

    vi. *IQR*

c. Construct a box plot and a histogram on the same set of axes. Make comments about the box plot, the histogram, and the chart.

Solution 2.33

a. See **Table 2.30**

b.   i. The sample mean = 73.5

    ii. The sample standard deviation = 17.9

    iii. The median = 73

    iv. The first quartile = 61

    v. The third quartile = 90

    vi. *IQR* = 90 − 61 = 29

c. The *x*-axis goes from 32.5 to 100.5; *y*-axis goes from –2.4 to 15 for the histogram. The number of intervals is five, so the width of an interval is (100.5 – 32.5) divided by five, is equal to 13.6. Endpoints of the intervals are as follows: the starting point is 32.5, 32.5 + 13.6 = 46.1, 46.1 + 13.6 = 59.7, 59.7 + 13.6 = 73.3, 73.3 + 13.6 = 86.9, 86.9 + 13.6 = 100.5 = the ending value; No data values fall on an interval boundary.

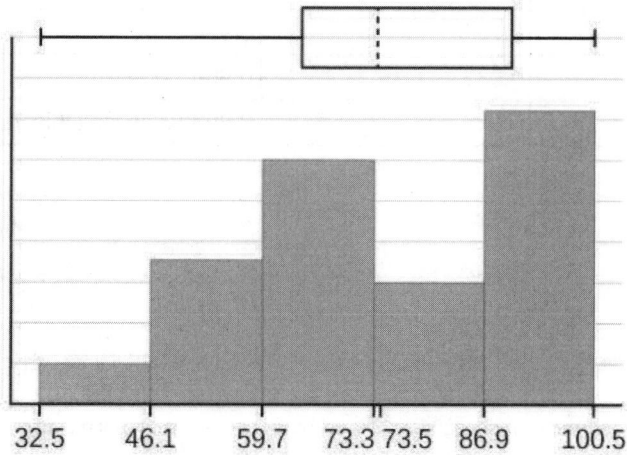

Figure 2.25

The long left whisker in the box plot is reflected in the left side of the histogram. The spread of the exam scores in the lower 50% is greater (73 – 33 = 40) than the spread in the upper 50% (100 – 73 = 27). The histogram, box plot, and chart all reflect this. There are a substantial number of A and B grades (80s, 90s, and 100). The histogram clearly shows this. The box plot shows us that the middle 50% of the exam scores (*IQR* = 29) are Ds, Cs, and Bs. The box plot also shows us that the lower 25% of the exam scores are Ds and Fs.

Data	Frequency	Relative Frequency	Cumulative Relative Frequency
33	1	0.032	0.032
42	1	0.032	0.064
49	2	0.065	0.129
53	1	0.032	0.161
55	2	0.065	0.226
61	1	0.032	0.258
63	1	0.032	0.29
67	1	0.032	0.322
68	2	0.065	0.387
69	2	0.065	0.452
72	1	0.032	0.484
73	1	0.032	0.516
74	1	0.032	0.548
78	1	0.032	0.580
80	1	0.032	0.612

Table 2.30

Data	Frequency	Relative Frequency	Cumulative Relative Frequency
83	1	0.032	0.644
88	3	0.097	0.741
90	1	0.032	0.773
92	1	0.032	0.805
94	4	0.129	0.934
96	1	0.032	0.966
100	1	0.032	0.998 (Why isn't this value 1?)

Table 2.30

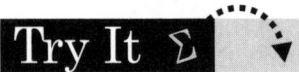

Try It

☞ **2.33** The following data show the different types of pet food stores in the area carry.
6; 6; 6; 6; 7; 7; 7; 7; 7; 8; 9; 9; 9; 9; 10; 10; 10; 10; 10; 11; 11; 11; 11; 12; 12; 12; 12; 12; 12;
Calculate the sample mean and the sample standard deviation to one decimal place using a TI-83+ or TI-84 calculator.

Standard deviation of Grouped Frequency Tables

Recall that for grouped data we do not know individual data values, so we cannot describe the typical value of the data with precision. In other words, we cannot find the exact mean, median, or mode. We can, however, determine the best estimate of the measures of center by finding the mean of the grouped data with the formula: $Mean\ of\ Frequency\ Table = \dfrac{\sum fm}{\sum f}$

where $f =$ interval frequencies and $m =$ interval midpoints.

Just as we could not find the exact mean, neither can we find the exact standard deviation. Remember that standard deviation describes numerically the expected deviation a data value has from the mean. In simple English, the standard deviation allows us to compare how "unusual" individual data is compared to the mean.

Example 2.34

Find the standard deviation for the data in **Table 2.31**.

Class	Frequency, f	Midpoint, m	m^2	$\bar{x}^2$	fm^2	Standard Deviation
0–2	1	1	1	7.58	1	3.5
3–5	6	4	16	7.58	96	3.5
6–8	10	7	49	7.58	490	3.5
9–11	7	10	100	7.58	700	3.5
12–14	0	13	169	7.58	0	3.5
15–17	2	16	256	7.58	512	3.5

Table 2.31

For this data set, we have the mean, $\bar{x}$ = 7.58 and the standard deviation, s_x = 3.5. This means that a randomly selected data value would be expected to be 3.5 units from the mean. If we look at the first class, we see that the class midpoint is equal to one. This is almost two full standard deviations from the mean since 7.58 – 3.5 – 3.5 = 0.58. While the formula for calculating the standard deviation is not complicated, $s_x = \sqrt{\dfrac{f(m - \bar{x})^2}{n - 1}}$ where s_x = sample standard deviation, $\bar{x}$ = sample mean, the calculations are tedious. It is usually best to use technology when performing the calculations.

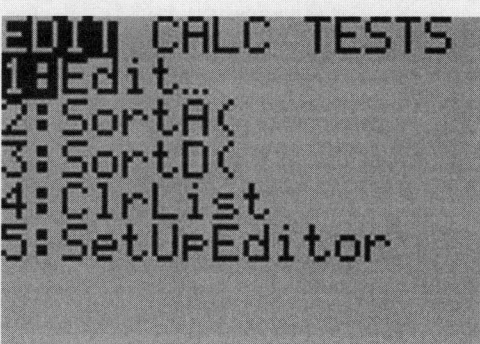

☞ **2.34** Find the standard deviation for the data from the previous example

Class	Frequency, *f*
0–2	1
3–5	6
6–8	10
9–11	7
12–14	0
15–17	2

Table 2.32

First, press the **STAT** key and select **1:Edit**

Figure 2.26

Input the midpoint values into **L1** and the frequencies into **L2**

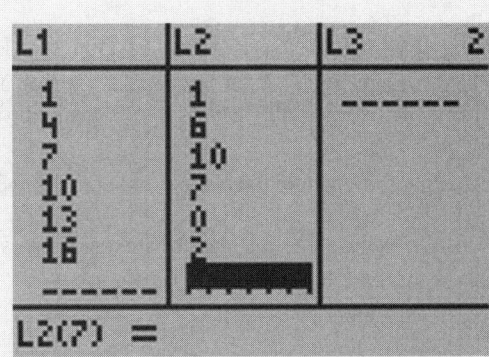

Figure 2.27

Select **STAT**, **CALC**, and **1: 1-Var Stats**

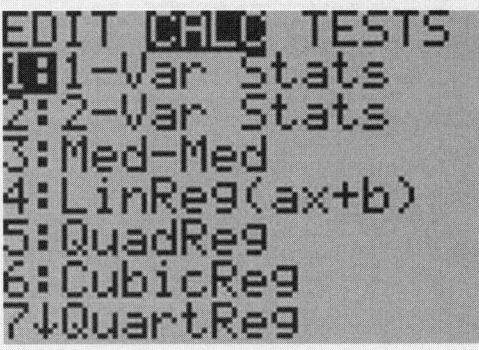

Figure 2.28

Select **2nd** then **1** then , **2nd** then **2 Enter**

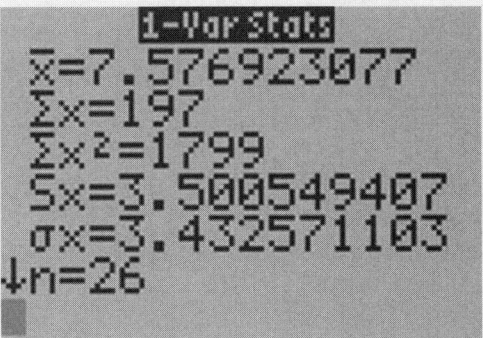

Figure 2.29

You will see displayed both a population standard deviation, σ_x, and the sample standard deviation, s_x.

Comparing Values from Different Data Sets

The standard deviation is useful when comparing data values that come from different data sets. If the data sets have different means and standard deviations, then comparing the data values directly can be misleading.

- For each data value, calculate how many standard deviations away from its mean the value is.
- Use the formula: value = mean + (#ofSTDEVs)(standard deviation); solve for #ofSTDEVs.

- $\# \, ofSTDEVs = \dfrac{\text{value} - \text{mean}}{\text{standard deviation}}$

- Compare the results of this calculation.

#ofSTDEVs is often called a "z-score"; we can use the symbol z. In symbols, the formulas become:

Sample	$x = \bar{x} + zs$	$z = \dfrac{x - \bar{x}}{s}$
Population	$x = \mu + z\sigma$	$z = \dfrac{x - \mu}{\sigma}$

Table 2.33

Example 2.35

Two students, John and Ali, from different high schools, wanted to find out who had the highest GPA when compared to his school. Which student had the highest GPA when compared to his school?

Student	GPA	School Mean GPA	School Standard Deviation
John	2.85	3.0	0.7
Ali	77	80	10

Table 2.34

Solution 2.35

For each student, determine how many standard deviations (#ofSTDEVs) his GPA is away from the average, for his school. Pay careful attention to signs when comparing and interpreting the answer.

$$z = \# \text{ of STDEVs} = \frac{\text{value} - \text{mean}}{\text{standard deviation}} = \frac{x - \mu}{\sigma}$$

For John, $z = \# \, ofSTDEVs = \dfrac{2.85 - 3.0}{0.7} = -0.21$

For Ali, $z = \# \, ofSTDEVs = \dfrac{77 - 80}{10} = -0.3$

John has the better GPA when compared to his school because his GPA is 0.21 standard deviations **below** his school's mean while Ali's GPA is 0.3 standard deviations **below** his school's mean.

John's z-score of –0.21 is higher than Ali's z-score of –0.3. For GPA, higher values are better, so we conclude that John has the better GPA when compared to his school.

Try It Σ

2.35 Two swimmers, Angie and Beth, from different teams, wanted to find out who had the fastest time for the 50 meter freestyle when compared to her team. Which swimmer had the fastest time when compared to her team?

Swimmer	Time (seconds)	Team Mean Time	Team Standard Deviation
Angie	26.2	27.2	0.8
Beth	27.3	30.1	1.4

Table 2.35

The following lists give a few facts that provide a little more insight into what the standard deviation tells us about the distribution of the data.

For ANY data set, no matter what the distribution of the data is:

- At least 75% of the data is within two standard deviations of the mean.

- At least 89% of the data is within three standard deviations of the mean.

- At least 95% of the data is within 4.5 standard deviations of the mean.

- This is known as Chebyshev's Rule.

For data having a distribution that is BELL-SHAPED and SYMMETRIC:

- Approximately 68% of the data is within one standard deviation of the mean.

- Approximately 95% of the data is within two standard deviations of the mean.

- More than 99% of the data is within three standard deviations of the mean.

- This is known as the Empirical Rule.

- It is important to note that this rule only applies when the shape of the distribution of the data is bell-shaped and symmetric. We will learn more about this when studying the "Normal" or "Gaussian" probability distribution in later chapters.

2.8 | Descriptive Statistics

Stats Lab

2.1 Descriptive Statistics

Class Time:

Names:

Student Learning Outcomes

- The student will construct a histogram and a box plot.
- The student will calculate univariate statistics.
- The student will examine the graphs to interpret what the data implies.

Collect the Data

Record the number of pairs of shoes you own.

1. Randomly survey 30 classmates about the number of pairs of shoes they own. Record their values.

Table 2.36 Survey Results

2. Construct a histogram. Make five to six intervals. Sketch the graph using a ruler and pencil and scale the axes.

Figure 2.30

3. Calculate the following values.

   a. $\bar{x}$ = _____

   b. s = _____

4. Are the data discrete or continuous? How do you know?

5. In complete sentences, describe the shape of the histogram.

6. Are there any potential outliers? List the value(s) that could be outliers. Use a formula to check the end values to determine if they are potential outliers.

Analyze the Data

1. Determine the following values.

    a. Min = _____

    b. M = _____

    c. Max = _____

    d. Q_1 = _____

    e. Q_3 = _____

    f. IQR = _____

2. Construct a box plot of data

3. What does the shape of the box plot imply about the concentration of data? Use complete sentences.

4. Using the box plot, how can you determine if there are potential outliers?

5. How does the standard deviation help you to determine concentration of the data and whether or not there are potential outliers?

6. What does the IQR represent in this problem?

7. Show your work to find the value that is 1.5 standard deviations:

    a. above the mean.

    b. below the mean.

KEY TERMS

Box plot a graph that gives a quick picture of the middle 50% of the data

First Quartile the value that is the median of the of the lower half of the ordered data set

Frequency the number of times a value of the data occurs

Frequency Polygon looks like a line graph but uses intervals to display ranges of large amounts of data

Frequency Table a data representation in which grouped data is displayed along with the corresponding frequencies

Histogram a graphical representation in *x-y* form of the distribution of data in a data set; *x* represents the data and *y* represents the frequency, or relative frequency. The graph consists of contiguous rectangles.

Interquartile Range or *IQR*, is the range of the middle 50 percent of the data values; the *IQR* is found by subtracting the first quartile from the third quartile.

Interval also called a class interval; an interval represents a range of data and is used when displaying large data sets

Mean a number that measures the central tendency of the data; a common name for mean is 'average.' The term 'mean' is a shortened form of 'arithmetic mean.' By definition, the mean for a sample (denoted by $\bar{x}$) is

$$\bar{x} = \frac{\text{Sum of all values in the sample}}{\text{Number of values in the sample}},$$ and the mean for a population (denoted by μ) is

$$\mu = \frac{\text{Sum of all values in the population}}{\text{Number of values in the population}}.$$

Median a number that separates ordered data into halves; half the values are the same number or smaller than the median and half the values are the same number or larger than the median. The median may or may not be part of the data.

Midpoint the mean of an interval in a frequency table

Mode the value that appears most frequently in a set of data

Outlier an observation that does not fit the rest of the data

Paired Data Set two data sets that have a one to one relationship so that:

- both data sets are the same size, and
- each data point in one data set is matched with exactly one point from the other set.

Percentile a number that divides ordered data into hundredths; percentiles may or may not be part of the data. The median of the data is the second quartile and the 50th percentile. The first and third quartiles are the 25th and the 75th percentiles, respectively.

Quartiles the numbers that separate the data into quarters; quartiles may or may not be part of the data. The second quartile is the median of the data.

Relative Frequency the ratio of the number of times a value of the data occurs in the set of all outcomes to the number of all outcomes

Skewed used to describe data that is not symmetrical; when the right side of a graph looks "chopped off" compared the left side, we say it is "skewed to the left." When the left side of the graph looks "chopped off" compared to the right side, we say the data is "skewed to the right." Alternatively: when the lower values of the data are more spread out, we say the data are skewed to the left. When the greater values are more spread out, the data are skewed to the right.

Standard Deviation a number that is equal to the square root of the variance and measures how far data values are from their mean; notation: *s* for sample standard deviation and σ for population standard deviation.

Variance mean of the squared deviations from the mean, or the square of the standard deviation; for a set of data, a deviation can be represented as $x - \bar{x}$ where x is a value of the data and $\bar{x}$ is the sample mean. The sample variance is equal to the sum of the squares of the deviations divided by the difference of the sample size and one.

CHAPTER REVIEW

2.1 Stem-and-Leaf Graphs (Stemplots), Line Graphs, and Bar Graphs

A **stem-and-leaf plot** is a way to plot data and look at the distribution. In a stem-and-leaf plot, all data values within a class are visible. The advantage in a stem-and-leaf plot is that all values are listed, unlike a histogram, which gives classes of data values. A **line graph** is often used to represent a set of data values in which a quantity varies with time. These graphs are useful for finding trends. That is, finding a general pattern in data sets including temperature, sales, employment, company profit or cost over a period of time. A **bar graph** is a chart that uses either horizontal or vertical bars to show comparisons among categories. One axis of the chart shows the specific categories being compared, and the other axis represents a discrete value. Some bar graphs present bars clustered in groups of more than one (grouped bar graphs), and others show the bars divided into subparts to show cumulative effect (stacked bar graphs). Bar graphs are especially useful when categorical data is being used.

2.2 Histograms, Frequency Polygons, and Time Series Graphs

A **histogram** is a graphic version of a frequency distribution. The graph consists of bars of equal width drawn adjacent to each other. The horizontal scale represents classes of quantitative data values and the vertical scale represents frequencies. The heights of the bars correspond to frequency values. Histograms are typically used for large, continuous, quantitative data sets. A frequency polygon can also be used when graphing large data sets with data points that repeat. The data usually goes on y-axis with the frequency being graphed on the x-axis. Time series graphs can be helpful when looking at large amounts of data for one variable over a period of time.

2.3 Measures of the Location of the Data

The values that divide a rank-ordered set of data into 100 equal parts are called percentiles. Percentiles are used to compare and interpret data. For example, an observation at the 50th percentile would be greater than 50 percent of the other obeservations in the set. Quartiles divide data into quarters. The first quartile (Q_1) is the 25th percentile,the second quartile (Q_2 or median) is 50th percentile, and the third quartile (Q_3) is the the 75th percentile. The interquartile range, or IQR, is the range of the middle 50 percent of the data values. The IQR is found by subtracting Q_1 from Q_3, and can help determine outliers by using the following two expressions.

- $Q_3 + IQR(1.5)$
- $Q_1 - IQR(1.5)$

2.4 Box Plots

Box plots are a type of graph that can help visually organize data. To graph a box plot the following data points must be calculated: the minimum value, the first quartile, the median, the third quartile, and the maximum value. Once the box plot is graphed, you can display and compare distributions of data.

2.5 Measures of the Center of the Data

The mean and the median can be calculated to help you find the "center" of a data set. The mean is the best estimate for the actual data set, but the median is the best measurement when a data set contains several outliers or extreme values. The mode will tell you the most frequently occuring datum (or data) in your data set. The mean, median, and mode are extremely helpful when you need to analyze your data, but if your data set consists of ranges which lack specific values, the mean may seem impossible to calculate. However, the mean can be approximated if you add the lower boundary with the upper boundary and divide by two to find the midpoint of each interval. Multiply each midpoint by the number of values found in the corresponding range. Divide the sum of these values by the total number of data values in the set.

2.6 Skewness and the Mean, Median, and Mode

Looking at the distribution of data can reveal a lot about the relationship between the mean, the median, and the mode. There are three types of distributions. A **right (or positive) skewed** distribution has a shape like **Figure 2.17**. A **left (or negative) skewed** distribution has a shape like **Figure 2.18**. A **symmetrical** distrubtion looks like **Figure 2.16**.

2.7 Measures of the Spread of the Data

The standard deviation can help you calculate the spread of data. There are different equations to use if are calculating the standard deviation of a sample or of a population.

- The Standard Deviation allows us to compare individual data or classes to the data set mean numerically.

- $s = \sqrt{\dfrac{\sum (x - \bar{x})^2}{n-1}}$ or $s = \sqrt{\dfrac{\sum f(x - \bar{x})^2}{n-1}}$ is the formula for calculating the standard deviation of a sample.

  To calculate the standard deviation of a population, we would use the population mean, μ, and the formula $\sigma = \sqrt{\dfrac{\sum (x - \mu)^2}{N}}$ or $\sigma = \sqrt{\dfrac{\sum f(x - \mu)^2}{N}}$.

FORMULA REVIEW

2.3 Measures of the Location of the Data

$i = \left(\dfrac{k}{100}\right)(n + 1)$

where i = the ranking or position of a data value,

k = the kth percentile,

n = total number of data.

Expression for finding the percentile of a data value:
$\left(\dfrac{x + 0.5y}{n}\right)(100)$

where x = the number of values counting from the bottom of the data list up to but not including the data value for which you want to find the percentile,

y = the number of data values equal to the data value for which you want to find the percentile,

n = total number of data

2.5 Measures of the Center of the Data

$\mu = \dfrac{\sum fm}{\sum f}$ Where f = interval frequencies and m = interval midpoints.

2.7 Measures of the Spread of the Data

$s_x = \sqrt{\dfrac{\sum fm^2}{n} - \bar{x}^2}$ where

s_x = sample standard deviation

$\bar{x}$ = sample mean

PRACTICE

2.1 Stem-and-Leaf Graphs (Stemplots), Line Graphs, and Bar Graphs

For each of the following data sets, create a stem plot and identify any outliers.

1. The miles per gallon rating for 30 cars are shown below (lowest to highest).
19, 19, 19, 20, 21, 21, 25, 25, 25, 26, 26, 28, 29, 31, 31, 32, 32, 33, 34, 35, 36, 37, 37, 38, 38, 38, 38, 41, 43, 43

2. The height in feet of 25 trees is shown below (lowest to highest).
25, 27, 33, 34, 34, 34, 35, 37, 37, 38, 39, 39, 39, 40, 41, 45, 46, 47, 49, 50, 50, 53, 53, 54, 54

3. The data are the prices of different laptops at an electronics store. Round each value to the nearest ten.
249, 249, 260, 265, 265, 280, 299, 299, 309, 319, 325, 326, 350, 350, 350, 365, 369, 389, 409, 459, 489, 559, 569, 570, 610

4. The data are daily high temperatures in a town for one month.
61, 61, 62, 64, 66, 67, 67, 67, 68, 69, 70, 70, 70, 71, 71, 72, 74, 74, 74, 75, 75, 75, 76, 76, 77, 78, 78, 79, 79, 95

For the next three exercises, use the data to construct a line graph.

5. In a survey, 40 people were asked how many times they visited a store before making a major purchase. The results are shown in **Table 2.37**.

Number of times in store	Frequency
1	4
2	10
3	16
4	6
5	4

Table 2.37

6. In a survey, several people were asked how many years it has been since they purchased a mattress. The results are shown in **Table 2.38**.

Years since last purchase	Frequency
0	2
1	8
2	13
3	22
4	16
5	9

Table 2.38

7. Several children were asked how many TV shows they watch each day. The results of the survey are shown in **Table 2.39**.

Number of TV Shows	Frequency
0	12
1	18
2	36
3	7
4	2

Table 2.39

8. The students in Ms. Ramirez's math class have birthdays in each of the four seasons. **Table 2.40** shows the four seasons, the number of students who have birthdays in each season, and the percentage (%) of students in each group. Construct a bar graph showing the number of students.

Seasons	Number of students	Proportion of population
Spring	8	24%
Summer	9	26%
Autumn	11	32%
Winter	6	18%

Table 2.40

9. Using the data from Mrs. Ramirez's math class supplied in **Exercise 2.8**, construct a bar graph showing the percentages.

10. David County has six high schools. Each school sent students to participate in a county-wide science competition. **Table 2.41** shows the percentage breakdown of competitors from each school, and the percentage of the entire student population of the county that goes to each school. Construct a bar graph that shows the population percentage of competitors from each school.

High School	Science competition population	Overall student population
Alabaster	28.9%	8.6%
Concordia	7.6%	23.2%
Genoa	12.1%	15.0%
Mocksville	18.5%	14.3%
Tynneson	24.2%	10.1%
West End	8.7%	28.8%

Table 2.41

11. Use the data from the David County science competition supplied in **Exercise 2.10**. Construct a bar graph that shows the county-wide population percentage of students at each school.

2.2 Histograms, Frequency Polygons, and Time Series Graphs

12. Sixty-five randomly selected car salespersons were asked the number of cars they generally sell in one week. Fourteen people answered that they generally sell three cars; nineteen generally sell four cars; twelve generally sell five cars; nine generally sell six cars; eleven generally sell seven cars. Complete the table.

Data Value (# cars)	Frequency	Relative Frequency	Cumulative Relative Frequency

Table 2.42

13. What does the frequency column in **Table 2.42** sum to? Why?

14. What does the relative frequency column in **Table 2.42** sum to? Why?

15. What is the difference between relative frequency and frequency for each data value in **Table 2.42**?

16. What is the difference between cumulative relative frequency and relative frequency for each data value?

17. To construct the histogram for the data in **Table 2.42**, determine appropriate minimum and maximum x and y values and the scaling. Sketch the histogram. Label the horizontal and vertical axes with words. Include numerical scaling.

Figure 2.31

18. Construct a frequency polygon for the following:

a.

Pulse Rates for Women	Frequency
60–69	12
70–79	14
80–89	11
90–99	1
100–109	1
110–119	0
120–129	1

Table 2.43

b.

Actual Speed in a 30 MPH Zone	Frequency
42–45	25
46–49	14
50–53	7
54–57	3
58–61	1

Table 2.44

c.

Tar (mg) in Nonfiltered Cigarettes	Frequency
10–13	1
14–17	0
18–21	15
22–25	7
26–29	2

Table 2.45

19. Construct a frequency polygon from the frequency distribution for the 50 highest ranked countries for depth of hunger.

Depth of Hunger	Frequency
230–259	21
260–289	13
290–319	5
320–349	7
350–379	1
380–409	1
410–439	1

Table 2.46

20. Use the two frequency tables to compare the life expectancy of men and women from 20 randomly selected countries. Include an overlayed frequency polygon and discuss the shapes of the distributions, the center, the spread, and any outliers. What can we conclude about the life expectancy of women compared to men?

Life Expectancy at Birth – Women	Frequency
49–55	3
56–62	3
63–69	1
70–76	3
77–83	8
84–90	2

Table 2.47

Life Expectancy at Birth – Men	Frequency
49–55	3
56–62	3
63–69	1
70–76	1
77–83	7
84–90	5

Table 2.48

21. Construct a times series graph for (a) the number of male births, (b) the number of female births, and (c) the total number of births.

Sex/Year	1855	1856	1857	1858	1859	1860	1861
Female	45,545	49,582	50,257	50,324	51,915	51,220	52,403
Male	47,804	52,239	53,158	53,694	54,628	54,409	54,606
Total	93,349	101,821	103,415	104,018	106,543	105,629	107,009

Table 2.49

Sex/Year	1862	1863	1864	1865	1866	1867	1868	1869
Female	51,812	53,115	54,959	54,850	55,307	55,527	56,292	55,033
Male	55,257	56,226	57,374	58,220	58,360	58,517	59,222	58,321
Total	107,069	109,341	112,333	113,070	113,667	114,044	115,514	113,354

Table 2.50

Sex/Year	1870	1871	1872	1873	1874	1875
Female	56,431	56,099	57,472	58,233	60,109	60,146
Male	58,959	60,029	61,293	61,467	63,602	63,432
Total	115,390	116,128	118,765	119,700	123,711	123,578

Table 2.51

22. The following data sets list full time police per 100,000 citizens along with homicides per 100,000 citizens for the city of Detroit, Michigan during the period from 1961 to 1973.

Year	1961	1962	1963	1964	1965	1966	1967
Police	260.35	269.8	272.04	272.96	272.51	261.34	268.89
Homicides	8.6	8.9	8.52	8.89	13.07	14.57	21.36

Table 2.52

Year	1968	1969	1970	1971	1972	1973
Police	295.99	319.87	341.43	356.59	376.69	390.19
Homicides	28.03	31.49	37.39	46.26	47.24	52.33

Table 2.53

a. Construct a double time series graph using a common *x*-axis for both sets of data.
b. Which variable increased the fastest? Explain.
c. Did Detroit's increase in police officers have an impact on the murder rate? Explain.

2.3 Measures of the Location of the Data

23. Listed are 29 ages for Academy Award winning best actors *in order from smallest to largest.*

18; 21; 22; 25; 26; 27; 29; 30; 31; 33; 36; 37; 41; 42; 47; 52; 55; 57; 58; 62; 64; 67; 69; 71; 72; 73; 74; 76; 77

    a. Find the 40th percentile.
    b. Find the 78th percentile.

24. Listed are 32 ages for Academy Award winning best actors *in order from smallest to largest.*

18; 18; 21; 22; 25; 26; 27; 29; 30; 31; 31; 33; 36; 37; 37; 41; 42; 47; 52; 55; 57; 58; 62; 64; 67; 69; 71; 72; 73; 74; 76; 77

    a. Find the percentile of 37.
    b. Find the percentile of 72.

25. Jesse was ranked 37th in his graduating class of 180 students. At what percentile is Jesse's ranking?

26.
    a. For runners in a race, a low time means a faster run. The winners in a race have the shortest running times. Is it more desirable to have a finish time with a high or a low percentile when running a race?
    b. The 20th percentile of run times in a particular race is 5.2 minutes. Write a sentence interpreting the 20th percentile in the context of the situation.
    c. A bicyclist in the 90th percentile of a bicycle race completed the race in 1 hour and 12 minutes. Is he among the fastest or slowest cyclists in the race? Write a sentence interpreting the 90th percentile in the context of the situation.

27.
    a. For runners in a race, a higher speed means a faster run. Is it more desirable to have a speed with a high or a low percentile when running a race?
    b. The 40th percentile of speeds in a particular race is 7.5 miles per hour. Write a sentence interpreting the 40th percentile in the context of the situation.

28. On an exam, would it be more desirable to earn a grade with a high or low percentile? Explain.

29. Mina is waiting in line at the Department of Motor Vehicles (DMV). Her wait time of 32 minutes is the 85th percentile of wait times. Is that good or bad? Write a sentence interpreting the 85th percentile in the context of this situation.

30. In a survey collecting data about the salaries earned by recent college graduates, Li found that her salary was in the 78th percentile. Should Li be pleased or upset by this result? Explain.

31. In a study collecting data about the repair costs of damage to automobiles in a certain type of crash tests, a certain model of car had $1,700 in damage and was in the 90th percentile. Should the manufacturer and the consumer be pleased or upset by this result? Explain and write a sentence that interprets the 90th percentile in the context of this problem.

32. The University of California has two criteria used to set admission standards for freshman to be admitted to a college in the UC system:
    a. Students' GPAs and scores on standardized tests (SATs and ACTs) are entered into a formula that calculates an "admissions index" score. The admissions index score is used to set eligibility standards intended to meet the goal of admitting the top 12% of high school students in the state. In this context, what percentile does the top 12% represent?
    b. Students whose GPAs are at or above the 96th percentile of all students at their high school are eligible (called eligible in the local context), even if they are not in the top 12% of all students in the state. What percentage of students from each high school are "eligible in the local context"?

33. Suppose that you are buying a house. You and your realtor have determined that the most expensive house you can afford is the 34th percentile. The 34th percentile of housing prices is $240,000 in the town you want to move to. In this town, can you afford 34% of the houses or 66% of the houses?

Use the following information to answer the next six exercises. Sixty-five randomly selected car salespersons were asked the number of cars they generally sell in one week. Fourteen people answered that they generally sell three cars; nineteen generally sell four cars; twelve generally sell five cars; nine generally sell six cars; eleven generally sell seven cars.

34. First quartile = _____

35. Second quartile = median = 50th percentile = _____

36. Third quartile = _____

37. Interquartile range (IQR) = _____ – _____ = _____

38. 10th percentile = _____

39. 70th percentile = _____

2.4 Box Plots

Use the following information to answer the next two exercises. Sixty-five randomly selected car salespersons were asked the number of cars they generally sell in one week. Fourteen people answered that they generally sell three cars; nineteen generally sell four cars; twelve generally sell five cars; nine generally sell six cars; eleven generally sell seven cars.

40. Construct a box plot below. Use a ruler to measure and scale accurately.

41. Looking at your box plot, does it appear that the data are concentrated together, spread out evenly, or concentrated in some areas, but not in others? How can you tell?

2.5 Measures of the Center of the Data

42. Find the mean for the following frequency tables.

a.

Grade	Frequency
49.5–59.5	2
59.5–69.5	3
69.5–79.5	8
79.5–89.5	12
89.5–99.5	5

Table 2.54

b.

Daily Low Temperature	Frequency
49.5–59.5	53
59.5–69.5	32
69.5–79.5	15
79.5–89.5	1
89.5–99.5	0

Table 2.55

c.

Points per Game	Frequency
49.5–59.5	14
59.5–69.5	32
69.5–79.5	15
79.5–89.5	23
89.5–99.5	2

Table 2.56

Use the following information to answer the next three exercises: The following data show the lengths of boats moored in a marina. The data are ordered from smallest to largest: 16; 17; 19; 20; 20; 21; 23; 24; 25; 25; 25; 26; 26; 27; 27; 27; 28; 29; 30; 32; 33; 33; 34; 35; 37; 39; 40

43. Calculate the mean.

44. Identify the median.

45. Identify the mode.

Use the following information to answer the next three exercises: Sixty-five randomly selected car salespersons were asked the number of cars they generally sell in one week. Fourteen people answered that they generally sell three cars; nineteen generally sell four cars; twelve generally sell five cars; nine generally sell six cars; eleven generally sell seven cars. Calculate the following:

46. sample mean = $\bar{x}$ = _____

47. median = _____

48. mode = _____

2.6 Skewness and the Mean, Median, and Mode

Use the following information to answer the next three exercises: State whether the data are symmetrical, skewed to the left, or skewed to the right.

49. 1; 1; 1; 2; 2; 2; 2; 3; 3; 3; 3; 3; 3; 3; 3; 4; 4; 4; 5; 5

50. 16; 17; 19; 22; 22; 22; 22; 22; 23

51. 87; 87; 87; 87; 87; 88; 89; 89; 90; 91

52. When the data are skewed left, what is the typical relationship between the mean and median?

53. When the data are symmetrical, what is the typical relationship between the mean and median?

54. What word describes a distribution that has two modes?

55. Describe the shape of this distribution.

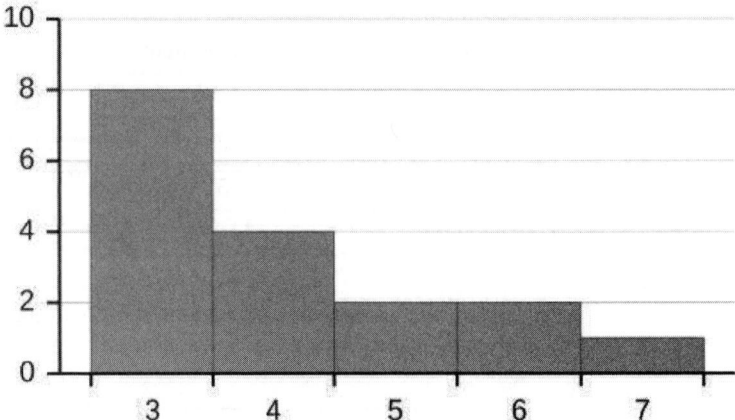

Figure 2.32

56. Describe the relationship between the mode and the median of this distribution.

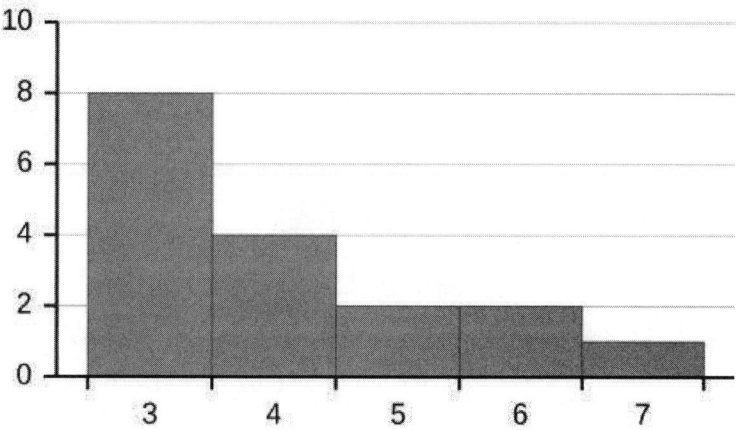

Figure 2.33

57. Describe the relationship between the mean and the median of this distribution.

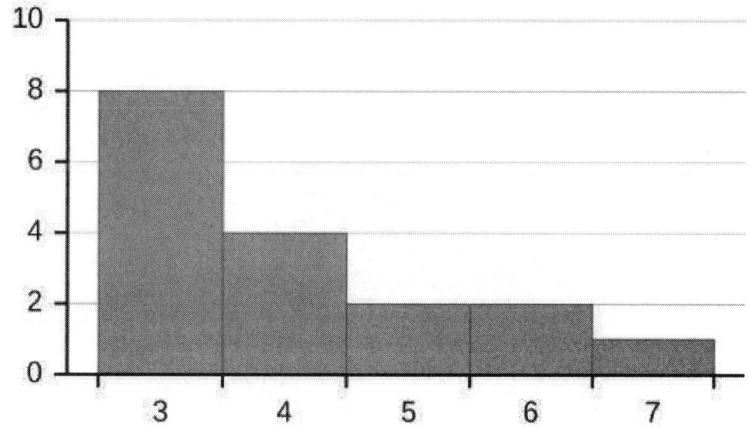

Figure 2.34

58. Describe the shape of this distribution.

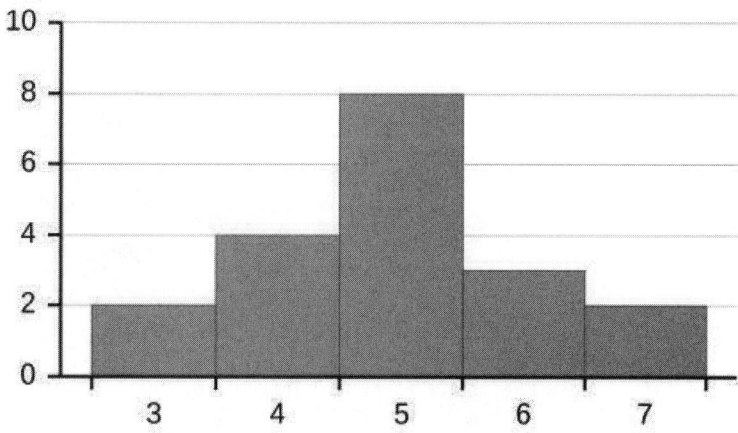

Figure 2.35

59. Describe the relationship between the mode and the median of this distribution.

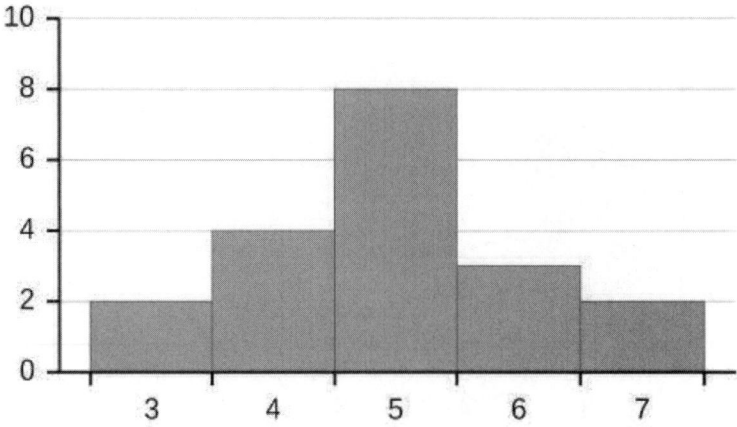

Figure 2.36

60. Are the mean and the median the exact same in this distribution? Why or why not?

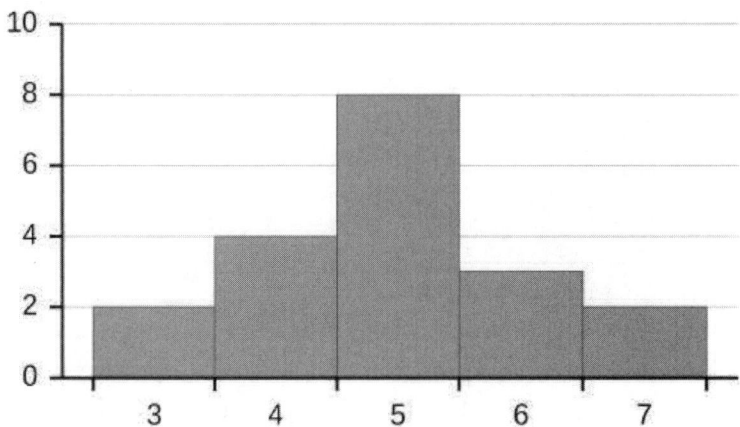

Figure 2.37

61. Describe the shape of this distribution.

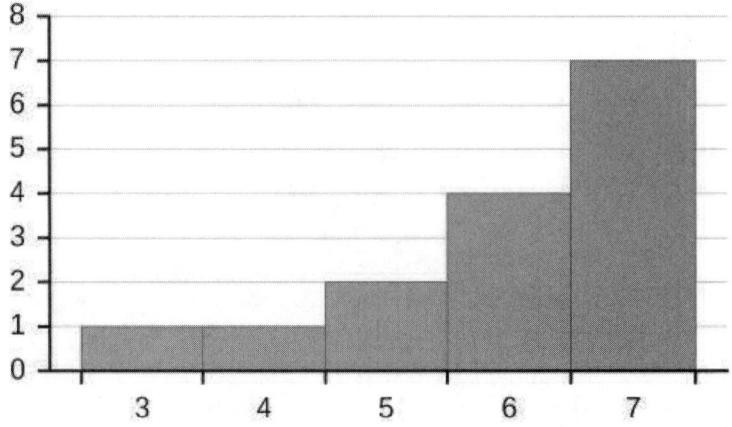

Figure 2.38

62. Describe the relationship between the mode and the median of this distribution.

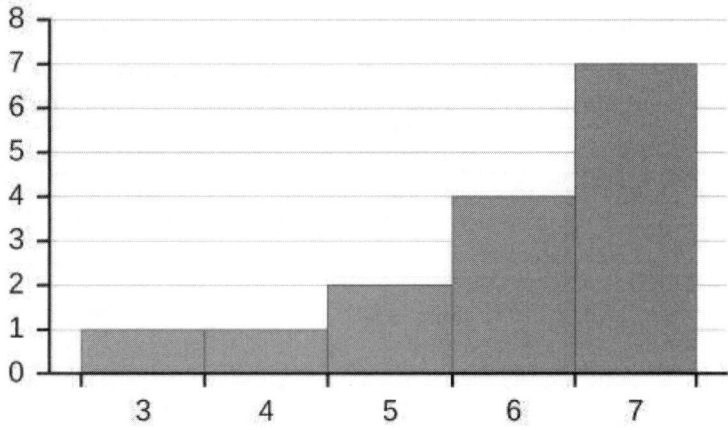

Figure 2.39

63. Describe the relationship between the mean and the median of this distribution.

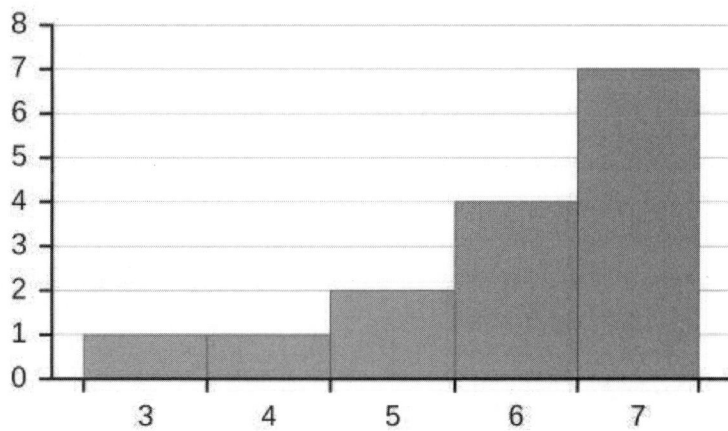

Figure 2.40

64. The mean and median for the data are the same.

3; 4; 5; 5; 6; 6; 6; 6; 7; 7; 7; 7; 7; 7; 7

Is the data perfectly symmetrical? Why or why not?

65. Which is the greatest, the mean, the mode, or the median of the data set?

11; 11; 12; 12; 12; 12; 13; 15; 17; 22; 22; 22

66. Which is the least, the mean, the mode, and the median of the data set?

56; 56; 56; 58; 59; 60; 62; 64; 64; 65; 67

67. Of the three measures, which tends to reflect skewing the most, the mean, the mode, or the median? Why?

68. In a perfectly symmetrical distribution, when would the mode be different from the mean and median?

2.7 Measures of the Spread of the Data

Use the following information to answer the next two exercises: The following data are the distances between 20 retail stores and a large distribution center. The distances are in miles.
29; 37; 38; 40; 58; 67; 68; 69; 76; 86; 87; 95; 96; 96; 99; 106; 112; 127; 145; 150

69. Use a graphing calculator or computer to find the standard deviation and round to the nearest tenth.

70. Find the value that is one standard deviation below the mean.

71. Two baseball players, Fredo and Karl, on different teams wanted to find out who had the higher batting average when compared to his team. Which baseball player had the higher batting average when compared to his team?

Baseball Player	Batting Average	Team Batting Average	Team Standard Deviation
Fredo	0.158	0.166	0.012
Karl	0.177	0.189	0.015

Table 2.57

72. Use **Table 2.57** to find the value that is three standard deviations:
a. above the mean
b. below the mean

Find the standard deviation for the following frequency tables using the formula. Check the calculations with the TI 83/84.

73. Find the standard deviation for the following frequency tables using the formula. Check the calculations with the TI 83/84.

a.

Grade	Frequency
49.5–59.5	2
59.5–69.5	3
69.5–79.5	8
79.5–89.5	12
89.5–99.5	5

Table 2.58

b.

Daily Low Temperature	Frequency
49.5–59.5	53
59.5–69.5	32
69.5–79.5	15
79.5–89.5	1
89.5–99.5	0

Table 2.59

c.

Points per Game	Frequency
49.5–59.5	14
59.5–69.5	32
69.5–79.5	15
79.5–89.5	23
89.5–99.5	2

Table 2.60

HOMEWORK

2.1 Stem-and-Leaf Graphs (Stemplots), Line Graphs, and Bar Graphs

74. Student grades on a chemistry exam were: 77, 78, 76, 81, 86, 51, 79, 82, 84, 99
   a. Construct a stem-and-leaf plot of the data.
   b. Are there any potential outliers? If so, which scores are they? Why do you consider them outliers?

75. Table 2.61 contains the 2010 obesity rates in U.S. states and Washington, DC.

State	Percent (%)	State	Percent (%)	State	Percent (%)
Alabama	32.2	Kentucky	31.3	North Dakota	27.2
Alaska	24.5	Louisiana	31.0	Ohio	29.2
Arizona	24.3	Maine	26.8	Oklahoma	30.4
Arkansas	30.1	Maryland	27.1	Oregon	26.8
California	24.0	Massachusetts	23.0	Pennsylvania	28.6
Colorado	21.0	Michigan	30.9	Rhode Island	25.5
Connecticut	22.5	Minnesota	24.8	South Carolina	31.5
Delaware	28.0	Mississippi	34.0	South Dakota	27.3
Washington, DC	22.2	Missouri	30.5	Tennessee	30.8
Florida	26.6	Montana	23.0	Texas	31.0
Georgia	29.6	Nebraska	26.9	Utah	22.5
Hawaii	22.7	Nevada	22.4	Vermont	23.2
Idaho	26.5	New Hampshire	25.0	Virginia	26.0
Illinois	28.2	New Jersey	23.8	Washington	25.5
Indiana	29.6	New Mexico	25.1	West Virginia	32.5
Iowa	28.4	New York	23.9	Wisconsin	26.3
Kansas	29.4	North Carolina	27.8	Wyoming	25.1

Table 2.61

a. Use a random number generator to randomly pick eight states. Construct a bar graph of the obesity rates of those eight states.
b. Construct a bar graph for all the states beginning with the letter "A."
c. Construct a bar graph for all the states beginning with the letter "M."

2.2 Histograms, Frequency Polygons, and Time Series Graphs

76. Suppose that three book publishers were interested in the number of fiction paperbacks adult consumers purchase per month. Each publisher conducted a survey. In the survey, adult consumers were asked the number of fiction paperbacks they had purchased the previous month. The results are as follows:

# of books	Freq.	Rel. Freq.
0	10	
1	12	
2	16	
3	12	
4	8	
5	6	
6	2	
8	2	

Table 2.62 Publisher A

# of books	Freq.	Rel. Freq.
0	18	
1	24	
2	24	
3	22	
4	15	
5	10	
7	5	
9	1	

Table 2.63 Publisher B

# of books	Freq.	Rel. Freq.
0–1	20	
2–3	35	
4–5	12	
6–7	2	
8–9	1	

Table 2.64 Publisher C

a. Find the relative frequencies for each survey. Write them in the charts.
b. Using either a graphing calculator, computer, or by hand, use the frequency column to construct a histogram for each publisher's survey. For Publishers A and B, make bar widths of one. For Publisher C, make bar widths of two.
c. In complete sentences, give two reasons why the graphs for Publishers A and B are not identical.
d. Would you have expected the graph for Publisher C to look like the other two graphs? Why or why not?
e. Make new histograms for Publisher A and Publisher B. This time, make bar widths of two.
f. Now, compare the graph for Publisher C to the new graphs for Publishers A and B. Are the graphs more similar or more different? Explain your answer.

77. Often, cruise ships conduct all on-board transactions, with the exception of gambling, on a cashless basis. At the end of the cruise, guests pay one bill that covers all onboard transactions. Suppose that 60 single travelers and 70 couples were surveyed as to their on-board bills for a seven-day cruise from Los Angeles to the Mexican Riviera. Following is a summary of the bills for each group.

Amount($)	Frequency	Rel. Frequency
51–100	5	
101–150	10	
151–200	15	
201–250	15	
251–300	10	
301–350	5	

Table 2.65 Singles

Amount($)	Frequency	Rel. Frequency
100–150	5	
201–250	5	
251–300	5	
301–350	5	
351–400	10	
401–450	10	
451–500	10	
501–550	10	
551–600	5	
601–650	5	

Table 2.66 Couples

a. Fill in the relative frequency for each group.
b. Construct a histogram for the singles group. Scale the *x*-axis by $50 widths. Use relative frequency on the *y*-axis.
c. Construct a histogram for the couples group. Scale the *x*-axis by $50 widths. Use relative frequency on the *y*-axis.
d. Compare the two graphs:
    i. List two similarities between the graphs.
    ii. List two differences between the graphs.
    iii. Overall, are the graphs more similar or different?
e. Construct a new graph for the couples by hand. Since each couple is paying for two individuals, instead of scaling the *x*-axis by $50, scale it by $100. Use relative frequency on the *y*-axis.
f. Compare the graph for the singles with the new graph for the couples:
    i. List two similarities between the graphs.
    ii. Overall, are the graphs more similar or different?
g. How did scaling the couples graph differently change the way you compared it to the singles graph?
h. Based on the graphs, do you think that individuals spend the same amount, more or less, as singles as they do person by person as a couple? Explain why in one or two complete sentences.

78. Twenty-five randomly selected students were asked the number of movies they watched the previous week. The results are as follows.

# of movies	Frequency	Relative Frequency	Cumulative Relative Frequency
0	5		
1	9		
2	6		
3	4		
4	1		

Table 2.67

    a.   Construct a histogram of the data.
    b.   Complete the columns of the chart.

Use the following information to answer the next two exercises: Suppose one hundred eleven people who shopped in a special t-shirt store were asked the number of t-shirts they own costing more than $19 each.

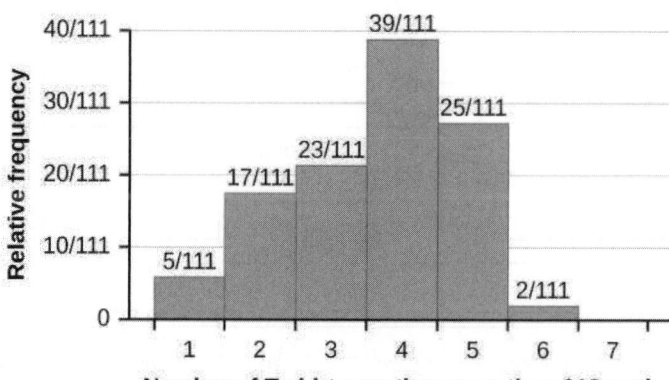

79. The percentage of people who own at most three t-shirts costing more than $19 each is approximately:
    a.   21
    b.   59
    c.   41
    d.   Cannot be determined

80. If the data were collected by asking the first 111 people who entered the store, then the type of sampling is:
    a.   cluster
    b.   simple random
    c.   stratified
    d.   convenience

81. Following are the 2010 obesity rates by U.S. states and Washington, DC.

State	Percent (%)	State	Percent (%)	State	Percent (%)
Alabama	32.2	Kentucky	31.3	North Dakota	27.2
Alaska	24.5	Louisiana	31.0	Ohio	29.2
Arizona	24.3	Maine	26.8	Oklahoma	30.4
Arkansas	30.1	Maryland	27.1	Oregon	26.8
California	24.0	Massachusetts	23.0	Pennsylvania	28.6
Colorado	21.0	Michigan	30.9	Rhode Island	25.5
Connecticut	22.5	Minnesota	24.8	South Carolina	31.5
Delaware	28.0	Mississippi	34.0	South Dakota	27.3
Washington, DC	22.2	Missouri	30.5	Tennessee	30.8
Florida	26.6	Montana	23.0	Texas	31.0
Georgia	29.6	Nebraska	26.9	Utah	22.5
Hawaii	22.7	Nevada	22.4	Vermont	23.2
Idaho	26.5	New Hampshire	25.0	Virginia	26.0
Illinois	28.2	New Jersey	23.8	Washington	25.5
Indiana	29.6	New Mexico	25.1	West Virginia	32.5
Iowa	28.4	New York	23.9	Wisconsin	26.3
Kansas	29.4	North Carolina	27.8	Wyoming	25.1

Table 2.68

Construct a bar graph of obesity rates of your state and the four states closest to your state. Hint: Label the *x*-axis with the states.

2.3 Measures of the Location of the Data

82. The median age for U.S. blacks currently is 30.9 years; for U.S. whites it is 42.3 years.
   a. Based upon this information, give two reasons why the black median age could be lower than the white median age.
   b. Does the lower median age for blacks necessarily mean that blacks die younger than whites? Why or why not?
   c. How might it be possible for blacks and whites to die at approximately the same age, but for the median age for whites to be higher?

83. Six hundred adult Americans were asked by telephone poll, "What do you think constitutes a middle-class income?" The results are in **Table 2.69**. Also, include left endpoint, but not the right endpoint.

Salary ($)	Relative Frequency
< 20,000	0.02
20,000–25,000	0.09
25,000–30,000	0.19
30,000–40,000	0.26
40,000–50,000	0.18
50,000–75,000	0.17
75,000–99,999	0.02
100,000+	0.01

Table 2.69

 a. What percentage of the survey answered "not sure"?
 b. What percentage think that middle-class is from $25,000 to $50,000?
 c. Construct a histogram of the data.
   i. Should all bars have the same width, based on the data? Why or why not?
   ii. How should the <20,000 and the 100,000+ intervals be handled? Why?
 d. Find the 40th and 80th percentiles
 e. Construct a bar graph of the data

84. Given the following box plot:

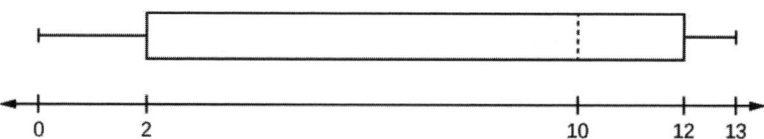

Figure 2.41
 a. which quarter has the smallest spread of data? What is that spread?
 b. which quarter has the largest spread of data? What is that spread?
 c. find the interquartile range (*IQR*).
 d. are there more data in the interval 5–10 or in the interval 10–13? How do you know this?
 e. which interval has the fewest data in it? How do you know this?
   i. 0–2
   ii. 2–4
   iii. 10–12
   iv. 12–13
   v. need more information

85. The following box plot shows the U.S. population for 1990, the latest available year.

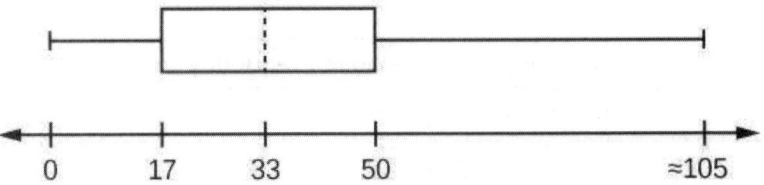

Figure 2.42

    a. Are there fewer or more children (age 17 and under) than senior citizens (age 65 and over)? How do you know?

    b. 12.6% are age 65 and over. Approximately what percentage of the population are working age adults (above age 17 to age 65)?

2.4 Box Plots

86. In a survey of 20-year-olds in China, Germany, and the United States, people were asked the number of foreign countries they had visited in their lifetime. The following box plots display the results.

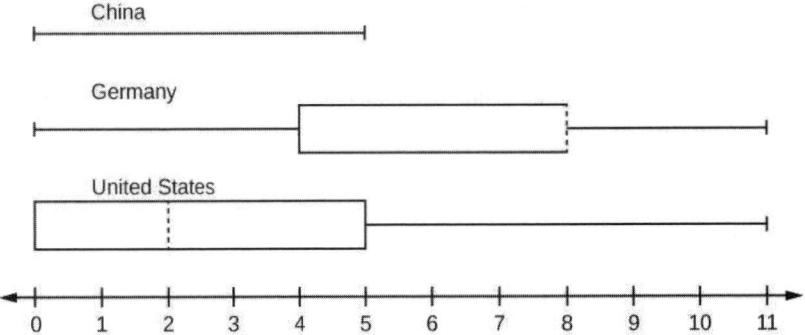

Figure 2.43

    a. In complete sentences, describe what the shape of each box plot implies about the distribution of the data collected.

    b. Have more Americans or more Germans surveyed been to over eight foreign countries?

    c. Compare the three box plots. What do they imply about the foreign travel of 20-year-old residents of the three countries when compared to each other?

87. Given the following box plot, answer the questions.

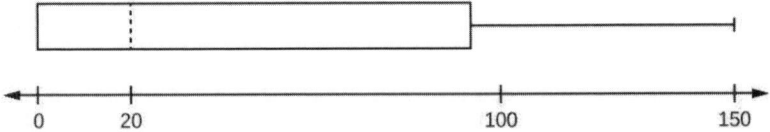

Figure 2.44

    a. Think of an example (in words) where the data might fit into the above box plot. In 2–5 sentences, write down the example.

    b. What does it mean to have the first and second quartiles so close together, while the second to third quartiles are far apart?

88. Given the following box plots, answer the questions.

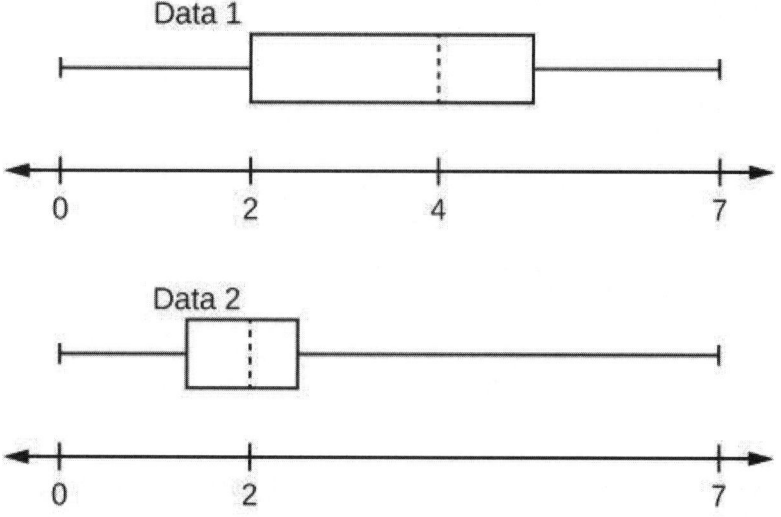

Figure 2.45

    a. In complete sentences, explain why each statement is false.

         i. **Data 1** has more data values above two than **Data 2** has above two.

        ii. The data sets cannot have the same mode.

       iii. For **Data 1**, there are more data values below four than there are above four.

    b. For which group, Data 1 or Data 2, is the value of "7" more likely to be an outlier? Explain why in complete sentences.

89. A survey was conducted of 130 purchasers of new BMW 3 series cars, 130 purchasers of new BMW 5 series cars, and 130 purchasers of new BMW 7 series cars. In it, people were asked the age they were when they purchased their car. The following box plots display the results.

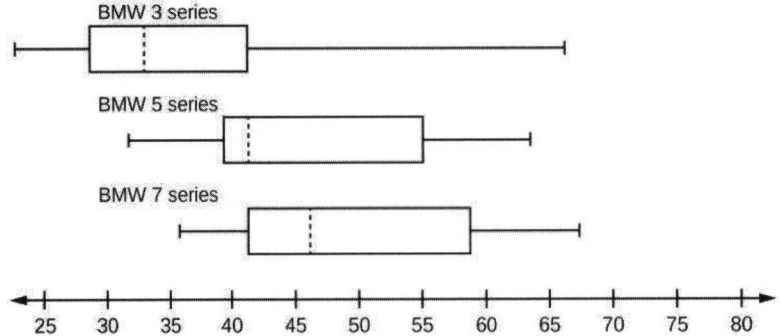

Figure 2.46

    a. In complete sentences, describe what the shape of each box plot implies about the distribution of the data collected for that car series.

    b. Which group is most likely to have an outlier? Explain how you determined that.

    c. Compare the three box plots. What do they imply about the age of purchasing a BMW from the series when compared to each other?

    d. Look at the BMW 5 series. Which quarter has the smallest spread of data? What is the spread?

    e. Look at the BMW 5 series. Which quarter has the largest spread of data? What is the spread?

    f. Look at the BMW 5 series. Estimate the interquartile range (IQR).

    g. Look at the BMW 5 series. Are there more data in the interval 31 to 38 or in the interval 45 to 55? How do you know this?

    h. Look at the BMW 5 series. Which interval has the fewest data in it? How do you know this?

        i.   31–35

        ii. 38–41

        iii. 41–64

90. Twenty-five randomly selected students were asked the number of movies they watched the previous week. The results are as follows:

# of movies	Frequency
0	5
1	9
2	6
3	4
4	1

Table 2.70

Construct a box plot of the data.

2.5 Measures of the Center of the Data

91. The most obese countries in the world have obesity rates that range from 11.4% to 74.6%. This data is summarized in the following table.

Percent of Population Obese	Number of Countries
11.4–20.45	29
20.45–29.45	13
29.45–38.45	4
38.45–47.45	0
47.45–56.45	2
56.45–65.45	1
65.45–74.45	0
74.45–83.45	1

Table 2.71

a.   What is the best estimate of the average obesity percentage for these countries?
b.   The United States has an average obesity rate of 33.9%. Is this rate above average or below?
c.   How does the United States compare to other countries?

92. Table 2.72 gives the percent of children under five considered to be underweight. What is the best estimate for the mean percentage of underweight children?

Percent of Underweight Children	Number of Countries
16–21.45	23
21.45–26.9	4
26.9–32.35	9
32.35–37.8	7
37.8–43.25	6
43.25–48.7	1

Table 2.72

2.6 Skewness and the Mean, Median, and Mode

93. The median age of the U.S. population in 1980 was 30.0 years. In 1991, the median age was 33.1 years.
a.   What does it mean for the median age to rise?
b.   Give two reasons why the median age could rise.
c.   For the median age to rise, is the actual number of children less in 1991 than it was in 1980? Why or why not?

2.7 Measures of the Spread of the Data

Use the following information to answer the next nine exercises: The population parameters below describe the full-time equivalent number of students (FTES) each year at Lake Tahoe Community College from 1976–1977 through 2004–2005.

- $\mu = 1000$ FTES

- median = 1,014 FTES

- $\sigma = 474$ FTES

- first quartile = 528.5 FTES

- third quartile = 1,447.5 FTES

- n = 29 years

94. A sample of 11 years is taken. About how many are expected to have a FTES of 1014 or above? Explain how you determined your answer.

95. 75% of all years have an FTES:
   a. at or below: _____
   b. at or above: _____

96. The population standard deviation = _____

97. What percent of the FTES were from 528.5 to 1447.5? How do you know?

98. What is the *IQR*? What does the *IQR* represent?

99. How many standard deviations away from the mean is the median?

Additional Information: The population FTES for 2005–2006 through 2010–2011 was given in an updated report. The data are reported here.

Year	2005–06	2006–07	2007–08	2008–09	2009–10	2010–11
Total FTES	1,585	1,690	1,735	1,935	2,021	1,890

Table 2.73

100. Calculate the mean, median, standard deviation, the first quartile, the third quartile and the *IQR*. Round to one decimal place.

101. What additional information is needed to construct a box plot for the FTES for 2005-2006 through 2010-2011 and a box plot for the FTES for 1976-1977 through 2004-2005?

102. Compare the *IQR* for the FTES for 1976–77 through 2004–2005 with the *IQR* for the FTES for 2005-2006 through 2010–2011. Why do you suppose the *IQR*s are so different?

103. Three students were applying to the same graduate school. They came from schools with different grading systems. Which student had the best GPA when compared to other students at his school? Explain how you determined your answer.

Student	GPA	School Average GPA	School Standard Deviation
Thuy	2.7	3.2	0.8
Vichet	87	75	20
Kamala	8.6	8	0.4

Table 2.74

104. A music school has budgeted to purchase three musical instruments. They plan to purchase a piano costing $3,000, a guitar costing $550, and a drum set costing $600. The mean cost for a piano is $4,000 with a standard deviation of $2,500. The mean cost for a guitar is $500 with a standard deviation of $200. The mean cost for drums is $700 with a standard deviation of $100. Which cost is the lowest, when compared to other instruments of the same type? Which cost is the highest when compared to other instruments of the same type. Justify your answer.

105. An elementary school class ran one mile with a mean of 11 minutes and a standard deviation of three minutes. Rachel, a student in the class, ran one mile in eight minutes. A junior high school class ran one mile with a mean of nine minutes and a standard deviation of two minutes. Kenji, a student in the class, ran 1 mile in 8.5 minutes. A high school class ran one mile with a mean of seven minutes and a standard deviation of four minutes. Nedda, a student in the class, ran one mile in eight minutes.
   a. Why is Kenji considered a better runner than Nedda, even though Nedda ran faster than he?
   b. Who is the fastest runner with respect to his or her class? Explain why.

106. The most obese countries in the world have obesity rates that range from 11.4% to 74.6%. This data is summarized in **Table 14**.

Percent of Population Obese	Number of Countries
11.4–20.45	29
20.45–29.45	13
29.45–38.45	4
38.45–47.45	0
47.45–56.45	2
56.45–65.45	1
65.45–74.45	0
74.45–83.45	1

Table 2.75

What is the best estimate of the average obesity percentage for these countries? What is the standard deviation for the listed obesity rates? The United States has an average obesity rate of 33.9%. Is this rate above average or below? How "unusual" is the United States' obesity rate compared to the average rate? Explain.

107. Table 2.76 gives the percent of children under five considered to be underweight.

Percent of Underweight Children	Number of Countries
16–21.45	23
21.45–26.9	4
26.9–32.35	9
32.35–37.8	7
37.8–43.25	6
43.25–48.7	1

Table 2.76

What is the best estimate for the mean percentage of underweight children? What is the standard deviation? Which interval(s) could be considered unusual? Explain.

BRINGING IT TOGETHER: HOMEWORK

108. Santa Clara County, CA, has approximately 27,873 Japanese-Americans. Their ages are as follows:

Age Group	Percent of Community
0–17	18.9
18–24	8.0
25–34	22.8
35–44	15.0
45–54	13.1
55–64	11.9
65+	10.3

Table 2.77

a. Construct a histogram of the Japanese-American community in Santa Clara County, CA. The bars will **not** be the same width for this example. Why not? What impact does this have on the reliability of the graph?
b. What percentage of the community is under age 35?
c. Which box plot most resembles the information above?

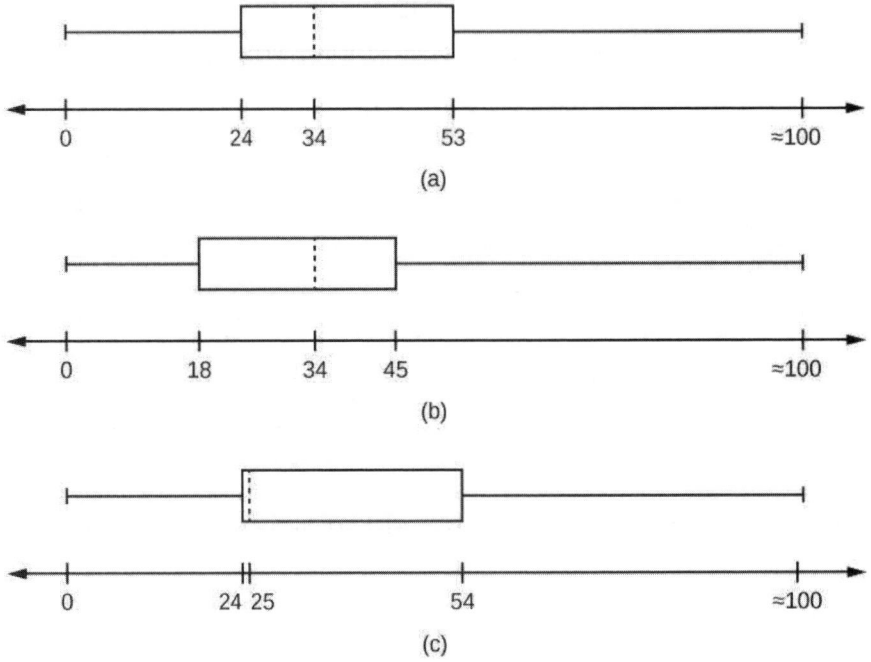

Figure 2.47

109. Javier and Ercilia are supervisors at a shopping mall. Each was given the task of estimating the mean distance that shoppers live from the mall. They each randomly surveyed 100 shoppers. The samples yielded the following information.

	Javier	Ercilia
$\bar{x}$	6.0 miles	6.0 miles
s	4.0 miles	7.0 miles

Table 2.78

a. How can you determine which survey was correct ?
b. Explain what the difference in the results of the surveys implies about the data.
c. If the two histograms depict the distribution of values for each supervisor, which one depicts Ercilia's sample? How do you know?

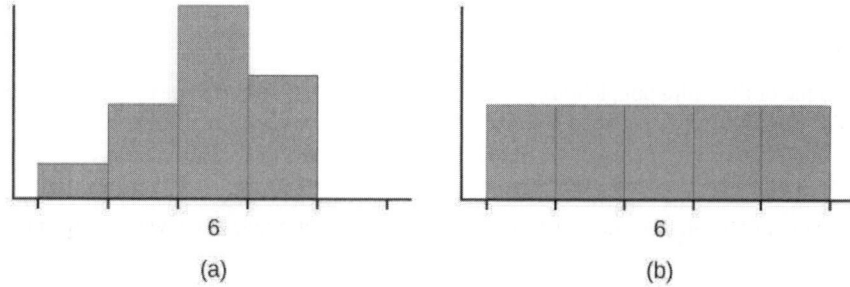

(a)   (b)

Figure 2.48

d. If the two box plots depict the distribution of values for each supervisor, which one depicts Ercilia's sample? How do you know?

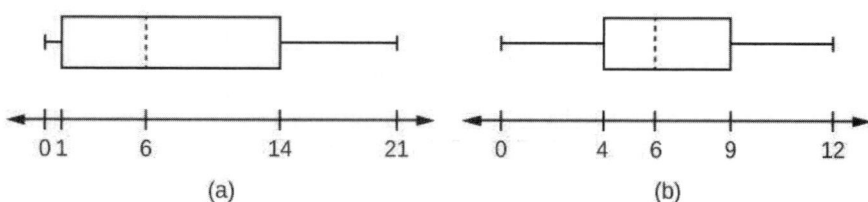

(a)   (b)

Figure 2.49

Use the following information to answer the next three exercises: We are interested in the number of years students in a particular elementary statistics class have lived in California. The information in the following table is from the entire section.

Number of years	Frequency	Number of years	Frequency
7	1	22	1
14	3	23	1
15	1	26	1
18	1	40	2
19	4	42	2
			Total = 20

Table 2.79

Number of years	Frequency	Number of years	Frequency
20	3		
			Total = 20

Table 2.79

110. What is the *IQR*?
- a.   8
- b.   11
- c.   15
- d.   35

111. What is the mode?
- a.   19
- b.   19.5
- c.   14 and 20
- d.   22.65

112. Is this a sample or the entire population?
- a.   sample
- b.   entire population
- c.   neither

113. Twenty-five randomly selected students were asked the number of movies they watched the previous week. The results are as follows:

# of movies	Frequency
0	5
1	9
2	6
3	4
4	1

Table 2.80

- a.   Find the sample mean $\bar{x}$.
- b.   Find the approximate sample standard deviation, *s*.

114. Forty randomly selected students were asked the number of pairs of sneakers they owned. Let X = the number of pairs of sneakers owned. The results are as follows:

X	Frequency
1	2
2	5
3	8
4	12
5	12
6	0
7	1

Table 2.81

  a. Find the sample mean $\bar{x}$
  b. Find the sample standard deviation, s
  c. Construct a histogram of the data.
  d. Complete the columns of the chart.
  e. Find the first quartile.
  f. Find the median.
  g. Find the third quartile.
  h. Construct a box plot of the data.
  i. What percent of the students owned at least five pairs?
  j. Find the 40th percentile.
  k. Find the 90th percentile.
  l. Construct a line graph of the data
  m. Construct a stemplot of the data

115. Following are the published weights (in pounds) of all of the team members of the San Francisco 49ers from a previous year.

177; 205; 210; 210; 232; 205; 185; 185; 178; 210; 206; 212; 184; 174; 185; 242; 188; 212; 215; 247; 241; 223; 220; 260; 245; 259; 278; 270; 280; 295; 275; 285; 290; 272; 273; 280; 285; 286; 200; 215; 185; 230; 250; 241; 190; 260; 250; 302; 265; 290; 276; 228; 265

  a. Organize the data from smallest to largest value.
  b. Find the median.
  c. Find the first quartile.
  d. Find the third quartile.
  e. Construct a box plot of the data.
  f. The middle 50% of the weights are from _____ to _____.
  g. If our population were all professional football players, would the above data be a sample of weights or the population of weights? Why?
  h. If our population included every team member who ever played for the San Francisco 49ers, would the above data be a sample of weights or the population of weights? Why?
  i. Assume the population was the San Francisco 49ers. Find:
      i. the population mean, μ.
      ii. the population standard deviation, σ.
      iii. the weight that is two standard deviations below the mean.
      iv. When Steve Young, quarterback, played football, he weighed 205 pounds. How many standard deviations above or below the mean was he?
  j. That same year, the mean weight for the Dallas Cowboys was 240.08 pounds with a standard deviation of 44.38 pounds. Emmit Smith weighed in at 209 pounds. With respect to his team, who was lighter, Smith or Young? How did you determine your answer?

116. One hundred teachers attended a seminar on mathematical problem solving. The attitudes of a representative sample of 12 of the teachers were measured before and after the seminar. A positive number for change in attitude indicates that a teacher's attitude toward math became more positive. The 12 change scores are as follows:

3; 8; –1; 2; 0; 5; –3; 1; –1; 6; 5; –2

  a. What is the mean change score?
  b. What is the standard deviation for this population?
  c. What is the median change score?
  d. Find the change score that is 2.2 standard deviations below the mean.

117. Refer to **Figure 2.50** determine which of the following are true and which are false. Explain your solution to each part in complete sentences.

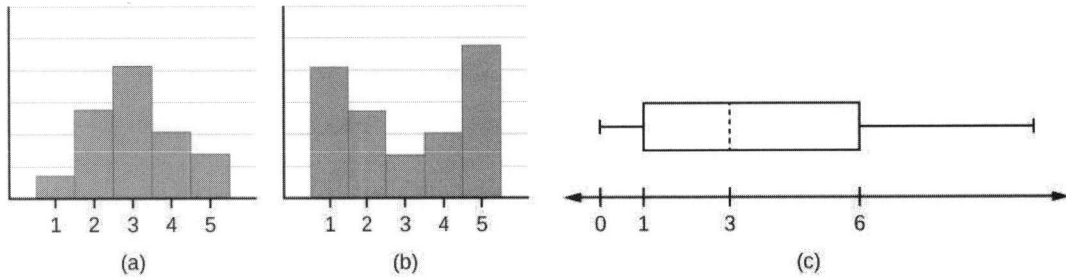

Figure 2.50
  a. The medians for all three graphs are the same.
  b. We cannot determine if any of the means for the three graphs is different.
  c. The standard deviation for graph b is larger than the standard deviation for graph a.
  d. We cannot determine if any of the third quartiles for the three graphs is different.

118. In a recent issue of the *IEEE Spectrum*, 84 engineering conferences were announced. Four conferences lasted two days. Thirty-six lasted three days. Eighteen lasted four days. Nineteen lasted five days. Four lasted six days. One lasted seven days. One lasted eight days. One lasted nine days. Let X = the length (in days) of an engineering conference.
  a. Organize the data in a chart.
  b. Find the median, the first quartile, and the third quartile.
  c. Find the 65th percentile.
  d. Find the 10th percentile.
  e. Construct a box plot of the data.
  f. The middle 50% of the conferences last from _____ days to _____ days.
  g. Calculate the sample mean of days of engineering conferences.
  h. Calculate the sample standard deviation of days of engineering conferences.
  i. Find the mode.
  j. If you were planning an engineering conference, which would you choose as the length of the conference: mean; median; or mode? Explain why you made that choice.
  k. Give two reasons why you think that three to five days seem to be popular lengths of engineering conferences.

119. A survey of enrollment at 35 community colleges across the United States yielded the following figures:

6414; 1550; 2109; 9350; 21828; 4300; 5944; 5722; 2825; 2044; 5481; 5200; 5853; 2750; 10012; 6357; 27000; 9414; 7681; 3200; 17500; 9200; 7380; 18314; 6557; 13713; 17768; 7493; 2771; 2861; 1263; 7285; 28165; 5080; 11622

  a. Organize the data into a chart with five intervals of equal width. Label the two columns "Enrollment" and "Frequency."
  b. Construct a histogram of the data.
  c. If you were to build a new community college, which piece of information would be more valuable: the mode or the mean?
  d. Calculate the sample mean.
  e. Calculate the sample standard deviation.
  f. A school with an enrollment of 8000 would be how many standard deviations away from the mean?

Use the following information to answer the next two exercises. X = the number of days per week that 100 clients use a particular exercise facility.

x	Frequency
0	3
1	12
2	33
3	28
4	11
5	9
6	4

Table 2.82

120. The 80th percentile is _____
   a. 5
   b. 80
   c. 3
   d. 4

121. The number that is 1.5 standard deviations BELOW the mean is approximately _____
   a. 0.7
   b. 4.8
   c. −2.8
   d. Cannot be determined

122. Suppose that a publisher conducted a survey asking adult consumers the number of fiction paperback books they had purchased in the previous month. The results are summarized in the **Table 2.83**.

# of books	Freq.	Rel. Freq.
0	18	
1	24	
2	24	
3	22	
4	15	
5	10	
7	5	
9	1	

Table 2.83

a. Are there any outliers in the data? Use an appropriate numerical test involving the *IQR* to identify outliers, if any, and clearly state your conclusion.
b. If a data value is identified as an outlier, what should be done about it?
c. Are any data values further than two standard deviations away from the mean? In some situations, statisticians may use this criteria to identify data values that are unusual, compared to the other data values. (Note that this criteria is most appropriate to use for data that is mound-shaped and symmetric, rather than for skewed data.)
d. Do parts a and c of this problem give the same answer?
e. Examine the shape of the data. Which part, a or c, of this question gives a more appropriate result for this data?
f. Based on the shape of the data which is the most appropriate measure of center for this data: mean, median or mode?

REFERENCES

2.1 Stem-and-Leaf Graphs (Stemplots), Line Graphs, and Bar Graphs

Burbary, Ken. *Facebook Demographics Revisited – 2001 Statistics*, 2011. Available online at http://www.kenburbary.com/2011/03/facebook-demographics-revisited-2011-statistics-2/ (accessed August 21, 2013).

"9th Annual AP Report to the Nation." CollegeBoard, 2013. Available online at http://apreport.collegeboard.org/goals-and-findings/promoting-equity (accessed September 13, 2013).

"Overweight and Obesity: Adult Obesity Facts." Centers for Disease Control and Prevention. Available online at http://www.cdc.gov/obesity/data/adult.html (accessed September 13, 2013).

2.2 Histograms, Frequency Polygons, and Time Series Graphs

Data on annual homicides in Detroit, 1961–73, from Gunst & Mason's book 'Regression Analysis and its Application', Marcel Dekker

"Timeline: Guide to the U.S. Presidents: Information on every president's birthplace, political party, term of office, and more." Scholastic, 2013. Available online at http://www.scholastic.com/teachers/article/timeline-guide-us-presidents (accessed April 3, 2013).

"Presidents." Fact Monster. Pearson Education, 2007. Available online at http://www.factmonster.com/ipka/A0194030.html (accessed April 3, 2013).

"Food Security Statistics." Food and Agriculture Organization of the United Nations. Available online at http://www.fao.org/economic/ess/ess-fs/en/ (accessed April 3, 2013).

"Consumer Price Index." United States Department of Labor: Bureau of Labor Statistics. Available online at http://data.bls.gov/pdq/SurveyOutputServlet (accessed April 3, 2013).

"CO2 emissions (kt)." The World Bank, 2013. Available online at http://databank.worldbank.org/data/home.aspx (accessed April 3, 2013).

"Births Time Series Data." General Register Office For Scotland, 2013. Available online at http://www.gro-scotland.gov.uk/statistics/theme/vital-events/births/time-series.html (accessed April 3, 2013).

"Demographics: Children under the age of 5 years underweight." Indexmundi. Available online at http://www.indexmundi.com/g/r.aspx?t=50&v=2224&aml=en (accessed April 3, 2013).

Gunst, Richard, Robert Mason. *Regression Analysis and Its Application: A Data-Oriented Approach*. CRC Press: 1980.

"Overweight and Obesity: Adult Obesity Facts." Centers for Disease Control and Prevention. Available online at http://www.cdc.gov/obesity/data/adult.html (accessed September 13, 2013).

2.3 Measures of the Location of the Data

Cauchon, Dennis, Paul Overberg. "Census data shows minorities now a majority of U.S. births." USA Today, 2012. Available online at http://usatoday30.usatoday.com/news/nation/story/2012-05-17/minority-birthscensus/55029100/1 (accessed April 3, 2013).

Data from the United States Department of Commerce: United States Census Bureau. Available online at http://www.census.gov/ (accessed April 3, 2013).

"1990 Census." United States Department of Commerce: United States Census Bureau. Available online at http://www.census.gov/main/www/cen1990.html (accessed April 3, 2013).

Data from *San Jose Mercury News*.

Data from *Time Magazine*; survey by Yankelovich Partners, Inc.

2.4 Box Plots

Data from *West Magazine*.

2.5 Measures of the Center of the Data

Data from The World Bank, available online at http://www.worldbank.org (accessed April 3, 2013).

"Demographics: Obesity – adult prevalence rate." Indexmundi. Available online at http://www.indexmundi.com/g/r.aspx?t=50&v=2228&l=en (accessed April 3, 2013).

2.7 Measures of the Spread of the Data

Data from Microsoft Bookshelf.

King, Bill."Graphically Speaking." Institutional Research, Lake Tahoe Community College. Available online at http://www.ltcc.edu/web/about/institutional-research (accessed April 3, 2013).

SOLUTIONS

1

Stem	Leaf
1	9 9 9
2	0 1 1 5 5 5 6 6 8 9
3	1 1 2 2 3 4 5 6 7 7 8 8 8 8
4	1 3 3

Table 2.84

3

Stem	Leaf
2	5 5 6 7 7 8
3	0 0 1 2 3 3 5 5 5 7 7 9
4	1 6 9
5	6 7 7
6	1

Table 2.85

5

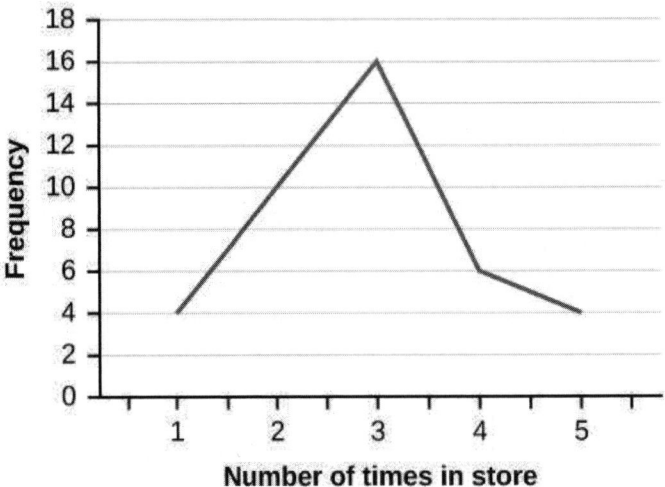

Figure 2.51

7

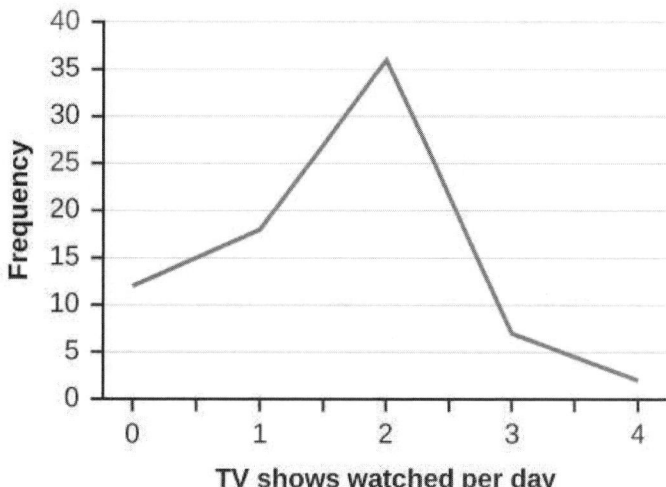

Figure 2.52

9

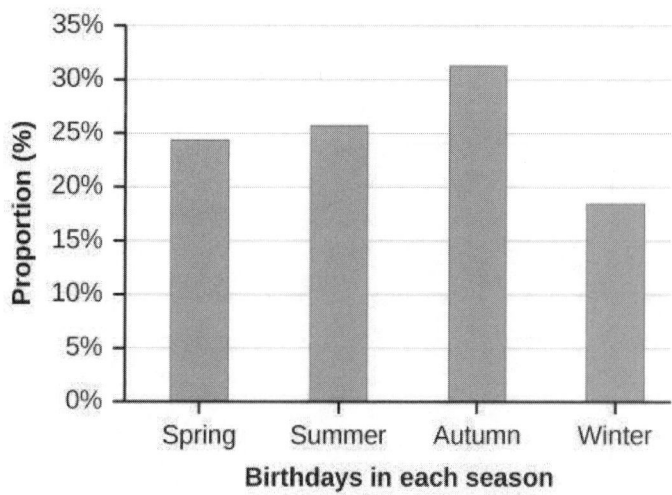

Figure 2.53

11

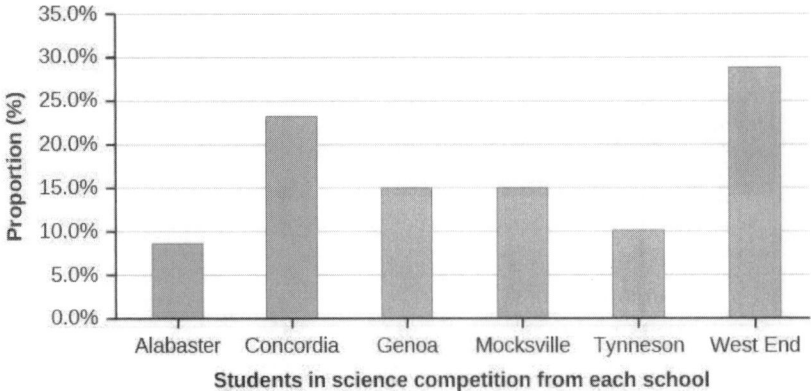

Figure 2.54

13 65

15 The relative frequency shows the *proportion* of data points that have each value. The frequency tells the *number* of data points that have each value.

17 Answers will vary. One possible histogram is shown:

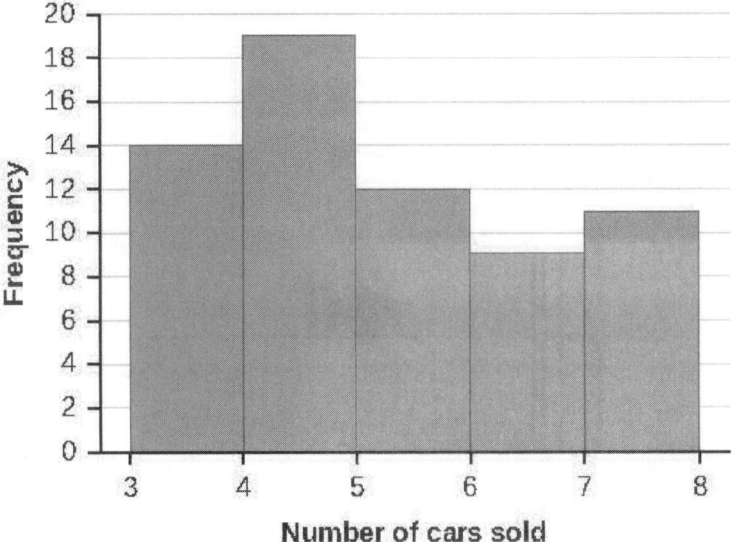

Figure 2.55

19 Find the midpoint for each class. These will be graphed on the *x*-axis. The frequency values will be graphed on the *y*-axis values.

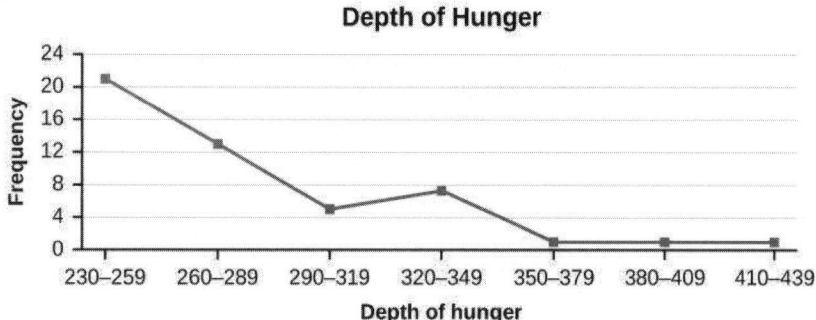

Figure 2.56

21

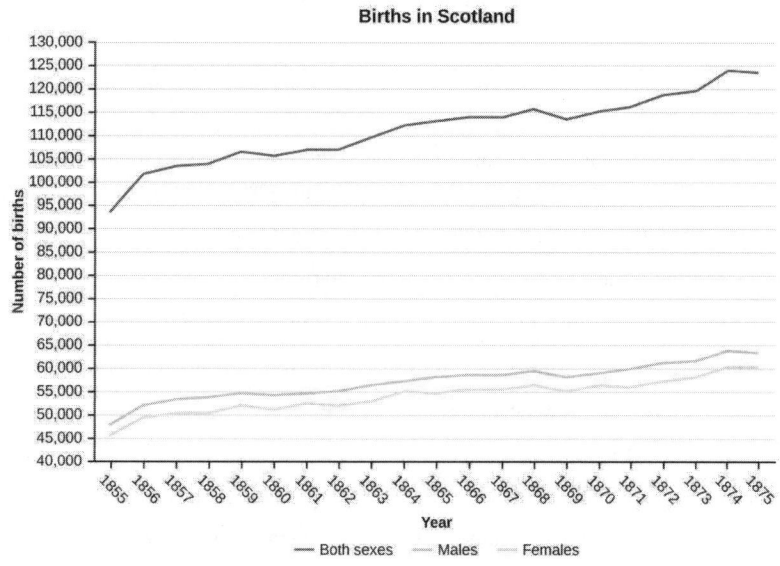

Figure 2.57

23

a. The 40th percentile is 37 years.

b. The 78th percentile is 70 years.

25 Jesse graduated 37th out of a class of 180 students. There are $180 - 37 = 143$ students ranked below Jesse. There is one rank of 37. $x = 143$ and $y = 1$. $\frac{x + 0.5y}{n}(100) = \frac{143 + 0.5(1)}{180}(100) = 79.72$. Jesse's rank of 37 puts him at the 80th percentile.

27

a. For runners in a race it is more desirable to have a high percentile for speed. A high percentile means a higher speed which is faster.

b. 40% of runners ran at speeds of 7.5 miles per hour or less (slower). 60% of runners ran at speeds of 7.5 miles per hour or more (faster).

29 When waiting in line at the DMV, the 85th percentile would be a long wait time compared to the other people waiting. 85% of people had shorter wait times than Mina. In this context, Mina would prefer a wait time corresponding to a lower percentile. 85% of people at the DMV waited 32 minutes or less. 15% of people at the DMV waited 32 minutes or longer.

31 The manufacturer and the consumer would be upset. This is a large repair cost for the damages, compared to the other cars in the sample. INTERPRETATION: 90% of the crash tested cars had damage repair costs of $1700 or less; only 10% had damage repair costs of $1700 or more.

33 You can afford 34% of houses. 66% of the houses are too expensive for your budget. INTERPRETATION: 34% of houses cost $240,000 or less. 66% of houses cost $240,000 or more.

35 4

37 $6 - 4 = 2$

39 6

41 More than 25% of salespersons sell four cars in a typical week. You can see this concentration in the box plot because the first quartile is equal to the median. The top 25% and the bottom 25% are spread out evenly; the whiskers have the same length.

43 Mean: $16 + 17 + 19 + 20 + 20 + 21 + 23 + 24 + 25 + 25 + 25 + 26 + 26 + 27 + 27 + 27 + 28 + 29 + 30 + 32 + 33 + 33 + 34 + 35 + 37 + 39 + 40 = 738$; $\frac{738}{27} = 27.33$

45 The most frequent lengths are 25 and 27, which occur three times. Mode = 25, 27

47 4

49 The data are symmetrical. The median is 3 and the mean is 2.85. They are close, and the mode lies close to the middle of the data, so the data are symmetrical.

51 The data are skewed right. The median is 87.5 and the mean is 88.2. Even though they are close, the mode lies to the left of the middle of the data, and there are many more instances of 87 than any other number, so the data are skewed right.

53 When the data are symmetrical, the mean and median are close or the same.

55 The distribution is skewed right because it looks pulled out to the right.

57 The mean is 4.1 and is slightly greater than the median, which is four.

59 The mode and the median are the same. In this case, they are both five.

61 The distribution is skewed left because it looks pulled out to the left.

63 The mean and the median are both six.

65 The mode is 12, the median is 12.5, and the mean is 15.1. The mean is the largest.

67 The mean tends to reflect skewing the most because it is affected the most by outliers.

69 $s = 34.5$

71 For Fredo: $z = \frac{0.158 - 0.166}{0.012} = -0.67$ For Karl: $z = \frac{0.177 - 0.189}{0.015} = -0.8$ Fredo's z-score of -0.67 is higher than Karl's z-score of -0.8. For batting average, higher values are better, so Fredo has a better batting average compared to his team.

73

a. $s_x = \sqrt{\frac{\sum fm^2}{n} - \bar{x}^2} = \sqrt{\frac{193157.45}{30} - 79.5^2} = 10.88$

b. $s_x = \sqrt{\frac{\sum fm^2}{n} - \bar{x}^2} = \sqrt{\frac{380945.3}{101} - 60.94^2} = 7.62$

c. $s_x = \sqrt{\frac{\sum fm^2}{n} - \bar{x}^2} = \sqrt{\frac{440051.5}{86} - 70.66^2} = 11.14$

75

a. Example solution for using the random number generator for the TI-84+ to generate a simple random sample of 8 states. Instructions are as follows.

Number the entries in the table 1–51 (Includes Washington, DC; Numbered vertically)

Press MATH

Arrow over to PRB

Press 5:randInt(

Enter 51,1,8)

Eight numbers are generated (use the right arrow key to scroll through the numbers). The numbers correspond to the numbered states (for this example: {47 21 9 23 51 13 25 4}. If any numbers are repeated, generate a different number by using 5:randInt(51,1)). Here, the states (and Washington DC) are {Arkansas, Washington DC, Idaho, Maryland, Michigan, Mississippi, Virginia, Wyoming}.

Corresponding percents are {30.1, 22.2, 26.5, 27.1, 30.9, 34.0, 26.0, 25.1}.

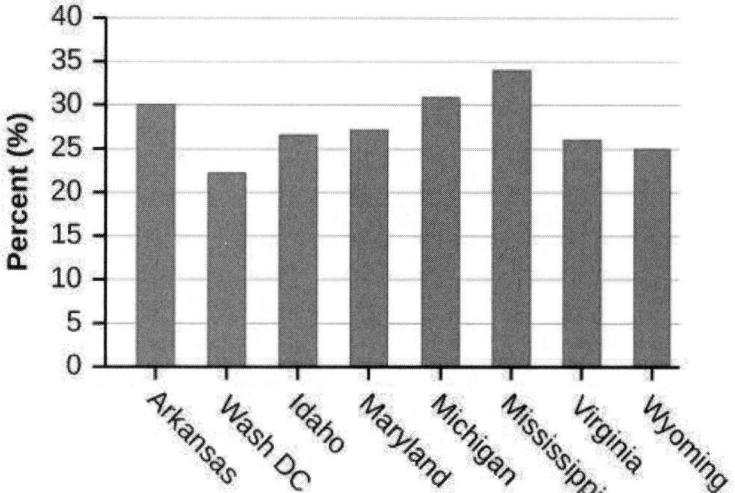

Figure 2.58

b.

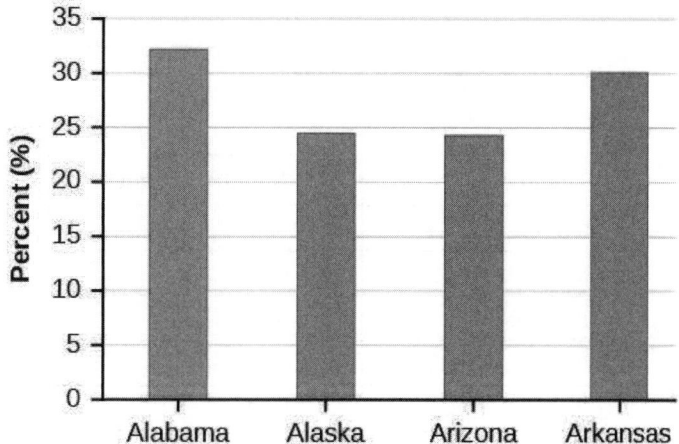

Figure 2.59

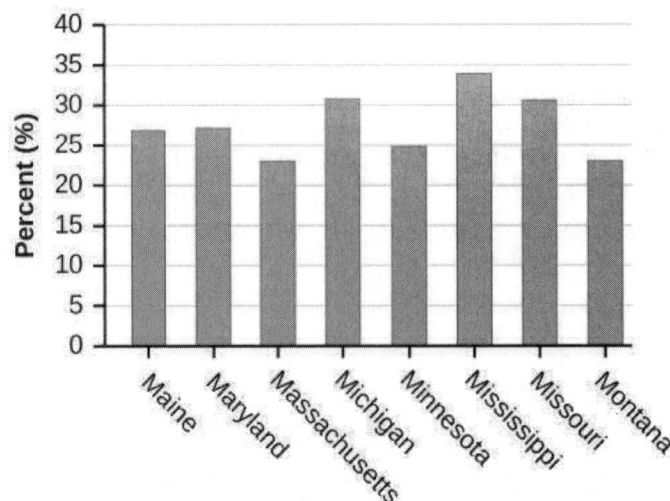

c.

Figure 2.60

77

Amount($)	Frequency	Relative Frequency
51–100	5	0.08
101–150	10	0.17
151–200	15	0.25
201–250	15	0.25
251–300	10	0.17
301–350	5	0.08

Table 2.86 Singles

Amount($)	Frequency	Relative Frequency
100–150	5	0.07
201–250	5	0.07
251–300	5	0.07
301–350	5	0.07
351–400	10	0.14
401–450	10	0.14
451–500	10	0.14
501–550	10	0.14
551–600	5	0.07
601–650	5	0.07

Table 2.87 Couples

a. See **Table 2.66** and **Table 2.66**.

b. In the following histogram data values that fall on the right boundary are counted in the class interval, while values that fall on the left boundary are not counted (with the exception of the first interval where both boundary values are included).

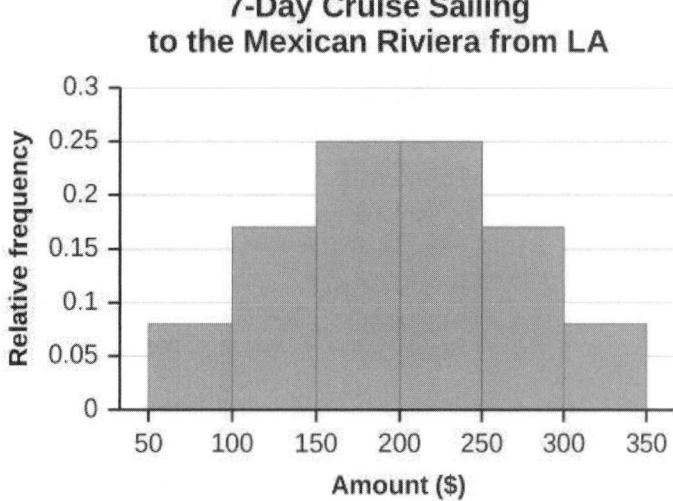

Figure 2.61

c. In the following histogram, the data values that fall on the right boundary are counted in the class interval, while values that fall on the left boundary are not counted (with the exception of the first interval where values on both boundaries are included).

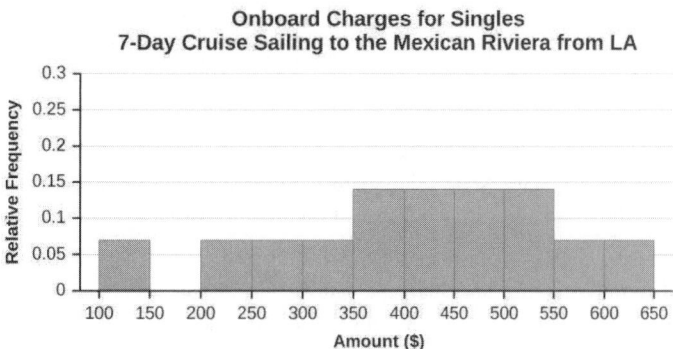

Figure 2.62

d. Compare the two graphs:

   i. Answers may vary. Possible answers include:

     ▪ Both graphs have a single peak.

     ▪ Both graphs use class intervals with width equal to $50.

   ii. Answers may vary. Possible answers include:

     ▪ The couples graph has a class interval with no values.

     ▪ It takes almost twice as many class intervals to display the data for couples.

   iii. Answers may vary. Possible answers include: The graphs are more similar than different because the overall patterns for the graphs are the same.

e. Check student's solution.

f. Compare the graph for the Singles with the new graph for the Couples:

   i.   ▪ Both graphs have a single peak.

        ▪ Both graphs display 6 class intervals.

        ▪ Both graphs show the same general pattern.

   ii. Answers may vary. Possible answers include: Although the width of the class intervals for couples is double that of the class intervals for singles, the graphs are more similar than they are different.

g. Answers may vary. Possible answers include: You are able to compare the graphs interval by interval. It is easier to compare the overall patterns with the new scale on the Couples graph. Because a couple represents two individuals, the new scale leads to a more accurate comparison.

h. Answers may vary. Possible answers include: Based on the histograms, it seems that spending does not vary much from singles to individuals who are part of a couple. The overall patterns are the same. The range of spending for couples is approximately double the range for individuals.

79 c

81 Answers will vary.

83

a. $1 - (0.02+0.09+0.19+0.26+0.18+0.17+0.02+0.01) = 0.06$

b. $0.19+0.26+0.18 = 0.63$

c. Check student's solution.

d. 40th percentile will fall between 30,000 and 40,000

    80th percentile will fall between 50,000 and 75,000

e. Check student's solution.

85

a. more children; the left whisker shows that 25% of the population are children 17 and younger. The right whisker shows that 25% of the population are adults 50 and older, so adults 65 and over represent less than 25%.

b. 62.4%

87

a. Answers will vary. Possible answer: State University conducted a survey to see how involved its students are in community service. The box plot shows the number of community service hours logged by participants over the past year.

b. Because the first and second quartiles are close, the data in this quarter is very similar. There is not much variation in the values. The data in the third quarter is much more variable, or spread out. This is clear because the second quartile is so far away from the third quartile.

89

a. Each box plot is spread out more in the greater values. Each plot is skewed to the right, so the ages of the top 50% of buyers are more variable than the ages of the lower 50%.

b. The BMW 3 series is most likely to have an outlier. It has the longest whisker.

c. Comparing the median ages, younger people tend to buy the BMW 3 series, while older people tend to buy the BMW 7 series. However, this is not a rule, because there is so much variability in each data set.

d. The second quarter has the smallest spread. There seems to be only a three-year difference between the first quartile and the median.

e. The third quarter has the largest spread. There seems to be approximately a 14-year difference between the median and the third quartile.

f. *IQR* ~ 17 years

g. There is not enough information to tell. Each interval lies within a quarter, so we cannot tell exactly where the data in that quarter is concentrated.

h. The interval from 31 to 35 years has the fewest data values. Twenty-five percent of the values fall in the interval 38 to 41, and 25% fall between 41 and 64. Since 25% of values fall between 31 and 38, we know that fewer than 25% fall between 31 and 35.

92 The mean percentage, $\bar{x} = \dfrac{1328.65}{50} = 26.75$

94 The median value is the middle value in the ordered list of data values. The median value of a set of 11 will be the 6th number in order. Six years will have totals at or below the median.

96 474 FTES

98 919

100
- mean = 1,809.3

- median = 1,812.5

- standard deviation = 151.2

- first quartile = 1,690

- third quartile = 1,935

- *IQR* = 245

102 Hint: Think about the number of years covered by each time period and what happened to higher education during those periods.

104 For pianos, the cost of the piano is 0.4 standard deviations BELOW the mean. For guitars, the cost of the guitar is 0.25 standard deviations ABOVE the mean. For drums, the cost of the drum set is 1.0 standard deviations BELOW the mean. Of the three, the drums cost the lowest in comparison to the cost of other instruments of the same type. The guitar costs the most in comparison to the cost of other instruments of the same type.

106
- $\bar{x} = 23.32$

- Using the TI 83/84, we obtain a standard deviation of: $s_x = 12.95$.

- The obesity rate of the United States is 10.58% higher than the average obesity rate.

- Since the standard deviation is 12.95, we see that 23.32 + 12.95 = 36.27 is the obesity percentage that is one standard deviation from the mean. The United States obesity rate is slightly less than one standard deviation from the mean. Therefore, we can assume that the United States, while 34% obese, does not hav e an unusually high percentage of obese people.

108
a. For graph, check student's solution.

b. 49.7% of the community is under the age of 35.

c. Based on the information in the table, graph (a) most closely represents the data.

110 a

112 b

113
a. 1.48

b. 1.12

115

a. 174; 177; 178; 184; 185; 185; 185; 185; 188; 190; 200; 205; 205; 206; 210; 210; 210; 212; 212; 215; 215; 220; 223; 228; 230; 232; 241; 241; 242; 245; 247; 250; 250; 259; 260; 260; 265; 265; 270; 272; 273; 275; 276; 278; 280; 280; 285; 285; 286; 290; 290; 295; 302

b. 241

c. 205.5

d. 272.5

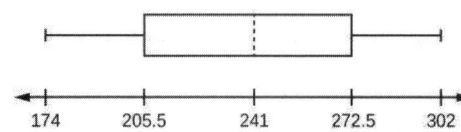

e.

f. 205.5, 272.5

g. sample

h. population

i.   i. 236.34

   ii. 37.50

   iii. 161.34

   iv. 0.84 std. dev. below the mean

j. Young

117

a. True

b. True

c. True

d. False

119

a.

Enrollment	Frequency
1000-5000	10
5000-10000	16
10000-15000	3
15000-20000	3
20000-25000	1
25000-30000	2

Table 2.88

b. Check student's solution.

c. mode

d. 8628.74

e. 6943.88

f. −0.09

121 a

3 | PROBABILITY TOPICS

Figure 3.1 Meteor showers are rare, but the probability of them occurring can be calculated. (credit: Navicore/flickr)

Introduction

Chapter Objectives
By the end of this chapter, the student should be able to: • Understand and use the terminology of probability. • Determine whether two events are mutually exclusive and whether two events are independent. • Calculate probabilities using the Addition Rules and Multiplication Rules. • Construct and interpret Contingency Tables. • Construct and interpret Venn Diagrams. • Construct and interpret Tree Diagrams.

It is often necessary to "guess" about the outcome of an event in order to make a decision. Politicians study polls to guess their likelihood of winning an election. Teachers choose a particular course of study based on what they think students can comprehend. Doctors choose the treatments needed for various diseases based on their assessment of likely results. You may have visited a casino where people play games chosen because of the belief that the likelihood of winning is good. You may have chosen your course of study based on the probable availability of jobs.

You have, more than likely, used probability. In fact, you probably have an intuitive sense of probability. Probability deals with the chance of an event occurring. Whenever you weigh the odds of whether or not to do your homework or to study for an exam, you are using probability. In this chapter, you will learn how to solve probability problems using a systematic approach.

Collaborative Exercise

Your instructor will survey your class. Count the number of students in the class today.

• Raise your hand if you have any change in your pocket or purse. Record the number of raised hands.

- Raise your hand if you rode a bus within the past month. Record the number of raised hands.

- Raise your hand if you answered "yes" to BOTH of the first two questions. Record the number of raised hands.

Use the class data as estimates of the following probabilities. P(change) means the probability that a randomly chosen person in your class has change in his/her pocket or purse. P(bus) means the probability that a randomly chosen person in your class rode a bus within the last month and so on. Discuss your answers.

- Find P(change).

- Find P(bus).

- Find P(change AND bus). Find the probability that a randomly chosen student in your class has change in his/her pocket or purse and rode a bus within the last month.

- Find P(change|bus). Find the probability that a randomly chosen student has change given that he or she rode a bus within the last month. Count all the students that rode a bus. From the group of students who rode a bus, count those who have change. The probability is equal to those who have change and rode a bus divided by those who rode a bus.

3.1 | Terminology

Probability is a measure that is associated with how certain we are of outcomes of a particular experiment or activity. An **experiment** is a planned operation carried out under controlled conditions. If the result is not predetermined, then the experiment is said to be a **chance** experiment. Flipping one fair coin twice is an example of an experiment.

A result of an experiment is called an **outcome**. The **sample space** of an experiment is the set of all possible outcomes. Three ways to represent a sample space are: to list the possible outcomes, to create a tree diagram, or to create a Venn diagram. The uppercase letter S is used to denote the sample space. For example, if you flip one fair coin, $S = \{H, T\}$ where H = heads and T = tails are the outcomes.

An **event** is any combination of outcomes. Upper case letters like A and B represent events. For example, if the experiment is to flip one fair coin, event A might be getting at most one head. The probability of an event A is written $P(A)$.

The **probability** of any outcome is the **long-term relative frequency** of that outcome. **Probabilities are between zero and one, inclusive** (that is, zero and one and all numbers between these values). $P(A) = 0$ means the event A can never happen. $P(A) = 1$ means the event A always happens. $P(A) = 0.5$ means the event A is equally likely to occur or not to occur. For example, if you flip one fair coin repeatedly (from 20 to 2,000 to 20,000 times) the relative frequency of heads approaches 0.5 (the probability of heads).

Equally likely means that each outcome of an experiment occurs with equal probability. For example, if you toss a **fair**, six-sided die, each face (1, 2, 3, 4, 5, or 6) is as likely to occur as any other face. If you toss a fair coin, a Head (H) and a Tail (T) are equally likely to occur. If you randomly guess the answer to a true/false question on an exam, you are equally likely to select a correct answer or an incorrect answer.

To calculate the probability of an event A when all outcomes in the sample space are equally likely, count the number of outcomes for event A and divide by the total number of outcomes in the sample space. For example, if you toss a fair dime and a fair nickel, the sample space is $\{HH, TH, HT, TT\}$ where T = tails and H = heads. The sample space has four outcomes. A = getting one head. There are two outcomes that meet this condition $\{HT, TH\}$, so $P(A) = \frac{2}{4} = 0.5$.

Suppose you roll one fair six-sided die, with the numbers $\{1, 2, 3, 4, 5, 6\}$ on its faces. Let event E = rolling a number that is at least five. There are two outcomes $\{5, 6\}$. $P(E) = \frac{2}{6}$. If you were to roll the die only a few times, you would not be surprised if your observed results did not match the probability. If you were to roll the die a very large number of times, you would expect that, overall, $\frac{2}{6}$ of the rolls would result in an outcome of "at least five". You would not expect exactly $\frac{2}{6}$.

The long-term relative frequency of obtaining this result would approach the theoretical probability of $\frac{2}{6}$ as the number of repetitions grows larger and larger.

This important characteristic of probability experiments is known as the **law of large numbers** which states that as the number of repetitions of an experiment is increased, the relative frequency obtained in the experiment tends to become closer and closer to the theoretical probability. Even though the outcomes do not happen according to any set pattern or order, overall, the long-term observed relative frequency will approach the theoretical probability. (The word **empirical** is often used instead of the word observed.)

It is important to realize that in many situations, the outcomes are not equally likely. A coin or die may be **unfair**, or **biased**. Two math professors in Europe had their statistics students test the Belgian one Euro coin and discovered that in 250 trials, a head was obtained 56% of the time and a tail was obtained 44% of the time. The data seem to show that the coin is not a fair coin; more repetitions would be helpful to draw a more accurate conclusion about such bias. Some dice may be biased. Look at the dice in a game you have at home; the spots on each face are usually small holes carved out and then painted to make the spots visible. Your dice may or may not be biased; it is possible that the outcomes may be affected by the slight weight differences due to the different numbers of holes in the faces. Gambling casinos make a lot of money depending on outcomes from rolling dice, so casino dice are made differently to eliminate bias. Casino dice have flat faces; the holes are completely filled with paint having the same density as the material that the dice are made out of so that each face is equally likely to occur. Later we will learn techniques to use to work with probabilities for events that are not equally likely.

"OR" Event:

An outcome is in the event A OR B if the outcome is in A or is in B or is in both A and B. For example, let $A = \{1, 2, 3, 4, 5\}$ and $B = \{4, 5, 6, 7, 8\}$. A OR $B = \{1, 2, 3, 4, 5, 6, 7, 8\}$. Notice that 4 and 5 are NOT listed twice.

"AND" Event:

An outcome is in the event A AND B if the outcome is in both A and B at the same time. For example, let A and B be $\{1, 2, 3, 4, 5\}$ and $\{4, 5, 6, 7, 8\}$, respectively. Then A AND $B = \{4, 5\}$.

The **complement** of event A is denoted A' (read "A prime"). A' consists of all outcomes that are **NOT** in A. Notice that $P(A) + P(A') = 1$. For example, let $S = \{1, 2, 3, 4, 5, 6\}$ and let $A = \{1, 2, 3, 4\}$. Then, $A' = \{5, 6\}$. $P(A) = \frac{4}{6}$, $P(A') = \frac{2}{6}$, and

$$P(A) + P(A') = \frac{4}{6} + \frac{2}{6} = 1$$

The **conditional probability** of A given B is written $P(A|B)$. $P(A|B)$ is the probability that event A will occur given that the event B has already occurred. **A conditional reduces the sample space**. We calculate the probability of A from the reduced sample space B. The formula to calculate $P(A|B)$ is $P(A|B) = \dfrac{P(A \text{ AND } B)}{P(B)}$ where $P(B)$ is greater than zero.

For example, suppose we toss one fair, six-sided die. The sample space $S = \{1, 2, 3, 4, 5, 6\}$. Let A = face is 2 or 3 and B = face is even (2, 4, 6). To calculate $P(A|B)$, we count the number of outcomes 2 or 3 in the sample space $B = \{2, 4, 6\}$. Then we divide that by the number of outcomes B (rather than S).

We get the same result by using the formula. Remember that S has six outcomes.

$$P(A|B) = \frac{P(A \text{ AND } B)}{P(B)} = \frac{\frac{(\text{the number of outcomes that are 2 or 3 and even in } S)}{6}}{\frac{(\text{the number of outcomes that are even in } S)}{6}} = \frac{\frac{1}{6}}{\frac{3}{6}} = \frac{1}{3}$$

Understanding Terminology and Symbols

It is important to read each problem carefully to think about and understand what the events are. Understanding the wording is the first very important step in solving probability problems. Reread the problem several times if necessary. Clearly identify the event of interest. Determine whether there is a condition stated in the wording that would indicate that the probability is conditional; carefully identify the condition, if any.

Example 3.1

The sample space S is the whole numbers starting at one and less than 20.

a. $S = $ _____

Let event A = the even numbers and event B = numbers greater than 13.

b. $A =$ _____ , $B =$ _____

c. $P(A) =$ _____ , $P(B) =$ _____

d. A AND $B =$ _____ , A OR $B =$ _____

e. $P(A$ AND $B) =$ _____ , $P(A$ OR $B) =$ _____

f. $A' =$ _____ , $P(A') =$ _____

g. $P(A) + P(A') =$ _____

h. $P(A|B) =$ _____ , $P(B|A) =$ _____ ; are the probabilities equal?

Solution 3.1

a. $S = \{1, 2, 3, 4, 5, 6, 7, 8, 9, 10, 11, 12, 13, 14, 15, 16, 17, 18, 19\}$

b. $A = \{2, 4, 6, 8, 10, 12, 14, 16, 18\}$, $B = \{14, 15, 16, 17, 18, 19\}$

c. $P(A) = \frac{9}{19}$, $P(B) = \frac{6}{19}$

d. A AND $B = \{14,16,18\}$, A OR $B = \{2, 4, 6, 8, 10, 12, 14, 15, 16, 17, 18, 19\}$

e. $P(A$ AND $B) = \frac{3}{19}$, $P(A$ OR $B) = \frac{12}{19}$

f. $A' = 1, 3, 5, 7, 9, 11, 13, 15, 17, 19$; $P(A') = \frac{10}{19}$

g. $P(A) + P(A') = 1$ $(\frac{9}{19} + \frac{10}{19} = 1)$

h. $P(A|B) = \frac{P(A \text{ AND } B)}{P(B)} = \frac{3}{6}$, $P(B|A) = \frac{P(A \text{ AND } B)}{P(A)} = \frac{3}{9}$, No

Try It Σ

3.1 The sample space S is all the ordered pairs of two whole numbers, the first from one to three and the second from one to four (Example: (1, 4)).

a. $S =$ _____

Let event $A =$ the sum is even and event $B =$ the first number is prime.

b. $A =$ _____ , $B =$ _____

c. $P(A) =$ _____ , $P(B) =$ _____

d. A AND $B =$ _____ , A OR $B =$ _____

e. $P(A$ AND $B) =$ _____ , $P(A$ OR $B) =$ _____

f. $B' =$ _____ , $P(B') =$ _____

g. $P(A) + P(A') =$ _____

h. $P(A|B) =$ _____ , $P(B|A) =$ _____ ; are the probabilities equal?

Example 3.2

A fair, six-sided die is rolled. Describe the sample space S, identify each of the following events with a subset of S and compute its probability (an outcome is the number of dots that show up).

    a.   Event T = the outcome is two.

    b.   Event A = the outcome is an even number.

    c.   Event B = the outcome is less than four.

    d.   The complement of A.

    e. A GIVEN B

    f. B GIVEN A

    g. A AND B

    h. A OR B

    i. A OR B'

    j.   Event N = the outcome is a prime number.

    k.   Event I = the outcome is seven.

Solution 3.2

    a. $T = \{2\}$, $P(T) = \frac{1}{6}$

    b. $A = \{2, 4, 6\}$, $P(A) = \frac{1}{2}$

    c. $B = \{1, 2, 3\}$, $P(B) = \frac{1}{2}$

    d. $A' = \{1, 3, 5\}$, $P(A') = \frac{1}{2}$

    e. $A|B = \{2\}$, $P(A|B) = \frac{1}{3}$

    f. $B|A = \{2\}$, $P(B|A) = \frac{1}{3}$

    g. A AND $B = \{2\}$, $P(A$ AND $B) = \frac{1}{6}$

    h. A OR $B = \{1, 2, 3, 4, 6\}$, $P(A$ OR $B) = \frac{5}{6}$

    i. A OR $B' = \{2, 4, 5, 6\}$, $P(A$ OR $B') = \frac{2}{3}$

    j. $N = \{2, 3, 5\}$, $P(N) = \frac{1}{2}$

    k.   A six-sided die does not have seven dots. $P(7) = 0$.

Example 3.3

Table 3.1 describes the distribution of a random sample *S* of 100 individuals, organized by gender and whether they are right- or left-handed.

	Right-handed	**Left-handed**
Males	43	9
Females	44	4

Table 3.1

Let's denote the events *M* = the subject is male, *F* = the subject is female, *R* = the subject is right-handed, *L* = the subject is left-handed. Compute the following probabilities:

  a. *P(M)*

  b. *P(F)*

  c. *P(R)*

  d. *P(L)*

  e. *P(M* AND *R)*

  f. *P(F* AND *L)*

  g. *P(M* OR *F)*

  h. *P(M* OR *R)*

  i. *P(F* OR *L)*

  j. *P(M')*

  k. *P(R|M)*

  l. *P(F|L)*

  m. *P(L|F)*

Solution 3.3

  a. *P(M)* = 0.52

  b. *P(F)* = 0.48

  c. *P(R)* = 0.87

  d. *P(L)* = 0.13

  e. *P(M* AND *R)* = 0.43

  f. *P(F* AND *L)* = 0.04

  g. *P(M* OR *F)* = 1

  h. *P(M* OR *R)* = 0.96

  i. *P(F* OR *L)* = 0.57

  j. *P(M')* = 0.48

  k. *P(R|M)* = 0.8269 (rounded to four decimal places)

  l. *P(F|L)* = 0.3077 (rounded to four decimal places)

  m. *P(L|F)* = 0.0833

3.2 | Independent and Mutually Exclusive Events

Independent and mutually exclusive do **not** mean the same thing.

Independent Events

Two events are independent if the following are true:

- $P(A|B) = P(A)$

- $P(B|A) = P(B)$

- $P(A \text{ AND } B) = P(A)P(B)$

Two events A and B are **independent** if the knowledge that one occurred does not affect the chance the other occurs. For example, the outcomes of two roles of a fair die are independent events. The outcome of the first roll does not change the probability for the outcome of the second roll. To show two events are independent, you must show **only one** of the above conditions. If two events are NOT independent, then we say that they are **dependent**.

Sampling may be done **with replacement** or **without replacement**.

- **With replacement**: If each member of a population is replaced after it is picked, then that member has the possibility of being chosen more than once. When sampling is done with replacement, then events are considered to be independent, meaning the result of the first pick will not change the probabilities for the second pick.

- **Without replacement**: When sampling is done without replacement, each member of a population may be chosen only once. In this case, the probabilities for the second pick are affected by the result of the first pick. The events are considered to be dependent or not independent.

If it is not known whether A and B are independent or dependent, **assume they are dependent until you can show otherwise**.

Example 3.4

You have a fair, well-shuffled deck of 52 cards. It consists of four suits. The suits are clubs, diamonds, hearts and spades. There are 13 cards in each suit consisting of 1, 2, 3, 4, 5, 6, 7, 8, 9, 10, J (jack), Q (queen), K (king) of that suit.

a. Sampling with replacement:
Suppose you pick three cards with replacement. The first card you pick out of the 52 cards is the Q of spades. You put this card back, reshuffle the cards and pick a second card from the 52-card deck. It is the ten of clubs. You put this card back, reshuffle the cards and pick a third card from the 52-card deck. This time, the card is the Q of spades again. Your picks are {Q of spades, ten of clubs, Q of spades}. You have picked the Q of spades twice. You pick each card from the 52-card deck.

b. Sampling without replacement:
Suppose you pick three cards without replacement. The first card you pick out of the 52 cards is the K of hearts. You put this card aside and pick the second card from the 51 cards remaining in the deck. It is the three of diamonds. You put this card aside and pick the third card from the remaining 50 cards in the deck. The third card is the J of spades. Your picks are {K of hearts, three of diamonds, J of spades}. Because you have picked the cards without replacement, you cannot pick the same card twice.

Try It Σ

3.4 You have a fair, well-shuffled deck of 52 cards. It consists of four suits. The suits are clubs, diamonds, hearts and spades. There are 13 cards in each suit consisting of 1, 2, 3, 4, 5, 6, 7, 8, 9, 10, J (jack), Q (queen), K (king) of that suit. Three cards are picked at random.

a. Suppose you know that the picked cards are Q of spades, K of hearts and Q of spades. Can you decide if the sampling was with or without replacement?

b. Suppose you know that the picked cards are *Q* of spades, *K* of hearts, and *J* of spades. Can you decide if the sampling was with or without replacement?

Example 3.5

You have a fair, well-shuffled deck of 52 cards. It consists of four suits. The suits are clubs, diamonds, hearts, and spades. There are 13 cards in each suit consisting of 1, 2, 3, 4, 5, 6, 7, 8, 9, 10, *J* (jack), *Q* (queen), and *K* (king) of that suit. *S* = spades, *H* = Hearts, *D* = Diamonds, *C* = Clubs.

a. Suppose you pick four cards, but do not put any cards back into the deck. Your cards are *QS*, *1D*, *1C*, *QD*.

b. Suppose you pick four cards and put each card back before you pick the next card. Your cards are *KH*, *7D*, *6D*, *KH*.

Which of a. or b. did you sample with replacement and which did you sample without replacement?

Solution 3.5

a. Without replacement; b. With replacement

Try It Σ

3.5 You have a fair, well-shuffled deck of 52 cards. It consists of four suits. The suits are clubs, diamonds, hearts, and spades. There are 13 cards in each suit consisting of 1, 2, 3, 4, 5, 6, 7, 8, 9, 10, *J* (jack), *Q* (queen), and *K* (king) of that suit. *S* = spades, *H* = Hearts, *D* = Diamonds, *C* = Clubs. Suppose that you sample four cards without replacement. Which of the following outcomes are possible? Answer the same question for sampling with replacement.

a. *QS*, *1D*, *1C*, *QD*

b. *KH*, *7D*, *6D*, *KH*

c. *QS*, *7D*, *6D*, *KS*

Mutually Exclusive Events

A and *B* are **mutually exclusive** events if they cannot occur at the same time. This means that *A* and *B* do not share any outcomes and *P(A* AND *B)* = 0.

For example, suppose the sample space *S* = {1, 2, 3, 4, 5, 6, 7, 8, 9, 10}. Let *A* = {1, 2, 3, 4, 5}, *B* = {4, 5, 6, 7, 8}, and *C* = {7, 9}. *A* AND *B* = {4, 5}. *P(A* AND *B)* = $\frac{2}{10}$ and is not equal to zero. Therefore, *A* and *B* are not mutually exclusive. *A* and *C* do not have any numbers in common so *P(A* AND *C)* = 0. Therefore, *A* and *C* are mutually exclusive.

If it is not known whether *A* and *B* are mutually exclusive, **assume they are not until you can show otherwise**. The following examples illustrate these definitions and terms.

Example 3.6

Flip two fair coins. (This is an experiment.)

The sample space is {*HH*, *HT*, *TH*, *TT*} where *T* = tails and *H* = heads. The outcomes are *HH*, *HT*, *TH*, and *TT*. The outcomes HT and TH are different. The *HT* means that the first coin showed heads and the second coin showed tails. The *TH* means that the first coin showed tails and the second coin showed heads.

• Let *A* = the event of getting **at most one tail**. (At most one tail means zero or one tail.) Then *A* can be written as {*HH*, *HT*, *TH*}. The outcome *HH* shows zero tails. *HT* and *TH* each show one tail.

- Let B = the event of getting all tails. B can be written as $\{TT\}$. B is the **complement** of A, so $B = A'$. Also, $P(A) + P(B) = P(A) + P(A') = 1$.

- The probabilities for A and for B are $P(A) = \frac{3}{4}$ and $P(B) = \frac{1}{4}$.

- Let C = the event of getting all heads. $C = \{HH\}$. Since $B = \{TT\}$, $P(B \text{ AND } C) = 0$. B and C are mutually exclusive. (B and C have no members in common because you cannot have all tails and all heads at the same time.)

- Let D = event of getting **more than one** tail. $D = \{TT\}$. $P(D) = \frac{1}{4}$

- Let E = event of getting a head on the first roll. (This implies you can get either a head or tail on the second roll.) $E = \{HT, HH\}$. $P(E) = \frac{2}{4}$

- Find the probability of getting **at least one** (one or two) tail in two flips. Let F = event of getting at least one tail in two flips. $F = \{HT, TH, TT\}$. $P(F) = \frac{3}{4}$

Try It Σ

3.6 Draw two cards from a standard 52-card deck with replacement. Find the probability of getting at least one black card.

Example 3.7

Flip two fair coins. Find the probabilities of the events.

a. Let F = the event of getting at most one tail (zero or one tail).

b. Let G = the event of getting two faces that are the same.

c. Let H = the event of getting a head on the first flip followed by a head or tail on the second flip.

d. Are F and G mutually exclusive?

e. Let J = the event of getting all tails. Are J and H mutually exclusive?

Solution 3.7

Look at the sample space in **Example 3.6**.

a. Zero (0) or one (1) tails occur when the outcomes HH, TH, HT show up. $P(F) = \frac{3}{4}$

b. Two faces are the same if HH or TT show up. $P(G) = \frac{2}{4}$

c. A head on the first flip followed by a head or tail on the second flip occurs when HH or HT show up. $P(H) = \frac{2}{4}$

d. F and G share HH so $P(F \text{ AND } G)$ is not equal to zero (0). F and G are not mutually exclusive.

e. Getting all tails occurs when tails shows up on both coins (TT). H's outcomes are HH and HT.

J and H have nothing in common so $P(J \text{ AND } H) = 0$. J and H are mutually exclusive.

Try It Σ

3.7 A box has two balls, one white and one red. We select one ball, put it back in the box, and select a second ball (sampling with replacement). Find the probability of the following events:

a. Let F = the event of getting the white ball twice.

b. Let G = the event of getting two balls of different colors.

c. Let H = the event of getting white on the first pick.

d. Are F and G mutually exclusive?

e. Are G and H mutually exclusive?

Example 3.8

Roll one fair, six-sided die. The sample space is {1, 2, 3, 4, 5, 6}. Let event A = a face is odd. Then A = {1, 3, 5}. Let event B = a face is even. Then B = {2, 4, 6}.

- Find the complement of A, A'. The complement of A, A', is B because A and B together make up the sample space. $P(A) + P(B) = P(A) + P(A') = 1$. Also, $P(A) = \frac{3}{6}$ and $P(B) = \frac{3}{6}$.

- Let event C = odd faces larger than two. Then C = {3, 5}. Let event D = all even faces smaller than five. Then D = {2, 4}. $P(C \text{ AND } D) = 0$ because you cannot have an odd and even face at the same time. Therefore, C and D are mutually exclusive events.

- Let event E = all faces less than five. E = {1, 2, 3, 4}.

Are C and E mutually exclusive events? (Answer yes or no.) Why or why not?

Solution 3.8

No. C = {3, 5} and E = {1, 2, 3, 4}. $P(C \text{ AND } E) = \frac{1}{6}$. To be mutually exclusive, $P(C \text{ AND } E)$ must be zero.

- Find $P(C|A)$. This is a conditional probability. Recall that the event C is {3, 5} and event A is {1, 3, 5}. To find $P(C|A)$, find the probability of C using the sample space A. You have reduced the sample space from the original sample space {1, 2, 3, 4, 5, 6} to {1, 3, 5}. So, $P(C|A) = \frac{2}{3}$.

Try It Σ

3.8 Let event A = learning Spanish. Let event B = learning German. Then A AND B = learning Spanish and German. Suppose $P(A) = 0.4$ and $P(B) = 0.2$. $P(A \text{ AND } B) = 0.08$. Are events A and B independent? Hint: You must show ONE of the following:

- $P(A|B) = P(A)$

- $P(B|A) = P(B)$

- $P(A \text{ AND } B) = P(A)P(B)$

Example 3.9

Let event G = taking a math class. Let event H = taking a science class. Then, G AND H = taking a math class and a science class. Suppose $P(G) = 0.6$, $P(H) = 0.5$, and $P(G \text{ AND } H) = 0.3$. Are G and H independent?

If G and H are independent, then you must show **ONE** of the following:

- $P(G|H) = P(G)$

- $P(H|G) = P(H)$

- $P(G \text{ AND } H) = P(G)P(H)$

NOTE

The choice you make depends on the information you have. You could choose any of the methods here because you have the necessary information.

a. Show that $P(G|H) = P(G)$.

Solution 3.9

$$P(G|H) = \frac{P(G \text{ AND } H)}{P(H)} = \frac{0.3}{0.5} = 0.6 = P(G)$$

b. Show $P(G \text{ AND } H) = P(G)P(H)$.

Solution 3.9

$P(G)P(H) = (0.6)(0.5) = 0.3 = P(G \text{ AND } H)$

Since G and H are independent, knowing that a person is taking a science class does not change the chance that he or she is taking a math class. If the two events had not been independent (that is, they are dependent) then knowing that a person is taking a science class would change the chance he or she is taking math. For practice, show that $P(H|G) = P(H)$ to show that G and H are independent events.

Try It Σ

3.9 In a bag, there are six red marbles and four green marbles. The red marbles are marked with the numbers 1, 2, 3, 4, 5, and 6. The green marbles are marked with the numbers 1, 2, 3, and 4.

- R = a red marble

- G = a green marble

- O = an odd-numbered marble

- The sample space is S = {$R1$, $R2$, $R3$, $R4$, $R5$, $R6$, $G1$, $G2$, $G3$, $G4$}.

S has ten outcomes. What is $P(G \text{ AND } O)$?

Example 3.10

Let event C = taking an English class. Let event D = taking a speech class.

Suppose $P(C) = 0.75$, $P(D) = 0.3$, $P(C|D) = 0.75$ and $P(C \text{ AND } D) = 0.225$.

Justify your answers to the following questions numerically.

a. Are C and D independent?

b. Are C and D mutually exclusive?

c. What is $P(D|C)$?

Solution 3.10

a.   Yes, because $P(C|D) = P(C)$.

b.   No, because $P(C \text{ AND } D)$ is not equal to zero.

c. $P(D|C) = \dfrac{P(C \text{ AND } D)}{P(C)} = \dfrac{0.225}{0.75} = 0.3$

Try It Σ

3.10 A student goes to the library. Let events B = the student checks out a book and D = the student checks out a DVD. Suppose that $P(B) = 0.40$, $P(D) = 0.30$ and $P(B \text{ AND } D) = 0.20$.

a.   Find $P(B|D)$.

b.   Find $P(D|B)$.

c.   Are B and D independent?

d.   Are B and D mutually exclusive?

Example 3.11

In a box there are three red cards and five blue cards. The red cards are marked with the numbers 1, 2, and 3, and the blue cards are marked with the numbers 1, 2, 3, 4, and 5. The cards are well-shuffled. You reach into the box (you cannot see into it) and draw one card.

Let R = red card is drawn, B = blue card is drawn, E = even-numbered card is drawn.

The sample space $S = R1, R2, R3, B1, B2, B3, B4, B5$. S has eight outcomes.

- $P(R) = \dfrac{3}{8}$. $P(B) = \dfrac{5}{8}$. $P(R \text{ AND } B) = 0$. (You cannot draw one card that is both red and blue.)

- $P(E) = \dfrac{3}{8}$. (There are three even-numbered cards, $R2$, $B2$, and $B4$.)

- $P(E|B) = \dfrac{2}{5}$. (There are five blue cards: $B1$, $B2$, $B3$, $B4$, and $B5$. Out of the blue cards, there are two even cards; $B2$ and $B4$.)

- $P(B|E) = \dfrac{2}{3}$. (There are three even-numbered cards: $R2$, $B2$, and $B4$. Out of the even-numbered cards, to are blue; $B2$ and $B4$.)

- The events R and B are mutually exclusive because $P(R \text{ AND } B) = 0$.

- Let G = card with a number greater than 3. $G = \{B4, B5\}$. $P(G) = \dfrac{2}{8}$. Let H = blue card numbered between one and four, inclusive. $H = \{B1, B2, B3, B4\}$. $P(G|H) = \dfrac{1}{4}$. (The only card in H that has a number greater than three is $B4$.) Since $\dfrac{2}{8} = \dfrac{1}{4}$, $P(G) = P(G|H)$, which means that G and H are independent.

Try It Σ

3.11 In a basketball arena,

- 70% of the fans are rooting for the home team.

- 25% of the fans are wearing blue.

- 20% of the fans are wearing blue and are rooting for the away team.

- Of the fans rooting for the away team, 67% are wearing blue.

Let A be the event that a fan is rooting for the away team.
Let B be the event that a fan is wearing blue.
Are the events of rooting for the away team and wearing blue independent? Are they mutually exclusive?

Example 3.12

In a particular college class, 60% of the students are female. Fifty percent of all students in the class have long hair. Forty-five percent of the students are female and have long hair. Of the female students, 75% have long hair. Let F be the event that a student is female. Let L be the event that a student has long hair. One student is picked randomly. Are the events of being female and having long hair independent?

- The following probabilities are given in this example:

- $P(F) = 0.60$; $P(L) = 0.50$

- $P(F \text{ AND } L) = 0.45$

- $P(L|F) = 0.75$

NOTE

The choice you make depends on the information you have. You could use the first or last condition on the list for this example. You do not know $P(F|L)$ yet, so you cannot use the second condition.

Solution 1

Check whether $P(F \text{ AND } L) = P(F)P(L)$. We are given that $P(F \text{ AND } L) = 0.45$, but $P(F)P(L) = (0.60)(0.50) = 0.30$. The events of being female and having long hair are not independent because $P(F \text{ AND } L)$ does not equal $P(F)P(L)$.

Solution 2

Check whether $P(L|F)$ equals $P(L)$. We are given that $P(L|F) = 0.75$, but $P(L) = 0.50$; they are not equal. The events of being female and having long hair are not independent.

Interpretation of Results

The events of being female and having long hair are not independent; knowing that a student is female changes the probability that a student has long hair.

Try It Σ

3.12 Mark is deciding which route to take to work. His choices are I = the Interstate and F = Fifth Street.

- $P(I) = 0.44$ and $P(F) = 0.56$

- $P(I \text{ AND } F) = 0$ because Mark will take only one route to work.

What is the probability of $P(I \text{ OR } F)$?

Example 3.13

a. Toss one fair coin (the coin has two sides, *H* and *T*). The outcomes are _____. Count the outcomes. There are ____ outcomes.

b. Toss one fair, six-sided die (the die has 1, 2, 3, 4, 5 or 6 dots on a side). The outcomes are _____. Count the outcomes. There are ____ outcomes.

c. Multiply the two numbers of outcomes. The answer is _____.

d. If you flip one fair coin and follow it with the toss of one fair, six-sided die, the answer in part c. is the number of outcomes (size of the sample space). What are the outcomes? (Hint: Two of the outcomes are *H*1 and *T*6.)

e. Event *A* = heads (*H*) on the coin followed by an even number (2, 4, 6) on the die.
   A = {_____}. Find *P*(*A*).

f. Event *B* = heads on the coin followed by a three on the die. *B* = {_____}. Find *P*(*B*).

g. Are *A* and *B* mutually exclusive? (Hint: What is *P*(*A* AND *B*)? If *P*(*A* AND *B*) = 0, then *A* and *B* are mutually exclusive.)

h. Are *A* and *B* independent? (Hint: Is *P*(*A* AND *B*) = *P*(*A*)*P*(*B*)? If *P*(*A* AND *B*) = *P*(*A*)*P*(*B*), then *A* and *B* are independent. If not, then they are dependent).

Solution 3.13

a. *H* and *T*; 2

b. 1, 2, 3, 4, 5, 6; 6

c. 2(6) = 12

d. *T*1, *T*2, *T*3, *T*4, *T*5, *T*6, *H*1, *H*2, *H*3, *H*4, *H*5, *H*6

e. *A* = {*H*2, *H*4, *H*6}; $P(A) = \frac{3}{12}$

f. *B* = {*H*3}; $P(B) = \frac{1}{12}$

g. Yes, because *P*(*A* AND *B*) = 0

h. $P(A \text{ AND } B) = 0. P(A)P(B) = \left(\frac{3}{12}\right)\left(\frac{1}{12}\right)$. *P*(*A* AND *B*) does not equal *P*(*A*)*P*(*B*), so *A* and *B* are dependent.

Try It Σ

3.13 A box has two balls, one white and one red. We select one ball, put it back in the box, and select a second ball (sampling with replacement). Let *T* be the event of getting the white ball twice, *F* the event of picking the white ball first, *S* the event of picking the white ball in the second drawing.

a. Compute *P*(*T*).

b. Compute *P*(*T*|*F*).

c. Are *T* and *F* independent?.

d. Are *F* and *S* mutually exclusive?

e. Are *F* and *S* independent?

3.3 | Two Basic Rules of Probability

When calculating probability, there are two rules to consider when determining if two events are independent or dependent and if they are mutually exclusive or not.

The Multiplication Rule

If A and B are two events defined on a **sample space**, then: $P(A \text{ AND } B) = P(B)P(A|B)$.

This rule may also be written as: $P(A|B) = \dfrac{P(A \text{ AND } B)}{P(B)}$

(The probability of A given B equals the probability of A and B divided by the probability of B.)

If A and B are **independent**, then $P(A|B) = P(A)$. Then $P(A \text{ AND } B) = P(A|B)P(B)$ becomes $P(A \text{ AND } B) = P(A)P(B)$.

The Addition Rule

If A and B are defined on a sample space, then: $P(A \text{ OR } B) = P(A) + P(B) - P(A \text{ AND } B)$.

If A and B are **mutually exclusive**, then $P(A \text{ AND } B) = 0$. Then $P(A \text{ OR } B) = P(A) + P(B) - P(A \text{ AND } B)$ becomes $P(A \text{ OR } B) = P(A) + P(B)$.

Example 3.14

Klaus is trying to choose where to go on vacation. His two choices are: A = New Zealand and B = Alaska

- Klaus can only afford one vacation. The probability that he chooses A is $P(A) = 0.6$ and the probability that he chooses B is $P(B) = 0.35$.

- $P(A \text{ AND } B) = 0$ because Klaus can only afford to take one vacation

- Therefore, the probability that he chooses either New Zealand or Alaska is $P(A \text{ OR } B) = P(A) + P(B) = 0.6 + 0.35 = 0.95$. Note that the probability that he does not choose to go anywhere on vacation must be 0.05.

Example 3.15

Carlos plays college soccer. He makes a goal 65% of the time he shoots. Carlos is going to attempt two goals in a row in the next game. A = the event Carlos is successful on his first attempt. $P(A) = 0.65$. B = the event Carlos is successful on his second attempt. $P(B) = 0.65$. Carlos tends to shoot in streaks. The probability that he makes the second goal **GIVEN** that he made the first goal is 0.90.

a. What is the probability that he makes both goals?

Solution 3.15

a. The problem is asking you to find $P(A \text{ AND } B) = P(B \text{ AND } A)$. Since $P(B|A) = 0.90$: $P(B \text{ AND } A) = P(B|A)P(A) = (0.90)(0.65) = 0.585$

Carlos makes the first and second goals with probability 0.585.

b. What is the probability that Carlos makes either the first goal or the second goal?

Solution 3.15

b. The problem is asking you to find $P(A \text{ OR } B)$.

$P(A \text{ OR } B) = P(A) + P(B) - P(A \text{ AND } B) = 0.65 + 0.65 - 0.585 = 0.715$

Carlos makes either the first goal or the second goal with probability 0.715.

c. Are A and B independent?

Solution 3.15

c. No, they are not, because $P(B \text{ AND } A) = 0.585$.

$P(B)P(A) = (0.65)(0.65) = 0.423$

$0.423 \neq 0.585 = P(B \text{ AND } A)$

So, $P(B \text{ AND } A)$ is **not** equal to $P(B)P(A)$.

d. Are A and B mutually exclusive?

Solution 3.15

d. No, they are not because $P(A \text{ and } B) = 0.585$.

To be mutually exclusive, $P(A \text{ AND } B)$ must equal zero.

Try It Σ

3.15 Helen plays basketball. For free throws, she makes the shot 75% of the time. Helen must now attempt two free throws. C = the event that Helen makes the first shot. $P(C) = 0.75$. D = the event Helen makes the second shot. $P(D) = 0.75$. The probability that Helen makes the second free throw given that she made the first is 0.85. What is the probability that Helen makes both free throws?

Example 3.16

A community swim team has **150** members. **Seventy-five** of the members are advanced swimmers. **Forty-seven** of the members are intermediate swimmers. The remainder are novice swimmers. **Forty** of the advanced swimmers practice four times a week. **Thirty** of the intermediate swimmers practice four times a week. **Ten** of the novice swimmers practice four times a week. Suppose one member of the swim team is chosen randomly.

a. What is the probability that the member is a novice swimmer?

Solution 3.16

a. $\dfrac{28}{150}$

b. What is the probability that the member practices four times a week?

Solution 3.16

b. $\dfrac{80}{150}$

c. What is the probability that the member is an advanced swimmer and practices four times a week?

Solution 3.16

c. $\dfrac{40}{150}$

d. What is the probability that a member is an advanced swimmer and an intermediate swimmer? Are being an advanced swimmer and an intermediate swimmer mutually exclusive? Why or why not?

Solution 3.16

d. $P(\text{advanced AND intermediate}) = 0$, so these are mutually exclusive events. A swimmer cannot be an advanced swimmer and an intermediate swimmer at the same time.

e. Are being a novice swimmer and practicing four times a week independent events? Why or why not?

Solution 3.16

e. No, these are not independent events.
P(novice AND practices four times per week) = 0.0667
P(novice)P(practices four times per week) = 0.0996
$0.0667 \neq 0.0996$

Try It Σ

3.16 A school has 200 seniors of whom 140 will be going to college next year. Forty will be going directly to work. The remainder are taking a gap year. Fifty of the seniors going to college play sports. Thirty of the seniors going directly to work play sports. Five of the seniors taking a gap year play sports. What is the probability that a senior is taking a gap year?

Example 3.17

Felicity attends Modesto JC in Modesto, CA. The probability that Felicity enrolls in a math class is 0.2 and the probability that she enrolls in a speech class is 0.65. The probability that she enrolls in a math class GIVEN that she enrolls in speech class is 0.25.

Let: M = math class, S = speech class, $M|S$ = math given speech

a. What is the probability that Felicity enrolls in math and speech?
Find $P(M \text{ AND } S) = P(M|S)P(S)$.

b. What is the probability that Felicity enrolls in math or speech classes?
Find $P(M \text{ OR } S) = P(M) + P(S) - P(M \text{ AND } S)$.

c. Are M and S independent? Is $P(M|S) = P(M)$?

d. Are M and S mutually exclusive? Is $P(M \text{ AND } S) = 0$?

Solution 3.17
a. 0.1625, b. 0.6875, c. No, d. No

Try It Σ

3.17 A student goes to the library. Let events B = the student checks out a book and D = the student check out a DVD. Suppose that $P(B) = 0.40$, $P(D) = 0.30$ and $P(D|B) = 0.5$.

a. Find $P(B \text{ AND } D)$.

b. Find $P(B \text{ OR } D)$.

Example 3.18

Studies show that about one woman in seven (approximately 14.3%) who live to be 90 will develop breast cancer. Suppose that of those women who develop breast cancer, a test is negative 2% of the time. Also suppose that in the general population of women, the test for breast cancer is negative about 85% of the time. Let B = woman develops breast cancer and let N = tests negative. Suppose one woman is selected at random.

a. What is the probability that the woman develops breast cancer? What is the probability that woman tests negative?

Solution 3.18
a. $P(B) = 0.143$; $P(N) = 0.85$

b. Given that the woman has breast cancer, what is the probability that she tests negative?

Solution 3.18
b. $P(N|B) = 0.02$

c. What is the probability that the woman has breast cancer AND tests negative?

Solution 3.18
c. $P(B \text{ AND } N) = P(B)P(N|B) = (0.143)(0.02) = 0.0029$

d. What is the probability that the woman has breast cancer or tests negative?

Solution 3.18
d. $P(B \text{ OR } N) = P(B) + P(N) - P(B \text{ AND } N) = 0.143 + 0.85 - 0.0029 = 0.9901$

e. Are having breast cancer and testing negative independent events?

Solution 3.18
e. No. $P(N) = 0.85$; $P(N|B) = 0.02$. So, $P(N|B)$ does not equal $P(N)$.

f. Are having breast cancer and testing negative mutually exclusive?

Solution 3.18
f. No. $P(B \text{ AND } N) = 0.0029$. For B and N to be mutually exclusive, $P(B \text{ AND } N)$ must be zero.

Try It Σ

3.18 A school has 200 seniors of whom 140 will be going to college next year. Forty will be going directly to work. The remainder are taking a gap year. Fifty of the seniors going to college play sports. Thirty of the seniors going directly to work play sports. Five of the seniors taking a gap year play sports. What is the probability that a senior is going to college and plays sports?

Example 3.19

Refer to the information in **Example 3.18**. P = tests positive.

a. Given that a woman develops breast cancer, what is the probability that she tests positive. Find $P(P|B) = 1 - P(N|B)$.

b. What is the probability that a woman develops breast cancer and tests positive. Find $P(B \text{ AND } P) = P(P|B)P(B)$.

c. What is the probability that a woman does not develop breast cancer. Find $P(B') = 1 - P(B)$.

d. What is the probability that a woman tests positive for breast cancer. Find $P(P) = 1 - P(N)$.

Solution 3.19
a. 0.98; b. 0.1401; c. 0.857; d. 0.15

3.19 A student goes to the library. Let events B = the student checks out a book and D = the student checks out a DVD. Suppose that $P(B) = 0.40$, $P(D) = 0.30$ and $P(D|B) = 0.5$.

a. Find $P(B')$.

b. Find $P(D \text{ AND } B)$.

c. Find $P(B|D)$.

d. Find $P(D \text{ AND } B')$.

e. Find $P(D|B')$.

3.4 | Contingency Tables

A **contingency table** provides a way of portraying data that can facilitate calculating probabilities. The table helps in determining conditional probabilities quite easily. The table displays sample values in relation to two different variables that may be dependent or contingent on one another. Later on, we will use contingency tables again, but in another manner.

Example 3.20

Suppose a study of speeding violations and drivers who use cell phones produced the following fictional data:

	Speeding violation in the last year	No speeding violation in the last year	Total
Uses cell phone while driving	25	280	305
Does not use cell phone while driving	45	405	450
Total	70	685	755

Table 3.2

The total number of people in the sample is 755. The row totals are 305 and 450. The column totals are 70 and 685. Notice that 305 + 450 = 755 and 70 + 685 = 755.

Calculate the following probabilities using the table.

a. Find P(Driver is a cell phone user).
b. Find P(driver had no violation in the last year).
c. Find P(Driver had no violation in the last year AND was a cell phone user).
d. Find P(Driver is a cell phone user OR driver had no violation in the last year).
e. Find P(Driver is a cell phone user GIVEN driver had a violation in the last year).
f. Find P(Driver had no violation last year GIVEN driver was not a cell phone user)

Solutions:

a. $\dfrac{\text{number of cell phone users}}{\text{total number in study}} = \dfrac{305}{755}$

b. $\dfrac{\text{number that had no violation}}{\text{total number in study}} = \dfrac{685}{755}$

c. $\dfrac{280}{755}$

d. $\left(\dfrac{305}{755} + \dfrac{685}{755}\right) - \dfrac{280}{755} = \dfrac{710}{755}$

e. $\dfrac{25}{70}$ (The sample space is reduced to the number of drivers who had a violation.)

f. $\dfrac{405}{450}$ (The sample space is reduced to the number of drivers who were not cell phone users.)

Try It Σ

3.20 Table 3.3 shows the number of athletes who stretch before exercising and how many had injuries within the past year.

	Injury in last year	No injury in last year	Total
Stretches	55	295	350
Does not stretch	231	219	450
Total	286	514	800

Table 3.3

a. What is P(athlete stretches before exercising)?
b. What is P(athlete stretches before exercising|no injury in the last year)?

Example 3.21

Table 3.4 shows a random sample of 100 hikers and the areas of hiking they prefer.

Sex	The Coastline	Near Lakes and Streams	On Mountain Peaks	Total
Female	18	16	____	45
Male	____	____	14	55
Total	____	41	____	____

Table 3.4 Hiking Area Preference

a. Complete the table.

Solution 3.21

a.

Sex	The Coastline	Near Lakes and Streams	On Mountain Peaks	Total
Female	18	16	**11**	45
Male	**16**	**25**	14	55
Total	**34**	41	**25**	**100**

Table 3.5 Hiking Area Preference

b. Are the events "being female" and "preferring the coastline" independent events?

Let F = being female and let C = preferring the coastline.

1. Find $P(F \text{ AND } C)$.

2. Find $P(F)P(C)$

Are these two numbers the same? If they are, then F and C are independent. If they are not, then F and C are not independent.

Solution 3.21

b.

1. $P(F \text{ AND } C) = \dfrac{18}{100} = 0.18$

2. $P(F)P(C) = \left(\dfrac{45}{100}\right)\left(\dfrac{34}{100}\right) = (0.45)(0.34) = 0.153$

$P(F \text{ AND } C) \neq P(F)P(C)$, so the events F and C are not independent.

c. Find the probability that a person is male given that the person prefers hiking near lakes and streams. Let M = being male, and let L = prefers hiking near lakes and streams.

1. What word tells you this is a conditional?

2. Fill in the blanks and calculate the probability: $P(\_\_\_|\_\_\_) = \_\_\_$.

3. Is the sample space for this problem all 100 hikers? If not, what is it?

Solution 3.21

c.

1. The word 'given' tells you that this is a conditional.

2. $P(M|L) = \dfrac{25}{41}$

3. No, the sample space for this problem is the 41 hikers who prefer lakes and streams.

d. Find the probability that a person is female or prefers hiking on mountain peaks. Let F = being female, and let P = prefers mountain peaks.

1. Find $P(F)$.

2. Find $P(P)$.

3. Find $P(F \text{ AND } P)$.

4. Find $P(F \text{ OR } P)$.

Solution 3.21

d.

1. $P(F) = \dfrac{45}{100}$

2. $P(P) = \dfrac{25}{100}$

3. $P(F \text{ AND } P) = \dfrac{11}{100}$

4. $P(F \text{ OR } P) = \dfrac{45}{100} + \dfrac{25}{100} - \dfrac{11}{100} = \dfrac{59}{100}$

Try It Σ

3.21 **Table 3.6** shows a random sample of 200 cyclists and the routes they prefer. Let M = males and H = hilly path.

Gender	Lake Path	Hilly Path	Wooded Path	Total
Female	45	38	27	110
Male	26	52	12	90
Total	71	90	39	200

Table 3.6

a. Out of the males, what is the probability that the cyclist prefers a hilly path?

b. Are the events "being male" and "preferring the hilly path" independent events?

Example 3.22

Muddy Mouse lives in a cage with three doors. If Muddy goes out the first door, the probability that he gets caught by Alissa the cat is $\dfrac{1}{5}$ and the probability he is not caught is $\dfrac{4}{5}$. If he goes out the second door, the probability he gets caught by Alissa is $\dfrac{1}{4}$ and the probability he is not caught is $\dfrac{3}{4}$. The probability that Alissa catches Muddy coming out of the third door is $\dfrac{1}{2}$ and the probability she does not catch Muddy is $\dfrac{1}{2}$. It is equally likely that Muddy will choose any of the three doors so the probability of choosing each door is $\dfrac{1}{3}$.

Caught or Not	Door One	Door Two	Door Three	Total
Caught	$\dfrac{1}{15}$	$\dfrac{1}{12}$	$\dfrac{1}{6}$	——

Table 3.7 Door Choice

Caught or Not	Door One	Door Two	Door Three	Total
Not Caught	$\frac{4}{15}$	$\frac{3}{12}$	$\frac{1}{6}$	____
Total	____	____	____	1

Table 3.7 Door Choice

- The first entry $\frac{1}{15} = \left(\frac{1}{5}\right)\left(\frac{1}{3}\right)$ is P(Door One AND Caught)

- The entry $\frac{4}{15} = \left(\frac{4}{5}\right)\left(\frac{1}{3}\right)$ is P(Door One AND Not Caught)

Verify the remaining entries.

a. Complete the probability contingency table. Calculate the entries for the totals. Verify that the lower-right corner entry is 1.

Solution 3.22
a.

Caught or Not	Door One	Door Two	Door Three	Total
Caught	$\frac{1}{15}$	$\frac{1}{12}$	$\frac{1}{6}$	$\frac{19}{60}$
Not Caught	$\frac{4}{15}$	$\frac{3}{12}$	$\frac{1}{6}$	$\frac{41}{60}$
Total	$\frac{5}{15}$	$\frac{4}{12}$	$\frac{2}{6}$	1

Table 3.8 Door Choice

b. What is the probability that Alissa does not catch Muddy?

Solution 3.22
b. $\frac{41}{60}$

c. What is the probability that Muddy chooses Door One OR Door Two given that Muddy is caught by Alissa?

Solution 3.22
c. $\frac{9}{19}$

Example 3.23

Table 3.9 contains the number of crimes per 100,000 inhabitants from 2008 to 2011 in the U.S.

Year	Robbery	Burglary	Rape	Vehicle	Total
2008	145.7	732.1	29.7	314.7	
2009	133.1	717.7	29.1	259.2	
2010	119.3	701	27.7	239.1	
2011	113.7	702.2	26.8	229.6	
Total					

Table 3.9 United States Crime Index Rates Per 100,000 Inhabitants 2008–2011

TOTAL each column and each row. Total data = 4,520.7

a. Find P(2009 AND Robbery).

b. Find P(2010 AND Burglary).

c. Find P(2010 OR Burglary).

d. Find P(2011|Rape).

e. Find P(Vehicle|2008).

Solution 3.23
a. 0.0294, b. 0.1551, c. 0.7165, d. 0.2365, e. 0.2575

Try It

3.23 Table 3.10 relates the weights and heights of a group of individuals participating in an observational study.

Weight/Height	Tall	Medium	Short	Totals
Obese	18	28	14	
Normal	20	51	28	
Underweight	12	25	9	
Totals				

Table 3.10

a. Find the total for each row and column

b. Find the probability that a randomly chosen individual from this group is Tall.

c. Find the probability that a randomly chosen individual from this group is Obese and Tall.

d. Find the probability that a randomly chosen individual from this group is Tall given that the idividual is Obese.

e. Find the probability that a randomly chosen individual from this group is Obese given that the individual is Tall.

f. Find the probability a randomly chosen individual from this group is Tall and Underweight.

g. Are the events Obese and Tall independent?

3.5 | Tree and Venn Diagrams

Sometimes, when the probability problems are complex, it can be helpful to graph the situation. Tree diagrams and Venn diagrams are two tools that can be used to visualize and solve conditional probabilities.

Tree Diagrams

A **tree diagram** is a special type of graph used to determine the outcomes of an experiment. It consists of "branches" that are labeled with either frequencies or probabilities. Tree diagrams can make some probability problems easier to visualize and solve. The following example illustrates how to use a tree diagram.

Example 3.24

In an urn, there are 11 balls. Three balls are red (*R*) and eight balls are blue (*B*). Draw two balls, one at a time, **with replacement**. "With replacement" means that you put the first ball back in the urn before you select the second ball. The tree diagram using frequencies that show all the possible outcomes follows.

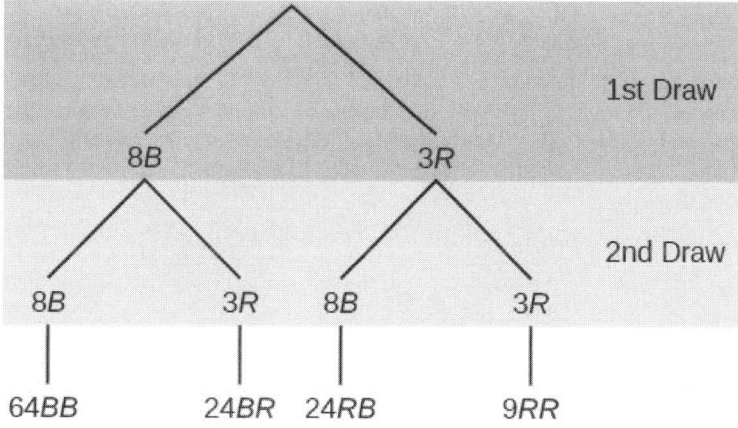

Figure 3.2   Total = 64 + 24 + 24 + 9 = 121

The first set of branches represents the first draw. The second set of branches represents the second draw. Each of the outcomes is distinct. In fact, we can list each red ball as *R*1, *R*2, and *R*3 and each blue ball as *B*1, *B*2, *B*3, *B*4, *B*5, *B*6, *B*7, and *B*8. Then the nine *RR* outcomes can be written as:

*R*1*R*1; *R*1*R*2; *R*1*R*3; *R*2*R*1; *R*2*R*2; *R*2*R*3; *R*3*R*1; *R*3*R*2; *R*3*R*3

The other outcomes are similar.

There are a total of 11 balls in the urn. Draw two balls, one at a time, with replacement. There are 11(11) = 121 outcomes, the size of the **sample space**.

a. List the 24 *BR* outcomes: *B*1*R*1, *B*1*R*2, *B*1*R*3, ...

Solution 3.24
a. *B*1*R*1; *B*1*R*2; *B*1*R*3; *B*2*R*1; *B*2*R*2; *B*2*R*3; *B*3*R*1; *B*3*R*2; *B*3*R*3; *B*4*R*1; *B*4*R*2; *B*4*R*3; *B*5*R*1; *B*5*R*2; *B*5*R*3; *B*6*R*1; *B*6*R*2; *B*6*R*3; *B*7*R*1; *B*7*R*2; *B*7*R*3; *B*8*R*1; *B*8*R*2; *B*8*R*3

b. Using the tree diagram, calculate *P*(*RR*).

Solution 3.24
b. $P(RR) = \left(\frac{3}{11}\right)\left(\frac{3}{11}\right) = \frac{9}{121}$

c. Using the tree diagram, calculate $P(RB \text{ OR } BR)$.

Solution 3.24

c. $P(RB \text{ OR } BR) = \left(\frac{3}{11}\right)\left(\frac{8}{11}\right) + \left(\frac{8}{11}\right)\left(\frac{3}{11}\right) = \frac{48}{121}$

d. Using the tree diagram, calculate $P(R \text{ on 1st draw AND } B \text{ on 2nd draw})$.

Solution 3.24

d. $P(R \text{ on 1st draw AND } B \text{ on 2nd draw}) = P(RB) = \left(\frac{3}{11}\right)\left(\frac{8}{11}\right) = \frac{24}{121}$

e. Using the tree diagram, calculate $P(R \text{ on 2nd draw GIVEN } B \text{ on 1st draw})$.

Solution 3.24

e. $P(R \text{ on 2nd draw GIVEN } B \text{ on 1st draw}) = P(R \text{ on 2nd}|B \text{ on 1st}) = \frac{24}{88} = \frac{3}{11}$

This problem is a conditional one. The sample space has been reduced to those outcomes that already have a blue on the first draw. There are $24 + 64 = 88$ possible outcomes ($24\ BR$ and $64\ BB$). Twenty-four of the 88 possible outcomes are BR. $\frac{24}{88} = \frac{3}{11}$.

f. Using the tree diagram, calculate $P(BB)$.

Solution 3.24

f. $P(BB) = \frac{64}{121}$

g. Using the tree diagram, calculate $P(B \text{ on the 2nd draw given } R \text{ on the first draw})$.

Solution 3.24

g. $P(B \text{ on 2nd draw}|R \text{ on 1st draw}) = \frac{8}{11}$

There are $9 + 24$ outcomes that have R on the first draw ($9\ RR$ and $24\ RB$). The sample space is then $9 + 24 = 33$. 24 of the 33 outcomes have B on the second draw. The probability is then $\frac{24}{33}$.

Try It ∑

3.24 In a standard deck, there are 52 cards. 12 cards are face cards (event F) and 40 cards are not face cards (event N). Draw two cards, one at a time, with replacement. All possible outcomes are shown in the tree diagram as frequencies. Using the tree diagram, calculate $P(FF)$.

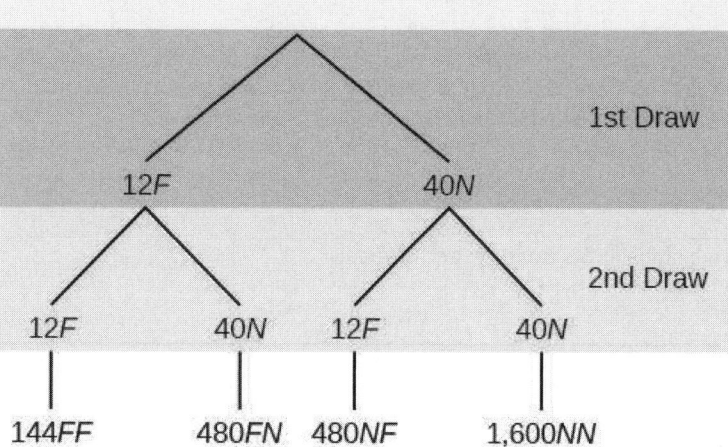

Figure 3.3

Example 3.25

An urn has three red marbles and eight blue marbles in it. Draw two marbles, one at a time, this time without replacement, from the urn. **"Without replacement"** means that you do not put the first ball back before you select the second marble. Following is a tree diagram for this situation. The branches are labeled with probabilities instead of frequencies. The numbers at the ends of the branches are calculated by multiplying the numbers on the two corresponding branches, for example, $\left(\frac{3}{11}\right)\left(\frac{2}{10}\right) = \frac{6}{110}$.

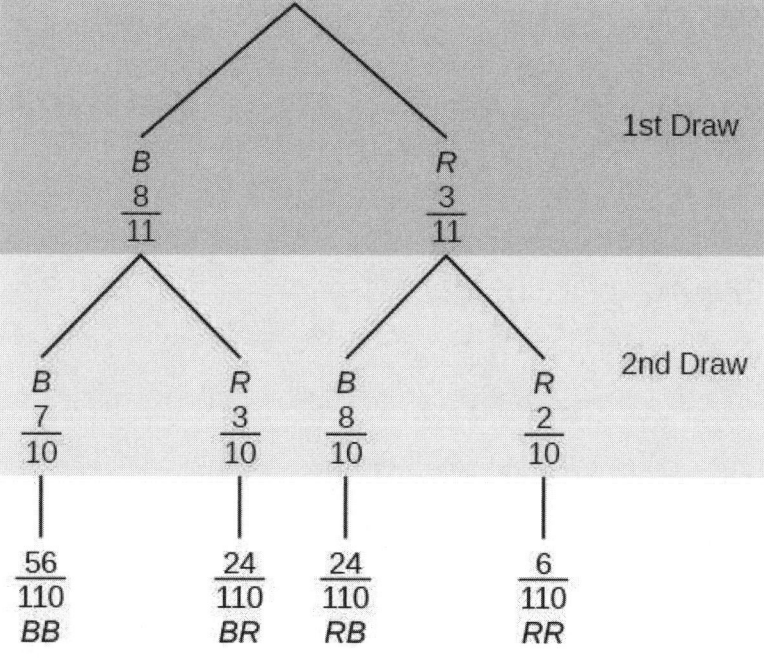

Figure 3.4   Total $= \dfrac{56 + 24 + 24 + 6}{110} = \dfrac{110}{110} = 1$

NOTE

If you draw a red on the first draw from the three red possibilities, there are two red marbles left to draw on the second draw. You do not put back or replace the first marble after you have drawn it. You draw **without replacement**, so that on the second draw there are ten marbles left in the urn.

Calculate the following probabilities using the tree diagram.

a. $P(RR)$ = _____

Solution 3.25

a. $P(RR) = \left(\frac{3}{11}\right)\left(\frac{2}{10}\right) = \frac{6}{110}$

b. Fill in the blanks:

$P(RB \text{ OR } BR) = \left(\frac{3}{11}\right)\left(\frac{8}{10}\right) + (\underline{\quad})(\underline{\quad}) = \frac{48}{110}$

Solution 3.25

b. $P(RB \text{ OR } BR) = \left(\frac{3}{11}\right)\left(\frac{8}{10}\right) + \left(\frac{8}{11}\right)\left(\frac{3}{10}\right) = \frac{48}{110}$

c. $P(R \text{ on 2nd}|B \text{ on 1st}) =$

Solution 3.25

c. $P(R \text{ on 2nd}|B \text{ on 1st}) = \frac{3}{10}$

d. Fill in the blanks.

$P(R \text{ on 1st AND } B \text{ on 2nd}) = P(RB) = (\underline{\quad})(\underline{\quad}) = \frac{24}{100}$

Solution 3.25

d. $P(R \text{ on 1st AND } B \text{ on 2nd}) = P(RB) = \left(\frac{3}{11}\right)\left(\frac{8}{10}\right) = \frac{24}{100}$

e. Find $P(BB)$.

Solution 3.25

e. $P(BB) = \left(\frac{8}{11}\right)\left(\frac{7}{10}\right)$

f. Find $P(B \text{ on 2nd}|R \text{ on 1st})$.

Solution 3.25

f. Using the tree diagram, $P(B \text{ on 2nd}|R \text{ on 1st}) = P(R|B) = \frac{8}{10}$.

If we are using probabilities, we can label the tree in the following general way.

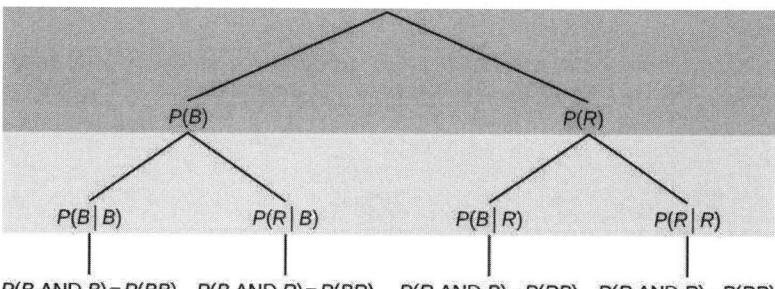

- $P(R|R)$ here means $P(R$ on 2nd$|R$ on 1st)
- $P(B|R)$ here means $P(B$ on 2nd$|R$ on 1st)
- $P(R|B)$ here means $P(R$ on 2nd$|B$ on 1st)
- $P(B|B)$ here means $P(B$ on 2nd$|B$ on 1st)

Try It Σ

3.25 In a standard deck, there are 52 cards. Twelve cards are face cards (F) and 40 cards are not face cards (N). Draw two cards, one at a time, without replacement. The tree diagram is labeled with all possible probabilities.

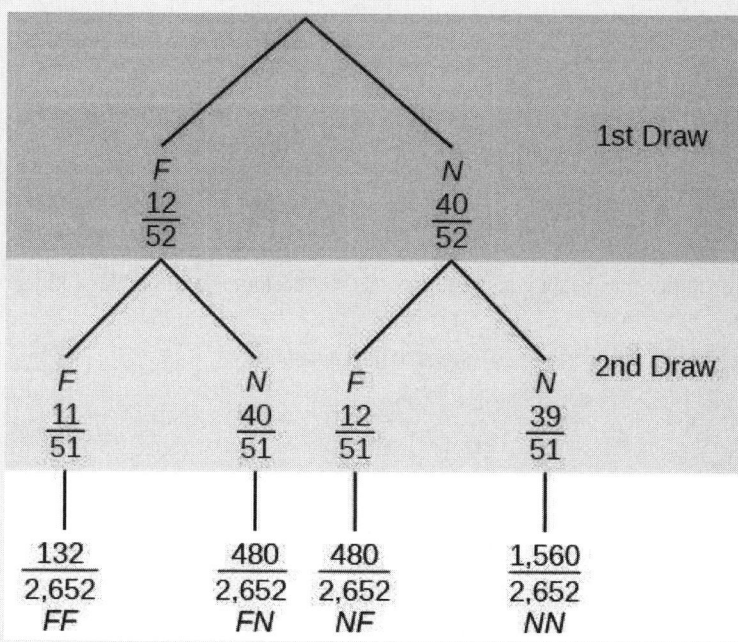

Figure 3.5

a. Find $P(FN$ OR $NF)$.

b. Find $P(N|F)$.

c. Find $P($at most one face card$)$.
   Hint: "At most one face card" means zero or one face card.

d. Find $P($at least on face card$)$.
   Hint: "At least one face card" means one or two face cards.

Example 3.26

A litter of kittens available for adoption at the Humane Society has four tabby kittens and five black kittens. A family comes in and randomly selects two kittens (without replacement) for adoption.

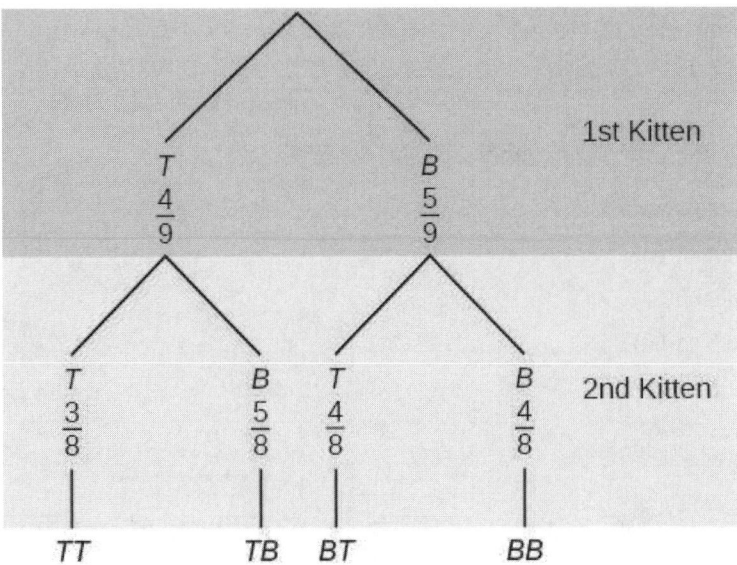

a. What is the probability that both kittens are tabby?

a. $\left(\frac{1}{2}\right)\left(\frac{1}{2}\right)$ b. $\left(\frac{4}{9}\right)\left(\frac{4}{9}\right)$ c. $\left(\frac{4}{9}\right)\left(\frac{3}{8}\right)$ d. $\left(\frac{4}{9}\right)\left(\frac{5}{9}\right)$

b. What is the probability that one kitten of each coloring is selected?

a. $\left(\frac{4}{9}\right)\left(\frac{5}{9}\right)$ b. $\left(\frac{4}{9}\right)\left(\frac{5}{8}\right)$ c. $\left(\frac{4}{9}\right)\left(\frac{5}{9}\right)+\left(\frac{5}{9}\right)\left(\frac{4}{9}\right)$ d. $\left(\frac{4}{9}\right)\left(\frac{5}{8}\right)+\left(\frac{5}{9}\right)\left(\frac{4}{8}\right)$

c. What is the probability that a tabby is chosen as the second kitten when a black kitten was chosen as the first?

d. What is the probability of choosing two kittens of the same color?

Solution 3.26

a. c, b. d, c. $\frac{4}{8}$, d. $\frac{32}{72}$

3.26 Suppose there are four red balls and three yellow balls in a box. Two balls are drawn from the box without replacement. What is the probability that one ball of each coloring is selected?

Venn Diagram

A **Venn diagram** is a picture that represents the outcomes of an experiment. It generally consists of a box that represents the sample space S together with circles or ovals. The circles or ovals represent events.

Example 3.27

Suppose an experiment has the outcomes 1, 2, 3, ... , 12 where each outcome has an equal chance of occurring. Let event A = {1, 2, 3, 4, 5, 6} and event B = {6, 7, 8, 9}. Then A AND B = {6} and A OR B = {1, 2, 3, 4, 5, 6, 7, 8, 9}. The Venn diagram is as follows:

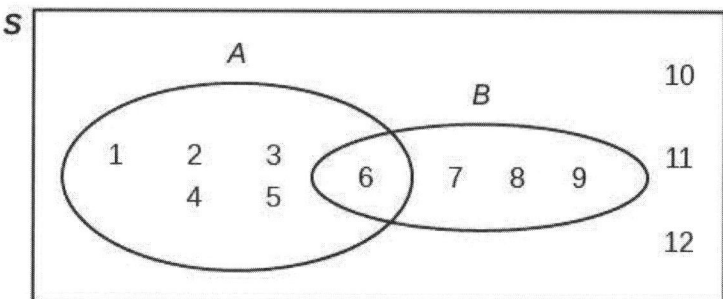

Figure 3.6

3.27 Suppose an experiment has outcomes black, white, red, orange, yellow, green, blue, and purple, where each outcome has an equal chance of occurring. Let event C = {green, blue, purple} and event P = {red, yellow, blue}. Then C AND P = {blue} and C OR P = {green, blue, purple, red, yellow}. Draw a Venn diagram representing this situation.

Example 3.28

Flip two fair coins. Let A = tails on the first coin. Let B = tails on the second coin. Then A = {TT, TH} and B = {TT, HT}. Therefore, A AND B = {TT}. A OR B = {TH, TT, HT}.

The sample space when you flip two fair coins is X = {HH, HT, TH, TT}. The outcome HH is in NEITHER A NOR B. The Venn diagram is as follows:

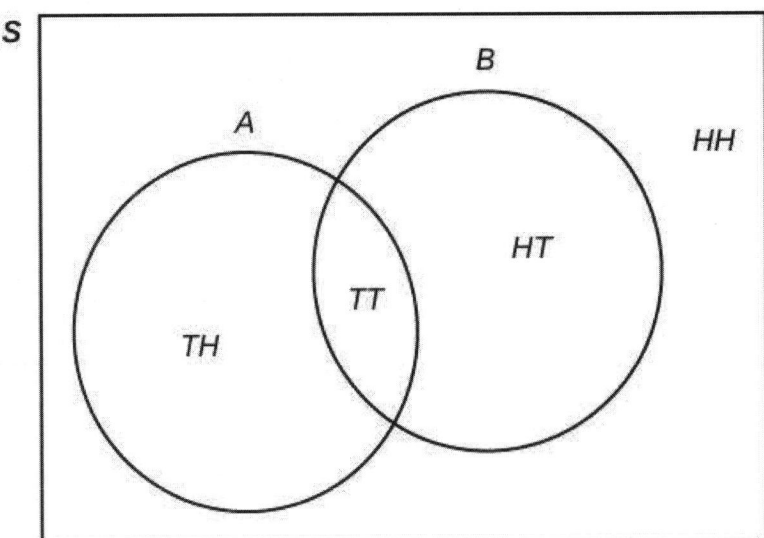

Figure 3.7

3.28 Roll a fair, six-sided die. Let *A* = a prime number of dots is rolled. Let *B* = an odd number of dots is rolled. Then *A* = {2, 3, 5} and *B* = {1, 3, 5}. Therefore, *A* AND *B* = {3, 5}. *A* OR *B* = {1, 2, 3, 5}. The sample space for rolling a fair die is *S* = {1, 2, 3, 4, 5, 6}. Draw a Venn diagram representing this situation.

Example 3.29

Forty percent of the students at a local college belong to a club and **50%** work part time. **Five percent** of the students work part time and belong to a club. Draw a Venn diagram showing the relationships. Let *C* = student belongs to a club and *PT* = student works part time.

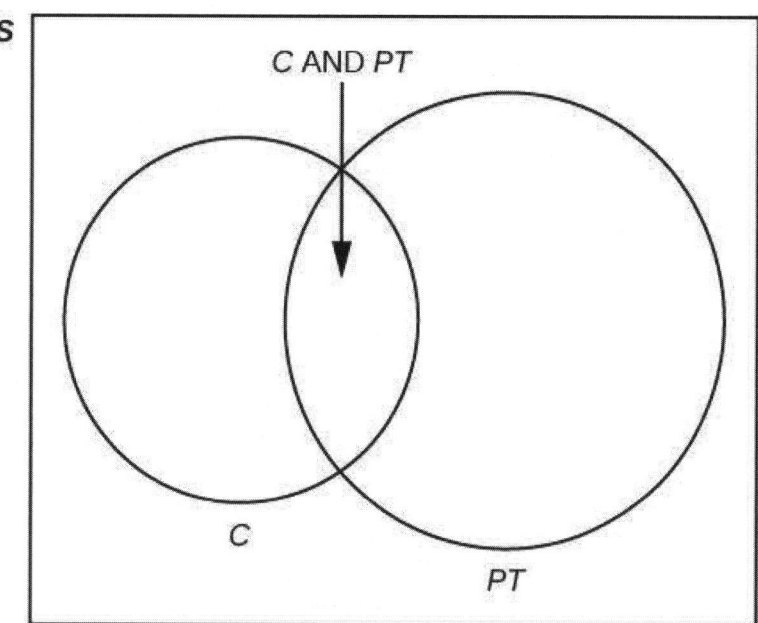

Figure 3.8

If a student is selected at random, find

- the probability that the student belongs to a club. $P(C) = 0.40$
- the probability that the student works part time. $P(PT) = 0.50$
- the probability that the student belongs to a club AND works part time. $P(C \text{ AND } PT) = 0.05$
- the probability that the student belongs to a club **given** that the student works part time.
  $$P(C|PT) \ = \ \frac{P(C \text{ AND } PT)}{P(PT)} \ = \ \frac{0.05}{0.50} \ = \ 0.1$$
- the probability that the student belongs to a club **OR** works part time. $P(C \text{ OR } PT) = P(C) + P(PT) - P(C \text{ AND } PT) = 0.40 + 0.50 - 0.05 = 0.85$

Try It Σ

3.29 Fifty percent of the workers at a factory work a second job, 25% have a spouse who also works, 5% work a second job and have a spouse who also works. Draw a Venn diagram showing the relationships. Let W = works a second job and S = spouse also works.

Example 3.30

A person with type O blood and a negative Rh factor (Rh-) can donate blood to any person with any blood type. Four percent of African Americans have type O blood and a negative RH factor, 5−10% of African Americans have the Rh- factor, and 51% have type O blood.

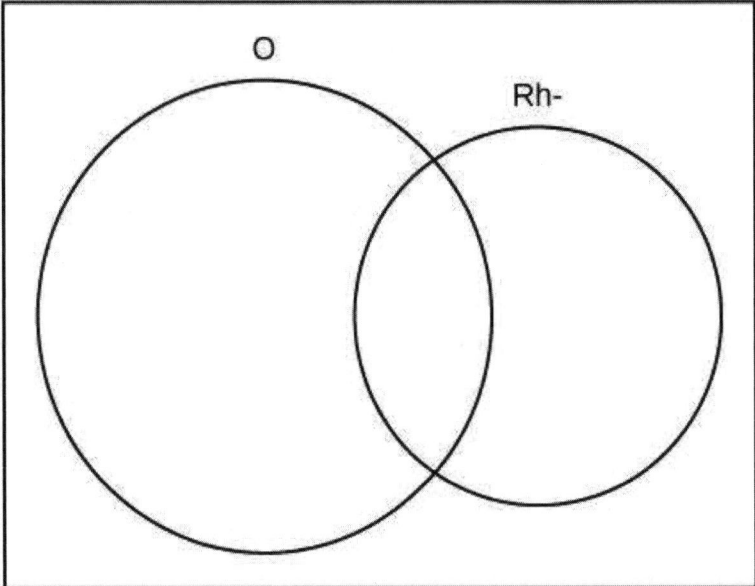

Figure 3.9

The "O" circle represents the African Americans with type O blood. The "Rh-" oval represents the African Americans with the Rh- factor.

We will take the average of 5% and 10% and use 7.5% as the percent of African Americans who have the Rh- factor. Let O = African American with Type O blood and R = African American with Rh- factor.

   a. $P(O) = $ _____

   b. $P(R) = $ _____

   c. $P(O \text{ AND } R) = $ _____

   d. $P(O \text{ OR } R) = $ _____

   e. In the Venn Diagram, describe the overlapping area using a complete sentence.

   f. In the Venn Diagram, describe the area in the rectangle but outside both the circle and the oval using a complete sentence.

Solution 3.30
a. 0.51; b. 0.075; c. 0.04; d. 0.545; e. The area represents the African Americans that have type O blood and the Rh- factor. f. The area represents the African Americans that have neither type O blood nor the Rh- factor.

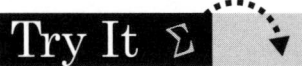

3.30 In a bookstore, the probability that the customer buys a novel is 0.6, and the probability that the customer buys a non-fiction book is 0.4. Suppose that the probability that the customer buys both is 0.2.

   a. Draw a Venn diagram representing the situation.

   b. Find the probability that the customer buys either a novel or anon-fiction book.

   c. In the Venn diagram, describe the overlapping area using a complete sentence.

   d. Suppose that some customers buy only compact disks. Draw an oval in your Venn diagram representing this event.

3.6 | Probability Topics

Stats Lab

3.1 Probability Topics

Class time:

Names:

Student Learning Outcomes

- The student will use theoretical and empirical methods to estimate probabilities.
- The student will appraise the differences between the two estimates.
- The student will demonstrate an understanding of long-term relative frequencies.

Do the Experiment

Count out 40 mixed-color M&Ms® which is approximately one small bag's worth. Record the number of each color in **Table 3.11**. Use the information from this table to complete **Table 3.12**. Next, put the M&Ms in a cup. The experiment is to pick two M&Ms, one at a time. Do **not** look at them as you pick them. The first time through, replace the first M&M before picking the second one. Record the results in the "With Replacement" column of **Table 3.13**. Do this 24 times. The second time through, after picking the first M&M, do **not** replace it before picking the second one. Then, pick the second one. Record the results in the "Without Replacement" column section of **Table 3.14**. After you record the pick, put **both** M&Ms back. Do this a total of 24 times, also. Use the data from **Table 3.14** to calculate the empirical probability questions. Leave your answers in unreduced fractional form. Do **not** multiply out any fractions.

Color	Quantity
Yellow (Y)	
Green (G)	
Blue (BL)	
Brown (B)	
Orange (O)	
Red (R)	

Table 3.11 Population

	With Replacement	Without Replacement
P(2 reds)		
$P(R_1B_2$ OR $B_1R_2)$		
$P(R_1$ AND $G_2)$		
$P(G_2|R_1)$		
P(no yellows)		
P(doubles)		
P(no doubles)		

Table 3.12 Theoretical Probabilities

NOTE

G_2 = green on second pick; R_1 = red on first pick; B_1 = brown on first pick; B_2 = brown on second pick; doubles = both picks are the same colour.

With Replacement	Without Replacement
(__ , __) (__ , __)	(__ , __) (__ , __)
(__ , __) (__ , __)	(__ , __) (__ , __)
(__ , __) (__ , __)	(__ , __) (__ , __)
(__ , __) (__ , __)	(__ , __) (__ , __)
(__ , __) (__ , __)	(__ , __) (__ , __)
(__ , __) (__ , __)	(__ , __) (__ , __)
(__ , __) (__ , __)	(__ , __) (__ , __)
(__ , __) (__ , __)	(__ , __) (__ , __)
(__ , __) (__ , __)	(__ , __) (__ , __)
(__ , __) (__ , __)	(__ , __) (__ , __)
(__ , __) (__ , __)	(__ , __) (__ , __)
(__ , __) (__ , __)	(__ , __) (__ , __)

Table 3.13 Empirical Results

	With Replacement	Without Replacement
P(2 reds)		
$P(R_1B_2$ OR $B_1R_2)$		
$P(R_1$ AND $G_2)$		
$P(G_2|R_1)$		
P(no yellows)		
P(doubles)		
P(no doubles)		

Table 3.14 Empirical Probabilities

Discussion Questions

1. Why are the "With Replacement" and "Without Replacement" probabilities different?

2. Convert P(no yellows) to decimal format for both Theoretical "With Replacement" and for Empirical "With Replacement". Round to four decimal places.

   a. Theoretical "With Replacement": P(no yellows) = _____

   b. Empirical "With Replacement": P(no yellows) = _____

   c. Are the decimal values "close"? Did you expect them to be closer together or farther apart? Why?

3. If you increased the number of times you picked two M&Ms to 240 times, why would empirical probability values change?

4. Would this change (see part 3) cause the empirical probabilities and theoretical probabilities to be closer together or farther apart? How do you know?

5. Explain the differences in what $P(G_1 \text{ AND } R_2)$ and $P(R_1|G_2)$ represent. Hint: Think about the sample space for each probability.

KEY TERMS

Conditional Probability the likelihood that an event will occur given that another event has already occurred

contingency table the method of displaying a frequency distribution as a table with rows and columns to show how two variables may be dependent (contingent) upon each other; the table provides an easy way to calculate conditional probabilities.

Dependent Events If two events are NOT independent, then we say that they are dependent.

Equally Likely Each outcome of an experiment has the same probability.

Event a subset of the set of all outcomes of an experiment; the set of all outcomes of an experiment is called a **sample space** and is usually denoted by *S*. An event is an arbitrary subset in *S*. It can contain one outcome, two outcomes, no outcomes (empty subset), the entire sample space, and the like. Standard notations for events are capital letters such as *A*, *B*, *C*, and so on.

Experiment a planned activity carried out under controlled conditions

Independent Events The occurrence of one event has no effect on the probability of the occurrence of another event. Events *A* and *B* are independent if one of the following is true:

1. $P(A|B) = P(A)$

2. $P(B|A) = P(B)$

3. $P(A \text{ AND } B) = P(A)P(B)$

Mutually Exclusive Two events are mutually exclusive if the probability that they both happen at the same time is zero. If events *A* and *B* are mutually exclusive, then $P(A \text{ AND } B) = 0$.

Outcome a particular result of an experiment

Probability a number between zero and one, inclusive, that gives the likelihood that a specific event will occur; the foundation of statistics is given by the following 3 axioms (by A.N. Kolmogorov, 1930's): Let *S* denote the sample space and *A* and *B* are two events in *S*. Then:

- $0 \le P(A) \le 1$

- If *A* and *B* are any two mutually exclusive events, then $P(A \text{ OR } B) = P(A) + P(B)$.

- $P(S) = 1$

Sample Space the set of all possible outcomes of an experiment

Sampling with Replacement If each member of a population is replaced after it is picked, then that member has the possibility of being chosen more than once.

Sampling without Replacement When sampling is done without replacement, each member of a population may be chosen only once.

The AND Event An outcome is in the event *A* AND *B* if the outcome is in both *A* AND *B* at the same time.

The Complement Event The complement of event *A* consists of all outcomes that are NOT in *A*.

The Conditional Probability of *A* GIVEN *B* $P(A|B)$ is the probability that event *A* will occur given that the event *B* has already occurred.

The Conditional Probability of One Event Given Another Event $P(A|B)$ is the probability that event *A* will occur given that the event *B* has already occurred.

The Or Event An outcome is in the event *A* OR *B* if the outcome is in *A* or is in *B* or is in both *A* and *B*.

The OR of Two Events An outcome is in the event *A* OR *B* if the outcome is in *A*, is in *B*, or is in both *A* and *B*.

Tree Diagram the useful visual representation of a sample space and events in the form of a "tree" with branches marked by possible outcomes together with associated probabilities (frequencies, relative frequencies)

Venn Diagram the visual representation of a sample space and events in the form of circles or ovals showing their intersections

CHAPTER REVIEW

3.1 Terminology

In this module we learned the basic terminology of probability. The set of all possible outcomes of an experiment is called the sample space. Events are subsets of the sample space, and they are assigned a probability that is a number between zero and one, inclusive.

3.2 Independent and Mutually Exclusive Events

Two events A and B are independent if the knowledge that one occurred does not affect the chance the other occurs. If two events are not independent, then we say that they are dependent.

In sampling with replacement, each member of a population is replaced after it is picked, so that member has the possibility of being chosen more than once, and the events are considered to be independent. In sampling without replacement, each member of a population may be chosen only once, and the events are considered not to be independent. When events do not share outcomes, they are mutually exclusive of each other.

3.3 Two Basic Rules of Probability

The multiplication rule and the addition rule are used for computing the probability of A and B, as well as the probability of A or B for two given events A, B defined on the sample space. In sampling with replacement each member of a population is replaced after it is picked, so that member has the possibility of being chosen more than once, and the events are considered to be independent. In sampling without replacement, each member of a population may be chosen only once, and the events are considered to be not independent. The events A and B are mutually exclusive events when they do not have any outcomes in common.

3.4 Contingency Tables

There are several tools you can use to help organize and sort data when calculating probabilities. Contingency tables help display data and are particularly useful when calculating probabilites that have multiple dependent variables.

3.5 Tree and Venn Diagrams

A tree diagram use branches to show the different outcomes of experiments and makes complex probability questions easy to visualize.

A Venn diagram is a picture that represents the outcomes of an experiment. It generally consists of a box that represents the sample space S together with circles or ovals. The circles or ovals represent events. A Venn diagram is especially helpful for visualizing the OR event, the AND event, and the complement of an event and for understanding conditional probabilities.

FORMULA REVIEW

3.1 Terminology

A and B are events

$P(S) = 1$ where S is the sample space

$0 \leq P(A) \leq 1$

$P(A|B) = \dfrac{P(A \text{ AND } B)}{P(B)}$

3.2 Independent and Mutually Exclusive Events

If A and B are independent, $P(A \text{ AND } B) = P(A)P(B)$, $P(A|B) = P(A)$ and $P(B|A) = P(B)$.

If A and B are mutually exclusive, $P(A \text{ OR } B) = P(A) + P(B)$ and $P(A \text{ AND } B) = 0$.

3.3 Two Basic Rules of Probability

The multiplication rule: $P(A \text{ AND } B) = P(A|B)P(B)$

The addition rule: $P(A$ OR $B) = P(A) + P(B) - P(A$ AND $B)$

PRACTICE

3.1 Terminology

1. In a particular college class, there are male and female students. Some students have long hair and some students have short hair. Write the **symbols** for the probabilities of the events for parts a through j. (Note that you cannot find numerical answers here. You were not given enough information to find any probability values yet; concentrate on understanding the symbols.)

- Let F be the event that a student is female.
- Let M be the event that a student is male.
- Let S be the event that a student has short hair.
- Let L be the event that a student has long hair.
    a. The probability that a student does not have long hair.
    b. The probability that a student is male or has short hair.
    c. The probability that a student is a female and has long hair.
    d. The probability that a student is male, given that the student has long hair.
    e. The probability that a student has long hair, given that the student is male.
    f. Of all the female students, the probability that a student has short hair.
    g. Of all students with long hair, the probability that a student is female.
    h. The probability that a student is female or has long hair.
    i. The probability that a randomly selected student is a male student with short hair.
    j. The probability that a student is female.

Use the following information to answer the next four exercises. A box is filled with several party favors. It contains 12 hats, 15 noisemakers, ten finger traps, and five bags of confetti.

Let H = the event of getting a hat.
Let N = the event of getting a noisemaker.
Let F = the event of getting a finger trap.
Let C = the event of getting a bag of confetti.

2. Find $P(H)$.

3. Find $P(N)$.

4. Find $P(F)$.

5. Find $P(C)$.

Use the following information to answer the next six exercises. A jar of 150 jelly beans contains 22 red jelly beans, 38 yellow, 20 green, 28 purple, 26 blue, and the rest are orange.

Let B = the event of getting a blue jelly bean
Let G = the event of getting a green jelly bean.
Let O = the event of getting an orange jelly bean.
Let P = the event of getting a purple jelly bean.
Let R = the event of getting a red jelly bean.
Let Y = the event of getting a yellow jelly bean.

6. Find $P(B)$.

7. Find $P(G)$.

8. Find $P(P)$.

9. Find $P(R)$.

10. Find $P(Y)$.

11. Find $P(O)$.

Use the following information to answer the next six exercises. There are 23 countries in North America, 12 countries in South America, 47 countries in Europe, 44 countries in Asia, 54 countries in Africa, and 14 in Oceania (Pacific Ocean region).

Let A = the event that a country is in Asia.
Let E = the event that a country is in Europe.
Let F = the event that a country is in Africa.
Let N = the event that a country is in North America.
Let O = the event that a country is in Oceania.
Let S = the event that a country is in South America.

12. Find $P(A)$.

13. Find $P(E)$.

14. Find $P(F)$.

15. Find $P(N)$.

16. Find $P(O)$.

17. Find $P(S)$.

18. What is the probability of drawing a red card in a standard deck of 52 cards?

19. What is the probability of drawing a club in a standard deck of 52 cards?

20. What is the probability of rolling an even number of dots with a fair, six-sided die numbered one through six?

21. What is the probability of rolling a prime number of dots with a fair, six-sided die numbered one through six?

Use the following information to answer the next two exercises. You see a game at a local fair. You have to throw a dart at a color wheel. Each section on the color wheel is equal in area.

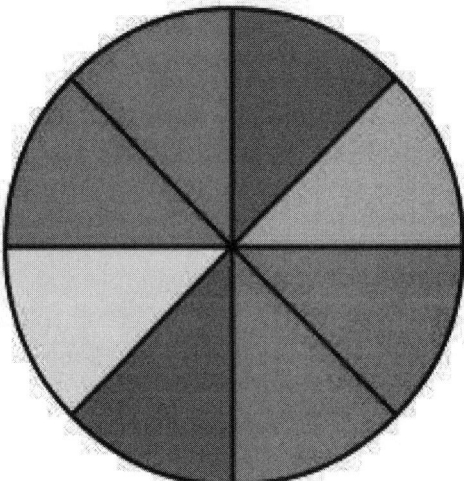

Figure 3.10

Let B = the event of landing on blue.
Let R = the event of landing on red.
Let G = the event of landing on green.
Let Y = the event of landing on yellow.

22. If you land on Y, you get the biggest prize. Find $P(Y)$.

23. If you land on red, you don't get a prize. What is $P(R)$?

Use the following information to answer the next ten exercises. On a baseball team, there are infielders and outfielders. Some players are great hitters, and some players are not great hitters.

Let I = the event that a player in an infielder.

Let O = the event that a player is an outfielder.

Let H = the event that a player is a great hitter.

Let N = the event that a player is not a great hitter.

24. Write the symbols for the probability that a player is not an outfielder.

25. Write the symbols for the probability that a player is an outfielder or is a great hitter.

26. Write the symbols for the probability that a player is an infielder and is not a great hitter.

27. Write the symbols for the probability that a player is a great hitter, given that the player is an infielder.

28. Write the symbols for the probability that a player is an infielder, given that the player is a great hitter.

29. Write the symbols for the probability that of all the outfielders, a player is not a great hitter.

30. Write the symbols for the probability that of all the great hitters, a player is an outfielder.

31. Write the symbols for the probability that a player is an infielder or is not a great hitter.

32. Write the symbols for the probability that a player is an outfielder and is a great hitter.

33. Write the symbols for the probability that a player is an infielder.

34. What is the word for the set of all possible outcomes?

35. What is conditional probability?

36. A shelf holds 12 books. Eight are fiction and the rest are nonfiction. Each is a different book with a unique title. The fiction books are numbered one to eight. The nonfiction books are numbered one to four. Randomly select one book

Let F = event that book is fiction

Let N = event that book is nonfiction

What is the sample space?

37. What is the sum of the probabilities of an event and its complement?

Use the following information to answer the next two exercises. You are rolling a fair, six-sided number cube. Let E = the event that it lands on an even number. Let M = the event that it lands on a multiple of three.

38. What does $P(E|M)$ mean in words?

39. What does $P(E$ OR $M)$ mean in words?

3.2 Independent and Mutually Exclusive Events

40. E and F are mutually exclusive events. $P(E) = 0.4$; $P(F) = 0.5$. Find $P(E|F)$.

41. J and K are independent events. $P(J|K) = 0.3$. Find $P(J)$.

42. U and V are mutually exclusive events. $P(U) = 0.26$; $P(V) = 0.37$. Find:
   a. $P(U$ AND $V) =$
   b. $P(U|V) =$
   c. $P(U$ OR $V) =$

43. Q and R are independent events. $P(Q) = 0.4$ and $P(Q$ AND $R) = 0.1$. Find $P(R)$.

3.3 Two Basic Rules of Probability

Use the following information to answer the next ten exercises. Forty-eight percent of all Californians registered voters prefer life in prison without parole over the death penalty for a person convicted of first degree murder. Among Latino California registered voters, 55% prefer life in prison without parole over the death penalty for a person convicted of first degree murder. 37.6% of all Californians are Latino.

In this problem, let:

- C = Californians (registered voters) preferring life in prison without parole over the death penalty for a person convicted of first degree murder.

- *L* = Latino Californians

Suppose that one Californian is randomly selected.

44. Find *P*(*C*).

45. Find *P*(*L*).

46. Find *P*(*C*|*L*).

47. In words, what is *C*|*L*?

48. Find *P*(*L* AND *C*).

49. In words, what is *L* AND *C*?

50. Are *L* and *C* independent events? Show why or why not.

51. Find *P*(*L* OR *C*).

52. In words, what is *L* OR *C*?

53. Are *L* and *C* mutually exclusive events? Show why or why not.

3.4 Contingency Tables

Use the following information to answer the next four exercises. **Table 3.15** shows a random sample of musicians and how they learned to play their instruments.

Gender	Self-taught	Studied in School	Private Instruction	Total
Female	12	38	22	72
Male	19	24	15	58
Total	31	62	37	130

Table 3.15

54. Find *P*(musician is a female).

55. Find *P*(musician is a male AND had private instruction).

56. Find *P*(musician is a female OR is self taught).

57. Are the events "being a female musician" and "learning music in school" mutually exclusive events?

3.5 Tree and Venn Diagrams

58. The probability that a man develops some form of cancer in his lifetime is 0.4567. The probability that a man has at least one false positive test result (meaning the test comes back for cancer when the man does not have it) is 0.51. Let: *C* = a man develops cancer in his lifetime; *P* = man has at least one false positive. Construct a tree diagram of the situation.

BRINGING IT TOGETHER: PRACTICE

Use the following information to answer the next seven exercises. An article in the *New England Journal of Medicine*, reported about a study of smokers in California and Hawaii. In one part of the report, the self-reported ethnicity and smoking levels per day were given. Of the people smoking at most ten cigarettes per day, there were 9,886 African Americans, 2,745 Native Hawaiians, 12,831 Latinos, 8,378 Japanese Americans, and 7,650 Whites. Of the people smoking 11 to 20 cigarettes per day, there were 6,514 African Americans, 3,062 Native Hawaiians, 4,932 Latinos, 10,680 Japanese Americans, and 9,877 Whites. Of the people smoking 21 to 30 cigarettes per day, there were 1,671 African Americans, 1,419 Native Hawaiians, 1,406 Latinos, 4,715 Japanese Americans, and 6,062 Whites. Of the people smoking at least 31 cigarettes per day, there were 759 African Americans, 788 Native Hawaiians, 800 Latinos, 2,305 Japanese Americans, and 3,970 Whites.

59. Complete the table using the data provided. Suppose that one person from the study is randomly selected. Find the probability that person smoked 11 to 20 cigarettes per day.

Smoking Level	African American	Native Hawaiian	Latino	Japanese Americans	White	TOTALS
1–10						
11–20						
21–30						
31+						
TOTALS						

Table 3.16 Smoking Levels by Ethnicity

60. Suppose that one person from the study is randomly selected. Find the probability that person smoked 11 to 20 cigarettes per day.

61. Find the probability that the person was Latino.

62. In words, explain what it means to pick one person from the study who is "Japanese American **AND** smokes 21 to 30 cigarettes per day." Also, find the probability.

63. In words, explain what it means to pick one person from the study who is "Japanese American **OR** smokes 21 to 30 cigarettes per day." Also, find the probability.

64. In words, explain what it means to pick one person from the study who is "Japanese American **GIVEN** that person smokes 21 to 30 cigarettes per day." Also, find the probability.

65. Prove that smoking level/day and ethnicity are dependent events.

HOMEWORK

3.1 Terminology

66.

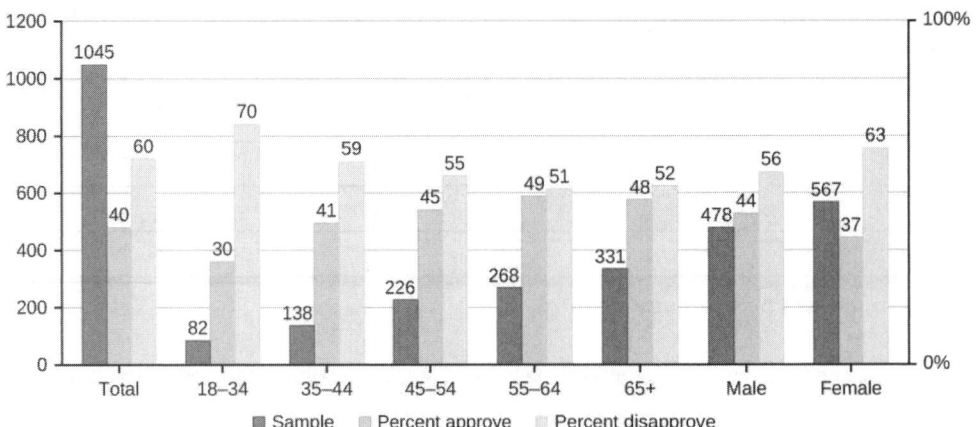

Figure 3.11 The graph in **Figure 3.11** displays the sample sizes and percentages of people in different age and gender groups who were polled concerning their approval of Mayor Ford's actions in office. The total number in the sample of all the age groups is 1,045.

    a. Define three events in the graph.
    b. Describe in words what the entry 40 means.
    c. Describe in words the complement of the entry in question 2.
    d. Describe in words what the entry 30 means.
    e. Out of the males and females, what percent are males?
    f. Out of the females, what percent disapprove of Mayor Ford?
    g. Out of all the age groups, what percent approve of Mayor Ford?
    h. Find P(Approve|Male).
    i. Out of the age groups, what percent are more than 44 years old?
    j. Find P(Approve|Age < 35).

67. Explain what is wrong with the following statements. Use complete sentences.

    a. If there is a 60% chance of rain on Saturday and a 70% chance of rain on Sunday, then there is a 130% chance of rain over the weekend.
    b. The probability that a baseball player hits a home run is greater than the probability that he gets a successful hit.

3.2 Independent and Mutually Exclusive Events

Use the following information to answer the next 12 exercises. The graph shown is based on more than 170,000 interviews done by Gallup that took place from January through December 2012. The sample consists of employed Americans 18 years of age or older. The Emotional Health Index Scores are the sample space. We randomly sample one Emotional Health Index Score.

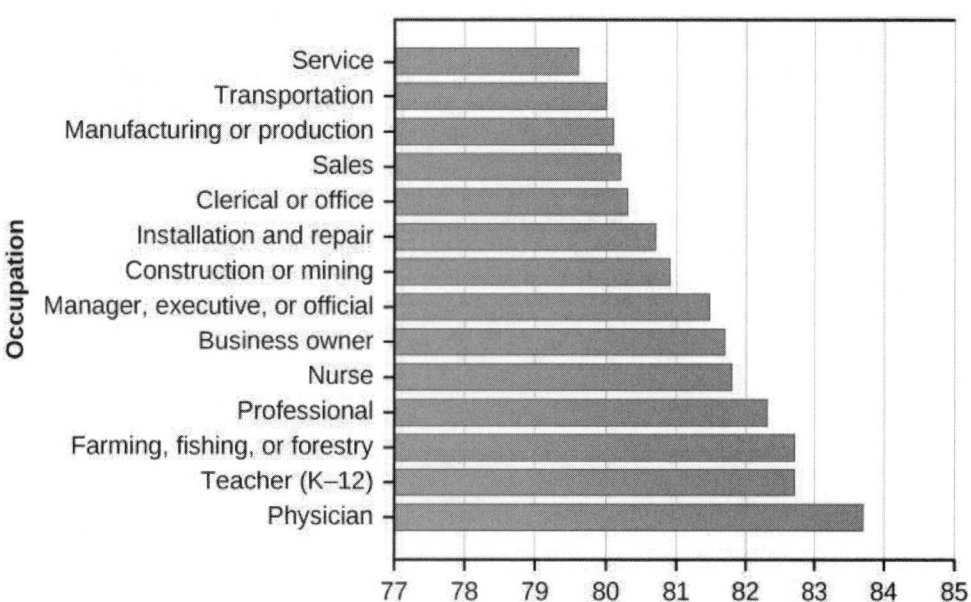

Figure 3.12

68. Find the probability that an Emotional Health Index Score is 82.7.

69. Find the probability that an Emotional Health Index Score is 81.0.

70. Find the probability that an Emotional Health Index Score is more than 81?

71. Find the probability that an Emotional Health Index Score is between 80.5 and 82?

72. If we know an Emotional Health Index Score is 81.5 or more, what is the probability that it is 82.7?

73. What is the probability that an Emotional Health Index Score is 80.7 or 82.7?

74. What is the probability that an Emotional Health Index Score is less than 80.2 given that it is already less than 81.

75. What occupation has the highest emotional index score?

76. What occupation has the lowest emotional index score?

77. What is the range of the data?

78. Compute the average EHIS.

79. If all occupations are equally likely for a certain individual, what is the probability that he or she will have an occupation with lower than average EHIS?

3.3 Two Basic Rules of Probability

80. On February 28, 2013, a Field Poll Survey reported that 61% of California registered voters approved of allowing two people of the same gender to marry and have regular marriage laws apply to them. Among 18 to 39 year olds (California registered voters), the approval rating was 78%. Six in ten California registered voters said that the upcoming Supreme Court's ruling about the constitutionality of California's Proposition 8 was either very or somewhat important to them. Out of those CA registered voters who support same-sex marriage, 75% say the ruling is important to them.

In this problem, let:

- C = California registered voters who support same-sex marriage.
- B = California registered voters who say the Supreme Court's ruling about the constitutionality of California's Proposition 8 is very or somewhat important to them
- A = California registered voters who are 18 to 39 years old.
    a. Find $P(C)$.
    b. Find $P(B)$.
    c. Find $P(C|A)$.
    d. Find $P(B|C)$.
    e. In words, what is $C|A$?
    f. In words, what is $B|C$?
    g. Find $P(C$ AND $B)$.
    h. In words, what is C AND B?
    i. Find $P(C$ OR $B)$.
    j. Are C and B mutually exclusive events? Show why or why not.

81. After Rob Ford, the mayor of Toronto, announced his plans to cut budget costs in late 2011, the Forum Research polled 1,046 people to measure the mayor's popularity. Everyone polled expressed either approval or disapproval. These are the results their poll produced:

- In early 2011, 60 percent of the population approved of Mayor Ford's actions in office.
- In mid-2011, 57 percent of the population approved of his actions.
- In late 2011, the percentage of popular approval was measured at 42 percent.
    a. What is the sample size for this study?
    b. What proportion in the poll disapproved of Mayor Ford, according to the results from late 2011?
    c. How many people polled responded that they approved of Mayor Ford in late 2011?
    d. What is the probability that a person supported Mayor Ford, based on the data collected in mid-2011?
    e. What is the probability that a person supported Mayor Ford, based on the data collected in early 2011?

Use the following information to answer the next three exercises. The casino game, roulette, allows the gambler to bet on the probability of a ball, which spins in the roulette wheel, landing on a particular color, number, or range of numbers. The table used to place bets contains of 38 numbers, and each number is assigned to a color and a range.

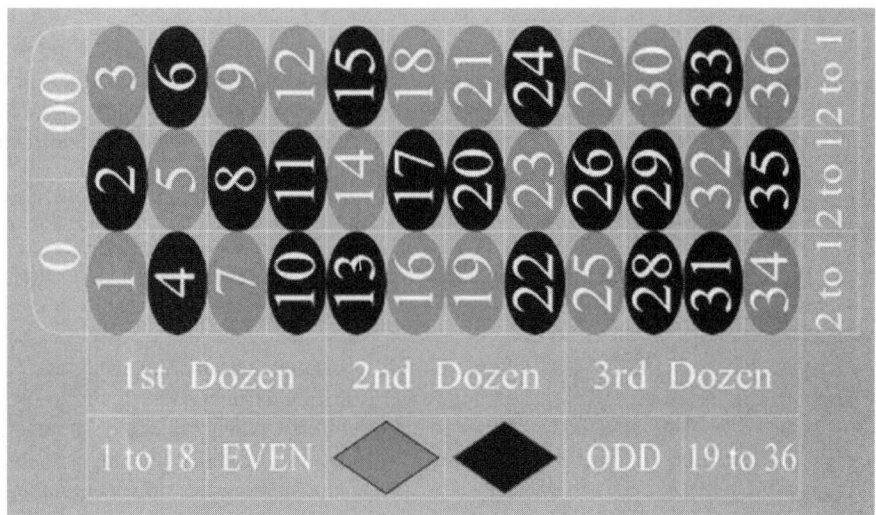

Figure 3.13 (credit: film8ker/wikibooks)

82.

a. List the sample space of the 38 possible outcomes in roulette.
b. You bet on red. Find *P*(red).
c. You bet on -1st 12- (1st Dozen). Find *P*(-1st 12-).
d. You bet on an even number. Find *P*(even number).
e. Is getting an odd number the complement of getting an even number? Why?
f. Find two mutually exclusive events.
g. Are the events Even and 1st Dozen independent?

83. Compute the probability of winning the following types of bets:

a. Betting on two lines that touch each other on the table as in 1-2-3-4-5-6
b. Betting on three numbers in a line, as in 1-2-3
c. Betting on one number
d. Betting on four numbers that touch each other to form a square, as in 10-11-13-14
e. Betting on two numbers that touch each other on the table, as in 10-11 or 10-13
f. Betting on 0-00-1-2-3
g. Betting on 0-1-2; or 0-00-2; or 00-2-3

84. Compute the probability of winning the following types of bets:

a. Betting on a color
b. Betting on one of the dozen groups
c. Betting on the range of numbers from 1 to 18
d. Betting on the range of numbers 19–36
e. Betting on one of the columns
f. Betting on an even or odd number (excluding zero)

85. Suppose that you have eight cards. Five are green and three are yellow. The five green cards are numbered 1, 2, 3, 4, and 5. The three yellow cards are numbered 1, 2, and 3. The cards are well shuffled. You randomly draw one card.

- *G* = card drawn is green
- *E* = card drawn is even-numbered

a. List the sample space.
b. *P*(*G*) = _____
c. *P*(*G*|*E*) = _____
d. *P*(*G* AND *E*) = _____
e. *P*(*G* OR *E*) = _____
f. Are *G* and *E* mutually exclusive? Justify your answer numerically.

86. Roll two fair dice separately. Each die has six faces.
   a. List the sample space.
   b. Let *A* be the event that either a three or four is rolled first, followed by an even number. Find *P*(*A*).
   c. Let *B* be the event that the sum of the two rolls is at most seven. Find *P*(*B*).
   d. In words, explain what "*P*(*A*|*B*)" represents. Find *P*(*A*|*B*).
   e. Are *A* and *B* mutually exclusive events? Explain your answer in one to three complete sentences, including numerical justification.
   f. Are *A* and *B* independent events? Explain your answer in one to three complete sentences, including numerical justification.

87. A special deck of cards has ten cards. Four are green, three are blue, and three are red. When a card is picked, its color of it is recorded. An experiment consists of first picking a card and then tossing a coin.
   a. List the sample space.
   b. Let *A* be the event that a blue card is picked first, followed by landing a head on the coin toss. Find *P*(*A*).
   c. Let *B* be the event that a red or green is picked, followed by landing a head on the coin toss. Are the events *A* and *B* mutually exclusive? Explain your answer in one to three complete sentences, including numerical justification.
   d. Let *C* be the event that a red or blue is picked, followed by landing a head on the coin toss. Are the events *A* and *C* mutually exclusive? Explain your answer in one to three complete sentences, including numerical justification.

88. An experiment consists of first rolling a die and then tossing a coin.
   a. List the sample space.
   b. Let *A* be the event that either a three or a four is rolled first, followed by landing a head on the coin toss. Find *P*(*A*).
   c. Let *B* be the event that the first and second tosses land on heads. Are the events *A* and *B* mutually exclusive? Explain your answer in one to three complete sentences, including numerical justification.

89. An experiment consists of tossing a nickel, a dime, and a quarter. Of interest is the side the coin lands on.
   a. List the sample space.
   b. Let *A* be the event that there are at least two tails. Find *P*(*A*).
   c. Let *B* be the event that the first and second tosses land on heads. Are the events *A* and *B* mutually exclusive? Explain your answer in one to three complete sentences, including justification.

90. Consider the following scenario:
Let *P*(*C*) = 0.4.
Let *P*(*D*) = 0.5.
Let *P*(*C*|*D*) = 0.6.
   a. Find *P*(*C* AND *D*).
   b. Are *C* and *D* mutually exclusive? Why or why not?
   c. Are *C* and *D* independent events? Why or why not?
   d. Find *P*(*C* OR *D*).
   e. Find *P*(*D*|*C*).

91. *Y* and *Z* are independent events.
   a. Rewrite the basic Addition Rule *P*(*Y* OR *Z*) = *P*(*Y*) + *P*(*Z*) - *P*(*Y* AND *Z*) using the information that *Y* and *Z* are independent events.
   b. Use the rewritten rule to find *P*(*Z*) if *P*(*Y* OR *Z*) = 0.71 and *P*(*Y*) = 0.42.

92. *G* and *H* are mutually exclusive events. *P*(*G*) = 0.5 *P*(*H*) = 0.3
   a. Explain why the following statement MUST be false: *P*(*H*|*G*) = 0.4.
   b. Find *P*(*H* OR *G*).
   c. Are *G* and *H* independent or dependent events? Explain in a complete sentence.

93. Approximately 281,000,000 people over age five live in the United States. Of these people, 55,000,000 speak a language other than English at home. Of those who speak another language at home, 62.3% speak Spanish.

Let: E = speaks English at home; E' = speaks another language at home; S = speaks Spanish;

Finish each probability statement by matching the correct answer.

Probability Statements	Answers
a. $P(E') =$	i. 0.8043
b. $P(E) =$	ii. 0.623
c. $P(S \text{ and } E') =$	iii. 0.1957
d. $P(S|E') =$	iv. 0.1219

Table 3.17

94. 1994, the U.S. government held a lottery to issue 55,000 Green Cards (permits for non-citizens to work legally in the U.S.). Renate Deutsch, from Germany, was one of approximately 6.5 million people who entered this lottery. Let G = won green card.
   a. What was Renate's chance of winning a Green Card? Write your answer as a probability statement.
   b. In the summer of 1994, Renate received a letter stating she was one of 110,000 finalists chosen. Once the finalists were chosen, assuming that each finalist had an equal chance to win, what was Renate's chance of winning a Green Card? Write your answer as a conditional probability statement. Let F = was a finalist.
   c. Are G and F independent or dependent events? Justify your answer numerically and also explain why.
   d. Are G and F mutually exclusive events? Justify your answer numerically and explain why.

95. Three professors at George Washington University did an experiment to determine if economists are more selfish than other people. They dropped 64 stamped, addressed envelopes with $10 cash in different classrooms on the George Washington campus. 44% were returned overall. From the economics classes 56% of the envelopes were returned. From the business, psychology, and history classes 31% were returned.

Let: R = money returned; E = economics classes; O = other classes

   a. Write a probability statement for the overall percent of money returned.
   b. Write a probability statement for the percent of money returned out of the economics classes.
   c. Write a probability statement for the percent of money returned out of the other classes.
   d. Is money being returned independent of the class? Justify your answer numerically and explain it.
   e. Based upon this study, do you think that economists are more selfish than other people? Explain why or why not. Include numbers to justify your answer.

96. The following table of data obtained from www.baseball-almanac.com shows hit information for four players. Suppose that one hit from the table is randomly selected.

Name	Single	Double	Triple	Home Run	Total Hits
Babe Ruth	1,517	506	136	714	2,873
Jackie Robinson	1,054	273	54	137	1,518
Ty Cobb	3,603	174	295	114	4,189
Hank Aaron	2,294	624	98	755	3,771
Total	8,471	1,577	583	1,720	12,351

Table 3.18

Are "the hit being made by Hank Aaron" and "the hit being a double" independent events?

a. Yes, because P(hit by Hank Aaron|hit is a double) = P(hit by Hank Aaron)
b. No, because P(hit by Hank Aaron|hit is a double) ≠ P(hit is a double)
c. No, because P(hit is by Hank Aaron|hit is a double) ≠ P(hit by Hank Aaron)
d. Yes, because P(hit is by Hank Aaron|hit is a double) = P(hit is a double)

97. United Blood Services is a blood bank that serves more than 500 hospitals in 18 states. According to their website, a person with type O blood and a negative Rh factor (Rh-) can donate blood to any person with any bloodtype. Their data show that 43% of people have type O blood and 15% of people have Rh- factor; 52% of people have type O or Rh- factor.
a. Find the probability that a person has both type O blood and the Rh- factor.
b. Find the probability that a person does NOT have both type O blood and the Rh- factor.

98. At a college, 72% of courses have final exams and 46% of courses require research papers. Suppose that 32% of courses have a research paper and a final exam. Let F be the event that a course has a final exam. Let R be the event that a course requires a research paper.
a. Find the probability that a course has a final exam or a research project.
b. Find the probability that a course has NEITHER of these two requirements.

99. In a box of assorted cookies, 36% contain chocolate and 12% contain nuts. Of those, 8% contain both chocolate and nuts. Sean is allergic to both chocolate and nuts.
a. Find the probability that a cookie contains chocolate or nuts (he can't eat it).
b. Find the probability that a cookie does not contain chocolate or nuts (he can eat it).

100. A college finds that 10% of students have taken a distance learning class and that 40% of students are part time students. Of the part time students, 20% have taken a distance learning class. Let D = event that a student takes a distance learning class and E = event that a student is a part time student
a. Find $P(D$ AND $E)$.
b. Find $P(E|D)$.
c. Find $P(D$ OR $E)$.
d. Using an appropriate test, show whether D and E are independent.
e. Using an appropriate test, show whether D and E are mutually exclusive.

3.4 Contingency Tables

Use the information in the Table 3.19 to answer the next eight exercises. The table shows the political party affiliation of each of 67 members of the US Senate in June 2012, and when they are up for reelection.

Up for reelection:	Democratic Party	Republican Party	Other	Total
November 2014	20	13	0	
November 2016	10	24	0	

Table 3.19

Up for reelection:	Democratic Party	Republican Party	Other	Total
Total				

Table 3.19

101. What is the probability that a randomly selected senator has an "Other" affiliation?

102. What is the probability that a randomly selected senator is up for reelection in November 2016?

103. What is the probability that a randomly selected senator is a Democrat and up for reelection in November 2016?

104. What is the probability that a randomly selected senator is a Republican or is up for reelection in November 2014?

105. Suppose that a member of the US Senate is randomly selected. Given that the randomly selected senator is up for reelection in November 2016, what is the probability that this senator is a Democrat?

106. Suppose that a member of the US Senate is randomly selected. What is the probability that the senator is up for reelection in November 2014, knowing that this senator is a Republican?

107. The events "Republican" and "Up for reelection in 2016" are _____
   a. mutually exclusive.
   b. independent.
   c. both mutually exclusive and independent.
   d. neither mutually exclusive nor independent.

108. The events "Other" and "Up for reelection in November 2016" are _____
   a. mutually exclusive.
   b. independent.
   c. both mutually exclusive and independent.
   d. neither mutually exclusive nor independent.

109. Table 3.20 gives the number of suicides estimated in the U.S. for a recent year by age, race (black or white), and sex. We are interested in possible relationships between age, race, and sex. We will let suicide victims be our population.

Race and Sex	1–14	15–24	25–64	over 64	TOTALS
white, male	210	3,360	13,610		22,050
white, female	80	580	3,380		4,930
black, male	10	460	1,060		1,670
black, female	0	40	270		330
all others					
TOTALS	310	4,650	18,780		29,760

Table 3.20

   a. Fill in the column for the suicides for individuals over age 64.
   b. Fill in the row for all other races.
   c. Find the probability that a randomly selected individual was a white male.
   d. Find the probability that a randomly selected individual was a black female.
   e. Find the probability that a randomly selected individual was black
   f. Find the probability that a randomly selected individual was a black or white male.
   g. Out of the individuals over age 64, find the probability that a randomly selected individual was a black or white male.

Use the following information to answer the next two exercises. The table of data obtained from *www.baseball-almanac.com* shows hit information for four well known baseball players. Suppose that one hit from the table is randomly selected.

NAME	Single	Double	Triple	Home Run	TOTAL HITS
Babe Ruth	1,517	506	136	714	2,873
Jackie Robinson	1,054	273	54	137	1,518
Ty Cobb	3,603	174	295	114	4,189
Hank Aaron	2,294	624	98	755	3,771
TOTAL	8,471	1,577	583	1,720	12,351

Table 3.21

110. Find P(hit was made by Babe Ruth).

    a. $\frac{1518}{2873}$

    b. $\frac{2873}{12351}$

    c. $\frac{583}{12351}$

    d. $\frac{4189}{12351}$

111. Find P(hit was made by Ty Cobb|The hit was a Home Run).

    a. $\frac{4189}{12351}$

    b. $\frac{114}{1720}$

    c. $\frac{1720}{4189}$

    d. $\frac{114}{12351}$

112. Table 3.22 identifies a group of children by one of four hair colors, and by type of hair.

Hair Type	Brown	Blond	Black	Red	Totals
Wavy	20		15	3	43
Straight	80	15		12	
Totals		20			215

Table 3.22

    a. Complete the table.
    b. What is the probability that a randomly selected child will have wavy hair?
    c. What is the probability that a randomly selected child will have either brown or blond hair?
    d. What is the probability that a randomly selected child will have wavy brown hair?
    e. What is the probability that a randomly selected child will have red hair, given that he or she has straight hair?
    f. If B is the event of a child having brown hair, find the probability of the complement of B.
    g. In words, what does the complement of B represent?

113. In a previous year, the weights of the members of the **San Francisco 49ers** and the **Dallas Cowboys** were published in the *San Jose Mercury News*. The factual data were compiled into the following table.

Shirt#	≤ 210	211–250	251–290	> 290
1–33	21	5	0	0
34–66	6	18	7	4
66–99	6	12	22	5

Table 3.23

For the following, suppose that you randomly select one player from the 49ers or Cowboys.

    a.   Find the probability that his shirt number is from 1 to 33.
    b.   Find the probability that he weighs at most 210 pounds.
    c.   Find the probability that his shirt number is from 1 to 33 AND he weighs at most 210 pounds.
    d.   Find the probability that his shirt number is from 1 to 33 OR he weighs at most 210 pounds.
    e.   Find the probability that his shirt number is from 1 to 33 GIVEN that he weighs at most 210 pounds.

3.5 Tree and Venn Diagrams

Use the following information to answer the next two exercises. This tree diagram shows the tossing of an unfair coin followed by drawing one bead from a cup containing three red (*R*), four yellow (*Y*) and five blue (*B*) beads. For the coin, $P(H) = \frac{2}{3}$ and $P(T) = \frac{1}{3}$ where *H* is heads and *T* is tails.

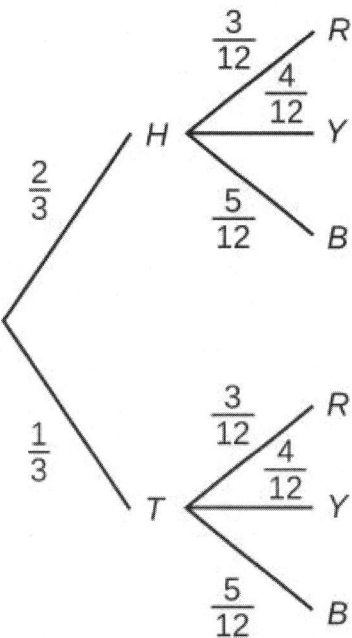

Figure 3.14

114. Find P(tossing a Head on the coin AND a Red bead)

  a. $\frac{2}{3}$

  b. $\frac{5}{15}$

  c. $\frac{6}{36}$

  d. $\frac{5}{36}$

115. Find P(Blue bead).

  a. $\frac{15}{36}$

  b. $\frac{10}{36}$

  c. $\frac{10}{12}$

  d. $\frac{6}{36}$

116. A box of cookies contains three chocolate and seven butter cookies. Miguel randomly selects a cookie and eats it. Then he randomly selects another cookie and eats it. (How many cookies did he take?)

  a. Draw the tree that represents the possibilities for the cookie selections. Write the probabilities along each branch of the tree.
  b. Are the probabilities for the flavor of the SECOND cookie that Miguel selects independent of his first selection? Explain.
  c. For each complete path through the tree, write the event it represents and find the probabilities.
  d. Let S be the event that both cookies selected were the same flavor. Find $P(S)$.
  e. Let T be the event that the cookies selected were different flavors. Find $P(T)$ by two different methods: by using the complement rule and by using the branches of the tree. Your answers should be the same with both methods.
  f. Let U be the event that the second cookie selected is a butter cookie. Find $P(U)$.

BRINGING IT TOGETHER: HOMEWORK

117. A previous year, the weights of the members of the **San Francisco 49ers** and the **Dallas Cowboys** were published in the *San Jose Mercury News*. The factual data are compiled into **Table 3.24**.

Shirt#	≤ 210	211–250	251–290	290≤
1–33	21	5	0	0
34–66	6	18	7	4
66–99	6	12	22	5

Table 3.24

For the following, suppose that you randomly select one player from the 49ers or Cowboys.

If having a shirt number from one to 33 and weighing at most 210 pounds were independent events, then what should be true about P(Shirt# 1–33|≤ 210 pounds)?

118. The probability that a male develops some form of cancer in his lifetime is 0.4567. The probability that a male has at least one false positive test result (meaning the test comes back for cancer when the man does not have it) is 0.51. Some of the following questions do not have enough information for you to answer them. Write "not enough information" for those answers. Let C = a man develops cancer in his lifetime and P = man has at least one false positive.

   a. $P(C) =$ _____
   b. $P(P|C) =$ _____
   c. $P(P|C') =$ _____
   d. If a test comes up positive, based upon numerical values, can you assume that man has cancer? Justify numerically and explain why or why not.

119. Given events G and H: $P(G) = 0.43$; $P(H) = 0.26$; $P(H$ AND $G) = 0.14$
   a. Find $P(H$ OR $G)$.
   b. Find the probability of the complement of event (H AND G).
   c. Find the probability of the complement of event (H OR G).

120. Given events J and K: $P(J) = 0.18$; $P(K) = 0.37$; $P(J$ OR $K) = 0.45$
   a. Find $P(J$ AND $K)$.
   b. Find the probability of the complement of event (J AND K).
   c. Find the probability of the complement of event (J OR K).

Use the following information to answer the next two exercises. Suppose that you have eight cards. Five are green and three are yellow. The cards are well shuffled.

121. Suppose that you randomly draw two cards, one at a time, **with replacement**.
Let G_1 = first card is green
Let G_2 = second card is green
   a. Draw a tree diagram of the situation.
   b. Find $P(G_1$ AND $G_2)$.
   c. Find P(at least one green).
   d. Find $P(G_2|G_1)$.
   e. Are G_2 and G_1 independent events? Explain why or why not.

122. Suppose that you randomly draw two cards, one at a time, **without replacement**.
G_1 = first card is green
G_2 = second card is green
   a. Draw a tree diagram of the situation.
   b. Find $P(G_1$ AND $G_2)$.
   c. Find P(at least one green).
   d. Find $P(G_2|G_1)$.
   e. Are G_2 and G_1 independent events? Explain why or why not.

Use the following information to answer the next two exercises. The percent of licensed U.S. drivers (from a recent year) that are female is 48.60. Of the females, 5.03% are age 19 and under; 81.36% are age 20–64; 13.61% are age 65 or over. Of the licensed U.S. male drivers, 5.04% are age 19 and under; 81.43% are age 20–64; 13.53% are age 65 or over.

123. Complete the following.
   a. Construct a table or a tree diagram of the situation.
   b. Find P(driver is female).
   c. Find P(driver is age 65 or over|driver is female).
   d. Find P(driver is age 65 or over AND female).
   e. In words, explain the difference between the probabilities in part c and part d.
   f. Find P(driver is age 65 or over).
   g. Are being age 65 or over and being female mutually exclusive events? How do you know?

124. Suppose that 10,000 U.S. licensed drivers are randomly selected.
   a. How many would you expect to be male?
   b. Using the table or tree diagram, construct a contingency table of gender versus age group.
   c. Using the contingency table, find the probability that out of the age 20–64 group, a randomly selected driver is female.

125. Approximately 86.5% of Americans commute to work by car, truck, or van. Out of that group, 84.6% drive alone and 15.4% drive in a carpool. Approximately 3.9% walk to work and approximately 5.3% take public transportation.
   a. Construct a table or a tree diagram of the situation. Include a branch for all other modes of transportation to work.
   b. Assuming that the walkers walk alone, what percent of all commuters travel alone to work?
   c. Suppose that 1,000 workers are randomly selected. How many would you expect to travel alone to work?
   d. Suppose that 1,000 workers are randomly selected. How many would you expect to drive in a carpool?

126. When the Euro coin was introduced in 2002, two math professors had their statistics students test whether the Belgian one Euro coin was a fair coin. They spun the coin rather than tossing it and found that out of 250 spins, 140 showed a head (event H) while 110 showed a tail (event T). On that basis, they claimed that it is not a fair coin.
   a. Based on the given data, find $P(H)$ and $P(T)$.
   b. Use a tree to find the probabilities of each possible outcome for the experiment of tossing the coin twice.
   c. Use the tree to find the probability of obtaining exactly one head in two tosses of the coin.
   d. Use the tree to find the probability of obtaining at least one head.

127. *Use the following information to answer the next two exercises.* The following are real data from Santa Clara County, CA. As of a certain time, there had been a total of 3,059 documented cases of AIDS in the county. They were grouped into the following categories:

	Homosexual/Bisexual	IV Drug User*	Heterosexual Contact	Other	Totals
Female	0	70	136	49	____
Male	2,146	463	60	135	____
Totals	____	____	____	____	____

Table 3.25 * includes homosexual/bisexual IV drug users

Suppose a person with AIDS in Santa Clara County is randomly selected.

   a. Find P(Person is female).
   b. Find P(Person has a risk factor heterosexual contact).
   c. Find P(Person is female OR has a risk factor of IV drug user).
   d. Find P(Person is female AND has a risk factor of homosexual/bisexual).
   e. Find P(Person is male AND has a risk factor of IV drug user).
   f. Find P(Person is female GIVEN person got the disease from heterosexual contact).
   g. Construct a Venn diagram. Make one group females and the other group heterosexual contact.

128. Answer these questions using probability rules. Do NOT use the contingency table. Three thousand fifty-nine cases of AIDS had been reported in Santa Clara County, CA, through a certain date. Those cases will be our population. Of those cases, 6.4% obtained the disease through heterosexual contact and 7.4% are female. Out of the females with the disease, 53.3% got the disease from heterosexual contact.
   a. Find P(Person is female).
   b. Find P(Person obtained the disease through heterosexual contact).
   c. Find P(Person is female GIVEN person got the disease from heterosexual contact)
   d. Construct a Venn diagram representing this situation. Make one group females and the other group heterosexual contact. Fill in all values as probabilities.

REFERENCES

3.1 Terminology

"Countries List by Continent." Worldatlas, 2013. Available online at http://www.worldatlas.com/cntycont.htm (accessed May 2, 2013).

3.2 Independent and Mutually Exclusive Events

Lopez, Shane, Preety Sidhu. "U.S. Teachers Love Their Lives, but Struggle in the Workplace." Gallup Wellbeing, 2013.

http://www.gallup.com/poll/161516/teachers-love-lives-struggle-workplace.aspx (accessed May 2, 2013).

Data from Gallup. Available online at www.gallup.com/ (accessed May 2, 2013).

3.3 Two Basic Rules of Probability

DiCamillo, Mark, Mervin Field. "The File Poll." Field Research Corporation. Available online at http://www.field.com/fieldpollonline/subscribers/Rls2443.pdf (accessed May 2, 2013).

Rider, David, "Ford support plummeting, poll suggests," The Star, September 14, 2011. Available online at http://www.thestar.com/news/gta/2011/09/14/ford_support_plummeting_poll_suggests.html (accessed May 2, 2013).

"Mayor's Approval Down." News Release by Forum Research Inc. Available online at http://www.forumresearch.com/forms/News Archives/News Releases/74209_TO_Issues_-_Mayoral_Approval_%28Forum_Research%29%2820130320%29.pdf (accessed May 2, 2013).

"Roulette." Wikipedia. Available online at http://en.wikipedia.org/wiki/Roulette (accessed May 2, 2013).

Shin, Hyon B., Robert A. Kominski. "Language Use in the United States: 2007." United States Census Bureau. Available online at http://www.census.gov/hhes/socdemo/language/data/acs/ACS-12.pdf (accessed May 2, 2013).

Data from the Baseball-Almanac, 2013. Available online at www.baseball-almanac.com (accessed May 2, 2013).

Data from U.S. Census Bureau.

Data from the Wall Street Journal.

Data from The Roper Center: Public Opinion Archives at the University of Connecticut. Available online at http://www.ropercenter.uconn.edu/ (accessed May 2, 2013).

Data from Field Research Corporation. Available online at www.field.com/fieldpollonline (accessed May 2,2 013).

3.4 Contingency Tables

"Blood Types." American Red Cross, 2013. Available online at http://www.redcrossblood.org/learn-about-blood/blood-types (accessed May 3, 2013).

Data from the National Center for Health Statistics, part of the United States Department of Health and Human Services.

Data from United States Senate. Available online at www.senate.gov (accessed May 2, 2013).

Haiman, Christopher A., Daniel O. Stram, Lynn R. Wilkens, Malcom C. Pike, Laurence N. Kolonel, Brien E. Henderson, and Loïc Le Marchand. "Ethnic and Racial Differences in the Smoking-Related Risk of Lung Cancer." The New England Journal of Medicine, 2013. Available online at http://www.nejm.org/doi/full/10.1056/NEJMoa033250 (accessed May 2, 2013).

"Human Blood Types." Unite Blood Services, 2011. Available online at http://www.unitedbloodservices.org/learnMore.aspx (accessed May 2, 2013).

Samuel, T. M. "Strange Facts about RH Negative Blood." eHow Health, 2013. Available online at http://www.ehow.com/facts_5552003_strange-rh-negative-blood.html (accessed May 2, 2013).

"United States: Uniform Crime Report – State Statistics from 1960–2011." The Disaster Center. Available online at http://www.disastercenter.com/crime/ (accessed May 2, 2013).

3.5 Tree and Venn Diagrams

Data from Clara County Public H.D.

Data from the American Cancer Society.

Data from The Data and Story Library, 1996. Available online at http://lib.stat.cmu.edu/DASL/ (accessed May 2, 2013).

Data from the Federal Highway Administration, part of the United States Department of Transportation.

Data from the United States Census Bureau, part of the United States Department of Commerce.

Data from USA Today.

"Environment." The World Bank, 2013. Available online at http://data.worldbank.org/topic/environment (accessed May 2,

2013).

"Search for Datasets." Roper Center: Public Opinion Archives, University of Connecticut., 2013. Available online at http://www.ropercenter.uconn.edu/data_access/data/search_for_datasets.html (accessed May 2, 2013).

SOLUTIONS

1
  a. $P(L') = P(S)$

  b. $P(M \text{ OR } S)$

  c. $P(F \text{ AND } L)$

  d. $P(M|L)$

  e. $P(L|M)$

  f. $P(S|F)$

  g. $P(F|L)$

  h. $P(F \text{ OR } L)$

  i. $P(M \text{ AND } S)$

  j. $P(F)$

3 $P(N) = \frac{15}{42} = \frac{5}{14} = 0.36$

5 $P(C) = \frac{5}{42} = 0.12$

7 $P(G) = \frac{20}{150} = \frac{2}{15} = 0.13$

9 $P(R) = \frac{22}{150} = \frac{11}{75} = 0.15$

11 $P(O) = \frac{150 - 22 - 38 - 20 - 28 - 26}{150} = \frac{16}{150} = \frac{8}{75} = 0.11$

13 $P(E) = \frac{47}{194} = 0.24$

15 $P(N) = \frac{23}{194} = 0.12$

17 $P(S) = \frac{12}{194} = \frac{6}{97} = 0.06$

19 $\frac{13}{52} = \frac{1}{4} = 0.25$

21 $\frac{3}{6} = \frac{1}{2} = 0.5$

23 $P(R) = \frac{4}{8} = 0.5$

25 $P(O \text{ OR } H)$

27 $P(H|I)$

29 $P(N|O)$

31 $P(I \text{ OR } N)$

33 $P(I)$

35 The likelihood that an event will occur given that another event has already occurred.

37 1

39 the probability of landing on an even number or a multiple of three

41 $P(J) = 0.3$

43 $P(Q \text{ AND } R) = P(Q)P(R)$ $0.1 = (0.4)P(R)$ $P(R) = 0.25$

45 0.376

47 $C|L$ means, given the person chosen is a Latino Californian, the person is a registered voter who prefers life in prison without parole for a person convicted of first degree murder.

49 L AND C is the event that the person chosen is a Latino California registered voter who prefers life without parole over the death penalty for a person convicted of first degree murder.

51 0.6492

53 No, because $P(L \text{ AND } C)$ does not equal 0.

55 $P(\text{musician is a male AND had private instruction}) = \dfrac{15}{130} = \dfrac{3}{26} = 0.12$

57 $P(\text{being a female musician AND learning music in school}) = \dfrac{38}{130} = \dfrac{19}{65} = 0.29$ $P(\text{being a female musician})P(\text{learning music in school}) = \left(\dfrac{72}{130}\right)\left(\dfrac{62}{130}\right) = \dfrac{4,464}{16,900} = \dfrac{1,116}{4,225} = 0.26$ No, they are not independent because $P(\text{being a female musician AND learning music in school})$ is not equal to $P(\text{being a female musician})P(\text{learning music in school})$.

58

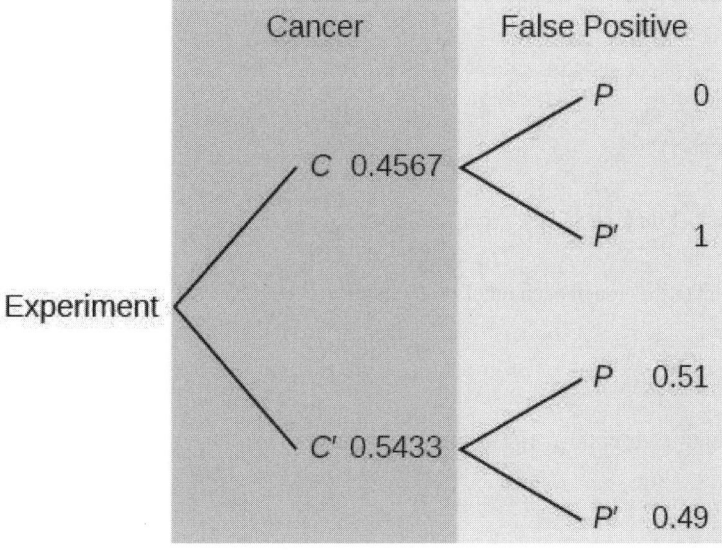

Figure 3.15

60 $\dfrac{35,065}{100,450}$

62 To pick one person from the study who is Japanese American AND smokes 21 to 30 cigarettes per day means that the person has to meet both criteria: both Japanese American and smokes 21 to 30 cigarettes. The sample space should include everyone in the study. The probability is $\dfrac{4,715}{100,450}$.

64 To pick one person from the study who is Japanese American given that person smokes 21-30 cigarettes per day, means that the person must fulfill both criteria and the sample space is reduced to those who smoke 21-30 cigarettes per day. The probability is $\frac{4715}{15,273}$.

67

a.   You can't calculate the joint probability knowing the probability of both events occurring, which is not in the information given; the probabilities should be multiplied, not added; and probability is never greater than 100%

b.   A home run by definition is a successful hit, so he has to have at least as many successful hits as home runs.

69 0

71 0.3571

73 0.2142

75 Physician (83.7)

77 83.7 − 79.6 = 4.1

79 P(Occupation < 81.3) = 0.5

81

a.   The Forum Research surveyed 1,046 Torontonians.

b.   58%

c.   42% of 1,046 = 439 (rounding to the nearest integer)

d.   0.57

e.   0.60.

83

a. P(Betting on two line that touch each other on the table) = $\frac{6}{38}$

b. P(Betting on three numbers in a line) = $\frac{3}{38}$

c. P(Bettting on one number) = $\frac{1}{38}$

d. P(Betting on four number that touch each other to form a square) = $\frac{4}{38}$

e. P(Betting on two number that touch each other on the table) = $\frac{2}{38}$

f. P(Betting on 0-00-1-2-3) = $\frac{5}{38}$

g. P(Betting on 0-1-2; or 0-00-2; or 00-2-3) = $\frac{3}{38}$

85

a. $\{G1, G2, G3, G4, G5, Y1, Y2, Y3\}$

b. $\frac{5}{8}$

c. $\frac{2}{3}$

d. $\frac{2}{8}$

e. $\frac{6}{8}$

f.   No, because $P(G$ AND $E)$ does not equal 0.

87

> **NOTE**
> _____
>
> The coin toss is independent of the card picked first.

a. $\{(G,H)\ (G,T)\ (B,H)\ (B,T)\ (R,H)\ (R,T)\}$

b. $P(A) = P(\text{blue})P(\text{head}) = \left(\dfrac{3}{10}\right)\left(\dfrac{1}{2}\right) = \dfrac{3}{20}$

c. Yes, A and B are mutually exclusive because they cannot happen at the same time; you cannot pick a card that is both blue and also (red or green). $P(A\ \text{AND}\ B) = 0$

d. No, A and C are not mutually exclusive because they can occur at the same time. In fact, C includes all of the outcomes of A; if the card chosen is blue it is also (red or blue). $P(A\ \text{AND}\ C) = P(A) = \dfrac{3}{20}$

89

a. $S = \{(HHH),\ (HHT),\ (HTH),\ (HTT),\ (THH),\ (THT),\ (TTH),\ (TTT)\}$

b. $\dfrac{4}{8}$

c. Yes, because if A has occurred, it is impossible to obtain two tails. In other words, $P(A\ \text{AND}\ B) = 0$.

91

a. If Y and Z are independent, then $P(Y\ \text{AND}\ Z) = P(Y)P(Z)$, so $P(Y\ \text{OR}\ Z) = P(Y) + P(Z) - P(Y)P(Z)$.

b. 0.5

93 iii; i; iv; ii

95

a. $P(R) = 0.44$

b. $P(R|E) = 0.56$

c. $P(R|O) = 0.31$

d. No, whether the money is returned is not independent of which class the money was placed in. There are several ways to justify this mathematically, but one is that the money placed in economics classes is not returned at the same overall rate; $P(R|E) \neq P(R)$.

e. No, this study definitely does not support that notion; _in fact_, it suggests the opposite. The money placed in the economics classrooms was returned at a higher rate than the money place in all classes collectively; $P(R|E) > P(R)$.

97

a. $P(\text{type O OR Rh-}) = P(\text{type O}) + P(\text{Rh-}) - P(\text{type O AND Rh-})$

   $0.52 = 0.43 + 0.15 - P(\text{type O AND Rh-})$; solve to find $P(\text{type O AND Rh-}) = 0.06$

   6% of people have type O, Rh- blood

b. $P(\text{NOT(type O AND Rh-)}) = 1 - P(\text{type O AND Rh-}) = 1 - 0.06 = 0.94$

   94% of people do not have type O, Rh- blood

99

a. Let $C =$ be the event that the cookie contains chocolate. Let $N =$ the event that the cookie contains nuts.

b. $P(C\ \text{OR}\ N) = P(C) + P(N) - P(C\ \text{AND}\ N) = 0.36 + 0.12 - 0.08 = 0.40$

c. $P(\text{NEITHER chocolate NOR nuts}) = 1 - P(C\ \text{OR}\ N) = 1 - 0.40 = 0.60$

101 0

103 $\frac{10}{67}$

105 $\frac{10}{34}$

107 d

109

a.

Race and Sex	1–14	15–24	25–64	over 64	TOTALS
white, male	210	3,360	13,610	4,870	22,050
white, female	80	580	3,380	890	4,930
black, male	10	460	1,060	140	1,670
black, female	0	40	270	20	330
all others				100	
TOTALS	310	4,650	18,780	6,020	29,760

Table 3.26

b.

Race and Sex	1–14	15–24	25–64	over 64	TOTALS
white, male	210	3,360	13,610	4,870	22,050
white, female	80	580	3,380	890	4,930
black, male	10	460	1,060	140	1,670
black, female	0	40	270	20	330
all others	10	210	460	100	780
TOTALS	310	4,650	18,780	6,020	29,760

Table 3.27

c. $\frac{22,050}{29,760}$

d. $\frac{330}{29,760}$

e. $\frac{2,000}{29,760}$

f. $\frac{23,720}{29,760}$

g. $\frac{5,010}{6,020}$

111 b

113

a. $\frac{26}{106}$

b. $\frac{33}{106}$

c. $\frac{21}{106}$

d. $\left(\frac{26}{106}\right) + \left(\frac{33}{106}\right) - \left(\frac{21}{106}\right) = \left(\frac{38}{106}\right)$

e. $\frac{21}{33}$

115 a

118

a. $P(C) = 0.4567$

b. not enough information

c. not enough information

d. No, because over half (0.51) of men have at least one false positive text

120

a. $P(J \text{ OR } K) = P(J) + P(K) - P(J \text{ AND } K)$; $0.45 = 0.18 + 0.37 - P(J \text{ AND } K)$; solve to find $P(J \text{ AND } K) = 0.10$

b. $P(\text{NOT } (J \text{ AND } K)) = 1 - P(J \text{ AND } K) = 1 - 0.10 = 0.90$

c. $P(\text{NOT } (J \text{ OR } K)) = 1 - P(J \text{ OR } K) = 1 - 0.45 = 0.55$

121

a.

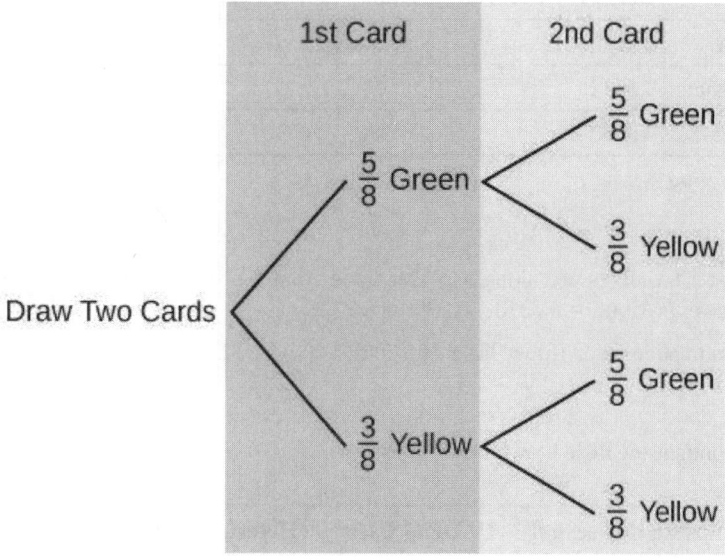

Figure 3.16

b. $P(GG) = \left(\frac{5}{8}\right)\left(\frac{5}{8}\right) = \frac{25}{64}$

c. $P(\text{at least one green}) = P(GG) + P(GY) + P(YG) = \frac{25}{64} + \frac{15}{64} + \frac{15}{64} = \frac{55}{64}$

d. $P(G|G) = \frac{5}{8}$

e. Yes, they are independent because the first card is placed back in the bag before the second card is drawn; the composition of cards in the bag remains the same from draw one to draw two.

123

	<20	20–64	>64	Totals
Female	0.0244	0.3954	0.0661	0.486
Male	0.0259	0.4186	0.0695	0.514
Totals	0.0503	0.8140	0.1356	1

Table 3.28

b. $P(F) = 0.486$

c. $P(>64|F) = 0.1361$

d. $P(>64 \text{ and } F) = P(F)\, P(>64|F) = (0.486)(0.1361) = 0.0661$

e. $P(>64|F)$ is the percentage of female drivers who are 65 or older and $P(>64 \text{ and } F)$ is the percentage of drivers who are female and 65 or older.

f. $P(>64) = P(>64 \text{ and } F) + P(>64 \text{ and } M) = 0.1356$

g. No, being female and 65 or older are not mutually exclusive because they can occur at the same time $P(>64 \text{ and } F) = 0.0661$.

125

a.

	Car, Truck or Van	Walk	Public Transportation	Other	Totals
Alone	0.7318				
Not Alone	0.1332				
Totals	0.8650	0.0390	0.0530	0.0430	1

Table 3.29

b. If we assume that all walkers are alone and that none from the other two groups travel alone (which is a big assumption) we have: $P(\text{Alone}) = 0.7318 + 0.0390 = 0.7708$.

c. Make the same assumptions as in (b) we have: $(0.7708)(1{,}000) = 771$

d. $(0.1332)(1{,}000) = 133$

127 The completed contingency table is as follows:

	Homosexual/Bisexual	IV Drug User*	Heterosexual Contact	Other	Totals
Female	0	70	136	49	**255**
Male	2,146	463	60	135	**2,804**
Totals	**2,146**	**533**	**196**	**184**	**3,059**

Table 3.30 * includes homosexual/bisexual IV drug users

a. $\dfrac{255}{3059}$

b. $\dfrac{196}{3059}$

c. $\dfrac{718}{3059}$

d. 0

e. $\frac{463}{3059}$

f. $\frac{136}{196}$

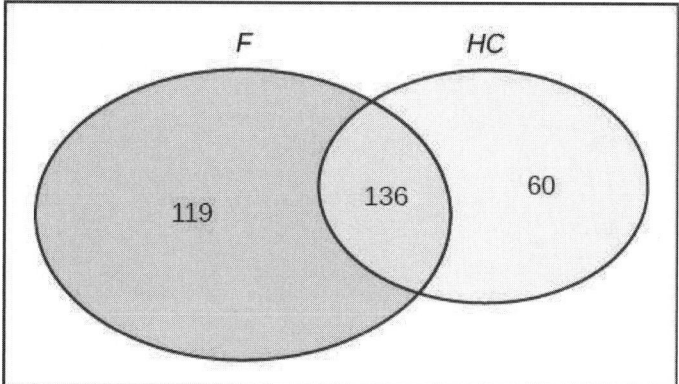

g.

Figure 3.17

4 | DISCRETE RANDOM VARIABLES

Figure 4.1 You can use probability and discrete random variables to calculate the likelihood of lightning striking the ground five times during a half-hour thunderstorm. (Credit: Leszek Leszczynski)

Introduction

Chapter Objectives
By the end of this chapter, the student should be able to: • Recognize and understand discrete probability distribution functions, in general. • Calculate and interpret expected values. • Recognize the binomial probability distribution and apply it appropriately. • Recognize the Poisson probability distribution and apply it appropriately. • Recognize the geometric probability distribution and apply it appropriately. • Recognize the hypergeometric probability distribution and apply it appropriately. • Classify discrete word problems by their distributions.

A student takes a ten-question, true-false quiz. Because the student had such a busy schedule, he or she could not study and guesses randomly at each answer. What is the probability of the student passing the test with at least a 70%?

Small companies might be interested in the number of long-distance phone calls their employees make during the peak time of the day. Suppose the average is 20 calls. What is the probability that the employees make more than 20 long-distance phone calls during the peak time?

These two examples illustrate two different types of probability problems involving discrete random variables. Recall that discrete data are data that you can count. A **random variable** describes the outcomes of a statistical experiment in words. The values of a random variable can vary with each repetition of an experiment.

Random Variable Notation

Upper case letters such as X or Y denote a random variable. Lower case letters like x or y denote the value of a random variable. If X **is a random variable, then** X **is written in words, and** x **is given as a number.**

For example, let X = the number of heads you get when you toss three fair coins. The sample space for the toss of three fair coins is *TTT*; *THH*; *HTH*; *HHT*; *HTT*; *THT*; *TTH*; *HHH*. Then, x = 0, 1, 2, 3. X is in words and x is a number. Notice that for this example, the x values are countable outcomes. Because you can count the possible values that X can take on and the outcomes are random (the x values 0, 1, 2, 3), X is a discrete random variable.

Collaborative Exercise

Toss a coin ten times and record the number of heads. After all members of the class have completed the experiment (tossed a coin ten times and counted the number of heads), fill in **Table 4.1**. Let X = the number of heads in ten tosses of the coin.

x	Frequency of x	Relative Frequency of x

Table 4.1

a. Which value(s) of x occurred most frequently?

b. If you tossed the coin 1,000 times, what values could x take on? Which value(s) of x do you think would occur most frequently?

c. What does the relative frequency column sum to?

4.1 | Probability Distribution Function (PDF) for a Discrete Random Variable

A discrete **probability distribution function** has two characteristics:

1. Each probability is between zero and one, inclusive.

2. The sum of the probabilities is one.

Example 4.1

A child psychologist is interested in the number of times a newborn baby's crying wakes its mother after midnight. For a random sample of 50 mothers, the following information was obtained. Let X = the number of times per week a newborn baby's crying wakes its mother after midnight. For this example, x = 0, 1, 2, 3, 4, 5.

$P(x)$ = probability that X takes on a value x.

x	P(x)
0	$P(x = 0) = \dfrac{2}{50}$
1	$P(x = 1) = \dfrac{11}{50}$
2	$P(x = 2) = \dfrac{23}{50}$
3	$P(x = 3) = \dfrac{9}{50}$
4	$P(x = 4) = \dfrac{4}{50}$
5	$P(x = 5) = \dfrac{1}{50}$

Table 4.2

X takes on the values 0, 1, 2, 3, 4, 5. This is a discrete PDF because:

a. Each $P(x)$ is between zero and one, inclusive.

b. The sum of the probabilities is one, that is,

$$\frac{2}{50} + \frac{11}{50} + \frac{23}{50} + \frac{9}{50} + \frac{4}{50} + \frac{1}{50} = 1$$

Try It Σ

4.1 A hospital researcher is interested in the number of times the average post-op patient will ring the nurse during a 12-hour shift. For a random sample of 50 patients, the following information was obtained. Let X = the number of times a patient rings the nurse during a 12-hour shift. For this exercise, x = 0, 1, 2, 3, 4, 5. $P(x)$ = the probability that X takes on value x. Why is this a discrete probability distribution function (two reasons)?

X	P(x)
0	$P(x = 0) = \dfrac{4}{50}$
1	$P(x = 1) = \dfrac{8}{50}$
2	$P(x = 2) = \dfrac{16}{50}$
3	$P(x = 3) = \dfrac{14}{50}$
4	$P(x = 4) = \dfrac{6}{50}$

Table 4.3

X	P(x)
5	$P(x = 5) = \frac{2}{50}$

Table 4.3

Example 4.2

Suppose Nancy has classes **three days** a week. She attends classes three days a week **80%** of the time, **two days 15%** of the time, **one day 4%** of the time, and **no days 1%** of the time. Suppose one week is randomly selected.

a. Let X = the number of days Nancy _____.

Solution 4.2
a. Let X = the number of days Nancy attends class per week.

b. X takes on what values?

Solution 4.2
b. 0, 1, 2, and 3

c. Suppose one week is randomly chosen. Construct a probability distribution table (called a PDF table) like the one in **Example 4.1**. The table should have two columns labeled x and $P(x)$. What does the $P(x)$ column sum to?

Solution 4.2
c.

x	P(x)
0	0.01
1	0.04
2	0.15
3	0.80

Table 4.4

Try It Σ

4.2 Jeremiah has basketball practice two days a week. Ninety percent of the time, he attends both practices. Eight percent of the time, he attends one practice. Two percent of the time, he does not attend either practice. What is X and what values does it take on?

4.2 | Mean or Expected Value and Standard Deviation

The **expected value** is often referred to as the **"long-term" average or mean**. This means that over the long term of doing an experiment over and over, you would **expect** this average.

You toss a coin and record the result. What is the probability that the result is heads? If you flip a coin two times, does probability tell you that these flips will result in one heads and one tail? You might toss a fair coin ten times and record nine heads. As you learned in **Section 3.**, probability does not describe the short-term results of an experiment. It gives information about what can be expected in the long term. To demonstrate this, Karl Pearson once tossed a fair coin 24,000 times! He recorded the results of each toss, obtaining heads 12,012 times. **In his experiment, Pearson illustrated the Law of Large Numbers**.

The Law of Large Numbers states that, as the number of trials in a probability experiment increases, the difference between the theoretical probability of an event and the relative frequency approaches zero **(the theoretical probability and the relative frequency get closer and closer together)**. When evaluating the long-term results of statistical experiments, we often want to know the "average" outcome. This "long-term average" is known as the **mean** or **expected value** of the experiment and is denoted by the Greek letter μ. In other words, after conducting many trials of an experiment, you would expect this average value.

NOTE

To find the expected value or long term average, μ, simply multiply each value of the random variable by its probability and add the products.

Example 4.3

A men's soccer team plays soccer zero, one, or two days a week. The probability that they play zero days is 0.2, the probability that they play one day is 0.5, and the probability that they play two days is 0.3. Find the long-term average or expected value, μ, of the number of days per week the men's soccer team plays soccer.

To do the problem, first let the random variable X = the number of days the men's soccer team plays soccer per week. X takes on the values 0, 1, 2. Construct a PDF table adding a column $x*P(x)$. In this column, you will multiply each x value by its probability.

x	P(x)	x*P(x)
0	0.2	(0)(0.2) = 0
1	0.5	(1)(0.5) = 0.5
2	0.3	(2)(0.3) = 0.6

Table 4.5 Expected Value Table This table is called an expected value table. The table helps you calculate the expected value or long-term average.

Add the last column $x*P(x)$ to find the long term average or expected value: $(0)(0.2) + (1)(0.5) + (2)(0.3) = 0 + 0.5 + 0.6 = 1.1$.

The expected value is 1.1. The men's soccer team would, on the average, expect to play soccer 1.1 days per week. The number 1.1 is the long-term average or expected value if the men's soccer team plays soccer week after week after week. We say $\mu = 1.1$.

Example 4.4

Find the expected value of the number of times a newborn baby's crying wakes its mother after midnight. The expected value is the expected number of times per week a newborn baby's crying wakes its mother after midnight. Calculate the standard deviation of the variable as well.

x	$P(x)$	$x*P(x)$	$(x - \mu)^2 \cdot P(x)$
0	$P(x = 0) = \dfrac{2}{50}$	$(0)\left(\dfrac{2}{50}\right) = 0$	$(0 - 2.1)^2 \cdot 0.04 = 0.1764$
1	$P(x = 1) = \left(\dfrac{11}{50}\right)$	$(1)\left(\dfrac{11}{50}\right) = \dfrac{11}{50}$	$(1 - 2.1)^2 \cdot 0.22 = 0.2662$
2	$P(x = 2) = \dfrac{23}{50}$	$(2)\left(\dfrac{23}{50}\right) = \dfrac{46}{50}$	$(2 - 2.1)^2 \cdot 0.46 = 0.0046$
3	$P(x = 3) = \dfrac{9}{50}$	$(3)\left(\dfrac{9}{50}\right) = \dfrac{27}{50}$	$(3 - 2.1)^2 \cdot 0.18 = 0.1458$
4	$P(x = 4) = \dfrac{4}{50}$	$(4)\left(\dfrac{4}{50}\right) = \dfrac{16}{50}$	$(4 - 2.1)^2 \cdot 0.08 = 0.2888$
5	$P(x = 5) = \dfrac{1}{50}$	$(5)\left(\dfrac{1}{50}\right) = \dfrac{5}{50}$	$(5 - 2.1)^2 \cdot 0.02 = 0.1682$

Table 4.6 You expect a newborn to wake its mother after midnight 2.1 times per week, on the average.

Add the values in the third column of the table to find the expected value of X:

μ = Expected Value = $\dfrac{105}{50}$ = 2.1

Use μ to complete the table. The fourth column of this table will provide the values you need to calculate the standard deviation. For each value x, multiply the square of its deviation by its probability. (Each deviation has the format $x - \mu$).

Add the values in the fourth column of the table:

0.1764 + 0.2662 + 0.0046 + 0.1458 + 0.2888 + 0.1682 = 1.05

The standard deviation of X is the square root of this sum: $\sigma = \sqrt{1.05} \approx 1.0247$

Try It Σ

4.4 A hospital researcher is interested in the number of times the average post-op patient will ring the nurse during a 12-hour shift. For a random sample of 50 patients, the following information was obtained. What is the expected value?

x	P(x)
0	$P(x = 0) = \frac{4}{50}$
1	$P(x = 1) = \frac{8}{50}$
2	$P(x = 2) = \frac{16}{50}$
3	$P(x = 3) = \frac{14}{50}$
4	$P(x = 4) = \frac{6}{50}$
5	$P(x = 5) = \frac{2}{50}$

Table 4.7

Example 4.5

Suppose you play a game of chance in which five numbers are chosen from 0, 1, 2, 3, 4, 5, 6, 7, 8, 9. A computer randomly selects five numbers from zero to nine with replacement. You pay $2 to play and could profit $100,000 if you match all five numbers in order (you get your $2 back plus $100,000). Over the long term, what is your **expected** profit of playing the game?

To do this problem, set up an expected value table for the amount of money you can profit.

Let X = the amount of money you profit. The values of x are not 0, 1, 2, 3, 4, 5, 6, 7, 8, 9. Since you are interested in your profit (or loss), the values of x are 100,000 dollars and −2 dollars.

To win, you must get all five numbers correct, in order. The probability of choosing one correct number is $\frac{1}{10}$ because there are ten numbers. You may choose a number more than once. The probability of choosing all five numbers correctly and in order is

$$\left(\frac{1}{10}\right)\left(\frac{1}{10}\right)\left(\frac{1}{10}\right)\left(\frac{1}{10}\right)\left(\frac{1}{10}\right) = (1)(10^{-5}) = 0.00001.$$

Therefore, the probability of winning is 0.00001 and the probability of losing is

$$1 - 0.00001 = 0.99999.$$

The expected value table is as follows:

	x	P(x)	x*P(x)
Loss	–2	0.99999	(–2)(0.99999) = –1.99998
Profit	100,000	0.00001	(100000)(0.00001) = 1

Table 4.8 Add the last column. –1.99998 + 1 = –0.99998

Since –0.99998 is about –1, you would, on average, expect to lose approximately $1 for each game you play. However, each time you play, you either lose $2 or profit $100,000. The $1 is the average or expected LOSS per game after playing this game over and over.

4.5 You are playing a game of chance in which four cards are drawn from a standard deck of 52 cards. You guess the suit of each card before it is drawn. The cards are replaced in the deck on each draw. You pay $1 to play. If you guess the right suit every time, you get your money back and $256. What is your expected profit of playing the game over the long term?

Example 4.6

Suppose you play a game with a biased coin. You play each game by tossing the coin once. $P(\text{heads}) = \frac{2}{3}$ and $P(\text{tails}) = \frac{1}{3}$. If you toss a head, you pay $6. If you toss a tail, you win $10. If you play this game many times, will you come out ahead?

a. Define a random variable X.

Solution 4.6
a. X = amount of profit

b. Complete the following expected value table.

	x		
WIN	10	$\frac{1}{3}$	_____
LOSE	____	_____	$\frac{-12}{3}$

Table 4.9

Solution 4.6
b.

	x	P(x)	xP(x)
WIN	10	$\frac{1}{3}$	$\frac{10}{3}$
LOSE	–6	$\frac{2}{3}$	$\frac{-12}{3}$

Table 4.10

c. What is the expected value, μ? Do you come out ahead?

Solution 4.6

c. Add the last column of the table. The expected value $\mu = \frac{-2}{3}$. You lose, on average, about 67 cents each time you play the game so you do not come out ahead.

Try It Σ

4.6 Suppose you play a game with a spinner. You play each game by spinning the spinner once. $P(\text{red}) = \frac{2}{5}$, $P(\text{blue}) = \frac{2}{5}$, and $P(\text{green}) = \frac{1}{5}$. If you land on red, you pay \$10. If you land on blue, you don't pay or win anything. If you land on green, you win \$10. Complete the following expected value table.

	x	P(x)	
Red			$-\frac{20}{5}$
Blue		$\frac{2}{5}$	
Green	10		

Table 4.11

Like data, probability distributions have standard deviations. To calculate the standard deviation (σ) of a probability distribution, find each deviation from its expected value, square it, multiply it by its probability, add the products, and take the square root. To understand how to do the calculation, look at the table for the number of days per week a men's soccer team plays soccer. To find the standard deviation, add the entries in the column labeled $(x - \mu)^2 P(x)$ and take the square root.

x	P(x)	x*P(x)	$(x - \mu)^2 P(x)$
0	0.2	(0)(0.2) = 0	$(0 - 1.1)^2(0.2) = 0.242$
1	0.5	(1)(0.5) = 0.5	$(1 - 1.1)^2(0.5) = 0.005$

Table 4.12

x	P(x)	x*P(x)	$(x - \mu)^2 P(x)$
2	0.3	(2)(0.3) = 0.6	$(2 - 1.1)^2(0.3) = 0.243$

Table 4.12

Add the last column in the table. 0.242 + 0.005 + 0.243 = 0.490. The standard deviation is the square root of 0.49, or $\sigma = \sqrt{0.49} = 0.7$

Generally for probability distributions, we use a calculator or a computer to calculate μ and σ to reduce roundoff error. For some probability distributions, there are short-cut formulas for calculating μ and σ.

Example 4.7

Toss a fair, six-sided die twice. Let X = the number of faces that show an even number. Construct a table like **Table 4.11** and calculate the mean μ and standard deviation σ of X.

Solution 4.7

Tossing one fair six-sided die twice has the same sample space as tossing two fair six-sided dice. The sample space has 36 outcomes:

(1, 1)	(1, 2)	(1, 3)	(1, 4)	(1, 5)	(1, 6)
(2, 1)	(2, 2)	(2, 3)	(2, 4)	(2, 5)	(2, 6)
(3, 1)	(3, 2)	(3, 3)	(3, 4)	(3, 5)	(3, 6)
(4, 1)	(4, 2)	(4, 3)	(4, 4)	(4, 5)	(4, 6)
(5, 1)	(5, 2)	(5, 3)	(5, 4)	(5, 5)	(5, 6)
(6, 1)	(6, 2)	(6, 3)	(6, 4)	(6, 5)	(6, 6)

Table 4.13

Use the sample space to complete the following table:

x	P(x)	xP(x)	$(x - \mu)^2 \cdot P(x)$
0	$\frac{9}{36}$	0	$(0 - 1)^2 \cdot \frac{9}{36} = \frac{9}{36}$
1	$\frac{18}{36}$	$\frac{18}{36}$	$(1 - 1)^2 \cdot \frac{18}{36} = 0$
2	$\frac{9}{36}$	$\frac{18}{36}$	$(1 - 1)^2 \cdot \frac{9}{36} = \frac{9}{36}$

Table 4.14 Calculating μ and σ.

Add the values in the third column to find the expected value: $\mu = \frac{36}{36} = 1$. Use this value to complete the fourth column.

Add the values in the fourth column and take the square root of the sum: $\sigma = \sqrt{\frac{18}{36}} \approx 0.7071$.

Example 4.8

On May 11, 2013 at 9:30 PM, the probability that moderate seismic activity (one moderate earthquake) would occur in the next 48 hours in Iran was about 21.42%. Suppose you make a bet that a moderate earthquake will occur in Iran during this period. If you win the bet, you win $50. If you lose the bet, you pay $20. Let X = the amount of profit from a bet.

$P(\text{win}) = P(\text{one moderate earthquake will occur}) = 21.42\%$

$P(\text{loss}) = P(\text{one moderate earthquake will } not \text{ occur}) = 100\% - 21.42\%$

If you bet many times, will you come out ahead? Explain your answer in a complete sentence using numbers. What is the standard deviation of X? Construct a table similar to **Table 4.12** and **Table 4.12** to help you answer these questions.

Solution 4.8

	x	$P(x)$	$x(Px)$	$(x-\mu)^2 P(x)$
win	50	0.2142	10.71	$[50 - (-5.006)]^2(0.2142) = 648.0964$
loss	-20	0.7858	-15.716	$[-20 - (-5.006)]^2(0.7858) = 176.6636$

Table 4.15

Mean = Expected Value = 10.71 + (−15.716) = −5.006.

If you make this bet many times under the same conditions, your long term outcome will be an average *loss* of $5.01 per bet.

Standard Deviation = $\sqrt{648.0964 + 176.6636} \approx 28.7186$

4.8 On May 11, 2013 at 9:30 PM, the probability that moderate seismic activity (one moderate earthquake) would occur in the next 48 hours in Japan was about 1.08%. As in **Example 4.8**, you bet that a moderate earthquake will occur in Japan during this period. If you win the bet, you win $100. If you lose the bet, you pay $10. Let X = the amount of profit from a bet. Find the mean and standard deviation of X.

Some of the more common discrete probability functions are binomial, geometric, hypergeometric, and Poisson. Most elementary courses do not cover the geometric, hypergeometric, and Poisson. Your instructor will let you know if he or she wishes to cover these distributions.

A probability distribution function is a pattern. You try to fit a probability problem into a **pattern** or distribution in order to perform the necessary calculations. These distributions are tools to make solving probability problems easier. Each distribution has its own special characteristics. Learning the characteristics enables you to distinguish among the different distributions.

4.3 | Binomial Distribution

There are three characteristics of a binomial experiment.

1. There are a fixed number of trials. Think of trials as repetitions of an experiment. The letter n denotes the number of trials.

2. There are only two possible outcomes, called "success" and "failure," for each trial. The letter p denotes the probability of a success on one trial, and q denotes the probability of a failure on one trial. $p + q = 1$.

3. The n trials are independent and are repeated using identical conditions. Because the n trials are independent, the outcome of one trial does not help in predicting the outcome of another trial. Another way of saying this is that for each individual trial, the probability, p, of a success and probability, q, of a failure remain the same. For example, randomly guessing at a true-false statistics question has only two outcomes. If a success is guessing correctly, then a failure is guessing incorrectly. Suppose Joe always guesses correctly on any statistics true-false question with probability $p =$ 0.6. Then, $q = 0.4$. This means that for every true-false statistics question Joe answers, his probability of success ($p =$ 0.6) and his probability of failure ($q = 0.4$) remain the same.

The outcomes of a binomial experiment fit a **binomial probability distribution**. The random variable $X =$ the number of successes obtained in the n independent trials.

The mean, μ, and variance, σ^2, for the binomial probability distribution are $\mu = np$ and $\sigma^2 = npq$. The standard deviation, σ, is then $\sigma = \sqrt{npq}$.

Any experiment that has characteristics two and three and where $n = 1$ is called a **Bernoulli Trial** (named after Jacob Bernoulli who, in the late 1600s, studied them extensively). A binomial experiment takes place when the number of successes is counted in one or more Bernoulli Trials.

Example 4.9

At ABC College, the withdrawal rate from an elementary physics course is 30% for any given term. This implies that, for any given term, 70% of the students stay in the class for the entire term. A "success" could be defined as an individual who withdrew. The random variable $X =$ the number of students who withdraw from the randomly selected elementary physics class.

4.9 The state health board is concerned about the amount of fruit available in school lunches. Forty-eight percent of schools in the state offer fruit in their lunches every day. This implies that 52% do not. What would a "success" be in this case?

Example 4.10

Suppose you play a game that you can only either win or lose. The probability that you win any game is 55%, and the probability that you lose is 45%. Each game you play is independent. If you play the game 20 times, write the function that describes the probability that you win 15 of the 20 times. Here, if you define X as the number of wins, then X takes on the values 0, 1, 2, 3, ..., 20. The probability of a success is $p = 0.55$. The probability of a failure is $q = 0.45$. The number of trials is $n = 20$. The probability question can be stated mathematically as $P(x = 15)$.

4.10 A trainer is teaching a dolphin to do tricks. The probability that the dolphin successfully performs the trick is 35%, and the probability that the dolphin does not successfully perform the trick is 65%. Out of 20 attempts, you want to find the probability that the dolphin succeeds 12 times. State the probability question mathematically.

Example 4.11

A fair coin is flipped 15 times. Each flip is independent. What is the probability of getting more than ten heads?

Let X = the number of heads in 15 flips of the fair coin. X takes on the values 0, 1, 2, 3, ..., 15. Since the coin is fair, $p = 0.5$ and $q = 0.5$. The number of trials is $n = 15$. State the probability question mathematically.

Solution 4.11
$P(x > 10)$

Try It Σ

4.11 A fair, six-sided die is rolled ten times. Each roll is independent. You want to find the probability of rolling a one more than three times. State the probability question mathematically.

Example 4.12

Approximately 70% of statistics students do their homework in time for it to be collected and graded. Each student does homework independently. In a statistics class of 50 students, what is the probability that at least 40 will do their homework on time? Students are selected randomly.

a. This is a binomial problem because there is only a success or a _____, there are a fixed number of trials, and the probability of a success is 0.70 for each trial.

Solution 4.12
a. failure

b. If we are interested in the number of students who do their homework on time, then how do we define X?

Solution 4.12
b. X = the number of statistics students who do their homework on time

c. What values does x take on?

Solution 4.12
c. 0, 1, 2, ..., 50

d. What is a "failure," in words?

Solution 4.12

d. Failure is defined as a student who does not complete his or her homework on time.

The probability of a success is $p = 0.70$. The number of trials is $n = 50$.

e. If $p + q = 1$, then what is q?

Solution 4.12
e. $q = 0.30$

f. The words "at least" translate as what kind of inequality for the probability question $P(x \_\_\_\_ 40)$.

Solution 4.12
f. greater than or equal to ($\geq$)

The probability question is $P(x \geq 40)$.

 **Try It** Σ

4.12 Sixty-five percent of people pass the state driver's exam on the first try. A group of 50 individuals who have taken the driver's exam is randomly selected. Give two reasons why this is a binomial problem.

Notation for the Binomial: B = Binomial Probability Distribution Function

$X \sim B(n, p)$

Read this as "X is a random variable with a binomial distribution." The parameters are n and p; n = number of trials, p = probability of a success on each trial.

Example 4.13

It has been stated that about 41% of adult workers have a high school diploma but do not pursue any further education. If 20 adult workers are randomly selected, find the probability that at most 12 of them have a high school diploma but do not pursue any further education. How many adult workers do you expect to have a high school diploma but do not pursue any further education?

Let X = the number of workers who have a high school diploma but do not pursue any further education.

X takes on the values 0, 1, 2, ..., 20 where n = 20, p = 0.41, and q = 1 – 0.41 = 0.59. $X \sim B(20, 0.41)$

Find $P(x \leq 12)$. $P(x \leq 12)$ = 0.9738. (calculator or computer)

 Using the TI-83, 83+, 84, 84+ Calculator

Go into 2nd DISTR. The syntax for the instructions are as follows:

To calculate (x = value): binompdf(n, p, number) if "number" is left out, the result is the binomial probability table.
To calculate $P(x \leq$ value): binomcdf(n, p, number) if "number" is left out, the result is the cumulative binomial probability table.
For this problem: After you are in 2nd DISTR, arrow down to binomcdf. Press ENTER. Enter 20,0.41,12). The result is $P(x \leq 12)$ = 0.9738.

> **NOTE**
>
> If you want to find $P(x = 12)$, use the pdf (binompdf). If you want to find $P(x > 12)$, use 1 - binomcdf(20,0.41,12).

The probability that at most 12 workers have a high school diploma but do not pursue any further education is 0.9738.

The graph of $X \sim B(20, 0.41)$ is as follows:

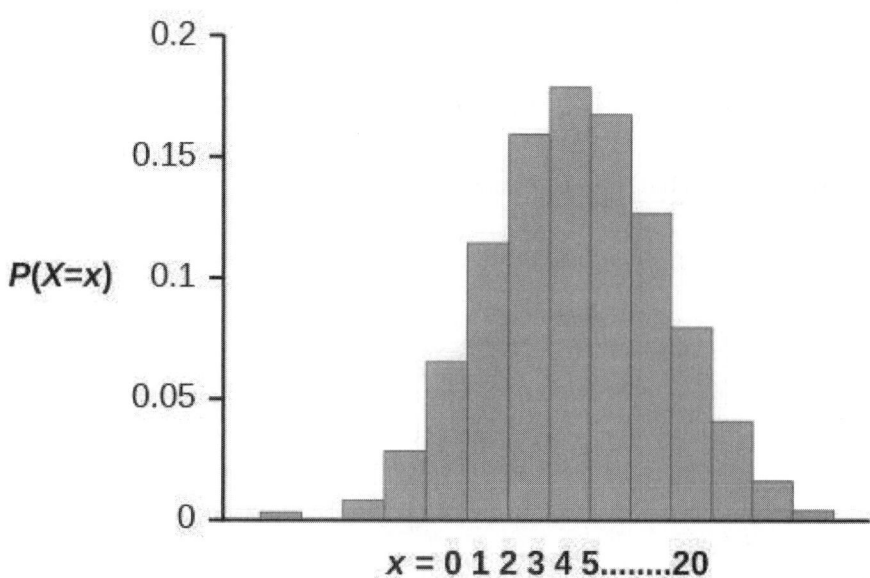

Figure 4.2

The *y*-axis contains the probability of *x*, where *X* = the number of workers who have only a high school diploma.

The number of adult workers that you expect to have a high school diploma but not pursue any further education is the mean, $\mu = np = (20)(0.41) = 8.2$.

The formula for the variance is $\sigma^2 = npq$. The standard deviation is $\sigma = \sqrt{npq}$.

$\sigma = \sqrt{(20)(0.41)(0.59)} = 2.20$.

Try It Σ

☞ **4.13** About 32% of students participate in a community volunteer program outside of school. If 30 students are selected at random, find the probability that at most 14 of them participate in a community volunteer program outside of school. Use the TI-83+ or TI-84 calculator to find the answer.

Example 4.14

In the 2013 *Jerry's Artarama* art supplies catalog, there are 560 pages. Eight of the pages feature signature artists. Suppose we randomly sample 100 pages. Let *X* = the number of pages that feature signature artists.

  a. What values does *x* take on?

  b. What is the probability distribution? Find the following probabilities:

   i. the probability that two pages feature signature artists

   ii. the probability that at most six pages feature signature artists

   iii. the probability that more than three pages feature signature artists.

  c. Using the formulas, calculate the (i) mean and (ii) standard deviation.

Solution 4.14
  a. *x* = 0, 1, 2, 3, 4, 5, 6, 7, 8

b. $X \sim B\left(100, \frac{8}{560}\right)$

    i. $P(x = 2) = \text{binompdf}\left(100, \frac{8}{560}, 2\right) = 0.2466$

    ii. $P(x \leq 6) = \text{binomcdf}\left(100, \frac{8}{560}, 6\right) = 0.9994$

    iii. $P(x > 3) = 1 - P(x \leq 3) = 1 - \text{binomcdf}\left(100, \frac{8}{560}, 3\right) = 1 - 0.9443 = 0.0557$

c.   i. Mean $= np = (100)\left(\frac{8}{560}\right) = \frac{800}{560} \approx 1.4286$

    ii. Standard Deviation $= \sqrt{npq} = \sqrt{(100)\left(\frac{8}{560}\right)\left(\frac{552}{560}\right)} \approx 1.1867$

Try It Σ

4.14 According to a Gallup poll, 60% of American adults prefer saving over spending. Let X = the number of American adults out of a random sample of 50 who prefer saving to spending.

a. What is the probability distribution for X?

b. Use your calculator to find the following probabilities:

    i. the probability that 25 adults in the sample prefer saving over spending

    ii. the probability that at most 20 adults prefer saving

    iii. the probability that more than 30 adults prefer saving

c. Using the formulas, calculate the (i) mean and (ii) standard deviation of X.

Example 4.15

The lifetime risk of developing pancreatic cancer is about one in 78 (1.28%). Suppose we randomly sample 200 people. Let X = the number of people who will develop pancreatic cancer.

a. What is the probability distribution for X?

b. Using the formulas, calculate the (i) mean and (ii) standard deviation of X.

c. Use your calculator to find the probability that at most eight people develop pancreatic cancer

d. Is it more likely that five or six people will develop pancreatic cancer? Justify your answer numerically.

Solution 4.15

a. $X \sim B(200, 0.0128)$

b.   i. Mean $= np = 200(0.0128) = 2.56$

    ii. Standard Deviation $= \sqrt{npq} = \sqrt{(200)(0.0128)(0.9872)} \approx 1.5897$

c. Using the TI-83, 83+, 84 calculator with instructions as provided in **Example 4.13**:
$P(x \leq 8) = \text{binomcdf}(200, 0.0128, 8) = 0.9988$

d. $P(x = 5) = \text{binompdf}(200, 0.0128, 5) = 0.0707$
$P(x = 6) = \text{binompdf}(200, 0.0128, 6) = 0.0298$
So $P(x = 5) > P(x = 6)$; it is more likely that five people will develop cancer than six.

4.15 During the 2013 regular NBA season, DeAndre Jordan of the Los Angeles Clippers had the highest field goal completion rate in the league. DeAndre scored with 61.3% of his shots. Suppose you choose a random sample of 80 shots made by DeAndre during the 2013 season. Let X = the number of shots that scored points.

   a. What is the probability distribution for X?

   b. Using the formulas, calculate the (i) mean and (ii) standard deviation of X.

   c. Use your calculator to find the probability that DeAndre scored with 60 of these shots.

   d. Find the probability that DeAndre scored with more than 50 of these shots.

Example 4.16

The following example illustrates a problem that is **not** binomial. It violates the condition of independence. ABC College has a student advisory committee made up of ten staff members and six students. The committee wishes to choose a chairperson and a recorder. What is the probability that the chairperson and recorder are both students? The names of all committee members are put into a box, and two names are drawn **without replacement**. The first name drawn determines the chairperson and the second name the recorder. There are two trials. However, the trials are not independent because the outcome of the first trial affects the outcome of the second trial. The probability of a student on the first draw is $\frac{6}{16}$. The probability of a student on the second draw is $\frac{5}{15}$, when the first draw selects a student. The probability is $\frac{6}{15}$, when the first draw selects a staff member. The probability of drawing a student's name changes for each of the trials and, therefore, violates the condition of independence.

4.16 A lacrosse team is selecting a captain. The names of all the seniors are put into a hat, and the first three that are drawn will be the captains. The names are not replaced once they are drawn (one person cannot be two captains). You want to see if the captains all play the same position. State whether this is binomial or not and state why.

4.4 | Geometric Distribution

There are three main characteristics of a geometric experiment.

1. There are one or more Bernoulli trials with all failures except the last one, which is a success. In other words, you keep repeating what you are doing until the first success. Then you stop. For example, you throw a dart at a bullseye until you hit the bullseye. The first time you hit the bullseye is a "success" so you stop throwing the dart. It might take six tries until you hit the bullseye. You can think of the trials as failure, failure, failure, failure, failure, success, STOP.

2. In theory, the number of trials could go on forever. There must be at least one trial.

3. The probability, p, of a success and the probability, q, of a failure is the same for each trial. $p + q = 1$ and $q = 1 - p$. For example, the probability of rolling a three when you throw one fair die is $\frac{1}{6}$. This is true no matter how many times you roll the die. Suppose you want to know the probability of getting the first three on the fifth roll. On rolls one through four, you do not get a face with a three. The probability for each of the rolls is $q = \frac{5}{6}$, the probability of a failure. The probability of getting a three on the fifth roll is $\left(\frac{5}{6}\right)\left(\frac{5}{6}\right)\left(\frac{5}{6}\right)\left(\frac{5}{6}\right)\left(\frac{1}{6}\right) = 0.0804$

X = the number of independent trials until the first success.

Example 4.17

You play a game of chance that you can either win or lose (there are no other possibilities) **until** you lose. Your probability of losing is $p = 0.57$. What is the probability that it takes five games until you lose? Let X = the number of games you play until you lose (includes the losing game). Then X takes on the values 1, 2, 3, ... (could go on indefinitely). The probability question is $P(x = 5)$.

4.17 You throw darts at a board until you hit the center area. Your probability of hitting the center area is $p = 0.17$. You want to find the probability that it takes eight throws until you hit the center. What values does X take on?

Example 4.18

A safety engineer feels that 35% of all industrial accidents in her plant are caused by failure of employees to follow instructions. She decides to look at the accident reports (selected randomly and replaced in the pile after reading) **until** she finds one that shows an accident caused by failure of employees to follow instructions. On average, how many reports would the safety engineer **expect** to look at until she finds a report showing an accident caused by employee failure to follow instructions? What is the probability that the safety engineer will have to examine at least three reports until she finds a report showing an accident caused by employee failure to follow instructions?

Let X = the number of accidents the safety engineer must examine **until** she finds a report showing an accident caused by employee failure to follow instructions. X takes on the values 1, 2, 3, ... The first question asks you to find the **expected value** or the mean. The second question asks you to find $P(x \geq 3)$. ("At least" translates to a "greater than or equal to" symbol).

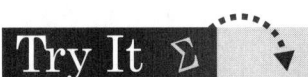

4.18 An instructor feels that 15% of students get below a C on their final exam. She decides to look at final exams (selected randomly and replaced in the pile after reading) until she finds one that shows a grade below a C. We want to know the probability that the instructor will have to examine at least ten exams until she finds one with a grade below a C. What is the probability question stated mathematically?

Example 4.19

Suppose that you are looking for a student at your college who lives within five miles of you. You know that 55% of the 25,000 students do live within five miles of you. You randomly contact students from the college **until** one says he or she lives within five miles of you. What is the probability that you need to contact four people?

This is a geometric problem because you may have a number of failures before you have the one success you desire. Also, the probability of a success stays the same each time you ask a student if he or she lives within five miles of you. There is no definite number of trials (number of times you ask a student).

a. Let X = the number of _____ you must ask _____ one says yes.

Solution 4.19
a. Let X = the number of **students** you must ask **until** one says yes.

b. What values does X take on?

Solution 4.19
b. 1, 2, 3, …, (total number of students)

c. What are p and q?

Solution 4.19
c. $p = 0.55$; $q = 0.45$

d. The probability question is $P(\underline{\hspace{1cm}})$.

Solution 4.19
d. $P(x = 4)$

 Try It Σ

4.19 You need to find a store that carries a special printer ink. You know that of the stores that carry printer ink, 10% of them carry the special ink. You randomly call each store until one has the ink you need. What are p and q?

Notation for the Geometric: G = Geometric Probability Distribution Function

$X \sim G(p)$

Read this as "X is a random variable with a **geometric distribution**." The parameter is p; p = the probability of a success for each trial.

Example 4.20

Assume that the probability of a defective computer component is 0.02. Components are randomly selected. Find the probability that the first defect is caused by the seventh component tested. How many components do you expect to test until one is found to be defective?

Let X = the number of computer components tested until the first defect is found.

X takes on the values 1, 2, 3, ... where $p = 0.02$. $X \sim G(0.02)$

Find $P(x = 7)$. $P(x = 7) = 0.0177$.

 Using the TI-83, 83+, 84, 84+ Calculator

To find the probability that $x = 7$,

- Enter 2nd, DISTR
- Scroll down and select geometpdf(
- Press ENTER
- Enter 0.02, 7); press ENTER to see the result: $P(x = 7) = 0.0177$

To find the probability that $x \leq 7$, follow the same instructions EXCEPT select E:geometcdf(as the distribution function.

The probability that the seventh component is the first defect is 0.0177.

The graph of $X \sim G(0.02)$ is:

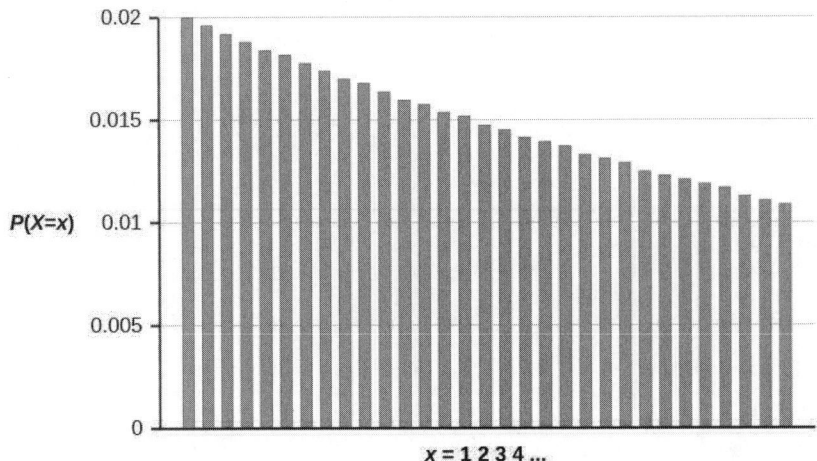

Figure 4.3

The y-axis contains the probability of x, where X = the number of computer components tested.

The number of components that you would expect to test until you find the first defective one is the mean, $\mu = 50$.

The formula for the mean is $\mu = \frac{1}{p} = \frac{1}{0.02} = 50$

The formula for the variance is $\sigma^2 = \left(\frac{1}{p}\right)\left(\frac{1}{p} - 1\right) = \left(\frac{1}{0.02}\right)\left(\frac{1}{0.02} - 1\right) = 2{,}450$

The standard deviation is $\sigma = \sqrt{\left(\frac{1}{p}\right)\left(\frac{1}{p} - 1\right)} = \sqrt{\left(\frac{1}{0.02}\right)\left(\frac{1}{0.02} - 1\right)} = 49.5$

☞ **4.20** The probability of a defective steel rod is 0.01. Steel rods are selected at random. Find the probability that the first defect occurs on the ninth steel rod. Use the TI-83+ or TI-84 calculator to find the answer.

Example 4.21

The lifetime risk of developing pancreatic cancer is about one in 78 (1.28%). Let X = the number of people you ask until one says he or she has pancreatic cancer. Then X is a discrete random variable with a geometric distribution: $X \sim G\left(\frac{1}{78}\right)$ or $X \sim G(0.0128)$.

   a. What is the probability of that you ask ten people before one says he or she has pancreatic cancer?

   b. What is the probability that you must ask 20 people?

   c. Find the (i) mean and (ii) standard deviation of X.

Solution 4.21

a. $P(x = 10)$ = geometpdf(0.0128, 10) = 0.0114

b. $P(x = 20)$ = geometpdf(0.0128, 20) = 0.01

c.   i.   Mean = $\mu = \frac{1}{p} = \frac{1}{0.0128} = 78$

    ii.   Standard Deviation = $\sigma = \sqrt{\frac{1-p}{p^2}} = \sqrt{\frac{1-0.0128}{0.0128^2}} \approx 77.6234$

Try It Σ

4.21 The literacy rate for a nation measures the proportion of people age 15 and over who can read and write. The literacy rate for women in Afghanistan is 12%. Let X = the number of Afghani women you ask until one says that she is literate.

a. What is the probability distribution of X?

b. What is the probability that you ask five women before one says she is literate?

c. What is the probability that you must ask ten women?

d. Find the (i) mean and (ii) standard deviation of X.

4.5 | Hypergeometric Distribution

There are five characteristics of a hypergeometric experiment.

1. You take samples from **two** groups.

2. You are concerned with a group of interest, called the first group.

3. You sample **without replacement** from the combined groups. For example, you want to choose a softball team from a combined group of 11 men and 13 women. The team consists of ten players.

4. Each pick is **not** independent, since sampling is without replacement. In the softball example, the probability of picking a woman first is $\frac{13}{24}$. The probability of picking a man second is $\frac{11}{23}$ if a woman was picked first. It is $\frac{10}{23}$ if a man was picked first. The probability of the second pick depends on what happened in the first pick.

5. You are **not** dealing with Bernoulli Trials.

The outcomes of a hypergeometric experiment fit a **hypergeometric probability** distribution. The random variable X = the number of items from the group of interest.

Example 4.22

A candy dish contains 100 jelly beans and 80 gumdrops. Fifty candies are picked at random. What is the probability that 35 of the 50 are gumdrops? The two groups are jelly beans and gumdrops. Since the probability question asks for the probability of picking gumdrops, the group of interest (first group) is gumdrops. The size of the group of interest (first group) is 80. The size of the second group is 100. The size of the sample is 50 (jelly beans or gumdrops). Let X = the number of gumdrops in the sample of 50. X takes on the values $x = 0, 1, 2, ...,$ 50. What is the probability statement written mathematically?

Solution 4.22

$P(x = 35)$

4.22 A bag contains letter tiles. Forty-four of the tiles are vowels, and 56 are consonants. Seven tiles are picked at random. You want to know the probability that four of the seven tiles are vowels. What is the group of interest, the size of the group of interest, and the size of the sample?

Example 4.23

Suppose a shipment of 100 DVD players is known to have ten defective players. An inspector randomly chooses 12 for inspection. He is interested in determining the probability that, among the 12 players, at most two are defective. The two groups are the 90 non-defective DVD players and the 10 defective DVD players. The group of interest (first group) is the defective group because the probability question asks for the probability of at most two defective DVD players. The size of the sample is 12 DVD players. (They may be non-defective or defective.) Let X = the number of defective DVD players in the sample of 12. X takes on the values 0, 1, 2, ..., 10. X may not take on the values 11 or 12. The sample size is 12, but there are only 10 defective DVD players. Write the probability statement mathematically.

Solution 4.23
$P(x \le 2)$

4.23 A gross of eggs contains 144 eggs. A particular gross is known to have 12 cracked eggs. An inspector randomly chooses 15 for inspection. She wants to know the probability that, among the 15, at most three are cracked. What is X, and what values does it take on?

Example 4.24

You are president of an on-campus special events organization. You need a committee of seven students to plan a special birthday party for the president of the college. Your organization consists of 18 women and 15 men. You are interested in the number of men on your committee. If the members of the committee are randomly selected, what is the probability that your committee has more than four men?

This is a hypergeometric problem because you are choosing your committee from two groups (men and women).

a. Are you choosing with or without replacement?

Solution 4.24
a. without

b. What is the group of interest?

Solution 4.24
b. the men

c. How many are in the group of interest?

Solution 4.24
c. 15 men

d. How many are in the other group?

Solution 4.24
d. 18 women

e. Let X = _____ on the committee. What values does X take on?

Solution 4.24
e. Let X = **the number of men** on the committee. x = 0, 1, 2, …, 7.

f. The probability question is P(_____).

Solution 4.24
f. $P(x > 4)$

4.24 A palette has 200 milk cartons. Of the 200 cartons, it is known that ten of them have leaked and cannot be sold. A stock clerk randomly chooses 18 for inspection. He wants to know the probability that among the 18, no more than two are leaking. Give five reasons why this is a hypergeometric problem.

Notation for the Hypergeometric: H = Hypergeometric Probability Distribution Function

$X \sim H(r, b, n)$

Read this as "X is a random variable with a hypergeometric distribution." The parameters are r, b, and n; r = the size of the group of interest (first group), b = the size of the second group, n = the size of the chosen sample.

Example 4.25

A school site committee is to be chosen randomly from six men and five women. If the committee consists of four members chosen randomly, what is the probability that two of them are men? How many men do you expect to be on the committee?

Let X = the number of men on the committee of four. The men are the group of interest (first group).

X takes on the values 0, 1, 2, 3, 4, where r = 6, b = 5, and n = 4. $X \sim H(6, 5, 4)$

Find $P(x = 2)$. $P(x = 2) = 0.4545$ (calculator or computer)

> **NOTE**
>
> Currently, the TI-83+ and TI-84 do not have hypergeometric probability functions. There are a number of computer packages, including Microsoft Excel, that do.

The probability that there are two men on the committee is about 0.45.

The graph of $X \sim H(6, 5, 4)$ is:

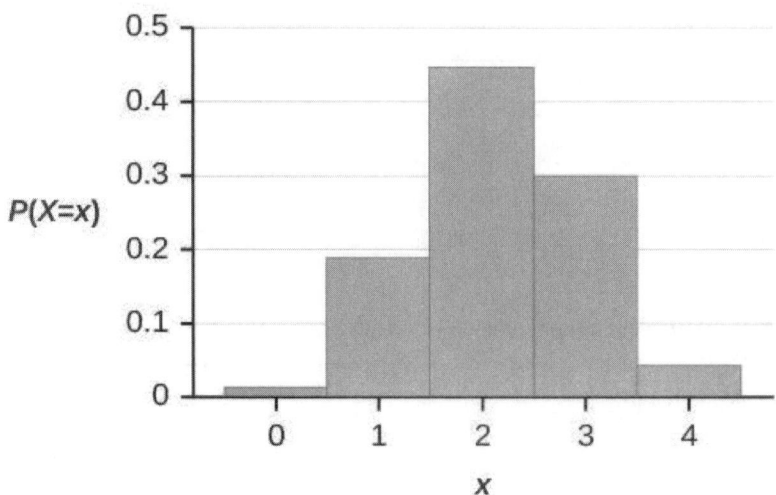

Figure 4.4

The y-axis contains the probability of X, where X = the number of men on the committee.

You would expect $m = 2.18$ (about two) men on the committee.

The formula for the mean is $\mu = \dfrac{nr}{r + b} = \dfrac{(4)(6)}{6 + 5} = 2.18$

4.25 An intramural basketball team is to be chosen randomly from 15 boys and 12 girls. The team has ten slots. You want to know the probability that eight of the players will be boys. What is the group of interest and the sample?

4.6 | Poisson Distribution

There are two main characteristics of a Poisson experiment.

1. The **Poisson probability distribution** gives the probability of a number of events occurring in a **fixed interval** of time or space if these events happen with a known average rate and independently of the time since the last event. For example, a book editor might be interested in the number of words spelled incorrectly in a particular book. It might be that, on the average, there are five words spelled incorrectly in 100 pages. The interval is the 100 pages.

2. The Poisson distribution may be used to approximate the binomial if the probability of success is "small" (such as 0.01) and the number of trials is "large" (such as 1,000). You will verify the relationship in the homework exercises. n is the number of trials, and p is the probability of a "success."

The random variable X = the number of occurrences in the interval of interest.

Example 4.26

The average number of loaves of bread put on a shelf in a bakery in a half-hour period is 12. Of interest is the number of loaves of bread put on the shelf in five minutes. The time interval of interest is five minutes. What is the probability that the number of loaves, selected randomly, put on the shelf in five minutes is three?

Let X = the number of loaves of bread put on the shelf in five minutes. If the average number of loaves put on the shelf in 30 minutes (half-hour) is 12, **then the average number of loaves put on the shelf in five minutes is** $\left(\frac{5}{30}\right)(12) = 2$ loaves of bread.

The probability question asks you to find $P(x = 3)$.

4.26 The average number of fish caught in an hour is eight. Of interest is the number of fish caught in 15 minutes. The time interval of interest is 15 minutes. What is the average number of fish caught in 15 minutes?

Example 4.27

A bank expects to receive six bad checks per day, on average. What is the probability of the bank getting fewer than five bad checks on any given day? Of interest is the number of checks the bank receives in one day, so the time interval of interest is one day. Let X = the number of bad checks the bank receives in one day. If the bank expects to receive six bad checks per day then the average is six checks per day. Write a mathematical statement for the probability question.

Solution 4.27
$P(x < 5)$

4.27 An electronics store expects to have ten returns per day on average. The manager wants to know the probability of the store getting fewer than eight returns on any given day. State the probability question mathematically.

Example 4.28

You notice that a news reporter says "uh," on average, two times per broadcast. What is the probability that the news reporter says "uh" more than two times per broadcast.

This is a Poisson problem because you are interested in knowing the number of times the news reporter says "uh" during a broadcast.

a. What is the interval of interest?

Solution 4.28
a. one broadcast

b. What is the average number of times the news reporter says "uh" during one broadcast?

Solution 4.28
b. 2

c. Let X = _____. What values does X take on?

Solution 4.28

c. Let X = the number of times the news reporter says "uh" during one broadcast.

$x = 0, 1, 2, 3, ...$

d. The probability question is $P(_____)$.

Solution 4.28

d. $P(x > 2)$

4.28 An emergency room at a particular hospital gets an average of five patients per hour. A doctor wants to know the probability that the ER gets more than five patients per hour. Give the reason why this would be a Poisson distribution.

Notation for the Poisson: P = Poisson Probability Distribution Function

$X \sim P(\mu)$

Read this as "X is a random variable with a Poisson distribution." The parameter is μ (or λ); μ (or λ) = the mean for the interval of interest.

Example 4.29

Leah's answering machine receives about six telephone calls between 8 a.m. and 10 a.m. What is the probability that Leah receives more than one call **in the next 15 minutes?**

Let X = the number of calls Leah receives in 15 minutes. (The **interval of interest** is 15 minutes or $\frac{1}{4}$ hour.)

$x = 0, 1, 2, 3, ...$

If Leah receives, on the average, six telephone calls in two hours, and there are eight 15 minute intervals in two hours, then Leah receives

$\left(\frac{1}{8}\right)(6) = 0.75$ calls in 15 minutes, on average. So, $\mu = 0.75$ for this problem.

$X \sim P(0.75)$

Find $P(x > 1)$. $P(x > 1) = 0.1734$ (calculator or computer)

 Using the TI-83, 83+, 84, 84+ Calculator

- Press 1 – and then press 2nd DISTR.
- Arrow down to poissoncdf. Press ENTER.
- Enter (.75,1).
- The result is $P(x > 1) = 0.1734$.

> **NOTE**
>
> The TI calculators use λ (lambda) for the mean.

The probability that Leah receives more than one telephone call in the next 15 minutes is about 0.1734:
$P(x > 1) = 1 - \text{poissoncdf}(0.75, 1)$.

The graph of $X \sim P(0.75)$ is:

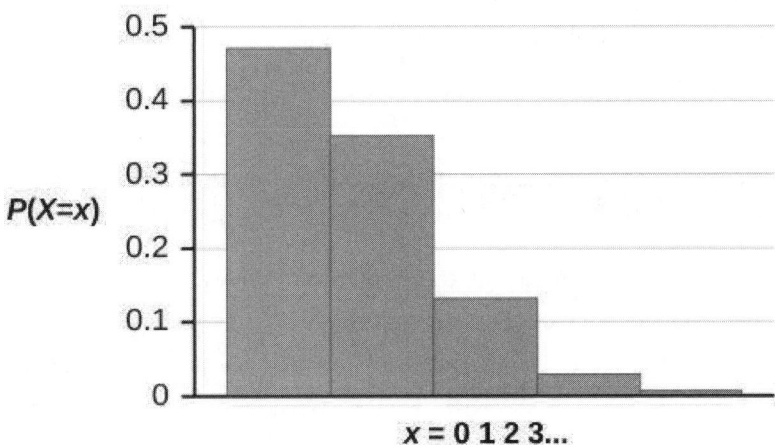

Figure 4.5

The y-axis contains the probability of x where X = the number of calls in 15 minutes.

Try It Σ

4.29 A customer service center receives about ten emails every half-hour. What is the probability that the customer service center receives more than four emails in the next six minutes? Use the TI-83+ or TI-84 calculator to find the answer.

Example 4.30

According to Baydin, an email management company, an email user gets, on average, 147 emails per day. Let X = the number of emails an email user receives per day. The discrete random variable X takes on the values $x = 0$, 1, 2 …. The random variable X has a Poisson distribution: $X \sim P(147)$. The mean is 147 emails.

a. What is the probability that an email user receives exactly 160 emails per day?

b. What is the probability that an email user receives at most 160 emails per day?

c. What is the standard deviation?

Solution 4.30

a. $P(x = 160) = \text{poissonpdf}(147, 160) \approx 0.0180$

b. $P(x \leq 160) = \text{poissoncdf}(147, 160) \approx 0.8666$

c. Standard Deviation = $\sigma = \sqrt{\mu} = \sqrt{147} \approx 12.1244$

Try It Σ

4.30 According to a recent poll by the Pew Internet Project, girls between the ages of 14 and 17 send an average of 187 text messages each day. Let X = the number of texts that a girl aged 14 to 17 sends per day. The discrete random variable X takes on the values x = 0, 1, 2 …. The random variable X has a Poisson distribution: $X \sim P(187)$. The mean is 187 text messages.

a. What is the probability that a teen girl sends exactly 175 texts per day?

b. What is the probability that a teen girl sends at most 150 texts per day?

c. What is the standard deviation?

Example 4.31

Text message users receive or send an average of 41.5 text messages per day.

a. How many text messages does a text message user receive or send per hour?

b. What is the probability that a text message user receives or sends two messages per hour?

c. What is the probability that a text message user receives or sends more than two messages per hour?

Solution 4.31

a. Let X = the number of texts that a user sends or receives in one hour. The average number of texts received per hour is $\frac{41.5}{24} \approx 1.7292$.

b. $X \sim P(1.7292)$, so $P(x = 2)$ = poissonpdf(1.7292, 2) ≈ 0.2653

c. $P(x > 2) = 1 - P(x \le 2) = 1 -$ poissoncdf(1.7292, 2) $\approx 1 - 0.7495 = 0.2505$

Try It Σ

4.31 Atlanta's Hartsfield-Jackson International Airport is the busiest airport in the world. On average there are 2,500 arrivals and departures each day.

a. How many airplanes arrive and depart the airport per hour?

b. What is the probability that there are exactly 100 arrivals and departures in one hour?

c. What is the probability that there are at most 100 arrivals and departures in one hour?

Example 4.32

On May 13, 2013, starting at 4:30 PM, the probability of low seismic activity for the next 48 hours in Alaska was reported as about 1.02%. Use this information for the next 200 days to find the probability that there will be low seismic activity in ten of the next 200 days. Use both the binomial and Poisson distributions to calculate the probabilities. Are they close?

Solution 4.32

Let X = the number of days with low seismic activity.

Using the binomial distribution:

- $P(x = 10) = \text{binompdf}(200, .0102, 10) \approx 0.000039$

Using the Poisson distribution:

- Calculate $\mu = np = 200(0.0102) \approx 2.04$

- $P(x = 10) = \text{poissonpdf}(2.04, 10) \approx 0.000045$

We expect the approximation to be good because n is large (greater than 20) and p is small (less than 0.05). The results are close—both probabilities reported are almost 0.

4.32 On May 13, 2013, starting at 4:30 PM, the probability of moderate seismic activity for the next 48 hours in the Kuril Islands off the coast of Japan was reported at about 1.43%. Use this information for the next 100 days to find the probability that there will be low seismic activity in five of the next 100 days. Use both the binomial and Poisson distributions to calculate the probabilities. Are they close?

4.7 | Discrete Distribution (Playing Card Experiment)

Stats **L**ab

4.1 Discrete Distribution (Playing Card Experiment)

Class Time:

Names:

Student Learning Outcomes

- The student will compare empirical data and a theoretical distribution to determine if an everyday experiment fits a discrete distribution.
- The student will compare technology-generated simulation and a theoretical distribution.
- The student will demonstrate an understanding of long-term probabilities.

Supplies

- One full deck of playing cards
- One programming calculator

Procedure

The experimental procedure for empirical data is to pick one card from a deck of shuffled cards.

1. The theoretical probability of picking a diamond from a deck is _____.
2. Shuffle a deck of cards.
3. Pick one card from it.
4. Record whether it was a diamond or not a diamond.
5. Put the card back and reshuffle.
6. Do this a total of ten times.
7. Record the number of diamonds picked.
8. Let X = number of diamonds. Theoretically, $X \sim B(\_\_\_\_\_, \_\_\_\_\_)$

Organize the Data

1. Record the number of diamonds picked for your class with playing cards in **Table 4.16**. Then calculate the relative frequency.

x	Frequency	Relative Frequency
0	_____	_____
1	_____	_____
2	_____	_____
3	_____	_____
4	_____	_____
5	_____	_____
6	_____	_____
7	_____	_____
8	_____	_____

x	Frequency	Relative Frequency
9	_____	_____
10	_____	_____

Table 4.16

2. Calculate the following:

   a. $\bar{x}$ = _____

   b. s = _____

3. Construct a histogram of the empirical data.

Figure 4.6

Theoretical Distribution

a. Build the theoretical PDF chart based on the distribution in the **Procedure** section.

x	P(x)
0	
1	
2	
3	
4	
5	
6	
7	
8	
9	
10	

b. Calculate the following:

    a. μ = _____

    b. σ = _____

c. Construct a histogram of the theoretical distribution.

This is a blank graph template. The x-axis is labeled Number of diamonds. The y-axis is labeled Probability.

Figure 4.7

Using the Data

NOTE

RF = relative frequency

Use the table from the **Theoretical Distribution** section to calculate the following answers. Round your answers to four decimal places.

- $P(x = 3)$ = _____

- $P(1 < x < 4)$ = _____

- $P(x \geq 8)$ = _____

Use the data from the **Organize the Data** section to calculate the following answers. Round your answers to four decimal places.

- $RF(x = 3)$ = _____

- $RF(1 < x < 4)$ = _____

- $RF(x \geq 8)$ = _____

Discussion Questions

For questions 1 and 2, think about the shapes of the two graphs, the probabilities, the relative frequencies, the means, and the standard deviations.

1. Knowing that data vary, describe three similarities between the graphs and distributions of the theoretical, empirical, and simulation distributions. Use complete sentences.

2. Describe the three most significant differences between the graphs or distributions of the theoretical, empirical, and simulation distributions.

3. Using your answers from questions 1 and 2, does it appear that the two sets of data fit the theoretical distribution? In complete sentences, explain why or why not.

4. Suppose that the experiment had been repeated 500 times. Would you expect **Table 4.16** or **Table 4.17** to change, and how would it change? Why? Why wouldn't the other table(s) change?

4.8 | Discrete Distribution (Lucky Dice Experiment)

Stats Lab

4.2 Discrete Distribution (Lucky Dice Experiment)

Class Time:

Names:

Student Learning Outcomes

- The student will compare empirical data and a theoretical distribution to determine if a Tet gambling game fits a discrete distribution.
- The student will demonstrate an understanding of long-term probabilities.

Supplies

- one "Lucky Dice" game or three regular dice

Procedure

Round answers to relative frequency and probability problems to four decimal places.

1. The experimental procedure is to bet on one object. Then, roll three Lucky Dice and count the number of matches. The number of matches will decide your profit.

2. What is the theoretical probability of one die matching the object?

3. Choose one object to place a bet on. Roll the three Lucky Dice. Count the number of matches.

4. Let X = number of matches. Theoretically, $X \sim B(_____,_____)$

5. Let Y = profit per game.

Organize the Data

In **Table 4.18**, fill in the y value that corresponds to each x value. Next, record the number of matches picked for your class. Then, calculate the relative frequency.

1. Complete the table.

x	y	Frequency	Relative Frequency
0			
1			
2			
3			

Table 4.18

2. Calculate the following:

    a. $\bar{x}$ = _____

    b. s_x = _____

    c. $\bar{y}$ = _____

    d. s_y = _____

3. Explain what $\bar{x}$ represents.

4. Explain what $\bar{y}$ represents.

5. Based upon the experiment:

   a. What was the average profit per game?

   b. Did this represent an average win or loss per game?

   c. How do you know? Answer in complete sentences.

6. Construct a histogram of the empirical data.

Figure 4.8

Theoretical Distribution

Build the theoretical PDF chart for x and y based on the distribution from the **Procedure** section.

1.

x	y	P(x) = P(y)
0		
1		
2		
3		

Table 4.19

2. Calculate the following:

   a. $\mu_x =$ _____

   b. $\sigma_x =$ _____

   c. $\mu_x =$ _____

3. Explain what μ_x represents.

4. Explain what μ_y represents.

5. Based upon theory:

   a. What was the expected profit per game?

   b. Did the expected profit represent an average win or loss per game?

c. How do you know? Answer in complete sentences.

6. Construct a histogram of the theoretical distribution.

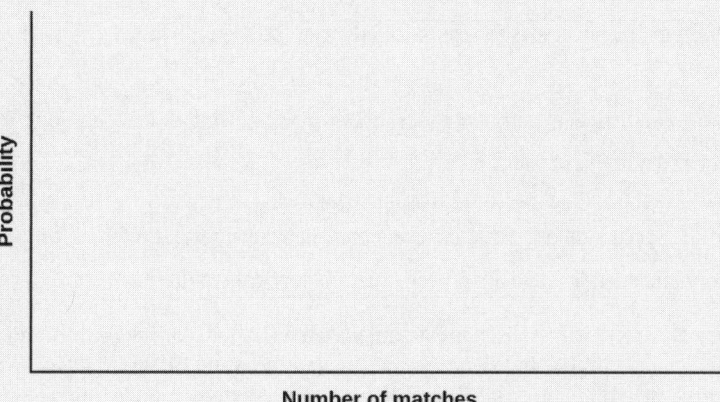

Figure 4.9

Use the Data

NOTE

RF = relative frequency

Use the data from the **Theoretical Distribution** section to calculate the following answers. Round your answers to four decimal places.

1. $P(x = 3) =$ _____

2. $P(0 < x < 3) =$ _____

3. $P(x \geq 2) =$ _____

Use the data from the **Organize the Data** section to calculate the following answers. Round your answers to four decimal places.

1. $RF(x = 3) =$ _____

2. $RF(0 < x < 3) =$ _____

3. $RF(x \geq 2) =$ _____

Discussion Question

For questions 1 and 2, consider the graphs, the probabilities, the relative frequencies, the means, and the standard deviations.

1. Knowing that data vary, describe three similarities between the graphs and distributions of the theoretical and empirical distributions. Use complete sentences.

2. Describe the three most significant differences between the graphs or distributions of the theoretical and empirical distributions.

3. Thinking about your answers to questions 1 and 2, does it appear that the data fit the theoretical distribution? In complete sentences, explain why or why not.

4. Suppose that the experiment had been repeated 500 times. Would you expect **Table 4.18** or **Table 4.19** to change, and how would it change? Why? Why wouldn't the other table change?

KEY TERMS

Bernoulli Trials an experiment with the following characteristics:

1. There are only two possible outcomes called "success" and "failure" for each trial.

2. The probability p of a success is the same for any trial (so the probability $q = 1 - p$ of a failure is the same for any trial).

Binomial Experiment a statistical experiment that satisfies the following three conditions:

1. There are a fixed number of trials, n.

2. There are only two possible outcomes, called "success" and, "failure," for each trial. The letter p denotes the probability of a success on one trial, and q denotes the probability of a failure on one trial.

3. The n trials are independent and are repeated using identical conditions.

Binomial Probability Distribution a discrete random variable (RV) that arises from Bernoulli trials; there are a fixed number, n, of independent trials. "Independent" means that the result of any trial (for example, trial one) does not affect the results of the following trials, and all trials are conducted under the same conditions. Under these circumstances the binomial RV X is defined as the number of successes in n trials. The notation is: $X \sim B(n, p)$. The mean is $\mu = np$ and the standard deviation is $\sigma = \sqrt{npq}$. The probability of exactly x successes in n trials is

$$P(X = x) = \binom{n}{x} p^x q^{n-x}.$$

Expected Value expected arithmetic average when an experiment is repeated many times; also called the mean. Notations: μ. For a discrete random variable (RV) with probability distribution function $P(x)$, the definition can also be written in the form $\mu = \sum x P(x)$.

Geometric Distribution a discrete random variable (RV) that arises from the Bernoulli trials; the trials are repeated until the first success. The geometric variable X is defined as the number of trials until the first success. Notation: $X \sim G(p)$. The mean is $\mu = \frac{1}{p}$ and the standard deviation is $\sigma = \sqrt{\frac{1}{p}\left(\frac{1}{p} - 1\right)}$. The probability of exactly x failures before the first success is given by the formula: $P(X = x) = p(1 - p)^{x-1}$.

Geometric Experiment a statistical experiment with the following properties:

1. There are one or more Bernoulli trials with all failures except the last one, which is a success.

2. In theory, the number of trials could go on forever. There must be at least one trial.

3. The probability, p, of a success and the probability, q, of a failure do not change from trial to trial.

Hypergeometric Experiment a statistical experiment with the following properties:

1. You take samples from two groups.

2. You are concerned with a group of interest, called the first group.

3. You sample without replacement from the combined groups.

4. Each pick is not independent, since sampling is without replacement.

5. You are not dealing with Bernoulli Trials.

Hypergeometric Probability a discrete random variable (RV) that is characterized by:

1. A fixed number of trials.

2. The probability of success is not the same from trial to trial.

We sample from two groups of items when we are interested in only one group. X is defined as the number of successes out of the total number of items chosen. Notation: $X \sim H(r, b, n)$, where r = the number of items in the group of interest, b = the number of items in the group not of interest, and n = the number of items chosen.

Mean a number that measures the central tendency; a common name for mean is 'average.' The term 'mean' is a shortened form of 'arithmetic mean.' By definition, the mean for a sample (detonated by $\bar{x}$) is

$$\bar{x} = \frac{\text{Sum of all values in the sample}}{\text{Number of values in the sample}}$$ and the mean for a population (denoted by μ) is $\mu =$ $$\frac{\text{Sum of all values in the population}}{\text{Number of values in the population}}.$$

Mean of a Probability Distribution the long-term average of many trials of a statistical experiment

Poisson Probability Distribution a discrete random variable (RV) that counts the number of times a certain event will occur in a specific interval; characteristics of the variable:

- The probability that the event occurs in a given interval is the same for all intervals.

- The events occur with a known mean and independently of the time since the last event.

The distribution is defined by the mean μ of the event in the interval. Notation: $X \sim P(\mu)$. The mean is $\mu = np$. The standard deviation is $\sigma = \sqrt{\mu}$. The probability of having exactly x successes in r trials is $P(X = \text{x}) = (e^{-\mu})\frac{\mu^x}{x!}$.

The Poisson distribution is often used to approximate the binomial distribution, when n is "large" and p is "small" (a general rule is that n should be greater than or equal to 20 and p should be less than or equal to 0.05).

Probability Distribution Function (PDF) a mathematical description of a discrete random variable (RV), given either in the form of an equation (formula) or in the form of a table listing all the possible outcomes of an experiment and the probability associated with each outcome.

Random Variable (RV) a characteristic of interest in a population being studied; common notation for variables are upper case Latin letters $X, Y, Z,...$; common notation for a specific value from the domain (set of all possible values of a variable) are lower case Latin letters $x, y,$ and z. For example, if X is the number of children in a family, then x represents a specific integer 0, 1, 2, 3,.... Variables in statistics differ from variables in intermediate algebra in the two following ways.

- The domain of the random variable (RV) is not necessarily a numerical set; the domain may be expressed in words; for example, if $X =$ hair color then the domain is {black, blond, gray, green, orange}.

- We can tell what specific value x the random variable X takes only after performing the experiment.

Standard Deviation of a Probability Distribution a number that measures how far the outcomes of a statistical experiment are from the mean of the distribution

The Law of Large Numbers As the number of trials in a probability experiment increases, the difference between the theoretical probability of an event and the relative frequency probability approaches zero.

CHAPTER REVIEW

4.1 Probability Distribution Function (PDF) for a Discrete Random Variable

The characteristics of a probability distribution function (PDF) for a discrete random variable are as follows:

1. Each probability is between zero and one, inclusive (*inclusive* means to include zero and one).

2. The sum of the probabilities is one.

4.2 Mean or Expected Value and Standard Deviation

The expected value, or mean, of a discrete random variable predicts the long-term results of a statistical experiment that has been repeated many times. The standard deviation of a probability distribution is used to measure the variability of possible outcomes.

4.3 Binomial Distribution

A statistical experiment can be classified as a binomial experiment if the following conditions are met:

1. There are a fixed number of trials, n.

2. There are only two possible outcomes, called "success" and, "failure" for each trial. The letter p denotes the

probability of a success on one trial and q denotes the probability of a failure on one trial.

3.   The n trials are independent and are repeated using identical conditions.

The outcomes of a binomial experiment fit a binomial probability distribution. The random variable X = the number of successes obtained in the n independent trials. The mean of X can be calculated using the formula $\mu = np$, and the standard deviation is given by the formula $\sigma = \sqrt{npq}$.

4.4 Geometric Distribution

There are three characteristics of a geometric experiment:

1.   There are one or more Bernoulli trials with all failures except the last one, which is a success.

2.   In theory, the number of trials could go on forever. There must be at least one trial.

3.   The probability, p, of a success and the probability, q, of a failure are the same for each trial.

In a geometric experiment, define the discrete random variable X as the number of independent trials until the first success. We say that X has a geometric distribution and write $X \sim G(p)$ where p is the probability of success in a single trial.

The mean of the geometric distribution $X \sim G(p)$ is $\mu = \frac{1}{p}$ and the standard deviation is $\sigma\sqrt{\frac{(1-p)}{p^2}} = \sqrt{\frac{1}{p}\left(\frac{1}{p}-1\right)}$.

4.5 Hypergeometric Distribution

A **hypergeometric experiment** is a statistical experiment with the following properties:

1.   You take samples from two groups.

2.   You are concerned with a group of interest, called the first group.

3.   You sample without replacement from the combined groups.

4.   Each pick is not independent, since sampling is without replacement.

5.   You are not dealing with Bernoulli Trials.

The outcomes of a hypergeometric experiment fit a hypergeometric probability distribution. The random variable X = the number of items from the group of interest. The distribution of X is denoted $X \sim H(r, b, n)$, where r = the size of the group of interest (first group), b = the size of the second group, and n = the size of the chosen sample. It follows that $n \leq r + b$. The mean of X is $\mu = \frac{nr}{r+b}$ and the standard deviation is $\sigma = \sqrt{\frac{rbn(r+b-n)}{(r+b)^2(r+b-1)}}$.

4.6 Poisson Distribution

A **Poisson probability distribution** of a discrete random variable gives the probability of a number of events occurring in a fixed interval of time or space, if these events happen at a known average rate and independently of the time since the last event. The Poisson distribution may be used to approximate the binomial, if the probability of success is "small" (less than or equal to 0.05) and the number of trials is "large" (greater than or equal to 20).

FORMULA REVIEW

4.2 Mean or Expected Value and Standard Deviation

Mean or Expected Value: $\mu = \sum_{x \in X} xP(x)$

Standard Deviation: $\sigma = \sqrt{\sum_{x \in X}(x-\mu)^2 P(x)}$

4.3 Binomial Distribution

$X \sim B(n, p)$ means that the discrete random variable X has a binomial probability distribution with n trials and probability of success p.

X = the number of successes in n independent trials

n = the number of independent trials

X takes on the values $x = 0, 1, 2, 3, ..., n$

p = the probability of a success for any trial

q = the probability of a failure for any trial

$p + q = 1$

$q = 1 - p$

The mean of X is $\mu = np$. The standard deviation of X is $\sigma = \sqrt{npq}$.

4.4 Geometric Distribution

$X \sim G(p)$ means that the discrete random variable X has a geometric probability distribution with probability of success in a single trial p.

X = the number of independent trials until the first success

X takes on the values $x = 1, 2, 3, \ldots$

p = the probability of a success for any trial

q = the probability of a failure for any trial $p + q = 1$
$q = 1 - p$

The mean is $\mu = \dfrac{1}{p}$.

The standard deviation is $\sigma = \sqrt{\dfrac{1 - p}{p^2}} = \sqrt{\dfrac{1}{p}\left(\dfrac{1}{p} - 1\right)}$.

4.5 Hypergeometric Distribution

$X \sim H(r, b, n)$ means that the discrete random variable X has a hypergeometric probability distribution with r = the size of the group of interest (first group), b = the size of the

second group, and n = the size of the chosen sample.

X = the number of items from the group of interest that are in the chosen sample, and X may take on the values $x = 0$, 1, ..., up to the size of the group of interest. (The minimum value for X may be larger than zero in some instances.)

$n \leq r + b$

The mean of X is given by the formula $\mu = \dfrac{nr}{r + b}$ and the

standard deviation is $= \sqrt{\dfrac{rbn(r + b - n)}{(r + b)^2(r + b - 1)}}$.

4.6 Poisson Distribution

$X \sim P(\mu)$ means that X has a Poisson probability distribution where X = the number of occurrences in the interval of interest.

X takes on the values $x = 0, 1, 2, 3, \ldots$

The mean μ is typically given.

The variance is $\sigma^2 = \mu$, and the standard deviation is $\sigma = \sqrt{\mu}$.

When $P(\mu)$ is used to approximate a binomial distribution, $\mu = np$ where n represents the number of independent trials and p represents the probability of success in a single trial.

PRACTICE

4.1 Probability Distribution Function (PDF) for a Discrete Random Variable

Use the following information to answer the next five exercises: A company wants to evaluate its attrition rate, in other words, how long new hires stay with the company. Over the years, they have established the following probability distribution.

Let X = the number of years a new hire will stay with the company.

Let $P(x)$ = the probability that a new hire will stay with the company x years.

1. Complete **Table 4.20** using the data provided.

x	P(x)
0	0.12
1	0.18
2	0.30
3	0.15
4	
5	0.10
6	0.05

Table 4.20

2. $P(x = 4) =$ _____

3. $P(x \geq 5) =$ _____

4. On average, how long would you expect a new hire to stay with the company?

5. What does the column "$P(x)$" sum to?

Use the following information to answer the next six exercises: A baker is deciding how many batches of muffins to make to sell in his bakery. He wants to make enough to sell every one and no fewer. Through observation, the baker has established a probability distribution.

x	P(x)
1	0.15
2	0.35
3	0.40
4	0.10

Table 4.21

6. Define the random variable X.

7. What is the probability the baker will sell more than one batch? $P(x > 1) =$ _____

8. What is the probability the baker will sell exactly one batch? $P(x = 1) =$ _____

9. On average, how many batches should the baker make?

Use the following information to answer the next four exercises: Ellen has music practice three days a week. She practices for all of the three days 85% of the time, two days 8% of the time, one day 4% of the time, and no days 3% of the time. One week is selected at random.

10. Define the random variable X.

11. Construct a probability distribution table for the data.

12. We know that for a probability distribution function to be discrete, it must have two characteristics. One is that the sum of the probabilities is one. What is the other characteristic?

Use the following information to answer the next five exercises: Javier volunteers in community events each month. He does not do more than five events in a month. He attends exactly five events 35% of the time, four events 25% of the time, three events 20% of the time, two events 10% of the time, one event 5% of the time, and no events 5% of the time.

13. Define the random variable X.

14. What values does x take on?

15. Construct a PDF table.

16. Find the probability that Javier volunteers for less than three events each month. $P(x < 3) =$ _____

17. Find the probability that Javier volunteers for at least one event each month. $P(x > 0) =$ _____

4.2 Mean or Expected Value and Standard Deviation

18. Complete the expected value table.

x	P(x)	x*P(x)
0	0.2	
1	0.2	
2	0.4	
3	0.2	

Table 4.22

19. Find the expected value from the expected value table.

x	P(x)	x*P(x)
2	0.1	2(0.1) = 0.2
4	0.3	4(0.3) = 1.2
6	0.4	6(0.4) = 2.4
8	0.2	8(0.2) = 1.6

Table 4.23

20. Find the standard deviation.

x	P(x)	x*P(x)	$(x - \mu)^2 P(x)$
2	0.1	2(0.1) = 0.2	$(2–5.4)^2(0.1) = 1.156$
4	0.3	4(0.3) = 1.2	$(4–5.4)^2(0.3) = 0.588$
6	0.4	6(0.4) = 2.4	$(6–5.4)^2(0.4) = 0.144$
8	0.2	8(0.2) = 1.6	$(8–5.4)^2(0.2) = 1.352$

Table 4.24

21. Identify the mistake in the probability distribution table.

x	P(x)	x*P(x)
1	0.15	0.15
2	0.25	0.50
3	0.30	0.90
4	0.20	0.80
5	0.15	0.75

Table 4.25

22. Identify the mistake in the probability distribution table.

x	P(x)	x*P(x)
1	0.15	0.15
2	0.25	0.40
3	0.25	0.65
4	0.20	0.85
5	0.15	1

Table 4.26

Use the following information to answer the next five exercises: A physics professor wants to know what percent of physics majors will spend the next several years doing post-graduate research. He has the following probability distribution.

x	P(x)	x*P(x)
1	0.35	
2	0.20	
3	0.15	
4		
5	0.10	
6	0.05	

Table 4.27

23. Define the random variable X.

24. Define $P(x)$, or the probability of x.

25. Find the probability that a physics major will do post-graduate research for four years. $P(x = 4) = $ _____

26. FInd the probability that a physics major will do post-graduate research for at most three years. $P(x \leq 3) = $ _____

27. On average, how many years would you expect a physics major to spend doing post-graduate research?

Use the following information to answer the next seven exercises: A ballet instructor is interested in knowing what percent of each year's class will continue on to the next, so that she can plan what classes to offer. Over the years, she has established the following probability distribution.

- Let X = the number of years a student will study ballet with the teacher.

- Let $P(x)$ = the probability that a student will study ballet x years.

28. Complete **Table 4.28** using the data provided.

x	P(x)	x*P(x)
1	0.10	
2	0.05	
3	0.10	
4		
5	0.30	
6	0.20	
7	0.10	

Table 4.28

29. In words, define the random variable X.

30. $P(x = 4) = $ _____

31. $P(x < 4) = $ _____

32. On average, how many years would you expect a child to study ballet with this teacher?

33. What does the column "$P(x)$" sum to and why?

34. What does the column "$x*P(x)$" sum to and why?

35. You are playing a game by drawing a card from a standard deck and replacing it. If the card is a face card, you win $30. If it is not a face card, you pay $2. There are 12 face cards in a deck of 52 cards. What is the expected value of playing the game?

36. You are playing a game by drawing a card from a standard deck and replacing it. If the card is a face card, you win $30. If it is not a face card, you pay $2. There are 12 face cards in a deck of 52 cards. Should you play the game?

4.3 Binomial Distribution

Use the following information to answer the next eight exercises: The Higher Education Research Institute at UCLA collected data from 203,967 incoming first-time, full-time freshmen from 270 four-year colleges and universities in the U.S. 71.3% of those students replied that, yes, they believe that same-sex couples should have the right to legal marital status. Suppose that you randomly pick eight first-time, full-time freshmen from the survey. You are interested in the number that believes that same sex-couples should have the right to legal marital status.

37. In words, define the random variable X.

38. $X \sim$ _____(_____,_____)

39. What values does the random variable X take on?

40. Construct the probability distribution function (PDF).

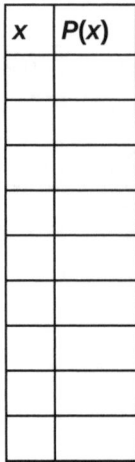

x	P(x)

Table 4.29

41. On average (μ), how many would you expect to answer yes?

42. What is the standard deviation (σ)?

43. What is the probability that at most five of the freshmen reply "yes"?

44. What is the probability that at least two of the freshmen reply "yes"?

4.4 Geometric Distribution

Use the following information to answer the next six exercises: The Higher Education Research Institute at UCLA collected data from 203,967 incoming first-time, full-time freshmen from 270 four-year colleges and universities in the U.S. 71.3% of those students replied that, yes, they believe that same-sex couples should have the right to legal marital status. Suppose that you randomly select freshman from the study until you find one who replies "yes." You are interested in the number of freshmen you must ask.

45. In words, define the random variable X.

46. $X \sim$ _____(_____,_____)

47. What values does the random variable X take on?

48. Construct the probability distribution function (PDF). Stop at $x = 6$.

x	P(x)
1	
2	
3	
4	
5	
6	

Table 4.30

49. On average (μ), how many freshmen would you expect to have to ask until you found one who replies "yes?"

50. What is the probability that you will need to ask fewer than three freshmen?

4.5 Hypergeometric Distribution

Use the following information to answer the next five exercises: Suppose that a group of statistics students is divided into two groups: business majors and non-business majors. There are 16 business majors in the group and seven non-business majors in the group. A random sample of nine students is taken. We are interested in the number of business majors in the sample.

51. In words, define the random variable X.

52. $X \sim$ _____(_____,_____)

53. What values does X take on?

54. Find the standard deviation.

55. On average (μ), how many would you expect to be business majors?

4.6 Poisson Distribution

Use the following information to answer the next six exercises: On average, a clothing store gets 120 customers per day.

56. Assume the event occurs independently in any given day. Define the random variable X.

57. What values does X take on?

58. What is the probability of getting 150 customers in one day?

59. What is the probability of getting 35 customers in the first four hours? Assume the store is open 12 hours each day.

60. What is the probability that the store will have more than 12 customers in the first hour?

61. What is the probability that the store will have fewer than 12 customers in the first two hours?

62. Which type of distribution can the Poisson model be used to approximate? When would you do this?

Use the following information to answer the next six exercises: On average, eight teens in the U.S. die from motor vehicle injuries per day. As a result, states across the country are debating raising the driving age.

63. Assume the event occurs independently in any given day. In words, define the random variable X.

64. $X \sim$ _____(_____,_____)

65. What values does X take on?

66. For the given values of the random variable X, fill in the corresponding probabilities.

67. Is it likely that there will be no teens killed from motor vehicle injuries on any given day in the U.S? Justify your answer numerically.

68. Is it likely that there will be more than 20 teens killed from motor vehicle injuries on any given day in the U.S.? Justify your answer numerically.

HOMEWORK

4.1 Probability Distribution Function (PDF) for a Discrete Random Variable

69. Suppose that the PDF for the number of years it takes to earn a Bachelor of Science (B.S.) degree is given in **Table 4.31**.

x	P(x)
3	0.05
4	0.40
5	0.30
6	0.15
7	0.10

Table 4.31

    a. In words, define the random variable X.
    b. What does it mean that the values zero, one, and two are not included for x in the PDF?

4.2 Mean or Expected Value and Standard Deviation

70. A theater group holds a fund-raiser. It sells 100 raffle tickets for $5 apiece. Suppose you purchase four tickets. The prize is two passes to a Broadway show, worth a total of $150.
    a. What are you interested in here?
    b. In words, define the random variable X.
    c. List the values that X may take on.
    d. Construct a PDF.
    e. If this fund-raiser is repeated often and you always purchase four tickets, what would be your expected average winnings per raffle?

71. A game involves selecting a card from a regular 52-card deck and tossing a coin. The coin is a fair coin and is equally likely to land on heads or tails.
    • If the card is a face card, and the coin lands on Heads, you win $6
    • If the card is a face card, and the coin lands on Tails, you win $2
    • If the card is not a face card, you lose $2, no matter what the coin shows.
    a. Find the expected value for this game (expected net gain or loss).
    b. Explain what your calculations indicate about your long-term average profits and losses on this game.
    c. Should you play this game to win money?

72. You buy a lottery ticket to a lottery that costs $10 per ticket. There are only 100 tickets available to be sold in this lottery. In this lottery there are one $500 prize, two $100 prizes, and four $25 prizes. Find your expected gain or loss.

73. Complete the PDF and answer the questions.

x	P(x)	xP(x)
0	0.3	
1	0.2	
2		
3	0.4	

Table 4.32

    a. Find the probability that $x = 2$.
    b. Find the expected value.

74. Suppose that you are offered the following "deal." You roll a die. If you roll a six, you win $10. If you roll a four or five, you win $5. If you roll a one, two, or three, you pay $6.
  a. What are you ultimately interested in here (the value of the roll or the money you win)?
  b. In words, define the Random Variable X.
  c. List the values that X may take on.
  d. Construct a PDF.
  e. Over the long run of playing this game, what are your expected average winnings per game?
  f. Based on numerical values, should you take the deal? Explain your decision in complete sentences.

75. A venture capitalist, willing to invest $1,000,000, has three investments to choose from. The first investment, a software company, has a 10% chance of returning $5,000,000 profit, a 30% chance of returning $1,000,000 profit, and a 60% chance of losing the million dollars. The second company, a hardware company, has a 20% chance of returning $3,000,000 profit, a 40% chance of returning $1,000,000 profit, and a 40% chance of losing the million dollars. The third company, a biotech firm, has a 10% chance of returning $6,000,000 profit, a 70% of no profit or loss, and a 20% chance of losing the million dollars.
  a. Construct a PDF for each investment.
  b. Find the expected value for each investment.
  c. Which is the safest investment? Why do you think so?
  d. Which is the riskiest investment? Why do you think so?
  e. Which investment has the highest expected return, on average?

76. Suppose that 20,000 married adults in the United States were randomly surveyed as to the number of children they have. The results are compiled and are used as theoretical probabilities. Let X = the number of children married people have.

x	P(x)	xP(x)
0	0.10	
1	0.20	
2	0.30	
3		
4	0.10	
5	0.05	
6 (or more)	0.05	

Table 4.33

  a. Find the probability that a married adult has three children.
  b. In words, what does the expected value in this example represent?
  c. Find the expected value.
  d. Is it more likely that a married adult will have two to three children or four to six children? How do you know?

77. Suppose that the PDF for the number of years it takes to earn a Bachelor of Science (B.S.) degree is given as in **Table 4.34**.

x	P(x)
3	0.05
4	0.40
5	0.30
6	0.15
7	0.10

Table 4.34

On average, how many years do you expect it to take for an individual to earn a B.S.?

78. People visiting video rental stores often rent more than one DVD at a time. The probability distribution for DVD rentals per customer at Video To Go is given in the following table. There is a five-video limit per customer at this store, so nobody ever rents more than five DVDs.

x	P(x)
0	0.03
1	0.50
2	0.24
3	
4	0.07
5	0.04

Table 4.35

   a. Describe the random variable X in words.
   b. Find the probability that a customer rents three DVDs.
   c. Find the probability that a customer rents at least four DVDs.
   d. Find the probability that a customer rents at most two DVDs.
     Another shop, Entertainment Headquarters, rents DVDs and video games. The probability distribution for DVD rentals per customer at this shop is given as follows. They also have a five-DVD limit per customer.

x	P(x)
0	0.35
1	0.25
2	0.20
3	0.10
4	0.05
5	0.05

Table 4.36

   e. At which store is the expected number of DVDs rented per customer higher?
   f. If Video to Go estimates that they will have 300 customers next week, how many DVDs do they expect to rent next week? Answer in sentence form.
   g. If Video to Go expects 300 customers next week, and Entertainment HQ projects that they will have 420 customers, for which store is the expected number of DVD rentals for next week higher? Explain.
   h. Which of the two video stores experiences more variation in the number of DVD rentals per customer? How do you know that?

79. A "friend" offers you the following "deal." For a $10 fee, you may pick an envelope from a box containing 100 seemingly identical envelopes. However, each envelope contains a coupon for a free gift.
- Ten of the coupons are for a free gift worth $6.
- Eighty of the coupons are for a free gift worth $8.
- Six of the coupons are for a free gift worth $12.
- Four of the coupons are for a free gift worth $40.

Based upon the financial gain or loss over the long run, should you play the game?

   a. Yes, I expect to come out ahead in money.
   b. No, I expect to come out behind in money.
   c. It doesn't matter. I expect to break even.

80. Florida State University has 14 statistics classes scheduled for its Summer 2013 term. One class has space available for 30 students, eight classes have space for 60 students, one class has space for 70 students, and four classes have space for 100 students.

    a. What is the average class size assuming each class is filled to capacity?

    b. Space is available for 980 students. Suppose that each class is filled to capacity and select a statistics student at random. Let the random variable X equal the size of the student's class. Define the PDF for X.

    c. Find the mean of X.

    d. Find the standard deviation of X.

81. In a lottery, there are 250 prizes of $5, 50 prizes of $25, and ten prizes of $100. Assuming that 10,000 tickets are to be issued and sold, what is a fair price to charge to break even?

4.3 Binomial Distribution

82. According to a recent article the average number of babies born with significant hearing loss (deafness) is approximately two per 1,000 babies in a healthy baby nursery. The number climbs to an average of 30 per 1,000 babies in an intensive care nursery.

Suppose that 1,000 babies from healthy baby nurseries were randomly surveyed. Find the probability that exactly two babies were born deaf.

Use the following information to answer the next four exercises. Recently, a nurse commented that when a patient calls the medical advice line claiming to have the flu, the chance that he or she truly has the flu (and not just a nasty cold) is only about 4%. Of the next 25 patients calling in claiming to have the flu, we are interested in how many actually have the flu.

83. Define the random variable and list its possible values.

84. State the distribution of X.

85. Find the probability that at least four of the 25 patients actually have the flu.

86. On average, for every 25 patients calling in, how many do you expect to have the flu?

87. People visiting video rental stores often rent more than one DVD at a time. The probability distribution for DVD rentals per customer at Video To Go is given **Table 4.37**. There is five-video limit per customer at this store, so nobody ever rents more than five DVDs.

x	P(x)
0	0.03
1	0.50
2	0.24
3	
4	0.07
5	0.04

Table 4.37

    a. Describe the random variable X in words.

    b. Find the probability that a customer rents three DVDs.

    c. Find the probability that a customer rents at least four DVDs.

    d. Find the probability that a customer rents at most two DVDs.

88. A school newspaper reporter decides to randomly survey 12 students to see if they will attend Tet (Vietnamese New Year) festivities this year. Based on past years, she knows that 18% of students attend Tet festivities. We are interested in the number of students who will attend the festivities.

    a. In words, define the random variable X.
    b. List the values that X may take on.
    c. Give the distribution of X. $X \sim$ _____(_____,_____)
    d. How many of the 12 students do we expect to attend the festivities?
    e. Find the probability that at most four students will attend.
    f. Find the probability that more than two students will attend.

Use the following information to answer the next two exercises: The probability that the San Jose Sharks will win any given game is 0.3694 based on a 13-year win history of 382 wins out of 1,034 games played (as of a certain date). An upcoming monthly schedule contains 12 games.

89. The expected number of wins for that upcoming month is:

    a. 1.67
    b. 12
    c. $\dfrac{382}{1043}$
    d. 4.43

Let X = the number of games won in that upcoming month.

90. What is the probability that the San Jose Sharks win six games in that upcoming month?

    a. 0.1476
    b. 0.2336
    c. 0.7664
    d. 0.8903

91. What is the probability that the San Jose Sharks win at least five games in that upcoming month

    a. 0.3694
    b. 0.5266
    c. 0.4734
    d. 0.2305

92. A student takes a ten-question true-false quiz, but did not study and randomly guesses each answer. Find the probability that the student passes the quiz with a grade of at least 70% of the questions correct.

93. A student takes a 32-question multiple-choice exam, but did not study and randomly guesses each answer. Each question has three possible choices for the answer. Find the probability that the student guesses **more than** 75% of the questions correctly.

94. Six different colored dice are rolled. Of interest is the number of dice that show a one.

    a. In words, define the random variable X.
    b. List the values that X may take on.
    c. Give the distribution of X. $X \sim$ _____(_____,_____)
    d. On average, how many dice would you expect to show a one?
    e. Find the probability that all six dice show a one.
    f. Is it more likely that three or that four dice will show a one? Use numbers to justify your answer numerically.

95. More than 96 percent of the very largest colleges and universities (more than 15,000 total enrollments) have some online offerings. Suppose you randomly pick 13 such institutions. We are interested in the number that offer distance learning courses.

    a. In words, define the random variable X.
    b. List the values that X may take on.
    c. Give the distribution of X. $X \sim$ _____(_____,_____)
    d. On average, how many schools would you expect to offer such courses?
    e. Find the probability that at most ten offer such courses.
    f. Is it more likely that 12 or that 13 will offer such courses? Use numbers to justify your answer numerically and answer in a complete sentence.

96. Suppose that about 85% of graduating students attend their graduation. A group of 22 graduating students is randomly chosen.
- a. In words, define the random variable X.
- b. List the values that X may take on.
- c. Give the distribution of X. X ~ _____(_____,_____)
- d. How many are expected to attend their graduation?
- e. Find the probability that 17 or 18 attend.
- f. Based on numerical values, would you be surprised if all 22 attended graduation? Justify your answer numerically.

97. At The Fencing Center, 60% of the fencers use the foil as their main weapon. We randomly survey 25 fencers at The Fencing Center. We are interested in the number of fencers who do **not** use the foil as their main weapon.
- a. In words, define the random variable X.
- b. List the values that X may take on.
- c. Give the distribution of X. X ~ _____(_____,_____)
- d. How many are expected to **not** to use the foil as their main weapon?
- e. Find the probability that six do **not** use the foil as their main weapon.
- f. Based on numerical values, would you be surprised if all 25 did **not** use foil as their main weapon? Justify your answer numerically.

98. Approximately 8% of students at a local high school participate in after-school sports all four years of high school. A group of 60 seniors is randomly chosen. Of interest is the number who participated in after-school sports all four years of high school.
- a. In words, define the random variable X.
- b. List the values that X may take on.
- c. Give the distribution of X. X ~ _____(_____,_____)
- d. How many seniors are expected to have participated in after-school sports all four years of high school?
- e. Based on numerical values, would you be surprised if none of the seniors participated in after-school sports all four years of high school? Justify your answer numerically.
- f. Based upon numerical values, is it more likely that four or that five of the seniors participated in after-school sports all four years of high school? Justify your answer numerically.

99. The chance of an IRS audit for a tax return with over $25,000 in income is about 2% per year. We are interested in the expected number of audits a person with that income has in a 20-year period. Assume each year is independent.
- a. In words, define the random variable X.
- b. List the values that X may take on.
- c. Give the distribution of X. X ~ _____(_____,_____)
- d. How many audits are expected in a 20-year period?
- e. Find the probability that a person is not audited at all.
- f. Find the probability that a person is audited more than twice.

100. It has been estimated that only about 30% of California residents have adequate earthquake supplies. Suppose you randomly survey 11 California residents. We are interested in the number who have adequate earthquake supplies.
- a. In words, define the random variable X.
- b. List the values that X may take on.
- c. Give the distribution of X. X ~ _____(_____,_____)
- d. What is the probability that at least eight have adequate earthquake supplies?
- e. Is it more likely that none or that all of the residents surveyed will have adequate earthquake supplies? Why?
- f. How many residents do you expect will have adequate earthquake supplies?

101. There are two similar games played for Chinese New Year and Vietnamese New Year. In the Chinese version, fair dice with numbers 1, 2, 3, 4, 5, and 6 are used, along with a board with those numbers. In the Vietnamese version, fair dice with pictures of a gourd, fish, rooster, crab, crayfish, and deer are used. The board has those six objects on it, also. We will play with bets being $1. The player places a bet on a number or object. The "house" rolls three dice. If none of the dice show the number or object that was bet, the house keeps the $1 bet. If one of the dice shows the number or object bet (and the other two do not show it), the player gets back his or her $1 bet, plus $1 profit. If two of the dice show the number or object bet (and the third die does not show it), the player gets back his or her $1 bet, plus $2 profit. If all three dice show the number or object bet, the player gets back his or her $1 bet, plus $3 profit. Let X = number of matches and Y = profit per game.

    a. In words, define the random variable X.
    b. List the values that X may take on.
    c. Give the distribution of X. X ~ _____(_____,_____)
    d. List the values that Y may take on. Then, construct one PDF table that includes both X and Y and their probabilities.
    e. Calculate the average expected matches over the long run of playing this game for the player.
    f. Calculate the average expected earnings over the long run of playing this game for the player.
    g. Determine who has the advantage, the player or the house.

102. According to The World Bank, only 9% of the population of Uganda had access to electricity as of 2009. Suppose we randomly sample 150 people in Uganda. Let X = the number of people who have access to electricity.

    a. What is the probability distribution for X?
    b. Using the formulas, calculate the mean and standard deviation of X.
    c. Use your calculator to find the probability that 15 people in the sample have access to electricity.
    d. Find the probability that at most ten people in the sample have access to electricity.
    e. Find the probability that more than 25 people in the sample have access to electricity.

103. The literacy rate for a nation measures the proportion of people age 15 and over that can read and write. The literacy rate in Afghanistan is 28.1%. Suppose you choose 15 people in Afghanistan at random. Let X = the number of people who are literate.

    a. Sketch a graph of the probability distribution of X.
    b. Using the formulas, calculate the (i) mean and (ii) standard deviation of X.
    c. Find the probability that more than five people in the sample are literate. Is it is more likely that three people or four people are literate.

4.4 Geometric Distribution

104. A consumer looking to buy a used red Miata car will call dealerships until she finds a dealership that carries the car. She estimates the probability that any independent dealership will have the car will be 28%. We are interested in the number of dealerships she must call.

    a. In words, define the random variable X.
    b. List the values that X may take on.
    c. Give the distribution of X. X ~ _____(_____,_____)
    d. On average, how many dealerships would we expect her to have to call until she finds one that has the car?
    e. Find the probability that she must call at most four dealerships.
    f. Find the probability that she must call three or four dealerships.

105. Suppose that the probability that an adult in America will watch the Super Bowl is 40%. Each person is considered independent. We are interested in the number of adults in America we must survey until we find one who will watch the Super Bowl.

    a. In words, define the random variable X.
    b. List the values that X may take on.
    c. Give the distribution of X. X ~ _____(_____,_____)
    d. How many adults in America do you expect to survey until you find one who will watch the Super Bowl?
    e. Find the probability that you must ask seven people.
    f. Find the probability that you must ask three or four people.

106. It has been estimated that only about 30% of California residents have adequate earthquake supplies. Suppose we are interested in the number of California residents we must survey until we find a resident who does **not** have adequate earthquake supplies.

    a. In words, define the random variable X.

    b. List the values that X may take on.

    c. Give the distribution of X. $X \sim$ _____(_____,_____)

    d. What is the probability that we must survey just one or two residents until we find a California resident who does not have adequate earthquake supplies?

    e. What is the probability that we must survey at least three California residents until we find a California resident who does not have adequate earthquake supplies?

    f. How many California residents do you expect to need to survey until you find a California resident who **does not** have adequate earthquake supplies?

    g. How many California residents do you expect to need to survey until you find a California resident who **does** have adequate earthquake supplies?

107. In one of its Spring catalogs, L.L. Bean® advertised footwear on 29 of its 192 catalog pages. Suppose we randomly survey 20 pages. We are interested in the number of pages that advertise footwear. Each page may be picked more than once.

    a. In words, define the random variable X.

    b. List the values that X may take on.

    c. Give the distribution of X. $X \sim$ _____(_____,_____)

    d. How many pages do you expect to advertise footwear on them?

    e. Is it probable that all twenty will advertise footwear on them? Why or why not?

    f. What is the probability that fewer than ten will advertise footwear on them?

    g. Reminder: A page may be picked more than once. We are interested in the number of pages that we must randomly survey until we find one that has footwear advertised on it. Define the random variable X and give its distribution.

    h. What is the probability that you only need to survey at most three pages in order to find one that advertises footwear on it?

    i. How many pages do you expect to need to survey in order to find one that advertises footwear?

108. Suppose that you are performing the probability experiment of rolling one fair six-sided die. Let F be the event of rolling a four or a five. You are interested in how many times you need to roll the die in order to obtain the first four or five as the outcome.

  • p = probability of success (event F occurs)

  • q = probability of failure (event F does not occur)

    a. Write the description of the random variable X.

    b. What are the values that X can take on?

    c. Find the values of p and q.

    d. Find the probability that the first occurrence of event F (rolling a four or five) is on the second trial.

109. Ellen has music practice three days a week. She practices for all of the three days 85% of the time, two days 8% of the time, one day 4% of the time, and no days 3% of the time. One week is selected at random. What values does X take on?

110. The World Bank records the prevalence of HIV in countries around the world. According to their data, "Prevalence of HIV refers to the percentage of people ages 15 to 49 who are infected with HIV."[1] In South Africa, the prevalence of HIV is 17.3%. Let X = the number of people you test until you find a person infected with HIV.

    a. Sketch a graph of the distribution of the discrete random variable X.

    b. What is the probability that you must test 30 people to find one with HIV?

    c. What is the probability that you must ask ten people?

    d. Find the (i) mean and (ii) standard deviation of the distribution of X.

---

1. "Prevalence of HIV, total (% of populations ages 15-49)," The World Bank, 2013. Available online at http://data.worldbank.org/indicator/ SH.DYN.AIDS.ZS?order=wbapi_data_value_2011+wbapi_data_value+wbapi_data_value-last&sort=desc (accessed May 15, 2013).

111. According to a recent Pew Research poll, 75% of millenials (people born between 1981 and 1995) have a profile on a social networking site. Let X = the number of millenials you ask until you find a person without a profile on a social networking site.
   a. Describe the distribution of X.
   b. Find the (i) mean and (ii) standard deviation of X.
   c. What is the probability that you must ask ten people to find one person without a social networking site?
   d. What is the probability that you must ask 20 people to find one person without a social networking site?
   e. What is the probability that you must ask *at most* five people?

4.5 Hypergeometric Distribution

112. A group of Martial Arts students is planning on participating in an upcoming demonstration. Six are students of Tae Kwon Do; seven are students of Shotokan Karate. Suppose that eight students are randomly picked to be in the first demonstration. We are interested in the number of Shotokan Karate students in that first demonstration.
   a. In words, define the random variable X.
   b. List the values that X may take on.
   c. Give the distribution of X. X ~ _____(_____,_____)
   d. How many Shotokan Karate students do we expect to be in that first demonstration?

113. In one of its Spring catalogs, L.L. Bean® advertised footwear on 29 of its 192 catalog pages. Suppose we randomly survey 20 pages. We are interested in the number of pages that advertise footwear. Each page may be picked at most once.
   a. In words, define the random variable X.
   b. List the values that X may take on.
   c. Give the distribution of X. X ~ _____(_____,_____)
   d. How many pages do you expect to advertise footwear on them?
   e. Calculate the standard deviation.

114. Suppose that a technology task force is being formed to study technology awareness among instructors. Assume that ten people will be randomly chosen to be on the committee from a group of 28 volunteers, 20 who are technically proficient and eight who are not. We are interested in the number on the committee who are **not** technically proficient.
   a. In words, define the random variable X.
   b. List the values that X may take on.
   c. Give the distribution of X. X ~ _____(_____,_____)
   d. How many instructors do you expect on the committee who are **not** technically proficient?
   e. Find the probability that at least five on the committee are not technically proficient.
   f. Find the probability that at most three on the committee are not technically proficient.

115. Suppose that nine Massachusetts athletes are scheduled to appear at a charity benefit. The nine are randomly chosen from eight volunteers from the Boston Celtics and four volunteers from the New England Patriots. We are interested in the number of Patriots picked.
   a. In words, define the random variable X.
   b. List the values that X may take on.
   c. Give the distribution of X. X ~ _____(_____,_____)
   d. Are you choosing the nine athletes with or without replacement?

116. A bridge hand is defined as 13 cards selected at random and without replacement from a deck of 52 cards. In a standard deck of cards, there are 13 cards from each suit: hearts, spades, clubs, and diamonds. What is the probability of being dealt a hand that does not contain a heart?
   a. What is the group of interest?
   b. How many are in the group of interest?
   c. How many are in the other group?
   d. Let X = _____. What values does X take on?
   e. The probability question is P(_____).
   f. Find the probability in question.
   g. Find the (i) mean and (ii) standard deviation of X.

4.6 Poisson Distribution

117. The switchboard in a Minneapolis law office gets an average of 5.5 incoming phone calls during the noon hour on Mondays. Experience shows that the existing staff can handle up to six calls in an hour. Let X = the number of calls received at noon.
- a. Find the mean and standard deviation of X.
- b. What is the probability that the office receives at most six calls at noon on Monday?
- c. Find the probability that the law office receives six calls at noon. What does this mean to the law office staff who get, on average, 5.5 incoming phone calls at noon?
- d. What is the probability that the office receives more than eight calls at noon?

118. The maternity ward at Dr. Jose Fabella Memorial Hospital in Manila in the Philippines is one of the busiest in the world with an average of 60 births per day. Let X = the number of births in an hour.
- a. Find the mean and standard deviation of X.
- b. Sketch a graph of the probability distribution of X.
- c. What is the probability that the maternity ward will deliver three babies in one hour?
- d. What is the probability that the maternity ward will deliver at most three babies in one hour?
- e. What is the probability that the maternity ward will deliver more than five babies in one hour?

119. A manufacturer of Christmas tree light bulbs knows that 3% of its bulbs are defective. Find the probability that a string of 100 lights contains at most four defective bulbs using both the binomial and Poisson distributions.

120. The average number of children a Japanese woman has in her lifetime is 1.37. Suppose that one Japanese woman is randomly chosen.
- a. In words, define the random variable X.
- b. List the values that X may take on.
- c. Give the distribution of X. X ~ _____(_____,_____)
- d. Find the probability that she has no children.
- e. Find the probability that she has fewer children than the Japanese average.
- f. Find the probability that she has more children than the Japanese average.

121. The average number of children a Spanish woman has in her lifetime is 1.47. Suppose that one Spanish woman is randomly chosen.
- a. In words, define the Random Variable X.
- b. List the values that X may take on.
- c. Give the distribution of X. X ~ _____(_____,_____)
- d. Find the probability that she has no children.
- e. Find the probability that she has fewer children than the Spanish average.
- f. Find the probability that she has more children than the Spanish average .

122. Fertile, female cats produce an average of three litters per year. Suppose that one fertile, female cat is randomly chosen. In one year, find the probability she produces:
- a. In words, define the random variable X.
- b. List the values that X may take on.
- c. Give the distribution of X. X ~ _____
- d. Find the probability that she has no litters in one year.
- e. Find the probability that she has at least two litters in one year.
- f. Find the probability that she has exactly three litters in one year.

123. The chance of having an extra fortune in a fortune cookie is about 3%. Given a bag of 144 fortune cookies, we are interested in the number of cookies with an extra fortune. Two distributions may be used to solve this problem, but only use one distribution to solve the problem.
- a. In words, define the random variable X.
- b. List the values that X may take on.
- c. Give the distribution of X. X ~ _____(_____,_____)
- d. How many cookies do we expect to have an extra fortune?
- e. Find the probability that none of the cookies have an extra fortune.
- f. Find the probability that more than three have an extra fortune.
- g. As n increases, what happens involving the probabilities using the two distributions? Explain in complete sentences.

124. According to the South Carolina Department of Mental Health web site, for every 200 U.S. women, the average number who suffer from anorexia is one. Out of a randomly chosen group of 600 U.S. women determine the following.
    a. In words, define the random variable X.
    b. List the values that X may take on.
    c. Give the distribution of X. $X \sim$ _____(_____,_____)
    d. How many are expected to suffer from anorexia?
    e. Find the probability that no one suffers from anorexia.
    f. Find the probability that more than four suffer from anorexia.

125. The chance of an IRS audit for a tax return with over $25,000 in income is about 2% per year. Suppose that 100 people with tax returns over $25,000 are randomly picked. We are interested in the number of people audited in one year. Use a Poisson distribution to anwer the following questions.
    a. In words, define the random variable X.
    b. List the values that X may take on.
    c. Give the distribution of X. $X \sim$ _____(_____,_____)
    d. How many are expected to be audited?
    e. Find the probability that no one was audited.
    f. Find the probability that at least three were audited.

126. Approximately 8% of students at a local high school participate in after-school sports all four years of high school. A group of 60 seniors is randomly chosen. Of interest is the number that participated in after-school sports all four years of high school.
    a. In words, define the random variable X.
    b. List the values that X may take on.
    c. Give the distribution of X. $X \sim$ _____(_____,_____)
    d. How many seniors are expected to have participated in after-school sports all four years of high school?
    e. Based on numerical values, would you be surprised if none of the seniors participated in after-school sports all four years of high school? Justify your answer numerically.
    f. Based on numerical values, is it more likely that four or that five of the seniors participated in after-school sports all four years of high school? Justify your answer numerically.

127. On average, Pierre, an amateur chef, drops three pieces of egg shell into every two cake batters he makes. Suppose that you buy one of his cakes.
    a. In words, define the random variable X.
    b. List the values that X may take on.
    c. Give the distribution of X. $X \sim$ _____(_____,_____)
    d. On average, how many pieces of egg shell do you expect to be in the cake?
    e. What is the probability that there will not be any pieces of egg shell in the cake?
    f. Let's say that you buy one of Pierre's cakes each week for six weeks. What is the probability that there will not be any egg shell in any of the cakes?
    g. Based upon the average given for Pierre, is it possible for there to be seven pieces of shell in the cake? Why?

Use the following information to answer the next two exercises: The average number of times per week that Mrs. Plum's cats wake her up at night because they want to play is ten. We are interested in the number of times her cats wake her up each week.

128. In words, the random variable X = _____
    a. the number of times Mrs. Plum's cats wake her up each week.
    b. the number of times Mrs. Plum's cats wake her up each hour.
    c. the number of times Mrs. Plum's cats wake her up each night.
    d. the number of times Mrs. Plum's cats wake her up.

129. Find the probability that her cats will wake her up no more than five times next week.
    a. 0.5000
    b. 0.9329
    c. 0.0378
    d. 0.0671

REFERENCES

4.2 Mean or Expected Value and Standard Deviation

Class Catalogue at the Florida State University. Available online at https://apps.oti.fsu.edu/RegistrarCourseLookup/SearchFormLegacy (accessed May 15, 2013).

"World Earthquakes: Live Earthquake News and Highlights," World Earthquakes, 2012. http://www.world-earthquakes.com/index.php?option=ethq_prediction (accessed May 15, 2013).

4.3 Binomial Distribution

"Access to electricity (% of population)," The World Bank, 2013. Available online at http://data.worldbank.org/indicator/EG.ELC.ACCS.ZS?order=wbapi_data_value_2009%20wbapi_data_value%20wbapi_data_value-first&sort=asc (accessed May 15, 2015).

"Distance Education." Wikipedia. Available online at http://en.wikipedia.org/wiki/Distance_education (accessed May 15, 2013).

"NBA Statistics – 2013," ESPN NBA, 2013. Available online at http://espn.go.com/nba/statistics/_/seasontype/2 (accessed May 15, 2013).

Newport, Frank. "Americans Still Enjoy Saving Rather than Spending: Few demographic differences seen in these views other than by income," GALLUP® Economy, 2013. Available online at http://www.gallup.com/poll/162368/americans-enjoy-saving-rather-spending.aspx (accessed May 15, 2013).

Pryor, John H., Linda DeAngelo, Laura Palucki Blake, Sylvia Hurtado, Serge Tran. *The American Freshman: National Norms Fall 2011*. Los Angeles: Cooperative Institutional Research Program at the Higher Education Research Institute at UCLA, 2011. Also available online at http://heri.ucla.edu/PDFs/pubs/TFS/Norms/Monographs/TheAmericanFreshman2011.pdf (accessed May 15, 2013).

"The World FactBook," Central Intelligence Agency. Available online at https://www.cia.gov/library/publications/the-world-factbook/geos/af.html (accessed May 15, 2013).

"What are the key statistics about pancreatic cancer?" American Cancer Society, 2013. Available online at http://www.cancer.org/cancer/pancreaticcancer/detailedguide/pancreatic-cancer-key-statistics (accessed May 15, 2013).

4.4 Geometric Distribution

"Millennials: A Portrait of Generation Next," PewResearchCenter. Available online at http://www.pewsocialtrends.org/files/2010/10/millennials-confident-connected-open-to-change.pdf (accessed May 15, 2013).

"Millennials: Confident. Connected. Open to Change." Executive Summary by PewResearch Social & Demographic Trends, 2013. Available online at http://www.pewsocialtrends.org/2010/02/24/millennials-confident-connected-open-to-change/ (accessed May 15, 2013).

"Prevalence of HIV, total (% of populations ages 15-49)," The World Bank, 2013. Available online at http://data.worldbank.org/indicator/SH.DYN.AIDS.ZS?order=wbapi_data_value_2011+wbapi_data_value+wbapi_data_value-last&sort=desc (accessed May 15, 2013).

Pryor, John H., Linda DeAngelo, Laura Palucki Blake, Sylvia Hurtado, Serge Tran. *The American Freshman: National Norms Fall 2011*. Los Angeles: Cooperative Institutional Research Program at the Higher Education Research Institute at UCLA, 2011. Also available online at http://heri.ucla.edu/PDFs/pubs/TFS/Norms/Monographs/TheAmericanFreshman2011.pdf (accessed May 15, 2013).

"Summary of the National Risk and Vulnerability Assessment 2007/8: A profile of Afghanistan," The European Union and ICON-Institute. Available online at http://ec.europa.eu/europeaid/where/asia/documents/afgh_brochure_summary_en.pdf (accessed May 15, 2013).

"The World FactBook," Central Intelligence Agency. Available online at https://www.cia.gov/library/publications/the-world-factbook/geos/af.html (accessed May 15, 2013).

"UNICEF reports on Female Literacy Centers in Afghanistan established to teach women and girls basic resading [sic] and writing skills," UNICEF Television. Video available online at http://www.unicefusa.org/assets/video/afghan-female-literacy-centers.html (accessed May 15, 2013).

4.6 Poisson Distribution

"ATL Fact Sheet," Department of Aviation at the Hartsfield-Jackson Atlanta International Airport, 2013. Available online at http://www.atlanta-airport.com/Airport/ATL/ATL_FactSheet.aspx (accessed May 15, 2013).

Center for Disease Control and Prevention. "Teen Drivers: Fact Sheet," Injury Prevention & Control: Motor Vehicle Safety, October 2, 2012. Available online at http://www.cdc.gov/Motorvehiclesafety/Teen_Drivers/teendrivers_factsheet.html (accessed May 15, 2013).

"Children and Childrearing," Ministry of Health, Labour, and Welfare. Available online at http://www.mhlw.go.jp/english/policy/children/children-childrearing/index.html (accessed May 15, 2013).

"Eating Disorder Statistics," South Carolina Department of Mental Health, 2006. Available online at http://www.state.sc.us/dmh/anorexia/statistics.htm (accessed May 15, 2013).

"Giving Birth in Manila: The maternity ward at the Dr Jose Fabella Memorial Hospital in Manila, the busiest in the Philippines, where there is an average of 60 births a day," theguardian, 2013. Available online at http://www.theguardian.com/world/gallery/2011/jun/08/philippines-health#/?picture=375471900&index=2 (accessed May 15, 2013).

"How Americans Use Text Messaging," Pew Internet, 2013. Available online at http://pewinternet.org/Reports/2011/Cell-Phone-Texting-2011/Main-Report.aspx (accessed May 15, 2013).

Lenhart, Amanda. "Teens, Smartphones & Testing: Texting volum is up while the frequency of voice calling is down. About one in four teens say they own smartphones," Pew Internet, 2012. Available online at http://www.pewinternet.org/~/media/Files/Reports/2012/PIP_Teens_Smartphones_and_Texting.pdf (accessed May 15, 2013).

"One born every minute: the maternity unit where mothers are THREE to a bed," MailOnline. Available online at http://www.dailymail.co.uk/news/article-2001422/Busiest-maternity-ward-planet-averages-60-babies-day-mothers-bed.html (accessed May 15, 2013).

Vanderkam, Laura. "Stop Checking Your Email, Now." CNNMoney, 2013. Available online at http://management.fortune.cnn.com/2012/10/08/stop-checking-your-email-now/ (accessed May 15, 2013).

"World Earthquakes: Live Earthquake News and Highlights," World Earthquakes, 2012. http://www.world-earthquakes.com/index.php?option=ethq_prediction (accessed May 15, 2013).

SOLUTIONS

1

x	P(x)
0	0.12
1	0.18
2	0.30
3	0.15
4	0.10
5	0.10
6	0.05

Table 4.38

3 0.10 + 0.05 = 0.15

5 1

7 $0.35 + 0.40 + 0.10 = 0.85$

9 $1(0.15) + 2(0.35) + 3(0.40) + 4(0.10) = 0.15 + 0.70 + 1.20 + 0.40 = 2.45$

11

x	P(x)
0	0.03
1	0.04
2	0.08
3	0.85

Table 4.39

13 Let X = the number of events Javier volunteers for each month.

15

x	P(x)
0	0.05
1	0.05
2	0.10
3	0.20
4	0.25
5	0.35

Table 4.40

17 $1 - 0.05 = 0.95$

19 $0.2 + 1.2 + 2.4 + 1.6 = 5.4$

21 The values of $P(x)$ do not sum to one.

23 Let X = the number of years a physics major will spend doing post-graduate research.

25 $1 - 0.35 - 0.20 - 0.15 - 0.10 - 0.05 = 0.15$

27 $1(0.35) + 2(0.20) + 3(0.15) + 4(0.15) + 5(0.10) + 6(0.05) = 0.35 + 0.40 + 0.45 + 0.60 + 0.50 + 0.30 = 2.6$ years

29 X is the number of years a student studies ballet with the teacher.

31 $0.10 + 0.05 + 0.10 = 0.25$

33 The sum of the probabilities sum to one because it is a probability distribution.

35 $-2\left(\frac{40}{52}\right) + 30\left(\frac{12}{52}\right) = -1.54 + 6.92 = 5.38$

37 X = the number that reply "yes"

39 0, 1, 2, 3, 4, 5, 6, 7, 8

41 5.7

43 0.4151

45 X = the number of freshmen selected from the study until one replied "yes" that same-sex couples should have the right to legal marital status.

47 1,2,…

49 1.4

51 X = the number of business majors in the sample.

53 2, 3, 4, 5, 6, 7, 8, 9

55 6.26

57 0, 1, 2, 3, 4, …

59 0.0485

61 0.0214

63 X = the number of U.S. teens who die from motor vehicle injuries per day.

65 0, 1, 2, 3, 4, ...

67 No

71 The variable of interest is X, or the gain or loss, in dollars. The face cards jack, queen, and king. There are (3)(4) = 12 face cards and 52 – 12 = 40 cards that are not face cards. We first need to construct the probability distribution for X. We use the card and coin events to determine the probability for each outcome, but we use the monetary value of X to determine the expected value.

Card Event	X net gain/loss	$P(X)$
Face Card and Heads	6	$\left(\frac{12}{52}\right)\left(\frac{1}{2}\right) = \left(\frac{6}{52}\right)$
Face Card and Tails	2	$\left(\frac{12}{52}\right)\left(\frac{1}{2}\right) = \left(\frac{6}{52}\right)$
(Not Face Card) and (H or T)	–2	$\left(\frac{40}{52}\right)(1) = \left(\frac{40}{52}\right)$

Table 4.41

- Expected value = $(6)\left(\frac{6}{52}\right) + (2)\left(\frac{6}{52}\right) + (-2)\left(\frac{40}{52}\right) = -\frac{32}{52}$

- Expected value = –$0.62, rounded to the nearest cent

- If you play this game repeatedly, over a long string of games, you would expect to lose 62 cents per game, on average.

- You should not play this game to win money because the expected value indicates an expected average loss.

73
a. 0.1
b. 1.6

75

a.

Software Company	
x	**P(x)**
5,000,000	0.10
1,000,000	0.30
−1,000,000	0.60

Table 4.42

Hardware Company	
x	**P(x)**
3,000,000	0.20
1,000,000	0.40
−1,000,00	0.40

Table 4.43

Biotech Firm	
x	**P(x)**
6,00,000	0.10
0	0.70
−1,000,000	0.20

Table 4.44

b. $200,000; $600,000; $400,000

c. third investment because it has the lowest probability of loss

d. first investment because it has the highest probability of loss

e. second investment

77 4.85 years

79 b

81 Let X = the amount of money to be won on a ticket. The following table shows the PDF for X.

x	P(x)
0	0.969
5	$\frac{250}{10,000} = 0.025$

Table 4.45

x	P(x)
25	$\dfrac{50}{10,000} = 0.005$
100	$\dfrac{10}{10,000} = 0.001$

Table 4.45

Calculate the expected value of X. 0(0.969) + 5(0.025) + 25(0.005) + 100(0.001) = 0.35 A fair price for a ticket is $0.35. Any price over $0.35 will enable the lottery to raise money.

83 X = the number of patients calling in claiming to have the flu, who actually have the flu. X = 0, 1, 2, ...25

85 0.0165

87

a. X = the number of DVDs a Video to Go customer rents

b. 0.12

c. 0.11

d. 0.77

89 d. 4.43

91 c

93

- X = number of questions answered correctly

- $X \sim B\left(32, \dfrac{1}{3}\right)$

- We are interested in MORE THAN 75% of 32 questions correct. 75% of 32 is 24. We want to find $P(x > 24)$. The event "more than 24" is the complement of "less than or equal to 24."

- Using your calculator's distribution menu: $1 - \text{binomcdf}\left(32, \dfrac{1}{3}, \ 24\right)$

- $P(x > 24) = 0$

- The probability of getting more than 75% of the 32 questions correct when randomly guessing is very small and practically zero.

95

a. X = the number of college and universities that offer online offerings.

b. 0, 1, 2, …, 13

c. $X \sim B(13, 0.96)$

d. 12.48

e. 0.0135

f. $P(x = 12) = 0.3186$ $P(x = 13) = 0.5882$ More likely to get 13.

97

a. X = the number of fencers who do **not** use the foil as their main weapon

b. 0, 1, 2, 3,... 25

c. $X \sim B(25, 0.40)$

d. 10

   e. 0.0442

   f. The probability that all 25 not use the foil is almost zero. Therefore, it would be very surprising.

99

   a. X = the number of audits in a 20-year period

   b. 0, 1, 2, …, 20

   c. $X \sim B(20, 0.02)$

   d. 0.4

   e. 0.6676

   f. 0.0071

101

   1. X = the number of matches

   2. 0, 1, 2, 3

   3. $X \sim B\left(3, \frac{1}{6}\right)$

   4. In dollars: −1, 1, 2, 3

   5. $\frac{1}{2}$

   6. Multiply each Y value by the corresponding X probability from the PDF table. The answer is −0.0787. You lose about eight cents, on average, per game.

   7. The house has the advantage.

103

   a. $X \sim B(15, 0.281)$

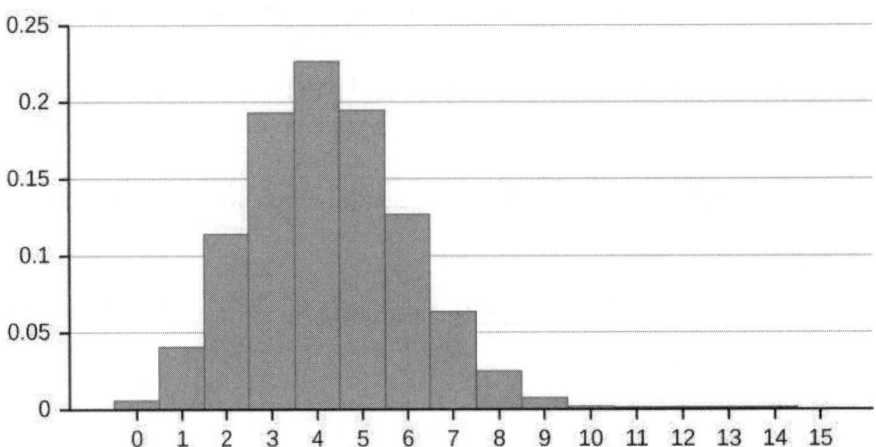

   Figure 4.10

   b.   i. Mean = μ = np = 15(0.281) = 4.215

        ii. Standard Deviation = σ = $\sqrt{npq}$ = $\sqrt{15(0.281)(0.719)}$ = 1.7409

   c. $P(x > 5) = 1 - P(x \le 5) = 1 - \text{binomcdf}(15, 0.281, 5) = 1 - 0.7754 = 0.2246$
      $P(x = 3) = \text{binompdf}(15, 0.281, 3) = 0.1927$
      $P(x = 4) = \text{binompdf}(15, 0.281, 4) = 0.2259$
      It is more likely that four people are literate that three people are.

105

a. X = the number of adults in America who are surveyed until one says he or she will watch the Super Bowl.

b. $X \sim G(0.40)$

c. 2.5

d. 0.0187

e. 0.2304

107

a. X = the number of pages that advertise footwear

b. X takes on the values 0, 1, 2, ..., 20

c. $X \sim B(20, \frac{29}{192})$

d. 3.02

e. No

f. 0.9997

g. X = the number of pages we must survey until we find one that advertises footwear. $X \sim G(\frac{29}{192})$

h. 0.3881

i. 6.6207 pages

109 0, 1, 2, and 3

111

a. $X \sim G(0.25)$

b. i. Mean = $\mu = \frac{1}{p} = \frac{1}{0.25} = 4$

 ii. Standard Deviation = $\sigma = \sqrt{\frac{1-p}{p^2}} = \sqrt{\frac{1-0.25}{0.25^2}} \approx 3.4641$

c. $P(x = 10)$ = geometpdf(0.25, 10) = 0.0188

d. $P(x = 20)$ = geometpdf(0.25, 20) = 0.0011

e. $P(x \leq 5)$ = geometcdf(0.25, 5) = 0.7627

113

a. X = the number of pages that advertise footwear

b. 0, 1, 2, 3, ..., 20

c. $X \sim H(29, 163, 20)$; $r = 29$, $b = 163$, $n = 20$

d. 3.03

e. 1.5197

115

a. X = the number of Patriots picked

b. 0, 1, 2, 3, 4

c. $X \sim H(4, 8, 9)$

d. Without replacement

117

a. $X \sim P(5.5)$; $\mu = 5.5$; $\sigma = \sqrt{5.5} \approx 2.3452$

b. $P(x \le 6) =$ poissoncdf(5.5, 6) ≈ 0.6860

c. There is a 15.7% probability that the law staff will receive more calls than they can handle.

d. $P(x > 8) = 1 - P(x \le 8) = 1 -$ poissoncdf(5.5, 8) $\approx 1 - 0.8944 = 0.1056$

119 Let $X =$ the number of defective bulbs in a string. Using the Poisson distribution:

- $\mu = np = 100(0.03) = 3$

- $X \sim P(3)$

- $P(x \le 4) =$ poissoncdf(3, 4) ≈ 0.8153

Using the binomial distribution:

- $X \sim B(100, 0.03)$

- $P(x \le 4) =$ binomcdf(100, 0.03, 4) ≈ 0.8179

The Poisson approximation is very good—the difference between the probabilities is only 0.0026.

121

a. $X =$ the number of children for a Spanish woman

b. 0, 1, 2, 3,...

c. $X \sim P(1.47)$

d. 0.2299

e. 0.5679

f. 0.4321

123

a. $X =$ the number of fortune cookies that have an extra fortune

b. 0, 1, 2, 3,... 144

c. $X \sim B(144, 0.03)$ or $P(4.32)$

d. 4.32

e. 0.0124 or 0.0133

f. 0.6300 or 0.6264

g. As n gets larger, the probabilities get closer together.

125

a. $X =$ the number of people audited in one year

b. 0, 1, 2, ..., 100

c. $X \sim P(2)$

d. 2

e. 0.1353

f. 0.3233

127

a. $X =$ the number of shell pieces in one cake

b. 0, 1, 2, 3,...

c. $X \sim P(1.5)$

d. 1.5

e. 0.2231

f. 0.0001

g. Yes

129 d

5 | CONTINUOUS RANDOM VARIABLES

Figure 5.1 The heights of these radish plants are continuous random variables. (Credit: Rev Stan)

Introduction

Chapter Objectives
By the end of this chapter, the student should be able to: • Recognize and understand continuous probability density functions in general. • Recognize the uniform probability distribution and apply it appropriately. • Recognize the exponential probability distribution and apply it appropriately.

Continuous random variables have many applications. Baseball batting averages, IQ scores, the length of time a long distance telephone call lasts, the amount of money a person carries, the length of time a computer chip lasts, and SAT scores are just a few. The field of reliability depends on a variety of continuous random variables.

> **NOTE**
>
> The values of discrete and continuous random variables can be ambiguous. For example, if X is equal to the number of miles (to the nearest mile) you drive to work, then X is a discrete random variable. You count the miles. If X is the distance you drive to work, then you measure values of X and X is a continuous random variable. For a second example, if X is equal to the number of books in a backpack, then X is a discrete random variable. If X is the weight of a book, then X is a continuous random variable because weights are measured. How the random variable is defined is very important.

Properties of Continuous Probability Distributions

The graph of a continuous probability distribution is a curve. Probability is represented by area under the curve.

The curve is called the **probability density function** (abbreviated as **pdf**). We use the symbol $f(x)$ to represent the curve. $f(x)$ is the function that corresponds to the graph; we use the density function $f(x)$ to draw the graph of the probability distribution.

Area under the curve is given by a different function called the **cumulative distribution function** (abbreviated as **cdf**). The cumulative distribution function is used to evaluate probability as area.

- The outcomes are measured, not counted.
- The entire area under the curve and above the x-axis is equal to one.
- Probability is found for intervals of x values rather than for individual x values.
- $P(c < x < d)$ is the probability that the random variable X is in the interval between the values c and d. $P(c < x < d)$ is the area under the curve, above the x-axis, to the right of c and the left of d.
- $P(x = c) = 0$ The probability that x takes on any single individual value is zero. The area below the curve, above the x-axis, and between $x = c$ and $x = c$ has no width, and therefore no area (area = 0). Since the probability is equal to the area, the probability is also zero.
- $P(c < x < d)$ is the same as $P(c \leq x \leq d)$ because probability is equal to area.

We will find the area that represents probability by using geometry, formulas, technology, or probability tables. In general, calculus is needed to find the area under the curve for many probability density functions. When we use formulas to find the area in this textbook, the formulas were found by using the techniques of integral calculus. However, because most students taking this course have not studied calculus, we will not be using calculus in this textbook.

There are many continuous probability distributions. When using a continuous probability distribution to model probability, the distribution used is selected to model and fit the particular situation in the best way.

In this chapter and the next, we will study the uniform distribution, the exponential distribution, and the normal distribution. The following graphs illustrate these distributions.

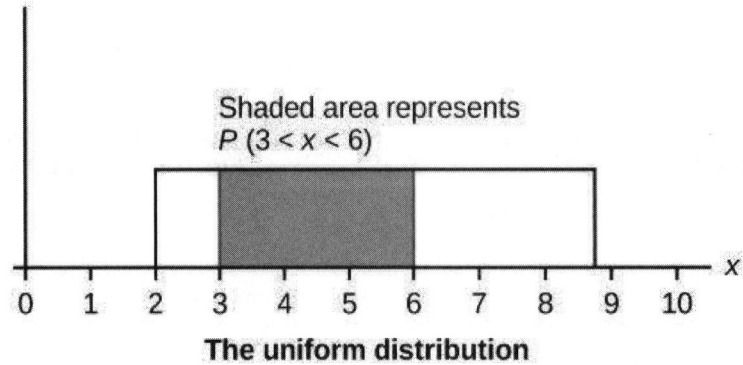

Figure 5.2 The graph shows a Uniform Distribution with the area between $x = 3$ and $x = 6$ shaded to represent the probability that the value of the random variable X is in the interval between three and six.

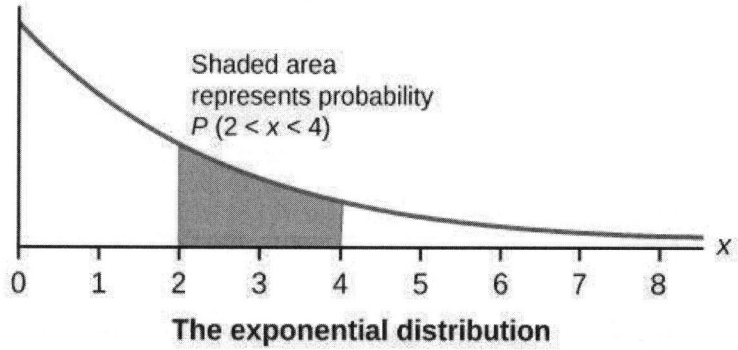

The exponential distribution

Figure 5.3 The graph shows an Exponential Distribution with the area between $x = 2$ and $x = 4$ shaded to represent the probability that the value of the random variable X is in the interval between two and four.

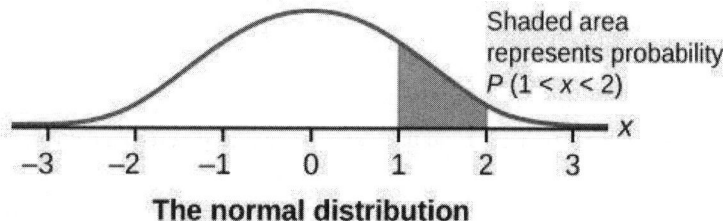

The normal distribution

Figure 5.4 The graph shows the Standard Normal Distribution with the area between $x = 1$ and $x = 2$ shaded to represent the probability that the value of the random variable X is in the interval between one and two.

5.1 | Continuous Probability Functions

We begin by defining a continuous probability density function. We use the function notation $f(x)$. Intermediate algebra may have been your first formal introduction to functions. In the study of probability, the functions we study are special. We define the function $f(x)$ so that the area between it and the x-axis is equal to a probability. Since the maximum probability is one, the maximum area is also one. **For continuous probability distributions, PROBABILITY = AREA.**

Example 5.1

Consider the function $f(x) = \frac{1}{20}$ for $0 \leq x \leq 20$. x = a real number. The graph of $f(x) = \frac{1}{20}$ is a horizontal line.

However, since $0 \leq x \leq 20$, $f(x)$ is restricted to the portion between $x = 0$ and $x = 20$, inclusive.

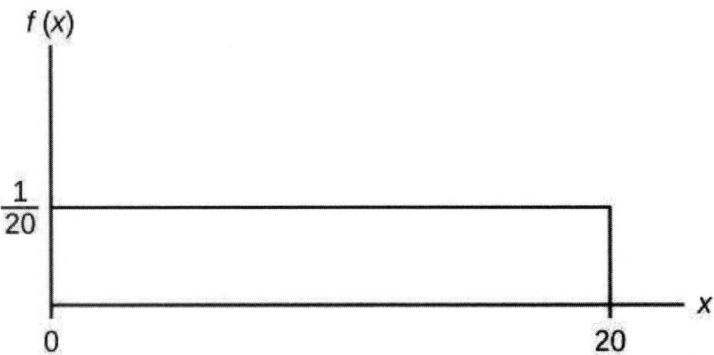

Figure 5.5

$f(x) = \frac{1}{20}$ **for** $0 \leq x \leq 20$.

The graph of $f(x) = \frac{1}{20}$ is a horizontal line segment when $0 \leq x \leq 20$.

The area between $f(x) = \frac{1}{20}$ where $0 \leq x \leq 20$ and the x-axis is the area of a rectangle with base = 20 and height = $\frac{1}{20}$.

$$\text{AREA} = 20\left(\frac{1}{20}\right) = 1$$

Suppose we want to find the area between $f(x) = \frac{1}{20}$ **and the x-axis where $0 < x < 2$.**

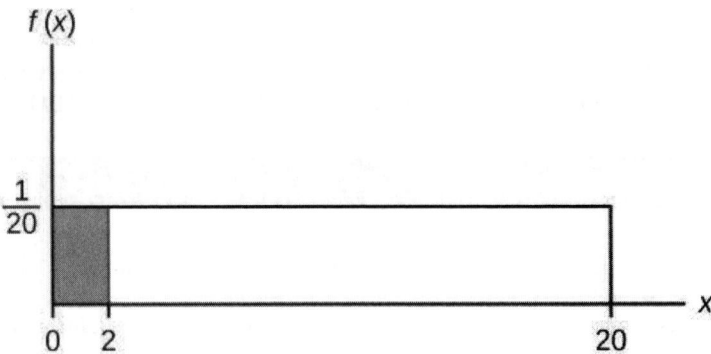

Figure 5.6

$$\text{AREA} = (2 - 0)\left(\frac{1}{20}\right) = 0.1$$

$(2 - 0) = 2 = $ base of a rectangle

REMINDER

area of a rectangle = (base)(height).

The area corresponds to a probability. The probability that x is between zero and two is 0.1, which can be written mathematically as $P(0 < x < 2) = P(x < 2) = 0.1$.

Suppose we want to find the area between $f(x) = \frac{1}{20}$ and the x-axis where $4 < x < 15$.

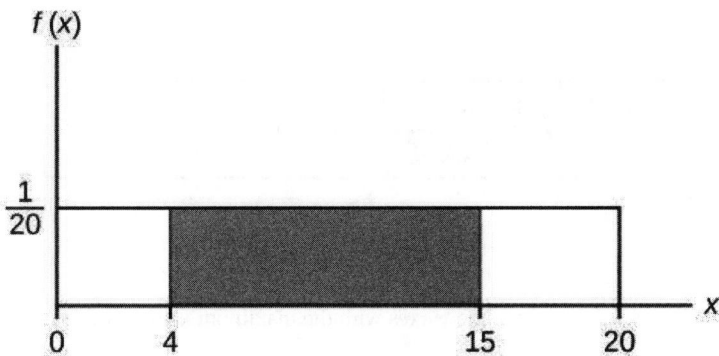

Figure 5.7

$$\text{AREA} = (15 - 4)\left(\frac{1}{20}\right) = 0.55$$

$(15 - 4) = 11 = $ the base of a rectangle

The area corresponds to the probability $P(4 < x < 15) = 0.55$.

Suppose we want to find $P(x = 15)$. On an x-y graph, $x = 15$ is a vertical line. A vertical line has no width (or zero width). Therefore, $P(x = 15) = $ (base)(height) $= (0)\left(\frac{1}{20}\right) = 0$

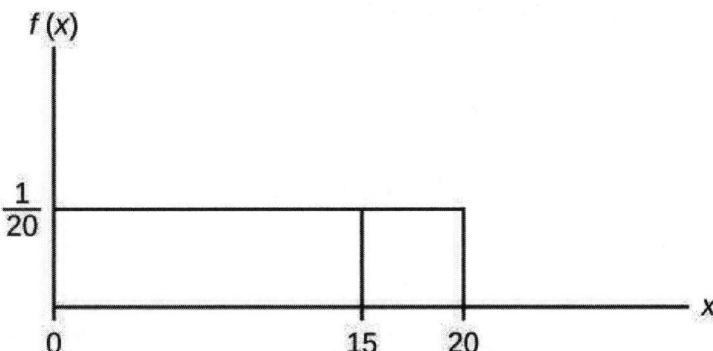

Figure 5.8

$P(X \leq x)$, which can also be written as $P(X < x)$ for continuous distributions, is called the cumulative distribution function or CDF. Notice the "less than or equal to" symbol. We can also use the CDF to calculate $P(X > x)$. The CDF gives "area to the left" and $P(X > x)$ gives "area to the right." We calculate $P(X > x)$ for continuous distributions as follows: $P(X > x) = 1 - P(X < x)$.

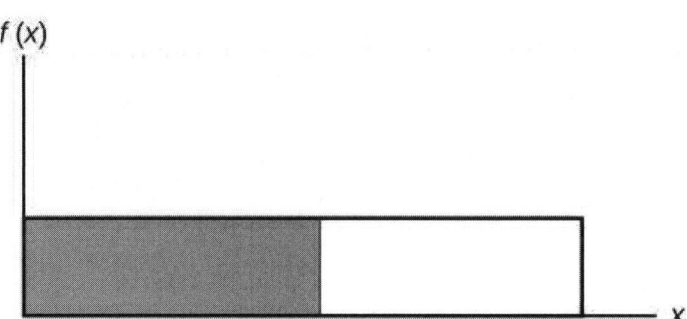

Figure 5.9

Label the graph with $f(x)$ and x. Scale the x and y axes with the maximum x and y values. $f(x) = \frac{1}{20}$, $0 \le x \le 20$.

To calculate the probability that x is between two values, look at the following graph. Shade the region between $x = 2.3$ and $x = 12.7$. Then calculate the shaded area of a rectangle.

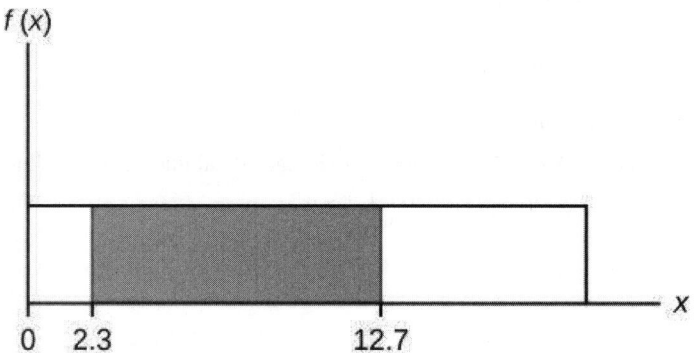

Figure 5.10

$$P(2.3 < x < 12.7) = (\text{base})(\text{height}) = (12.7 - 2.3)\left(\frac{1}{20}\right) = 0.52$$

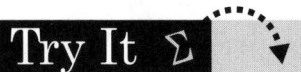

5.1 Consider the function $f(x) = \frac{1}{8}$ for $0 \le x \le 8$. Draw the graph of $f(x)$ and find $P(2.5 < x < 7.5)$.

5.2 | The Uniform Distribution

The uniform distribution is a continuous probability distribution and is concerned with events that are equally likely to occur. When working out problems that have a uniform distribution, be careful to note if the data is inclusive or exclusive of endpoints.

Example 5.2

The data in **Table 5.1** are 55 smiling times, in seconds, of an eight-week-old baby.

10.4	19.6	18.8	13.9	17.8	16.8	21.6	17.9	12.5	11.1	4.9
12.8	14.8	22.8	20.0	15.9	16.3	13.4	17.1	14.5	19.0	22.8
1.3	0.7	8.9	11.9	10.9	7.3	5.9	3.7	17.9	19.2	9.8
5.8	6.9	2.6	5.8	21.7	11.8	3.4	2.1	4.5	6.3	10.7
8.9	9.4	9.4	7.6	10.0	3.3	6.7	7.8	11.6	13.8	18.6

Table 5.1

The sample mean = 11.49 and the sample standard deviation = 6.23.

We will assume that the smiling times, in seconds, follow a uniform distribution between zero and 23 seconds, inclusive. This means that any smiling time from zero to and including 23 seconds is **equally likely**. The histogram that could be constructed from the sample is an empirical distribution that closely matches the theoretical uniform distribution.

Let X = length, in seconds, of an eight-week-old baby's smile.

The notation for the uniform distribution is

$X \sim U(a, b)$ where a = the lowest value of x and b = the highest value of x.

The probability density function is $f(x) = \dfrac{1}{b-a}$ for $a \le x \le b$.

For this example, $X \sim U(0, 23)$ and $f(x) = \dfrac{1}{23-0}$ for $0 \le X \le 23$.

Formulas for the theoretical mean and standard deviation are

$$\mu = \frac{a+b}{2} \text{ and } \sigma = \sqrt{\frac{(b-a)^2}{12}}$$

For this problem, the theoretical mean and standard deviation are

$$\mu = \frac{0+23}{2} = 11.50 \text{ seconds and } \sigma = \sqrt{\frac{(23-0)^2}{12}} = 6.64 \text{ seconds.}$$

Notice that the theoretical mean and standard deviation are close to the sample mean and standard deviation in this example.

Try It ∑

5.2 The data that follow are the number of passengers on 35 different charter fishing boats. The sample mean = 7.9 and the sample standard deviation = 4.33. The data follow a uniform distribution where all values between and including zero and 14 are equally likely. State the values of a and b. Write the distribution in proper notation, and calculate the theoretical mean and standard deviation.

1	12	4	10	4	14	11
7	11	4	13	2	4	6
3	10	0	12	6	9	10
5	13	4	10	14	12	11
6	10	11	0	11	13	2

Table 5.2

Example 5.3

a. Refer to **Example 5.2**. What is the probability that a randomly chosen eight-week-old baby smiles between two and 18 seconds?

Solution 5.3

$P(2 < x < 18) = \text{(base)(height)} = (18 - 2)\left(\frac{1}{23}\right) = \frac{16}{23}$.

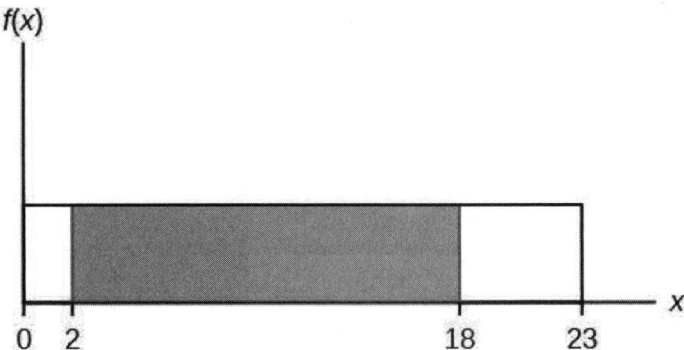

Figure 5.11

b. Find the 90th percentile for an eight-week-old baby's smiling time.

Solution 5.3

b. Ninety percent of the smiling times fall below the 90th percentile, k, so $P(x < k) = 0.90$.

$P(x < k) = 0.90$

$\text{(base)(height)} = 0.90$

$(k - 0)\left(\dfrac{1}{23}\right) = 0.90$

$k = (23)(0.90) = 20.7$

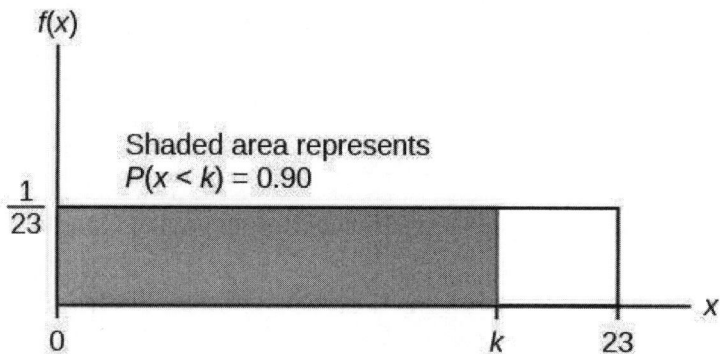

Figure 5.12

c. Find the probability that a random eight-week-old baby smiles more than 12 seconds **KNOWING** that the baby smiles **MORE THAN EIGHT SECONDS**.

Solution 5.3

c. This probability question is a **conditional**. You are asked to find the probability that an eight-week-old baby smiles more than 12 seconds when you **already know** the baby has smiled for more than eight seconds.

Find $P(x > 12 | x > 8)$ There are two ways to do the problem. **For the first way**, use the fact that this is a **conditional** and changes the sample space. The graph illustrates the new sample space. You already know the baby smiled more than eight seconds.

Write a new $f(x)$: $f(x) = \dfrac{1}{23 - 8} = \dfrac{1}{15}$ for $8 < x < 23$

$P(x > 12 | x > 8) = (23 - 12)\left(\dfrac{1}{15}\right) = \dfrac{11}{15}$

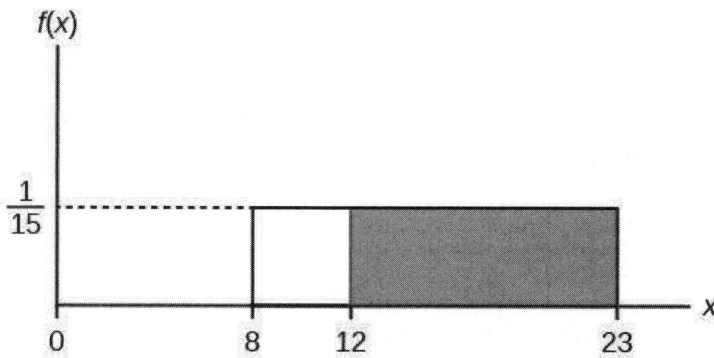

Figure 5.13

For the second way, use the conditional formula from **Probability Topics** with the original distribution $X \sim U$ (0, 23):

$$P(A|B) = \frac{P(A \text{ AND } B)}{P(B)}$$

For this problem, A is $(x > 12)$ and B is $(x > 8)$.

So, $P(x > 12 | x > 8) = \frac{(x > 12 \text{ AND } x > 8)}{P(x > 8)} = \frac{P(x > 12)}{P(x > 8)} = \frac{\frac{11}{23}}{\frac{15}{23}} = \frac{11}{15}$

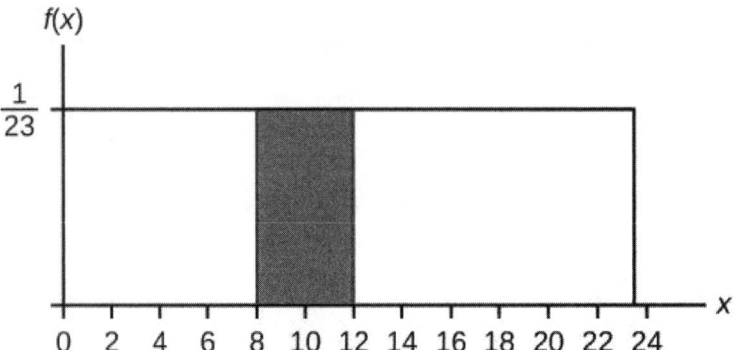

Figure 5.14

Try It Σ

5.3 A distribution is given as $X \sim U(0, 20)$. What is $P(2 < x < 18)$? Find the 90th percentile.

Example 5.4

The amount of time, in minutes, that a person must wait for a bus is uniformly distributed between zero and 15 minutes, inclusive.

a. What is the probability that a person waits fewer than 12.5 minutes?

Solution 5.4

a. Let X = the number of minutes a person must wait for a bus. $a = 0$ and $b = 15$. $X \sim U(0, 15)$. Write the probability density function. $f(x) = \frac{1}{15 - 0} = \frac{1}{15}$ for $0 \leq x \leq 15$.

Find $P(x < 12.5)$. Draw a graph.

$$P(x < k) = (\text{base})(\text{height}) = (12.5 - 0)\left(\frac{1}{15}\right) = 0.8333$$

The probability a person waits less than 12.5 minutes is 0.8333.

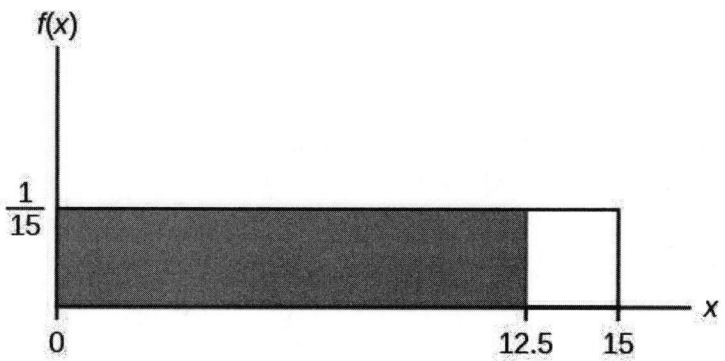

Figure 5.15

b. On the average, how long must a person wait? Find the mean, μ, and the standard deviation, σ.

Solution 5.4

b. $\mu = \dfrac{a + b}{2} = \dfrac{15 + 0}{2} = 7.5$. On the average, a person must wait 7.5 minutes.

$\sigma = \sqrt{\dfrac{(b\text{ - }a)^2}{12}} = \sqrt{\dfrac{(15\text{ - }0)^2}{12}} = 4.3$. The Standard deviation is 4.3 minutes.

c. Ninety percent of the time, the time a person must wait falls below what value?

This asks for the 90th percentile.

Solution 5.4

c. Find the 90th percentile. Draw a graph. Let k = the 90th percentile.

$P(x < k) = (\text{base})(\text{height}) = (k - 0)(\frac{1}{15})$

$0.90 = (k)\left(\frac{1}{15}\right)$

$k = (0.90)(15) = 13.5$

k is sometimes called a critical value.

The 90th percentile is 13.5 minutes. Ninety percent of the time, a person must wait at most 13.5 minutes.

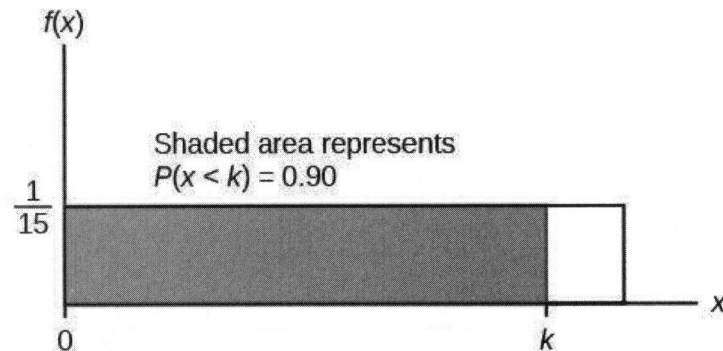

Figure 5.16

Try It Σ

5.4 The total duration of baseball games in the major league in the 2011 season is uniformly distributed between 447 hours and 521 hours inclusive.

   a. Find a and b and describe what they represent.

   b. Write the distribution.

   c. Find the mean and the standard deviation.

   d. What is the probability that the duration of games for a team for the 2011 season is between 480 and 500 hours?

   e. What is the 65th percentile for the duration of games for a team for the 2011 season?

Example 5.5

Suppose the time it takes a nine-year old to eat a donut is between 0.5 and 4 minutes, inclusive. Let X = the time, in minutes, it takes a nine-year old child to eat a donut. Then $X \sim U(0.5, 4)$.

a. The probability that a randomly selected nine-year old child eats a donut in at least two minutes is _____.

Solution 5.5
a. 0.5714

b. Find the probability that a different nine-year old child eats a donut in more than two minutes given that the child has already been eating the donut for more than 1.5 minutes.

The second question has a **conditional probability**. You are asked to find the probability that a nine-year old child eats a donut in more than two minutes given that the child has already been eating the donut for more than 1.5 minutes. Solve the problem two different ways (see **Exercise 5.0**). You must reduce the sample space. **First way**: Since you know the child has already been eating the donut for more than 1.5 minutes, you are no longer starting at a = 0.5 minutes. Your starting point is 1.5 minutes.

Write a new $f(x)$:

$$f(x) = \frac{1}{4 - 1.5} = \frac{2}{5} \text{ for } 1.5 \le x \le 4.$$

Find $P(x > 2 | x > 1.5)$. Draw a graph.

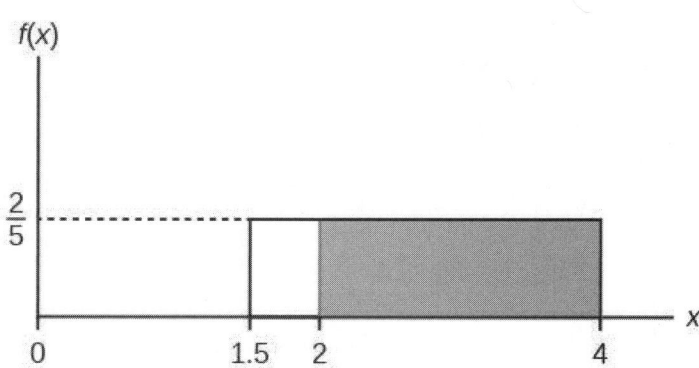

Figure 5.17

$P(x > 2|x > 1.5) = \text{(base)(new height)} = (4 - 2)\left(\frac{2}{5}\right) = \frac{4}{5}$

Solution 5.5

b. $\frac{4}{5}$

The probability that a nine-year old child eats a donut in more than two minutes given that the child has already been eating the donut for more than 1.5 minutes is $\frac{4}{5}$.

Second way: Draw the original graph for $X \sim U$ (0.5, 4). Use the conditional formula

$P(x > 2|x > 1.5) = \dfrac{P(x > 2 \text{ AND } x > 1.5)}{P(x > 1.5)} = \dfrac{P(x > 2)}{P(x > 1.5)} = \dfrac{\frac{2}{3.5}}{\frac{2.5}{3.5}} = 0.8 = \dfrac{4}{5}$

Try It Σ

5.5 Suppose the time it takes a student to finish a quiz is uniformly distributed between six and 15 minutes, inclusive. Let X = the time, in minutes, it takes a student to finish a quiz. Then $X \sim U$ (6, 15).

Find the probability that a randomly selected student needs at least eight minutes to complete the quiz. Then find the probability that a different student needs at least eight minutes to finish the quiz given that she has already taken more than seven minutes.

Example 5.6

Ace Heating and Air Conditioning Service finds that the amount of time a repairman needs to fix a furnace is uniformly distributed between 1.5 and four hours. Let x = the time needed to fix a furnace. Then $x \sim U$ (1.5, 4).

a. Find the probability that a randomly selected furnace repair requires more than two hours.

b. Find the probability that a randomly selected furnace repair requires less than three hours.

c. Find the 30th percentile of furnace repair times.

d. The longest 25% of furnace repair times take at least how long? (In other words: find the minimum time for the longest 25% of repair times.) What percentile does this represent?

e. Find the mean and standard deviation

Solution 5.6

a. To find $f(x)$: $f(x) = \dfrac{1}{4 - 1.5} = \dfrac{1}{2.5}$ so $f(x) = 0.4$

$P(x > 2) = $ (base)(height) $= (4 - 2)(0.4) = 0.8$

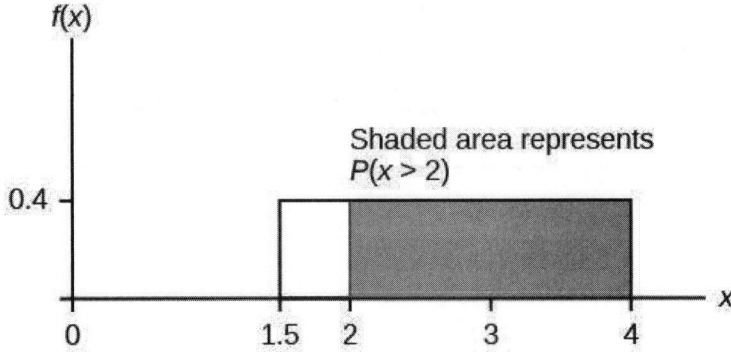

Figure 5.18 Uniform Distribution between 1.5 and four with shaded area between two and four representing the probability that the repair time x is greater than two

Solution 5.6

b. $P(x < 3) = $ (base)(height) $= (3 - 1.5)(0.4) = 0.6$

The graph of the rectangle showing the entire distribution would remain the same. However the graph should be shaded between $x = 1.5$ and $x = 3$. Note that the shaded area starts at $x = 1.5$ rather than at $x = 0$; since $X \sim U(1.5, 4)$, x can not be less than 1.5.

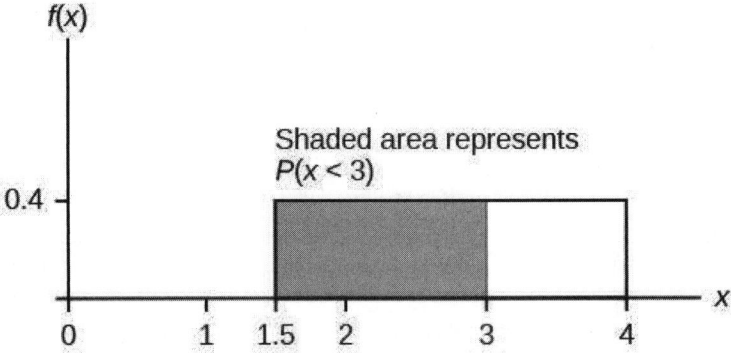

Figure 5.19 Uniform Distribution between 1.5 and four with shaded area between 1.5 and three representing the probability that the repair time x is less than three

Solution 5.6

c.

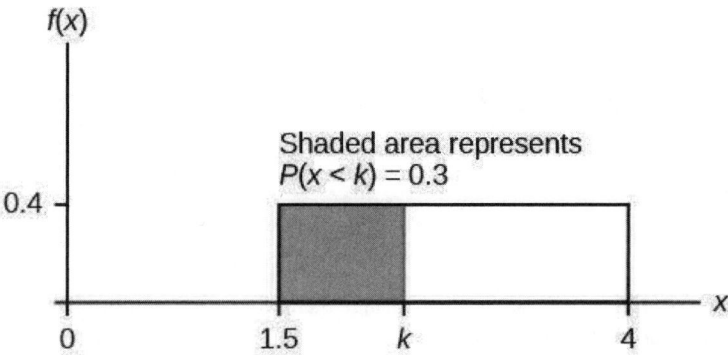

Figure 5.20 Uniform Distribution between 1.5 and 4 with an area of 0.30 shaded to the left, representing the shortest 30% of repair times.

$P (x < k) = 0.30$
$P(x < k) = (\text{base})(\text{height}) = (k - 1.5)(0.4)$
$0.3 = (k - 1.5) (0.4)$; Solve to find k:
$0.75 = k - 1.5$, obtained by dividing both sides by 0.4
$k = 2.25$, obtained by adding 1.5 to both sides
The 30th percentile of repair times is 2.25 hours. 30% of repair times are 2.5 hours or less.

Solution 5.6

d.

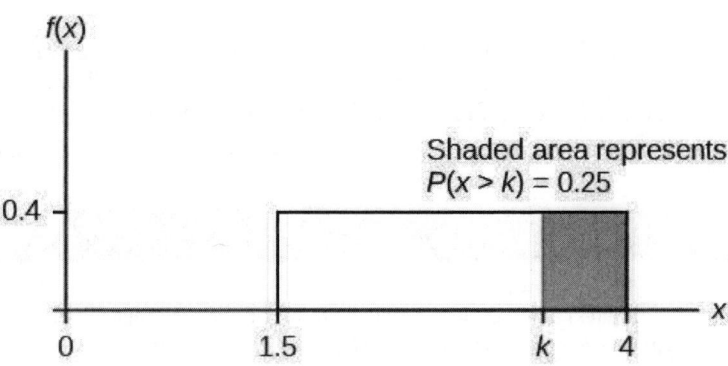

Figure 5.21 Uniform Distribution between 1.5 and 4 with an area of 0.25 shaded to the right representing the longest 25% of repair times.

$P(x > k) = 0.25$
$P(x > k) = (\text{base})(\text{height}) = (4 - k)(0.4)$
$0.25 = (4 - k)(0.4)$; Solve for k:
$0.625 = 4 - k$,
obtained by dividing both sides by 0.4
$-3.375 = -k$,
obtained by subtracting four from both sides: **$k = 3.375$**
The longest 25% of furnace repairs take at least 3.375 hours (3.375 hours or longer).
Note: Since 25% of repair times are 3.375 hours or longer, that means that 75% of repair times are 3.375 hours or less. 3.375 hours is the **75th percentile** of furnace repair times.

Solution 5.6

e. $\mu = \dfrac{a+b}{2}$ and $\sigma = \sqrt{\dfrac{(b-a)^2}{12}}$

$\mu = \dfrac{1.5+4}{2} = 2.75$ hours and $\sigma = \sqrt{\dfrac{(4-1.5)^2}{12}} = 0.7217$ hours

Try It Σ

5.6 The amount of time a service technician needs to change the oil in a car is uniformly distributed between 11 and 21 minutes. Let $X =$ the time needed to change the oil on a car.

a. Write the random variable X in words. $X =$ _____.

b. Write the distribution.

c. Graph the distribution.

d. Find $P(x > 19)$.

e. Find the 50th percentile.

5.3 | The Exponential Distribution

The **exponential distribution** is often concerned with the amount of time until some specific event occurs. For example, the amount of time (beginning now) until an earthquake occurs has an exponential distribution. Other examples include the length, in minutes, of long distance business telephone calls, and the amount of time, in months, a car battery lasts. It can be shown, too, that the value of the change that you have in your pocket or purse approximately follows an exponential distribution.

Values for an exponential random variable occur in the following way. There are fewer large values and more small values. For example, the amount of money customers spend in one trip to the supermarket follows an exponential distribution. There are more people who spend small amounts of money and fewer people who spend large amounts of money.

Exponential distributions are commonly used in calculations of product reliability, or the length of time a product lasts.

Example 5.7

Let $X =$ amount of time (in minutes) a postal clerk spends with his or her customer. The time is known to have an exponential distribution with the average amount of time equal to four minutes.

X is a **continuous random variable** since time is measured. It is given that $\mu = 4$ minutes. To do any calculations, you must know m, the decay parameter.

$m = \dfrac{1}{\mu}$. Therefore, $m = \dfrac{1}{4} = 0.25$.

The standard deviation, σ, is the same as the mean. $\mu = \sigma$

The distribution notation is $X \sim Exp(m)$. Therefore, $X \sim Exp(0.25)$.

The probability density function is $f(x) = me^{-mx}$. The number $e = 2.71828182846...$ It is a number that is used often in mathematics. Scientific calculators have the key "e^x." If you enter one for x, the calculator will display the value e.

The curve is:

$f(x) = 0.25e^{-0.25x}$ where x is at least zero and $m = 0.25$.

For example, $f(5) = 0.25e^{(-0.25)(5)} = 0.072$. The probability that the postal clerk spends five minutes with the customers is 0.072.

The graph is as follows:

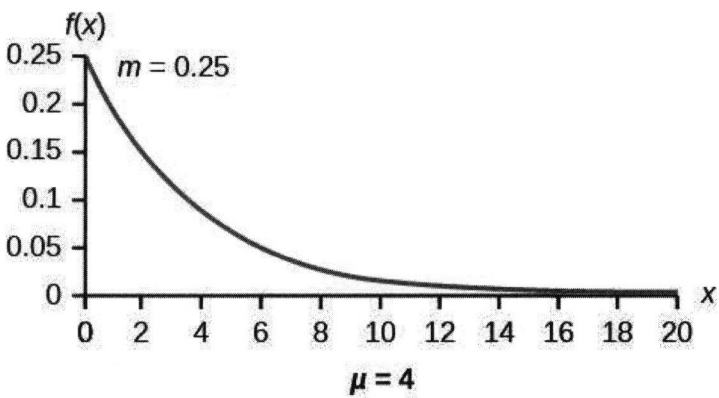

Figure 5.22

Notice the graph is a declining curve. When $x = 0$,

$f(x) = 0.25e^{(-0.25)(0)} = (0.25)(1) = 0.25 = m$. The maximum value on the y-axis is m.

Try It Σ

5.7 The amount of time spouses shop for anniversary cards can be modeled by an exponential distribution with the average amount of time equal to eight minutes. Write the distribution, state the probability density function, and graph the distribution.

Example 5.8

a. Using the information in **Example 5.7**, find the probability that a clerk spends four to five minutes with a randomly selected customer.

Solution 5.8

a. Find $P(4 < x < 5)$.

The **cumulative distribution function (CDF)** gives the area to the left.

$P(x < x) = 1 - e^{-mx}$

$P(x < 5) = 1 - e^{(-0.25)(5)} = 0.7135$ and $P(x < 4) = 1 - e^{(-0.25)(4)} = 0.6321$

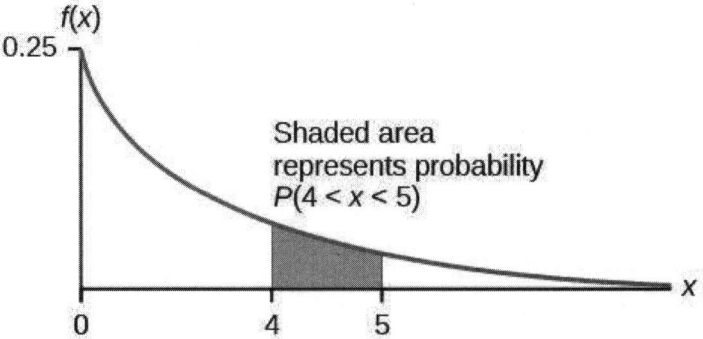

Figure 5.23

NOTE

You can do these calculations easily on a calculator.

The probability that a postal clerk spends four to five minutes with a randomly selected customer is $P(4 < x < 5)$ = $P(x < 5) - P(x < 4) = 0.7135 - 0.6321 = 0.0814$.

 Using the TI-83, 83+, 84, 84+ Calculator

On the home screen, enter $(1 - e^{(-0.25*5)})-(1-e^{(-0.25*4)})$ or enter $e^{(-0.25*4)} - e^{(-0.25*5)}$.

b. Half of all customers are finished within how long? (Find the 50th percentile)

Solution 5.8

b. Find the 50th percentile.

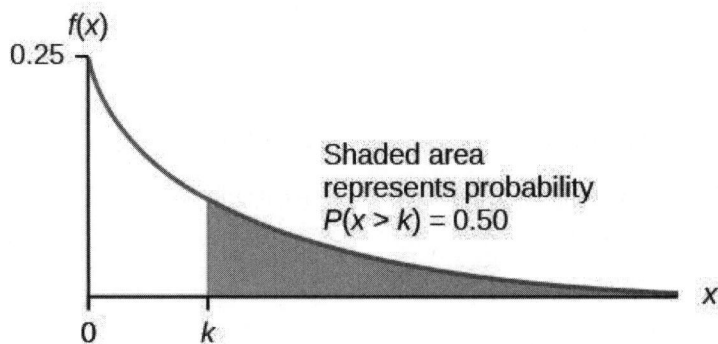

Figure 5.24

$P(x < k) = 0.50$, $k = 2.8$ minutes (calculator or computer)

Half of all customers are finished within 2.8 minutes.

You can also do the calculation as follows:

$P(x < k) = 0.50$ and $P(x < k) = 1 - e^{-0.25k}$

Therefore, $0.50 = 1 - e^{-0.25k}$ and $e^{-0.25k} = 1 - 0.50 = 0.5$

Take natural logs: $ln(e^{-0.25k}) = ln(0.50)$. So, $-0.25k = ln(0.50)$

Solve for k: $k = \dfrac{ln(0.50)}{-0.25} = 2.8$ minutes. The calculator simplifies the calculation for percentile k. See the following two notes.

NOTE

A formula for the percentile k is $k = \dfrac{ln(1 - AreaToTheLeft)}{-m}$ where ln is the natural log.

 Using the TI-83, 83+, 84, 84+ Calculator

On the home screen, enter $ln(1 - 0.50)/{-0.25}$. Press the (-) for the negative.

c. Which is larger, the mean or the median?

Solution 5.8

c. From part b, the median or 50th percentile is 2.8 minutes. The theoretical mean is four minutes. The mean is larger.

Try It Σ

5.8 The number of days ahead travelers purchase their airline tickets can be modeled by an exponential distribution with the average amount of time equal to 15 days. Find the probability that a traveler will purchase a ticket fewer than ten days in advance. How many days do half of all travelers wait?

Collaborative Exercise

Have each class member count the change he or she has in his or her pocket or purse. Your instructor will record the amounts in dollars and cents. Construct a histogram of the data taken by the class. Use five intervals. Draw a smooth curve through the bars. The graph should look approximately exponential. Then calculate the mean.

Let X = the amount of money a student in your class has in his or her pocket or purse.

The distribution for X is approximately exponential with mean, $\mu =$ _____ and $m =$ _____. The standard deviation, $\sigma =$ _____.

Draw the appropriate exponential graph. You should label the x– and y–axes, the decay rate, and the mean. Shade the area that represents the probability that one student has less than $.40 in his or her pocket or purse. (Shade $P(x < 0.40)$).

Example 5.9

On the average, a certain computer part lasts ten years. The length of time the computer part lasts is exponentially distributed.

a. What is the probability that a computer part lasts more than 7 years?

Solution 5.9

a. Let x = the amount of time (in years) a computer part lasts.

$\mu = 10$ so $m = \frac{1}{\mu} = \frac{1}{10} = 0.1$

Find $P(x > 7)$. Draw the graph.
$P(x > 7) = 1 - P(x < 7)$.
Since $P(X < x) = 1 - e^{-mx}$ then $P(X > x) = 1 - (1 - e^{-mx}) = e^{-mx}$
$P(x > 7) = e^{(-0.1)(7)} = 0.4966$. The probability that a computer part lasts more than seven years is 0.4966.

Using the TI-83, 83+, 84, 84+ Calculator

On the home screen, enter e^(-.1*7).

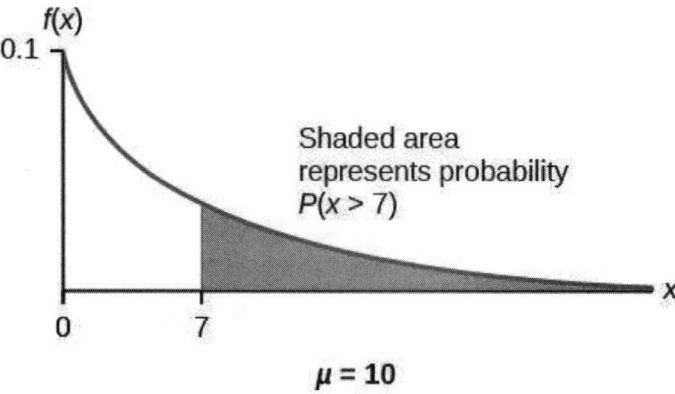

Figure 5.25

b. On the average, how long would five computer parts last if they are used one after another?

Solution 5.9

b. On the average, one computer part lasts ten years. Therefore, five computer parts, if they are used one right after the other would last, on the average, (5)(10) = 50 years.

c. Eighty percent of computer parts last at most how long?

Solution 5.9

c. Find the 80th percentile. Draw the graph. Let k = the 80th percentile.

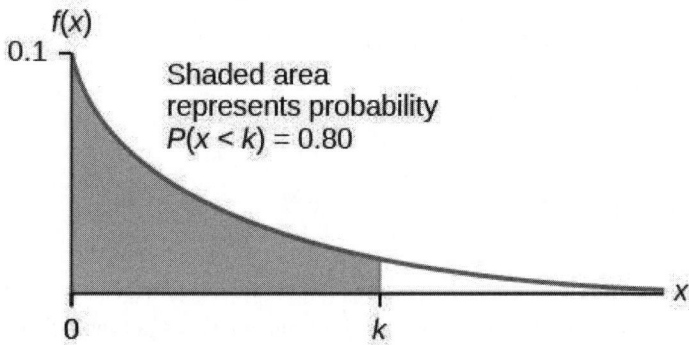

Figure 5.26

Solve for k: $k = \dfrac{ln(1 - 0.80)}{-0.1} = 16.1$ years

Eighty percent of the computer parts last at most 16.1 years.

 Using the TI-83, 83+, 84, 84+ Calculator

On the home screen, enter $\dfrac{ln(1 - 0.80)}{-0.1}$

d. What is the probability that a computer part lasts between nine and 11 years?

Solution 5.9

d. Find $P(9 < x < 11)$. Draw the graph.

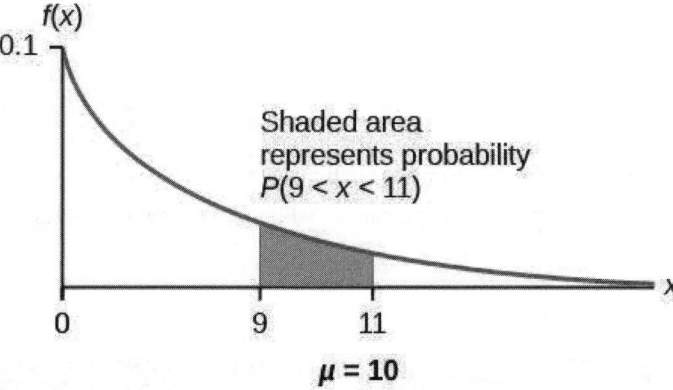

Figure 5.27

$P(9 < x < 11) = P(x < 11) - P(x < 9) = (1 - e^{(-0.1)(11)}) - (1 - e^{(-0.1)(9)}) = 0.6671 - 0.5934 = 0.0737$. The probability that a computer part lasts between nine and 11 years is 0.0737.

Using the TI-83, 83+, 84, 84+ Calculator

On the home screen, enter $e^{\wedge}(-0.1*9) - e^{\wedge}(-0.1*11)$.

Try It Σ

5.9 On average, a pair of running shoes can last 18 months if used every day. The length of time running shoes last is exponentially distributed. What is the probability that a pair of running shoes last more than 15 months? On average, how long would six pairs of running shoes last if they are used one after the other? Eighty percent of running shoes last at most how long if used every day?

Example 5.10

Suppose that the length of a phone call, in minutes, is an exponential random variable with decay parameter $\frac{1}{12}$.

If another person arrives at a public telephone just before you, find the probability that you will have to wait more than five minutes. Let X = the length of a phone call, in minutes.

What is m, μ, and σ? The probability that you must wait more than five minutes is _____ .

Solution 5.10

- $m = \frac{1}{12}$

- $\mu = 12$

- $\sigma = 12$

$P(x > 5) = 0.6592$

Try It Σ

5.10 Suppose that the distance, in miles, that people are willing to commute to work is an exponential random variable with a decay parameter $\frac{1}{20}$. Let X = the distance people are willing to commute in miles. What is m, μ, and σ? What is the probability that a person is willing to commute more than 25 miles?

Example 5.11

The time spent waiting between events is often modeled using the exponential distribution. For example, suppose that an average of 30 customers per hour arrive at a store and the time between arrivals is exponentially distributed.

  a. On average, how many minutes elapse between two successive arrivals?

  b. When the store first opens, how long on average does it take for three customers to arrive?

  c. After a customer arrives, find the probability that it takes less than one minute for the next customer to arrive.

d. After a customer arrives, find the probability that it takes more than five minutes for the next customer to arrive.

e. Seventy percent of the customers arrive within how many minutes of the previous customer?

f. Is an exponential distribution reasonable for this situation?

Solution 5.11

a. Since we expect 30 customers to arrive per hour (60 minutes), we expect on average one customer to arrive every two minutes on average.

b. Since one customer arrives every two minutes on average, it will take six minutes on average for three customers to arrive.

c. Let X = the time between arrivals, in minutes. By part a, $\mu = 2$, so $m = \frac{1}{2} = 0.5$.

Therefore, $X \sim Exp(0.5)$.
The cumulative distribution function is $P(X < x) = 1 - e^{(-0.5)(x)}$.
Therefore $P(X < 1) = 1 - e^{(-0.5)(1)} \approx 0.3935$.

$1 - e^{\wedge}(-0.5) \approx 0.3935$

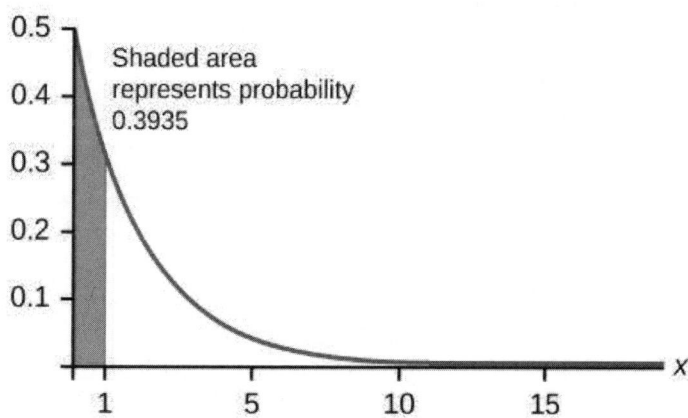

Figure 5.28

d. $P(X > 5) = 1 - P(X < 5) = 1 - (1 - e^{(-0.50)(5)}) = e^{-2.5} \approx 0.0821$.

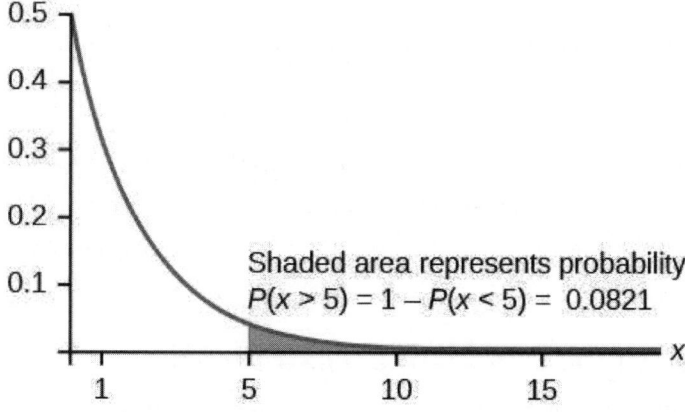

Figure 5.29

$1 - (1 - e^{\wedge}((-0.50)(5)))$ or $e^{\wedge}(-5*0.5)$

e. We want to solve $0.70 = P(X < x)$ for x.

Substituting in the cumulative distribution function gives $0.70 = 1 - e^{-0.5x}$, so that $e^{-0.5x} = 0.30$. Converting this to logarithmic form gives $-0.5x = ln(0.30)$, or $x = \dfrac{ln(0.30)}{-0.5} \approx 2.41$ minutes.

Thus, seventy percent of customers arrive within 2.41 minutes of the previous customer.

You are finding the 70th percentile k so you can use the formula $k = \dfrac{ln(1 - Area\_To\_The\_Left\_Of\_k)}{(-m)}$

$k = \dfrac{ln(1 - 0.70)}{(-0.5)} \approx 2.41$ minutes

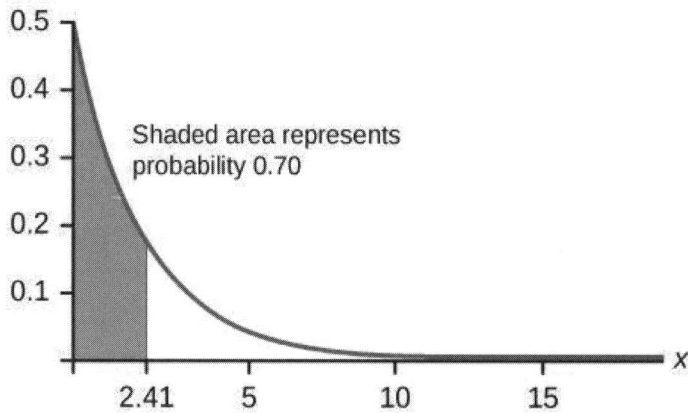

Figure 5.30

f. This model assumes that a single customer arrives at a time, which may not be reasonable since people might shop in groups, leading to several customers arriving at the same time. It also assumes that the flow of customers does not change throughout the day, which is not valid if some times of the day are busier than others.

Try It Σ

5.11 Suppose that on a certain stretch of highway, cars pass at an average rate of five cars per minute. Assume that the duration of time between successive cars follows the exponential distribution.

a. On average, how many seconds elapse between two successive cars?

b. After a car passes by, how long on average will it take for another seven cars to pass by?

c. Find the probability that after a car passes by, the next car will pass within the next 20 seconds.

d. Find the probability that after a car passes by, the next car will not pass for at least another 15 seconds.

Memorylessness of the Exponential Distribution

In **Example 5.7** recall that the amount of time between customers is exponentially distributed with a mean of two minutes ($X \sim Exp$ (0.5)). Suppose that five minutes have elapsed since the last customer arrived. Since an unusually long amount of time has now elapsed, it would seem to be more likely for a customer to arrive within the next minute. With the exponential distribution, this is not the case–the additional time spent waiting for the next customer does not depend on how much time has already elapsed since the last customer. This is referred to as the **memoryless property**. Specifically, the **memoryless property** says that

$P(X > r + t \mid X > r) = P(X > t)$ for all $r \geq 0$ and $t \geq 0$

For example, if five minutes have elapsed since the last customer arrived, then the probability that more than one minute will elapse before the next customer arrives is computed by using $r = 5$ and $t = 1$ in the foregoing equation.

$P(X > 5 + 1 \mid X > 5) = P(X > 1) = e^{(-0.5)(1)} \approx 0.6065.$

This is the same probability as that of waiting more than one minute for a customer to arrive after the previous arrival.

The exponential distribution is often used to model the longevity of an electrical or mechanical device. In **Example 5.9**, the lifetime of a certain computer part has the exponential distribution with a mean of ten years ($X \sim Exp(0.1)$). The **memoryless property** says that knowledge of what has occurred in the past has no effect on future probabilities. In this case it means that an old part is not any more likely to break down at any particular time than a brand new part. In other words, the part stays as good as new until it suddenly breaks. For example, if the part has already lasted ten years, then the probability that it lasts another seven years is $P(X > 17 \mid X > 10) = P(X > 7) = 0.4966$.

Example 5.12

Refer to **Example 5.7** where the time a postal clerk spends with his or her customer has an exponential distribution with a mean of four minutes. Suppose a customer has spent four minutes with a postal clerk. What is the probability that he or she will spend at least an additional three minutes with the postal clerk?

The decay parameter of X is $m = \dfrac{1}{4} = 0.25$, so $X \sim Exp(0.25)$.

The cumulative distribution function is $P(X < x) = 1 - e^{-0.25x}$.

We want to find $P(X > 7 \mid X > 4)$. The **memoryless property** says that $P(X > 7 \mid X > 4) = P(X > 3)$, so we just need to find the probability that a customer spends more than three minutes with a postal clerk.

This is $P(X > 3) = 1 - P(X < 3) = 1 - (1 - e^{-0.25 \cdot 3}) = e^{-0.75} \approx 0.4724$.

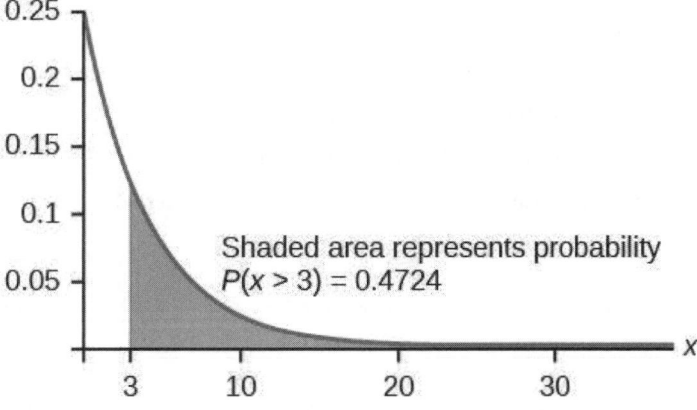

Figure 5.31

🖩 Using the TI-83, 83+, 84, 84+ Calculator

$1-(1-e^{\wedge}(-0.25*3)) = e^{\wedge}(-0.25*3).$

5.12 Suppose that the longevity of a light bulb is exponential with a mean lifetime of eight years. If a bulb has already lasted 12 years, find the probability that it will last a total of over 19 years.

Relationship between the Poisson and the Exponential Distribution

There is an interesting relationship between the exponential distribution and the Poisson distribution. Suppose that the time that elapses between two successive events follows the exponential distribution with a mean of μ units of time. Also assume that these times are independent, meaning that the time between events is not affected by the times between previous events. If these assumptions hold, then the number of events per unit time follows a Poisson distribution with mean $\lambda = 1/\mu$. Recall from the chapter on **Discrete Random Variables** that if X has the Poisson distribution with mean λ, then $P(X = k) = \frac{\lambda^k e^{-\lambda}}{k!}$. Conversely, if the number of events per unit time follows a Poisson distribution, then the amount of time between events follows the exponential distribution. ($k! = k*(k–1*)(k–2)*(k–3)…3*2*1$)

 Using the TI-83, 83+, 84, 84+ Calculator

Suppose X has the Poisson distribution with mean λ. Compute $P(X = k)$ by entering 2nd, VARS(DISTR), C: poissonpdf(λ, k). To compute $P(X \leq k)$, enter 2nd, VARS (DISTR), D:poissoncdf(λ, k).

Example 5.13

At a police station in a large city, calls come in at an average rate of four calls per minute. Assume that the time that elapses from one call to the next has the exponential distribution. Take note that we are concerned only with the rate at which calls come in, and we are ignoring the time spent on the phone. We must also assume that the times spent between calls are independent. This means that a particularly long delay between two calls does not mean that there will be a shorter waiting period for the next call. We may then deduce that the total number of calls received during a time period has the Poisson distribution.

a. Find the average time between two successive calls.

b. Find the probability that after a call is received, the next call occurs in less than ten seconds.

c. Find the probability that exactly five calls occur within a minute.

d. Find the probability that less than five calls occur within a minute.

e. Find the probability that more than 40 calls occur in an eight-minute period.

Solution 5.13

a. On average there are four calls occur per minute, so 15 seconds, or $\frac{15}{60} = 0.25$ minutes occur between successive calls on average.

b. Let T = time elapsed between calls. From part a, $\mu = 0.25$, so $m = \frac{1}{0.25} = 4$. Thus, $T \sim Exp(4)$.

The cumulative distribution function is $P(T < t) = 1 - e^{-4t}$.

The probability that the next call occurs in less than ten seconds (ten seconds = 1/6 minute) is

$$P\left(T < \frac{1}{6}\right) = 1 - e^{\left(-4\right)\left(\frac{1}{6}\right)} \approx 0.4866.$$

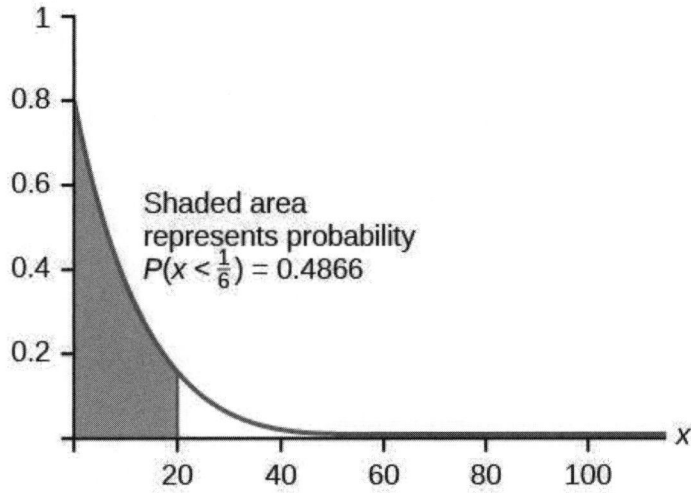

Figure 5.32

c. Let X = the number of calls per minute. As previously stated, the number of calls per minute has a Poisson distribution, with a mean of four calls per minute.

Therefore, $X \sim Poisson(4)$, and so $P(X = 5) = \dfrac{4^5 e^{-4}}{5!} \approx 0.1563$. ($5! = (5)(4)(3)(2)(1)$)

poissonpdf(4, 5) = 0.1563.

d. Keep in mind that X must be a whole number, so $P(X < 5) = P(X \leq 4)$.
    To compute this, we could take $P(X = 0) + P(X = 1) + P(X = 2) + P(X = 3) + P(X = 4)$.
    Using technology, we see that $P(X \leq 4) = 0.6288$.

poisssoncdf(4, 4) = 0.6288

e. Let Y = the number of calls that occur during an eight minute period.
    Since there is an average of four calls per minute, there is an average of $(8)(4) = 32$ calls during each eight minute period.
    Hence, $Y \sim Poisson(32)$. Therefore, $P(Y > 40) = 1 - P(Y \leq 40) = 1 - 0.9294 = 0.0707$.

1 – poissoncdf(32, 40). = 0.0707

Try It Σ

5.13 In a small city, the number of automobile accidents occur with a Poisson distribution at an average of three per week.

a. Calculate the probability that there are at most 2 accidents occur in any given week.

b. What is the probability that there is at least two weeks between any 2 accidents?

5.4 | Continuous Distribution

Stats Lab

5.1 Continuous Distribution

Class Time:

Names:

Student Learning Outcomes

- The student will compare and contrast empirical data from a random number generator with the uniform distribution.

Collect the Data

Use a random number generator to generate 50 values between zero and one (inclusive). List them in **Table 5.3**. Round the numbers to four decimal places or set the calculator MODE to four places.

1. Complete the table.

Table 5.3

2. Calculate the following:

   a. $\bar{x} =$ _____

   b. $s =$ _____

   c. first quartile = _____

   d. third quartile = _____

   e. median = _____

Organize the Data

1. Construct a histogram of the empirical data. Make eight bars.

Figure 5.33

2. Construct a histogram of the empirical data. Make five bars.

Figure 5.34

Describe the Data

1. In two to three complete sentences, describe the shape of each graph. (Keep it simple. Does the graph go straight across, does it have a V shape, does it have a hump in the middle or at either end, and so on. One way to help you determine a shape is to draw a smooth curve roughly through the top of the bars.)

2. Describe how changing the number of bars might change the shape.

Theoretical Distribution

1. In words, $X =$ _____.

2. The theoretical distribution of X is $X \sim U(0,1)$.

3. In theory, based upon the distribution $X \sim U(0,1)$, complete the following.

   a. $\mu =$ _____

   b. $\sigma =$ _____

   c. first quartile = _____

   d. third quartile = _____

   e. median = _____

4. Are the empirical values (the data) in the section titled **Collect the Data** close to the corresponding theoretical values? Why or why not?

Plot the Data

1. Construct a box plot of the data. Be sure to use a ruler to scale accurately and draw straight edges.

2. Do you notice any potential outliers? If so, which values are they? Either way, justify your answer numerically. (Recall that any DATA that are less than $Q_1 - 1.5(IQR)$ or more than $Q_3 + 1.5(IQR)$ are potential outliers. IQR means interquartile range.)

Compare the Data

1. For each of the following parts, use a complete sentence to comment on how the value obtained from the data compares to the theoretical value you expected from the distribution in the section titled **Theoretical Distribution**.

   a. minimum value: _____

   b. first quartile: _____

   c. median: _____

   d. third quartile: _____

   e. maximum value: _____

   f. width of IQR: _____

   g. overall shape: _____

2. Based on your comments in the section titled **Collect the Data**, how does the box plot fit or not fit what you would expect of the distribution in the section titled **Theoretical Distribution**?

Discussion Question

1. Suppose that the number of values generated was 500, not 50. How would that affect what you would expect the empirical data to be and the shape of its graph to look like?

KEY TERMS

Conditional Probability the likelihood that an event will occur given that another event has already occurred.

decay parameter The decay parameter describes the rate at which probabilities decay to zero for increasing values of x. It is the value m in the probability density function $f(x) = me^{(-mx)}$ of an exponential random variable. It is also equal to $m = \frac{1}{\mu}$, where μ is the mean of the random variable.

Exponential Distribution a continuous random variable (RV) that appears when we are interested in the intervals of time between some random events, for example, the length of time between emergency arrivals at a hospital; the notation is $X \sim Exp(m)$. The mean is $\mu = \frac{1}{m}$ and the standard deviation is $\sigma = \frac{1}{m}$. The probability density function is $f(x) = me^{-mx}$, $x \geq 0$ and the cumulative distribution function is $P(X \leq x) = 1 - e^{-mx}$.

memoryless property For an exponential random variable X, the memoryless property is the statement that knowledge of what has occurred in the past has no effect on future probabilities. This means that the probability that X exceeds $x + k$, given that it has exceeded x, is the same as the probability that X would exceed k if we had no knowledge about it. In symbols we say that $P(X > x + k | X > x) = P(X > k)$.

Poisson distribution If there is a known average of λ events occurring per unit time, and these events are independent of each other, then the number of events X occurring in one unit of time has the Poisson distribution. The probability of k events occurring in one unit time is equal to $P(X = k) = \frac{\lambda^k e^{-\lambda}}{k!}$.

Uniform Distribution a continuous random variable (RV) that has equally likely outcomes over the domain, $a < x < b$. Notation: $X \sim U(a,b)$. The mean is $\mu = \frac{a+b}{2}$ and the standard deviation is $\sigma = \sqrt{\frac{(b-a)^2}{12}}$. The probability density function is $f(x) = \frac{1}{b-a}$ for $a < x < b$ or $a \leq x \leq b$. The cumulative distribution is $P(X \leq x) = \frac{x-a}{b-a}$.

CHAPTER REVIEW

5.1 Continuous Probability Functions

The probability density function (pdf) is used to describe probabilities for continuous random variables. The area under the density curve between two points corresponds to the probability that the variable falls between those two values. In other words, the area under the density curve between points a and b is equal to $P(a < x < b)$. The cumulative distribution function (cdf) gives the probability as an area. If X is a continuous random variable, the probability density function (pdf), $f(x)$, is used to draw the graph of the probability distribution. The total area under the graph of $f(x)$ is one. The area under the graph of $f(x)$ and between values a and b gives the probability $P(a < x < b)$.

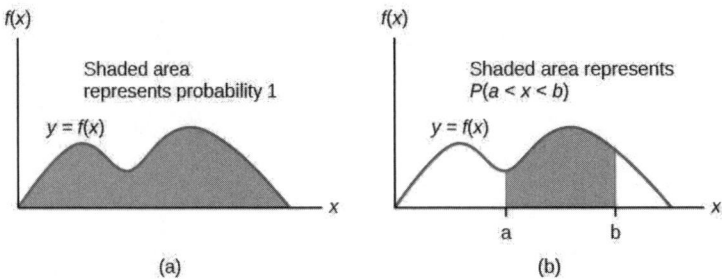

Figure 5.35

The cumulative distribution function (cdf) of X is defined by $P(X \leq x)$. It is a function of x that gives the probability that the random variable is less than or equal to x.

5.2 The Uniform Distribution

If X has a uniform distribution where $a < x < b$ or $a \leq x \leq b$, then X takes on values between a and b (may include a and b). All values x are equally likely. We write $X \sim U(a, b)$. The mean of X is $\mu = \frac{a+b}{2}$. The standard deviation of X is

$\sigma = \sqrt{\frac{(b-a)^2}{12}}$. The probability density function of X is $f(x) = \frac{1}{b-a}$ for $a \leq x \leq b$. The cumulative distribution function

of X is $P(X \leq x) = \frac{x-a}{b-a}$. X is continuous.

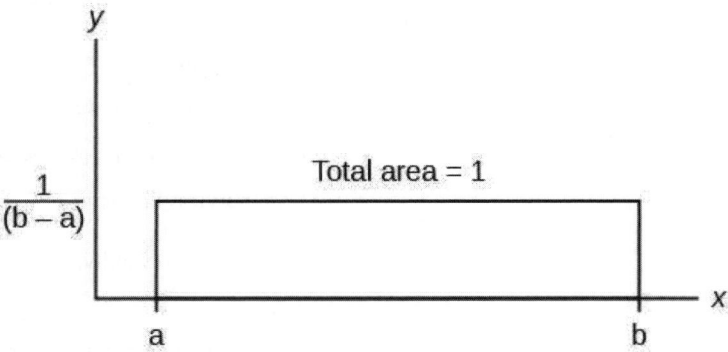

Figure 5.36

The probability $P(c < X < d)$ may be found by computing the area under $f(x)$, between c and d. Since the corresponding area is a rectangle, the area may be found simply by multiplying the width and the height.

5.3 The Exponential Distribution

If X has an **exponential distribution** with mean μ, then the **decay parameter** is $m = \frac{1}{\mu}$, and we write $X \sim Exp(m)$ where

$x \geq 0$ and $m > 0$. The probability density function of X is $f(x) = me^{-mx}$ (or equivalently $f(x) = \frac{1}{\mu}e^{-x/\mu}$. The cumulative

distribution function of X is $P(X \leq x) = 1 - e^{-mx}$.

The exponential distribution has the **memoryless property**, which says that future probabilities do not depend on any past information. Mathematically, it says that $P(X > x + k | X > x) = P(X > k)$.

If T represents the waiting time between events, and if $T \sim Exp(\lambda)$, then the number of events X per unit time follows the

Poisson distribution with mean λ. The probability density function of X is $\mathrm{P}(X = k) = \frac{\lambda^k e^{-k}}{k!}$. This may be computed

using a TI-83, 83+, 84, 84+ calculator with the command poissonpdf(λ, k). The cumulative distribution function $P(X \leq k)$ may be computed using the TI-83, 83+,84, 84+ calculator with the command poissoncdf(λ, k).

FORMULA REVIEW

5.1 Continuous Probability Functions

Probability density function (pdf) $f(x)$:

- $f(x) \geq 0$
- The total area under the curve $f(x)$ is one.

Cumulative distribution function (cdf): $P(X \leq x)$

5.2 The Uniform Distribution

X = a real number between a and b (in some instances, X can take on the values a and b). a = smallest X; b = largest X

$X \sim U$ (a, b)

The mean is $\mu = \frac{a+b}{2}$

The standard deviation is $\sigma = \sqrt{\dfrac{(b-a)^2}{12}}$

Probability density function: $f(x) = \dfrac{1}{b-a}$ for $a \le X \le b$

Area to the Left of x: $P(X < x) = (x-a)\left(\dfrac{1}{b-a}\right)$

Area to the Right of x: $P(X > x) = (b-x)\left(\dfrac{1}{b-a}\right)$

Area Between c and d: $P(c < x < d) = (\text{base})(\text{height}) = (d-c)\left(\dfrac{1}{b-a}\right)$

Uniform: $X \sim U(a, b)$ where $a < x < b$

- pdf: $f(x) = \dfrac{1}{b-a}$ for $a \le x \le b$

- cdf: $P(X \le x) = \dfrac{x-a}{b-a}$

- mean $\mu = \dfrac{a+b}{2}$

- standard deviation $\sigma = \sqrt{\dfrac{(b-a)^2}{12}}$

- $P(c < X < d) = (d-c)\left(\dfrac{1}{b-a}\right)$

5.3 The Exponential Distribution

Exponential: $X \sim Exp(m)$ where m = the decay parameter

- pdf: $f(x) = me^{(-mx)}$ where $x \ge 0$ and $m > 0$

- cdf: $P(X \le x) = 1 - e^{(-mx)}$

- mean $\mu = \dfrac{1}{m}$

- standard deviation $\sigma = \mu$

- percentile k: $k = \dfrac{ln(1 - AreaToTheLeftOfk)}{(-m)}$

- Additionally
  - $P(X > x) = e^{(-mx)}$
  - $P(a < X < b) = e^{(-ma)} - e^{(-mb)}$

- Memoryless Property: $P(X > x + k | X > x) = P(X > k)$

- Poisson probability: $P(X = k) = \dfrac{\lambda^k e^{-k}}{k!}$ with mean λ

- $k! = k*(k-1)*(k-2)*(k-3)\ldots3*2*1$

PRACTICE

5.1 Continuous Probability Functions

1. Which type of distribution does the graph illustrate?

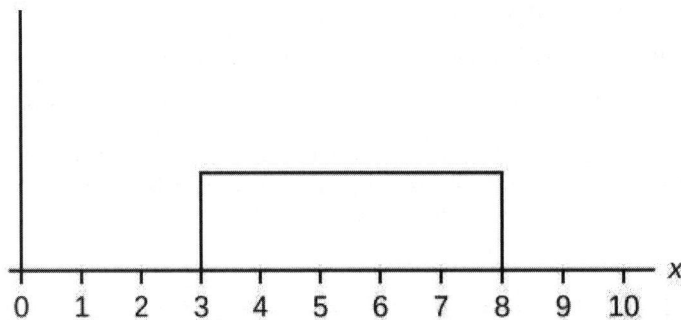

Figure 5.37

2. Which type of distribution does the graph illustrate?

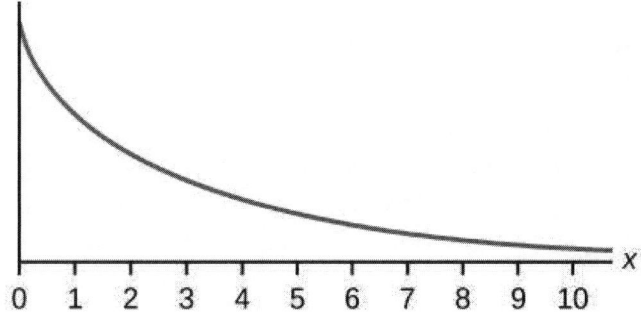

Figure 5.38

3. Which type of distribution does the graph illustrate?

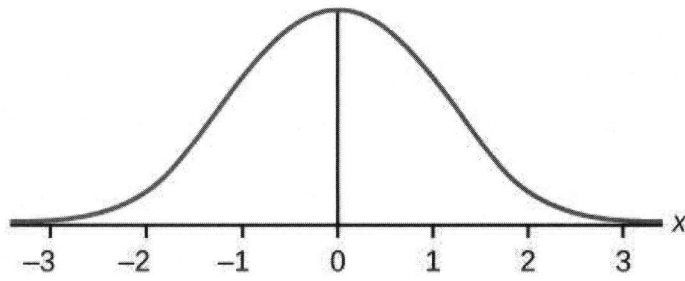

Figure 5.39

4. What does the shaded area represent? $P(\_\_\_ < x < \_\_\_)$

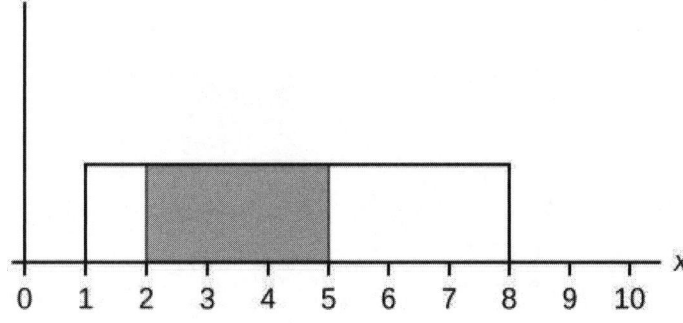

Figure 5.40

5. What does the shaded area represent? $P(\_\_\_ < x < \_\_\_)$

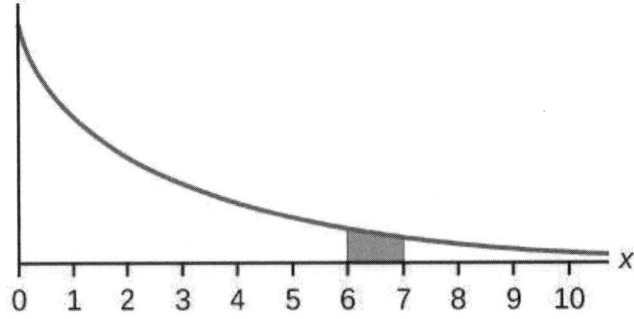

Figure 5.41

6. For a continuous probablity distribution, $0 \leq x \leq 15$. What is $P(x > 15)$?

7. What is the area under $f(x)$ if the function is a continuous probability density function?

8. For a continuous probability distribution, $0 \leq x \leq 10$. What is $P(x = 7)$?

9. A **continuous** probability function is restricted to the portion between $x = 0$ and 7. What is $P(x = 10)$?

10. $f(x)$ for a continuous probability function is $\frac{1}{5}$, and the function is restricted to $0 \leq x \leq 5$. What is $P(x < 0)$?

11. $f(x)$, a continuous probability function, is equal to $\frac{1}{12}$, and the function is restricted to $0 \leq x \leq 12$. What is $P (0 < x < 12)$?

12. Find the probability that x falls in the shaded area.

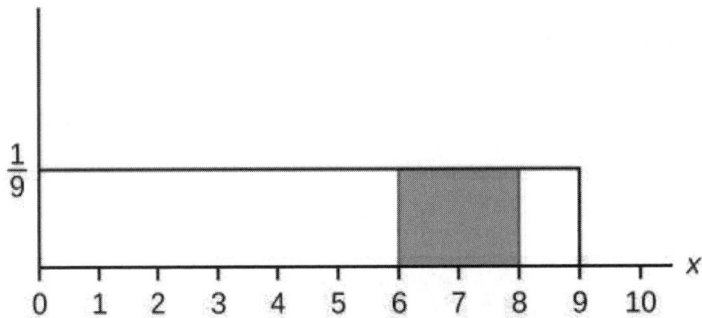

Figure 5.42

13. Find the probability that *x* falls in the shaded area.

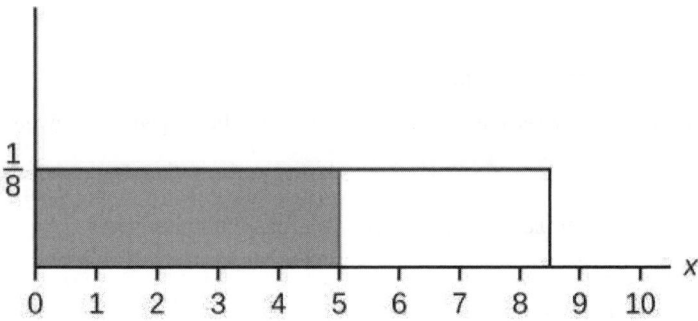

Figure 5.43

14. Find the probability that *x* falls in the shaded area.

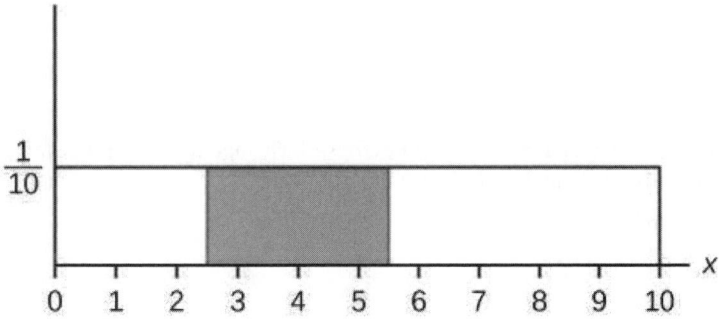

Figure 5.44

15. *f*(*x*), a continuous probability function, is equal to $\frac{1}{3}$ and the function is restricted to $1 \leq x \leq 4$. Describe $P\left(x > \frac{3}{2}\right)$.

5.2 The Uniform Distribution

Use the following information to answer the next ten questions. The data that follow are the square footage (in 1,000 feet squared) of 28 homes.

1.5	2.4	3.6	2.6	1.6	2.4	2.0
3.5	2.5	1.8	2.4	2.5	3.5	4.0
2.6	1.6	2.2	1.8	3.8	2.5	1.5
2.8	1.8	4.5	1.9	1.9	3.1	1.6

Table 5.4

The sample mean = 2.50 and the sample standard deviation = 0.8302.

The distribution can be written as $X \sim U(1.5, 4.5)$.

16. What type of distribution is this?

17. In this distribution, outcomes are equally likely. What does this mean?

18. What is the height of *f*(*x*) for the continuous probability distribution?

19. What are the constraints for the values of *x*?

20. Graph $P(2 < x < 3)$.

21. What is $P(2 < x < 3)$?

22. What is $P(x < 3.5| x < 4)$?

23. What is $P(x = 1.5)$?

24. What is the 90th percentile of square footage for homes?

25. Find the probability that a randomly selected home has more than 3,000 square feet given that you already know the house has more than 2,000 square feet.

Use the following information to answer the next eight exercises. A distribution is given as $X \sim U(0, 12)$.

26. What is a? What does it represent?

27. What is b? What does it represent?

28. What is the probability density function?

29. What is the theoretical mean?

30. What is the theoretical standard deviation?

31. Draw the graph of the distribution for $P(x > 9)$.

32. Find $P(x > 9)$.

33. Find the 40th percentile.

Use the following information to answer the next eleven exercises. The age of cars in the staff parking lot of a suburban college is uniformly distributed from six months (0.5 years) to 9.5 years.

34. What is being measured here?

35. In words, define the random variable X.

36. Are the data discrete or continuous?

37. The interval of values for x is _____.

38. The distribution for X is _____.

39. Write the probability density function.

40. Graph the probability distribution.

    a. Sketch the graph of the probability distribution.

    Figure 5.45

    b. Identify the following values:

        i. Lowest value for $\bar{x}$: _____

        ii. Highest value for $\bar{x}$: _____

        iii. Height of the rectangle: _____

        iv. Label for *x*-axis (words): _____

        v. Label for *y*-axis (words): _____

41. Find the average age of the cars in the lot.

42. Find the probability that a randomly chosen car in the lot was less than four years old.

    a. Sketch the graph, and shade the area of interest.

    Figure 5.46

    b. Find the probability. $P(x < 4) =$ _____

43. Considering only the cars less than 7.5 years old, find the probability that a randomly chosen car in the lot was less than four years old.
a. Sketch the graph, shade the area of interest.

Figure 5.47
b. Find the probability. $P(x < 4 | x < 7.5) =$ _____

44. What has changed in the previous two problems that made the solutions different?

45. Find the third quartile of ages of cars in the lot. This means you will have to find the value such that $\frac{3}{4}$, or 75%, of the cars are at most (less than or equal to) that age.
a. Sketch the graph, and shade the area of interest.

Figure 5.48
b. Find the value k such that $P(x < k) = 0.75$.
c. The third quartile is _____

5.3 The Exponential Distribution

Use the following information to answer the next ten exercises. A customer service representative must spend different amounts of time with each customer to resolve various concerns. The amount of time spent with each customer can be modeled by the following distribution: $X \sim Exp(0.2)$

46. What type of distribution is this?

47. Are outcomes equally likely in this distribution? Why or why not?

48. What is m? What does it represent?

49. What is the mean?

50. What is the standard deviation?

51. State the probability density function.

52. Graph the distribution.

53. Find $P(2 < x < 10)$.

54. Find $P(x > 6)$.

55. Find the 70th percentile.

Use the following information to answer the next seven exercises. A distribution is given as $X \sim Exp(0.75)$.

56. What is m?

57. What is the probability density function?

58. What is the cumulative distribution function?

59. Draw the distribution.

60. Find $P(x < 4)$.

61. Find the 30th percentile.

62. Find the median.

63. Which is larger, the mean or the median?

Use the following information to answer the next 16 exercises. Carbon-14 is a radioactive element with a half-life of about 5,730 years. Carbon-14 is said to decay exponentially. The decay rate is 0.000121. We start with one gram of carbon-14. We are interested in the time (years) it takes to decay carbon-14.

64. What is being measured here?

65. Are the data discrete or continuous?

66. In words, define the random variable X.

67. What is the decay rate (m)?

68. The distribution for X is _____.

69. Find the amount (percent of one gram) of carbon-14 lasting less than 5,730 years. This means, find $P(x < 5,730)$.
   a.   Sketch the graph, and shade the area of interest.

   Figure 5.49
   b.   Find the probability. $P(x < 5,730) =$ _____

70. Find the percentage of carbon-14 lasting longer than 10,000 years.
   a.   Sketch the graph, and shade the area of interest.

   Figure 5.50
   b.   Find the probability. $P(x > 10,000) =$ _____

71. Thirty percent (30%) of carbon-14 will decay within how many years?
   a.   Sketch the graph, and shade the area of interest.

   Figure 5.51
   b.   Find the value k such that $P(x < k) = 0.30$.

HOMEWORK

5.1 Continuous Probability Functions

For each probability and percentile problem, draw the picture.

72. Consider the following experiment. You are one of 100 people enlisted to take part in a study to determine the percent of nurses in America with an R.N. (registered nurse) degree. You ask nurses if they have an R.N. degree. The nurses answer "yes" or "no." You then calculate the percentage of nurses with an R.N. degree. You give that percentage to your supervisor.
   a.   What part of the experiment will yield discrete data?
   b.   What part of the experiment will yield continuous data?

73. When age is rounded to the nearest year, do the data stay continuous, or do they become discrete? Why?

5.2 The Uniform Distribution

For each probability and percentile problem, draw the picture.

74. Births are approximately uniformly distributed between the 52 weeks of the year. They can be said to follow a uniform distribution from one to 53 (spread of 52 weeks).

    a. $X \sim$ _____
    b. Graph the probability distribution.
    c. $f(x) =$ _____
    d. $\mu =$ _____
    e. $\sigma =$ _____
    f. Find the probability that a person is born at the exact moment week 19 starts. That is, find $P(x = 19) =$ _____
    g. $P(2 < x < 31) =$ _____
    h. Find the probability that a person is born after week 40.
    i. $P(12 < x | x < 28) =$ _____
    j. Find the 70th percentile.
    k. Find the minimum for the upper quarter.

75. A random number generator picks a number from one to nine in a uniform manner.

    a. $X \sim$ _____
    b. Graph the probability distribution.
    c. $f(x) =$ _____
    d. $\mu =$ _____
    e. $\sigma =$ _____
    f. $P(3.5 < x < 7.25) =$ _____
    g. $P(x > 5.67)$
    h. $P(x > 5 | x > 3) =$ _____
    i. Find the 90th percentile.

76. According to a study by Dr. John McDougall of his live-in weight loss program, the people who follow his program lose between six and 15 pounds a month until they approach trim body weight. Let's suppose that the weight loss is uniformly distributed. We are interested in the weight loss of a randomly selected individual following the program for one month.

    a. Define the random variable. $X =$ _____
    b. $X \sim$ _____
    c. Graph the probability distribution.
    d. $f(x) =$ _____
    e. $\mu =$ _____
    f. $\sigma =$ _____
    g. Find the probability that the individual lost more than ten pounds in a month.
    h. Suppose it is known that the individual lost more than ten pounds in a month. Find the probability that he lost less than 12 pounds in the month.
    i. $P(7 < x < 13 | x > 9) =$ _____. State this in a probability question, similarly to parts g and h, draw the picture, and find the probability.

77. A subway train arrives every eight minutes during rush hour. We are interested in the length of time a commuter must wait for a train to arrive. The time follows a uniform distribution.

    a. Define the random variable. $X =$ _____
    b. $X \sim$ _____
    c. Graph the probability distribution.
    d. $f(x) =$ _____
    e. $\mu =$ _____
    f. $\sigma =$ _____
    g. Find the probability that the commuter waits less than one minute.
    h. Find the probability that the commuter waits between three and four minutes.
    i. Sixty percent of commuters wait more than how long for the train? State this in a probability question, similarly to parts g and h, draw the picture, and find the probability.

78. The age of a first grader on September 1 at Garden Elementary School is uniformly distributed from 5.8 to 6.8 years. We randomly select one first grader from the class.
   a. Define the random variable. $X =$ _____
   b. $X \sim$ _____
   c. Graph the probability distribution.
   d. $f(x) =$ _____
   e. $\mu =$ _____
   f. $\sigma =$ _____
   g. Find the probability that she is over 6.5 years old.
   h. Find the probability that she is between four and six years old.
   i. Find the 70th percentile for the age of first graders on September 1 at Garden Elementary School.

Use the following information to answer the next three exercises. The Sky Train from the terminal to the rental–car and long–term parking center is supposed to arrive every eight minutes. The waiting times for the train are known to follow a uniform distribution.

79. What is the average waiting time (in minutes)?
   a. zero
   b. two
   c. three
   d. four

80. Find the 30th percentile for the waiting times (in minutes).
   a. two
   b. 2.4
   c. 2.75
   d. three

81. The probability of waiting more than seven minutes given a person has waited more than four minutes is?
   a. 0.125
   b. 0.25
   c. 0.5
   d. 0.75

82. The time (in minutes) until the next bus departs a major bus depot follows a distribution with $f(x) = \frac{1}{20}$ where x goes from 25 to 45 minutes.
   a. Define the random variable. $X =$ _____
   b. $X \sim$ _____
   c. Graph the probability distribution.
   d. The distribution is _____ (name of distribution). It is _____ (discrete or continuous).
   e. $\mu =$ _____
   f. $\sigma =$ _____
   g. Find the probability that the time is at most 30 minutes. Sketch and label a graph of the distribution. Shade the area of interest. Write the answer in a probability statement.
   h. Find the probability that the time is between 30 and 40 minutes. Sketch and label a graph of the distribution. Shade the area of interest. Write the answer in a probability statement.
   i. $P(25 < x < 55) =$ _____. State this in a probability statement, similarly to parts g and h, draw the picture, and find the probability.
   j. Find the 90th percentile. This means that 90% of the time, the time is less than _____ minutes.
   k. Find the 75th percentile. In a complete sentence, state what this means. (See part j.)
   l. Find the probability that the time is more than 40 minutes given (or knowing that) it is at least 30 minutes.

83. Suppose that the value of a stock varies each day from $16 to $25 with a uniform distribution.
   a. Find the probability that the value of the stock is more than $19.
   b. Find the probability that the value of the stock is between $19 and $22.
   c. Find the upper quartile - 25% of all days the stock is above what value? Draw the graph.
   d. Given that the stock is greater than $18, find the probability that the stock is more than $21.

84. A fireworks show is designed so that the time between fireworks is between one and five seconds, and follows a uniform distribution.
   a. Find the average time between fireworks.
   b. Find probability that the time between fireworks is greater than four seconds.

85. The number of miles driven by a truck driver falls between 300 and 700, and follows a uniform distribution.
   a. Find the probability that the truck driver goes more than 650 miles in a day.
   b. Find the probability that the truck drivers goes between 400 and 650 miles in a day.
   c. At least how many miles does the truck driver travel on the furthest 10% of days?

5.3 The Exponential Distribution

86. Suppose that the length of long distance phone calls, measured in minutes, is known to have an exponential distribution with the average length of a call equal to eight minutes.
   a. Define the random variable. $X = $ _____.
   b. Is X continuous or discrete?
   c. $X \sim$ _____
   d. $\mu = $ _____
   e. $\sigma = $ _____
   f. Draw a graph of the probability distribution. Label the axes.
   g. Find the probability that a phone call lasts less than nine minutes.
   h. Find the probability that a phone call lasts more than nine minutes.
   i. Find the probability that a phone call lasts between seven and nine minutes.
   j. If 25 phone calls are made one after another, on average, what would you expect the total to be? Why?

87. Suppose that the useful life of a particular car battery, measured in months, decays with parameter 0.025. We are interested in the life of the battery.
   a. Define the random variable. $X = $ _____.
   b. Is X continuous or discrete?
   c. $X \sim$ _____
   d. On average, how long would you expect one car battery to last?
   e. On average, how long would you expect nine car batteries to last, if they are used one after another?
   f. Find the probability that a car battery lasts more than 36 months.
   g. Seventy percent of the batteries last at least how long?

88. The percent of persons (ages five and older) in each state who speak a language at home other than English is approximately exponentially distributed with a mean of 9.848. Suppose we randomly pick a state.
   a. Define the random variable. $X = $ _____.
   b. Is X continuous or discrete?
   c. $X \sim$ _____
   d. $\mu = $ _____
   e. $\sigma = $ _____
   f. Draw a graph of the probability distribution. Label the axes.
   g. Find the probability that the percent is less than 12.
   h. Find the probability that the percent is between eight and 14.
   i. The percent of all individuals living in the United States who speak a language at home other than English is 13.8.

       i. Why is this number different from 9.848%?
       ii. What would make this number higher than 9.848%?

89. The time (in years) **after** reaching age 60 that it takes an individual to retire is approximately exponentially distributed with a mean of about five years. Suppose we randomly pick one retired individual. We are interested in the time after age 60 to retirement.
  a. Define the random variable. X = _____.
  b. Is X continuous or discrete?
  c. $X \sim$ = _____
  d. μ = _____
  e. σ = _____
  f. Draw a graph of the probability distribution. Label the axes.
  g. Find the probability that the person retired after age 70.
  h. Do more people retire before age 65 or after age 65?
  i. In a room of 1,000 people over age 80, how many do you expect will NOT have retired yet?

90. The cost of all maintenance for a car during its first year is approximately exponentially distributed with a mean of $150.
  a. Define the random variable. X = _____.
  b. $X \sim$ = _____
  c. μ = _____
  d. σ = _____
  e. Draw a graph of the probability distribution. Label the axes.
  f. Find the probability that a car required over $300 for maintenance during its first year.

Use the following information to answer the next three exercises. The average lifetime of a certain new cell phone is three years. The manufacturer will replace any cell phone failing within two years of the date of purchase. The lifetime of these cell phones is known to follow an exponential distribution.

91. The decay rate is:
  a. 0.3333
  b. 0.5000
  c. 2
  d. 3

92. What is the probability that a phone will fail within two years of the date of purchase?
  a. 0.8647
  b. 0.4866
  c. 0.2212
  d. 0.9997

93. What is the median lifetime of these phones (in years)?
  a. 0.1941
  b. 1.3863
  c. 2.0794
  d. 5.5452

94. Let $X \sim Exp(0.1)$.
  a. decay rate = _____
  b. μ = _____
  c. Graph the probability distribution function.
  d. On the graph, shade the area corresponding to $P(x < 6)$ and find the probability.
  e. Sketch a new graph, shade the area corresponding to $P(3 < x < 6)$ and find the probability.
  f. Sketch a new graph, shade the area corresponding to $P(x < 7)$ and find the probability.
  g. Sketch a new graph, shade the area corresponding to the 40th percentile and find the value.
  h. Find the average value of x.

95. Suppose that the longevity of a light bulb is exponential with a mean lifetime of eight years.
  a. Find the probability that a light bulb lasts less than one year.
  b. Find the probability that a light bulb lasts between six and ten years.
  c. Seventy percent of all light bulbs last at least how long?
  d. A company decides to offer a warranty to give refunds to light bulbs whose lifetime is among the lowest two percent of all bulbs. To the nearest month, what should be the cutoff lifetime for the warranty to take place?
  e. If a light bulb has lasted seven years, what is the probability that it fails within the 8th year.

96. At a 911 call center, calls come in at an average rate of one call every two minutes. Assume that the time that elapses from one call to the next has the exponential distribution.

    a. On average, how much time occurs between five consecutive calls?

    b. Find the probability that after a call is received, it takes more than three minutes for the next call to occur.

    c. Ninety-percent of all calls occur within how many minutes of the previous call?

    d. Suppose that two minutes have elapsed since the last call. Find the probability that the next call will occur within the next minute.

    e. Find the probability that less than 20 calls occur within an hour.

97. In major league baseball, a no-hitter is a game in which a pitcher, or pitchers, doesn't give up any hits throughout the game. No-hitters occur at a rate of about three per season. Assume that the duration of time between no-hitters is exponential.

    a. What is the probability that an entire season elapses with a single no-hitter?

    b. If an entire season elapses without any no-hitters, what is the probability that there are no no-hitters in the following season?

    c. What is the probability that there are more than 3 no-hitters in a single season?

98. During the years 1998–2012, a total of 29 earthquakes of magnitude greater than 6.5 have occurred in Papua New Guinea. Assume that the time spent waiting between earthquakes is exponential.

    a. What is the probability that the next earthquake occurs within the next three months?

    b. Given that six months has passed without an earthquake in Papua New Guinea, what is the probability that the next three months will be free of earthquakes?

    c. What is the probability of zero earthquakes occurring in 2014?

    d. What is the probability that at least two earthquakes will occur in 2014?

99. According to the American Red Cross, about one out of nine people in the U.S. have Type B blood. Suppose the blood types of people arriving at a blood drive are independent. In this case, the number of Type B blood types that arrive roughly follows the Poisson distribution.

    a. If 100 people arrive, how many on average would be expected to have Type B blood?

    b. What is the probability that over 10 people out of these 100 have type B blood?

    c. What is the probability that more than 20 people arrive before a person with type B blood is found?

100. A web site experiences traffic during normal working hours at a rate of 12 visits per hour. Assume that the duration between visits has the exponential distribution.

    a. Find the probability that the duration between two successive visits to the web site is more than ten minutes.

    b. The top 25% of durations between visits are at least how long?

    c. Suppose that 20 minutes have passed since the last visit to the web site. What is the probability that the next visit will occur within the next 5 minutes?

    d. Find the probability that less than 7 visits occur within a one-hour period.

101. At an urgent care facility, patients arrive at an average rate of one patient every seven minutes. Assume that the duration between arrivals is exponentially distributed.

    a. Find the probability that the time between two successive visits to the urgent care facility is less than 2 minutes.

    b. Find the probability that the time between two successive visits to the urgent care facility is more than 15 minutes.

    c. If 10 minutes have passed since the last arrival, what is the probability that the next person will arrive within the next five minutes?

    d. Find the probability that more than eight patients arrive during a half-hour period.

REFERENCES

5.2 The Uniform Distribution

McDougall, John A. The McDougall Program for Maximum Weight Loss. Plume, 1995.

5.3 The Exponential Distribution

Data from the United States Census Bureau.

Data from World Earthquakes, 2013. Available online at http://www.world-earthquakes.com/ (accessed June 11, 2013).

"No-hitter." Baseball-Reference.com, 2013. Available online at http://www.baseball-reference.com/bullpen/No-hitter (accessed June 11, 2013).

Zhou, Rick. "Exponential Distribution lecture slides." Available online at www.public.iastate.edu/~riczw/stat330s11/lecture/lec13.pdf (accessed June 11, 2013).

SOLUTIONS

1 Uniform Distribution

3 Normal Distribution

5 $P(6 < x < 7)$

7 one

9 zero

11 one

13 0.625

15 The probability is equal to the area from $x = \frac{3}{2}$ to $x = 4$ above the x-axis and up to $f(x) = \frac{1}{3}$.

17 It means that the value of x is just as likely to be any number between 1.5 and 4.5.

19 $1.5 \le x \le 4.5$

21 0.3333

23 zero

25 0.6

27 b is 12, and it represents the highest value of x.

29 six

31

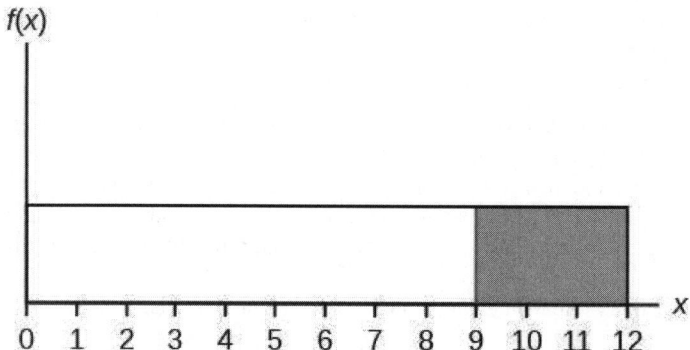

Figure 5.52

33 4.8

35 X = The age (in years) of cars in the staff parking lot

37 0.5 to 9.5

39 $f(x) = \frac{1}{9}$ where x is between 0.5 and 9.5, inclusive.

41 $\mu = 5$

43

a. Check student's solution.

b. $\frac{3.5}{7}$

45

a. Check student's solution.

b. $k = 7.25$

c. 7.25

47 No, outcomes are not equally likely. In this distribution, more people require a little bit of time, and fewer people require a lot of time, so it is more likely that someone will require less time.

49 five

51 $f(x) = 0.2e^{-0.2x}$

53 0.5350

55 6.02

57 $f(x) = 0.75e^{-0.75x}$

59

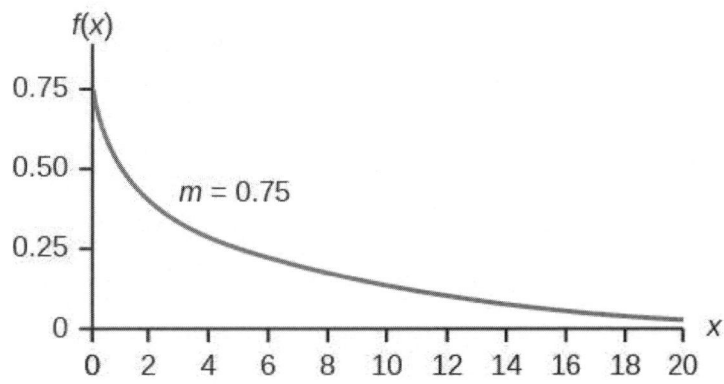

Figure 5.53

61 0.4756

63 The mean is larger. The mean is $\frac{1}{m} = \frac{1}{0.75} \approx 1.33$, which is greater than 0.9242.

65 continuous

67 $m = 0.000121$

69

a. Check student's solution

b. $P(x < 5{,}730) = 0.5001$

71

a. Check student's solution.

b. $k = 2947.73$

73 Age is a measurement, regardless of the accuracy used.

75

a. $X \sim U(1, 9)$

b. Check student's solution.

c. $f(x) = \frac{1}{8}$ where $1 \le x \le 9$

d. five

e. 2.3

f. $\frac{15}{32}$

g. $\frac{333}{800}$

h. $\frac{2}{3}$

i. 8.2

77

a. *X* represents the length of time a commuter must wait for a train to arrive on the Red Line.

b. $X \sim U(0, 8)$

c. Graph the probability distribution.

d. $f(x) = \frac{1}{8}$ where $0 \le x \le 8$

e. four

f. 2.31

g. $\frac{1}{8}$

h. $\frac{1}{8}$

i. 3.2

79 d

81 b

83

a. The probability density function of *X* is $\frac{1}{25 - 16} = \frac{1}{9}$.

   $P(X > 19) = (25 - 19)\left(\frac{1}{9}\right) = \frac{6}{9} = \frac{2}{3}$.

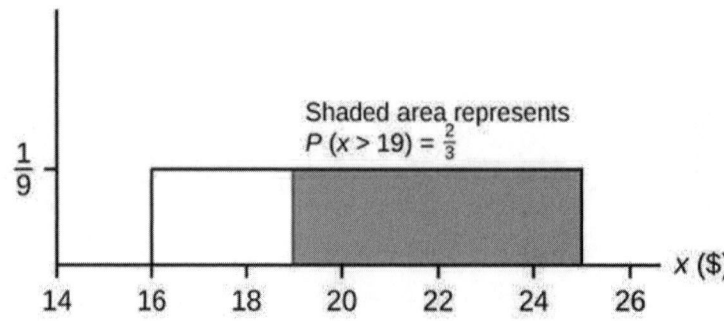

Figure 5.54

b. $P(19 < X < 22) = (22 - 19)\left(\frac{1}{9}\right) = \frac{3}{9} = \frac{1}{3}$.

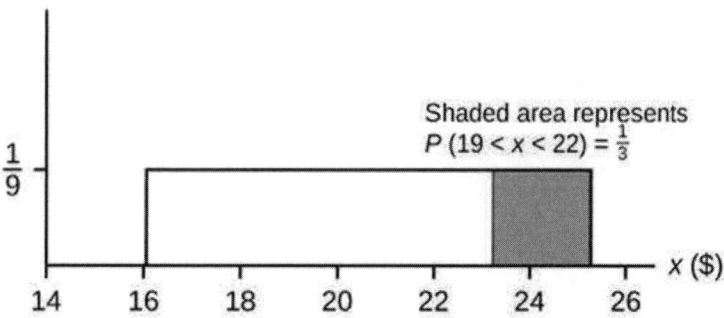

Figure 5.55

c. The area must be 0.25, and $0.25 = (\text{width})\left(\frac{1}{9}\right)$, so width $= (0.25)(9) = 2.25$. Thus, the value is $25 - 2.25 = 22.75$.

d. This is a conditional probability question. $P(x > 21 \mid x > 18)$. You can do this two ways:

  ◦ Draw the graph where a is now 18 and b is still 25. The height is $\frac{1}{(25 - 18)} = \frac{1}{7}$

    So, $P(x > 21 \mid x > 18) = (25 - 21)\left(\frac{1}{7}\right) = 4/7$.

  ◦ Use the formula: $P(x > 21 \mid x > 18) = \dfrac{P(x > 21 \text{ AND } x > 18)}{P(x > 18)}$

    $= \dfrac{P(x > 21)}{P(x > 18)} = \dfrac{(25 - 21)}{(25 - 18)} = \dfrac{4}{7}$.

85

a. $P(X > 650) = \dfrac{700 - 650}{700 - 300} = \dfrac{50}{400} = \dfrac{1}{8} = 0.125$.

b. $P(400 < X < 650) = \dfrac{650 - 400}{700 - 300} = \dfrac{250}{400} = 0.625$

c. $0.10 = \dfrac{\text{width}}{700 - 300}$, so width $= 400(0.10) = 40$. Since $700 - 40 = 660$, the drivers travel at least 660 miles on the furthest 10% of days.

87

a. $X =$ the useful life of a particular car battery, measured in months.

b. X is continuous.

c. $X \sim Exp(0.025)$

d. 40 months

e. 360 months

f. 0.4066

g. 14.27

89

a. $X =$ the time (in years) after reaching age 60 that it takes an individual to retire

b. X is continuous.

c. $X \sim Exp\left(\frac{1}{5}\right)$

d.   five

e.   five

f.   Check student's solution.

g.   0.1353

h.   before

i.   18.3

91 a

93 c

95 Let T = the life time of a light bulb. The decay parameter is m = 1/8, and $T \sim$ Exp(1/8). The cumulative distribution function is $P(T < t) = 1 - e^{-\frac{t}{8}}$

a.   Therefore, $P(T < 1) = 1 - e^{-\frac{1}{8}} \approx 0.1175$.

b.   We want to find $P(6 < t < 10)$.
     To do this, $P(6 < t < 10) - P(t < 6)$
     $$= = \left(1 - e^{-\frac{1}{8}*10}\right) - \left(1 - e^{-\frac{1}{8}*6}\right) \approx 0.7135 - 0.5276 = 0.1859$$

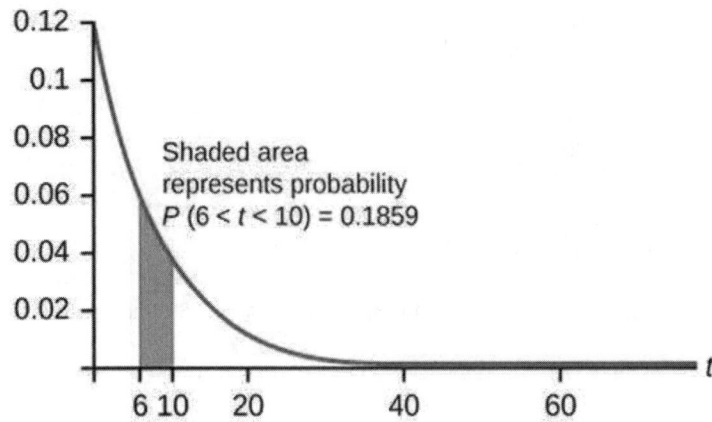

Figure 5.56

c.   We want to find $0.70 = P(T > t) = 1 - \left(1 - e^{-\frac{t}{8}}\right) = e^{-\frac{t}{8}}$.

Solving for t, $e^{-\frac{t}{8}} = 0.70$, so $-\frac{t}{8} = ln(0.70)$, and $t = -8ln(0.70) \approx 2.85$ years.

Or use $t = \frac{ln(\text{area\_to\_the\_right})}{(-m)} = \frac{ln(0.70)}{-\frac{1}{8}} \approx 2.85$ years .

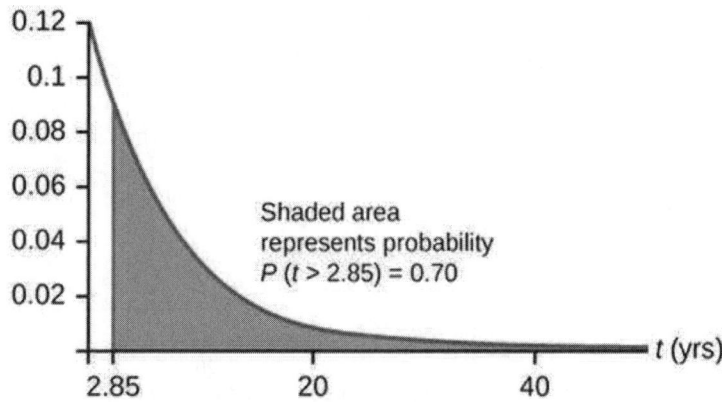

Figure 5.57

d. We want to find $0.02 = P(T < t) = 1 - e^{-\frac{t}{8}}$.

Solving for t, $e^{-\frac{t}{8}} = 0.98$, so $-\frac{t}{8} = ln(0.98)$, and $t = -8ln(0.98) \approx 0.1616$ years, or roughly two months.

The warranty should cover light bulbs that last less than 2 months.

Or use $\dfrac{ln(\text{area\_to\_the\_right})}{(-m)} = \dfrac{ln(1 - 0.2)}{-\frac{1}{8}} = 0.1616$.

e. We must find $P(T < 8 | T > 7)$.
Notice that by the rule of complement events, $P(T < 8 | T > 7) = 1 - P(T > 8 | T > 7)$.
By the memoryless property $(P(X > r + t | X > r) = P(X > t))$.

So $P(T > 8 | T > 7) = P(T > 1) = 1 - \left(1 - e^{-\frac{1}{8}}\right) = e^{-\frac{1}{8}} \approx 0.8825$

Therefore, $P(T < 8 | T > 7) = 1 - 0.8825 = 0.1175$.

97 Let X = the number of no-hitters throughout a season. Since the duration of time between no-hitters is exponential, the <u>number</u> of no-hitters <u>per season</u> is Poisson with mean $\lambda = 3$.

Therefore, $(X = 0) = \dfrac{3^0 e^{-3}}{0!} = e^{-3} \approx 0.0498$

> **NOTE**
>
> You could let T = duration of time between no-hitters. Since the time is exponential and there are 3 no-hitters per season, then the time between no-hitters is $\frac{1}{3}$ season. For the exponential, $\mu = \frac{1}{3}$.
>
> Therefore, $m = \frac{1}{\mu} = 3$ and $T \sim Exp(3)$.

a. The desired probability is $P(T > 1) = 1 - P(T < 1) = 1 - (1 - e^{-3}) = e^{-3} \approx 0.0498$.

b. Let T = duration of time between no-hitters. We find $P(T > 2 | T > 1)$, and by the **memoryless property** this is simply $P(T > 1)$, which we found to be 0.0498 in part a.

c. Let X = the <u>number</u> of no-hitters is a season. Assume that X is Poisson with mean $\lambda = 3$. Then $P(X > 3) = 1 - P(X \le 3)$ $= 0.3528$.

99

a. $\dfrac{100}{9} = 11.11$

b. $P(X > 10) = 1 - P(X \le 10) = 1 - \text{Poissoncdf}(11.11, 10) \approx 0.5532$.

c. The number of people with Type B blood encountered roughly follows the Poisson distribution, so the number of people X who arrive between successive Type B arrivals is roughly exponential with mean $\mu = 9$ and $m = \frac{1}{9}$. The cumulative distribution function of X is $P(X < x) = 1 - e^{-\frac{x}{9}}$. Thus hus, $P(X > 20) = 1 - P(X \le 20) = 1 - \left(1 - e^{-\frac{20}{9}}\right) \approx 0.1084$.

NOTE

We could also deduce that each person arriving has a 8/9 chance of not having Type B blood. So the probability that none of the first 20 people arrive have Type B blood is $\left(\frac{8}{9}\right)^{20} \approx 0.0948$. (The geometric distribution is more appropriate than the exponential because the number of people between Type B people is discrete instead of continuous.)

---

101 Let T = duration (in minutes) between successive visits. Since patients arrive at a rate of one patient every seven minutes, $\mu = 7$ and the decay constant is $m = \frac{1}{7}$. The cdf is $P(T < t) = 1 - e^{\frac{t}{7}}$

a. $P(T < 2) = 1 - 1 - e^{-\frac{2}{7}} \approx 0.2485$.

b. $P(T > 15) = 1 - P(T < 15) = 1 - \left(1 - e^{-\frac{15}{7}}\right) \approx e^{-\frac{15}{7}} \approx 0.1173$.

c. $P(T > 15 | T > 10) = P(T > 5) = 1 - \left(1 - e^{-\frac{5}{7}}\right) = e^{-\frac{5}{7}} \approx 0.4895$.

d. Let X = # of patients arriving during a half-hour period. Then X has the Poisson distribution with a mean of $\frac{30}{7}$, $X \sim$ Poisson$\left(\frac{30}{7}\right)$. Find $P(X > 8) = 1 - P(X \le 8) \approx 0.0311$.

6 | THE NORMAL DISTRIBUTION

Figure 6.1 If you ask enough people about their shoe size, you will find that your graphed data is shaped like a bell curve and can be described as normally distributed. (credit: Ömer Ünlü)

Introduction

Chapter Objectives

By the end of this chapter, the student should be able to:

- Recognize the normal probability distribution and apply it appropriately.
- Recognize the standard normal probability distribution and apply it appropriately.
- Compare normal probabilities by converting to the standard normal distribution.

The normal, a continuous distribution, is the most important of all the distributions. It is widely used and even more widely abused. Its graph is bell-shaped. You see the bell curve in almost all disciplines. Some of these include psychology, business, economics, the sciences, nursing, and, of course, mathematics. Some of your instructors may use the normal distribution to help determine your grade. Most IQ scores are normally distributed. Often real-estate prices fit a normal distribution. The normal distribution is extremely important, but it cannot be applied to everything in the real world.

In this chapter, you will study the normal distribution, the standard normal distribution, and applications associated with them.

The normal distribution has two parameters (two numerical descriptive measures): the mean (μ) and the standard deviation (σ). If X is a quantity to be measured that has a normal distribution with mean (μ) and standard deviation (σ), we designate this by writing

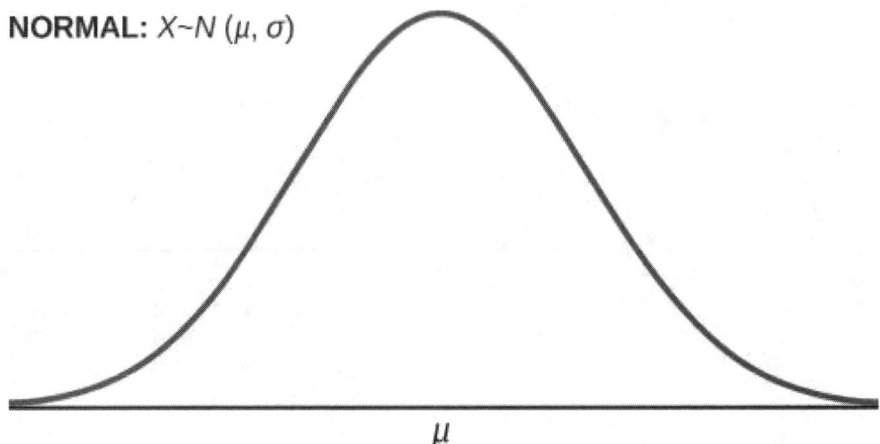

NORMAL: $X \sim N(\mu, \sigma)$

μ

Figure 6.2

The probability density function is a rather complicated function. **Do not memorize it**. It is not necessary.

$$f(x) = \frac{1}{\sigma \cdot \sqrt{2 \cdot \pi}} \cdot e^{-\frac{1}{2} \cdot \left(\frac{x - \mu}{\sigma}\right)^2}$$

The cumulative distribution function is $P(X < x)$. It is calculated either by a calculator or a computer, or it is looked up in a table. Technology has made the tables virtually obsolete. For that reason, as well as the fact that there are various table formats, we are not including table instructions.

The curve is symmetric about a vertical line drawn through the mean, μ. In theory, the mean is the same as the median, because the graph is symmetric about μ. As the notation indicates, the normal distribution depends only on the mean and the standard deviation. Since the area under the curve must equal one, a change in the standard deviation, σ, causes a change in the shape of the curve; the curve becomes fatter or skinnier depending on σ. A change in μ causes the graph to shift to the left or right. This means there are an infinite number of normal probability distributions. One of special interest is called the **standard normal distribution**.

Collaborative Exercise

Your instructor will record the heights of both men and women in your class, separately. Draw histograms of your data. Then draw a smooth curve through each histogram. Is each curve somewhat bell-shaped? Do you think that if you had recorded 200 data values for men and 200 for women that the curves would look bell-shaped? Calculate the mean for each data set. Write the means on the x-axis of the appropriate graph below the peak. Shade the approximate area that represents the probability that one randomly chosen male is taller than 72 inches. Shade the approximate area that represents the probability that one randomly chosen female is shorter than 60 inches. If the total area under each curve is one, does either probability appear to be more than 0.5?

6.1 | The Standard Normal Distribution

The **standard normal distribution** is a normal distribution of **standardized values called z-scores. A z-score is measured in units of the standard deviation.** For example, if the mean of a normal distribution is five and the standard deviation is two, the value 11 is three standard deviations above (or to the right of) the mean. The calculation is as follows:

$x = \mu + (z)(\sigma) = 5 + (3)(2) = 11$

The z-score is three.

The mean for the standard normal distribution is zero, and the standard deviation is one. The transformation $z = \frac{x - \mu}{\sigma}$ produces the distribution $Z \sim N(0, 1)$. The value x in the given equation comes from a normal distribution with mean μ and standard deviation σ.

Z-Scores

If X is a normally distributed random variable and $X \sim N(\mu, \sigma)$, then the z-score is:

$$z = \frac{x - \mu}{\sigma}$$

The z-score tells you how many standard deviations the value x is above (to the right of) or below (to the left of) the mean, μ. Values of x that are larger than the mean have positive z-scores, and values of x that are smaller than the mean have negative z-scores. If x equals the mean, then x has a z-score of zero.

Example 6.1

Suppose $X \sim N(5, 6)$. This says that X is a normally distributed random variable with mean $\mu = 5$ and standard deviation $\sigma = 6$. Suppose $x = 17$. Then:

$$z = \frac{x - \mu}{\sigma} = \frac{17 - 5}{6} = 2$$

This means that $x = 17$ is **two standard deviations** (2σ) above or to the right of the mean $\mu = 5$.

Notice that: $5 + (2)(6) = 17$ (The pattern is $\mu + z\sigma = x$)

Now suppose $x = 1$. Then: $z = \frac{x - \mu}{\sigma} = \frac{1 - 5}{6} = -0.67$ (rounded to two decimal places)

This means that $x = 1$ is 0.67 standard deviations (-0.67σ) below or to the left of the mean $\mu = 5$. Notice that: $5 + (-0.67)(6)$ is approximately equal to one (This has the pattern $\mu + (-0.67)\sigma = 1$)

Summarizing, when z is positive, x is above or to the right of μ and when z is negative, x is to the left of or below μ. Or, when z is positive, x is greater than μ, and when z is negative x is less than μ.

Try It Σ

6.1 What is the z-score of x, when $x = 1$ and $X \sim N(12,3)$?

Example 6.2

Some doctors believe that a person can lose five pounds, on the average, in a month by reducing his or her fat intake and by exercising consistently. Suppose weight loss has a normal distribution. Let X = the amount of weight lost (in pounds) by a person in a month. Use a standard deviation of two pounds. $X \sim N(5, 2)$. Fill in the blanks.

a. Suppose a person **lost** ten pounds in a month. The z-score when $x = 10$ pounds is $z = 2.5$ (verify). This z-score tells you that $x = 10$ is _____ standard deviations to the _____ (right or left) of the mean _____ (What is the mean?).

Solution 6.2
a. This z-score tells you that $x = 10$ is **2.5** standard deviations to the **right** of the mean **five**.

b. Suppose a person **gained** three pounds (a negative weight loss). Then $z =$ _____. This z-score tells you that $x = -3$ is _____ standard deviations to the _____ (right or left) of the mean.

Solution 6.2

b. $z = -4$. This z-score tells you that $x = -3$ is **four** standard deviations to the **left** of the mean.

c. Suppose the random variables X and Y have the following normal distributions: $X \sim N(5, 6)$ and $Y \sim N(2, 1)$. If $x = 17$, then $z = 2$. (This was previously shown.) If $y = 4$, what is z?

Solution 6.2

c. $z = \dfrac{y - \mu}{\sigma} = \dfrac{4 - 2}{1} = 2$ where $\mu = 2$ and $\sigma = 1$.

The z-score for $y = 4$ is $z = 2$. This means that four is $z = 2$ standard deviations to the right of the mean. Therefore, $x = 17$ and $y = 4$ are both two (of **their own**) standard deviations to the right of **their** respective means.

The z-score allows us to compare data that are scaled differently. To understand the concept, suppose $X \sim N(5, 6)$ represents weight gains for one group of people who are trying to gain weight in a six week period and $Y \sim N(2, 1)$ measures the same weight gain for a second group of people. A negative weight gain would be a weight loss. Since $x = 17$ and $y = 4$ are each two standard deviations to the right of their means, they represent the same, standardized weight gain **relative to their means**.

6.2 Fill in the blanks.

Jerome averages 16 points a game with a standard deviation of four points. $X \sim N(16,4)$. Suppose Jerome scores ten points in a game. The z–score when $x = 10$ is -1.5. This score tells you that $x = 10$ is _____ standard deviations to the _____(right or left) of the mean_____(What is the mean?).

The Empirical Rule

If X is a random variable and has a normal distribution with mean μ and standard deviation σ, then the **Empirical Rule** states the following:

- About 68% of the x values lie between -1σ and $+1\sigma$ of the mean μ (within one standard deviation of the mean).
- About 95% of the x values lie between -2σ and $+2\sigma$ of the mean μ (within two standard deviations of the mean).
- About 99.7% of the x values lie between -3σ and $+3\sigma$ of the mean μ (within three standard deviations of the mean). Notice that almost all the x values lie within three standard deviations of the mean.
- The z-scores for $+1\sigma$ and -1σ are $+1$ and -1, respectively.
- The z-scores for $+2\sigma$ and -2σ are $+2$ and -2, respectively.
- The z-scores for $+3\sigma$ and -3σ are $+3$ and -3 respectively.

The empirical rule is also known as the 68-95-99.7 rule.

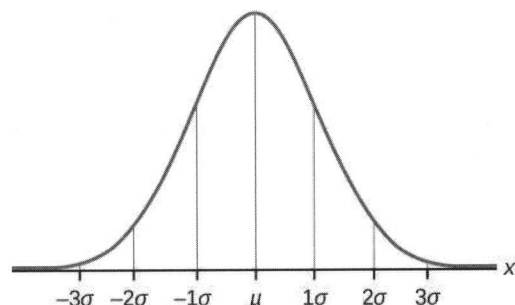

Figure 6.3

Example 6.3

The mean height of 15 to 18-year-old males from Chile from 2009 to 2010 was 170 cm with a standard deviation of 6.28 cm. Male heights are known to follow a normal distribution. Let X = the height of a 15 to 18-year-old male from Chile in 2009 to 2010. Then $X \sim N(170, 6.28)$.

a. Suppose a 15 to 18-year-old male from Chile was 168 cm tall from 2009 to 2010. The z-score when $x = 168$ cm is $z =$ _____. This z-score tells you that $x = 168$ is _____ standard deviations to the _____ (right or left) of the mean _____ (What is the mean?).

Solution 6.3
a. –0.32, 0.32, left, 170

b. Suppose that the height of a 15 to 18-year-old male from Chile from 2009 to 2010 has a z-score of $z = 1.27$. What is the male's height? The z-score ($z = 1.27$) tells you that the male's height is _____ standard deviations to the _____ (right or left) of the mean.

Solution 6.3
b. 177.98 cm, 1.27, right

Try It Σ

6.3 Use the information in **Example 6.3** to answer the following questions.

a. Suppose a 15 to 18-year-old male from Chile was 176 cm tall from 2009 to 2010. The z-score when $x = 176$ cm is $z =$ _____. This z-score tells you that $x = 176$ cm is _____ standard deviations to the _____ (right or left) of the mean _____ (What is the mean?).

b. Suppose that the height of a 15 to 18-year-old male from Chile from 2009 to 2010 has a z-score of $z = -2$. What is the male's height? The z-score ($z = -2$) tells you that the male's height is _____ standard deviations to the _____ (right or left) of the mean.

Example 6.4

From 1984 to 1985, the mean height of 15 to 18-year-old males from Chile was 172.36 cm, and the standard deviation was 6.34 cm. Let Y = the height of 15 to 18-year-old males from 1984 to 1985. Then $Y \sim N(172.36, 6.34)$.

The mean height of 15 to 18-year-old males from Chile from 2009 to 2010 was 170 cm with a standard deviation of 6.28 cm. Male heights are known to follow a normal distribution. Let X = the height of a 15 to 18-year-old male from Chile in 2009 to 2010. Then $X \sim N(170, 6.28)$.

Find the z-scores for x = 160.58 cm and y = 162.85 cm. Interpret each z-score. What can you say about x = 160.58 cm and y = 162.85 cm as they compare to their respective means and standard deviations?

Solution 6.4
The z-score for x = -160.58 is z = –1.5.
The z-score for y = 162.85 is z = –1.5.
Both x = 160.58 and y = 162.85 deviate the same number of standard deviations from their respective means and in the same direction.

Try It Σ

6.4 In 2012, 1,664,479 students took the SAT exam. The distribution of scores in the verbal section of the SAT had a mean μ = 496 and a standard deviation σ = 114. Let X = a SAT exam verbal section score in 2012. Then $X \sim N(496, 114)$.

Find the z-scores for x_1 = 325 and x_2 = 366.21. Interpret each z-score. What can you say about x_1 = 325 and x_2 = 366.21 as they compare to their respective means and standard deviations?

Example 6.5

Suppose x has a normal distribution with mean 50 and standard deviation 6.

- About 68% of the x values lie within one standard deviation of the mean. Therefore, about 68% of the x values lie between $-1\sigma = (-1)(6) = -6$ and $1\sigma = (1)(6) = 6$ of the mean 50. The values $50 - 6 = 44$ and $50 + 6 = 56$ are within one standard deviation from the mean 50. The z-scores are –1 and +1 for 44 and 56, respectively.

- About 95% of the x values lie within two standard deviations of the mean. Therefore, about 95% of the x values lie between $-2\sigma = (-2)(6) = -12$ and $2\sigma = (2)(6) = 12$. The values $50 - 12 = 38$ and $50 + 12 = 62$ are within two standard deviations from the mean 50. The z-scores are –2 and +2 for 38 and 62, respectively.

- About 99.7% of the x values lie within three standard deviations of the mean. Therefore, about 95% of the x values lie between $-3\sigma = (-3)(6) = -18$ and $3\sigma = (3)(6) = 18$ from the mean 50. The values $50 - 18 = 32$ and $50 + 18 = 68$ are within three standard deviations of the mean 50. The z-scores are –3 and +3 for 32 and 68, respectively.

Try It Σ

6.5 Suppose X has a normal distribution with mean 25 and standard deviation five. Between what values of x do 68% of the values lie?

Example 6.6

From 1984 to 1985, the mean height of 15 to 18-year-old males from Chile was 172.36 cm, and the standard deviation was 6.34 cm. Let Y = the height of 15 to 18-year-old males in 1984 to 1985. Then $Y \sim N(172.36, 6.34)$.

a. About 68% of the y values lie between what two values? These values are _____. The z-scores are _____, respectively.

b. About 95% of the *y* values lie between what two values? These values are _____. The *z*-scores are _____ respectively.

c. About 99.7% of the *y* values lie between what two values? These values are _____. The *z*-scores are _____, respectively.

Solution 6.6

a. About 68% of the values lie between 166.02 cm and 178.7 cm. The *z*-scores are –1 and 1.

b. About 95% of the values lie between 159.68 cm and 185.04 cm. The *z*-scores are –2 and 2.

c. About 99.7% of the values lie between 153.34 cm and 191.38 cm. The *z*-scores are –3 and 3.

Try It Σ

6.6 The scores on a college entrance exam have an approximate normal distribution with mean, μ = 52 points and a standard deviation, σ = 11 points.

a. About 68% of the *y* values lie between what two values? These values are _____. The *z*-scores are _____, respectively.

b. About 95% of the *y* values lie between what two values? These values are _____. The *z*-scores are _____, respectively.

c. About 99.7% of the *y* values lie between what two values? These values are _____. The *z*-scores are _____, respectively.

6.2 | Using the Normal Distribution

The shaded area in the following graph indicates the area to the left of *x*. This area is represented by the probability $P(X < x)$. Normal tables, computers, and calculators provide or calculate the probability $P(X < x)$.

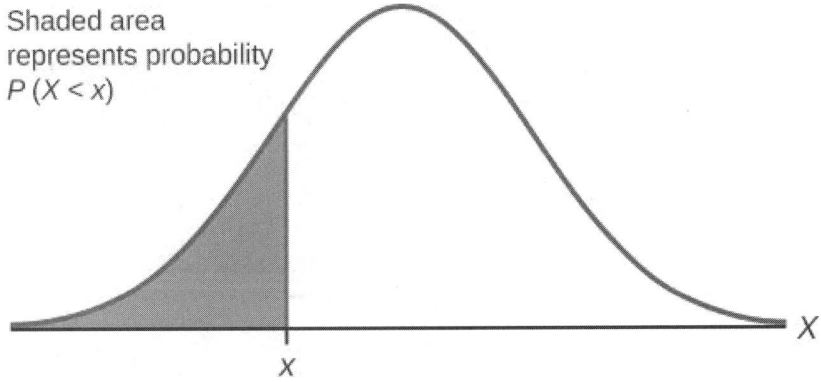

Figure 6.4

The area to the right is then $P(X > x) = 1 - P(X < x)$. Remember, $P(X < x) =$ **Area to the left** of the vertical line through *x*. $P(X < x) = 1 - P(X < x) =$ **Area to the right** of the vertical line through *x*. $P(X < x)$ is the same as $P(X \le x)$ and $P(X > x)$ is the same as $P(X \ge x)$ for continuous distributions.

Calculations of Probabilities

Probabilities are calculated using technology. There are instructions given as necessary for the TI-83+ and TI-84 calculators.

NOTE

To calculate the probability, use the probability tables provided in **Appendix H** without the use of technology. The tables include instructions for how to use them.

Example 6.7

If the area to the left is 0.0228, then the area to the right is 1 − 0.0228 = 0.9772.

 **Try It**

6.7 If the area to the left of *x* is 0.012, then what is the area to the right?

Example 6.8

The final exam scores in a statistics class were normally distributed with a mean of 63 and a standard deviation of five.

a. Find the probability that a randomly selected student scored more than 65 on the exam.

Solution 6.8

a. Let *X* = a score on the final exam. *X* ~ *N*(63, 5), where *μ* = 63 and *σ* = 5.

Draw a graph.

Then, find *P*(*x* > 65).

P(*x* > 65) = 0.3446

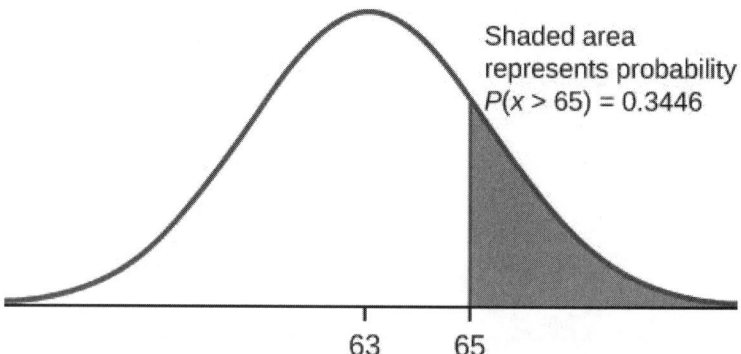

Figure 6.5

The probability that any student selected at random scores more than 65 is 0.3446.

 Using the TI-83, 83+, 84, 84+ Calculator

Go into **2nd DISTR.**

After pressing **2nd DISTR**, press **2:normalcdf**.

The syntax for the instructions are as follows:

normalcdf(lower value, upper value, mean, standard deviation) For this problem: normalcdf(65,1E99,63,5) = 0.3446. You get 1E99 (= 10^{99}) by pressing **1**, the **EE** key (a 2nd key) and then **99**. Or, you can enter **10^99** instead. The number 10^{99} is way out in the right tail of the normal curve. We are calculating the area between 65 and 10^{99}. In some instances, the lower number of the area might be –1E99 (= -10^{99}). The number -10^{99} is way out in the left tail of the normal curve.

HISTORICAL NOTE

The TI probability program calculates a z-score and then the probability from the z-score. Before technology, the z-score was looked up in a standard normal probability table (because the math involved is too cumbersome) to find the probability. In this example, a standard normal table with area to the left of the z-score was used. You calculate the z-score and look up the area to the left. The probability is the area to the right.

$$z = \frac{65 - 63}{5} = 0.4$$

Area to the left is 0.6554.

$P(x > 65) = P(z > 0.4) = 1 - 0.6554 = 0.3446$

Using the TI-83, 83+, 84, 84+ Calculator

Find the percentile for a student scoring 65:

*Press **2nd Distr**
*Press **2:normalcdf(**
*Enter lower bound, upper bound, mean, standard deviation followed by)
*Press **ENTER**.
For this Example, the steps are
2nd Distr
2:normalcdf(65,1,2nd EE,99,63,5) **ENTER**
The probability that a selected student scored more than 65 is 0.3446.

b. Find the probability that a randomly selected student scored less than 85.

Solution 6.8

b. Draw a graph.

Then find $P(x < 85)$, and shade the graph.

Using a computer or calculator, find $P(x < 85) = 1$.

normalcdf(0,85,63,5) = 1 (rounds to one)

The probability that one student scores less than 85 is approximately one (or 100%).

c. Find the 90th percentile (that is, find the score k that has 90% of the scores below k and 10% of the scores above k).

Solution 6.8

c. Find the 90th percentile. For each problem or part of a problem, draw a new graph. Draw the *x*-axis. Shade the area that corresponds to the 90th percentile.

Let *k* = the 90th percentile. The variable *k* is located on the *x*-axis. $P(x < k)$ is the area to the left of *k*. The 90th percentile *k* separates the exam scores into those that are the same or lower than *k* and those that are the same or higher. Ninety percent of the test scores are the same or lower than *k*, and ten percent are the same or higher. The variable *k* is often called a **critical value**.

k = 69.4

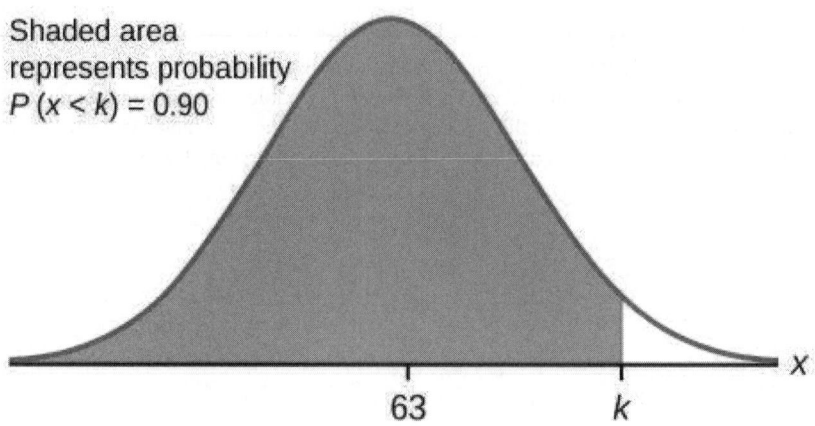

Figure 6.6

The 90th percentile is 69.4. This means that 90% of the test scores fall at or below 69.4 and 10% fall at or above. To get this answer on the calculator, follow this step:

 Using the TI-83, 83+, 84, 84+ Calculator

invNorm in 2nd DISTR. invNorm(area to the left, mean, standard deviation)
For this problem, invNorm(0.90,63,5) = 69.4

d. Find the 70th percentile (that is, find the score *k* such that 70% of scores are below *k* and 30% of the scores are above *k*).

Solution 6.8

d. Find the 70th percentile.

Draw a new graph and label it appropriately. *k* = 65.6

The 70th percentile is 65.6. This means that 70% of the test scores fall at or below 65.5 and 30% fall at or above.

invNorm(0.70,63,5) = 65.6

Try It Σ

6.8 The golf scores for a school team were normally distributed with a mean of 68 and a standard deviation of three. Find the probability that a randomly selected golfer scored less than 65.

Example 6.9

A personal computer is used for office work at home, research, communication, personal finances, education, entertainment, social networking, and a myriad of other things. Suppose that the average number of hours a household personal computer is used for entertainment is two hours per day. Assume the times for entertainment are normally distributed and the standard deviation for the times is half an hour.

a. Find the probability that a household personal computer is used for entertainment between 1.8 and 2.75 hours per day.

Solution 6.9

a. Let X = the amount of time (in hours) a household personal computer is used for entertainment. $X \sim N(2, 0.5)$ where $\mu = 2$ and $\sigma = 0.5$.

Find $P(1.8 < x < 2.75)$.

The probability for which you are looking is the area **between** $x = 1.8$ and $x = 2.75$. $P(1.8 < x < 2.75) = 0.5886$

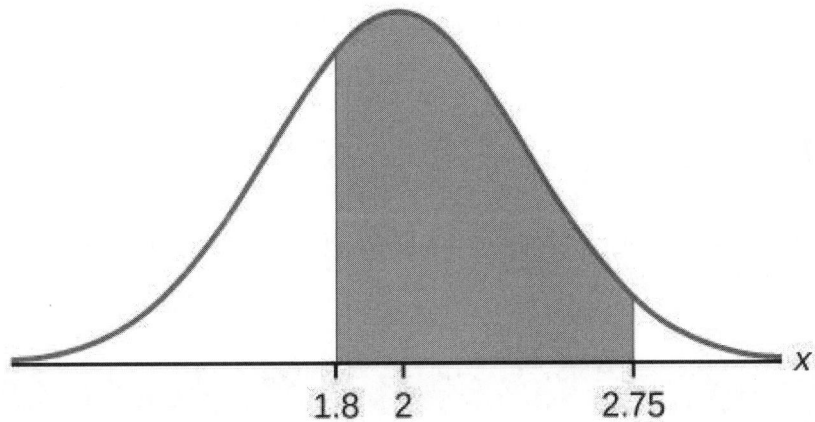

Figure 6.7

normalcdf(1.8,2.75,2,0.5) = 0.5886

The probability that a household personal computer is used between 1.8 and 2.75 hours per day for entertainment is 0.5886.

b. Find the maximum number of hours per day that the bottom quartile of households uses a personal computer for entertainment.

Solution 6.9

b. To find the maximum number of hours per day that the bottom quartile of households uses a personal computer for entertainment, **find the 25th percentile**, k, where $P(x < k) = 0.25$.

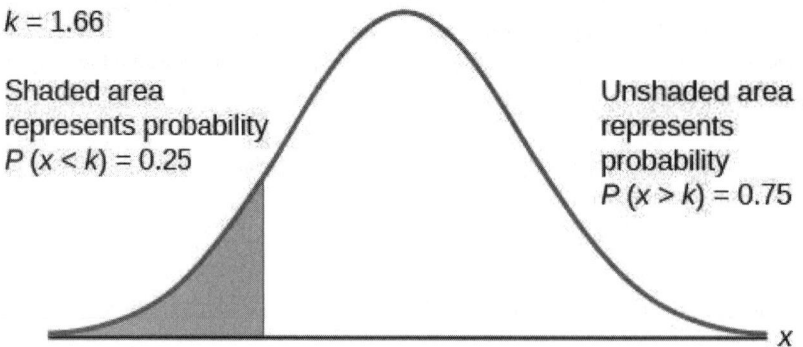

Figure 6.8

invNorm(0.25,2,0.5) = 1.66

The maximum number of hours per day that the bottom quartile of households uses a personal computer for entertainment is 1.66 hours.

Try It Σ

6.9 The golf scores for a school team were normally distributed with a mean of 68 and a standard deviation of three. Find the probability that a golfer scored between 66 and 70.

Example 6.10

In the United States the ages 13 to 55+ of smartphone users approximately follow a normal distribution with approximate mean and standard deviation of 36.9 years and 13.9 years, respectively.

a. Determine the probability that a random smartphone user in the age range 13 to 55+ is between 23 and 64.7 years old.

Solution 6.10
a. normalcdf(23,64.7,36.9,13.9) = 0.8186

b. Determine the probability that a randomly selected smartphone user in the age range 13 to 55+ is at most 50.8 years old.

Solution 6.10
b. normalcdf(-10^{99},50.8,36.9,13.9) = 0.8413

c. Find the 80th percentile of this distribution, and interpret it in a complete sentence.

Solution 6.10
c.
invNorm(0.80,36.9,13.9) = 48.6
The 80th percentile is 48.6 years.

80% of the smartphone users in the age range 13 – 55+ are 48.6 years old or less.

Try It Σ

6.10 Use the information in **Example 6.10** to answer the following questions.

a. Find the 30th percentile, and interpret it in a complete sentence.

b. What is the probability that the age of a randomly selected smartphone user in the range 13 to 55+ is less than 27 years old.

Example 6.11

In the United States the ages 13 to 55+ of smartphone users approximately follow a normal distribution with approximate mean and standard deviation of 36.9 years and 13.9 years respectively. Using this information, answer the following questions (round answers to one decimal place).

a. Calculate the interquartile range (*IQR*).

Solution 6.11
a.
$IQR = Q_3 - Q_1$
Calculate $Q_3 = 75^{th}$ percentile and $Q_1 = 25^{th}$ percentile.
invNorm(0.75,36.9,13.9) = Q_3 = 46.2754
invNorm(0.25,36.9,13.9) = Q_1 = 27.5246
$IQR = Q_3 - Q_1 = 18.8$

b. Forty percent of the ages that range from 13 to 55+ are at least what age?

Solution 6.11
b.
Find k where $P(x \geq k) = 0.40$ ("At least" translates to "greater than or equal to.")
0.40 = the area to the right.
Area to the left = 1 – 0.40 = 0.60.
The area to the left of k = 0.60.
invNorm(0.60,36.9,13.9) = 40.4215.
$k = 40.4$.
Forty percent of the ages that range from 13 to 55+ are at least 40.4 years.

Try It Σ

6.11 Two thousand students took an exam. The scores on the exam have an approximate normal distribution with a mean $\mu = 81$ points and standard deviation $\sigma = 15$ points.

a. Calculate the first- and third-quartile scores for this exam.

b. The middle 50% of the exam scores are between what two values?

Example 6.12

A citrus farmer who grows mandarin oranges finds that the diameters of mandarin oranges harvested on his farm follow a normal distribution with a mean diameter of 5.85 cm and a standard deviation of 0.24 cm.

a. Find the probability that a randomly selected mandarin orange from this farm has a diameter larger than 6.0 cm. Sketch the graph.

Solution 6.12

a. normalcdf(6,10^99,5.85,0.24) = 0.2660

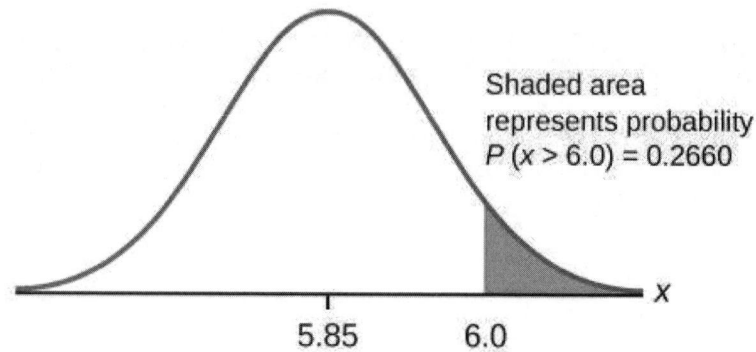

Figure 6.9

b. The middle 20% of mandarin oranges from this farm have diameters between _____ and _____.

Solution 6.12
b.
$1 - 0.20 = 0.80$
The tails of the graph of the normal distribution each have an area of 0.40.
Find $k1$, the 40th percentile, and $k2$, the 60th percentile ($0.40 + 0.20 = 0.60$).
$k1 = $ invNorm(0.40,5.85,0.24) = 5.79 cm
$k2 = $ invNorm(0.60,5.85,0.24) = 5.91 cm

c. Find the 90th percentile for the diameters of mandarin oranges, and interpret it in a complete sentence.

Solution 6.12
c. 6.16: Ninety percent of the diameter of the mandarin oranges is at most 6.16 cm.

6.12 Using the information from **Example 6.12**, answer the following:

a. The middle 40% of mandarin oranges from this farm are between _____ and _____.

b. Find the 16th percentile and interpret it in a complete sentence.

6.3 | Normal Distribution (Lap Times)

Stats Lab

6.1 Normal Distribution (Lap Times)

Class Time:

Names:

Student Learning Outcome

- The student will compare and contrast empirical data and a theoretical distribution to determine if Terry Vogel's lap times fit a continuous distribution.

Directions

Round the relative frequencies and probabilities to four decimal places. Carry all other decimal answers to two places.

Collect the Data

1. Use the data from **Appendix C**. Use a stratified sampling method by lap (races 1 to 20) and a random number generator to pick six lap times from each stratum. Record the lap times below for laps two to seven.

Table 6.1

2. Construct a histogram. Make five to six intervals. Sketch the graph using a ruler and pencil. Scale the axes.

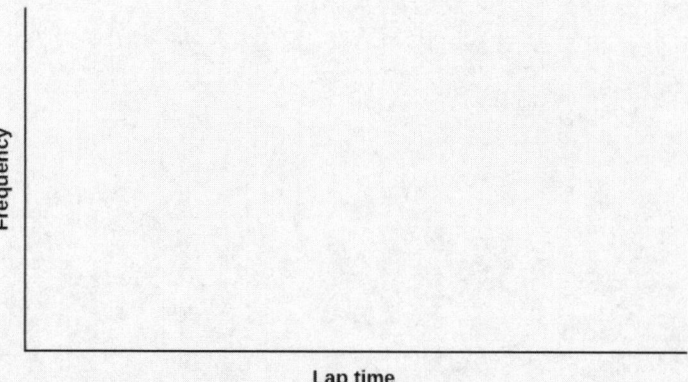

Figure 6.10

3. Calculate the following:

   a. $\bar{x} =$ _____

   b. $s =$ _____

4. Draw a smooth curve through the tops of the bars of the histogram. Write one to two complete sentences to

describe the general shape of the curve. (Keep it simple. Does the graph go straight across, does it have a v-shape, does it have a hump in the middle or at either end, and so on?)

Analyze the Distribution

Using your sample mean, sample standard deviation, and histogram to help, what is the approximate theoretical distribution of the data?

- $X \sim$ _____ (_____ , _____)
- How does the histogram help you arrive at the approximate distribution?

Describe the Data

Use the data you collected to complete the following statements.

- The *IQR* goes from _____ to _____.
- *IQR* = _____. ($IQR = Q_3 - Q_1$)
- The 15th percentile is _____.
- The 85th percentile is _____.
- The median is _____.
- The empirical probability that a randomly chosen lap time is more than 130 seconds is _____.
- Explain the meaning of the 85th percentile of this data.

Theoretical Distribution

Using the theoretical distribution, complete the following statements. You should use a normal approximation based on your sample data.

- The *IQR* goes from _____ to _____.
- *IQR* = _____.
- The 15th percentile is _____.
- The 85th percentile is _____.
- The median is _____.
- The probability that a randomly chosen lap time is more than 130 seconds is _____.
- Explain the meaning of the 85th percentile of this distribution.

Discussion Questions

Do the data from the section titled **Collect the Data** give a close approximation to the theoretical distribution in the section titled **Analyze the Distribution**? In complete sentences and comparing the result in the sections titled **Describe the Data** and **Theoretical Distribution**, explain why or why not.

6.4 | Normal Distribution (Pinkie Length)

Stats Lab

6.2 Normal Distribution (Pinkie Length)

Class Time:

Names:

Student Learning Outcomes

- The student will compare empirical data and a theoretical distribution to determine if data from the experiment follow a continuous distribution.

Collect the Data

Measure the length of your pinky finger (in centimeters).

1. Randomly survey 30 adults for their pinky finger lengths. Round the lengths to the nearest 0.5 cm.

Table 6.2

2. Construct a histogram. Make five to six intervals. Sketch the graph using a ruler and pencil. Scale the axes.

Figure 6.11

3. Calculate the following.

   a. $\bar{x}$ = _____

   b. s = _____

4. Draw a smooth curve through the top of the bars of the histogram. Write one to two complete sentences to describe the general shape of the curve. (Keep it simple. Does the graph go straight across, does it have a v-shape, does it have a hump in the middle or at either end, and so on?)

Analyze the Distribution

Using your sample mean, sample standard deviation, and histogram, what was the approximate theoretical distribution of the data you collected?

- $X \sim$ _____(_____, _____)
- How does the histogram help you arrive at the approximate distribution?

Describe the Data

Using the data you collected complete the following statements. (Hint: order the data)

REMEMBER

$(IQR = Q_3 - Q_1)$

- $IQR =$ _____
- The 15th percentile is _____.
- The 85th percentile is _____.
- Median is _____.
- What is the theoretical probability that a randomly chosen pinky length is more than 6.5 cm?
- Explain the meaning of the 85th percentile of this data.

Theoretical Distribution

Using the theoretical distribution, complete the following statements. Use a normal approximation based on the sample mean and standard deviation.

- $IQR =$ _____
- The 15th percentile is _____.
- The 85th percentile is _____.
- Median is _____.
- What is the theoretical probability that a randomly chosen pinky length is more than 6.5 cm?
- Explain the meaning of the 85th percentile of this data.

Discussion Questions

Do the data you collected give a close approximation to the theoretical distribution? In complete sentences and comparing the results in the sections titled **Describe the Data** and **Theoretical Distribution**, explain why or why not.

KEY TERMS

Normal Distribution

a continuous random variable (RV) with pdf $f(x) = \dfrac{1}{\sigma\sqrt{2\pi}}\,e^{\dfrac{-(x-\mu)^2}{2\sigma^2}}$, where μ is the mean of the distribution and σ is the standard deviation; notation: $X \sim N(\mu, \sigma)$. If $\mu = 0$ and $\sigma = 1$, the RV is called the **standard normal distribution**.

Standard Normal Distribution a continuous random variable (RV) $X \sim N(0, 1)$; when X follows the standard normal distribution, it is often noted as $Z \sim N(0, 1)$.

z-score the linear transformation of the form $z = \dfrac{x-\mu}{\sigma}$; if this transformation is applied to any normal distribution $X \sim N(\mu, \sigma)$ the result is the standard normal distribution $Z \sim N(0,1)$. If this transformation is applied to any specific value x of the RV with mean μ and standard deviation σ, the result is called the z-score of x. The z-score allows us to compare data that are normally distributed but scaled differently.

CHAPTER REVIEW

6.1 The Standard Normal Distribution

A z-score is a standardized value. Its distribution is the standard normal, $Z \sim N(0, 1)$. The mean of the z-scores is zero and the standard deviation is one. If z is the z-score for a value x from the normal distribution $N(\mu, \sigma)$ then z tells you how many standard deviations x is above (greater than) or below (less than) μ.

6.2 Using the Normal Distribution

The normal distribution, which is continuous, is the most important of all the probability distributions. Its graph is bell-shaped. This bell-shaped curve is used in almost all disciplines. Since it is a continuous distribution, the total area under the curve is one. The parameters of the normal are the mean μ and the standard deviation σ. A special normal distribution, called the standard normal distribution is the distribution of z-scores. Its mean is zero, and its standard deviation is one.

FORMULA REVIEW

6.0 Introduction

$X \sim N(\mu, \sigma)$

μ = the mean; σ = the standard deviation

6.1 The Standard Normal Distribution

z = a standardized value (z-score)

mean = 0; standard deviation = 1

To find the kth percentile of X when the z-scores is known:
$k = \mu + (z)\sigma$

z-score: $z = \dfrac{x-\mu}{\sigma}$

Z = the random variable for z-scores

$Z \sim N(0, 1)$

6.2 Using the Normal Distribution

Normal Distribution: $X \sim N(\mu, \sigma)$ where μ is the mean and σ is the standard deviation.

Standard Normal Distribution: $Z \sim N(0, 1)$.

Calculator function for probability: normalcdf (lower x value of the area, upper x value of the area, mean, standard deviation)

Calculator function for the kth percentile: k = invNorm (area to the left of k, mean, standard deviation)

PRACTICE

6.1 The Standard Normal Distribution

1. A bottle of water contains 12.05 fluid ounces with a standard deviation of 0.01 ounces. Define the random variable X in words. $X =$ _____.

2. A normal distribution has a mean of 61 and a standard deviation of 15. What is the median?

3. $X \sim N(1, 2)$

$\sigma =$ _____

4. A company manufactures rubber balls. The mean diameter of a ball is 12 cm with a standard deviation of 0.2 cm. Define the random variable X in words. $X =$ _____.

5. $X \sim N(-4, 1)$

What is the median?

6. $X \sim N(3, 5)$

$\sigma =$ _____

7. $X \sim N(-2, 1)$

$\mu =$ _____

8. What does a z-score measure?

9. What does standardizing a normal distribution do to the mean?

10. Is $X \sim N(0, 1)$ a standardized normal distribution? Why or why not?

11. What is the z-score of $x = 12$, if it is two standard deviations to the right of the mean?

12. What is the z-score of $x = 9$, if it is 1.5 standard deviations to the left of the mean?

13. What is the z-score of $x = -2$, if it is 2.78 standard deviations to the right of the mean?

14. What is the z-score of $x = 7$, if it is 0.133 standard deviations to the left of the mean?

15. Suppose $X \sim N(2, 6)$. What value of x has a z-score of three?

16. Suppose $X \sim N(8, 1)$. What value of x has a z-score of -2.25?

17. Suppose $X \sim N(9, 5)$. What value of x has a z-score of -0.5?

18. Suppose $X \sim N(2, 3)$. What value of x has a z-score of -0.67?

19. Suppose $X \sim N(4, 2)$. What value of x is 1.5 standard deviations to the left of the mean?

20. Suppose $X \sim N(4, 2)$. What value of x is two standard deviations to the right of the mean?

21. Suppose $X \sim N(8, 9)$. What value of x is 0.67 standard deviations to the left of the mean?

22. Suppose $X \sim N(-1, 2)$. What is the z-score of $x = 2$?

23. Suppose $X \sim N(12, 6)$. What is the z-score of $x = 2$?

24. Suppose $X \sim N(9, 3)$. What is the z-score of $x = 9$?

25. Suppose a normal distribution has a mean of six and a standard deviation of 1.5. What is the z-score of $x = 5.5$?

26. In a normal distribution, $x = 5$ and $z = -1.25$. This tells you that $x = 5$ is ____ standard deviations to the ____ (right or left) of the mean.

27. In a normal distribution, $x = 3$ and $z = 0.67$. This tells you that $x = 3$ is ____ standard deviations to the ____ (right or left) of the mean.

28. In a normal distribution, $x = -2$ and $z = 6$. This tells you that $x = -2$ is ____ standard deviations to the ____ (right or left) of the mean.

29. In a normal distribution, $x = -5$ and $z = -3.14$. This tells you that $x = -5$ is ____ standard deviations to the ____ (right or left) of the mean.

30. In a normal distribution, $x = 6$ and $z = -1.7$. This tells you that $x = 6$ is ____ standard deviations to the ____ (right or left) of the mean.

31. About what percent of *x* values from a normal distribution lie within one standard deviation (left and right) of the mean of that distribution?

32. About what percent of the *x* values from a normal distribution lie within two standard deviations (left and right) of the mean of that distribution?

33. About what percent of *x* values lie between the second and third standard deviations (both sides)?

34. Suppose $X \sim N(15, 3)$. Between what *x* values does 68.27% of the data lie? The range of *x* values is centered at the mean of the distribution (i.e., 15).

35. Suppose $X \sim N(-3, 1)$. Between what *x* values does 95.45% of the data lie? The range of *x* values is centered at the mean of the distribution(i.e., −3).

36. Suppose $X \sim N(-3, 1)$. Between what *x* values does 34.14% of the data lie?

37. About what percent of *x* values lie between the mean and three standard deviations?

38. About what percent of *x* values lie between the mean and one standard deviation?

39. About what percent of *x* values lie between the first and second standard deviations from the mean (both sides)?

40. About what percent of *x* values lie betwween the first and third standard deviations(both sides)?

Use the following information to answer the next two exercises: The life of Sunshine CD players is normally distributed with mean of 4.1 years and a standard deviation of 1.3 years. A CD player is guaranteed for three years. We are interested in the length of time a CD player lasts.

41. Define the random variable *X* in words. *X* = _____.

42. $X \sim$ _____(_____,_____)

6.2 Using the Normal Distribution

43. How would you represent the area to the left of one in a probability statement?

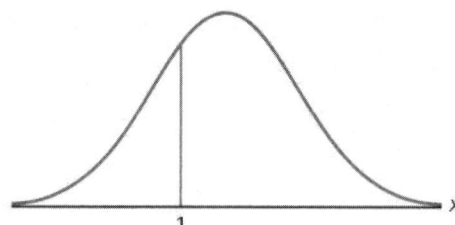

Figure 6.12

44. What is the area to the right of one?

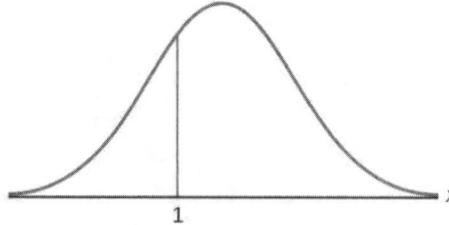

Figure 6.13

45. Is $P(x < 1)$ equal to $P(x \le 1)$? Why?

46. How would you represent the area to the left of three in a probability statement?

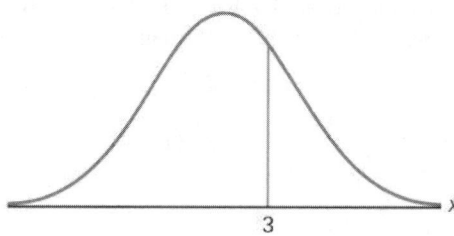

Figure 6.14

47. What is the area to the right of three?

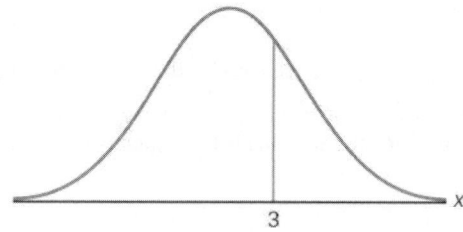

Figure 6.15

48. If the area to the left of x in a normal distribution is 0.123, what is the area to the right of x?

49. If the area to the right of x in a normal distribution is 0.543, what is the area to the left of x?

Use the following information to answer the next four exercises:

$X \sim N(54, 8)$

50. Find the probability that $x > 56$.

51. Find the probability that $x < 30$.

52. Find the 80th percentile.

53. Find the 60th percentile.

54. $X \sim N(6, 2)$

Find the probability that x is between three and nine.

55. $X \sim N(-3, 4)$

Find the probability that x is between one and four.

56. $X \sim N(4, 5)$

Find the maximum of x in the bottom quartile.

57. *Use the following information to answer the next three exercise:* The life of Sunshine CD players is normally distributed with a mean of 4.1 years and a standard deviation of 1.3 years. A CD player is guaranteed for three years. We are interested in the length of time a CD player lasts. Find the probability that a CD player will break down during the guarantee period.

    a. Sketch the situation. Label and scale the axes. Shade the region corresponding to the probability.

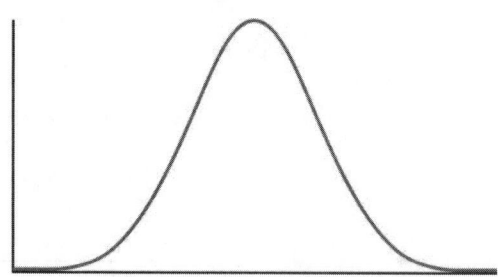

Figure 6.16

    b. $P(0 < x < $ _____ $) = $ _____ (Use zero for the minimum value of x.)

58. Find the probability that a CD player will last between 2.8 and six years.

    a. Sketch the situation. Label and scale the axes. Shade the region corresponding to the probability.

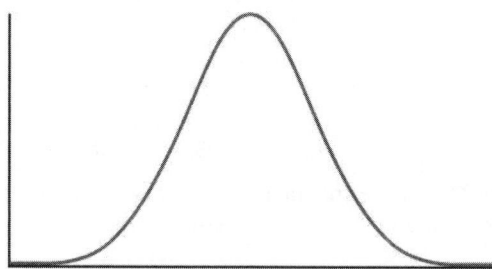

Figure 6.17

    b. $P($ _____ $< x < $ _____ $) = $ _____

59. Find the 70th percentile of the distribution for the time a CD player lasts.

    a. Sketch the situation. Label and scale the axes. Shade the region corresponding to the lower 70%.

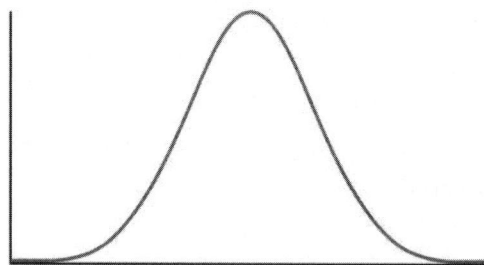

Figure 6.18

    b. $P(x < k) = $ _____ Therefore, $k = $ _____

HOMEWORK

6.1 The Standard Normal Distribution

Use the following information to answer the next two exercises: The patient recovery time from a particular surgical procedure is normally distributed with a mean of 5.3 days and a standard deviation of 2.1 days.

60. What is the median recovery time?
   a. 2.7
   b. 5.3
   c. 7.4
   d. 2.1

61. What is the *z*-score for a patient who takes ten days to recover?
   a. 1.5
   b. 0.2
   c. 2.2
   d. 7.3

62. The length of time to find it takes to find a parking space at 9 A.M. follows a normal distribution with a mean of five minutes and a standard deviation of two minutes. If the mean is significantly greater than the standard deviation, which of the following statements is true?
   I.   The data cannot follow the uniform distribution.
   II. The data cannot follow the exponential distribution..
   III. The data cannot follow the normal distribution.
   a. I only
   b. II only
   c. III only
   d. I, II, and III

63. The heights of the 430 National Basketball Association players were listed on team rosters at the start of the 2005–2006 season. The heights of basketball players have an approximate normal distribution with mean, $\mu = 79$ inches and a standard deviation, $\sigma = 3.89$ inches. For each of the following heights, calculate the *z*-score and interpret it using complete sentences.

   a. 77 inches
   b. 85 inches
   c. If an NBA player reported his height had a *z*-score of 3.5, would you believe him? Explain your answer.

64. The systolic blood pressure (given in millimeters) of males has an approximately normal distribution with mean $\mu = 125$ and standard deviation $\sigma = 14$. Systolic blood pressure for males follows a normal distribution.
   a. Calculate the *z*-scores for the male systolic blood pressures 100 and 150 millimeters.
   b. If a male friend of yours said he thought his systolic blood pressure was 2.5 standard deviations below the mean, but that he believed his blood pressure was between 100 and 150 millimeters, what would you say to him?

65. Kyle's doctor told him that the *z*-score for his systolic blood pressure is 1.75. Which of the following is the best interpretation of this standardized score? The systolic blood pressure (given in millimeters) of males has an approximately normal distribution with mean $\mu = 125$ and standard deviation $\sigma = 14$. If $X = $ a systolic blood pressure score then $X \sim N(125, 14)$.
   a. Which answer(s) **is/are** correct?
       i.   Kyle's systolic blood pressure is 175.
       ii. Kyle's systolic blood pressure is 1.75 times the average blood pressure of men his age.
       iii. Kyle's systolic blood pressure is 1.75 above the average systolic blood pressure of men his age.
       iv. Kyles's systolic blood pressure is 1.75 standard deviations above the average systolic blood pressure for men.
   b. Calculate Kyle's blood pressure.

66. Height and weight are two measurements used to track a child's development. The World Health Organization measures child development by comparing the weights of children who are the same height and the same gender. In 2009, weights for all 80 cm girls in the reference population had a mean $\mu = 10.2$ kg and standard deviation $\sigma = 0.8$ kg. Weights are normally distributed. $X \sim N(10.2, 0.8)$. Calculate the z-scores that correspond to the following weights and interpret them.
   a. 11 kg
   b. 7.9 kg
   c. 12.2 kg

67. In 2005, 1,475,623 students heading to college took the SAT. The distribution of scores in the math section of the SAT follows a normal distribution with mean $\mu = 520$ and standard deviation $\sigma = 115$.
   a. Calculate the z-score for an SAT score of 720. Interpret it using a complete sentence.
   b. What math SAT score is 1.5 standard deviations above the mean? What can you say about this SAT score?
   c. For 2012, the SAT math test had a mean of 514 and standard deviation 117. The ACT math test is an alternate to the SAT and is approximately normally distributed with mean 21 and standard deviation 5.3. If one person took the SAT math test and scored 700 and a second person took the ACT math test and scored 30, who did better with respect to the test they took?

6.2 Using the Normal Distribution

Use the following information to answer the next two exercises: The patient recovery time from a particular surgical procedure is normally distributed with a mean of 5.3 days and a standard deviation of 2.1 days.

68. What is the probability of spending more than two days in recovery?
   a. 0.0580
   b. 0.8447
   c. 0.0553
   d. 0.9420

69. The 90th percentile for recovery times is?
   a. 8.89
   b. 7.07
   c. 7.99
   d. 4.32

Use the following information to answer the next three exercises: The length of time it takes to find a parking space at 9 A.M. follows a normal distribution with a mean of five minutes and a standard deviation of two minutes.

70. Based upon the given information and numerically justified, would you be surprised if it took less than one minute to find a parking space?
   a. Yes
   b. No
   c. Unable to determine

71. Find the probability that it takes at least eight minutes to find a parking space.
   a. 0.0001
   b. 0.9270
   c. 0.1862
   d. 0.0668

72. Seventy percent of the time, it takes more than how many minutes to find a parking space?
   a. 1.24
   b. 2.41
   c. 3.95
   d. 6.05

73. According to a study done by De Anza students, the height for Asian adult males is normally distributed with an average of 66 inches and a standard deviation of 2.5 inches. Suppose one Asian adult male is randomly chosen. Let X = height of the individual.
   a. $X \sim$ _____(_____,_____)
   b. Find the probability that the person is between 65 and 69 inches. Include a sketch of the graph, and write a probability statement.
   c. Would you expect to meet many Asian adult males over 72 inches? Explain why or why not, and justify your answer numerically.

74. IQ is normally distributed with a mean of 100 and a standard deviation of 15. Suppose one individual is randomly chosen. Let X = IQ of an individual.
   a. $X \sim$ _____(_____,_____)
   b. Find the probability that the person has an IQ greater than 120. Include a sketch of the graph, and write a probability statement.
   c. MENSA is an organization whose members have the top 2% of all IQs. Find the minimum IQ needed to qualify for the MENSA organization. Sketch the graph, and write the probability statement.
   d. The middle 50% of IQs fall between what two values? Sketch the graph and write the probability statement.

75. The percent of fat calories that a person in America consumes each day is normally distributed with a mean of about 36 and a standard deviation of 10. Suppose that one individual is randomly chosen. Let X = percent of fat calories.
   a. $X \sim$ _____(_____,_____)
   b. Find the probability that the percent of fat calories a person consumes is more than 40. Graph the situation. Shade in the area to be determined.
   c. Find the maximum number for the lower quarter of percent of fat calories. Sketch the graph and write the probability statement.

76. Suppose that the distance of fly balls hit to the outfield (in baseball) is normally distributed with a mean of 250 feet and a standard deviation of 50 feet.
   a. If X = distance in feet for a fly ball, then $X \sim$ _____(_____,_____)
   b. If one fly ball is randomly chosen from this distribution, what is the probability that this ball traveled fewer than 220 feet? Sketch the graph. Scale the horizontal axis X. Shade the region corresponding to the probability. Find the probability.
   c. Find the 80th percentile of the distribution of fly balls. Sketch the graph, and write the probability statement.

77. In China, four-year-olds average three hours a day unsupervised. Most of the unsupervised children live in rural areas, considered safe. Suppose that the standard deviation is 1.5 hours and the amount of time spent alone is normally distributed. We randomly select one Chinese four-year-old living in a rural area. We are interested in the amount of time the child spends alone per day.
   a. In words, define the random variable X.
   b. $X \sim$ _____(_____,_____)
   c. Find the probability that the child spends less than one hour per day unsupervised. Sketch the graph, and write the probability statement.
   d. What percent of the children spend over ten hours per day unsupervised?
   e. Seventy percent of the children spend at least how long per day unsupervised?

78. In the 1992 presidential election, Alaska's 40 election districts averaged 1,956.8 votes per district for President Clinton. The standard deviation was 572.3. (There are only 40 election districts in Alaska.) The distribution of the votes per district for President Clinton was bell-shaped. Let X = number of votes for President Clinton for an election district.
   a. State the approximate distribution of X.
   b. Is 1,956.8 a population mean or a sample mean? How do you know?
   c. Find the probability that a randomly selected district had fewer than 1,600 votes for President Clinton. Sketch the graph and write the probability statement.
   d. Find the probability that a randomly selected district had between 1,800 and 2,000 votes for President Clinton.
   e. Find the third quartile for votes for President Clinton.

79. Suppose that the duration of a particular type of criminal trial is known to be normally distributed with a mean of 21 days and a standard deviation of seven days.
   a. In words, define the random variable X.
   b. $X \sim$ _____(_____,_____)
   c. If one of the trials is randomly chosen, find the probability that it lasted at least 24 days. Sketch the graph and write the probability statement.
   d. Sixty percent of all trials of this type are completed within how many days?

80. Terri Vogel, an amateur motorcycle racer, averages 129.71 seconds per 2.5 mile lap (in a seven-lap race) with a standard deviation of 2.28 seconds. The distribution of her race times is normally distributed. We are interested in one of her randomly selected laps.

    a. In words, define the random variable X.

    b. $X \sim$ _____(_____,_____)

    c. Find the percent of her laps that are completed in less than 130 seconds.

    d. The fastest 3% of her laps are under _____.

    e. The middle 80% of her laps are from _____ seconds to _____ seconds.

81. Thuy Dau, Ngoc Bui, Sam Su, and Lan Voung conducted a survey as to how long customers at Lucky claimed to wait in the checkout line until their turn. Let X = time in line. **Table 6.3** displays the ordered real data (in minutes):

0.50	4.25	5	6	7.25
1.75	4.25	5.25	6	7.25
2	4.25	5.25	6.25	7.25
2.25	4.25	5.5	6.25	7.75
2.25	4.5	5.5	6.5	8
2.5	4.75	5.5	6.5	8.25
2.75	4.75	5.75	6.5	9.5
3.25	4.75	5.75	6.75	9.5
3.75	5	6	6.75	9.75
3.75	5	6	6.75	10.75

Table 6.3

    a. Calculate the sample mean and the sample standard deviation.

    b. Construct a histogram.

    c. Draw a smooth curve through the midpoints of the tops of the bars.

    d. In words, describe the shape of your histogram and smooth curve.

    e. Let the sample mean approximate μ and the sample standard deviation approximate σ. The distribution of X can then be approximated by $X \sim$ _____(_____,_____)

    f. Use the distribution in part e to calculate the probability that a person will wait fewer than 6.1 minutes.

    g. Determine the cumulative relative frequency for waiting less than 6.1 minutes.

    h. Why aren't the answers to part f and part g exactly the same?

    i. Why are the answers to part f and part g as close as they are?

    j. If only ten customers has been surveyed rather than 50, do you think the answers to part f and part g would have been closer together or farther apart? Explain your conclusion.

82. Suppose that Ricardo and Anita attend different colleges. Ricardo's GPA is the same as the average GPA at his school. Anita's GPA is 0.70 standard deviations above her school average. In complete sentences, explain why each of the following statements may be false.

    a. Ricardo's actual GPA is lower than Anita's actual GPA.

    b. Ricardo is not passing because his z-score is zero.

    c. Anita is in the 70th percentile of students at her college.

83. Table 6.4 shows a sample of the maximum capacity (maximum number of spectators) of sports stadiums. The table does not include horse-racing or motor-racing stadiums.

40,000	40,000	45,050	45,500	46,249	48,134
49,133	50,071	50,096	50,466	50,832	51,100
51,500	51,900	52,000	52,132	52,200	52,530
52,692	53,864	54,000	55,000	55,000	55,000
55,000	55,000	55,000	55,082	57,000	58,008
59,680	60,000	60,000	60,492	60,580	62,380
62,872	64,035	65,000	65,050	65,647	66,000
66,161	67,428	68,349	68,976	69,372	70,107
70,585	71,594	72,000	72,922	73,379	74,500
75,025	76,212	78,000	80,000	80,000	82,300

Table 6.4

   a. Calculate the sample mean and the sample standard deviation for the maximum capacity of sports stadiums (the data).
   b. Construct a histogram.
   c. Draw a smooth curve through the midpoints of the tops of the bars of the histogram.
   d. In words, describe the shape of your histogram and smooth curve.
   e. Let the sample mean approximate μ and the sample standard deviation approximate σ. The distribution of X can then be approximated by $X \sim$ _____(_____,_____).
   f. Use the distribution in part e to calculate the probability that the maximum capacity of sports stadiums is less than 67,000 spectators.
   g. Determine the cumulative relative frequency that the maximum capacity of sports stadiums is less than 67,000 spectators. Hint: Order the data and count the sports stadiums that have a maximum capacity less than 67,000. Divide by the total number of sports stadiums in the sample.
   h. Why aren't the answers to part f and part g exactly the same?

84. An expert witness for a paternity lawsuit testifies that the length of a pregnancy is normally distributed with a mean of 280 days and a standard deviation of 13 days. An alleged father was out of the country from 240 to 306 days before the birth of the child, so the pregnancy would have been less than 240 days or more than 306 days long if he was the father. The birth was uncomplicated, and the child needed no medical intervention. What is the probability that he was NOT the father? What is the probability that he could be the father? Calculate the z-scores first, and then use those to calculate the probability.

85. A NUMMI assembly line, which has been operating since 1984, has built an average of 6,000 cars and trucks a week. Generally, 10% of the cars were defective coming off the assembly line. Suppose we draw a random sample of $n = 100$ cars. Let X represent the number of defective cars in the sample. What can we say about X in regard to the 68-95-99.7 empirical rule (one standard deviation, two standard deviations and three standard deviations from the mean are being referred to)? Assume a normal distribution for the defective cars in the sample.

86. We flip a coin 100 times ($n = 100$) and note that it only comes up heads 20% ($p = 0.20$) of the time. The mean and standard deviation for the number of times the coin lands on heads is $\mu = 20$ and $\sigma = 4$ (verify the mean and standard deviation). Solve the following:
   a. There is about a 68% chance that the number of heads will be somewhere between ___ and ___.
   b. There is about a _____chance that the number of heads will be somewhere between 12 and 28.
   c. There is about a _____ chance that the number of heads will be somewhere between eight and 32.

87. A $1 scratch off lotto ticket will be a winner one out of five times. Out of a shipment of $n = 190$ lotto tickets, find the probability for the lotto tickets that there are
   a. somewhere between 34 and 54 prizes.
   b. somewhere between 54 and 64 prizes.
   c. more than 64 prizes.

88. Facebook provides a variety of statistics on its Web site that detail the growth and popularity of the site.

On average, 28 percent of 18 to 34 year olds check their Facebook profiles before getting out of bed in the morning. Suppose this percentage follows a normal distribution with a standard deviation of five percent.

  a. Find the probability that the percent of 18 to 34-year-olds who check Facebook before getting out of bed in the morning is at least 30.
  b. Find the 95th percentile, and express it in a sentence.

REFERENCES

6.1 The Standard Normal Distribution

"Blood Pressure of Males and Females." StatCruch, 2013. Available online at http://www.statcrunch.com/5.0/viewreport.php?reportid=11960 (accessed May 14, 2013).

"The Use of Epidemiological Tools in Conflict-affected populations: Open-access educational resources for policy-makers: Calculation of z-scores." London School of Hygiene and Tropical Medicine, 2009. Available online at http://conflict.lshtm.ac.uk/page_125.htm (accessed May 14, 2013).

"2012 College-Bound Seniors Total Group Profile Report." CollegeBoard, 2012. Available online at http://media.collegeboard.com/digitalServices/pdf/research/TotalGroup-2012.pdf (accessed May 14, 2013).

"Digest of Education Statistics: ACT score average and standard deviations by sex and race/ethnicity and percentage of ACT test takers, by selected composite score ranges and planned fields of study: Selected years, 1995 through 2009." National Center for Education Statistics. Available online at http://nces.ed.gov/programs/digest/d09/tables/dt09_147.asp (accessed May 14, 2013).

Data from the *San Jose Mercury News*.

Data from *The World Almanac and Book of Facts*.

"List of stadiums by capacity." Wikipedia. Available online at https://en.wikipedia.org/wiki/List_of_stadiums_by_capacity (accessed May 14, 2013).

Data from the National Basketball Association. Available online at www.nba.com (accessed May 14, 2013).

6.2 Using the Normal Distribution

"Naegele's rule." Wikipedia. Available online at http://en.wikipedia.org/wiki/Naegele's_rule (accessed May 14, 2013).

"403: NUMMI." Chicago Public Media & Ira Glass, 2013. Available online at http://www.thisamericanlife.org/radio-archives/episode/403/nummi (accessed May 14, 2013).

"Scratch-Off Lottery Ticket Playing Tips." WinAtTheLottery.com, 2013. Available online at http://www.winatthelottery.com/public/department40.cfm (accessed May 14, 2013).

"Smart Phone Users, By The Numbers." Visual.ly, 2013. Available online at http://visual.ly/smart-phone-users-numbers (accessed May 14, 2013).

"Facebook Statistics." Statistics Brain. Available online at http://www.statisticbrain.com/facebook-statistics/(accessed May 14, 2013).

SOLUTIONS

1 ounces of water in a bottle

3 2

5 –4

7 –2

9 The mean becomes zero.

11 $z = 2$

13 $z = 2.78$

15 $x = 20$

17 $x = 6.5$

19 $x = 1$

21 $x = 1.97$

23 $z = -1.67$

25 $z \approx -0.33$

27 0.67, right

29 3.14, left

31 about 68%

33 about 4%

35 between -5 and -1

37 about 50%

39 about 27%

41 The lifetime of a Sunshine CD player measured in years.

43 $P(x < 1)$

45 Yes, because they are the same in a continuous distribution: $P(x = 1) = 0$

47 $1 - P(x < 3)$ or $P(x > 3)$

49 $1 - 0.543 = 0.457$

51 0.0013

53 56.03

55 0.1186

57

   a. Check student's solution.

   b. 3, 0.1979

59

   a. Check student's solution.

   b. 0.70, 4.78 years

61 c

63

   a. Use the z-score formula. $z = -0.5141$. The height of 77 inches is 0.5141 standard deviations below the mean. An NBA player whose height is 77 inches is shorter than average.

   b. Use the z-score formula. $z = 1.5424$. The height 85 inches is 1.5424 standard deviations above the mean. An NBA player whose height is 85 inches is taller than average.

   c. Height = $79 + 3.5(3.89) = 92.615$ inches, which is taller than 7 feet, 8 inches. There are very few NBA players this tall so the answer is no, not likely.

65

   a. iv

   b. Kyle's blood pressure is equal to $125 + (1.75)(14) = 149.5$.

67 Let X = an SAT math score and Y = an ACT math score.

a. $X = 720$ $\frac{720-520}{15} = 1.74$ The exam score of 720 is 1.74 standard deviations above the mean of 520.

b. $z = 1.5$

The math SAT score is $520 + 1.5(115) \approx 692.5$. The exam score of 692.5 is 1.5 standard deviations above the mean of 520.

c. $\frac{X - \mu}{\sigma} = \frac{700-514}{117} \approx 1.59$, the z-score for the SAT. $\frac{Y - \mu}{\sigma} = \frac{30-21}{5.3} \approx 1.70$, the z-scores for the ACT. With respect to the test they took, the person who took the ACT did better (has the higher z-score).

69 c

71 d

73

a. $X \sim N(66, 2.5)$

b. 0.5404

c. No, the probability that an Asian male is over 72 inches tall is 0.0082

75

a. $X \sim N(36, 10)$

b. The probability that a person consumes more than 40% of their calories as fat is 0.3446.

c. Approximately 25% of people consume less than 29.26% of their calories as fat.

77

a. X = number of hours that a Chinese four-year-old in a rural area is unsupervised during the day.

b. $X \sim N(3, 1.5)$

c. The probability that the child spends less than one hour a day unsupervised is 0.0918.

d. The probability that a child spends over ten hours a day unsupervised is less than 0.0001.

e. 2.21 hours

79

a. X = the distribution of the number of days a particular type of criminal trial will take

b. $X \sim N(21, 7)$

c. The probability that a randomly selected trial will last more than 24 days is 0.3336.

d. 22.77

81

a. mean = 5.51, $s = 2.15$

b. Check student's solution.

c. Check student's solution.

d. Check student's solution.

e. $X \sim N(5.51, 2.15)$

f. 0.6029

g. The cumulative frequency for less than 6.1 minutes is 0.64.

h. The answers to part f and part g are not exactly the same, because the normal distribution is only an approximation to the real one.

i. The answers to part f and part g are close, because a normal distribution is an excellent approximation when the sample size is greater than 30.

j. The approximation would have been less accurate, because the smaller sample size means that the data does not fit normal curve as well.

83

1. mean = 60,136
   s = 10,468

2. Answers will vary.

3. Answers will vary.

4. Answers will vary.

5. $X \sim N(60136, 10468)$

6. 0.7440

7. The cumulative relative frequency is 43/60 = 0.717.

8. The answers for part f and part g are not the same, because the normal distribution is only an approximation.

85

$n = 100; p = 0.1; q = 0.9$

$\mu = np = (100)(0.10) = 10$

$\sigma = \sqrt{npq} = \sqrt{(100)(0.1)(0.9)} = 3$

i. $z = \pm1$: $x_1 = \mu + z\sigma = 10 + 1(3) = 13$ and $x2 = \mu - z\sigma = 10 - 1(3) = 7$. 68% of the defective cars will fall between seven and 13.

ii. $z = \pm2$: $x_1 = \mu + z\sigma = 10 + 2(3) = 16$ and $x2 = \mu - z\sigma = 10 - 2(3) = 4$. 95 % of the defective cars will fall between four and 16

iii. $z = \pm3$: $x_1 = \mu + z\sigma = 10 + 3(3) = 19$ and $x2 = \mu - z\sigma = 10 - 3(3) = 1$. 99.7% of the defective cars will fall between one and 19.

87

$n = 190; p = \dfrac{1}{5} = 0.2; q = 0.8$

$\mu = np = (190)(0.2) = 38$

$\sigma = \sqrt{npq} = \sqrt{(190)(0.2)(0.8)} = 5.5136$

a. For this problem: $P(34 < x < 54)$ = normalcdf(34,54,48,5.5136) = 0.7641

b. For this problem: $P(54 < x < 64)$ = normalcdf(54,64,48,5.5136) = 0.0018

c. For this problem: $P(x > 64)$ = normalcdf(64,10^{99},48,5.5136) = 0.0000012 (approximately 0)

7 | THE CENTRAL LIMIT THEOREM

Figure 7.1 If you want to figure out the distribution of the change people carry in their pockets, using the central limit theorem and assuming your sample is large enough, you will find that the distribution is normal and bell-shaped. (credit: John Lodder)

Introduction

Chapter Objectives
By the end of this chapter, the student should be able to: • Recognize central limit theorem problems. • Classify continuous word problems by their distributions. • Apply and interpret the central limit theorem for means. • Apply and interpret the central limit theorem for sums.

Why are we so concerned with means? Two reasons are: they give us a middle ground for comparison, and they are easy to calculate. In this chapter, you will study means and the **central limit theorem**.

The **central limit theorem** (clt for short) is one of the most powerful and useful ideas in all of statistics. There are two alternative forms of the theorem, and both alternatives are concerned with drawing finite samples size n from a population with a known mean, μ, and a known standard deviation, σ. The first alternative says that if we collect samples of size n with a "large enough n," calculate each sample's mean, and create a histogram of those means, then the resulting histogram will tend to have an approximate normal bell shape. The second alternative says that if we again collect samples of size n that are "large enough," calculate the sum of each sample and create a histogram, then the resulting histogram will again tend to have a normal bell-shape.

The size of the sample, n, that is required in order to be "large enough" depends on the original population from which the samples are drawn (the sample size should be at least 30 or the data should come from a normal distribution). If the original population is far from normal, then more observations are needed for the sample means or sums to be normal. **Sampling is done with replacement.**

It would be difficult to overstate the importance of the central limit theorem in statistical theory. Knowing that data, even if its distribution is not normal, behaves in a predictable way is a powerful tool.

Collaborative Exercise

Suppose eight of you roll one fair die ten times, seven of you roll two fair dice ten times, nine of you roll five fair dice ten times, and 11 of you roll ten fair dice ten times.

Each time a person rolls more than one die, he or she calculates the sample **mean** of the faces showing. For example, one person might roll five fair dice and get 2, 2, 3, 4, 6 on one roll.

The mean is $\frac{2 + 2 + 3 + 4 + 6}{5}$ = 3.4. The 3.4 is one mean when five fair dice are rolled. This same person would roll the five dice nine more times and calculate nine more means for a total of ten means.

Your instructor will pass out the dice to several people. Roll your dice ten times. For each roll, record the faces, and find the mean. Round to the nearest 0.5.

Your instructor (and possibly you) will produce one graph (it might be a histogram) for one die, one graph for two dice, one graph for five dice, and one graph for ten dice. Since the "mean" when you roll one die is just the face on the die, what distribution do these **means** appear to be representing?

Draw the graph for the means using two dice. Do the sample means show any kind of pattern?

Draw the graph for the means using five dice. Do you see any pattern emerging?

Finally, draw the graph for the means using ten dice. Do you see any pattern to the graph? What can you conclude as you increase the number of dice?

As the number of dice rolled increases from one to two to five to ten, the following is happening:

1. The mean of the sample means remains approximately the same.

2. The spread of the sample means (the standard deviation of the sample means) gets smaller.

3. The graph appears steeper and thinner.

You have just demonstrated the central limit theorem (clt).

The central limit theorem tells you that as you increase the number of dice, **the sample means tend toward a normal distribution (the sampling distribution).**

7.1 | The Central Limit Theorem for Sample Means (Averages)

Suppose X is a random variable with a distribution that may be known or unknown (it can be any distribution). Using a subscript that matches the random variable, suppose:

a. μ_X = the mean of X

b. σ_X = the standard deviation of X

If you draw random samples of size n, then as n increases, the random variable $\overline{X}$ which consists of sample means, tends

to be **normally distributed** and

$$\overline{X} \sim N\left(\mu_x, \frac{\sigma_x}{\sqrt{n}}\right).$$

The **central limit theorem** for sample means says that if you keep drawing larger and larger samples (such as rolling one, two, five, and finally, ten dice) and **calculating their means,** the sample means form their own **normal distribution** (the sampling distribution). The normal distribution has the same mean as the original distribution and a variance that equals the original variance divided by the sample size. Standard deviation is the square root of variance, so the standard deviation of the sampling distribution is the standard deviation of the original distribution divided by the square root of *n*. The variable *n* is the number of values that are averaged together, not the number of times the experiment is done.

To put it more formally, if you draw random samples of size *n*, the distribution of the random variable $\overline{X}$, which consists of sample means, is called the **sampling distribution of the mean**. The sampling distribution of the mean approaches a normal distribution as *n*, the **sample size**, increases.

The random variable $\overline{X}$ has a different z-score associated with it from that of the random variable *X*. The mean $\overline{x}$ is the value of $\overline{X}$ in one sample.

$$z = \frac{\overline{x} - \mu_x}{\left(\frac{\sigma_x}{\sqrt{n}}\right)}$$

μ_X is the average of both *X* and $\overline{X}$.

$\sigma\overline{x} = \frac{\sigma_x}{\sqrt{n}}$ = standard deviation of $\overline{X}$ and is called the **standard error of the mean.**

 Using the TI-83, 83+, 84, 84+ Calculator

To find probabilities for means on the calculator, follow these steps.

2nd DISTR
2:normalcdf

$$normalcdf\left(lower\ value\ of\ the\ area,\ \ upper\ value\ of\ the\ area,\ \ mean,\ \ \frac{standard\ \ deviation}{\sqrt{sample\ \ size}}\right)$$

where:

- *mean* is the mean of the original distribution

- *standard deviation* is the standard deviation of the original distribution

- *sample size* = n

Example 7.1

An unknown distribution has a mean of 90 and a standard deviation of 15. Samples of size *n* = 25 are drawn randomly from the population.

a. Find the probability that the **sample mean** is between 85 and 92.

Solution 7.1

a. Let *X* = one value from the original unknown population. The probability question asks you to find a probability for the **sample mean**.

Let $\overline{X}$ = the mean of a sample of size 25. Since μ_X = 90, σ_X = 15, and *n* = 25,

$$\overline{X} \sim N\left(90, \frac{15}{\sqrt{25}}\right).$$

Find $P(85 < \overline{x} < 92)$. Draw a graph.

$$P(85 < \overline{x} < 92) = 0.6997$$

The probability that the sample mean is between 85 and 92 is 0.6997.

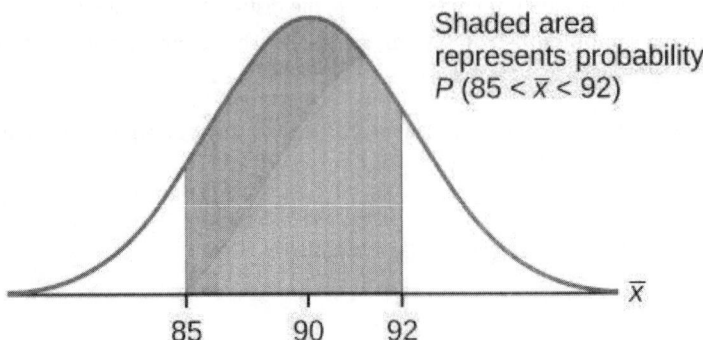

Figure 7.2

 Using the TI-83, 83+, 84, 84+ Calculator

normalcdf(lower value, upper value, mean, standard error of the mean)

The parameter list is abbreviated (lower value, upper value, μ, $\frac{\sigma}{\sqrt{n}}$)

normalcdf$(85,92,90,\frac{15}{\sqrt{25}}) = 0.6997$

b. Find the value that is two standard deviations above the expected value, 90, of the sample mean.

Solution 7.1

b. To find the value that is two standard deviations above the expected value 90, use the formula:

$$\text{value} = \mu_x + (\#\text{ofTSDEVs})\left(\frac{\sigma_x}{\sqrt{n}}\right)$$

$$\text{value} = 90 + 2\left(\frac{15}{\sqrt{25}}\right) = 96$$

The value that is two standard deviations above the expected value is 96.

The standard error of the mean is $\frac{\sigma_x}{\sqrt{n}} = \frac{15}{\sqrt{25}} = 3$. Recall that the standard error of the mean is a description of how far (on average) that the sample mean will be from the population mean in repeated simple random samples of size n.

Try It Σ

7.1 An unknown distribution has a mean of 45 and a standard deviation of eight. Samples of size $n = 30$ are drawn randomly from the population. Find the probability that the sample mean is between 42 and 50.

Example 7.2

The length of time, in hours, it takes an "over 40" group of people to play one soccer match is normally distributed with a **mean of two hours** and a **standard deviation of 0.5 hours**. A **sample of size $n = 50$** is drawn randomly from the population. Find the probability that the **sample mean** is between 1.8 hours and 2.3 hours.

Solution 7.2

Let X = the time, in hours, it takes to play one soccer match.

The probability question asks you to find a probability for the **sample mean time, in hours**, it takes to play one soccer match.

Let $\bar{X}$ = the **mean** time, in hours, it takes to play one soccer match.

If $\mu_X =$ _____, $\sigma_X =$ _____, and $n =$ _____, then $X \sim N($_____, _____$)$ by the **central limit theorem for means**.

$\mu_X = 2$, $\sigma_X = 0.5$, $n = 50$, and $X \sim N\left(2, \frac{0.5}{\sqrt{50}}\right)$

Find $P(1.8 < \bar{x} < 2.3)$. Draw a graph.

$P(1.8 < \bar{x} < 2.3) = 0.9977$

$\texttt{normalcdf}\left(1.8, 2.3, 2, \frac{.5}{\sqrt{50}}\right) = 0.9977$

The probability that the mean time is between 1.8 hours and 2.3 hours is 0.9977.

Try It Σ

7.2 The length of time taken on the SAT for a group of students is normally distributed with a mean of 2.5 hours and a standard deviation of 0.25 hours. A sample size of $n = 60$ is drawn randomly from the population. Find the probability that the sample mean is between two hours and three hours.

Using the TI-83, 83+, 84, 84+ Calculator

To find percentiles for means on the calculator, follow these steps.

2nd DIStR

3:invNorm

$k = \text{invNorm}\left(\text{area to the left of } k, \text{mean}, \frac{standard\ deviation}{\sqrt{sample\ size}}\right)$

where:

- k = the kth percentile
- *mean* is the mean of the original distribution
- *standard deviation* is the standard deviation of the original distribution
- *sample size* = n

Example 7.3

In a recent study reported Oct. 29, 2012 on the Flurry Blog, the mean age of tablet users is 34 years. Suppose the standard deviation is 15 years. Take a sample of size $n = 100$.

   a. What are the mean and standard deviation for the sample mean ages of tablet users?

   b. What does the distribution look like?

   c. Find the probability that the sample mean age is more than 30 years (the reported mean age of tablet users in this particular study).

   d. Find the 95th percentile for the sample mean age (to one decimal place).

Solution 7.3

   a. Since the sample mean tends to target the population mean, we have $\mu_X = \mu = 34$. The sample standard deviation is given by $\sigma_X = \dfrac{\sigma}{\sqrt{n}} = \dfrac{15}{\sqrt{100}} = \dfrac{15}{10} = 1.5$

   b. The central limit theorem states that for large sample sizes(n), the sampling distribution will be approximately normal.

   c. The probability that the sample mean age is more than 30 is given by $P(X > 30) =$ `normalcdf`$(30,\text{E}99,34,1.5) = 0.9962$

   d. Let k = the 95th percentile.

$$k = \text{invNorm}\left(0.95,34,\dfrac{15}{\sqrt{100}}\right) = 36.5$$

Try It Σ

7.3 In an article on Flurry Blog, a gaming marketing gap for men between the ages of 30 and 40 is identified. You are researching a startup game targeted at the 35-year-old demographic. Your idea is to develop a strategy game that can be played by men from their late 20s through their late 30s. Based on the article's data, industry research shows that the average strategy player is 28 years old with a standard deviation of 4.8 years. You take a sample of 100 randomly selected gamers. If your target market is 29- to 35-year-olds, should you continue with your development strategy?

Example 7.4

The mean number of minutes for app engagement by a tablet user is 8.2 minutes. Suppose the standard deviation is one minute. Take a sample of 60.

   a. What are the mean and standard deviation for the sample mean number of app engagement by a tablet user?

   b. What is the standard error of the mean?

   c. Find the 90th percentile for the sample mean time for app engagement for a tablet user. Interpret this value in a complete sentence.

   d. Find the probability that the sample mean is between eight minutes and 8.5 minutes.

Solution 7.4

a. $\mu_{\bar{x}} = \mu = 8.2 \ \sigma_{\bar{x}} = \frac{\sigma}{\sqrt{n}} = \frac{1}{\sqrt{60}} = 0.13$

b. This allows us to calculate the probability of sample means of a particular distance from the mean, in repeated samples of size 60.

c. Let k = the 90th percentile

$k = \mathtt{invNorm}\left(0.90, 8.2, \frac{1}{\sqrt{60}}\right) = 8.37$. This values indicates that 90 percent of the average app engagement time for table users is less than 8.37 minutes.

d. $P(8 < \bar{x} < 8.5) = \mathtt{normalcdf}\left(8, 8.5, 8.2, \frac{1}{\sqrt{60}}\right) = 0.9293$

Try It Σ

7.4 Cans of a cola beverage claim to contain 16 ounces. The amounts in a sample are measured and the statistics are $n = 34$, $\bar{x} = 16.01$ ounces. If the cans are filled so that $\mu = 16.00$ ounces (as labeled) and $\sigma = 0.143$ ounces, find the probability that a sample of 34 cans will have an average amount greater than 16.01 ounces. Do the results suggest that cans are filled with an amount greater than 16 ounces?

7.2 | The Central Limit Theorem for Sums

Suppose X is a random variable with a distribution that may be **known or unknown** (it can be any distribution) and suppose:

a. μ_X = the mean of X

b. σ_X = the standard deviation of X

If you draw random samples of size n, then as n increases, the random variable ΣX consisting of sums tends to be **normally distributed** and $\Sigma X \sim N((n)(\mu_X), (\sqrt{n})(\sigma_X))$.

The central limit theorem for sums says that if you keep drawing larger and larger samples and taking their sums, the sums form their own normal distribution (the sampling distribution), which approaches a normal distribution as the sample size increases. **The normal distribution has a mean equal to the original mean multiplied by the sample size and a standard deviation equal to the original standard deviation multiplied by the square root of the sample size.**

The random variable ΣX has the following z-score associated with it:

a. Σx is one sum.

b. $z = \dfrac{\Sigma x - (n)(\mu_X)}{(\sqrt{n})(\sigma_X)}$

    i. $(n)(\mu_X)$ = the mean of ΣX

    ii. $(\sqrt{n})(\sigma_X)$ = standard deviation of ΣX

 Using the TI-83, 83+, 84, 84+ Calculator

To find probabilities for sums on the calculator, follow these steps.

2nd `DISTR`
2:`normalcdf`
`normalcdf`(lower value of the area, upper value of the area, (n)(mean), $(\sqrt{n})$(standard deviation))

where:

- *mean* is the mean of the original distribution
- *standard deviation* is the standard deviation of the original distribution
- **sample size** = n

Example 7.5

An unknown distribution has a mean of 90 and a standard deviation of 15. A sample of size 80 is drawn randomly from the population.

   a. Find the probability that the sum of the 80 values (or the total of the 80 values) is more than 7,500.

   b. Find the sum that is 1.5 standard deviations above the mean of the sums.

Solution 7.5

Let X = one value from the original unknown population. The probability question asks you to find a probability for **the sum (or total of) 80 values.**

ΣX = the sum or total of 80 values. Since $\mu_X = 90$, $\sigma_X = 15$, and $n = 80$, $\Sigma X \sim N((80)(90),$
$(\sqrt{80})(15))$

- mean of the sums = $(n)(\mu_X) = (80)(90) = 7{,}200$
- standard deviation of the sums = $(\sqrt{n})(\sigma_X) = (\sqrt{80})(15)$

- sum of 80 values = $\Sigma x = 7{,}500$

a. Find $P(\Sigma x > 7{,}500)$

$P(\Sigma x > 7{,}500) = 0.0127$

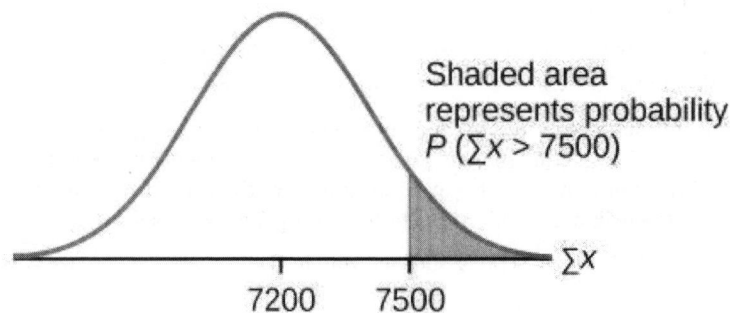

Figure 7.3

 Using the TI-83, 83+, 84, 84+ Calculator

normalcdf(lower value, upper value, mean of sums, stdev of sums)

The parameter list is abbreviated(lower, upper, $(n)(\mu_X,$ $(\sqrt{n})(\sigma_X))$

normalcdf $(7500,\text{1E99},(80)(90),(\sqrt{80})(15)) = 0.0127$

REMINDER

$1E99 = 10^{99}$.

Press the **EE** key for E.

b. Find Σx where $z = 1.5$.

$\Sigma x = (n)(\mu_X) + (z)(\sqrt{n})(\sigma_X) = (80)(90) + (1.5)(\sqrt{80})(15) = 7{,}401.2$

Try It Σ

7.5 An unknown distribution has a mean of 45 and a standard deviation of eight. A sample size of 50 is drawn randomly from the population. Find the probability that the sum of the 50 values is more than 2,400.

 Using the TI-83, 83+, 84, 84+ Calculator

To find percentiles for sums on the calculator, follow these steps.

2nd DIStR
3:invNorm
$k =$ invNorm (area to the left of k, (n)(mean), $(\sqrt{n})$(standard deviation))

where:

- k is the kth **percentile**
- *mean* is the mean of the original distribution
- *standard deviation* is the standard deviation of the original distribution
- *sample size* = n

Example 7.6

In a recent study reported Oct. 29, 2012 on the Flurry Blog, the mean age of tablet users is 34 years. Suppose the standard deviation is 15 years. The sample of size is 50.

a. What are the mean and standard deviation for the sum of the ages of tablet users? What is the distribution?

b. Find the probability that the sum of the ages is between 1,500 and 1,800 years.

c. Find the 80th percentile for the sum of the 50 ages.

Solution 7.6

a. $\mu_{\Sigma x} = n\mu_x = 50(34) = 1{,}700$ and $\sigma_{\Sigma x} = \sqrt{n}\,\sigma_x = (\sqrt{50})(15) = 106.07$

The distribution is normal for sums by the central limit theorem.

b. $P(1500 < \Sigma x < 1800) = \texttt{normalcdf}(1{,}500, 1{,}800, (50)(34), (\sqrt{50})(15)) = 0.7974$

c. Let $k =$ the 80th percentile.
$k = \texttt{invNorm}(0.80, (50)(34), (\sqrt{50})(15)) = 1{,}789.3$

Try It ⅀

7.6 In a recent study reported Oct.29, 2012 on the Flurry Blog, the mean age of tablet users is 35 years. Suppose the standard deviation is ten years. The sample size is 39.

a. What are the mean and standard deviation for the sum of the ages of tablet users? What is the distribution?

b. Find the probability that the sum of the ages is between 1,400 and 1,500 years.

c. Find the 90th percentile for the sum of the 39 ages.

Example 7.7

The mean number of minutes for app engagement by a tablet user is 8.2 minutes. Suppose the standard deviation is one minute. Take a sample of size 70.

a. What are the mean and standard deviation for the sums?

b. Find the 95th percentile for the sum of the sample. Interpret this value in a complete sentence.

c. Find the probability that the sum of the sample is at least ten hours.

Solution 7.7

a. $\mu_{\Sigma x} = n\mu_x = 70(8.2) = 574$ minutes and $\sigma_{\Sigma x} = (\sqrt{n})(\sigma_x) = (\sqrt{70})(1) = 8.37$ minutes

b. Let k = the 95th percentile.

k = invNorm $(0.95,(70)(8.2), (\sqrt{70})(1)) = 587.76$ minutes

Ninety five percent of the sums of app engagement times are at most 587.76 minutes.

c. ten hours = 600 minutes

$P(\Sigma x \geq 600) =$ `normalcdf`$(600,\text{E}99,(70)(8.2), (\sqrt{70})(1)) = 0.0009$

Try It ⅀

7.7 The mean number of minutes for app engagement by a table use is 8.2 minutes. Suppose the standard deviation is one minute. Take a sample size of 70.

a. What is the probability that the sum of the sample is between seven hours and ten hours? What does this mean in context of the problem?

b. Find the 84th and 16th percentiles for the sum of the sample. Interpret these values in context.

7.3 | Using the Central Limit Theorem

It is important for you to understand when to use the **central limit theorem**. If you are being asked to find the probability of the mean, use the clt for the mean. If you are being asked to find the probability of a sum or total, use the clt for sums. This also applies to percentiles for means and sums.

NOTE

If you are being asked to find the probability of an **individual** value, do **not** use the clt. **Use the distribution of its random variable.**

Examples of the Central Limit Theorem

Law of Large Numbers

The **law of large numbers** says that if you take samples of larger and larger size from any population, then the mean $\bar{x}$ of the sample tends to get closer and closer to μ. From the central limit theorem, we know that as n gets larger and larger, the sample means follow a normal distribution. The larger n gets, the smaller the standard deviation gets. (Remember that the standard deviation for $\bar{X}$ is $\frac{\sigma}{\sqrt{n}}$.) This means that the sample mean $\bar{x}$ must be close to the population mean μ. We can say that μ is the value that the sample means approach as n gets larger. The central limit theorem illustrates the law of large numbers.

Central Limit Theorem for the Mean and Sum Examples

Example 7.8

A study involving stress is conducted among the students on a college campus. **The stress scores follow a uniform distribution** with the lowest stress score equal to one and the highest equal to five. Using a sample of 75 students, find:

a. The probability that the **mean stress score** for the 75 students is less than two.

b. The 90th percentile for the **mean stress score** for the 75 students.

c. The probability that the **total of the 75 stress scores** is less than 200.

d. The 90th percentile for the **total stress score** for the 75 students.

Let X = one stress score.

Problems a and b ask you to find a probability or a percentile for a **mean**. Problems c and d ask you to find a probability or a percentile for a **total or sum**. The sample size, n, is equal to 75.

Since the individual stress scores follow a uniform distribution, $X \sim U(1, 5)$ where $a = 1$ and $b = 5$ (See **Continuous Random Variables** for an explanation on the uniform distribution).

$$\mu_X = \frac{a + b}{2} = \frac{1 + 5}{2} = 3$$

$$\sigma_X = \sqrt{\frac{(b - a)^2}{12}} = \sqrt{\frac{(5 - 1)^2}{12}} = 1.15$$

For problems a. and b., let $\bar{X}$ = the mean stress score for the 75 students. Then,

$$\bar{X} \sim N\left(3, \frac{1.15}{\sqrt{75}}\right)$$

a. Find $P(\bar{x} < 2)$. Draw the graph.

Solution 7.8

a. $P(\bar{x} < 2) = 0$

The probability that the mean stress score is less than two is about zero.

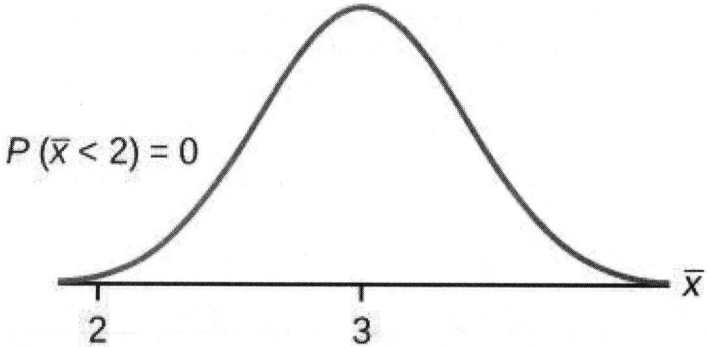

Figure 7.4

$$\text{normalcdf}\left(1,2,3,\frac{1.15}{\sqrt{75}}\right) = 0$$

b. Find the 90th percentile for the mean of 75 stress scores. Draw a graph.

Solution 7.8

b. Let k = the 90th precentile.

Find k, where $P(\bar{x} < k) = 0.90$.

$k = 3.2$

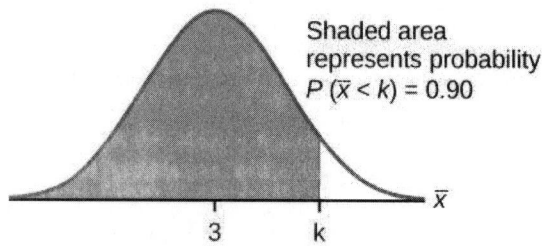

Figure 7.5

The 90th percentile for the mean of 75 scores is about 3.2. This tells us that 90% of all the means of 75 stress scores are at most 3.2, and that 10% are at least 3.2.

$$\text{invNorm}\left(0.90,3,\frac{1.15}{\sqrt{75}}\right) = 3.2$$

For problems c and d, let ΣX = the sum of the 75 stress scores. Then, $\Sigma X \sim N[(75)(3), (\sqrt{75})(1.15)]$

c. Find $P(\Sigma x < 200)$. Draw the graph.

Solution 7.8

c. The mean of the sum of 75 stress scores is $(75)(3) = 225$

The standard deviation of the sum of 75 stress scores is $(\sqrt{75})(1.15) = 9.96$

$P(\Sigma x < 200) = 0$

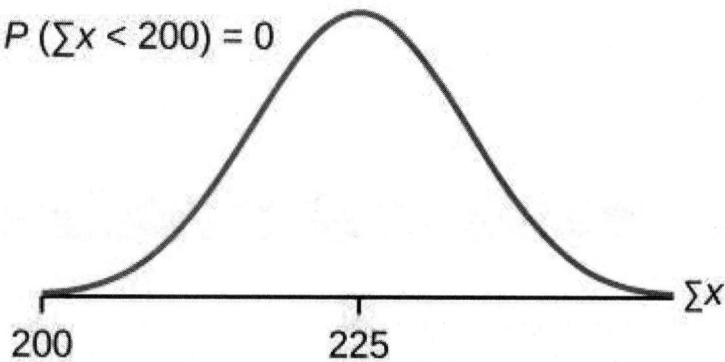

Figure 7.6

The probability that the total of 75 scores is less than 200 is about zero.

`normalcdf`$(75,200,(75)(3),(\sqrt{75})(1.15))$.

> **REMINDER**
>
> The smallest total of 75 stress scores is 75, because the smallest single score is one.

d. Find the 90th percentile for the total of 75 stress scores. Draw a graph.

Solution 7.8

d. Let k = the 90th percentile.

Find k where $P(\Sigma x < k) = 0.90$.

$k = 237.8$

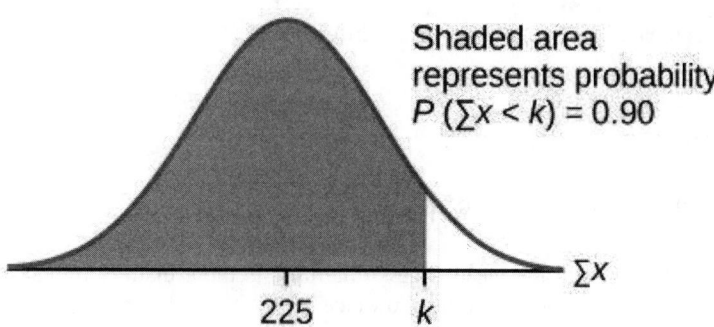

Figure 7.7

The 90th percentile for the sum of 75 scores is about 237.8. This tells us that 90% of all the sums of 75 scores are no more than 237.8 and 10% are no less than 237.8.

`invNorm`$(0.90,(75)(3),(\sqrt{75})(1.15)) = 237.8$

Try It Σ

7.8 Use the information in **Example 7.8**, but use a sample size of 55 to answer the following questions.

a. Find $P(\bar{x} < 7)$.

b. Find $P(\Sigma x > 170)$.

c. Find the 80th percentile for the mean of 55 scores.

d. Find the 85th percentile for the sum of 55 scores.

Example 7.9

Suppose that a market research analyst for a cell phone company conducts a study of their customers who exceed the time allowance included on their basic cell phone contract; the analyst finds that for those people who exceed the time included in their basic contract, the **excess time used** follows an **exponential distribution** with a mean of 22 minutes.

Consider a random sample of 80 customers who exceed the time allowance included in their basic cell phone contract.

Let X = the excess time used by one INDIVIDUAL cell phone customer who exceeds his contracted time allowance.

$X \sim Exp\left(\frac{1}{22}\right)$. From previous chapters, we know that $\mu = 22$ and $\sigma = 22$.

Let $\bar{X}$ = the mean excess time used by a sample of $n = 80$ customers who exceed their contracted time allowance.

$\bar{X} \sim N\left(22, \frac{22}{\sqrt{80}}\right)$ by the central limit theorem for sample means

Using the clt to find probability

a. Find the probability that the mean excess time used by the 80 customers in the sample is longer than 20 minutes. This is asking us to find $P(\bar{x} > 20)$. Draw the graph.

b. Suppose that one customer who exceeds the time limit for his cell phone contract is randomly selected. Find the probability that this individual customer's excess time is longer than 20 minutes. This is asking us to find $P(x > 20)$.

c. Explain why the probabilities in parts a and b are different.

Solution 7.9

a. Find: $P(\bar{x} > 20)$

$P(\bar{x} > 20) = 0.79199$ using `normalcdf`$\left(20, 1E99, 22, \frac{22}{\sqrt{80}}\right)$

The probability is 0.7919 that the mean excess time used is more than 20 minutes, for a sample of 80 customers who exceed their contracted time allowance.

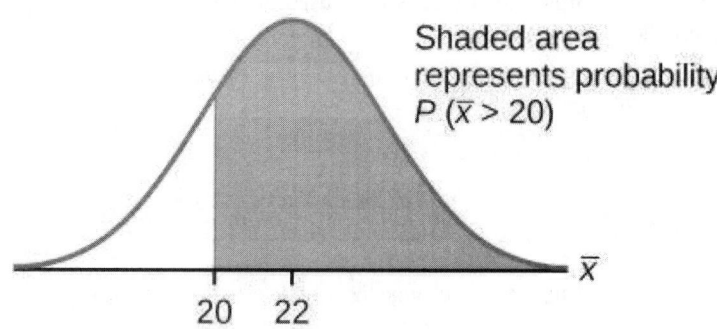

Figure 7.8

b. Find $P(x > 20)$. Remember to use the exponential distribution for an **individual:** $X \sim Exp\left(\frac{1}{22}\right)$.

$$P(x > 20) = e^{\left(-\left(\frac{1}{22}\right)(20)\right)} \text{ or } e^{(-0.04545(20))} = 0.4029$$

c. 1. $P(x > 20) = 0.4029$ but $P(\overline{x} > 20) = 0.7919$

2. The probabilities are not equal because we use different distributions to calculate the probability for individuals and for means.

3. When asked to find the probability of an individual value, use the stated distribution of its random variable; do not use the clt. Use the clt with the normal distribution when you are being asked to find the probability for a mean.

Using the clt to find percentiles Find the 95th percentile for the **sample mean excess time** for samples of 80 customers who exceed their basic contract time allowances. Draw a graph.

Solution 7.9

Let k = the 95th percentile. Find k where $P(\overline{x} < k) = 0.95$

$k = 26.0$ using $\texttt{invNorm}\left(0.95, 22, \frac{22}{\sqrt{80}}\right) = 26.0$

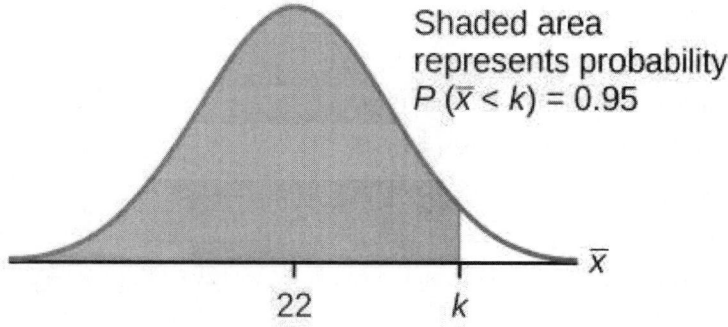

Figure 7.9

The 95th percentile for the **sample mean excess time used** is about 26.0 minutes for random samples of 80 customers who exceed their contractual allowed time.

Ninety five percent of such samples would have means under 26 minutes; only five percent of such samples would have means above 26 minutes.

7.9 Use the information in **Example 7.9**, but change the sample size to 144.

a. Find $P(20 < \bar{x} < 30)$.

b. Find $P(\Sigma x$ is at least 3,000).

c. Find the 75th percentile for the sample mean excess time of 144 customers.

d. Find the 85th percentile for the sum of 144 excess times used by customers.

Example 7.10

In the United States, someone is sexually assaulted every two minutes, on average, according to a number of studies. Suppose the standard deviation is 0.5 minutes and the sample size is 100.

a. Find the median, the first quartile, and the third quartile for the sample mean time of sexual assaults in the United States.

b. Find the median, the first quartile, and the third quartile for the sum of sample times of sexual assaults in the United States.

c. Find the probability that a sexual assault occurs on the average between 1.75 and 1.85 minutes.

d. Find the value that is two standard deviations above the sample mean.

e. Find the *IQR* for the sum of the sample times.

Solution 7.10

a. We have, $\mu_x = \mu = 2$ and $\sigma_x = \dfrac{\sigma}{\sqrt{n}} = \dfrac{0.5}{10} = 0.05$. Therefore:

    1. 50th percentile = $\mu_x = \mu = 2$

    2. 25th percentile = $invNorm(0.25,2,0.05) = 1.97$

    3. 75th percentile = $invNorm(0.75,2,0.05) = 2.03$

b. We have $\mu_{\Sigma x} = n(\mu_x) = 100(2) = 200$ and $\sigma_{\mu x} = \sqrt{n}\,(\sigma_x) = 10(0.5) = 5$. Therefore

    1. 50th percentile = $\mu_{\Sigma x} = n(\mu_x) = 100(2) = 200$

    2. 25th percentile = $invNorm(0.25,200,5) = 196.63$

    3. 75th percentile = $invNorm(0.75,200,5) = 203.37$

c. $P(1.75 < \bar{x} < 1.85) = \mathtt{normalcdf}(1.75,1.85,2,0.05) = 0.0013$

d. Using the *z*-score equation, $z = \dfrac{\bar{x} - \mu_{\bar{x}}}{\sigma_{\bar{x}}}$, and solving for *x*, we have $x = 2(0.05) + 2 = 2.1$

e. The *IQR* is 75th percentile − 25th percentile = $203.37 - 196.63 = 6.74$

7.10 Based on data from the National Health Survey, women between the ages of 18 and 24 have an average systolic blood pressures (in mm Hg) of 114.8 with a standard deviation of 13.1. Systolic blood pressure for women between the ages of 18 to 24 follow a normal distribution.

a. If one woman from this population is randomly selected, find the probability that her systolic blood pressure is greater than 120.

b. If 40 women from this population are randomly selected, find the probability that their mean systolic blood pressure is greater than 120.

c. If the sample were four women between the ages of 18 to 24 and we did not know the original distribution, could the central limit theorem be used?

Example 7.11

A study was done about violence against prostitutes and the symptoms of the posttraumatic stress that they developed. The age range of the prostitutes was 14 to 61. The mean age was 30.9 years with a standard deviation of nine years.

a. In a sample of 25 prostitutes, what is the probability that the mean age of the prostitutes is less than 35?

b. Is it likely that the mean age of the sample group could be more than 50 years? Interpret the results.

c. In a sample of 49 prostitutes, what is the probability that the sum of the ages is no less than 1,600?

d. Is it likely that the sum of the ages of the 49 prostitutes is at most 1,595? Interpret the results.

e. Find the 95th percentile for the sample mean age of 65 prostitutes. Interpret the results.

f. Find the 90th percentile for the sum of the ages of 65 prostitutes. Interpret the results.

Solution 7.11

a. $P(\bar{x} < 35) = \texttt{normalcdf}(\text{-}E99,35,30.9,1.8) = 0.9886$

b. $P(\bar{x} > 50) = \texttt{normalcdf}(50, E99,30.9,1.8) \approx 0$. For this sample group, it is almost impossible for the group's average age to be more than 50. However, it is still possible for an individual in this group to have an age greater than 50.

c. $P(\Sigma x \geq 1,600) = \texttt{normalcdf}(1600,E99,1514.10,63) = 0.0864$

d. $P(\Sigma x \leq 1,595) = \texttt{normalcdf}(\text{-}E99,1595,1514.10,63) = 0.9005$. This means that there is a 90% chance that the sum of the ages for the sample group $n = 49$ is at most 1595.

e. The 95th percentile $= \texttt{invNorm}(0.95,30.9,1.1) = 32.7$. This indicates that 95% of the prostitutes in the sample of 65 are younger than 32.7 years, on average.

f. The 90th percentile $= \texttt{invNorm}(0.90,2008.5,72.56) = 2101.5$. This indicates that 90% of the prostitutes in the sample of 65 have a sum of ages less than 2,101.5 years.

Try It Σ

7.11 According to Boeing data, the 757 airliner carries 200 passengers and has doors with a height of 72 inches. Assume for a certain population of men we have a mean height of 69.0 inches and a standard deviation of 2.8 inches.

a. What doorway height would allow 95% of men to enter the aircraft without bending?

b. Assume that half of the 200 passengers are men. What mean doorway height satisfies the condition that there is a 0.95 probability that this height is greater than the mean height of 100 men?

c. For engineers designing the 757, which result is more relevant: the height from part a or part b? Why?

HISTORICAL NOTE

: Normal Approximation to the Binomial

Historically, being able to compute binomial probabilities was one of the most important applications of the central limit theorem. Binomial probabilities with a small value for n(say, 20) were displayed in a table in a book. To calculate the probabilities with large values of n, you had to use the binomial formula, which could be very complicated. Using the **normal approximation to the binomial** distribution simplified the process. To compute the normal approximation to the binomial distribution, take a simple random sample from a population. You must meet the conditions for a **binomial distribution**:

- there are a certain number n of independent trials
- the outcomes of any trial are success or failure
- each trial has the same probability of a success p

Recall that if X is the binomial random variable, then $X \sim B(n, p)$. The shape of the binomial distribution needs to be similar to the shape of the normal distribution. To ensure this, the quantities np and nq must both be greater than five ($np > 5$ and $nq > 5$; the approximation is better if they are both greater than or equal to 10). Then the binomial can be approximated by the normal distribution with mean $\mu = np$ and standard deviation $\sigma = \sqrt{npq}$. Remember that $q = 1 - p$. In order to get the best approximation, add 0.5 to x or subtract 0.5 from x (use $x + 0.5$ or $x - 0.5$). The number 0.5 is called the **continuity correction factor** and is used in the following example.

Example 7.12

Suppose in a local Kindergarten through 12th grade (K - 12) school district, 53 percent of the population favor a charter school for grades K through 5. A simple random sample of 300 is surveyed.

a. Find the probability that **at least 150** favor a charter school.

b. Find the probability that **at most 160** favor a charter school.

c. Find the probability that **more than 155** favor a charter school.

d. Find the probability that **fewer than 147** favor a charter school.

e. Find the probability that **exactly 175** favor a charter school.

Let X = the number that favor a charter school for grades K trough 5. $X \sim B(n, p)$ where $n = 300$ and $p = 0.53$. Since $np > 5$ and $nq > 5$, use the normal approximation to the binomial. The formulas for the mean and standard deviation are $\mu = np$ and $\sigma = \sqrt{npq}$. The mean is 159 and the standard deviation is 8.6447. The random variable for the normal distribution is Y. $Y \sim N(159, 8.6447)$. See **The Normal Distribution** for help with calculator instructions.

For part a, you **include 150** so $P(X \geq 150)$ has normal approximation $P(Y \geq 149.5) = 0.8641$.

normalcdf(149.5,10^99,159,8.6447) = 0.8641.

For part b, you **include 160** so $P(X \leq 160)$ has normal appraximation $P(Y \leq 160.5) = 0.5689$.

normalcdf(0,160.5,159,8.6447) = 0.5689

For part c, you **exclude 155** so $P(X > 155)$ has normal approximation $P(y > 155.5) = 0.6572$.

normalcdf(155.5,10^99,159,8.6447) = 0.6572.

For part d, you **exclude 147** so $P(X < 147)$ has normal approximation $P(Y < 146.5) = 0.0741$.

normalcdf(0,146.5,159,8.6447) = 0.0741

For part e,$P(X = 175)$ has normal approximation $P(174.5 < Y < 175.5) = 0.0083$.

normalcdf(174.5,175.5,159,8.6447) = 0.0083

Because of calculators and computer software that let you calculate binomial probabilities for large values of *n* easily, it is not necessary to use the the normal approximation to the binomial distribution, provided that you have access to these technology tools. Most school labs have Microsoft Excel, an example of computer software that calculates binomial probabilities. Many students have access to the TI-83 or 84 series calculators, and they easily calculate probabilities for the binomial distribution. If you type in "binomial probability distribution calculation" in an Internet browser, you can find at least one online calculator for the binomial.

For **Example 7.10**, the probabilities are calculated using the following binomial distribution: (*n* = 300 and *p* = 0.53). Compare the binomial and normal distribution answers. See **Discrete Random Variables** for help with calculator instructions for the binomial.

$P(X \geq 150)$:1 - binomialcdf(300,0.53,149) = 0.8641

$P(X \leq 160)$:binomialcdf(300,0.53,160) = 0.5684

$P(X > 155)$:1 - binomialcdf(300,0.53,155) = 0.6576

$P(X < 147)$:binomialcdf(300,0.53,146) = 0.0742

$P(X = 175)$:(You use the binomial pdf.)binomialpdf(300,0.53,175) = 0.0083

Try It Σ

7.12 In a city, 46 percent of the population favor the incumbent, Dawn Morgan, for mayor. A simple random sample of 500 is taken. Using the continuity correction factor, find the probability that at least 250 favor Dawn Morgan for mayor.

7.4 | Central Limit Theorem (Pocket Change)

Stats Lab

7.1 Central Limit Theorem (Pocket Change)

Class Time:

Names:

Student Learning Outcomes

- The student will demonstrate and compare properties of the central limit theorem.

NOTE

This lab works best when sampling from several classes and combining data.

Collect the Data

1. Count the change in your pocket. (Do not include bills.)

2. Randomly survey 30 classmates. Record the values of the change in **Table 7.1**.

Table 7.1

3. Construct a histogram. Make five to six intervals. Sketch the graph using a ruler and pencil. Scale the axes.

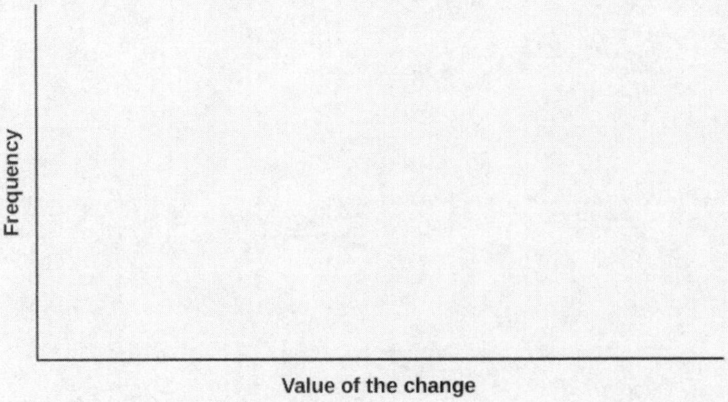

Frequency

Value of the change

Figure 7.10

4. Calculate the following ($n = 1$; surveying one person at a time):

   a. $\bar{x} =$ _____

   b. $s =$ _____

5. Draw a smooth curve through the tops of the bars of the histogram. Use one to two complete sentences to describe the general shape of the curve.

Collecting Averages of Pairs

Repeat steps one through five of the section **Collect the Data.** with one exception. Instead of recording the change of 30 classmates, record the average change of 30 pairs.

1. Randomly survey 30 **pairs** of classmates.

2. Record the values of the average of their change in **Table 7.2**.

Table 7.2

3. Construct a histogram. Scale the axes using the same scaling you used for the section titled **Collect the Data.** Sketch the graph using a ruler and a pencil.

Figure 7.11

4. Calculate the following ($n = 2$; surveying two people at a time):

    a. $\bar{x} =$ _____

    b. $s =$ _____

5. Draw a smooth curve through tops of the bars of the histogram. Use one to two complete sentences to describe the general shape of the curve.

Collecting Averages of Groups of Five

Repeat steps one through five (of the section titled **Collect the Data**) with one exception. Instead of recording the change of 30 classmates, record the average change of 30 groups of five.

1. Randomly survey 30 **groups of five** classmates.

2. Record the values of the average of their change.

Table 7.3

3. Construct a histogram. Scale the axes using the same scaling you used for the section titled **Collect the Data**. Sketch the graph using a ruler and a pencil.

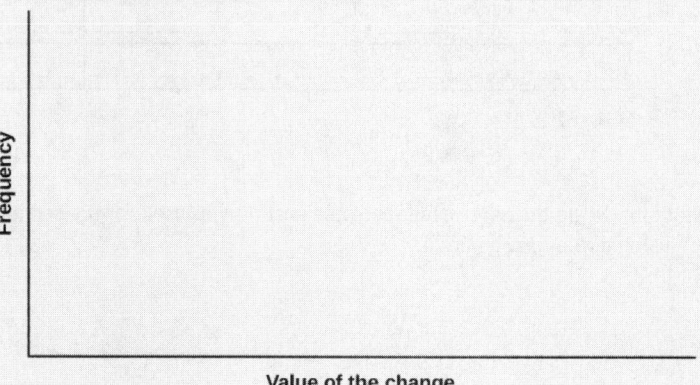

Figure 7.12

4. Calculate the following ($n = 5$; surveying five people at a time):

   a. $\bar{x}$ = _____

   b. s = _____

5. Draw a smooth curve through tops of the bars of the histogram. Use one to two complete sentences to describe the general shape of the curve.

Discussion Questions

1. Why did the shape of the distribution of the data change, as n changed? Use one to two complete sentences to explain what happened.

2. In the section titled **Collect the Data**, what was the approximate distribution of the data? $X \sim$ _____(_____,_____)

3. In the section titled **Collecting Averages of Groups of Five**, what was the approximate distribution of the averages? $\bar{X} \sim$ _____(_____,_____)

4. In one to two complete sentences, explain any differences in your answers to the previous two questions.

7.5 | Central Limit Theorem (Cookie Recipes)

Stats Lab

7.2 Central Limit Theorem (Cookie Recipes)

Class Time:

Names:

Student Learning Outcomes

- The student will demonstrate and compare properties of the central limit theorem.

Given

X = length of time (in days) that a cookie recipe lasted at the Olmstead Homestead. (Assume that each of the different recipes makes the same quantity of cookies.)

Recipe #	X		Recipe #	X		Recipe #	X		Recipe #	X
1	1		16	2		31	3		46	2
2	5		17	2		32	4		47	2
3	2		18	4		33	5		48	11
4	5		19	6		34	6		49	5
5	6		20	1		35	6		50	5
6	1		21	6		36	1		51	4
7	2		22	5		37	1		52	6
8	6		23	2		38	2		53	5
9	5		24	5		39	1		54	1
10	2		25	1		40	6		55	1
11	5		26	6		41	1		56	2
12	1		27	4		42	6		57	4
13	1		28	1		43	2		58	3
14	3		29	6		44	6		59	6
15	2		30	2		45	2		60	5

Table 7.4

Calculate the following:

a. $\mu_x = $ _____

b. $\sigma_x = $ _____

Collect the Data

Use a random number generator to randomly select four samples of size $n = 5$ from the given population. Record your samples in **Table 7.5**. Then, for each sample, calculate the mean to the nearest tenth. Record them in the spaces provided. Record the sample means for the rest of the class.

1. Complete the table:

	Sample 1	Sample 2	Sample 3	Sample 4	Sample means from other groups:
Means:	$\overline{x}$ = _____	$\overline{x}$ = _____	$\overline{x}$ = _____	$\overline{x}$ = _____	

Table 7.5

2. Calculate the following:

    a. $\overline{x}$ = _____

    b. $s_{\overline{x}}$ = _____

3. Again, use a random number generator to randomly select four samples from the population. This time, make the samples of size $n = 10$. Record the samples in **Table 7.6**. As before, for each sample, calculate the mean to the nearest tenth. Record them in the spaces provided. Record the sample means for the rest of the class.

	Sample 1	Sample 2	Sample 3	Sample 4	Sample means from other groups
Means:	$\overline{x}$ = _____	$\overline{x}$ = _____	$\overline{x}$ = _____	$\overline{x}$ = _____	

Table 7.6

4. Calculate the following:

    a. $\overline{x}$ = _____

    b. $s_{\overline{x}}$ = _____

5. For the original population, construct a histogram. Make intervals with a bar width of one day. Sketch the graph using a ruler and pencil. Scale the axes.

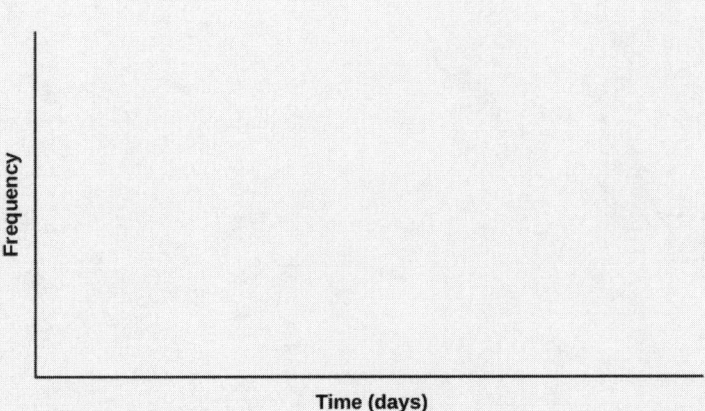

Figure 7.13

6. Draw a smooth curve through the tops of the bars of the histogram. Use one to two complete sentences to describe the general shape of the curve.

Repeat the Procedure for *n* = 5

1. For the sample of *n* = 5 days averaged together, construct a histogram of the averages (your means together with the means of the other groups). Make intervals with bar widths of $\frac{1}{2}$ a day. Sketch the graph using a ruler and pencil. Scale the axes.

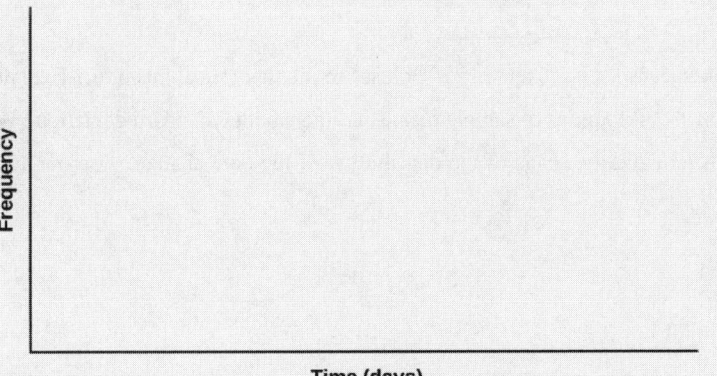

Figure 7.14

2. Draw a smooth curve through the tops of the bars of the histogram. Use one to two complete sentences to describe the general shape of the curve.

Repeat the Procedure for *n* = 10

1. For the sample of *n* = 10 days averaged together, construct a histogram of the averages (your means together with the means of the other groups). Make intervals with bar widths of $\frac{1}{2}$ a day. Sketch the graph using a ruler and pencil. Scale the axes.

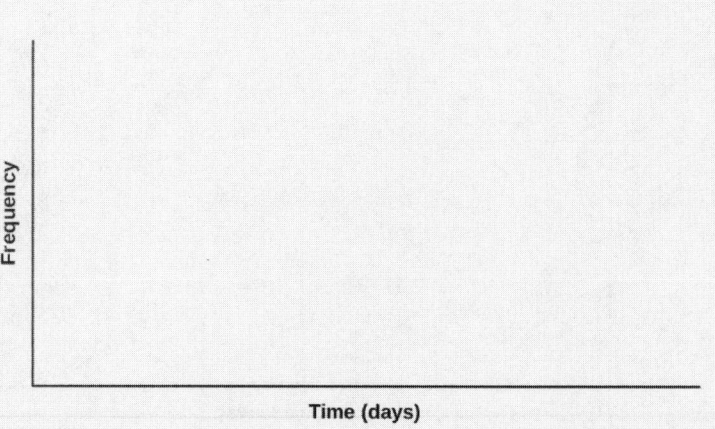

Figure 7.15

2. Draw a smooth curve through the tops of the bars of the histogram. Use one to two complete sentences to describe the general shape of the curve.

Discussion Questions

1. Compare the three histograms you have made, the one for the population and the two for the sample means. In three to five sentences, describe the similarities and differences.

2. State the theoretical (according to the clt) distributions for the sample means.

   a. $n = 5$: $\bar{x} \sim$ _____(_____, _____)

   b. $n = 10$: $\bar{x} \sim$ _____(_____, _____)

3. Are the sample means for $n = 5$ and $n = 10$ "close" to the theoretical mean, μ_x? Explain why or why not.

4. Which of the two distributions of sample means has the smaller standard deviation? Why?

5. As n changed, why did the shape of the distribution of the data change? Use one to two complete sentences to explain what happened.

KEY TERMS

Average a number that describes the central tendency of the data; there are a number of specialized averages, including the arithmetic mean, weighted mean, median, mode, and geometric mean.

Central Limit Theorem Given a random variable (RV) with known mean μ and known standard deviation, σ, we are sampling with size n, and we are interested in two new RVs: the sample mean, $\bar{X}$, and the sample sum, ΣX. If the size (n) of the sample is sufficiently large, then $\bar{X} \sim N(\mu, \frac{\sigma}{\sqrt{n}})$ and $\Sigma X \sim N(n\mu, (\sqrt{n})(\sigma))$. If the size ($n$) of the sample is sufficiently large, then the distribution of the sample means and the distribution of the sample sums will approximate a normal distributions regardless of the shape of the population. The mean of the sample means will equal the population mean, and the mean of the sample sums will equal n times the population mean. The standard deviation of the distribution of the sample means, $\frac{\sigma}{\sqrt{n}}$, is called the standard error of the mean.

Exponential Distribution a continuous random variable (RV) that appears when we are interested in the intervals of time between some random events, for example, the length of time between emergency arrivals at a hospital, notation: $X \sim Exp(m)$. The mean is $\mu = \frac{1}{m}$ and the standard deviation is $\sigma = \frac{1}{m}$. The probability density function is $f(x) = me^{-mx}$, $x \geq 0$ and the cumulative distribution function is $P(X \leq x) = 1 - e^{-mx}$.

Mean a number that measures the central tendency; a common name for mean is "average." The term "mean" is a shortened form of "arithmetic mean." By definition, the mean for a sample (denoted by $\bar{x}$) is $\bar{x} = \frac{\text{Sum of all values in the sample}}{\text{Number of values in the sample}}$, and the mean for a population (denoted by μ) is $\mu = \frac{\text{Sum of all values in the population}}{\text{Number of values in the population}}$.

Normal Distribution

a continuous random variable (RV) with pdf $f(x) = \frac{1}{\sigma\sqrt{2\pi}} e^{\frac{-(x-\mu)^2}{2\sigma^2}}$, where μ is the mean of the distribution and σ is the standard deviation; notation: $X \sim N(\mu, \sigma)$. If $\mu = 0$ and $\sigma = 1$, the RV is called a **standard normal distribution**.

Normal Distribution

a continuous random variable (RV) with pdf $f(x) = \frac{1}{\sigma\sqrt{2\pi}} e^{\frac{-(x-\mu)^2}{2\sigma^2}}$, where μ is the mean of the distribution and σ is the standard deviation.; notation: $X \sim N(\mu, \sigma)$. If $\mu = 0$ and $\sigma = 1$, the RV is called the **standard normal distribution**.

Sampling Distribution Given simple random samples of size n from a given population with a measured characteristic such as mean, proportion, or standard deviation for each sample, the probability distribution of all the measured characteristics is called a sampling distribution.

Standard Error of the Mean the standard deviation of the distribution of the sample means, or $\frac{\sigma}{\sqrt{n}}$.

Uniform Distribution a continuous random variable (RV) that has equally likely outcomes over the domain, $a < x < b$; often referred as the **Rectangular Distribution** because the graph of the pdf has the form of a rectangle. Notation: $X \sim U(a, b)$. The mean is $\mu = \frac{a+b}{2}$ and the standard deviation is $\sigma = \sqrt{\frac{(b-a)^2}{12}}$. The probability density function is $f(x) = \frac{1}{b-a}$ for $a < x < b$ or $a \leq x \leq b$. The cumulative distribution is $P(X \leq x) = \frac{x-a}{b-a}$.

CHAPTER REVIEW

7.1 The Central Limit Theorem for Sample Means (Averages)

In a population whose distribution may be known or unknown, if the size (n) of samples is sufficiently large, the distribution of the sample means will be approximately normal. The mean of the sample means will equal the population mean. The standard deviation of the distribution of the sample means, called the standard error of the mean, is equal to the population standard deviation divided by the square root of the sample size (n).

7.2 The Central Limit Theorem for Sums

The central limit theorem tells us that for a population with any distribution, the distribution of the sums for the sample means approaches a normal distribution as the sample size increases. In other words, if the sample size is large enough, the distribution of the sums can be approximated by a normal distribution even if the original population is not normally distributed. Additionally, if the original population has a mean of μ_X and a standard deviation of σ_x, the mean of the sums is $n\mu_x$ and the standard deviation is $(\sqrt{n})(\sigma_x)$ where n is the sample size.

7.3 Using the Central Limit Theorem

The central limit theorem can be used to illustrate the law of large numbers. The law of large numbers states that the larger the sample size you take from a population, the closer the sample mean $\bar{x}$ gets to μ.

FORMULA REVIEW

7.1 The Central Limit Theorem for Sample Means (Averages)

The Central Limit Theorem for Sample Means: $\bar{X} \sim N\left(\mu_x, \frac{\sigma x}{\sqrt{n}}\right)$

The Mean $\bar{X}$: μ_x

Central Limit Theorem for Sample Means z-score and standard error of the mean: $z = \dfrac{x - \mu_x}{\left(\frac{\sigma_x}{\sqrt{n}}\right)}$

Standard Error of the Mean (Standard Deviation ($\bar{X}$)): $\dfrac{\sigma_x}{\sqrt{n}}$

7.2 The Central Limit Theorem for Sums

The Central Limit Theorem for Sums: $\sum X \sim N[(n)(\mu_x), (\sqrt{n})(\sigma_x)]$

Mean for Sums ($\sum X$): $(n)(\mu_x)$

The Central Limit Theorem for Sums z-score and standard deviation for sums: z for the sample mean $= \dfrac{\sum x - (n)(\mu_X)}{(\sqrt{n})(\sigma_X)}$

Standard deviation for Sums ($\sum X$): $(\sqrt{n})(\sigma_x)$

PRACTICE

7.1 The Central Limit Theorem for Sample Means (Averages)

Use the following information to answer the next six exercises: Yoonie is a personnel manager in a large corporation. Each month she must review 16 of the employees. From past experience, she has found that the reviews take her approximately four hours each to do with a population standard deviation of 1.2 hours. Let X be the random variable representing the time it takes her to complete one review. Assume X is normally distributed. Let $\bar{X}$ be the random variable representing the mean time to complete the 16 reviews. Assume that the 16 reviews represent a random set of reviews.

1. What is the mean, standard deviation, and sample size?

2. Complete the distributions.

    a. $X \sim$ _____(_____,_____)

    b. $\bar{X} \sim$ _____(_____,_____)

3. Find the probability that **one** review will take Yoonie from 3.5 to 4.25 hours. Sketch the graph, labeling and scaling the horizontal axis. Shade the region corresponding to the probability.

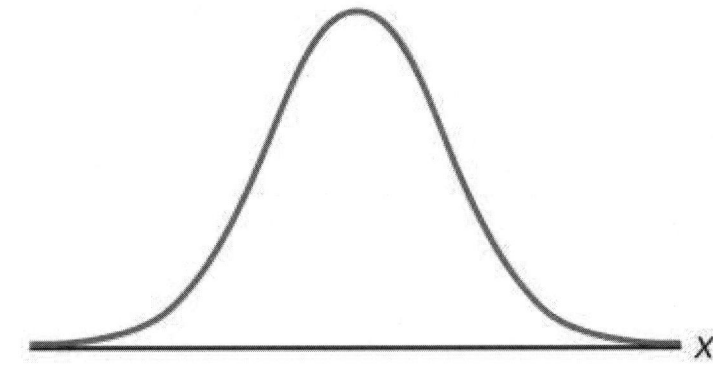

    a.

    Figure 7.16

    b. $P($_____ $< x <$ _____$) =$ _____

4. Find the probability that the **mean** of a month's reviews will take Yoonie from 3.5 to 4.25 hrs. Sketch the graph, labeling and scaling the horizontal axis. Shade the region corresponding to the probability.

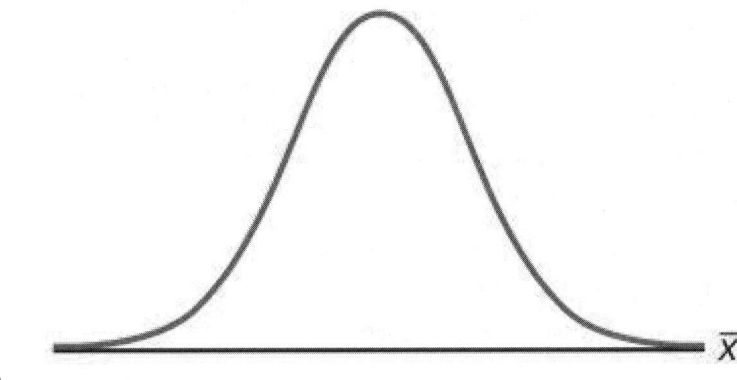

    a.

    Figure 7.17

    b. $P($_____$) =$ _____

5. What causes the probabilities in **Exercise 7.3** and **Exercise 7.4** to be different?

6. Find the 95ᵗʰ percentile for the mean time to complete one month's reviews. Sketch the graph.

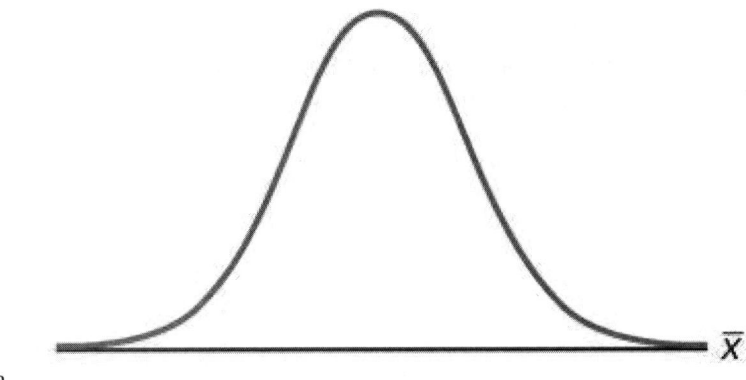

a.

Figure 7.18

b.   The 95ᵗʰ Percentile =_____

7.2 The Central Limit Theorem for Sums

Use the following information to answer the next four exercises: An unknown distribution has a mean of 80 and a standard deviation of 12. A sample size of 95 is drawn randomly from the population.

7. Find the probability that the sum of the 95 values is greater than 7,650.

8. Find the probability that the sum of the 95 values is less than 7,400.

9. Find the sum that is two standard deviations above the mean of the sums.

10. Find the sum that is 1.5 standard deviations below the mean of the sums.

Use the following information to answer the next five exercises: The distribution of results from a cholesterol test has a mean of 180 and a standard deviation of 20. A sample size of 40 is drawn randomly.

11. Find the probability that the sum of the 40 values is greater than 7,500.

12. Find the probability that the sum of the 40 values is less than 7,000.

13. Find the sum that is one standard deviation above the mean of the sums.

14. Find the sum that is 1.5 standard deviations below the mean of the sums.

15. Find the percentage of sums between 1.5 standard deviations below the mean of the sums and one standard deviation above the mean of the sums.

Use the following information to answer the next six exercises: A researcher measures the amount of sugar in several cans of the same soda. The mean is 39.01 with a standard deviation of 0.5. The researcher randomly selects a sample of 100.

16. Find the probability that the sum of the 100 values is greater than 3,910.

17. Find the probability that the sum of the 100 values is less than 3,900.

18. Find the probability that the sum of the 100 values falls between the numbers you found in and .

19. Find the sum with a z–score of –2.5.

20. Find the sum with a z–score of 0.5.

21. Find the probability that the sums will fall between the z-scores –2 and 1.

Use the following information to answer the next four exercises: An unknown distribution has a mean 12 and a standard deviation of one. A sample size of 25 is taken. Let X = the object of interest.

22. What is the mean of ΣX?

23. What is the standard deviation of ΣX?

24. What is $P(\Sigma x = 290)$?

25. What is $P(\Sigma x > 290)$?

26. True or False: only the sums of normal distributions are also normal distributions.

27. In order for the sums of a distribution to approach a normal distribution, what must be true?

28. What three things must you know about a distribution to find the probability of sums?

29. An unknown distribution has a mean of 25 and a standard deviation of six. Let X = one object from this distribution. What is the sample size if the standard deviation of ΣX is 42?

30. An unknown distribution has a mean of 19 and a standard deviation of 20. Let X = the object of interest. What is the sample size if the mean of ΣX is 15,200?

Use the following information to answer the next three exercises. A market researcher analyzes how many electronics devices customers buy in a single purchase. The distribution has a mean of three with a standard deviation of 0.7. She samples 400 customers.

31. What is the z-score for $\Sigma x = 840$?

32. What is the z-score for $\Sigma x = 1,186$?

33. What is $P(\Sigma x < 1,186)$?

Use the following information to answer the next three exercises: An unkwon distribution has a mean of 100, a standard deviation of 100, and a sample size of 100. Let X = one object of interest.

34. What is the mean of ΣX?

35. What is the standard deviation of ΣX?

36. What is $P(\Sigma x > 9,000)$?

7.3 Using the Central Limit Theorem

Use the following information to answer the next ten exercises: A manufacturer produces 25-pound lifting weights. The lowest actual weight is 24 pounds, and the highest is 26 pounds. Each weight is equally likely so the distribution of weights is uniform. A sample of 100 weights is taken.

37.
    a. What is the distribution for the weights of one 25-pound lifting weight? What is the mean and standard deivation?
    b. What is the distribution for the mean weight of 100 25-pound lifting weights?
    c. Find the probability that the mean actual weight for the 100 weights is less than 24.9.

38. Draw the graph from **Exercise 7.37**

39. Find the probability that the mean actual weight for the 100 weights is greater than 25.2.

40. Draw the graph from **Exercise 7.39**

41. Find the 90th percentile for the mean weight for the 100 weights.

42. Draw the graph from **Exercise 7.41**

43.
    a. What is the distribution for the sum of the weights of 100 25-pound lifting weights?
    b. Find $P(\Sigma x < 2,450)$.

44. Draw the graph from **Exercise 7.43**

45. Find the 90th percentile for the total weight of the 100 weights.

46. Draw the graph from **Exercise 7.45**

Use the following information to answer the next five exercises: The length of time a particular smartphone's battery lasts follows an exponential distribution with a mean of ten months. A sample of 64 of these smartphones is taken.

47.
  a. What is the standard deviation?
  b. What is the parameter m?

48. What is the distribution for the length of time one battery lasts?

49. What is the distribution for the mean length of time 64 batteries last?

50. What is the distribution for the total length of time 64 batteries last?

51. Find the probability that the sample mean is between seven and 11.

52. Find the 80th percentile for the total length of time 64 batteries last.

53. Find the IQR for the mean amount of time 64 batteries last.

54. Find the middle 80% for the total amount of time 64 batteries last.

Use the following information to answer the next eight exercises: A uniform distribution has a minimum of six and a maximum of ten. A sample of 50 is taken.

55. Find $P(\Sigma x > 420)$.

56. Find the 90th percentile for the sums.

57. Find the 15th percentile for the sums.

58. Find the first quartile for the sums.

59. Find the third quartile for the sums.

60. Find the 80th percentile for the sums.

HOMEWORK

7.1 The Central Limit Theorem for Sample Means (Averages)

61. Previously, De Anza statistics students estimated that the amount of change daytime statistics students carry is exponentially distributed with a mean of $0.88. Suppose that we randomly pick 25 daytime statistics students.
  a. In words, $X =$ _____
  b. $X \sim$ _____(_____,_____)
  c. In words, $\overline{X} =$ _____
  d. $\overline{X} \sim$ _____ (_____, _____)
  e. Find the probability that an individual had between $0.80 and $1.00. Graph the situation, and shade in the area to be determined.
  f. Find the probability that the average of the 25 students was between $0.80 and $1.00. Graph the situation, and shade in the area to be determined.
  g. Explain why there is a difference in part e and part f.

62. Suppose that the distance of fly balls hit to the outfield (in baseball) is normally distributed with a mean of 250 feet and a standard deviation of 50 feet. We randomly sample 49 fly balls.
  a. If $\overline{X} =$ average distance in feet for 49 fly balls, then $\overline{X} \sim$ _____(_____,_____)
  b. What is the probability that the 49 balls traveled an average of less than 240 feet? Sketch the graph. Scale the horizontal axis for $\overline{X}$. Shade the region corresponding to the probability. Find the probability.
  c. Find the 80th percentile of the distribution of the average of 49 fly balls.

63. According to the Internal Revenue Service, the average length of time for an individual to complete (keep records for, learn, prepare, copy, assemble, and send) IRS Form 1040 is 10.53 hours (without any attached schedules). The distribution is unknown. Let us assume that the standard deviation is two hours. Suppose we randomly sample 36 taxpayers.

    a. In words, X = _____

    b. In words, $\bar{X}$ = _____

    c. $\bar{X}$ ~ _____(_____,_____)

    d. Would you be surprised if the 36 taxpayers finished their Form 1040s in an average of more than 12 hours? Explain why or why not in complete sentences.

    e. Would you be surprised if one taxpayer finished his or her Form 1040 in more than 12 hours? In a complete sentence, explain why.

64. Suppose that a category of world-class runners are known to run a marathon (26 miles) in an average of 145 minutes with a standard deviation of 14 minutes. Consider 49 of the races. Let $\bar{X}$ the average of the 49 races.

    a. $\bar{X}$ ~ _____(_____,_____)

    b. Find the probability that the runner will average between 142 and 146 minutes in these 49 marathons.

    c. Find the 80th percentile for the average of these 49 marathons.

    d. Find the median of the average running times.

65. The length of songs in a collector's iTunes album collection is uniformly distributed from two to 3.5 minutes. Suppose we randomly pick five albums from the collection. There are a total of 43 songs on the five albums.

    a. In words, X = _____

    b. X ~ _____

    c. In words, $\bar{X}$ = _____

    d. $\bar{X}$ ~ _____(_____,_____)

    e. Find the first quartile for the average song length, $\bar{X}$.

    f. The IQR (interquartile range) for the average song length, $\bar{X}$, is from ___ - ___.

66. In 1940 the average size of a U.S. farm was 174 acres. Let's say that the standard deviation was 55 acres. Suppose we randomly survey 38 farmers from 1940.

    a. In words, X = _____

    b. In words, $\bar{X}$ = _____

    c. $\bar{X}$ ~ _____(_____,_____)

    d. The IQR for $\bar{X}$ is from _____ acres to _____ acres.

67. Determine which of the following are true and which are false. Then, in complete sentences, justify your answers.

    a. When the sample size is large, the mean of $\bar{X}$ is approximately equal to the mean of X.

    b. When the sample size is large, $\bar{X}$ is approximately normally distributed.

    c. When the sample size is large, the standard deviation of $\bar{X}$ is approximately the same as the standard deviation of X.

68. The percent of fat calories that a person in America consumes each day is normally distributed with a mean of about 36 and a standard deviation of about ten. Suppose that 16 individuals are randomly chosen. Let $\bar{X}$ = average percent of fat calories.

    a. $\bar{X}$ ~ _____(_____, _____)

    b. For the group of 16, find the probability that the average percent of fat calories consumed is more than five. Graph the situation and shade in the area to be determined.

    c. Find the first quartile for the average percent of fat calories.

69. The distribution of income in some Third World countries is considered wedge shaped (many very poor people, very few middle income people, and even fewer wealthy people). Suppose we pick a country with a wedge shaped distribution. Let the average salary be $2,000 per year with a standard deviation of $8,000. We randomly survey 1,000 residents of that country.

  a. In words, $X =$ _____
  b. In words, $\bar{X} =$ _____
  c. $\bar{X} \sim$ _____(_____,_____)
  d. How is it possible for the standard deviation to be greater than the average?
  e. Why is it more likely that the average of the 1,000 residents will be from $2,000 to $2,100 than from $2,100 to $2,200?

70. Which of the following is NOT TRUE about the distribution for averages?

  a. The mean, median, and mode are equal.
  b. The area under the curve is one.
  c. The curve never touches the x-axis.
  d. The curve is skewed to the right.

71. The cost of unleaded gasoline in the Bay Area once followed an unknown distribution with a mean of $4.59 and a standard deviation of $0.10. Sixteen gas stations from the Bay Area are randomly chosen. We are interested in the average cost of gasoline for the 16 gas stations. The distribution to use for the average cost of gasoline for the 16 gas stations is:

  a. $\bar{X} \sim N(4.59, 0.10)$
  b. $\bar{X} \sim N\left(4.59, \dfrac{0.10}{\sqrt{16}}\right)$
  c. $\bar{X} \sim N\left(4.59, \dfrac{16}{0.10}\right)$
  d. $\bar{X} \sim N\left(4.59, \dfrac{\sqrt{16}}{0.10}\right)$

7.2 The Central Limit Theorem for Sums

72. Which of the following is NOT TRUE about the theoretical distribution of sums?

  a. The mean, median and mode are equal.
  b. The area under the curve is one.
  c. The curve never touches the x-axis.
  d. The curve is skewed to the right.

73. Suppose that the duration of a particular type of criminal trial is known to have a mean of 21 days and a standard deviation of seven days. We randomly sample nine trials.

  a. In words, $\Sigma X =$ _____
  b. $\Sigma X \sim$ _____(_____,_____)
  c. Find the probability that the total length of the nine trials is at least 225 days.
  d. Ninety percent of the total of nine of these types of trials will last at least how long?

74. Suppose that the weight of open boxes of cereal in a home with children is uniformly distributed from two to six pounds with a mean of four pounds and standard deviation of 1.1547. We randomly survey 64 homes with children.

  a. In words, $X =$ _____
  b. The distribution is _____.
  c. In words, $\Sigma X =$ _____
  d. $\Sigma X \sim$ _____(_____,_____)
  e. Find the probability that the total weight of open boxes is less than 250 pounds.
  f. Find the 35th percentile for the total weight of open boxes of cereal.

75. Salaries for teachers in a particular elementary school district are normally distributed with a mean of $44,000 and a standard deviation of $6,500. We randomly survey ten teachers from that district.
   a. In words, $X =$ _____
   b. $X \sim$ _____(_____,_____)
   c. In words, $\Sigma X =$ _____
   d. $\Sigma X \sim$ _____(_____,_____)
   e. Find the probability that the teachers earn a total of over $400,000.
   f. Find the 90th percentile for an individual teacher's salary.
   g. Find the 90th percentile for the sum of ten teachers' salary.
   h. If we surveyed 70 teachers instead of ten, graphically, how would that change the distribution in part d?
   i. If each of the 70 teachers received a $3,000 raise, graphically, how would that change the distribution in part b?

7.3 Using the Central Limit Theorem

76. The attention span of a two-year-old is exponentially distributed with a mean of about eight minutes. Suppose we randomly survey 60 two-year-olds.
   a. In words, $X =$ _____
   b. $X \sim$ _____(_____,_____)
   c. In words, $\bar{X} =$ _____
   d. $\bar{X} \sim$ _____(_____,_____)
   e. Before doing any calculations, which do you think will be higher? Explain why.
      i. The probability that an individual attention span is less than ten minutes.
      ii. The probability that the average attention span for the 60 children is less than ten minutes?
   f. Calculate the probabilities in part e.
   g. Explain why the distribution for $\bar{X}$ is not exponential.

77. The closing stock prices of 35 U.S. semiconductor manufacturers are given as follows.

8.625; 30.25; 27.625; 46.75; 32.875; 18.25; 5; 0.125; 2.9375; 6.875; 28.25; 24.25; 21; 1.5; 30.25; 71; 43.5; 49.25; 2.5625; 31; 16.5; 9.5; 18.5; 18; 9; 10.5; 16.625; 1.25; 18; 12.87; 7; 12.875; 2.875; 60.25; 29.25

   a. In words, $X =$ _____
   b.   i. $\bar{x} =$ _____
         ii. $s_x =$ _____
         iii. $n =$ _____
   c. Construct a histogram of the distribution of the averages. Start at $x = -0.0005$. Use bar widths of ten.
   d. In words, describe the distribution of stock prices.
   e. Randomly average five stock prices together. (Use a random number generator.) Continue averaging five pieces together until you have ten averages. List those ten averages.
   f. Use the ten averages from part e to calculate the following.
         i. $\bar{x} =$ _____
         ii. $s_x =$ _____
   g. Construct a histogram of the distribution of the averages. Start at $x = -0.0005$. Use bar widths of ten.
   h. Does this histogram look like the graph in part c?
   i. In one or two complete sentences, explain why the graphs either look the same or look different?
   j. Based upon the theory of the **central limit theorem**, $\bar{X} \sim$ _____(_____,_____)

Use the following information to answer the next three exercises: Richard's Furniture Company delivers furniture from 10 A.M. to 2 P.M. continuously and uniformly. We are interested in how long (in hours) past the 10 A.M. start time that individuals wait for their delivery.

78. $X \sim$ _____(_____,_____)
   a. $U(0,4)$
   b. $U(10,2)$
   c. $Exp(2)$
   d. $N(2,1)$

79. The average wait time is:
    a. one hour.
    b. two hours.
    c. two and a half hours.
    d. four hours.

80. Suppose that it is now past noon on a delivery day. The probability that a person must wait at least one and a half **more** hours is:
    a. $\frac{1}{4}$

    b. $\frac{1}{2}$

    c. $\frac{3}{4}$

    d. $\frac{3}{8}$

Use the following information to answer the next two exercises: The time to wait for a particular rural bus is distributed uniformly from zero to 75 minutes. One hundred riders are randomly sampled to learn how long they waited.

81. The 90th percentile sample average wait time (in minutes) for a sample of 100 riders is:
    a. 315.0
    b. 40.3
    c. 38.5
    d. 65.2

82. Would you be surprised, based upon numerical calculations, if the sample average wait time (in minutes) for 100 riders was less than 30 minutes?
    a. yes
    b. no
    c. There is not enough information.

Use the following to answer the next two exercises: The cost of unleaded gasoline in the Bay Area once followed an unknown distribution with a mean of $4.59 and a standard deviation of $0.10. Sixteen gas stations from the Bay Area are randomly chosen. We are interested in the average cost of gasoline for the 16 gas stations.

83. What's the approximate probability that the average price for 16 gas stations is over $4.69?
    a. almost zero
    b. 0.1587
    c. 0.0943
    d. unknown

84. Find the probability that the average price for 30 gas stations is less than $4.55.
    a. 0.6554
    b. 0.3446
    c. 0.0142
    d. 0.9858
    e. 0

85. Suppose in a local Kindergarten through 12th grade (K - 12) school district, 53 percent of the population favor a charter school for grades K through five. A simple random sample of 300 is surveyed. Calculate following using the normal approximation to the binomial distribtion.
    a. Find the probability that less than 100 favor a charter school for grades K through 5.
    b. Find the probability that 170 or more favor a charter school for grades K through 5.
    c. Find the probability that no more than 140 favor a charter school for grades K through 5.
    d. Find the probability that there are fewer than 130 that favor a charter school for grades K through 5.
    e. Find the probability that exactly 150 favor a charter school for grades K through 5.

If you have access to an appropriate calculator or computer software, try calculating these probabilities using the technology.

86. Four friends, Janice, Barbara, Kathy and Roberta, decided to carpool together to get to school. Each day the driver would be chosen by randomly selecting one of the four names. They carpool to school for 96 days. Use the normal approximation to the binomial to calculate the following probabilities. Round the standard deviation to four decimal places.

    a. Find the probability that Janice is the driver at most 20 days.
    b. Find the probability that Roberta is the driver more than 16 days.
    c. Find the probability that Barbara drives exactly 24 of those 96 days.

87. $X \sim N(60, 9)$. Suppose that you form random samples of 25 from this distribution. Let $\bar{X}$ be the random variable of averages. Let ΣX be the random variable of sums. For parts c through f, sketch the graph, shade the region, label and scale the horizontal axis for $\bar{X}$, and find the probability.

    a. Sketch the distributions of X and $\bar{X}$ on the same graph.
    b. $\bar{X} \sim$ _____(_____,_____)
    c. $P(\bar{x} < 60) =$ _____
    d. Find the 30th percentile for the mean.
    e. $P(56 < \bar{x} < 62) =$ _____
    f. $P(18 < \bar{x} < 58) =$ _____
    g. $\Sigma x \sim$ _____(_____,_____)
    h. Find the minimum value for the upper quartile for the sum.
    i. $P(1,400 < \Sigma x < 1,550) =$ _____

88. Suppose that the length of research papers is uniformly distributed from ten to 25 pages. We survey a class in which 55 research papers were turned in to a professor. The 55 research papers are considered a random collection of all papers. We are interested in the average length of the research papers.

    a. In words, $X =$ _____
    b. $X \sim$ _____(_____,_____)
    c. $\mu_x =$ _____
    d. $\sigma_x =$ _____
    e. In words, $\bar{X} =$ _____
    f. $\bar{X} \sim$ _____(_____,_____)
    g. In words, $\Sigma X =$ _____
    h. $\Sigma X \sim$ _____(_____,_____)
    i. Without doing any calculations, do you think that it's likely that the professor will need to read a total of more than 1,050 pages? Why?
    j. Calculate the probability that the professor will need to read a total of more than 1,050 pages.
    k. Why is it so unlikely that the average length of the papers will be less than 12 pages?

89. Salaries for teachers in a particular elementary school district are normally distributed with a mean of $44,000 and a standard deviation of $6,500. We randomly survey ten teachers from that district.

    a. Find the 90th percentile for an individual teacher's salary.
    b. Find the 90th percentile for the average teacher's salary.

90. The average length of a maternity stay in a U.S. hospital is said to be 2.4 days with a standard deviation of 0.9 days. We randomly survey 80 women who recently bore children in a U.S. hospital.

    a. In words, $X =$ _____

    b. In words, $\bar{X} =$ _____

    c. $\bar{X} \sim$ _____(_____,_____)

    d. In words, $\Sigma X =$ _____

    e. $\Sigma X \sim$ _____(_____,_____)

    f. Is it likely that an individual stayed more than five days in the hospital? Why or why not?

    g. Is it likely that the average stay for the 80 women was more than five days? Why or why not?

    h. Which is more likely:

        i. An individual stayed more than five days.

        ii. the average stay of 80 women was more than five days.

    i. If we were to sum up the women's stays, is it likely that, collectively they spent more than a year in the hospital? Why or why not?

For each problem, wherever possible, provide graphs and use the calculator.

91. NeverReady batteries has engineered a newer, longer lasting AAA battery. The company claims this battery has an average life span of 17 hours with a standard deviation of 0.8 hours. Your statistics class questions this claim. As a class, you randomly select 30 batteries and find that the sample mean life span is 16.7 hours. If the process is working properly, what is the probability of getting a random sample of 30 batteries in which the sample mean lifetime is 16.7 hours or less? Is the company's claim reasonable?

92. Men have an average weight of 172 pounds with a standard deviation of 29 pounds.

    a. Find the probability that 20 randomly selected men will have a sum weight greater than 3600 lbs.

    b. If 20 men have a sum weight greater than 3500 lbs, then their total weight exceeds the safety limits for water taxis. Based on (a), is this a safety concern? Explain.

93. M&M candies large candy bags have a claimed net weight of 396.9 g. The standard deviation for the weight of the individual candies is 0.017 g. The following table is from a stats experiment conducted by a statistics class.

Red	Orange	Yellow	Brown	Blue	Green
0.751	0.735	0.883	0.696	0.881	0.925
0.841	0.895	0.769	0.876	0.863	0.914
0.856	0.865	0.859	0.855	0.775	0.881
0.799	0.864	0.784	0.806	0.854	0.865
0.966	0.852	0.824	0.840	0.810	0.865
0.859	0.866	0.858	0.868	0.858	1.015
0.857	0.859	0.848	0.859	0.818	0.876
0.942	0.838	0.851	0.982	0.868	0.809
0.873	0.863			0.803	0.865
0.809	0.888			0.932	0.848
0.890	0.925			0.842	0.940
0.878	0.793			0.832	0.833
0.905	0.977			0.807	0.845
	0.850			0.841	0.852
	0.830			0.932	0.778
	0.856			0.833	0.814
	0.842			0.881	0.791
	0.778			0.818	0.810
	0.786			0.864	0.881
	0.853			0.825	
	0.864			0.855	
	0.873			0.942	
	0.880			0.825	
	0.882			0.869	
	0.931			0.912	
				0.887	

Table 7.7

The bag contained 465 candies and he listed weights in the table came from randomly selected candies. Count the weights.

a. Find the mean sample weight and the standard deviation of the sample weights of candies in the table.
b. Find the sum of the sample weights in the table and the standard deviation of the sum of the weights.
c. If 465 M&Ms are randomly selected, find the probability that their weights sum to at least 396.9.
d. Is the Mars Company's M&M labeling accurate?

94. The Screw Right Company claims their $\frac{3}{4}$ inch screws are within ±0.23 of the claimed mean diameter of 0.750 inches with a standard deviation of 0.115 inches. The following data were recorded.

0.757	0.723	0.754	0.737	0.757	0.741	0.722	0.741	0.743	0.742
0.740	0.758	0.724	0.739	0.736	0.735	0.760	0.750	0.759	0.754
0.744	0.758	0.765	0.756	0.738	0.742	0.758	0.757	0.724	0.757
0.744	0.738	0.763	0.756	0.760	0.768	0.761	0.742	0.734	0.754
0.758	0.735	0.740	0.743	0.737	0.737	0.725	0.761	0.758	0.756

Table 7.8

The screws were randomly selected from the local home repair store.

    a. Find the mean diameter and standard deviation for the sample
    b. Find the probability that 50 randomly selected screws will be within the stated tolerance levels. Is the company's diameter claim plausible?

95. Your company has a contract to perform preventive maintenance on thousands of air-conditioners in a large city. Based on service records from previous years, the time that a technician spends servicing a unit averages one hour with a standard deviation of one hour. In the coming week, your company will service a simple random sample of 70 units in the city. You plan to budget an average of 1.1 hours per technician to complete the work. Will this be enough time?

96. A typical adult has an average IQ score of 105 with a standard deviation of 20. If 20 randomly selected adults are given an IQ tesst, what is the probability that the sample mean scores will be between 85 and 125 points?

97. Certain coins have an average weight of 5.201 grams with a standard deviation of 0.065 g. If a vending machine is designed to accept coins whose weights range from 5.111 g to 5.291 g, what is the expected number of rejected coins when 280 randomly selected coins are inserted into the machine?

REFERENCES

7.1 The Central Limit Theorem for Sample Means (Averages)

Baran, Daya. "20 Percent of Americans Have Never Used Email."WebGuild, 2010. Available online at http://www.webguild.org/20080519/20-percent-of-americans-have-never-used-email (accessed May 17, 2013).

Data from The Flurry Blog, 2013. Available online at http://blog.flurry.com (accessed May 17, 2013).

Data from the United States Department of Agriculture.

7.2 The Central Limit Theorem for Sums

Farago, Peter. "The Truth About Cats and Dogs: Smartphone vs Tablet Usage Differences." The Flurry Blog, 2013. Posted October 29, 2012. Available online at http://blog.flurry.com (accessed May 17, 2013).

7.3 Using the Central Limit Theorem

Data from the Wall Street Journal.

"National Health and Nutrition Examination Survey." Center for Disease Control and Prevention. Available online at http://www.cdc.gov/nchs/nhanes.htm (accessed May 17, 2013).

SOLUTIONS

1 mean = 4 hours; standard deviation = 1.2 hours; sample size = 16

3 a. Check student's solution.

b. 3.5, 4.25, 0.2441

5 The fact that the two distributions are different accounts for the different probabilities.

7 0.3345

9 7,833.92

11 0.0089

13 7,326.49

15 77.45%

17 0.4207

19 3,888.5

21 0.8186

23 5

25 0.9772

27 The sample size, n, gets larger.

29 49

31 26.00

33 0.1587

35 1,000

37

  a. $U(24, 26)$, 25, 0.5774

  b. $N(25, 0.0577)$

  c. 0.0416

39 0.0003

41 25.07

43

  a. $N(2,500, 5.7735)$

  b. 0

45 2,507.40

47

  a. 10

  b. $\frac{1}{10}$

49 $N\left(10, \frac{10}{8}\right)$

51 0.7799

53 1.69

55 0.0072

57 391.54

59 405.51

61

  a. X = amount of change students carry

b. $X \sim E(0.88, 0.88)$

c. $\overline{X}$ = average amount of change carried by a sample of 25 sstudents.

d. $\overline{X} \sim N(0.88, 0.176)$

e. 0.0819

f. 0.1882

g. The distributions are different. Part a is exponential and part b is normal.

63

a. length of time for an individual to complete IRS form 1040, in hours.

b. mean length of time for a sample of 36 taxpayers to complete IRS form 1040, in hours.

c. $N\left(10.53, \frac{1}{3}\right)$

d. Yes. I would be surprised, because the probability is almost 0.

e. No. I would not be totally surprised because the probability is 0.2312

65

a. the length of a song, in minutes, in the collection

b. $U(2, 3.5)$

c. the average length, in minutes, of the songs from a sample of five albums from the collection

d. $N(2.75, 0.0660)$

e. 2.71 minutes

f. 0.09 minutes

67

a. True. The mean of a sampling distribution of the means is approximately the mean of the data distribution.

b. True. According to the Central Limit Theorem, the larger the sample, the closer the sampling distribution of the means becomes normal.

c. The standard deviation of the sampling distribution of the means will decrease making it approximately the same as the standard deviation of X as the sample size increases.

69

a. X = the yearly income of someone in a third world country

b. the average salary from samples of 1,000 residents of a third world country

c. $\overline{X} \sim N\left(2000, \frac{8000}{\sqrt{1000}}\right)$

d. Very wide differences in data values can have averages smaller than standard deviations.

e. The distribution of the sample mean will have higher probabilities closer to the population mean.

   $P(2000 < \overline{X} < 2100) = 0.1537$

   $P(2100 < \overline{X} < 2200) = 0.1317$

71 b

73

a. the total length of time for nine criminal trials

b. $N(189, 21)$

c. 0.0432

d. 162.09; ninety percent of the total nine trials of this type will last 162 days or more.

75

a. X = the salary of one elementary school teacher in the district

b. $X \sim N(44{,}000, 6{,}500)$

c. $\Sigma X \sim$ sum of the salaries of ten elementary school teachers in the sample

d. $\Sigma X \sim N(44000, 20554.80)$

e. 0.9742

f. $52,330.09

g. 466,342.04

h. Sampling 70 teachers instead of ten would cause the distribution to be more spread out. It would be a more symmetrical normal curve.

i. If every teacher received a $3,000 raise, the distribution of X would shift to the right by $3,000. In other words, it would have a mean of $47,000.

77

a. X = the closing stock prices for U.S. semiconductor manufacturers

b. i. $20.71; ii. $17.31; iii. 35

d. Exponential distribution, $X \sim Exp\left(\frac{1}{20.71}\right)$

e. Answers will vary.

f. i. $20.71; ii. $11.14

g. Answers will vary.

h. Answers will vary.

i. Answers will vary.

j. $N\left(20.71, \frac{17.31}{\sqrt{5}}\right)$

79 b

81 b

83 a

85

a. 0

b. 0.1123

c. 0.0162

d. 0.0003

e. 0.0268

87

a. Check student's solution.

b. $\bar{X} \sim N\left(60, \frac{9}{\sqrt{25}}\right)$

c. 0.5000

d. 59.06

e. 0.8536

   f. 0.1333

   g. $N(1500, 45)$

   h. 1530.35

   i. 0.6877

89

   a. $52,330

   b. $46,634

91

- We have $\mu = 17$, $\sigma = 0.8$, $\bar{x} = 16.7$, and $n = 30$. To calculate the probability, we use $\mathtt{normalcdf}$(lower, upper, μ, $\frac{\sigma}{\sqrt{n}}$) = $\mathtt{normalcdf}\left(E - 99, 16.7, 17, \frac{0.8}{\sqrt{30}}\right)$ = 0.0200.

- If the process is working properly, then the probability that a sample of 30 batteries would have at most 16.7 lifetime hours is only 2%. Therefore, the class was justified to question the claim.

93

   a. For the sample, we have $n = 100$, $\bar{x} = 0.862$, $s = 0.05$

   b. $\Sigma \bar{x} = 85.65$, $\Sigma s = 5.18$

   c. $\mathtt{normalcdf}(396.9, E99, (465)(0.8565), (0.05)(\sqrt{465})) \approx 1$

   d. Since the probability of a sample of size 465 having at least a mean sum of 396.9 is appproximately 1, we can conclude that Mars is correctly labeling their M&M packages.

95 Use $\mathtt{normalcdf}\left(E - 99, 1.1, 1, \frac{1}{\sqrt{70}}\right)$ = 0.7986. This means that there is an 80% chance that the service time will be less than 1.1 hours. It could be wise to schedule more time since there is an associated 20% chance that the maintenance time will be greater than 1.1 hours.

97 We assume that the weights of coins are normally distributed in the population. Since we have $\mathtt{normalcdf}$ $\left(5.111, 5.291, 5.201, \frac{0.065}{\sqrt{280}}\right) \approx 0.8338$, we expect $(1 - 0.8338)280 \approx 47$ coins to be rejected.

8 | CONFIDENCE INTERVALS

Figure 8.1 Have you ever wondered what the average number of M&Ms in a bag at the grocery store is? You can use confidence intervals to answer this question. (credit: comedy_nose/flickr)

Introduction

Chapter Objectives

By the end of this chapter, the student should be able to:

- Calculate and interpret confidence intervals for estimating a population mean and a population proportion.
- Interpret the Student's t probability distribution as the sample size changes.
- Discriminate between problems applying the normal and the Student's *t* distributions.
- Calculate the sample size required to estimate a population mean and a population proportion given a desired confidence level and margin of error.

Suppose you were trying to determine the mean rent of a two-bedroom apartment in your town. You might look in the classified section of the newspaper, write down several rents listed, and average them together. You would have obtained a point estimate of the true mean. If you are trying to determine the percentage of times you make a basket when shooting a basketball, you might count the number of shots you make and divide that by the number of shots you attempted. In this case, you would have obtained a point estimate for the true proportion.

We use sample data to make generalizations about an unknown population. This part of statistics is called **inferential statistics**. **The sample data help us to make an estimate of a population parameter**. We realize that the point estimate is most likely not the exact value of the population parameter, but close to it. After calculating point estimates, we construct interval estimates, called confidence intervals.

In this chapter, you will learn to construct and interpret confidence intervals. You will also learn a new distribution, the Student's-t, and how it is used with these intervals. Throughout the chapter, it is important to keep in mind that the confidence interval is a random variable. It is the population parameter that is fixed.

If you worked in the marketing department of an entertainment company, you might be interested in the mean number of songs a consumer downloads a month from iTunes. If so, you could conduct a survey and calculate the sample mean, $\bar{x}$, and the sample standard deviation, s. You would use $\bar{x}$ to estimate the population mean and s to estimate the population standard deviation. The sample mean, $\bar{x}$, is the **point estimate** for the population mean, μ. The sample standard deviation, s, is the point estimate for the population standard deviation, σ.

Each of $\bar{x}$ and s is called a statistic.

A **confidence interval** is another type of estimate but, instead of being just one number, it is an interval of numbers. It provides a range of reasonable values in which we expect the population parameter to fall. There is no guarantee that a given confidence interval does capture the parameter, but there is a predictable probability of success.

Suppose, for the iTunes example, we do not know the population mean μ, but we do know that the population standard deviation is $\sigma = 1$ and our sample size is 100. Then, by the central limit theorem, the standard deviation for the sample mean is

$$\frac{\sigma}{\sqrt{n}} = \frac{1}{\sqrt{100}} = 0.1 \, .$$

The **empirical rule**, which applies to bell-shaped distributions, says that in approximately 95% of the samples, the sample mean, $\bar{x}$, will be within two standard deviations of the population mean μ. For our iTunes example, two standard deviations is $(2)(0.1) = 0.2$. The sample mean $\bar{x}$ is likely to be within 0.2 units of μ.

Because $\bar{x}$ is within 0.2 units of μ, which is unknown, then μ is likely to be within 0.2 units of $\bar{x}$ in 95% of the samples. The population mean μ is contained in an interval whose lower number is calculated by taking the sample mean and subtracting two standard deviations $(2)(0.1)$ and whose upper number is calculated by taking the sample mean and adding two standard deviations. In other words, μ is between $\bar{x} - 0.2$ and $\bar{x} + 0.2$ in 95% of all the samples.

For the iTunes example, suppose that a sample produced a sample mean $\bar{x} = 2$. Then the unknown population mean μ is between

$$\bar{x} - 0.2 = 2 - 0.2 = 1.8 \text{ and } \bar{x} + 0.2 = 2 + 0.2 = 2.2$$

We say that we are **95% confident** that the unknown population mean number of songs downloaded from iTunes per month is between 1.8 and 2.2. **The 95% confidence interval is (1.8, 2.2).**

The 95% confidence interval implies two possibilities. Either the interval (1.8, 2.2) contains the true mean μ or our sample produced an $\bar{x}$ that is not within 0.2 units of the true mean μ. The second possibility happens for only 5% of all the samples (95–100%).

Remember that a confidence interval is created for an unknown population parameter like the population mean, μ. Confidence intervals for some parameters have the form:

(point estimate – margin of error, point estimate + margin of error)

The margin of error depends on the confidence level or percentage of confidence and the standard error of the mean.

When you read newspapers and journals, some reports will use the phrase "margin of error." Other reports will not use that phrase, but include a confidence interval as the point estimate plus or minus the margin of error. These are two ways of expressing the same concept.

NOTE

Although the text only covers symmetrical confidence intervals, there are non-symmetrical confidence intervals (for example, a confidence interval for the standard deviation).

Collaborative Exercise

Have your instructor record the number of meals each student in your class eats out in a week. Assume that the standard deviation is known to be three meals. Construct an approximate 95% confidence interval for the true mean number of meals students eat out each week.

1. Calculate the sample mean.

2. Let $\sigma = 3$ and n = the number of students surveyed.

3. Construct the interval $\left(\bar{x} - 2 \cdot \frac{\sigma}{\sqrt{n}}, \bar{x} + 2 \cdot \frac{\sigma}{\sqrt{n}} \right)$.

We say we are approximately 95% confident that the true mean number of meals that students eat out in a week is between _____ and _____.

8.1 | A Single Population Mean using the Normal Distribution

A confidence interval for a population mean with a known standard deviation is based on the fact that the sample means follow an approximately normal distribution. Suppose that our sample has a mean of $\bar{x} = 10$ and we have constructed the 90% confidence interval (5, 15) where $EBM = 5$.

Calculating the Confidence Interval

To construct a confidence interval for a single unknown population mean μ, **where the population standard deviation is known**, we need $\bar{x}$ as an estimate for μ and we need the margin of error. Here, the margin of error (EBM) is called the **error bound for a population mean** (abbreviated EBM). The sample mean $\bar{x}$ is the **point estimate** of the unknown population mean μ.

The confidence interval estimate will have the form:

(point estimate - error bound, point estimate + error bound) or, in symbols,($\bar{x} - EBM$, $\bar{x} + EBM$)

The margin of error (EBM) depends on the **confidence level** (abbreviated **CL**). The confidence level is often considered the probability that the calculated confidence interval estimate will contain the true population parameter. However, it is more accurate to state that the confidence level is the percent of confidence intervals that contain the true population parameter when repeated samples are taken. Most often, it is the choice of the person constructing the confidence interval to choose a confidence level of 90% or higher because that person wants to be reasonably certain of his or her conclusions.

There is another probability called alpha (α). α is related to the confidence level, CL. α is the probability that the interval does not contain the unknown population parameter.
Mathematically, $\alpha + CL = 1$.

Example 8.1

Suppose we have collected data from a sample. We know the sample mean but we do not know the mean for the entire population.

The sample mean is seven, and the error bound for the mean is 2.5.

$\bar{x}$ = 7 and EBM = 2.5

The confidence interval is (7 – 2.5, 7 + 2.5), and calculating the values gives (4.5, 9.5).

If the confidence level (CL) is 95%, then we say that, "We estimate with 95% confidence that the true value of the population mean is between 4.5 and 9.5."

8.1 Suppose we have data from a sample. The sample mean is 15, and the error bound for the mean is 3.2.

What is the confidence interval estimate for the population mean?

A confidence interval for a population mean with a known standard deviation is based on the fact that the sample means follow an approximately normal distribution. Suppose that our sample has a mean of $\bar{x}$ = 10, and we have constructed the 90% confidence interval (5, 15) where EBM = 5.

To get a 90% confidence interval, we must include the central 90% of the probability of the normal distribution. If we include the central 90%, we leave out a total of α = 10% in both tails, or 5% in each tail, of the normal distribution.

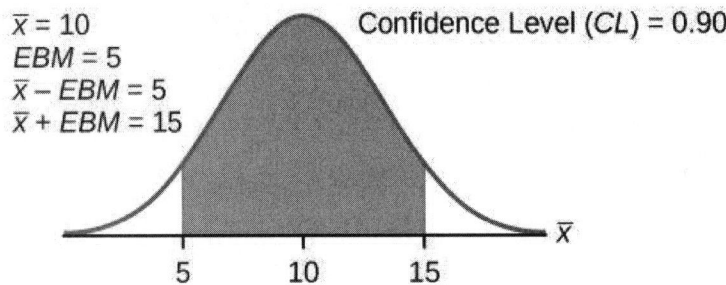

Figure 8.2

To capture the central 90%, we must go out 1.645 "standard deviations" on either side of the calculated sample mean. The value 1.645 is the z-score from a standard normal probability distribution that puts an area of 0.90 in the center, an area of 0.05 in the far left tail, and an area of 0.05 in the far right tail.

It is important that the "standard deviation" used must be appropriate for the parameter we are estimating, so in this section we need to use the standard deviation that applies to sample means, which is $\frac{\sigma}{\sqrt{n}}$. The fraction $\frac{\sigma}{\sqrt{n}}$, is commonly called the "standard error of the mean" in order to distinguish clearly the standard deviation for a mean from the population standard deviation σ.

In summary, as a result of the central limit theorem:

- $\bar{X}$ is normally distributed, that is, $\bar{X} \sim N\left(\mu_X, \frac{\sigma}{\sqrt{n}}\right)$.

- **When the population standard deviation σ is known, we use a normal distribution to calculate the error bound.**

Calculating the Confidence Interval

To construct a confidence interval estimate for an unknown population mean, we need data from a random sample. The steps to construct and interpret the confidence interval are:

- Calculate the sample mean $\bar{x}$ from the sample data. Remember, in this section we already know the population standard deviation σ.

- Find the z-score that corresponds to the confidence level.

- Calculate the error bound *EBM*.

- Construct the confidence interval.

- Write a sentence that interprets the estimate in the context of the situation in the problem. (Explain what the confidence interval means, in the words of the problem.)

We will first examine each step in more detail, and then illustrate the process with some examples.

Finding the *z*-score for the Stated Confidence Level

When we know the population standard deviation σ, we use a standard normal distribution to calculate the error bound EBM and construct the confidence interval. We need to find the value of z that puts an area equal to the confidence level (in decimal form) in the middle of the standard normal distribution $Z \sim N(0, 1)$.

The confidence level, *CL*, is the area in the middle of the standard normal distribution. $CL = 1 - \alpha$, so α is the area that is split equally between the two tails. Each of the tails contains an area equal to $\frac{\alpha}{2}$.

The z-score that has an area to the right of $\frac{\alpha}{2}$ is denoted by $z_{\frac{\alpha}{2}}$.

For example, when $CL = 0.95$, $\alpha = 0.05$ and $\frac{\alpha}{2} = 0.025$; we write $z_{\frac{\alpha}{2}} = z_{0.025}$.

The area to the right of $z_{0.025}$ is 0.025 and the area to the left of $z_{0.025}$ is $1 - 0.025 = 0.975$.

$z_{\frac{\alpha}{2}} = z_{0.025} = 1.96$, using a calculator, computer or a standard normal probability table.

 Using the TI-83, 83+, 84, 84+ Calculator

invNorm(0.975, 0, 1) = 1.96

NOTE

Remember to use the area to the LEFT of $z_{\frac{\alpha}{2}}$; in this chapter the last two inputs in the invNorm command are 0, 1, because you are using a standard normal distribution $Z \sim N(0, 1)$.

Calculating the Error Bound (*EBM*)

The error bound formula for an unknown population mean μ when the population standard deviation σ is known is

- $EBM = \left(z_{\frac{\alpha}{2}}\right)\left(\frac{\sigma}{\sqrt{n}}\right)$

Constructing the Confidence Interval

- The confidence interval estimate has the format $(\bar{x} - EBM, \ \bar{x} + EBM)$.

The graph gives a picture of the entire situation.

$CL + \frac{\alpha}{2} + \frac{\alpha}{2} = CL + \alpha = 1$.

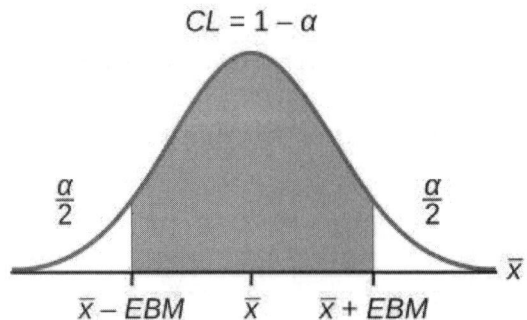

Figure 8.3

Writing the Interpretation

The interpretation should clearly state the confidence level (*CL*), explain what population parameter is being estimated (here, a **population mean**), and state the confidence interval (both endpoints). "We estimate with ___% confidence that the true population mean (include the context of the problem) is between ___ and ___ (include appropriate units)."

Example 8.2

Suppose scores on exams in statistics are normally distributed with an unknown population mean and a population standard deviation of three points. A random sample of 36 scores is taken and gives a sample mean (sample mean score) of 68. Find a confidence interval estimate for the population mean exam score (the mean score on all exams).

Find a 90% confidence interval for the true (population) mean of statistics exam scores.

Solution 8.2

- You can use technology to calculate the confidence interval directly.

- The first solution is shown step-by-step (Solution A).

- The second solution uses the TI-83, 83+, and 84+ calculators (Solution B).

Solution A

To find the confidence interval, you need the sample mean, $\bar{x}$, and the *EBM*.

$\bar{x} = 68$

$EBM = \left(z_{\frac{\alpha}{2}}\right)\left(\frac{\sigma}{\sqrt{n}}\right)$

$\sigma = 3$; $n = 36$; The confidence level is 90% (*CL* = 0.90)

$CL = 0.90$ so $\alpha = 1 - CL = 1 - 0.90 = 0.10$

$\frac{\alpha}{2} = 0.05 \quad z_{\frac{\alpha}{2}} = z_{0.05}$

The area to the right of $z_{0.05}$ is 0.05 and the area to the left of $z_{0.05}$ is $1 - 0.05 = 0.95$.

$z_{\frac{\alpha}{2}} = z_{0.05} = 1.645$

using invNorm(0.95, 0, 1) on the TI-83,83+, and 84+ calculators. This can also be found using appropriate commands on other calculators, using a computer, or using a probability table for the standard normal distribution.

$EBM = (1.645)\left(\frac{3}{\sqrt{36}}\right) = 0.8225$

$$\bar{x} - EBM = 68 - 0.8225 = 67.1775$$

$$\bar{x} + EBM = 68 + 0.8225 = 68.8225$$

The 90% confidence interval is **(67.1775, 68.8225).**

Solution 8.2

Solution B

Using the TI-83, 83+, 84, 84+ Calculator

Press STAT and arrow over to TESTS.
Arrow down to 7:ZInterval.
Press ENTER.
Arrow to Stats and press ENTER.
Arrow down and enter three for σ, 68 for $\bar{x}$, 36 for n, and .90 for C-level.
Arrow down to Calculate and press ENTER.
The confidence interval is (to three decimal places)(67.178, 68.822).

Interpretation

We estimate with 90% confidence that the true population mean exam score for all statistics students is between 67.18 and 68.82.

Explanation of 90% Confidence Level

Ninety percent of all confidence intervals constructed in this way contain the true mean statistics exam score. For example, if we constructed 100 of these confidence intervals, we would expect 90 of them to contain the true population mean exam score.

8.2 Suppose average pizza delivery times are normally distributed with an unknown population mean and a population standard deviation of six minutes. A random sample of 28 pizza delivery restaurants is taken and has a sample mean delivery time of 36 minutes.

Find a 90% confidence interval estimate for the population mean delivery time.

Example 8.3

The Specific Absorption Rate (SAR) for a cell phone measures the amount of radio frequency (RF) energy absorbed by the user's body when using the handset. Every cell phone emits RF energy. Different phone models have different SAR measures. To receive certification from the Federal Communications Commission (FCC) for sale in the United States, the SAR level for a cell phone must be no more than 1.6 watts per kilogram. **Table 8.1** shows the highest SAR level for a random selection of cell phone models as measured by the FCC.

Phone Model	SAR	Phone Model	SAR	Phone Model	SAR
Apple iPhone 4S	1.11	LG Ally	1.36	Pantech Laser	0.74
BlackBerry Pearl 8120	1.48	LG AX275	1.34	Samsung Character	0.5
BlackBerry Tour 9630	1.43	LG Cosmos	1.18	Samsung Epic 4G Touch	0.4
Cricket TXTM8	1.3	LG CU515	1.3	Samsung M240	0.867
HP/Palm Centro	1.09	LG Trax CU575	1.26	Samsung Messager III SCH-R750	0.68
HTC One V	0.455	Motorola Q9h	1.29	Samsung Nexus S	0.51
HTC Touch Pro 2	1.41	Motorola Razr2 V8	0.36	Samsung SGH-A227	1.13
Huawei M835 Ideos	0.82	Motorola Razr2 V9	0.52	SGH-a107 GoPhone	0.3
Kyocera DuraPlus	0.78	Motorola V195s	1.6	Sony W350a	1.48
Kyocera K127 Marbl	1.25	Nokia 1680	1.39	T-Mobile Concord	1.38

Table 8.1

Find a 98% confidence interval for the true (population) mean of the Specific Absorption Rates (SARs) for cell phones. Assume that the population standard deviation is $\sigma = 0.337$.

Solution 8.3

Solution A

To find the confidence interval, start by finding the point estimate: the sample mean.

$$\bar{x} = 1.024$$

Next, find the *EBM*. Because you are creating a 98% confidence interval, *CL* = 0.98.

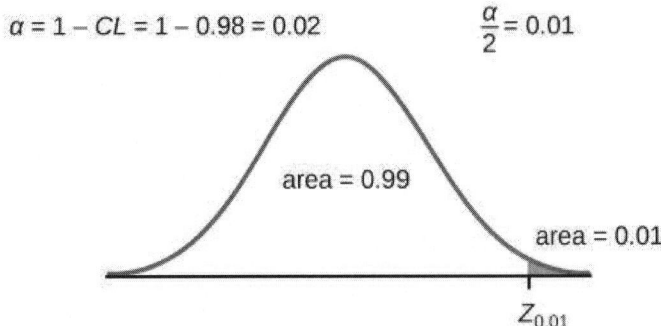

$$\alpha = 1 - CL = 1 - 0.98 = 0.02 \qquad \frac{\alpha}{2} = 0.01$$

area = 0.99

area = 0.01

$z_{0.01}$

Figure 8.4

You need to find $z_{0.01}$ having the property that the area under the normal density curve to the right of $z_{0.01}$ is 0.01 and the area to the left is 0.99. Use your calculator, a computer, or a probability table for the standard normal distribution to find $z_{0.01} = 2.326$.

$$EBM = (z_{0.01})\frac{\sigma}{\sqrt{n}} = (2.326)\frac{0.337}{\sqrt{30}} = 0.1431$$

To find the 98% confidence interval, find $\bar{x} \pm EBM$.

$\overline{x} - EBM = 1.024 - 0.1431 = 0.8809$

$\overline{x} - EBM = 1.024 - 0.1431 = 1.1671$

We estimate with 98% confidence that the true SAR mean for the population of cell phones in the United States is between 0.8809 and 1.1671 watts per kilogram.

Solution 8.3

Solution B

 Using the TI-83, 83+, 84, 84+ Calculator

Press STAT and arrow over to TESTS.
Arrow down to 7:ZInterval.
Press ENTER.
Arrow to Stats and press ENTER.
Arrow down and enter the following values:
σ: 0.337
$\overline{x}$: 1.024
n: 30
C-level: 0.98

Arrow down to Calculate and press ENTER.
The confidence interval is (to three decimal places) (0.881, 1.167).

8.3 **Table 8.2** shows a different random sampling of 20 cell phone models. Use this data to calculate a 93% confidence interval for the true mean SAR for cell phones certified for use in the United States. As previously, assume that the population standard deviation is $\sigma = 0.337$.

Phone Model	SAR	Phone Model	SAR
Blackberry Pearl 8120	1.48	Nokia E71x	1.53
HTC Evo Design 4G	0.8	Nokia N75	0.68
HTC Freestyle	1.15	Nokia N79	1.4
LG Ally	1.36	Sagem Puma	1.24
LG Fathom	0.77	Samsung Fascinate	0.57
LG Optimus Vu	0.462	Samsung Infuse 4G	0.2
Motorola Cliq XT	1.36	Samsung Nexus S	0.51
Motorola Droid Pro	1.39	Samsung Replenish	0.3
Motorola Droid Razr M	1.3	Sony W518a Walkman	0.73
Nokia 7705 Twist	0.7	ZTE C79	0.869

Table 8.2

Notice the difference in the confidence intervals calculated in **Example 8.3** and the following **Try It** exercise. These intervals are different for several reasons: they were calculated from different samples, the samples were different sizes, and the intervals were calculated for different levels of confidence. Even though the intervals are different, they do not yield conflicting information. The effects of these kinds of changes are the subject of the next section in this chapter.

Changing the Confidence Level or Sample Size

Example 8.4

Suppose we change the original problem in **Example 8.2** by using a 95% confidence level. Find a 95% confidence interval for the true (population) mean statistics exam score.

Solution 8.4

To find the confidence interval, you need the sample mean, $\bar{x}$, and the *EBM*.

$$\bar{x} = 68$$

$$EBM = \left(z_{\frac{\alpha}{2}} \right) \left(\frac{\sigma}{\sqrt{n}} \right)$$

$\sigma = 3$; $n = 36$; The confidence level is 95% ($CL = 0.95$).

$CL = 0.95$ so $\alpha = 1 - CL = 1 - 0.95 = 0.05$

$\frac{\alpha}{2} = 0.025 \quad z_{\frac{\alpha}{2}} = z_{0.025}$

The area to the right of $z_{0.025}$ is 0.025 and the area to the left of $z_{0.025}$ is $1 - 0.025 = 0.975$.

$$z_{\frac{\alpha}{2}} = z_{0.025} = 1.96$$

when using invnorm(0.975,0,1) on the TI-83, 83+, or 84+ calculators. (This can also be found using appropriate commands on other calculators, using a computer, or using a probability table for the standard normal distribution.)

$$EBM = (1.96)\left(\frac{3}{\sqrt{36}}\right) = 0.98$$

$$\bar{x} - EBM = 68 - 0.98 = 67.02$$

$$\bar{x} + EBM = 68 + 0.98 = 68.98$$

Notice that the *EBM* is larger for a 95% confidence level in the original problem.

Interpretation

We estimate with 95% confidence that the true population mean for all statistics exam scores is between 67.02 and 68.98.

Explanation of 95% Confidence Level

Ninety-five percent of all confidence intervals constructed in this way contain the true value of the population mean statistics exam score.

Comparing the results

The 90% confidence interval is (67.18, 68.82). The 95% confidence interval is (67.02, 68.98). The 95% confidence interval is wider. If you look at the graphs, because the area 0.95 is larger than the area 0.90, it makes sense that the 95% confidence interval is wider. To be more confident that the confidence interval actually does contain the true value of the population mean for all statistics exam scores, the confidence interval necessarily needs to be wider.

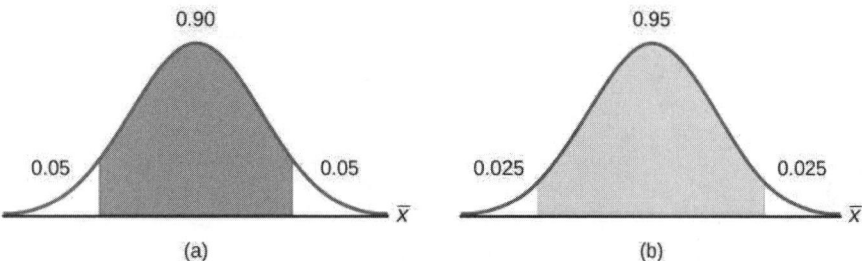

Figure 8.5

Summary: Effect of Changing the Confidence Level
- Increasing the confidence level increases the error bound, making the confidence interval wider.
- Decreasing the confidence level decreases the error bound, making the confidence interval narrower.

Try It Σ

8.4 Refer back to the pizza-delivery **Try It** exercise. The population standard deviation is six minutes and the sample mean deliver time is 36 minutes. Use a sample size of 20. Find a 95% confidence interval estimate for the true mean pizza delivery time.

Example 8.5

Suppose we change the original problem in **Example 8.2** to see what happens to the error bound if the sample size is changed.

Leave everything the same except the sample size. Use the original 90% confidence level. What happens to the error bound and the confidence interval if we increase the sample size and use $n = 100$ instead of $n = 36$? What happens if we decrease the sample size to $n = 25$ instead of $n = 36$?

- $\bar{x} = 68$

- $EBM = \left(z_{\frac{\alpha}{2}}\right)\left(\frac{\sigma}{\sqrt{n}}\right)$

- $\sigma = 3$; The confidence level is 90% ($CL = 0.90$); $z_{\frac{\alpha}{2}} = z_{0.05} = 1.645$.

Solution 8.5
Solution A

If we **increase** the sample size n to 100, we **decrease** the error bound.

When $n = 100$: $EBM = \left(z_{\frac{\alpha}{2}}\right)\left(\frac{\sigma}{\sqrt{n}}\right) = (1.645)\left(\frac{3}{\sqrt{100}}\right) = 0.4935$.

Solution 8.5
Solution B

If we **decrease** the sample size n to 25, we **increase** the error bound.

When $n = 25$: $EBM = \left(z_{\frac{\alpha}{2}}\right)\left(\frac{\sigma}{\sqrt{n}}\right) = (1.645)\left(\frac{3}{\sqrt{25}}\right) = 0.987$.

Summary: Effect of Changing the Sample Size
- Increasing the sample size causes the error bound to decrease, making the confidence interval narrower.
- Decreasing the sample size causes the error bound to increase, making the confidence interval wider.

8.5 Refer back to the pizza-delivery **Try It** exercise. The mean delivery time is 36 minutes and the population standard deviation is six minutes. Assume the sample size is changed to 50 restaurants with the same sample mean. Find a 90% confidence interval estimate for the population mean delivery time.

Working Backwards to Find the Error Bound or Sample Mean

When we calculate a confidence interval, we find the sample mean, calculate the error bound, and use them to calculate the confidence interval. However, sometimes when we read statistical studies, the study may state the confidence interval only. If we know the confidence interval, we can work backwards to find both the error bound and the sample mean.

Finding the Error Bound
- From the upper value for the interval, subtract the sample mean,
- OR, from the upper value for the interval, subtract the lower value. Then divide the difference by two.

Finding the Sample Mean
- Subtract the error bound from the upper value of the confidence interval,

- OR, average the upper and lower endpoints of the confidence interval.

Notice that there are two methods to perform each calculation. You can choose the method that is easier to use with the information you know.

Example 8.6

Suppose we know that a confidence interval is **(67.18, 68.82)** and we want to find the error bound. We may know that the sample mean is 68, or perhaps our source only gave the confidence interval and did not tell us the value of the sample mean.

Calculate the Error Bound:
- If we know that the sample mean is 68: $EBM = 68.82 - 68 = 0.82$.

- If we don't know the sample mean: $EBM = \dfrac{(68.82 - 67.18)}{2} = 0.82$.

Calculate the Sample Mean:
- If we know the error bound: $\bar{x} = 68.82 - 0.82 = 68$

- If we don't know the error bound: $\bar{x} = \dfrac{(67.18 + 68.82)}{2} = 68$.

Try It Σ

8.6 Suppose we know that a confidence interval is (42.12, 47.88). Find the error bound and the sample mean.

Calculating the Sample Size *n*

If researchers desire a specific margin of error, then they can use the error bound formula to calculate the required sample size.

The error bound formula for a population mean when the population standard deviation is known is

$$EBM = \left(z_{\frac{\alpha}{2}}\right)\left(\frac{\sigma}{\sqrt{n}}\right).$$

The formula for sample size is $n = \dfrac{z^2 \sigma^2}{EBM^2}$, found by solving the error bound formula for *n*.

In this formula, *z* is $z_{\frac{\alpha}{2}}$, corresponding to the desired confidence level. A researcher planning a study who wants a specified confidence level and error bound can use this formula to calculate the size of the sample needed for the study.

Example 8.7

The population standard deviation for the age of Foothill College students is 15 years. If we want to be 95% confident that the sample mean age is within two years of the true population mean age of Foothill College students, how many randomly selected Foothill College students must be surveyed?

From the problem, we know that $\sigma = 15$ and $EBM = 2$.

$z = z_{0.025} = 1.96$, because the confidence level is 95%.

$n = \dfrac{z^2 \sigma^2}{EBM^2} = \dfrac{(1.96)^2 (15)^2}{2^2} = 216.09$ using the sample size equation.

Use $n = 217$: Always round the answer UP to the next higher integer to ensure that the sample size is large enough.

Therefore, 217 Foothill College students should be surveyed in order to be 95% confident that we are within two years of the true population mean age of Foothill College students.

8.7 The population standard deviation for the height of high school basketball players is three inches. If we want to be 95% confident that the sample mean height is within one inch of the true population mean height, how many randomly selected students must be surveyed?

8.2 | A Single Population Mean using the Student t Distribution

In practice, we rarely know the population **standard deviation**. In the past, when the sample size was large, this did not present a problem to statisticians. They used the sample standard deviation s as an estimate for σ and proceeded as before to calculate a **confidence interval** with close enough results. However, statisticians ran into problems when the sample size was small. A small sample size caused inaccuracies in the confidence interval.

William S. Goset (1876–1937) of the Guinness brewery in Dublin, Ireland ran into this problem. His experiments with hops and barley produced very few samples. Just replacing σ with s did not produce accurate results when he tried to calculate a confidence interval. He realized that he could not use a normal distribution for the calculation; he found that the actual distribution depends on the sample size. This problem led him to "discover" what is called the **Student's t-distribution**. The name comes from the fact that Gosset wrote under the pen name "Student."

Up until the mid-1970s, some statisticians used the **normal distribution** approximation for large sample sizes and used the Student's t-distribution only for sample sizes of at most 30. With graphing calculators and computers, the practice now is to use the Student's t-distribution whenever s is used as an estimate for σ.

If you draw a simple random sample of size n from a population that has an approximately normal distribution with mean μ and unknown population standard deviation σ and calculate the t-score $t = \dfrac{\overline{x} - \mu}{\left(\frac{s}{\sqrt{n}}\right)}$, then the t-scores follow a **Student's t-distribution with $n-1$ degrees of freedom**. The t-score has the same interpretation as the **z-score**. It measures how far $\overline{x}$ is from its mean μ. For each sample size n, there is a different Student's t-distribution.

The **degrees of freedom**, $n-1$, come from the calculation of the sample standard deviation s. In **Appendix H**, we used n deviations $(x - \overline{x}$ values$)$ to calculate s. Because the sum of the deviations is zero, we can find the last deviation once we know the other $n-1$ deviations. The other $n-1$ deviations can change or vary freely. **We call the number $n-1$ the degrees of freedom (df).**

Properties of the Student's t-Distribution
- The graph for the Student's t-distribution is similar to the standard normal curve.

- The mean for the Student's t-distribution is zero and the distribution is symmetric about zero.

- The Student's t-distribution has more probability in its tails than the standard normal distribution because the spread of the t-distribution is greater than the spread of the standard normal. So the graph of the Student's t-distribution will be thicker in the tails and shorter in the center than the graph of the standard normal distribution.

- The exact shape of the Student's t-distribution depends on the degrees of freedom. As the degrees of freedom increases, the graph of Student's t-distribution becomes more like the graph of the standard normal distribution.

- The underlying population of individual observations is assumed to be normally distributed with unknown population mean μ and unknown population standard deviation σ. The size of the underlying population is generally not relevant unless it is very small. If it is bell shaped (normal) then the assumption is met and doesn't need discussion. Random sampling is assumed, but that is a completely separate assumption from normality.

Calculators and computers can easily calculate any Student's t-probabilities. The TI-83,83+, and 84+ have a tcdf function to find the probability for given values of *t*. The grammar for the tcdf command is tcdf(lower bound, upper bound, degrees of freedom). However for confidence intervals, we need to use **inverse** probability to find the value of *t* when we know the probability.

For the TI-84+ you can use the invT command on the DISTRibution menu. The invT command works similarly to the invnorm. The invT command requires two inputs: **invT(area to the left, degrees of freedom)** The output is the t-score that corresponds to the area we specified.

The TI-83 and 83+ do not have the invT command. (The TI-89 has an inverse T command.)

A probability table for the Student's t-distribution can also be used. The table gives t-scores that correspond to the confidence level (column) and degrees of freedom (row). (The TI-86 does not have an invT program or command, so if you are using that calculator, you need to use a probability table for the Student's t-Distribution.) When using a *t*-table, note that some tables are formatted to show the confidence level in the column headings, while the column headings in some tables may show only corresponding area in one or both tails.

A Student's t table (See **Appendix H**) gives *t*-scores given the degrees of freedom and the right-tailed probability. The table is very limited. **Calculators and computers can easily calculate any Student's t-probabilities.**

The notation for the Student's t-distribution (using *T* as the random variable) is:

* $T \sim t_{df}$ where $df = n - 1$.

*   For example, if we have a sample of size $n = 20$ items, then we calculate the degrees of freedom as $df = n - 1 = 20 - 1 = 19$ and we write the distribution as $T \sim t_{19}$.

If the population standard deviation is not known, the **error bound for a population mean** is:

* $EBM = \left(t_{\frac{\alpha}{2}}\right)\left(\frac{s}{\sqrt{n}}\right),$

* $t_{\frac{\alpha}{2}}$ is the *t*-score with area to the right equal to $\frac{\alpha}{2}$,

*   use $df = n - 1$ degrees of freedom, and

*   *s* = sample standard deviation.

The format for the confidence interval is:

$(\bar{x} - EBM, \ \bar{x} + EBM).$

 Using the TI-83, 83+, 84, 84+ Calculator

To calculate the confidence interval directly:
Press STAT.
Arrow over to TESTS.
Arrow down to 8:TInterval and press ENTER (or just press 8).

Example 8.8

Suppose you do a study of acupuncture to determine how effective it is in relieving pain. You measure sensory rates for 15 subjects with the results given. Use the sample data to construct a 95% confidence interval for the mean sensory rate for the population (assumed normal) from which you took the data.
The solution is shown step-by-step and by using the TI-83, 83+, or 84+ calculators.

8.6; 9.4; 7.9; 6.8; 8.3; 7.3; 9.2; 9.6; 8.7; 11.4; 10.3; 5.4; 8.1; 5.5; 6.9

Solution 8.8
*   The first solution is step-by-step (Solution A).

*   The second solution uses the TI-83+ and TI-84 calculators (Solution B).

Solution A

To find the confidence interval, you need the sample mean, $\bar{x}$, and the *EBM*.

$\bar{x}$ = 8.2267 *s* = 1.6722 *n* = 15

df = 15 − 1 = 14 *CL* so *α* = 1 − *CL* = 1 − 0.95 = 0.05

$\frac{\alpha}{2}$ = 0.025 $t_{\frac{\alpha}{2}} = t_{0.025}$

The area to the right of $t_{0.025}$ is 0.025, and the area to the left of $t_{0.025}$ is 1 − 0.025 = 0.975

$t_{\frac{\alpha}{2}} = t_{0.025} = 2.14$ using invT(.975,14) on the TI-84+ calculator.

$$EBM = \left(t_{\frac{\alpha}{2}}\right)\left(\frac{s}{\sqrt{n}}\right)$$

$$EBM = (2.14)\left(\frac{1.6722}{\sqrt{15}}\right) = 0.924$$

$\bar{x}$ − *EBM* = 8.2267 − 0.9240 = 7.3

$\bar{x}$ + *EBM* = 8.2267 + 0.9240 = 9.15

The 95% confidence interval is (7.30, 9.15).

We estimate with 95% confidence that the true population mean sensory rate is between 7.30 and 9.15.

Solution 8.8

 Using the TI-83, 83+, 84, 84+ Calculator

Press **STAT** and arrow over to **TESTS**.
Arrow down to **8:TInterval** and press **ENTER** (or you can just press **8**).
Arrow to **Data** and press **ENTER**.
Arrow down to **List** and enter the list name where you put the data.
There should be a 1 after **Freq**.
Arrow down to **C-level** and enter 0.95
Arrow down to **Calculate** and press **ENTER**.
The 95% confidence interval is (7.3006, 9.1527)

NOTE

When calculating the error bound, a probability table for the Student's t-distribution can also be used to find the value of *t*. The table gives *t*-scores that correspond to the confidence level (column) and degrees of freedom (row); the *t*-score is found where the row and column intersect in the table.

8.8 You do a study of hypnotherapy to determine how effective it is in increasing the number of hours of sleep subjects get each night. You measure hours of sleep for 12 subjects with the following results. Construct a 95% confidence interval for the mean number of hours slept for the population (assumed normal) from which you took the data.

8.2; 9.1; 7.7; 8.6; 6.9; 11.2; 10.1; 9.9; 8.9; 9.2; 7.5; 10.5

Example 8.9

The Human Toxome Project (HTP) is working to understand the scope of industrial pollution in the human body. Industrial chemicals may enter the body through pollution or as ingredients in consumer products. In October 2008, the scientists at HTP tested cord blood samples for 20 newborn infants in the United States. The cord blood of the "In utero/newborn" group was tested for 430 industrial compounds, pollutants, and other chemicals, including chemicals linked to brain and nervous system toxicity, immune system toxicity, and reproductive toxicity, and fertility problems. There are health concerns about the effects of some chemicals on the brain and nervous system. **Table 8.2** shows how many of the targeted chemicals were found in each infant's cord blood.

| 79 | 145 | 147 | 160 | 116 | 100 | 159 | 151 | 156 | 126 |
| 137 | 83 | 156 | 94 | 121 | 144 | 123 | 114 | 139 | 99 |

Table 8.3

Use this sample data to construct a 90% confidence interval for the mean number of targeted industrial chemicals to be found in an in infant's blood.

Solution 8.9

Solution A

From the sample, you can calculate $\bar{x}$ = 127.45 and s = 25.965. There are 20 infants in the sample, so n = 20, and df = 20 – 1 = 19.

You are asked to calculate a 90% confidence interval: CL = 0.90, so α = 1 – CL = 1 – 0.90 = 0.10 $\frac{\alpha}{2} = 0.05, t_{\frac{\alpha}{2}} = t_{0.05}$

By definition, the area to the right of $t_{0.05}$ is 0.05 and so the area to the left of $t_{0.05}$ is 1 – 0.05 = 0.95.

Use a table, calculator, or computer to find that $t_{0.05}$ = 1.729.

$$EBM = t_{\frac{\alpha}{2}}\left(\frac{s}{\sqrt{n}}\right) = 1.729\left(\frac{25.965}{\sqrt{20}}\right) \approx 10.038$$

$$\bar{x} - EBM = 127.45 - 10.038 = 117.412$$

$$\bar{x} + EBM = 127.45 + 10.038 = 137.488$$

We estimate with 90% confidence that the mean number of all targeted industrial chemicals found in cord blood in the United States is between 117.412 and 137.488.

Solution 8.9

Solution B

Using the TI-83, 83+, 84, 84+ Calculator

Enter the data as a list.
Press STAT and arrow over to TESTS.
Arrow down to 8:TInterval and press ENTER (or you can just press 8). Arrow to Data and press ENTER.
Arrow down to List and enter the list name where you put the data.
Arrow down to Freq and enter 1.
Arrow down to C-level and enter 0.90
Arrow down to Calculate and press ENTER.
The 90% confidence interval is (117.41, 137.49).

Try It Σ

8.9 A random sample of statistics students were asked to estimate the total number of hours they spend watching television in an average week. The responses are recorded in **Table 8.4**. Use this sample data to construct a 98% confidence interval for the mean number of hours statistics students will spend watching television in one week.

0	3	1	20	9
5	10	1	10	4
14	2	4	4	5

Table 8.4

8.3 | A Population Proportion

During an election year, we see articles in the newspaper that state **confidence intervals** in terms of proportions or percentages. For example, a poll for a particular candidate running for president might show that the candidate has 40% of the vote within three percentage points (if the sample is large enough). Often, election polls are calculated with 95% confidence, so, the pollsters would be 95% confident that the true proportion of voters who favored the candidate would be between 0.37 and 0.43: (0.40 – 0.03,0.40 + 0.03).

Investors in the stock market are interested in the true proportion of stocks that go up and down each week. Businesses that sell personal computers are interested in the proportion of households in the United States that own personal computers. Confidence intervals can be calculated for the true proportion of stocks that go up or down each week and for the true proportion of households in the United States that own personal computers.

The procedure to find the confidence interval, the sample size, the **error bound**, and the **confidence level** for a proportion is similar to that for the population mean, but the formulas are different.

How do you know you are dealing with a proportion problem? First, the underlying **distribution is a binomial distribution**. (There is no mention of a mean or average.) If X is a binomial random variable, then $X \sim B(n, p)$ where n is the number of trials and p is the probability of a success. To form a proportion, take X, the random variable for the number of successes and divide it by n, the number of trials (or the sample size). The random variable P' (read "P prime") is that proportion,

$$P' = \frac{X}{n}$$

(Sometimes the random variable is denoted as $\hat{P}$, read "P hat".)

When n is large and p is not close to zero or one, we can use the **normal distribution** to approximate the binomial.

$X \sim N(np, \sqrt{npq})$

If we divide the random variable, the mean, and the standard deviation by n, we get a normal distribution of proportions with P', called the estimated proportion, as the random variable. (Recall that a proportion as the number of successes divided by n.)

$\frac{X}{n} = P' \sim N\left(\frac{np}{n}, \frac{\sqrt{npq}}{n}\right)$

Using algebra to simplify : $\frac{\sqrt{npq}}{n} = \sqrt{\frac{pq}{n}}$

P' follows a normal distribution for proportions: $\frac{X}{n} = P' \sim N\left(\frac{np}{n}, \frac{\sqrt{npq}}{n}\right)$

The confidence interval has the form $(p' - EBP, p' + EBP)$. *EBP* is error bound for the proportion.

$p' = \frac{x}{n}$

p' = the **estimated proportion** of successes (p' is a **point estimate** for p, the true proportion.)

x = the **number** of successes

n = the size of the sample

The error bound for a proportion is

$EBP = \left(z_{\frac{\alpha}{2}}\right)\left(\sqrt{\frac{p'q'}{n}}\right)$ where $q' = 1 - p'$

This formula is similar to the error bound formula for a mean, except that the "appropriate standard deviation" is different. For a mean, when the population standard deviation is known, the appropriate standard deviation that we use is $\frac{\sigma}{\sqrt{n}}$. For a proportion, the appropriate standard deviation is $\sqrt{\frac{pq}{n}}$.

However, in the error bound formula, we use $\sqrt{\frac{p'q'}{n}}$ as the standard deviation, instead of $\sqrt{\frac{pq}{n}}$.

In the error bound formula, the **sample proportions p' and q' are estimates of the unknown population proportions p and q**. The estimated proportions p' and q' are used because p and q are not known. The sample proportions p' and q' are calculated from the data: p' is the estimated proportion of successes, and q' is the estimated proportion of failures.

The confidence interval can be used only if the number of successes np' and the number of failures nq' are both greater than five.

NOTE

For the normal distribution of proportions, the z-score formula is as follows.

If $P' \sim N\left(p, \sqrt{\frac{pq}{n}}\right)$ then the z-score formula is $z = \dfrac{p' - p}{\sqrt{\frac{pq}{n}}}$

Example 8.10

Suppose that a market research firm is hired to estimate the percent of adults living in a large city who have cell phones. Five hundred randomly selected adult residents in this city are surveyed to determine whether they have cell phones. Of the 500 people surveyed, 421 responded yes - they own cell phones. Using a 95% confidence level, compute a confidence interval estimate for the true proportion of adult residents of this city who have cell phones.

Solution 8.10
Solution A

- The first solution is step-by-step (Solution A).

- The second solution uses a function of the TI-83, 83+ or 84 calculators (Solution B).

Let X = the number of people in the sample who have cell phones. X is binomial. $X \sim B\left(500, \frac{421}{500}\right)$.

To calculate the confidence interval, you must find p', q', and EBP.

$n = 500$

x = the number of successes = 421

$$p' = \frac{x}{n} = \frac{421}{500} = 0.842$$

$p' = 0.842$ is the sample proportion; this is the point estimate of the population proportion.

$q' = 1 - p' = 1 - 0.842 = 0.158$

Since $CL = 0.95$, then $\alpha = 1 - CL = 1 - 0.95 = 0.05 \left(\frac{\alpha}{2}\right) = 0.025$.

Then $z_{\frac{\alpha}{2}} = z_{0.025} = 1.96$

Use the TI-83, 83+, or 84+ calculator command invNorm(0.975,0,1) to find $z_{0.025}$. Remember that the area to the right of $z_{0.025}$ is 0.025 and the area to the left of $z_{0.025}$ is 0.975. This can also be found using appropriate commands on other calculators, using a computer, or using a Standard Normal probability table.

$$EBP = \left(z_{\frac{\alpha}{2}}\right)\sqrt{\frac{p'q'}{n}} = (1.96)\sqrt{\frac{(0.842)(0.158)}{500}} = 0.032$$

$p' - EBP = 0.842 - 0.032 = 0.81$

$p' + EBP = 0.842 + 0.032 = 0.874$

The confidence interval for the true binomial population proportion is $(p' - EBP, p' + EBP) = (0.810, 0.874)$.

Interpretation

We estimate with 95% confidence that between 81% and 87.4% of all adult residents of this city have cell phones.

Explanation of 95% Confidence Level

Ninety-five percent of the confidence intervals constructed in this way would contain the true value for the population proportion of all adult residents of this city who have cell phones.

Solution 8.10

Solution B

 Using the TI-83, 83+, 84, 84+ Calculator

Press STAT and arrow over to TESTS.
Arrow down to A:1-PropZint. Press ENTER.
Arrow down to x and enter 421.
Arrow down to n and enter 500.
Arrow down to C-Level and enter .95.
Arrow down to Calculate and press ENTER.

The confidence interval is (0.81003, 0.87397).

8.10 Suppose 250 randomly selected people are surveyed to determine if they own a tablet. Of the 250 surveyed, 98 reported owning a tablet. Using a 95% confidence level, compute a confidence interval estimate for the true proportion of people who own tablets.

Example 8.11

For a class project, a political science student at a large university wants to estimate the percent of students who are registered voters. He surveys 500 students and finds that 300 are registered voters. Compute a 90% confidence interval for the true percent of students who are registered voters, and interpret the confidence interval.

Solution 8.11
- The first solution is step-by-step (Solution A).

- The second solution uses a function of the TI-83, 83+, or 84 calculators (Solution B).

Solution A

$x = 300$ and $n = 500$

$p' = \frac{x}{n} = \frac{300}{500} = 0.600$

$q' = 1 - p' = 1 - 0.600 = 0.400$

Since $CL = 0.90$, then $\alpha = 1 - CL = 1 - 0.90 = 0.10 \left(\frac{\alpha}{2}\right) = 0.05$

$z_{\frac{\alpha}{2}} = z_{0.05} = 1.645$

Use the TI-83, 83+, or 84+ calculator command invNorm(0.95,0,1) to find $z_{0.05}$. Remember that the area to the right of $z_{0.05}$ is 0.05 and the area to the left of $z_{0.05}$ is 0.95. This can also be found using appropriate commands on other calculators, using a computer, or using a standard normal probability table.

$EBP = \left(z_{\frac{\alpha}{2}}\right)\sqrt{\frac{p'q'}{n}} = (1.645)\sqrt{\frac{(0.60)(0.40)}{500}} = 0.036$

$p' - EBP = 0.60 - 0.036 = 0.564$

$p' + EBP = 0.60 + 0.036 = 0.636$

The confidence interval for the true binomial population proportion is $(p' - EBP, p' + EBP) = (0.564, 0.636)$.

Interpretation
- We estimate with 90% confidence that the true percent of all students that are registered voters is between 56.4% and 63.6%.

- Alternate Wording: We estimate with 90% confidence that between 56.4% and 63.6% of ALL students are registered voters.

Explanation of 90% Confidence Level

Ninety percent of all confidence intervals constructed in this way contain the true value for the population percent of students that are registered voters.

Solution 8.11

Solution B

 Using the TI-83, 83+, 84, 84+ Calculator

Press STAT and arrow over to TESTS.
Arrow down to A:1-PropZint. Press ENTER.
Arrow down to x and enter 300.
Arrow down to n and enter 500.
Arrow down to C-Level and enter 0.90.
Arrow down to Calculate and press ENTER.
The confidence interval is (0.564, 0.636).

Try It Σ

8.11 A student polls his school to see if students in the school district are for or against the new legislation regarding school uniforms. She surveys 600 students and finds that 480 are against the new legislation.

a. Compute a 90% confidence interval for the true percent of students who are against the new legislation, and interpret the confidence interval.

b. In a sample of 300 students, 68% said they own an iPod and a smart phone. Compute a 97% confidence interval for the true percent of students who own an iPod and a smartphone.

"Plus Four" Confidence Interval for p

There is a certain amount of error introduced into the process of calculating a confidence interval for a proportion. Because we do not know the true proportion for the population, we are forced to use point estimates to calculate the appropriate standard deviation of the sampling distribution. Studies have shown that the resulting estimation of the standard deviation can be flawed.

Fortunately, there is a simple adjustment that allows us to produce more accurate confidence intervals. We simply pretend that we have four additional observations. Two of these observations are successes and two are failures. The new sample size, then, is $n + 4$, and the new count of successes is $x + 2$.

Computer studies have demonstrated the effectiveness of this method. It should be used when the confidence level desired is at least 90% and the sample size is at least ten.

Example 8.12

A random sample of 25 statistics students was asked: "Have you smoked a cigarette in the past week?" Six students reported smoking within the past week. Use the "plus-four" method to find a 95% confidence interval for the true proportion of statistics students who smoke.

Solution 8.12

Solution A

Six students out of 25 reported smoking within the past week, so $x = 6$ and $n = 25$. Because we are using the "plus-four" method, we will use $x = 6 + 2 = 8$ and $n = 25 + 4 = 29$.

$$p' = \frac{x}{n} = \frac{8}{29} \approx 0.276$$

$$q' = 1 - p' = 1 - 0.276 = 0.724$$

Since $CL = 0.95$, we know $\alpha = 1 - 0.95 = 0.05$ and $\frac{\alpha}{2} = 0.025$.

$$z_{0.025} = 1.96$$

$$EPB = \left(z_{\frac{\alpha}{2}}\right)\sqrt{\frac{p'q'}{n}} = (1.96)\sqrt{\frac{0.276(0.724)}{29}} \approx 0.163$$

$$p' - EPB = 0.276 - 0.163 = 0.113$$

$$p' + EPB = 0.276 + 0.163 = 0.439$$

We are 95% confident that the true proportion of all statistics students who smoke cigarettes is between 0.113 and 0.439.

Solution 8.12

Solution B

 Using the TI-83, 83+, 84, 84+ Calculator

Press STAT and arrow over to TESTS.
Arrow down to A:1-PropZint. Press ENTER.

> **REMINDER**
>
> Remember that the plus-four method assume an additional four trials: two successes and two failures. You do not need to change the process for calculating the confidence interval; simply update the values of x and n to reflect these additional trials.

Arrow down to x and enter eight.
Arrow down to n and enter 29.
Arrow down to C-Level and enter 0.95.
Arrow down to Calculate and press ENTER.
The confidence interval is (0.113, 0.439).

Try It Σ

8.12 Out of a random sample of 65 freshmen at State University, 31 students have declared a major. Use the "plus-four" method to find a 96% confidence interval for the true proportion of freshmen at State University who have declared a major.

Example 8.13

The Berkman Center for Internet & Society at Harvard recently conducted a study analyzing the privacy management habits of teen internet users. In a group of 50 teens, 13 reported having more than 500 friends on Facebook. Use the "plus four" method to find a 90% confidence interval for the true proportion of teens who would report having more than 500 Facebook friends.

Solution 8.13
Solution A

Using "plus-four," we have $x = 13 + 2 = 15$ and $n = 50 + 4 = 54$.

$$p' = \frac{15}{54} \approx 0.278$$

$$q' = 1 - p' = 1 - 0.241 = 0.722$$

Since $CL = 0.90$, we know $\alpha = 1 - 0.90 = 0.10$ and $\frac{\alpha}{2} = 0.05$.

$$z_{0.05} = 1.645$$

$$EPB = (z_{\frac{\alpha}{2}})\left(\sqrt{\frac{p'q'}{n}}\right) = (1.645)\left(\sqrt{\frac{(0.278)(0.722)}{54}}\right) \approx 0.100$$

$p' - EPB = 0.278 - 0.100 = 0.178$

$p' + EPB = 0.278 + 0.100 = 0.378$

We are 90% confident that between 17.8% and 37.8% of all teens would report having more than 500 friends on Facebook.

Solution 8.13
Solution B

 Using the TI-83, 83+, 84, 84+ Calculator

Press STAT and arrow over to TESTS.
Arrow down to A:1-PropZint. Press ENTER.
Arrow down to x and enter 15.
Arrow down to n and enter 54.
Arrow down to C-Level and enter 0.90.
Arrow down to Calculate and press ENTER.
The confidence interval is (0.178, 0.378).

Try It Σ

8.13 The Berkman Center Study referenced in **Example 8.13** talked to teens in smaller focus groups, but also interviewed additional teens over the phone. When the study was complete, 588 teens had answered the question about their Facebook friends with 159 saying that they have more than 500 friends. Use the "plus-four" method to find a 90% confidence interval for the true proportion of teens that would report having more than 500 Facebook friends based on this larger sample. Compare the results to those in **Example 8.13**.

Calculating the Sample Size n

If researchers desire a specific margin of error, then they can use the error bound formula to calculate the required sample size.

The error bound formula for a population proportion is

- $EBP = \left(z_{\frac{\alpha}{2}} \right)\left(\sqrt{\frac{p' q'}{n}} \right)$

- Solving for n gives you an equation for the sample size.

- $n = \dfrac{\left(z_{\frac{\alpha}{2}} \right)^2 (p' q')}{EBP^2}$

Example 8.14

Suppose a mobile phone company wants to determine the current percentage of customers aged 50+ who use text messaging on their cell phones. How many customers aged 50+ should the company survey in order to be 90% confident that the estimated (sample) proportion is within three percentage points of the true population proportion of customers aged 50+ who use text messaging on their cell phones.

Solution 8.14

From the problem, we know that **$EBP = 0.03$** (3%=0.03) and $z_{\frac{\alpha}{2}}$ $z_{0.05} = 1.645$ because the confidence level is 90%.

However, in order to find n, we need to know the estimated (sample) proportion p'. Remember that $q' = 1 - p'$. But, we do not know p' yet. Since we multiply p' and q' together, we make them both equal to 0.5 because $p'q' = (0.5)(0.5) = 0.25$ results in the largest possible product. (Try other products: $(0.6)(0.4) = 0.24$; $(0.3)(0.7) = 0.21$; $(0.2)(0.8) = 0.16$ and so on). The largest possible product gives us the largest n. This gives us a large enough sample so that we can be 90% confident that we are within three percentage points of the true population proportion. To calculate the sample size n, use the formula and make the substitutions.

$n = \dfrac{z^2 p' q'}{EBP^2}$ gives $n = \dfrac{1.645^2 (0.5)(0.5)}{0.03^2} = 751.7$

Round the answer to the next higher value. The sample size should be 752 cell phone customers aged 50+ in order to be 90% confident that the estimated (sample) proportion is within three percentage points of the true population proportion of all customers aged 50+ who use text messaging on their cell phones.

Try It Σ

8.14 Suppose an internet marketing company wants to determine the current percentage of customers who click on ads on their smartphones. How many customers should the company survey in order to be 90% confident that the estimated proportion is within five percentage points of the true population proportion of customers who click on ads on their smartphones?

8.4 | Confidence Interval (Home Costs)

Stats Lab

8.1 Confidence Interval (Home Costs)

Class Time:

Names:

Student Learning Outcomes

- The student will calculate the 90% confidence interval for the mean cost of a home in the area in which this school is located.
- The student will interpret confidence intervals.
- The student will determine the effects of changing conditions on the confidence interval.

Collect the Data

Check the Real Estate section in your local newspaper. Record the sale prices for 35 randomly selected homes recently listed in the county.

NOTE

Many newspapers list them only one day per week. Also, we will assume that homes come up for sale randomly.

1. Complete the table:

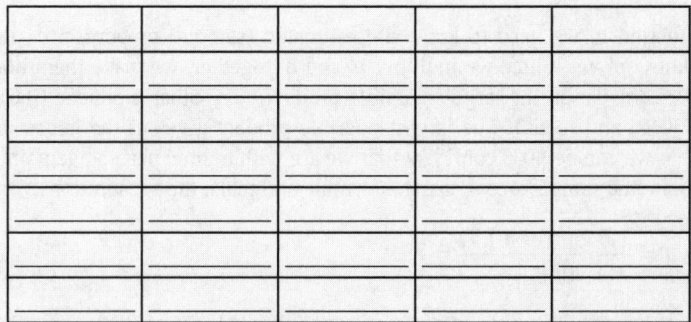

Table 8.5

Describe the Data

1. Compute the following:

   a. $\bar{x}$ = _____

   b. s_x = _____

   c. n = _____

2. In words, define the random variable $\bar{X}$.

3. State the estimated distribution to use. Use both words and symbols.

Find the Confidence Interval

1. Calculate the confidence interval and the error bound.

   a. Confidence Interval: _____

   b. Error Bound: _____

2. How much area is in both tails (combined)? α = _____

3. How much area is in each tail? $\frac{\alpha}{2}$ = _____

4. Fill in the blanks on the graph with the area in each section. Then, fill in the number line with the upper and lower limits of the confidence interval and the sample mean.

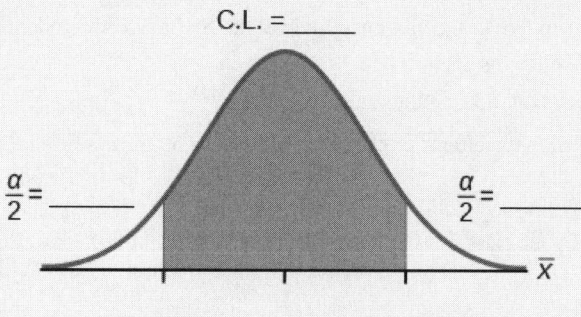

C.L. =_____

$\frac{\alpha}{2}$ = _____

$\frac{\alpha}{2}$ = _____

$\overline{x}$

Figure 8.6

5. Some students think that a 90% confidence interval contains 90% of the data. Use the list of data on the first page and count how many of the data values lie within the confidence interval. What percent is this? Is this percent close to 90%? Explain why this percent should or should not be close to 90%.

Describe the Confidence Interval

1. In two to three complete sentences, explain what a confidence interval means (in general), as if you were talking to someone who has not taken statistics.

2. In one to two complete sentences, explain what this confidence interval means for this particular study.

Use the Data to Construct Confidence Intervals

1. Using the given information, construct a confidence interval for each confidence level given.

Confidence level	EBM/Error Bound	Confidence Interval
50%		
80%		
95%		
99%		

Table 8.6

2. What happens to the EBM as the confidence level increases? Does the width of the confidence interval increase or decrease? Explain why this happens.

8.5 | Confidence Interval (Place of Birth)

Stats Lab

8.2 Confidence Interval (Place of Birth)

Class Time:

Names:

Student Learning Outcomes

- The student will calculate the 90% confidence interval the proportion of students in this school who were born in this state.
- The student will interpret confidence intervals.
- The student will determine the effects of changing conditions on the confidence interval.

Collect the Data

1. Survey the students in your class, asking them if they were born in this state. Let X = the number that were born in this state.

    a. $n =$ _____

    b. $x =$ _____

2. In words, define the random variable P'.

3. State the estimated distribution to use.

Find the Confidence Interval and Error Bound

1. Calculate the confidence interval and the error bound.

    a. Confidence Interval: _____

    b. Error Bound: _____

2. How much area is in both tails (combined)? $\alpha =$ _____

3. How much area is in each tail? $\frac{\alpha}{2} =$ _____

4. Fill in the blanks on the graph with the area in each section. Then, fill in the number line with the upper and lower limits of the confidence interval and the sample proportion.

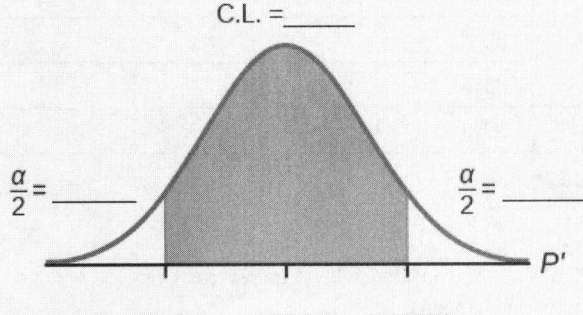

Figure 8.7

Describe the Confidence Interval

1. In two to three complete sentences, explain what a confidence interval means (in general), as though you were talking to someone who has not taken statistics.

2. In one to two complete sentences, explain what this confidence interval means for this particular study.

3. Construct a confidence interval for each confidence level given.

Confidence level	EBP/Error Bound	Confidence Interval
50%		
80%		
95%		
99%		

Table 8.7

4. What happens to the EBP as the confidence level increases? Does the width of the confidence interval increase or decrease? Explain why this happens.

8.6 | Confidence Interval (Women's Heights)

Stats Lab

8.3 Confidence Interval (Women's Heights)

Class Time:

Names:

Student Learning Outcomes

- The student will calculate a 90% confidence interval using the given data.
- The student will determine the relationship between the confidence level and the percentage of constructed intervals that contain the population mean.

Given:

59.4	71.6	69.3	65.0	62.9	66.5	61.7	55.2
67.5	67.2	63.8	62.9	63.0	63.9	68.7	65.5
61.9	69.6	58.7	63.4	61.8	60.6	69.8	60.0
64.9	66.1	66.8	60.6	65.6	63.8	61.3	59.2
64.1	59.3	64.9	62.4	63.5	60.9	63.3	66.3
61.5	64.3	62.9	60.6	63.8	58.8	64.9	65.7
62.5	70.9	62.9	63.1	62.2	58.7	64.7	66.0
60.5	64.7	65.4	60.2	65.0	64.1	61.1	65.3
64.6	59.2	61.4	62.0	63.5	61.4	65.5	62.3
65.5	64.7	58.8	66.1	64.9	66.9	57.9	69.8
58.5	63.4	69.2	65.9	62.2	60.0	58.1	62.5
62.4	59.1	66.4	61.2	60.4	58.7	66.7	67.5
63.2	56.6	67.7	62.5				

Table 8.8 Heights of 100 Women (in Inches)

1. **Table 8.8** lists the heights of 100 women. Use a random number generator to select ten data values randomly.

2. Calculate the sample mean and the sample standard deviation. Assume that the population standard deviation is known to be 3.3 inches. With these values, construct a 90% confidence interval for your sample of ten values. Write the confidence interval you obtained in the first space of **Table 8.9**.

3. Now write your confidence interval on the board. As others in the class write their confidence intervals on the board, copy them into **Table 8.9**.

___	___	___	___	___
___	___	___	___	___
___	___	___	___	___
___	___	___	___	___

Table 8.9 90% Confidence Intervals

Discussion Questions

1. The actual population mean for the 100 heights given **Table 8.8** is $\mu = 63.4$. Using the class listing of confidence intervals, count how many of them contain the population mean μ; i.e., for how many intervals does the value of μ lie between the endpoints of the confidence interval?

2. Divide this number by the total number of confidence intervals generated by the class to determine the percent of confidence intervals that contains the mean μ. Write this percent here: _____.

3. Is the percent of confidence intervals that contain the population mean μ close to 90%?

4. Suppose we had generated 100 confidence intervals. What do you think would happen to the percent of confidence intervals that contained the population mean?

5. When we construct a 90% confidence interval, we say that we are **90% confident that the true population mean lies within the confidence interval.** Using complete sentences, explain what we mean by this phrase.

6. Some students think that a 90% confidence interval contains 90% of the data. Use the list of data given (the heights of women) and count how many of the data values lie within the confidence interval that you generated based on that data. How many of the 100 data values lie within your confidence interval? What percent is this? Is this percent close to 90%?

7. Explain why it does not make sense to count data values that lie in a confidence interval. Think about the random variable that is being used in the problem.

8. Suppose you obtained the heights of ten women and calculated a confidence interval from this information. Without knowing the population mean μ, would you have any way of knowing **for certain** if your interval actually contained the value of μ? Explain.

KEY TERMS

Binomial Distribution a discrete random variable (RV) which arises from Bernoulli trials; there are a fixed number, n, of independent trials. "Independent" means that the result of any trial (for example, trial 1) does not affect the results of the following trials, and all trials are conducted under the same conditions. Under these circumstances the binomial RV X is defined as the number of successes in n trials. The notation is: $X \sim B(\mathbf{n}, \mathbf{p})$. The mean is $\mu = np$ and the standard deviation is $\sigma = \sqrt{npq}$. The probability of exactly x successes in n trials is $P(X = x) = \binom{n}{x} p^x q^{n-x}$.

Confidence Interval (CI) an interval estimate for an unknown population parameter. This depends on:

- the desired confidence level,

- information that is known about the distribution (for example, known standard deviation),

- the sample and its size.

Confidence Level (CL) the percent expression for the probability that the confidence interval contains the true population parameter; for example, if the CL = 90%, then in 90 out of 100 samples the interval estimate will enclose the true population parameter.

Degrees of Freedom (*df*) the number of objects in a sample that are free to vary

Error Bound for a Population Mean (*EBM*) the margin of error; depends on the confidence level, sample size, and known or estimated population standard deviation.

Error Bound for a Population Proportion (EBP) the margin of error; depends on the confidence level, the sample size, and the estimated (from the sample) proportion of successes.

Inferential Statistics also called statistical inference or inductive statistics; this facet of statistics deals with estimating a population parameter based on a sample statistic. For example, if four out of the 100 calculators sampled are defective we might infer that four percent of the production is defective.

Normal Distribution
a continuous random variable (RV) with pdf $f(x) = \dfrac{1}{\sigma\sqrt{2\pi}} e^{-(x-\mu)^2 \big/ 2\sigma^2}$, where μ is the mean of the distribution and σ is the standard deviation, notation: $X \sim N(\mu, \sigma)$. If $\mu = 0$ and $\sigma = 1$, the RV is called **the standard normal distribution**.

Parameter a numerical characteristic of a population

Point Estimate a single number computed from a sample and used to estimate a population parameter

Standard Deviation a number that is equal to the square root of the variance and measures how far data values are from their mean; notation: s for sample standard deviation and σ for population standard deviation

Student's t-Distribution investigated and reported by William S. Gossett in 1908 and published under the pseudonym Student; the major characteristics of the random variable (RV) are:

- It is continuous and assumes any real values.

- The pdf is symmetrical about its mean of zero. However, it is more spread out and flatter at the apex than the normal distribution.

- It approaches the standard normal distribution as n get larger.

- There is a "family of t–distributions: each representative of the family is completely defined by the number of degrees of freedom, which is one less than the number of data.

CHAPTER REVIEW

8.1 A Single Population Mean using the Normal Distribution

In this module, we learned how to calculate the confidence interval for a single population mean where the population standard deviation is known. When estimating a population mean, the margin of error is called the error bound for a population mean (*EBM*). A confidence interval has the general form:

(lower bound, upper bound) = (point estimate – *EBM*, point estimate + *EBM*)

The calculation of *EBM* depends on the size of the sample and the level of confidence desired. The confidence level is the percent of all possible samples that can be expected to include the true population parameter. As the confidence level increases, the corresponding *EBM* increases as well. As the sample size increases, the *EBM* decreases. By the central limit theorem,

$$EBM = z\frac{\sigma}{\sqrt{n}}$$

Given a confidence interval, you can work backwards to find the error bound (*EBM*) or the sample mean. To find the error bound, find the difference of the upper bound of the interval and the mean. If you do not know the sample mean, you can find the error bound by calculating half the difference of the upper and lower bounds. To find the sample mean given a confidence interval, find the difference of the upper bound and the error bound. If the error bound is unknown, then average the upper and lower bounds of the confidence interval to find the sample mean.

Sometimes researchers know in advance that they want to estimate a population mean within a specific margin of error for a given level of confidence. In that case, solve the *EBM* formula for *n* to discover the size of the sample that is needed to achieve this goal:

$$n = \frac{z^2\sigma^2}{EBM^2}$$

8.2 A Single Population Mean using the Student t Distribution

In many cases, the researcher does not know the population standard deviation, σ, of the measure being studied. In these cases, it is common to use the sample standard deviation, *s*, as an estimate of σ. The normal distribution creates accurate confidence intervals when σ is known, but it is not as accurate when *s* is used as an estimate. In this case, the Student's t-distribution is much better. Define a t-score using the following formula:

$$t = \frac{\bar{x} - \mu}{\frac{s}{\sqrt{n}}}$$

The *t*-score follows the Student's t-distribution with $n - 1$ degrees of freedom. The confidence interval under this distribution is calculated with $EBM = \left(t_{\frac{\alpha}{2}}\right)\frac{s}{\sqrt{n}}$ where $t_{\frac{\alpha}{2}}$ is the *t*-score with area to the right equal to $\frac{\alpha}{2}$, *s* is the sample standard deviation, and *n* is the sample size. Use a table, calculator, or computer to find $t_{\frac{\alpha}{2}}$ for a given α.

8.3 A Population Proportion

Some statistical measures, like many survey questions, measure qualitative rather than quantitative data. In this case, the population parameter being estimated is a proportion. It is possible to create a confidence interval for the true population proportion following procedures similar to those used in creating confidence intervals for population means. The formulas are slightly different, but they follow the same reasoning.

Let p' represent the sample proportion, *x/n*, where *x* represents the number of successes and *n* represents the sample size. Let $q' = 1 - p'$. Then the confidence interval for a population proportion is given by the following formula:

(lower bound, upper bound) $= (p' - EBP, p' + EBP) = \left(p' - z\sqrt{\frac{p'q'}{n}}, p' + z\sqrt{\frac{p'q'}{n}}\right)$

The "plus four" method for calculating confidence intervals is an attempt to balance the error introduced by using estimates of the population proportion when calculating the standard deviation of the sampling distribution. Simply imagine four additional trials in the study; two are successes and two are failures. Calculate $p' = \frac{x+2}{n+4}$, and proceed to find the confidence interval. When sample sizes are small, this method has been demonstrated to provide more accurate confidence intervals than the standard formula used for larger samples.

FORMULA REVIEW

8.1 A Single Population Mean using the Normal Distribution

$\bar{X} \sim N\left(\mu_X, \frac{\sigma}{\sqrt{n}}\right)$ The distribution of sample means is normally distributed with mean equal to the population mean and standard deviation given by the population standard deviation divided by the square root of the sample size.

The general form for a confidence interval for a single population mean, known standard deviation, normal distribution is given by
(lower bound, upper bound) = (point estimate – EBM, point estimate + EBM)

$= (\bar{x} - EBM, \ \bar{x} + EBM)$

$= \left(\bar{x} - z\frac{\sigma}{\sqrt{n}}, \ \bar{x} + z\frac{\sigma}{\sqrt{n}}\right)$

$EBM = z\frac{\sigma}{\sqrt{n}}$ = the error bound for the mean, or the margin of error for a single population mean; this formula is used when the population standard deviation is known.

CL = confidence level, or the proportion of confidence intervals created that are expected to contain the true population parameter

$\alpha = 1 - CL$ = the proportion of confidence intervals that will not contain the population parameter

$z_{\frac{\alpha}{2}}$ = the z-score with the property that the area to the right of the z-score is $\frac{\alpha}{2}$ this is the z-score used in the calculation of "EBM where $\alpha = 1 - CL$.

$n = \frac{z^2 \sigma^2}{EBM^2}$ = the formula used to determine the sample size (n) needed to achieve a desired margin of error at a given level of confidence

General form of a confidence interval

(lower value, upper value) = (point estimate−error bound, point estimate + error bound)

To find the error bound when you know the confidence interval

error bound = upper value−point estimate OR error bound
$= \frac{\text{upper value} - \text{lower value}}{2}$

Single Population Mean, Known Standard Deviation, Normal Distribution

Use the Normal Distribution for Means, Population

Standard Deviation is Known $EBM = z\frac{\alpha}{2} \cdot \frac{\sigma}{\sqrt{n}}$

The confidence interval has the format ($\bar{x} - EBM, \ \bar{x} + EBM$).

8.2 A Single Population Mean using the Student t Distribution

s = the standard deviation of sample values.

$t = \frac{\bar{x} - \mu}{\frac{s}{\sqrt{n}}}$ is the formula for the t-score which measures how far away a measure is from the population mean in the Student's t-distribution

$df = n - 1$; the degrees of freedom for a Student's t-distribution where n represents the size of the sample

$T \sim t_{df}$ the random variable, T, has a Student's t-distribution with df degrees of freedom

$EBM = t_{\frac{\alpha}{2}}\frac{s}{\sqrt{n}}$ = the error bound for the population mean when the population standard deviation is unknown

$t_{\frac{\alpha}{2}}$ is the t-score in the Student's t-distribution with area to the right equal to $\frac{\alpha}{2}$

The general form for a confidence interval for a single mean, population standard deviation unknown, Student's t is given by (lower bound, upper bound)
= (point estimate – EBM, point estimate + EBM)
$= \left(\bar{x} - \frac{ts}{\sqrt{n}}, \ \bar{x} + \frac{ts}{\sqrt{n}}\right)$

8.3 A Population Proportion

$p' = x/n$ where x represents the number of successes and n represents the sample size. The variable p' is the sample proportion and serves as the point estimate for the true population proportion.

$q' = 1 - p'$

$p' \sim N\left(p, \sqrt{\frac{pq}{n}}\right)$ The variable p' has a binomial distribution that can be approximated with the normal distribution shown here.

EBP = the error bound for a proportion = $z_{\frac{\alpha}{2}}\sqrt{\frac{p'q'}{n}}$

Confidence interval for a proportion:

(lower bound, upper bound) $= (p' - EBP, \ p' + EBP) = \left(p' - z\sqrt{\frac{p'q'}{n}}, \ p' + z\sqrt{\frac{p'q'}{n}}\right)$

$n = \dfrac{z_{\frac{\alpha}{2}}^{2} p' q'}{EBP^2}$ provides the number of participants needed to estimate the population proportion with confidence $1 - \alpha$ and margin of error *EBP*.

Use the normal distribution for a single population proportion $p' = \frac{x}{n}$

$$EBP = \left(z_{\frac{\alpha}{2}}\right)\sqrt{\dfrac{p'q'}{n}} \quad p' + q' = 1$$

The confidence interval has the format $(p' - EBP, p' + EBP)$.

$\bar{x}$ is a point estimate for μ

p' is a point estimate for ρ

s is a point estimate for σ

PRACTICE

8.1 A Single Population Mean using the Normal Distribution

Use the following information to answer the next five exercises: The standard deviation of the weights of elephants is known to be approximately 15 pounds. We wish to construct a 95% confidence interval for the mean weight of newborn elephant calves. Fifty newborn elephants are weighed. The sample mean is 244 pounds. The sample standard deviation is 11 pounds.

1. Identify the following:

    a. $\bar{x}$ = _____

    b. σ = _____

    c. n = _____

2. In words, define the random variables X and $\bar{X}$.

3. Which distribution should you use for this problem?

4. Construct a 95% confidence interval for the population mean weight of newborn elephants. State the confidence interval, sketch the graph, and calculate the error bound.

5. What will happen to the confidence interval obtained, if 500 newborn elephants are weighed instead of 50? Why?

Use the following information to answer the next seven exercises: The U.S. Census Bureau conducts a study to determine the time needed to complete the short form. The Bureau surveys 200 people. The sample mean is 8.2 minutes. There is a known standard deviation of 2.2 minutes. The population distribution is assumed to be normal.

6. Identify the following:

    a. $\bar{x}$ = _____

    b. σ = _____

    c. n = _____

7. In words, define the random variables X and $\bar{X}$.

8. Which distribution should you use for this problem?

9. Construct a 90% confidence interval for the population mean time to complete the forms. State the confidence interval, sketch the graph, and calculate the error bound.

10. If the Census wants to increase its level of confidence and keep the error bound the same by taking another survey, what changes should it make?

11. If the Census did another survey, kept the error bound the same, and surveyed only 50 people instead of 200, what would happen to the level of confidence? Why?

12. Suppose the Census needed to be 98% confident of the population mean length of time. Would the Census have to survey more people? Why or why not?

Use the following information to answer the next ten exercises: A sample of 20 heads of lettuce was selected. Assume that the population distribution of head weight is normal. The weight of each head of lettuce was then recorded. The mean weight was 2.2 pounds with a standard deviation of 0.1 pounds. The population standard deviation is known to be 0.2 pounds.

13. Identify the following:

    a. $\bar{x}$ = _____

    b. σ = _____

    c. n = _____

14. In words, define the random variable X.

15. In words, define the random variable $\bar{X}$.

16. Which distribution should you use for this problem?

17. Construct a 90% confidence interval for the population mean weight of the heads of lettuce. State the confidence interval, sketch the graph, and calculate the error bound.

18. Construct a 95% confidence interval for the population mean weight of the heads of lettuce. State the confidence interval, sketch the graph, and calculate the error bound.

19. In complete sentences, explain why the confidence interval in **Exercise 8.17** is larger than in **Exercise 8.18**.

20. In complete sentences, give an interpretation of what the interval in **Exercise 8.18** means.

21. What would happen if 40 heads of lettuce were sampled instead of 20, and the error bound remained the same?

22. What would happen if 40 heads of lettuce were sampled instead of 20, and the confidence level remained the same?

Use the following information to answer the next 14 exercises: The mean age for all Foothill College students for a recent Fall term was 33.2. The population standard deviation has been pretty consistent at 15. Suppose that twenty-five Winter students were randomly selected. The mean age for the sample was 30.4. We are interested in the true mean age for Winter Foothill College students. Let X = the age of a Winter Foothill College student.

23. $\bar{x}$ = _____

24. n = _____

25. _____ = 15

26. In words, define the random variable $\bar{X}$.

27. What is $\bar{x}$ estimating?

28. Is σ_x known?

29. As a result of your answer to **Exercise 8.26**, state the exact distribution to use when calculating the confidence interval.

Construct a 95% Confidence Interval for the true mean age of Winter Foothill College students by working out then answering the next seven exercises.

30. How much area is in both tails (combined)? α = _____

31. How much area is in each tail? $\frac{\alpha}{2}$ = _____

32. Identify the following specifications:

    a. lower limit

    b. upper limit

    c. error bound

33. The 95% confidence interval is:_____.

34. Fill in the blanks on the graph with the areas, upper and lower limits of the confidence interval, and the sample mean.

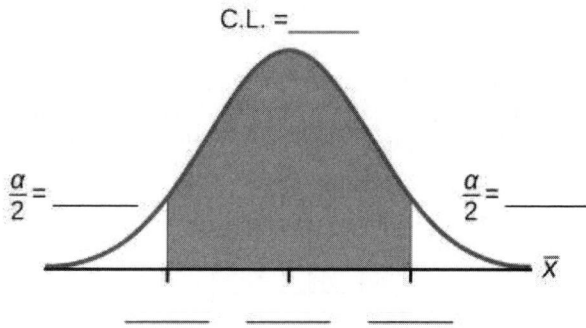

Figure 8.8

35. In one complete sentence, explain what the interval means.

36. Using the same mean, standard deviation, and level of confidence, suppose that n were 69 instead of 25. Would the error bound become larger or smaller? How do you know?

37. Using the same mean, standard deviation, and sample size, how would the error bound change if the confidence level were reduced to 90%? Why?

8.2 A Single Population Mean using the Student t Distribution

Use the following information to answer the next five exercises. A hospital is trying to cut down on emergency room wait times. It is interested in the amount of time patients must wait before being called back to be examined. An investigation committee randomly surveyed 70 patients. The sample mean was 1.5 hours with a sample standard deviation of 0.5 hours.

38. Identify the following:

    a. $\bar{x}$ =_____
    b. s_x =_____
    c. n =_____
    d. $n - 1$ =_____

39. Define the random variables X and $\bar{X}$ in words.

40. Which distribution should you use for this problem?

41. Construct a 95% confidence interval for the population mean time spent waiting. State the confidence interval, sketch the graph, and calculate the error bound.

42. Explain in complete sentences what the confidence interval means.

Use the following information to answer the next six exercises: One hundred eight Americans were surveyed to determine the number of hours they spend watching television each month. It was revealed that they watched an average of 151 hours each month with a standard deviation of 32 hours. Assume that the underlying population distribution is normal.

43. Identify the following:

    a. $\bar{x}$ =_____
    b. s_x =_____
    c. n =_____
    d. $n - 1$ =_____

44. Define the random variable X in words.

45. Define the random variable $\bar{X}$ in words.

46. Which distribution should you use for this problem?

47. Construct a 99% confidence interval for the population mean hours spent watching television per month. (a) State the confidence interval, (b) sketch the graph, and (c) calculate the error bound.

48. Why would the error bound change if the confidence level were lowered to 95%?

Use the following information to answer the next 13 exercises: The data in **Table 8.10** are the result of a random survey of 39 national flags (with replacement between picks) from various countries. We are interested in finding a confidence interval for the true mean number of colors on a national flag. Let X = the number of colors on a national flag.

X	Freq.
1	1
2	7
3	18
4	7
5	6

Table 8.10

49. Calculate the following:

    a. $\bar{x}$ =_____

    b. s_x =_____

    c. n =_____

50. Define the random variable $\bar{X}$ in words.

51. What is $\bar{x}$ estimating?

52. Is σ_x known?

53. As a result of your answer to **Exercise 8.52**, state the exact distribution to use when calculating the confidence interval.

Construct a 95% confidence interval for the true mean number of colors on national flags.

54. How much area is in both tails (combined)?

55. How much area is in each tail?

56. Calculate the following:
    a. lower limit
    b. upper limit
    c. error bound

57. The 95% confidence interval is_____.

58. Fill in the blanks on the graph with the areas, the upper and lower limits of the Confidence Interval and the sample mean.

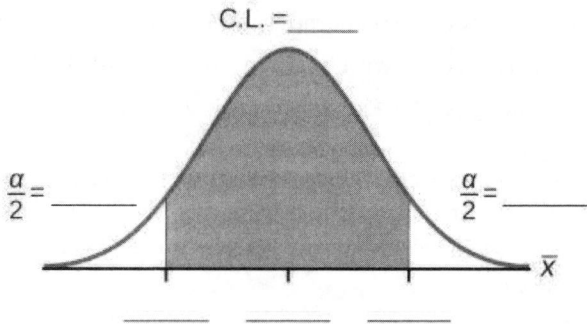

Figure 8.9

59. In one complete sentence, explain what the interval means.

60. Using the same $\bar{x}$, s_x, and level of confidence, suppose that n were 69 instead of 39. Would the error bound become larger or smaller? How do you know?

61. Using the same $\bar{x}$, s_x, and $n = 39$, how would the error bound change if the confidence level were reduced to 90%? Why?

8.3 A Population Proportion

Use the following information to answer the next two exercises: Marketing companies are interested in knowing the population percent of women who make the majority of household purchasing decisions.

62. When designing a study to determine this population proportion, what is the minimum number you would need to survey to be 90% confident that the population proportion is estimated to within 0.05?

63. If it were later determined that it was important to be more than 90% confident and a new survey were commissioned, how would it affect the minimum number you need to survey? Why?

Use the following information to answer the next five exercises: Suppose the marketing company did do a survey. They randomly surveyed 200 households and found that in 120 of them, the woman made the majority of the purchasing decisions. We are interested in the population proportion of households where women make the majority of the purchasing decisions.

64. Identify the following:
    a. $x =$ _____
    b. $n =$ _____
    c. $p' =$ _____

65. Define the random variables X and P' in words.

66. Which distribution should you use for this problem?

67. Construct a 95% confidence interval for the population proportion of households where the women make the majority of the purchasing decisions. State the confidence interval, sketch the graph, and calculate the error bound.

68. List two difficulties the company might have in obtaining random results, if this survey were done by email.

Use the following information to answer the next five exercises: Of 1,050 randomly selected adults, 360 identified themselves as manual laborers, 280 identified themselves as non-manual wage earners, 250 identified themselves as mid-level managers, and 160 identified themselves as executives. In the survey, 82% of manual laborers preferred trucks, 62% of non-manual wage earners preferred trucks, 54% of mid-level managers preferred trucks, and 26% of executives preferred trucks.

69. We are interested in finding the 95% confidence interval for the percent of executives who prefer trucks. Define random variables X and P' in words.

70. Which distribution should you use for this problem?

71. Construct a 95% confidence interval. State the confidence interval, sketch the graph, and calculate the error bound.

72. Suppose we want to lower the sampling error. What is one way to accomplish that?

73. The sampling error given in the survey is ±2%. Explain what the ±2% means.

Use the following information to answer the next five exercises: A poll of 1,200 voters asked what the most significant issue was in the upcoming election. Sixty-five percent answered the economy. We are interested in the population proportion of voters who feel the economy is the most important.

74. Define the random variable X in words.

75. Define the random variable P' in words.

76. Which distribution should you use for this problem?

77. Construct a 90% confidence interval, and state the confidence interval and the error bound.

78. What would happen to the confidence interval if the level of confidence were 95%?

Use the following information to answer the next 16 exercises: The Ice Chalet offers dozens of different beginning ice-skating classes. All of the class names are put into a bucket. The 5 P.M., Monday night, ages 8 to 12, beginning ice-skating class was picked. In that class were 64 girls and 16 boys. Suppose that we are interested in the true proportion of girls, ages 8 to 12, in all beginning ice-skating classes at the Ice Chalet. Assume that the children in the selected class are a random sample of the population.

79. What is being counted?

80. In words, define the random variable X.

81. Calculate the following:
   a. $x =$ _____
   b. $n =$ _____
   c. $p' =$ _____

82. State the estimated distribution of X. $X\sim$_____

83. Define a new random variable P'. What is p' estimating?

84. In words, define the random variable P'.

85. State the estimated distribution of P'. Construct a 92% Confidence Interval for the true proportion of girls in the ages 8 to 12 beginning ice-skating classes at the Ice Chalet.

86. How much area is in both tails (combined)?

87. How much area is in each tail?

88. Calculate the following:
   a. lower limit
   b. upper limit
   c. error bound

89. The 92% confidence interval is _____.

90. Fill in the blanks on the graph with the areas, upper and lower limits of the confidence interval, and the sample proportion.

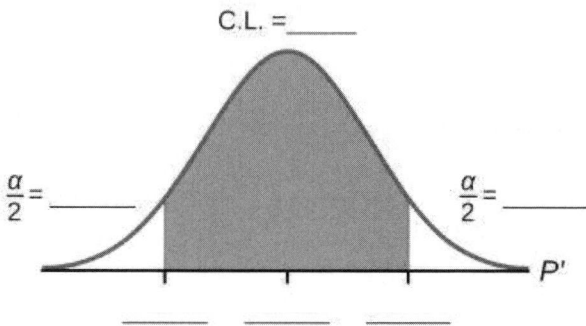

Figure 8.10

91. In one complete sentence, explain what the interval means.

92. Using the same p' and level of confidence, suppose that n were increased to 100. Would the error bound become larger or smaller? How do you know?

93. Using the same p' and $n = 80$, how would the error bound change if the confidence level were increased to 98%? Why?

94. If you decreased the allowable error bound, why would the minimum sample size increase (keeping the same level of confidence)?

HOMEWORK

8.1 A Single Population Mean using the Normal Distribution

95. Among various ethnic groups, the standard deviation of heights is known to be approximately three inches. We wish to construct a 95% confidence interval for the mean height of male Swedes. Forty-eight male Swedes are surveyed. The sample mean is 71 inches. The sample standard deviation is 2.8 inches.

    a.
        i. $\bar{x}$ =_____
        ii. σ =_____
        iii. n =_____

    b. In words, define the random variables X and $\bar{X}$.
    c. Which distribution should you use for this problem? Explain your choice.
    d. Construct a 95% confidence interval for the population mean height of male Swedes.
        i. State the confidence interval.
        ii. Sketch the graph.
        iii. Calculate the error bound.

    e. What will happen to the level of confidence obtained if 1,000 male Swedes are surveyed instead of 48? Why?

96. Announcements for 84 upcoming engineering conferences were randomly picked from a stack of IEEE Spectrum magazines. The mean length of the conferences was 3.94 days, with a standard deviation of 1.28 days. Assume the underlying population is normal.

    a. In words, define the random variables X and $\bar{X}$.
    b. Which distribution should you use for this problem? Explain your choice.
    c. Construct a 95% confidence interval for the population mean length of engineering conferences.
        i. State the confidence interval.
        ii. Sketch the graph.
        iii. Calculate the error bound.

97. Suppose that an accounting firm does a study to determine the time needed to complete one person's tax forms. It randomly surveys 100 people. The sample mean is 23.6 hours. There is a known standard deviation of 7.0 hours. The population distribution is assumed to be normal.

    a.   i. $\bar{x}$ =_____
                ii. σ =_____
                iii. n =_____

    b. In words, define the random variables X and $\bar{X}$.
    c. Which distribution should you use for this problem? Explain your choice.
    d. Construct a 90% confidence interval for the population mean time to complete the tax forms.
         i. State the confidence interval.
         ii. Sketch the graph.
         iii. Calculate the error bound.

    e. If the firm wished to increase its level of confidence and keep the error bound the same by taking another survey, what changes should it make?
    f. If the firm did another survey, kept the error bound the same, and only surveyed 49 people, what would happen to the level of confidence? Why?
    g. Suppose that the firm decided that it needed to be at least 96% confident of the population mean length of time to within one hour. How would the number of people the firm surveys change? Why?

98. A sample of 16 small bags of the same brand of candies was selected. Assume that the population distribution of bag weights is normal. The weight of each bag was then recorded. The mean weight was two ounces with a standard deviation of 0.12 ounces. The population standard deviation is known to be 0.1 ounce.

    a.   i. $\bar{x}$ =_____
                ii. σ =_____
                iii. s_x =_____

    b. In words, define the random variable X.
    c. In words, define the random variable $\bar{X}$.
    d. Which distribution should you use for this problem? Explain your choice.
    e. Construct a 90% confidence interval for the population mean weight of the candies.
         i. State the confidence interval.
         ii. Sketch the graph.
         iii. Calculate the error bound.

    f. Construct a 98% confidence interval for the population mean weight of the candies.
         i. State the confidence interval.
         ii. Sketch the graph.
         iii. Calculate the error bound.

    g. In complete sentences, explain why the confidence interval in part f is larger than the confidence interval in part e.
    h. In complete sentences, give an interpretation of what the interval in part f means.

99. A camp director is interested in the mean number of letters each child sends during his or her camp session. The population standard deviation is known to be 2.5. A survey of 20 campers is taken. The mean from the sample is 7.9 with a sample standard deviation of 2.8.

    a.   i. $\bar{x}$ =_____
                ii. σ =_____
                iii. n =_____

    b. Define the random variables X and $\bar{X}$ in words.
    c. Which distribution should you use for this problem? Explain your choice.
    d. Construct a 90% confidence interval for the population mean number of letters campers send home.
         i. State the confidence interval.
         ii. Sketch the graph.
         iii. Calculate the error bound.

    e. What will happen to the error bound and confidence interval if 500 campers are surveyed? Why?

100. What is meant by the term "90% confident" when constructing a confidence interval for a mean?
   a. If we took repeated samples, approximately 90% of the samples would produce the same confidence interval.
   b. If we took repeated samples, approximately 90% of the confidence intervals calculated from those samples would contain the sample mean.
   c. If we took repeated samples, approximately 90% of the confidence intervals calculated from those samples would contain the true value of the population mean.
   d. If we took repeated samples, the sample mean would equal the population mean in approximately 90% of the samples.

101. The Federal Election Commission collects information about campaign contributions and disbursements for candidates and political committees each election cycle. During the 2012 campaign season, there were 1,619 candidates for the House of Representatives across the United States who received contributions from individuals. **Table 8.11** shows the total receipts from individuals for a random selection of 40 House candidates rounded to the nearest $100. The standard deviation for this data to the nearest hundred is $\sigma = \$909,200$.

$3,600	$1,243,900	$10,900	$385,200	$581,500
$7,400	$2,900	$400	$3,714,500	$632,500
$391,000	$467,400	$56,800	$5,800	$405,200
$733,200	$8,000	$468,700	$75,200	$41,000
$13,300	$9,500	$953,800	$1,113,500	$1,109,300
$353,900	$986,100	$88,600	$378,200	$13,200
$3,800	$745,100	$5,800	$3,072,100	$1,626,700
$512,900	$2,309,200	$6,600	$202,400	$15,800

Table 8.11

   a. Find the point estimate for the population mean.
   b. Using 95% confidence, calculate the error bound.
   c. Create a 95% confidence interval for the mean total individual contributions.
   d. Interpret the confidence interval in the context of the problem.

102. The American Community Survey (ACS), part of the United States Census Bureau, conducts a yearly census similar to the one taken every ten years, but with a smaller percentage of participants. The most recent survey estimates with 90% confidence that the mean household income in the U.S. falls between $69,720 and $69,922. Find the point estimate for mean U.S. household income and the error bound for mean U.S. household income.

103. The average height of young adult males has a normal distribution with standard deviation of 2.5 inches. You want to estimate the mean height of students at your college or university to within one inch with 93% confidence. How many male students must you measure?

8.2 A Single Population Mean using the Student t Distribution

104. In six packages of "The Flintstones® Real Fruit Snacks" there were five Bam-Bam snack pieces. The total number of snack pieces in the six bags was 68. We wish to calculate a 96% confidence interval for the population proportion of Bam-Bam snack pieces.
   a. Define the random variables X and P' in words.
   b. Which distribution should you use for this problem? Explain your choice
   c. Calculate p'.
   d. Construct a 96% confidence interval for the population proportion of Bam-Bam snack pieces per bag.
       i. State the confidence interval.
       ii. Sketch the graph.
       iii. Calculate the error bound.
   e. Do you think that six packages of fruit snacks yield enough data to give accurate results? Why or why not?

105. A random survey of enrollment at 35 community colleges across the United States yielded the following figures: 6,414; 1,550; 2,109; 9,350; 21,828; 4,300; 5,944; 5,722; 2,825; 2,044; 5,481; 5,200; 5,853; 2,750; 10,012; 6,357; 27,000; 9,414; 7,681; 3,200; 17,500; 9,200; 7,380; 18,314; 6,557; 13,713; 17,768; 7,493; 2,771; 2,861; 1,263; 7,285; 28,165; 5,080; 11,622. Assume the underlying population is normal.

    a.
        i. $\bar{x}$ = _____
        ii. s_x = _____
        iii. n = _____
        iv. $n - 1$ = _____

    b. Define the random variables X and $\bar{X}$ in words.

    c. Which distribution should you use for this problem? Explain your choice.

    d. Construct a 95% confidence interval for the population mean enrollment at community colleges in the United States.
        i. State the confidence interval.
        ii. Sketch the graph.
        iii. Calculate the error bound.

    e. What will happen to the error bound and confidence interval if 500 community colleges were surveyed? Why?

106. Suppose that a committee is studying whether or not there is waste of time in our judicial system. It is interested in the mean amount of time individuals waste at the courthouse waiting to be called for jury duty. The committee randomly surveyed 81 people who recently served as jurors. The sample mean wait time was eight hours with a sample standard deviation of four hours.

    a.
        i. $\bar{x}$ = _____
        ii. s_x = _____
        iii. n = _____
        iv. $n - 1$ = _____

    b. Define the random variables X and $\bar{X}$ in words.

    c. Which distribution should you use for this problem? Explain your choice.

    d. Construct a 95% confidence interval for the population mean time wasted.
        i. State the confidence interval.
        ii. Sketch the graph.
        iii. Calculate the error bound.

    e. Explain in a complete sentence what the confidence interval means.

107. A pharmaceutical company makes tranquilizers. It is assumed that the distribution for the length of time they last is approximately normal. Researchers in a hospital used the drug on a random sample of nine patients. The effective period of the tranquilizer for each patient (in hours) was as follows: 2.7; 2.8; 3.0; 2.3; 2.3; 2.2; 2.8; 2.1; and 2.4.

    a.
        i. $\bar{x}$ = _____
        ii. s_x = _____
        iii. n = _____
        iv. $n - 1$ = _____

    b. Define the random variable X in words.

    c. Define the random variable $\bar{X}$ in words.

    d. Which distribution should you use for this problem? Explain your choice.

    e. Construct a 95% confidence interval for the population mean length of time.
        i. State the confidence interval.
        ii. Sketch the graph.
        iii. Calculate the error bound.

    f. What does it mean to be "95% confident" in this problem?

108. Suppose that 14 children, who were learning to ride two-wheel bikes, were surveyed to determine how long they had to use training wheels. It was revealed that they used them an average of six months with a sample standard deviation of three months. Assume that the underlying population distribution is normal.

    a.   i. $\bar{x}$ = _____

           ii. s_x = _____

          iii. n = _____

          iv. $n - 1$ = _____

    b. Define the random variable X in words.

    c. Define the random variable $\bar{X}$ in words.

    d. Which distribution should you use for this problem? Explain your choice.

    e. Construct a 99% confidence interval for the population mean length of time using training wheels.

          i. State the confidence interval.

          ii. Sketch the graph.

          iii. Calculate the error bound.

    f. Why would the error bound change if the confidence level were lowered to 90%?

109. The Federal Election Commission (FEC) collects information about campaign contributions and disbursements for candidates and political committees each election cycle. A political action committee (PAC) is a committee formed to raise money for candidates and campaigns. A Leadership PAC is a PAC formed by a federal politician (senator or representative) to raise money to help other candidates' campaigns.

The FEC has reported financial information for 556 Leadership PACs that operating during the 2011–2012 election cycle. The following table shows the total receipts during this cycle for a random selection of 30 Leadership PACs.

$46,500.00	$0	$40,966.50	$105,887.20	$5,175.00
$29,050.00	$19,500.00	$181,557.20	$31,500.00	$149,970.80
$2,555,363.20	$12,025.00	$409,000.00	$60,521.70	$18,000.00
$61,810.20	$76,530.80	$119,459.20	$0	$63,520.00
$6,500.00	$502,578.00	$705,061.10	$708,258.90	$135,810.00
$2,000.00	$2,000.00	$0	$1,287,933.80	$219,148.30

Table 8.12

$\bar{x} = \$251,854.23$

$s = \$521,130.41$

Use this sample data to construct a 96% confidence interval for the mean amount of money raised by all Leadership PACs during the 2011–2012 election cycle. Use the Student's t-distribution.

110. *Forbes* magazine published data on the best small firms in 2012. These were firms that had been publicly traded for at least a year, have a stock price of at least $5 per share, and have reported annual revenue between $5 million and $1 billion. The **Table 8.13** shows the ages of the corporate CEOs for a random sample of these firms.

48	58	51	61	56
59	74	63	53	50
59	60	60	57	46
55	63	57	47	55
57	43	61	62	49
67	67	55	55	49

Table 8.13

Use this sample data to construct a 90% confidence interval for the mean age of CEO's for these top small firms. Use the Student's t-distribution.

111. Unoccupied seats on flights cause airlines to lose revenue. Suppose a large airline wants to estimate its mean number of unoccupied seats per flight over the past year. To accomplish this, the records of 225 flights are randomly selected and the number of unoccupied seats is noted for each of the sampled flights. The sample mean is 11.6 seats and the sample standard deviation is 4.1 seats.

    a.   i. $\bar{x}$ = _____

           ii. s_x = _____

           iii. n = _____

           iv. n-1 = _____

    b. Define the random variables X and $\bar{X}$ in words.

    c. Which distribution should you use for this problem? Explain your choice.

    d. Construct a 92% confidence interval for the population mean number of unoccupied seats per flight.

           i. State the confidence interval.

           ii. Sketch the graph.

           iii. Calculate the error bound.

112. In a recent sample of 84 used car sales costs, the sample mean was $6,425 with a standard deviation of $3,156. Assume the underlying distribution is approximately normal.

    a. Which distribution should you use for this problem? Explain your choice.

    b. Define the random variable $\bar{X}$ in words.

    c. Construct a 95% confidence interval for the population mean cost of a used car.

           i. State the confidence interval.

           ii. Sketch the graph.

           iii. Calculate the error bound.

    d. Explain what a "95% confidence interval" means for this study.

113. Six different national brands of chocolate chip cookies were randomly selected at the supermarket. The grams of fat per serving are as follows: 8; 8; 10; 7; 9; 9. Assume the underlying distribution is approximately normal.

    a. Construct a 90% confidence interval for the population mean grams of fat per serving of chocolate chip cookies sold in supermarkets.

           i. State the confidence interval.

           ii. Sketch the graph.

           iii. Calculate the error bound.

    b. If you wanted a smaller error bound while keeping the same level of confidence, what should have been changed in the study before it was done?

    c. Go to the store and record the grams of fat per serving of six brands of chocolate chip cookies.

    d. Calculate the mean.

    e. Is the mean within the interval you calculated in part a? Did you expect it to be? Why or why not?

114. A survey of the mean number of cents off that coupons give was conducted by randomly surveying one coupon per page from the coupon sections of a recent San Jose Mercury News. The following data were collected: 20¢; 75¢; 50¢; 65¢; 30¢; 55¢; 40¢; 40¢; 30¢; 55¢; $1.50; 40¢; 65¢; 40¢. Assume the underlying distribution is approximately normal.

   a.   i. $\bar{x}$ = _____

        ii. s_x = _____

        iii. n = _____

        iv. n-1 = _____

   b. Define the random variables X and $\bar{X}$ in words.
   c. Which distribution should you use for this problem? Explain your choice.
   d. Construct a 95% confidence interval for the population mean worth of coupons.
        i. State the confidence interval.
        ii. Sketch the graph.
        iii. Calculate the error bound.

   e. If many random samples were taken of size 14, what percent of the confidence intervals constructed should contain the population mean worth of coupons? Explain why.

Use the following information to answer the next two exercises: A quality control specialist for a restaurant chain takes a random sample of size 12 to check the amount of soda served in the 16 oz. serving size. The sample mean is 13.30 with a sample standard deviation of 1.55. Assume the underlying population is normally distributed.

115. Find the 95% Confidence Interval for the true population mean for the amount of soda served.
   a. (12.42, 14.18)
   b. (12.32, 14.29)
   c. (12.50, 14.10)
   d. Impossible to determine

116. What is the error bound?
   a. 0.87
   b. 1.98
   c. 0.99
   d. 1.74

8.3 A Population Proportion

117. Insurance companies are interested in knowing the population percent of drivers who always buckle up before riding in a car.
   a. When designing a study to determine this population proportion, what is the minimum number you would need to survey to be 95% confident that the population proportion is estimated to within 0.03?
   b. If it were later determined that it was important to be more than 95% confident and a new survey was commissioned, how would that affect the minimum number you would need to survey? Why?

118. Suppose that the insurance companies did do a survey. They randomly surveyed 400 drivers and found that 320 claimed they always buckle up. We are interested in the population proportion of drivers who claim they always buckle up.
   a.   i. x = _____

        ii. n = _____

        iii. p' = _____

   b. Define the random variables X and P', in words.
   c. Which distribution should you use for this problem? Explain your choice.
   d. Construct a 95% confidence interval for the population proportion who claim they always buckle up.
        i. State the confidence interval.
        ii. Sketch the graph.
        iii. Calculate the error bound.

   e. If this survey were done by telephone, list three difficulties the companies might have in obtaining random results.

119. According to a recent survey of 1,200 people, 61% feel that the president is doing an acceptable job. We are interested in the population proportion of people who feel the president is doing an acceptable job.
  a. Define the random variables X and P' in words.
  b. Which distribution should you use for this problem? Explain your choice.
  c. Construct a 90% confidence interval for the population proportion of people who feel the president is doing an acceptable job.
      i. State the confidence interval.
      ii. Sketch the graph.
      iii. Calculate the error bound.

120. An article regarding interracial dating and marriage recently appeared in the *Washington Post*. Of the 1,709 randomly selected adults, 315 identified themselves as Latinos, 323 identified themselves as blacks, 254 identified themselves as Asians, and 779 identified themselves as whites. In this survey, 86% of blacks said that they would welcome a white person into their families. Among Asians, 77% would welcome a white person into their families, 71% would welcome a Latino, and 66% would welcome a black person.
  a. We are interested in finding the 95% confidence interval for the percent of all black adults who would welcome a white person into their families. Define the random variables X and P', in words.
  b. Which distribution should you use for this problem? Explain your choice.
  c. Construct a 95% confidence interval.
      i. State the confidence interval.
      ii. Sketch the graph.
      iii. Calculate the error bound.

121. Refer to the information in **Exercise 8.120**.
  a. Construct three 95% confidence intervals.
      i. percent of all Asians who would welcome a white person into their families.
      ii. percent of all Asians who would welcome a Latino into their families.
      iii. percent of all Asians who would welcome a black person into their families.
  b. Even though the three point estimates are different, do any of the confidence intervals overlap? Which?
  c. For any intervals that do overlap, in words, what does this imply about the significance of the differences in the true proportions?
  d. For any intervals that do not overlap, in words, what does this imply about the significance of the differences in the true proportions?

122. Stanford University conducted a study of whether running is healthy for men and women over age 50. During the first eight years of the study, 1.5% of the 451 members of the 50-Plus Fitness Association died. We are interested in the proportion of people over 50 who ran and died in the same eight-year period.
  a. Define the random variables X and P' in words.
  b. Which distribution should you use for this problem? Explain your choice.
  c. Construct a 97% confidence interval for the population proportion of people over 50 who ran and died in the same eight–year period.
      i. State the confidence interval.
      ii. Sketch the graph.
      iii. Calculate the error bound.
  d. Explain what a "97% confidence interval" means for this study.

123. A telephone poll of 1,000 adult Americans was reported in an issue of *Time Magazine*. One of the questions asked was "What is the main problem facing the country?" Twenty percent answered "crime." We are interested in the population proportion of adult Americans who feel that crime is the main problem.
  a. Define the random variables X and P' in words.
  b. Which distribution should you use for this problem? Explain your choice.
  c. Construct a 95% confidence interval for the population proportion of adult Americans who feel that crime is the main problem.
      i. State the confidence interval.
      ii. Sketch the graph.
      iii. Calculate the error bound.
  d. Suppose we want to lower the sampling error. What is one way to accomplish that?
  e. The sampling error given by Yankelovich Partners, Inc. (which conducted the poll) is ±3%. In one to three complete sentences, explain what the ±3% represents.

124. Refer to **Exercise 8.123**. Another question in the poll was "[How much are] you worried about the quality of education in our schools?" Sixty-three percent responded "a lot". We are interested in the population proportion of adult Americans who are worried a lot about the quality of education in our schools.
  a. Define the random variables X and P' in words.
  b. Which distribution should you use for this problem? Explain your choice.
  c. Construct a 95% confidence interval for the population proportion of adult Americans who are worried a lot about the quality of education in our schools.
     i. State the confidence interval.
     ii. Sketch the graph.
     iii. Calculate the error bound.
  d. The sampling error given by Yankelovich Partners, Inc. (which conducted the poll) is ±3%. In one to three complete sentences, explain what the ±3% represents.

Use the following information to answer the next three exercises: According to a Field Poll, 79% of California adults (actual results are 400 out of 506 surveyed) feel that "education and our schools" is one of the top issues facing California. We wish to construct a 90% confidence interval for the true proportion of California adults who feel that education and the schools is one of the top issues facing California.

125. A point estimate for the true population proportion is:
  a. 0.90
  b. 1.27
  c. 0.79
  d. 400

126. A 90% confidence interval for the population proportion is _____.
  a. (0.761, 0.820)
  b. (0.125, 0.188)
  c. (0.755, 0.826)
  d. (0.130, 0.183)

127. The error bound is approximately _____.
  a. 1.581
  b. 0.791
  c. 0.059
  d. 0.030

Use the following information to answer the next two exercises: Five hundred and eleven (511) homes in a certain southern California community are randomly surveyed to determine if they meet minimal earthquake preparedness recommendations. One hundred seventy-three (173) of the homes surveyed met the minimum recommendations for earthquake preparedness, and 338 did not.

128. Find the confidence interval at the 90% Confidence Level for the true population proportion of southern California community homes meeting at least the minimum recommendations for earthquake preparedness.
  a. (0.2975, 0.3796)
  b. (0.6270, 0.6959)
  c. (0.3041, 0.3730)
  d. (0.6204, 0.7025)

129. The point estimate for the population proportion of homes that do not meet the minimum recommendations for earthquake preparedness is _____.
  a. 0.6614
  b. 0.3386
  c. 173
  d. 338

130. On May 23, 2013, Gallup reported that of the 1,005 people surveyed, 76% of U.S. workers believe that they will continue working past retirement age. The confidence level for this study was reported at 95% with a ±3% margin of error.
   a. Determine the estimated proportion from the sample.
   b. Determine the sample size.
   c. Identify *CL* and α.
   d. Calculate the error bound based on the information provided.
   e. Compare the error bound in part d to the margin of error reported by Gallup. Explain any differences between the values.
   f. Create a confidence interval for the results of this study.
   g. A reporter is covering the release of this study for a local news station. How should she explain the confidence interval to her audience?

131. A national survey of 1,000 adults was conducted on May 13, 2013 by Rasmussen Reports. It concluded with 95% confidence that 49% to 55% of Americans believe that big-time college sports programs corrupt the process of higher education.
   a. Find the point estimate and the error bound for this confidence interval.
   b. Can we (with 95% confidence) conclude that more than half of all American adults believe this?
   c. Use the point estimate from part a and *n* = 1,000 to calculate a 75% confidence interval for the proportion of American adults that believe that major college sports programs corrupt higher education.
   d. Can we (with 75% confidence) conclude that at least half of all American adults believe this?

132. Public Policy Polling recently conducted a survey asking adults across the U.S. about music preferences. When asked, 80 of the 571 participants admitted that they have illegally downloaded music.
   a. Create a 99% confidence interval for the true proportion of American adults who have illegally downloaded music.
   b. This survey was conducted through automated telephone interviews on May 6 and 7, 2013. The error bound of the survey compensates for sampling error, or natural variability among samples. List some factors that could affect the survey's outcome that are not covered by the margin of error.
   c. Without performing any calculations, describe how the confidence interval would change if the confidence level changed from 99% to 90%.

133. You plan to conduct a survey on your college campus to learn about the political awareness of students. You want to estimate the true proportion of college students on your campus who voted in the 2012 presidential election with 95% confidence and a margin of error no greater than five percent. How many students must you interview?

134. In a recent Zogby International Poll, nine of 48 respondents rated the likelihood of a terrorist attack in their community as "likely" or "very likely." Use the "plus four" method to create a 97% confidence interval for the proportion of American adults who believe that a terrorist attack in their community is likely or very likely. Explain what this confidence interval means in the context of the problem.

REFERENCES

8.1 A Single Population Mean using the Normal Distribution

"American Fact Finder." U.S. Census Bureau. Available online at http://factfinder2.census.gov/faces/nav/jsf/pages/searchresults.xhtml?refresh=t (accessed July 2, 2013).

"Disclosure Data Catalog: Candidate Summary Report 2012." U.S. Federal Election Commission. Available online at http://www.fec.gov/data/index.jsp (accessed July 2, 2013).

"Headcount Enrollment Trends by Student Demographics Ten-Year Fall Trends to Most Recently Completed Fall." Foothill De Anza Community College District. Available online at http://research.fhda.edu/factbook/FH_Demo_Trends/FoothillDemographicTrends.htm (accessed September 30,2013).

Kuczmarski, Robert J., Cynthia L. Ogden, Shumei S. Guo, Laurence M. Grummer-Strawn, Katherine M. Flegal, Zuguo Mei, Rong Wei, Lester R. Curtin, Alex F. Roche, Clifford L. Johnson. "2000 CDC Growth Charts for the United States: Methods and Development." Centers for Disease Control and Prevention. Available online at http://www.cdc.gov/growthcharts/2000growthchart-us.pdf (accessed July 2, 2013).

La, Lynn, Kent German. "Cell Phone Radiation Levels." c|net part of CBX Interactive Inc. Available online at http://reviews.cnet.com/cell-phone-radiation-levels/ (accessed July 2, 2013).

"Mean Income in the Past 12 Months (in 2011 Inflaction-Adjusted Dollars): 2011 American Community Survey 1-Year Estimates." American Fact Finder, U.S. Census Bureau. Available online at http://factfinder2.census.gov/faces/tableservices/jsf/pages/productview.xhtml?pid=ACS_11_1YR_S1902&prodType=table (accessed July 2, 2013).

"Metadata Description of Candidate Summary File." U.S. Federal Election Commission. Available online at http://www.fec.gov/finance/disclosure/metadata/metadataforcandidatesummary.shtml (accessed July 2, 2013).

"National Health and Nutrition Examination Survey." Centers for Disease Control and Prevention. Available online at http://www.cdc.gov/nchs/nhanes.htm (accessed July 2, 2013).

8.2 A Single Population Mean using the Student t Distribution

"America's Best Small Companies." Forbes, 2013. Available online at http://www.forbes.com/best-small-companies/list/ (accessed July 2, 2013).

Data from *Microsoft Bookshelf.*

Data from http://www.businessweek.com/.

Data from http://www.forbes.com/.

"Disclosure Data Catalog: Leadership PAC and Sponsors Report, 2012." Federal Election Commission. Available online at http://www.fec.gov/data/index.jsp (accessed July 2,2013).

"Human Toxome Project: Mapping the Pollution in People." Environmental Working Group. Available online at http://www.ewg.org/sites/humantoxome/participants/participant-group.php?group=in+utero%2Fnewborn (accessed July 2, 2013).

"Metadata Description of Leadership PAC List." Federal Election Commission. Available online at http://www.fec.gov/finance/disclosure/metadata/metadataLeadershipPacList.shtml (accessed July 2, 2013).

8.3 A Population Proportion

Jensen, Tom. "Democrats, Republicans Divided on Opinion of Music Icons." Public Policy Polling. Available online at http://www.publicpolicypolling.com/Day2MusicPoll.pdf (accessed July 2, 2013).

Madden, Mary, Amanda Lenhart, Sandra Coresi, Urs Gasser, Maeve Duggan, Aaron Smith, and Meredith Beaton. "Teens, Social Media, and Privacy." PewInternet, 2013. Available online at http://www.pewinternet.org/Reports/2013/Teens-Social-Media-And-Privacy.aspx (accessed July 2, 2013).

Prince Survey Research Associates International. "2013 Teen and Privacy Management Survey." Pew Research Center: Internet and American Life Project. Available online at http://www.pewinternet.org/~/media//Files/Questionnaire/2013/Methods%20and%20Questions_Teens%20and%20Social%20Media.pdf (accessed July 2, 2013).

Saad, Lydia. "Three in Four U.S. Workers Plan to Work Pas Retirement Age: Slightly more say they will do this by choice rather than necessity." Gallup® Economy, 2013. Available online at http://www.gallup.com/poll/162758/three-four-workers-plan-work-past-retirement-age.aspx (accessed July 2, 2013).

The Field Poll. Available online at http://field.com/fieldpollonline/subscribers/ (accessed July 2, 2013).

Zogby. "New SUNYIT/Zogby Analytics Poll: Few Americans Worry about Emergency Situations Occurring in Their Community; Only one in three have an Emergency Plan; 70% Support Infrastructure 'Investment' for National Security." Zogby Analytics, 2013. Available online at http://www.zogbyanalytics.com/news/299-americans-neither-worried-nor-prepared-in-case-of-a-disaster-sunyit-zogby-analytics-poll (accessed July 2, 2013).

"52% Say Big-Time College Athletics Corrupt Education Process." Rasmussen Reports, 2013. Available online at http://www.rasmussenreports.com/public_content/lifestyle/sports/may_2013/52_say_big_time_college_athletics_corrupt_education_process (accessed July 2, 2013).

SOLUTIONS

1
  a. 244

  b. 15

  c. 50

3 $N\left(244, \dfrac{15}{\sqrt{50}}\right)$

5 As the sample size increases, there will be less variability in the mean, so the interval size decreases.

7 X is the time in minutes it takes to complete the U.S. Census short form. $\overline{X}$ is the mean time it took a sample of 200 people to complete the U.S. Census short form.

9 CI: (7.9441, 8.4559)

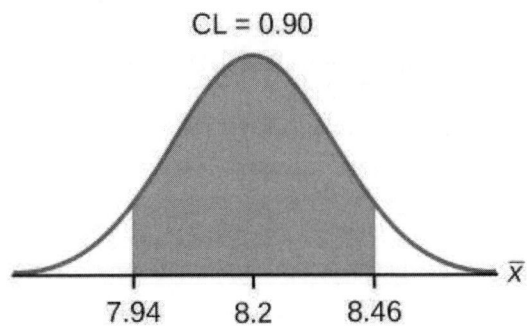

Figure 8.11

$EBM = 0.26$

11 The level of confidence would decrease because decreasing n makes the confidence interval wider, so at the same error bound, the confidence level decreases.

13
  a. $\overline{x} = 2.2$

  b. $\sigma = 0.2$

  c. $n = 20$

15 $\overline{X}$ is the mean weight of a sample of 20 heads of lettuce.

17 $EBM = 0.07$
CI: (2.1264, 2.2736)

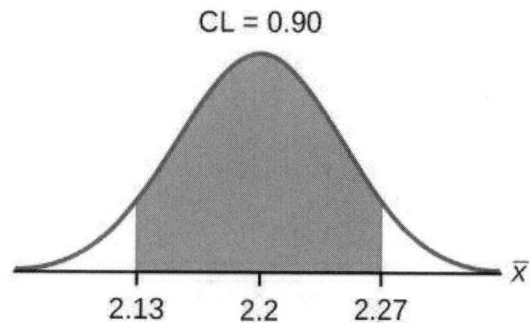

Figure 8.12

19 The interval is greater because the level of confidence increased. If the only change made in the analysis is a change in confidence level, then all we are doing is changing how much area is being calculated for the normal distribution. Therefore, a larger confidence level results in larger areas and larger intervals.

21 The confidence level would increase.

23 30.4

25 σ

27 μ

29 normal

31 0.025

33 (24.52,36.28)

35 We are 95% confident that the true mean age for Winger Foothill College students is between 24.52 and 36.28.

37 The error bound for the mean would decrease because as the CL decreases, you need less area under the normal curve (which translates into a smaller interval) to capture the true population mean.

39 X is the number of hours a patient waits in the emergency room before being called back to be examined. $\overline{X}$ is the mean wait time of 70 patients in the emergency room.

41 CI: (1.3808, 1.6192)

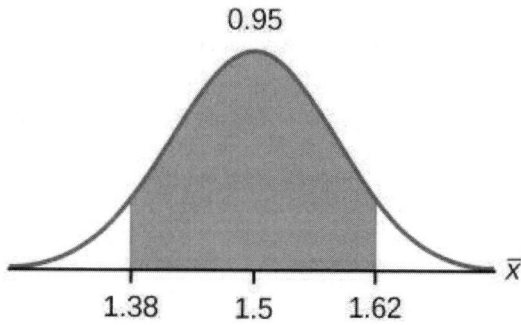

Figure 8.13

$EBM = 0.12$

43
    a. $\overline{x} = 151$

    b. $s_x = 32$

    c. $n = 108$

    d. $n - 1 = 107$

45 $\bar{X}$ is the mean number of hours spent watching television per month from a sample of 108 Americans.

47 CI: (142.92, 159.08)

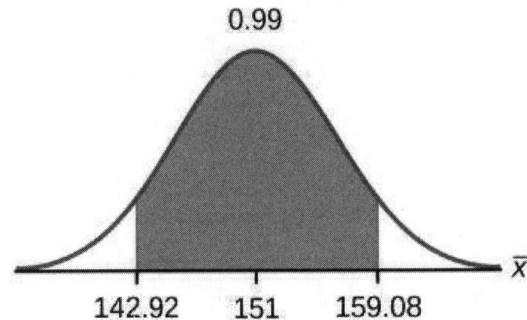

Figure 8.14

$EBM = 8.08$

49

    a. 3.26

    b. 1.02

    c. 39

51 μ

53 t_{38}

55 0.025

57 (2.93, 3.59)

59 We are 95% confident that the true mean number of colors for national flags is between 2.93 colors and 3.59 colors.

60 The error bound would become EBM = 0.245. This error bound decreases because as sample sizes increase, variability decreases and we need less interval length to capture the true mean.

63 It would decrease, because the z-score would decrease, which reducing the numerator and lowering the number.

65 X is the number of "successes" where the woman makes the majority of the purchasing decisions for the household. P' is the percentage of households sampled where the woman makes the majority of the purchasing decisions for the household.

67 CI: (0.5321, 0.6679)

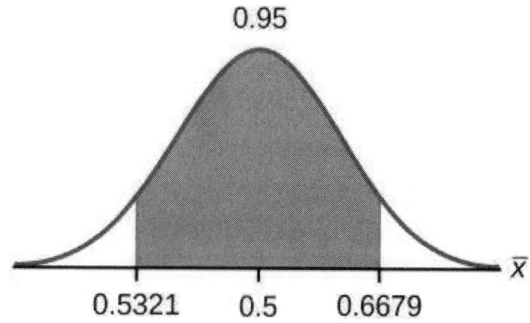

Figure 8.15

EBM: 0.0679

69 *X* is the number of "successes" where an executive prefers a truck. *P′* is the percentage of executives sampled who prefer a truck.

71 CI: (0.19432, 0.33068)

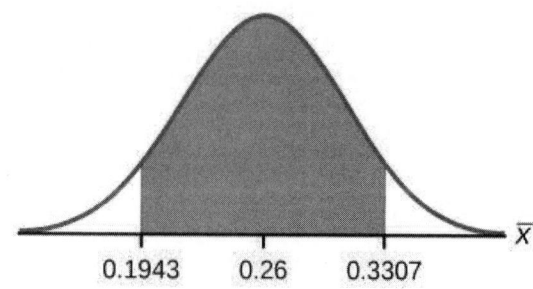

Figure 8.16

EBM: 0.0707

73 The sampling error means that the true mean can be 2% above or below the sample mean.

75 *P′* is the proportion of voters sampled who said the economy is the most important issue in the upcoming election.

77 CI: (0.62735, 0.67265) *EBM*: 0.02265

79 The number of girls, ages 8 to 12, in the 5 P.M. Monday night beginning ice-skating class.

81
   a. *x* = 64
   b. *n* = 80
   c. *p′* = 0.8

83 *p*

85 $P' \sim N\left(0.8, \sqrt{\frac{(0.8)(0.2)}{80}}\right)$. (0.72171, 0.87829).

87 0.04

89 (0.72; 0.88)

91 With 92% confidence, we estimate the proportion of girls, ages 8 to 12, in a beginning ice-skating class at the Ice Chalet to be between 72% and 88%.

93 The error bound would increase. Assuming all other variables are kept constant, as the confidence level increases, the area under the curve corresponding to the confidence level becomes larger, which creates a wider interval and thus a larger error.

95

- a.   i.   71

     ii.   3

     iii.   48

- b.   X is the height of a Swiss male, and is the mean height from a sample of 48 Swiss males.

- c.   Normal. We know the standard deviation for the population, and the sample size is greater than 30.

- d.   i.   CI: (70.151, 71.49)

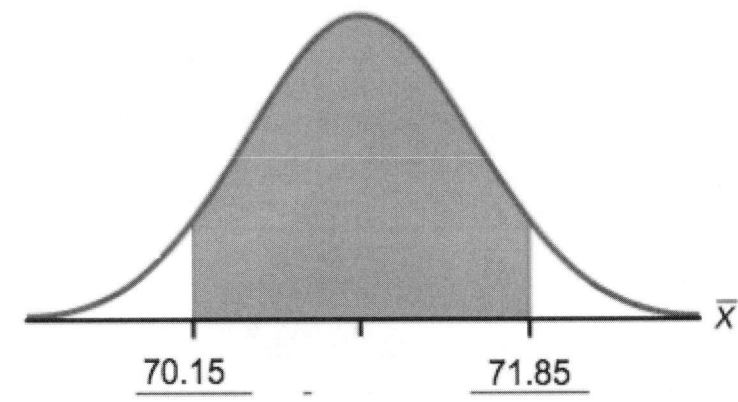

     ii.

Figure 8.17

     iii.   *EBM* = 0.849

- e.   The confidence interval will decrease in size, because the sample size increased. Recall, when all factors remain unchanged, an increase in sample size decreases variability. Thus, we do not need as large an interval to capture the true population mean.

97

- a.   i. $\bar{x}$ = 23.6

     ii. σ = 7

     iii.   n = 100

- b.   X is the time needed to complete an individual tax form. $\bar{X}$ is the mean time to complete tax forms from a sample of 100 customers.

- c. $N\left(23.6, \frac{7}{\sqrt{100}}\right)$ because we know sigma.

- d.   ii.   (22.228, 24.972)

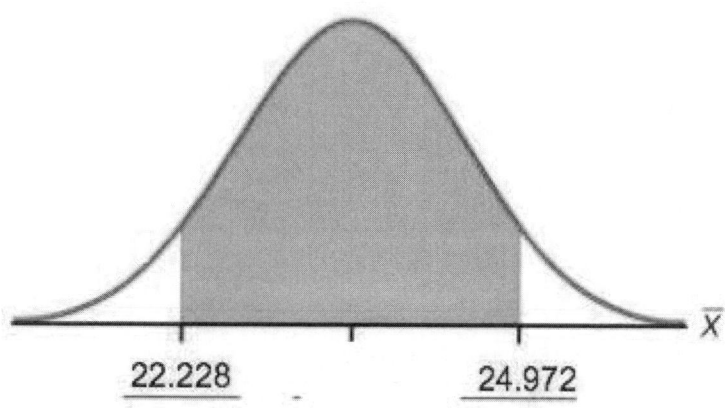

Figure 8.18

   iii. *EBM* = 1.372

e. It will need to change the sample size. The firm needs to determine what the confidence level should be, then apply the error bound formula to determine the necessary sample size.

f. The confidence level would increase as a result of a larger interval. Smaller sample sizes result in more variability. To capture the true population mean, we need to have a larger interval.

g. According to the error bound formula, the firm needs to survey 206 people. Since we increase the confidence level, we need to increase either our error bound or the sample size.

99

a.   i. 7.9

     ii. 2.5

    iii. 20

b. X is the number of letters a single camper will send home. $\overline{X}$ is the mean number of letters sent home from a sample of 20 campers.

c. $N\ 7.9\left(\dfrac{2.5}{\sqrt{20}}\right)$

d.   i. CI: (6.98, 8.82)

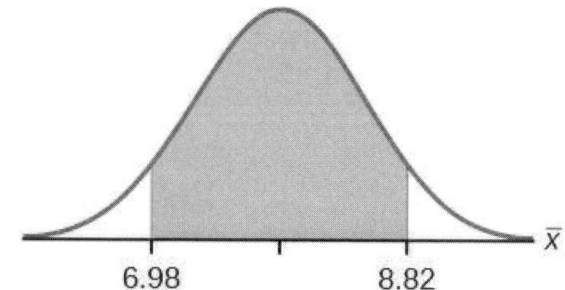

   ii.

Figure 8.19

   iii. *EBM*: 0.92

e. The error bound and confidence interval will decrease.

101

a. $\bar{x}$ = \$568,873

b. $CL = 0.95 \; \alpha = 1 - 0.95 = 0.05 \; z_{\frac{\alpha}{2}} = 1.96$

$EBM = z_{0.025}\frac{\sigma}{\sqrt{n}} = 1.96 \; \frac{909200}{\sqrt{40}} = \$281,764$

c. $\bar{x} - EBM = 568,873 - 281,764 = 287,109$

$\bar{x} + EBM = 568,873 + 281,764 = 850,637$

Alternate solution:

 Using the TI-83, 83+, 84, 84+ Calculator

1. Press **STAT** and arrow over to **TESTS**.

2. Arrow down to **7:ZInterval**.

3. Press **ENTER**.

4. Arrow to Stats and press **ENTER**.

5. Arrow down and enter the following values:

   σ : 909,200

   $\bar{x}$: 568,873

   n: 40

   CL: 0.95

6. Arrow down to Calculate and press **ENTER**.

7. The confidence interval is (\$287,114, \$850,632).

8. Notice the small difference between the two solutions–these differences are simply due to rounding error in the hand calculations.

d. We estimate with 95% confidence that the mean amount of contributions received from all individuals by House candidates is between \$287,109 and \$850,637.

103 Use the formula for *EBM*, solved for *n*:

$n = \frac{z^2\sigma^2}{EBM^2}$ From the statement of the problem, you know that $\sigma = 2.5$, and you need $EBM = 1$. $z = z_{0.035} = 1.812$ (This is the value of z for which the area under the density curve to the **right** of z is 0.035.)

$n = \frac{z^2\sigma^2}{EBM^2} = \frac{1.812^2 2.5^2}{1^2} \approx 20.52$ You need to measure at least 21 male students to achieve your goal.

105

a.   i.   8629

  ii.   6944

  iii.   35

  iv.   34

b. t_{34}

c.   i.   CI: (6244, 11,014)

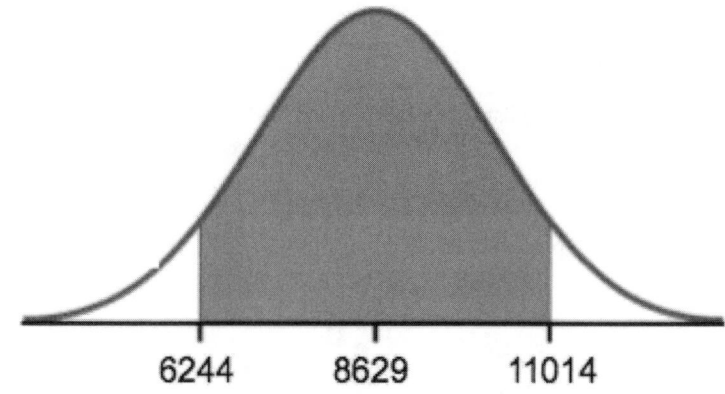

ii.

Figure 8.20

    iii. EB = 2385

d. It will become smaller

107

a.   i. $\bar{x}$ = 2.51

    ii. s_x = 0.318

    iii. $n = 9$

    iv. $n - 1 = 8$

b. the effective length of time for a tranquilizer

c. the mean effective length of time of tranquilizers from a sample of nine patients

d. We need to use a Student's-t distribution, because we do not know the population standard deviation.

e.   i. CI: (2.27, 2.76)

    ii. Check student's solution.

    iii. *EBM*: 0.25

f. If we were to sample many groups of nine patients, 95% of the samples would contain the true population mean length of time.

109 $\bar{x} = \$251, 854.23$ $s = \$521, 130.41$ Note that we are not given the population standard deviation, only the standard deviation of the sample. There are 30 measures in the sample, so $n = 30$, and $df = 30 - 1 = 29$ $CL = 0.96$, so $\alpha = 1 - CL = 1 - 0.96 = 0.04$ $\frac{\alpha}{2} = 0.02$ $t_{\frac{\alpha}{2}} = t_{0.02} = 2.150$ $EBM = t_{\frac{\alpha}{2}}\left(\frac{s}{\sqrt{n}}\right) = 2.150\left(\frac{521, 130.41}{\sqrt{30}}\right)$ ~ $\$204, 561.66$ $\bar{x}$ -

$EBM = \$251,854.23 - \$204,561.66 = \$47,292.57$ $\bar{x} + EBM = \$251,854.23 + \$204,561.66 = \$456,415.89$ We estimate with 96% confidence that the mean amount of money raised by all Leadership PACs during the 2011–2012 election cycle lies between \$47,292.57 and \$456,415.89.

Alternate Solution

 Using the TI-83, 83+, 84, 84+ Calculator

Enter the data as a list.

Press **STAT** and arrow over to **TESTS**.

Arrow down to 8:TInterval.

Press ENTER.

Arrow to Data and press ENTER.

Arrow down and enter the name of the list where the data is stored.

Enter Freq: 1

Enter C-Level: 0.96

Arrow down to Calculate and press Enter.

The 96% confidence interval is ($47,262, $456,447).

The difference between solutions arises from rounding differences.

111

a.   i. $\bar{x}$ = 11.6

    ii. s_x = 4.1

    iii. n = 225

    iv. $n - 1 = 224$

b. X is the number of unoccupied seats on a single flight. $\bar{X}$ is the mean number of unoccupied seats from a sample of 225 flights.

c.   We will use a Student's-t distribution, because we do not know the population standard deviation.

d.   i.   CI: (11.12 , 12.08)

    ii.   Check student's solution.

    iii.   *EBM*: 0.48

113

a.   i.   CI: (7.64 , 9.36)

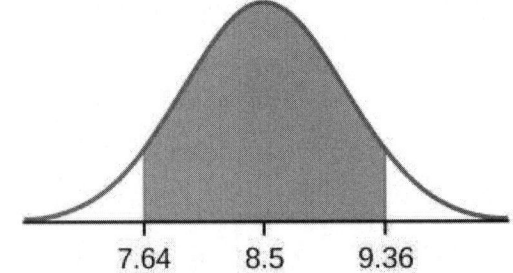

    ii.

Figure 8.21

    iii.   *EBM*: 0.86

b.   The sample should have been increased.

c.   Answers will vary.

d.   Answers will vary.

e.   Answers will vary.

115 b

117

a. 1,068

b. The sample size would need to be increased since the critical value increases as the confidence level increases.

119

a. X = the number of people who feel that the president is doing an acceptable job;

P' = the proportion of people in a sample who feel that the president is doing an acceptable job.

b. $N\left(0.61, \sqrt{\dfrac{(0.61)(0.39)}{1200}}\right)$

c. i. CI: (0.59, 0.63)

ii. Check student's solution

iii. *EBM*: 0.02

121

a. i. (0.72, 0.82)

ii. (0.65, 0.76)

iii. (0.60, 0.72)

b. Yes, the intervals (0.72, 0.82) and (0.65, 0.76) overlap, and the intervals (0.65, 0.76) and (0.60, 0.72) overlap.

c. We can say that there does not appear to be a significant difference between the proportion of Asian adults who say that their families would welcome a white person into their families and the proportion of Asian adults who say that their families would welcome a Latino person into their families.

d. We can say that there is a significant difference between the proportion of Asian adults who say that their families would welcome a white person into their families and the proportion of Asian adults who say that their families would welcome a black person into their families.

123

a. X = the number of adult Americans who feel that crime is the main problem; P' = the proportion of adult Americans who feel that crime is the main problem

b. Since we are estimating a proportion, given P' = 0.2 and n = 1000, the distribution we should use is $N\left(0.2, \sqrt{\dfrac{(0.2)(0.8)}{1000}}\right)$.

c. i. CI: (0.18, 0.22)

ii. Check student's solution.

iii. *EBM*: 0.02

d. One way to lower the sampling error is to increase the sample size.

e. The stated "± 3%" represents the maximum error bound. This means that those doing the study are reporting a maximum error of 3%. Thus, they estimate the percentage of adult Americans who feel that crime is the main problem to be between 18% and 22%.

125 c

127 d

129 a

131

a. $p' = \dfrac{(0.55 + 0.49)}{2} = 0.52$; *EBP* = 0.55 - 0.52 = 0.03

b. No, the confidence interval includes values less than or equal to 0.50. It is possible that less than half of the population believe this.

c. $CL = 0.75$, so $\alpha = 1 - 0.75 = 0.25$ and $\frac{\alpha}{2} = 0.125$ $z_{\frac{\alpha}{2}} = 1.150$. (The area to the right of this z is 0.125, so the area to

the left is $1 - 0.125 = 0.875$.)

$$EBP = (1.150)\sqrt{\frac{0.52(0.48)}{1,000}} \approx 0.018$$

$(p' - EBP, p' + EBP) = (0.52 - 0.018, 0.52 + 0.018) = (0.502, 0.538)$
Alternate Solution

 Using the TI-83, 83+, 84, 84+ Calculator

STAT TESTS A: 1-PropZinterval with $x = (0.52)(1,000)$, $n = 1,000$, CL = 0.75.

Answer is (0.502, 0.538)

d. Yes – this interval does not fall less than 0.50 so we can conclude that at least half of all American adults believe that major sports programs corrupt education – but we do so with only 75% confidence.

133 $CL = 0.95$ $\alpha = 1 - 0.95 = 0.05$ $\frac{\alpha}{2} = 0.025$ $z_{\frac{\alpha}{2}} = 1.96$. Use $p' = q' = 0.5$.

$$n = \frac{z_{\frac{\alpha}{2}}^2 p' q'}{EBP^2} = \frac{1.96^2(0.5)(0.5)}{0.05^2} = 384.16$$ You need to interview at least 385 students to estimate the proportion to within 5% at 95% confidence.

9 | HYPOTHESIS TESTING WITH ONE SAMPLE

Figure 9.1 You can use a hypothesis test to decide if a dog breeder's claim that every Dalmatian has 35 spots is statistically sound. (Credit: Robert Neff)

Introduction

Chapter Objectives
By the end of this chapter, the student should be able to: • Differentiate between Type I and Type II Errors • Describe hypothesis testing in general and in practice • Conduct and interpret hypothesis tests for a single population mean, population standard deviation known. • Conduct and interpret hypothesis tests for a single population mean, population standard deviation unknown. • Conduct and interpret hypothesis tests for a single population proportion.

One job of a statistician is to make statistical inferences about populations based on samples taken from the population.

Confidence intervals are one way to estimate a population parameter. Another way to make a statistical inference is to make a decision about a parameter. For instance, a car dealer advertises that its new small truck gets 35 miles per gallon, on average. A tutoring service claims that its method of tutoring helps 90% of its students get an A or a B. A company says that women managers in their company earn an average of $60,000 per year.

A statistician will make a decision about these claims. This process is called " **hypothesis testing**." A hypothesis test involves collecting data from a sample and evaluating the data. Then, the statistician makes a decision as to whether or not there is sufficient evidence, based upon analyses of the data, to reject the null hypothesis.

In this chapter, you will conduct hypothesis tests on single means and single proportions. You will also learn about the errors associated with these tests.

Hypothesis testing consists of two contradictory hypotheses or statements, a decision based on the data, and a conclusion. To perform a hypothesis test, a statistician will:

1. Set up two contradictory hypotheses.

2. Collect sample data (in homework problems, the data or summary statistics will be given to you).

3. Determine the correct distribution to perform the hypothesis test.

4. Analyze sample data by performing the calculations that ultimately will allow you to reject or decline to reject the null hypothesis.

5. Make a decision and write a meaningful conclusion.

> **NOTE**
>
> To do the hypothesis test homework problems for this chapter and later chapters, make copies of the appropriate special solution sheets. See **Appendix E**.

9.1 | Null and Alternative Hypotheses

The actual test begins by considering two **hypotheses**. They are called the **null hypothesis** and the **alternative hypothesis**. These hypotheses contain opposing viewpoints.

H_0: **The null hypothesis:** It is a statement of no difference between sample means or proportions or no difference between a sample mean or proportion and a population mean or proportion. In other words, the difference equals 0.

H_a: **The alternative hypothesis:** It is a claim about the population that is contradictory to H_0 and what we conclude when we reject H_0.

Since the null and alternative hypotheses are contradictory, you must examine evidence to decide if you have enough evidence to reject the null hypothesis or not. The evidence is in the form of sample data.

After you have determined which hypothesis the sample supports, you make a **decision.** There are two options for a decision. They are "reject H_0" if the sample information favors the alternative hypothesis or "do not reject H_0" or "decline to reject H_0" if the sample information is insufficient to reject the null hypothesis.

Mathematical Symbols Used in H_0 and H_a:

H_0	H_a
equal (=)	not equal (≠) **or** greater than (>) **or** less than (<)
greater than or equal to (≥)	less than (<)
less than or equal to (≤)	more than (>)

Table 9.1

> **NOTE**
>
> H_0 always has a symbol with an equal in it. H_a never has a symbol with an equal in it. The choice of symbol depends

on the wording of the hypothesis test. However, be aware that many researchers (including one of the co-authors in research work) use = in the null hypothesis, even with > or < as the symbol in the alternative hypothesis. This practice is acceptable because we only make the decision to reject or not reject the null hypothesis.

Example 9.1

H_0: No more than 30% of the registered voters in Santa Clara County voted in the primary election. $p \leq 30$
H_a: More than 30% of the registered voters in Santa Clara County voted in the primary election. $p > 30$

9.1 A medical trial is conducted to test whether or not a new medicine reduces cholesterol by 25%. State the null and alternative hypotheses.

Example 9.2

We want to test whether the mean GPA of students in American colleges is different from 2.0 (out of 4.0). The null and alternative hypotheses are:
H_0: $\mu = 2.0$
H_a: $\mu \neq 2.0$

9.2 We want to test whether the mean height of eighth graders is 66 inches. State the null and alternative hypotheses. Fill in the correct symbol (=, ≠, ≥, <, ≤, >) for the null and alternative hypotheses.

a. H_0: μ ___ 66

b. H_a: μ ___ 66

Example 9.3

We want to test if college students take less than five years to graduate from college, on the average. The null and alternative hypotheses are:
H_0: $\mu \geq 5$
H_a: $\mu < 5$

9.3 We want to test if it takes fewer than 45 minutes to teach a lesson plan. State the null and alternative hypotheses. Fill in the correct symbol (=, ≠, ≥, <, ≤, >) for the null and alternative hypotheses.

a. H_0: μ ___ 45

b. H_a: μ ___ 45

Example 9.4

In an issue of *U. S. News and World Report*, an article on school standards stated that about half of all students in France, Germany, and Israel take advanced placement exams and a third pass. The same article stated that 6.6% of U.S. students take advanced placement exams and 4.4% pass. Test if the percentage of U.S. students who take advanced placement exams is more than 6.6%. State the null and alternative hypotheses.
H_0: $p \leq 0.066$
H_a: $p > 0.066$

 Try It Σ

9.4 On a state driver's test, about 40% pass the test on the first try. We want to test if more than 40% pass on the first try. Fill in the correct symbol (=, ≠, ≥, <, ≤, >) for the null and alternative hypotheses.

a. H_0: p ___ 0.40

b. H_a: p ___ 0.40

Collaborative Exercise

Bring to class a newspaper, some news magazines, and some Internet articles . In groups, find articles from which your group can write null and alternative hypotheses. Discuss your hypotheses with the rest of the class.

9.2 | Outcomes and the Type I and Type II Errors

When you perform a hypothesis test, there are four possible outcomes depending on the actual truth (or falseness) of the null hypothesis H_0 and the decision to reject or not. The outcomes are summarized in the following table:

ACTION	H_0 IS ACTUALLY	...
	True	False
Do not reject H_0	Correct Outcome	Type II error
Reject H_0	Type I Error	Correct Outcome

Table 9.2

The four possible outcomes in the table are:

1.   The decision is **not to reject H_0** when **H_0 is true (correct decision).**
2.   The decision is to **reject H_0** when **H_0 is true** (incorrect decision known as a **Type I error**).
3.   The decision is **not to reject H_0** when, in fact, **H_0 is false** (incorrect decision known as a **Type II error**).
4.   The decision is to **reject H_0** when **H_0 is false** (**correct decision** whose probability is called the **Power of the Test**).

Each of the errors occurs with a particular probability. The Greek letters α and β represent the probabilities.

α = probability of a Type I error = **P(Type I error)** = probability of rejecting the null hypothesis when the null hypothesis is true.

β = probability of a Type II error = **P(Type II error)** = probability of not rejecting the null hypothesis when the null hypothesis is false.

α and β should be as small as possible because they are probabilities of errors. They are rarely zero.

The Power of the Test is $1 - \beta$. Ideally, we want a high power that is as close to one as possible. Increasing the sample size can increase the Power of the Test.

The following are examples of Type I and Type II errors.

Example 9.5

Suppose the null hypothesis, H_0, is: Frank's rock climbing equipment is safe.

Type I error: Frank thinks that his rock climbing equipment may not be safe when, in fact, it really is safe. **Type II error**: Frank thinks that his rock climbing equipment may be safe when, in fact, it is not safe.

α = **probability** that Frank thinks his rock climbing equipment may not be safe when, in fact, it really is safe. β = **probability** that Frank thinks his rock climbing equipment may be safe when, in fact, it is not safe.

Notice that, in this case, the error with the greater consequence is the Type II error. (If Frank thinks his rock climbing equipment is safe, he will go ahead and use it.)

9.5 Suppose the null hypothesis, H_0, is: the blood cultures contain no traces of pathogen X. State the Type I and Type II errors.

Example 9.6

Suppose the null hypothesis, H_0, is: The victim of an automobile accident is alive when he arrives at the emergency room of a hospital.

Type I error: The emergency crew thinks that the victim is dead when, in fact, the victim is alive. **Type II error**: The emergency crew does not know if the victim is alive when, in fact, the victim is dead.

α = **probability** that the emergency crew thinks the victim is dead when, in fact, he is really alive = P(Type I error). β = **probability** that the emergency crew does not know if the victim is alive when, in fact, the victim is dead = P(Type II error).

The error with the greater consequence is the Type I error. (If the emergency crew thinks the victim is dead, they will not treat him.)

9.6 Suppose the null hypothesis, H_0, is: a patient is not sick. Which type of error has the greater consequence, Type I or Type II?

Example 9.7

It's a Boy Genetic Labs claim to be able to increase the likelihood that a pregnancy will result in a boy being born. Statisticians want to test the claim. Suppose that the null hypothesis, H_0, is: It's a Boy Genetic Labs has no effect on gender outcome.

Type I error: This results when a true null hypothesis is rejected. In the context of this scenario, we would state that we believe that It's a Boy Genetic Labs influences the gender outcome, when in fact it has no effect. The probability of this error occurring is denoted by the Greek letter alpha, α.

Type II error: This results when we fail to reject a false null hypothesis. In context, we would state that It's a Boy Genetic Labs does not influence the gender outcome of a pregnancy when, in fact, it does. The probability of this error occurring is denoted by the Greek letter beta, β.

The error of greater consequence would be the Type I error since couples would use the It's a Boy Genetic Labs product in hopes of increasing the chances of having a boy.

Try It Σ

9.7 "Red tide" is a bloom of poison-producing algae–a few different species of a class of plankton called dinoflagellates. When the weather and water conditions cause these blooms, shellfish such as clams living in the area develop dangerous levels of a paralysis-inducing toxin. In Massachusetts, the Division of Marine Fisheries (DMF) monitors levels of the toxin in shellfish by regular sampling of shellfish along the coastline. If the mean level of toxin in clams exceeds 800 μg (micrograms) of toxin per kg of clam meat in any area, clam harvesting is banned there until the bloom is over and levels of toxin in clams subside. Describe both a Type I and a Type II error in this context, and state which error has the greater consequence.

Example 9.8

A certain experimental drug claims a cure rate of at least 75% for males with prostate cancer. Describe both the Type I and Type II errors in context. Which error is the more serious?

Type I: A cancer patient believes the cure rate for the drug is less than 75% when it actually is at least 75%.

Type II: A cancer patient believes the experimental drug has at least a 75% cure rate when it has a cure rate that is less than 75%.

In this scenario, the Type II error contains the more severe consequence. If a patient believes the drug works at least 75% of the time, this most likely will influence the patient's (and doctor's) choice about whether to use the drug as a treatment option.

Try It Σ

9.8 Determine both Type I and Type II errors for the following scenario:

Assume a null hypothesis, H_0, that states the percentage of adults with jobs is at least 88%.

Identify the Type I and Type II errors from these four statements.

a. Not to reject the null hypothesis that the percentage of adults who have jobs is at least 88% when that percentage is actually less than 88%

b. Not to reject the null hypothesis that the percentage of adults who have jobs is at least 88% when the percentage is actually at least 88%.

c. Reject the null hypothesis that the percentage of adults who have jobs is at least 88% when the percentage is actually at least 88%.

d. Reject the null hypothesis that the percentage of adults who have jobs is at least 88% when that percentage is actually less than 88%.

9.3 | Distribution Needed for Hypothesis Testing

Earlier in the course, we discussed sampling distributions. **Particular distributions are associated with hypothesis**

testing. Perform tests of a population mean using a **normal distribution** or a **Student's *t*-distribution**. (Remember, use a Student's *t*-distribution when the population **standard deviation** is unknown and the distribution of the sample mean is approximately normal.) We perform tests of a population proportion using a normal distribution (usually *n* is large).

If you are testing a **single population mean**, the distribution for the test is for **means**:

$$\bar{X} \sim N\left(\mu_X, \frac{\sigma_X}{\sqrt{n}}\right) \text{ or } t_{df}$$

The population parameter is μ. The estimated value (point estimate) for μ is $\bar{x}$, the sample mean.

If you are testing a **single population proportion**, the distribution for the test is for proportions or percentages:

$$P' \sim N\left(p, \sqrt{\frac{p \cdot q}{n}}\right)$$

The population parameter is *p*. The estimated value (point estimate) for *p* is *p'*. $p' = \frac{x}{n}$ where *x* is the number of successes and *n* is the sample size.

Assumptions

When you perform a **hypothesis test of a single population mean μ** using a **Student's *t*-distribution** (often called a t-test), there are fundamental assumptions that need to be met in order for the test to work properly. Your data should be a **simple random sample** that comes from a population that is approximately **normally distributed**. You use the sample **standard deviation** to approximate the population standard deviation. (Note that if the sample size is sufficiently large, a t-test will work even if the population is not approximately normally distributed).

When you perform a **hypothesis test of a single population mean μ** using a normal distribution (often called a *z*-test), you take a simple random sample from the population. The population you are testing is normally distributed or your sample size is sufficiently large. You know the value of the population standard deviation which, in reality, is rarely known.

When you perform a **hypothesis test of a single population proportion *p***, you take a simple random sample from the population. You must meet the conditions for a **binomial distribution** which are: there are a certain number *n* of independent trials, the outcomes of any trial are success or failure, and each trial has the same probability of a success *p*. The shape of the binomial distribution needs to be similar to the shape of the normal distribution. To ensure this, the quantities *np* and *nq* must both be greater than five ($np > 5$ and $nq > 5$). Then the binomial distribution of a sample (estimated) proportion can be approximated by the normal distribution with $\mu = p$ and $\sigma = \sqrt{\frac{pq}{n}}$. Remember that $q = 1 - p$.

9.4 | Rare Events, the Sample, Decision and Conclusion

Establishing the type of distribution, sample size, and known or unknown standard deviation can help you figure out how to go about a hypothesis test. However, there are several other factors you should consider when working out a hypothesis test.

Rare Events

Suppose you make an assumption about a property of the population (this assumption is the **null hypothesis**). Then you gather sample data randomly. If the sample has properties that would be very **unlikely** to occur if the assumption is true, then you would conclude that your assumption about the population is probably incorrect. (Remember that your assumption is just an **assumption**—it is not a fact and it may or may not be true. But your sample data are real and the data are showing you a fact that seems to contradict your assumption.)

For example, Didi and Ali are at a birthday party of a very wealthy friend. They hurry to be first in line to grab a prize from a tall basket that they cannot see inside because they will be blindfolded. There are 200 plastic bubbles in the basket and Didi and Ali have been told that there is only one with a $100 bill. Didi is the first person to reach into the basket and pull out a bubble. Her bubble contains a $100 bill. The probability of this happening is $\frac{1}{200} = 0.005$. Because this is so unlikely,

Ali is hoping that what the two of them were told is wrong and there are more $100 bills in the basket. A "rare event" has occurred (Didi getting the $100 bill) so Ali doubts the assumption about only one $100 bill being in the basket.

Using the Sample to Test the Null Hypothesis

Use the sample data to calculate the actual probability of getting the test result, called the *p*-value. The *p*-value is the **probability that, if the null hypothesis is true, the results from another randomly selected sample will be as extreme**

or more extreme as the results obtained from the given sample.

A large *p*-value calculated from the data indicates that we should not reject the **null hypothesis**. The smaller the *p*-value, the more unlikely the outcome, and the stronger the evidence is against the null hypothesis. We would reject the null hypothesis if the evidence is strongly against it.

Draw a graph that shows the *p*-value. The hypothesis test is easier to perform if you use a graph because you see the problem more clearly.

Example 9.9

Suppose a baker claims that his bread height is more than 15 cm, on average. Several of his customers do not believe him. To persuade his customers that he is right, the baker decides to do a hypothesis test. He bakes 10 loaves of bread. The mean height of the sample loaves is 17 cm. The baker knows from baking hundreds of loaves of bread that the **standard deviation** for the height is 0.5 cm. and the distribution of heights is normal.

The null hypothesis could be H_0: $\mu \leq 15$ The alternate hypothesis is H_a: $\mu > 15$

The words **"is more than"** translates as a ">" so "$\mu > 15$" goes into the alternate hypothesis. The null hypothesis must contradict the alternate hypothesis.

Since σ **is known** ($\sigma = 0.5$ cm.), the distribution for the population is known to be normal with mean $\mu = 15$ and standard deviation $\frac{\sigma}{\sqrt{n}} = \frac{0.5}{\sqrt{10}} = 0.16$.

Suppose the null hypothesis is true (the mean height of the loaves is no more than 15 cm). Then is the mean height (17 cm) calculated from the sample unexpectedly large? The hypothesis test works by asking the question how **unlikely** the sample mean would be if the null hypothesis were true. The graph shows how far out the sample mean is on the normal curve. The *p*-value is the probability that, if we were to take other samples, any other sample mean would fall at least as far out as 17 cm.

The *p*-value, then, is the probability that a sample mean is the same or greater than 17 cm. when the population mean is, in fact, 15 cm. We can calculate this probability using the normal distribution for means.

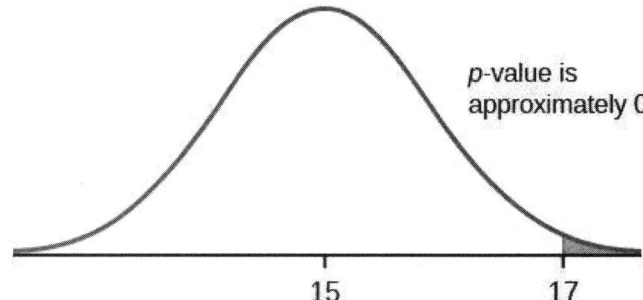

Figure 9.2

p-value= $P(\bar{x} > 17)$ which is approximately zero.

A *p*-value of approximately zero tells us that it is highly unlikely that a loaf of bread rises no more than 15 cm, on average. That is, almost 0% of all loaves of bread would be at least as high as 17 cm. **purely by CHANCE** had the population mean height really been 15 cm. Because the outcome of 17 cm. is so **unlikely (meaning it is happening NOT by chance alone)**, we conclude that the evidence is strongly against the null hypothesis (the mean height is at most 15 cm.). There is sufficient evidence that the true mean height for the population of the baker's loaves of bread is greater than 15 cm.

Try It Σ

9.9 A normal distribution has a standard deviation of 1. We want to verify a claim that the mean is greater than 12. A sample of 36 is taken with a sample mean of 12.5.

H_0: $\mu \leq 12$
H_a: $\mu > 12$
The *p*-value is 0.0013
Draw a graph that shows the *p*-value.

Decision and Conclusion

A systematic way to make a decision of whether to reject or not reject the **null hypothesis** is to compare the *p*-value and a **preset or preconceived α (also called a "significance level")**. A preset α is the probability of a **Type I error** (rejecting the null hypothesis when the null hypothesis is true). It may or may not be given to you at the beginning of the problem.

When you make a **decision** to reject or not reject H_0, do as follows:

- If $\alpha > p$-value, reject H_0. The results of the sample data are significant. There is sufficient evidence to conclude that H_0 is an incorrect belief and that the **alternative hypothesis**, H_a, may be correct.

- If $\alpha \leq p$-value, do not reject H_0. The results of the sample data are not significant. There is not sufficient evidence to conclude that the alternative hypothesis, H_a, may be correct.

- When you "do not reject H_0", it does not mean that you should believe that H_0 is true. It simply means that the sample data have **failed** to provide sufficient evidence to cast serious doubt about the truthfulness of H_o.

Conclusion: After you make your decision, write a thoughtful **conclusion** about the hypotheses in terms of the given problem.

Example 9.10

When using the *p*-value to evaluate a hypothesis test, it is sometimes useful to use the following memory device

If the *p*-value is low, the null must go.

If the *p*-value is high, the null must fly.

This memory aid relates a *p*-value less than the established alpha (the *p* is low) as rejecting the null hypothesis and, likewise, relates a *p*-value higher than the established alpha (the *p* is high) as not rejecting the null hypothesis.

Fill in the blanks.

Reject the null hypothesis when _____.

The results of the sample data _____.

Do not reject the null when hypothesis when _____.

The results of the sample data _____.

Solution 9.10

Reject the null hypothesis when **the *p*-value is less than the established alpha value**. The results of the sample data **support the alternative hypothesis**.

Do not reject the null hypothesis when **the *p*-value is greater than the established alpha value**. The results of the sample data **do not support the alternative hypothesis**.

9.10 It's a Boy Genetics Labs claim their procedures improve the chances of a boy being born. The results for a test of a single population proportion are as follows:

H_0: $p = 0.50$, H_a: $p > 0.50$

$\alpha = 0.01$

p-value $= 0.025$

Interpret the results and state a conclusion in simple, non-technical terms.

9.5 | Additional Information and Full Hypothesis Test Examples

- In a **hypothesis test** problem, you may see words such as "the level of significance is 1%." The "1%" is the preconceived or preset α.
- The statistician setting up the hypothesis test selects the value of α to use **before** collecting the sample data.
- **If no level of significance is given, a common standard to use is $\alpha = 0.05$.**
- When you calculate the p-value and draw the picture, the p-value is the area in the left tail, the right tail, or split evenly between the two tails. For this reason, we call the hypothesis test left, right, or two tailed.
- The **alternative hypothesis**, H_a, tells you if the test is left, right, or two-tailed. It is the **key** to conducting the appropriate test.
- H_a **never** has a symbol that contains an equal sign.
- **Thinking about the meaning of the p-value**: A data analyst (and anyone else) should have more confidence that he made the correct decision to reject the null hypothesis with a smaller p-value (for example, 0.001 as opposed to 0.04) even if using the 0.05 level for alpha. Similarly, for a large p-value such as 0.4, as opposed to a p-value of 0.056 (alpha = 0.05 is less than either number), a data analyst should have more confidence that she made the correct decision in not rejecting the null hypothesis. This makes the data analyst use judgment rather than mindlessly applying rules.

The following examples illustrate a left-, right-, and two-tailed test.

Example 9.11

H_o: $\mu = 5$, H_a: $\mu < 5$

Test of a single population mean. H_a tells you the test is left-tailed. The picture of the p-value is as follows:

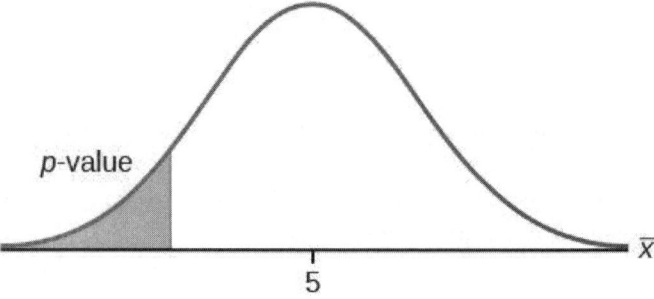

Figure 9.3

Try It Σ

9.11 H_0: $\mu = 10$, H_a: $\mu < 10$

Assume the *p*-value is 0.0935. What type of test is this? Draw the picture of the *p*-value.

Example 9.12

H_0: $p \leq 0.2$ H_a: $p > 0.2$

This is a test of a single population proportion. H_a tells you the test is **right-tailed**. The picture of the *p*-value is as follows:

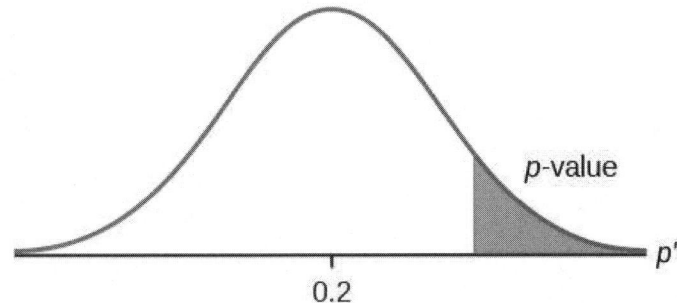

Figure 9.4

Try It Σ

9.12 H_0: $\mu \leq 1$, H_a: $\mu > 1$

Assume the *p*-value is 0.1243. What type of test is this? Draw the picture of the *p*-value.

Example 9.13

H_0: $p = 50$ H_a: $p \neq 50$

This is a test of a single population mean. H_a tells you the test is **two-tailed**. The picture of the *p*-value is as follows.

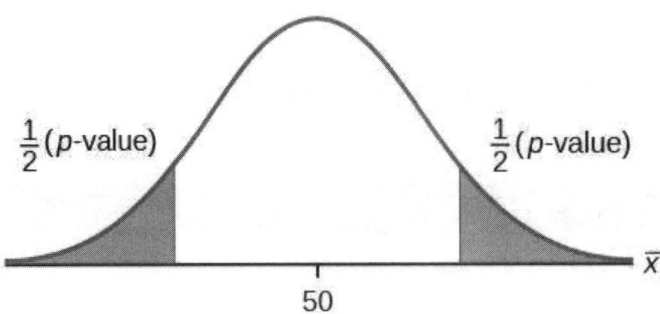

Figure 9.5

9.13 H_0: $p = 0.5$, H_a: $p \neq 0.5$

Assume the *p*-value is 0.2564. What type of test is this? Draw the picture of the *p*-value.

Full Hypothesis Test Examples

Example 9.14

Jeffrey, as an eight-year old, **established a mean time of 16.43 seconds** for swimming the 25-yard freestyle, with a **standard deviation of 0.8 seconds**. His dad, Frank, thought that Jeffrey could swim the 25-yard freestyle faster using goggles. Frank bought Jeffrey a new pair of expensive goggles and timed Jeffrey for **15 25-yard freestyle swims**. For the 15 swims, **Jeffrey's mean time was 16 seconds. Frank thought that the goggles helped Jeffrey to swim faster than the 16.43 seconds.** Conduct a hypothesis test using a preset $\alpha = 0.05$. Assume that the swim times for the 25-yard freestyle are normal.

Solution 9.14

Set up the Hypothesis Test:

Since the problem is about a mean, this is a **test of a single population mean**.

H_0: $\mu = 16.43$ H_a: $\mu < 16.43$

For Jeffrey to swim faster, his time will be less than 16.43 seconds. The "<" tells you this is left-tailed.

Determine the distribution needed:

Random variable: $\bar{X}$ = the mean time to swim the 25-yard freestyle.

Distribution for the test: $\bar{X}$ is normal (population **standard deviation** is known: $\sigma = 0.8$)

$$\bar{X} \sim N\left(\mu, \frac{\sigma_X}{\sqrt{n}}\right) \text{ Therefore, } \bar{X} \sim N\left(16.43, \frac{0.8}{\sqrt{15}}\right)$$

$\mu = 16.43$ comes from H_0 and not the data. $\sigma = 0.8$, and $n = 15$.

Calculate the *p*-value using the normal distribution for a mean:

p-value = $P(\bar{x} < 16) = 0.0187$ where the sample mean in the problem is given as 16.

p-value = 0.0187 (This is called the **actual level of significance**.) The *p*-value is the area to the left of the sample mean is given as 16.

Graph:

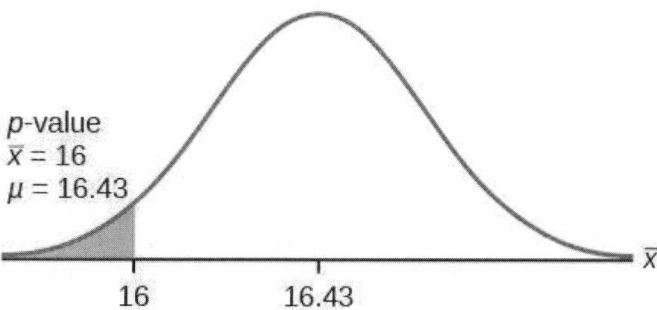

Figure 9.6

$\mu = 16.43$ comes from H_0. Our assumption is $\mu = 16.43$.

Interpretation of the *p*-value: If H_0 is true, there is a 0.0187 probability (1.87%)that Jeffrey's mean time to swim the 25-yard freestyle is 16 seconds or less. Because a 1.87% chance is small, the mean time of 16 seconds or less is unlikely to have happened randomly. It is a rare event.

Compare α and the *p*-value:

$\alpha = 0.05$ *p*-value = 0.0187 $\alpha >$ *p*-value

Make a decision: Since $\alpha >$ *p*-value, reject H_0.

This means that you reject $\mu = 16.43$. In other words, you do not think Jeffrey swims the 25-yard freestyle in 16.43 seconds but faster with the new goggles.

Conclusion: At the 5% significance level, we conclude that Jeffrey swims faster using the new goggles. The sample data show there is sufficient evidence that Jeffrey's mean time to swim the 25-yard freestyle is less than 16.43 seconds.

The *p*-value can easily be calculated.

 Using the TI-83, 83+, 84, 84+ Calculator

Press **STAT** and arrow over to **TESTS**. Press **1:Z-Test**. Arrow over to **Stats** and press **ENTER**. Arrow down and enter 16.43 for μ_0 (null hypothesis), .8 for σ, 16 for the sample mean, and 15 for *n*. Arrow down to μ : (alternate hypothesis) and arrow over to $< \mu_0$. Press **ENTER**. Arrow down to **Calculate** and press **ENTER**. The calculator not only calculates the *p*-value ($p = 0.0187$) but it also calculates the test statistic (*z*-score) for the sample mean. $\mu < 16.43$ is the alternative hypothesis. Do this set of instructions again except arrow to **Draw**(instead of **Calculate**). Press **ENTER**. A shaded graph appears with $z = -2.08$ (test statistic) and $p = 0.0187$ (*p*-value). Make sure when you use **Draw** that no other equations are highlighted in $Y =$ and the plots are turned off.

When the calculator does a *Z*-Test, the **Z-Test** function finds the *p*-value by doing a normal probability calculation using the **central limit theorem**:

$$P(\overline{x} < 16) = \text{2nd DISTR normcdf} \left(-10^{\wedge}99, 16, 16.43, 0.8 / \sqrt{15} \right).$$

The Type I and Type II errors for this problem are as follows:

The Type I error is to conclude that Jeffrey swims the 25-yard freestyle, on average, in less than 16.43 seconds when, in fact, he actually swims the 25-yard freestyle, on average, in 16.43 seconds. (Reject the null hypothesis when the null hypothesis is true.)

The Type II error is that there is not evidence to conclude that Jeffrey swims the 25-yard free-style, on average, in less than 16.43 seconds when, in fact, he actually does swim the 25-yard free-style, on average, in less than 16.43 seconds. (Do not reject the null hypothesis when the null hypothesis is false.)

 Try It Σ

9.14 The mean throwing distance of a football for Marco, a high school freshman quarterback, is 40 yards, with a standard deviation of two yards. The team coach tells Marco to adjust his grip to get more distance. The coach records the distances for 20 throws. For the 20 throws, Marco's mean distance was 45 yards. The coach thought the different grip helped Marco throw farther than 40 yards. Conduct a hypothesis test using a preset $\alpha = 0.05$. Assume the throw distances for footballs are normal.

First, determine what type of test this is, set up the hypothesis test, find the *p*-value, sketch the graph, and state your conclusion.

 Using the TI-83, 83+, 84, 84+ Calculator

Press STAT and arrow over to TESTS. Press 1:Z-Test. Arrow over to Stats and press ENTER. Arrow down and enter 40 for $\mu 0$ (null hypothesis), 2 for σ, 45 for the sample mean, and 20 for *n*. Arrow down to μ: (alternative hypothesis) and set it either as $<$, $\neq$, or $>$. Press ENTER. Arrow down to Calculate and press ENTER. The calculator not only calculates the *p*-value but it also calculates the test statistic (*z*-score) for the sample mean. Select $<$, $\neq$, or $>$ for the alternative hypothesis. Do this set of instructions again except arrow to Draw (instead of Calculate). Press ENTER. A shaded graph appears with test statistic and *p*-value. Make sure when you use Draw that no other equations are highlighted in $Y =$ and the plots are turned off.

HISTORICAL NOTE (EXAMPLE 9.11)

The traditional way to compare the two probabilities, α and the *p*-value, is to compare the critical value (*z*-score from α) to the test statistic (*z*-score from data). The calculated test statistic for the *p*-value is –2.08. (From the Central Limit Theorem, the test statistic formula is $z = \dfrac{\bar{x} - \mu_X}{\left(\frac{\sigma_X}{\sqrt{n}}\right)}$. For this problem, $\bar{x} = 16$, $\mu_X = 16.43$ from the null hypothes is, $\sigma_X = 0.8$, and $n = 15$.) You can find the critical value for $\alpha = 0.05$ in the normal table (see **15.Tables** in the Table of Contents). The *z*-score for an area to the left equal to 0.05 is midway between –1.65 and –1.64 (0.05 is midway between 0.0505 and 0.0495). The *z*-score is –1.645. Since –1.645 > –2.08 (which demonstrates that $\alpha > p$-value), reject H_0. Traditionally, the decision to reject or not reject was done in this way. Today, comparing the two probabilities α and the *p*-value is very common. For this problem, the *p*-value, 0.0187 is considerably smaller than α, 0.05. You can be confident about your decision to reject. The graph shows α, the *p*-value, and the test statistic and the critical value.

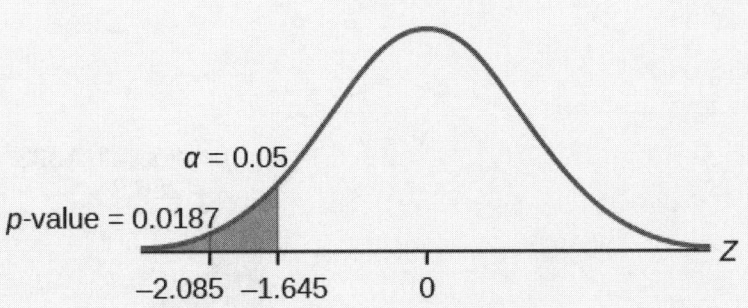

Figure 9.7

Example 9.15

A college football coach records the mean weight that his players can bench press as **275 pounds**, with a **standard deviation of 55 pounds**. Three of his players thought that the mean weight was **more than** that amount. They asked **30** of their teammates for their estimated maximum lift on the bench press exercise. The data ranged from 205 pounds to 385 pounds. The actual different weights were (frequencies are in parentheses) 205(3); 215(3); 225(1); 241(2); 252(2); 265(2); 275(2); 313(2); 316(5); 338(2); 341(1); 345(2); 368(2); 385(1).

Conduct a hypothesis test using a 2.5% level of significance to determine if the bench press mean is **more than 275 pounds**.

Solution 9.15

Set up the Hypothesis Test:

Since the problem is about a mean weight, this is a **test of a single population mean**.

$H_0: \mu = 275$
$H_a: \mu > 275$
This is a right-tailed test.

Calculating the distribution needed:

Random variable: $\bar{X}$ = the mean weight, in pounds, lifted by the football players.

Distribution for the test: It is normal because σ is known.

$$\bar{X} \sim N\left(275, \frac{55}{\sqrt{30}}\right)$$

$\bar{x} = 286.2$ pounds (from the data).

$\sigma = 55$ pounds **(Always use σ if you know it.)** We assume $\mu = 275$ pounds unless our data shows us otherwise.

Calculate the p-value using the normal distribution for a mean and using the sample mean as input (see **Appendix G** for using the data as input):

p-value $= P(\bar{x} > 286.2) = 0.1323$.

Interpretation of the p-value: If H_0 is true, then there is a 0.1331 probability (13.23%) that the football players can lift a mean weight of 286.2 pounds or more. Because a 13.23% chance is large enough, a mean weight lift of 286.2 pounds or more is not a rare event.

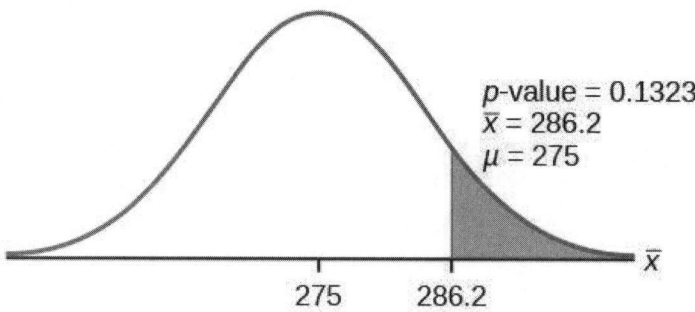

Figure 9.8

Compare α and the p-value:

$\alpha = 0.025$ p-value $= 0.1323$

Make a decision: Since $\alpha < p$-value, do not reject H_0.

Conclusion: At the 2.5% level of significance, from the sample data, there is not sufficient evidence to conclude that the true mean weight lifted is more than 275 pounds.

The p-value can easily be calculated.

 Using the TI-83, 83+, 84, 84+ Calculator

Put the data and frequencies into lists. Press **STAT** and arrow over to **TESTS**. Press **1:Z-Test**. Arrow over to **Data** and press **ENTER**. Arrow down and enter 275 for μ_0, 55 for σ, the name of the list where you put the data, and the name of the list where you put the frequencies. Arrow down to μ: and arrow over to $> \mu_0$. Press **ENTER**. Arrow down to **Calculate** and press **ENTER**. The calculator not only calculates the p-value ($p = 0.1331$, a little different from the previous calculation - in it we used the sample mean rounded to one decimal place instead of the data) but it also calculates the test statistic (z-score) for the sample mean, the sample mean, and the sample standard deviation. $\mu > 275$ is the alternative hypothesis. Do this set of instructions again except arrow to **Draw** (instead of **Calculate**). Press **ENTER**. A shaded graph appears with $z = 1.112$ (test statistic) and $p = 0.1331$ (p-value). Make sure when you use **Draw** that no other equations are highlighted in $Y =$ and the plots are turned off.

Example 9.16

Statistics students believe that the mean score on the first statistics test is 65. A statistics instructor thinks the mean score is higher than 65. He samples ten statistics students and obtains the scores 65; 65; 70; 67; 66; 63; 63; 68; 72; 71. He performs a hypothesis test using a 5% level of significance. The data are assumed to be from a normal distribution.

Solution 9.16

Set up the hypothesis test:

A 5% level of significance means that $\alpha = 0.05$. This is a test of a **single population mean**.

$H_0: \mu = 65$ $H_a: \mu > 65$

Since the instructor thinks the average score is higher, use a ">". The ">" means the test is right-tailed.

Determine the distribution needed:

Random variable: $\bar{X}$ = average score on the first statistics test.

Distribution for the test: If you read the problem carefully, you will notice that there is **no population standard deviation given**. You are only given $n = 10$ sample data values. Notice also that the data come from a normal distribution. This means that the distribution for the test is a student's t.

Use t_{df}. Therefore, the distribution for the test is t_9 where $n = 10$ and $df = 10 - 1 = 9$.

Calculate the p-value using the Student's t-distribution:

p-value = $P(\bar{x} > 67) = 0.0396$ where the sample mean and sample standard deviation are calculated as 67 and 3.1972 from the data.

Interpretation of the p-value: If the null hypothesis is true, then there is a 0.0396 probability (3.96%) that the sample mean is 65 or more.

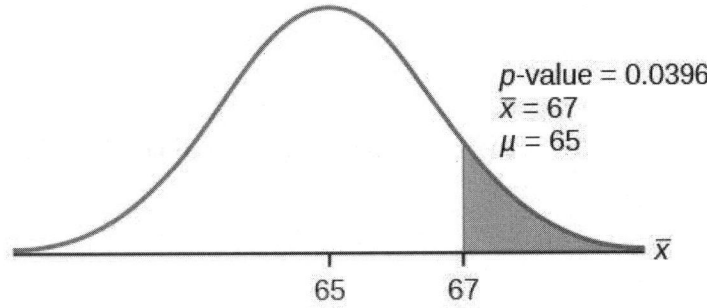

Figure 9.9

Compare α and the p-value:

Since $\alpha = 0.05$ and p-value = 0.0396. $\alpha > p$-value.

Make a decision: Since $\alpha > p$-value, reject H_0.

This means you reject $\mu = 65$. In other words, you believe the average test score is more than 65.

Conclusion: At a 5% level of significance, the sample data show sufficient evidence that the mean (average) test score is more than 65, just as the math instructor thinks.

The p-value can easily be calculated.

 Using the TI-83, 83+, 84, 84+ Calculator

Put the data into a list. Press **STAT** and arrow over to **TESTS**. Press **2:T-Test**. Arrow over to **Data** and press **ENTER**. Arrow down and enter 65 for μ_0, the name of the list where you put the data, and 1 for **Freq:**. Arrow down to μ: and arrow over to > μ_0. Press **ENTER**. Arrow down to **Calculate** and press **ENTER**. The calculator not only calculates the p-value ($p = 0.0396$) but it also calculates the test statistic (t-score) for the sample mean, the sample mean, and the sample standard deviation. $\mu > 65$ is the alternative hypothesis. Do this set of instructions again except arrow to **Draw** (instead of **Calculate**). Press **ENTER**. A shaded graph appears with $t = 1.9781$ (test statistic) and $p = 0.0396$ (p-value). Make sure when you use **Draw** that no other equations are highlighted in $Y =$ and the plots are turned off.

Try It Σ

9.16 It is believed that a stock price for a particular company will grow at a rate of $5 per week with a standard deviation of $1. An investor believes the stock won't grow as quickly. The changes in stock price is recorded for ten weeks and are as follows: $4, $3, $2, $3, $1, $7, $2, $1, $1, $2. Perform a hypothesis test using a 5% level of significance. State the null and alternative hypotheses, find the *p*-value, state your conclusion, and identify the Type I and Type II errors.

Example 9.17

Joon believes that 50% of first-time brides in the United States are younger than their grooms. She performs a hypothesis test to determine if the percentage is **the same or different from 50%**. Joon samples **100 first-time brides** and **53** reply that they are younger than their grooms. For the hypothesis test, she uses a 1% level of significance.

Solution 9.17

Set up the hypothesis test:

The 1% level of significance means that $\alpha = 0.01$. This is a **test of a single population proportion**.

$H_0: p = 0.50 \qquad H_a: p \neq 0.50$

The words **"is the same or different from"** tell you this is a two-tailed test.

Calculate the distribution needed:

Random variable: P' = the percent of of first-time brides who are younger than their grooms.

Distribution for the test: The problem contains no mention of a mean. The information is given in terms of percentages. Use the distribution for P', the estimated proportion.

$P' \sim N\left(p, \sqrt{\dfrac{p \cdot q}{n}}\right)$ Therefore, $P' \sim N\left(0.5, \sqrt{\dfrac{0.5 \cdot 0.5}{100}}\right)$

where $p = 0.50$, $q = 1 - p = 0.50$, and $n = 100$

Calculate the *p*-value using the normal distribution for proportions:

p-value = $P(p' < 0.47 \text{ or } p' > 0.53) = 0.5485$

where $x = 53$, $p' = \dfrac{x}{n} = \dfrac{53}{100} = 0.53$.

Interpretation of the *p*-value: If the null hypothesis is true, there is 0.5485 probability (54.85%) that the sample (estimated) proportion p' is 0.53 or more OR 0.47 or less (see the graph in **Figure 9.9**).

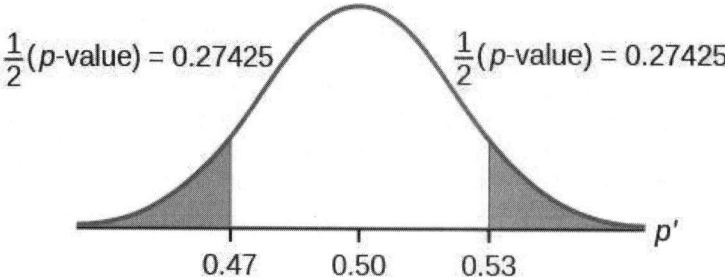

Figure 9.10

$\mu = p = 0.50$ comes from H_0, the null hypothesis.

$p' = 0.53$. Since the curve is symmetrical and the test is two-tailed, the p' for the left tail is equal to $0.50 - 0.03 = 0.47$ where $\mu = p = 0.50$. (0.03 is the difference between 0.53 and 0.50.)

Compare α and the p-value:

Since $\alpha = 0.01$ and p-value = 0.5485. $\alpha < p$-value.

Make a decision: Since $\alpha < p$-value, you cannot reject H_0.

Conclusion: At the 1% level of significance, the sample data do not show sufficient evidence that the percentage of first-time brides who are younger than their grooms is different from 50%.

The p-value can easily be calculated.

 Using the TI-83, 83+, 84, 84+ Calculator

Press **STAT** and arrow over to **TESTS**. Press **5:1-PropZTest**. Enter .5 for p_0, 53 for x and 100 for n. Arrow down to **Prop** and arrow to **not equals** p_0. Press **ENTER**. Arrow down to **Calculate** and press **ENTER**. The calculator calculates the p-value ($p = 0.5485$) and the test statistic (z-score). **Prop not equals** .5 is the alternate hypothesis. Do this set of instructions again except arrow to **Draw** (instead of **Calculate**). Press **ENTER**. A shaded graph appears with $z = 0.6$ (test statistic) and $p = 0.5485$ (p-value). Make sure when you use **Draw** that no other equations are highlighted in $Y =$ and the plots are turned off.

The Type I and Type II errors are as follows:

The Type I error is to conclude that the proportion of first-time brides who are younger than their grooms is different from 50% when, in fact, the proportion is actually 50%. (Reject the null hypothesis when the null hypothesis is true).

The Type II error is there is not enough evidence to conclude that the proportion of first time brides who are younger than their grooms differs from 50% when, in fact, the proportion does differ from 50%. (Do not reject the null hypothesis when the null hypothesis is false.)

Try It Σ

9.17 A teacher believes that 85% of students in the class will want to go on a field trip to the local zoo. She performs a hypothesis test to determine if the percentage is the same or different from 85%. The teacher samples 50 students and 39 reply that they would want to go to the zoo. For the hypothesis test, use a 1% level of significance.

First, determine what type of test this is, set up the hypothesis test, find the p-value, sketch the graph, and state your conclusion.

Example 9.18

Suppose a consumer group suspects that the proportion of households that have three cell phones is 30%. A cell phone company has reason to believe that the proportion is not 30%. Before they start a big advertising campaign, they conduct a hypothesis test. Their marketing people survey 150 households with the result that 43 of the households have three cell phones.

Solution 9.18

Set up the Hypothesis Test:

$H_0: p = 0.30$ $H_a: p \neq 0.30$

Determine the distribution needed:

The **random variable** is $P' =$ proportion of households that have three cell phones.

The **distribution** for the hypothesis test is $P' \sim N\left(0.30, \sqrt{\dfrac{(0.30) \cdot (0.70)}{150}}\right)$

a. The value that helps determine the p-value is p'. Calculate p'.

Solution 9.18

a. $p' = \dfrac{x}{n}$ where x is the number of successes and n is the total number in the sample.

$x = 43$, $n = 150$

$p' = \dfrac{43}{150}$

b. What is a **success** for this problem?

Solution 9.18

b. A success is having three cell phones in a household.

c. What is the level of significance?

Solution 9.18

c. The level of significance is the preset α. Since α is not given, assume that $\alpha = 0.05$.

d. Draw the graph for this problem. Draw the horizontal axis. Label and shade appropriately. Calculate the p-value.

Solution 9.18

d. p-value = 0.7216

e. Make a decision. _____ (Reject/Do not reject) H_0 because_____.

Solution 9.18

e. Assuming that $\alpha = 0.05$, $\alpha < p$-value. The decision is do not reject H_0 because there is not sufficient evidence to conclude that the proportion of households that have three cell phones is not 30%.

9.18 Marketers believe that 92% of adults in the United States own a cell phone. A cell phone manufacturer believes that number is actually lower. 200 American adults are surveyed, of which, 174 report having cell phones. Use a 5% level of significance. State the null and alternative hypothesis, find the p-value, state your conclusion, and identify the Type I and Type II errors.

The next example is a poem written by a statistics student named Nicole Hart. The solution to the problem follows the poem. Notice that the hypothesis test is for a single population proportion. This means that the null and alternate hypotheses use the parameter p. The distribution for the test is normal. The estimated proportion p' is the proportion of fleas killed to the total fleas found on Fido. This is sample information. The problem gives a preconceived $\alpha = 0.01$, for comparison, and a 95% confidence interval computation. The poem is clever and humorous, so please enjoy it!

Example 9.19

My dog has so many fleas,
They do not come off with ease.
As for shampoo, I have tried many types
Even one called Bubble Hype,
Which only killed 25% of the fleas,
Unfortunately I was not pleased.

I've used all kinds of soap,
Until I had given up hope
Until one day I saw
An ad that put me in awe.

A shampoo used for dogs
Called GOOD ENOUGH to Clean a Hog
Guaranteed to kill more fleas.

I gave Fido a bath
And after doing the math
His number of fleas
Started dropping by 3's!

Before his shampoo
I counted 42.
At the end of his bath,
I redid the math
And the new shampoo had killed 17 fleas.
So now I was pleased.

Now it is time for you to have some fun
With the level of significance being .01,
You must help me figure out
Use the new shampoo or go without?

Solution 9.19

Set up the hypothesis test:

H_0: $p \le 0.25$ H_a: $p > 0.25$

Determine the distribution needed:

In words, CLEARLY state what your random variable $\bar{X}$ or P' represents.

P' = The proportion of fleas that are killed by the new shampoo

State the distribution to use for the test.

Normal: $N\left(0.25, \sqrt{\dfrac{(0.25)(1 - 0.25)}{42}}\right)$

Test Statistic: $z = 2.3163$

Calculate the p-value using the normal distribution for proportions:

p-value = 0.0103

In one to two complete sentences, explain what the p-value means for this problem.

If the null hypothesis is true (the proportion is 0.25), then there is a 0.0103 probability that the sample (estimated) proportion is 0.4048 $\left(\dfrac{17}{42}\right)$ or more.

Use the previous information to sketch a picture of this situation. CLEARLY, label and scale the horizontal axis and shade the region(s) corresponding to the *p*-value.

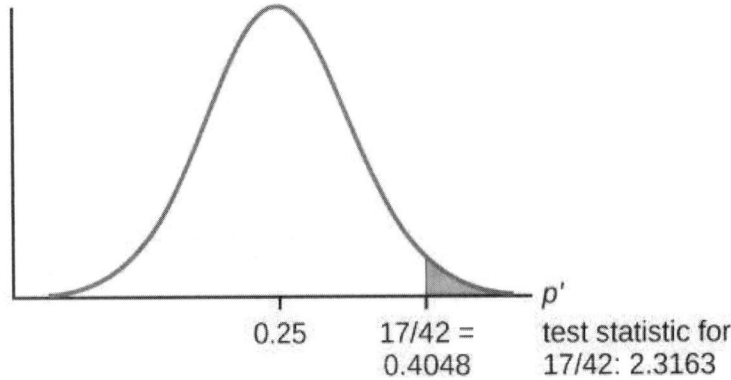

Figure 9.11

Compare α and the *p*-value:

Indicate the correct decision ("reject" or "do not reject" the null hypothesis), the reason for it, and write an appropriate conclusion, using complete sentences.

alpha	decision	reason for decision
0.01	Do not reject H_0	$\alpha < p$-value

Table 9.3

Conclusion: At the 1% level of significance, the sample data do not show sufficient evidence that the percentage of fleas that are killed by the new shampoo is more than 25%.

Construct a 95% confidence interval for the true mean or proportion. Include a sketch of the graph of the situation. Label the point estimate and the lower and upper bounds of the confidence interval.

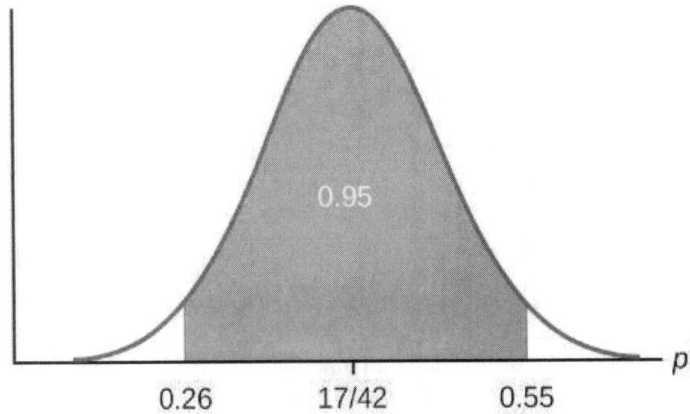

Figure 9.12

Confidence Interval: (0.26,0.55) We are 95% confident that the true population proportion p of fleas that are killed by the new shampoo is between 26% and 55%.

NOTE

This test result is not very definitive since the *p*-value is very close to alpha. In reality, one would probably do more tests by giving the dog another bath after the fleas have had a chance to return.

Example 9.20

The National Institute of Standards and Technology provides exact data on conductivity properties of materials. Following are conductivity measurements for 11 randomly selected pieces of a particular type of glass.

1.11; 1.07; 1.11; 1.07; 1.12; 1.08; .98; .98 1.02; .95; .95

Is there convincing evidence that the average conductivity of this type of glass is greater than one? Use a significance level of 0.05. Assume the population is normal.

Solution 9.20
Let's follow a four-step process to answer this statistical question.

1. **State the Question**: We need to determine if, at a 0.05 significance level, the average conductivity of the selected glass is greater than one. Our hypotheses will be

   a. $H_0: \mu \leq 1$

   b. $H_a: \mu > 1$

2. **Plan**: We are testing a sample mean without a known population standard deviation. Therefore, we need to use a Student's-t distribution. Assume the underlying population is normal.

3. **Do the calculations**: We will input the sample data into the TI-83 as follows.

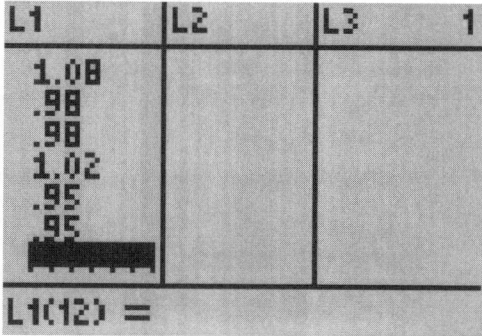

Figure 9.13

Figure 9.14

Figure 9.15

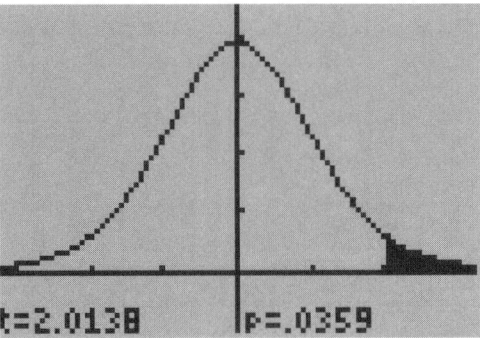

Figure 9.16

4. **State the Conclusions**: Since the *p*-value* (*p* = 0.036) is less than our alpha value, we will reject the null hypothesis. It is reasonable to state that the data supports the claim that the average conductivity level is greater than one.

Example 9.21

In a study of 420,019 cell phone users, 172 of the subjects developed brain cancer. Test the claim that cell phone users developed brain cancer at a greater rate than that for non-cell phone users (the rate of brain cancer for non-cell phone users is 0.0340%). Since this is a critical issue, use a 0.005 significance level. Explain why the significance level should be so low in terms of a Type I error.

Solution 9.21

We will follow the four-step process.

1. We need to conduct a hypothesis test on the claimed cancer rate. Our hypotheses will be
   a. $H_0: p \leq 0.00034$

   b. $H_a: p > 0.00034$

   If we commit a Type I error, we are essentially accepting a false claim. Since the claim describes cancer-causing environments, we want to minimize the chances of incorrectly identifying causes of cancer.

2. We will be testing a sample proportion with $x = 172$ and $n = 420,019$. The sample is sufficiently large because we have $np = 420,019(0.00034) = 142.8$, $nq = 420,019(0.99966) = 419,876.2$, two independent outcomes, and a fixed probability of success $p = 0.00034$. Thus we will be able to generalize our results to the population.

3. The associated TI results are

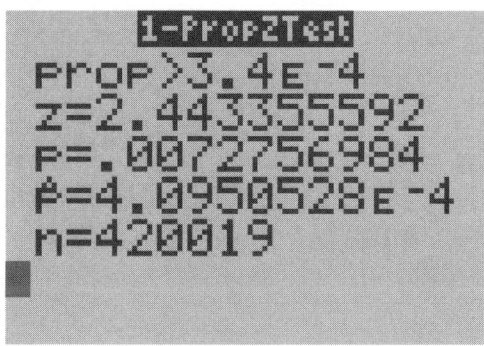

Figure 9.17

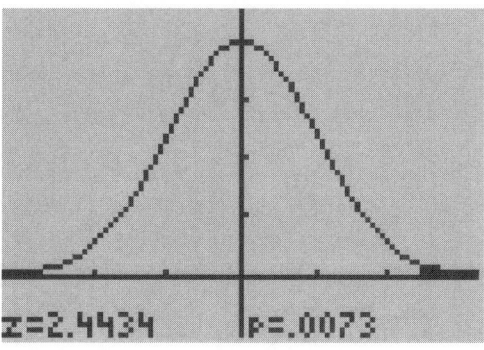

Figure 9.18

4. Since the p-value $= 0.0073$ is greater than our alpha value $= 0.005$, we cannot reject the null. Therefore, we conclude that there is not enough evidence to support the claim of higher brain cancer rates for the cell phone users.

Example 9.22

According to the US Census there are approximately 268,608,618 residents aged 12 and older. Statistics from the Rape, Abuse, and Incest National Network indicate that, on average, 207,754 rapes occur each year (male and female) for persons aged 12 and older. This translates into a percentage of sexual assaults of 0.078%. In Daviess County, KY, there were reported 11 rapes for a population of 37,937. Conduct an appropriate hypothesis test to determine if there is a statistically significant difference between the local sexual assault percentage and the national sexual assault percentage. Use a significance level of 0.01.

Solution 9.22

We will follow the four-step plan.

1. We need to test whether the proportion of sexual assaults in Daviess County, KY is significantly different from the national average.

2. Since we are presented with proportions, we will use a one-proportion z-test. The hypotheses for the test will be

   a. H_0: $p = 0.00078$

   b. H_a: $p \neq 0.00078$

3. The following screen shots display the summary statistics from the hypothesis test.

Figure 9.19

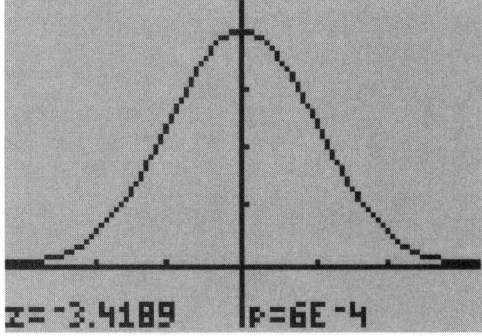

Figure 9.20

4. Since the p-value, $p = 0.00063$, is less than the alpha level of 0.01, the sample data indicates that we should reject the null hypothesis. In conclusion, the sample data support the claim that the proportion of sexual assaults in Daviess County, Kentucky is different from the national average proportion.

9.6 | Hypothesis Testing of a Single Mean and Single Proportion

Stats Lab

9.1 Hypothesis Testing of a Single Mean and Single Proportion

Class Time:

Names:

Student Learning Outcomes

- The student will select the appropriate distributions to use in each case.
- The student will conduct hypothesis tests and interpret the results.

Television Survey

In a recent survey, it was stated that Americans watch television on average four hours per day. Assume that $\sigma = 2$. Using your class as the sample, conduct a hypothesis test to determine if the average for students at your school is lower.

1. H_0: _____

2. H_a: _____

3. In words, define the random variable. _____ = _____

4. The distribution to use for the test is _____.

5. Determine the test statistic using your data.

6. Draw a graph and label it appropriately. Shade the actual level of significance.

   a. Graph:

   Figure 9.21

   b. Determine the *p*-value.

7. Do you or do you not reject the null hypothesis? Why?

8. Write a clear conclusion using a complete sentence.

Language Survey

About 42.3% of Californians and 19.6% of all Americans over age five speak a language other than English at home. Using your class as the sample, conduct a hypothesis test to determine if the percent of the students at your school who speak a language other than English at home is different from 42.3%.

1. H_0: _____
2. H_a: _____
3. In words, define the random variable. _____ = _____
4. The distribution to use for the test is _____
5. Determine the test statistic using your data.
6. Draw a graph and label it appropriately. Shade the actual level of significance.

    a. Graph:

Figure 9.22

    b. Determine the *p*-value.
7. Do you or do you not reject the null hypothesis? Why?
8. Write a clear conclusion using a complete sentence.

Jeans Survey

Suppose that young adults own an average of three pairs of jeans. Survey eight people from your class to determine if the average is higher than three. Assume the population is normal.

1. H_0: _____
2. H_a: _____
3. In words, define the random variable. _____ = _____
4. The distribution to use for the test is _____.
5. Determine the test statistic using your data.
6. Draw a graph and label it appropriately. Shade the actual level of significance.

    a. Graph:

Figure 9.23

    b. Determine the *p*-value.

7. Do you or do you not reject the null hypothesis? Why?

8. Write a clear conclusion using a complete sentence.

KEY TERMS

Binomial Distribution a discrete random variable (RV) that arises from Bernoulli trials. There are a fixed number, n, of independent trials. "Independent" means that the result of any trial (for example, trial 1) does not affect the results of the following trials, and all trials are conducted under the same conditions. Under these circumstances the binomial RV X is defined as the number of successes in n trials. The notation is: $X \sim B(n, p)$ $\mu = np$ and the standard deviation is $\sigma = \sqrt{npq}$. The probability of exactly x successes in n trials is $P(X = x) = \binom{n}{x} p^x q^{n-x}$.

Central Limit Theorem Given a random variable (RV) with known mean μ and known standard deviation σ. We are sampling with size n and we are interested in two new RVs - the sample mean, $\bar{X}$, and the sample sum, ΣX. If the size n of the sample is sufficiently large, then $\bar{X} \sim N\left(\mu, \frac{\sigma}{\sqrt{n}}\right)$ and $\Sigma X \sim N(n\mu, \sqrt{n}\sigma)$. If the size n of the sample is sufficiently large, then the distribution of the sample means and the distribution of the sample sums will approximate a normal distribution regardless of the shape of the population. The mean of the sample means will equal the population mean and the mean of the sample sums will equal n times the population mean. The standard deviation of the distribution of the sample means, $\frac{\sigma}{\sqrt{n}}$, is called the standard error of the mean.

Confidence Interval (CI) an interval estimate for an unknown population parameter. This depends on:

- The desired confidence level.
- Information that is known about the distribution (for example, known standard deviation).
- The sample and its size.

Hypothesis a statement about the value of a population parameter, in case of two hypotheses, the statement assumed to be true is called the null hypothesis (notation H_0) and the contradictory statement is called the alternative hypothesis (notation H_a).

Hypothesis Testing Based on sample evidence, a procedure for determining whether the hypothesis stated is a reasonable statement and should not be rejected, or is unreasonable and should be rejected.

Level of Significance of the Test probability of a Type I error (reject the null hypothesis when it is true). Notation: α. In hypothesis testing, the Level of Significance is called the preconceived α or the preset α.

Normal Distribution
a continuous random variable (RV) with pdf $f(x) = \frac{1}{\sigma\sqrt{2\pi}} e^{\frac{-(x-\mu)^2}{2\sigma^2}}$, where μ is the mean of the distribution, and σ is the standard deviation, notation: $X \sim N(\mu, \sigma)$. If $\mu = 0$ and $\sigma = 1$, the RV is called **the standard normal distribution**.

p-value the probability that an event will happen purely by chance assuming the null hypothesis is true. The smaller the p-value, the stronger the evidence is against the null hypothesis.

Standard Deviation a number that is equal to the square root of the variance and measures how far data values are from their mean; notation: s for sample standard deviation and σ for population standard deviation.

Student's t-Distribution investigated and reported by William S. Gossett in 1908 and published under the pseudonym Student. The major characteristics of the random variable (RV) are:

- It is continuous and assumes any real values.
- The pdf is symmetrical about its mean of zero. However, it is more spread out and flatter at the apex than the normal distribution.
- It approaches the standard normal distribution as n gets larger.
- There is a "family" of t distributions: every representative of the family is completely defined by the number of degrees of freedom which is one less than the number of data items.

Type 1 Error The decision is to reject the null hypothesis when, in fact, the null hypothesis is true.

Type 2 Error The decision is not to reject the null hypothesis when, in fact, the null hypothesis is false.

CHAPTER REVIEW

9.1 Null and Alternative Hypotheses

In a **hypothesis test**, sample data is evaluated in order to arrive at a decision about some type of claim. If certain conditions about the sample are satisfied, then the claim can be evaluated for a population. In a hypothesis test, we:

1. Evaluate the **null hypothesis**, typically denoted with H_0. The null is not rejected unless the hypothesis test shows otherwise. The null statement must always contain some form of equality ($=$, $\leq$ or $\geq$)

2. Always write the **alternative hypothesis**, typically denoted with H_a or H_1, using less than, greater than, or not equals symbols, i.e., ($\neq$, $>$, or $<$).

3. If we reject the null hypothesis, then we can assume there is enough evidence to support the alternative hypothesis.

4. Never state that a claim is proven true or false. Keep in mind the underlying fact that hypothesis testing is based on probability laws; therefore, we can talk only in terms of non-absolute certainties.

9.2 Outcomes and the Type I and Type II Errors

In every hypothesis test, the outcomes are dependent on a correct interpretation of the data. Incorrect calculations or misunderstood summary statistics can yield errors that affect the results. A **Type I** error occurs when a true null hypothesis is rejected. A **Type II error** occurs when a false null hypothesis is not rejected.

The probabilities of these errors are denoted by the Greek letters α and β, for a Type I and a Type II error respectively. The power of the test, $1 - \beta$, quantifies the likelihood that a test will yield the correct result of a true alternative hypothesis being accepted. A high power is desirable.

9.3 Distribution Needed for Hypothesis Testing

In order for a hypothesis test's results to be generalized to a population, certain requirements must be satisfied.

When testing for a single population mean:

1. A Student's t-test should be used if the data come from a simple, random sample and the population is approximately normally distributed, or the sample size is large, with an unknown standard deviation.

2. The normal test will work if the data come from a simple, random sample and the population is approximately normally distributed, or the sample size is large, with a known standard deviation.

When testing a single population proportion use a normal test for a single population proportion if the data comes from a simple, random sample, fill the requirements for a binomial distribution, and the mean number of success and the mean number of failures satisfy the conditions: $np > 5$ and $nq > n$ where n is the sample size, p is the probability of a success, and q is the probability of a failure.

9.4 Rare Events, the Sample, Decision and Conclusion

When the probability of an event occurring is low, and it happens, it is called a rare event. Rare events are important to consider in hypothesis testing because they can inform your willingness not to reject or to reject a null hypothesis. To test a null hypothesis, find the p-value for the sample data and graph the results. When deciding whether or not to reject the null the hypothesis, keep these two parameters in mind:

1. $\alpha > p$-value, reject the null hypothesis

2. $\alpha \leq p$-value, do not reject the null hypothesis

9.5 Additional Information and Full Hypothesis Test Examples

The **hypothesis test** itself has an established process. This can be summarized as follows:

1. Determine H_0 and H_a. Remember, they are contradictory.

2. Determine the random variable.

3. Determine the distribution for the test.

4. Draw a graph, calculate the test statistic, and use the test statistic to calculate the *p*-value. (A *z*-score and a *t*-score are examples of test statistics.)

5. Compare the preconceived α with the *p*-value, make a decision (reject or do not reject H_0), and write a clear conclusion using English sentences.

Notice that in performing the hypothesis test, you use α and not β. β is needed to help determine the sample size of the data that is used in calculating the *p*-value. Remember that the quantity $1 - \beta$ is called the **Power of the Test**. A high power is desirable. If the power is too low, statisticians typically increase the sample size while keeping α the same.If the power is low, the null hypothesis might not be rejected when it should be.

FORMULA REVIEW

9.1 Null and Alternative Hypotheses

H_0 and H_a are contradictory.

If H_o has:	equal (=)	greater than or equal to ($\geq$)	less than or equal to ($\leq$)
then H_a has:	not equal ($\neq$) **or** greater than (>) **or** less than (<)	less than (<)	greater than (>)

Table 9.4

If $\alpha \leq$ *p*-value, then do not reject H_0.

If $\alpha >$ *p*-value, then reject H_0.

α is preconceived. Its value is set before the hypothesis test starts. The *p*-value is calculated from the data.

9.2 Outcomes and the Type I and Type II Errors

α = probability of a Type I error = P(Type I error) = probability of rejecting the null hypothesis when the null hypothesis is true.

β = probability of a Type II error = P(Type II error) = probability of not rejecting the null hypothesis when the null hypothesis is false.

9.3 Distribution Needed for Hypothesis Testing

If there is no given preconceived α, then use $\alpha = 0.05$.

Types of Hypothesis Tests

- Single population mean, **known** population variance (or standard deviation): **Normal test**.
- Single population mean, **unknown** population variance (or standard deviation): **Student's *t*-test**.
- Single population proportion: **Normal test**.
- For a **single population mean**, we may use a normal distribution with the following mean and standard deviation. Means: $\mu = \mu_{\bar{x}}$ and $\sigma_{\bar{x}} = \frac{\sigma_x}{\sqrt{n}}$
- A **single population proportion**, we may use a normal distribution with the following mean and standard deviation. Proportions: $\mu = p$ and $\sigma = \sqrt{\frac{pq}{n}}$.

PRACTICE

9.1 Null and Alternative Hypotheses

1. You are testing that the mean speed of your cable Internet connection is more than three Megabits per second. What is the random variable? Describe in words.

2. You are testing that the mean speed of your cable Internet connection is more than three Megabits per second. State the null and alternative hypotheses.

3. The American family has an average of two children. What is the random variable? Describe in words.

4. The mean entry level salary of an employee at a company is $58,000. You believe it is higher for IT professionals in the company. State the null and alternative hypotheses.

5. A sociologist claims the probability that a person picked at random in Times Square in New York City is visiting the area is 0.83. You want to test to see if the proportion is actually less. What is the random variable? Describe in words.

6. A sociologist claims the probability that a person picked at random in Times Square in New York City is visiting the area is 0.83. You want to test to see if the claim is correct. State the null and alternative hypotheses.

7. In a population of fish, approximately 42% are female. A test is conducted to see if, in fact, the proportion is less. State the null and alternative hypotheses.

8. Suppose that a recent article stated that the mean time spent in jail by a first–time convicted burglar is 2.5 years. A study was then done to see if the mean time has increased in the new century. A random sample of 26 first-time convicted burglars in a recent year was picked. The mean length of time in jail from the survey was 3 years with a standard deviation of 1.8 years. Suppose that it is somehow known that the population standard deviation is 1.5. If you were conducting a hypothesis test to determine if the mean length of jail time has increased, what would the null and alternative hypotheses be? The distribution of the population is normal.
   a. H_0: _____
   b. H_a: _____

9. A random survey of 75 death row inmates revealed that the mean length of time on death row is 17.4 years with a standard deviation of 6.3 years. If you were conducting a hypothesis test to determine if the population mean time on death row could likely be 15 years, what would the null and alternative hypotheses be?
   a. H_0: _____
   b. H_a: _____

10. The National Institute of Mental Health published an article stating that in any one-year period, approximately 9.5 percent of American adults suffer from depression or a depressive illness. Suppose that in a survey of 100 people in a certain town, seven of them suffered from depression or a depressive illness. If you were conducting a hypothesis test to determine if the true proportion of people in that town suffering from depression or a depressive illness is lower than the percent in the general adult American population, what would the null and alternative hypotheses be?
   a. H_0: _____
   b. H_a: _____

9.2 Outcomes and the Type I and Type II Errors

11. The mean price of mid-sized cars in a region is $32,000. A test is conducted to see if the claim is true. State the Type I and Type II errors in complete sentences.

12. A sleeping bag is tested to withstand temperatures of –15 °F. You think the bag cannot stand temperatures that low. State the Type I and Type II errors in complete sentences.

13. For **Exercise 9.12**, what are α and β in words?

14. In words, describe $1 - \beta$ For **Exercise 9.12**.

15. A group of doctors is deciding whether or not to perform an operation. Suppose the null hypothesis, H_0, is: the surgical procedure will go well. State the Type I and Type II errors in complete sentences.

16. A group of doctors is deciding whether or not to perform an operation. Suppose the null hypothesis, H_0, is: the surgical procedure will go well. Which is the error with the greater consequence?

17. The power of a test is 0.981. What is the probability of a Type II error?

18. A group of divers is exploring an old sunken ship. Suppose the null hypothesis, H_0, is: the sunken ship does not contain buried treasure. State the Type I and Type II errors in complete sentences.

19. A microbiologist is testing a water sample for E-coli. Suppose the null hypothesis, H_0, is: the sample does not contain E-coli. The probability that the sample does not contain E-coli, but the microbiologist thinks it does is 0.012. The probability that the sample does contain E-coli, but the microbiologist thinks it does not is 0.002. What is the power of this test?

20. A microbiologist is testing a water sample for E-coli. Suppose the null hypothesis, H_0, is: the sample contains E-coli. Which is the error with the greater consequence?

9.3 Distribution Needed for Hypothesis Testing

21. Which two distributions can you use for hypothesis testing for this chapter?

22. Which distribution do you use when you are testing a population mean and the population standard deviation is known? Assume a normal distribution, with n ≥ 30.

23. Which distribution do you use when the standard deviation is not known and you are testing one population mean? Assume sample size is large.

24. A population mean is 13. The sample mean is 12.8, and the sample standard deviation is two. The sample size is 20. What distribution should you use to perform a hypothesis test? Assume the underlying population is normal.

25. A population has a mean is 25 and a standard deviation of five. The sample mean is 24, and the sample size is 108. What distribution should you use to perform a hypothesis test?

26. It is thought that 42% of respondents in a taste test would prefer Brand *A*. In a particular test of 100 people, 39% preferred Brand *A*. What distribution should you use to perform a hypothesis test?

27. You are performing a hypothesis test of a single population mean using a Student's *t*-distribution. What must you assume about the distribution of the data?

28. You are performing a hypothesis test of a single population mean using a Student's *t*-distribution. The data are not from a simple random sample. Can you accurately perform the hypothesis test?

29. You are performing a hypothesis test of a single population proportion. What must be true about the quantities of np and nq?

30. You are performing a hypothesis test of a single population proportion. You find out that np is less than five. What must you do to be able to perform a valid hypothesis test?

31. You are performing a hypothesis test of a single population proportion. The data come from which distribution?

9.4 Rare Events, the Sample, Decision and Conclusion

32. When do you reject the null hypothesis?

33. The probability of winning the grand prize at a particular carnival game is 0.005. Is the outcome of winning very likely or very unlikely?

34. The probability of winning the grand prize at a particular carnival game is 0.005. Michele wins the grand prize. Is this considered a rare or common event? Why?

35. It is believed that the mean height of high school students who play basketball on the school team is 73 inches with a standard deviation of 1.8 inches. A random sample of 40 players is chosen. The sample mean was 71 inches, and the sample standard deviation was 1.5 years. Do the data support the claim that the mean height is less than 73 inches? The *p*-value is almost zero. State the null and alternative hypotheses and interpret the *p*-value.

36. The mean age of graduate students at a University is at most 31 y ears with a standard deviation of two years. A random sample of 15 graduate students is taken. The sample mean is 32 years and the sample standard deviation is three years. Are the data significant at the 1% level? The *p*-value is 0.0264. State the null and alternative hypotheses and interpret the *p*-value.

37. Does the shaded region represent a low or a high *p*-value compared to a level of significance of 1%?

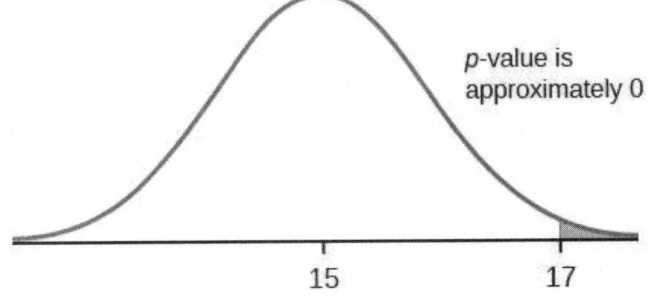

Figure 9.24

38. What should you do when $\alpha > p$-value?

39. What should you do if $\alpha = p$-value?

40. If you do not reject the null hypothesis, then it must be true. Is this statement correct? State why or why not in complete sentences.

Use the following information to answer the next seven exercises: Suppose that a recent article stated that the mean time spent in jail by a first-time convicted burglar is 2.5 years. A study was then done to see if the mean time has increased in the new century. A random sample of 26 first-time convicted burglars in a recent year was picked. The mean length of time in jail from the survey was three years with a standard deviation of 1.8 years. Suppose that it is somehow known that the population standard deviation is 1.5. Conduct a hypothesis test to determine if the mean length of jail time has increased. Assume the distribution of the jail times is approximately normal.

41. Is this a test of means or proportions?

42. What symbol represents the random variable for this test?

43. In words, define the random variable for this test.

44. Is σ known and, if so, what is it?

45. Calculate the following:

    a. $\bar{x}$ _____

    b. σ _____

    c. s_x _____

    d. n _____

46. Since both σ and s_x are given, which should be used? In one to two complete sentences, explain why.

47. State the distribution to use for the hypothesis test.

48. A random survey of 75 death row inmates revealed that the mean length of time on death row is 17.4 years with a standard deviation of 6.3 years. Conduct a hypothesis test to determine if the population mean time on death row could likely be 15 years.

    a. Is this a test of one mean or proportion?

    b. State the null and alternative hypotheses.

       H_0: _____ H_a : _____

    c. Is this a right-tailed, left-tailed, or two-tailed test?

    d. What symbol represents the random variable for this test?

    e. In words, define the random variable for this test.

    f. Is the population standard deviation known and, if so, what is it?

    g. Calculate the following:

       i. $\bar{x}$ = _____

       ii. s = _____

       iii. n = _____

    h. Which test should be used?

    i. State the distribution to use for the hypothesis test.

    j. Find the *p*-value.

    k. At a pre-conceived $\alpha = 0.05$, what is your:

       i. Decision:

       ii. Reason for the decision:

       iii. Conclusion (write out in a complete sentence):

9.5 Additional Information and Full Hypothesis Test Examples

49. Assume H_0: $\mu = 9$ and H_a: $\mu < 9$. Is this a left-tailed, right-tailed, or two-tailed test?

50. Assume H_0: $\mu \leq 6$ and H_a: $\mu > 6$. Is this a left-tailed, right-tailed, or two-tailed test?

51. Assume H_0: $p = 0.25$ and H_a: $p \neq 0.25$. Is this a left-tailed, right-tailed, or two-tailed test?

52. Draw the general graph of a left-tailed test.

53. Draw the graph of a two-tailed test.

54. A bottle of water is labeled as containing 16 fluid ounces of water. You believe it is less than that. What type of test would you use?

55. Your friend claims that his mean golf score is 63. You want to show that it is higher than that. What type of test would you use?

56. A bathroom scale claims to be able to identify correctly any weight within a pound. You think that it cannot be that accurate. What type of test would you use?

57. You flip a coin and record whether it shows heads or tails. You know the probability of getting heads is 50%, but you think it is less for this particular coin. What type of test would you use?

58. If the alternative hypothesis has a not equals (≠) symbol, you know to use which type of test?

59. Assume the null hypothesis states that the mean is at least 18. Is this a left-tailed, right-tailed, or two-tailed test?

60. Assume the null hypothesis states that the mean is at most 12. Is this a left-tailed, right-tailed, or two-tailed test?

61. Assume the null hypothesis states that the mean is equal to 88. The alternative hypothesis states that the mean is not equal to 88. Is this a left-tailed, right-tailed, or two-tailed test?

HOMEWORK

9.1 Null and Alternative Hypotheses

62. Some of the following statements refer to the null hypothesis, some to the alternate hypothesis.

State the null hypothesis, H_0, and the alternative hypothesis. H_a, in terms of the appropriate parameter (μ or p).

  a. The mean number of years Americans work before retiring is 34.
  b. At most 60% of Americans vote in presidential elections.
  c. The mean starting salary for San Jose State University graduates is at least $100,000 per year.
  d. Twenty-nine percent of high school seniors get drunk each month.
  e. Fewer than 5% of adults ride the bus to work in Los Angeles.
  f. The mean number of cars a person owns in her lifetime is not more than ten.
  g. About half of Americans prefer to live away from cities, given the choice.
  h. Europeans have a mean paid vacation each year of six weeks.
  i. The chance of developing breast cancer is under 11% for women.
  j. Private universities' mean tuition cost is more than $20,000 per year.

63. Over the past few decades, public health officials have examined the link between weight concerns and teen girls' smoking. Researchers surveyed a group of 273 randomly selected teen girls living in Massachusetts (between 12 and 15 years old). After four years the girls were surveyed again. Sixty-three said they smoked to stay thin. Is there good evidence that more than thirty percent of the teen girls smoke to stay thin? The alternative hypothesis is:
  a. $p < 0.30$
  b. $p \le 0.30$
  c. $p \ge 0.30$
  d. $p > 0.30$

64. A statistics instructor believes that fewer than 20% of Evergreen Valley College (EVC) students attended the opening night midnight showing of the latest Harry Potter movie. She surveys 84 of her students and finds that 11 attended the midnight showing. An appropriate alternative hypothesis is:
  a. $p = 0.20$
  b. $p > 0.20$
  c. $p < 0.20$
  d. $p \le 0.20$

65. Previously, an organization reported that teenagers spent 4.5 hours per week, on average, on the phone. The organization thinks that, currently, the mean is higher. Fifteen randomly chosen teenagers were asked how many hours per week they spend on the phone. The sample mean was 4.75 hours with a sample standard deviation of 2.0. Conduct a hypothesis test. The null and alternative hypotheses are:

    a. H_o: $\bar{x}$ = 4.5, H_a: $\bar{x}$ > 4.5

    b. H_o: $\mu \geq 4.5$, H_a: $\mu < 4.5$

    c. H_o: $\mu = 4.75$, H_a: $\mu > 4.75$

    d. H_o: $\mu = 4.5$, H_a: $\mu > 4.5$

9.2 Outcomes and the Type I and Type II Errors

66. State the Type I and Type II errors in complete sentences given the following statements.

    a. The mean number of years Americans work before retiring is 34.

    b. At most 60% of Americans vote in presidential elections.

    c. The mean starting salary for San Jose State University graduates is at least $100,000 per year.

    d. Twenty-nine percent of high school seniors get drunk each month.

    e. Fewer than 5% of adults ride the bus to work in Los Angeles.

    f. The mean number of cars a person owns in his or her lifetime is not more than ten.

    g. About half of Americans prefer to live away from cities, given the choice.

    h. Europeans have a mean paid vacation each year of six weeks.

    i. The chance of developing breast cancer is under 11% for women.

    j. Private universities mean tuition cost is more than $20,000 per year.

67. For statements a-j in **Exercise 9.109**, answer the following in complete sentences.

    a. State a consequence of committing a Type I error.

    b. State a consequence of committing a Type II error.

68. When a new drug is created, the pharmaceutical company must subject it to testing before receiving the necessary permission from the Food and Drug Administration (FDA) to market the drug. Suppose the null hypothesis is "the drug is unsafe." What is the Type II Error?

    a. To conclude the drug is safe when in, fact, it is unsafe.

    b. Not to conclude the drug is safe when, in fact, it is safe.

    c. To conclude the drug is safe when, in fact, it is safe.

    d. Not to conclude the drug is unsafe when, in fact, it is unsafe.

69. A statistics instructor believes that fewer than 20% of Evergreen Valley College (EVC) students attended the opening midnight showing of the latest Harry Potter movie. She surveys 84 of her students and finds that 11 of them attended the midnight showing. The Type I error is to conclude that the percent of EVC students who attended is _____.

    a. at least 20%, when in fact, it is less than 20%.

    b. 20%, when in fact, it is 20%.

    c. less than 20%, when in fact, it is at least 20%.

    d. less than 20%, when in fact, it is less than 20%.

70. It is believed that Lake Tahoe Community College (LTCC) Intermediate Algebra students get less than seven hours of sleep per night, on average. A survey of 22 LTCC Intermediate Algebra students generated a mean of 7.24 hours with a standard deviation of 1.93 hours. At a level of significance of 5%, do LTCC Intermediate Algebra students get less than seven hours of sleep per night, on average?

The Type II error is not to reject that the mean number of hours of sleep LTCC students get per night is at least seven when, in fact, the mean number of hours

    a. is more than seven hours.

    b. is at most seven hours.

    c. is at least seven hours.

    d. is less than seven hours.

71. Previously, an organization reported that teenagers spent 4.5 hours per week, on average, on the phone. The organization thinks that, currently, the mean is higher. Fifteen randomly chosen teenagers were asked how many hours per week they spend on the phone. The sample mean was 4.75 hours with a sample standard deviation of 2.0. Conduct a hypothesis test, the Type I error is:

    a. to conclude that the current mean hours per week is higher than 4.5, when in fact, it is higher

    b. to conclude that the current mean hours per week is higher than 4.5, when in fact, it is the same

    c. to conclude that the mean hours per week currently is 4.5, when in fact, it is higher

    d. to conclude that the mean hours per week currently is no higher than 4.5, when in fact, it is not higher

9.3 Distribution Needed for Hypothesis Testing

72. It is believed that Lake Tahoe Community College (LTCC) Intermediate Algebra students get less than seven hours of sleep per night, on average. A survey of 22 LTCC Intermediate Algebra students generated a mean of 7.24 hours with a standard deviation of 1.93 hours. At a level of significance of 5%, do LTCC Intermediate Algebra students get less than seven hours of sleep per night, on average? The distribution to be used for this test is $\bar{X} \sim$ _____

    a. $N\left(7.24, \dfrac{1.93}{\sqrt{22}}\right)$

    b. $N(7.24, 1.93)$

    c. t_{22}

    d. t_{21}

9.4 Rare Events, the Sample, Decision and Conclusion

73. The National Institute of Mental Health published an article stating that in any one-year period, approximately 9.5 percent of American adults suffer from depression or a depressive illness. Suppose that in a survey of 100 people in a certain town, seven of them suffered from depression or a depressive illness. Conduct a hypothesis test to determine if the true proportion of people in that town suffering from depression or a depressive illness is lower than the percent in the general adult American population.

    a. Is this a test of one mean or proportion?

    b. State the null and alternative hypotheses.

        H_0: _____ H_a: _____

    c. Is this a right-tailed, left-tailed, or two-tailed test?

    d. What symbol represents the random variable for this test?

    e. In words, define the random variable for this test.

    f. Calculate the following:

        i. $x =$ _____

        ii. $n =$ _____

        iii. $p' =$ _____

    g. Calculate $\sigma_x =$ _____. Show the formula set-up.

    h. State the distribution to use for the hypothesis test.

    i. Find the *p*-value.

    j. At a pre-conceived $\alpha = 0.05$, what is your:

        i. Decision:

        ii. Reason for the decision:

        iii. Conclusion (write out in a complete sentence):

9.5 Additional Information and Full Hypothesis Test Examples

*For each of the word problems, use a solution sheet to do the hypothesis test. The solution sheet is found in **Appendix E**. Please feel free to make copies of the solution sheets. For the online version of the book, it is suggested that you copy the .doc or the .pdf files.*

NOTE

If you are using a Student's-t distribution for one of the following homework problems, you may assume that the underlying population is normally distributed. (In general, you must first prove that assumption, however.)

74. A particular brand of tires claims that its deluxe tire averages at least 50,000 miles before it needs to be replaced. From past studies of this tire, the standard deviation is known to be 8,000. A survey of owners of that tire design is conducted. From the 28 tires surveyed, the mean lifespan was 46,500 miles with a standard deviation of 9,800 miles. Using alpha = 0.05, is the data highly inconsistent with the claim?

75. From generation to generation, the mean age when smokers first start to smoke varies. However, the standard deviation of that age remains constant of around 2.1 years. A survey of 40 smokers of this generation was done to see if the mean starting age is at least 19. The sample mean was 18.1 with a sample standard deviation of 1.3. Do the data support the claim at the 5% level?

76. The cost of a daily newspaper varies from city to city. However, the variation among prices remains steady with a standard deviation of 20¢. A study was done to test the claim that the mean cost of a daily newspaper is $1.00. Twelve costs yield a mean cost of 95¢ with a standard deviation of 18¢. Do the data support the claim at the 1% level?

77. An article in the *San Jose Mercury News* stated that students in the California state university system take 4.5 years, on average, to finish their undergraduate degrees. Suppose you believe that the mean time is longer. You conduct a survey of 49 students and obtain a sample mean of 5.1 with a sample standard deviation of 1.2. Do the data support your claim at the 1% level?

78. The mean number of sick days an employee takes per year is believed to be about ten. Members of a personnel department do not believe this figure. They randomly survey eight employees. The number of sick days they took for the past year are as follows: 12; 4; 15; 3; 11; 8; 6; 8. Let x = the number of sick days they took for the past year. Should the personnel team believe that the mean number is ten?

79. In 1955, *Life Magazine* reported that the 25 year-old mother of three worked, on average, an 80 hour week. Recently, many groups have been studying whether or not the women's movement has, in fact, resulted in an increase in the average work week for women (combining employment and at-home work). Suppose a study was done to determine if the mean work week has increased. 81 women were surveyed with the following results. The sample mean was 83; the sample standard deviation was ten. Does it appear that the mean work week has increased for women at the 5% level?

80. Your statistics instructor claims that 60 percent of the students who take her Elementary Statistics class go through life feeling more enriched. For some reason that she can't quite figure out, most people don't believe her. You decide to check this out on your own. You randomly survey 64 of her past Elementary Statistics students and find that 34 feel more enriched as a result of her class. Now, what do you think?

81. A Nissan Motor Corporation advertisement read, "The average man's I.Q. is 107. The average brown trout's I.Q. is 4. So why can't man catch brown trout?" Suppose you believe that the brown trout's mean I.Q. is greater than four. You catch 12 brown trout. A fish psychologist determines the I.Q.s as follows: 5; 4; 7; 3; 6; 4; 5; 3; 6; 3; 8; 5. Conduct a hypothesis test of your belief.

82. Refer to **Exercise 9.119**. Conduct a hypothesis test to see if your decision and conclusion would change if your belief were that the brown trout's mean I.Q. is **not** four.

83. According to an article in *Newsweek*, the natural ratio of girls to boys is 100:105. In China, the birth ratio is 100: 114 (46.7% girls). Suppose you don't believe the reported figures of the percent of girls born in China. You conduct a study. In this study, you count the number of girls and boys born in 150 randomly chosen recent births. There are 60 girls and 90 boys born of the 150. Based on your study, do you believe that the percent of girls born in China is 46.7?

84. A poll done for *Newsweek* found that 13% of Americans have seen or sensed the presence of an angel. A contingent doubts that the percent is really that high. It conducts its own survey. Out of 76 Americans surveyed, only two had seen or sensed the presence of an angel. As a result of the contingent's survey, would you agree with the *Newsweek* poll? In complete sentences, also give three reasons why the two polls might give different results.

85. The mean work week for engineers in a start-up company is believed to be about 60 hours. A newly hired engineer hopes that it's shorter. She asks ten engineering friends in start-ups for the lengths of their mean work weeks. Based on the results that follow, should she count on the mean work week to be shorter than 60 hours?

Data (length of mean work week): 70; 45; 55; 60; 65; 55; 55; 60; 50; 55.

86. Use the "Lap time" data for Lap 4 (see **Appendix C**) to test the claim that Terri finishes Lap 4, on average, in less than 129 seconds. Use all twenty races given.

87. Use the "Initial Public Offering" data (see **Appendix C**) to test the claim that the mean offer price was $18 per share. Do not use all the data. Use your random number generator to randomly survey 15 prices.

NOTE
_____

The following questions were written by past students. They are excellent problems!

88. "Asian Family Reunion," by Chau Nguyen

Every two years it comes around.

We all get together from different towns.

In my honest opinion,

It's not a typical family reunion.

Not forty, or fifty, or sixty,

But how about seventy companions!

The kids would play, scream, and shout

One minute they're happy, another they'll pout.

The teenagers would look, stare, and compare

From how they look to what they wear.

The men would chat about their business

That they make more, but never less.

Money is always their subject

And there's always talk of more new projects.

The women get tired from all of the chats

They head to the kitchen to set out the mats.

Some would sit and some would stand

Eating and talking with plates in their hands.

Then come the games and the songs

And suddenly, everyone gets along!

With all that laughter, it's sad to say

That it always ends in the same old way.

They hug and kiss and say "good-bye"

And then they all begin to cry!

I say that 60 percent shed their tears

But my mom counted 35 people this year.

She said that boys and men will always have their pride,

So we won't ever see them cry.

I myself don't think she's correct,

So could you please try this problem to see if you object?

89. "The Problem with Angels," by Cyndy Dowling

Although this problem is wholly mine,

The catalyst came from the magazine, Time.

On the magazine cover I did find

The realm of angels tickling my mind.

Inside, 69% I found to be

In angels, Americans do believe.

Then, it was time to rise to the task,

Ninety-five high school and college students I did ask.

Viewing all as one group,

Random sampling to get the scoop.

So, I asked each to be true,

"Do you believe in angels?" Tell me, do!

Hypothesizing at the start,

Totally believing in my heart

That the proportion who said yes

Would be equal on this test.

Lo and behold, seventy-three did arrive,

Out of the sample of ninety-five.

Now your job has just begun,

Solve this problem and have some fun.

90. "Blowing Bubbles," by Sondra Prull

Studying stats just made me tense,

I had to find some sane defense.

Some light and lifting simple play

To float my math anxiety away.

Blowing bubbles lifts me high

Takes my troubles to the sky.

POIK! They're gone, with all my stress

Bubble therapy is the best.

The label said each time I blew

The average number of bubbles would be at least 22.

I blew and blew and this I found

From 64 blows, they all are round!

But the number of bubbles in 64 blows

Varied widely, this I know.

20 per blow became the mean

They deviated by 6, and not 16.

From counting bubbles, I sure did relax

But now I give to you your task.

Was 22 a reasonable guess?

Find the answer and pass this test!

91. "Dalmatian Darnation," by Kathy Sparling

A greedy dog breeder named Spreckles

Bred puppies with numerous freckles

The Dalmatians he sought

Possessed spot upon spot

The more spots, he thought, the more shekels.

His competitors did not agree

That freckles would increase the fee.

They said, "Spots are quite nice

But they don't affect price;

One should breed for improved pedigree."

The breeders decided to prove

This strategy was a wrong move.

Breeding only for spots

Would wreak havoc, they thought.

His theory they want to disprove.

They proposed a contest to Spreckles

Comparing dog prices to freckles.

In records they looked up

One hundred one pups:

Dalmatians that fetched the most shekels.

They asked Mr. Spreckles to name

An average spot count he'd claim

To bring in big bucks.

Said Spreckles, "Well, shucks,

It's for one hundred one that I aim."

Said an amateur statistician

Who wanted to help with this mission.

"Twenty-one for the sample

Standard deviation's ample:

They examined one hundred and one

Dalmatians that fetched a good sum.

They counted each spot,

Mark, freckle and dot

And tallied up every one.

Instead of one hundred one spots

They averaged ninety six dots

Can they muzzle Spreckles'

Obsession with freckles

Based on all the dog data they've got?

92. "Macaroni and Cheese, please!!" by Nedda Misherghi and Rachelle Hall

As a poor starving student I don't have much money to spend for even the bare necessities. So my favorite and main staple food is macaroni and cheese. It's high in taste and low in cost and nutritional value.

One day, as I sat down to determine the meaning of life, I got a serious craving for this, oh, so important, food of my life. So I went down the street to Greatway to get a box of macaroni and cheese, but it was SO expensive! $2.02 !!! Can you believe it? It made me stop and think. The world is changing fast. I had thought that the mean cost of a box (the normal size, not some super-gigantic-family-value-pack) was at most $1, but now I wasn't so sure. However, I was determined to find out. I went to 53 of the closest grocery stores and surveyed the prices of macaroni and cheese. Here are the data I wrote in my notebook:

Price per box of Mac and Cheese:
- 5 stores @ $2.02
- 15 stores @ $0.25
- 3 stores @ $1.29
- 6 stores @ $0.35
- 4 stores @ $2.27
- 7 stores @ $1.50
- 5 stores @ $1.89
- 8 stores @ 0.75.

I could see that the cost varied but I had to sit down to figure out whether or not I was right. If it does turn out that this mouth-watering dish is at most $1, then I'll throw a big cheesy party in our next statistics lab, with enough macaroni and cheese for just me. (After all, as a poor starving student I can't be expected to feed our class of animals!)

93. "William Shakespeare: The Tragedy of Hamlet, Prince of Denmark," by Jacqueline Ghodsi THE CHARACTERS (in order of appearance):

- HAMLET, Prince of Denmark and student of Statistics
- POLONIUS, Hamlet's tutor
- HOROTIO, friend to Hamlet and fellow student

Scene: The great library of the castle, in which Hamlet does his lessons

Act I

(The day is fair, but the face of Hamlet is clouded. He paces the large room. His tutor, Polonius, is reprimanding Hamlet regarding the latter's recent experience. Horatio is seated at the large table at right stage.)

POLONIUS: My Lord, how cans't thou admit that thou hast seen a ghost! It is but a figment of your imagination!

HAMLET: I beg to differ; I know of a certainty that five-and-seventy in one hundred of us, condemned to the whips and scorns of time as we are, have gazed upon a spirit of health, or goblin damn'd, be their intents wicked or charitable.

POLONIUS If thou doest insist upon thy wretched vision then let me invest your time; be true to thy work and speak to me through the reason of the null and alternate hypotheses. (He turns to Horatio.) Did not Hamlet himself say, "What piece of work is man, how noble in reason, how infinite in faculties? Then let not this foolishness persist. Go, Horatio, make a survey of three-and-sixty and discover what the true proportion be. For my part, I will never succumb to this fantasy, but deem man to be devoid of all reason should thy proposal of at least five-and-seventy in one hundred hold true.

HORATIO (to Hamlet): What should we do, my Lord?

HAMLET: Go to thy purpose, Horatio.

HORATIO: To what end, my Lord?

HAMLET: That you must teach me. But let me conjure you by the rights of our fellowship, by the consonance of our youth, but the obligation of our ever-preserved love, be even and direct with me, whether I am right or no.

(Horatio exits, followed by Polonius, leaving Hamlet to ponder alone.)

Act II

(The next day, Hamlet awaits anxiously the presence of his friend, Horatio. Polonius enters and places some books upon the table just a moment before Horatio enters.)

POLONIUS: So, Horatio, what is it thou didst reveal through thy deliberations?

HORATIO: In a random survey, for which purpose thou thyself sent me forth, I did discover that one-and-forty believe fervently that the spirits of the dead walk with us. Before my God, I might not this believe, without the sensible and true avouch of mine own eyes.

POLONIUS: Give thine own thoughts no tongue, Horatio. (Polonius turns to Hamlet.) But look to't I charge you, my Lord. Come Horatio, let us go together, for this is not our test. (Horatio and Polonius leave together.)

HAMLET: To reject, or not reject, that is the question: whether 'tis nobler in the mind to suffer the slings and arrows of outrageous statistics, or to take arms against a sea of data, and, by opposing, end them. (Hamlet resignedly attends to his task.)

(Curtain falls)

94. "Untitled," by Stephen Chen

I've often wondered how software is released and sold to the public. Ironically, I work for a company that sells products with known problems. Unfortunately, most of the problems are difficult to create, which makes them difficult to fix. I usually use the test program X, which tests the product, to try to create a specific problem. When the test program is run to make an error occur, the likelihood of generating an error is 1%.

So, armed with this knowledge, I wrote a new test program Y that will generate the same error that test program X creates, but more often. To find out if my test program is better than the original, so that I can convince the management that I'm right, I ran my test program to find out how often I can generate the same error. When I ran my test program 50 times, I generated the error twice. While this may not seem much better, I think that I can convince the management to use my test program instead of the original test program. Am I right?

95. "Japanese Girls' Names"

by Kumi Furuichi

It used to be very typical for Japanese girls' names to end with "ko." (The trend might have started around my grandmothers' generation and its peak might have been around my mother's generation.) "Ko" means "child" in Chinese characters. Parents would name their daughters with "ko" attaching to other Chinese characters which have meanings that they want their daughters to become, such as Sachiko—happy child, Yoshiko—a good child, Yasuko—a healthy child, and so on.

However, I noticed recently that only two out of nine of my Japanese girlfriends at this school have names which end with "ko." More and more, parents seem to have become creative, modernized, and, sometimes, westernized in naming their children.

I have a feeling that, while 70 percent or more of my mother's generation would have names with "ko" at the end, the proportion has dropped among my peers. I wrote down all my Japanese friends', ex-classmates', co-workers, and acquaintances' names that I could remember. Following are the names. (Some are repeats.) Test to see if the proportion has dropped for this generation.

Ai, Akemi, Akiko, Ayumi, Chiaki, Chie, Eiko, Eri, Eriko, Fumiko, Harumi, Hitomi, Hiroko, Hiroko, Hidemi, Hisako, Hinako, Izumi, Izumi, Junko, Junko, Kana, Kanako, Kanayo, Kayo, Kayoko, Kazumi, Keiko, Keiko, Kei, Kumi, Kumiko, Kyoko, Kyoko, Madoka, Maho, Mai, Maiko, Maki, Miki, Miki, Mikiko, Mina, Minako, Miyako, Momoko, Nana, Naoko, Naoko, Naoko, Noriko, Rieko, Rika, Rika, Rumiko, Rei, Reiko, Reiko, Sachiko, Sachiko, Sachiyo, Saki, Sayaka, Sayoko, Sayuri, Seiko, Shiho, Shizuka, Sumiko, Takako, Takako, Tomoe, Tomoe, Tomoko, Touko, Yasuko, Yasuko, Yasuyo, Yoko, Yoko, Yoko, Yoshiko, Yoshiko, Yoshiko, Yuka, Yuki, Yuki, Yukiko, Yuko, Yuko.

96. "Phillip's Wish," by Suzanne Osorio

My nephew likes to play

Chasing the girls makes his day.

He asked his mother

If it is okay

To get his ear pierced.

She said, "No way!"

To poke a hole through your ear,

Is not what I want for you, dear.

He argued his point quite well,

Says even my macho pal, Mel,

Has gotten this done.

It's all just for fun.

C'mon please, mom, please, what the hell.

Again Phillip complained to his mother,

Saying half his friends (including their brothers)

Are piercing their ears

And they have no fears

He wants to be like the others.

She said, "I think it's much less.

We must do a hypothesis test.

And if you are right,

I won't put up a fight.

But, if not, then my case will rest."

We proceeded to call fifty guys

To see whose prediction would fly.

Nineteen of the fifty

Said piercing was nifty

And earrings they'd occasionally buy.

Then there's the other thirty-one,

Who said they'd never have this done.

So now this poem's finished.

Will his hopes be diminished,

Or will my nephew have his fun?

97. "The Craven," by Mark Salangsang

Once upon a morning dreary

In stats class I was weak and weary.

Pondering over last night's homework

Whose answers were now on the board

This I did and nothing more.

While I nodded nearly napping

Suddenly, there came a tapping.

As someone gently rapping,

Rapping my head as I snore.

Quoth the teacher, "Sleep no more."

"In every class you fall asleep,"

The teacher said, his voice was deep.

"So a tally I've begun to keep

Of every class you nap and snore.

The percentage being forty-four."

"My dear teacher I must confess,

While sleeping is what I do best.

The percentage, I think, must be less,

A percentage less than forty-four."

This I said and nothing more.

"We'll see," he said and walked away,

And fifty classes from that day

He counted till the month of May

The classes in which I napped and snored.

The number he found was twenty-four.

At a significance level of 0.05,

Please tell me am I still alive?

Or did my grade just take a dive

Plunging down beneath the floor?

Upon thee I hereby implore.

98. Toastmasters International cites a report by Gallop Poll that 40% of Americans fear public speaking. A student believes that less than 40% of students at her school fear public speaking. She randomly surveys 361 schoolmates and finds that 135 report they fear public speaking. Conduct a hypothesis test to determine if the percent at her school is less than 40%.

99. Sixty-eight percent of online courses taught at community colleges nationwide were taught by full-time faculty. To test if 68% also represents California's percent for full-time faculty teaching the online classes, Long Beach City College (LBCC) in California, was randomly selected for comparison. In the same year, 34 of the 44 online courses LBCC offered were taught by full-time faculty. Conduct a hypothesis test to determine if 68% represents California. NOTE: For more accurate results, use more California community colleges and this past year's data.

100. According to an article in *Bloomberg Businessweek*, New York City's most recent adult smoking rate is 14%. Suppose that a survey is conducted to determine this year's rate. Nine out of 70 randomly chosen N.Y. City residents reply that they smoke. Conduct a hypothesis test to determine if the rate is still 14% or if it has decreased.

101. The mean age of De Anza College students in a previous term was 26.6 years old. An instructor thinks the mean age for online students is older than 26.6. She randomly surveys 56 online students and finds that the sample mean is 29.4 with a standard deviation of 2.1. Conduct a hypothesis test.

102. Registered nurses earned an average annual salary of $69,110. For that same year, a survey was conducted of 41 California registered nurses to determine if the annual salary is higher than $69,110 for California nurses. The sample average was $71,121 with a sample standard deviation of $7,489. Conduct a hypothesis test.

103. La Leche League International reports that the mean age of weaning a child from breastfeeding is age four to five worldwide. In America, most nursing mothers wean their children much earlier. Suppose a random survey is conducted of 21 U.S. mothers who recently weaned their children. The mean weaning age was nine months (3/4 year) with a standard deviation of 4 months. Conduct a hypothesis test to determine if the mean weaning age in the U.S. is less than four years old.

104. Over the past few decades, public health officials have examined the link between weight concerns and teen girls' smoking. Researchers surveyed a group of 273 randomly selected teen girls living in Massachusetts (between 12 and 15 years old). After four years the girls were surveyed again. Sixty-three said they smoked to stay thin. Is there good evidence that more than thirty percent of the teen girls smoke to stay thin?
After conducting the test, your decision and conclusion are
    a. Reject H_0: There is sufficient evidence to conclude that more than 30% of teen girls smoke to stay thin.
    b. Do not reject H_0: There is not sufficient evidence to conclude that less than 30% of teen girls smoke to stay thin.
    c. Do not reject H_0: There is not sufficient evidence to conclude that more than 30% of teen girls smoke to stay thin.
    d. Reject H_0: There is sufficient evidence to conclude that less than 30% of teen girls smoke to stay thin.

105. A statistics instructor believes that fewer than 20% of Evergreen Valley College (EVC) students attended the opening night midnight showing of the latest Harry Potter movie. She surveys 84 of her students and finds that 11 of them attended the midnight showing.
At a 1% level of significance, an appropriate conclusion is:
    a. There is insufficient evidence to conclude that the percent of EVC students who attended the midnight showing of Harry Potter is less than 20%.
    b. There is sufficient evidence to conclude that the percent of EVC students who attended the midnight showing of Harry Potter is more than 20%.
    c. There is sufficient evidence to conclude that the percent of EVC students who attended the midnight showing of Harry Potter is less than 20%.
    d. There is insufficient evidence to conclude that the percent of EVC students who attended the midnight showing of Harry Potter is at least 20%.

106. Previously, an organization reported that teenagers spent 4.5 hours per week, on average, on the phone. The organization thinks that, currently, the mean is higher. Fifteen randomly chosen teenagers were asked how many hours per week they spend on the phone. The sample mean was 4.75 hours with a sample standard deviation of 2.0. Conduct a hypothesis test.

At a significance level of $a = 0.05$, what is the correct conclusion?
    a. There is enough evidence to conclude that the mean number of hours is more than 4.75
    b. There is enough evidence to conclude that the mean number of hours is more than 4.5
    c. There is not enough evidence to conclude that the mean number of hours is more than 4.5
    d. There is not enough evidence to conclude that the mean number of hours is more than 4.75

Instructions: For the following ten exercises,
Hypothesis testing: For the following ten exercises, answer each question.

    a. State the null and alternate hypothesis.

    b. State the *p*-value.

    c. State alpha.

    d. What is your decision?

    e. Write a conclusion.

    f. Answer any other questions asked in the problem.

107. According to the Center for Disease Control website, in 2011 at least 18% of high school students have smoked a cigarette. An Introduction to Statistics class in Davies County, KY conducted a hypothesis test at the local high school (a medium sized–approximately 1,200 students–small city demographic) to determine if the local high school's percentage was lower. One hundred fifty students were chosen at random and surveyed. Of the 150 students surveyed, 82 have smoked. Use a significance level of 0.05 and using appropriate statistical evidence, conduct a hypothesis test and state the conclusions.

108. A recent survey in the *N.Y. Times Almanac* indicated that 48.8% of families own stock. A broker wanted to determine if this survey could be valid. He surveyed a random sample of 250 families and found that 142 owned some type of stock. At the 0.05 significance level, can the survey be considered to be accurate?

109. Driver error can be listed as the cause of approximately 54% of all fatal auto accidents, according to the American Automobile Association. Thirty randomly selected fatal accidents are examined, and it is determined that 14 were caused by driver error. Using $\alpha = 0.05$, is the AAA proportion accurate?

110. The US Department of Energy reported that 51.7% of homes were heated by natural gas. A random sample of 221 homes in Kentucky found that 115 were heated by natural gas. Does the evidence support the claim for Kentucky at the $\alpha = 0.05$ level in Kentucky? Are the results applicable across the country? Why?

111. For Americans using library services, the American Library Association claims that at most 67% of patrons borrow books. The library director in Owensboro, Kentucky feels this is not true, so she asked a local college statistic class to conduct a survey. The class randomly selected 100 patrons and found that 82 borrowed books. Did the class demonstrate that the percentage was higher in Owensboro, KY? Use $\alpha = 0.01$ level of significance. What is the possible proportion of patrons that do borrow books from the Owensboro Library?

112. The Weather Underground reported that the mean amount of summer rainfall for the northeastern US is at least 11.52 inches. Ten cities in the northeast are randomly selected and the mean rainfall amount is calculated to be 7.42 inches with a standard deviation of 1.3 inches. At the $\alpha = 0.05$ level, can it be concluded that the mean rainfall was below the reported average? What if $\alpha = 0.01$? Assume the amount of summer rainfall follows a normal distribution.

113. A survey in the *N.Y. Times Almanac* finds the mean commute time (one way) is 25.4 minutes for the 15 largest US cities. The Austin, TX chamber of commerce feels that Austin's commute time is less and wants to publicize this fact. The mean for 25 randomly selected commuters is 22.1 minutes with a standard deviation of 5.3 minutes. At the $\alpha = 0.10$ level, is the Austin, TX commute significantly less than the mean commute time for the 15 largest US cities?

114. A report by the Gallup Poll found that a woman visits her doctor, on average, at most 5.8 times each year. A random sample of 20 women results in these yearly visit totals

3; 2; 1; 3; 7; 2; 9; 4; 6; 6; 8; 0; 5; 6; 4; 2; 1; 3; 4; 1

At the $\alpha = 0.05$ level can it be concluded that the sample mean is higher than 5.8 visits per year?

115. According to the *N.Y. Times Almanac* the mean family size in the U.S. is 3.18. A sample of a college math class resulted in the following family sizes:

5; 4; 5; 4; 4; 3; 6; 4; 3; 3; 5; 5; 6; 3; 3; 2; 7; 4; 5; 2; 2; 2; 3; 2

At $\alpha = 0.05$ level, is the class' mean family size greater than the national average? Does the Almanac result remain valid? Why?

116. The student academic group on a college campus claims that freshman students study at least 2.5 hours per day, on average. One Introduction to Statistics class was skeptical. The class took a random sample of 30 freshman students and found a mean study time of 137 minutes with a standard deviation of 45 minutes. At $\alpha = 0.01$ level, is the student academic group's claim correct?

REFERENCES

9.1 Null and Alternative Hypotheses

Data from the National Institute of Mental Health. Available online at http://www.nimh.nih.gov/publicat/depression.cfm.

9.5 Additional Information and Full Hypothesis Test Examples

Data from Amit Schitai. Director of Instructional Technology and Distance Learning. LBCC.

Data from *Bloomberg Businessweek*. Available online at http://www.businessweek.com/news/2011- 09-15/nyc-smoking-rate-falls-to-record-low-of-14-bloomberg-says.html.

Data from energy.gov. Available online at http://energy.gov (accessed June 27. 2013).

Data from Gallup®. Available online at www.gallup.com (accessed June 27, 2013).

Data from *Growing by Degrees* by Allen and Seaman.

Data from La Leche League International. Available online at http://www.lalecheleague.org/Law/BAFeb01.html.

Data from the American Automobile Association. Available online at www.aaa.com (accessed June 27, 2013).

Data from the American Library Association. Available online at www.ala.org (accessed June 27, 2013).

Data from the Bureau of Labor Statistics. Available online at http://www.bls.gov/oes/current/oes291111.htm.

Data from the Centers for Disease Control and Prevention. Available online at www.cdc.gov (accessed June 27, 2013)

Data from the U.S. Census Bureau, available online at http://quickfacts.census.gov/qfd/states/00000.html (accessed June 27, 2013).

Data from the United States Census Bureau. Available online at http://www.census.gov/hhes/socdemo/language/.

Data from Toastmasters International. Available online at http://toastmasters.org/artisan/detail.asp?CategoryID=1&SubCategoryID=10&ArticleID=429&Page=1.

Data from Weather Underground. Available online at www.wunderground.com (accessed June 27, 2013).

Federal Bureau of Investigations. "Uniform Crime Reports and Index of Crime in Daviess in the State of Kentucky enforced by Daviess County from 1985 to 2005." Available online at http://www.disastercenter.com/kentucky/crime/3868.htm (accessed June 27, 2013).

"Foothill-De Anza Community College District." De Anza College, Winter 2006. Available online at http://research.fhda.edu/factbook/DAdemofs/Fact_sheet_da_2006w.pdf.

Johansen, C., J. Boice, Jr., J. McLaughlin, J. Olsen. "Cellular Telephones and Cancer—a Nationwide Cohort Study in Denmark." Institute of Cancer Epidemiology and the Danish Cancer Society, 93(3):203-7. Available online at http://www.ncbi.nlm.nih.gov/pubmed/11158188 (accessed June 27, 2013).

Rape, Abuse & Incest National Network. "How often does sexual assault occur?" RAINN, 2009. Available online at http://www.rainn.org/get-information/statistics/frequency-of-sexual-assault (accessed June 27, 2013).

SOLUTIONS

1 The random variable is the mean Internet speed in Megabits per second.

3 The random variable is the mean number of children an American family has.

5 The random variable is the proportion of people picked at random in Times Square visiting the city.

7
  a. H_0: $p = 0.42$

  b. H_a: $p < 0.42$

9
  a. H_0: $\mu = 15$

  b. H_a: $\mu \neq 15$

11 Type I: The mean price of mid-sized cars is $32,000, but we conclude that it is not $32,000. Type II: The mean price of mid-sized cars is not $32,000, but we conclude that it is $32,000.

13 α = the probability that you think the bag cannot withstand -15 degrees F, when in fact it can β = the probability that you think the bag can withstand -15 degrees F, when in fact it cannot

15 Type I: The procedure will go well, but the doctors think it will not. Type II: The procedure will not go well, but the doctors think it will.

17 0.019

19 0.998

21 A normal distribution or a Student's *t*-distribution

23 Use a Student's *t*-distribution

25 a normal distribution for a single population mean

27 It must be approximately normally distributed.

29 They must both be greater than five.

31 binomial distribution

33 The outcome of winning is very unlikely.

35 $H_0: \mu >= 73$
$H_a: \mu < 73$
The *p*-value is almost zero, which means there is sufficient data to conclude that the mean height of high school students who play basketball on the school team is less than 73 inches at the 5% level. The data do support the claim.

37 The shaded region shows a low *p*-value.

39 Do not reject H_0.

41 means

43 the mean time spent in jail for 26 first time convicted burglars

45
  a. 3
  b. 1.5
  c. 1.8
  d. 26

47 $\bar{X} \sim N\left(2.5, \frac{1.5}{\sqrt{26}}\right)$

49 This is a left-tailed test.

51 This is a two-tailed test.

53

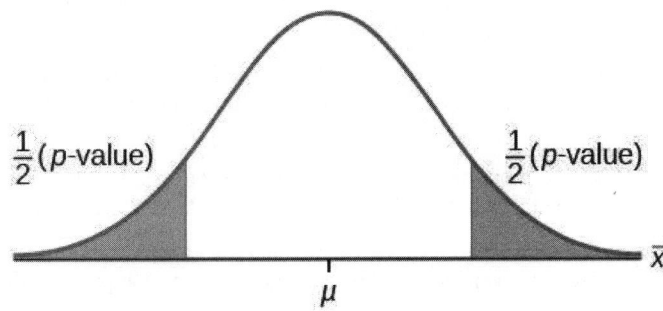

Figure 9.25

55 a right-tailed test

57 a left-tailed test

59 This is a left-tailed test.

61 This is a two-tailed test.

62

    a. H_0: $\mu = 34$; H_a: $\mu \neq 34$

    b. H_0: $p \leq 0.60$; H_a: $p > 0.60$

    c. H_0: $\mu \geq 100,000$; H_a: $\mu < 100,000$

    d. H_0: $p = 0.29$; H_a: $p \neq 0.29$

    e. H_0: $p = 0.05$; H_a: $p < 0.05$

    f. H_0: $\mu \leq 10$; H_a: $\mu > 10$

    g. H_0: $p = 0.50$; H_a: $p \neq 0.50$

    h. H_0: $\mu = 6$; H_a: $\mu \neq 6$

    i. H_0: $p \geq 0.11$; H_a: $p < 0.11$

    j. H_0: $\mu \leq 20,000$; H_a: $\mu > 20,000$

64 c

66

    a.   Type I error: We conclude that the mean is not 34 years, when it really is 34 years. Type II error: We conclude that the mean is 34 years, when in fact it really is not 34 years.

    b.   Type I error: We conclude that more than 60% of Americans vote in presidential elections, when the actual percentage is at most 60%. Type II error: We conclude that at most 60% of Americans vote in presidential elections when, in fact, more than 60% do.

    c.   Type I error: We conclude that the mean starting salary is less than $100,000, when it really is at least $100,000. Type II error: We conclude that the mean starting salary is at least $100,000 when, in fact, it is less than $100,000.

    d.   Type I error: We conclude that the proportion of high school seniors who get drunk each month is not 29%, when it really is 29%. Type II error: We conclude that the proportion of high school seniors who get drunk each month is 29% when, in fact, it is not 29%.

    e.   Type I error: We conclude that fewer than 5% of adults ride the bus to work in Los Angeles, when the percentage that do is really 5% or more. Type II error: We conclude that 5% or more adults ride the bus to work in Los Angeles when, in fact, fewer that 5% do.

    f.   Type I error: We conclude that the mean number of cars a person owns in his or her lifetime is more than 10, when in reality it is not more than 10. Type II error: We conclude that the mean number of cars a person owns in his or her lifetime is not more than 10 when, in fact, it is more than 10.

    g.   Type I error: We conclude that the proportion of Americans who prefer to live away from cities is not about half, though the actual proportion is about half. Type II error: We conclude that the proportion of Americans who prefer to live away from cities is half when, in fact, it is not half.

    h.   Type I error: We conclude that the duration of paid vacations each year for Europeans is not six weeks, when in fact it is six weeks. Type II error: We conclude that the duration of paid vacations each year for Europeans is six weeks when, in fact, it is not.

    i.   Type I error: We conclude that the proportion is less than 11%, when it is really at least 11%. Type II error: We conclude that the proportion of women who develop breast cancer is at least 11%, when in fact it is less than 11%.

    j.   Type I error: We conclude that the average tuition cost at private universities is more than $20,000, though in reality it is at most $20,000. Type II error: We conclude that the average tuition cost at private universities is at most $20,000 when, in fact, it is more than $20,000.

68 b

70 d

72 d

74

    a. H_0: $\mu \geq 50,000$

    b. H_a: $\mu < 50,000$

c. Let $\bar{X}$ = the average lifespan of a brand of tires.

d. normal distribution

e. $z = -2.315$

f. p-value = 0.0103

g. Check student's solution.

h.   i.   alpha: 0.05

    ii. Decision: Reject the null hypothesis.

    iii. Reason for decision: The p-value is less than 0.05.

    iv. Conclusion: There is sufficient evidence to conclude that the mean lifespan of the tires is less than 50,000 miles.

i. (43,537, 49,463)

76

a. H_0: μ = \$1.00

b. H_a: $\mu \neq$ \$1.00

c. Let $\bar{X}$ = the average cost of a daily newspaper.

d. normal distribution

e. $z = -0.866$

f. p-value = 0.3865

g. Check student's solution.

h.   i.   Alpha: 0.01

    ii. Decision: Do not reject the null hypothesis.

    iii. Reason for decision: The p-value is greater than 0.01.

    iv. Conclusion: There is sufficient evidence to support the claim that the mean cost of daily papers is \$1. The mean cost could be \$1.

i. (\$0.84, \$1.06)

78

a. H_0: μ = 10

b. H_a: $\mu \neq$ 10

c. Let $\bar{X}$ the mean number of sick days an employee takes per year.

d. Student's t-distribution

e. $t = -1.12$

f. p-value = 0.300

g. Check student's solution.

h.   i.   Alpha: 0.05

    ii. Decision: Do not reject the null hypothesis.

    iii. Reason for decision: The p-value is greater than 0.05.

    iv. Conclusion: At the 5% significance level, there is insufficient evidence to conclude that the mean number of sick days is not ten.

i. (4.9443, 11.806)

80

a. H_0: $p \geq 0.6$

b. H_a: $p < 0.6$

c. Let P' = the proportion of students who feel more enriched as a result of taking Elementary Statistics.

d. normal for a single proportion

e. 1.12

f. p-value = 0.1308

g. Check student's solution.

h.   i.   Alpha: 0.05

    ii.   Decision: Do not reject the null hypothesis.

    iii.   Reason for decision: The p-value is greater than 0.05.

    iv.   Conclusion: There is insufficient evidence to conclude that less than 60 percent of her students feel more enriched.

i. Confidence Interval: (0.409, 0.654)
The "plus-4s" confidence interval is (0.411, 0.648)

82

a. H_0: $\mu = 4$

b. H_a: $\mu \neq 4$

c. Let $\bar{X}$ the average I.Q. of a set of brown trout.

d. two-tailed Student's t-test

e. $t = 1.95$

f. p-value = 0.076

g. Check student's solution.

h.   i.   Alpha: 0.05

    ii.   Decision: Reject the null hypothesis.

    iii.   Reason for decision: The p-value is greater than 0.05

    iv.   Conclusion: There is insufficient evidence to conclude that the average IQ of brown trout is not four.

i. (3.8865,5.9468)

84

a. H_0: $p \geq 0.13$

b. H_a: $p < 0.13$

c. Let P' = the proportion of Americans who have seen or sensed angels

d. normal for a single proportion

e. −2.688

f. p-value = 0.0036

g. Check student's solution.

h.   i.   alpha: 0.05

    ii.   Decision: Reject the null hypothesis.

    iii.   Reason for decision: The p-value is less than 0.05.

    iv.   Conclusion: There is sufficient evidence to conclude that the percentage of Americans who have seen or sensed an angel is less than 13%.

i. (0, 0.0623).
The "plus-4s" confidence interval is (0.0022, 0.0978)

86

a. $H_0: \mu \geq 129$

b. $H_a: \mu < 129$

c. Let $\bar{X}$ = the average time in seconds that Terri finishes Lap 4.

d. Student's t-distribution

e. $t = 1.209$

f. 0.8792

g. Check student's solution.

h. i. Alpha: 0.05

 ii. Decision: Do not reject the null hypothesis.

 iii. Reason for decision: The p-value is greater than 0.05.

 iv. Conclusion: There is insufficient evidence to conclude that Terri's mean lap time is less than 129 seconds.

i. (128.63, 130.37)

88

a. $H_0: p = 0.60$

b. $H_a: p < 0.60$

c. Let P' = the proportion of family members who shed tears at a reunion.

d. normal for a single proportion

e. −1.71

f. 0.0438

g. Check student's solution.

h. i. alpha: 0.05

 ii. Decision: Reject the null hypothesis.

 iii. Reason for decision: p-value < alpha

 iv. Conclusion: At the 5% significance level, there is sufficient evidence to conclude that the proportion of family members who shed tears at a reunion is less than 0.60. However, the test is weak because the p-value and alpha are quite close, so other tests should be done.

i. We are 95% confident that between 38.29% and 61.71% of family members will shed tears at a family reunion. (0.3829, 0.6171). The "plus-4s" confidence interval (see chapter 8) is (0.3861, 0.6139)

Note that here the "large-sample" 1 − PropZTest provides the approximate p-value of 0.0438. Whenever a p-value based on a normal approximation is close to the level of significance, the exact p-value based on binomial probabilities should be calculated whenever possible. This is beyond the scope of this course.

90

a. $H_0: \mu \geq 22$

b. $H_a: \mu < 22$

c. Let $\bar{X}$ = the mean number of bubbles per blow.

d. Student's t-distribution

e. −2.667

f. p-value = 0.00486

g. Check student's solution.

h. i. Alpha: 0.05

    ii. Decision: Reject the null hypothesis.

    iii. Reason for decision: The *p*-value is less than 0.05.

    iv. Conclusion: There is sufficient evidence to conclude that the mean number of bubbles per blow is less than 22.

i. (18.501, 21.499)

92

a. H_0: $\mu \leq 1$

b. H_a: $\mu > 1$

c. Let $\bar{X}$ = the mean cost in dollars of macaroni and cheese in a certain town.

d. Student's *t*-distribution

e. $t = 0.340$

f. *p*-value = 0.36756

g. Check student's solution.

h. i. Alpha: 0.05

    ii. Decision: Do not reject the null hypothesis.

    iii. Reason for decision: The *p*-value is greater than 0.05

    iv. Conclusion: The mean cost could be \$1, or less. At the 5% significance level, there is insufficient evidence to conclude that the mean price of a box of macaroni and cheese is more than \$1.

i. (0.8291, 1.241)

94

a. H_0: $p = 0.01$

b. H_a: $p > 0.01$

c. Let P' = the proportion of errors generated

d. Normal for a single proportion

e. 2.13

f. 0.0165

g. Check student's solution.

h. i. Alpha: 0.05

    ii. Decision: Reject the null hypothesis

    iii. Reason for decision: The *p*-value is less than 0.05.

    iv. Conclusion: At the 5% significance level, there is sufficient evidence to conclude that the proportion of errors generated is more than 0.01.

i. Confidence interval: (0, 0.094).
The "plus-4s" confidence interval is (0.004, 0.144).

96

a. H_0: $p = 0.50$

b. H_a: $p < 0.50$

c. Let P' = the proportion of friends that has a pierced ear.

d. normal for a single proportion

e. −1.70

    f.   *p*-value = 0.0448

    g.   Check student's solution.

    h.   i.   Alpha: 0.05

           ii.   Decision: Reject the null hypothesis

           iii.   Reason for decision: The *p*-value is less than 0.05. (However, they are very close.)

           iv.   Conclusion: There is sufficient evidence to support the claim that less than 50% of his friends have pierced ears.

    i.   Confidence Interval: (0.245, 0.515): The "plus-4s" confidence interval is (0.259, 0.519).

98

    a. H_0: $p = 0.40$

    b. H_a: $p < 0.40$

    c.   Let P' = the proportion of schoolmates who fear public speaking.

    d.   normal for a single proportion

    e.   −1.01

    f.   *p*-value = 0.1563

    g.   Check student's solution.

    h.   i.   Alpha: 0.05

           ii.   Decision: Do not reject the null hypothesis.

           iii.   Reason for decision: The *p*-value is greater than 0.05.

           iv.   Conclusion: There is insufficient evidence to support the claim that less than 40% of students at the school fear public speaking.

    i.   Confidence Interval: (0.3241, 0.4240): The "plus-4s" confidence interval is (0.3257, 0.4250).

100

    a. H_0: $p = 0.14$

    b. H_a: $p < 0.14$

    c.   Let P' = the proportion of NYC residents that smoke.

    d.   normal for a single proportion

    e.   −0.2756

    f.   *p*-value = 0.3914

    g.   Check student's solution.

    h.   i.   alpha: 0.05

           ii.   Decision: Do not reject the null hypothesis.

           iii.   Reason for decision: The *p*-value is greater than 0.05.

           iv.   At the 5% significance level, there is insufficient evidence to conclude that the proportion of NYC residents who smoke is less than 0.14.

    i.   Confidence Interval: (0.0502, 0.2070): The "plus-4s" confidence interval (see chapter 8) is (0.0676, 0.2297).

102

    a. H_0: $\mu = 69{,}110$

    b. H_a: $\mu > 69{,}110$

    c.   Let $\bar{X}$ = the mean salary in dollars for California registered nurses.

    d.   Student's *t*-distribution

e. $t = 1.719$

f. *p*-value: 0.0466

g. Check student's solution.

h.   i.   Alpha: 0.05

    ii.   Decision: Reject the null hypothesis.

    iii.   Reason for decision: The *p*-value is less than 0.05.

    iv.   Conclusion: At the 5% significance level, there is sufficient evidence to conclude that the mean salary of California registered nurses exceeds $69,110.

i. ($68,757, $73,485)

104 c

106 c

108

a. H_0: $p = 0.488$ H_a: $p \neq 0.488$

b. *p*-value = 0.0114

c. alpha = 0.05

d. Reject the null hypothesis.

e. At the 5% level of significance, there is enough evidence to conclude that 48.8% of families own stocks.

f. The survey does not appear to be accurate.

110

a. H_0: $p = 0.517$ H_a: $p \neq 0.517$

b. *p*-value = 0.9203.

c. alpha = 0.05.

d. Do not reject the null hypothesis.

e. At the 5% significance level, there is not enough evidence to conclude that the proportion of homes in Kentucky that are heated by natural gas is 0.517.

f. However, we cannot generalize this result to the entire nation. First, the sample's population is only the state of Kentucky. Second, it is reasonable to assume that homes in the extreme north and south will have extreme high usage and low usage, respectively. We would need to expand our sample base to include these possibilities if we wanted to generalize this claim to the entire nation.

112

a. H_0: $\mu \geq 11.52$ H_a: $\mu < 11.52$

b. *p*-value = 0.000002 which is almost 0.

c. alpha = 0.05.

d. Reject the null hypothesis.

e. At the 5% significance level, there is enough evidence to conclude that the mean amount of summer rain in the northeaster US is less than 11.52 inches, on average.

f. We would make the same conclusion if alpha was 1% because the *p*-value is almost 0.

114

a. H_0: $\mu \leq 5.8$ H_a: $\mu > 5.8$

b. *p*-value = 0.9987

c. alpha = 0.05

d. Do not reject the null hypothesis.

e. At the 5% level of significance, there is not enough evidence to conclude that a woman visits her doctor, on average, more than 5.8 times a year.

116

a. H_0: $\mu \geq 150$ H_a: $\mu < 150$

b. p-value = 0.0622

c. alpha = 0.01

d. Do not reject the null hypothesis.

e. At the 1% significance level, there is not enough evidence to conclude that freshmen students study less than 2.5 hours per day, on average.

f. The student academic group's claim appears to be correct.

10 | HYPOTHESIS TESTING WITH TWO SAMPLES

Figure 10.1 If you want to test a claim that involves two groups (the types of breakfasts eaten east and west of the Mississippi River) you can use a slightly different technique when conducting a hypothesis test. (credit: Chloe Lim)

Introduction

Chapter Objectives

By the end of this chapter, the student should be able to:

- Classify hypothesis tests by type.
- Conduct and interpret hypothesis tests for two population means, population standard deviations known.
- Conduct and interpret hypothesis tests for two population means, population standard deviations unknown.
- Conduct and interpret hypothesis tests for two population proportions.
- Conduct and interpret hypothesis tests for matched or paired samples.

Studies often compare two groups. For example, researchers are interested in the effect aspirin has in preventing heart attacks. Over the last few years, newspapers and magazines have reported various aspirin studies involving two groups. Typically, one group is given aspirin and the other group is given a placebo. Then, the heart attack rate is studied over several years.

There are other situations that deal with the comparison of two groups. For example, studies compare various diet and exercise programs. Politicians compare the proportion of individuals from different income brackets who might vote for them. Students are interested in whether SAT or GRE preparatory courses really help raise their scores.

You have learned to conduct hypothesis tests on single means and single proportions. You will expand upon that in this chapter. You will compare two means or two proportions to each other. The general procedure is still the same, just expanded.

To compare two means or two proportions, you work with two groups. The groups are classified either as **independent** or **matched pairs**. **Independent groups** consist of two samples that are independent, that is, sample values selected from one population are not related in any way to sample values selected from the other population. **Matched pairs** consist of two samples that are dependent. The parameter tested using matched pairs is the population mean. The parameters tested using independent groups are either population means or population proportions.

NOTE

☞   This chapter relies on either a calculator or a computer to calculate the degrees of freedom, the test statistics, and p-values. TI-83+ and TI-84 instructions are included as well as the test statistic formulas. When using a TI-83+ or TI-84 calculator, we do not need to separate two population means, independent groups, or population variances unknown into large and small sample sizes. However, most statistical computer software has the ability to differentiate these tests.

This chapter deals with the following hypothesis tests:

Independent groups (samples are independent)
- Test of two population means.
- Test of two population proportions.

Matched or paired samples (samples are dependent)
- Test of the two population proportions by testing one population mean of differences.

10.1 | Two Population Means with Unknown Standard Deviations

1. The two independent samples are simple random samples from two distinct populations.

2. For the two distinct populations:
   ◦ if the sample sizes are small, the distributions are important (should be normal)
   ◦ if the sample sizes are large, the distributions are not important (need not be normal)

The test comparing two independent population means with unknown and possibly unequal population standard deviations is called the Aspin-Welch t-test. The degrees of freedom formula was developed by Aspin-Welch.

The comparison of two population means is very common. A difference between the two samples depends on both the means and the standard deviations. Very different means can occur by chance if there is great variation among the individual samples. In order to account for the variation, we take the difference of the sample means, $\bar{X}_1 - \bar{X}_2$, and divide by the standard error in order to standardize the difference. The result is a t-score test statistic.

Because we do not know the population standard deviations, we estimate them using the two sample standard deviations from our independent samples. For the hypothesis test, we calculate the estimated standard deviation, or **standard error**, of **the difference in sample means**, $\bar{X}_1 - \bar{X}_2$.

The standard error is:

$$\sqrt{\frac{(s_1)^2}{n_1} + \frac{(s_2)^2}{n_2}}$$

The test statistic (*t*-score) is calculated as follows:

$$\frac{(\bar{x}_1 - \bar{x}_2) - (\mu_1 - \mu_2)}{\sqrt{\frac{(s_1)^2}{n_1} + \frac{(s_2)^2}{n_2}}}$$

where:

- s_1 and s_2, the sample standard deviations, are estimates of σ_1 and σ_2, respectively.

- σ_1 and σ_1 are the unknown population standard deviations.

- $\bar{x}_1$ and $\bar{x}_2$ are the sample means. μ_1 and μ_2 are the population means.

The number of **degrees of freedom (*df*)** requires a somewhat complicated calculation. However, a computer or calculator calculates it easily. The *df* are not always a whole number. The test statistic calculated previously is approximated by the Student's *t*-distribution with *df* as follows:

Degrees of freedom

$$df = \frac{\left(\frac{(s_1)^2}{n_1} + \frac{(s_2)^2}{n_2}\right)^2}{\left(\frac{1}{n_1 - 1}\right)\left(\frac{(s_1)^2}{n_1}\right)^2 + \left(\frac{1}{n_2 - 1}\right)\left(\frac{(s_2)^2}{n_2}\right)^2}$$

When both sample sizes n_1 and n_2 are five or larger, the Student's *t* approximation is very good. Notice that the sample variances $(s_1)^2$ and $(s_2)^2$ are not pooled. (If the question comes up, do not pool the variances.)

☞ It is not necessary to compute this by hand. A calculator or computer easily computes it.

Example 10.1 Independent groups

The average amount of time boys and girls aged seven to 11 spend playing sports each day is believed to be the same. A study is done and data are collected, resulting in the data in **Table 10.1**. Each populations has a normal distribution.

	Sample Size	Average Number of Hours Playing Sports Per Day	Sample Standard Deviation
Girls	9	2	0.866
Boys	16	3.2	1.00

Table 10.1

Is there a difference in the mean amount of time boys and girls aged seven to 11 play sports each day? Test at the 5% level of significance.

Solution 10.1

The population standard deviations are not known. Let *g* be the subscript for girls and *b* be the subscript for boys. Then, μ_g is the population mean for girls and μ_b is the population mean for boys. This is a test of two **independent groups**, two population **means**.

Random variable: $\overline{X}_g - \overline{X}_b$ = difference in the sample mean amount of time girls and boys play sports each day.

$H_0: \mu_g = \mu_b \qquad H_0: \mu_g - \mu_b = 0$
$H_a: \mu_g \neq \mu_b \qquad H_a: \mu_g - \mu_b \neq 0$

The words **"the same"** tell you H_0 has an "=". Since there are no other words to indicate H_a, assume it says **"is different."** This is a two-tailed test.

Distribution for the test: Use t_{df} where df is calculated using the df formula for independent groups, two population means. Using a calculator, df is approximately 18.8462. **Do not pool the variances.**

Calculate the p-value using a Student's t-distribution: p-value = 0.0054

Graph:

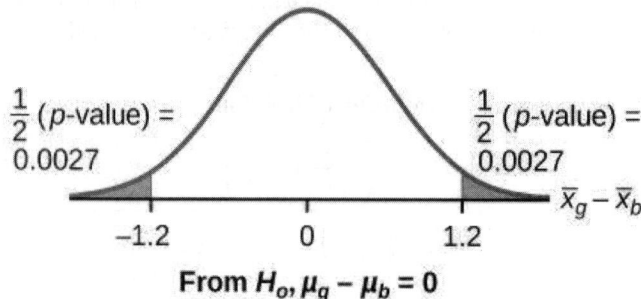

Figure 10.2

$s_g = 0.866$

$s_b = 1$

So, $\overline{x}_g - \overline{x}_b = 2 - 3.2 = -1.2$

Half the p-value is below −1.2 and half is above 1.2.

Make a decision: Since $\alpha > p$-value, reject H_0. This means you reject $\mu_g = \mu_b$. The means are different.

 Using the TI-83, 83+, 84, 84+ Calculator

Press STAT. Arrow over to TESTS and press 4:2-SampTTest. Arrow over to Stats and press ENTER. Arrow down and enter 2 for the first sample mean, 0.866 for Sx1, 9 for n1, 3.2 for the second sample mean, 1 for Sx2, and 16 for n2. Arrow down to µ1: and arrow to does not equal µ2. Press ENTER. Arrow down to Pooled: and No. Press ENTER. Arrow down to Calculate and press ENTER. The p-value is $p = 0.0054$, the dfs are approximately 18.8462, and the test statistic is -3.14. Do the procedure again but instead of Calculate do Draw.

Conclusion: At the 5% level of significance, the sample data show there is sufficient evidence to conclude that the mean number of hours that girls and boys aged seven to 11 play sports per day is different (mean number of hours boys aged seven to 11 play sports per day is greater than the mean number of hours played by girls OR the mean number of hours girls aged seven to 11 play sports per day is greater than the mean number of hours played by boys).

Try It Σ

10.1 Two samples are shown in **Table 10.2**. Both have normal distributions. The means for the two populations are thought to be the same. Is there a difference in the means? Test at the 5% level of significance.

	Sample Size	Sample Mean	Sample Standard Deviation
Population A	25	5	1
Population B	16	4.7	1.2

Table 10.2

NOTE

When the sum of the sample sizes is larger than 30 ($n_1 + n_2 > 30$) you can use the normal distribution to approximate the Student's t.

Example 10.2

A study is done by a community group in two neighboring colleges to determine which one graduates students with more math classes. College A samples 11 graduates. Their average is four math classes with a standard deviation of 1.5 math classes. College B samples nine graduates. Their average is 3.5 math classes with a standard deviation of one math class. The community group believes that a student who graduates from college A **has taken more math classes,** on the average. Both populations have a normal distribution. Test at a 1% significance level. Answer the following questions.

a. Is this a test of two means or two proportions?

Solution 10.2
a. two means

b. Are the populations standard deviations known or unknown?

Solution 10.2
b. unknown

c. Which distribution do you use to perform the test?

Solution 10.2
c. Student's t

d. What is the random variable?

Solution 10.2
d. $\bar{X}_A - \bar{X}_B$

e. What are the null and alternate hypotheses? Write the null and alternate hypotheses in words and in symbols.

Solution 10.2

e.

- $H_o : \mu_A \le \mu_B$

- $H_a : \mu_A > \mu_B$

f. Is this test right-, left-, or two-tailed?

Solution 10.2

f.

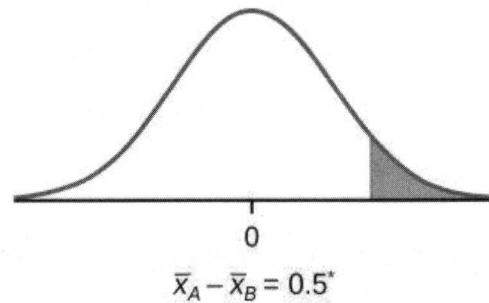

Figure 10.3

right

g. What is the *p*-value?

Solution 10.2

g. 0.1928

h. Do you reject or not reject the null hypothesis?

Solution 10.2

h. Do not reject.

i. **Conclusion:**

Solution 10.2

i. At the 1% level of significance, from the sample data, there is not sufficient evidence to conclude that a student who graduates from college A has taken more math classes, on the average, than a student who graduates from college B.

10.2 A study is done to determine if Company A retains its workers longer than Company B. Company A samples 15 workers, and their average time with the company is five years with a standard deviation of 1.2. Company B samples

20 workers, and their average time with the company is 4.5 years with a standard deviation of 0.8. The populations are normally distributed.

a. Are the population standard deviations known?

b. Conduct an appropriate hypothesis test. At the 5% significance level, what is your conclusion?

Example 10.3

A professor at a large community college wanted to determine whether there is a difference in the means of final exam scores between students who took his statistics course online and the students who took his face-to-face statistics class. He believed that the mean of the final exam scores for the online class would be lower than that of the face-to-face class. Was the professor correct? The randomly selected 30 final exam scores from each group are listed in **Table 10.3** and **Table 10.4**.

67.6	41.2	85.3	55.9	82.4	91.2	73.5	94.1	64.7	64.7
70.6	38.2	61.8	88.2	70.6	58.8	91.2	73.5	82.4	35.5
94.1	88.2	64.7	55.9	88.2	97.1	85.3	61.8	79.4	79.4

Table 10.3 Online Class

77.9	95.3	81.2	74.1	98.8	88.2	85.9	92.9	87.1	88.2
69.4	57.6	69.4	67.1	97.6	85.9	88.2	91.8	78.8	71.8
98.8	61.2	92.9	90.6	97.6	100	95.3	83.5	92.9	89.4

Table 10.4 Face-to-face Class

Is the mean of the Final Exam scores of the online class lower than the mean of the Final Exam scores of the face-to-face class? Test at a 5% significance level. Answer the following questions:

a. Is this a test of two means or two proportions?

b. Are the population standard deviations known or unknown?

c. Which distribution do you use to perform the test?

d. What is the random variable?

e. What are the null and alternative hypotheses? Write the null and alternative hypotheses in words and in symbols.

f. Is this test right, left, or two tailed?

g. What is the *p*-value?

h. Do you reject or not reject the null hypothesis?

i. At the ___ level of significance, from the sample data, there _____ (is/is not) sufficient evidence to conclude that _____.

(See the conclusion in **Example 10.2**, and write yours in a similar fashion)

Using the TI-83, 83+, 84, 84+ Calculator

First put the data for each group into two lists (such as L1 and L2). Press STAT. Arrow over to TESTS and press 4:2SampTTest. Make sure Data is highlighted and press ENTER. Arrow down and enter L1 for the first list and L2 for the second list. Arrow down to μ_1: and arrow to $\neq \mu_2$ (does not equal). Press ENTER. Arrow down to Pooled: No. Press ENTER. Arrow down to Calculate and press ENTER.

NOTE

Be careful not to mix up the information for Group 1 and Group 2!

Solution 10.3

a. two means

b. unknown

c. Student's t

d. $\overline{X}_1 - \overline{X}_2$

e. 1. H_0: $\mu_1 = \mu_2$ Null hypothesis: the means of the final exam scores are equal for the online and face-to-face statistics classes.

    2. H_a: $\mu_1 < \mu_2$ Alternative hypothesis: the mean of the final exam scores of the online class is less than the mean of the final exam scores of the face-to-face class.

f. left-tailed

g. p-value = 0.0011

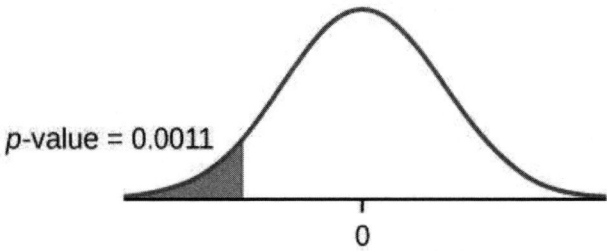

Figure 10.4

h. Reject the null hypothesis

i. The professor was correct. The evidence shows that the mean of the final exam scores for the online class is lower than that of the face-to-face class.
    At the 5% level of significance, from the sample data, there is (is/is not) sufficient evidence to conclude that the mean of the final exam scores for the online class is less than the mean of final exam scores of the face-to-face class.

Cohen's Standards for Small, Medium, and Large Effect Sizes

Cohen's d is a measure of effect size based on the differences between two means. Cohen's d, named for United States statistician Jacob Cohen, measures the relative strength of the differences between the means of two populations based on sample data. The calculated value of effect size is then compared to Cohen's standards of small, medium, and large effect sizes.

Size of effect	d
Small	0.2
medium	0.5
Large	0.8

**Table 10.5 Cohen's
Standard Effect
Sizes**

Cohen's d is the measure of the difference between two means divided by the pooled standard deviation: $d = \dfrac{\bar{x}_1 - \bar{x}_2}{s_{pooled}}$

where $s_{pooled} = \sqrt{\dfrac{(n_1 - 1)s_1^2 + (n_2 - 1)s_2^2}{n_1 + n_2 - 2}}$

Example 10.4

Calculate Cohen's d for **Example 10.2**. Is the size of the effect small, medium, or large? Explain what the size of the effect means for this problem.

Solution 10.4
$\mu_1 = 4 \; s_1 = 1.5 \; n_1 = 11$
$\mu_2 = 3.5 \; s_2 = 1 \; n_2 = 9$
$d = 0.384$
The effect is small because 0.384 is between Cohen's value of 0.2 for small effect size and 0.5 for medium effect size. The size of the differences of the means for the two colleges is small indicating that there is not a significant difference between them.

Example 10.5

Calculate Cohen's d for **Example 10.3**. Is the size of the effect small, medium or large? Explain what the size of the effect means for this problem.

Solution 10.5
$d = 0.834$; Large, because 0.834 is greater than Cohen's 0.8 for a large effect size. The size of the differences between the means of the Final Exam scores of online students and students in a face-to-face class is large indicating a significant difference.

10.5 Weighted alpha is a measure of risk-adjusted performance of stocks over a period of a year. A high positive weighted alpha signifies a stock whose price has risen while a small positive weighted alpha indicates an unchanged stock price during the time period. Weighted alpha is used to identify companies with strong upward or downward trends. The weighted alpha for the top 30 stocks of banks in the northeast and in the west as identified by Nasdaq on May 24, 2013 are listed in **Table 10.6** and **Table 10.7**, respectively.

94.2	75.2	69.6	52.0	48.0	41.9	36.4	33.4	31.5	27.6
77.3	71.9	67.5	50.6	46.2	38.4	35.2	33.0	28.7	26.5
76.3	71.7	56.3	48.7	43.2	37.6	33.7	31.8	28.5	26.0

Table 10.6 Northeast

126.0	70.6	65.2	51.4	45.5	37.0	33.0	29.6	23.7	22.6
116.1	70.6	58.2	51.2	43.2	36.0	31.4	28.7	23.5	21.6
78.2	68.2	55.6	50.3	39.0	34.1	31.0	25.3	23.4	21.5

Table 10.7 West

Is there a difference in the weighted alpha of the top 30 stocks of banks in the northeast and in the west? Test at a 5% significance level. Answer the following questions:

a. Is this a test of two means or two proportions?

b. Are the population standard deviations known or unknown?

c. Which distribution do you use to perform the test?

d. What is the random variable?

e. What are the null and alternative hypotheses? Write the null and alternative hypotheses in words and in symbols.

f. Is this test right, left, or two tailed?

g. What is the p-value?

h. Do you reject or not reject the null hypothesis?

i. At the ___ level of significance, from the sample data, there _____ (is/is not) sufficient evidence to conclude that _____.

j. Calculate Cohen's d and interpret it.

10.2 | Two Population Means with Known Standard Deviations

Even though this situation is not likely (knowing the population standard deviations is not likely), the following example illustrates hypothesis testing for independent means, known population standard deviations. The sampling distribution for the difference between the means is normal and both populations must be normal. The random variable is $\overline{X}_1 - \overline{X}_2$. The normal distribution has the following format:

Normal distribution is:

$$\overline{X}_1 - \overline{X}_2 \sim N\left[\mu_1 - \mu_2, \sqrt{\frac{(\sigma_1)^2}{n_1} + \frac{(\sigma_2)^2}{n_2}}\right]$$

The standard deviation is:

$$\sqrt{\frac{(\sigma_1)^2}{n_1} + \frac{(\sigma_2)^2}{n_2}}$$

The test statistic (z-score) is:

$$z = \frac{(\bar{x}_1 - \bar{x}_2) - (\mu_1 - \mu_2)}{\sqrt{\frac{(\sigma_1)^2}{n_1} + \frac{(\sigma_2)^2}{n_2}}}$$

Example 10.6

Independent groups, population standard deviations known: The mean lasting time of two competing floor waxes is to be compared. **Twenty floors** are randomly assigned **to test each wax**. Both populations have a normal distributions. The data are recorded in **Table 10.8**.

Wax	Sample Mean Number of Months Floor Wax Lasts	Population Standard Deviation
1	3	0.33
2	2.9	0.36

Table 10.8

Does the data indicate that **wax 1 is more effective than wax 2**? Test at a 5% level of significance.

Solution 10.6

This is a test of two independent groups, two population means, population standard deviations known.

Random Variable: $\bar{X}_1 - \bar{X}_2$ = difference in the mean number of months the competing floor waxes last.

$H_0: \mu_1 \le \mu_2$

$H_a: \mu_1 > \mu_2$

The words **"is more effective"** says that **wax 1 lasts longer than wax 2**, on average. "Longer" is a ">" symbol and goes into H_a. Therefore, this is a right-tailed test.

Distribution for the test: The population standard deviations are known so the distribution is normal. Using the formula, the distribution is:

$$\bar{X}_1 - \bar{X}_2 \sim N\left(0, \sqrt{\frac{0.33^2}{20} + \frac{0.36^2}{20}}\right)$$

Since $\mu_1 \le \mu_2$ then $\mu_1 - \mu_2 \le 0$ and the mean for the normal distribution is zero.

Calculate the *p*-value using the normal distribution: *p*-value = 0.1799

Graph:

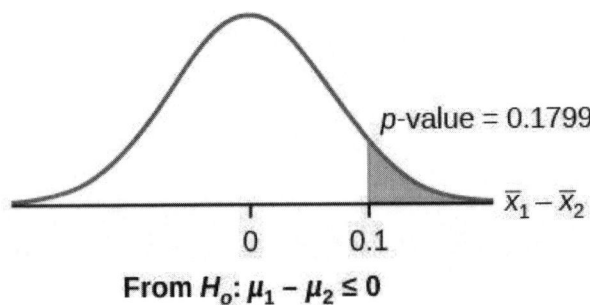

Figure 10.5

$$\overline{X}_1 - \overline{X}_2 = 3 - 2.9 = 0.1$$

Compare α and the *p*-value: $\alpha = 0.05$ and *p*-value $= 0.1799$. Therefore, $\alpha < $ *p*-value.

Make a decision: Since $\alpha < $ *p*-value, do not reject H_0.

Conclusion: At the 5% level of significance, from the sample data, there is not sufficient evidence to conclude that the mean time wax 1 lasts is longer (wax 1 is more effective) than the mean time wax 2 lasts.

 Using the TI-83, 83+, 84, 84+ Calculator

Press **STAT**. Arrow over to **TESTS** and press **3:2-SampZTest**. Arrow over to **Stats** and press **ENTER**. Arrow down and enter **.33** for sigma1, **.36** for sigma2, **3** for the first sample mean, **20** for n1, **2.9** for the second sample mean, and **20** for n2. Arrow down to μ1: and arrow to $> \mu_2$. Press **ENTER**. Arrow down to **Calculate** and press **ENTER**. The *p*-value is $p = 0.1799$ and the test statistic is 0.9157. Do the procedure again, but instead of **Calculate** do **Draw**.

Try It Σ

10.6 The means of the number of revolutions per minute of two competing engines are to be compared. Thirty engines are randomly assigned to be tested. Both populations have normal distributions. **Table 10.9** shows the result. Do the data indicate that Engine 2 has higher RPM than Engine 1? Test at a 5% level of significance.

Engine	Sample Mean Number of RPM	Population Standard Deviation
1	1,500	50
2	1,600	60

Table 10.9

Example 10.7

An interested citizen wanted to know if Democratic U. S. senators are older than Republican U.S. senators, on average. On May 26 2013, the mean age of 30 randomly selected Republican Senators was 61 years 247 days old (61.675 years) with a standard deviation of 10.17 years. The mean age of 30 randomly selected Democratic senators was 61 years 257 days old (61.704 years) with a standard deviation of 9.55 years.

Do the data indicate that Democratic senators are older than Republican senators, on average? Test at a 5% level of significance.

Solution 10.7

This is a test of two independent groups, two population means. The population standard deviations are unknown, but the sum of the sample sizes is 30 + 30 = 60, which is greater than 30, so we can use the normal approximation to the Student's-t distribution. Subscripts: 1: Democratic senators 2: Republican senators

Random variable: $\bar{X}_1 - \bar{X}_2$ = difference in the mean age of Democratic and Republican U.S. senators.

$H_0: \mu_1 \le \mu_2$ $H_0: \mu_1 - \mu_2 \le 0$

$H_a: \mu_1 > \mu_2$ $H_a: \mu_1 - \mu_2 > 0$

The words "older than" translates as a ">" symbol and goes into H_a. Therefore, this is a right-tailed test.

Distribution for the test: The distribution is the normal approximation to the Student's t for means, independent groups. Using the formula, the distribution is: $\bar{X}_1 - \bar{X}_2 \sim N[0, \sqrt{\frac{(9.55)^2}{30} + \frac{(10.17)^2}{30}}]$

Since $\mu_1 \le \mu_2$, $\mu_1 - \mu_2 \le 0$ and the mean for the normal distribution is zero.

(Calculating the p-value using the normal distribution gives p-value = 0.4955)

Graph:

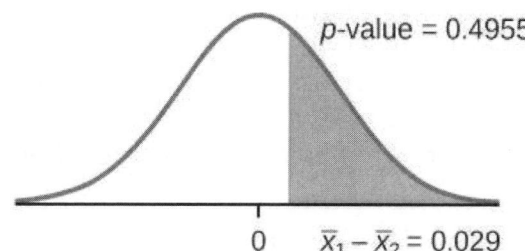

Figure 10.6

Compare α and the p-value: α = 0.05 and p-value = 0.4955. Therefore, $\alpha < p$-value.

Make a decision: Since $\alpha < p$-value, do not reject H_0.

Conclusion: At the 5% level of significance, from the sample data, there is not sufficient evidence to conclude that the mean age of Democratic senators is greater than the mean age of the Republican senators.

10.3 | Comparing Two Independent Population Proportions

When conducting a hypothesis test that compares two independent population proportions, the following characteristics should be present:

1. The two independent samples are simple random samples that are independent.

2. The number of successes is at least five, and the number of failures is at least five, for each of the samples.

3. Growing literature states that the population must be at least ten or 20 times the size of the sample. This keeps each population from being over-sampled and causing incorrect results.

Comparing two proportions, like comparing two means, is common. If two estimated proportions are different, it may be due to a difference in the populations or it may be due to chance. A hypothesis test can help determine if a difference in the estimated proportions reflects a difference in the population proportions.

The difference of two proportions follows an approximate normal distribution. Generally, the null hypothesis states that the two proportions are the same. That is, $H_0: p_A = p_B$. To conduct the test, we use a pooled proportion, p_c.

The pooled proportion is calculated as follows:
$$p_c = \frac{x_A + x_B}{n_A + n_B}$$

The distribution for the differences is:
$$P'_A - P'_B \sim N[0, \sqrt{p_c(1 - p_c)(\frac{1}{n_A} + \frac{1}{n_B})}]$$

The test statistic (z-score) is:
$$z = \frac{(p'_A - p'_B) - (p_A - p_B)}{\sqrt{p_c(1 - p_c)(\frac{1}{n_A} + \frac{1}{n_B})}}$$

Example 10.8

Two types of medication for hives are being tested to determine if there is a **difference in the proportions of adult patient reactions**. **Twenty** out of a random **sample of 200** adults given medication A still had hives 30 minutes after taking the medication. **Twelve** out of another **random sample of 200 adults** given medication B still had hives 30 minutes after taking the medication. Test at a 1% level of significance.

Solution 10.8

The problem asks for a difference in proportions, making it a test of two proportions.

Let A and B be the subscripts for medication A and medication B, respectively. Then p_A and p_B are the desired population proportions.

Random Variable:

$P'_A - P'_B$ = difference in the proportions of adult patients who did not react after 30 minutes to medication A and to medication B.

$H_0: p_A = p_B$

$p_A - p_B = 0$

$H_a: p_A \neq p_B$

$p_A - p_B \neq 0$

The words **"is a difference"** tell you the test is two-tailed.

Distribution for the test: Since this is a test of two binomial population proportions, the distribution is normal:

$$p_c = \frac{x_A + x_B}{n_A + n_B} = \frac{20 + 12}{200 + 200} = 0.08 \quad 1 - p_c = 0.92$$

$$P'_A - P'_B \sim N\left[0, \sqrt{(0.08)(0.92)(\frac{1}{200} + \frac{1}{200})}\right]$$

$P'_A - P'_B$ follows an approximate normal distribution.

Calculate the *p*-value using the normal distribution: *p*-value = 0.1404.

Estimated proportion for group A: $p'_A = \frac{x_A}{n_A} = \frac{20}{200} = 0.1$

Estimated proportion for group B: $p'_B = \frac{x_B}{n_B} = \frac{12}{200} = 0.06$

Graph:

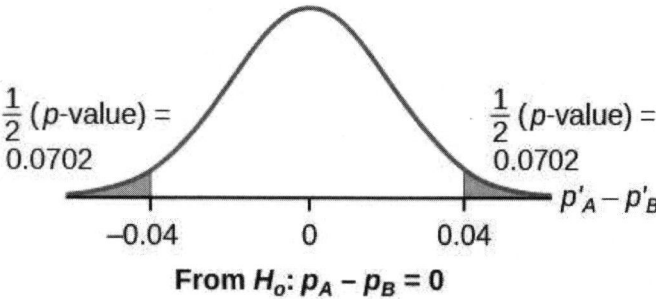

Figure 10.7

$P'_A - P'_B = 0.1 - 0.06 = 0.04$.

Half the p-value is below -0.04, and half is above 0.04.

Compare α and the p-value: $\alpha = 0.01$ and the p-value $= 0.1404$. $\alpha < p$-value.

Make a decision: Since $\alpha < p$-value, do not reject H_0.

Conclusion: At a 1% level of significance, from the sample data, there is not sufficient evidence to conclude that there is a difference in the proportions of adult patients who did not react after 30 minutes to medication A and medication B.

 Using the TI-83, 83+, 84, 84+ Calculator

Press STAT. Arrow over to TESTS and press 6:2-PropZTest. Arrow down and enter 20 for x1, 200 for n1, 12 for x2, and 200 for n2. Arrow down to p1: and arrow to not equal p2. Press ENTER. Arrow down to Calculate and press ENTER. The p-value is $p = 0.1404$ and the test statistic is 1.47. Do the procedure again, but instead of Calculate do Draw.

Try It Σ

10.8 Two types of valves are being tested to determine if there is a difference in pressure tolerances. Fifteen out of a random sample of 100 of Valve A cracked under 4,500 psi. Six out of a random sample of 100 of Valve B cracked under 4,500 psi. Test at a 5% level of significance.

Example 10.9

A research study was conducted about gender differences in "sexting." The researcher believed that the proportion of girls involved in "sexting" is less than the proportion of boys involved. The data collected in the spring of 2010 among a random sample of middle and high school students in a large school district in the southern United States is summarized in **Table 10.9**. Is the proportion of girls sending sexts less than the proportion of boys "sexting?" Test at a 1% level of significance.

	Males	**Females**
Sent "sexts"	183	156
Total number surveyed	2231	2169

Table 10.10

Solution 10.9

This is a test of two population proportions. Let M and F be the subscripts for males and females. Then p_M and p_F are the desired population proportions.

Random variable:

$p'_F - p'_M$ = difference in the proportions of males and females who sent "sexts."

$H_0: p_F = p_M \quad H_0: p_F - p_M = 0$

$H_a: p_F < p_M \quad H_a: p_F - p_M < 0$

The words **"less than"** tell you the test is left-tailed.

Distribution for the test: Since this is a test of two population proportions, the distribution is normal:

$$p_c = \frac{x_F + x_M}{n_F + n_M} = \frac{156 + 183}{2169 + 2231} = 0.077$$

$1 - p_c = 0.923$

Therefore,

$$p'_F - p'_M \sim N\left(0, \ \sqrt{(0.077)(0.923)\left(\frac{1}{2169} + \frac{1}{2231}\right)}\right)$$

$p'_F - p'_M$ follows an approximate normal distribution.

Calculate the p-value using the normal distribution:
p-value = 0.1045
Estimated proportion for females: 0.0719
Estimated proportion for males: 0.082

Graph:

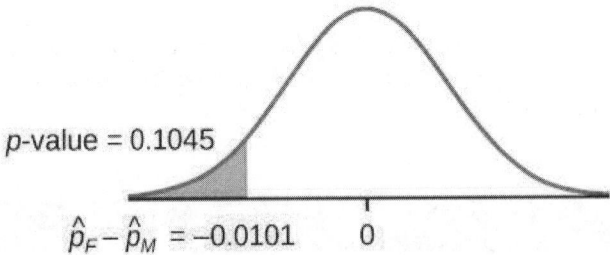

Figure 10.8

Decision: Since $\alpha < p$-value, Do not reject H_0

Conclusion: At the 1% level of significance, from the sample data, there is not sufficient evidence to conclude that the proportion of girls sending "sexts" is less than the proportion of boys sending "sexts."

Using the TI-83, 83+, 84, 84+ Calculator

Press STAT. Arrow over to TESTS and press 6:2-PropZTest. Arrow down and enter 156 for x1, 2169 for n1, 183 for x2, and 2231 for n2. Arrow down to p1: and arrow to less than p2. Press ENTER. Arrow down to Calculate and press ENTER. The *p*-value is $P = 0.1045$ and the test statistic is $z = -1.256$.

Example 10.10

Researchers conducted a study of smartphone use among adults. A cell phone company claimed that iPhone smartphones are more popular with whites (non-Hispanic) than with African Americans. The results of the survey indicate that of the 232 African American cell phone owners randomly sampled, 5% have an iPhone. Of the 1,343 white cell phone owners randomly sampled, 10% own an iPhone. Test at the 5% level of significance. Is the proportion of white iPhone owners greater than the proportion of African American iPhone owners?

Solution 10.10

This is a test of two population proportions. Let W and A be the subscripts for the whites and African Americans. Then p_W and p_A are the desired population proportions.

Random variable:

$p'_W - p'_A$ = difference in the proportions of Android and iPhone users.

$H_0: p_W = p_A$ $H_0: p_W - p_A = 0$

$H_a: p_W > p_A$ $H_a: p_W - p_A > 0$

The words "more popular" indicate that the test is right-tailed.

Distribution for the test: The distribution is approximately normal:

$$p_c = \frac{x_W + x_A}{n_W + n_A} = \frac{134 + 12}{1343 + 232} = 0.0927$$

$1 - p_c = 0.9073$

Therefore,

$$p'_W - p'_A \sim N\left(0, \ \sqrt{(0.0927)(0.9073)\left(\frac{1}{1343} + \frac{1}{232}\right)}\right)$$

$p'_W - p'_A$ follows an approximate normal distribution.

Calculate the *p*-value using the normal distribution:

p-value = 0.0077
Estimated proportion for group A: 0.10
Estimated proportion for group B: 0.05

Graph:

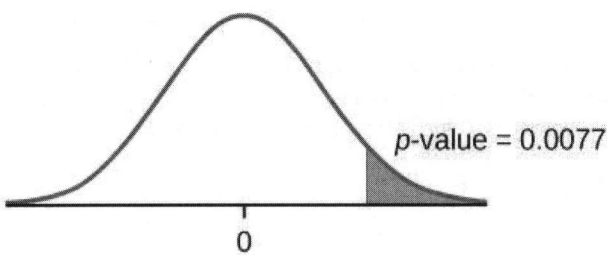

Figure 10.9

Decision: Since $\alpha > p$-value, reject the H_0.

Conclusion: At the 5% level of significance, from the sample data, there is sufficient evidence to conclude that a larger proportion of white cell phone owners use iPhones than African Americans.

 Using the TI-83, 83+, 84, 84+ Calculator

TI-83+ and TI-84: Press STAT. Arrow over to TESTS and press 6:2-PropZTest. Arrow down and enter 135 for x1, 1343 for n1, 12 for x2, and 232 for n2. Arrow down to p1: and arrow to greater than p2. Press ENTER. Arrow down to Calculate and press ENTER. The P-value is P = 0.0092 and the test statistic is Z = 2.33.

 **Try It** Σ

10.10 A concerned group of citizens wanted to know if the proportion of forcible rapes in Texas was different in 2011 than in 2010. Their research showed that of the 113,231 violent crimes in Texas in 2010, 7,622 of them were forcible rapes. In 2011, 7,439 of the 104,873 violent crimes were in the forcible rape category. Test at a 5% significance level. Answer the following questions:

a. Is this a test of two means or two proportions?

b. Which distribution do you use to perform the test?

c. What is the random variable?

d. What are the null and alternative hypothesis? Write the null and alternative hypothesis in symbols.

e. Is this test right-, left-, or two-tailed?

f. What is the p-value?

g. Do you reject or not reject the null hypothesis?

h. At the ___ level of significance, from the sample data, there _____ (is/is not) sufficient evidence to conclude that _____.

10.4 | Matched or Paired Samples

When using a hypothesis test for matched or paired samples, the following characteristics should be present:

1. Simple random sampling is used.

2. Sample sizes are often small.

3. Two measurements (samples) are drawn from the same pair of individuals or objects.

4. Differences are calculated from the matched or paired samples.

5. The differences form the sample that is used for the hypothesis test.

6. Either the matched pairs have differences that come from a population that is normal or the number of differences is sufficiently large so that distribution of the sample mean of differences is approximately normal.

In a hypothesis test for matched or paired samples, subjects are matched in pairs and differences are calculated. The differences are the data. The population mean for the differences, μ_d, is then tested using a Student's-t test for a single population mean with $n - 1$ degrees of freedom, where n is the number of differences.

The test statistic (*t*-score) is:

$$t = \frac{\overline{x}_d - \mu_d}{\left(\frac{s_d}{\sqrt{n}}\right)}$$

Example 10.11

A study was conducted to investigate the effectiveness of hypnotism in reducing pain. Results for randomly selected subjects are shown in **Table 10.10**. A lower score indicates less pain. The "before" value is matched to an "after" value and the differences are calculated. The differences have a normal distribution. Are the sensory measurements, on average, lower after hypnotism? Test at a 5% significance level.

Subject:	A	B	C	D	E	F	G	H
Before	6.6	6.5	9.0	10.3	11.3	8.1	6.3	11.6
After	6.8	2.4	7.4	8.5	8.1	6.1	3.4	2.0

Table 10.11

Solution 10.11

Corresponding "before" and "after" values form matched pairs. (Calculate "after" – "before.")

After Data	Before Data	Difference
6.8	6.6	0.2
2.4	6.5	-4.1
7.4	9	-1.6
8.5	10.3	-1.8
8.1	11.3	-3.2
6.1	8.1	-2
3.4	6.3	-2.9
2	11.6	-9.6

Table 10.12

The data **for the test** are the differences: {0.2, –4.1, –1.6, –1.8, –3.2, –2, –2.9, –9.6}

The sample mean and sample standard deviation of the differences are: $\overline{x}_d = -3.13$ and $s_d = 2.91$ Verify these values.

Let μ_d be the population mean for the differences. We use the subscript d to denote "differences."

Random variable: $\overline{X}_d$ = the mean difference of the sensory measurements

$H_0: \mu_d \geq 0$

The null hypothesis is zero or positive, meaning that there is the same or more pain felt after hypnotism. That means the subject shows no improvement. μ_d is the population mean of the differences.)

$H_a: \mu_d < 0$

The alternative hypothesis is negative, meaning there is less pain felt after hypnotism. That means the subject shows improvement. The score should be lower after hypnotism, so the difference ought to be negative to indicate improvement.

Distribution for the test: The distribution is a Student's t with $df = n - 1 = 8 - 1 = 7$. Use t_7. **(Notice that the test is for a single population mean.)**

Calculate the p-value using the Student's-t distribution: p-value = 0.0095

Graph:

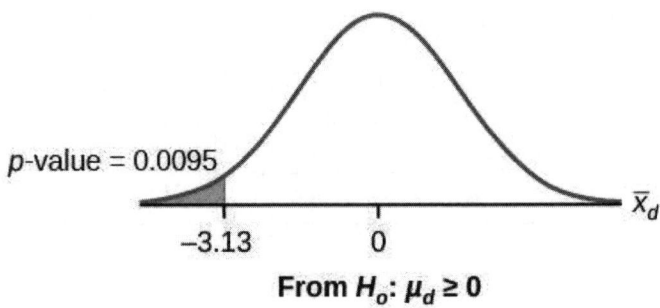

Figure 10.10

$\overline{X}_d$ is the random variable for the differences.

The sample mean and sample standard deviation of the differences are:

$\overline{x}_d = -3.13$

$\overline{s}_d = 2.91$

Compare α and the p-value: $\alpha = 0.05$ and p-value = 0.0095. $\alpha > p$-value.

Make a decision: Since $\alpha > p$-value, reject H_0. This means that $\mu_d < 0$ and there is improvement.

Conclusion: At a 5% level of significance, from the sample data, there is sufficient evidence to conclude that the sensory measurements, on average, are lower after hypnotism. Hypnotism appears to be effective in reducing pain.

NOTE

👉 For the TI-83+ and TI-84 calculators, you can either calculate the differences ahead of time (**after - before**) and put the differences into a list or you can put the **after** data into a first list and the **before** data into a second list. Then go to a third list and arrow up to the name. Enter 1st list name - 2nd list name. The calculator will do the subtraction, and you will have the differences in the third list.

Using the TI-83, 83+, 84, 84+ Calculator

Use your list of differences as the data. Press STAT and arrow over to TESTS. Press 2:T-Test. Arrow over to Data and press ENTER. Arrow down and enter 0 for μ_0, the name of the list where you put the data, and 1 for Freq:. Arrow down to μ: and arrow over to $< \mu_0$. Press ENTER. Arrow down to Calculate and press ENTER. The *p*-value is 0.0094, and the test statistic is -3.04. Do these instructions again except, arrow to Draw (instead of Calculate). Press ENTER.

Try It Σ

10.11 A study was conducted to investigate how effective a new diet was in lowering cholesterol. Results for the randomly selected subjects are shown in the table. The differences have a normal distribution. Are the subjects' cholesterol levels lower on average after the diet? Test at the 5% level.

Subject	A	B	C	D	E	F	G	H	I
Before	209	210	205	198	216	217	238	240	222
After	199	207	189	209	217	202	211	223	201

Table 10.13

Example 10.12

A college football coach was interested in whether the college's strength development class increased his players' maximum lift (in pounds) on the bench press exercise. He asked four of his players to participate in a study. The amount of weight they could each lift was recorded before they took the strength development class. After completing the class, the amount of weight they could each lift was again measured. The data are as follows:

Weight (in pounds)	Player 1	Player 2	Player 3	Player 4
Amount of weight lifted prior to the class	205	241	338	368
Amount of weight lifted after the class	295	252	330	360

Table 10.14

The coach wants to know if the strength development class makes his players stronger, on average.
Record the **differences** data. Calculate the differences by subtracting the amount of weight lifted prior to the class from the weight lifted after completing the class. The data for the differences are: {90, 11, -8, -8}. Assume the differences have a normal distribution.

Using the differences data, calculate the sample mean and the sample standard deviation.

$\bar{x}_d = 21.3, s_d = 46.7$

NOTE

The data given here would indicate that the distribution is actually right-skewed. The difference 90 may be an extreme outlier? It is pulling the sample mean to be 21.3 (positive). The means of the other three data values are actually negative.

Using the difference data, this becomes a test of a single _____ (fill in the blank).

Define the random variable: $\bar{X}_d$ mean difference in the maximum lift per player.

The distribution for the hypothesis test is t_3.

$H_0: \mu_d \leq 0, H_a: \mu_d > 0$

Graph:

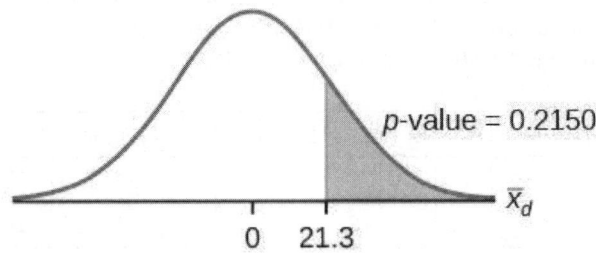

Figure 10.11

Calculate the *p*-value: The *p*-value is 0.2150

Decision: If the level of significance is 5%, the decision is not to reject the null hypothesis, because $\alpha < p$-value.

What is the conclusion?

At a 5% level of significance, from the sample data, there is not sufficient evidence to conclude that the strength development class helped to make the players stronger, on average.

10.12 A new prep class was designed to improve SAT test scores. Five students were selected at random. Their scores on two practice exams were recorded, one before the class and one after. The data recorded in **Table 10.15**. Are the scores, on average, higher after the class? Test at a 5% level.

SAT Scores	Student 1	Student 2	Student 3	Student 4
Score before class	1840	1960	1920	2150
Score after class	1920	2160	2200	2100

Table 10.15

Example 10.13

Seven eighth graders at Kennedy Middle School measured how far they could push the shot-put with their dominant (writing) hand and their weaker (non-writing) hand. They thought that they could push equal distances with either hand. The data were collected and recorded in **Table 10.16**.

Distance (in feet) using	Student 1	Student 2	Student 3	Student 4	Student 5	Student 6	Student 7
Dominant Hand	30	26	34	17	19	26	20
Weaker Hand	28	14	27	18	17	26	16

Table 10.16

Conduct a hypothesis test to determine whether the mean difference in distances between the children's dominant versus weaker hands is significant.

Record the **differences** data. Calculate the differences by subtracting the distances with the weaker hand from the distances with the dominant hand. The data for the differences are: {2, 12, 7, –1, 2, 0, 4}. The differences have a normal distribution.

Using the differences data, calculate the sample mean and the sample standard deviation. $\bar{x}_d = 3.71$, $s_d = 4.5$.

Random variable: $\bar{X}_d$ = mean difference in the distances between the hands.

Distribution for the hypothesis test: t_6

$H_0: \mu_d = 0 \quad H_a: \mu_d \neq 0$

Graph:

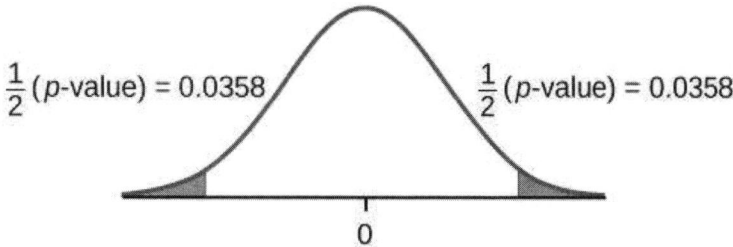

Figure 10.12

Calculate the p-value: The p-value is 0.0716 (using the data directly).

(test statistic = 2.18. p-value = 0.0719 using $\left(\bar{x}_d = 3.71, \ s_d = 4.5. \right)$

Decision: Assume $\alpha = 0.05$. Since $\alpha < p$-value, Do not reject H_0.

Conclusion: At the 5% level of significance, from the sample data, there is not sufficient evidence to conclude that there is a difference in the children's weaker and dominant hands to push the shot-put.

10.13 Five ball players think they can throw the same distance with their dominant hand (throwing) and off-hand (catching hand). The data were collected and recorded in **Table 10.17**. Conduct a hypothesis test to determine whether the mean difference in distances between the dominant and off-hand is significant. Test at the 5% level.

	Player 1	Player 2	Player 3	Player 4	Player 5
Dominant Hand	120	111	135	140	125
Off-hand	105	109	98	111	99

Table 10.17

10.5 | Hypothesis Testing for Two Means and Two Proportions

Stats Lab

10.1 Hypothesis Testing for Two Means and Two Proportions

Class Time:

Names:

Student Learning Outcomes

- The student will select the appropriate distributions to use in each case.
- The student will conduct hypothesis tests and interpret the results.

Supplies:

- the business section from two consecutive days' newspapers
- three small packages of M&Ms®
- five small packages of Reese's Pieces®

Increasing Stocks Survey

Look at yesterday's newspaper business section. Conduct a hypothesis test to determine if the proportion of New York Stock Exchange (NYSE) stocks that increased is greater than the proportion of NASDAQ stocks that increased. As randomly as possible, choose 40 NYSE stocks, and 32 NASDAQ stocks and complete the following statements.

1. H_0: _____
2. H_a: _____
3. In words, define the random variable.
4. The distribution to use for the test is _____.
5. Calculate the test statistic using your data.
6. Draw a graph and label it appropriately. Shade the actual level of significance.

    a. Graph:

Figure 10.13

    b. Calculate the p-value.

7. Do you reject or not reject the null hypothesis? Why?

8. Write a clear conclusion using a complete sentence.

Decreasing Stocks Survey

Randomly pick eight stocks from the newspaper. Using two consecutive days' business sections, test whether the stocks went down, on average, for the second day.

1. H_0: _____
2. H_a: _____
3. In words, define the random variable.
4. The distribution to use for the test is _____.
5. Calculate the test statistic using your data.
6. Draw a graph and label it appropriately. Shade the actual level of significance.

   a. Graph:

Figure 10.14

   b. Calculate the p-value:

7. Do you reject or not reject the null hypothesis? Why?
8. Write a clear conclusion using a complete sentence.

Candy Survey

Buy three small packages of M&Ms and five small packages of Reese's Pieces (same net weight as the M&Ms). Test whether or not the mean number of candy pieces per package is the same for the two brands.

1. H_0: _____
2. H_a: _____
3. In words, define the random variable.
4. What distribution should be used for this test?
5. Calculate the test statistic using your data.
6. Draw a graph and label it appropriately. Shade the actual level of significance.

   a. Graph:

Figure 10.15

b. Calculate the *p*-value.

7. Do you reject or not reject the null hypothesis? Why?

8. Write a clear conclusion using a complete sentence.

Shoe Survey

Test whether women have, on average, more pairs of shoes than men. Include all forms of sneakers, shoes, sandals, and boots. Use your class as the sample.

1. H_0: _____

2. H_a: _____

3. In words, define the random variable.

4. The distribution to use for the test is _____.

5. Calculate the test statistic using your data.

6. Draw a graph and label it appropriately. Shade the actual level of significance.

   a. Graph:

Figure 10.16

b. Calculate the *p*-value.

7. Do you reject or not reject the null hypothesis? Why?

8. Write a clear conclusion using a complete sentence.

KEY TERMS

Degrees of Freedom (*df*) the number of objects in a sample that are free to vary.

Pooled Proportion estimate of the common value of p_1 and p_2.

Standard Deviation A number that is equal to the square root of the variance and measures how far data values are from their mean; notation: s for sample standard deviation and σ for population standard deviation.

Variable (Random Variable) a characteristic of interest in a population being studied. Common notation for variables are upper-case Latin letters X, Y, Z,... Common notation for a specific value from the domain (set of all possible values of a variable) are lower-case Latin letters x, y, z,.... For example, if X is the number of children in a family, then x represents a specific integer 0, 1, 2, 3, ... Variables in statistics differ from variables in intermediate algebra in two following ways.

- The domain of the random variable (RV) is not necessarily a numerical set; the domain may be expressed in words; for example, if X = hair color, then the domain is {black, blond, gray, green, orange}.
- We can tell what specific value x of the random variable X takes only after performing the experiment.

CHAPTER REVIEW

10.1 Two Population Means with Unknown Standard Deviations

Two population means from independent samples where the population standard deviations are not known

- Random Variable: $\bar{X}_1 - \bar{X}_2$ = the difference of the sampling means
- Distribution: Student's t-distribution with degrees of freedom (variances not pooled)

10.2 Two Population Means with Known Standard Deviations

A hypothesis test of two population means from independent samples where the population standard deviations are known (typically approximated with the sample standard deviations), will have these characteristics:

- Random variable: $\bar{X}_1 - \bar{X}_2$ = the difference of the means
- Distribution: normal distribution

10.3 Comparing Two Independent Population Proportions

Test of two population proportions from independent samples.

- Random variable: $\hat{p}_A - \hat{p}_B =$ difference between the two estimated proportions
- Distribution: normal distribution

10.4 Matched or Paired Samples

A hypothesis test for matched or paired samples (t-test) has these characteristics:

- Test the differences by subtracting one measurement from the other measurement
- Random Variable: $\bar{x}_d$ = mean of the differences
- Distribution: Student's-t distribution with $n - 1$ degrees of freedom
- If the number of differences is small (less than 30), the differences must follow a normal distribution.
- Two samples are drawn from the same set of objects.
- Samples are dependent.

FORMULA REVIEW

10.1 Two Population Means with Unknown Standard Deviations

Standard error: $SE = \sqrt{\dfrac{(s_1)^2}{n_1} + \dfrac{(s_2)^2}{n_2}}$

Test statistic (t-score): $t = \dfrac{(\bar{x}_1 - \bar{x}_2) - (\mu_1 - \mu_2)}{\sqrt{\dfrac{(s_1)^2}{n_1} + \dfrac{(s_2)^2}{n_2}}}$

Degrees of freedom:

$$df = \dfrac{\left(\dfrac{(s_1)^2}{n_1} + \dfrac{(s_2)^2}{n_2}\right)^2}{\left(\dfrac{1}{n_1-1}\right)\left(\dfrac{(s_1)^2}{n_1}\right)^2 + \left(\dfrac{1}{n_2-1}\right)\left(\dfrac{(s_2)^2}{n_2}\right)^2}$$

where:

s_1 and s_2 are the sample standard deviations, and n_1 and n_2 are the sample sizes.

$\bar{x}_1$ and $\bar{x}_2$ are the sample means.

Cohen's d is the measure of effect size:

$d = \dfrac{\bar{x}_1 - \bar{x}_2}{s_{pooled}}$

where $s_{pooled} = \sqrt{\dfrac{(n_1-1)s_1^2 + (n_2-1)s_2^2}{n_1 + n_2 - 2}}$

10.2 Two Population Means with Known Standard Deviations

Normal Distribution:

$\bar{X}_1 - \bar{X}_2 \sim N\left[\mu_1 - \mu_2, \sqrt{\dfrac{(\sigma_1)^2}{n_1} + \dfrac{(\sigma_2)^2}{n_2}}\right]$.

Generally $\boldsymbol{\mu_1 - \mu_2 = 0.}$

Test Statistic (z-score):

$z = \dfrac{(\bar{x}_1 - \bar{x}_2) - (\mu_1 - \mu_2)}{\sqrt{\dfrac{(\sigma_1)^2}{n_1} + \dfrac{(\sigma_2)^2}{n_2}}}$

Generally $\boldsymbol{\mu_1 - \mu_2 = 0.}$

where:

σ_1 and σ_2 are the known population standard deviations. n_1 and n_2 are the sample sizes. $\bar{x}_1$ and $\bar{x}_2$ are the sample means. μ_1 and μ_2 are the population means.

10.3 Comparing Two Independent Population Proportions

Pooled Proportion: $p_c = \dfrac{x_F + x_M}{n_F + n_M}$

Distribution for the differences:

$p'_A - p'_B \sim N\left[0, \sqrt{p_c(1-p_c)\left(\dfrac{1}{n_A} + \dfrac{1}{n_B}\right)}\right]$

where the null hypothesis is $H_0: p_A = p_B$ or $H_0: p_A - p_B = 0$.

Test Statistic (z-score): $z = \dfrac{(p'_A - p'_B)}{\sqrt{p_c(1-p_c)\left(\dfrac{1}{n_A} + \dfrac{1}{n_B}\right)}}$

where the null hypothesis is $H_0: p_A = p_B$ or $H_0: p_A - p_B = 0$.

where

p'_A and p'_B are the sample proportions, p_A and p_B are the population proportions,

P_c is the pooled proportion, and $\boldsymbol{n_A}$ and $\boldsymbol{n_B}$ are the sample sizes.

10.4 Matched or Paired Samples

Test Statistic (t-score): $t = \dfrac{\bar{x}_d - \mu_d}{\left(\dfrac{s_d}{\sqrt{n}}\right)}$

where:

$\bar{x}_d$ is the mean of the sample differences. μ_d is the mean of the population differences. s_d is the sample standard deviation of the differences. n is the sample size.

PRACTICE

10.1 Two Population Means with Unknown Standard Deviations

Use the following information to answer the next 15 exercises: Indicate if the hypothesis test is for

    a.   independent group means, population standard deviations, and/or variances known

  b. independent group means, population standard deviations, and/or variances unknown

  c. matched or paired samples

  d. single mean

  e. two proportions

  f. single proportion

1. It is believed that 70% of males pass their drivers test in the first attempt, while 65% of females pass the test in the first attempt. Of interest is whether the proportions are in fact equal.

2. A new laundry detergent is tested on consumers. Of interest is the proportion of consumers who prefer the new brand over the leading competitor. A study is done to test this.

3. A new windshield treatment claims to repel water more effectively. Ten windshields are tested by simulating rain without the new treatment. The same windshields are then treated, and the experiment is run again. A hypothesis test is conducted.

4. The known standard deviation in salary for all mid-level professionals in the financial industry is $11,000. Company A and Company B are in the financial industry. Suppose samples are taken of mid-level professionals from Company A and from Company B. The sample mean salary for mid-level professionals in Company A is $80,000. The sample mean salary for mid-level professionals in Company B is $96,000. Company A and Company B management want to know if their mid-level professionals are paid differently, on average.

5. The average worker in Germany gets eight weeks of paid vacation.

6. According to a television commercial, 80% of dentists agree that Ultrafresh toothpaste is the best on the market.

7. It is believed that the average grade on an English essay in a particular school system for females is higher than for males. A random sample of 31 females had a mean score of 82 with a standard deviation of three, and a random sample of 25 males had a mean score of 76 with a standard deviation of four.

8. The league mean batting average is 0.280 with a known standard deviation of 0.06. The Rattlers and the Vikings belong to the league. The mean batting average for a sample of eight Rattlers is 0.210, and the mean batting average for a sample of eight Vikings is 0.260. There are 24 players on the Rattlers and 19 players on the Vikings. Are the batting averages of the Rattlers and Vikings statistically different?

9. In a random sample of 100 forests in the United States, 56 were coniferous or contained conifers. In a random sample of 80 forests in Mexico, 40 were coniferous or contained conifers. Is the proportion of conifers in the United States statistically more than the proportion of conifers in Mexico?

10. A new medicine is said to help improve sleep. Eight subjects are picked at random and given the medicine. The means hours slept for each person were recorded before starting the medication and after.

11. It is thought that teenagers sleep more than adults on average. A study is done to verify this. A sample of 16 teenagers has a mean of 8.9 hours slept and a standard deviation of 1.2. A sample of 12 adults has a mean of 6.9 hours slept and a standard deviation of 0.6.

12. Varsity athletes practice five times a week, on average.

13. A sample of 12 in-state graduate school programs at school A has a mean tuition of $64,000 with a standard deviation of $8,000. At school B, a sample of 16 in-state graduate programs has a mean of $80,000 with a standard deviation of $6,000. On average, are the mean tuitions different?

14. A new WiFi range booster is being offered to consumers. A researcher tests the native range of 12 different routers under the same conditions. The ranges are recorded. Then the researcher uses the new WiFi range booster and records the new ranges. Does the new WiFi range booster do a better job?

15. A high school principal claims that 30% of student athletes drive themselves to school, while 4% of non-athletes drive themselves to school. In a sample of 20 student athletes, 45% drive themselves to school. In a sample of 35 non-athlete students, 6% drive themselves to school. Is the percent of student athletes who drive themselves to school more than the percent of nonathletes?

Use the following information to answer the next three exercises: A study is done to determine which of two soft drinks has more sugar. There are 13 cans of Beverage A in a sample and six cans of Beverage B. The mean amount of sugar in Beverage A is 36 grams with a standard deviation of 0.6 grams. The mean amount of sugar in Beverage B is 38 grams with a standard deviation of 0.8 grams. The researchers believe that Beverage B has more sugar than Beverage A, on average.

Both populations have normal distributions.

16. Are standard deviations known or unknown?

17. What is the random variable?

18. Is this a one-tailed or two-tailed test?

Use the following information to answer the next 12 exercises: The U.S. Center for Disease Control reports that the mean life expectancy was 47.6 years for whites born in 1900 and 33.0 years for nonwhites. Suppose that you randomly survey death records for people born in 1900 in a certain county. Of the 124 whites, the mean life span was 45.3 years with a standard deviation of 12.7 years. Of the 82 nonwhites, the mean life span was 34.1 years with a standard deviation of 15.6 years. Conduct a hypothesis test to see if the mean life spans in the county were the same for whites and nonwhites.

19. Is this a test of means or proportions?

20. State the null and alternative hypotheses.
    a. H_0: _____
    b. H_a: _____

21. Is this a right-tailed, left-tailed, or two-tailed test?

22. In symbols, what is the random variable of interest for this test?

23. In words, define the random variable of interest for this test.

24. Which distribution (normal or Student's t) would you use for this hypothesis test?

25. Explain why you chose the distribution you did for **Exercise 10.24**.

26. Calculate the test statistic and p-value.

27. Sketch a graph of the situation. Label the horizontal axis. Mark the hypothesized difference and the sample difference. Shade the area corresponding to the p-value.

28. Find the p-value.

29. At a pre-conceived $\alpha = 0.05$, what is your:
    a. Decision:
    b. Reason for the decision:
    c. Conclusion (write out in a complete sentence):

30. Does it appear that the means are the same? Why or why not?

10.2 Two Population Means with Known Standard Deviations

Use the following information to answer the next five exercises. The mean speeds of fastball pitches from two different baseball pitchers are to be compared. A sample of 14 fastball pitches is measured from each pitcher. The populations have normal distributions. **Table 10.18** shows the result. Scouters believe that Rodriguez pitches a speedier fastball.

Pitcher	Sample Mean Speed of Pitches (mph)	Population Standard Deviation
Wesley	86	3
Rodriguez	91	7

Table 10.18

31. What is the random variable?

32. State the null and alternative hypotheses.

33. What is the test statistic?

34. What is the p-value?

35. At the 1% significance level, what is your conclusion?

Use the following information to answer the next five exercises. A researcher is testing the effects of plant food on plant growth. Nine plants have been given the plant food. Another nine plants have not been given the plant food. The heights of the plants are recorded after eight weeks. The populations have normal distributions. The following table is the result. The researcher thinks the food makes the plants grow taller.

Plant Group	Sample Mean Height of Plants (inches)	Population Standard Deviation
Food	16	2.5
No food	14	1.5

Table 10.19

36. Is the population standard deviation known or unknown?

37. State the null and alternative hypotheses.

38. What is the *p*-value?

39. Draw the graph of the *p*-value.

40. At the 1% significance level, what is your conclusion?

Use the following information to answer the next five exercises. Two metal alloys are being considered as material for ball bearings. The mean melting point of the two alloys is to be compared. 15 pieces of each metal are being tested. Both populations have normal distributions. The following table is the result. It is believed that Alloy Zeta has a different melting point.

	Sample Mean Melting Temperatures (°F)	Population Standard Deviation
Alloy Gamma	800	95
Alloy Zeta	900	105

Table 10.20

41. State the null and alternative hypotheses.

42. Is this a right-, left-, or two-tailed test?

43. What is the *p*-value?

44. Draw the graph of the *p*-value.

45. At the 1% significance level, what is your conclusion?

10.3 Comparing Two Independent Population Proportions

Use the following information for the next five exercises. Two types of phone operating system are being tested to determine if there is a difference in the proportions of system failures (crashes). Fifteen out of a random sample of 150 phones with OS_1 had system failures within the first eight hours of operation. Nine out of another random sample of 150 phones with OS_2 had system failures within the first eight hours of operation. OS_2 is believed to be more stable (have fewer crashes) than OS_1.

46. Is this a test of means or proportions?

47. What is the random variable?

48. State the null and alternative hypotheses.

49. What is the *p*-value?

50. What can you conclude about the two operating systems?

Use the following information to answer the next twelve exercises. In the recent Census, three percent of the U.S. population reported being of two or more races. However, the percent varies tremendously from state to state. Suppose that two random surveys are conducted. In the first random survey, out of 1,000 North Dakotans, only nine people reported being of two or more races. In the second random survey, out of 500 Nevadans, 17 people reported being of two or more races. Conduct a hypothesis test to determine if the population percents are the same for the two states or if the percent for Nevada is statistically higher than for North Dakota.

51. Is this a test of means or proportions?

52. State the null and alternative hypotheses.

  a. H_0: _____

  b. H_a: _____

53. Is this a right-tailed, left-tailed, or two-tailed test? How do you know?

54. What is the random variable of interest for this test?

55. In words, define the random variable for this test.

56. Which distribution (normal or Student's t) would you use for this hypothesis test?

57. Explain why you chose the distribution you did for the **Exercise 10.56**.

58. Calculate the test statistic.

59. Sketch a graph of the situation. Mark the hypothesized difference and the sample difference. Shade the area corresponding to the p-value.

$p'_N - p'_{ND}$

Figure 10.17

60. Find the p-value.

61. At a pre-conceived $\alpha = 0.05$, what is your:

  a. Decision:

  b. Reason for the decision:

  c. Conclusion (write out in a complete sentence):

62. Does it appear that the proportion of Nevadans who are two or more races is higher than the proportion of North Dakotans? Why or why not?

10.4 Matched or Paired Samples

Use the following information to answer the next five exercises. A study was conducted to test the effectiveness of a software patch in reducing system failures over a six-month period. Results for randomly selected installations are shown in **Table 10.21**. The "before" value is matched to an "after" value, and the differences are calculated. The differences have a normal distribution. Test at the 1% significance level.

Installation	A	B	C	D	E	F	G	H
Before	3	6	4	2	5	8	2	6
After	1	5	2	0	1	0	2	2

Table 10.21

63. What is the random variable?

64. State the null and alternative hypotheses.

65. What is the p-value?

66. Draw the graph of the p-value.

67. What conclusion can you draw about the software patch?

Use the following information to answer next five exercises. A study was conducted to test the effectiveness of a juggling class. Before the class started, six subjects juggled as many balls as they could at once. After the class, the same six subjects juggled as many balls as they could. The differences in the number of balls are calculated. The differences have a normal distribution. Test at the 1% significance level.

Subject	A	B	C	D	E	F
Before	3	4	3	2	4	5
After	4	5	6	4	5	7

Table 10.22

68. State the null and alternative hypotheses.

69. What is the *p*-value?

70. What is the sample mean difference?

71. Draw the graph of the *p*-value.

72. What conclusion can you draw about the juggling class?

Use the following information to answer the next five exercises. A doctor wants to know if a blood pressure medication is effective. Six subjects have their blood pressures recorded. After twelve weeks on the medication, the same six subjects have their blood pressure recorded again. For this test, only systolic pressure is of concern. Test at the 1% significance level.

Patient	A	B	C	D	E	F
Before	161	162	165	162	166	171
After	158	159	166	160	167	169

Table 10.23

73. State the null and alternative hypotheses.

74. What is the test statistic?

75. What is the *p*-value?

76. What is the sample mean difference?

77. What is the conclusion?

HOMEWORK

10.1 Two Population Means with Unknown Standard Deviations

DIRECTIONS: For each of the word problems, use a solution sheet to do the hypothesis test. The solution sheet is found in **Appendix E**. *Please feel free to make copies of the solution sheets. For the online version of the book, it is suggested that you copy the .doc or the .pdf files.*

> **NOTE**
>
> If you are using a Student's *t*-distribution for a homework problem in what follows, including for paired data, you may assume that the underlying population is normally distributed. (When using these tests in a real situation, you must first prove that assumption, however.)

78. The mean number of English courses taken in a two–year time period by male and female college students is believed to be about the same. An experiment is conducted and data are collected from 29 males and 16 females. The males took an average of three English courses with a standard deviation of 0.8. The females took an average of four English courses with a standard deviation of 1.0. Are the means statistically the same?

79. A student at a four-year college claims that mean enrollment at four–year colleges is higher than at two–year colleges in the United States. Two surveys are conducted. Of the 35 two–year colleges surveyed, the mean enrollment was 5,068 with a standard deviation of 4,777. Of the 35 four-year colleges surveyed, the mean enrollment was 5,466 with a standard deviation of 8,191.

80. At Rachel's 11th birthday party, eight girls were timed to see how long (in seconds) they could hold their breath in a relaxed position. After a two-minute rest, they timed themselves while jumping. The girls thought that the mean difference between their jumping and relaxed times would be zero. Test their hypothesis.

Relaxed time (seconds)	Jumping time (seconds)
26	21
47	40
30	28
22	21
23	25
45	43
37	35
29	32

Table 10.24

81. Mean entry-level salaries for college graduates with mechanical engineering degrees and electrical engineering degrees are believed to be approximately the same. A recruiting office thinks that the mean mechanical engineering salary is actually lower than the mean electrical engineering salary. The recruiting office randomly surveys 50 entry level mechanical engineers and 60 entry level electrical engineers. Their mean salaries were $46,100 and $46,700, respectively. Their standard deviations were $3,450 and $4,210, respectively. Conduct a hypothesis test to determine if you agree that the mean entry-level mechanical engineering salary is lower than the mean entry-level electrical engineering salary.

82. Marketing companies have collected data implying that teenage girls use more ring tones on their cellular phones than teenage boys do. In one particular study of 40 randomly chosen teenage girls and boys (20 of each) with cellular phones, the mean number of ring tones for the girls was 3.2 with a standard deviation of 1.5. The mean for the boys was 1.7 with a standard deviation of 0.8. Conduct a hypothesis test to determine if the means are approximately the same or if the girls' mean is higher than the boys' mean.

*Use the information from **Appendix C** to answer the next four exercises.*

83. Using the data from Lap 1 only, conduct a hypothesis test to determine if the mean time for completing a lap in races is the same as it is in practices.

84. Repeat the test in **Exercise 10.83**, but use Lap 5 data this time.

85. Repeat the test in **Exercise 10.83**, but this time combine the data from Laps 1 and 5.

86. In two to three complete sentences, explain in detail how you might use Terri Vogel's data to answer the following question. "Does Terri Vogel drive faster in races than she does in practices?"

Use the following information to answer the next two exercises. The Eastern and Western Major League Soccer conferences have a new Reserve Division that allows new players to develop their skills. Data for a randomly picked date showed the following annual goals.

Western	Eastern
Los Angeles 9	D.C. United 9
FC Dallas 3	Chicago 8

Table 10.25

Western	Eastern
Chivas USA 4	Columbus 7
Real Salt Lake 3	New England 6
Colorado 4	MetroStars 5
San Jose 4	Kansas City 3

Table 10.25

Conduct a hypothesis test to answer the next two exercises.

87. The **exact** distribution for the hypothesis test is:
    a. the normal distribution
    b. the Student's *t*-distribution
    c. the uniform distribution
    d. the exponential distribution

88. If the level of significance is 0.05, the conclusion is:
    a. There is sufficient evidence to conclude that the **W** Division teams score fewer goals, on average, than the **E** teams
    b. There is insufficient evidence to conclude that the **W** Division teams score more goals, on average, than the **E** teams.
    c. There is insufficient evidence to conclude that the **W** teams score fewer goals, on average, than the **E** teams score.
    d. Unable to determine

89. Suppose a statistics instructor believes that there is no significant difference between the mean class scores of statistics day students on Exam 2 and statistics night students on Exam 2. She takes random samples from each of the populations. The mean and standard deviation for 35 statistics day students were 75.86 and 16.91. The mean and standard deviation for 37 statistics night students were 75.41 and 19.73. The "day" subscript refers to the statistics day students. The "night" subscript refers to the statistics night students. A concluding statement is:
    a. There is sufficient evidence to conclude that statistics night students' mean on Exam 2 is better than the statistics day students' mean on Exam 2.
    b. There is insufficient evidence to conclude that the statistics day students' mean on Exam 2 is better than the statistics night students' mean on Exam 2.
    c. There is insufficient evidence to conclude that there is a significant difference between the means of the statistics day students and night students on Exam 2.
    d. There is sufficient evidence to conclude that there is a significant difference between the means of the statistics day students and night students on Exam 2.

90. Researchers interviewed street prostitutes in Canada and the United States. The mean age of the 100 Canadian prostitutes upon entering prostitution was 18 with a standard deviation of six. The mean age of the 130 United States prostitutes upon entering prostitution was 20 with a standard deviation of eight. Is the mean age of entering prostitution in Canada lower than the mean age in the United States? Test at a 1% significance level.

91. A powder diet is tested on 49 people, and a liquid diet is tested on 36 different people. Of interest is whether the liquid diet yields a higher mean weight loss than the powder diet. The powder diet group had a mean weight loss of 42 pounds with a standard deviation of 12 pounds. The liquid diet group had a mean weight loss of 45 pounds with a standard deviation of 14 pounds.

92. Suppose a statistics instructor believes that there is no significant difference between the mean class scores of statistics day students on Exam 2 and statistics night students on Exam 2. She takes random samples from each of the populations. The mean and standard deviation for 35 statistics day students were 75.86 and 16.91, respectively. The mean and standard deviation for 37 statistics night students were 75.41 and 19.73. The "day" subscript refers to the statistics day students. The "night" subscript refers to the statistics night students. An appropriate alternative hypothesis for the hypothesis test is:
    a. $\mu_{day} > \mu_{night}$
    b. $\mu_{day} < \mu_{night}$
    c. $\mu_{day} = \mu_{night}$
    d. $\mu_{day} \neq \mu_{night}$

10.2 Two Population Means with Known Standard Deviations

DIRECTIONS: For each of the word problems, use a solution sheet to do the hypothesis test. The solution sheet is found in **Appendix E**. *Please feel free to make copies of the solution sheets. For the online version of the book, it is suggested that you copy the .doc or the .pdf files.*

NOTE

If you are using a Student's *t*-distribution for one of the following homework problems, including for paired data, you may assume that the underlying population is normally distributed. (When using these tests in a real situation, you must first prove that assumption, however.)

---

93. A study is done to determine if students in the California state university system take longer to graduate, on average, than students enrolled in private universities. One hundred students from both the California state university system and private universities are surveyed. Suppose that from years of research, it is known that the population standard deviations are 1.5811 years and 1 year, respectively. The following data are collected. The California state university system students took on average 4.5 years with a standard deviation of 0.8. The private university students took on average 4.1 years with a standard deviation of 0.3.

94. Parents of teenage boys often complain that auto insurance costs more, on average, for teenage boys than for teenage girls. A group of concerned parents examines a random sample of insurance bills. The mean annual cost for 36 teenage boys was $679. For 23 teenage girls, it was $559. From past years, it is known that the population standard deviation for each group is $180. Determine whether or not you believe that the mean cost for auto insurance for teenage boys is greater than that for teenage girls.

95. A group of transfer bound students wondered if they will spend the same mean amount on texts and supplies each year at their four-year university as they have at their community college. They conducted a random survey of 54 students at their community college and 66 students at their local four-year university. The sample means were $947 and $1,011, respectively. The population standard deviations are known to be $254 and $87, respectively. Conduct a hypothesis test to determine if the means are statistically the same.

96. Some manufacturers claim that non-hybrid sedan cars have a lower mean miles-per-gallon (mpg) than hybrid ones. Suppose that consumers test 21 hybrid sedans and get a mean of 31 mpg with a standard deviation of seven mpg. Thirty-one non-hybrid sedans get a mean of 22 mpg with a standard deviation of four mpg. Suppose that the population standard deviations are known to be six and three, respectively. Conduct a hypothesis test to evaluate the manufacturers claim.

97. A baseball fan wanted to know if there is a difference between the number of games played in a World Series when the American League won the series versus when the National League won the series. From 1922 to 2012, the population standard deviation of games won by the American League was 1.14, and the population standard deviation of games won by the National League was 1.11. Of 19 randomly selected World Series games won by the American League, the mean number of games won was 5.76. The mean number of 17 randomly selected games won by the National League was 5.42. Conduct a hypothesis test.

98. One of the questions in a study of marital satisfaction of dual-career couples was to rate the statement "I'm pleased with the way we divide the responsibilities for childcare." The ratings went from one (strongly agree) to five (strongly disagree). **Table 10.26** contains ten of the paired responses for husbands and wives. Conduct a hypothesis test to see if the mean difference in the husband's versus the wife's satisfaction level is negative (meaning that, within the partnership, the husband is happier than the wife).

Wife's Score	2	2	3	3	4	2	1	1	2	4
Husband's Score	2	2	1	3	2	1	1	1	2	4

Table 10.26

10.3 Comparing Two Independent Population Proportions

DIRECTIONS: For each of the word problems, use a solution sheet to do the hypothesis test. The solution sheet is found in

Appendix E. Please feel free to make copies of the solution sheets. For the online version of the book, it is suggested that you copy the .doc or the .pdf files.

> **NOTE**
>
> If you are using a Student's *t*-distribution for one of the following homework problems, including for paired data, you may assume that the underlying population is normally distributed. (In general, you must first prove that assumption, however.)

99. A recent drug survey showed an increase in the use of drugs and alcohol among local high school seniors as compared to the national percent. Suppose that a survey of 100 local seniors and 100 national seniors is conducted to see if the proportion of drug and alcohol use is higher locally than nationally. Locally, 65 seniors reported using drugs or alcohol within the past month, while 60 national seniors reported using them.

100. We are interested in whether the proportions of female suicide victims for ages 15 to 24 are the same for the whites and the blacks races in the United States. We randomly pick one year, 1992, to compare the races. The number of suicides estimated in the United States in 1992 for white females is 4,930. Five hundred eighty were aged 15 to 24. The estimate for black females is 330. Forty were aged 15 to 24. We will let female suicide victims be our population.

101. Elizabeth Mjelde, an art history professor, was interested in whether the value from the Golden Ratio formula, $\left(\dfrac{\text{larger} + \text{smaller dimension}}{\text{larger dimension}} \right)$ was the same in the Whitney Exhibit for works from 1900 to 1919 as for works from 1920 to 1942. Thirty-seven early works were sampled, averaging 1.74 with a standard deviation of 0.11. Sixty-five of the later works were sampled, averaging 1.746 with a standard deviation of 0.1064. Do you think that there is a significant difference in the Golden Ratio calculation?

102. A recent year was randomly picked from 1985 to the present. In that year, there were 2,051 Hispanic students at Cabrillo College out of a total of 12,328 students. At Lake Tahoe College, there were 321 Hispanic students out of a total of 2,441 students. In general, do you think that the percent of Hispanic students at the two colleges is basically the same or different?

Use the following information to answer the next three exercises. Neuroinvasive West Nile virus is a severe disease that affects a person's nervous system . It is spread by the Culex species of mosquito. In the United States in 2010 there were 629 reported cases of neuroinvasive West Nile virus out of a total of 1,021 reported cases and there were 486 neuroinvasive reported cases out of a total of 712 cases reported in 2011. Is the 2011 proportion of neuroinvasive West Nile virus cases more than the 2010 proportion of neuroinvasive West Nile virus cases? Using a 1% level of significance, conduct an appropriate hypothesis test.

- "2011" subscript: 2011 group.
- "2010" subscript: 2010 group

103. This is:
   a. a test of two proportions
   b. a test of two independent means
   c. a test of a single mean
   d. a test of matched pairs.

104. An appropriate null hypothesis is:
   a. $p_{2011} \le p_{2010}$
   b. $p_{2011} \ge p_{2010}$
   c. $\mu_{2011} \le \mu_{2010}$
   d. $p_{2011} > p_{2010}$

105. The *p*-value is 0.0022. At a 1% level of significance, the appropriate conclusion is

    a. There is sufficient evidence to conclude that the proportion of people in the United States in 2011 who contracted neuroinvasive West Nile disease is less than the proportion of people in the United States in 2010 who contracted neuroinvasive West Nile disease.

    b. There is insufficient evidence to conclude that the proportion of people in the United States in 2011 who contracted neuroinvasive West Nile disease is more than the proportion of people in the United States in 2010 who contracted neuroinvasive West Nile disease.

    c. There is insufficient evidence to conclude that the proportion of people in the United States in 2011 who contracted neuroinvasive West Nile disease is less than the proportion of people in the United States in 2010 who contracted neuroinvasive West Nile disease.

    d. There is sufficient evidence to conclude that the proportion of people in the United States in 2011 who contracted neuroinvasive West Nile disease is more than the proportion of people in the United States in 2010 who contracted neuroinvasive West Nile disease.

106. Researchers conducted a study to find out if there is a difference in the use of eReaders by different age groups. Randomly selected participants were divided into two age groups. In the 16- to 29-year-old group, 7% of the 628 surveyed use eReaders, while 11% of the 2,309 participants 30 years old and older use eReaders.

107. Adults aged 18 years old and older were randomly selected for a survey on obesity. Adults are considered obese if their body mass index (BMI) is at least 30. The researchers wanted to determine if the proportion of women who are obese in the south is less than the proportion of southern men who are obese. The results are shown in **Table 10.27**. Test at the 1% level of significance.

	Number who are obese	Sample size
Men	42,769	155,525
Women	67,169	248,775

Table 10.27

108. Two computer users were discussing tablet computers. A higher proportion of people ages 16 to 29 use tablets than the proportion of people age 30 and older. **Table 10.28** details the number of tablet owners for each age group. Test at the 1% level of significance.

	16–29 year olds	30 years old and older
Own a Tablet	69	231
Sample Size	628	2,309

Table 10.28

109. A group of friends debated whether more men use smartphones than women. They consulted a research study of smartphone use among adults. The results of the survey indicate that of the 973 men randomly sampled, 379 use smartphones. For women, 404 of the 1,304 who were randomly sampled use smartphones. Test at the 5% level of significance.

110. While her husband spent 2½ hours picking out new speakers, a statistician decided to determine whether the percent of men who enjoy shopping for electronic equipment is higher than the percent of women who enjoy shopping for electronic equipment. The population was Saturday afternoon shoppers. Out of 67 men, 24 said they enjoyed the activity. Eight of the 24 women surveyed claimed to enjoy the activity. Interpret the results of the survey.

111. We are interested in whether children's educational computer software costs less, on average, than children's entertainment software. Thirty-six educational software titles were randomly picked from a catalog. The mean cost was $31.14 with a standard deviation of $4.69. Thirty-five entertainment software titles were randomly picked from the same catalog. The mean cost was $33.86 with a standard deviation of $10.87. Decide whether children's educational software costs less, on average, than children's entertainment software.

112. Joan Nguyen recently claimed that the proportion of college-age males with at least one pierced ear is as high as the proportion of college-age females. She conducted a survey in her classes. Out of 107 males, 20 had at least one pierced ear. Out of 92 females, 47 had at least one pierced ear. Do you believe that the proportion of males has reached the proportion of females?

113. Use the data sets found in **Appendix C** to answer this exercise. Is the proportion of race laps Terri completes slower than 130 seconds less than the proportion of practice laps she completes slower than 135 seconds?

114. "To Breakfast or Not to Breakfast?" by Richard Ayore

In the American society, birthdays are one of those days that everyone looks forward to. People of different ages and peer groups gather to mark the 18th, 20th, …, birthdays. During this time, one looks back to see what he or she has achieved for the past year and also focuses ahead for more to come.

If, by any chance, I am invited to one of these parties, my experience is always different. Instead of dancing around with my friends while the music is booming, I get carried away by memories of my family back home in Kenya. I remember the good times I had with my brothers and sister while we did our daily routine.

Every morning, I remember we went to the shamba (garden) to weed our crops. I remember one day arguing with my brother as to why he always remained behind just to join us an hour later. In his defense, he said that he preferred waiting for breakfast before he came to weed. He said, "This is why I always work more hours than you guys!"

And so, to prove him wrong or right, we decided to give it a try. One day we went to work as usual without breakfast, and recorded the time we could work before getting tired and stopping. On the next day, we all ate breakfast before going to work. We recorded how long we worked again before getting tired and stopping. Of interest was our mean increase in work time. Though not sure, my brother insisted that it was more than two hours. Using the data in **Table 10.29**, solve our problem.

Work hours with breakfast	Work hours without breakfast
8	6
7	5
9	5
5	4
9	7
8	7
10	7
7	5
6	6
9	5

Table 10.29

10.4 Matched or Paired Samples

DIRECTIONS: For each of the word problems, use a solution sheet to do the hypothesis test. The solution sheet is found in **Appendix E**. *Please feel free to make copies of the solution sheets. For the online version of the book, it is suggested that you copy the .doc or the .pdf files.*

NOTE

If you are using a Student's *t*-distribution for the homework problems, including for paired data, you may assume that the underlying population is normally distributed. (When using these tests in a real situation, you must first prove that assumption, however.)

115. Ten individuals went on a low–fat diet for 12 weeks to lower their cholesterol. The data are recorded in **Table 10.30**. Do you think that their cholesterol levels were significantly lowered?

Starting cholesterol level	Ending cholesterol level
140	140
220	230
110	120
240	220
200	190
180	150
190	200
360	300
280	300
260	240

Table 10.30

Use the following information to answer the next two exercises. A new AIDS prevention drug was tried on a group of 224 HIV positive patients. Forty-five patients developed AIDS after four years. In a control group of 224 HIV positive patients, 68 developed AIDS after four years. We want to test whether the method of treatment reduces the proportion of patients that develop AIDS after four years or if the proportions of the treated group and the untreated group stay the same.

Let the subscript t = treated patient and ut = untreated patient.

116. The appropriate hypotheses are:
   a. H_0: $p_t < p_{ut}$ and H_a: $p_t \geq p_{ut}$
   b. H_0: $p_t \leq p_{ut}$ and H_a: $p_t > p_{ut}$
   c. H_0: $p_t = p_{ut}$ and H_a: $p_t \neq p_{ut}$
   d. H_0: $p_t = p_{ut}$ and H_a: $p_t < p_{ut}$

117. If the p-value is 0.0062 what is the conclusion (use $\alpha = 0.05$)?
   a. The method has no effect.
   b. There is sufficient evidence to conclude that the method reduces the proportion of HIV positive patients who develop AIDS after four years.
   c. There is sufficient evidence to conclude that the method increases the proportion of HIV positive patients who develop AIDS after four years.
   d. There is insufficient evidence to conclude that the method reduces the proportion of HIV positive patients who develop AIDS after four years.

Use the following information to answer the next two exercises. An experiment is conducted to show that blood pressure can be consciously reduced in people trained in a "biofeedback exercise program." Six subjects were randomly selected and blood pressure measurements were recorded before and after the training. The difference between blood pressures was calculated (after - before) producing the following results: $\bar{x}_d = -10.2$ $s_d = 8.4$. Using the data, test the hypothesis that the blood pressure has decreased after the training.

118. The distribution for the test is:
   a. t_5
   b. t_6
   c. $N(-10.2, 8.4)$
   d. $N(-10.2, \dfrac{8.4}{\sqrt{6}})$

119. If $\alpha = 0.05$, the p-value and the conclusion are

    a. 0.0014; There is sufficient evidence to conclude that the blood pressure decreased after the training.

    b. 0.0014; There is sufficient evidence to conclude that the blood pressure increased after the training.

    c. 0.0155; There is sufficient evidence to conclude that the blood pressure decreased after the training.

    d. 0.0155; There is sufficient evidence to conclude that the blood pressure increased after the training.

120. A golf instructor is interested in determining if her new technique for improving players' golf scores is effective. She takes four new students. She records their 18-hole scores before learning the technique and then after having taken her class. She conducts a hypothesis test. The data are as follows.

	Player 1	Player 2	Player 3	Player 4
Mean score before class	83	78	93	87
Mean score after class	80	80	86	86

Table 10.31

The correct decision is:

    a. Reject H_0.

    b. Do not reject the H_0.

121. A local cancer support group believes that the estimate for new female breast cancer cases in the south is higher in 2013 than in 2012. The group compared the estimates of new female breast cancer cases by southern state in 2012 and in 2013. The results are in **Table 10.32**.

Southern States	2012	2013
Alabama	3,450	3,720
Arkansas	2,150	2,280
Florida	15,540	15,710
Georgia	6,970	7,310
Kentucky	3,160	3,300
Louisiana	3,320	3,630
Mississippi	1,990	2,080
North Carolina	7,090	7,430
Oklahoma	2,630	2,690
South Carolina	3,570	3,580
Tennessee	4,680	5,070
Texas	15,050	14,980
Virginia	6,190	6,280

Table 10.32

122. A traveler wanted to know if the prices of hotels are different in the ten cities that he visits the most often. The list of the cities with the corresponding hotel prices for his two favorite hotel chains is in **Table 10.33**. Test at the 1% level of significance.

Cities	Hyatt Regency prices in dollars	Hilton prices in dollars
Atlanta	107	169
Boston	358	289
Chicago	209	299
Dallas	209	198
Denver	167	169
Indianapolis	179	214
Los Angeles	179	169
New York City	625	459
Philadelphia	179	159
Washington, DC	245	239

Table 10.33

123. A politician asked his staff to determine whether the underemployment rate in the northeast decreased from 2011 to 2012. The results are in **Table 10.34**.

Northeastern States	2011	2012
Connecticut	17.3	16.4
Delaware	17.4	13.7
Maine	19.3	16.1
Maryland	16.0	15.5
Massachusetts	17.6	18.2
New Hampshire	15.4	13.5
New Jersey	19.2	18.7
New York	18.5	18.7
Ohio	18.2	18.8
Pennsylvania	16.5	16.9
Rhode Island	20.7	22.4
Vermont	14.7	12.3
West Virginia	15.5	17.3

Table 10.34

BRINGING IT TOGETHER: HOMEWORK

Use the following information to answer the next ten exercises. indicate which of the following choices best identifies the hypothesis test.

    a. independent group means, population standard deviations and/or variances known

    b. independent group means, population standard deviations and/or variances unknown

    c. matched or paired samples

    d. single mean

    e. two proportions

    f. single proportion

124. A powder diet is tested on 49 people, and a liquid diet is tested on 36 different people. The population standard deviations are two pounds and three pounds, respectively. Of interest is whether the liquid diet yields a higher mean weight loss than the powder diet.

125. A new chocolate bar is taste-tested on consumers. Of interest is whether the proportion of children who like the new chocolate bar is greater than the proportion of adults who like it.

126. The mean number of English courses taken in a two–year time period by male and female college students is believed to be about the same. An experiment is conducted and data are collected from nine males and 16 females.

127. A football league reported that the mean number of touchdowns per game was five. A study is done to determine if the mean number of touchdowns has decreased.

128. A study is done to determine if students in the California state university system take longer to graduate than students enrolled in private universities. One hundred students from both the California state university system and private universities are surveyed. From years of research, it is known that the population standard deviations are 1.5811 years and one year, respectively.

129. According to a YWCA Rape Crisis Center newsletter, 75% of rape victims know their attackers. A study is done to verify this.

130. According to a recent study, U.S. companies have a mean maternity-leave of six weeks.

131. A recent drug survey showed an increase in use of drugs and alcohol among local high school students as compared to the national percent. Suppose that a survey of 100 local youths and 100 national youths is conducted to see if the proportion of drug and alcohol use is higher locally than nationally.

132. A new SAT study course is tested on 12 individuals. Pre-course and post-course scores are recorded. Of interest is the mean increase in SAT scores. The following data are collected:

Pre-course score	Post-course score
1	300
960	920
1010	1100
840	880
1100	1070
1250	1320
860	860
1330	1370
790	770
990	1040
1110	1200
740	850

Table 10.35

133. University of Michigan researchers reported in the *Journal of the National Cancer Institute* that quitting smoking is especially beneficial for those under age 49. In this American Cancer Society study, the risk (probability) of dying of lung cancer was about the same as for those who had never smoked.

134. Lesley E. Tan investigated the relationship between left-handedness vs. right-handedness and motor competence in preschool children. Random samples of 41 left-handed preschool children and 41 right-handed preschool children were given several tests of motor skills to determine if there is evidence of a difference between the children based on this experiment. The experiment produced the means and standard deviations shown **Table 10.36**. Determine the appropriate test and best distribution to use for that test.

	Left-handed	Right-handed
Sample size	41	41
Sample mean	97.5	98.1
Sample standard deviation	17.5	19.2

Table 10.36

    a. Two independent means, normal distribution
    b. Two independent means, Student's-t distribution
    c. Matched or paired samples, Student's-t distribution
    d. Two population proportions, normal distribution

135. A golf instructor is interested in determining if her new technique for improving players' golf scores is effective. She takes four (4) new students. She records their 18-hole scores before learning the technique and then after having taken her class. She conducts a hypothesis test. The data are as **Table 10.37**.

	Player 1	Player 2	Player 3	Player 4
Mean score before class	83	78	93	87
Mean score after class	80	80	86	86

Table 10.37

This is:

    a. a test of two independent means.
    b. a test of two proportions.
    c. a test of a single mean.
    d. a test of a single proportion.

REFERENCES

10.1 Two Population Means with Unknown Standard Deviations

Data from Graduating Engineer + Computer Careers. Available online at http://www.graduatingengineer.com

Data from *Microsoft Bookshelf*.

Data from the United States Senate website, available online at www.Senate.gov (accessed June 17, 2013).

"List of current United States Senators by Age." Wikipedia. Available online at http://en.wikipedia.org/wiki/List_of_current_United_States_Senators_by_age (accessed June 17, 2013).

"Sectoring by Industry Groups." Nasdaq. Available online at http://www.nasdaq.com/markets/barchart-sectors.aspx?page=sectors&base=industry (accessed June 17, 2013).

"Strip Clubs: Where Prostitution and Trafficking Happen." Prostitution Research and Education, 2013. Available online at www.prostitutionresearch.com/ProsViolPosttrauStress.html (accessed June 17, 2013).

"World Series History." Baseball-Almanac, 2013. Available online at http://www.baseball-almanac.com/ws/wsmenu.shtml (accessed June 17, 2013).

10.2 Two Population Means with Known Standard Deviations

Data from the United States Census Bureau. Available online at http://www.census.gov/prod/cen2010/briefs/c2010br-02.pdf

Hinduja, Sameer. "Sexting Research and Gender Differences." Cyberbulling Research Center, 2013. Available online at http://cyberbullying.us/blog/sexting-research-and-gender-differences/ (accessed June 17, 2013).

"Smart Phone Users, By the Numbers." Visually, 2013. Available online at http://visual.ly/smart-phone-users-numbers (accessed June 17, 2013).

Smith, Aaron. "35% of American adults own a Smartphone." Pew Internet, 2013. Available online at http://www.pewinternet.org/~/media/Files/Reports/2011/PIP_Smartphones.pdf (accessed June 17, 2013).

"State-Specific Prevalence of Obesity AmongAduls—Unites States, 2007." MMWR, CDC. Available online at http://www.cdc.gov/mmwr/preview/mmwrhtml/mm5728a1.htm (accessed June 17, 2013).

"Texas Crime Rates 1960–1012." FBI, Uniform Crime Reports, 2013. Available online at: http://www.disastercenter.com/crime/txcrime.htm (accessed June 17, 2013).

10.3 Comparing Two Independent Population Proportions

Data from *Educational Resources*, December catalog.

Data from Hilton Hotels. Available online at http://www.hilton.com (accessed June 17, 2013).

Data from Hyatt Hotels. Available online at http://hyatt.com (accessed June 17, 2013).

Data from Statistics, United States Department of Health and Human Services.

Data from Whitney Exhibit on loan to San Jose Museum of Art.

Data from the American Cancer Society. Available online at http://www.cancer.org/index (accessed June 17, 2013).

Data from the Chancellor's Office, California Community Colleges, November 1994.

"State of the States." Gallup, 2013. Available online at http://www.gallup.com/poll/125066/State-States.aspx?ref=interactive (accessed June 17, 2013).

"West Nile Virus." Centers for Disease Control and Prevention. Available online at http://www.cdc.gov/ncidod/dvbid/westnile/index.htm (accessed June 17, 2013).

SOLUTIONS

1 two proportions

3 matched or paired samples

5 single mean

7 independent group means, population standard deviations and/or variances unknown

9 two proportions

11 independent group means, population standard deviations and/or variances unknown

13 independent group means, population standard deviations and/or variances unknown

15 two proportions

17 The random variable is the difference between the mean amounts of sugar in the two soft drinks.

19 means

21 two-tailed

23 the difference between the mean life spans of whites and nonwhites

25 This is a comparison of two population means with unknown population standard deviations.

27 Check student's solution.

29

a. Reject the null hypothesis

b. p-value < 0.05

c. There is not enough evidence at the 5% level of significance to support the claim that life expectancy in the 1900s is different between whites and nonwhites.

31 The difference in mean speeds of the fastball pitches of the two pitchers

33 –2.46

35 At the 1% significance level, we can reject the null hypothesis. There is sufficient data to conclude that the mean speed of Rodriguez's fastball is faster than Wesley's.

37 Subscripts: 1 = Food, 2 = No Food
$H_0: \mu_1 \le \mu_2$
$H_a: \mu_1 > \mu_2$

39

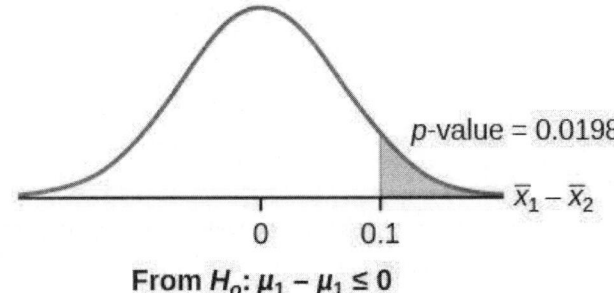

Figure 10.18

41 Subscripts: 1 = Gamma, 2 = Zeta
$H_0: \mu_1 = \mu_2$
$H_a: \mu_1 \ne \mu_2$

43 0.0062

45 There is sufficient evidence to reject the null hypothesis. The data support that the melting point for Alloy Zeta is different from the melting point of Alloy Gamma.

47 $P'_{OS1} - P'_{OS2}$ = difference in the proportions of phones that had system failures within the first eight hours of operation with OS_1 and OS_2.

49 0.1018

51 proportions

53 right-tailed

55 The random variable is the difference in proportions (percents) of the populations that are of two or more races in Nevada and North Dakota.

57 Our sample sizes are much greater than five each, so we use the normal for two proportions distribution for this hypothesis test.

59 Check student's solution.

61

a. Reject the null hypothesis.

b. p-value $<$ alpha

c. At the 5% significance level, there is sufficient evidence to conclude that the proportion (percent) of the population that is of two or more races in Nevada is statistically higher than that in North Dakota.

63 the mean difference of the system failures

65 0.0067

67 With a p-value 0.0067, we can reject the null hypothesis. There is enough evidence to support that the software patch is effective in reducing the number of system failures.

69 0.0021

71

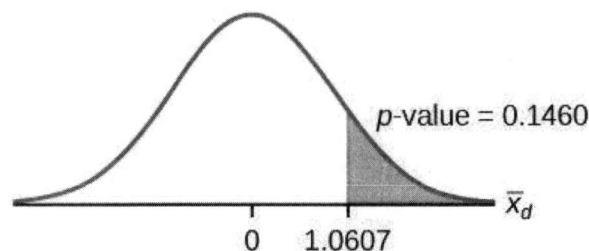

Figure 10.19

73 $H_0: \mu_d \geq 0$ $H_a: \mu_d < 0$

75 0.0699

77 We decline to reject the null hypothesis. There is not sufficient evidence to support that the medication is effective.

79 Subscripts: 1: two-year colleges; 2: four-year colleges
  a. $H_0: \mu_1 \geq \mu_2$

  b. $H_a: \mu_1 < \mu_2$

  c. $\overline{X}_1 - \overline{X}_2$ is the difference between the mean enrollments of the two-year colleges and the four-year colleges.

  d. Student's-t

  e. test statistic: -0.2480

  f. p-value: 0.4019

  g. Check student's solution.

  h.   i. Alpha: 0.05

      ii. Decision: Do not reject

     iii. Reason for Decision: p-value > alpha

      iv. Conclusion: At the 5% significance level, there is sufficient evidence to conclude that the mean enrollment at four-year colleges is higher than at two-year colleges.

81 Subscripts: 1: mechanical engineering; 2: electrical engineering
  a. $H_0: \mu_1 \geq \mu_2$

  b. $H_a: \mu_1 < \mu_2$

  c. $\overline{X}_1 - \overline{X}_2$ is the difference between the mean entry level salaries of mechanical engineers and electrical engineers.

  d. t_{108}

  e. test statistic: $t = -0.82$

  f. p-value: 0.2061

g. Check student's solution.

h. i. Alpha: 0.05

 ii. Decision: Do not reject the null hypothesis.

 iii. Reason for Decision: p-value > alpha

 iv. Conclusion: At the 5% significance level, there is insufficient evidence to conclude that the mean entry-level salaries of mechanical engineers is lower than that of electrical engineers.

83

a. $H_0: \mu_1 = \mu_2$

b. $H_a: \mu_1 \neq \mu_2$

c. $\bar{X}_1 - \bar{X}_2$ is the difference between the mean times for completing a lap in races and in practices.

d. $t_{20.32}$

e. test statistic: –4.70

f. p-value: 0.0001

g. Check student's solution.

h. i. Alpha: 0.05

 ii. Decision: Reject the null hypothesis.

 iii. Reason for Decision: p-value < alpha

 iv. Conclusion: At the 5% significance level, there is sufficient evidence to conclude that the mean time for completing a lap in races is different from that in practices.

85

a. $H_0: \mu_1 = \mu_2$

b. $H_a: \mu_1 \neq \mu_2$

c. is the difference between the mean times for completing a lap in races and in practices.

d. $t_{40.94}$

e. test statistic: –5.08

f. p-value: zero

g. Check student's solution.

h. i. Alpha: 0.05

 ii. Decision: Reject the null hypothesis.

 iii. Reason for Decision: p-value < alpha

 iv. Conclusion: At the 5% significance level, there is sufficient evidence to conclude that the mean time for completing a lap in races is different from that in practices.

88 c

90 Test: two independent sample means, population standard deviations unknown. Random variable: $\bar{X}_1 - \bar{X}_2$ Distribution: $H_0: \mu_1 = \mu_2$ $H_a: \mu_1 < \mu_2$ The mean age of entering prostitution in Canada is lower than the mean age in the United States.

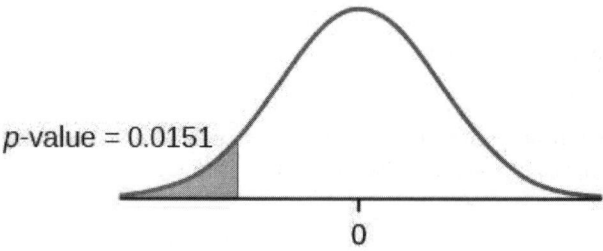

Figure 10.20

Graph: left-tailed p-value : 0.0151 Decision: Do not reject H_0. Conclusion: At the 1% level of significance, from the sample data, there is not sufficient evidence to conclude that the mean age of entering prostitution in Canada is lower than the mean age in the United States.

92 d

94 Subscripts: 1 = boys, 2 = girls
  a. H_0: $\mu_1 \leq \mu_2$

  b. H_a: $\mu_1 > \mu_2$

  c. The random variable is the difference in the mean auto insurance costs for boys and girls.

  d. normal

  e. test statistic: $z = 2.50$

  f. p-value: 0.0062

  g. Check student's solution.

  h.   i. Alpha: 0.05

      ii. Decision: Reject the null hypothesis.

      iii. Reason for Decision: p-value < alpha

      iv. Conclusion: At the 5% significance level, there is sufficient evidence to conclude that the mean cost of auto insurance for teenage boys is greater than that for girls.

96 Subscripts: 1 = non-hybrid sedans, 2 = hybrid sedans
  a. H_0: $\mu_1 \geq \mu_2$

  b. H_a: $\mu_1 < \mu_2$

  c. The random variable is the difference in the mean miles per gallon of non-hybrid sedans and hybrid sedans.

  d. normal

  e. test statistic: 6.36

  f. p-value: 0

  g. Check student's solution.

  h.   i. Alpha: 0.05

      ii. Decision: Reject the null hypothesis.

      iii. Reason for decision: p-value < alpha

      iv. Conclusion: At the 5% significance level, there is sufficient evidence to conclude that the mean miles per gallon of non-hybrid sedans is less than that of hybrid sedans.

98
  a. H_0: $\mu_d = 0$

  b. H_a: $\mu_d < 0$

c. The random variable X_d is the average difference between husband's and wife's satisfaction level.

d. t_9

e. test statistic: $t = -1.86$

f. p-value: 0.0479

g. Check student's solution

h.   i. Alpha: 0.05

    ii. Decision: Reject the null hypothesis, but run another test.

    iii. Reason for Decision: p-value < alpha

    iv. Conclusion: This is a weak test because alpha and the p-value are close. However, there is insufficient evidence to conclude that the mean difference is negative.

100

a. $H_0: P_W = P_B$

b. $H_a: P_W \neq P_B$

c. The random variable is the difference in the proportions of white and black suicide victims, aged 15 to 24.

d. normal for two proportions

e. test statistic: -0.1944

f. p-value: 0.8458

g. Check student's solution.

h.   i. Alpha: 0.05

    ii. Decision: Reject the null hypothesis.

    iii. Reason for decision: p-value > alpha

    iv. Conclusion: At the 5% significance level, there is insufficient evidence to conclude that the proportions of white and black female suicide victims, aged 15 to 24, are different.

102 Subscripts: 1 = Cabrillo College, 2 = Lake Tahoe College

a. $H_0: p_1 = p_2$

b. $H_a: p_1 \neq p_2$

c. The random variable is the difference between the proportions of Hispanic students at Cabrillo College and Lake Tahoe College.

d. normal for two proportions

e. test statistic: 4.29

f. p-value: 0.00002

g. Check student's solution.

h.   i. Alpha: 0.05

    ii. Decision: Reject the null hypothesis.

    iii. Reason for decision: p-value < alpha

    iv. Conclusion: There is sufficient evidence to conclude that the proportions of Hispanic students at Cabrillo College and Lake Tahoe College are different.

104 a

106 Test: two independent sample proportions. Random variable: $p'_1 - p'_2$ Distribution:
$H_0: p_1 = p_2$
$H_a: p_1 \neq p_2$ The proportion of eReader users is different for the 16- to 29-year-old users from that of the 30 and older users.
Graph: two-tailed

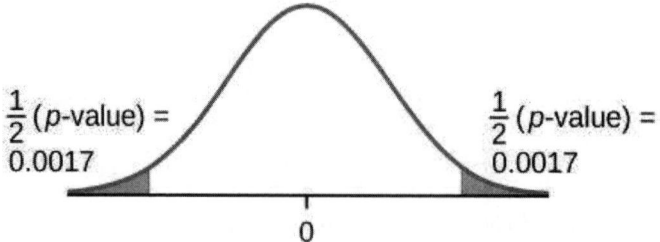

Figure 10.21

p-value : 0.0033 Decision: Reject the null hypothesis. Conclusion: At the 5% level of significance, from the sample data, there is sufficient evidence to conclude that the proportion of eReader users 16 to 29 years old is different from the proportion of eReader users 30 and older.

108 Test: two independent sample proportions Random variable: $p'_1 - p'_2$ Distribution: H_0: $p_1 = p_2$ H_a: $p_1 > p_2$ A higher proportion of tablet owners are aged 16 to 29 years old than are 30 years old and older. Graph: right-tailed

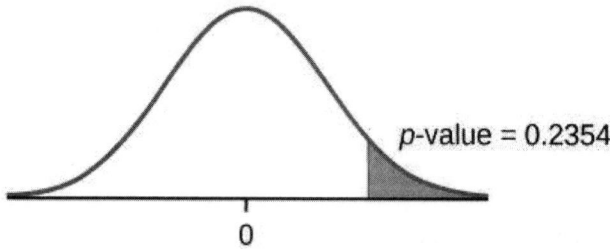

Figure 10.22

p-value: 0.2354 Decision: Do not reject the H_0. Conclusion: At the 1% level of significance, from the sample data, there is not sufficient evidence to conclude that a higher proportion of tablet owners are aged 16 to 29 years old than are 30 years old and older.

110 Subscripts: 1: men; 2: women

a. H_0: $p_1 \le p_2$

b. H_a: $p_1 > p_2$

c. $P'_1 - P'_2$ is the difference between the proportions of men and women who enjoy shopping for electronic equipment.

d. normal for two proportions

e. test statistic: 0.22

f. *p*-value: 0.4133

g. Check student's solution.

h. i. Alpha: 0.05

    ii. Decision: Do not reject the null hypothesis.

    iii. Reason for Decision: *p*-value > alpha

    iv. Conclusion: At the 5% significance level, there is insufficient evidence to conclude that the proportion of men who enjoy shopping for electronic equipment is more than the proportion of women.

112

a. H_0: $p_1 = p_2$

b. H_a: $p_1 \ne p_2$

c. $P'_1 - P'_2$ is the difference between the proportions of men and women that have at least one pierced ear.

d. normal for two proportions

e. test statistic: –4.82

f. *p*-value: zero

g. Check student's solution.

h.   i.   Alpha: 0.05

   ii.   Decision: Reject the null hypothesis.

   iii.   Reason for Decision: *p*-value < alpha

   iv.   Conclusion: At the 5% significance level, there is sufficient evidence to conclude that the proportions of males and females with at least one pierced ear is different.

114

a. $H_0: \mu_d = 0$

b. $H_a: \mu_d > 0$

c. The random variable X_d is the mean difference in work times on days when eating breakfast and on days when not eating breakfast.

d. t_9

e. test statistic: 4.8963

f. *p*-value: 0.0004

g. Check student's solution.

h.   i.   Alpha: 0.05

   ii.   Decision: Reject the null hypothesis.

   iii.   Reason for Decision: *p*-value < alpha

   iv.   Conclusion: At the 5% level of significance, there is sufficient evidence to conclude that the mean difference in work times on days when eating breakfast and on days when not eating breakfast has increased.

115 *p*-value = 0.1494 At the 5% significance level, there is insufficient evidence to conclude that the medication lowered cholesterol levels after 12 weeks.

117 b

119 c

121 Test: two matched pairs or paired samples (*t*-test) Random variable: $\overline{X}_d$ Distribution: t_{12} $H_0: \mu_d = 0$ $H_a: \mu_d > 0$ The mean of the differences of new female breast cancer cases in the south between 2013 and 2012 is greater than zero. The estimate for new female breast cancer cases in the south is higher in 2013 than in 2012. Graph: right-tailed *p*-value: 0.0004

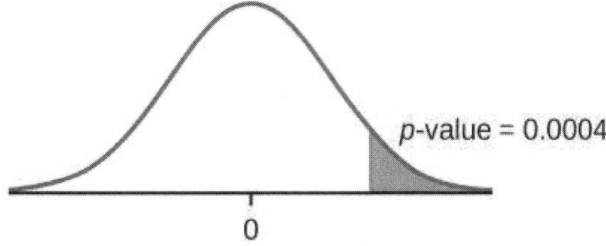

Figure 10.23

Decision: Reject H_0 Conclusion: At the 5% level of significance, from the sample data, there is sufficient evidence to conclude that there was a higher estimate of new female breast cancer cases in 2013 than in 2012.

123 Test: matched or paired samples (*t*-test) Difference data: {–0.9, –3.7, –3.2, –0.5, 0.6, –1.9, –0.5, 0.2, 0.6, 0.4, 1.7, –2.4, 1.8} Random Variable: $\overline{X}_d$ Distribution: H_0: $\mu_d = 0$ H_a: $\mu_d < 0$ The mean of the differences of the rate of underemployment in the northeastern states between 2012 and 2011 is less than zero. The underemployment rate went down from 2011 to 2012. Graph: left-tailed.

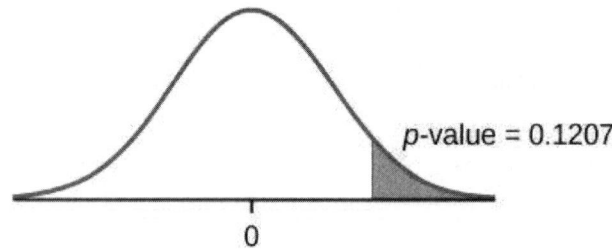

Figure 10.24

p-value: 0.1207 Decision: Do not reject H_0. Conclusion: At the 5% level of significance, from the sample data, there is not sufficient evidence to conclude that there was a decrease in the underemployment rates of the northeastern states from 2011 to 2012.

125 e

127 d

129 f

131 e

133 f

135 a

11 | THE CHI-SQUARE DISTRIBUTION

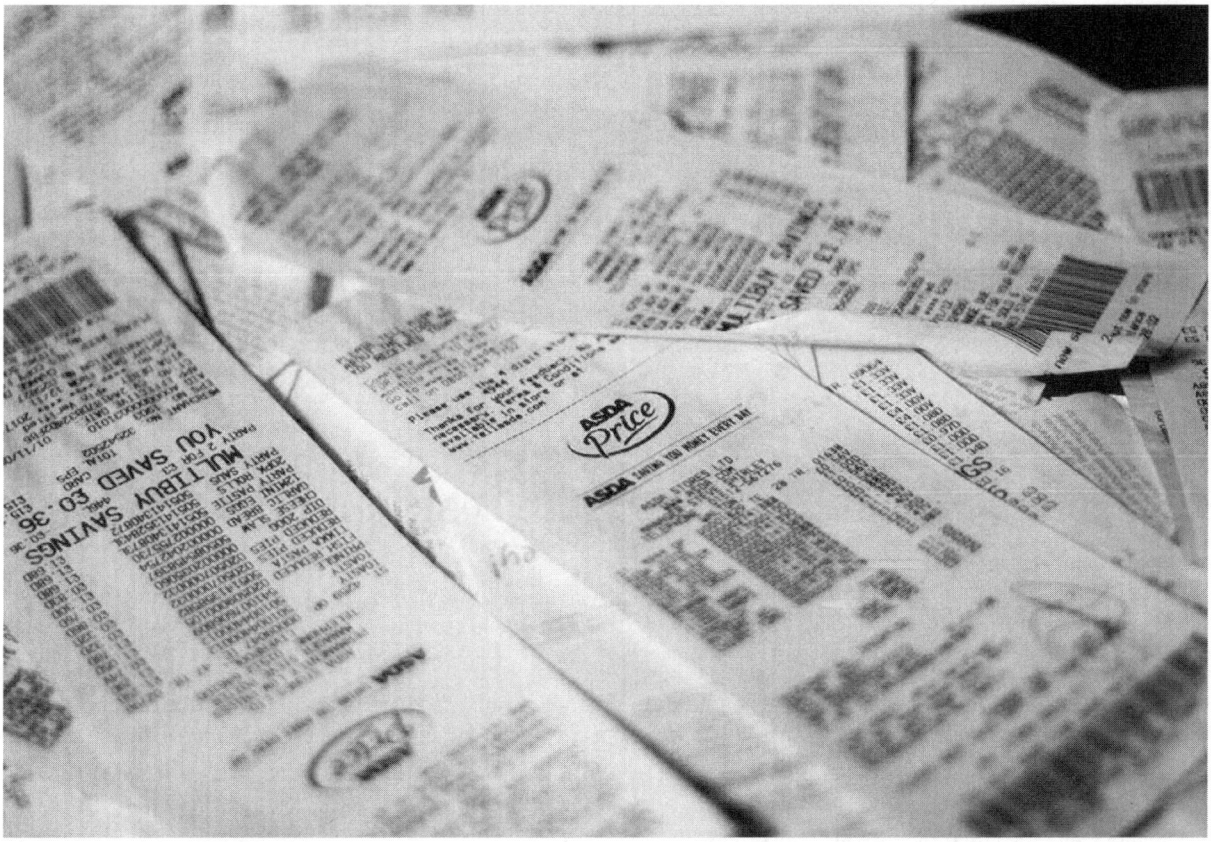

Figure 11.1 The chi-square distribution can be used to find relationships between two things, like grocery prices at different stores. (credit: Pete/flickr)

Introduction

Chapter Objectives

By the end of this chapter, the student should be able to:

- Interpret the chi-square probability distribution as the sample size changes.
- Conduct and interpret chi-square goodness-of-fit hypothesis tests.
- Conduct and interpret chi-square test of independence hypothesis tests.
- Conduct and interpret chi-square homogeneity hypothesis tests.
- Conduct and interpret chi-square single variance hypothesis tests.

Have you ever wondered if lottery numbers were evenly distributed or if some numbers occurred with a greater frequency? How about if the types of movies people preferred were different across different age groups? What about if a coffee machine was dispensing approximately the same amount of coffee each time? You could answer these questions by conducting a hypothesis test.

You will now study a new distribution, one that is used to determine the answers to such questions. This distribution is called the chi-square distribution.

In this chapter, you will learn the three major applications of the chi-square distribution:

1. the goodness-of-fit test, which determines if data fit a particular distribution, such as in the lottery example

2. the test of independence, which determines if events are independent, such as in the movie example

3. the test of a single variance, which tests variability, such as in the coffee example

NOTE

 Though the chi-square distribution depends on calculators or computers for most of the calculations, there is a table available (see **Appendix G**). TI-83+ and TI-84 calculator instructions are included in the text.

Collaborative Exercise

Look in the sports section of a newspaper or on the Internet for some sports data (baseball averages, basketball scores, golf tournament scores, football odds, swimming times, and the like). Plot a histogram and a boxplot using your data. See if you can determine a probability distribution that your data fits. Have a discussion with the class about your choice.

11.1 | Facts About the Chi-Square Distribution

The notation for the **chi-square distribution** is:

$$\chi \sim \chi^2_{df}$$

where df = degrees of freedom which depends on how chi-square is being used. (If you want to practice calculating chi-square probabilities then use $df = n - 1$. The degrees of freedom for the three major uses are each calculated differently.)

For the χ^2 distribution, the population mean is $\mu = df$ and the population standard deviation is $\sigma = \sqrt{2(df)}$.

The random variable is shown as χ^2, but may be any upper case letter.

The random variable for a chi-square distribution with k degrees of freedom is the sum of k independent, squared standard normal variables.

$\chi^2 = (Z_1)^2 + (Z_2)^2 + ... + (Z_k)^2$

1. The curve is nonsymmetrical and skewed to the right.

2. There is a different chi-square curve for each df.

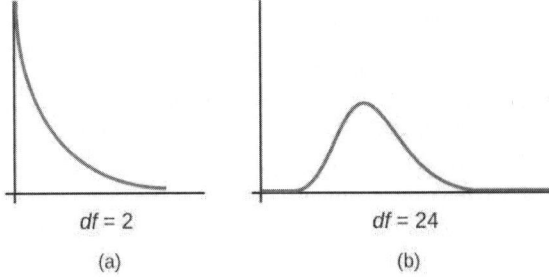

Figure 11.2

3. The test statistic for any test is always greater than or equal to zero.

4. When $df > 90$, the chi-square curve approximates the normal distribution. For $X \sim \chi^2_{1,000}$ the mean, $\mu = df = 1,000$ and the standard deviation, $\sigma = \sqrt{2(1,000)} = 44.7$. Therefore, $X \sim N(1,000, 44.7)$, approximately.

5. The mean, μ, is located just to the right of the peak.

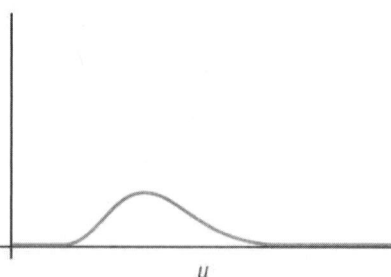

Figure 11.3

11.2 | Goodness-of-Fit Test

In this type of hypothesis test, you determine whether the data **"fit"** a particular distribution or not. For example, you may suspect your unknown data fit a binomial distribution. You use a chi-square test (meaning the distribution for the hypothesis test is chi-square) to determine if there is a fit or not. **The null and the alternative hypotheses for this test may be written in sentences or may be stated as equations or inequalities.**

The test statistic for a goodness-of-fit test is:

$$\sum_k \frac{(O - E)^2}{E}$$

where:

- O = **observed values** (data)
- E = **expected values** (from theory)
- k = the number of different data cells or categories

The observed values are the data values and the expected values are the values you would expect to get if the null hypothesis were true. There are n terms of the form $\frac{(O - E)^2}{E}$.

The number of degrees of freedom is df = (number of categories – 1).

The goodness-of-fit test is almost always right-tailed. If the observed values and the corresponding expected values are not close to each other, then the test statistic can get very large and will be way out in the right tail of the chi-square curve.

> **NOTE**
>
> The expected value for each cell needs to be at least five in order for you to use this test.

Example 11.1

Absenteeism of college students from math classes is a major concern to math instructors because missing class appears to increase the drop rate. Suppose that a study was done to determine if the actual student absenteeism rate follows faculty perception. The faculty expected that a group of 100 students would miss class according to **Table 11.1**.

Number of absences per term	Expected number of students
0–2	50
3–5	30
6–8	12
9–11	6
12+	2

Table 11.1

A random survey across all mathematics courses was then done to determine the actual number **(observed)** of absences in a course. The chart in **Table 11.2** displays the results of that survey.

Number of absences per term	Actual number of students
0–2	35
3–5	40
6–8	20
9–11	1
12+	4

Table 11.2

Determine the null and alternative hypotheses needed to conduct a goodness-of-fit test.

H_0: Student absenteeism **fits** faculty perception.

The alternative hypothesis is the opposite of the null hypothesis.

H_a: Student absenteeism **does not fit** faculty perception.

a. Can you use the information as it appears in the charts to conduct the goodness-of-fit test?

Solution 11.1
a. **No.** Notice that the expected number of absences for the "12+" entry is less than five (it is two). Combine that group with the "9–11" group to create new tables where the number of students for each entry are at least five. The new results are in **Table 11.2** and **Table 11.3**.

Number of absences per term	Expected number of students
0–2	50
3–5	30
6–8	12
9+	8

Table 11.3

Number of absences per term	Actual number of students
0–2	35
3–5	40
6–8	20
9+	5

Table 11.4

b. What is the number of degrees of freedom (*df*)?

Solution 11.1

b. There are four "cells" or categories in each of the new tables.

df = number of cells − 1 = 4 − 1 = 3

11.1 A factory manager needs to understand how many products are defective versus how many are produced. The number of expected defects is listed in **Table 11.5**.

Number produced	Number defective
0–100	5
101–200	6
201–300	7
301–400	8
401–500	10

Table 11.5

A random sample was taken to determine the actual number of defects. **Table 11.6** shows the results of the survey.

Number produced	Number defective
0–100	5
101–200	7
201–300	8
301–400	9
401–500	11

Table 11.6

State the null and alternative hypotheses needed to conduct a goodness-of-fit test, and state the degrees of freedom.

Example 11.2

Employers want to know which days of the week employees are absent in a five-day work week. Most employers would like to believe that employees are absent equally during the week. Suppose a random sample of 60 managers were asked on which day of the week they had the highest number of employee absences. The results were distributed as in **Table 11.6**. For the population of employees, do the days for the highest number of absences occur with equal frequencies during a five-day work week? Test at a 5% significance level.

	Monday	Tuesday	Wednesday	Thursday	Friday
Number of Absences	15	12	9	9	15

Table 11.7 Day of the Week Employees were Most Absent

Solution 11.2

The null and alternative hypotheses are:

- H_0: The absent days occur with equal frequencies, that is, they fit a uniform distribution.
- H_a: The absent days occur with unequal frequencies, that is, they do not fit a uniform distribution.

If the absent days occur with equal frequencies, then, out of 60 absent days (the total in the sample: $15 + 12 + 9 + 9 + 15 = 60$), there would be 12 absences on Monday, 12 on Tuesday, 12 on Wednesday, 12 on Thursday, and 12 on Friday. These numbers are the **expected** (E) values. The values in the table are the **observed** (O) values or data.

This time, calculate the χ^2 test statistic by hand. Make a chart with the following headings and fill in the columns:

- Expected (E) values (12, 12, 12, 12, 12)
- Observed (O) values (15, 12, 9, 9, 15)
- $(O - E)$
- $(O - E)^2$
- $\dfrac{(O - E)^2}{E}$

Now add (sum) the last column. The sum is three. This is the χ^2 test statistic.

To find the *p*-value, calculate $P(\chi^2 > 3)$. This test is right-tailed. (Use a computer or calculator to find the *p*-value. You should get *p*-value = 0.5578.)

The *dfs* are the number of cells $- 1 = 5 - 1 = 4$

 Using the TI-83, 83+, 84, 84+ Calculator

Press 2nd DISTR. Arrow down to χ^2cdf. Press ENTER. Enter (3,10^99,4). Rounded to four decimal places, you should see 0.5578, which is the p-value.

Next, complete a graph like the following one with the proper labeling and shading. (You should shade the right tail.)

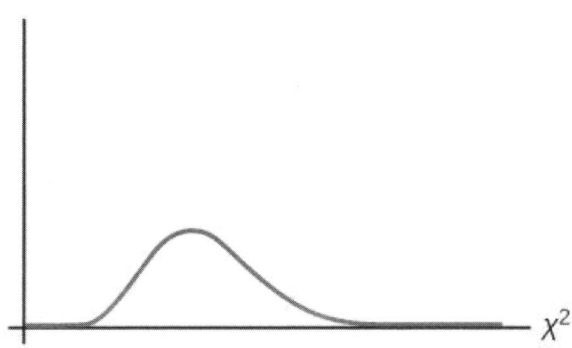

Figure 11.4

The decision is not to reject the null hypothesis.

Conclusion: At a 5% level of significance, from the sample data, there is not sufficient evidence to conclude that the absent days do not occur with equal frequencies.

Using the TI-83, 83+, 84, 84+ Calculator

TI-83+ and some TI-84 calculators do not have a special program for the test statistic for the goodness-of-fit test. The next example **Example 11.3** has the calculator instructions. The newer TI-84 calculators have in STAT TESTS the test Chi2 GOF. To run the test, put the observed values (the data) into a first list and the expected values (the values you expect if the null hypothesis is true) into a second list. Press STAT TESTS and Chi2 GOF. Enter the list names for the Observed list and the Expected list. Enter the degrees of freedom and press calculate or draw. Make sure you clear any lists before you start. **To Clear Lists in the calculators:** Go into STAT EDIT and arrow up to the list name area of the particular list. Press CLEAR and then arrow down. The list will be cleared. Alternatively, you can press STAT and press 4 (for ClrList). Enter the list name and press ENTER.

Try It Σ

11.2 Teachers want to know which night each week their students are doing most of their homework. Most teachers think that students do homework equally throughout the week. Suppose a random sample of 56 students were asked on which night of the week they did the most homework. The results were distributed as in **Table 11.8**.

	Sunday	Monday	Tuesday	Wednesday	Thursday	Friday	Saturday
Number of Students	11	8	10	7	10	5	5

Table 11.8

From the population of students, do the nights for the highest number of students doing the majority of their homework occur with equal frequencies during a week? What type of hypothesis test should you use?

Example 11.3

One study indicates that the number of televisions that American families have is distributed (this is the **given** distribution for the American population) as in **Table 11.9**.

Number of Televisions	Percent
0	10
1	16
2	55
3	11
4+	8

Table 11.9

The table contains expected (E) percents.

A random sample of 600 families in the far western United States resulted in the data in **Table 11.10**.

Number of Televisions	Frequency
0	66
1	119
2	340
3	60
4+	15
	Total = 600

Table 11.10

The table contains observed (O) frequency values.

At the 1% significance level, does it appear that the distribution "number of televisions" of far western United States families is different from the distribution for the American population as a whole?

Solution 11.3

This problem asks you to test whether the far western United States families distribution fits the distribution of the American families. This test is always right-tailed.

The first table contains expected percentages. To get expected (E) frequencies, multiply the percentage by 600. The expected frequencies are shown in **Table 11.10**.

Number of Televisions	Percent	Expected Frequency
0	10	(0.10)(600) = 60
1	16	(0.16)(600) = 96
2	55	(0.55)(600) = 330
3	11	(0.11)(600) = 66
over 3	8	(0.08)(600) = 48

Therefore, the expected frequencies are 60, 96, 330, 66, and 48. In the TI calculators, you can let the calculator do the math. For example, instead of 60, enter 0.10*600.

H_0: The "number of televisions" distribution of far western United States families is the same as the "number of televisions" distribution of the American population.

H_a: The "number of televisions" distribution of far western United States families is different from the "number of televisions" distribution of the American population.

Distribution for the test: χ^2_4 where df = (the number of cells) – 1 = 5 – 1 = 4.

NOTE

$df \neq 600 - 1$

Calculate the test statistic: $\chi 2 = 29.65$

Graph:

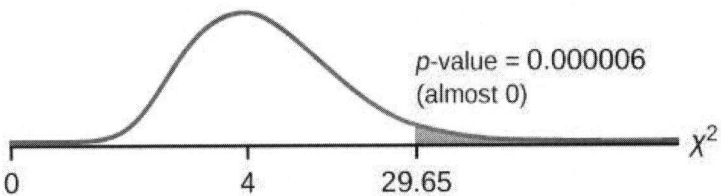

Figure 11.5

Probability statement: p-value = $P(\chi^2 > 29.65) = 0.000006$

Compare α and the p-value:

- $\alpha = 0.01$

- p-value = 0.000006

So, $\alpha > p$-value.

Make a decision: Since $\alpha > p$-value, reject H_o.

This means you reject the belief that the distribution for the far western states is the same as that of the American population as a whole.

Conclusion: At the 1% significance level, from the data, there is sufficient evidence to conclude that the "number of televisions" distribution for the far western United States is different from the "number of televisions" distribution for the American population as a whole.

Using the TI-83, 83+, 84, 84+ Calculator

Press STAT and ENTER. Make sure to clear lists L1, L2, and L3 if they have data in them (see the note at the end of **Example 11.2**). Into L1, put the observed frequencies 66, 119, 349, 60, 15. Into L2, put the expected frequencies .10*600, .16*600, .55*600, .11*600, .08*600. Arrow over to list L3 and up to the name area "L3". Enter (L1-L2)^2/L2 and ENTER. Press 2nd QUIT. Press 2nd LIST and arrow over to MATH. Press 5. You should see "sum" (Enter L3). Rounded to 2 decimal places, you should see 29.65. Press 2nd DISTR. Press 7 or Arrow down to 7:χ2cdf and press ENTER. Enter (29.65,1E99,4). Rounded to four places, you should see 5.77E-6 = .000006 (rounded to six decimal places), which is the p-value.

The newer TI-84 calculators have in STAT TESTS the test Chi2 GOF. To run the test, put the observed values (the data) into a first list and the expected values (the values you expect if the null hypothesis is true) into a second list. Press STAT TESTS and Chi2 GOF. Enter the list names for the Observed list and the Expected list. Enter the degrees of freedom and press calculate or draw. Make sure you clear any lists before you start.

11.3 The expected percentage of the number of pets students have in their homes is distributed (this is the given distribution for the student population of the United States) as in **Table 11.12**.

Number of Pets	Percent
0	18
1	25
2	30
3	18
4+	9

Table 11.12

A random sample of 1,000 students from the Eastern United States resulted in the data in **Table 11.13**.

Number of Pets	Frequency
0	210
1	240
2	320
3	140
4+	90

Table 11.13

At the 1% significance level, does it appear that the distribution "number of pets" of students in the Eastern United

States is different from the distribution for the United States student population as a whole? What is the *p*-value?

Example 11.4

Suppose you flip two coins 100 times. The results are 20 *HH*, 27 *HT*, 30 *TH*, and 23 *TT*. Are the coins fair? Test at a 5% significance level.

Solution 11.4

This problem can be set up as a goodness-of-fit problem. The sample space for flipping two fair coins is {*HH*, *HT*, *TH*, *TT*}. Out of 100 flips, you would expect 25 *HH*, 25 *HT*, 25 *TH*, and 25 *TT*. This is the expected distribution. The question, "Are the coins fair?" is the same as saying, "Does the distribution of the coins (20 *HH*, 27 *HT*, 30 *TH*, 23 *TT*) fit the expected distribution?"

Random Variable: Let X = the number of heads in one flip of the two coins. X takes on the values 0, 1, 2. (There are 0, 1, or 2 heads in the flip of two coins.) Therefore, the **number of cells is three**. Since X = the number of heads, the observed frequencies are 20 (for two heads), 57 (for one head), and 23 (for zero heads or both tails). The expected frequencies are 25 (for two heads), 50 (for one head), and 25 (for zero heads or both tails). This test is right-tailed.

H_0: The coins are fair.

H_a: The coins are not fair.

Distribution for the test: χ_2^2 where $df = 3 - 1 = 2$.

Calculate the test statistic: $\chi^2 = 2.14$

Graph:

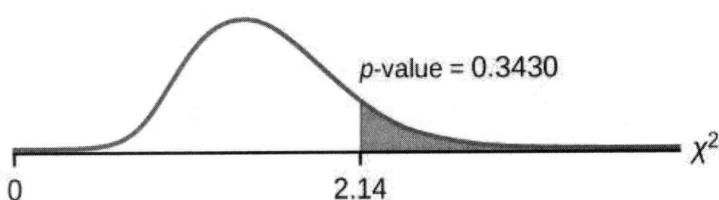

Figure 11.6

Probability statement: *p*-value = $P(\chi^2 > 2.14) = 0.3430$

Compare α and the *p*-value:

- $\alpha = 0.05$
- *p*-value = 0.3430

$\alpha < p$-value.

Make a decision: Since $\alpha < p$-value, do not reject H_0.

Conclusion: There is insufficient evidence to conclude that the coins are not fair.

Using the TI-83, 83+, 84, 84+ Calculator

Press **STAT** and **ENTER**. Make sure you clear lists L1, L2, and L3 if they have data in them. Into L1, put the observed frequencies 20, 57, 23. Into L2, put the expected frequencies 25, 50, 25. Arrow over to list L3 and up to the name area "L3". Enter (L1-L2)^2/L2 and ENTER. Press 2nd QUIT. Press 2nd LIST and arrow over to MATH. Press 5. You should see "sum". Enter L3. Rounded to two decimal places, you should see 2.14. Press 2nd DISTR. Arrow down to 7:χ2cdf (or press 7). Press ENTER. Enter 2.14,1E99,2). Rounded to four places, you should see .3430, which is the p-value.

The newer TI-84 calculators have in STAT TESTS the test Chi2 GOF. To run the test, put the observed values (the data) into a first list and the expected values (the values you expect if the null hypothesis is true) into a second list. Press STAT TESTS and Chi2 GOF. Enter the list names for the Observed list and the Expected list. Enter the degrees of freedom and press calculate or draw. Make sure you clear any lists before you start.

Try It Σ

☞ **11.4** Students in a social studies class hypothesize that the literacy rates across the world for every region are 82%. **Table 11.14** shows the actual literacy rates across the world broken down by region. What are the test statistic and the degrees of freedom?

MDG Region	Adult Literacy Rate (%)
Developed Regions	99.0
Commonwealth of Independent States	99.5
Northern Africa	67.3
Sub-Saharan Africa	62.5
Latin America and the Caribbean	91.0
Eastern Asia	93.8
Southern Asia	61.9
South-Eastern Asia	91.9
Western Asia	84.5
Oceania	66.4

Table 11.14

11.3 | Test of Independence

Tests of independence involve using a **contingency table** of observed (data) values.

The test statistic for a **test of independence** is similar to that of a goodness-of-fit test:

$$\sum_{(i \cdot j)} \frac{(O - E)^2}{E}$$

where:

- O = observed values
- E = expected values
- i = the number of rows in the table

- j = the number of columns in the table

There are $i \cdot j$ terms of the form $\dfrac{(O - E)^2}{E}$.

A test of independence determines whether two factors are independent or not. You first encountered the term independence in **Probability Topics**. As a review, consider the following example.

NOTE

The expected value for each cell needs to be at least five in order for you to use this test.

Example 11.5

Suppose A = a speeding violation in the last year and B = a cell phone user while driving. If A and B are independent then $P(A \text{ AND } B) = P(A)P(B)$. A AND B is the event that a driver received a speeding violation last year and also used a cell phone while driving. Suppose, in a study of drivers who received speeding violations in the last year, and who used cell phone while driving, that 755 people were surveyed. Out of the 755, 70 had a speeding violation and 685 did not; 305 used cell phones while driving and 450 did not.

Let y = expected number of drivers who used a cell phone while driving and received speeding violations.

If A and B are independent, then $P(A \text{ AND } B) = P(A)P(B)$. By substitution,

$$\frac{y}{755} = \left(\frac{70}{755}\right)\left(\frac{305}{755}\right)$$

Solve for y: $y = \dfrac{(70)(305)}{755} = 28.3$

About 28 people from the sample are expected to use cell phones while driving and to receive speeding violations.

In a test of independence, we state the null and alternative hypotheses in words. Since the contingency table consists of **two factors**, the null hypothesis states that the factors are **independent** and the alternative hypothesis states that they are **not independent (dependent)**. If we do a test of independence using the example, then the null hypothesis is:

H_0: Being a cell phone user while driving and receiving a speeding violation are independent events.

If the null hypothesis were true, we would expect about 28 people to use cell phones while driving and to receive a speeding violation.

The test of independence is always right-tailed because of the calculation of the test statistic. If the expected and observed values are not close together, then the test statistic is very large and way out in the right tail of the chi-square curve, as it is in a goodness-of-fit.

The number of degrees of freedom for the test of independence is:

df = (number of columns - 1)(number of rows - 1)

The following formula calculates the **expected number** (E):

$$E = \frac{(\text{row total})(\text{column total})}{\text{total number surveyed}}$$

Try It Σ

11.5 A sample of 300 students is taken. Of the students surveyed, 50 were music students, while 250 were not. Ninety-seven were on the honor roll, while 203 were not. If we assume being a music student and being on the honor roll are independent events, what is the expected number of music students who are also on the honor roll?

Example 11.6

In a volunteer group, adults 21 and older volunteer from one to nine hours each week to spend time with a disabled senior citizen. The program recruits among community college students, four-year college students, and nonstudents. In **Table 11.15** is a **sample** of the adult volunteers and the number of hours they volunteer per week.

Type of Volunteer	1–3 Hours	4–6 Hours	7–9 Hours	Row Total
Community College Students	111	96	48	255
Four-Year College Students	96	133	61	290
Nonstudents	91	150	53	294
Column Total	298	379	162	839

Table 11.15 Number of Hours Worked Per Week by Volunteer Type (Observed) The table contains **observed (O)** values (data).

Is the number of hours volunteered **independent** of the type of volunteer?

Solution 11.6

The **observed table** and the question at the end of the problem, "Is the number of hours volunteered independent of the type of volunteer?" tell you this is a test of independence. The two factors are **number of hours volunteered** and **type of volunteer**. This test is always right-tailed.

H_0: The number of hours volunteered is **independent** of the type of volunteer.

H_a: The number of hours volunteered is **dependent** on the type of volunteer.

The expected result are in **Table 11.15**.

Type of Volunteer	1-3 Hours	4-6 Hours	7-9 Hours
Community College Students	90.57	115.19	49.24
Four-Year College Students	103.00	131.00	56.00
Nonstudents	104.42	132.81	56.77

Table 11.16 Number of Hours Worked Per Week by Volunteer Type (Expected) The table contains **expected (E)** values (data).

For example, the calculation for the expected frequency for the top left cell is

$$E = \frac{(\text{row total})(\text{column total})}{\text{total number surveyed}} = \frac{(255)(298)}{839} = 90.57$$

Calculate the test statistic: $\chi^2 = 12.99$ (calculator or computer)

Distribution for the test: χ_4^2

$df = (3 \text{ columns} - 1)(3 \text{ rows} - 1) = (2)(2) = 4$

Graph:

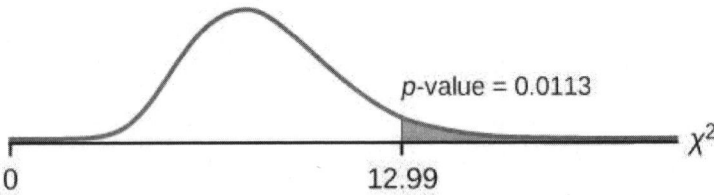

Figure 11.7

Probability statement: p-value$=P(\chi^2 > 12.99) = 0.0113$

Compare α and the p-value: Since no α is given, assume $\alpha = 0.05$. p-value $= 0.0113$. $\alpha > p$-value.

Make a decision: Since $\alpha > p$-value, reject H_0. This means that the factors are not independent.

Conclusion: At a 5% level of significance, from the data, there is sufficient evidence to conclude that the number of hours volunteered and the type of volunteer are dependent on one another.

For the example in **Table 11.15**, if there had been another type of volunteer, teenagers, what would the degrees of freedom be?

 Using the TI-83, 83+, 84, 84+ Calculator

Press the MATRX key and arrow over to EDIT. Press 1:[A]. Press 3 ENTER 3 ENTER. Enter the table values by row from **Table 11.15**. Press ENTER after each. Press 2nd   QUIT. Press STAT and arrow over to TESTS. Arrow down to C:χ2-TEST. Press ENTER. You should see Observed:[A] and Expected:[B]. Arrow down to Calculate. Press ENTER. The test statistic is 12.9909 and the p-value = 0.0113. Do the procedure a second time, but arrow down to Draw instead of calculate.

Try It Σ

11.6 The Bureau of Labor Statistics gathers data about employment in the United States. A sample is taken to calculate the number of U.S. citizens working in one of several industry sectors over time. **Table 11.17** shows the results:

Industry Sector	2000	2010	2020	Total
Nonagriculture wage and salary	13,243	13,044	15,018	41,305
Goods-producing, excluding agriculture	2,457	1,771	1,950	6,178
Services-providing	10,786	11,273	13,068	35,127
Agriculture, forestry, fishing, and hunting	240	214	201	655
Nonagriculture self-employed and unpaid family worker	931	894	972	2,797
Secondary wage and salary jobs in agriculture and private household industries	14	11	11	36
Secondary jobs as a self-employed or unpaid family worker	196	144	152	492

Table 11.17

Industry Sector	2000	2010	2020	Total
Total	27,867	27,351	31,372	86,590

Table 11.17

We want to know if the change in the number of jobs is independent of the change in years. State the null and alternative hypotheses and the degrees of freedom.

Example 11.7

De Anza College is interested in the relationship between anxiety level and the need to succeed in school. A random sample of 400 students took a test that measured anxiety level and need to succeed in school. **Table 11.18** shows the results. De Anza College wants to know if anxiety level and need to succeed in school are independent events.

Need to Succeed in School	High Anxiety	Med-high Anxiety	Medium Anxiety	Med-low Anxiety	Low Anxiety	Row Total
High Need	35	42	53	15	10	155
Medium Need	18	48	63	33	31	193
Low Need	4	5	11	15	17	52
Column Total	57	95	127	63	58	400

Table 11.18 Need to Succeed in School vs. Anxiety Level

a. How many high anxiety level students are expected to have a high need to succeed in school?

Solution 11.7

a. The column total for a high anxiety level is 57. The row total for high need to succeed in school is 155. The sample size or total surveyed is 400.

$$E = \frac{\text{(row total)(column total)}}{\text{total surveyed}} = \frac{155 \cdot 57}{400} = 22.09$$

The expected number of students who have a high anxiety level and a high need to succeed in school is about 22.

b. If the two variables are independent, how many students do you expect to have a low need to succeed in school and a med-low level of anxiety?

Solution 11.7

b. The column total for a med-low anxiety level is 63. The row total for a low need to succeed in school is 52. The sample size or total surveyed is 400.

c. $E = \frac{\text{(row total)(column total)}}{\text{total surveyed}} = \underline{\hspace{2cm}}$

Solution 11.7

c. $E = \dfrac{\text{(row total)(column total)}}{\text{total surveyed}} = 8.19$

d. The expected number of students who have a med-low anxiety level and a low need to succeed in school is about _____.

Solution 11.7

d. 8

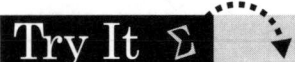

11.7 Refer back to the information in **Try It**. How many service providing jobs are there expected to be in 2020? How many nonagriculture wage and salary jobs are there expected to be in 2020?

11.4 | Test for Homogeneity

The goodness–of–fit test can be used to decide whether a population fits a given distribution, but it will not suffice to decide whether two populations follow the same unknown distribution. A different test, called the **test for homogeneity**, can be used to draw a conclusion about whether two populations have the same distribution. To calculate the test statistic for a test for homogeneity, follow the same procedure as with the test of independence.

NOTE

The expected value for each cell needs to be at least five in order for you to use this test.

Hypotheses

H_0: The distributions of the two populations are the same.

H_a: The distributions of the two populations are not the same.

Test Statistic

Use a χ^2 test statistic. It is computed in the same way as the test for independence.

Degrees of Freedom (*df*)

df = number of columns - 1

Requirements

All values in the table must be greater than or equal to five.

Common Uses

Comparing two populations. For example: men vs. women, before vs. after, east vs. west. The variable is categorical with more than two possible response values.

Example 11.8

Do male and female college students have the same distribution of living arrangements? Use a level of significance of 0.05. Suppose that 250 randomly selected male college students and 300 randomly selected female college students were asked about their living arrangements: dormitory, apartment, with parents, other.

The results are shown in **Table 11.18**. Do male and female college students have the same distribution of living arrangements?

	Dormitory	Apartment	With Parents	Other
Males	72	84	49	45
Females	91	86	88	35

Table 11.19 Distribution of Living Arragements for College Males and College Females

Solution 11.8

H_0: The distribution of living arrangements for male college students is the same as the distribution of living arrangements for female college students.

H_a: The distribution of living arrangements for male college students is not the same as the distribution of living arrangements for female college students.

Degrees of Freedom (*df*):
df = number of columns − 1 = 4 − 1 = 3

Distribution for the test: χ_3^2

Calculate the test statistic: $\chi^2 = 10.1287$ (calculator or computer)

Probability statement: *p*-value = $P(\chi^2 > 10.1287) = 0.0175$

Using the TI-83, 83+, 84, 84+ Calculator

Press the MATRX key and arrow over to EDIT. Press 1:[A]. Press 2 ENTER 4 ENTER. Enter the table values by row. Press ENTER after each. Press 2nd QUIT. Press STAT and arrow over to TESTS. Arrow down to C:χ2-TEST. Press ENTER. You should see Observed:[A] and Expected:[B]. Arrow down to Calculate. Press ENTER. The test statistic is 10.1287 and the *p*-value = 0.0175. Do the procedure a second time but arrow down to Draw instead of calculate.

Compare α and the *p*-value: Since no α is given, assume α = 0.05. *p*-value = 0.0175. α > *p*-value.

Make a decision: Since α > *p*-value, reject H_0. This means that the distributions are not the same.

Conclusion: At a 5% level of significance, from the data, there is sufficient evidence to conclude that the distributions of living arrangements for male and female college students are not the same.

Notice that the conclusion is only that the distributions are not the same. We cannot use the test for homogeneity to draw any conclusions about how they differ.

11.8 Do families and singles have the same distribution of cars? Use a level of significance of 0.05. Suppose that 100

randomly selected families and 200 randomly selected singles were asked what type of car they drove: sport, sedan, hatchback, truck, van/SUV. The results are shown in **Table 11.20**. Do families and singles have the same distribution of cars? Test at a level of significance of 0.05.

	Sport	Sedan	Hatchback	Truck	Van/SUV
Family	5	15	35	17	28
Single	45	65	37	46	7

Table 11.20

Example 11.9

Both before and after a recent earthquake, surveys were conducted asking voters which of the three candidates they planned on voting for in the upcoming city council election. Has there been a change since the earthquake? Use a level of significance of 0.05. **Table 11.20** shows the results of the survey. Has there been a change in the distribution of voter preferences since the earthquake?

	Perez	Chung	Stevens
Before	167	128	135
After	214	197	225

Table 11.21

Solution 11.9

H_0: The distribution of voter preferences was the same before and after the earthquake.

H_a: The distribution of voter preferences was not the same before and after the earthquake.

Degrees of Freedom (df):
df = number of columns − 1 = 3 − 1 = 2

Distribution for the test: χ^2_2

Calculate the test statistic: χ^2 = 3.2603 (calculator or computer)

Probability statement: p-value=$P(\chi^2 > 3.2603)$ = 0.1959

▯ **Using the TI-83, 83+, 84, 84+ Calculator**

Press the MATRX key and arrow over to EDIT. Press 1:[A]. Press 2 ENTER 3 ENTER. Enter the table values by row. Press ENTER after each. Press 2nd QUIT. Press STAT and arrow over to TESTS. Arrow down to C:χ2-TEST. Press ENTER. You should see Observed:[A] and Expected:[B]. Arrow down to Calculate. Press ENTER. The test statistic is 3.2603 and the p-value = 0.1959. Do the procedure a second time but arrow down to Draw instead of calculate.

Compare α and the p-value: $\alpha = 0.05$ and the p-value = 0.1959. $\alpha < p$-value.

Make a decision: Since $\alpha < p$-value, do not reject H_o.

Conclusion: At a 5% level of significance, from the data, there is insufficient evidence to conclude that the distribution of voter preferences was not the same before and after the earthquake.

Try It Σ

☞ **11.9** Ivy League schools receive many applications, but only some can be accepted. At the schools listed in **Table 11.22**, two types of applications are accepted: regular and early decision.

Application Type Accepted	Brown	Columbia	Cornell	Dartmouth	Penn	Yale
Regular	2,115	1,792	5,306	1,734	2,685	1,245
Early Decision	577	627	1,228	444	1,195	761

Table 11.22

We want to know if the number of regular applications accepted follows the same distribution as the number of early applications accepted. State the null and alternative hypotheses, the degrees of freedom and the test statistic, sketch the graph of the p-value, and draw a conclusion about the test of homogeneity.

11.5 | Comparison of the Chi-Square Tests

You have seen the χ^2 test statistic used in three different circumstances. The following bulleted list is a summary that will help you decide which χ^2 test is the appropriate one to use.

- **Goodness-of-Fit:** Use the goodness-of-fit test to decide whether a population with an unknown distribution "fits" a known distribution. In this case there will be a single qualitative survey question or a single outcome of an experiment from a single population. Goodness-of-Fit is typically used to see if the population is uniform (all outcomes occur with equal frequency), the population is normal, or the population is the same as another population with a known distribution. The null and alternative hypotheses are:
  H_0: The population fits the given distribution.
  H_a: The population does not fit the given distribution.

- **Independence:** Use the test for independence to decide whether two variables (factors) are independent or dependent. In this case there will be two qualitative survey questions or experiments and a contingency table will be constructed. The goal is to see if the two variables are unrelated (independent) or related (dependent). The null and alternative hypotheses are:
  H_0: The two variables (factors) are independent.
  H_a: The two variables (factors) are dependent.

- **Homogeneity:** Use the test for homogeneity to decide if two populations with unknown distributions have the same distribution as each other. In this case there will be a single qualitative survey question or experiment given to two different populations. The null and alternative hypotheses are:
  H_0: The two populations follow the same distribution.
  H_a: The two populations have different distributions.

11.6 | Test of a Single Variance

A **test of a single variance** assumes that the underlying distribution is **normal**. The null and alternative hypotheses are stated in terms of the **population variance** (or population standard deviation). The test statistic is:

$$\frac{(n-1)s^2}{\sigma^2}$$

where:

- n = the total number of data
- s^2 = sample variance
- σ^2 = population variance

You may think of s as the random variable in this test. The number of degrees of freedom is $df = n - 1$. **A test of a single variance may be right-tailed, left-tailed, or two-tailed. Example 11.10** will show you how to set up the null and alternative hypotheses. The null and alternative hypotheses contain statements about the population variance.

Example 11.10

Math instructors are not only interested in how their students do on exams, on average, but how the exam scores vary. To many instructors, the variance (or standard deviation) may be more important than the average.

Suppose a math instructor believes that the standard deviation for his final exam is five points. One of his best students thinks otherwise. The student claims that the standard deviation is more than five points. If the student were to conduct a hypothesis test, what would the null and alternative hypotheses be?

Solution 11.10

Even though we are given the population standard deviation, we can set up the test using the population variance as follows.

- H_0: $\sigma^2 = 5^2$
- H_a: $\sigma^2 > 5^2$

11.10 A SCUBA instructor wants to record the collective depths each of his students dives during their checkout. He is interested in how the depths vary, even though everyone should have been at the same depth. He believes the standard deviation is three feet. His assistant thinks the standard deviation is less than three feet. If the instructor were to conduct a test, what would the null and alternative hypotheses be?

Example 11.11

With individual lines at its various windows, a post office finds that the standard deviation for normally distributed waiting times for customers on Friday afternoon is 7.2 minutes. The post office experiments with a single, main waiting line and finds that for a random sample of 25 customers, the waiting times for customers have a standard deviation of 3.5 minutes.

With a significance level of 5%, test the claim that **a single line causes lower variation among waiting times (shorter waiting times) for customers**.

Solution 11.11

Since the claim is that a single line causes less variation, this is a test of a single variance. The parameter is the population variance, σ^2, or the population standard deviation, σ.

Random Variable: The sample standard deviation, s, is the random variable. Let s = standard deviation for the waiting times.

- H_0: $\sigma^2 = 7.2^2$
- H_a: $\sigma^2 < 7.2^2$

The word **"less"** tells you this is a left-tailed test.

Distribution for the test: χ^2_{24}, where:

- n = the number of customers sampled
- $df = n - 1 = 25 - 1 = 24$

Calculate the test statistic:

$$\chi^2 = \frac{(n-1)s^2}{\sigma^2} = \frac{(25-1)(3.5)^2}{7.2^2} = 5.67$$

where $n = 25$, $s = 3.5$, and $\sigma = 7.2$.

Graph:

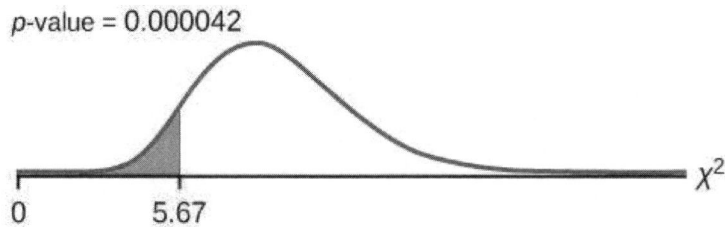

p-value = 0.000042

0   5.67

Figure 11.8

Probability statement: p-value = $P(\chi^2 < 5.67) = 0.000042$

Compare α and the p-value:
$\alpha = 0.05$; p-value = 0.000042; $\alpha > p$-value

Make a decision: Since $\alpha > p$-value, reject H_0. This means that you reject $\sigma^2 = 7.2^2$. In other words, you do not think the variation in waiting times is 7.2 minutes; you think the variation in waiting times is less.

Conclusion: At a 5% level of significance, from the data, there is sufficient evidence to conclude that a single line causes a lower variation among the waiting times **or** with a single line, the customer waiting times vary less than 7.2 minutes.

 Using the TI-83, 83+, 84, 84+ Calculator

In **2nd DISTR**, use **7:χ2cdf**. The syntax is **(lower, upper, df)** for the parameter list. For **Example 11.11**, χ2cdf(-1E99,5.67,24). The p-value = 0.000042.

Try It Σ

11.11 The FCC conducts broadband speed tests to measure how much data per second passes between a consumer's computer and the internet. As of August of 2012, the standard deviation of Internet speeds across Internet Service Providers (ISPs) was 12.2 percent. Suppose a sample of 15 ISPs is taken, and the standard deviation is 13.2. An analyst claims that the standard deviation of speeds is more than what was reported. State the null and alternative hypotheses, compute the degrees of freedom, the test statistic, sketch the graph of the p-value, and draw a conclusion. Test at the

1% significance level.

11.7 | Lab 1: Chi-Square Goodness-of-Fit

Stats Lab

11.1 Lab 1: Chi-Square Goodness-of-Fit

Class Time:

Names:

Student Learning Outcome

- The student will evaluate data collected to determine if they fit either the uniform or exponential distributions.

Collect the Data

Go to your local supermarket. Ask 30 people as they leave for the total amount on their grocery receipts. (Or, ask three cashiers for the last ten amounts. Be sure to include the express lane, if it is open.)

NOTE

You may need to combine two categories so that each cell has an expected value of at least five.

1. Record the values.

Table 11.23

2. Construct a histogram of the data. Make five to six intervals. Sketch the graph using a ruler and pencil. Scale the axes.

Figure 11.9

3. Calculate the following:

a. $\bar{x}$ = _____

b. s = _____

c. s^2 = _____

Uniform Distribution

Test to see if grocery receipts follow the uniform distribution.

1. Using your lowest and highest values, $X \sim U$ (_____, _____)

2. Divide the distribution into fifths.

3. Calculate the following:

    a. lowest value = _____

    b. 20th percentile = _____

    c. 40th percentile = _____

    d. 60th percentile = _____

    e. 80th percentile = _____

    f. highest value = _____

4. For each fifth, count the observed number of receipts and record it. Then determine the expected number of receipts and record that.

Fifth	Observed	Expected
1st		
2nd		
3rd		
4th		
5th		

Table 11.24

5. H_0: _____

6. H_a: _____

7. What distribution should you use for a hypothesis test?

8. Why did you choose this distribution?

9. Calculate the test statistic.

10. Find the p-value.

11. Sketch a graph of the situation. Label and scale the x-axis. Shade the area corresponding to the p-value.

Figure 11.10

12. State your decision.

13. State your conclusion in a complete sentence.

Exponential Distribution

Test to see if grocery receipts follow the exponential distribution with decay parameter $\frac{1}{x}$.

1. Using $\frac{1}{x}$ as the decay parameter, $X \sim Exp(\underline{\hspace{2cm}})$.

2. Calculate the following:

    a. lowest value = _____

    b. first quartile = _____

    c. 37th percentile = _____

    d. median = _____

    e. 63rd percentile = _____

    f. 3rd quartile = _____

    g. highest value = _____

3. For each cell, count the observed number of receipts and record it. Then determine the expected number of receipts and record that.

Cell	Observed	Expected
1st		
2nd		
3rd		
4th		
5th		
6th		

Table 11.25

4. H_0: _____

5. H_a: _____

6. What distribution should you use for a hypothesis test?

7. Why did you choose this distribution?

8. Calculate the test statistic.

9. Find the *p*-value.

10. Sketch a graph of the situation. Label and scale the *x*-axis. Shade the area corresponding to the *p*-value.

Figure 11.11

11. State your decision.

12. State your conclusion in a complete sentence.

Discussion Questions

1. Did your data fit either distribution? If so, which?

2. In general, do you think it's likely that data could fit more than one distribution? In complete sentences, explain why or why not.

11.8 | Lab 2: Chi-Square Test of Independence

Stats Lab

11.2 Lab 2: Chi-Square Test of Independence

Class Time:

Names:

Student Learning Outcome

- The student will evaluate if there is a significant relationship between favorite type of snack and gender.

Collect the Data

1. Using your class as a sample, complete the following chart. Ask each other what your favorite snack is, then total the results.

   NOTE _____

   You may need to combine two food categories so that each cell has an expected value of at least five.

	sweets (candy & baked goods)	ice cream	chips & pretzels	fruits & vegetables	Total
male					
female					
Total					

Table 11.26 Favorite type of snack

2. Looking at **Table 11.26**, does it appear to you that there is a dependence between gender and favorite type of snack food? Why or why not?

Hypothesis Test

Conduct a hypothesis test to determine if the factors are independent:

1. H_0: _____
2. H_a: _____
3. What distribution should you use for a hypothesis test?
4. Why did you choose this distribution?
5. Calculate the test statistic.
6. Find the p-value.
7. Sketch a graph of the situation. Label and scale the x-axis. Shade the area corresponding to the p-value.

Figure 11.12

8. State your decision.

9. State your conclusion in a complete sentence.

Discussion Questions

1. Is the conclusion of your study the same as or different from your answer to answer to question two under **Collect the Data**?

2. Why do you think that occurred?

KEY TERMS

Contingency Table a table that displays sample values for two different factors that may be dependent or contingent on one another; it facilitates determining conditional probabilities.

CHAPTER REVIEW

11.1 Facts About the Chi-Square Distribution

The chi-square distribution is a useful tool for assessment in a series of problem categories. These problem categories include primarily (i) whether a data set fits a particular distribution, (ii) whether the distributions of two populations are the same, (iii) whether two events might be independent, and (iv) whether there is a different variability than expected within a population.

An important parameter in a chi-square distribution is the degrees of freedom df in a given problem. The random variable in the chi-square distribution is the sum of squares of df standard normal variables, which must be independent. The key characteristics of the chi-square distribution also depend directly on the degrees of freedom.

The chi-square distribution curve is skewed to the right, and its shape depends on the degrees of freedom df. For $df > 90$, the curve approximates the normal distribution. Test statistics based on the chi-square distribution are always greater than or equal to zero. Such application tests are almost always right-tailed tests.

11.2 Goodness-of-Fit Test

To assess whether a data set fits a specific distribution, you can apply the goodness-of-fit hypothesis test that uses the chi-square distribution. The null hypothesis for this test states that the data come from the assumed distribution. The test compares observed values against the values you would expect to have if your data followed the assumed distribution. The test is almost always right-tailed. Each observation or cell category must have an expected value of at least five.

11.3 Test of Independence

To assess whether two factors are independent or not, you can apply the test of independence that uses the chi-square distribution. The null hypothesis for this test states that the two factors are independent. The test compares observed values to expected values. The test is right-tailed. Each observation or cell category must have an expected value of at least 5.

11.4 Test for Homogeneity

To assess whether two data sets are derived from the same distribution—which need not be known, you can apply the test for homogeneity that uses the chi-square distribution. The null hypothesis for this test states that the populations of the two data sets come from the same distribution. The test compares the observed values against the expected values if the two populations followed the same distribution. The test is right-tailed. Each observation or cell category must have an expected value of at least five.

11.5 Comparison of the Chi-Square Tests

The goodness-of-fit test is typically used to determine if data fits a particular distribution. The test of independence makes use of a contingency table to determine the independence of two factors. The test for homogeneity determines whether two populations come from the same distribution, even if this distribution is unknown.

11.6 Test of a Single Variance

To test variability, use the chi-square test of a single variance. The test may be left-, right-, or two-tailed, and its hypotheses are always expressed in terms of the variance (or standard deviation).

FORMULA REVIEW

11.1 Facts About the Chi-Square Distribution

$\chi^2 = (Z_1)^2 + (Z_2)^2 + \dots (Z_{df})^2$ chi-square distribution random variable

$\mu_{\chi^2} = df$ chi-square distribution population mean

$\sigma_{\chi^2} = \sqrt{2(df)}$ Chi-Square distribution population standard deviation

11.2 Goodness-of-Fit Test

$\sum_{k} \frac{(O-E)^2}{E}$ goodness-of-fit test statistic where:

O: observed values
E: expected values

k: number of different data cells or categories

$df = k - 1$ degrees of freedom

11.3 Test of Independence

Test of Independence

- The number of degrees of freedom is equal to (number of columns - 1)(number of rows - 1).

- The test statistic is $\sum_{(i \cdot j)} \frac{(O-E)^2}{E}$ where O = observed values, E = expected values, i = the number of rows in the table, and j = the number of columns in the table.

- If the null hypothesis is true, the expected number $E = \frac{(\text{row total})(\text{column total})}{\text{total surveyed}}$.

11.4 Test for Homogeneity

$\sum_{i \cdot j} \frac{(O-E)^2}{E}$ Homogeneity test statistic where: O = observed values
E = expected values
i = number of rows in data contingency table
j = number of columns in data contingency table
$df = (i-1)(j-1)$ Degrees of freedom

11.6 Test of a Single Variance

$\chi^2 = \frac{(n-1) \cdot s^2}{\sigma^2}$ Test of a single variance statistic where:
n: sample size
s: sample standard deviation
σ: population standard deviation

$df = n - 1$ Degrees of freedom

Test of a Single Variance

- Use the test to determine variation.

- The degrees of freedom is the number of samples – 1.

- The test statistic is $\frac{(n-1) \cdot s^2}{\sigma^2}$, where n = the total number of data, s^2 = sample variance, and σ^2 = population variance.

- The test may be left-, right-, or two-tailed.

PRACTICE

11.1 Facts About the Chi-Square Distribution

1. If the number of degrees of freedom for a chi-square distribution is 25, what is the population mean and standard deviation?

2. If $df > 90$, the distribution is _____. If $df = 15$, the distribution is _____.

3. When does the chi-square curve approximate a normal distribution?

4. Where is μ located on a chi-square curve?

5. Is it more likely the *df* is 90, 20, or two in the graph?

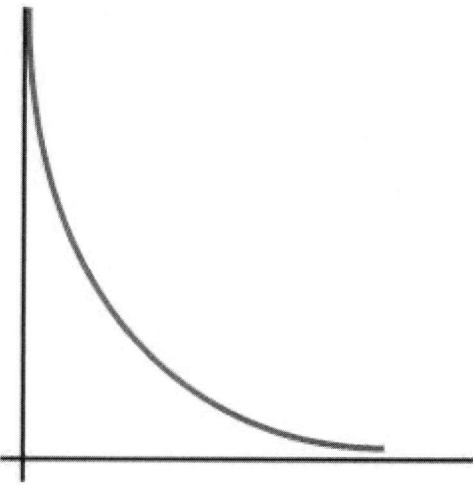

Figure 11.13

11.2 Goodness-of-Fit Test

Determine the appropriate test to be used in the next three exercises.

6. An archeologist is calculating the distribution of the frequency of the number of artifacts she finds in a dig site. Based on previous digs, the archeologist creates an expected distribution broken down by grid sections in the dig site. Once the site has been fully excavated, she compares the actual number of artifacts found in each grid section to see if her expectation was accurate.

7. An economist is deriving a model to predict outcomes on the stock market. He creates a list of expected points on the stock market index for the next two weeks. At the close of each day's trading, he records the actual points on the index. He wants to see how well his model matched what actually happened.

8. A personal trainer is putting together a weight-lifting program for her clients. For a 90-day program, she expects each client to lift a specific maximum weight each week. As she goes along, she records the actual maximum weights her clients lifted. She wants to know how well her expectations met with what was observed.

Use the following information to answer the next five exercises: A teacher predicts that the distribution of grades on the final exam will be and they are recorded in **Table 11.27**.

Grade	Proportion
A	0.25
B	0.30
C	0.35
D	0.10

Table 11.27

The actual distribution for a class of 20 is in **Table 11.28**.

Grade	Frequency
A	7

Table 11.28

Grade	Frequency
B	7
C	5
D	1

Table 11.28

9. $df =$ _____

10. State the null and alternative hypotheses.

11. χ^2 test statistic = _____

12. p-value = _____

13. At the 5% significance level, what can you conclude?

Use the following information to answer the next nine exercises: The following data are real. The cumulative number of AIDS cases reported for Santa Clara County is broken down by ethnicity as in **Table 11.29**.

Ethnicity	Number of Cases
White	2,229
Hispanic	1,157
Black/African-American	457
Asian, Pacific Islander	232
	Total = 4,075

Table 11.29

The percentage of each ethnic group in Santa Clara County is as in **Table 11.30**.

Ethnicity	Percentage of total county population	Number expected (round to two decimal places)
White	42.9%	1748.18
Hispanic	26.7%	
Black/African-American	2.6%	
Asian, Pacific Islander	27.8%	
	Total = 100%	

Table 11.30

14. If the ethnicities of AIDS victims followed the ethnicities of the total county population, fill in the expected number of cases per ethnic group.
Perform a goodness-of-fit test to determine whether the occurrence of AIDS cases follows the ethnicities of the general population of Santa Clara County.

15. H_0: _____

16. H_a: _____

17. Is this a right-tailed, left-tailed, or two-tailed test?

18. degrees of freedom = _____

19. χ^2 test statistic = _____

20. *p*-value = _____

21. Graph the situation. Label and scale the horizontal axis. Mark the mean and test statistic. Shade in the region corresponding to the *p*-value.

Figure 11.14

Let $\alpha = 0.05$

Decision: _____

Reason for the Decision: _____

Conclusion (write out in complete sentences): _____

22. Does it appear that the pattern of AIDS cases in Santa Clara County corresponds to the distribution of ethnic groups in this county? Why or why not?

11.3 Test of Independence

Determine the appropriate test to be used in the next three exercises.

23. A pharmaceutical company is interested in the relationship between age and presentation of symptoms for a common viral infection. A random sample is taken of 500 people with the infection across different age groups.

24. The owner of a baseball team is interested in the relationship between player salaries and team winning percentage. He takes a random sample of 100 players from different organizations.

25. A marathon runner is interested in the relationship between the brand of shoes runners wear and their run times. She takes a random sample of 50 runners and records their run times as well as the brand of shoes they were wearing.

Use the following information to answer the next seven exercises: Transit Railroads is interested in the relationship between travel distance and the ticket class purchased. A random sample of 200 passengers is taken. **Table 11.31** shows the results. The railroad wants to know if a passenger's choice in ticket class is independent of the distance they must travel.

Traveling Distance	Third class	Second class	First class	Total
1–100 miles	21	14	6	41
101–200 miles	18	16	8	42
201–300 miles	16	17	15	48

Table 11.31

Traveling Distance	Third class	Second class	First class	Total
301–400 miles	12	14	21	47
401–500 miles	6	6	10	22
Total	73	67	60	200

Table 11.31

26. State the hypotheses.

H_0: _____

H_a: _____

27. $df = $ _____

28. How many passengers are expected to travel between 201 and 300 miles and purchase second-class tickets?

29. How many passengers are expected to travel between 401 and 500 miles and purchase first-class tickets?

30. What is the test statistic?

31. What is the p-value?

32. What can you conclude at the 5% level of significance?

Use the following information to answer the next eight exercises: An article in the New England Journal of Medicine, discussed a study on smokers in California and Hawaii. In one part of the report, the self-reported ethnicity and smoking levels per day were given. Of the people smoking at most ten cigarettes per day, there were 9,886 African Americans, 2,745 Native Hawaiians, 12,831 Latinos, 8,378 Japanese Americans and 7,650 whites. Of the people smoking 11 to 20 cigarettes per day, there were 6,514 African Americans, 3,062 Native Hawaiians, 4,932 Latinos, 10,680 Japanese Americans, and 9,877 whites. Of the people smoking 21 to 30 cigarettes per day, there were 1,671 African Americans, 1,419 Native Hawaiians, 1,406 Latinos, 4,715 Japanese Americans, and 6,062 whites. Of the people smoking at least 31 cigarettes per day, there were 759 African Americans, 788 Native Hawaiians, 800 Latinos, 2,305 Japanese Americans, and 3,970 whites.

33. Complete the table.

Smoking Level Per Day	African American	Native Hawaiian	Latino	Japanese Americans	White	TOTALS
1-10						
11-20						
21-30						
31+						
TOTALS						

Table 11.32 Smoking Levels by Ethnicity (Observed)

34. State the hypotheses.

H_0: _____

H_a: _____

35. Enter expected values in **Table 11.32**. Round to two decimal places.

Calculate the following values:

36. $df = $ _____

37. χ^2 test statistic = _____

38. p-value = _____

39. Is this a right-tailed, left-tailed, or two-tailed test? Explain why.

40. Graph the situation. Label and scale the horizontal axis. Mark the mean and test statistic. Shade in the region corresponding to the *p*-value.

Figure 11.15

State the decision and conclusion (in a complete sentence) for the following preconceived levels of α.

41. $\alpha = 0.05$
   a. Decision: _____
   b. Reason for the decision: _____
   c. Conclusion (write out in a complete sentence): _____

42. $\alpha = 0.01$
   a. Decision: _____
   b. Reason for the decision: _____
   c. Conclusion (write out in a complete sentence): _____

11.4 Test for Homogeneity

43. A math teacher wants to see if two of her classes have the same distribution of test scores. What test should she use?

44. What are the null and alternative hypotheses for **Exercise 11.43**?

45. A market researcher wants to see if two different stores have the same distribution of sales throughout the year. What type of test should he use?

46. A meteorologist wants to know if East and West Australia have the same distribution of storms. What type of test should she use?

47. What condition must be met to use the test for homogeneity?

Use the following information to answer the next five exercises: Do private practice doctors and hospital doctors have the same distribution of working hours? Suppose that a sample of 100 private practice doctors and 150 hospital doctors are selected at random and asked about the number of hours a week they work. The results are shown in **Table 11.33**.

	20–30	30–40	40–50	50–60
Private Practice	16	40	38	6
Hospital	8	44	59	39

Table 11.33

48. State the null and alternative hypotheses.

49. *df* = _____

50. What is the test statistic?

51. What is the *p*-value?

52. What can you conclude at the 5% significance level?

11.5 Comparison of the Chi-Square Tests

53. Which test do you use to decide whether an observed distribution is the same as an expected distribution?

54. What is the null hypothesis for the type of test from **Exercise 11.53**?

55. Which test would you use to decide whether two factors have a relationship?

56. Which test would you use to decide if two populations have the same distribution?

57. How are tests of independence similar to tests for homogeneity?

58. How are tests of independence different from tests for homogeneity?

11.6 Test of a Single Variance

Use the following information to answer the next three exercises: An archer's standard deviation for his hits is six (data is measured in distance from the center of the target). An observer claims the standard deviation is less.

59. What type of test should be used?

60. State the null and alternative hypotheses.

61. Is this a right-tailed, left-tailed, or two-tailed test?

Use the following information to answer the next three exercises: The standard deviation of heights for students in a school is 0.81. A random sample of 50 students is taken, and the standard deviation of heights of the sample is 0.96. A researcher in charge of the study believes the standard deviation of heights for the school is greater than 0.81.

62. What type of test should be used?

63. State the null and alternative hypotheses.

64. *df* = _____

Use the following information to answer the next four exercises: The average waiting time in a doctor's office varies. The standard deviation of waiting times in a doctor's office is 3.4 minutes. A random sample of 30 patients in the doctor's office has a standard deviation of waiting times of 4.1 minutes. One doctor believes the variance of waiting times is greater than originally thought.

65. What type of test should be used?

66. What is the test statistic?

67. What is the *p*-value?

68. What can you conclude at the 5% significance level?

HOMEWORK

11.1 Facts About the Chi-Square Distribution

Decide whether the following statements are true or false.

69. As the number of degrees of freedom increases, the graph of the chi-square distribution looks more and more symmetrical.

70. The standard deviation of the chi-square distribution is twice the mean.

71. The mean and the median of the chi-square distribution are the same if *df* = 24.

11.2 Goodness-of-Fit Test

*For each problem, use a solution sheet to solve the hypothesis test problem. Go to **Appendix E** for the chi-square solution sheet. Round expected frequency to two decimal places.*

72. A six-sided die is rolled 120 times. Fill in the expected frequency column. Then, conduct a hypothesis test to determine if the die is fair. The data in **Table 11.34** are the result of the 120 rolls.

Face Value	Frequency	Expected Frequency
1	15	
2	29	
3	16	
4	15	
5	30	
6	15	

Table 11.34

73. The marital status distribution of the U.S. male population, ages 15 and older, is as shown in **Table 11.35**.

Marital Status	Percent	Expected Frequency
never married	31.3	
married	56.1	
widowed	2.5	
divorced/separated	10.1	

Table 11.35

Suppose that a random sample of 400 U.S. young adult males, 18 to 24 years old, yielded the following frequency distribution. We are interested in whether this age group of males fits the distribution of the U.S. adult population. Calculate the frequency one would expect when surveying 400 people. Fill in **Table 11.35**, rounding to two decimal places.

Marital Status	Frequency
never married	140
married	238
widowed	2
divorced/separated	20

Table 11.36

Use the following information to answer the next two exercises: The columns in **Table 11.37** contain the Race/Ethnicity of U.S. Public Schools for a recent year, the percentages for the Advanced Placement Examinee Population for that class, and the Overall Student Population. Suppose the right column contains the result of a survey of 1,000 local students from that year who took an AP Exam.

Race/Ethnicity	AP Examinee Population	Overall Student Population	Survey Frequency
Asian, Asian American, or Pacific Islander	10.2%	5.4%	113
Black or African-American	8.2%	14.5%	94
Hispanic or Latino	15.5%	15.9%	136
American Indian or Alaska Native	0.6%	1.2%	10
White	59.4%	61.6%	604
Not reported/other	6.1%	1.4%	43

Table 11.37

74. Perform a goodness-of-fit test to determine whether the local results follow the distribution of the U.S. overall student population based on ethnicity.

75. Perform a goodness-of-fit test to determine whether the local results follow the distribution of U.S. AP examinee population, based on ethnicity.

76. The City of South Lake Tahoe, CA, has an Asian population of 1,419 people, out of a total population of 23,609. Suppose that a survey of 1,419 self-reported Asians in the Manhattan, NY, area yielded the data in **Table 11.38**. Conduct a goodness-of-fit test to determine if the self-reported sub-groups of Asians in the Manhattan area fit that of the Lake Tahoe area.

Race	Lake Tahoe Frequency	Manhattan Frequency
Asian Indian	131	174
Chinese	118	557
Filipino	1,045	518
Japanese	80	54
Korean	12	29
Vietnamese	9	21
Other	24	66

Table 11.38

Use the following information to answer the next two exercises: UCLA conducted a survey of more than 263,000 college freshmen from 385 colleges in fall 2005. The results of students' expected majors by gender were reported in *The Chronicle of Higher Education (2/2/2006)*. Suppose a survey of 5,000 graduating females and 5,000 graduating males was done as a follow-up last year to determine what their actual majors were. The results are shown in the tables for **Exercise 11.77** and **Exercise 11.78**. The second column in each table does not add to 100% because of rounding.

77. Conduct a goodness-of-fit test to determine if the actual college majors of graduating females fit the distribution of their expected majors.

Major	Women - Expected Major	Women - Actual Major
Arts & Humanities	14.0%	670
Biological Sciences	8.4%	410
Business	13.1%	685
Education	13.0%	650
Engineering	2.6%	145
Physical Sciences	2.6%	125
Professional	18.9%	975
Social Sciences	13.0%	605
Technical	0.4%	15
Other	5.8%	300
Undecided	8.0%	420

Table 11.39

78. Conduct a goodness-of-fit test to determine if the actual college majors of graduating males fit the distribution of their expected majors.

Major	Men - Expected Major	Men - Actual Major
Arts & Humanities	11.0%	600
Biological Sciences	6.7%	330
Business	22.7%	1130
Education	5.8%	305
Engineering	15.6%	800
Physical Sciences	3.6%	175
Professional	9.3%	460
Social Sciences	7.6%	370
Technical	1.8%	90
Other	8.2%	400
Undecided	6.6%	340

Table 11.40

Read the statement and decide whether it is true or false.

79. In a goodness-of-fit test, the expected values are the values we would expect if the null hypothesis were true.

80. In general, if the observed values and expected values of a goodness-of-fit test are not close together, then the test statistic can get very large and on a graph will be way out in the right tail.

81. Use a goodness-of-fit test to determine if high school principals believe that students are absent equally during the week or not.

82. The test to use to determine if a six-sided die is fair is a goodness-of-fit test.

83. In a goodness-of fit test, if the *p*-value is 0.0113, in general, do not reject the null hypothesis.

84. A sample of 212 commercial businesses was surveyed for recycling one commodity; a commodity here means any one type of recyclable material such as plastic or aluminum. **Table 11.41** shows the business categories in the survey, the sample size of each category, and the number of businesses in each category that recycle one commodity. Based on the study, on average half of the businesses were expected to be recycling one commodity. As a result, the last column shows the expected number of businesses in each category that recycle one commodity. At the 5% significance level, perform a hypothesis test to determine if the observed number of businesses that recycle one commodity follows the uniform distribution of the expected values.

Business Type	Number in class	Observed Number that recycle one commodity	Expected number that recycle one commodity
Office	35	19	17.5
Retail/Wholesale	48	27	24
Food/Restaurants	53	35	26.5
Manufacturing/Medical	52	21	26
Hotel/Mixed	24	9	12

Table 11.41

85. Table 11.42 contains information from a survey among 499 participants classified according to their age groups. The second column shows the percentage of obese people per age class among the study participants. The last column comes from a different study at the national level that shows the corresponding percentages of obese people in the same age classes in the USA. Perform a hypothesis test at the 5% significance level to determine whether the survey participants are a representative sample of the USA obese population.

Age Class (Years)	Obese Expected (Percentage)	Obese-Observed (Frequencies)
20–30	22.4	122
31–40	18.6	104
41–50	12.8	78
51–60	10.4	64
61–70	35.8	168

Table 11.42

11.3 Test of Independence

*For each problem, use a solution sheet to solve the hypothesis test problem. Go to **Appendix E** for the chi-square solution sheet. Round expected frequency to two decimal places.*

86. A recent debate about where in the United States skiers believe the skiing is best prompted the following survey. Test to see if the best ski area is independent of the level of the skier.

U.S. Ski Area	Beginner	Intermediate	Advanced
Tahoe	20	30	40
Utah	10	30	60
Colorado	10	40	50

Table 11.43

87. Car manufacturers are interested in whether there is a relationship between the size of car an individual drives and the number of people in the driver's family (that is, whether car size and family size are independent). To test this, suppose that 800 car owners were randomly surveyed with the results in **Table 11.44**. Conduct a test of independence.

Family Size	Sub & Compact	Mid-size	Full-size	Van & Truck
1	20	35	40	35
2	20	50	70	80
3–4	20	50	100	90
5+	20	30	70	70

Table 11.44

88. College students may be interested in whether or not their majors have any effect on starting salaries after graduation. Suppose that 300 recent graduates were surveyed as to their majors in college and their starting salaries after graduation. **Table 11.45** shows the data. Conduct a test of independence.

Major	< $50,000	$50,000 – $68,999	$69,000 +
English	5	20	5
Engineering	10	30	60
Nursing	10	15	15
Business	10	20	30
Psychology	20	30	20

Table 11.45

89. Some travel agents claim that honeymoon hot spots vary according to age of the bride. Suppose that 280 recent brides were interviewed as to where they spent their honeymoons. The information is given in **Table 11.46**. Conduct a test of independence.

Location	20–29	30–39	40–49	50 and over
Niagara Falls	15	25	25	20
Poconos	15	25	25	10
Europe	10	25	15	5
Virgin Islands	20	25	15	5

Table 11.46

90. A manager of a sports club keeps information concerning the main sport in which members participate and their ages. To test whether there is a relationship between the age of a member and his or her choice of sport, 643 members of the sports club are randomly selected. Conduct a test of independence.

Sport	18 - 25	26 - 30	31 - 40	41 and over
racquetball	42	58	30	46
tennis	58	76	38	65
swimming	72	60	65	33

Table 11.47

91. A major food manufacturer is concerned that the sales for its skinny french fries have been decreasing. As a part of a feasibility study, the company conducts research into the types of fries sold across the country to determine if the type of fries sold is independent of the area of the country. The results of the study are shown in **Table 11.48**. Conduct a test of independence.

Type of Fries	Northeast	South	Central	West
skinny fries	70	50	20	25
curly fries	100	60	15	30
steak fries	20	40	10	10

Table 11.48

92. According to Dan Lenard, an independent insurance agent in the Buffalo, N.Y. area, the following is a breakdown of the amount of life insurance purchased by males in the following age groups. He is interested in whether the age of the male and the amount of life insurance purchased are independent events. Conduct a test for independence.

Age of Males	None	< $200,000	$200,000–$400,000	$401,001–$1,000,000	$1,000,001+
20–29	40	15	40	0	5
30–39	35	5	20	20	10
40–49	20	0	30	0	30
50+	40	30	15	15	10

Table 11.49

93. Suppose that 600 thirty-year-olds were surveyed to determine whether or not there is a relationship between the level of education an individual has and salary. Conduct a test of independence.

Annual Salary	Not a high school graduate	High school graduate	College graduate	Masters or doctorate
< $30,000	15	25	10	5
$30,000–$40,000	20	40	70	30
$40,000–$50,000	10	20	40	55
$50,000–$60,000	5	10	20	60
$60,000+	0	5	10	150

Table 11.50

Read the statement and decide whether it is true or false.

94. The number of degrees of freedom for a test of independence is equal to the sample size minus one.

95. The test for independence uses tables of observed and expected data values.

96. The test to use when determining if the college or university a student chooses to attend is related to his or her socioeconomic status is a test for independence.

97. In a test of independence, the expected number is equal to the row total multiplied by the column total divided by the total surveyed.

98. An ice cream maker performs a nationwide survey about favorite flavors of ice cream in different geographic areas of the U.S. Based on **Table 11.51**, do the numbers suggest that geographic location is independent of favorite ice cream flavors? Test at the 5% significance level.

U.S. region/ Flavor	Strawberry	Chocolate	Vanilla	Rocky Road	Mint Chocolate Chip	Pistachio	Row total
West	12	21	22	19	15	8	97
Midwest	10	32	22	11	15	6	96
East	8	31	27	8	15	7	96
South	15	28	30	8	15	6	102
Column Total	45	112	101	46	60	27	391

Table 11.51

99. **Table 11.52** provides a recent survey of the youngest online entrepreneurs whose net worth is estimated at one million dollars or more. Their ages range from 17 to 30. Each cell in the table illustrates the number of entrepreneurs who correspond to the specific age group and their net worth. Are the ages and net worth independent? Perform a test of independence at the 5% significance level.

Age Group\ Net Worth Value (in millions of US dollars)	1–5	6–24	≥25	Row Total
17–25	8	7	5	20
26–30	6	5	9	20
Column Total	14	12	14	40

Table 11.52

100. A 2013 poll in California surveyed people about taxing sugar-sweetened beverages. The results are presented in **Table 11.53**, and are classified by ethnic group and response type. Are the poll responses independent of the participants' ethnic group? Conduct a test of independence at the 5% significance level.

Opinion/ Ethnicity	Asian-American	White/Non-Hispanic	African-American	Latino	Row Total
Against tax	48	433	41	160	682
In Favor of tax	54	234	24	147	459
No opinion	16	43	16	19	94
Column Total	118	710	81	326	1235

Table 11.53

11.4 Test for Homogeneity

*For each word problem, use a solution sheet to solve the hypothesis test problem. Go to **Appendix E** for the chi-square solution sheet. Round expected frequency to two decimal places.*

101. A psychologist is interested in testing whether there is a difference in the distribution of personality types for business majors and social science majors. The results of the study are shown in **Table 11.54**. Conduct a test of homogeneity. Test at a 5% level of significance.

	Open	Conscientious	Extrovert	Agreeable	Neurotic
Business	41	52	46	61	58
Social Science	72	75	63	80	65

Table 11.54

102. Do men and women select different breakfasts? The breakfasts ordered by randomly selected men and women at a popular breakfast place is shown in **Table 11.55**. Conduct a test for homogeneity at a 5% level of significance.

	French Toast	Pancakes	Waffles	Omelettes
Men	47	35	28	53
Women	65	59	55	60

Table 11.55

103. A fisherman is interested in whether the distribution of fish caught in Green Valley Lake is the same as the distribution of fish caught in Echo Lake. Of the 191 randomly selected fish caught in Green Valley Lake, 105 were rainbow trout, 27 were other trout, 35 were bass, and 24 were catfish. Of the 293 randomly selected fish caught in Echo Lake, 115 were rainbow trout, 58 were other trout, 67 were bass, and 53 were catfish. Perform a test for homogeneity at a 5% level of significance.

104. In 2007, the United States had 1.5 million homeschooled students, according to the U.S. National Center for Education Statistics. In **Table 11.56** you can see that parents decide to homeschool their children for different reasons, and some reasons are ranked by parents as more important than others. According to the survey results shown in the table, is the distribution of applicable reasons the same as the distribution of the most important reason? Provide your assessment at the 5% significance level. Did you expect the result you obtained?

Reasons for Homeschooling	Applicable Reason (in thousands of respondents)	Most Important Reason (in thousands of respondents)	Row Total
Concern about the environment of other schools	1,321	309	1,630
Dissatisfaction with academic instruction at other schools	1,096	258	1,354
To provide religious or moral instruction	1,257	540	1,797
Child has special needs, other than physical or mental	315	55	370
Nontraditional approach to child's education	984	99	1,083
Other reasons (e.g., finances, travel, family time, etc.)	485	216	701
Column Total	5,458	1,477	6,935

Table 11.56

105. When looking at energy consumption, we are often interested in detecting trends over time and how they correlate among different countries. The information in **Table 11.57** shows the average energy use (in units of kg of oil equivalent per capita) in the USA and the joint European Union countries (EU) for the six-year period 2005 to 2010. Do the energy use values in these two areas come from the same distribution? Perform the analysis at the 5% significance level.

Year	European Union	United States	Row Total
2010	3,413	7,164	10,557
2009	3,302	7,057	10,359
2008	3,505	7,488	10,993
2007	3,537	7,758	11,295
2006	3,595	7,697	11,292
2005	3,613	7,847	11,460
Column Total	20,965	45,011	65,976

Table 11.57

106. The Insurance Institute for Highway Safety collects safety information about all types of cars every year, and publishes a report of Top Safety Picks among all cars, makes, and models. **Table 11.58** presents the number of Top Safety Picks in six car categories for the two years 2009 and 2013. Analyze the table data to conclude whether the distribution of cars that earned the Top Safety Picks safety award has remained the same between 2009 and 2013. Derive your results at the 5% significance level.

Year \ Car Type	Small	Mid-Size	Large	Small SUV	Mid-Size SUV	Large SUV	Row Total
2009	12	22	10	10	27	6	87
2013	31	30	19	11	29	4	124
Column Total	43	52	29	21	56	10	211

Table 11.58

11.5 Comparison of the Chi-Square Tests

*For each word problem, use a solution sheet to solve the hypothesis test problem. Go to **Appendix E** for the chi-square solution sheet. Round expected frequency to two decimal places.*

107. Is there a difference between the distribution of community college statistics students and the distribution of university statistics students in what technology they use on their homework? Of some randomly selected community college students, 43 used a computer, 102 used a calculator with built in statistics functions, and 65 used a table from the textbook. Of some randomly selected university students, 28 used a computer, 33 used a calculator with built in statistics functions, and 40 used a table from the textbook. Conduct an appropriate hypothesis test using a 0.05 level of significance.

Read the statement and decide whether it is true or false.

108. If $df = 2$, the chi-square distribution has a shape that reminds us of the exponential.

11.6 Test of a Single Variance

Use the following information to answer the next twelve exercises: Suppose an airline claims that its flights are consistently on time with an average delay of at most 15 minutes. It claims that the average delay is so consistent that the variance is no more than 150 minutes. Doubting the consistency part of the claim, a disgruntled traveler calculates the delays for his next 25 flights. The average delay for those 25 flights is 22 minutes with a standard deviation of 15 minutes.

109. Is the traveler disputing the claim about the average or about the variance?

110. A sample standard deviation of 15 minutes is the same as a sample variance of _____ minutes.

111. Is this a right-tailed, left-tailed, or two-tailed test?

112. H_0: _____

113. $df =$ _____

114. chi-square test statistic = _____

115. p-value = _____

116. Graph the situation. Label and scale the horizontal axis. Mark the mean and test statistic. Shade the p-value.

117. Let $\alpha = 0.05$
Decision: _____
Conclusion (write out in a complete sentence.): _____

118. How did you know to test the variance instead of the mean?

119. If an additional test were done on the claim of the average delay, which distribution would you use?

120. If an additional test were done on the claim of the average delay, but 45 flights were surveyed, which distribution would you use?

*For each word problem, use a solution sheet to solve the hypothesis test problem. Go to **Appendix E** for the chi-square solution sheet. Round expected frequency to two decimal places.*

121. A plant manager is concerned her equipment may need recalibrating. It seems that the actual weight of the 15 oz. cereal boxes it fills has been fluctuating. The standard deviation should be at most 0.5 oz. In order to determine if the machine needs to be recalibrated, 84 randomly selected boxes of cereal from the next day's production were weighed. The standard deviation of the 84 boxes was 0.54. Does the machine need to be recalibrated?

122. Consumers may be interested in whether the cost of a particular calculator varies from store to store. Based on surveying 43 stores, which yielded a sample mean of $84 and a sample standard deviation of $12, test the claim that the standard deviation is greater than $15.

123. Isabella, an accomplished **Bay to Breakers** runner, claims that the standard deviation for her time to run the 7.5 mile race is at most three minutes. To test her claim, Rupinder looks up five of her race times. They are 55 minutes, 61 minutes, 58 minutes, 63 minutes, and 57 minutes.

124. Airline companies are interested in the consistency of the number of babies on each flight, so that they have adequate safety equipment. They are also interested in the variation of the number of babies. Suppose that an airline executive believes the average number of babies on flights is six with a variance of nine at most. The airline conducts a survey. The results of the 18 flights surveyed give a sample average of 6.4 with a sample standard deviation of 3.9. Conduct a hypothesis test of the airline executive's belief.

125. The number of births per woman in China is 1.6 down from 5.91 in 1966. This fertility rate has been attributed to the law passed in 1979 restricting births to one per woman. Suppose that a group of students studied whether or not the standard deviation of births per woman was greater than 0.75. They asked 50 women across China the number of births they had had. The results are shown in **Table 11.59**. Does the students' survey indicate that the standard deviation is greater than 0.75?

# of births	Frequency
0	5
1	30
2	10
3	5

Table 11.59

126. According to an avid aquarist, the average number of fish in a 20-gallon tank is 10, with a standard deviation of two. His friend, also an aquarist, does not believe that the standard deviation is two. She counts the number of fish in 15 other 20-gallon tanks. Based on the results that follow, do you think that the standard deviation is different from two? Data: 11; 10; 9; 10; 10; 11; 11; 10; 12; 9; 7; 9; 11; 10; 11

127. The manager of "Frenchies" is concerned that patrons are not consistently receiving the same amount of French fries with each order. The chef claims that the standard deviation for a ten-ounce order of fries is at most 1.5 oz., but the manager thinks that it may be higher. He randomly weighs 49 orders of fries, which yields a mean of 11 oz. and a standard deviation of two oz.

128. You want to buy a specific computer. A sales representative of the manufacturer claims that retail stores sell this computer at an average price of $1,249 with a very narrow standard deviation of $25. You find a website that has a price comparison for the same computer at a series of stores as follows: $1,299; $1,229.99; $1,193.08; $1,279; $1,224.95; $1,229.99; $1,269.95; $1,249. Can you argue that pricing has a larger standard deviation than claimed by the manufacturer? Use the 5% significance level. As a potential buyer, what would be the practical conclusion from your analysis?

129. A company packages apples by weight. One of the weight grades is Class A apples. Class A apples have a mean weight of 150 g, and there is a maximum allowed weight tolerance of 5% above or below the mean for apples in the same consumer package. A batch of apples is selected to be included in a Class A apple package. Given the following apple weights of the batch, does the fruit comply with the Class A grade weight tolerance requirements. Conduct an appropriate hypothesis test.

(a) at the 5% significance level

(b) at the 1% significance level

Weights in selected apple batch (in grams): 158; 167; 149; 169; 164; 139; 154; 150; 157; 171; 152; 161; 141; 166; 172;

BRINGING IT TOGETHER: HOMEWORK

130.

    a. Explain why a goodness-of-fit test and a test of independence are generally right-tailed tests.

    b. If you did a left-tailed test, what would you be testing?

REFERENCES

11.1 Facts About the Chi-Square Distribution

Data from *Parade Magazine*.

"HIV/AIDS Epidemiology Santa Clara County."Santa Clara County Public Health Department, May 2011.

11.2 Goodness-of-Fit Test

Data from the U.S. Census Bureau

Data from the College Board. Available online at http://www.collegeboard.com.

Data from the U.S. Census Bureau, Current Population Reports.

Ma, Y., E.R. Bertone, E.J. Stanek III, G.W. Reed, J.R. Hebert, N.L. Cohen, P.A. Merriam, I.S. Ockene, "Association between Eating Patterns and Obesity in a Free-living US Adult Population." *American Journal of Epidemiology* volume 158, no. 1, pages 85-92.

Ogden, Cynthia L., Margaret D. Carroll, Brian K. Kit, Katherine M. Flegal, "Prevalence of Obesity in the United States, 2009–2010." NCHS Data Brief no. 82, January 2012. Available online at http://www.cdc.gov/nchs/data/databriefs/db82.pdf (accessed May 24, 2013).

Stevens, Barbara J., "Multi-family and Commercial Solid Waste and Recycling Survey." Arlington Count, VA. Available online at http://www.arlingtonva.us/departments/EnvironmentalServices/SW/file84429.pdf (accessed May 24,2013).

11.3 Test of Independence

DiCamilo, Mark, Mervin Field, "Most Californians See a Direct Linkage between Obesity and Sugary Sodas. Two in Three Voters Support Taxing Sugar-Sweetened Beverages If Proceeds are Tied to Improving School Nutrition and Physical Activity Programs." The Field Poll, released Feb. 14, 2013. Available online at http://field.com/fieldpollonline/subscribers/Rls2436.pdf (accessed May 24, 2013).

Harris Interactive, "Favorite Flavor of Ice Cream." Available online at http://www.statisticbrain.com/favorite-flavor-of-ice-cream (accessed May 24, 2013)

"Youngest Online Entrepreneurs List." Available online at http://www.statisticbrain.com/youngest-online-entrepreneur-list (accessed May 24, 2013).

11.4 Test for Homogeneity

Data from the Insurance Institute for Highway Safety, 2013. Available online at www.iihs.org/iihs/ratings (accessed May 24, 2013).

"Energy use (kg of oil equivalent per capita)." The World Bank, 2013. Available online at http://data.worldbank.org/indicator/EG.USE.PCAP.KG.OE/countries (accessed May 24, 2013).

"Parent and Family Involvement Survey of 2007 National Household Education Survey Program (NHES)," U.S. Department of Education, National Center for Education Statistics. Available online at http://nces.ed.gov/pubsearch/pubsinfo.asp?pubid=2009030 (accessed May 24, 2013).

"Parent and Family Involvement Survey of 2007 National Household Education Survey Program (NHES)," U.S. Department of Education, National Center for Education Statistics. Available online at http://nces.ed.gov/pubs2009/

2009030_sup.pdf (accessed May 24, 2013).

11.6 Test of a Single Variance

"AppleInsider Price Guides." Apple Insider, 2013. Available online at http://appleinsider.com/mac_price_guide (accessed May 14, 2013).

Data from the World Bank, June 5, 2012.

SOLUTIONS

1 mean = 25 and standard deviation = 7.0711

3 when the number of degrees of freedom is greater than 90

5 $df = 2$

7 a goodness-of-fit test

9 3

11 2.04

13 We decline to reject the null hypothesis. There is not enough evidence to suggest that the observed test scores are significantly different from the expected test scores.

15 H_0: the distribution of AIDS cases follows the ethnicities of the general population of Santa Clara County.

17 right-tailed

19 2016.136

21 Graph: Check student's solution. Decision: Reject the null hypothesis. Reason for the Decision: p-value < alpha Conclusion (write out in complete sentences): The make-up of AIDS cases does not fit the ethnicities of the general population of Santa Clara County.

23 a test of independence

25 a test of independence

27 8

29 6.6

31 0.0435

33

Smoking Level Per Day	African American	Native Hawaiian	Latino	Japanese Americans	White	Totals
1-10	9,886	2,745	12,831	8,378	7,650	41,490
11-20	6,514	3,062	4,932	10,680	9,877	35,065
21-30	1,671	1,419	1,406	4,715	6,062	15,273
31+	759	788	800	2,305	3,970	8,622
Totals	18,830	8,014	19,969	26,078	27,559	10,0450

Table 11.60

35

Smoking Level Per Day	African American	Native Hawaiian	Latino	Japanese Americans	White
1-10	7777.57	3310.11	8248.02	10771.29	11383.01
11-20	6573.16	2797.52	6970.76	9103.29	9620.27
21-30	2863.02	1218.49	3036.20	3965.05	4190.23
31+	1616.25	687.87	1714.01	2238.37	2365.49

Table 11.61

37 10,301.8

39 right

41
  a.   Reject the null hypothesis.

  b.   *p*-value < alpha

  c.   There is sufficient evidence to conclude that smoking level is dependent on ethnic group.

43 test for homogeneity

45 test for homogeneity

47 All values in the table must be greater than or equal to five.

49 3

51 0.00005

53 a goodness-of-fit test

55 a test for independence

57 Answers will vary. Sample answer: Tests of independence and tests for homogeneity both calculate the test statistic the same way $\sum\limits_{(i\,j)} \frac{(O - E)^2}{E}$. In addition, all values must be greater than or equal to five.

59 a test of a single variance

61 a left-tailed test

63 H_0: $\sigma^2 = 0.81^2$; H_a: $\sigma^2 > 0.81^2$

65 a test of a single variance

67 0.0542

69 true

71 false

73

Marital Status	Percent	Expected Frequency
never married	31.3	125.2
married	56.1	224.4
widowed	2.5	10
divorced/separated	10.1	40.4

Table 11.62

a. The data fits the distribution.

b. The data does not fit the distribution.

c. 3

d. chi-square distribution with $df = 3$

e. 19.27

f. 0.0002

g. Check student's solution.

h.   i.   Alpha = 0.05

  ii.   Decision: Reject null

  iii.   Reason for decision: p-value < alpha

  iv.   Conclusion: Data does not fit the distribution.

75

a. H_0: The local results follow the distribution of the U.S. AP examinee population

b. H_a: The local results do not follow the distribution of the U.S. AP examinee population

c. $df = 5$

d. chi-square distribution with $df = 5$

e. chi-square test statistic = 13.4

f. p-value = 0.0199

g. Check student's solution.

h.   i.   Alpha = 0.05

  ii.   Decision: Reject null when $a = 0.05$

  iii.   Reason for Decision: p-value < alpha

  iv.   Conclusion: Local data do not fit the AP Examinee Distribution.

  v.   Decision: Do not reject null when $a = 0.01$

  vi.   Conclusion: There is insufficient evidence to conclude that local data do not follow the distribution of the U.S. AP examinee distribution.

77

a. H_0: The actual college majors of graduating females fit the distribution of their expected majors

b. H_a: The actual college majors of graduating females do not fit the distribution of their expected majors

c. $df = 10$

d. chi-square distribution with $df = 10$

e. test statistic = 11.48

f. *p*-value = 0.3211

g. Check student's solution.

h. i.   Alpha = 0.05

   ii.   Decision: Do not reject null when *a* = 0.05 and *a* = 0.01

   iii. Reason for decision: *p*-value > alpha

   iv.   Conclusion: There is insufficient evidence to conclude that the distribution of actual college majors of graduating females do not fit the distribution of their expected majors.

79 true

81 true

83 false

85

a. H_0: Surveyed obese fit the distribution of expected obese

b. H_a: Surveyed obese do not fit the distribution of expected obese

c. *df* = 4

d. chi-square distribution with *df* = 4

e. test statistic = 507.6

f. *p*-value = 0

g. Check student's solution.

h. i.   Alpha: 0.05

   ii.   Decision: Reject the null hypothesis.

   iii. Reason for decision: *p*-value < alpha

   iv.   Conclusion: At the 5% level of significance, from the data, there is sufficient evidence to conclude that the surveyed obese do not fit the distribution of expected obese.

87

a. H_0: Car size is independent of family size.

b. H_a: Car size is dependent on family size.

c. *df* = 9

d. chi-square distribution with *df* = 9

e. test statistic = 15.8284

f. *p*-value = 0.0706

g. Check student's solution.

h. i.   Alpha: 0.05

   ii.   Decision: Do not reject the null hypothesis.

   iii. Reason for decision: *p*-value > alpha

   iv.   Conclusion: At the 5% significance level, there is insufficient evidence to conclude that car size and family size are dependent.

89

a. H_0: Honeymoon locations are independent of bride's age.

b. H_a: Honeymoon locations are dependent on bride's age.

c. *df* = 9

d. chi-square distribution with $df = 9$

e. test statistic = 15.7027

f. p-value = 0.0734

g. Check student's solution.

h.   i. Alpha: 0.05

    ii. Decision: Do not reject the null hypothesis.

    iii. Reason for decision: p-value > alpha

    iv. Conclusion: At the 5% significance level, there is insufficient evidence to conclude that honeymoon location and bride age are dependent.

91

a. H_0: The types of fries sold are independent of the location.

b. H_a: The types of fries sold are dependent on the location.

c. $df = 6$

d. chi-square distribution with $df = 6$

e. test statistic =18.8369

f. p-value = 0.0044

g. Check student's solution.

h.   i. Alpha: 0.05

    ii. Decision: Reject the null hypothesis.

    iii. Reason for decision: p-value < alpha

    iv. Conclusion: At the 5% significance level, There is sufficient evidence that types of fries and location are dependent.

93

a. H_0: Salary is independent of level of education.

b. H_a: Salary is dependent on level of education.

c. $df = 12$

d. chi-square distribution with $df = 12$

e. test statistic = 255.7704

f. p-value = 0

g. Check student's solution.

h. Alpha: 0.05

Decision: Reject the null hypothesis.

Reason for decision: p-value < alpha

Conclusion: At the 5% significance level, there is sufficient evidence to conclude that salary and level of education are dependent.

95 true

97 true

99

a. H_0: Age is independent of the youngest online entrepreneurs' net worth.

b. H_a: Age is dependent on the net worth of the youngest online entrepreneurs.

c. $df = 2$

   d. chi-square distribution with $df = 2$

   e. test statistic = 1.76

   f. *p*-value 0.4144

   g. Check student's solution.

   h.   i. Alpha: 0.05

       ii. Decision: Do not reject the null hypothesis.

       iii. Reason for decision: *p*-value > alpha

       iv. Conclusion: At the 5% significance level, there is insufficient evidence to conclude that age and net worth for the youngest online entrepreneurs are dependent.

101

   a. H_0: The distribution for personality types is the same for both majors

   b. H_a: The distribution for personality types is not the same for both majors

   c. $df = 4$

   d. chi-square with $df = 4$

   e. test statistic = 3.01

   f. *p*-value = 0.5568

   g. Check student's solution.

   h.   i. Alpha: 0.05

       ii. Decision: Do not reject the null hypothesis.

       iii. Reason for decision: *p*-value > alpha

       iv. Conclusion: There is insufficient evidence to conclude that the distribution of personality types is different for business and social science majors.

103

   a. H_0: The distribution for fish caught is the same in Green Valley Lake and in Echo Lake.

   b. H_a: The distribution for fish caught is not the same in Green Valley Lake and in Echo Lake.

   c. 3

   d. chi-square with $df = 3$

   e. 11.75

   f. *p*-value = 0.0083

   g. Check student's solution.

   h.   i. Alpha: 0.05

       ii. Decision: Reject the null hypothesis.

       iii. Reason for decision: *p*-value < alpha

       iv. Conclusion: There is evidence to conclude that the distribution of fish caught is different in Green Valley Lake and in Echo Lake

105

   a. H_0: The distribution of average energy use in the USA is the same as in Europe between 2005 and 2010.

   b. H_a: The distribution of average energy use in the USA is not the same as in Europe between 2005 and 2010.

   c. $df = 4$

   d. chi-square with $df = 4$

   e. test statistic = 2.7434

    f. p-value = 0.7395

    g.   Check student's solution.

    h.   i.   Alpha: 0.05

         ii.   Decision: Do not reject the null hypothesis.

         iii.   Reason for decision: p-value > alpha

         iv.   Conclusion: At the 5% significance level, there is insufficient evidence to conclude that the average energy use values in the US and EU are not derived from different distributions for the period from 2005 to 2010.

107

    a. H_0: The distribution for technology use is the same for community college students and university students.

    b. H_a: The distribution for technology use is not the same for community college students and university students.

    c.   2

    d.   chi-square with $df = 2$

    e.   7.05

    f. p-value = 0.0294

    g.   Check student's solution.

    h.   i.   Alpha: 0.05

         ii.   Decision: Reject the null hypothesis.

         iii.   Reason for decision: p-value < alpha

         iv.   Conclusion: There is sufficient evidence to conclude that the distribution of technology use for statistics homework is not the same for statistics students at community colleges and at universities.

110 225

112 H_0: $\sigma^2 \le 150$

114 36

116 Check student's solution.

118 The claim is that the variance is no more than 150 minutes.

120 a Student's t- or normal distribution

122

    a. H_0: $\sigma = 15$

    b. H_a: $\sigma > 15$

    c. $df = 42$

    d.   chi-square with $df = 42$

    e.   test statistic = 26.88

    f. p-value = 0.9663

    g.   Check student's solution.

    h.   i.   Alpha = 0.05

         ii.   Decision: Do not reject null hypothesis.

         iii.   Reason for decision: p-value > alpha

         iv.   Conclusion: There is insufficient evidence to conclude that the standard deviation is greater than 15.

124

    a. H_0: $\sigma \le 3$

    b. H_a: $\sigma > 3$

c. $df = 17$

d. chi-square distribution with $df = 17$

e. test statistic = 28.73

f. p-value = 0.0371

g. Check student's solution.

h.   i. Alpha: 0.05

    ii. Decision: Reject the null hypothesis.

    iii. Reason for decision: p-value < alpha

    iv. Conclusion: There is sufficient evidence to conclude that the standard deviation is greater than three.

126

a. H_0: $\sigma = 2$

b. H_a: $\sigma \neq 2$

c. $df = 14$

d. chi-square distiribution with $df = 14$

e. chi-square test statistic = 5.2094

f. p-value = 0.0346

g. Check student's solution.

h.   i. Alpha = 0.05

    ii. Decision: Reject the null hypothesis

    iii. Reason for decision: p-value < alpha

    iv. Conclusion: There is sufficient evidence to conclude that the standard deviation is different than 2.

128 The sample standard deviation is \$34.29. $H_0 : \sigma^2 = 25^2$
$H_a : \sigma^2 > 25^2$
$df = n - 1 = 7.$

test statistic: $x^2 = \quad x_7^2 = \quad \dfrac{(n-1)s^2}{25^2} = \quad \dfrac{(8-1)(34.29)^2}{25^2} = 13.169$;

p-value: $P\left(x_7^2 > 13.169\right) = 1 - P\left(x_7^2 \leq 13.169\right) = 0.0681$

Alpha: 0.05
Decision: Do not reject the null hypothesis.
Reason for decision: p-value > alpha
Conclusion: At the 5% level, there is insufficient evidence to conclude that the variance is more than 625.

130

a. The test statistic is always positive and if the expected and observed values are not close together, the test statistic is large and the null hypothesis will be rejected.

b. Testing to see if the data fits the distribution "too well" or is too perfect.

12 | LINEAR REGRESSION AND CORRELATION

Figure 12.1 Linear regression and correlation can help you determine if an auto mechanic's salary is related to his work experience. (credit: Joshua Rothhaas)

Introduction

Chapter Objectives
By the end of this chapter, the student should be able to: • Discuss basic ideas of linear regression and correlation. • Create and interpret a line of best fit. • Calculate and interpret the correlation coefficient. • Calculate and interpret outliers.

Professionals often want to know how two or more numeric variables are related. For example, is there a relationship between the grade on the second math exam a student takes and the grade on the final exam? If there is a relationship, what is the relationship and how strong is it?

In another example, your income may be determined by your education, your profession, your years of experience, and your ability. The amount you pay a repair person for labor is often determined by an initial amount plus an hourly fee.

The type of data described in the examples is **bivariate** data — "bi" for two variables. In reality, statisticians use **multivariate** data, meaning many variables.

In this chapter, you will be studying the simplest form of regression, "linear regression" with one independent variable (x). This involves data that fits a line in two dimensions. You will also study correlation which measures how strong the relationship is.

12.1 | Linear Equations

Linear regression for two variables is based on a linear equation with one independent variable. The equation has the form:

$$y = a + \mathrm{bx}$$

where a and b are constant numbers.

The variable x **is the independent variable, and y is the dependent variable.** Typically, you choose a value to substitute for the independent variable and then solve for the dependent variable.

Example 12.1

The following examples are linear equations.

$$y = 3 + 2\mathrm{x}$$
$$y = -0.01 + 1.2\mathrm{x}$$

Try It Σ

12.1 Is the following an example of a linear equation?

$y = -0.125 - 3.5x$

The graph of a linear equation of the form $y = a + bx$ is a **straight line**. Any line that is not vertical can be described by this equation.

Example 12.2

Graph the equation $y = -1 + 2x$.

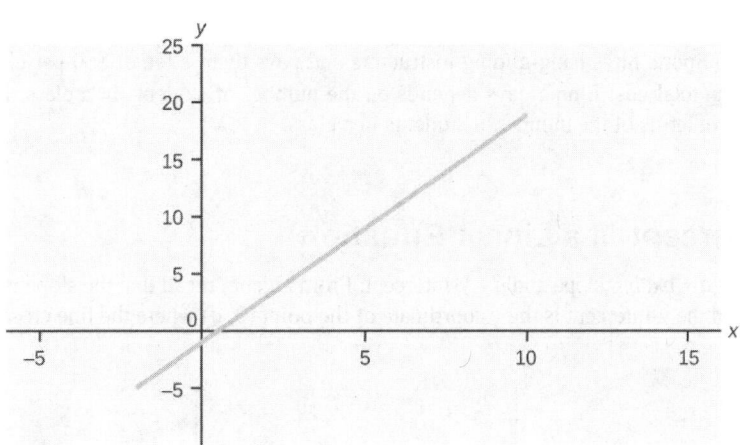

Figure 12.2

Try It Σ

12.2 Is the following an example of a linear equation? Why or why not?

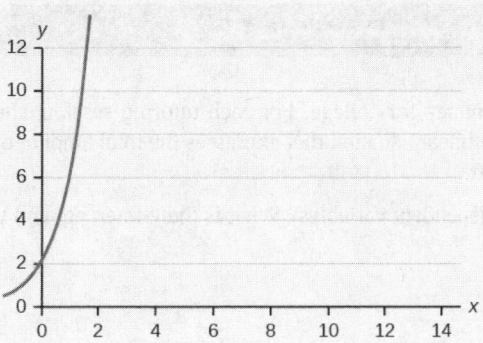

Figure 12.3

Example 12.3

Aaron's Word Processing Service (AWPS) does word processing. The rate for services is $32 per hour plus a $31.50 one-time charge. The total cost to a customer depends on the number of hours it takes to complete the job.

Find the equation that expresses the **total cost** in terms of the **number of hours** required to complete the job.

Solution 12.3

Let x = the number of hours it takes to get the job done.
Let y = the total cost to the customer.

The $31.50 is a fixed cost. If it takes x hours to complete the job, then $(32)(x)$ is the cost of the word processing only. The total cost is: $y = 31.50 + 32x$

12.3 Emma's Extreme Sports hires hang-gliding instructors and pays them a fee of $50 per class as well as $20 per student in the class. The total cost Emma pays depends on the number of students in a class. Find the equation that expresses the total cost in terms of the number of students in a class.

Slope and *Y*-Intercept of a Linear Equation

For the linear equation $y = a + bx$, b = slope and a = y-intercept. From algebra recall that the slope is a number that describes the steepness of a line, and the y-intercept is the y coordinate of the point $(0, a)$ where the line crosses the y-axis.

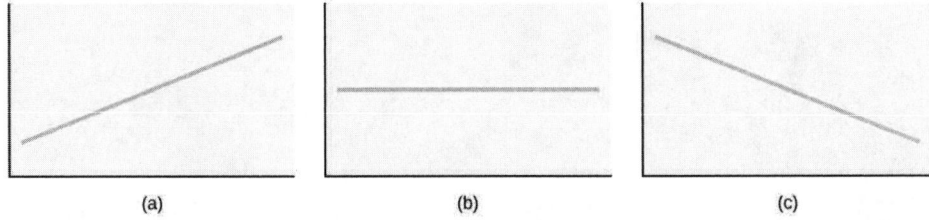

Figure 12.4 Three possible graphs of $y = a + bx$. (a) If $b > 0$, the line slopes upward to the right. (b) If $b = 0$, the line is horizontal. (c) If $b < 0$, the line slopes downward to the right.

Example 12.4

Svetlana tutors to make extra money for college. For each tutoring session, she charges a one-time fee of $25 plus $15 per hour of tutoring. A linear equation that expresses the total amount of money Svetlana earns for each session she tutors is $y = 25 + 15x$.

What are the independent and dependent variables? What is the y-intercept and what is the slope? Interpret them using complete sentences.

Solution 12.4

The independent variable (x) is the number of hours Svetlana tutors each session. The dependent variable (y) is the amount, in dollars, Svetlana earns for each session.

The y-intercept is 25 $(a = 25)$. At the start of the tutoring session, Svetlana charges a one-time fee of $25 (this is when $x = 0$). The slope is 15 $(b = 15)$. For each session, Svetlana earns $15 for each hour she tutors.

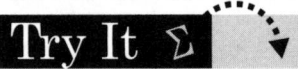

12.4 Ethan repairs household appliances like dishwashers and refrigerators. For each visit, he charges $25 plus $20 per hour of work. A linear equation that expresses the total amount of money Ethan earns per visit is $y = 25 + 20x$.

What are the independent and dependent variables? What is the y-intercept and what is the slope? Interpret them using complete sentences.

12.2 | Scatter Plots

Before we take up the discussion of linear regression and correlation, we need to examine a way to display the relation between two variables x and y. The most common and easiest way is a **scatter plot**. The following example illustrates a scatter plot.

Example 12.5

In Europe and Asia, m-commerce is popular. M-commerce users have special mobile phones that work like electronic wallets as well as provide phone and Internet services. Users can do everything from paying for parking to buying a TV set or soda from a machine to banking to checking sports scores on the Internet. For the years 2000 through 2004, was there a relationship between the year and the number of m-commerce users? Construct a scatter plot. Let x = the year and let y = the number of m-commerce users, in millions.

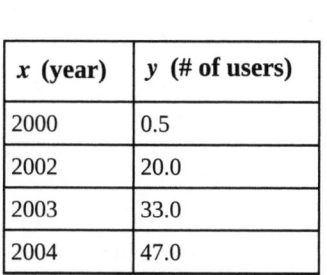

x (year)	y (# of users)
2000	0.5
2002	20.0
2003	33.0
2004	47.0

Table 12.1

(a) Table showing the number of m-commerce users (in millions) by year.

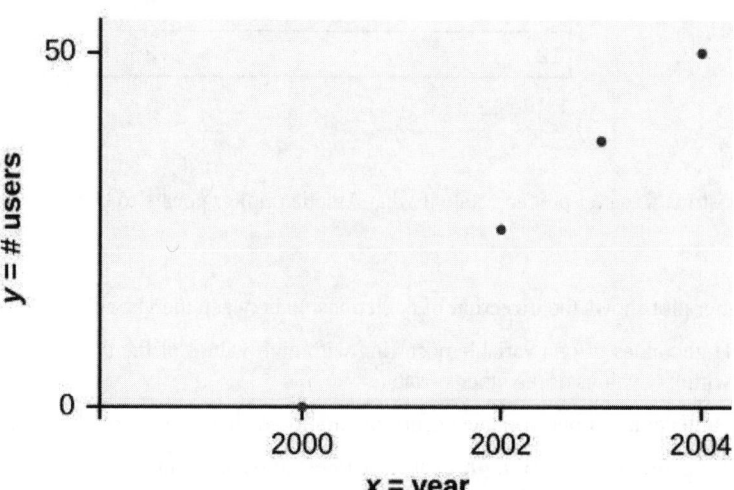

(b) Scatter plot showing the number of m-commerce users (in millions) by year.

Figure 12.5

 ## Using the TI-83, 83+, 84, 84+ Calculator

To create a scatter plot:

1. Enter your X data into list L1 and your Y data into list L2.

2. Press 2nd STATPLOT ENTER to use Plot 1. On the input screen for PLOT 1, highlight On and press ENTER. (Make sure the other plots are OFF.)

3. For TYPE: highlight the very first icon, which is the scatter plot, and press ENTER.

4. For Xlist:, enter L1 ENTER and for Ylist: L2 ENTER.

5. For Mark: it does not matter which symbol you highlight, but the square is the easiest to see. Press ENTER.

6. Make sure there are no other equations that could be plotted. Press Y = and clear any equations out.

7. Press the ZOOM key and then the number 9 (for menu item "ZoomStat") ; the calculator will fit the window to the data. You can press WINDOW to see the scaling of the axes.

 ## Try It ∑

12.5 Amelia plays basketball for her high school. She wants to improve to play at the college level. She notices that the number of points she scores in a game goes up in response to the number of hours she practices her jump shot each week. She records the following data:

X (hours practicing jump shot)	Y (points scored in a game)
5	15
7	22
9	28
10	31
11	33
12	36

Table 12.2

Construct a scatter plot and state if what Amelia thinks appears to be true.

A scatter plot shows the **direction** of a relationship between the variables. A clear direction happens when there is either:

- High values of one variable occurring with high values of the other variable or low values of one variable occurring with low values of the other variable.

- High values of one variable occurring with low values of the other variable.

You can determine the **strength** of the relationship by looking at the scatter plot and seeing how close the points are to a line, a power function, an exponential function, or to some other type of function. For a linear relationship there is an exception. Consider a scatter plot where all the points fall on a horizontal line providing a "perfect fit." The horizontal line would in fact show no relationship.

When you look at a scatterplot, you want to notice the **overall pattern** and any **deviations** from the pattern. The following scatterplot examples illustrate these concepts.

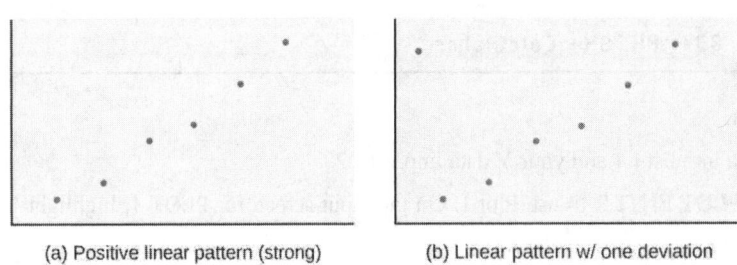

(a) Positive linear pattern (strong)   (b) Linear pattern w/ one deviation

Figure 12.6

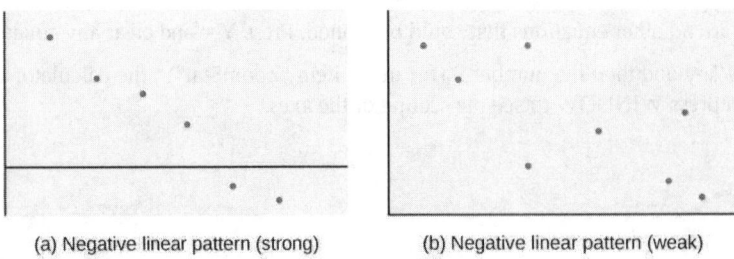

(a) Negative linear pattern (strong)   (b) Negative linear pattern (weak)

Figure 12.7

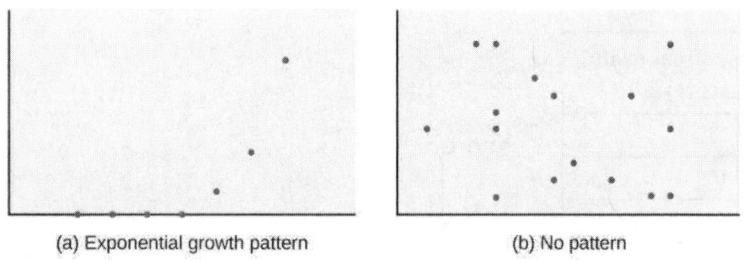

(a) Exponential growth pattern   (b) No pattern

Figure 12.8

In this chapter, we are interested in scatter plots that show a linear pattern. Linear patterns are quite common. The linear relationship is strong if the points are close to a straight line, except in the case of a horizontal line where there is no relationship. If we think that the points show a linear relationship, we would like to draw a line on the scatter plot. This line can be calculated through a process called **linear regression**. However, we only calculate a regression line if one of the variables helps to explain or predict the other variable. If x is the independent variable and y the dependent variable, then we can use a regression line to predict y for a given value of x

12.3 | The Regression Equation

Data rarely fit a straight line exactly. Usually, you must be satisfied with rough predictions. Typically, you have a set of data whose scatter plot appears to **"fit"** a straight line. This is called a **Line of Best Fit or Least-Squares Line**.

Collaborative Exercise

If you know a person's pinky (smallest) finger length, do you think you could predict that person's height? Collect data from your class (pinky finger length, in inches). The independent variable, x, is pinky finger length and the dependent variable, y, is height. For each set of data, plot the points on graph paper. Make your graph big enough and **use a ruler**. Then "by eye" draw a line that appears to "fit" the data. For your line, pick two convenient points and use them to find the slope of the line. Find the y-intercept of the line by extending your line so it crosses the y-axis. Using the slopes and the y-intercepts, write your equation of "best fit." Do you think everyone will have the same equation? Why or why not? According to your equation, what is the predicted height for a pinky length of 2.5 inches?

Example 12.6

A random sample of 11 statistics students produced the following data, where x is the third exam score out of 80, and y is the final exam score out of 200. Can you predict the final exam score of a random student if you know the third exam score?

x (third exam score)	y (final exam score)
65	175
67	133
71	185
71	163
66	126
75	198
67	153
70	163
71	159
69	151
69	159

Table 12.3

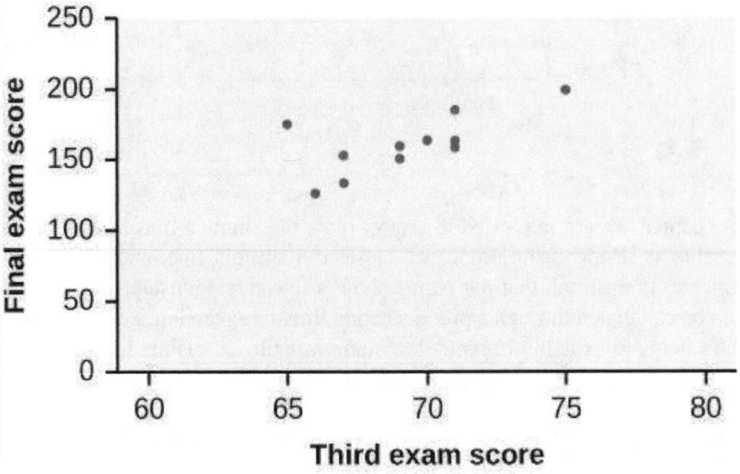

(b) Scatter plot showing the scores on the final exam based on scores from the third exam.

(a) Table showing the scores on the final exam based on scores from the third exam.

Figure 12.9

Try It Σ

☞ **12.6** SCUBA divers have maximum dive times they cannot exceed when going to different depths. The data in **Table 12.4** show different depths with the maximum dive times in minutes. Use your calculator to find the least squares regression line and predict the maximum dive time for 110 feet.

X (depth in feet)	Y (maximum dive time)
50	80
60	55
70	45
80	35
90	25
100	22

Table 12.4

The third exam score, x, is the independent variable and the final exam score, y, is the dependent variable. We will plot a regression line that best "fits" the data. If each of you were to fit a line "by eye," you would draw different lines. We can use what is called a **least-squares regression line** to obtain the best fit line.

Consider the following diagram. Each point of data is of the the form (x, y) and each point ofthe line of best fit using least-squares linear regression has the form $(x, \hat{y})$.

The $\hat{y}$ is read **"y hat"** and is the **estimated value of y**. It is the value of y obtained using the regression line. It is not generally equal to y from data.

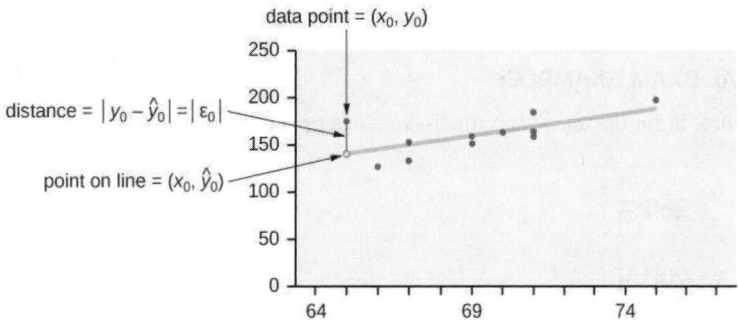

Figure 12.10

The term $y_0 - \hat{y}_0 = \varepsilon_0$ is called the **"error" or residual**. It is not an error in the sense of a mistake. The **absolute value of a residual** measures the vertical distance between the actual value of y and the estimated value of y. In other words, it measures the vertical distance between the actual data point and the predicted point on the line.

If the observed data point lies above the line, the residual is positive, and the line underestimates the actual data value for y. If the observed data point lies below the line, the residual is negative, and the line overestimates that actual data value for y.

In the diagram in **Figure 12.10**, $y_0 - \hat{y}_0 = \varepsilon_0$ is the residual for the point shown. Here the point lies above the line and the residual is positive.

ε = the Greek letter **epsilon**

For each data point, you can calculate the residuals or errors, $y_i - \hat{y}_i = \varepsilon_i$ for $i = 1, 2, 3, ..., 11$.

Each $|\varepsilon|$ is a vertical distance.

For the example about the third exam scores and the final exam scores for the 11 statistics students, there are 11 data points. Therefore, there are 11 ε values. If yousquare each ε and add, you get

$$(\varepsilon_1)^2 + (\varepsilon_2)^2 + ... + (\varepsilon_{11})^2 = \sum_{i=1}^{11} \varepsilon^2$$

This is called the **Sum of Squared Errors (SSE)**.

Using calculus, you can determine the values of a and b that make the **SSE** a minimum. When you make the **SSE** a minimum, you have determined the points that are on the line of best fit. It turns out that the line of best fit has the equation:

$$\hat{y} = a + bx$$

where $a = \bar{y} - b\bar{x}$ and $b = \dfrac{\Sigma(x - \bar{x})(y - \bar{y})}{\Sigma(x - \bar{x})^2}$.

The sample means of the x values and the y values are $\bar{x}$ and $\bar{y}$, respectively. The best fit line always passes through the point $(\bar{x}, \bar{y})$.

The slope b can be written as $b = r\left(\dfrac{s_y}{s_x}\right)$ where s_y = the standard deviation of the y values and s_x = the standard deviation of the x values. r is the correlation coefficient, which is discussed in the next section.

Least Squares Criteria for Best Fit

The process of fitting the best-fit line is called **linear regression**. The idea behind finding the best-fit line is based on the assumption that the data are scattered about a straight line. The criteria for the best fit line is that the sum of the squared errors (SSE) is minimized, that is, made as small as possible. Any other line you might choose would have a higher SSE than the best fit line. This best fit line is called the **least-squares regression line**.

NOTE

☞   Computer spreadsheets, statistical software, and many calculators can quickly calculate the best-fit line and create the graphs. The calculations tend to be tedious if done by hand. Instructions to use the TI-83, TI-83+, and TI-84+ calculators to find the best-fit line and create a scatterplot are shown at the end of this section.

THIRD EXAM vs FINAL EXAM EXAMPLE:

The graph of the line of best fit for the third-exam/final-exam example is as follows:

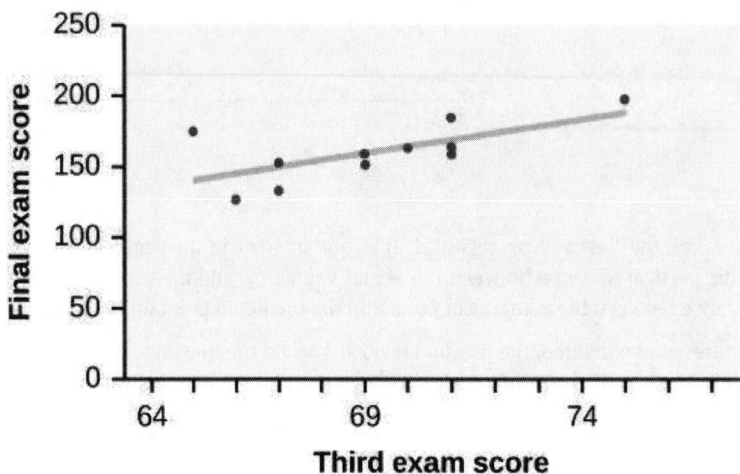

Figure 12.11

The least squares regression line (best-fit line) for the third-exam/final-exam example has the equation:

$$\hat{y} = -173.51 + 4.83x$$

REMINDER

Remember, it is always important to plot a scatter diagram first. If the scatter plot indicates that there is a linear relationship between the variables, then it is reasonable to use a best fit line to make predictions for y given x within the domain of x-values in the sample data, **but not necessarily for x-values outside that domain.** You could use the line to predict the final exam score for a student who earned a grade of 73 on the third exam. You should NOT use the line to predict the final exam score for a student who earned a grade of 50 on the third exam, because 50 is not within the domain of the x-values in the sample data, which are between 65 and 75.

UNDERSTANDING SLOPE

The slope of the line, b, describes how changes in the variables are related. It is important to interpret the slope of the line in the context of the situation represented by the data. You should be able to write a sentence interpreting the slope in plain English.

INTERPRETATION OF THE SLOPE: The slope of the best-fit line tells us how the dependent variable (y) changes for every one unit increase in the independent (x) variable, on average.

THIRD EXAM vs FINAL EXAM EXAMPLE

Slope: The slope of the line is b = 4.83.
Interpretation: For a one-point increase in the score on the third exam, the final exam score increases by 4.83 points, on average.

Using the TI-83, 83+, 84, 84+ Calculator

Using the Linear Regression T Test: LinRegTTest

1. In the STAT list editor, enter the X data in list L1 and the Y data in list L2, paired so that the corresponding (x,y) values are next to each other in the lists. (If a particular pair of values is repeated, enter it as many times as it appears in the data.)

2. On the STAT TESTS menu, scroll down with the cursor to select the LinRegTTest. (Be careful to select LinRegTTest, as some calculators may also have a different item called LinRegTInt.)

3. On the LinRegTTest input screen enter: Xlist: L1 ; Ylist: L2 ; Freq: 1

4. On the next line, at the prompt β or ρ, highlight "$\neq 0$" and press ENTER

5. Leave the line for "RegEq:" blank

6. Highlight Calculate and press ENTER.

LinRegTTest Input Screen and Output Screen

```
LinRegTTest
Xlist: L1
Ylist: L2
Freq: 1
β or ρ: [≠0] <0 >0
RegEQ:
Calculate
```

TI-83+ and TI-84+
calculators

```
LinRegTTest
y = a + bx
β ≠ 0 and ρ ≠ 0
t = 2.657560155
p = .0261501512
df = 9
↓a = −173.513363
b = 4.827394209
s = 16.41237711
r² = .4396931104
r = .663093591
```

Figure 12.12

The output screen contains a lot of information. For now we will focus on a few items from the output, and will return later to the other items.

The second line says $y = a + bx$. Scroll down to find the values $a = -173.513$, and $b = 4.8273$; the equation of the best fit line is $\hat{y} = -173.51 + 4.83x$

The two items at the bottom are $r_2 = 0.43969$ and $r = 0.663$. For now, just note where to find these values; we will discuss them in the next two sections.

Graphing the Scatterplot and Regression Line

1. We are assuming your X data is already entered in list L1 and your Y data is in list L2

2. Press 2nd STATPLOT ENTER to use Plot 1

3. On the input screen for PLOT 1, highlight **On**, and press ENTER

4. For TYPE: highlight the very first icon which is the scatterplot and press ENTER

5. Indicate Xlist: L1 and Ylist: L2

6. For Mark: it does not matter which symbol you highlight.

7. Press the ZOOM key and then the number 9 (for menu item "ZoomStat") ; the calculator will fit the window to the data

8. To graph the best-fit line, press the "Y=" key and type the equation −173.5 + 4.83X into equation Y1. (The X key is immediately left of the STAT key). Press ZOOM 9 again to graph it.

9. Optional: If you want to change the viewing window, press the WINDOW key. Enter your desired window using Xmin, Xmax, Ymin, Ymax

---

NOTE

Another way to graph the line after you create a scatter plot is to use LinRegTTest.

1. Make sure you have done the scatter plot. Check it on your screen.
2. Go to LinRegTTest and enter the lists.
3. At RegEq: press VARS and arrow over to Y-VARS. Press 1 for 1:Function. Press 1 for 1:Y1. Then arrow down to Calculate and do the calculation for the line of best fit.
4. Press Y = (you will see the regression equation).
5. Press GRAPH. The line will be drawn."

The Correlation Coefficient *r*

Besides looking at the scatter plot and seeing that a line seems reasonable, how can you tell if the line is a good predictor? Use the correlation coefficient as another indicator (besides the scatterplot) of the strength of the relationship between *x* and *y*.

The **correlation coefficient, *r*,** developed by Karl Pearson in the early 1900s, is numerical and provides a measure of strength and direction of the linear association between the independent variable *x* and the dependent variable *y*.

The correlation coefficient is calculated as

$$r = \frac{n\Sigma(xy) - (\Sigma x)(\Sigma y)}{\sqrt{\left[n\Sigma x^2 - (\Sigma x)^2\right]\left[n\Sigma y^2 - (\Sigma y)^2\right]}}$$

where *n* = the number of data points.

If you suspect a linear relationship between *x* and *y*, then *r* can measure how strong the linear relationship is.

What the VALUE of *r* tells us:

- The value of *r* is always between –1 and +1: $-1 \leq r \leq 1$.
- The size of the correlation *r* indicates the strength of the linear relationship between *x* and *y*. Values of *r* close to –1 or to +1 indicate a stronger linear relationship between *x* and *y*.
- If *r* = 0 there is absolutely no linear relationship between *x* and *y* **(no linear correlation)**.
- If *r* = 1, there is perfect positive correlation. If *r* = –1, there is perfect negative correlation. In both these cases, all of the original data points lie on a straight line. Of course,in the real world, this will not generally happen.

What the SIGN of *r* tells us

- A positive value of *r* means that when *x* increases, *y* tends to increase and when *x* decreases, *y* tends to decrease **(positive correlation)**.
- A negative value of *r* means that when *x* increases, *y* tends to decrease and when *x* decreases, *y* tends to increase **(negative correlation)**.
- The sign of *r* is the same as the sign of the slope, *b*, of the best-fit line.

NOTE

Strong correlation does not suggest that *x* causes *y* or *y* causes *x*. We say **"correlation does not imply causation."**

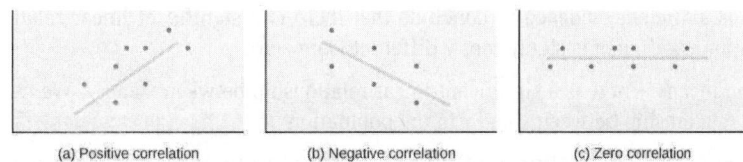

Figure 12.13 (a) A scatter plot showing data with a positive correlation. $0 < r < 1$ (b) A scatter plot showing data with a negative correlation. $-1 < r < 0$ (c) A scatter plot showing data with zero correlation. $r = 0$

The formula for r looks formidable. However, computer spreadsheets, statistical software, and many calculators can quickly calculate r. The correlation coefficient r is the bottom item in the output screens for the LinRegTTest on the TI-83, TI-83+, or TI-84+ calculator (see previous section for instructions).

The Coefficient of Determination

The variable r^2 is called the coefficient of determination and is the square of the correlation coefficient, but is usually stated as a percent, rather than in decimal form. It has an interpretation in the context of the data:

- r^2, when expressed as a percent, represents the percent of variation in the dependent (predicted) variable y that can be explained by variation in the independent (explanatory) variable x using the regression (best-fit) line.

- $1 - r^2$, when expressed as a percentage, represents the percent of variation in y that is NOT explained by variation in x using the regression line. This can be seen as the scattering of the observed data points about the regression line.

Consider the **third exam/final exam example** introduced in the previous section

- The line of best fit is: $\hat{y} = -173.51 + 4.83x$

- The correlation coefficient is $r = 0.6631$

- The coefficient of determination is $r^2 = 0.6631^2 = 0.4397$

- **Interpretation of r^2 in the context of this example:**

- Approximately 44% of the variation (0.4397 is approximately 0.44) in the final-exam grades can be explained by the variation in the grades on the third exam, using the best-fit regression line.

- Therefore, approximately 56% of the variation ($1 - 0.44 = 0.56$) in the final exam grades can NOT be explained by the variation in the grades on the third exam, using the best-fit regression line. (This is seen as the scattering of the points about the line.)

12.4 | Testing the Significance of the Correlation Coefficient

The correlation coefficient, r, tells us about the strength and direction of the linear relationship between x and y. However, the reliability of the linear model also depends on how many observed data points are in the sample. We need to look at both the value of the correlation coefficient r and the sample size n, together.

We perform a hypothesis test of the **"significance of the correlation coefficient"** to decide whether the linear relationship in the sample data is strong enough to use to model the relationship in the population.

The sample data are used to compute r, the correlation coefficient for the sample. If we had data for the entire population, we could find the population correlation coefficient. But because we have only have sample data, we cannot calculate the population correlation coefficient. The sample correlation coefficient, r, is our estimate of the unknown population correlation coefficient.

The symbol for the population correlation coefficient is ρ, the Greek letter "rho."
ρ = population correlation coefficient (unknown)
r = sample correlation coefficient (known; calculated from sample data)

The hypothesis test lets us decide whether the value of the population correlation coefficient ρ is "close to zero" or "significantly different from zero". We decide this based on the sample correlation coefficient r and the sample size n.

If the test concludes that the correlation coefficient is significantly different from zero, we say that the

correlation coefficient is "significant."
- Conclusion: There is sufficient evidence to conclude that there is a significant linear relationship between x and y because the correlation coefficient is significantly different from zero.

- What the conclusion means: There is a significant linear relationship between x and y. We can use the regression line to model the linear relationship between x and y in the population.

If the test concludes that the correlation coefficient is not significantly different from zero (it is close to zero), we say that correlation coefficient is "not significant".
- Conclusion: "There is insufficient evidence to conclude that there is a significant linear relationship between x and y because the correlation coefficient is not significantly different from zero."

- What the conclusion means: There is not a significant linear relationship between x and y. Therefore, we CANNOT use the regression line to model a linear relationship between x and y in the population.

NOTE

- If r is significant and the scatter plot shows a linear trend, the line can be used to predict the value of y for values of x that are within the domain of observed x values.

- If r is not significant OR if the scatter plot does not show a linear trend, the line should not be used for prediction.

- If r is significant and if the scatter plot shows a linear trend, the line may NOT be appropriate or reliable for prediction OUTSIDE the domain of observed x values in the data.

PERFORMING THE HYPOTHESIS TEST

- **Null Hypothesis: H_0: $\rho = 0$**

- **Alternate Hypothesis: H_a: $\rho \neq 0$**

WHAT THE HYPOTHESES MEAN IN WORDS:

- **Null Hypothesis H_0:** The population correlation coefficient IS NOT significantly different from zero. There IS NOT a significant linear relationship(correlation) between x and y in the population.

- **Alternate Hypothesis H_a:** The population correlation coefficient IS significantly DIFFERENT FROM zero. There IS A SIGNIFICANT LINEAR RELATIONSHIP (correlation) between x and y in the population.

DRAWING A CONCLUSION:

There are two methods of making the decision. The two methods are equivalent and give the same result.

- **Method 1: Using the p-value**

- **Method 2: Using a table of critical values**

In this chapter of this textbook, we will always use a significance level of 5%, $\alpha = 0.05$

NOTE

Using the p-value method, you could choose any appropriate significance level you want; you are not limited to using $\alpha = 0.05$. But the table of critical values provided in this textbook assumes that we are using a significance level of 5%, $\alpha = 0.05$. (If we wanted to use a different significance level than 5% with the critical value method, we would need different tables of critical values that are not provided in this textbook.)

METHOD 1: Using a p-value to make a decision

Using the TI-83, 83+, 84, 84+ Calculator

To calculate the p-value using LinRegTTEST:
On the LinRegTTEST input screen, on the line prompt for β or ρ, highlight "$\neq 0$"
The output screen shows the p-value on the line that reads "p =".
(Most computer statistical software can calculate the p-value.)

If the *p*-value is less than the significance level ($\alpha = 0.05$):
- Decision: Reject the null hypothesis.

- Conclusion: "There is sufficient evidence to conclude that there is a significant linear relationship between *x* and *y* because the correlation coefficient is significantly different from zero."

If the *p*-value is NOT less than the significance level ($\alpha = 0.05$)
- Decision: DO NOT REJECT the null hypothesis.

- Conclusion: "There is insufficient evidence to conclude that there is a significant linear relationship between *x* and *y* because the correlation coefficient is NOT significantly different from zero."

You will use technology to calculate the *p*-value. The following describes the calculations to compute the test statistics and the *p*-value:

The *p*-value is calculated using a *t*-distribution with *n* - 2 degrees of freedom.

The formula for the test statistic is $t = \dfrac{r\sqrt{n-2}}{\sqrt{1-r^2}}$. The value of the test statistic, *t*, is shown in the computer or calculator output along with the *p*-value. The test statistic *t* has the same sign as the correlation coefficient *r*. The *p*-value is the combined area in both tails.

An alternative way to calculate the *p*-value (**p**) given by LinRegTTest is the command 2*tcdf(abs(t),10^99, n-2) in 2nd DISTR.

THIRD-EXAM vs FINAL-EXAM EXAMPLE: *p*-value method
- Consider the **third exam/final exam example**.

- The line of best fit is: $\hat{y}$ = -173.51 + 4.83*x* with *r* = 0.6631 and there are *n* = 11 data points.

- Can the regression line be used for prediction? **Given a third exam score (*x* value), can we use the line to predict the final exam score (predicted *y* value)?**

H_0: $\rho = 0$

H_a: $\rho \neq 0$

$\alpha = 0.05$

- The *p*-value is 0.026 (from LinRegTTest on your calculator or from computer software).

- The *p*-value, 0.026, is less than the significance level of $\alpha = 0.05$.

- Decision: Reject the Null Hypothesis H_0

- Conclusion: There is sufficient evidence to conclude that there is a significant linear relationship between the third exam score (*x*) and the final exam score (*y*) because the correlation coefficient is significantly different from zero.

Because *r* is significant and the scatter plot shows a linear trend, the regression line can be used to predict final exam scores.

METHOD 2: Using a table of Critical Values to make a decision

The **95% Critical Values of the Sample Correlation Coefficient Table** can be used to give you a good idea of whether the computed value of *r* **is significant or not**. Compare *r* to the appropriate critical value in the table. If *r* is not between the positive and negative critical values, then the correlation coefficient is significant. If *r* is significant, then you may want to use the line for prediction.

Example 12.7

Suppose you computed *r* = 0.801 using *n* = 10 data points. *df* = *n* - 2 = 10 - 2 = 8. The critical values associated with *df* = 8 are -0.632 and + 0.632. If *r* < negative critical value or *r* > positive critical value, then *r* issignificant. Since *r* = 0.801 and 0.801 > 0.632, *r* is significant and the line may be usedfor prediction. If you view this example on a number line, it will help you.

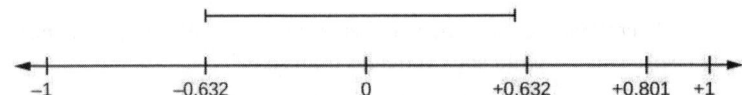

Figure 12.14 r is not significant between -0.632 and +0.632. $r = 0.801 > +0.632$. Therefore, r is significant.

Try It Σ

12.7 For a given line of best fit, you computed that $r = 0.6501$ using $n = 12$ data points and the critical value is 0.576. Can the line be used for prediction? Why or why not?

Example 12.8

Suppose you computed $r = -0.624$ with 14 data points. $df = 14 - 2 = 12$. The critical values are -0.532 and 0.532. Since $-0.624 < -0.532$, r is significant and the line can be used for prediction

Figure 12.15 $r = -0.624 < -0.532$. Therefore, r is significant.

Try It Σ

12.8 For a given line of best fit, you compute that $r = 0.5204$ using $n = 9$ data points, and the critical value is 0.666. Can the line be used for prediction? Why or why not?

Example 12.9

Suppose you computed $r = 0.776$ and $n = 6$. $df = 6 - 2 = 4$. The critical values are -0.811 and 0.811. Since $-0.811 < 0.776 < 0.811$, r is not significant, and the line should not be used for prediction.

Figure 12.16 $-0.811 < r = 0.776 < 0.811$. Therefore, r is not significant.

Try It Σ

12.9 For a given line of best fit, you compute that $r = -0.7204$ using $n = 8$ data points, and the critical value is = 0.707. Can the line be used for prediction? Why or why not?

THIRD-EXAM vs FINAL-EXAM EXAMPLE: critical value method

Consider the **third exam/final exam example**. The line of best fit is: $\hat{y} = -173.51+4.83x$ with $r = 0.6631$ and there are $n = 11$ data points. Can the regression line be used for prediction? **Given a third-exam score (x value), can we use the line to predict the final exam score (predicted y value)?**

H_0: $\rho = 0$
H_a: $\rho \neq 0$
$\alpha = 0.05$

- Use the "95% Critical Value" table for r with $df = n - 2 = 11 - 2 = 9$.

- The critical values are -0.602 and $+0.602$

- Since $0.6631 > 0.602$, r is significant.

- Decision: Reject the null hypothesis.

- Conclusion:There is sufficient evidence to conclude that there is a significant linear relationship between the third exam score (x) and the final exam score (y) because the correlation coefficient is significantly different from zero.

Because r is significant and the scatter plot shows a linear trend, the regression line can be used to predict final exam scores.

Example 12.10

Suppose you computed the following correlation coefficients. Using the table at the end of the chapter, determine if r is significant and the line of best fit associated with each r can be used to predict a y value. If it helps, draw a number line.

a. $r = -0.567$ and the sample size, n, is 19. The $df = n - 2 = 17$. The critical value is -0.456. $-0.567 < -0.456$ so r is significant.

b. $r = 0.708$ and the sample size, n, is nine. The $df = n - 2 = 7$. The critical value is 0.666. $0.708 > 0.666$ so r is significant.

c. $r = 0.134$ and the sample size, n, is 14. The $df = 14 - 2 = 12$. The critical value is 0.532. 0.134 is between -0.532 and 0.532 so r is not significant.

d. $r = 0$ and the sample size, n, is five. No matter what the dfs are, $r = 0$ is between the two critical values so r is not significant.

Try It

12.10 For a given line of best fit, you compute that $r = 0$ using $n = 100$ data points. Can the line be used for prediction? Why or why not?

Assumptions in Testing the Significance of the Correlation Coefficient

Testing the significance of the correlation coefficient requires that certain assumptions about the data are satisfied. The premise of this test is that the data are a sample of observed points taken from a larger population. We have not examined the entire population because it is not possible or feasible to do so. We are examining the sample to draw a conclusion about whether the linear relationship that we see between x and y in the sample data provides strong enough evidence so that we can conclude that there is a linear relationship between x and y in the population.

The regression line equation that we calculate from the sample data gives the best-fit line for our particular sample. We want to use this best-fit line for the sample as an estimate of the best-fit line for the population. Examining the scatterplot and testing the significance of the correlation coefficient helps us determine if it is appropriate to do this.

The assumptions underlying the test of significance are:
- There is a linear relationship in the population that models the average value of y for varying values of x. In other words, the expected value of y for each particular value lies on a straight line in the population. (We do not know the

equation for the line for the population. Our regression line from the sample is our best estimate of this line in the population.)

- The *y* values for any particular *x* value are normally distributed about the line. This implies that there are more *y* values scattered closer to the line than are scattered farther away. Assumption (1) implies that these normal distributions are centered on the line: the means of these normal distributions of *y* values lie on the line.

- The standard deviations of the population *y* values about the line are equal for each value of *x*. In other words, each of these normal distributions of *y* values has the same shape and spread about the line.

- The residual errors are mutually independent (no pattern).

- The data are produced from a well-designed, random sample or randomized experiment.

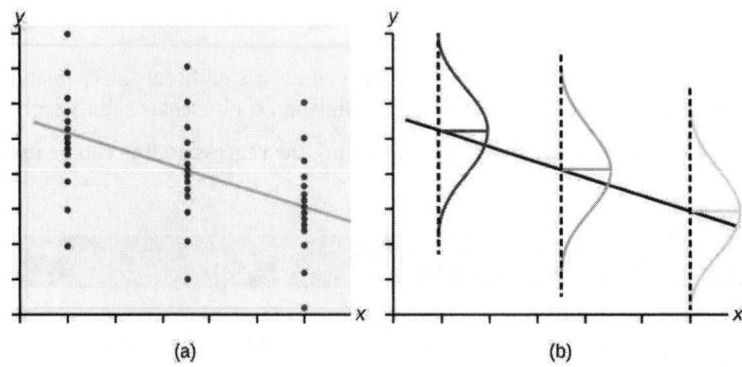

Figure 12.17 The *y* values for each *x* value are normally distributed about the line with the same standard deviation. For each *x* value, the mean of the *y* values lies on the regression line. More *y* values lie near the line than are scattered further away.

12.5 | Prediction

Recall the **third exam/final exam example**.

We examined the scatterplot and showed that the correlation coefficient is significant. We found the equation of the best-fit line for the final exam grade as a function of the grade on the third-exam. We can now use the least-squares regression line for prediction.

Suppose you want to estimate, or predict, the mean final exam score of statistics students who received 73 on the third exam. The exam scores (*x-values*) range from 65 to 75. **Since 73 is between the *x*-values 65 and 75**, substitute *x* = 73 into the equation. Then:

$$\hat{y} = -173.51 + 4.83(73) = 179.08$$

We predict that statistics students who earn a grade of 73 on the third exam will earn a grade of 179.08 on the final exam, on average.

Example 12.11

Recall the **third exam/final exam example**.

a. What would you predict the final exam score to be for a student who scored a 66 on the third exam?

Solution 12.11
a. 145.27

b. What would you predict the final exam score to be for a student who scored a 90 on the third exam?

Solution 12.11

b. The *x* values in the data are between 65 and 75. Ninety is outside of the domain of the observed *x* values in the data (independent variable), so you cannot reliably predict the final exam score for this student. (Even though it is possible to enter 90 into the equation for *x* and calculate a corresponding *y* value, the *y* value that you get will not be reliable.)

To understand really how unreliable the prediction can be outside of the observed *x* values observed in the data, make the substitution *x* = 90 into the equation.

$$\hat{y} = -173.51 + 4.83(90) = 261.19$$

The final-exam score is predicted to be 261.19. The largest the final-exam score can be is 200.

> **NOTE**
>
> The process of predicting inside of the observed *x* values observed in the data is called **interpolation**. The process of predicting outside of the observed *x* values observed in the data is called **extrapolation**.

Try It Σ

12.11 Data are collected on the relationship between the number of hours per week practicing a musical instrument and scores on a math test. The line of best fit is as follows:

$\hat{y} = 72.5 + 2.8x$

What would you predict the score on a math test would be for a student who practices a musical instrument for five hours a week?

12.6 | Outliers

In some data sets, there are values **(observed data points)** called **outliers**. **Outliers are observed data points that are far from the least squares line.** They have large "errors", where the "error" or residual is the vertical distance from the line to the point.

Outliers need to be examined closely. Sometimes, for some reason or another, they should not be included in the analysis of the data. It is possible that an outlier is a result of erroneous data. Other times, an outlier may hold valuable information about the population under study and should remain included in the data. The key is to examine carefully what causes a data point to be an outlier.

Besides outliers, a sample may contain one or a few points that are called **influential points**. Influential points are observed data points that are far from the other observed data points in the horizontal direction. These points may have a big effect on the slope of the regression line. To begin to identify an influential point, you can remove it from the data set and see if the slope of the regression line is changed significantly.

Computers and many calculators can be used to identify outliers from the data. Computer output for regression analysis will often identify both outliers and influential points so that you can examine them.

Identifying Outliers

We could guess at outliers by looking at a graph of the scatterplot and best fit-line. However, we would like some guideline as to how far away a point needs to be in order to be considered an outlier. **As a rough rule of thumb, we can flag any point that is located further than two standard deviations above or below the best-fit line as an outlier**. The standard deviation used is the standard deviation of the residuals or errors.

We can do this visually in the scatter plot by drawing an extra pair of lines that are two standard deviations above and below the best-fit line. Any data points that are outside this extra pair of lines are flagged as potential outliers. Or we can do this numerically by calculating each residual and comparing it to twice the standard deviation. On the TI-83, 83+, or 84+, the graphical approach is easier. The graphical procedure is shown first, followed by the numerical calculations. You would generally need to use only one of these methods.

Example 12.12

In the **third exam/final exam example**, you can determine if there is an outlier or not. If there is an outlier, as an exercise, delete it and fit the remaining data to a new line. For this example, the new line ought to fit the remaining data better. This means the **SSE** should be smaller and the correlation coefficient ought to be closer to 1 or –1.

Solution 12.12

Graphical Identification of Outliers

With the TI-83, 83+, 84+ graphing calculators, it is easy to identify the outliers graphically and visually. If we were to measure the vertical distance from any data point to the corresponding point on the line of best fit and that distance were equal to 2s or more, then we would consider the data point to be "too far" from the line of best fit. We need to find and graph the lines that are two standard deviations below and above the regression line. Any points that are outside these two lines are outliers. We will call these lines Y2 and Y3:

As we did with the equation of the regression line and the correlation coefficient, we will use technology to calculate this standard deviation for us. Using the **LinRegTTest** with this data, scroll down through the output screens to find s = **16.412**.

Line Y2 = –173.5 + 4.83x –2(16.4) and line Y3 = –173.5 + 4.83x + 2(16.4)

where $\hat{y}$ = –173.5 + 4.83x is the line of best fit. Y2 and Y3 have the same slope as the line of best fit.

Graph the scatterplot with the best fit line in equation Y1, then enter the two extra lines as Y2 and Y3 in the "Y="equation editor and press ZOOM 9. You will find that the only data point that is not between lines Y2 and Y3 is the point x = 65, y = 175. On the calculator screen it is just barely outside these lines. The outlier is the student who had a grade of 65 on the third exam and 175 on the final exam; this point is further than two standard deviations away from the best-fit line.

Sometimes a point is so close to the lines used to flag outliers on the graph that it is difficult to tell if the point is between or outside the lines. On a computer, enlarging the graph may help; on a small calculator screen, zooming in may make the graph clearer. Note that when the graph does not give a clear enough picture, you can use the numerical comparisons to identify outliers.

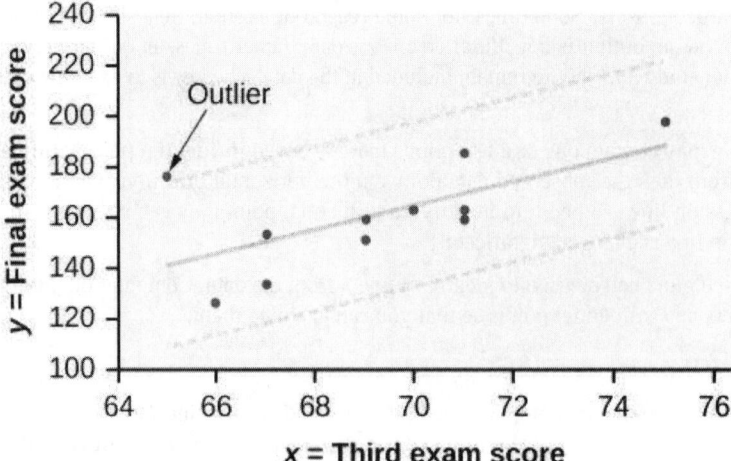

Figure 12.18

Try It Σ

12.12 Identify the potential outlier in the scatter plot. The standard deviation of the residuals or errors is approximately 8.6.

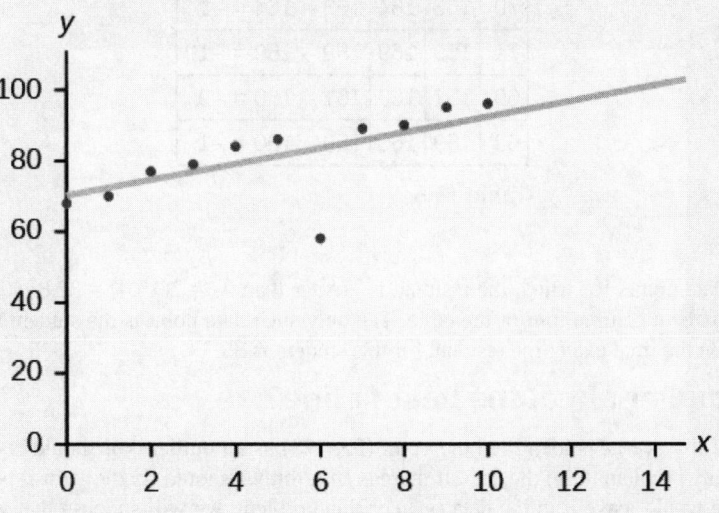

Figure 12.19

Numerical Identification of Outliers

In **Table 12.5**, the first two columns are the third-exam and final-exam data. The third column shows the predicted $\hat{y}$ values calculated from the line of best fit: $\hat{y} = -173.5 + 4.83x$. The residuals, or errors, have been calculated in the fourth column of the table: observed y value−predicted y value = $y - \hat{y}$.

s is the standard deviation of all the $y - \hat{y} = \varepsilon$ values where n = the total number of data points. If each residual is calculated and squared, and the results are added, we get the SSE. The standard deviation of the residuals is calculated from the SSE as:

$$s = \sqrt{\frac{SSE}{n-2}}$$

NOTE

We divide by $(n-2)$ because the regression model involves two estimates.

Rather than calculate the value of s ourselves, we can find s using the computer or calculator. For this example, the calculator function LinRegTTest found s = 16.4 as the standard deviation of the residuals 35; –17; 16; –6; –19; 9; 3; –1; –10; –9; –1.

x	y	$\hat{y}$	$y - \hat{y}$
65	175	140	175 – 140 = 35
67	133	150	133 – 150= –17
71	185	169	185 – 169 = 16
71	163	169	163 – 169 = –6

Table 12.5

x	y	ŷ	y − ŷ
66	126	145	126 − 145 = −19
75	198	189	198 − 189 = 9
67	153	150	153 − 150 = 3
70	163	164	163 − 164 = −1
71	159	169	159 − 169 = −10
69	151	160	151 − 160 = −9
69	159	160	159 − 160 = −1

Table 12.5

We are looking for all data points for which the residual is greater than $2s = 2(16.4) = 32.8$ or less than −32.8. Compare these values to the residuals in column four of the table. The only such data point is the student who had a grade of 65 on the third exam and 175 on the final exam; the residual for this student is 35.

How does the outlier affect the best fit line?

Numerically and graphically, we have identified the point (65, 175) as an outlier. We should re-examine the data for this point to see if there are any problems with the data. If there is an error, we should fix the error if possible, or delete the data. If the data is correct, we would leave it in the data set. For this problem, we will suppose that we examined the data and found that this outlier data was an error. Therefore we will continue on and delete the outlier, so that we can explore how it affects the results, as a learning experience.

Compute a new best-fit line and correlation coefficient using the ten remaining points:

On the TI-83, TI-83+, TI-84+ calculators, delete the outlier from L1 and L2. Using the LinRegTTest, the new line of best fit and the correlation coefficient are:

$\hat{y} = -355.19 + 7.39x$ and $r = 0.9121$

The new line with $r = 0.9121$ is a stronger correlation than the original ($r = 0.6631$) because $r = 0.9121$ is closer to one. This means that the new line is a better fit to the ten remaining data values. The line can better predict the final exam score given the third exam score.

Numerical Identification of Outliers: Calculating *s* and Finding Outliers Manually

If you do not have the function LinRegTTest, then you can calculate the outlier in the first example by doing the following.

First, **square each $|y − \hat{y}|$**

The squares are 35^2; 17^2; 16^2; 6^2; 19^2; 9^2; 3^2; 1^2; 10^2; 9^2; 1^2

Then, add (sum) all the $|y − \hat{y}|$ squared terms using the formula

$$\sum_{i=1}^{11} \left(\left|y_i - \hat{y}_i\right|\right)^2 = \sum_{i=1}^{11} \varepsilon_i^2 \text{ (Recall that } y_i - \hat{y}_i = \varepsilon_i.)$$

$$= 35^2 + 17^2 + 16^2 + 6^2 + 19^2 + 9^2 + 3^2 + 1^2 + 10^2 + 9^2 + 1^2$$

$= 2440 = $ **SSE**. The result, **SSE** is the Sum of Squared Errors.

Next, calculate *s*, the standard deviation of all the $y − \hat{y} = \varepsilon$ values where n = the total number of data points.

The calculation is $s = \sqrt{\dfrac{\text{SSE}}{n-2}}$.

For the third exam/final exam problem, $s = \sqrt{\dfrac{2440}{11-2}} = 16.47$.

Next, multiply *s* by 2:
$(2)(16.47) = 32.94$

32.94 is 2 standard deviations away from the mean of the $y - \hat{y}$ values.

If we were to measure the vertical distance from any data point to the corresponding point on the line of best fit and that distance is at least $2s$, then we would consider the data point to be "too far" from the line of best fit. We call that point a **potential outlier**.

For the example, if any of the $|y - \hat{y}|$ values are **at least** 32.94, the corresponding (x, y) data point is a potential outlier.

For the third exam/final exam problem, all the $|y - \hat{y}|$'s are less than 31.29 except for the first one which is 35.

$35 > 31.29$ That is, $|y - \hat{y}| \geq (2)(s)$

The point which corresponds to $|y - \hat{y}| = 35$ is (65, 175). **Therefore, the data point (65,175) is a potential outlier.** For this example, we will delete it. (Remember, we do not always delete an outlier.)

NOTE

When outliers are deleted, the researcher should either record that data was deleted, and why, or the researcher should provide results both with and without the deleted data. If data is erroneous and the correct values are known (e.g., student one actually scored a 70 instead of a 65), then this correction can be made to the data.

The next step is to compute a new best-fit line using the ten remaining points. The new line of best fit and the correlation coefficient are:

$\hat{y} = -355.19 + 7.39x$ and $r = 0.9121$

Example 12.13

Using this new line of best fit (based on the remaining ten data points in the **third exam/final exam example**), what would a student who receives a 73 on the third exam expect to receive on the final exam? Is this the same as the prediction made using the original line?

Solution 12.13
Using the new line of best fit, $\hat{y} = -355.19 + 7.39(73) = 184.28$. A student who scored 73 points on the third exam would expect to earn 184 points on the final exam.

The original line predicted $\hat{y} = -173.51 + 4.83(73) = 179.08$ so the prediction using the new line with the outlier eliminated differs from the original prediction.

12.13 The data points for the graph from the **third exam/final exam example** are as follows: (1, 5), (2, 7), (2, 6), (3, 9), (4, 12), (4, 13), (5, 18), (6, 19), (7, 12), and (7, 21). Remove the outlier and recalculate the line of best fit. Find the value of $\hat{y}$ when $x = 10$.

Example 12.14

The Consumer Price Index (CPI) measures the average change over time in the prices paid by urban consumers for consumer goods and services. The CPI affects nearly all Americans because of the many ways it is used. One of its biggest uses is as a measure of inflation. By providing information about price changes in the Nation's economy to government, business, and labor, the CPI helps them to make economic decisions. The President, Congress, and the Federal Reserve Board use the CPI's trends to formulate monetary and fiscal policies. In the following table, x is the year and y is the CPI.

x	y	x	y
1915	10.1	1969	36.7
1926	17.7	1975	49.3
1935	13.7	1979	72.6
1940	14.7	1980	82.4
1947	24.1	1986	109.6
1952	26.5	1991	130.7
1964	31.0	1999	166.6

Table 12.6 Data

a. Draw a scatterplot of the data.

b. Calculate the least squares line. Write the equation in the form $\hat{y} = a + bx$.

c. Draw the line on the scatterplot.

d. Find the correlation coefficient. Is it significant?

e. What is the average CPI for the year 1990?

Solution 12.14

a. See **Figure 12.19**.

b. $\hat{y} = -3204 + 1.662x$ is the equation of the line of best fit.

c. $r = 0.8694$

d. The number of data points is $n = 14$. Use the 95% Critical Values of the Sample Correlation Coefficient table at the end of Chapter 12. $n - 2 = 12$. The corresponding critical value is 0.532. Since $0.8694 > 0.532$, r is significant.
$\hat{y} = -3204 + 1.662(1990) = 103.4$ CPI

e. Using the calculator LinRegTTest, we find that $s = 25.4$; graphing the lines Y2 = –3204 + 1.662X – 2(25.4) and Y3 = –3204 + 1.662X + 2(25.4) shows that no data values are outside those lines, identifying no outliers. (Note that the year 1999 was very close to the upper line, but still inside it.)

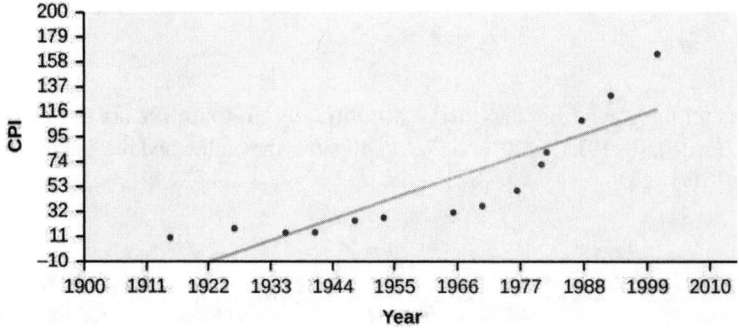

Figure 12.20

NOTE

In the example, notice the pattern of the points compared to the line. Although the correlation coefficient is significant, the pattern in the scatterplot indicates that a curve would be a more appropriate model to use than a line. In this example, a statistician should prefer to use other methods to fit a curve to this data, rather than model the data with the line we found. In addition to doing the calculations, it is always important to look at the scatterplot when deciding whether a linear model is appropriate.

If you are interested in seeing more years of data, visit the Bureau of Labor Statistics CPI website ftp://ftp.bls.gov/pub/special.requests/cpi/cpiai.txt; our data is taken from the column entitled "Annual Avg." (third column from the right). For example you could add more current years of data. Try adding the more recent years: 2004: CPI = 188.9; 2008: CPI = 215.3; 2011: CPI = 224.9. See how it affects the model. (Check: $\hat{y} = -4436 + 2.295x$; $r = 0.9018$. Is r significant? Is the fit better with the addition of the new points?)

12.14 The following table shows economic development measured in per capita income PCINC.

Year	PCINC	Year	PCINC
1870	340	1920	1050
1880	499	1930	1170
1890	592	1940	1364
1900	757	1950	1836
1910	927	1960	2132

Table 12.7

a. What are the independent and dependent variables?

b. Draw a scatter plot.

c. Use regression to find the line of best fit and the correlation coefficient.

d. Interpret the significance of the correlation coefficient.

e. Is there a linear relationship between the variables?

f. Find the coefficient of determination and interpret it.

g. What is the slope of the regression equation? What does it mean?

h. Use the line of best fit to estimate PCINC for 1900, for 2000.

i. Determine if there are any outliers.

95% Critical Values of the Sample Correlation Coefficient Table

Degrees of Freedom: $n - 2$	Critical Values: (+ and −)
1	0.997
2	0.950
3	0.878

Table 12.8

Degrees of Freedom: $n - 2$	Critical Values: (+ and −)
4	0.811
5	0.754
6	0.707
7	0.666
8	0.632
9	0.602
10	0.576
11	0.555
12	0.532
13	0.514
14	0.497
15	0.482
16	0.468
17	0.456
18	0.444
19	0.433
20	0.423
21	0.413
22	0.404
23	0.396
24	0.388
25	0.381
26	0.374
27	0.367
28	0.361
29	0.355
30	0.349
40	0.304
50	0.273
60	0.250
70	0.232
80	0.217
90	0.205
100	0.195

Table 12.8

12.7 | Regression (Distance from School)

Stats Lab

12.1 Regression (Distance from School)

Class Time:

Names:

Student Learning Outcomes

- The student will calculate and construct the line of best fit between two variables.
- The student will evaluate the relationship between two variables to determine if that relationship is significant.

Collect the Data

Use eight members of your class for the sample. Collect bivariate data (distance an individual lives from school, the cost of supplies for the current term).

1. Complete the table.

Distance from school	Cost of supplies this term

Table 12.9

2. Which variable should be the dependent variable and which should be the independent variable? Why?

3. Graph "distance" vs. "cost." Plot the points on the graph. Label both axes with words. Scale both axes.

Figure 12.21

Analyze the Data

Enter your data into your calculator or computer. Write the linear equation, rounding to four decimal places.

1. Calculate the following:

    a. $a =$ _____

    b. $b =$ _____

    c. correlation = _____

    d. $n =$ _____

    e. equation: $\hat{y} =$ _____

    f. Is the correlation significant? Why or why not? (Answer in one to three complete sentences.)

2. Supply an answer for the following senarios:

    a. For a person who lives eight miles from campus, predict the total cost of supplies this term:

    b. For a person who lives eighty miles from campus, predict the total cost of supplies this term:

3. Obtain the graph on your calculator or computer. Sketch the regression line.

Figure 12.22

Discussion Questions

1. Answer each question in complete sentences.

    a. Does the line seem to fit the data? Why?

    b. What does the correlation imply about the relationship between the distance and the cost?

2. Are there any outliers? If so, which point is an outlier?

3. Should the outlier, if it exists, be removed? Why or why not?

12.8 | Regression (Textbook Cost)

Stats Lab

12.2 Regression (Textbook Cost)

Class Time:

Names:

Student Learning Outcomes

- The student will calculate and construct the line of best fit between two variables.
- The student will evaluate the relationship between two variables to determine if that relationship is significant.

Collect the Data

Survey ten textbooks. Collect bivariate data (number of pages in a textbook, the cost of the textbook).

1. Complete the table.

Number of pages	Cost of textbook

Table 12.10

2. Which variable should be the dependent variable and which should be the independent variable? Why?

3. Graph "pages" vs. "cost." Plot the points on the graph in **Analyze the Data**. Label both axes with words. Scale both axes.

Analyze the Data

Enter your data into your calculator or computer. Write the linear equation, rounding to four decimal places.

1. Calculate the following:

    a. $a =$ _____

    b. $b =$ _____

    c. correlation = _____

    d. $n =$ _____

    e. equation: $y =$ _____

    f. Is the correlation significant? Why or why not? (Answer in complete sentences.)

2. Supply an answer for the following senarios:

    a. For a textbook with 400 pages, predict the cost.

    b. For a textbook with 600 pages, predict the cost.

3. Obtain the graph on your calculator or computer. Sketch the regression line.

Figure 12.23

Discussion Questions

1. Answer each question in complete sentences.
   a. Does the line seem to fit the data? Why?
   b. What does the correlation imply about the relationship between the number of pages and the cost?
2. Are there any outliers? If so, which point(s) is an outlier?
3. Should the outlier, if it exists, be removed? Why or why not?

12.9 | Regression (Fuel Efficiency)

Stats Lab

12.3 Regression (Fuel Efficiency)

Class Time:

Names:

Student Learning Outcomes

- The student will calculate and construct the line of best fit between two variables.
- The student will evaluate the relationship between two variables to determine if that relationship is significant.

Collect the Data

Find a reputable source that provides information on total fuel efficiency (in miles per gallon) and weight (in pounds) of new model cars with automatic transmissions. We will use this data to determine the relationship, if any, between the fuel efficiency of a car and its weight.

1. Using your random number generator, randomly select 20 cars from the list and record their weights and fuel efficiency into **Table 12.11**.

Weight	Fuel Efficiency

Table 12.11

2. Which variable should be the dependent variable and which should be the independent variable? Why?

3. By hand, do a scatterplot of "weight" vs. "fuel efficiency". Plot the points on graph paper. Label both axes with

words. Scale both axes accurately.

Figure 12.24

Analyze the Data

Enter your data into your calculator or computer. Write the linear equation, rounding to 4 decimal places.

1. Calculate the following:

   a. $a =$ _____

   b. $b =$ _____

   c. correlation = _____

   d. $n =$ _____

   e. equation: $\hat{y} =$ _____

2. Obtain the graph of the regression line on your calculator. Sketch the regression line on the same axes as your scatter plot.

Discussion Questions

1. Is the correlation significant? Explain how you determined this in complete sentences.

2. Is the relationship a positive one or a negative one? Explain how you can tell and what this means in terms of weight and fuel efficiency.

3. In one or two complete sentences, what is the practical interpretation of the slope of the least squares line in terms of fuel efficiency and weight?

4. For a car that weighs 4,000 pounds, predict its fuel efficiency. Include units.

5. Can we predict the fuel efficiency of a car that weighs 10,000 pounds using the least squares line? Explain why or why not.

6. Answer each question in complete sentences.

   a. Does the line seem to fit the data? Why or why not?

   b. What does the correlation imply about the relationship between fuel efficiency and weight of a car? Is this what you expected?

7. Are there any outliers? If so, which point is an outlier?

KEY TERMS

Coefficient of Correlation a measure developed by Karl Pearson (early 1900s) that gives the strength of association between the independent variable and the dependent variable; the formula is:

$$r = \frac{n\Sigma(xy) - (\Sigma x)(\Sigma y)}{\sqrt{\left[n\Sigma x^2 - (\Sigma x)^2\right]\left[n\Sigma y^2 - (\Sigma y)^2\right]}}$$

where n is the number of data points. The coefficient cannot be more then 1 and less then –1. The closer the coefficient is to ±1, the stronger the evidence of a significant linear relationship between x and y.

Outlier an observation that does not fit the rest of the data

CHAPTER REVIEW

12.1 Linear Equations

The most basic type of association is a linear association. This type of relationship can be defined algebraically by the equations used, numerically with actual or predicted data values, or graphically from a plotted curve. (Lines are classified as straight curves.) Algebraically, a linear equation typically takes the form $y = mx + b$, where m and b are constants, x is the independent variable, y is the dependent variable. In a statistical context, a linear equation is written in the form $y = a + bx$, where a and b are the constants. This form is used to help readers distinguish the statistical context from the algebraic context. In the equation $y = a + bx$, the constant b that multiplies the x variable (b is called a coefficient) is called as the **slope**. The slope describes the rate of change between the independent and dependent variables; in other words, the rate of change describes the change that occurs in the dependent variable as the independent variable is changed. In the equation $y = a + bx$, the constant a is called as the y-intercept. Graphically, the y-intercept is the y coordinate of the point where the graph of the line crosses the y axis. At this point $x = 0$.

The **slope of a line** is a value that describes the rate of change between the independent and dependent variables. The **slope** tells us how the dependent variable (y) changes for every one unit increase in the independent (x) variable, on average. The **y-intercept** is used to describe the dependent variable when the independent variable equals zero. Graphically, the slope is represented by three line types in elementary statistics.

12.2 Scatter Plots

Scatter plots are particularly helpful graphs when we want to see if there is a linear relationship among data points. They indicate both the direction of the relationship between the x variables and the y variables, and the strength of the relationship. We calculate the strength of the relationship between an independent variable and a dependent variable using linear regression.

12.3 The Regression Equation

A regression line, or a line of best fit, can be drawn on a scatter plot and used to predict outcomes for the x and y variables in a given data set or sample data. There are several ways to find a regression line, but usually the least-squares regression line is used because it creates a uniform line. Residuals, also called "errors," measure the distance from the actual value of y and the estimated value of y. The Sum of Squared Errors, when set to its minimum, calculates the points on the line of best fit. Regression lines can be used to predict values within the given set of data, but should not be used to make predictions for values outside the set of data.

The correlation coefficient r measures the strength of the linear association between x and y. The variable r has to be between –1 and +1. When r is positive, the x and y will tend to increase and decrease together. When r is negative, x will increase and y will decrease, or the opposite, x will decrease and y will increase. The coefficient of determination r^2, is equal to the square of the correlation coefficient. When expressed as a percent, r^2 represents the percent of variation in the dependent variable y that can be explained by variation in the independent variable x using the regression line.

12.4 Testing the Significance of the Correlation Coefficient

Linear regression is a procedure for fitting a straight line of the form $\hat{y} = a + bx$ to data. The conditions for regression are:

- **Linear** In the population, there is a linear relationship that models the average value of y for different values of x.

- **Independent** The residuals are assumed to be independent.

- **Normal** The y values are distributed normally for any value of x.
- **Equal variance** The standard deviation of the y values is equal for each x value.
- **Random** The data are produced from a well-designed random sample or randomized experiment.

The slope b and intercept a of the least-squares line estimate the slope β and intercept α of the population (true) regression line. To estimate the population standard deviation of y, σ, use the standard deviation of the residuals, s. $s = \sqrt{\dfrac{SEE}{n-2}}$. The variable ρ (rho) is the population correlation coefficient. To test the null hypothesis H_0: $\rho = hypothesized\ value$, use a linear regression t-test. The most common null hypothesis is H_0: $\rho = 0$ which indicates there is no linear relationship between x and y in the population. The TI-83, 83+, 84, 84+ calculator function LinRegTTest can perform this test (STATS TESTS LinRegTTest).

12.5 Prediction

After determining the presence of a strong correlation coefficient and calculating the line of best fit, you can use the least squares regression line to make predictions about your data.

12.6 Outliers

To determine if a point is an outlier, do one of the following:

1. Input the following equations into the TI 83, 83+,84, 84+:

$y_1 = a + bx$

$y_2 = a + bx + 2s$ where s is the standard deviation of the residuals

$y_3 = a + bx - 2s$

If any point is above y_2 or below y_3 then the point is considered to be an outlier.

2. Use the residuals and compare their absolute values to $2s$ where s is the standard deviation of the residuals. If the absolute value of any residual is greater than or equal to $2s$, then the corresponding point is an outlier.

3. Note: The calculator function LinRegTTest (STATS TESTS LinRegTTest) calculates s.

FORMULA REVIEW

12.1 Linear Equations

$y = a + bx$ where a is the y-intercept and b is the slope. The variable x is the independent variable and y is the dependent variable.

12.4 Testing the Significance of the Correlation Coefficient

Least Squares Line or Line of Best Fit:

$\hat{y} = a + bx$

where

$a = y$-intercept

$b = $ slope

Standard deviation of the residuals:

$$s = \sqrt{\frac{SEE}{n-2}}.$$

where

SSE = sum of squared errors

$n = $ the number of data points

PRACTICE

12.1 Linear Equations

Use the following information to answer the next three exercises. A vacation resort rents SCUBA equipment to certified divers. The resort charges an up-front fee of $25 and another fee of $12.50 an hour.

1. What are the dependent and independent variables?

2. Find the equation that expresses the total fee in terms of the number of hours the equipment is rented.

3. Graph the equation from **Exercise 12.2**.

Use the following information to answer the next two exercises. A credit card company charges $10 when a payment is late, and $5 a day each day the payment remains unpaid.

4. Find the equation that expresses the total fee in terms of the number of days the payment is late.

5. Graph the equation from **Exercise 12.4**.

6. Is the equation $y = 10 + 5x - 3x^2$ linear? Why or why not?

7. Which of the following equations are linear?

a. $y = 6x + 8$

b. $y + 7 = 3x$

c. $y - x = 8x^2$

d. $4y = 8$

8. Does the graph show a linear equation? Why or why not?

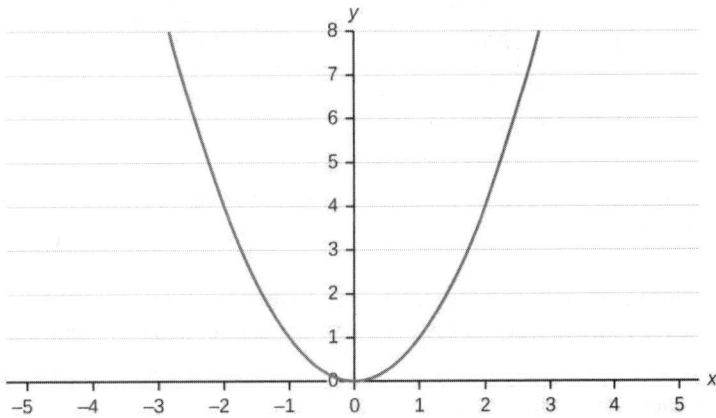

Figure 12.25

Table 12.12 contains real data for the first two decades of flu reporting.

Year	# flu cases diagnosed	# flu deaths
Pre-1981	91	29
1981	319	121
1982	1,170	453
1983	3,076	1,482
1984	6,240	3,466
1985	11,776	6,878
1986	19,032	11,987
1987	28,564	16,162
1988	35,447	20,868

Table 12.12 Adults and Adolescents only, United States

1989	42,674	27,591
1990	48,634	31,335
1991	59,660	36,560
1992	78,530	41,055
1993	78,834	44,730
1994	71,874	49,095
1995	68,505	49,456
1996	59,347	38,510
1997	47,149	20,736
1998	38,393	19,005
1999	25,174	18,454
2000	25,522	17,347
2001	25,643	17,402
2002	26,464	16,371
Total	**802,118**	**489,093**

**Table 12.12 Adults and Adolescents only,
United States**

9. Use the columns "year" and "# flu cases diagnosed. Why is "year" the independent variable and "# flu cases diagnosed." the dependent variable (instead of the reverse)?

Use the following information to answer the next two exercises. A specialty cleaning company charges an equipment fee and an hourly labor fee. A linear equation that expresses the total amount of the fee the company charges for each session is $y = 50 + 100x$.

10. What are the independent and dependent variables?

11. What is the y-intercept and what is the slope? Interpret them using complete sentences.

Use the following information to answer the next three questions. Due to erosion, a river shoreline is losing several thousand pounds of soil each year. A linear equation that expresses the total amount of soil lost per year is $y = 12,000x$.

12. What are the independent and dependent variables?

13. How many pounds of soil does the shoreline lose in a year?

14. What is the y-intercept? Interpret its meaning.

Use the following information to answer the next two exercises. The price of a single issue of stock can fluctuate throughout the day. A linear equation that represents the price of stock for Shipment Express is $y = 15 - 1.5x$ where x is the number of hours passed in an eight-hour day of trading.

15. What are the slope and y-intercept? Interpret their meaning.

16. If you owned this stock, would you want a positive or negative slope? Why?

12.2 Scatter Plots

17. Does the scatter plot appear linear? Strong or weak? Positive or negative?

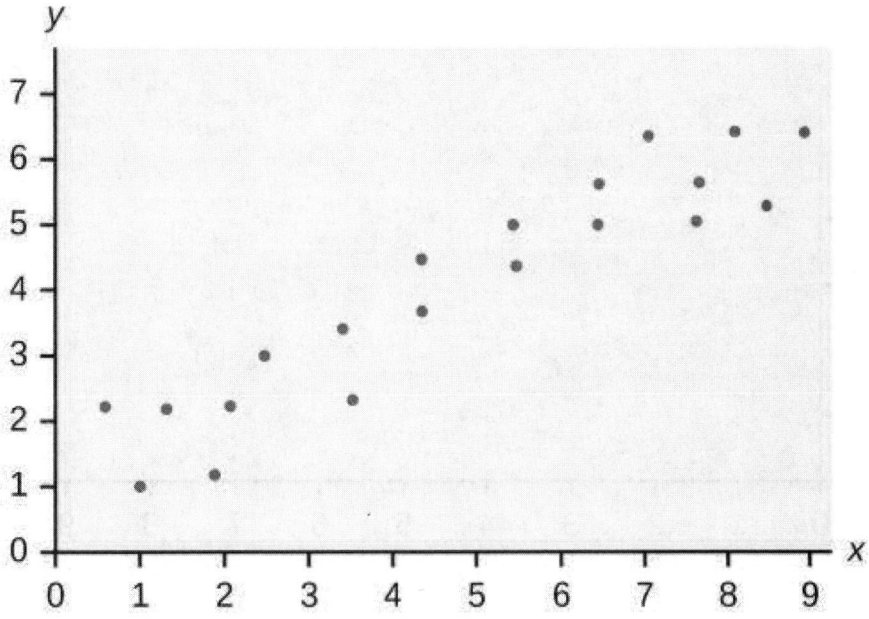

Figure 12.26

18. Does the scatter plot appear linear? Strong or weak? Positive or negative?

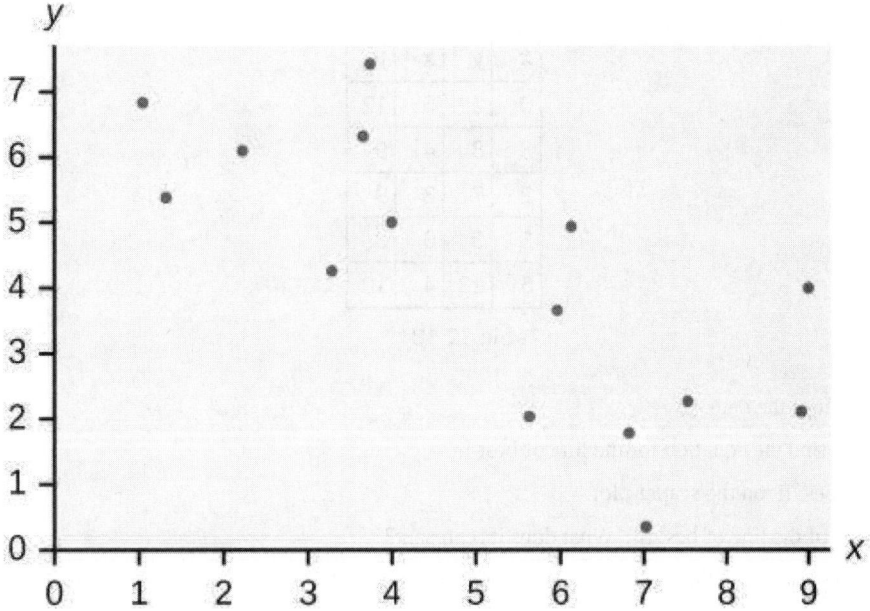

Figure 12.27

19. Does the scatter plot appear linear? Strong or weak? Positive or negative?

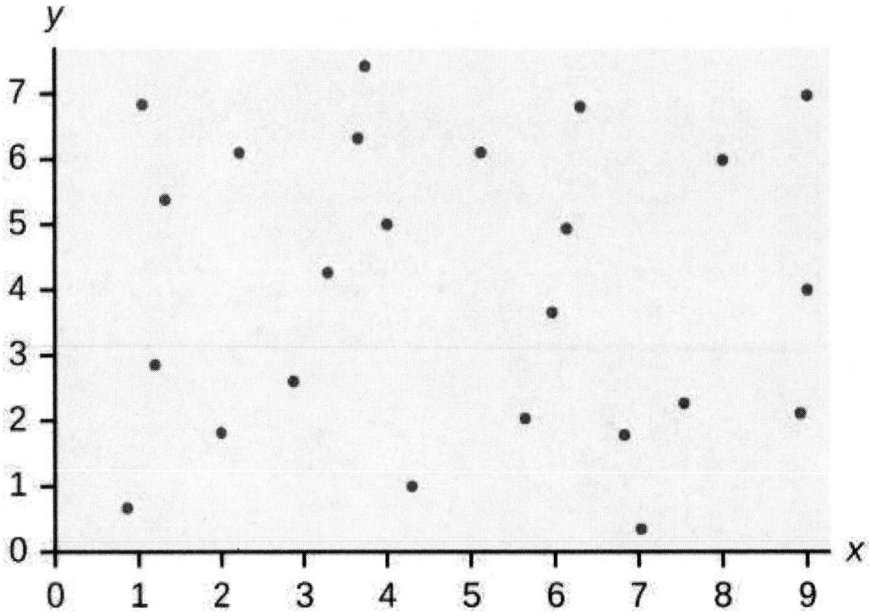

Figure 12.28

12.3 The Regression Equation

Use the following information to answer the next five exercises. A random sample of ten professional athletes produced the following data where x is the number of endorsements the player has and y is the amount of money made (in millions of dollars).

x	y	x	y
0	2	5	12
3	8	4	9
2	7	3	9
1	3	0	3
5	13	4	10

Table 12.13

20. Draw a scatter plot of the data.

21. Use regression to find the equation for the line of best fit.

22. Draw the line of best fit on the scatter plot.

23. What is the slope of the line of best fit? What does it represent?

24. What is the y-intercept of the line of best fit? What does it represent?

25. What does an r value of zero mean?

26. When $n = 2$ and $r = 1$, are the data significant? Explain.

27. When $n = 100$ and $r = -0.89$, is there a significant correlation? Explain.

12.4 Testing the Significance of the Correlation Coefficient

28. When testing the significance of the correlation coefficient, what is the null hypothesis?

29. When testing the significance of the correlation coefficient, what is the alternative hypothesis?

30. If the level of significance is 0.05 and the *p*-value is 0.04, what conclusion can you draw?

12.5 Prediction

Use the following information to answer the next two exercises. An electronics retailer used regression to find a simple model to predict sales growth in the first quarter of the new year (January through March). The model is good for 90 days, where *x* is the day. The model can be written as follows:

$\hat{y} = 101.32 + 2.48x$ where $\hat{y}$ is in thousands of dollars.

31. What would you predict the sales to be on day 60?

32. What would you predict the sales to be on day 90?

Use the following information to answer the next three exercises. A landscaping company is hired to mow the grass for several large properties. The total area of the properties combined is 1,345 acres. The rate at which one person can mow is as follows:

$\hat{y} = 1350 - 1.2x$ where *x* is the number of hours and $\hat{y}$ represents the number of acres left to mow.

33. How many acres will be left to mow after 20 hours of work?

34. How many acres will be left to mow after 100 hours of work?

35. How many hours will it take to mow all of the lawns? (When is $\hat{y} = 0$?)

Table 12.14 contains real data for the first two decades of flu cases reporting.

Year	# flu cases diagnosed	# flu deaths
Pre-1981	91	29
1981	319	121
1982	1,170	453
1983	3,076	1,482
1984	6,240	3,466
1985	11,776	6,878
1986	19,032	11,987
1987	28,564	16,162
1988	35,447	20,868
1989	42,674	27,591
1990	48,634	31,335
1991	59,660	36,560
1992	78,530	41,055
1993	78,834	44,730
1994	71,874	49,095
1995	68,505	49,456

**Table 12.14 Adults and Adolescents only,
United States**

1996	59,347	38,510
1997	47,149	20,736
1998	38,393	19,005
1999	25,174	18,454
2000	25,522	17,347
2001	25,643	17,402
2002	26,464	16,371
Total	**802,118**	**489,093**

Table 12.14 Adults and Adolescents only, United States

36. Graph "year" versus "# flu cases diagnosed" (plot the scatter plot). Do not include pre-1981 data.

37. Perform linear regression. What is the linear equation? Round to the nearest whole number.

38. Find the correlation coefficient.

     a. $r = $ _____

39. Solve.
     a. When $x = 1985$, $\hat{y} = $ _____
     b. When $x = 1990$, $\hat{y} = $ _____
     c. When $x = 1970$, $\hat{y} = $ _____ Why doesn't this answer make sense?

40. Does the line seem to fit the data? Why or why not?

41. What does the correlation imply about the relationship between time (years) and the number of diagnosed flu cases reported in the U.S.?

42. Plot the two given points on the following graph. Then, connect the two points to form the regression line.

Figure 12.29

Obtain the graph on your calculator or computer.

43. Write the equation: $\hat{y} = $ _____

44. Hand draw a smooth curve on the graph that shows the flow of the data.

45. Does the line seem to fit the data? Why or why not?

46. Do you think a linear fit is best? Why or why not?

47. What does the correlation imply about the relationship between time (years) and the number of diagnosed flu cases reported in the U.S.?

48. Graph "year" vs. "# flu cases diagnosed." Do not include pre-1981. Label both axes with words. Scale both axes.

49. Enter your data into your calculator or computer. The pre-1981 data should not be included. Why is that so?

Write the linear equation, rounding to four decimal places:

50. Find the correlation coefficient.
   a.   correlation = _____

12.6 Outliers

Use the following information to answer the next four exercises. The scatter plot shows the relationship between hours spent studying and exam scores. The line shown is the calculated line of best fit. The correlation coefficient is 0.69.

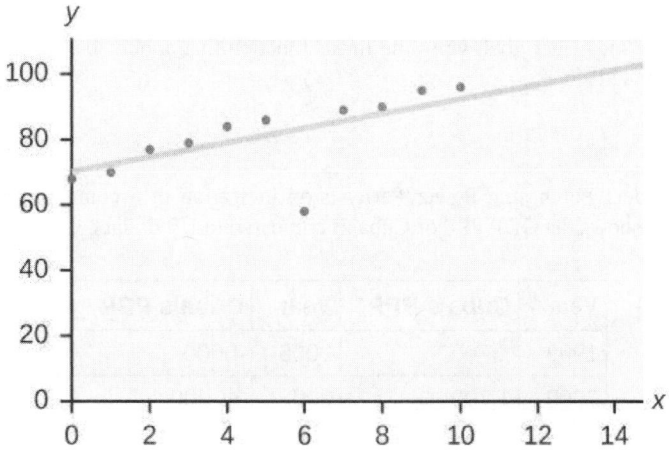

Figure 12.30

51. Do there appear to be any outliers?

52. A point is removed, and the line of best fit is recalculated. The new correlation coefficient is 0.98. Does the point appear to have been an outlier? Why?

53. What effect did the potential outlier have on the line of best fit?

54. Are you more or less confident in the predictive ability of the new line of best fit?

55. The Sum of Squared Errors for a data set of 18 numbers is 49. What is the standard deviation?

56. The Standard Deviation for the Sum of Squared Errors for a data set is 9.8. What is the cutoff for the vertical distance that a point can be from the line of best fit to be considered an outlier?

HOMEWORK

12.1 Linear Equations

57. For each of the following situations, state the independent variable and the dependent variable.
   a.   A study is done to determine if elderly drivers are involved in more motor vehicle fatalities than other drivers. The number of fatalities per 100,000 drivers is compared to the age of drivers.
   b.   A study is done to determine if the weekly grocery bill changes based on the number of family members.
   c.   Insurance companies base life insurance premiums partially on the age of the applicant.
   d.   Utility bills vary according to power consumption.
   e.   A study is done to determine if a higher education reduces the crime rate in a population.

58. Piece-rate systems are widely debated incentive payment plans. In a recent study of loan officer effectiveness, the following piece-rate system was examined:

% of goal reached	< 80	80	100	120
Incentive	n/a	$4,000 with an additional $125 added per percentage point from 81–99%	$6,500 with an additional $125 added per percentage point from 101–119%	$9,500 with an additional $125 added per percentage point starting at 121%

Table 12.15

If a loan officer makes 95% of his or her goal, write the linear function that applies based on the incentive plan table. In context, explain the *y*-intercept and slope.

12.2 Scatter Plots

59. The Gross Domestic Product Purchasing Power Parity is an indication of a country's currency value compared to another country. **Table 12.16** shows the GDP PPP of Cuba as compared to US dollars. Construct a scatter plot of the data.

Year	Cuba's PPP	Year	Cuba's PPP
1999	1,700	2006	4,000
2000	1,700	2007	11,000
2002	2,300	2008	9,500
2003	2,900	2009	9,700
2004	3,000	2010	9,900
2005	3,500		

Table 12.16

60. The following table shows the poverty rates and cell phone usage in the United States. Construct a scatter plot of the data

Year	Poverty Rate	Cellular Usage per Capita
2003	12.7	54.67
2005	12.6	74.19
2007	12	84.86
2009	12	90.82

Table 12.17

61. Does the higher cost of tuition translate into higher-paying jobs? The table lists the top ten colleges based on mid-career salary and the associated yearly tuition costs. Construct a scatter plot of the data.

School	Mid-Career Salary (in thousands)	Yearly Tuition
Princeton	137	28,540
Harvey Mudd	135	40,133
CalTech	127	39,900
US Naval Academy	122	0
West Point	120	0
MIT	118	42,050
Lehigh University	118	43,220
NYU-Poly	117	39,565
Babson College	117	40,400
Stanford	114	54,506

Table 12.18

62. If the level of significance is 0.05 and the p-value is 0.06, what conclusion can you draw?

63. If there are 15 data points in a set of data, what is the number of degree of freedom?

12.3 The Regression Equation

64. What is the process through which we can calculate a line that goes through a scatter plot with a linear pattern?

65. Explain what it means when a correlation has an r^2 of 0.72.

66. Can a coefficient of determination be negative? Why or why not?

12.5 Prediction

67. Recently, the annual number of driver deaths per 100,000 for the selected age groups was as follows:

Age	Number of Driver Deaths per 100,000
16–19	38
20–24	36
25–34	24
35–54	20
55–74	18
75+	28

Table 12.19

a. For each age group, pick the midpoint of the interval for the x value. (For the 75+ group, use 80.)
b. Using "ages" as the independent variable and "Number of driver deaths per 100,000" as the dependent variable, make a scatter plot of the data.
c. Calculate the least squares (best–fit) line. Put the equation in the form of: $\hat{y} = a + bx$
d. Find the correlation coefficient. Is it significant?
e. Predict the number of deaths for ages 40 and 60.
f. Based on the given data, is there a linear relationship between age of a driver and driver fatality rate?
g. What is the slope of the least squares (best-fit) line? Interpret the slope.

68. Table 12.20 shows the life expectancy for an individual born in the United States in certain years.

Year of Birth	Life Expectancy
1930	59.7
1940	62.9
1950	70.2
1965	69.7
1973	71.4
1982	74.5
1987	75
1992	75.7
2010	78.7

Table 12.20

a. Decide which variable should be the independent variable and which should be the dependent variable.
b. Draw a scatter plot of the ordered pairs.
c. Calculate the least squares line. Put the equation in the form of: $\hat{y} = a + bx$
d. Find the correlation coefficient. Is it significant?
e. Find the estimated life expectancy for an individual born in 1950 and for one born in 1982.
f. Why aren't the answers to part e the same as the values in **Table 12.20** that correspond to those years?
g. Use the two points in part e to plot the least squares line on your graph from part b.
h. Based on the data, is there a linear relationship between the year of birth and life expectancy?
i. Are there any outliers in the data?
j. Using the least squares line, find the estimated life expectancy for an individual born in 1850. Does the least squares line give an accurate estimate for that year? Explain why or why not.
k. What is the slope of the least-squares (best-fit) line? Interpret the slope.

69. The maximum discount value of the Entertainment® card for the "Fine Dining" section, Edition ten, for various pages is given in **Table 12.21**

Page number	Maximum value ($)
4	16
14	19
25	15
32	17
43	19
57	15
72	16
85	15
90	17

Table 12.21

a. Decide which variable should be the independent variable and which should be the dependent variable.
b. Draw a scatter plot of the ordered pairs.
c. Calculate the least-squares line. Put the equation in the form of: $\hat{y} = a + bx$
d. Find the correlation coefficient. Is it significant?
e. Find the estimated maximum values for the restaurants on page ten and on page 70.
f. Does it appear that the restaurants giving the maximum value are placed in the beginning of the "Fine Dining" section? How did you arrive at your answer?
g. Suppose that there were 200 pages of restaurants. What do you estimate to be the maximum value for a restaurant listed on page 200?
h. Is the least squares line valid for page 200? Why or why not?
i. What is the slope of the least-squares (best-fit) line? Interpret the slope.

70. Table 12.22 gives the gold medal times for every other Summer Olympics for the women's 100-meter freestyle (swimming).

Year	Time (seconds)
1912	82.2
1924	72.4
1932	66.8
1952	66.8
1960	61.2
1968	60.0
1976	55.65
1984	55.92
1992	54.64
2000	53.8
2008	53.1

Table 12.22

a. Decide which variable should be the independent variable and which should be the dependent variable.
b. Draw a scatter plot of the data.
c. Does it appear from inspection that there is a relationship between the variables? Why or why not?
d. Calculate the least squares line. Put the equation in the form of: $\hat{y} = a + bx$.
e. Find the correlation coefficient. Is the decrease in times significant?
f. Find the estimated gold medal time for 1932. Find the estimated time for 1984.
g. Why are the answers from part f different from the chart values?
h. Does it appear that a line is the best way to fit the data? Why or why not?
i. Use the least-squares line to estimate the gold medal time for the next Summer Olympics. Do you think that your answer is reasonable? Why or why not?

71.

State	# letters in name	Year entered the Union	Rank for entering the Union	Area (square miles)
Alabama	7	1819	22	52,423
Colorado	8	1876	38	104,100
Hawaii	6	1959	50	10,932
Iowa	4	1846	29	56,276
Maryland	8	1788	7	12,407
Missouri	8	1821	24	69,709
New Jersey	9	1787	3	8,722
Ohio	4	1803	17	44,828
South Carolina	13	1788	8	32,008
Utah	4	1896	45	84,904
Wisconsin	9	1848	30	65,499

Table 12.23

We are interested in whether or not the number of letters in a state name depends upon the year the state entered the Union.

    a. Decide which variable should be the independent variable and which should be the dependent variable.
    b. Draw a scatter plot of the data.
    c. Does it appear from inspection that there is a relationship between the variables? Why or why not?
    d. Calculate the least-squares line. Put the equation in the form of: $\hat{y} = a + bx$.
    e. Find the correlation coefficient. What does it imply about the significance of the relationship?
    f. Find the estimated number of letters (to the nearest integer) a state would have if it entered the Union in 1900. Find the estimated number of letters a state would have if it entered the Union in 1940.
    g. Does it appear that a line is the best way to fit the data? Why or why not?
    h. Use the least-squares line to estimate the number of letters a new state that enters the Union this year would have. Can the least squares line be used to predict it? Why or why not?

12.6 Outliers

72. The height (sidewalk to roof) of notable tall buildings in America is compared to the number of stories of the building (beginning at street level).

Height (in feet)	Stories
1,050	57
428	28
362	26
529	40
790	60
401	22
380	38
1,454	110
1,127	100
700	46

Table 12.24

  a. Using "stories" as the independent variable and "height" as the dependent variable, make a scatter plot of the data.
  b. Does it appear from inspection that there is a relationship between the variables?
  c. Calculate the least squares line. Put the equation in the form of: $\hat{y} = a + bx$
  d. Find the correlation coefficient. Is it significant?
  e. Find the estimated heights for 32 stories and for 94 stories.
  f. Based on the data in **Table 12.24**, is there a linear relationship between the number of stories in tall buildings and the height of the buildings?
  g. Are there any outliers in the data? If so, which point(s)?
  h. What is the estimated height of a building with six stories? Does the least squares line give an accurate estimate of height? Explain why or why not.
  i. Based on the least squares line, adding an extra story is predicted to add about how many feet to a building?
  j. What is the slope of the least squares (best-fit) line? Interpret the slope.

73. Ornithologists, scientists who study birds, tag sparrow hawks in 13 different colonies to study their population. They gather data for the percent of new sparrow hawks in each colony and the percent of those that have returned from migration.

Percent return:74; 66; 81; 52; 73; 62; 52; 45; 62; 46; 60; 46; 38
Percent new:5; 6; 8; 11; 12; 15; 16; 17; 18; 18; 19; 20; 20

  a. Enter the data into your calculator and make a scatter plot.
  b. Use your calculator's regression function to find the equation of the least-squares regression line. Add this to your scatter plot from part a.
  c. Explain in words what the slope and y-intercept of the regression line tell us.
  d. How well does the regression line fit the data? Explain your response.
  e. Which point has the largest residual? Explain what the residual means in context. Is this point an outlier? An influential point? Explain.
  f. An ecologist wants to predict how many birds will join another colony of sparrow hawks to which 70% of the adults from the previous year have returned. What is the prediction?

74. The following table shows data on average per capita coffee consumption and heart disease rate in a random sample of 10 countries.

Yearly coffee consumption in liters	2.5	3.9	2.9	2.4	2.9	0.8	9.1	2.7	0.8	0.7
Death from heart diseases	221	167	131	191	220	297	71	172	211	300

Table 12.25

    a. Enter the data into your calculator and make a scatter plot.
    b. Use your calculator's regression function to find the equation of the least-squares regression line. Add this to your scatter plot from part a.
    c. Explain in words what the slope and y-intercept of the regression line tell us.
    d. How well does the regression line fit the data? Explain your response.
    e. Which point has the largest residual? Explain what the residual means in context. Is this point an outlier? An influential point? Explain.
    f. Do the data provide convincing evidence that there is a linear relationship between the amount of coffee consumed and the heart disease death rate? Carry out an appropriate test at a significance level of 0.05 to help answer this question.

75. The following table consists of one student athlete's time (in minutes) to swim 2000 yards and the student's heart rate (beats per minute) after swimming on a random sample of 10 days:

Swim Time	Heart Rate
34.12	144
35.72	152
34.72	124
34.05	140
34.13	152
35.73	146
36.17	128
35.57	136
35.37	144
35.57	148

Table 12.26

    a. Enter the data into your calculator and make a scatter plot.
    b. Use your calculator's regression function to find the equation of the least-squares regression line. Add this to your scatter plot from part a.
    c. Explain in words what the slope and y-intercept of the regression line tell us.
    d. How well does the regression line fit the data? Explain your response.
    e. Which point has the largest residual? Explain what the residual means in context. Is this point an outlier? An influential point? Explain.

76. A researcher is investigating whether population impacts homicide rate. He uses demographic data from Detroit, MI to compare homicide rates and the number of the population that are white males.

Population Size	Homicide rate per 100,000 people
558,724	8.6
538,584	8.9
519,171	8.52
500,457	8.89
482,418	13.07
465,029	14.57
448,267	21.36
432,109	28.03
416,533	31.49
401,518	37.39
387,046	46.26
373,095	47.24
359,647	52.33

Table 12.27

   a. Use your calculator to construct a scatter plot of the data. What should the independent variable be? Why?
   b. Use your calculator's regression function to find the equation of the least-squares regression line. Add this to your scatter plot.
   c. Discuss what the following mean in context.
        i. The slope of the regression equation
        ii. The y-intercept of the regression equation
        iii. The correlation r
        iv. The coefficient of determination r2.

   d. Do the data provide convincing evidence that there is a linear relationship between population size and homicide rate? Carry out an appropriate test at a significance level of 0.05 to help answer this question.

77.

School	Mid-Career Salary (in thousands)	Yearly Tuition
Princeton	137	28,540
Harvey Mudd	135	40,133
CalTech	127	39,900
US Naval Academy	122	0
West Point	120	0
MIT	118	42,050
Lehigh University	118	43,220
NYU-Poly	117	39,565
Babson College	117	40,400
Stanford	114	54,506

Table 12.28

Using the data to determine the linear-regression line equation with the outliers removed. Is there a linear correlation for the data set with outliers removed? Justify your answer.

REFERENCES

12.1 Linear Equations

Data from the Centers for Disease Control and Prevention.

Data from the National Center for agency reporting flu cases and TB Prevention.

12.5 Prediction

Data from the Centers for Disease Control and Prevention.

Data from the National Center for agency reporting flu cases and TB Prevention.

Data from the United States Census Bureau. Available online at http://www.census.gov/compendia/statab/cats/transportation/motor_vehicle_accidents_and_fatalities.html

Data from the National Center for Health Statistics.

12.6 Outliers

Data from the House Ways and Means Committee, the Health and Human Services Department.

Data from Microsoft Bookshelf.

Data from the United States Department of Labor, the Bureau of Labor Statistics.

Data from the Physician's Handbook, 1990.

Data from the United States Department of Labor, the Bureau of Labor Statistics.

BRINGING IT TOGETHER: HOMEWORK

78. The average number of people in a family that attended college for various years is given in **Table 12.29**.

Year	Number of Family Members Attending College
1969	4.0
1973	3.6
1975	3.2
1979	3.0
1983	3.0
1988	3.0
1991	2.9

Table 12.29

a. Using "year" as the independent variable and "Number of Family Members Attending College" as the dependent variable, draw a scatter plot of the data.
b. Calculate the least-squares line. Put the equation in the form of: $\hat{y} = a + bx$
c. Find the correlation coefficient. Is it significant?
d. Pick two years between 1969 and 1991 and find the estimated number of family members attending college.
e. Based on the data in **Table 12.29**, is there a linear relationship between the year and the average number of family members attending college?
f. Using the least-squares line, estimate the number of family members attending college for 1960 and 1995. Does the least-squares line give an accurate estimate for those years? Explain why or why not.
g. Are there any outliers in the data?
h. What is the estimated average number of family members attending college for 1986? Does the least squares line give an accurate estimate for that year? Explain why or why not.
i. What is the slope of the least squares (best-fit) line? Interpret the slope.

79. The percent of female wage and salary workers who are paid hourly rates is given in **Table 12.30** for the years 1979 to 1992.

Year	Percent of workers paid hourly rates
1979	61.2
1980	60.7
1981	61.3
1982	61.3
1983	61.8
1984	61.7
1985	61.8
1986	62.0
1987	62.7
1990	62.8
1992	62.9

Table 12.30

a. Using "year" as the independent variable and "percent" as the dependent variable, draw a scatter plot of the data.
b. Does it appear from inspection that there is a relationship between the variables? Why or why not?
c. Calculate the least-squares line. Put the equation in the form of: $\hat{y} = a + bx$
d. Find the correlation coefficient. Is it significant?
e. Find the estimated percents for 1991 and 1988.
f. Based on the data, is there a linear relationship between the year and the percent of female wage and salary earners who are paid hourly rates?
g. Are there any outliers in the data?
h. What is the estimated percent for the year 2050? Does the least-squares line give an accurate estimate for that year? Explain why or why not.
i. What is the slope of the least-squares (best-fit) line? Interpret the slope.

Use the following information to answer the next two exercises. The cost of a leading liquid laundry detergent in different sizes is given in **Table 12.31**.

Size (ounces)	Cost ($)	Cost per ounce
16	3.99	
32	4.99	
64	5.99	
200	10.99	

Table 12.31

80.

    a. Using "size" as the independent variable and "cost" as the dependent variable, draw a scatter plot.

    b. Does it appear from inspection that there is a relationship between the variables? Why or why not?

    c. Calculate the least-squares line. Put the equation in the form of: $\hat{y} = a + bx$

    d. Find the correlation coefficient. Is it significant?

    e. If the laundry detergent were sold in a 40-ounce size, find the estimated cost.

    f. If the laundry detergent were sold in a 90-ounce size, find the estimated cost.

    g. Does it appear that a line is the best way to fit the data? Why or why not?

    h. Are there any outliers in the given data?

    i. Is the least-squares line valid for predicting what a 300-ounce size of the laundry detergent would you cost? Why or why not?

    j. What is the slope of the least-squares (best-fit) line? Interpret the slope.

81.

    a. Complete **Table 12.31** for the cost per ounce of the different sizes.

    b. Using "size" as the independent variable and "cost per ounce" as the dependent variable, draw a scatter plot of the data.

    c. Does it appear from inspection that there is a relationship between the variables? Why or why not?

    d. Calculate the least-squares line. Put the equation in the form of: $\hat{y} = a + bx$

    e. Find the correlation coefficient. Is it significant?

    f. If the laundry detergent were sold in a 40-ounce size, find the estimated cost per ounce.

    g. If the laundry detergent were sold in a 90-ounce size, find the estimated cost per ounce.

    h. Does it appear that a line is the best way to fit the data? Why or why not?

    i. Are there any outliers in the the data?

    j. Is the least-squares line valid for predicting what a 300-ounce size of the laundry detergent would cost per ounce? Why or why not?

    k. What is the slope of the least-squares (best-fit) line? Interpret the slope.

82. According to a flyer by a Prudential Insurance Company representative, the costs of approximate probate fees and taxes for selected net taxable estates are as follows:

Net Taxable Estate ($)	Approximate Probate Fees and Taxes ($)
600,000	30,000
750,000	92,500
1,000,000	203,000
1,500,000	438,000
2,000,000	688,000
2,500,000	1,037,000
3,000,000	1,350,000

Table 12.32

    a. Decide which variable should be the independent variable and which should be the dependent variable.

    b. Draw a scatter plot of the data.

    c. Does it appear from inspection that there is a relationship between the variables? Why or why not?

    d. Calculate the least-squares line. Put the equation in the form of: $\hat{y} = a + bx$.

    e. Find the correlation coefficient. Is it significant?

    f. Find the estimated total cost for a next taxable estate of $1,000,000. Find the cost for $2,500,000.

    g. Does it appear that a line is the best way to fit the data? Why or why not?

    h. Are there any outliers in the data?

    i. Based on these results, what would be the probate fees and taxes for an estate that does not have any assets?

    j. What is the slope of the least-squares (best-fit) line? Interpret the slope.

83. The following are advertised sale prices of color televisions at Anderson's.

Size (inches)	Sale Price ($)
9	147
20	197
27	297
31	447
35	1177
40	2177
60	2497

Table 12.33

   a. Decide which variable should be the independent variable and which should be the dependent variable.
   b. Draw a scatter plot of the data.
   c. Does it appear from inspection that there is a relationship between the variables? Why or why not?
   d. Calculate the least-squares line. Put the equation in the form of: $\hat{y} = a + bx$
   e. Find the correlation coefficient. Is it significant?
   f. Find the estimated sale price for a 32 inch television. Find the cost for a 50 inch television.
   g. Does it appear that a line is the best way to fit the data? Why or why not?
   h. Are there any outliers in the data?
   i. What is the slope of the least-squares (best-fit) line? Interpret the slope.

84. Table 12.34 shows the average heights for American boy s in 1990.

Age (years)	Height (cm)
birth	50.8
2	83.8
3	91.4
5	106.6
7	119.3
10	137.1
14	157.5

Table 12.34

   a. Decide which variable should be the independent variable and which should be the dependent variable.
   b. Draw a scatter plot of the data.
   c. Does it appear from inspection that there is a relationship between the variables? Why or why not?
   d. Calculate the least-squares line. Put the equation in the form of: $\hat{y} = a + bx$
   e. Find the correlation coefficient. Is it significant?
   f. Find the estimated average height for a one-year-old. Find the estimated average height for an eleven-year-old.
   g. Does it appear that a line is the best way to fit the data? Why or why not?
   h. Are there any outliers in the data?
   i. Use the least squares line to estimate the average height for a sixty-two-year-old man. Do you think that your answer is reasonable? Why or why not?
   j. What is the slope of the least-squares (best-fit) line? Interpret the slope.

85.

State	# letters in name	Year entered the Union	Ranks for entering the Union	Area (square miles)
Alabama	7	1819	22	52,423
Colorado	8	1876	38	104,100
Hawaii	6	1959	50	10,932
Iowa	4	1846	29	56,276
Maryland	8	1788	7	12,407
Missouri	8	1821	24	69,709
New Jersey	9	1787	3	8,722
Ohio	4	1803	17	44,828
South Carolina	13	1788	8	32,008
Utah	4	1896	45	84,904
Wisconsin	9	1848	30	65,499

Table 12.35

We are interested in whether there is a relationship between the ranking of a state and the area of the state.
   a. What are the independent and dependent variables?
   b. What do you think the scatter plot will look like? Make a scatter plot of the data.
   c. Does it appear from inspection that there is a relationship between the variables? Why or why not?
   d. Calculate the least-squares line. Put the equation in the form of: $\hat{y} = a + bx$
   e. Find the correlation coefficient. What does it imply about the significance of the relationship?
   f. Find the estimated areas for Alabama and for Colorado. Are they close to the actual areas?
   g. Use the two points in part f to plot the least-squares line on your graph from part b.
   h. Does it appear that a line is the best way to fit the data? Why or why not?
   i. Are there any outliers?
   j. Use the least squares line to estimate the area of a new state that enters the Union. Can the least-squares line be used to predict it? Why or why not?
   k. Delete "Hawaii" and substitute "Alaska" for it. Alaska is the forty-ninth, state with an area of 656,424 square miles.
   l. Calculate the new least-squares line.
   m. Find the estimated area for Alabama. Is it closer to the actual area with this new least-squares line or with the previous one that included Hawaii? Why do you think that's the case?
   n. Do you think that, in general, newer states are larger than the original states?

SOLUTIONS

1 dependent variable: fee amount; independent variable: time

3

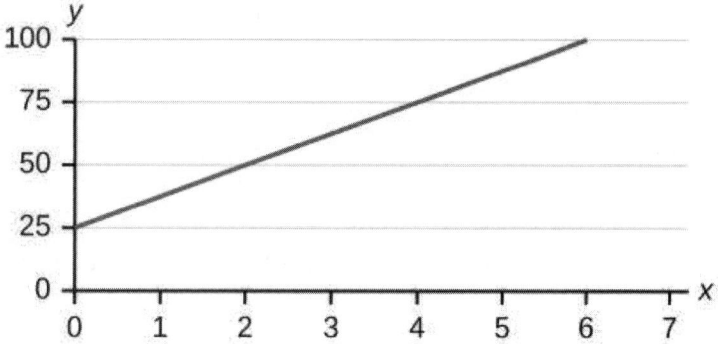

Figure 12.31

5

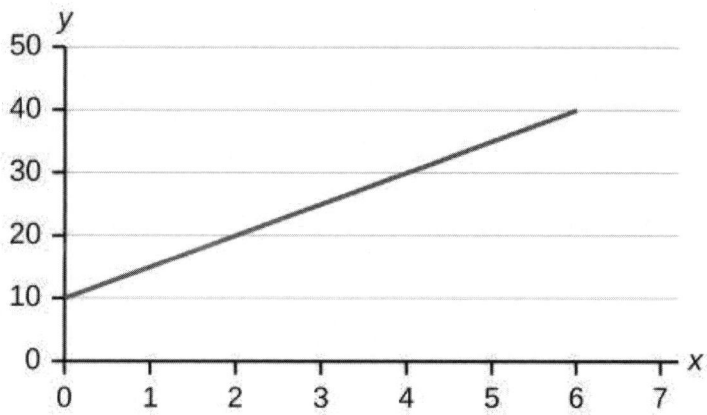

Figure 12.32

7 $y = 6x + 8$, $4y = 8$, and $y + 7 = 3x$ are all linear equations.

9 The number of flu cases depends on the year. Therefore, year becomes the independent variable and the number of flu cases is the dependent variable.

11 The y-intercept is 50 ($a = 50$). At the start of the cleaning, the company charges a one-time fee of $50 (this is when $x = 0$). The slope is 100 ($b = 100$). For each session, the company charges $100 for each hour they clean.

13 12,000 pounds of soil

15 The slope is -1.5 ($b = -1.5$). This means the stock is losing value at a rate of $1.50 per hour. The y-intercept is $15 ($a = 15$). This means the price of stock before the trading day was $15.

17 The data appear to be linear with a strong, positive correlation.

19 The data appear to have no correlation.

21 $\hat{y} = 2.23 + 1.99x$

23 The slope is 1.99 ($b = 1.99$). It means that for every endorsement deal a professional player gets, he gets an average of another $1.99 million in pay each year.

25 It means that there is no correlation between the data sets.

27 Yes, there are enough data points and the value of r is strong enough to show that there is a strong negative correlation between the data sets.

29 H_a: $\rho \neq 0$

31 $250,120

33 1,326 acres

35 1,125 hours, or when $x = 1,125$

37 Check student's solution.

39

 a. When $x = 1985$, $\hat{y} = 25,52$

 b. When $x = 1990$, $\hat{y} = 34,275$

 c. When $x = 1970$, $\hat{y} = -725$ Why doesn't this answer make sense? The range of x values was 1981 to 2002; the year 1970 is not in this range. The regression equation does not apply, because predicting for the year 1970 is extrapolation, which requires a different process. Also, a negative number does not make sense in this context, where we are predicting flu cases diagnosed.

41 Also, the correlation $r = 0.4526$. If r is compared to the value in the 95% Critical Values of the Sample Correlation Coefficient Table, because $r > 0.423$, r is significant, and you would think that the line could be used for prediction. But the scatter plot indicates otherwise.

43 $\hat{y} = 3,448,225 + 1750x$

45 There was an increase in flu cases diagnosed until 1993. From 1993 through 2002, the number of flu cases diagnosed declined each year. It is not appropriate to use a linear regression line to fit to the data.

47 Since there is no linear association between year and # of flu cases diagnosed, it is not appropriate to calculate a linear correlation coefficient. When there is a linear association and it is appropriate to calculate a correlation, we cannot say that one variable "causes" the other variable.

49 We don't know if the pre-1981 data was collected from a single year. So we don't have an accurate x value for this figure. Regression equation: $\hat{y}$ (#Flu Cases) = $-3,448,225 + 1749.777$ (year)

	Coefficients
Intercept	–3,448,225
X Variable 1	1,749.777

Table 12.36

51 Yes, there appears to be an outlier at (6, 58).

53 The potential outlier flattened the slope of the line of best fit because it was below the data set. It made the line of best fit less accurate is a predictor for the data.

55 $s = 1.75$

57

 a. independent variable: age; dependent variable: fatalities

 b. independent variable: # of family members; dependent variable: grocery bill

 c. independent variable: age of applicant; dependent variable: insurance premium

 d. independent variable: power consumption; dependent variable: utility

 e. independent variable: higher education (years); dependent variable: crime rates

59 Check student's solution.

61 For graph: check student's solution. Note that tuition is the independent variable and salary is the dependent variable.

63 13

65 It means that 72% of the variation in the dependent variable (y) can be explained by the variation in the independent variable (x).

67

a.

Age	Number of Driver Deaths per 100,000
16–19	38
20–24	36
25–34	24
35–54	20
55–74	18
75+	28

Table 12.37

b. Check student's solution.

c. $\hat{y} = 35.5818045 - 0.19182491x$

d. $r = -0.57874$
For four df and alpha = 0.05, the LinRegTTest gives p-value = 0.2288 so we do not reject the null hypothesis; there is not a significant linear relationship between deaths and age.
Using the table of critical values for the correlation coefficient, with four df, the critical value is 0.811. The correlation coefficient $r = -0.57874$ is not less than -0.811, so we do not reject the null hypothesis.

e. There is not a linear relationship between the two variables, as evidenced by a p-value greater than 0.05.

69

a. We wonder if the better discounts appear earlier in the book so we select page as X and discount as Y.

b. Check student's solution.

c. $\hat{y} = 17.21757 - 0.01412x$

d. $r = -0.2752$
For seven df and alpha = 0.05, using LinRegTTest p-value = 0.4736 so we do not reject; there is a not a significant linear relationship between page and discount.
Using the table of critical values for the correlation coefficient, with seven df, the critical value is 0.666. The correlation coefficient $xi = -0.2752$ is not less than 0.666 so we do not reject.

e. There is not a significant linear correlation so it appears there is no relationship between the page and the amount of the discount.

As the page number increases by one page, the discount decreases by $0.01412

71

a. Year is the independent or x variable; the number of letters is the dependent or y variable.

b. Check student's solution.

c. no

d. $\hat{y} = 47.03 - 0.0216x$

e. -0.4280 The r-value indicates that there is not a significant correlation between the year the state entered the union and the number of letters in the name.

f. No, the relationship does not appear to be linear; the correlation is not significant.

73 a. and b. Check student's solution. c. The slope of the regression line is -0.3031 with a y-intercept of 31.93. In context, the y-intercept indicates that when there are no returning sparrow hawks, there will be almost 32% new sparrow hawks, which doesn't make sense since if there are no returning birds, then the new percentage would have to be 100% (this is an example of why we do not extrapolate). The slope tells us that for each percentage increase in returning birds, the percentage of new birds in the colony decreases by 30.3%. d. If we examine r2, we see that only 57.52% of the variation in the percent of new birds is explained by the model and the correlation coefficient, r = −.7584 only indicates a somewhat strong correlation between returning and new percentages. e. The ordered pair (66, 6) generates the largest residual of 6.0. This means that when the observed return percentage is 66%, our observed new percentage, 6%, is almost 6% less than the predicted new value of 11.98%. If we remove this data pair, we see only an adjusted slope of -.2789 and an adjusted intercept of 30.9816. In other words, even though this data generates the largest residual, it is not an outlier, nor is the data pair an influential point. f. If there are 70% returning birds, we would expect to see y = −.2789(70) + 30.9816 = 0.114 or 11.4% new birds in the colony.

75

a. Check student's solution.

b. Check student's solution.

c. We have a slope of −1.4946 with a y-intercept of 193.88. The slope, in context, indicates that for each additional minute added to the swim time, the heart rate will decrease by 1.5 beats per minute. If the student is not swimming at all, the y-intercept indicates that his heart rate will be 193.88 beats per minute. While the slope has meaning (the longer it takes to swim 2,000 meters, the less effort the heart puts out), the y-intercept does not make sense. If the athlete is not swimming (resting), then his heart rate should be very low.

d. Since only 1.5% of the heart rate variation is explained by this regression equation, we must conclude that this association is not explained with a linear relationship.

e. The point (34.72, 124) generates the largest residual of −11.82. This means that our observed heart rate is almost 12 beats less than our predicted rate of 136 beats per minute. When this point is removed, the slope becomes −2.953 with the y-intercept changing to 247.1616. While the linear association is still very weak, we see that the removed data pair can be considered an influential point in the sense that the y-intercept becomes more meaningful.

77 If we remove the two service academies (the tuition is $0.00), we construct a new regression equation of y = −0.0009x + 160 with a correlation coefficient of 0.71397 and a coefficient of determination of 0.50976. This allows us to say there is a fairly strong linear association between tuition costs and salaries if the service academies are removed from the data set.

79

a. Check student's solution.

b. yes

c. $\hat{y}$ = −266.8863+0.1656x

d. 0.9448; Yes

e. 62.8233; 62.3265

f. yes

g. no; (1987, 62.7)

h. 72.5937; no

i. slope = 0.1656.
   As the year increases by one, the percent of workers paid hourly rates tends to increase by 0.1656.

81

a.

Size (ounces)	Cost ($)	cents/oz
16	3.99	24.94
32	4.99	15.59
64	5.99	9.36
200	10.99	5.50

Table 12.38

b. Check student's solution.

c. There is a linear relationship for the sizes 16 through 64, but that linear trend does not continue to the 200-oz size.

d. $\hat{y} = 20.2368 - 0.0819x$

e. $r = -0.8086$

f. 40-oz: 16.96 cents/oz

g. 90-oz: 12.87 cents/oz

h. The relationship is not linear; the least squares line is not appropriate.

i. no outliers

j. No, you would be extrapolating. The 300-oz size is outside the range of x.

k. slope = -0.08194; for each additional ounce in size, the cost per ounce decreases by 0.082 cents.

83

a. Size is x, the independent variable, price is y, the dependent variable.

b. Check student's solution.

c. The relationship does not appear to be linear.

d. $\hat{y} = -745.252 + 54.75569x$

e. $r = 0.8944$, yes it is significant

f. 32-inch: $1006.93, 50-inch: $1992.53

g. No, the relationship does not appear to be linear. However, r is significant.

h. no, the 60-inch TV

i. For each additional inch, the price increases by $54.76

85

  a. Let rank be the independent variable and area be the dependent variable.

  b. Check student's solution.

  c. There appears to be a linear relationship, with one outlier.

  d. $\hat{y}$ (area) = 24177.06 + 1010.478x

  e. $r = 0.50047$, r is not significant so there is no relationship between the variables.

  f. Alabama: 46407.576 Colorado: 62575.224

  g. Alabama estimate is closer than Colorado estimate.

  h. If the outlier is removed, there is a linear relationship.

  i. There is one outlier (Hawaii).

  j. rank 51: 75711.4; no

  k.

Alabama	7	1819	22	52,423
Colorado	8	1876	38	104,100
Hawaii	6	1959	50	10,932
Iowa	4	1846	29	56,276
Maryland	8	1788	7	12,407
Missouri	8	1821	24	69,709
New Jersey	9	1787	3	8,722
Ohio	4	1803	17	44,828
South Carolina	13	1788	8	32,008
Utah	4	1896	45	84,904
Wisconsin	9	1848	30	65,499

Table 12.39

  l. $\hat{y} = -87065.3 + 7828.532x$

  m. Alabama: 85,162.404; the prior estimate was closer. Alaska is an outlier.

  n. yes, with the exception of Hawaii

79

  a. Check student's solution.

  b. yes

  c. $\hat{y} = -266.8863 + 0.1656x$

  d. 0.9448; Yes

  e. 62.8233; 62.3265

  f. yes

  g. no; (1987, 62.7)

  h. 72.5937; no

  i. slope = 0.1656.
     As the year increases by one, the percent of workers paid hourly rates tends to increase by 0.1656.

81.

Size (ounces)	Cost ($)	cents/oz
16	3.99	24.94
32	4.99	15.59
64	5.99	9.36
200	10.99	5.50

Table 12.40

b. Check student's solution.

c. There is a linear relationship for the sizes 16 through 64, but that linear trend does not continue to the 200-oz size.

d. $\hat{y} = 20.2368 - 0.0819x$

e. $r = -0.8086$

f. 40-oz: 16.96 cents/oz

g. 90-oz: 12.87 cents/oz

h. The relationship is not linear; the least squares line is not appropriate.

i. no outliers

j. No, you would be extrapolating. The 300-oz size is outside the range of x.

k. slope = -0.08194; for each additional ounce in size, the cost per ounce decreases by 0.082 cents.

83

a. Size is x, the independent variable, price is y, the dependent variable.

b. Check student's solution.

c. The relationship does not appear to be linear.

d. $\hat{y} = -745.252 + 54.75569x$

e. $r = 0.8944$, yes it is significant

f. 32-inch: $1006.93, 50-inch: $1992.53

g. No, the relationship does not appear to be linear. However, r is significant.

h. no, the 60-inch TV

i. For each additional inch, the price increases by $54.76

85

a. Let rank be the independent variable and area be the dependent variable.

b. Check student's solution.

c. There appears to be a linear relationship, with one outlier.

d. $\hat{y}$ (area) = $24177.06 + 1010.478x$

e. $r = 0.50047$, r is not significant so there is no relationship between the variables.

f. Alabama: 46407.576 Colorado: 62575.224

g. Alabama estimate is closer than Colorado estimate.

h. If the outlier is removed, there is a linear relationship.

i. There is one outlier (Hawaii).

j. rank 51: 75711.4; no

k.

Alabama	7	1819	22	52,423
Colorado	8	1876	38	104,100
Hawaii	6	1959	50	10,932
Iowa	4	1846	29	56,276
Maryland	8	1788	7	12,407
Missouri	8	1821	24	69,709
New Jersey	9	1787	3	8,722
Ohio	4	1803	17	44,828
South Carolina	13	1788	8	32,008
Utah	4	1896	45	84,904
Wisconsin	9	1848	30	65,499

Table 12.41

l. $\hat{y} = -87065.3 + 7828.532x$

m. Alabama: 85,162.404; the prior estimate was closer. Alaska is an outlier.

n. yes, with the exception of Hawaii

13 | F DISTRIBUTION AND ONE-WAY ANOVA

Figure 13.1 One-way ANOVA is used to measure information from several groups.

Introduction

Chapter Objectives
By the end of this chapter, the student should be able to: • Interpret the F probability distribution as the number of groups and the sample size change. • Discuss two uses for the F distribution: one-way ANOVA and the test of two variances. • Conduct and interpret one-way ANOVA. • Conduct and interpret hypothesis tests of two variances.

Many statistical applications in psychology, social science, business administration, and the natural sciences involve several groups. For example, an environmentalist is interested in knowing if the average amount of pollution varies in several bodies of water. A sociologist is interested in knowing if the amount of income a person earns varies according to his or her upbringing. A consumer looking for a new car might compare the average gas mileage of several models.

For hypothesis tests comparing averages between more than two groups, statisticians have developed a method called "Analysis of Variance" (abbreviated ANOVA). In this chapter, you will study the simplest form of ANOVA called single factor or one-way ANOVA. You will also study the *F* distribution, used for one-way ANOVA, and the test of two variances. This is just a very brief overview of one-way ANOVA. You will study this topic in much greater detail in future statistics courses. One-Way ANOVA, as it is presented here, relies heavily on a calculator or computer.

13.1 | One-Way ANOVA

The purpose of a one-way ANOVA test is to determine the existence of a statistically significant difference among several group means. The test actually uses **variances** to help determine if the means are equal or not. In order to perform a one-way ANOVA test, there are five basic **assumptions** to be fulfilled:

1. Each population from which a sample is taken is assumed to be normal.
2. All samples are randomly selected and independent.
3. The populations are assumed to have **equal standard deviations (or variances)**.
4. The factor is a categorical variable.
5. The response is a numerical variable.

The Null and Alternative Hypotheses

The null hypothesis is simply that all the group population means are the same. The alternative hypothesis is that at least one pair of means is different. For example, if there are *k* groups:

$H_0: \mu_1 = \mu_2 = \mu_3 = ... = \mu_k$

H_a: At least two of the group means $\mu_1, \mu_2, \mu_3, ..., \mu_k$ are not equal. That is, $\mu_i \neq \mu_j$ for some $i \neq j$.

The graphs, a set of box plots representing the distribution of values with the group means indicated by a horizontal line through the box, help in the understanding of the hypothesis test. In the first graph (red box plots), $H_0: \mu_1 = \mu_2 = \mu_3$ and the three populations have the same distribution if the null hypothesis is true. The variance of the combined data is approximately the same as the variance of each of the populations.

If the null hypothesis is false, then the variance of the combined data is larger which is caused by the different means as shown in the second graph (green box plots).

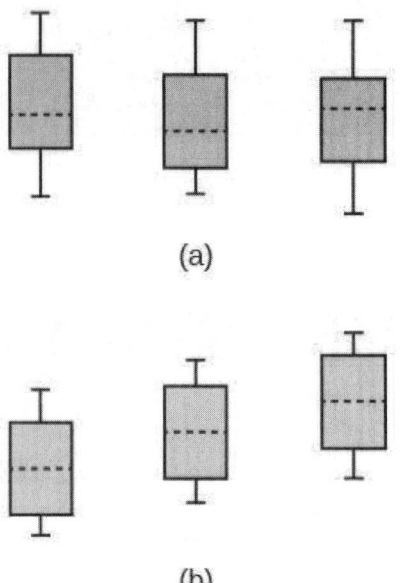

Figure 13.2 (a) H_0 is true. All means are the same; the differences are due to random variation. (b) H_0 is not true. All means are not the same; the differences are too large to be due to random variation.

13.2 | The F Distribution and the F-Ratio

The distribution used for the hypothesis test is a new one. It is called the **F distribution**, named after Sir Ronald Fisher, an English statistician. The F statistic is a ratio (a fraction). There are two sets of degrees of freedom; one for the numerator and one for the denominator.

For example, if F follows an F distribution and the number of degrees of freedom for the numerator is four, and the number of degrees of freedom for the denominator is ten, then $F \sim F_{4,10}$.

> **NOTE**
>
> The F distribution is derived from the Student's t-distribution. The values of the F distribution are squares of the corresponding values of the t-distribution. One-Way ANOVA expands the t-test for comparing more than two groups. The scope of that derivation is beyond the level of this course. It is preferable to use ANOVA when there are more than two groups instead of performing pairwise t-tests because performing multiple tests introduces the likelihood of making a Type 1 error.

To calculate the **F ratio**, two estimates of the variance are made.

1. **Variance between samples:** An estimate of σ^2 that is the variance of the sample means multiplied by n (when the sample sizes are the same.). If the samples are different sizes, the variance between samples is weighted to account for the different sample sizes. The variance is also called **variation due to treatment or explained variation.**

2. **Variance within samples:** An estimate of σ^2 that is the average of the sample variances (also known as a pooled variance). When the sample sizes are different, the variance within samples is weighted. The variance is also called the **variation due to error or unexplained variation.**

- SS_{between} = the **sum of squares** that represents the variation among the different samples

- SS_{within} = the sum of squares that represents the variation within samples that is due to chance.

To find a "sum of squares" means to add together squared quantities that, in some cases, may be weighted. We used sum of squares to calculate the sample variance and the sample standard deviation in **Descriptive Statistics**.

MS means " **mean square**." MS_{between} is the variance between groups, and MS_{within} is the variance within groups.

Calculation of Sum of Squares and Mean Square

- k = the number of different groups

- n_j = the size of the jth group

- s_j = the sum of the values in the jth group

- n = total number of all the values combined (total sample size: $\sum n_j$)

- x = one value: $\sum x = \sum s_j$

- Sum of squares of all values from every group combined: $\sum x^2$

- Between group variability: $SS_{\text{total}} = \sum x^2 - \dfrac{\left(\sum x^2\right)}{n}$

- Total sum of squares: $\sum x^2 - \dfrac{\left(\sum x\right)^2}{n}$

- Explained variation: sum of squares representing variation among the different samples: $SS_{\text{between}} = \sum \left[\dfrac{(s_j)^2}{n_j} \right] - \dfrac{\left(\sum s_j\right)^2}{n}$

- Unexplained variation: sum of squares representing variation within samples due to chance: $SS_{\text{within}} = SS_{\text{total}} - SS_{\text{between}}$

- df's for different groups (df's for the numerator): $df = k - 1$

- Equation for errors within samples (df's for the denominator): $df_{\text{within}} = n - k$

- Mean square (variance estimate) explained by the different groups: $MS_{\text{between}} = \dfrac{SS_{\text{between}}}{df_{\text{between}}}$

- Mean square (variance estimate) that is due to chance (unexplained): $MS_{\text{within}} = \dfrac{SS_{\text{within}}}{df_{\text{within}}}$

MS_{between} and MS_{within} can be written as follows:

- $MS_{\text{between}} = \dfrac{SS_{\text{between}}}{df_{\text{between}}} = \dfrac{SS_{\text{between}}}{k-1}$

- $MS_{\text{within}} = \dfrac{SS_{\text{within}}}{df_{\text{within}}} = \dfrac{SS_{\text{within}}}{n-k}$

The one-way ANOVA test depends on the fact that MS_{between} can be influenced by population differences among means of the several groups. Since MS_{within} compares values of each group to its own group mean, the fact that group means might be different does not affect MS_{within}.

The null hypothesis says that all groups are samples from populations having the same normal distribution. The alternate hypothesis says that at least two of the sample groups come from populations with different normal distributions. If the null hypothesis is true, MS_{between} and MS_{within} should both estimate the same value.

NOTE

The null hypothesis says that all the group population means are equal. The hypothesis of equal means implies that the populations have the same normal distribution, because it is assumed that the populations are normal and that they have equal variances.

F-Ratio or F Statistic

$$F = \frac{MS_{\text{between}}}{MS_{\text{within}}}$$

If MS_{between} and MS_{within} estimate the same value (following the belief that H_0 is true), then the F-ratio should be approximately equal to one. Mostly, just sampling errors would contribute to variations away from one. As it turns out, MS_{between} consists of the population variance plus a variance produced from the differences between the samples. MS_{within} is an estimate of the population variance. Since variances are always positive, if the null hypothesis is false, MS_{between} will generally be larger than MS_{within}. Then the F-ratio will be larger than one. However, if the population effect is small, it is not unlikely that MS_{within} will be larger in a given sample.

The foregoing calculations were done with groups of different sizes. If the groups are the same size, the calculations simplify somewhat and the F-ratio can be written as:

F-Ratio Formula when the groups are the same size

$$F = \frac{n \cdot s_{\bar{x}}^{2}}{s^{2}_{\text{pooled}}}$$

where ...

- n = the sample size
- $df_{\text{numerator}} = k - 1$
- $df_{\text{denominator}} = n - k$
- s^2 pooled = the mean of the sample variances (pooled variance)
- $s_{\bar{x}}^{2}$ = the variance of the sample means

Data are typically put into a table for easy viewing. One-Way ANOVA results are often displayed in this manner by computer software.

Source of Variation	Sum of Squares (*SS*)	Degrees of Freedom (*df*)	Mean Square (*MS*)	F
Factor (Between)	SS(Factor)	$k - 1$	$MS\text{(Factor)} = SS\text{(Factor)}/(k - 1)$	$F = MS\text{(Factor)}/MS\text{(Error)}$
Error (Within)	SS(Error)	$n - k$	$MS\text{(Error)} = SS\text{(Error)}/(n - k)$	
Total	SS(Total)	$n - 1$		

Table 13.1

Example 13.1

Three different diet plans are to be tested for mean weight loss. The entries in the table are the weight losses for the different plans. The one-way ANOVA results are shown in **Table 13.2**.

Plan 1: $n_1 = 4$	Plan 2: $n_2 = 3$	Plan 3: $n_3 = 3$
5	3.5	8
4.5	7	4
4		3.5
3	4.5	

Table 13.2

$s_1 = 16.5$, $s_2 = 15$, $s_3 = 15.5$

Following are the calculations needed to fill in the one-way ANOVA table. The table is used to conduct a hypothesis test.

$$SS(between) = \sum \left[\frac{(s_j)^2}{n_j} \right] - \frac{\left(\sum s_j \right)^2}{n}$$

$$= \frac{s_1^2}{4} + \frac{s_2^2}{3} + \frac{s_3^2}{3} - \frac{(s_1 + s_2 + s_3)^2}{10}$$

where $n_1 = 4$, $n_2 = 3$, $n_3 = 3$ and $n = n_1 + n_2 + n_3 = 10$

$$= \frac{(16.5)^2}{4} + \frac{(15)^2}{3} + \frac{(15.5)^2}{3} - \frac{(16.5 + 15 + 15.5)^2}{10}$$

$$SS(between) = 2.2458$$

$$S(total) = \sum x^2 - \frac{\left(\sum x \right)^2}{n}$$

$$= \left(5^2 + 4.5^2 + 4^2 + 3^2 + 3.5^2 + 7^2 + 4.5^2 + 8^2 + 4^2 + 3.5^2 \right)$$

$$- \frac{(5 + 4.5 + 4 + 3 + 3.5 + 7 + 4.5 + 8 + 4 + 3.5)^2}{10}$$

$$= 244 - \frac{47^2}{10} = 244 - 220.9$$

$$SS(total) = 23.1$$

$$SS(within) = SS(total) - SS(between)$$

$$= 23.1 - 2.2458$$

$$SS(within) = 20.8542$$

Using the TI-83, 83+, 84, 84+ Calculator

One-Way ANOVA Table: The formulas for SS(Total), SS(Factor) = SS(Between) and SS(Error) = SS(Within) as shown previously. The same information is provided by the TI calculator hypothesis test function ANOVA in STAT TESTS (syntax is ANOVA(L1, L2, L3) where L1, L2, L3 have the data from Plan 1, Plan 2, Plan 3 respectively).

Source of Variation	Sum of Squares (*SS*)	Degrees of Freedom (*df*)	Mean Square (*MS*)	*F*
Factor (Between)	SS(Factor) = SS(Between) = 2.2458	$k - 1$ = 3 groups − 1 = 2	MS(Factor) = SS(Factor)/$(k - 1)$ = 2.2458/2 = 1.1229	$F =$ MS(Factor)/MS(Error) = 1.1229/2.9792 = 0.3769
Error (Within)	SS(Error) = SS(Within) = 20.8542	$n - k$ = 10 total data − 3 groups = 7	MS(Error) = SS(Error)/$(n - k)$ = 20.8542/7 = 2.9792	
Total	SS(Total) = 2.2458 + 20.8542 = 23.1	$n - 1$ = 10 total data − 1 = 9		

Table 13.3

☞ **13.1** As part of an experiment to see how different types of soil cover would affect slicing tomato production, Marist College students grew tomato plants under different soil cover conditions. Groups of three plants each had one of the following treatments

- bare soil

- a commercial ground cover

- black plastic

- straw

- compost

All plants grew under the same conditions and were the same variety. Students recorded the weight (in grams) of tomatoes produced by each of the $n = 15$ plants:

Bare: $n_1 = 3$	Ground Cover: $n_2 = 3$	Plastic: $n_3 = 3$	Straw: $n_4 = 3$	Compost: $n_5 = 3$
2,625	5,348	6,583	7,285	6,277
2,997	5,682	8,560	6,897	7,818
4,915	5,482	3,830	9,230	8,677

Table 13.4

Create the one-way ANOVA table.

The one-way ANOVA hypothesis test is always right-tailed because larger F-values are way out in the right tail of the F-distribution curve and tend to make us reject H_0.

Notation

The notation for the F distribution is $F \sim F_{df(num),df(denom)}$

where $df(num) = df_{\text{between}}$ and $df(denom) = df_{\text{within}}$

The mean for the F distribution is $\mu = \dfrac{df(denom)}{df(denom) - 2}$

13.3 | Facts About the F Distribution

Here are some facts about the F distribution.

1. The curve is not symmetrical but skewed to the right.

2. There is a different curve for each set of dfs.

3. The F statistic is greater than or equal to zero.

4. As the degrees of freedom for the numerator and for the denominator get larger, the curve approximates the normal.

5. Other uses for the F distribution include comparing two variances and two-way Analysis of Variance. Two-Way Analysis is beyond the scope of this chapter.

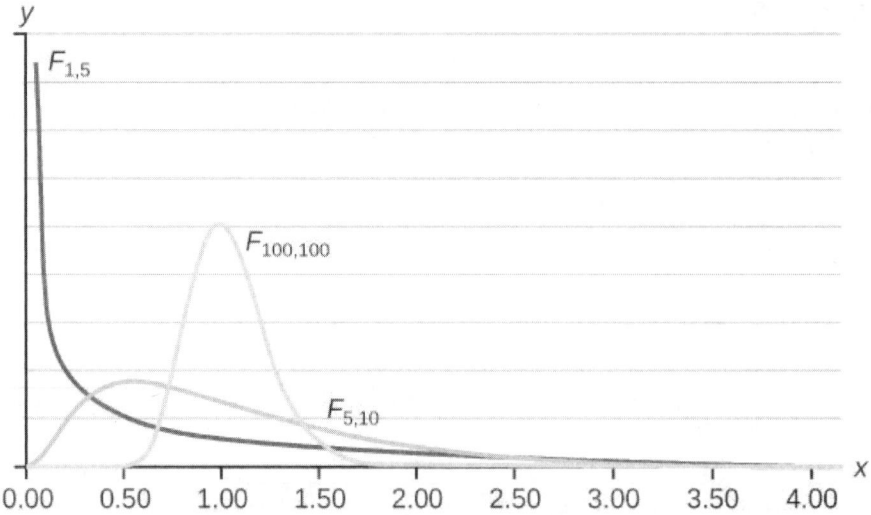

Figure 13.3

Example 13.2

Let's return to the slicing tomato exercise in **Try It**. The means of the tomato yields under the five mulching conditions are represented by μ_1, μ_2, μ_3, μ_4, μ_5. We will conduct a hypothesis test to determine if all means are the same or at least one is different. Using a significance level of 5%, test the null hypothesis that there is no difference in mean yields among the five groups against the alternative hypothesis that at least one mean is different from the rest.

Solution 13.2

The null and alternative hypotheses are:

H_0: $\mu_1 = \mu_2 = \mu_3 = \mu_4 = \mu_5$

H_a: $\mu_i \neq \mu_j$ some $i \neq j$

The one-way ANOVA results are shown in **Figure 13.50**

Source of Variation	Sum of Squares (*SS*)	Degrees of Freedom (*df*)	Mean Square (*MS*)	F
Factor (Between)	36,648,561	5 − 1 = 4	$\frac{36,648,561}{4} = 9,162,140$	$\frac{9,162,140}{2,044,672.6} = 4.4810$
Error (Within)	20,446,726	15 − 5 = 10	$\frac{20,446,726}{10} = 2,044,672.6$	
Total	57,095,287	15 − 1 = 14		

Table 13.5

Distribution for the test: $F_{4,10}$

$df(num) = 5 − 1 = 4$

$df(denom) = 15 − 5 = 10$

Test statistic: $F = 4.4810$

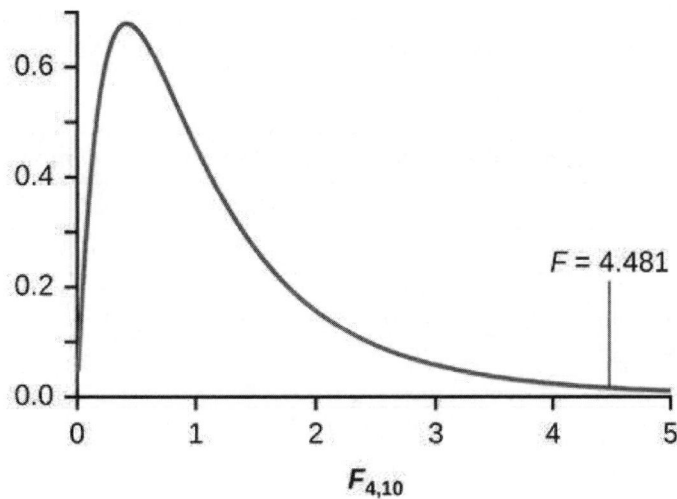

Figure 13.4

Probability Statement: p-value $= P(F > 4.481) = 0.0248$.

Compare α and the p-value: $\alpha = 0.05$, p-value $= 0.0248$

Make a decision: Since $\alpha > p$-value, we reject H_0.

Conclusion: At the 5% significance level, we have reasonably strong evidence that differences in mean yields for slicing tomato plants grown under different mulching conditions are unlikely to be due to chance alone. We may conclude that at least some of mulches led to different mean yields.

 Using the TI-83, 83+, 84, 84+ Calculator

To find these results on the calculator:

Press STAT. Press 1:EDIT. Put the data into the lists L_1, L_2, L_3, L_4, L_5.

Press STAT, and arrow over to TESTS, and arrow down to ANOVA. Press ENTER, and then enter L_1, L_2, L_3, L_4, L_5). Press ENTER. You will see that the values in the foregoing ANOVA table are easily produced by the calculator, including the test statistic and the p-value of the test.

The calculator displays:
$F = 4.4810$
$p = 0.0248$ (p-value)
Factor
$df = 4$
$SS = 36648560.9$
$MS = 9162140.23$
Error
$df = 10$
$SS = 20446726$
$MS = 2044672.6$

13.2 MRSA, or *Staphylococcus aureus*, can cause a serious bacterial infections in hospital patients. **Table 13.6** shows various colony counts from different patients who may or may not have MRSA. The data from the table is plotted in Figure 13.5.

Conc = 0.6	Conc = 0.8	Conc = 1.0	Conc = 1.2	Conc = 1.4
9	16	22	30	27
66	93	147	199	168
98	82	120	148	132

Table 13.6

Plot of the data for the different concentrations:

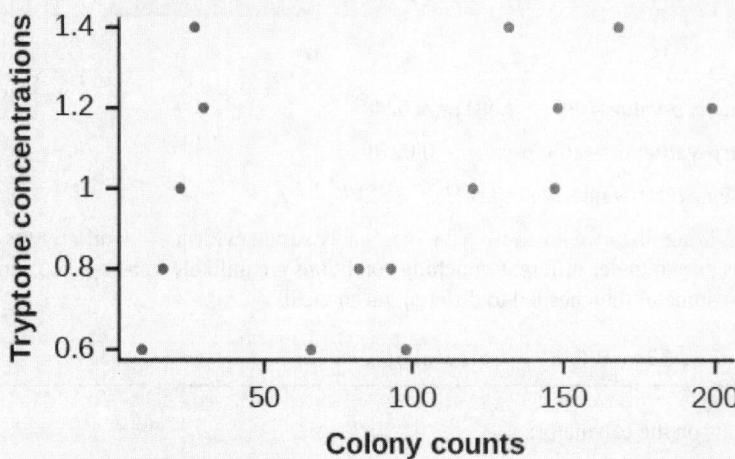

Figure 13.5

Test whether the mean number of colonies are the same or are different. Construct the ANOVA table (by hand or by using a TI-83, 83+, or 84+ calculator), find the *p*-value, and state your conclusion. Use a 5% significance level.

Example 13.3

Four sororities took a random sample of sisters regarding their grade means for the past term. The results are shown in **Table 13.7**.

Sorority 1	Sorority 2	Sorority 3	Sorority 4
2.17	2.63	2.63	3.79
1.85	1.77	3.78	3.45
2.83	3.25	4.00	3.08

Table 13.7 MEAN GRADES FOR FOUR SORORITIES

Sorority 1	Sorority 2	Sorority 3	Sorority 4
1.69	1.86	2.55	2.26
3.33	2.21	2.45	3.18

Table 13.7 MEAN GRADES FOR FOUR SORORITIES

Using a significance level of 1%, is there a difference in mean grades among the sororities?

Solution 13.3

Let μ_1, μ_2, μ_3, μ_4 be the population means of the sororities. Remember that the null hypothesis claims that the sorority groups are from the same normal distribution. The alternate hypothesis says that at least two of the sorority groups come from populations with different normal distributions. Notice that the four sample sizes are each five.

> **NOTE**
>
> This is an example of a **balanced design**, because each factor (i.e., sorority) has the same number of observations.

H_0: $\mu_1 = \mu_2 = \mu_3 = \mu_4$

H_a: Not all of the means μ_1, μ_2, μ_3, μ_4 are equal.

Distribution for the test: $F_{3,16}$

where $k = 4$ groups and $n = 20$ samples in total

$df(num) = k - 1 = 4 - 1 = 3$

$df(denom) = n - k = 20 - 4 = 16$

Calculate the test statistic: $F = 2.23$

Graph:

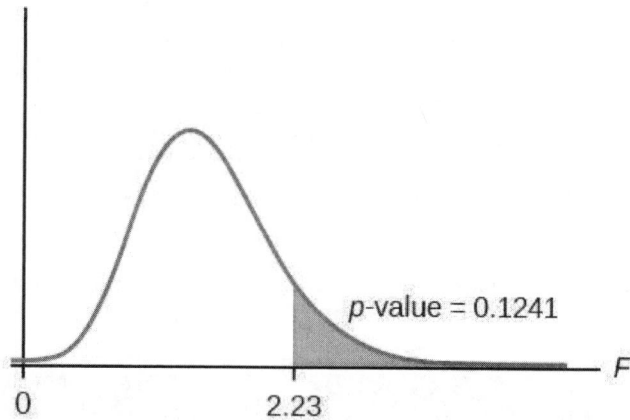

Figure 13.6

Probability statement: p-value = $P(F > 2.23) = 0.1241$

Compare α and the p-value: $\alpha = 0.01$
p-value = 0.1241

$\alpha < p$-value

Make a decision: Since $\alpha < p$-value, you cannot reject H_0.

Conclusion: There is not sufficient evidence to conclude that there is a difference among the mean grades for the sororities.

 Using the TI-83, 83+, 84, 84+ Calculator

Put the data into lists L_1, L_2, L_3, and L_4. Press **STAT** and arrow over to **TESTS**. Arrow down to **F:ANOVA**. Press **ENTER** and Enter (**L1,L2,L3,L4**).

The calculator displays the F statistic, the p-value and the values for the one-way ANOVA table:
$F = 2.2303$
$p = 0.1241$ (p-value)
Factor
$df = 3$
$SS = 2.88732$
$MS = 0.96244$
Error
$df = 16$
$SS = 6.9044$
$MS = 0.431525$

Try It Σ

13.3 Four sports teams took a random sample of players regarding their GPAs for the last year. The results are shown in **Table 13.8**.

Basketball	Baseball	Hockey	Lacrosse
3.6	2.1	4.0	2.0
2.9	2.6	2.0	3.6
2.5	3.9	2.6	3.9
3.3	3.1	3.2	2.7
3.8	3.4	3.2	2.5

Table 13.8 GPAs FOR FOUR SPORTS TEAMS

Use a significance level of 5%, and determine if there is a difference in GPA among the teams.

Example 13.4

A fourth grade class is studying the environment. One of the assignments is to grow bean plants in different soils. Tommy chose to grow his bean plants in soil found outside his classroom mixed with dryer lint. Tara chose to grow her bean plants in potting soil bought at the local nursery. Nick chose to grow his bean plants in soil from his mother's garden. No chemicals were used on the plants, only water. They were grown inside the classroom next to a large window. Each child grew five plants. At the end of the growing period, each plant was measured, producing the data (in inches) in **Table 13.9**.

Tommy's Plants	Tara's Plants	Nick's Plants
24	25	23
21	31	27
23	23	22
30	20	30
23	28	20

Table 13.9

Does it appear that the three media in which the bean plants were grown produce the same mean height? Test at a 3% level of significance.

Solution 13.4

This time, we will perform the calculations that lead to the F' statistic. Notice that each group has the same number of plants, so we will use the formula $F' = \dfrac{n \cdot s_{\bar{x}}^{2}}{s_{pooled}^{2}}$.

First, calculate the sample mean and sample variance of each group.

	Tommy's Plants	Tara's Plants	Nick's Plants
Sample Mean	24.2	25.4	24.4
Sample Variance	11.7	18.3	16.3

Table 13.10

Next, calculate the variance of the three group means (Calculate the variance of 24.2, 25.4, and 24.4). **Variance of the group means = 0.413** = $s_{\bar{x}}^{2}$

Then $MS_{between} = ns_{\bar{x}}^{2} = (5)(0.413)$ where $n = 5$ is the sample size (number of plants each child grew).

Calculate the mean of the three sample variances (Calculate the mean of 11.7, 18.3, and 16.3). **Mean of the sample variances = 15.433** = s^2 *pooled*

Then $MS_{within} = s^2{}_{pooled} = 15.433$.

The F statistic (or F ratio) is $F = \dfrac{MS_{between}}{MS_{within}} = \dfrac{ns_{\bar{x}}^{2}}{s_{pooled}^{2}} = \dfrac{(5)(0.413)}{15.433} = 0.134$

The *dfs* for the numerator = the number of groups $- 1 = 3 - 1 = 2$.

The *dfs* for the denominator = the total number of samples $-$ the number of groups $= 15 - 3 = 12$

The distribution for the test is $F_{2,12}$ and the F statistic is $F = 0.134$

The p-value is $P(F > 0.134) = 0.8759$.

Decision: Since $\alpha = 0.03$ and the p-value $= 0.8759$, do not reject H_0. (Why?)

Conclusion: With a 3% level of significance, from the sample data, the evidence is not sufficient to conclude that the mean heights of the bean plants are different.

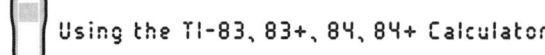

Using the TI-83, 83+, 84, 84+ Calculator

To calculate the *p*-value:

*Press 2nd DISTR

*Arrow down to Fcdf(and press ENTER.

*Enter 0.134, E99, 2, 12)

*Press ENTER

The *p*-value is 0.8759.

Try It Σ

13.4 Another fourth grader also grew bean plants, but this time in a jelly-like mass. The heights were (in inches) 24, 28, 25, 30, and 32. Do a one-way ANOVA test on the four groups. Are the heights of the bean plants different? Use the same method as shown in **Example 13.4**.

Collaborative Exercise

From the class, create four groups of the same size as follows: men under 22, men at least 22, women under 22, women at least 22. Have each member of each group record the number of states in the United States he or she has visited. Run an ANOVA test to determine if the average number of states visited in the four groups are the same. Test at a 1% level of significance. Use one of the solution sheets in **Appendix E**.

13.4 | Test of Two Variances

Another of the uses of the *F* distribution is testing two variances. It is often desirable to compare two variances rather than two averages. For instance, college administrators would like two college professors grading exams to have the same variation in their grading. In order for a lid to fit a container, the variation in the lid and the container should be the same. A supermarket might be interested in the variability of check-out times for two checkers.

In order to perform a *F* test of two variances, it is important that the following are true:

1. The populations from which the two samples are drawn are normally distributed.

2. The two populations are independent of each other.

Unlike most other tests in this book, the *F* test for equality of two variances is very sensitive to deviations from normality. If the two distributions are not normal, the test can give higher *p*-values than it should, or lower ones, in ways that are unpredictable. Many texts suggest that students not use this test at all, but in the interest of completeness we include it here.

Suppose we sample randomly from two independent normal populations. Let σ_1^2 and σ_2^2 be the population variances and s_1^2 and s_2^2 be the sample variances. Let the sample sizes be n_1 and n_2. Since we are interested in comparing the two sample variances, we use the *F* ratio:

$$F = \frac{\left[\frac{(s_1)^2}{(\sigma_1)^2}\right]}{\left[\frac{(s_2)^2}{(\sigma_2)^2}\right]}$$

F has the distribution $F \sim F(n_1 - 1, n_2 - 1)$

where $n_1 - 1$ are the degrees of freedom for the numerator and $n_2 - 1$ are the degrees of freedom for the denominator.

If the null hypothesis is $\sigma_1^2 = \sigma_2^2$, then the F Ratio becomes $F = \frac{\left[\frac{(s_1)^2}{(\sigma_1)^2}\right]}{\left[\frac{(s_2)^2}{(\sigma_2)^2}\right]} = \frac{(s_1)^2}{(s_2)^2}$.

NOTE

The F ratio could also be $\frac{(s_2)^2}{(s_1)^2}$. It depends on H_a and on which sample variance is larger.

If the two populations have equal variances, then s_1^2 and s_2^2 are close in value and $F = \frac{(s_1)^2}{(s_2)^2}$ is close to one. But if the two population variances are very different, s_1^2 and s_2^2 tend to be very different, too. Choosing s_1^2 as the larger sample variance causes the ratio $\frac{(s_1)^2}{(s_2)^2}$ to be greater than one. If s_1^2 and s_2^2 are far apart, then $F = \frac{(s_1)^2}{(s_2)^2}$ is a large number.

Therefore, if F is close to one, the evidence favors the null hypothesis (the two population variances are equal). But if F is much larger than one, then the evidence is against the null hypothesis. **A test of two variances may be left, right, or two-tailed.**

Example 13.5

Two college instructors are interested in whether or not there is any variation in the way they grade math exams. They each grade the same set of 30 exams. The first instructor's grades have a variance of 52.3. The second instructor's grades have a variance of 89.9. Test the claim that the first instructor's variance is smaller. (In most colleges, it is desirable for the variances of exam grades to be nearly the same among instructors.) The level of significance is 10%.

Solution 13.5

Let 1 and 2 be the subscripts that indicate the first and second instructor, respectively.

$n_1 = n_2 = 30$.

H_0: $\sigma_1^2 = \sigma_2^2$ and H_a: $\sigma_1^2 < \sigma_2^2$

Calculate the test statistic: By the null hypothesis ($\sigma_1^2 = \sigma_2^2$), the F statistic is:

$$F = \frac{\left[\frac{(s_1)^2}{(\sigma_1)^2}\right]}{\left[\frac{(s_2)^2}{(\sigma_2)^2}\right]} = \frac{(s_1)^2}{(s_2)^2} = \frac{52.3}{89.9} = 0.5818$$

Distribution for the test: $F_{29,29}$ where $n_1 - 1 = 29$ and $n_2 - 1 = 29$.

Graph: This test is left tailed.

Draw the graph labeling and shading appropriately.

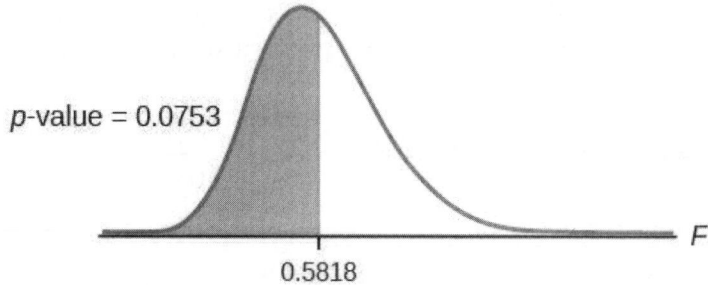

Figure 13.7

Probability statement: p-value $= P(F < 0.5818) = 0.0753$

Compare α and the p-value: $\alpha = 0.10$ $\alpha > p$-value.

Make a decision: Since $\alpha > p$-value, reject H_0.

Conclusion: With a 10% level of significance, from the data, there is sufficient evidence to conclude that the variance in grades for the first instructor is smaller.

 Using the TI-83, 83+, 84, 84+ Calculator

Press **STAT** and arrow over to **TESTS**. Arrow down to **D:2-SampFTest**. Press **ENTER**. Arrow to **Stats** and press **ENTER**. For **Sx1**, **n1**, **Sx2**, and **n2**, enter $\sqrt{(52.3)}$, **30**, $\sqrt{(89.9)}$, and **30**. Press **ENTER** after each. Arrow to **σ1:** and **< σ2**. Press **ENTER**. Arrow down to **Calculate** and press **ENTER**. $F = 0.5818$ and p-value $= 0.0753$. Do the procedure again and try **Draw** instead of **Calculate**.

13.5 The New York Choral Society divides male singers up into four categories from highest voices to lowest: Tenor1, Tenor2, Bass1, Bass2. In the table are heights of the men in the Tenor1 and Bass2 groups. One suspects that taller men will have lower voices, and that the variance of height may go up with the lower voices as well. Do we have good evidence that the variance of the heights of singers in each of these two groups (Tenor1 and Bass2) are different?

Tenor1	Bass2	Tenor 1	Bass 2	Tenor 1	Bass 2
69	72	67	72	68	67
72	75	70	74	67	70
71	67	65	70	64	70
66	75	72	66		69
76	74	70	68		72
74	72	68	75		71
71	72	64	68		74
66	74	73	70		75
68	72	66	72		

Table 13.11

13.5 | Lab: One-Way ANOVA

Stats Lab

13.1 One-Way ANOVA

Class Time:

Names:

Student Learning Outcome

- The student will conduct a simple one-way ANOVA test involving three variables.

Collect the Data

1. Record the price per pound of eight fruits, eight vegetables, and eight breads in your local supermarket.

Fruits	Vegetables	Breads

Table 13.12

2. Explain how you could try to collect the data randomly.

Analyze the Data and Conduct a Hypothesis Test

1. State the null hypothesis and the alternative hypothesis.

2. Compute the following:

   a. Fruit:

      i. $\bar{x}$ = _____

      ii. s_x = _____

      iii. n = _____

   b. Vegetables:

      i. $\bar{x}$ = _____

      ii. s_x = _____

      iii. n = _____

   c. Bread:

      i. $\bar{x}$ = _____

      ii. s_x = _____

      iii. n = _____

3. Find the following:

    a. *df(num)* = _____

    b. *df(denom)* = _____

4. State the approximate distribution for the test.

5. Test statistic: F = _____

6. Sketch a graph of this situation. CLEARLY, label and scale the horizontal axis and shade the region(s) corresponding to the *p*-value.

7. *p*-value = _____

8. Test at $\alpha = 0.05$. State your decision and conclusion.

9. a. Decision: Why did you make this decision?

    b. Conclusion (write a complete sentence).

    c. Based on the results of your study, is there a need to investigate any of the food groups' prices? Why or why not?

KEY TERMS

Analysis of Variance also referred to as ANOVA, is a method of testing whether or not the means of three or more populations are equal. The method is applicable if:

- all populations of interest are normally distributed.
- the populations have equal standard deviations.
- samples (not necessarily of the same size) are randomly and independently selected from each population.

The test statistic for analysis of variance is the F-ratio.

One-Way ANOVA a method of testing whether or not the means of three or more populations are equal; the method is applicable if:

- all populations of interest are normally distributed.
- the populations have equal standard deviations.
- samples (not necessarily of the same size) are randomly and independently selected from each population.
- there is one independent variable and one dependent variable.

The test statistic for analysis of variance is the F-ratio.

Variance mean of the squared deviations from the mean; the square of the standard deviation. For a set of data, a deviation can be represented as $x - \bar{x}$ where x is a value of the data and $\bar{x}$ is the sample mean. The sample variance is equal to the sum of the squares of the deviations divided by the difference of the sample size and one.

CHAPTER REVIEW

13.1 One-Way ANOVA

Analysis of variance extends the comparison of two groups to several, each a level of a categorical variable (factor). Samples from each group are independent, and must be randomly selected from normal populations with equal variances. We test the null hypothesis of equal means of the response in every group versus the alternative hypothesis of one or more group means being different from the others. A one-way ANOVA hypothesis test determines if several population means are equal. The distribution for the test is the F distribution with two different degrees of freedom.

Assumptions:

1. Each population from which a sample is taken is assumed to be normal.
2. All samples are randomly selected and independent.
3. The populations are assumed to have equal standard deviations (or variances).

13.2 The F Distribution and the F-Ratio

Analysis of variance compares the means of a response variable for several groups. ANOVA compares the variation within each group to the variation of the mean of each group. The ratio of these two is the F statistic from an F distribution with (number of groups − 1) as the numerator degrees of freedom and (number of observations − number of groups) as the denominator degrees of freedom. These statistics are summarized in the ANOVA table.

13.3 Facts About the F Distribution

The graph of the F distribution is always positive and skewed right, though the shape can be mounded or exponential depending on the combination of numerator and denominator degrees of freedom. The F statistic is the ratio of a measure of the variation in the group means to a similar measure of the variation within the groups. If the null hypothesis is correct, then the numerator should be small compared to the denominator. A small F statistic will result, and the area under the F curve to the right will be large, representing a large p-value. When the null hypothesis of equal group means is incorrect, then the numerator should be large compared to the denominator, giving a large F statistic and a small area (small p-value) to the right of the statistic under the F curve.

When the data have unequal group sizes (unbalanced data), then techniques from **Section 13.2** need to be used for hand calculations. In the case of balanced data (the groups are the same size) however, simplified calculations based on group means and variances may be used. In practice, of course, software is usually employed in the analysis. As in any analysis, graphs of various sorts should be used in conjunction with numerical techniques. Always look of your data!

13.4 Test of Two Variances

The F test for the equality of two variances rests heavily on the assumption of normal distributions. The test is unreliable if this assumption is not met. If both distributions are normal, then the ratio of the two sample variances is distributed as an F statistic, with numerator and denominator degrees of freedom that are one less than the samples sizes of the corresponding two groups. A **test of two variances** hypothesis test determines if two variances are the same. The distribution for the hypothesis test is the F distribution with two different degrees of freedom.

Assumptions:

1. The populations from which the two samples are drawn are normally distributed.

2. The two populations are independent of each other.

FORMULA REVIEW

13.2 The F Distribution and the F-Ratio

$$SS_{between} = \sum \left[\frac{(s_j)^2}{n_j} \right] - \frac{\left(\sum s_j \right)^2}{n}$$

$$SS_{total} = \sum x^2 - \frac{\left(\sum x \right)^2}{n}$$

$$SS_{within} = SS_{total} - SS_{between}$$

$df_{between} = df(num) = k - 1$

$df_{within} = df(denom) = n - k$

$$MS_{between} = \frac{SS_{between}}{df_{between}}$$

$$MS_{within} = \frac{SS_{within}}{df_{within}}$$

$$F = \frac{MS_{between}}{MS_{within}}$$

F ratio when the groups are the same size: $F = \dfrac{ns_{\bar{x}}^2}{s^2_{pooled}}$

Mean of the F distribution: $\mu = \dfrac{df(num)}{df(denom) - 1}$

where:

- k = the number of groups
- n_j = the size of the jth group
- s_j = the sum of the values in the jth group
- n = the total number of all values (observations) combined
- x = one value (one observation) from the data
- $s_{\bar{x}}^2$ = the variance of the sample means
- s^2_{pooled} = the mean of the sample variances (pooled variance)

13.4 Test of Two Variances

F has the distribution $F \sim F(n_1 - 1, n_2 - 1)$

$$F = \frac{\frac{s_1^2}{\sigma_1^2}}{\frac{s_2^2}{\sigma_2^2}}$$

If $\sigma_1 = \sigma_2$, then $F = \dfrac{s_1^2}{s_2^2}$

PRACTICE

13.1 One-Way ANOVA

Use the following information to answer the next five exercises. There are five basic assumptions that must be fulfilled in order to perform a one-way ANOVA test. What are they?

1. Write one assumption.

2. Write another assumption.

3. Write a third assumption.

4. Write a fourth assumption.

5. Write the final assumption.

6. State the null hypothesis for a one-way ANOVA test if there are four groups.

7. State the alternative hypothesis for a one-way ANOVA test if there are three groups.

8. When do you use an ANOVA test?

13.2 The F Distribution and the F-Ratio

Use the following information to answer the next eight exercises. Groups of men from three different areas of the country are to be tested for mean weight. The entries in **Table 13.13** are the weights for the different groups.

Group 1	Group 2	Group 3
216	202	170
198	213	165
240	284	182
187	228	197
176	210	201

Table 13.13

9. What is the Sum of Squares Factor?

10. What is the Sum of Squares Error?

11. What is the *df* for the numerator?

12. What is the *df* for the denominator?

13. What is the Mean Square Factor?

14. What is the Mean Square Error?

15. What is the *F* statistic?

Use the following information to answer the next eight exercises. Girls from four different soccer teams are to be tested for mean goals scored per game. The entries in the table are the goals per game for the different teams. The one-way ANOVA results are shown in **Table 13.14**.

Team 1	Team 2	Team 3	Team 4
1	2	0	3
2	3	1	4
0	2	1	4
3	4	0	3
2	4	0	2

Table 13.14

16. What is $SS_{between}$?

17. What is the *df* for the numerator?

18. What is $MS_{between}$?

19. What is SS_{within}?

20. What is the *df* for the denominator?

21. What is MS_{within}?

22. What is the *F* statistic?

23. Judging by the *F* statistic, do you think it is likely or unlikely that you will reject the null hypothesis?

13.3 Facts About the F Distribution

24. An *F* statistic can have what values?

25. What happens to the curves as the degrees of freedom for the numerator and the denominator get larger?
Use the following information to answer the next seven exercise. Four basketball teams took a random sample of players regarding how high each player can jump (in inches). The results are shown in **Table 13.15**.

Team 1	Team 2	Team 3	Team 4	Team 5
36	32	48	38	41
42	35	50	44	39
51	38	39	46	40

Table 13.15

26. What is the *df(num)*?

27. What is the *df(denom)*?

28. What are the Sum of Squares and Mean Squares Factors?

29. What are the Sum of Squares and Mean Squares Errors?

30. What is the *F* statistic?

31. What is the *p*-value?

32. At the 5% significance level, is there a difference in the mean jump heights among the teams?

Use the following information to answer the next seven exercises. A video game developer is testing a new game on three different groups. Each group represents a different target market for the game. The developer collects scores from a random sample from each group. The results are shown in **Table 13.16**

Group A	Group B	Group C
101	151	101
108	149	109
98	160	198
107	112	186
111	126	160

Table 13.16

33. What is the *df(num)*?

34. What is the *df(denom)*?

35. What are the $SS_{between}$ and $MS_{between}$?

36. What are the SS_{within} and MS_{within}?

37. What is the F Statistic?

38. What is the p-value?

39. At the 10% significance level, are the scores among the different groups different?

Use the following information to answer the next three exercises. Suppose a group is interested in determining whether teenagers obtain their drivers licenses at approximately the same average age across the country. Suppose that the following data are randomly collected from five teenagers in each region of the country. The numbers represent the age at which teenagers obtained their drivers licenses.

	Northeast	South	West	Central	East
	16.3	16.9	16.4	16.2	17.1
	16.1	16.5	16.5	16.6	17.2
	16.4	16.4	16.6	16.5	16.6
	16.5	16.2	16.1	16.4	16.8
$\bar{x} =$	_____	_____	_____	_____	_____
$s^2 =$	_____	_____	_____	_____	_____

Table 13.17

Enter the data into your calculator or computer.

40. p-value = _____

State the decisions and conclusions (in complete sentences) for the following preconceived levels of α.

41. $\alpha = 0.05$

a. Decision: _____

b. Conclusion: _____

42. $\alpha = 0.01$

a. Decision: _____

b. Conclusion: _____

13.4 Test of Two Variances

Use the following information to answer the next two exercises. There are two assumptions that must be true in order to perform an F test of two variances.

43. Name one assumption that must be true.

44. What is the other assumption that must be true?

Use the following information to answer the next five exercises. Two coworkers commute from the same building. They are interested in whether or not there is any variation in the time it takes them to drive to work. They each record their times for 20 commutes. The first worker's times have a variance of 12.1. The second worker's times have a variance of 16.9. The first worker thinks that he is more consistent with his commute times. Test the claim at the 10% level. Assume that commute times are normally distributed.

45. State the null and alternative hypotheses.

46. What is s_1 in this problem?

47. What is s_2 in this problem?

48. What is n?

49. What is the F statistic?

50. What is the p-value?

51. Is the claim accurate?

Use the following information to answer the next four exercises. Two students are interested in whether or not there is variation in their test scores for math class. There are 15 total math tests they have taken so far. The first student's grades have a standard deviation of 38.1. The second student's grades have a standard deviation of 22.5. The second student thinks his scores are more consistent.

52. State the null and alternative hypotheses.

53. What is the F Statistic?

54. What is the p-value?

55. At the 5% significance level, do we reject the null hypothesis?

Use the following information to answer the next three exercises. Two cyclists are comparing the variances of their overall paces going uphill. Each cyclist records his or her speeds going up 35 hills. The first cyclist has a variance of 23.8 and the second cyclist has a variance of 32.1. The cyclists want to see if their variances are the same or different. Assume that commute times are normally distributed.

56. State the null and alternative hypotheses.

57. What is the F Statistic?

58. At the 5% significance level, what can we say about the cyclists' variances?

HOMEWORK

13.1 One-Way ANOVA

59. Three different traffic routes are tested for mean driving time. The entries in the **Table 13.18** are the driving times in minutes on the three different routes.

Route 1	Route 2	Route 3
30	27	16
32	29	41
27	28	22
35	36	31

Table 13.18

State $SS_{between}$, SS_{within}, and the F statistic.

60. Suppose a group is interested in determining whether teenagers obtain their drivers licenses at approximately the same average age across the country. Suppose that the following data are randomly collected from five teenagers in each region of the country. The numbers represent the age at which teenagers obtained their drivers licenses.

	Northeast	South	West	Central	East
	16.3	16.9	16.4	16.2	17.1
	16.1	16.5	16.5	16.6	17.2
	16.4	16.4	16.6	16.5	16.6
	16.5	16.2	16.1	16.4	16.8
$\bar{x} =$	_____	_____	_____	_____	_____
$s^2 =$	_____	_____	_____	_____	_____

Table 13.19

State the hypotheses.

H_0: _____

H_a: _____

13.2 The F Distribution and the F-Ratio

Use the following information to answer the next three exercises. Suppose a group is interested in determining whether teenagers obtain their drivers licenses at approximately the same average age across the country. Suppose that the following data are randomly collected from five teenagers in each region of the country. The numbers represent the age at which teenagers obtained their drivers licenses.

	Northeast	South	West	Central	East
	16.3	16.9	16.4	16.2	17.1
	16.1	16.5	16.5	16.6	17.2
	16.4	16.4	16.6	16.5	16.6
	16.5	16.2	16.1	16.4	16.8
$\bar{x} =$	_____	_____	_____	_____	_____
$s^2 =$	_____	_____	_____	_____	_____

Table 13.20

H_0: $\mu_1 = \mu_2 = \mu_3 = \mu_4 = \mu_5$

$H\alpha$: At least any two of the group means $\mu_1, \mu_2, ..., \mu_5$ are not equal.

61. degrees of freedom – numerator: $df(num) =$ _____

62. degrees of freedom – denominator: $df(denom) =$ _____

63. F statistic = _____

13.3 Facts About the F Distribution

DIRECTIONS

Use a solution sheet to conduct the following hypothesis tests. The solution sheet can be found in **Appendix E**.

64. Three students, Linda, Tuan, and Javier, are given five laboratory rats each for a nutritional experiment. Each rat's weight is recorded in grams. Linda feeds her rats Formula A, Tuan feeds his rats Formula B, and Javier feeds his rats Formula C. At the end of a specified time period, each rat is weighed again, and the net gain in grams is recorded. Using a significance level of 10%, test the hypothesis that the three formulas produce the same mean weight gain.

Linda's rats	Tuan's rats	Javier's rats
43.5	47.0	51.2
39.4	40.5	40.9
41.3	38.9	37.9
46.0	46.3	45.0
38.2	44.2	48.6

Table 13.21 Weights of Student Lab Rats

65. A grassroots group opposed to a proposed increase in the gas tax claimed that the increase would hurt working-class people the most, since they commute the farthest to work. Suppose that the group randomly surveyed 24 individuals and asked them their daily one-way commuting mileage. The results are in **Table 13.22**. Using a 5% significance level, test the hypothesis that the three mean commuting mileages are the same.

working-class	professional (middle incomes)	professional (wealthy)
17.8	16.5	8.5
26.7	17.4	6.3
49.4	22.0	4.6
9.4	7.4	12.6
65.4	9.4	11.0
47.1	2.1	28.6
19.5	6.4	15.4
51.2	13.9	9.3

Table 13.22

Use the following information to answer the next two exercises. **Table 13.23** lists the number of pages in four different types of magazines.

home decorating	news	health	computer
172	87	82	104
286	94	153	136

Table 13.23

home decorating	news	health	computer
163	123	87	98
205	106	103	207
197	101	96	146

Table 13.23

66. Using a significance level of 5%, test the hypothesis that the four magazine types have the same mean length.

67. Eliminate one magazine type that you now feel has a mean length different from the others. Redo the hypothesis test, testing that the remaining three means are statistically the same. Use a new solution sheet. Based on this test, are the mean lengths for the remaining three magazines statistically the same?

68. A researcher wants to know if the mean times (in minutes) that people watch their favorite news station are the same. Suppose that **Table 13.24** shows the results of a study.

CNN	FOX	Local
45	15	72
12	43	37
18	68	56
38	50	60
23	31	51
35	22	

Table 13.24

Assume that all distributions are normal, the four population standard deviations are approximately the same, and the data were collected independently and randomly. Use a level of significance of 0.05.

69. Are the means for the final exams the same for all statistics class delivery types? **Table 13.25** shows the scores on final exams from several randomly selected classes that used the different delivery types.

Online	Hybrid	Face-to-Face
72	83	80
84	73	78
77	84	84
80	81	81
81		86
		79
		82

Table 13.25

Assume that all distributions are normal, the four population standard deviations are approximately the same, and the data were collected independently and randomly. Use a level of significance of 0.05.

70. Are the mean number of times a month a person eats out the same for whites, blacks, Hispanics and Asians? Suppose that **Table 13.26** shows the results of a study.

White	Black	Hispanic	Asian
6	4	7	8
8	1	3	3
2	5	5	5
4	2	4	1
6		6	7

Table 13.26

Assume that all distributions are normal, the four population standard deviations are approximately the same, and the data were collected independently and randomly. Use a level of significance of 0.05.

71. Are the mean numbers of daily visitors to a ski resort the same for the three types of snow conditions? Suppose that **Table 13.27** shows the results of a study.

Powder	Machine Made	Hard Packed
1,210	2,107	2,846
1,080	1,149	1,638
1,537	862	2,019
941	1,870	1,178
	1,528	2,233
	1,382	

Table 13.27

Assume that all distributions are normal, the four population standard deviations are approximately the same, and the data were collected independently and randomly. Use a level of significance of 0.05.

72. Sanjay made identical paper airplanes out of three different weights of paper, light, medium and heavy. He made four airplanes from each of the weights, and launched them himself across the room. Here are the distances (in meters) that his planes flew.

Paper Type/Trial	Trial 1	Trial 2	Trial 3	Trial 4
Heavy	5.1 meters	3.1 meters	4.7 meters	5.3 meters
Medium	4 meters	3.5 meters	4.5 meters	6.1 meters
Light	3.1 meters	3.3 meters	2.1 meters	1.9 meters

Table 13.28

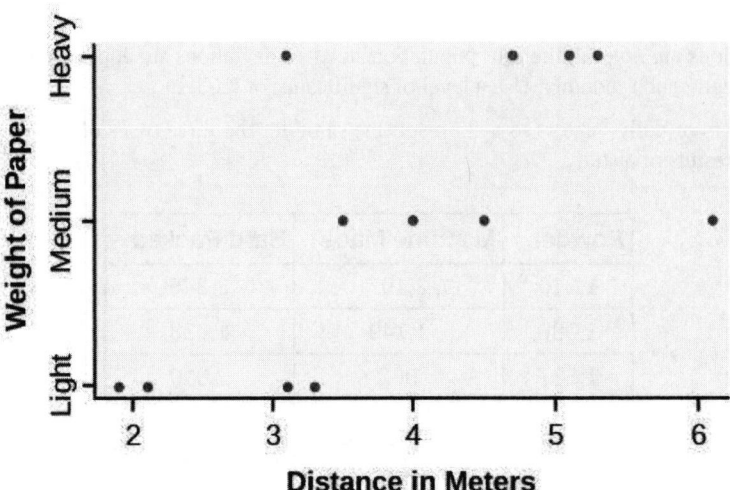

Figure 13.8

    a. Take a look at the data in the graph. Look at the spread of data for each group (light, medium, heavy). Does it seem reasonable to assume a normal distribution with the same variance for each group? Yes or No.

    b. Why is this a balanced design?

    c. Calculate the sample mean and sample standard deviation for each group.

    d. Does the weight of the paper have an effect on how far the plane will travel? Use a 1% level of significance. Complete the test using the method shown in the bean plant example in **Example 13.4**.

        ◦ variance of the group means _____

        ◦ $MS_{between}$ = _____

        ◦ mean of the three sample variances _____

        ◦ MS_{within} = _____

        ◦ F statistic = _____

        ◦ $df(num)$ = _____, $df(denom)$ = _____

        ◦ number of groups _____

        ◦ number of observations _____

        ◦ p-value = _____ ($P(F >$ _____$)$ = _____)

        ◦ Graph the p-value.

        ◦ decision: _____

        ◦ conclusion: _____

73. DDT is a pesticide that has been banned from use in the United States and most other areas of the world. It is quite effective, but persisted in the environment and over time became seen as harmful to higher-level organisms. Famously, egg shells of eagles and other raptors were believed to be thinner and prone to breakage in the nest because of ingestion of DDT in the food chain of the birds.

An experiment was conducted on the number of eggs (fecundity) laid by female fruit flies. There are three groups of flies. One group was bred to be resistant to DDT (the RS group). Another was bred to be especially susceptible to DDT (SS). Finally there was a control line of non-selected or typical fruitflies (NS). Here are the data:

RS	SS	NS	RS	SS	NS
12.8	38.4	35.4	22.4	23.1	22.6
21.6	32.9	27.4	27.5	29.4	40.4
14.8	48.5	19.3	20.3	16	34.4
23.1	20.9	41.8	38.7	20.1	30.4
34.6	11.6	20.3	26.4	23.3	14.9
19.7	22.3	37.6	23.7	22.9	51.8
22.6	30.2	36.9	26.1	22.5	33.8
29.6	33.4	37.3	29.5	15.1	37.9
16.4	26.7	28.2	38.6	31	29.5
20.3	39	23.4	44.4	16.9	42.4
29.3	12.8	33.7	23.2	16.1	36.6
14.9	14.6	29.2	23.6	10.8	47.4
27.3	12.2	41.7			

Table 13.29

The values are the average number of eggs laid daily for each of 75 flies (25 in each group) over the first 14 days of their lives. Using a 1% level of significance, are the mean rates of egg selection for the three strains of fruitfly different? If so, in what way? Specifically, the researchers were interested in whether or not the selectively bred strains were different from the nonselected line, and whether the two selected lines were different from each other.

Here is a chart of the three groups:

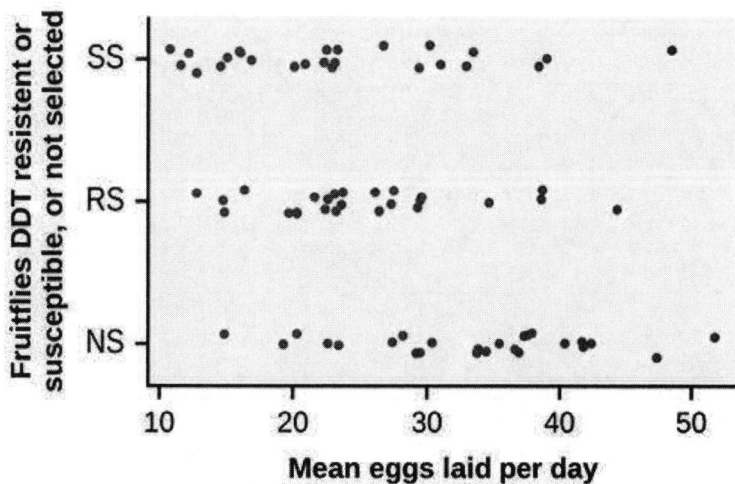

Figure 13.9

74. The data shown is the recorded body temperatures of 130 subjects as estimated from available histograms.

Traditionally we are taught that the normal human body temperature is 98.6 F. This is not quite correct for everyone. Are the mean temperatures among the four groups different?

Calculate 95% confidence intervals for the mean body temperature in each group and comment about the confidence intervals.

FL	FH	ML	MH	FL	FH	ML	MH
96.4	96.8	96.3	96.9	98.4	98.6	98.1	98.6
96.7	97.7	96.7	97	98.7	98.6	98.1	98.6
97.2	97.8	97.1	97.1	98.7	98.6	98.2	98.7
97.2	97.9	97.2	97.1	98.7	98.7	98.2	98.8
97.4	98	97.3	97.4	98.7	98.7	98.2	98.8
97.6	98	97.4	97.5	98.8	98.8	98.2	98.8
97.7	98	97.4	97.6	98.8	98.8	98.3	98.9
97.8	98	97.4	97.7	98.8	98.8	98.4	99
97.8	98.1	97.5	97.8	98.8	98.9	98.4	99
97.9	98.3	97.6	97.9	99.2	99	98.5	99
97.9	98.3	97.6	98	99.3	99	98.5	99.2
98	98.3	97.8	98		99.1	98.6	99.5
98.2	98.4	97.8	98		99.1	98.6	
98.2	98.4	97.8	98.3		99.2	98.7	
98.2	98.4	97.9	98.4		99.4	99.1	
98.2	98.4	98	98.4		99.9	99.3	
98.2	98.5	98	98.6		100	99.4	
98.2	98.6	98	98.6		100.8		

Table 13.30

13.4 Test of Two Variances

75. Three students, Linda, Tuan, and Javier, are given five laboratory rats each for a nutritional experiment. Each rat's weight is recorded in grams. Linda feeds her rats Formula A, Tuan feeds his rats Formula B, and Javier feeds his rats Formula C. At the end of a specified time period, each rat is weighed again and the net gain in grams is recorded.

Linda's rats	Tuan's rats	Javier's rats
43.5	47.0	51.2
39.4	40.5	40.9
41.3	38.9	37.9
46.0	46.3	45.0
38.2	44.2	48.6

Table 13.31

Determine whether or not the variance in weight gain is statistically the same among Javier's and Linda's rats. Test at a significance level of 10%.

76. A grassroots group opposed to a proposed increase in the gas tax claimed that the increase would hurt working-class people the most, since they commute the farthest to work. Suppose that the group randomly surveyed 24 individuals and asked them their daily one-way commuting mileage. The results are as follows.

working-class	professional (middle incomes)	professional (wealthy)
17.8	16.5	8.5
26.7	17.4	6.3
49.4	22.0	4.6
9.4	7.4	12.6
65.4	9.4	11.0
47.1	2.1	28.6
19.5	6.4	15.4
51.2	13.9	9.3

Table 13.32

Determine whether or not the variance in mileage driven is statistically the same among the working class and professional (middle income) groups. Use a 5% significance level.

77. Which two magazine types do you think have the same variance in length?

78. Which two magazine types do you think have different variances in length?

79. Is the variance for the amount of money, in dollars, that shoppers spend on Saturdays at the mall the same as the variance for the amount of money that shoppers spend on Sundays at the mall? Suppose that the **Table 13.33** shows the results of a study.

Saturday	Sunday	Saturday	Sunday
75	44	62	137
18	58	0	82
150	61	124	39
94	19	50	127
62	99	31	141
73	60	118	73
	89		

Table 13.33

80. Are the variances for incomes on the East Coast and the West Coast the same? Suppose that **Table 13.34** shows the results of a study. Income is shown in thousands of dollars. Assume that both distributions are normal. Use a level of significance of 0.05.

East	West
38	71
47	126
30	42
82	51
75	44
52	90
115	88
67	

Table 13.34

81. Thirty men in college were taught a method of finger tapping. They were randomly assigned to three groups of ten, with each receiving one of three doses of caffeine: 0 mg, 100 mg, 200 mg. This is approximately the amount in no, one, or two cups of coffee. Two hours after ingesting the caffeine, the men had the rate of finger tapping per minute recorded. The experiment was double blind, so neither the recorders nor the students knew which group they were in. Does caffeine affect the rate of tapping, and if so how?

Here are the data:

0 mg	100 mg	200 mg	0 mg	100 mg	200 mg
242	248	246	245	246	248
244	245	250	248	247	252
247	248	248	248	250	250
242	247	246	244	246	248
246	243	245	242	244	250

Table 13.35

82. King Manuel I, Komnenus ruled the Byzantine Empire from Constantinople (Istanbul) during the years 1145 to 1180 A.D. The empire was very powerful during his reign, but declined significantly afterwards. Coins minted during his era were found in Cyprus, an island in the eastern Mediterranean Sea. Nine coins were from his first coinage, seven from the second, four from the third, and seven from a fourth. These spanned most of his reign. We have data on the silver content of the coins:

First Coinage	Second Coinage	Third Coinage	Fourth Coinage
5.9	6.9	4.9	5.3
6.8	9.0	5.5	5.6
6.4	6.6	4.6	5.5
7.0	8.1	4.5	5.1
6.6	9.3		6.2
7.7	9.2		5.8
7.2	8.6		5.8
6.9			
6.2			

Table 13.36

Did the silver content of the coins change over the course of Manuel's reign?

Here are the means and variances of each coinage. The data are unbalanced.

	First	Second	Third	Fourth
Mean	6.7444	8.2429	4.875	5.6143
Variance	0.2953	1.2095	0.2025	0.1314

Table 13.37

83. The American League and the National League of Major League Baseball are each divided into three divisions: East, Central, and West. Many years, fans talk about some divisions being stronger (having better teams) than other divisions. This may have consequences for the postseason. For instance, in 2012 Tampa Bay won 90 games and did not play in the postseason, while Detroit won only 88 and did play in the postseason. This may have been an oddity, but is there good evidence that in the 2012 season, the American League divisions were significantly different in overall records? Use the following data to test whether the mean number of wins per team in the three American League divisions were the same or not. Note that the data are not balanced, as two divisions had five teams, while one had only four.

Division	Team	Wins
East	NY Yankees	95
East	Baltimore	93
East	Tampa Bay	90
East	Toronto	73
East	Boston	69

Table 13.38

Division	Team	Wins
Central	Detroit	88
Central	Chicago Sox	85
Central	Kansas City	72
Central	Cleveland	68
Central	Minnesota	66

Table 13.39

Division	Team	Wins
West	Oakland	94
West	Texas	93
West	LA Angels	89
West	Seattle	75

Table 13.40

REFERENCES

13.2 The F Distribution and the F-Ratio

Tomato Data, Marist College School of Science (unpublished student research)

13.3 Facts About the F Distribution

Data from a fourth grade classroom in 1994 in a private K – 12 school in San Jose, CA.

Hand, D.J., F. Daly, A.D. Lunn, K.J. McConway, and E. Ostrowski. *A Handbook of Small Datasets: Data for Fruitfly Fecundity.* London: Chapman & Hall, 1994.

Hand, D.J., F. Daly, A.D. Lunn, K.J. McConway, and E. Ostrowski. *A Handbook of Small Datasets.* London: Chapman & Hall, 1994, pg. 50.

Hand, D.J., F. Daly, A.D. Lunn, K.J. McConway, and E. Ostrowski. A Handbook of Small Datasets. London: Chapman & Hall, 1994, pg. 118.

"MLB Standings – 2012." Available online at http://espn.go.com/mlb/standings/_/year/2012.

Mackowiak, P. A., Wasserman, S. S., and Levine, M. M. (1992), "A Critical Appraisal of 98.6 Degrees F, the Upper Limit of the Normal Body Temperature, and Other Legacies of Carl Reinhold August Wunderlich," *Journal of the American Medical Association*, 268, 1578-1580.

13.4 Test of Two Variances

"MLB Vs. Division Standings – 2012." Available online at http://espn.go.com/mlb/standings/_/year/2012/type/vs-division/order/true.

SOLUTIONS

1 Each population from which a sample is taken is assumed to be normal.

3 The populations are assumed to have equal standard deviations (or variances).

5 The response is a numerical value.

7 H_a: At least two of the group means μ_1, μ_2, μ_3 are not equal.

9 4,939.2

11 2

13 2,469.6

15 3.7416

17 3

19 13.2

21 0.825

23 Because a one-way ANOVA test is always right-tailed, a high F statistic corresponds to a low p-value, so it is likely that we will reject the null hypothesis.

25 The curves approximate the normal distribution.

27 ten

29 $SS = 237.33$; $MS = 23.73$

31 0.1614

33 two

35 $SS = 5,700.4$; $MS = 2,850.2$

37 3.6101

39 Yes, there is enough evidence to show that the scores among the groups are statistically significant at the 10% level.

43 The populations from which the two samples are drawn are normally distributed.

45 H_0: $\sigma_1 = \sigma_2$ H_a: $\sigma_1 < \sigma_2$ or H_0: $\sigma_1^2 = \sigma_2^2$ H_a: $\sigma_1^2 < \sigma_2^2$

47 4.11

49 0.7159

51 No, at the 10% level of significance, we do not reject the null hypothesis and state that the data do not show that the variation in drive times for the first worker is less than the variation in drive times for the second worker.

53 2.8674

55 Reject the null hypothesis. There is enough evidence to say that the variance of the grades for the first student is higher than the variance in the grades for the second student.

57 0.7414

59 $SS_{between} = 26$
$SS_{within} = 441$
$F = 0.2653$

62 $df(denom) = 15$

64

a. $H_0: \mu_L = \mu_T = \mu_J$

b. H_a: at least any two of the means are different

c. $df(num) = 2$; $df(denom) = 12$

d. F distribution

e. 0.67

f. 0.5305

g. Check student's solution.

h. Decision: Do not reject null hypothesis; Conclusion: There is insufficient evidence to conclude that the means are different.

67

a. $H_a: \mu_c = \mu_n = \mu_h$

b. At least any two of the magazines have different mean lengths.

c. $df(num) = 2$, $df(denom) = 12$

d. F distribtuion

e. $F = 15.28$

f. p-value = 0.0005

g. Check student's solution.

h.   i. Alpha: 0.05

    ii. Decision: Reject the Null Hypothesis.

    iii. Reason for decision: p-value < alpha

    iv. Conclusion: There is sufficient evidence to conclude that the mean lengths of the magazines are different.

69

a. $H_0: \mu_o = \mu_h = \mu_f$

b. At least two of the means are different.

c. $df(n) = 2$, $df(d) = 13$

d. $F_{2,13}$

e. 0.64

f. 0.5437

g. Check student's solution.

h.   i. Alpha: 0.05

    ii. Decision: Do not reject the null hypothesis.

    iii. Reason for decision: p-value > alpha

    iv. Conclusion: The mean scores of different class delivery are not different.

71

a. $H_0: \mu_p = \mu_m = \mu_h$

b. At least any two of the means are different.

c. $df(n) = 2$, $df(d) = 12$

d. $F_{2,12}$

e. 3.13

f. 0.0807

g. Check student's solution.

h.   i. Alpha: 0.05

     ii. Decision: Do not reject the null hypothesis.

     iii. Reason for decision: p-value > alpha

     iv. Conclusion: There is not sufficient evidence to conclude that the mean numbers of daily visitors are different.

73 The data appear normally distributed from the chart and of similar spread. There do not appear to be any serious outliers, so we may proceed with our ANOVA calculations, to see if we have good evidence of a difference between the three groups. $H_0: \mu_1 = \mu_2 = \mu_3$; $H_a: \mu_i \neq \mu_j$ some $i \neq j$. Define μ_1, μ_2, μ_3, as the population mean number of eggs laid by the three groups of fruit flies. F statistic = 8.6657; p-value = 0.0004

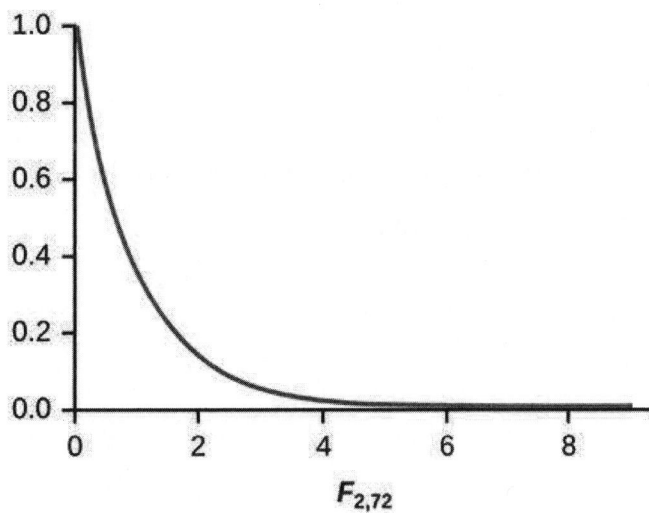

Figure 13.10

Decision: Since the p-value is less than the level of significance of 0.01, we reject the null hypothesis. **Conclusion:** We have good evidence that the average number of eggs laid during the first 14 days of life for these three strains of fruitflies are different. Interestingly, if you perform a two sample t-test to compare the RS and NS groups they are significantly different ($p = 0.0013$). Similarly, SS and NS are significantly different ($p = 0.0006$). However, the two selected groups, RS and SS are *not* significantly different ($p = 0.5176$). Thus we appear to have good evidence that selection either for resistance or for susceptibility involves a reduced rate of egg production (for these specific strains) as compared to flies that were not selected for resistance or susceptibility to DDT. Here, genetic selection has apparently involved a loss of fecundity.

75

a. $H_0: \sigma_1^2 = \sigma_2^2$

b. $H_a: \sigma_1^2 \neq \sigma_1^2$

c. $df(num) = 4$; $df(denom) = 4$

d. $F_{4,\,4}$

e. 3.00

f. 2(0.1563) = 0.3126. Using the TI-83+/84+ function 2-SampFtest, you get the test statistic as 2.9986 and *p*-value directly as 0.3127. If you input the lists in a different order, you get a test statistic of 0.3335 but the *p*-value is the same because this is a two-tailed test.

g. Check student't solution.

h. Decision: Do not reject the null hypothesis; Conclusion: There is insufficient evidence to conclude that the variances are different.

78 The answers may vary. Sample answer: Home decorating magazines and news magazines have different variances.

80

a. $H_0: = \sigma_1^2 = \sigma_2^2$

b. $H_a: \sigma_1^2 \neq \sigma_1^2$

c. $df(n) = 7$, $df(d) = 6$

d. $F_{7,6}$

e. 0.8117

f. 0.7825

g. Check student's solution.

h.   i. Alpha: 0.05

     ii. Decision: Do not reject the null hypothesis.

    iii. Reason for decision: *p*-value > alpha

     iv. Conclusion: There is not sufficient evidence to conclude that the variances are different.

82 Here is a strip chart of the silver content of the coins:

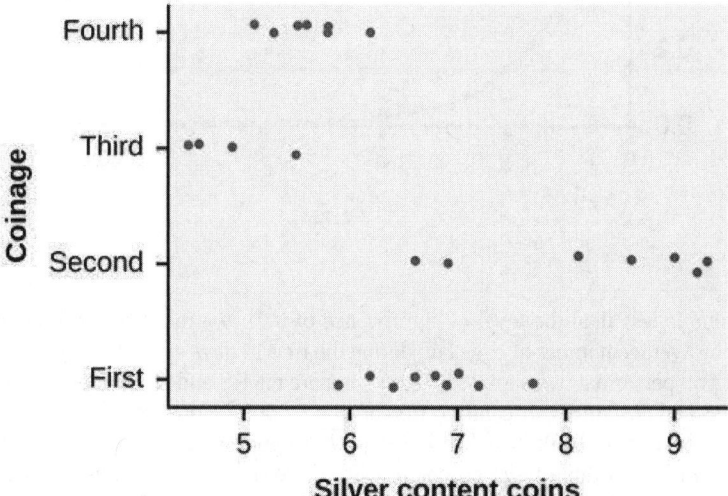

Figure 13.11

While there are differences in spread, it is not unreasonable to use ANOVA techniques. Here is the completed ANOVA table:

Source of Variation	Sum of Squares (*SS*)	Degrees of Freedom (*df*)	Mean Square (*MS*)	*F*
Factor (Between)	37.748	4 − 1 = 3	12.5825	26.272
Error (Within)	11.015	27 − 4 = 23	0.4789	
Total	48.763	27 − 1 = 26		

Table 13.41

$P(F > 26.272) = 0$; Reject the null hypothesis for any alpha. There is sufficient evidence to conclude that the mean silver content among the four coinages are different. From the strip chart, it appears that the first and second coinages had higher silver contents than the third and fourth.

83 Here is a stripchart of the number of wins for the 14 teams in the AL for the 2012 season.

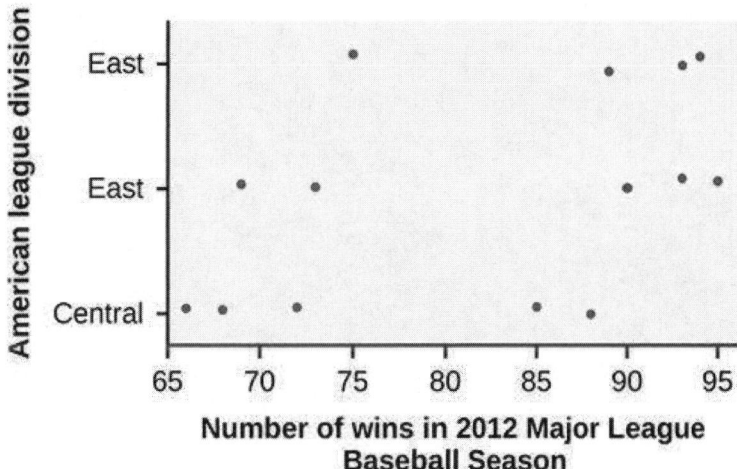

Figure 13.12

While the spread seems similar, there may be some question about the normality of the data, given the wide gaps in the middle near the 0.500 mark of 82 games (teams play 162 games each season in MLB). However, one-way ANOVA is robust. Here is the ANOVA table for the data:

Source of Variation	Sum of Squares (*SS*)	Degrees of Freedom (*df*)	Mean Square (*MS*)	*F*
Factor (Between)	344.16	3 − 1 = 2	172.08	
Error (Within)	1,219.55	14 − 3 = 11	110.87	1.5521
Total	1,563.71	14 − 1 = 13		

Table 13.42

$P(F > 1.5521) = 0.2548$

Since the *p*-value is so large, there is not good evidence against the null hypothesis of equal means. We decline to reject the null hypothesis. Thus, for 2012, there is not any have any good evidence of a significant difference in mean number of wins between the divisions of the American League.

APPENDIX A: REVIEW EXERCISES (CH 3-13)

These review exercises are designed to provide extra practice on concepts learned before a particular chapter. For example, the review exercises for Chapter 3, cover material learned in chapters 1 and 2.

Chapter 3

Use the following information to answer the next six exercises: In a survey of 100 stocks on NASDAQ, the average percent increase for the past year was 9% for NASDAQ stocks.

1. The "average increase" for all NASDAQ stocks is the:

   a. population

   b. statistic

   c. parameter

   d. sample

   e. variable

2. All of the NASDAQ stocks are the:

   a. population

   b. statistics

   c. parameter

   d. sample

   e. variable

3. Nine percent is the:

   a. population

   b. statistics

   c. parameter

   d. sample

   e. variable

4. The 100 NASDAQ stocks in the survey are the:

   a. population

   b. statistic

   c. parameter

   d. sample

   e. variable

5. The percent increase for one stock in the survey is the:

   a. population

b. statistic

c. parameter

d. sample

e. variable

6. Would the data collected by qualitative, quantitative discrete, or quantitative continuous?

Use the following information to answer the next two exercises: Thirty people spent two weeks around Mardi Gras in New Orleans. Their two-week weight gain is below. (Note: a loss is shown by a negative weight gain.)

Weight Gain	Frequency
−2	3
−1	5
0	2
1	4
4	13
6	2
11	1

Table A1

7. Calculate the following values:

a. the average weight gain for the two weeks

b. the standard deviation

c. the first, second, and third quartiles

8. Construct a histogram and box plot of the data.

Chapter 4

Use the following information to answer the next two exercises: A recent poll concerning credit cards found that 35 percent of respondents use a credit card that gives them a mile of air travel for every dollar they charge. Thirty percent of the respondents charge more than $2,000 per month. Of those respondents who charge more than $2,000, 80 percent use a credit card that gives them a mile of air travel for every dollar they charge.

9. What is the probability that a randomly selected respondent will spend more than $2,000 AND use a credit card that gives them a mile of air travel for every dollar they charge?

a. (0.30)(0.35)

b. (0.80)(0.35)

c. (0.80)(0.30)

d. (0.80)

10. Are using a credit card that gives a mile of air travel for each dollar spent AND charging more than $2,000 per month independent events?

a. Yes

b. No, and they are not mutually exclusive either.

c. No, but they are mutually exclusive.

d. Not enough information given to determine the answer

11. A sociologist wants to know the opinions of employed adult women about government funding for day care. She obtains a list of 520 members of a local business and professional women's club and mails a questionnaire to 100 of these women selected at random. Sixty-eight questionnaires are returned. What is the population in this study?

a. all employed adult women

b. all the members of a local business and professional women's club

c. the 100 women who received the questionnaire

d. all employed women with children

Use the following information to answer the next two exercises: The next two questions refer to the following: An article from The San Jose Mercury News was concerned with the racial mix of the 1500 students at Prospect High School in Saratoga, CA. The table summarizes the results. (Male and female values are approximate.) Suppose one Prospect High School student is randomly selected.

Gender/Ethnic group	White	Asian	Hispanic	Black	American Indian
Male	400	468	115	35	16
Female	440	132	140	40	14

Table A2

12. Find the probability that a student is Asian or Male.

13. Find the probability that a student is Black given that the student is female.

14. A sample of pounds lost, in a certain month, by individual members of a weight reducing clinic produced the following statistics:

- Mean = 5 lbs.
- Median = 4.5 lbs.
- Mode = 4 lbs.
- Standard deviation = 3.8 lbs.
- First quartile = 2 lbs.
- Third quartile = 8.5 lbs.

The correct statement is:

a. One fourth of the members lost exactly two pounds.

b. The middle fifty percent of the members lost from two to 8.5 lbs.

c. Most people lost 3.5 to 4.5 lbs.

d. All of the choices above are correct.

15. What does it mean when a data set has a standard deviation equal to zero?

a. All values of the data appear with the same frequency.

b. The mean of the data is also zero.

c. All of the data have the same value.

d. There are no data to begin with.

16. The statement that describe the illustration is:

Figure A1

  a. the mean is equal to the median.

  b. There is no first quartile.

  c. The lowest data value is the median.

  d. The median equals $\dfrac{Q_1 + Q_3}{2}$.

17. According to a recent article in the *San Jose Mercury News* the average number of babies born with significant hearing loss (deafness) is approximately 2 per 1000 babies in a healthy baby nursery. The number climbs to an average of 30 per 1000 babies in an intensive care nursery. Suppose that 1,000 babies from healthy baby nurseries were randomly surveyed. Find the probability that exactly two babies were born deaf.

18. A "friend" offers you the following "deal." For a $10 fee, you may pick an envelope from a box containing 100 seemingly identical envelopes. However, each envelope contains a coupon for a free gift.

  • Ten of the coupons are for a free gift worth $6.

  • Eighty of the coupons are for a free gift worth $8.

  • Six of the coupons are for a free gift worth $12.

  • Four of the coupons are for a free gift worth $40.

Based upon the financial gain or loss over the long run, should you play the game?

  a. Yes, I expect to come out ahead in money.

  b. No, I expect to come out behind in money.

  c. It doesn't matter. I expect to break even.

Use the following information to answer the next four exercises: Recently, a nurse commented that when a patient calls the medical advice line claiming to have the flu, the chance that he/she truly has the flu (and not just a nasty cold) is only about 4%. Of the next 25 patients calling in claiming to have the flu, we are interested in how many actually have the flu.

19. Define the random variable and list its possible values.

20. State the distribution of X.

21. Find the probability that at least four of the 25 patients actually have the flu.

22. On average, for every 25 patients calling in, how many do you expect to have the flu?

Use the following information to answer the next two exercises: Different types of writing can sometimes be distinguished by the number of letters in the words used. A student interested in this fact wants to study the number of letters of words used by Tom Clancy in his novels. She opens a Clancy novel at random and records the number of letters of the first 250 words on the page.

23. What kind of data was collected?

  a. qualitative

  b. quantitative continuous

  c. quantitative discrete

24. What is the population under study?

Chapter 5

Use the following information to answer the next seven exercises: A recent study of mothers of junior high school children in Santa Clara County reported that 76% of the mothers are employed in paid positions. Of those mothers who are employed, 64% work full-time (over 35 hours per week), and 36% work part-time. However, out of all of the mothers in the population, 49% work full-time. The population under study is made up of mothers of junior high school children in Santa Clara County. Let E = employed and F = full-time employment.

25.

a. Find the percent of all mothers in the population that are NOT employed.

b. Find the percent of mothers in the population that are employed part-time.

26. The "type of employment" is considered to be what type of data?

27. Find the probability that a randomly selected mother works part-time given that she is employed.

28. Find the probability that a randomly selected person from the population will be employed or work full-time.

29. Being employed and working part-time:

a. mutually exclusive events? Why or why not?

b. independent events? Why or why not?

Use the following additional information to answer the next two exercises: We randomly pick ten mothers from the above population. We are interested in the number of the mothers that are employed. Let *X* = number of mothers that are employed.

30. State the distribution for *X*.

31. Find the probability that at least six are employed.

32. We expect the statistics discussion board to have, on average, 14 questions posted to it per week. We are interested in the number of questions posted to it per day.

a. Define *X*.

b. What are the values that the random variable may take on?

c. State the distribution for *X*.

d. Find the probability that from ten to 14 (inclusive) questions are posted to the listserv on a randomly picked day.

33. A person invests $1,000 into stock of a company that hopes to go public in one year. The probability that the person will lose all his money after one year (i.e. his stock will be worthless) is 35%. The probability that the person's stock will still have a value of $1,000 after one year (i.e. no profit and no loss) is 60%. The probability that the person's stock will increase in value by $10,000 after one year (i.e. will be worth $11,000) is 5%. Find the expected profit after one year.

34. Rachel's piano cost $3,000. The average cost for a piano is $4,000 with a standard deviation of $2,500. Becca's guitar cost $550. The average cost for a guitar is $500 with a standard deviation of $200. Matt's drums cost $600. The average cost for drums is $700 with a standard deviation of $100. Whose cost was lowest when compared to his or her own instrument?

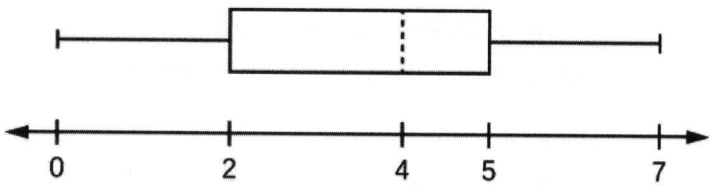

Figure A2

35. Explain why each statement is either true or false given the box plot in **Figure A2**.

a. Twenty-five percent of the data re at most five.

b. There is the same amount of data from 4–5 as there is from 5–7.

c. There are no data values of three.

d. Fifty percent of the data are four.

Using the following information to answer the next two exercises: 64 faculty members were asked the number of cars they owned (including spouse and children's cars). The results are given in the following graph:

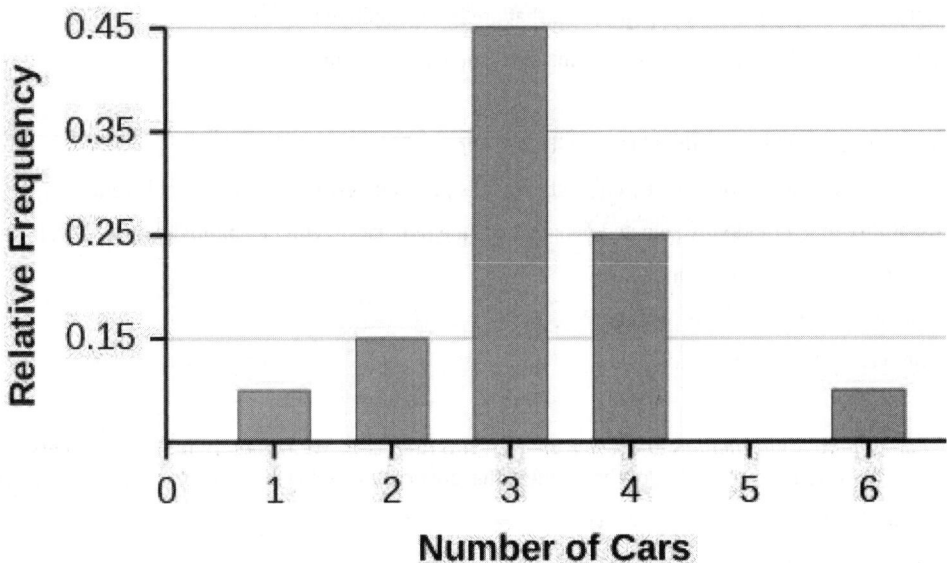

Figure A3

36. Find the approximate number of responses that were three.

37. Find the first, second and third quartiles. Use them to construct a box plot of the data.

Use the following information to answer the next three exercises: **Table A3** shows data gathered from 15 girls on the Snow Leopard soccer team when they were asked how they liked to wear their hair. Supposed one girl from the team is randomly selected.

Hair Style/Hair Color	Blond	Brown	Black
Ponytail	3	2	5
Plain	2	2	1

Table A3

38. Find the probability that the girl has black hair GIVEN that she wears a ponytail.

39. Find the probability that the girl wears her hair plain OR has brown hair.

40. Find the probability that the girl has blond hair AND that she wears her hair plain.

Chapter 6

Use the following information to answer the next two exercises: $X \sim U(3, 13)$

41. Explain which of the following are false and which are true.

a. $f(x) = \frac{1}{10}, 3 \le x \le 13$

b. There is no mode

   c. The median is less than the mean.

   d. $P(x > 10) = P(x \le 6)$

42. Calculate:

   a. the mean.

   b. the median.

   c. the 65th percentile.

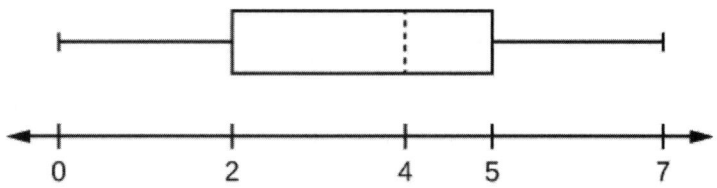

Figure A4

43. Which of the following is true for the box plot in **Figure A4**?

   a. Twenty-five percent of the data are at most five.

   b. There is about the same amount of data from 4–5 as there is from 5–7.

   c. There are no data values of three.

   d. Fifty percent of the data are four.

44. If $P(G|H) = P(G)$, then which of the following is correct?

   a. G and H are mutually exclusive events.

   b. $P(G) = P(H)$

   c. Knowing that H has occurred will affect the chance that G will happen.

   d. G and H are independent events.

45. If $P(J) = 0.3$, $P(K) = 0.63$, and J and K are independent events, then explain which are correct and which are incorrect.

   a. $P(J \text{ AND } K) = 0$

   b. $P(J \text{ OR } K) = 0.9$

   c. $P(J \text{ OR } K) = 0.72$

   d. $P(J) \ne P(J|K)$

46. On average, five students from each high school class get full scholarships to four-year colleges. Assume that most high school classes have about 500 students. X = the number of students from a high school class that get full scholarships to four-year schools. Which of the following is the distribution of X?

   a. $P(5)$

   b. $B(500, 5)$

   c. $Exp\left(\frac{1}{5}\right)$

   d. $N\left(5, \frac{(0.01)(0.99)}{500}\right)$

Chapter 7

Use the following information to answer the next three exercises: Richard's Furniture Company delivers furniture from 10 A.M. to 2 P.M. continuously and uniformly. We are interested in how long (in hours) past the 10 A.M. start time that individuals wait for their delivery.

47. $X \sim$ _____

  a. $U(0, 4)$

  b. $U(10, 20)$

  c. $Exp(2)$

  d. $N(2, 1)$

48. The average wait time is:

  a. 1 hour.

  b. 2 hours.

  c. 2.5 hours.

  d. 4 hours.

49. Suppose that it is now past noon on a delivery day. The probability that a person must wait at least 1.5 more hours is:

  a. $\frac{1}{4}$

  b. $\frac{1}{2}$

  c. $\frac{3}{4}$

  d. $\frac{3}{8}$

50. Given: $X \sim Exp\left(\frac{1}{3}\right)$

  a. Find $P(x > 1)$.

  b. Calculate the minimum value for the upper quartile.

  c. Find $P\left(x = \frac{1}{3}\right)$

51.

- 40% of full-time students took 4 years to graduate
- 30% of full-time students took 5 years to graduate
- 20% of full-time students took 6 years to graduate
- 10% of full-time students took 7 years to graduate

The expected time for full-time students to graduate is:

  a. 4 years

  b. 4.5 years

  c. 5 years

d. 5.5 years

52. Which of the following distributions is described by the following example?
Many people can run a short distance of under two miles, but as the distance increases, fewer people can run that far.

a. binomial

b. uniform

c. exponential

d. normal

53. The length of time to brush one's teeth is generally thought to be exponentially distributed with a mean of $\frac{3}{4}$ minutes.

Find the probability that a randomly selected person brushes his or her teeth less than $\frac{3}{4}$ minutes.

a. 0.5

b. $\frac{3}{4}$

c. 0.43

d. 0.63

54. Which distribution accurately describes the following situation?
The chance that a teenage boy regularly gives his mother a kiss goodnight is about 20%. Fourteen teenage boys are randomly surveyed. Let X = the number of teenage boys that regularly give their mother a kiss goodnight.

a. $B(14,0.20)$

b. $P(2.8)$

c. $N(2.8,2.24)$

d. $Exp\left(\frac{1}{0.20}\right)$

55. A 2008 report on technology use states that approximately 20% of U.S. households have never sent an e-mail. Suppose that we select a random sample of fourteen U.S. households. Let X = the number of households in a 2008 sample of 14 households that have never sent an email

a. $B(14,0.20)$

b. $P(2.8)$

c. $N(2.8,2.24)$

d. $Exp\left(\frac{1}{0.20}\right)$

Chapter 8

Use the following information to answer the next three exercises: Suppose that a sample of 15 randomly chosen people were put on a special weight loss diet. The amount of weight lost, in pounds, follows an unknown distribution with mean equal to 12 pounds and standard deviation equal to three pounds. Assume that the distribution for the weight loss is normal.

56. To find the probability that the mean amount of weight lost by 15 people is no more than 14 pounds, the random variable should be:

a. number of people who lost weight on the special weight loss diet.

b. the number of people who were on the diet.

   c. the mean amount of weight lost by 15 people on the special weight loss diet.

   d. the total amount of weight lost by 15 people on the special weight loss diet.

57. Find the probability asked for in **Question 56**.

58. Find the 90th percentile for the mean amount of weight lost by 15 people.

Using the following information to answer the next three exercises: The time of occurrence of the first accident during rush-hour traffic at a major intersection is uniformly distributed between the three hour interval 4 p.m. to 7 p.m. Let X = the amount of time (hours) it takes for the first accident to occur.

59. What is the probability that the time of occurrence is within the first half-hour or the last hour of the period from 4 to 7 p.m.?

   a. cannot be determined from the information given

   b. $\dfrac{1}{6}$

   c. $\dfrac{1}{2}$

   d. $\dfrac{1}{3}$

60. The 20th percentile occurs after how many hours?

   a. 0.20

   b. 0.60

   c. 0.50

   d. 1

61. Assume Ramon has kept track of the times for the first accidents to occur for 40 different days. Let C = the total cumulative time. Then C follows which distribution?

   a. $U(0,3)$

   b. $Exp(13)$

   c. $N(60, 5.477)$

   d. $N(1.5, 0.01875)$

62. Using the information in **Question 61**, find the probability that the total time for all first accidents to occur is more than 43 hours.

Use the following information to answer the next two exercises: The length of time a parent must wait for his children to clean their rooms is uniformly distributed in the time interval from one to 15 days.

63. How long must a parent expect to wait for his children to clean their rooms?

   a. eight days

   b. three days

   c. 14 days

   d. six days

64. What is the probability that a parent will wait more than six days given that the parent has already waited more than three days?

   a. 0.5174

   b. 0.0174

c. 0.7500

d. 0.2143

Use the following information to answer the next five exercises: Twenty percent of the students at a local community college live in within five miles of the campus. Thirty percent of the students at the same community college receive some kind of financial aid. Of those who live within five miles of the campus, 75% receive some kind of financial aid.

65. Find the probability that a randomly chosen student at the local community college does not live within five miles of the campus.

a. 80%

b. 20%

c. 30%

d. cannot be determined

66. Find the probability that a randomly chosen student at the local community college lives within five miles of the campus or receives some kind of financial aid.

a. 50%

b. 35%

c. 27.5%

d. 75%

67. Are living in student housing within five miles of the campus and receiving some kind of financial aid mutually exclusive?

a. yes

b. no

c. cannot be determined

68. The interest rate charged on the financial aid is _____ data.

a. quantitative discrete

b. quantitative continuous

c. qualitative discrete

d. qualitative

69. The following information is about the students who receive financial aid at the local community college.

- 1st quartile = $250

- 2nd quartile = $700

- 3rd quartile = $1200

These amounts are for the school year. If a sample of 200 students is taken, how many are expected to receive $250 or more?

a. 50

b. 250

c. 150

d. cannot be determined

Use the following information to answer the next two exercises: $P(A) = 0.2$, $P(B) = 0.3$; A and B are independent events.

70. $P(A \text{ AND } B) = $ _____

a. 0.5

b. 0.6

c. 0

d. 0.06

71. $P(A \text{ OR } B) = $ _____

a. 0.56

b. 0.5

c. 0.44

d. 1

72. If H and D are mutually exclusive events, $P(H) = 0.25$, $P(D) = 0.15$, then $P(H|D)$.

a. 1

b. 0

c. 0.40

d. 0.0375

Chapter 9

73. Rebecca and Matt are 14 year old twins. Matt's height is two standard deviations below the mean for 14 year old boys' height. Rebecca's height is 0.10 standard deviations above the mean for 14 year old girls' height. Interpret this.

a. Matt is 2.1 inches shorter than Rebecca.

b. Rebecca is very tall compared to other 14 year old girls.

c. Rebecca is taller than Matt.

d. Matt is shorter than the average 14 year old boy.

74. Construct a histogram of the IPO data (see **Appendix C**).

Use the following information to answer the next three exercises: Ninety homeowners were asked the number of estimates they obtained before having their homes fumigated. Let $X = $ the number of estimates.

x	Relative Frequency	Cumulative Relative Frequency
1	0.3	
2	0.2	
4	0.4	
5	0.1	

Table A4

75. Complete the cumulative frequency column.

76. Calculate the sample mean (a), the sample standard deviation (b) and the percent of the estimates that fall at or below four (c).

77. Calculate the median, M, the first quartile, Q_1, the third quartile, Q_3. Then construct a box plot of the data.

78. The middle 50% of the data are between _____ and _____.

Use the following information to answer the next three exercises: Seventy 5th and 6th graders were asked their favorite dinner.

	Pizza	Hamburgers	Spaghetti	Fried shrimp
5th grader	15	6	9	0
6th grader	15	7	10	8

Table A5

79. Find the probability that one randomly chosen child is in the 6th grade and prefers fried shrimp.

a. $\frac{32}{70}$

b. $\frac{8}{32}$

c. $\frac{8}{8}$

d. $\frac{8}{70}$

80. Find the probability that a child does not prefer pizza.

a. $\frac{30}{70}$

b. $\frac{30}{40}$

c. $\frac{40}{70}$

d. 1

81. Find the probability a child is in the 5th grade given that the child prefers spaghetti.

a. $\frac{9}{19}$

b. $\frac{9}{70}$

c. $\frac{9}{30}$

d. $\frac{19}{70}$

82. A sample of convenience is a random sample.

a. true

b. false

83. A statistic is a number that is a property of the population.

a. true

b. false

84. You should always throw out any data that are outliers.

  a. true

  b. false

85. Lee bakes pies for a small restaurant in Felton, CA. She generally bakes 20 pies in a day, on average. Of interest is the number of pies she bakes each day.

  a. Define the random variable X.

  b. State the distribution for X.

  c. Find the probability that Lee bakes more than 25 pies in any given day.

86. Six different brands of Italian salad dressing were randomly selected at a supermarket. The grams of fat per serving are 7, 7, 9, 6, 8, 5. Assume that the underlying distribution is normal. Calculate a 95% confidence interval for the population mean grams of fat per serving of Italian salad dressing sold in supermarkets.

87. Given: uniform, exponential, normal distributions. Match each to a statement below.

  a. mean = median ≠ mode

  b. mean > median > mode

  c. mean = median = mode

Chapter 10

Use the following information to answer the next three exercises: In a survey at Kirkwood Ski Resort the following information was recorded:

	0–10	11–20	21–40	40+
Ski	10	12	30	8
Snowboard	6	17	12	5

Table A6

Suppose that one person from **Table A6** was randomly selected.

88. Find the probability that the person was a skier or was age 11–20.

89. Find the probability that the person was a snowboarder given he or she was age 21–40.

90. Explain which of the following are true and which are false.

  a. Sport and age are independent events.

  b. Ski and age 11–20 are mutually exclusive events.

  c. $P(\text{Ski AND age } 21\text{–}40) < P(\text{Ski|age } 21\text{–}40)$

  d. $P(\text{Snowboard OR age } 0\text{–}10) < P(\text{Snowboard|age } 0\text{–}10)$

91. The average length of time a person with a broken leg wears a cast is approximately six weeks. The standard deviation is about three weeks. Thirty people who had recently healed from broken legs were interviewed. State the distribution that most accurately reflects total time to heal for the thirty people.

92. The distribution for X is uniform. What can we say for certain about the distribution for $\bar{X}$ when $n = 1$?

  a. The distribution for $\bar{X}$ is still uniform with the same mean and standard deviation as the distribution for X.

b.   The distribution for $\bar{X}$ is normal with the different mean and a different standard deviation as the distribution for X.

c.   The distribution for $\bar{X}$ is normal with the same mean but a larger standard deviation than the distribution for X.

d.   The distribution for $\bar{X}$ is normal with the same mean but a smaller standard deviation than the distribution for X.

93. The distribution for X is uniform. What can we say for certain about the distribution for $\sum X$ when $n = 50$?

a.   distribution for $\sum X$ is still uniform with the same mean and standard deviation as the distribution for X.

b.   The distribution for $\sum X$ is normal with the same mean but a larger standard deviation as the distribution for X.

c.   The distribution for $\sum X$ is normal with a larger mean and a larger standard deviation than the distribution for X.

d.   The distribution for $\sum X$ is normal with the same mean but a smaller standard deviation than the distribution for X.

Use the following information to answer the next three exercises: A group of students measured the lengths of all the carrots in a five-pound bag of baby carrots. They calculated the average length of baby carrots to be 2.0 inches with a standard deviation of 0.25 inches. Suppose we randomly survey 16 five-pound bags of baby carrots.

94. State the approximate distribution for $\bar{X}$, the distribution for the average lengths of baby carrots in 16 five-pound bags.

$\bar{X}$ ~ _____

95. Explain why we cannot find the probability that one individual randomly chosen carrot is greater than 2.25 inches.

96. Find the probability that $\bar{x}$ is between two and 2.25 inches.

Use the following information to answer the next three exercises: At the beginning of the term, the amount of time a student waits in line at the campus store is normally distributed with a mean of five minutes and a standard deviation of two minutes.

97. Find the 90th percentile of waiting time in minutes.

98. Find the median waiting time for one student.

99. Find the probability that the average waiting time for 40 students is at least 4.5 minutes.

Chapter 11

Use the following information to answer the next four exercises: Suppose that the time that owners keep their cars (purchased new) is normally distributed with a mean of seven years and a standard deviation of two years. We are interested in how long an individual keeps his car (purchased new). Our population is people who buy their cars new.

100. Sixty percent of individuals keep their cars **at most** how many years?

101. Suppose that we randomly survey one person. Find the probability that person keeps his or her car **less than** 2.5 years.

102. If we are to pick individuals ten at a time, find the distribution for the **mean** car length ownership.

103. If we are to pick ten individuals, find the probability that the **sum** of their ownership time is more than 55 years.

104. For which distribution is the median not equal to the mean?

a.   Uniform

b.   Exponential

c.   Normal

d.   Student t

105. Compare the standard normal distribution to the Student's t-distribution, centered at zero. Explain which of the following are true and which are false.

a. As the number surveyed increases, the area to the left of –1 for the Student's *t*-distribution approaches the area for the standard normal distribution.

b. As the degrees of freedom decrease, the graph of the Student's *t*-distribution looks more like the graph of the standard normal distribution.

c. If the number surveyed is 15, the normal distribution should never be used.

Use the following information to answer the next five exercises: We are interested in the checking account balance of twenty-year-old college students. We randomly survey 16 twenty-year-old college students. We obtain a sample mean of $640 and a sample standard deviation of $150. Let *X* = checking account balance of an individual twenty year old college student.

106. Explain why we cannot determine the distribution of *X*.

107. If you were to create a confidence interval or perform a hypothesis test for the population mean checking account balance of twenty-year-old college students, what distribution would you use?

108. Find the 95% confidence interval for the true mean checking account balance of a twenty-year-old college student.

109. What type of data is the balance of the checking account considered to be?

110. What type of data is the number of twenty-year-olds considered to be?

111. On average, a busy emergency room gets a patient with a shotgun wound about once per week. We are interested in the number of patients with a shotgun wound the emergency room gets per 28 days.

a. Define the random variable *X*.

b. State the distribution for *X*.

c. Find the probability that the emergency room gets no patients with shotgun wounds in the next 28 days.

Use the following information to answer the next two exercises: The probability that a certain slot machine will pay back money when a quarter is inserted is 0.30. Assume that each play of the slot machine is independent from each other. A person puts in 15 quarters for 15 plays.

112. Is the expected number of plays of the slot machine that will pay back money greater than, less than or the same as the median? Explain your answer.

113. Is it likely that exactly eight of the 15 plays would pay back money? Justify your answer numerically.

114. A game is played with the following rules:

• it costs $10 to enter.

• a fair coin is tossed four times.

• if you do not get four heads or four tails, you lose your $10.

• if you get four heads or four tails, you get back your $10, plus $30 more.

Over the long run of playing this game, what are your expected earnings?

115.

• The mean grade on a math exam in Rachel's class was 74, with a standard deviation of five. Rachel earned an 80.

• The mean grade on a math exam in Becca's class was 47, with a standard deviation of two. Becca earned a 51.

• The mean grade on a math exam in Matt's class was 70, with a standard deviation of eight. Matt earned an 83.

Find whose score was the best, compared to his or her own class. Justify your answer numerically.

Use the following information to answer the next two exercises: A random sample of 70 compulsive gamblers were asked the number of days they go to casinos per week. The results are given in the following graph:

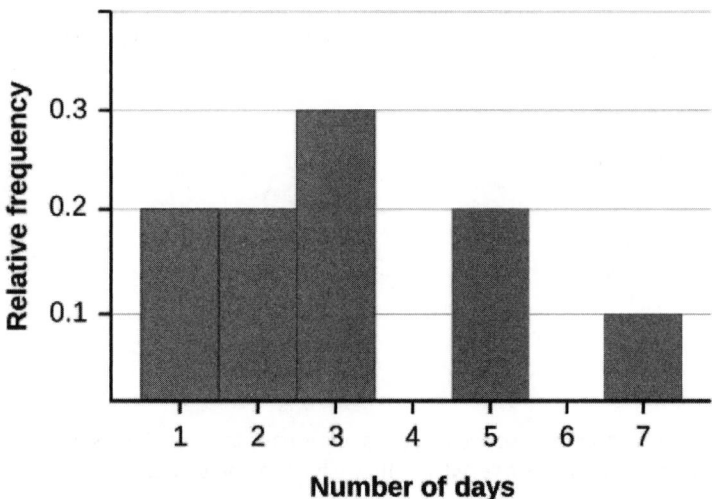

Figure A5

116. Find the number of responses that were five.

117. Find the mean, standard deviation, the median, the first quartile, the third quartile and the *IQR*.

118. Based upon research at De Anza College, it is believed that about 19% of the student population speaks a language other than English at home. Suppose that a study was done this year to see if that percent has decreased. Ninety-eight students were randomly surveyed with the following results. Fourteen said that they speak a language other than English at home.

   a. State an appropriate null hypothesis.

   b. State an appropriate alternative hypothesis.

   c. Define the random variable, P'.

   d. Calculate the test statistic.

   e. Calculate the *p*-value.

   f. At the 5% level of decision, what is your decision about the null hypothesis?

   g. What is the Type I error?

   h. What is the Type II error?

119. Assume that you are an emergency paramedic called in to rescue victims of an accident. You need to help a patient who is bleeding profusely. The patient is also considered to be a high risk for contracting AIDS. Assume that the null hypothesis is that the patient does **not** have the HIV virus. What is a Type I error?

120. It is often said that Californians are more casual than the rest of Americans. Suppose that a survey was done to see if the proportion of Californian professionals that wear jeans to work is greater than the proportion of non-Californian professionals. Fifty of each was surveyed with the following results. Fifteen Californians wear jeans to work and six non-Californians wear jeans to work.
Let C = Californian professional; NC = non-Californian professional

   a. State appropriate null and alternate hypotheses.

   b. Define the random variable.

   c. Calculate the test statistic and *p*-value.

   d. At the 5% significance level, what is your decision?

   e. What is the Type I error?

   f. What is the Type II error?

Use the following information to answer the next two exercises: A group of Statistics students have developed a technique that they feel will lower their anxiety level on statistics exams. They measured their anxiety level at the start of the quarter and again at the end of the quarter. Recorded is the paired data in that order: (1000, 900); (1200, 1050); (600, 700); (1300, 1100); (1000, 900); (900, 900).

121. This is a test of (pick the best answer):

a. large samples, independent means

b. small samples, independent means

c. dependent means

122. State the distribution to use for the test.

Chapter 12

Use the following information to answer the next two exercises: A recent survey of U.S. teenage pregnancy was answered by 720 girls, age 12–19. Six percent of the girls surveyed said they have been pregnant. We are interested in the true proportion of U.S. girls, age 12–19, who have been pregnant.

123. Find the 95% confidence interval for the true proportion of U.S. girls, age 12–19, who have been pregnant.

124. The report also stated that the results of the survey are accurate to within ±3.7% at the 95% confidence level. Suppose that a new study is to be done. It is desired to be accurate to within 2% of the 95% confidence level. What is the minimum number that should be surveyed?

125. Given: $X \sim Exp\left(\frac{1}{3}\right)$. Sketch the graph that depicts: $P(x > 1)$.

Use the following information to answer the next three exercises: The amount of money a customer spends in one trip to the supermarket is known to have an exponential distribution. Suppose the mean amount of money a customer spends in one trip to the supermarket is $72.

126. Find the probability that one customer spends less than $72 in one trip to the supermarket?

127. Suppose five customers pool their money. How much money altogether would you expect the five customers to spend in one trip to the supermarket (in dollars)?

128. State the distribution to use if you want to find the probability that the **mean** amount spent by five customers in one trip to the supermarket is less than $60.

Chapter 13

Use the following information to answer the next two exercises: Suppose that the probability of a drought in any independent year is 20%. Out of those years in which a drought occurs, the probability of water rationing is 10%. However, in any year, the probability of water rationing is 5%.

129. What is the probability of both a drought **and** water rationing occurring?

130. Out of the years with water rationing, find the probability that there is a drought.

Use the following information to answer the next three exercises:

	Apple	Pumpkin	Pecan
Female	40	10	30
Male	20	30	10

Table A7

131. Suppose that one individual is randomly chosen. Find the probability that the person's favorite pie is apple **or** the person is male.

132. Suppose that one male is randomly chosen. Find the probability his favorite pie is pecan.

133. Conduct a hypothesis test to determine if favorite pie type and gender are independent.

Use the following information to answer the next two exercises: Let's say that the probability that an adult watches the news at least once per week is 0.60.

134. We randomly survey 14 people. On average, how many people do we expect to watch the news at least once per week?

135. We randomly survey 14 people. Of interest is the number that watch the news at least once per week. State the distribution of *X*. *X* ~ _____

136. The following histogram is most likely to be a result of sampling from which distribution?

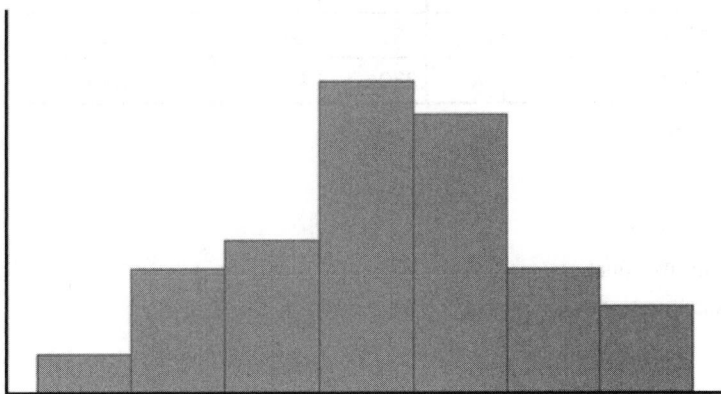

Figure A6

a. Chi-Square

b. Geometric

c. Uniform

d. Binomial

137. The ages of De Anza evening students is known to be normally distributed with a population mean of 40 and a population standard deviation of six. A sample of six De Anza evening students reported their ages (in years) as: 28; 35; 47; 45; 30; 50. Find the probability that the mean of six ages of randomly chosen students is less than 35 years. Hint: Find the sample mean.

138. A math exam was given to all the fifth grade children attending Country School. Two random samples of scores were taken. The null hypothesis is that the mean math scores for boys and girls in fifth grade are the same. Conduct a hypothesis test.

	n	$\bar{x}$	s^2
Boys	55	82	29
Girls	60	86	46

Table A8

139. In a survey of 80 males, 55 had played an organized sport growing up. Of the 70 females surveyed, 25 had played an organized sport growing up. We are interested in whether the proportion for males is higher than the proportion for females. Conduct a hypothesis test.

140. Which of the following is preferable when designing a hypothesis test?

a. Maximize α and minimize β

b. Minimize α and maximize β

c. Maximize α and β

d. Minimize α and β

Use the following information to answer the next three exercises: 120 people were surveyed as to their favorite beverage (non-alcoholic). The results are below.

Beverage/Age	0–9	10–19	20–29	30+	Totals
Milk	14	10	6	0	30
Soda	3	8	26	15	52
Juice	7	12	12	7	38
Totals	24	330	44	22	120

Table A9

141. Are the events of milk and 30+:

a. independent events? Justify your answer.

b. mutually exclusive events? Justify your answer.

142. Suppose that one person is randomly chosen. Find the probability that person is 10–19 given that he or she prefers juice.

143. Are "Preferred Beverage" and "Age" independent events? Conduct a hypothesis test.

144. Given the following histogram, which distribution is the data most likely to come from?

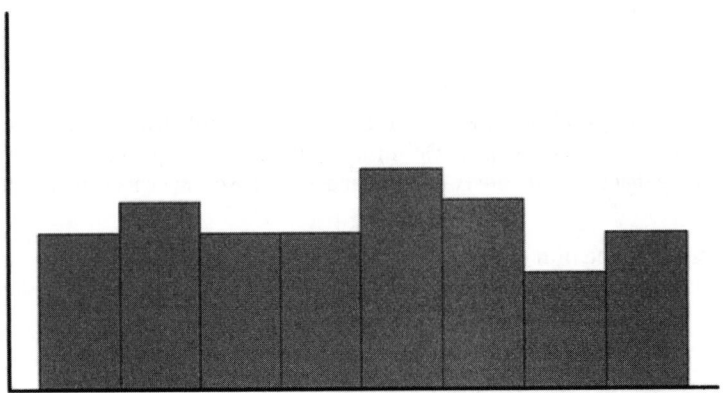

Figure A7

a. uniform

b. exponential

c. normal

d. chi-square

Solutions
Chapter 3

1. c. parameter

2. a. population

3. b. statistic

4. d. sample

5. e. variable

6. quantitative continuous

7.

  a. 2.27

  b. 3.04

  c. −1, 4, 4

8. Answers will vary.

Chapter 4

9. c. (0.80)(0.30)

10. b. No, and they are not mutually exclusive either.

11. a. all employed adult women

12. 0.5773

13. 0.0522

14. b. The middle fifty percent of the members lost from 2 to 8.5 lbs.

15. c. All of the data have the same value.

16. c. The lowest data value is the median.

17. 0.279

18. b. No, I expect to come out behind in money.

19. X = the number of patients calling in claiming to have the flu, who actually have the flu. X = 0, 1, 2, …25

20. $B(25, 0.04)$

21. 0.0165

22. 1

23. c. quantitative discrete

24. all words used by Tom Clancy in his novels

Chapter 5

25.

  a. 24%

  b. 27%

26. qualitative

27. 0.36

28. 0.7636

29.

  a. No

  b. No

30. $B(10, 0.76)$

31. 0.9330

32.

    a. X = the number of questions posted to the statistics listserv per day.

    b. $X = 0, 1, 2,\ldots$

    c. $X \sim P(2)$

    d. 0

33. $150

34. Matt

35.

    a. false

    b. true

    c. false

    d. false

36. 16

37. first quartile: 2
second quartile: 2
third quartile: 3

38. 0.5

39. $\dfrac{7}{15}$

40. $\dfrac{2}{15}$

Chapter 6

41.

    a. true

    b. true

    c. False – the median and the mean are the same for this symmetric distribution.

    d. true

42.

    a. 8

    b. 8

    c. $P(x < k) = 0.65 = (k - 3)\left(\dfrac{1}{10}\right)$. $k = 9.5$

43.

    a. False – $\dfrac{3}{4}$ of the data are at most five.

    b. True – each quartile has 25% of the data.

    c. False – that is unknown.

    d. False – 50% of the data are four or less.

44. d. *G* and *H* are independent events.

45.

a. False – *J* and *K* are independent so they are not mutually exclusive which would imply dependency (meaning *P*(*J* AND *K*) is not 0).

b. False – see answer c.

c. True – *P*(*J* OR *K*) = *P*(*J*) + *P*(*K*) – *P*(*J* AND *K*) = *P*(*J*) + *P*(*K*) – *P*(*J*)*P*(*K*) = 0.3 + 0.6 – (0.3)(0.6) = 0.72. Note the *P*(*J* AND *K*) = *P*(*J*)*P*(*K*) because *J* and *K* are independent.

d. False – *J* and *K* are independent so *P*(*J*) = *P*(*J*|*K*)

46. a. *P*(5)

Chapter 7

47. a. *U*(0, 4)

48. b. 2 hour

49. a. $\frac{1}{4}$

50.

a. 0.7165

b. 4.16

c. 0

51. c. 5 years

52. c. exponential

53. 0.63

54. *B*(14, 0.20)

55. *B*(14, 0.20)

Chapter 8

56. c. the mean amount of weight lost by 15 people on the special weight loss diet.

57. 0.9951

58. 12.99

59. c. $\frac{1}{2}$

60. b. 0.60

61. c. *N*(60, 5.477)

62. 0.9990

63. a. eight days

64. c. 0.7500

65. a. 80%

66. b. 35%

67. b. no

68. b. quantitative continuous

69. c. 150

70. d. 0.06

71. c. 0.44

72. b. 0

Chapter 9

73. d. Matt is shorter than the average 14 year old boy.

74. Answers will vary.

75.

x	Relative Frequency	Cumulative Relative Frequency
1	0.3	0.3
2	0.2	0.2
4	0.4	0.4
5	0.1	0.1

Table A10

76.

a. 2.8

b. 1.48

c. 90%

77. $M = 3$; $Q_1 = 1$; $Q_3 = 4$

78. 1 and 4

79. d. $\frac{8}{70}$

80. c. $\frac{40}{70}$

81. a. $\frac{9}{19}$

82. b. false

83. b. false

84. b. false

85.

a. X = the number of pies Lee bakes every day.

b. $P(20)$

c. 0.1122

86. CI: (5.25, 8.48)

87.

a. uniform

b. exponential

c. normal

Chapter 10

88. $\frac{77}{100}$

89. $\frac{12}{42}$

90.

   a.   false

   b.   false

   c.   true

   d.   false

91. $N(180, 16.43)$

92. a. The distribution for $\bar{X}$ is still uniform with the same mean and standard deviation as the distribution for X.

93. c. The distribution for $\sum X$ is normal with a larger mean and a larger standard deviation than the distribution for X.

94. $N\left(2, \ \frac{0.25}{\sqrt{16}}\right)$

95. Answers will vary.

96. 0.5000

97. 7.6

98. 5

99. 0.9431

Chapter 11

100. 7.5

101. 0.0122

102. $N(7, 0.63)$

103. 0.9911

104. b. Exponential

105.

   a.   true

   b.   false

   c.   false

106. Answers will vary.

107. Student's t with $df = 15$

108. (560.07, 719.93)

109. quantitative continuous data

110. quantitative discrete data

111.

   a. X = the number of patients with a shotgun wound the emergency room gets per 28 days

   b. $P(4)$

   c.   0.0183

112. greater than

113. No; $P(x = 8) = 0.0348$

114. You will lose $5.

115. Becca

116. 14

117. Sample mean = 3.2
Sample standard deviation = 1.85
Median = 3
$Q_1 = 2$
$Q_3 = 5$
$IQR = 3$

118. d. $z = -1.19$
e. 0.1171
f. Do not reject the null hypothesis.

119. We conclude that the patient does have the HIV virus when, in fact, the patient does not.

120. c. $z = 2.21$; $p = 0.0136$
d. Reject the null hypothesis.
e. We conclude that the proportion of Californian professionals that wear jeans to work is greater than the proportion of non-Californian professionals when, in fact, it is not greater.
f. We cannot conclude that the proportion of Californian professionals that wear jeans to work is greater than the proportion of non-Californian professionals when, in fact, it is greater.

121. c. dependent means

122. t_5

Chapter 12

123. (0.0424, 0.0770)

124. 2,401

125. Check student's solution.

126. 0.6321

127. $360

128. $N\left(72, \ \frac{72}{\sqrt{5}}\right)$

Chapter 13

129. 0.02

130. 0.40

131. $\frac{100}{140}$

132. $\frac{10}{60}$

133. p-value = 0; Reject the null hypothesis; conclude that they are dependent events

134. 8.4

135. $B(14, 0.60)$

136. d. Binomial

137. 0.3669

138. p-value = 0.0006; reject the null hypothesis; conclude that the averages are not equal

139. *p*-value = 0; reject the null hypothesis; conclude that the proportion of males is higher

140. Minimize α and β

141.

   a. No

   b. Yes, $P(M$ AND $30+) = 0$

142. $\frac{12}{38}$

143. No; *p*-value = 0

144. a. uniform

References

Data from the *San Jose Mercury News*.

Baran, Daya. "20 Percent of Americans Have Never Used Email." Webguild.org, 2010. Available online at: http://www.webguild.org/20080519/20-percent-of-americans-have-never-used-email (accessed October 17, 2013).

Data from *Parade Magazine*.

APPENDIX B: PRACTICE TESTS (1-4) AND FINAL EXAMS

Practice Test 1

1.1: Definitions of Statistics, Probability, and Key Terms

Use the following information to answer the next three exercises. A grocery store is interested in how much money, on average, their customers spend each visit in the produce department. Using their store records, they draw a sample of 1,000 visits and calculate each customer's average spending on produce.

1. Identify the population, sample, parameter, statistic, variable, and data for this example.

  a. population

  b. sample

  c. parameter

  d. statistic

  e. variable

  f. data

2. What kind of data is "amount of money spent on produce per visit"?

  a. qualitative

  b. quantitative-continuous

  c. quantitative-discrete

3. The study finds that the mean amount spent on produce per visit by the customers in the sample is $12.84. This is an example of a:

  a. population

  b. sample

  c. parameter

  d. statistic

  e. variable

1.2: Data, Sampling, and Variation in Data and Sampling

Use the following information to answer the next two exercises. A health club is interested in knowing how many times a typical member uses the club in a week. They decide to ask every tenth customer on a specified day to complete a short survey including information about how many times they have visited the club in the past week.

4. What kind of a sampling design is this?

  a. cluster

  b. stratified

c. simple random

d. systematic

5. "Number of visits per week" is what kind of data?

a. qualitative

b. quantitative-continuous

c. quantitative-discrete

6. Describe a situation in which you would calculate a parameter, rather than a statistic.

7. The U.S. federal government conducts a survey of high school seniors concerning their plans for future education and employment. One question asks whether they are planning to attend a four-year college or university in the following year. Fifty percent answer yes to this question; that fifty percent is a:

a. parameter

b. statistic

c. variable

d. data

8. Imagine that the U.S. federal government had the means to survey all high school seniors in the U.S. concerning their plans for future education and employment, and found that 50 percent were planning to attend a 4-year college or university in the following year. This 50 percent is an example of a:

a. parameter

b. statistic

c. variable

d. data

Use the following information to answer the next three exercises. A survey of a random sample of 100 nurses working at a large hospital asked how many years they had been working in the profession. Their answers are summarized in the following (incomplete) table.

9. Fill in the blanks in the table and round your answers to two decimal places for the Relative Frequency and Cumulative Relative Frequency cells.

# of years	Frequency	Relative Frequency	Cumulative Relative Frequency
< 5	25		
5–10	30		
> 10	empty		

Table B1

10. What proportion of nurses have five or more years of experience?

11. What proportion of nurses have ten or fewer years of experience?

12. Describe how you might draw a random sample of 30 students from a lecture class of 200 students.

13. Describe how you might draw a stratified sample of students from a college, where the strata are the students' class standing (freshman, sophomore, junior, or senior).

14. A manager wants to draw a sample, without replacement, of 30 employees from a workforce of 150. Describe how the chance of being selected will change over the course of drawing the sample.

15. The manager of a department store decides to measure employee satisfaction by selecting four departments at random, and conducting interviews with all the employees in those four departments. What type of survey design is this?

   a. cluster

   b. stratified

   c. simple random

   d. systematic

16. A popular American television sports program conducts a poll of viewers to see which team they believe will win the NFL (National Football League) championship this year. Viewers vote by calling a number displayed on the television screen and telling the operator which team they think will win. Do you think that those who participate in this poll are representative of all football fans in America?

17. Two researchers studying vaccination rates independently draw samples of 50 children, ages 3–18 months, from a large urban area, and determine if they are up to date on their vaccinations. One researcher finds that 84 percent of the children in her sample are up to date, and the other finds that 86 percent in his sample are up to date. Assuming both followed proper sampling procedures and did their calculations correctly, what is a likely explanation for this discrepancy?

18. A high school increased the length of the school day from 6.5 to 7.5 hours. Students who wished to attend this high school were required to sign contracts pledging to put forth their best effort on their school work and to obey the school rules; if they did not wish to do so, they could attend another high school in the district. At the end of one year, student performance on statewide tests had increased by ten percentage points over the previous year. Does this improvement prove that a longer school day improves student achievement?

19. You read a newspaper article reporting that eating almonds leads to increased life satisfaction. The study was conducted by the Almond Growers Association, and was based on a randomized survey asking people about their consumption of various foods, including almonds, and also about their satisfaction with different aspects of their life. Does anything about this poll lead you to question its conclusion?

20. Why is non-response a problem in surveys?

1.3: Frequency, Frequency Tables, and Levels of Measurement

21. Compute the mean of the following numbers, and report your answer using one more decimal place than is present in the original data:
14, 5, 18, 23, 6

1.4: Experimental Design and Ethics

22. A psychologist is interested in whether the size of tableware (bowls, plates, etc.) influences how much college students eat. He randomly assigns 100 college students to one of two groups: the first is served a meal using normal-sized tableware, while the second is served the same meal, but using tableware that it 20 percent smaller than normal. He records how much food is consumed by each group. Identify the following components of this study.

   a. population

   b. sample

   c. experimental units

   d. explanatory variable

   e. treatment

   f. response variable

23. A researcher analyzes the results of the SAT (Scholastic Aptitude Test) over a five-year period and finds that male students on average score higher on the math section, and female students on average score higher on the verbal section. She concludes that these observed differences in test performance are due to genetic factors. Explain how lurking variables could offer an alternative explanation for the observed differences in test scores.

24. Explain why it would not be possible to use random assignment to study the health effects of smoking.

25. A professor conducts a telephone survey of a city's population by drawing a sample of numbers from the phone book and having her student assistants call each of the selected numbers once to administer the survey. What are some sources of bias with this survey?

26. A professor offers extra credit to students who take part in her research studies. What is an ethical problem with this method of recruiting subjects?

2.1: Stem-and Leaf Graphs (Stemplots), Line Graphs, and Bar Graphs

Use the following information to answer the next four exercises. The midterm grades on a chemistry exam, graded on a scale of 0 to 100, were:

62, 64, 65, 65, 68, 70, 72, 72, 74, 75, 75, 75, 76,78, 78, 81, 83, 83, 84, 85, 87, 88, 92, 95, 98, 98, 100, 100, 740

27. Do you see any outliers in this data? If so, how would you address the situation?

28. Construct a stem plot for this data, using only the values in the range 0–100.

29. Describe the distribution of exam scores.

2.2: Histograms, Frequency Polygons, and Time Series Graphs

30. In a class of 35 students, seven students received scores in the 70–79 range. What is the relative frequency of scores in this range?

Use the following information to answer the next three exercises. You conduct a poll of 30 students to see how many classes they are taking this term. Your results are:

1; 1; 1; 1
2; 2; 2; 2; 2
3; 3; 3; 3; 3; 3; 3; 3
4; 4; 4; 4; 4; 4; 4; 4; 4
5; 5; 5; 5

31. You decide to construct a histogram of this data. What will be the range of your first bar, and what will be the central point?

32. What will be the widths and central points of the other bars?

33. Which bar in this histogram will be the tallest, and what will be its height?

34. You get data from the U.S. Census Bureau on the median household income for your city, and decide to display it graphically. Which is the better choice for this data, a bar graph or a histogram?

35. You collect data on the color of cars driven by students in your statistics class, and want to display this information graphically. Which is the better choice for this data, a bar graph or a histogram?

2.3: Measures of the Location of the Data

36. Your daughter brings home test scores showing that she scored in the 80th percentile in math and the 76th percentile in reading for her grade. Interpret these scores.

37. You have to wait 90 minutes in the emergency room of a hospital before you can see a doctor. You learn that your wait time was in the 82nd percentile of all wait times. Explain what this means, and whether you think it is good or bad.

2.4: Box Plots

Use the following information to answer the next three exercises. 1; 1; 2; 3; 4; 4; 5; 5; 6; 7; 7; 8; 9

38. What is the median for this data?

39. What is the first quartile for this data?

40. What is the third quartile for this data?

Use the following information to answer the next four exercises. This box plot represents scores on the final exam for a physics class.

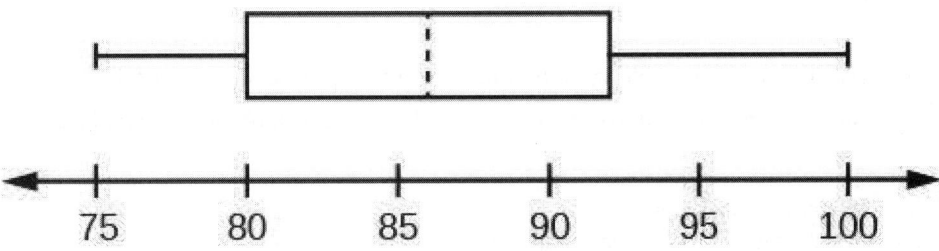

Figure B1

41. What is the median for this data, and how do you know?

42. What are the first and third quartiles for this data, and how do you know?

43. What is the interquartile range for this data?

44. What is the range for this data?

2.5: Measures of the Center of the Data

45. In a marathon, the median finishing time was 3:35:04 (three hours, 35 minutes, and four seconds). You finished in 3:34:10. Interpret the meaning of the median time, and discuss your time in relation to it.

Use the following information to answer the next three exercises. The value, in thousands of dollars, for houses on a block, are: 45; 47; 47.5; 51; 53.5; 125.

46. Calculate the mean for this data.

47. Calculate the median for this data.

48. Which do you think better reflects the average value of the homes on this block?

2.6: Skewness and the Mean, Median, and Mode

49. In a left-skewed distribution, which is greater?

  a. the mean

  b. the media

  c. the mode

50. In a right-skewed distribution, which is greater?

  a. the mean

  b. the median

  c. the mode

51. In a symmetrical distribution what will be the relationship among the mean, median, and mode?

2.7: Measures of the Spread of the Data

Use the following information to answer the next four exercises. 10; 11; 15; 15; 17; 22

52. Compute the mean and standard deviation for this data; use the sample formula for the standard deviation.

53. What number is two standard deviations above the mean of this data?

54. Express the number 13.7 in terms of the mean and standard deviation of this data.

55. In a biology class, the scores on the final exam were normally distributed, with a mean of 85, and a standard deviation of five. Susan got a final exam score of 95. Express her exam result as a *z*-score, and interpret its meaning.

3.1: Terminology

Use the following information to answer the next two exercises. You have a jar full of marbles: 50 are red, 25 are blue, and 15 are yellow. Assume you draw one marble at random for each trial, and replace it before the next trial.
Let $P(R)$ = the probability of drawing a red marble.
Let $P(B)$ = the probability of drawing a blue marble.

Let $P(Y)$ = the probability of drawing a yellow marble.

56. Find $P(B)$.

57. Which is more likely, drawing a red marble or a yellow marble? Justify your answer numerically.

Use the following information to answer the next two exercises. The following are probabilities describing a group of college students.
Let $P(M)$ = the probability that the student is male
Let $P(F)$ = the probability that the student is female
Let $P(E)$ = the probability the student is majoring in education
Let $P(S)$ = the probability the student is majoring in science

58. Write the symbols for the probability that a student, selected at random, is both female and a science major.

59. Write the symbols for the probability that the student is an education major, given that the student is male.

3.2: Independent and Mutually Exclusive Events

60. Events A and B are independent.
If $P(A)$ = 0.3 and $P(B)$ = 0.5, find $P(A$ AND $B)$.

61. C and D are mutually exclusive events.
If $P(C)$ = 0.18 and $P(D)$ = 0.03, find $P(C$ OR $D)$.

3.3: Two Basic Rules of Probability

62. In a high school graduating class of 300, 200 students are going to college, 40 are planning to work full-time, and 80 are taking a gap year. Are these events mutually exclusive?

Use the following information to answer the next two exercises. An archer hits the center of the target (the bullseye) 70 percent of the time. However, she is a streak shooter, and if she hits the center on one shot, her probability of hitting it on the shot immediately following is 0.85. Written in probability notation:
$P(A) = P(B) = P$(hitting the center on one shot) = 0.70
$P(B|A) = P$(hitting the center on a second shot, given that she hit it on the first) = 0.85

63. Calculate the probability that she will hit the center of the target on two consecutive shots.

64. Are $P(A)$ and $P(B)$ independent in this example?

3.4: Contingency Tables

Use the following information to answer the next three exercises. The following contingency table displays the number of students who report studying at least 15 hours per week, and how many made the honor roll in the past semester.

	Honor roll	No honor roll	Total
Study at least 15 hours/week		200	
Study less than 15 hours/week	125	193	
Total			1,000

Table B2

65. Complete the table.

66. Find P(honor roll|study at least 15 hours per week).

67. What is the probability a student studies less than 15 hours per week?

68. Are the events "study at least 15 hours per week" and "makes the honor roll" independent? Justify your answer numerically.

3.5: Tree and Venn Diagrams

69. At a high school, some students play on the tennis team, some play on the soccer team, but neither plays both tennis and soccer. Draw a Venn diagram illustrating this.

70. At a high school, some students play tennis, some play soccer, and some play both. Draw a Venn diagram illustrating this.

Practice Test 1 Solutions
1.1: Definitions of Statistics, Probability, and Key Terms

1.

   a. population: all the shopping visits by all the store's customers

   b. sample: the 1,000 visits drawn for the study

   c. parameter: the average expenditure on produce per visit by all the store's customers

   d. statistic: the average expenditure on produce per visit by the sample of 1,000

   e. variable: the expenditure on produce for each visit

   f. data: the dollar amounts spent on produce; for instance, $15.40, $11.53, etc

2. c

3. d

1.2: Data, Sampling, and Variation in Data and Sampling

4. d

5. c

6. Answers will vary.
Sample Answer: Any solution in which you use data from the entire population is acceptable. For instance, a professor might calculate the average exam score for her class: because the scores of all members of the class were used in the calculation, the average is a parameter.

7. b

8. a

9.

# of years	Frequency	Relative Frequency	Cumulative Relative Frequency
< 5	25	0.25	0.25
5–10	30	0.30	0.55
> 10	45	0.45	1.00

Table B3

10. 0.75

11. 0.55

12. Answers will vary.
Sample Answer: One possibility is to obtain the class roster and assign each student a number from 1 to 200. Then use a random number generator or table of random number to generate 30 numbers between 1 and 200, and select the students matching the random numbers. It would also be acceptable to write each student's name on a card, shuffle them in a box, and draw 30 names at random.

13. One possibility would be to obtain a roster of students enrolled in the college, including the class standing for each student. Then you would draw a proportionate random sample from within each class (for instance, if 30 percent of the students in the college are freshman, then 30 percent of your sample would be drawn from the freshman class).

14. For the first person picked, the chance of any individual being selected is one in 150. For the second person, it is one in 149, for the third it is one in 148, and so on. For the 30th person selected, the chance of selection is one in 121.

15. a

16. No. There are at least two chances for bias. First, the viewers of this particular program may not be representative of American football fans as a whole. Second, the sample will be self-selected, because people have to make a phone call in order to take part, and those people are probably not representative of the American football fan population as a whole.

17. These results (84 percent in one sample, 86 percent in the other) are probably due to sampling variability. Each researcher drew a different sample of children, and you would not expect them to get exactly the same result, although you would expect the results to be similar, as they are in this case.

18. No. The improvement could also be due to self-selection: only motivated students were willing to sign the contract, and they would have done well even in a school with 6.5 hour days. Because both changes were implemented at the same time, it is not possible to separate out their influence.

19. At least two aspects of this poll are troublesome. The first is that it was conducted by a group who would benefit by the result—almond sales are likely to increase if people believe that eating almonds will make them happier. The second is that this poll found that almond consumption and life satisfaction are correlated, but does not establish that eating almonds causes satisfaction. It is equally possible, for instance, that people with higher incomes are more likely to eat almonds, and are also more satisfied with their lives.

20. You want the sample of people who take part in a survey to be representative of the population from which they are drawn. People who refuse to take part in a survey often have different views than those who do participate, and so even a random sample may produce biased results if a large percentage of those selected refuse to participate in a survey.

1.3: Frequency, Frequency Tables, and Levels of Measurement

21. 13.2

1.4: Experimental Design and Ethics

22.

  a. population: all college students

  b. sample: the 100 college students in the study

  c. experimental units: each individual college student who participated

  d. explanatory variable: the size of the tableware

  e. treatment: tableware that is 20 percent smaller than normal

  f. response variable: the amount of food eaten

23. There are many lurking variables that could influence the observed differences in test scores. Perhaps the boys, on average, have taken more math courses than the girls, and the girls have taken more English classes than the boys. Perhaps the boys have been encouraged by their families and teachers to prepare for a career in math and science, and thus have put more effort into studying math, while the girls have been encouraged to prepare for fields like communication and psychology that are more focused on language use. A study design would have to control for these and other potential lurking variables (anything that could explain the observed difference in test scores, other than the genetic explanation) in order to draw a scientifically sound conclusion about genetic differences.

24. To use random assignment, you would have to be able to assign people to either smoke or not smoke. Because smoking has many harmful effects, this would not be an ethical experiment. Instead, we study people who have chosen to smoke, and compare them to others who have chosen not to smoke, and try to control for the other ways those two groups may differ (lurking variables).

25. Sources of bias include the fact that not everyone has a telephone, that cell phone numbers are often not listed in published directories, and that an individual might not be at home at the time of the phone call; all these factors make it likely that the respondents to the survey will not be representative of the population as a whole.

26. Research subjects should not be coerced into participation, and offering extra credit in exchange for participation could be construed as coercion. In addition, this method will result in a volunteer sample, which cannot be assumed to be representative of the population as a whole.

2.1: Stem-and Leaf Graphs (Stemplots), Line Graphs, and Bar Graphs

27. The value 740 is an outlier, because the exams were graded on a scale of 0 to 100, and 740 is far outside that range. It may be a data entry error, with the actual score being 74, so the professor should check that exam again to see what the actual score was.

28.

Stem	Leaf
6	2 4 5 5 8
7	0 2 2 4 5 5 5 6 8 8
8	1 3 3 4 5 7 8
9	2 5 8 8
10	0 0

Table B4

29. Most scores on this exam were in the range of 70–89, with a few scoring in the 60–69 range, and a few in the 90–100 range.

2.2: Histograms, Frequency Polygons, and Time Series Graphs

30. $RF = \frac{7}{35} = 0.2$

31. The range will be 0.5–1.5, and the central point will be 1.

32. Range 1.5–2.5, central point 2; range 2.5–3.5, central point 3; range 3.5–4.5, central point 4; range 4.5–5.5., central point 5.

33. The bar from 3.5 to 4.5, with a central point of 4, will be tallest; its height will be nine, because there are nine students taking four courses.

34. The histogram is a better choice, because income is a continuous variable.

35. A bar graph is the better choice, because this data is categorical rather than continuous.

2.3: Measures of the Location of the Data

36. Your daughter scored better than 80 percent of the students in her grade on math and better than 76 percent of the students in reading. Both scores are very good, and place her in the upper quartile, but her math score is slightly better in relation to her peers than her reading score.

37. You had an unusually long wait time, which is bad: 82 percent of patients had a shorter wait time than you, and only 18 percent had a longer wait time.

2.4: Box Plots

38. 5

39. 3

40. 7

41. The median is 86, as represented by the vertical line in the box.

42. The first quartile is 80, and the third quartile is 92, as represented by the left and right boundaries of the box.

43. $IQR = 92 - 80 = 12$

44. Range = 100 – 75 = 25

2.5: Measures of the Center of the Data

45. Half the runners who finished the marathon ran a time faster than 3:35:04, and half ran a time slower than 3:35:04. Your time is faster than the median time, so you did better than more than half of the runners in this race.

46. 61.5, or $61,500

47. 49.25 or $49,250

48. The median, because the mean is distorted by the high value of one house.

2.6: Skewness and the Mean, Median, and Mode

49. c

50. a

51. They will all be fairly close to each other.

2.7: Measures of the Spread of the Data

52. Mean: 15
Standard deviation: 4.3

$$\mu = \frac{10 + 11 + 15 + 15 + 17 + 22}{6} = 15$$

$$s = \sqrt{\frac{\sum \left(x - \bar{x}\right)^2}{n - 1}} = \sqrt{\frac{94}{5}} = 4.3$$

53. 15 + (2)(4.3) = 23.6

54. 13.7 is one standard deviation below the mean of this data, because 15 − 4.3 = 10.7

55. $z = \frac{95 - 85}{5} = 2.0$

Susan's z-score was 2.0, meaning she scored two standard deviations above the class mean for the final exam.

3.1: Terminology

56. $P(B) = \frac{25}{90} = 0.28$

57. Drawing a red marble is more likely.
$P(R) = \frac{50}{80} = 0.62$

$P(Y) = \frac{15}{80} = 0.19$

58. $P(F \text{ AND } S)$

59. $P(E|M)$

3.2: Independent and Mutually Exclusive Events

60. $P(A \text{ AND } B) = (0.3)(0.5) = 0.15$

61. $P(C \text{ OR } D) = 0.18 + 0.03 = 0.21$

3.3: Two Basic Rules of Probability

62. No, they cannot be mutually exclusive, because they add up to more than 300. Therefore, some students must fit into two or more categories (e.g., both going to college and working full time).

63. $P(A \text{ and } B) = (P(B|A))(P(A)) = (0.85)(0.70) = 0.595$

64. No. If they were independent, $P(B)$ would be the same as $P(B|A)$. We know this is not the case, because $P(B) = 0.70$ and $P(B|A) = 0.85$.

3.4: Contingency Tables

65.

	Honor roll	No honor roll	Total
Study at least 15 hours/week	482	200	682
Study less than 15 hours/week	125	193	318
Total	607	393	1,000

Table B5

66. $P(\text{honor roll}|\text{study at least 15 hours word per week}) = \frac{482}{1000} = 0.482$

67. $P(\text{studies less than 15 hours word per week}) = \frac{125 + 193}{1000} = 0.318$

68. Let $P(S)$ = study at least 15 hours per week
Let $P(H)$ = makes the honor roll
From the table, $P(S) = 0.682$, $P(H) = 0.607$, and $P(S \text{ AND } H) = 0.482$.
If $P(S)$ and $P(H)$ were independent, then $P(S \text{ AND } H)$ would equal $(P(S))(P(H))$.
However, $(P(S))(P(H)) = (0.682)(0.607) = 0.414$, while $P(S \text{ AND } H) = 0.482$.
Therefore, $P(S)$ and $P(H)$ are not independent.

3.5: Tree and Venn Diagrams

69.

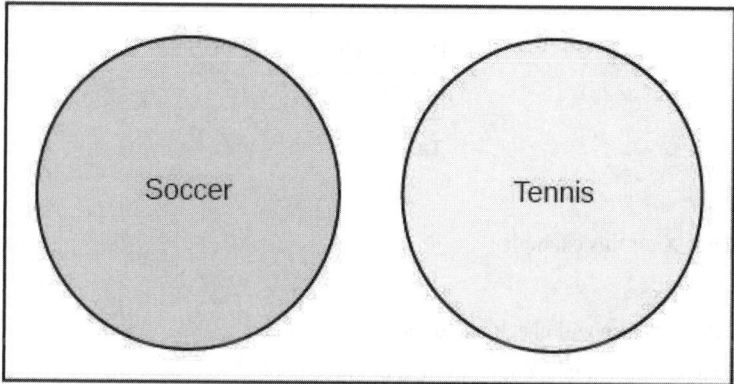

Figure B2

70.

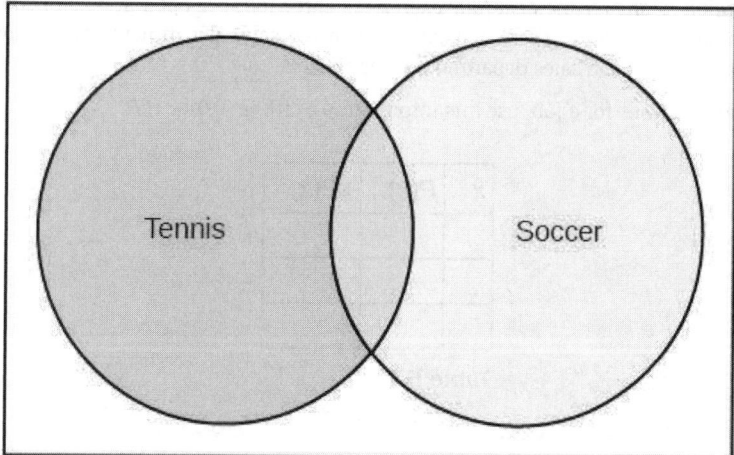

Figure B3

Practice Test 2
4.1: Probability Distribution Function (PDF) for a Discrete Random Variable

Use the following information to answer the next five exercises. You conduct a survey among a random sample of students at a particular university. The data collected includes their major, the number of classes they took the previous semester, and amount of money they spent on books purchased for classes in the previous semester.

1. If X = student's major, then what is the domain of X?

2. If Y = the number of classes taken in the previous semester, what is the domain of Y?

3. If Z = the amount of money spent on books in the previous semester, what is the domain of Z?

4. Why are X, Y, and Z in the previous example random variables?

5. After collecting data, you find that for one case, $z = -7$. Is this a possible value for Z?

6. What are the two essential characteristics of a discrete probability distribution?

Use this discrete probability distribution represented in this table to answer the following six questions. The university library records the number of books checked out by each patron over the course of one day, with the following result:

x	P(x)
0	0.20
1	0.45
2	0.20
3	0.10
4	0.05

Table B6

7. Define the random variable X for this example.

8. What is $P(x > 2)$?

9. What is the probability that a patron will check out at least one book?

10. What is the probability a patron will take out no more than three books?

11. If the table listed $P(x)$ as 0.15, how would you know that there was a mistake?

12. What is the average number of books taken out by a patron?

4.2: Mean or Expected Value and Standard Deviation

Use the following information to answer the next four exercises. Three jobs are open in a company: one in the accounting department, one in the human resources department, and one in the sales department. The accounting job receives 30 applicants, and the human resources and sales department 60 applicants.

13. If X = the number of applications for a job, use this information to fill in **Table B7**.

x	P(x)	xP(x)

Table B7

14. What is the mean number of applicants?

15. What is the PDF for X?

16. Add a fourth column to the table, for $(x - \mu)^2 P(x)$.

17. What is the standard deviation of X?

4.3: Binomial Distribution

18. In a binomial experiment, if $p = 0.65$, what does q equal?

19. What are the required characteristics of a binomial experiment?

20. Joe conducts an experiment to see how many times he has to flip a coin before he gets four heads in a row. Does this qualify as a binomial experiment?

Use the following information to answer the next three exercises. In a particularly community, 65 percent of households include at least one person who has graduated from college. You randomly sample 100 households in this community. Let X = the number of households including at least one college graduate.

21. Describe the probability distribution of X.

22. What is the mean of X?

23. What is the standard deviation of X?

Use the following information to answer the next four exercises. Joe is the star of his school's baseball team. His batting average is 0.400, meaning that for every ten times he comes to bat (an at-bat), four of those times he gets a hit. You decide to track his batting performance his next 20 at-bats.

24. Define the random variable X in this experiment.

25. Assuming Joe's probability of getting a hit is independent and identical across all 20 at-bats, describe the distribution of X.

26. Given this information, what number of hits do you predict Joe will get?

27. What is the standard deviation of X?

4.4: Geometric Distribution

28. What are the three major characteristics of a geometric experiment?

29. You decide to conduct a geometric experiment by flipping a coin until it comes up heads. This takes five trials. Represent the outcomes of this trial, using H for heads and T for tails.

30. You are conducting a geometric experiment by drawing cards from a normal 52-card pack, with replacement, until you draw the Queen of Hearts. What is the domain of X for this experiment?

31. You are conducting a geometric experiment by drawing cards from a normal 52-card deck, without replacement, until you draw a red card. What is the domain of X for this experiment?

Use the following information to answer the next three exercises. In a particular university, 27 percent of students are engineering majors. You decide to select students at random until you choose one that is an engineering major. Let X = the number of students you select until you find one that is an engineering major.

32. What is the probability distribution of X?

33. What is the mean of X?

34. What is the standard deviation of X?

4.5: Hypergeometric Distribution

35. You draw a random sample of ten students to participate in a survey, from a group of 30, consisting of 16 boys and 14 girls. You are interested in the probability that seven of the students chosen will be boys. Does this qualify as a hypergeometric experiment? List the conditions and whether or not they are met.

36. You draw five cards, without replacement, from a normal 52-card deck of playing cards, and are interested in the probability that two of the cards are spades. What are the group of interest, size of the group of interest, and sample size for this example?

4.6: Poisson Distribution

37. What are the key characteristics of the Poisson distribution?

Use the following information to answer the next three exercises. The number of drivers to arrive at a toll booth in an hour can be modeled by the Poisson distribution.

38. If X = the number of drivers, and the average numbers of drivers per hour is four, how would you express this distribution?

39. What is the domain of X?

40. What are the mean and standard deviation of X?

5.1: Continuous Probability Functions

41. You conduct a survey of students to see how many books they purchased the previous semester, the total amount they paid for those books, the number they sold after the semester was over, and the amount of money they received for the books they sold. Which variables in this survey are discrete, and which are continuous?

42. With continuous random variables, we never calculate the probability that X has a particular value, but always speak in terms of the probability that X has a value within a particular range. Why is this?

43. For a continuous random variable, why are $P(x < c)$ and $P(x \leq c)$ equivalent statements?

44. For a continuous probability function, $P(x < 5) = 0.35$. What is $P(x > 5)$, and how do you know?

45. Describe how you would draw the continuous probability distribution described by the function $f(x) = \frac{1}{10}$ for $0 \leq x \leq 10$. What type of a distribution is this?

46. For the continuous probability distribution described by the function $f(x) = \frac{1}{10}$ for $0 \leq x \leq 10$, what is the $P(0 < x < 4)$?

5.2: The Uniform Distribution

47. For the continuous probability distribution described by the function $f(x) = \frac{1}{10}$ for $0 \leq x \leq 10$, what is the $P(2 < x < 5)$?

Use the following information to answer the next four exercises. The number of minutes that a patient waits at a medical clinic to see a doctor is represented by a uniform distribution between zero and 30 minutes, inclusive.

48. If X equals the number of minutes a person waits, what is the distribution of X?

49. Write the probability density function for this distribution.

50. What is the mean and standard deviation for waiting time?

51. What is the probability that a patient waits less than ten minutes?

5.3: The Exponential Distribution

52. The distribution of the variable X, representing the average time to failure for an automobile battery, can be written as: $X \sim Exp(m)$. Describe this distribution in words.

53. If the value of m for an exponential distribution is ten, what are the mean and standard deviation for the distribution?

54. Write the probability density function for a variable distributed as: $X \sim Exp(0.2)$.

6.1: The Standard Normal Distribution

55. Translate this statement about the distribution of a random variable X into words: $X \sim (100, 15)$.

56. If the variable X has the standard normal distribution, express this symbolically.

Use the following information for the next six exercises. According to the World Health Organization, distribution of height in centimeters for girls aged five years and no months has the distribution: $X \sim N(109, 4.5)$.

57. What is the z-score for a height of 112 inches?

58. What is the z-score for a height of 100 centimeters?

59. Find the z-score for a height of 105 centimeters and explain what that means In the context of the population.

60. What height corresponds to a z-score of 1.5 in this population?

61. Using the empirical rule, we expect about 68 percent of the values in a normal distribution to lie within one standard deviation above or below the mean. What does this mean, in terms of a specific range of values, for this distribution?

62. Using the empirical rule, about what percent of heights in this distribution do you expect to be between 95.5 cm and 122.5 cm?

6.2: Using the Normal Distribution

Use the following information to answer the next four exercises. The distributor of lotto tickets claims that 20 percent of the tickets are winners. You draw a sample of 500 tickets to test this proposition.

63. Can you use the normal approximation to the binomial for your calculations? Why or why not.

64. What are the expected mean and standard deviation for your sample, assuming the distributor's claim is true?

65. What is the probability that your sample will have a mean greater than 100?

66. If the z-score for your sample result is –2.00, explain what this means, using the empirical rule.

7.1: The Central Limit Theorem for Sample Means (Averages)

67. What does the central limit theorem state with regard to the distribution of sample means?

68. The distribution of results from flipping a fair coin is uniform: heads and tails are equally likely on any flip, and over a large number of trials, you expect about the same number of heads and tails. Yet if you conduct a study by flipping 30 coins and recording the number of heads, and repeat this 100 times, the distribution of the mean number of heads will be approximately normal. How is this possible?

69. The mean of a normally-distributed population is 50, and the standard deviation is four. If you draw 100 samples of size 40 from this population, describe what you would expect to see in terms of the sampling distribution of the sample mean.

70. X is a random variable with a mean of 25 and a standard deviation of two. Write the distribution for the sample mean of samples of size 100 drawn from this population.

71. Your friend is doing an experiment drawing samples of size 50 from a population with a mean of 117 and a standard deviation of 16. This sample size is large enough to allow use of the central limit theorem, so he says the standard deviation of the sampling distribution of sample means will also be 16. Explain why this is wrong, and calculate the correct value.

72. You are reading a research article that refers to "the standard error of the mean." What does this mean, and how is it calculated?

Use the following information to answer the next six exercises. You repeatedly draw samples of $n = 100$ from a population with a mean of 75 and a standard deviation of 4.5.

73. What is the expected distribution of the sample means?

74. One of your friends tries to convince you that the standard error of the mean should be 4.5. Explain what error your friend made.

75. What is the z-score for a sample mean of 76?

76. What is the z-score for a sample mean of 74.7?

77. What sample mean corresponds to a z-score of 1.5?

78. If you decrease the sample size to 50, will the standard error of the mean be smaller or larger? What would be its value?

Use the following information to answer the next two questions. We use the empirical rule to analyze data for samples of size 60 drawn from a population with a mean of 70 and a standard deviation of 9.

79. What range of values would you expect to include 68 percent of the sample means?

80. If you increased the sample size to 100, what range would you expect to contain 68 percent of the sample means, applying the empirical rule?

7.2: The Central Limit Theorem for Sums

81. How does the central limit theorem apply to sums of random variables?

82. Explain how the rules applying the central limit theorem to sample means, and to sums of a random variable, are similar.

83. If you repeatedly draw samples of size 50 from a population with a mean of 80 and a standard deviation of four, and calculate the sum of each sample, what is the expected distribution of these sums?

Use the following information to answer the next four exercises. You draw one sample of size 40 from a population with a mean of 125 and a standard deviation of seven.

84. Compute the sum. What is the probability that the sum for your sample will be less than 5,000?

85. If you drew samples of this size repeatedly, computing the sum each time, what range of values would you expect to contain 95 percent of the sample sums?

86. What value is one standard deviation below the mean?

87. What value corresponds to a z-score of 2.2?

7.3: Using the Central Limit Theorem

88. What does the law of large numbers say about the relationship between the sample mean and the population mean?

89. Applying the law of large numbers, which sample mean would expect to be closer to the population mean, a sample of size ten or a sample of size 100?

Use this information for the next three questions. A manufacturer makes screws with a mean diameter of 0.15 cm (centimeters) and a range of 0.10 cm to 0.20 cm; within that range, the distribution is uniform.

90. If X = the diameter of one screw, what is the distribution of X?

91. Suppose you repeatedly draw samples of size 100 and calculate their mean. Applying the central limit theorem, what is the distribution of these sample means?

92. Suppose you repeatedly draw samples of 60 and calculate their sum. Applying the central limit theorem, what is the distribution of these sample sums?

Practice Test 2 Solutions
Probability Distribution Function (PDF) for a Discrete Random Variable

1. The domain of X = {English, Mathematics,….], i.e., a list of all the majors offered at the university, plus "undeclared."

2. The domain of Y = {0, 1, 2, …}, i.e., the integers from 0 to the upper limit of classes allowed by the university.

3. The domain of Z = any amount of money from 0 upwards.

4. Because they can take any value within their domain, and their value for any particular case is not known until the survey is completed.

5. No, because the domain of Z includes only positive numbers (you can't spend a negative amount of money). Possibly the value –7 is a data entry error, or a special code to indicated that the student did not answer the question.

6. The probabilities must sum to 1.0, and the probabilities of each event must be between 0 and 1, inclusive.

7. Let X = the number of books checked out by a patron.

8. $P(x > 2) = 0.10 + 0.05 = 0.15$

9. $P(x \geq 0) = 1 – 0.20 = 0.80$

10. $P(x \leq 3) = 1 – 0.05 = 0.95$

11. The probabilities would sum to 1.10, and the total probability in a distribution must always equal 1.0.

12. $\bar{x} = 0(0.20) + 1(0.45) + 2(0.20) + 3(0.10) + 4(0.05) = 1.35$

Mean or Expected Value and Standard Deviation

13.

x	P(x)	xP(x)
30	0.33	9.90
40	0.33	13.20
60	0.33	19.80

Table B8

14. $\bar{x} = 9.90 + 13.20 + 19.80 = 42.90$

15. $P(x = 30) = 0.33$
$P(x = 40) = 0.33$
$P(x = 60) = 0.33$

16.

x	P(x)	xP(x)	$(x - \mu)^2 P(x)$
30	0.33	9.90	$(30 - 42.90)^2(0.33) = 54.91$
40	0.33	13.20	$(40 - 42.90)^2(0.33) = 2.78$
60	0.33	19.90	$(60 - 42.90)^2(0.33) = 96.49$

Table B9

17. $\sigma_x = \sqrt{54.91 + 2.78 + 96.49} = 12.42$

Binomial Distribution

18. $q = 1 - 0.65 = 0.35$

19.

   1. There are a fixed number of trials.

   2. There are only two possible outcomes, and they add up to 1.

   3. The trials are independent and conducted under identical conditions.

20. No, because there are not a fixed number of trials

21. $X \sim B(100, 0.65)$

22. $\mu = np = 100(0.65) = 65$

23. $\sigma_x = \sqrt{npq} = \sqrt{100(0.65)(0.35)} = 4.77$

24. X = Joe gets a hit in one at-bat (in one occasion of his coming to bat)

25. $X \sim B(20, 0.4)$

26. $\mu = np = 20(0.4) = 8$

27. $\sigma_x = \sqrt{npq} = \sqrt{20(0.40)(0.60)} = 2.19$

4.4: Geometric Distribution

28.

   1. A series of Bernoulli trials are conducted until one is a success, and then the experiment stops.

   2. At least one trial is conducted, but there is no upper limit to the number of trials.

   3. The probability of success or failure is the same for each trial.

29. $T\,T\,T\,T\,H$

30. The domain of $X = \{1, 2, 3, 4, 5, ...n\}$. Because you are drawing with replacement, there is no upper bound to the number of draws that may be necessary.

31. The domain of $X = \{1, 2, 3, 4, 5, 6, 7, 8., 9, 10, 11, 12…27\}$. Because you are drawing without replacement, and 26 of the 52 cards are red, you have to draw a red card within the first 17 draws.

32. $X \sim G(0.24)$

33. $\mu = \frac{1}{p} = \frac{1}{0.27} = 3.70$

34. $\sigma = \sqrt{\frac{1 - p}{p^2}} = \sqrt{\frac{1 - 0.27}{0.27^2}} = 3.16$

4.5: Hypergeometric Distribution

35. Yes, because you are sampling from a population composed of two groups (boys and girls), have a group of interest (boys), and are sampling without replacement (hence, the probabilities change with each pick, and you are not performing Bernoulli trials).

36. The group of interest is the cards that are spades, the size of the group of interest is 13, and the sample size is five.

4.6: Poisson Distribution

37. A Poisson distribution models the number of events occurring in a fixed interval of time or space, when the events are independent and the average rate of the events is known.

38. $X \sim P(4)$

39. The domain of X = {0, 1, 2, 3, ...} i.e., any integer from 0 upwards.

40. $\mu = 4$

$\sigma = \sqrt{4} = 2$

5.1: Continuous Probability Functions

41. The discrete variables are the number of books purchased, and the number of books sold after the end of the semester. The continuous variables are the amount of money spent for the books, and the amount of money received when they were sold.

42. Because for a continuous random variable, $P(x = c) = 0$, where c is any single value. Instead, we calculate $P(c < x < d)$, i.e., the probability that the value of x is between the values c and d.

43. Because $P(x = c) = 0$ for any continuous random variable.

44. $P(x > 5) = 1 - 0.35 = 0.65$, because the total probability of a continuous probability function is always 1.

45. This is a uniform probability distribution. You would draw it as a rectangle with the vertical sides at 0 and 20, and the horizontal sides at $\frac{1}{10}$ and 0.

46. $P(0 < x < 4) = (4 - 0)\left(\frac{1}{10}\right) = 0.4$

5.2: The Uniform Distribution

47. $P(2 < x < 5) = (5 - 2)\left(\frac{1}{10}\right) = 0.3$

48. $X \sim U(0, 15)$

49. $f(x) = \frac{1}{b - a}$ for $(a \leq x \leq b)$ so $f(x) = \frac{1}{30}$ for $(0 \leq x \leq 30)$

50. $\mu = \frac{a + b}{2} = \frac{0 + 30}{5} = 15.0$

$\sigma = \sqrt{\frac{(b - a)^2}{12}} = \sqrt{\frac{(30 - 0)^2}{12}} = 8.66$

51. $P(x < 10) = (10)\left(\frac{1}{30}\right) = 0.33$

5.3: The Exponential Distribution

52. X has an exponential distribution with decay parameter m and mean and standard deviation $\frac{1}{m}$. In this distribution, there will be a relatively large numbers of small values, with values becoming less common as they become larger.

53. $\mu = \sigma = \frac{1}{m} = \frac{1}{10} = 0.1$

54. $f(x) = 0.2e^{-0.2x}$ where $x \geq 0$.

6.1: The Standard Normal Distribution

55. The random variable X has a normal distribution with a mean of 100 and a standard deviation of 15.

56. $X \sim N(0,1)$

57. $z = \dfrac{x - \mu}{\sigma}$ so $z = \dfrac{112 - 109}{4.5} = 0.67$

58. $z = \dfrac{x - \mu}{\sigma}$ so $z = \dfrac{100 - 109}{4.5} = -2.00$

59. $z = \dfrac{105 - 109}{4.5} = -0.89$

This girl is shorter than average for her age, by 0.89 standard deviations.

60. $109 + (1.5)(4.5) = 115.75$ cm

61. We expect about 68 percent of the heights of girls of age five years and zero months to be between 104.5 cm and 113.5 cm.

62. We expect 99.7 percent of the heights in this distribution to be between 95.5 cm and 122.5 cm, because that range represents the values three standard deviations above and below the mean.

6.2: Using the Normal Distribution

63. Yes, because both np and nq are greater than five.
$np = (500)(0.20) = 100$ and $nq = 500(0.80) = 400$

64. $\mu = np = (500)(0.20) = 100$

$$\sigma = \sqrt{npq} = \sqrt{500(0.20)(0.80)} = 8.94$$

65. Fifty percent, because in a normal distribution, half the values lie above the mean.

66. The results of our sample were two standard deviations below the mean, suggesting it is unlikely that 20 percent of the lotto tickets are winners, as claimed by the distributor, and that the true percent of winners is lower. Applying the Empirical Rule, If that claim were true, we would expect to see a result this far below the mean only about 2.5 percent of the time.

7.1: The Central Limit Theorem for Sample Means (Averages)

67. The central limit theorem states that if samples of sufficient size drawn from a population, the distribution of sample means will be normal, even if the distribution of the population is not normal.

68. The sample size of 30 is sufficiently large in this example to apply the central limit theorem. This theorem] states that for samples of sufficient size drawn from a population, the sampling distribution of the sample mean will approach normality, regardless of the distribution of the population from which the samples were drawn.

69. You would not expect each sample to have a mean of 50, because of sampling variability. However, you would expect the sampling distribution of the sample means to cluster around 50, with an approximately normal distribution, so that values close to 50 are more common than values further removed from 50.

70. $\bar{X} \sim N(25, 0.2)$ because $\bar{X} \sim N\left(\mu_x, \dfrac{\sigma_x}{\sqrt{n}}\right)$

71. The standard deviation of the sampling distribution of the sample means can be calculated using the formula $\left(\dfrac{\sigma_x}{\sqrt{n}}\right)$, which in this case is $\left(\dfrac{16}{\sqrt{50}}\right)$. The correct value for the standard deviation of the sampling distribution of the sample means is therefore 2.26.

72. The standard error of the mean is another name for the standard deviation of the sampling distribution of the sample mean. Given samples of size n drawn from a population with standard deviation σ_x, the standard error of the mean is $\left(\dfrac{\sigma_x}{\sqrt{n}}\right)$.

73. $X \sim N(75, 0.45)$

74. Your friend forgot to divide the standard deviation by the square root of *n*.

75. $z = \dfrac{\bar{x} - \mu_x}{\sigma_x} = \dfrac{76 - 75}{4.5} = 2.2$

76. $z = \dfrac{\bar{x} - \mu_x}{\sigma_x} = \dfrac{74.7 - 75}{4.5} = -0.67$

77. $75 + (1.5)(0.45) = 75.675$

78. The standard error of the mean will be larger, because you will be dividing by a smaller number. The standard error of the mean for samples of size $n = 50$ is:

$$\left(\frac{\sigma_x}{\sqrt{n}}\right) = \frac{4.5}{\sqrt{50}} = 0.64$$

79. You would expect this range to include values up to one standard deviation above or below the mean of the sample means. In this case:

$70 + \frac{9}{\sqrt{60}} = 71.16$ and $70 - \frac{9}{\sqrt{60}} = 68.84$ so you would expect 68 percent of the sample means to be between 68.84 and 71.16.

80. $70 + \frac{9}{\sqrt{100}} = 70.9$ and $70 - \frac{9}{\sqrt{100}} = 69.1$ so you would expect 68 percent of the sample means to be between 69.1

and 70.9. Note that this is a narrower interval due to the increased sample size.

7.2: The Central Limit Theorem for Sums

81. For a random variable X, the random variable ΣX will tend to become normally distributed as the size n of the samples used to compute the sum increases.

82. Both rules state that the distribution of a quantity (the mean or the sum) calculated on samples drawn from a population will tend to have a normal distribution, as the sample size increases, regardless of the distribution of population from which the samples are drawn.

83. $\Sigma X \sim N(n\mu_x, (\sqrt{n})(\sigma_x))$ so $\Sigma X \sim N(4000, 28.3)$

84. The probability is 0.50, because 5,000 is the mean of the sampling distribution of sums of size 40 from this population. Sums of random variables computed from a sample of sufficient size are normally distributed, and in a normal distribution, half the values lie below the mean.

85. Using the empirical rule, you would expect 95 percent of the values to be within two standard deviations of the mean. Using the formula for the standard deviation is for a sample sum: $(\sqrt{n})(\sigma_x) = (\sqrt{40})(7) = 44.3$ so you would expect 95

percent of the values to be between $5{,}000 + (2)(44.3)$ and $5{,}000 - (2)(44.3)$, or between 4,911.4 and 588.6.

86. $\mu - (\sqrt{n})(\sigma_x) = 5000 - (\sqrt{40})(7) = 4955.7$

87. $5000 + (2.2)(\sqrt{40})(7) = 5097.4$

7.3: Using the Central Limit Theorem

88. The law of large numbers says that as sample size increases, the sample mean tends to get nearer and nearer to the population mean.

89. You would expect the mean from a sample of size 100 to be nearer to the population mean, because the law of large numbers says that as sample size increases, the sample mean tends to approach the population mea.

90. $X \sim N(0.10, 0.20)$

91. $\bar{X} \sim N\left(\mu_x, \frac{\sigma_x}{\sqrt{n}}\right)$ and the standard deviation of a uniform distribution is $\frac{b-a}{\sqrt{12}}$. In this example, the standard deviation

of the distribution is $\frac{b-a}{\sqrt{12}} = \frac{0.10}{\sqrt{12}} = 0.03$

so $\bar{X} \sim N(0.15, 0.003)$

92. $\Sigma X \sim N((n)(\mu_x), (\sqrt{n})(\sigma_x))$ so $\Sigma X \sim N(9.0, 0.23)$

Practice Test 3
8.1: Confidence Interval, Single Population Mean, Population Standard Deviation Known, Normal

Use the following information to answer the next seven exercises. You draw a sample of size 30 from a normally distributed population with a standard deviation of four.

1. What is the standard error of the sample mean in this scenario, rounded to two decimal places?

2. What is the distribution of the sample mean?

3. If you want to construct a two-sided 95% confidence interval, how much probability will be in each tail of the distribution?

4. What is the appropriate *z*-score and error bound or margin of error (*EBM*) for a 95% confidence interval for this data?

5. Rounding to two decimal places, what is the 95% confidence interval if the sample mean is 41?

6. What is the 90% confidence interval if the sample mean is 41? Round to two decimal places

7. Suppose the sample size in this study had been 50, rather than 30. What would the 95% confidence interval be if the sample mean is 41? Round your answer to two decimal places.

8. For any given data set and sampling situation, which would you expect to be wider: a 95% confidence interval or a 99% confidence interval?

8.2: Confidence Interval, Single Population Mean, Standard Deviation Unknown, Student's *t*

9. Comparing graphs of the standard normal distribution (*z*-distribution) and a *t*-distribution with 15 degrees of freedom (*df*), how do they differ?

10. Comparing graphs of the standard normal distribution (*z*-distribution) and a *t*-distribution with 15 degrees of freedom (*df*), how are they similar?

Use the following information to answer the next five exercises. Body temperature is known to be distributed normally among healthy adults. Because you do not know the population standard deviation, you use the t-distribution to study body temperature. You collect data from a random sample of 20 healthy adults and find that your sample temperatures have a mean of 98.4 and a sample standard deviation of 0.3 (both in degrees Fahrenheit).

11. What is the degrees of freedom (*df*) for this study?

12. For a two-tailed 95% confidence interval, what is the appropriate *t*-value to use in the formula?

13. What is the 95% confidence interval?

14. What is the 99% confidence interval? Round to two decimal places.

15. Suppose your sample size had been 30 rather than 20. What would the 95% confidence interval be then? Round to two decimal places

8.3: Confidence Interval for a Population Proportion

Use this information to answer the next four exercises. You conduct a poll of 500 randomly selected city residents, asking them if they own an automobile. 280 say they do own an automobile, and 220 say they do not.

16. Find the sample proportion and sample standard deviation for this data.

17. What is the 95% two-sided confidence interval? Round to four decimal places.

18. Calculate the 90% confidence interval. Round to four decimal places.

19. Calculate the 99% confidence interval. Round to four decimal places.

Use the following information to answer the next three exercises. You are planning to conduct a poll of community members age 65 and older, to determine how many own mobile phones. You want to produce an estimate whose 95% confidence interval will be within four percentage points (plus or minus) the true population proportion. Use an estimated population proportion of 0.5.

20. What sample size do you need?

21. Suppose you knew from prior research that the population proportion was 0.6. What sample size would you need?

22. Suppose you wanted a 95% confidence interval within three percentage points of the population. Assume the population proportion is 0.5. What sample size do you need?

9.1: Null and Alternate Hypotheses

23. In your state, 58 percent of registered voters in a community are registered as Republicans. You want to conduct a study to see if this also holds up in your community. State the null and alternative hypotheses to test this.

24. You believe that at least 58 percent of registered voters in a community are registered as Republicans. State the null and alternative hypotheses to test this.

25. The mean household value in a city is $268,000. You believe that the mean household value in a particular neighborhood is lower than the city average. Write the null and alternative hypotheses to test this.

26. State the appropriate alternative hypothesis to this null hypothesis: H_0: $\mu = 107$

27. State the appropriate alternative hypothesis to this null hypothesis: H_0: $p < 0.25$

9.2: Outcomes and the Type I and Type II Errors

28. If you reject H_0 when H_0 is correct, what type of error is this?

29. If you fail to reject H_0 when H_0 is false, what type of error is this?

30. What is the relationship between the Type II error and the power of a test?

31. A new blood test is being developed to screen patients for cancer. Positive results are followed up by a more accurate (and expensive) test. It is assumed that the patient does not have cancer. Describe the null hypothesis, the Type I and Type II errors for this situation, and explain which type of error is more serious.

32. Explain in words what it means that a screening test for TB has an α level of 0.10. The null hypothesis is that the patient does not have TB.

33. Explain in words what it means that a screening test for TB has a β level of 0.20. The null hypothesis is that the patient does not have TB.

34. Explain in words what it means that a screening test for TB has a power of 0.80.

9.3: Distribution Needed for Hypothesis Testing

35. If you are conducting a hypothesis test of a single population mean, and you do not know the population variance, what test will you use if the sample size is 10 and the population is normal?

36. If you are conducting a hypothesis test of a single population mean, and you know the population variance, what test will you use?

37. If you are conducting a hypothesis test of a single population proportion, with np and nq greater than or equal to five, what test will you use, and with what parameters?

38. Published information indicates that, on average, college students spend less than 20 hours studying per week. You draw a sample of 25 students from your college, and find the sample mean to be 18.5 hours, with a standard deviation of 1.5 hours. What distribution will you use to test whether study habits at your college are the same as the national average, and why?

39. A published study says that 95 percent of American children are vaccinated against measles, with a standard deviation of 1.5 percent. You draw a sample of 100 children from your community and check their vaccination records, to see if the vaccination rate in your community is the same as the national average. What distribution will you use for this test, and why?

9.4: Rare Events, the Sample, Decision, and Conclusion

40. You are conducting a study with an α level of 0.05. If you get a result with a p-value of 0.07, what will be your decision?

41. You are conducting a study with $\alpha = 0.01$. If you get a result with a p-value of 0.006, what will be your decision?

Use the following information to answer the next five exercises. According to the World Health Organization, the average height of a one-year-old child is 29". You believe children with a particular disease are smaller than average, so you draw a sample of 20 children with this disease and find a mean height of 27.5" and a sample standard deviation of 1.5".

42. What are the null and alternative hypotheses for this study?

43. What distribution will you use to test your hypothesis, and why?

44. What is the test statistic and the p-value?

45. Based on your sample results, what is your decision?

46. Suppose the mean for your sample was 25.0. Redo the calculations and describe what your decision would be.

9.5: Additional Information and Full Hypothesis Test Examples

47. You conduct a study using $\alpha = 0.05$. What is the level of significance for this study?

48. You conduct a study, based on a sample drawn from a normally distributed population with a known variance, with the following hypotheses:
H_0: $\mu = 35.5$
H_a: $\mu \neq 35.5$
Will you conduct a one-tailed or two-tailed test?

49. You conduct a study, based on a sample drawn from a normally distributed population with a known variance, with the following hypotheses:
H_0: $\mu \geq 35.5$
H_a: $\mu < 35.5$
Will you conduct a one-tailed or two-tailed test?

Use the following information to answer the next three exercises. Nationally, 80 percent of adults own an automobile. You are interested in whether the same proportion in your community own cars. You draw a sample of 100 and find that 75 percent own cars.

50. What are the null and alternative hypotheses for this study?

51. What test will you use, and why?

10.1: Comparing Two Independent Population Means with Unknown Population Standard Deviations

52. You conduct a poll of political opinions, interviewing both members of 50 married couples. Are the groups in this study independent or matched?

53. You are testing a new drug to treat insomnia. You randomly assign 80 volunteer subjects to either the experimental (new drug) or control (standard treatment) conditions. Are the groups in this study independent or matched?

54. You are investigating the effectiveness of a new math textbook for high school students. You administer a pretest to a group of students at the beginning of the semester, and a posttest at the end of a year's instruction using this textbook, and compare the results. Are the groups in this study independent or matched?

Use the following information to answer the next two exercises. You are conducting a study of the difference in time at two colleges for undergraduate degree completion. At College A, students take an average of 4.8 years to complete an undergraduate degree, while at College B, they take an average of 4.2 years. The pooled standard deviation for this data is 1.6 years

55. Calculate Cohen's *d* and interpret it.

56. Suppose the mean time to earn an undergraduate degree at College A was 5.2 years. Calculate the effect size and interpret it.

57. You conduct an independent-samples t-test with sample size ten in each of two groups. If you are conducting a two-tailed hypothesis test with $\alpha = 0.01$, what p-values will cause you to reject the null hypothesis?

58. You conduct an independent samples *t*-test with sample size 15 in each group, with the following hypotheses:
H_0: $\mu \geq 110$
H_a: $\mu < 110$
If $\alpha = 0.05$, what *t*-values will cause you to reject the null hypothesis?

10.2: Comparing Two Independent Population Means with Known Population Standard Deviations

Use the following information to answer the next six exercises. College students in the sciences often complain that they must spend more on textbooks each semester than students in the humanities. To test this, you draw random samples of 50 science and 50 humanities students from your college, and record how much each spent last semester on textbooks. Consider the science students to be group one, and the humanities students to be group two.

59. What is the random variable for this study?

60. What are the null and alternative hypotheses for this study?

61. If the 50 science students spent an average of $530 with a sample standard deviation of $20 and the 50 humanities students spent an average of $380 with a sample standard deviation of $15, would you not reject or reject the null hypothesis? Use an alpha level of 0.05. What is your conclusion?

62. What would be your decision, if you were using $\alpha = 0.01$?

10.3: Comparing Two Independent Population Proportions

Use the information to answer the next six exercises. You want to know if proportion of homes with cable television service differs between Community A and Community B. To test this, you draw a random sample of 100 for each and record whether they have cable service.

63. What are the null and alternative hypotheses for this study

64. If 65 households in Community A have cable service, and 78 households in community B, what is the pooled proportion?

65. At $\alpha = 0.03$, will you reject the null hypothesis? What is your conclusion? 65 households in Community A have cable service, and 78 households in community B. 100 households in each community were surveyed.

66. Using an alpha value of 0.01, would you reject the null hypothesis? What is your conclusion? 65 households in Community A have cable service, and 78 households in community B. 100 households in each community were surveyed.

10.4: Matched or Paired Samples

Use the following information to answer the next five exercises. You are interested in whether a particular exercise program helps people lose weight. You conduct a study in which you weigh the participants at the start of the study, and again at the conclusion, after they have participated in the exercise program for six months. You compare the results using a matched-pairs t-test, in which the data is {weight at conclusion – weight at start}. You believe that, on average, the participants will have lost weight after six months on the exercise program.

67. What are the null and alternative hypotheses for this study?

68. Calculate the test statistic, assuming that $\bar{x}_d = -5$, $s_d = 6$, and $n = 30$ (pairs).

69. What are the degrees of freedom for this statistic?

70. Using $\alpha = 0.05$, what is your decision regarding the effectiveness of this program in causing weight loss? What is the conclusion?

71. What would it mean if the *t*-statistic had been 4.56, and what would have been your decision in that case?

11.1: Facts About the Chi-Square Distribution

72. What is the mean and standard deviation for a chi-square distribution with 20 degrees of freedom?

11.2: Goodness-of-Fit Test

Use the following information to answer the next four exercises. Nationally, about 66 percent of high school graduates enroll in higher education. You perform a chi-square goodness of fit test to see if this same proportion applies to your high school's most recent graduating class of 200. Your null hypothesis is that the national distribution also applies to your high school.

73. What are the expected numbers of students from your high school graduating class enrolled and not enrolled in higher education?

74. Fill out the rest of this table.

	Observed (*O*)	Expected (*E*)	*O – E*	(*O – E*)2	$\frac{(O-E)^2}{z}$
Enrolled	145				
Not enrolled	55				

Table B10

75. What are the degrees of freedom for this chi-square test?

76. What is the chi-square test statistic and the *p*-value. At the 5% significance level, what do you conclude?

77. For a chi-square distribution with 92 degrees of freedom, the curve _____.

78. For a chi-square distribution with five degrees of freedom, the curve is _____.

11.3: Test of Independence

Use the following information to answer the next four exercises. You are considering conducting a chi-square test of independence for the data in this table, which displays data about cell phone ownership for freshman and seniors at a high school. Your null hypothesis is that cell phone ownership is independent of class standing.

79. Compute the expected values for the cells.

	Cell = Yes	Cell = No
Freshman	100	150
Senior	200	50

Table B11

80. Compute $\frac{(O - E)^2}{z}$ for each cell, where O = observed and E = expected.

81. What is the chi-square statistic and degrees of freedom for this study?

82. At the $\alpha = 0.5$ significance level, what is your decision regarding the null hypothesis?

11.4: Test of Homogeneity

83. You conduct a chi-square test of homogeneity for data in a five by two table. What is the degrees of freedom for this test?

11.5: Comparison Summary of the Chi-Square Tests: Goodness-of-Fit, Independence and Homogeneity

84. A 2013 poll in the State of California surveyed people about taxing sugar-sweetened beverages. The results are presented in the following table, and are classified by ethnic group and response type. Are the poll responses independent of the participants' ethnic group? Conduct a hypothesis test at the 5% significance level.

Ethnic Group \ Response Type	Favor	Oppose	No Opinion	Row Total
White / Non-Hispanic	234	433	43	710
Latino	147	106	19	272
African American	24	41	6	71
Asian American	54	48	16	118
Column Total	459	628	84	1171

Table B12

85. In a test of homogeneity, what must be true about the expected value of each cell?

86. Stated in general terms, what are the null and alternative hypotheses for the chi-square test of independence?

87. Stated in general terms, what are the null and alternative hypotheses for the chi-square test of homogeneity?

11.6: Test of a Single Variance

88. A lab test claims to have a variance of no more than five. You believe the variance is greater. What are the null and alternative hypothesis to test this?

Practice Test 3 Solutions

8.1: Confidence Interval, Single Population Mean, Population Standard Deviation Known, Normal

1. $\frac{\sigma}{\sqrt{n}} = \frac{4}{\sqrt{30}} = 0.73$

2. normal

3. 0.025 or 2.5%; A 95% confidence interval contains 95% of the probability, and excludes five percent, and the five percent excluded is split evenly between the upper and lower tails of the distribution.

4. z-score = 1.96; $EBM = z_{\frac{\alpha}{2}}\left(\frac{\sigma}{\sqrt{n}}\right) = (1.96)(0.73) = 1.4308$

5. $41 \pm 1.43 = (39.57, 42.43)$; Using the calculator function Zinterval, answer is (40.74, 41.26. Answers differ due to rounding.

6. The z-value for a 90% confidence interval is 1.645, so $EBM = 1.645(0.73) = 1.20085$.
The 90% confidence interval is $41 \pm 1.20 = (39.80, 42.20)$.
The calculator function Zinterval answer is (40.78, 41.23). Answers differ due to rounding.

7. The standard error of measurement is: $\frac{\sigma}{\sqrt{n}} = \frac{4}{\sqrt{50}} = 0.57$

$EBM = z_{\frac{\alpha}{2}}\left(\frac{\sigma}{\sqrt{n}}\right) = (1.96)(0.57) = 1.12$

The 95% confidence interval is $41 \pm 1.12 = (39.88, 42.12)$.
The calculator function Zinterval answer is (40.84, 41.16). Answers differ due to rounding.

8. The 99% confidence interval, because it includes all but one percent of the distribution. The 95% confidence interval will be narrower, because it excludes five percent of the distribution.

8.2: Confidence Interval, Single Population Mean, Standard Deviation Unknown, Student's t

9. The t-distribution will have more probability in its tails ("thicker tails") and less probability near the mean of the distribution ("shorter in the center").

10. Both distributions are symmetrical and centered at zero.

11. $df = n - 1 = 20 - 1 = 19$

12. You can get the t-value from a probability table or a calculator. In this case, for a t-distribution with 19 degrees of freedom, and a 95% two-sided confidence interval, the value is 2.093, i.e.,
$t_{\frac{\alpha}{2}} = 2.093$. The calculator function is invT(0.975, 19).

13. $EBM = t_{\frac{\alpha}{2}}\left(\frac{s}{\sqrt{n}}\right) = (2.093)\left(\frac{0.3}{\sqrt{20}}\right) = 0.140$

$98.4 \pm 0.14 = (98.26, 98.54)$.
The calculator function Tinterval answer is (98.26, 98.54).

14. $t_{\frac{\alpha}{2}} = 2.861$. The calculator function is invT(0.995, 19).

$EBM = t_{\frac{\alpha}{2}}\left(\frac{s}{\sqrt{n}}\right) = (2.861)\left(\frac{0.3}{\sqrt{20}}\right) = 0.192$

$98.4 \pm 0.19 = (98.21, 98.59)$. The calculator function Tinterval answer is (98.21, 98.59).

15. $df = n - 1 = 30 - 1 = 29$. $t_{\frac{\alpha}{2}} = 2.045$

$EBM = z_t\left(\frac{s}{\sqrt{n}}\right) = (2.045)\left(\frac{0.3}{\sqrt{30}}\right) = 0.112$

$98.4 \pm 0.11 = (98.29, 98.51)$. The calculator function Tinterval answer is (98.29, 98.51).

8.3: Confidence Interval for a Population Proportion

16. $p' = \frac{280}{500} = 0.56$

$q' = 1 - p' = 1 - 0.56 = 0.44$

$s = \sqrt{\frac{pq}{n}} = \sqrt{\frac{0.56(0.44)}{500}} = 0.0222$

17. Because you are using the normal approximation to the binomial, $z_{\frac{\alpha}{2}} = 1.96$.

Calculate the error bound for the population (*EBP*):

$EBP = z_{\frac{\alpha}{2}}\sqrt{\frac{pq}{n}} = 1.96(0.222) = 0.0435$

Calculate the 95% confidence interval:
$0.56 \pm 0.0435 = (0.5165, 0.6035)$.
The calculator function 1-PropZint answer is (0.5165, 0.6035).

18. $z_{\frac{\alpha}{2}} = 1.64$

$EBP = z_{\frac{\alpha}{2}}\sqrt{\frac{pq}{n}} = 1.64(0.0222) = 0.0364$

$0.56 \pm 0.03 = (0.5236, 0.5964)$. The calculator function 1-PropZint answer is (0.5235, 0.5965)

19. $z_{\frac{\alpha}{2}} = 2.58$

$EBP = z_{\frac{\alpha}{2}}\sqrt{\frac{pq}{n}} = 2.58(0.0222) = 0.0573$

$0.56 \pm 0.05 = (0.5127, 0.6173)$.
The calculator function 1-PropZint answer is (0.5028, 0.6172).

20. *EBP* = 0.04 (because 4% = 0.04)
$z_{\frac{\alpha}{2}} = 1.96$ for a 95% confidence interval

$n = \frac{z^2 pq}{EBP^2} = \frac{1.96^2(0.5)(0.5)}{0.04^2} = \frac{0.9604}{0.0016} = 600.25$

You need 601 subjects (rounding upward from 600.25).

21. $n = \frac{n^2 pq}{EBP^2} = \frac{1.96^2(0.6)(0.4)}{0.04^2} = \frac{0.9220}{0.0016} = 576.24$

You need 577 subjects (rounding upward from 576.24).

22. $n = \frac{n^2 pq}{EBP^2} = \frac{1.96^2(0.5)(0.5)}{0.03^2} = \frac{0.9604}{0.0009} = 1067.11$

You need 1,068 subjects (rounding upward from 1,067.11).

9.1: Null and Alternate Hypotheses

23. H_0: $p = 0.58$
H_a: $p \neq 0.58$

24. H_0: $p \geq 0.58$
H_a: $p < 0.58$

25. H_0: $\mu \geq \$268,000$
H_a: $\mu < \$268,000$

26. H_a: $\mu \neq 107$

27. H_a: $p \geq 0.25$

9.2: Outcomes and the Type I and Type II Errors

28. a Type I error

29. a Type II error

30. Power $= 1 - \beta = 1 - P$(Type II error).

31. The null hypothesis is that the patient does not have cancer. A Type I error would be detecting cancer when it is not present. A Type II error would be not detecting cancer when it is present. A Type II error is more serious, because failure to detect cancer could keep a patient from receiving appropriate treatment.

32. The screening test has a ten percent probability of a Type I error, meaning that ten percent of the time, it will detect TB when it is not present.

33. The screening test has a 20 percent probability of a Type II error, meaning that 20 percent of the time, it will fail to detect TB when it is in fact present.

34. Eighty percent of the time, the screening test will detect TB when it is actually present.

9.3: Distribution Needed for Hypothesis Testing

35. The Student's t-test.

36. The normal distribution or z-test.

37. The normal distribution with $\mu = p$ and $\sigma = \sqrt{\dfrac{pq}{n}}$

38. t_{24}. You use the t-distribution because you don't know the population standard deviation, and the degrees of freedom are 24 because $df = n - 1$.

39. $\bar{X} \sim N\left(0.95, \dfrac{0.051}{\sqrt{100}}\right)$

Because you know the population standard deviation, and have a large sample, you can use the normal distribution.

9.4: Rare Events, the Sample, Decision, and Conclusion

40. Fail to reject the null hypothesis, because $\alpha \leq p$

41. Reject the null hypothesis, because $\alpha \geq p$.

42. H_0: $\mu \geq 29.0$"
H_a: $\mu < 29.0$"

43. t_{19}. Because you do not know the population standard deviation, use the t-distribution. The degrees of freedom are 19, because $df = n - 1$.

44. The test statistic is -4.4721 and the p-value is 0.00013 using the calculator function TTEST.

45. With $\alpha = 0.05$, reject the null hypothesis.

46. With $\alpha = 0.05$, the p-value is almost zero using the calculator function TTEST so reject the null hypothesis.

9.5: Additional Information and Full Hypothesis Test Examples

47. The level of significance is five percent.

48. two-tailed

49. one-tailed

50. H_0: $p = 0.8$
H_a: $p \neq 0.8$

51. You will use the normal test for a single population proportion because np and nq are both greater than five.

10.1: Comparing Two Independent Population Means with Unknown Population Standard Deviations

52. They are matched (paired), because you interviewed married couples.

53. They are independent, because participants were assigned at random to the groups.

54. They are matched (paired), because you collected data twice from each individual.

55. $d = \dfrac{\bar{x}_1 - \bar{x}_2}{s_{pooled}} = \dfrac{4.8 - 4.2}{1.6} = 0.375$

This is a small effect size, because 0.375 falls between Cohen's small (0.2) and medium (0.5) effect sizes.

56. $d = \dfrac{\bar{x}_1 - \bar{x}_2}{s_{pooled}} = \dfrac{5.2 - 4.2}{1.6} = 0.625$

The effect size is 0.625. By Cohen's standard, this is a medium effect size, because it falls between the medium (0.5) and large (0.8) effect sizes.

57. p-value < 0.01.

58. You will only reject the null hypothesis if you get a value significantly below the hypothesized mean of 110.

10.2: Comparing Two Independent Population Means with Known Population Standard Deviations

59. $\bar{X}_1 - \bar{X}_2$, i.e., the mean difference in amount spent on textbooks for the two groups.

60. H_0: $\bar{X}_1 - \bar{X}_2 \leq 0$

H_a: $\bar{X}_1 - \bar{X}_2 > 0$

This could also be written as:

H_0: $\bar{X}_1 \leq \bar{X}_2$

H_a: $\bar{X}_1 > \bar{X}_2$

61. Using the calculator function 2-SampTtest, reject the null hypothesis. At the 5% significance level, there is sufficient evidence to conclude that the science students spend more on textbooks than the humanities students.

62. Using the calculator function 2-SampTtest, reject the null hypothesis. At the 1% significance level, there is sufficient evidence to conclude that the science students spend more on textbooks than the humanities students.

10.3: Comparing Two Independent Population Proportions

63. H_0: $p_A = p_B$
H_a: $p_A \neq p_B$

64. $p_c = \dfrac{x_A + x_A}{n_A + n_A} = \dfrac{65 + 78}{100 + 100} = 0.715$

65. Using the calculator function 2-PropZTest, the p-value = 0.0417. Reject the null hypothesis. At the 3% significance level, here is sufficient evidence to conclude that there is a difference between the proportions of households in the two communities that have cable service.

66. Using the calculator function 2-PropZTest, the p-value = 0.0417. Do not reject the null hypothesis. At the 1% significance level, there is insufficient evidence to conclude that there is a difference between the proportions of households in the two communities that have cable service.

10.4: Matched or Paired Samples

67. H_0: $\bar{x}_d \geq 0$

H_a: $\bar{x}_d < 0$

68. $t = -4.5644$

69. $df = 30 - 1 = 29$.

70. Using the calculator function TTEST, the p-value = 0.00004 so reject the null hypothesis. At the 5% level, there is sufficient evidence to conclude that the participants lost weight, on average.

71. A positive t-statistic would mean that participants, on average, gained weight over the six months.

11.1: Facts About the Chi-Square Distribution

72. $\mu = df = 20$
$\sigma = \sqrt{2(df)} = \sqrt{40} = 6.32$

11.2: Goodness-of-Fit Test

73. Enrolled = 200(0.66) = 132. Not enrolled = 200(0.34) = 68

74.

	Observed (O)	Expected (E)	O – E	(O – E)2	$\frac{(O-E)^2}{z}$
Enrolled	145	132	145 – 132 = 13	169	$\frac{169}{132} = 1.280$
Not enrolled	55	68	55 – 68 = –13	169	$\frac{169}{68} = 2.485$

Table B13

75. $df = n - 1 = 2 - 1 = 1$.

76. Using the calculator function Chi-square GOF – Test (in STAT TESTS), the test statistic is 3.7656 and the p-value is 0.0523. Do not reject the null hypothesis. At the 5% significance level, there is insufficient evidence to conclude that high school most recent graduating class distribution of enrolled and not enrolled does not fit that of the national distribution.

77. approximates the normal

78. skewed right

11.3: Test of Independence

79.

	Cell = Yes	Cell = No	Total
Freshman	$\frac{250(300)}{500} = 150$	$\frac{250(200)}{500} = 100$	250
Senior	$\frac{250(300)}{500} = 150$	$\frac{250(200)}{500} = 100$	250
Total	300	200	500

Table B14

80. $\frac{(100 - 150)^2}{150} = 16.67$

$\frac{(150 - 100)^2}{100} = 25$

$\frac{(200 - 100)^2}{150} = 16.67$

$\frac{(50 - 100)^2}{100} = 25$

81. Chi-square = 16.67 + 25 + 16.67 + 25 = 83.34.
$df = (r - 1)(c - 1) = 1$

82. p-value = P(Chi-square, 83.34) = 0
Reject the null hypothesis.
You could also use the calculator function STAT TESTS Chi-Square – Test.

11.4: Test of Homogeneity

83. The table has five rows and two columns. $df = (r - 1)(c - 1) = (4)(1) = 4$.

11.5: Comparison Summary of the Chi-Square Tests: Goodness-of-Fit, Independence and Homogeneity

84. Using the calculator function (STAT TESTS) Chi-square Test, the p-value = 0. Reject the null hypothesis. At the 5% significance level, there is sufficient evidence to conclude that the poll responses independent of the participants' ethnic group.

85. The expected value of each cell must be at least five.

86. H_0: The variables are independent.
H_a: The variables are not independent.

87. H_0: The populations have the same distribution.
H_a: The populations do not have the same distribution.

11.6: Test of a Single Variance

88. H_0: $\sigma^2 \leq 5$
H_a: $\sigma^2 > 5$

Practice Test 4
12.1 Linear Equations

1. Which of the following equations is/are linear?

  a. $y = -3x$

  b. $y = 0.2 + 0.74x$

  c. $y = -9.4 - 2x$

  d. A and B

  e. A, B, and C

2. To complete a painting job requires four hours setup time plus one hour per 1,000 square feet. How would you express this information in a linear equation?

3. A statistics instructor is paid a per-class fee of $2,000 plus $100 for each student in the class. How would you express this information in a linear equation?

4. A tutoring school requires students to pay a one-time enrollment fee of $500 plus tuition of $3,000 per year. Express this information in an equation.

12.2: Slope and *Y*-intercept of a Linear Equation

Use the following information to answer the next four exercises. For the labor costs of doing repairs, an auto mechanic charges a flat fee of $75 per car, plus an hourly rate of $55.

5. What are the independent and dependent variables for this situation?

6. Write the equation and identify the slope and intercept.

7. What is the labor charge for a job that takes 3.5 hours to complete?

8. One job takes 2.4 hours to complete, while another takes 6.3 hours. What is the difference in labor costs for these two jobs?

12.3: Scatter Plots

9. Describe the pattern in this scatter plot, and decide whether the X and Y variables would be good candidates for linear regression.

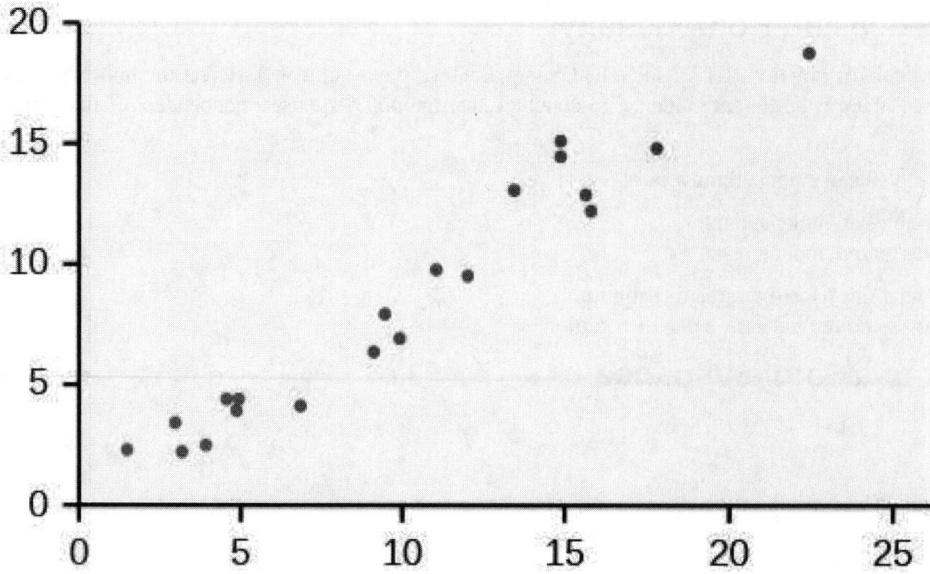

Figure B4

10. Describe the pattern in this scatter plot, and decide whether the X and Y variables would be good candidates for linear regression.

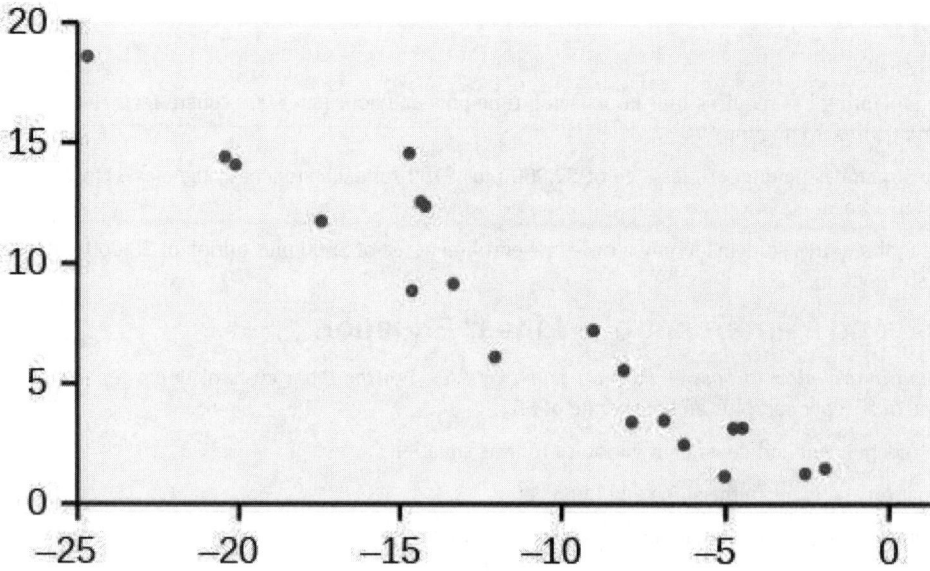

Figure B5

11. Describe the pattern in this scatter plot, and decide whether the X and Y variables would be good candidates for linear regression.

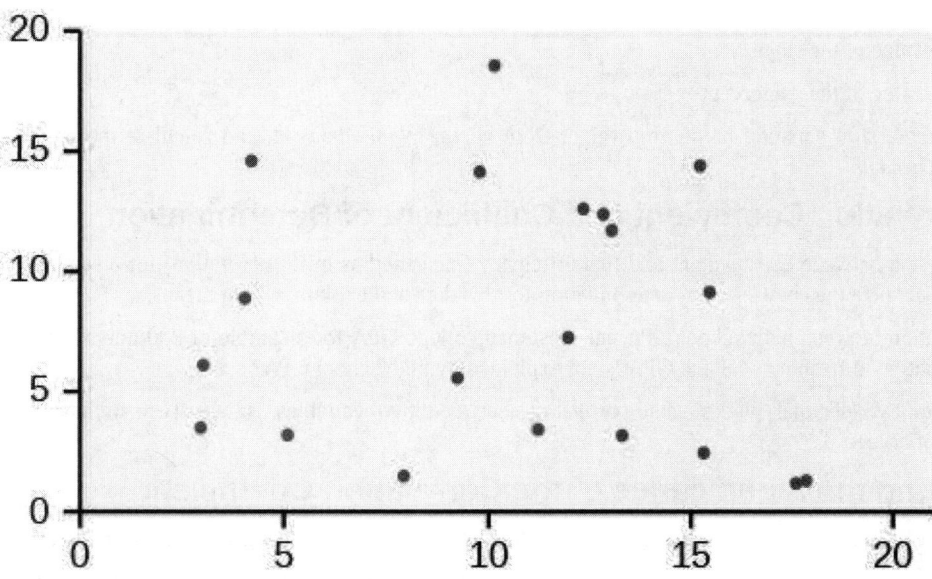

Figure B6

12. Describe the pattern in this scatter plot, and decide whether the X and Y variables would be good candidates for linear regression.

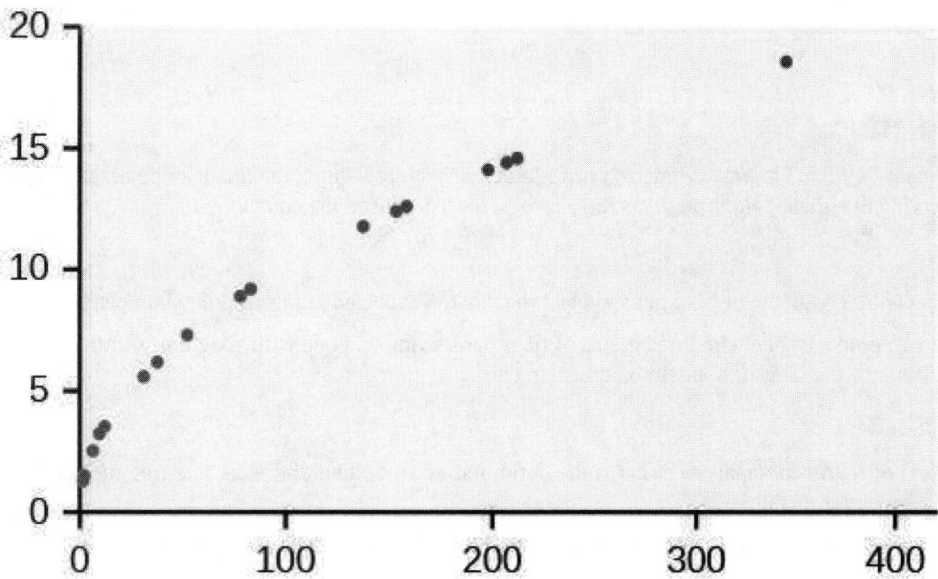

Figure B7

12.4: The Regression Equation

Use the following information to answer the next four exercises. Height (in inches) and weight (In pounds) in a sample of college freshman men have a linear relationship with the following summary statistics:

$\bar{x} = 68.4$

$\bar{y} = 141.6$

$s_x = 4.0$
$s_y = 9.6$
$r = 0.73$

Let Y = weight and X = height, and write the regression equation in the form:

$$\hat{y} = a + bx$$

13. What is the value of the slope?

14. What is the value of the y intercept?

15. Write the regression equation predicting weight from height in this data set, and calculate the predicted weight for someone 68 inches tall.

12.5: Correlation Coefficient and Coefficient of Determination

16. The correlation between body weight and fuel efficiency (measured as miles per gallon) for a sample of 2,012 model cars is –0.56. Calculate the coefficient of determination for this data and explain what it means.

17. The correlation between high school GPA and freshman college GPA for a sample of 200 university students is 0.32. How much variation in freshman college GPA is not explained by high school GPA?

18. Rounded to two decimal places what correlation between two variables is necessary to have a coefficient of determination of at least 0.50?

12.6: Testing the Significance of the Correlation Coefficient

19. Write the null and alternative hypotheses for a study to determine if two variables are significantly correlated.

20. In a sample of 30 cases, two variables have a correlation of 0.33. Do a t-test to see if this result is significant at the $\alpha = 0.05$ level. Use the formula:

$$t = \frac{r\sqrt{n-2}}{\sqrt{1-r^2}}$$

21. In a sample of 25 cases, two variables have a correlation of 0.45. Do a t-test to see if this result is significant at the $\alpha = 0.05$ level. Use the formula:

$$t = \frac{r\sqrt{n-2}}{\sqrt{1-r^2}}$$

12.7: Prediction

Use the following information to answer the next two exercises. A study relating the grams of potassium (Y) to the grams of fiber (X) per serving in enriched flour products (bread, rolls, etc.) produced the equation:

$$\hat{y} = 25 + 16x$$

22. For a product with five grams of fiber per serving, what are the expected grams of potassium per serving?

23. Comparing two products, one with three grams of fiber per serving and one with six grams of fiber per serving, what is the expected difference in grams of potassium per serving?

12.8: Outliers

24. In the context of regression analysis, what is the definition of an outlier, and what is a rule of thumb to evaluate if a given value in a data set is an outlier?

25. In the context of regression analysis, what is the definition of an influential point, and how does an influential point differ from an outlier?

26. The least squares regression line for a data set is $\hat{y} = 5 + 0.3x$ and the standard deviation of the residuals is 0.4. Does a case with the values $x = 2$, $y = 6.2$ qualify as an outlier?

27. The least squares regression line for a data set is $\hat{y} = 2.3 - 0.1x$ and the standard deviation of the residuals is 0.13. Does a case with the values $x = 4.1$, $y = 2.34$ qualify as an outlier?

13.1: One-Way ANOVA

28. What are the five basic assumptions to be met if you want to do a one-way ANOVA?

29. You are conducting a one-way ANOVA comparing the effectiveness of four drugs in lowering blood pressure in hypertensive patients. What are the null and alternative hypotheses for this study?

30. What is the primary difference between the independent samples t-test and one-way ANOVA?

31. You are comparing the results of three methods of teaching geometry to high school students. The final exam scores X_1, X_2, X_3, for the samples taught by the different methods have the following distributions:

$X_1 \sim N(85, 3.6)$

$X_1 \sim N(82, 4.8)$

$X_1 \sim N(79, 2.9)$

Each sample includes 100 students, and the final exam scores have a range of 0–100. Assuming the samples are independent and randomly selected, have the requirements for conducting a one-way ANOVA been met? Explain why or why not for each assumption.

32. You conduct a study comparing the effectiveness of four types of fertilizer to increase crop yield on wheat farms. When examining the sample results, you find that two of the samples have an approximately normal distribution, and two have an approximately uniform distribution. Is this a violation of the assumptions for conducting a one-way ANOVA?

13.2: The *F* Distribution

Use the following information to answer the next seven exercises. You are conducting a study of three types of feed supplements for cattle to test their effectiveness in producing weight gain among calves whose feed includes one of the supplements. You have four groups of 30 calves (one is a control group receiving the usual feed, but no supplement). You will conduct a one-way ANOVA after one year to see if there are difference in the mean weight for the four groups.

33. What is SS_{within} in this experiment, and what does it mean?

34. What is $SS_{between}$ in this experiment, and what does it mean?

35. What are k and i for this experiment?

36. If $SS_{within} = 374.5$ and $SS_{total} = 621.4$ for this data, what is $SS_{between}$?

37. What are $MS_{between}$, and MS_{within}, for this experiment?

38. What is the *F* Statistic for this data?

39. If there had been 35 calves in each group, instead of 30, with the sums of squares remaining the same, would the *F* Statistic be larger or smaller?

13.3: Facts About the *F* Distribution

40. Which of the following numbers are possible *F* Statistics?

a. 2.47

b. 5.95

c. –3.61

d. 7.28

e. 0.97

41. Histograms $F1$ and $F2$ below display the distribution of cases from samples from two populations, one distributed $F_{3,15}$ and one distributed $F_{5,500}$. Which sample came from which population?

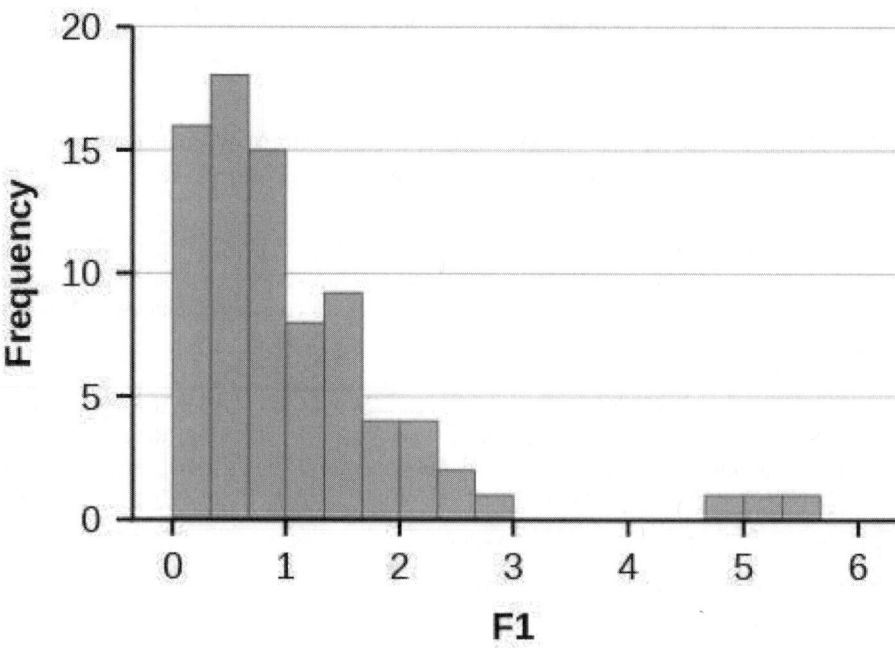

Figure B8

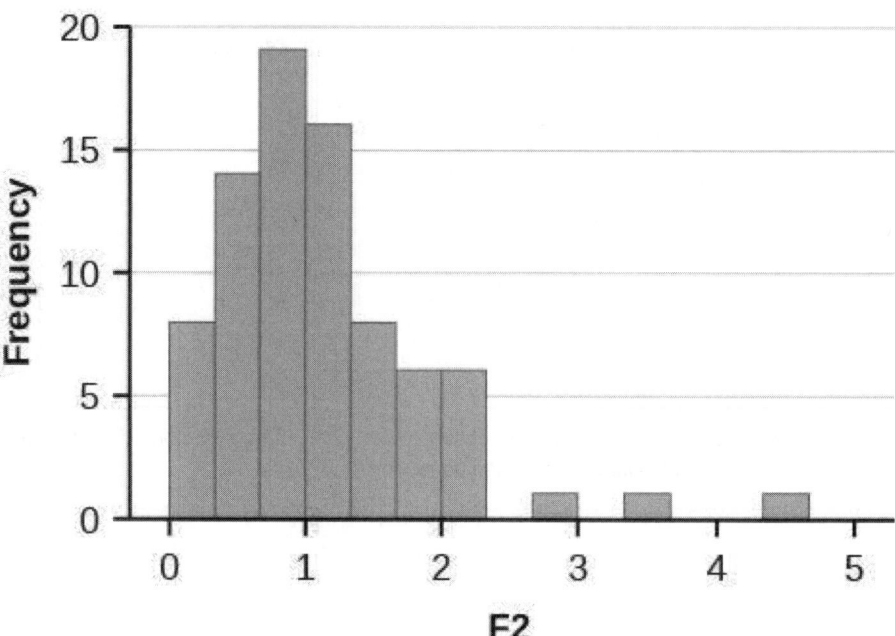

Figure B9

42. The F Statistic from an experiment with $k = 3$ and $n = 50$ is 3.67. At $\alpha = 0.05$, will you reject the null hypothesis?

43. The F Statistic from an experiment with $k = 4$ and $n = 100$ is 4.72. At $\alpha = 0.01$, will you reject the null hypothesis?

13.4: Test of Two Variances

44. What assumptions must be met to perform the F test of two variances?

45. You believe there is greater variance in grades given by the math department at your university than in the English department. You collect all the grades for undergraduate classes in the two departments for a semester, and compute the variance of each, and conduct an F test of two variances. What are the null and alternative hypotheses for this study?

Practice Test 4 Solutions
12.1 Linear Equations

1. e. A, B, and C.
All three are linear equations of the form $y = mx + b$.

2. Let y = the total number of hours required, and x the square footage, measured in units of 1,000. The equation is: $y = x + 4$

3. Let y = the total payment, and x the number of students in a class. The equation is: $y = 100(x) + 2,000$

4. Let y = the total cost of attendance, and x the number of years enrolled. The equation is: $y = 3,000(x) + 500$

12.2: Slope and Y-intercept of a Linear Equation

5. The independent variable is the hours worked on a car. The dependent variable is the total labor charges to fix a car.

6. Let y = the total charge, and x the number of hours required. The equation is: $y = 55x + 75$
The slope is 55 and the intercept is 75.

7. $y = 55(3.5) + 75 = 267.50$

8. Because the intercept is included in both equations, while you are only interested in the difference in costs, you do not need to include the intercept in the solution. The difference in number of hours required is: $6.3 - 2.4 = 3.9$.
Multiply this difference by the cost per hour: $55(3.9) = 214.5$.
The difference in cost between the two jobs is $214.50.

12.3: Scatter Plots

9. The X and Y variables have a strong linear relationship. These variables would be good candidates for analysis with linear regression.

10. The X and Y variables have a strong negative linear relationship. These variables would be good candidates for analysis with linear regression.

11. There is no clear linear relationship between the X and Y variables, so they are not good candidates for linear regression.

12. The X and Y variables have a strong positive relationship, but it is curvilinear rather than linear. These variables are not good candidates for linear regression.

12.4: The Regression Equation

13. $r\left(\frac{s_y}{s_x}\right) = 0.73\left(\frac{9.6}{4.0}\right) = 1.752 \approx 1.75$

14. $a = \bar{y} - b\bar{x} = 141.6 - 1.752(68.4) = 21.7632 \approx 21.76$

15. $\hat{y} = 21.76 + 1.75(68) = 140.76$

12.5: Correlation Coefficient and Coefficient of Determination

16. The coefficient of determination is the square of the correlation, or r^2.
For this data, $r^2 = (-0.56)2 = 0.3136 \approx 0.31$ or 31%. This means that 31 percent of the variation in fuel efficiency can be explained by the bodyweight of the automobile.

17. The coefficient of determination $= 0.32^2 = 0.1024$. This is the amount of variation in freshman college GPA that can be explained by high school GPA. The amount that cannot be explained is $1 - 0.1024 = 0.8976 \approx 0.90$. So about 90 percent of variance in freshman college GPA in this data is not explained by high school GPA.

18. $r = \sqrt{r^2}$

$\sqrt{0.5} = 0.707106781 \approx 0.71$

You need a correlation of 0.71 or higher to have a coefficient of determination of at least 0.5.

12.6: Testing the Significance of the Correlation Coefficient

19. $H_0: \rho = 0$
$H_a: \rho \neq 0$

20. $t = \frac{r\sqrt{n-2}}{\sqrt{1-r^2}} = \frac{0.33\sqrt{30-2}}{\sqrt{1-0.33^2}} = 1.85$

The critical value for $\alpha = 0.05$ for a two-tailed test using the t_{29} distribution is 2.045. Your value is less than this, so you fail to reject the null hypothesis and conclude that the study produced no evidence that the variables are significantly correlated.

Using the calculator function tcdf, the p-value is 2tcdf(1.85, 10^99, 29) = 0.0373. Do not reject the null hypothesis and conclude that the study produced no evidence that the variables are significantly correlated.

21. $t = \frac{r\sqrt{n-2}}{\sqrt{1-r^2}} = \frac{0.45\sqrt{25-2}}{\sqrt{1-0.45^2}} = 2.417$

The critical value for $\alpha = 0.05$ for a two-tailed test using the t_{24} distribution is 2.064. Your value is greater than this, so you reject the null hypothesis and conclude that the study produced evidence that the variables are significantly correlated. Using the calculator function tcdf, the p-value is 2tcdf(2.417, 10^99, 24) = 0.0118. Reject the null hypothesis and conclude that the study produced evidence that the variables are significantly correlated.

12.7: Prediction

22. $\hat{y} = 25 + 16(5) = 105$

23. Because the intercept appears in both predicted values, you can ignore it in calculating a predicted difference score. The difference in grams of fiber per serving is $6 - 3 = 3$ and the predicted difference in grams of potassium per serving is $(16)(3) = 48$.

12.8: Outliers

24. An outlier is an observed value that is far from the least squares regression line. A rule of thumb is that a point more than two standard deviations of the residuals from its predicted value on the least squares regression line is an outlier.

25. An influential point is an observed value in a data set that is far from other points in the data set, in a horizontal direction. Unlike an outlier, an influential point is determined by its relationship with other values in the data set, not by its relationship to the regression line.

26. The predicted value for y is: $\hat{y} = 5 + 0.3x = 5.6$. The value of 6.2 is less than two standard deviations from the predicted value, so it does not qualify as an outlier.
Residual for (2, 6.2): $6.2 - 5.6 = 0.6$ $(0.6 < 2(0.4))$

27. The predicted value for y is: $\hat{y} = 2.3 - 0.1(4.1) = 1.89$. The value of 2.32 is more than two standard deviations from the predicted value, so it qualifies as an outlier.
Residual for (4.1, 2.34): $2.32 - 1.89 = 0.43$ $(0.43 > 2(0.13))$

13.1: One-Way ANOVA

28.

1. Each sample is drawn from a normally distributed population

2. All samples are independent and randomly selected.

3. The populations from which the samples are draw have equal standard deviations.

4. The factor is a categorical variable.

5. The response is a numerical variable.

29. H_0: $\mu 1 = \mu 2 = \mu 3 = \mu 4$
H_a: At least two of the group means $\mu 1$, $\mu 2$, $\mu 3$, $\mu 4$ are not equal.

30. The independent samples t-test can only compare means from two groups, while one-way ANOVA can compare means of more than two groups.

31. Each sample appears to have been drawn from a normally distributed populations, the factor is a categorical variable (method), the outcome is a numerical variable (test score), and you were told the samples were independent and randomly selected, so those requirements are met. However, each sample has a different standard deviation, and this suggests that the populations from which they were drawn also have different standard deviations, which is a violation of an assumption for one-way ANOVA. Further statistical testing will be necessary to test the assumption of equal variance before proceeding with the analysis.

32. One of the assumptions for a one-way ANOVA is that the samples are drawn from normally distributed populations. Since two of your samples have an approximately uniform distribution, this casts doubt on whether this assumption has been met. Further statistical testing will be necessary to determine if you can proceed with the analysis.

13.2: The *F* Distribution

33. SS_{within} is the sum of squares within groups, representing the variation in outcome that cannot be attributed to the different feed supplements, but due to individual or chance factors among the calves in each group.

34. $SS_{between}$ is the sum of squares between groups, representing the variation in outcome that can be attributed to the different feed supplements.

35. k = the number of groups = 4
n_1 = the number of cases in group 1 = 30
n = the total number of cases = 4(30) = 120

36. $SS_{total} = SS_{within} + SS_{between}$ so $SS_{between} = SS_{total} - SS_{within}$
$621.4 - 374.5 = 246.9$

37. The mean squares in an ANOVA are found by dividing each sum of squares by its respective degrees of freedom (df).
For SS_{total}, $df = n - 1 = 120 - 1 = 119$.
For $SS_{between}$, $df = k - 1 = 4 - 1 = 3$.
For SS_{within}, $df = 120 - 4 = 116$.

$$MS_{between} = \frac{246.9}{3} = 82.3$$

$$MS_{within} = \frac{374.5}{116} = 3.23$$

38. $F = \dfrac{MS_{between}}{MS_{within}} = \dfrac{82.3}{3.23} = 25.48$

39. It would be larger, because you would be dividing by a smaller number. The value of $MS_{between}$ would not change with a change of sample size, but the value of MS_{within} would be smaller, because you would be dividing by a larger number (df_{within} would be 136, not 116). Dividing a constant by a smaller number produces a larger result.

13.3: Facts About the *F* Distribution

40. All but choice c, -3.61. *F* Statistics are always greater than or equal to 0.

41. As the degrees of freedom increase in an *F* distribution, the distribution becomes more nearly normal. Histogram *F2* is closer to a normal distribution than histogram *F1*, so the sample displayed in histogram *F1* was drawn from the $F_{3,15}$ population, and the sample displayed in histogram *F2* was drawn from the $F_{5,500}$ population.

42. Using the calculator function Fcdf, *p*-value = Fcdf(3.67, 1E, 3,50) = 0.0182. Reject the null hypothesis.

43. Using the calculator function Fcdf, *p*-value = Fcdf(4.72, 1E, 4, 100) = 0.0016 Reject the null hypothesis.

13.4: Test of Two Variances

44. The samples must be drawn from populations that are normally distributed, and must be drawn from independent populations.

45. Let σ_M^2 = variance in math grades, and σ_E^2 = variance in English grades.

H_0: $\sigma_M^2 \leq \sigma_E^2$

H_a: $\sigma_M^2 > \sigma_E^2$

Practice Final Exam 1

Use the following information to answer the next two exercises: An experiment consists of tossing two, 12-sided dice (the numbers 1–12 are printed on the sides of each die).

- Let Event *A* = both dice show an even number.
- Let Event *B* = both dice show a number more than eight

1. Events *A* and *B* are:

a. mutually exclusive.

b. independent.

c. mutually exclusive and independent.

d. neither mutually exclusive nor independent.

2. Find $P(A|B)$.

a. $\frac{2}{4}$

b. $\frac{16}{144}$

c. $\frac{4}{16}$

d. $\frac{2}{144}$

3. Which of the following are TRUE when we perform a hypothesis test on matched or paired samples?

a. Sample sizes are almost never small.

b. Two measurements are drawn from the same pair of individuals or objects.

c. Two sample means are compared to each other.

d. Answer choices b and c are both true.

Use the following information to answer the next two exercises: One hundred eighteen students were asked what type of color their bedrooms were painted: light colors, dark colors, or vibrant colors. The results were tabulated according to gender.

	Light colors	Dark colors	Vibrant colors
Female	20	22	28
Male	10	30	8

Table B15

4. Find the probability that a randomly chosen student is male or has a bedroom painted with light colors.

a. $\frac{10}{118}$

b. $\frac{68}{118}$

c. $\frac{48}{118}$

d. $\frac{10}{48}$

5. Find the probability that a randomly chosen student is male given the student's bedroom is painted with dark colors.

a. $\frac{30}{118}$

b. $\frac{30}{48}$

c. $\frac{22}{118}$

d. $\frac{30}{52}$

Use the following information to answer the next two exercises: We are interested in the number of times a teenager must be reminded to do his or her chores each week. A survey of 40 mothers was conducted. **Table B16** shows the results of the survey.

x	P (x)
0	$\frac{2}{40}$
1	$\frac{5}{40}$
2	
3	$\frac{14}{40}$
4	$\frac{7}{40}$
5	$\frac{4}{40}$

Table B16

6. Find the probability that a teenager is reminded two times.

a. 8

b. $\frac{8}{40}$

c. $\frac{6}{40}$

d. 2

7. Find the expected number of times a teenager is reminded to do his or her chores.

a. 15

b. 2.78

c. 1.0

d. 3.13

Use the following information to answer the next two exercises: On any given day, approximately 37.5% of the cars parked in the De Anza parking garage are parked crookedly. We randomly survey 22 cars. We are interested in the number of cars that are parked crookedly.

8. For every 22 cars, how many would you expect to be parked crookedly, on average?

a. 8.25

b. 11

c. 18

d. 7.5

9. What is the probability that at least ten of the 22 cars are parked crookedly.

a. 0.1263

b. 0.1607

c. 0.2870

d. 0.8393

10. Using a sample of 15 Stanford-Binet IQ scores, we wish to conduct a hypothesis test. Our claim is that the mean IQ score on the Stanford-Binet IQ test is more than 100. It is known that the standard deviation of all Stanford-Binet IQ scores is 15 points. The correct distribution to use for the hypothesis test is:

a. Binomial

b. Student's t

c. Normal

d. Uniform

Use the following information to answer the next three exercises: De Anza College keeps statistics on the pass rate of students who enroll in math classes. In a sample of 1,795 students enrolled in Math 1A (1st quarter calculus), 1,428 passed the course. In a sample of 856 students enrolled in Math 1B (2nd quarter calculus), 662 passed. In general, are the pass rates of Math 1A and Math 1B statistically the same? Let A = the subscript for Math 1A and B = the subscript for Math 1B.

11. If you were to conduct an appropriate hypothesis test, the alternate hypothesis would be:

a. $H_a: p_A = p_B$

b. $H_a: p_A > p_B$

c. $H_o: p_A = p_B$

d. $H_a: p_A \neq p_B$

12. The Type I error is to:

a. conclude that the pass rate for Math 1A is the same as the pass rate for Math 1B when, in fact, the pass rates are different.

b. conclude that the pass rate for Math 1A is different than the pass rate for Math 1B when, in fact, the pass rates are the same.

c. conclude that the pass rate for Math 1A is greater than the pass rate for Math 1B when, in fact, the pass rate for Math 1A is less than the pass rate for Math 1B.

d. conclude that the pass rate for Math 1A is the same as the pass rate for Math 1B when, in fact, they are the same.

13. The correct decision is to:

a. reject H_0

b. not reject H_0

c. There is not enough information given to conduct the hypothesis test

Kia, Alejandra, and Iris are runners on the track teams at three different schools. Their running times, in minutes, and the statistics for the track teams at their respective schools, for a one mile run, are given in the table below:

	Running Time	School Average Running Time	School Standard Deviation
Kia	4.9	5.2	0.15
Alejandra	4.2	4.6	0.25
Iris	4.5	4.9	0.12

Table B17

14. Which student is the BEST when compared to the other runners at her school?

a. Kia

b. Alejandra

c. Iris

d. Impossible to determine

Use the following information to answer the next two exercises: The following adult ski sweater prices are from the Gorsuch Ltd. Winter catalog: $212, $292, $278, $199, $280, $236

Assume the underlying sweater price population is approximately normal. The null hypothesis is that the mean price of adult ski sweaters from Gorsuch Ltd. is at least $275.

15. The correct distribution to use for the hypothesis test is:

a. Normal

b. Binomial

c. Student's *t*

d. Exponential

16. The hypothesis test:

a. is two-tailed.

b. is left-tailed.

c. is right-tailed.

d. has no tails.

17. Sara, a statistics student, wanted to determine the mean number of books that college professors have in their office. She randomly selected two buildings on campus and asked each professor in the selected buildings how many books are in his or her office. Sara surveyed 25 professors. The type of sampling selected is

a. simple random sampling.

b. systematic sampling.

c. cluster sampling.

d. stratified sampling.

18. A clothing store would use which measure of the center of data when placing orders for the typical "middle" customer?

a. mean

b. median

c. mode

d. IQR

19. In a hypothesis test, the *p*-value is

a. the probability that an outcome of the data will happen purely by chance when the null hypothesis is true.

b. called the preconceived alpha.

c. compared to beta to decide whether to reject or not reject the null hypothesis.

d. Answer choices A and B are both true.

Use the following information to answer the next three exercises: A community college offers classes 6 days a week: Monday through Saturday. Maria conducted a study of the students in her classes to determine how many days per week the students who are in her classes come to campus for classes. In each of her 5 classes she randomly selected 10 students and asked them how many days they come to campus for classes. Each of her classes are the same size. The results of her survey are summarized in **Table B18**.

Number of Days on Campus	Frequency	Relative Frequency	Cumulative Relative Frequency
1	2		

Table B18

Number of Days on Campus	Frequency	Relative Frequency	Cumulative Relative Frequency
2	12	.24	
3	10	.20	
4			.98
5	0		
6	1	.02	1.00

Table B18

20. Combined with convenience sampling, what other sampling technique did Maria use?

  a. simple random

  b. systematic

  c. cluster

  d. stratified

21. How many students come to campus for classes four days a week?

  a. 49

  b. 25

  c. 30

  d. 13

22. What is the 60th percentile for the this data?

  a. 2

  b. 3

  c. 4

  d. 5

Use the following information to answer the next two exercises: The following data are the results of a random survey of 110 Reservists called to active duty to increase security at California airports.

Number of Dependents	Frequency
0	11
1	27
2	33
3	20
4	19

Table B19

23. Construct a 95% confidence interval for the true population mean number of dependents of Reservists called to active duty to increase security at California airports.

  a. (1.85, 2.32)

  b. (1.80, 2.36)

  c. (1.97, 2.46)

  d. (1.92, 2.50)

24. The 95% confidence interval above means:

a. Five percent of confidence intervals constructed this way will not contain the true population aveage number of dependents.

b. We are 95% confident the true population mean number of dependents falls in the interval.

c. Both of the above answer choices are correct.

d. None of the above.

25. $X \sim U(4, 10)$. Find the 30th percentile.

a. 0.3000

b. 3

c. 5.8

d. 6.1

26. If $X \sim Exp(0.8)$, then $P(x < \mu) =$ _____

a. 0.3679

b. 0.4727

c. 0.6321

d. cannot be determined

27. The lifetime of a computer circuit board is normally distributed with a mean of 2,500 hours and a standard deviation of 60 hours. What is the probability that a randomly chosen board will last at most 2,560 hours?

a. 0.8413

b. 0.1587

c. 0.3461

d. 0.6539

28. A survey of 123 reservists called to active duty as a result of the September 11, 2001, attacks was conducted to determine the proportion that were married. Eighty-six reported being married. Construct a 98% confidence interval for the true population proportion of reservists called to active duty that are married.

a. (0.6030, 0.7954)

b. (0.6181, 0.7802)

c. (0.5927, 0.8057)

d. (0.6312, 0.7672)

29. Winning times in 26 mile marathons run by world class runners average 145 minutes with a standard deviation of 14 minutes. A sample of the last ten marathon winning times is collected. Let x = mean winning times for ten marathons. The distribution for x is:

a. $N\left(145, \frac{14}{\sqrt{10}}\right)$

b. $N(145, 14)$

c. t_9

d. t_{10}

30. Suppose that Phi Beta Kappa honors the top one percent of college and university seniors. Assume that grade point means (GPA) at a certain college are normally distributed with a 2.5 mean and a standard deviation of 0.5. What would be the minimum GPA needed to become a member of Phi Beta Kappa at that college?

a. 3.99

b. 1.34

c. 3.00

d. 3.66

The number of people living on American farms has declined steadily during the 20th century. Here are data on the farm population (in millions of persons) from 1935 to 1980.

Year	1935	1940	1945	1950	1955	1960	1965	1970	1975	1980
Population	32.1	30.5	24.4	23.0	19.1	15.6	12.4	9.7	8.9	7.2

Table B20

31. The linear regression equation is $\hat{y}$ = 1166.93 − 0.5868x. What was the expected farm population (in millions of persons) for 1980?

a. 7.2

b. 5.1

c. 6.0

d. 8.0

32. In linear regression, which is the best possible *SSE*?

a. 13.46

b. 18.22

c. 24.05

d. 16.33

33. In regression analysis, if the correlation coefficient is close to one what can be said about the best fit line?

a. It is a horizontal line. Therefore, we can not use it.

b. There is a strong linear pattern. Therefore, it is most likely a good model to be used.

c. The coefficient correlation is close to the limit. Therefore, it is hard to make a decision.

d. We do not have the equation. Therefore, we cannot say anything about it.

Use the following information to answer the next three exercises: A study of the career plans of young women and men sent questionnaires to all 722 members of the senior class in the College of Business Administration at the University of Illinois. One question asked which major within the business program the student had chosen. Here are the data from the students who responded.

	Female	Male
Accounting	68	56
Administration	91	40
Economics	5	6
Finance	61	59

Table B21 Does the data suggest that there is a relationship between the gender of students and their choice of major?

34. The distribution for the test is:

a. Chi^2_8 .

b. Chi^2_3.

c. t_{721}.

d. $N(0, 1)$.

35. The expected number of female who choose finance is:

a. 37.

b. 61.

c. 60.

d. 70.

36. The *p*-value is 0.0127 and the level of significance is 0.05. The conclusion to the test is:

a. there is insufficient evidence to conclude that the choice of major and the gender of the student are not independent of each other.

b. there is sufficient evidence to conclude that the choice of major and the gender of the student are not independent of each other.

c. there is sufficient evidence to conclude that students find economics very hard.

d. there is in sufficient evidence to conclude that more females prefer administration than males.

37. An agency reported that the work force nationwide is composed of 10% professional, 10% clerical, 30% skilled, 15% service, and 35% semiskilled laborers. A random sample of 100 San Jose residents indicated 15 professional, 15 clerical, 40 skilled, 10 service, and 20 semiskilled laborers. At $\alpha = 0.10$ does the work force in San Jose appear to be consistent with the agency report for the nation? Which kind of test is it?

a. Chi^2 goodness of fit

b. Chi^2 test of independence

c. Independent groups proportions

d. Unable to determine

Practice Final Exam 1 Solutions
Solutions

1. b. independent

2. c. $\frac{4}{16}$

3. b. Two measurements are drawn from the same pair of individuals or objects.

4. b. $\frac{68}{118}$

5. d. $\frac{30}{52}$

6. b. $\frac{8}{40}$

7. b. 2.78

8. a. 8.25

9. c. 0.2870

10. c. Normal

11. d. $H_a: p_A \neq p_B$

12. b. conclude that the pass rate for Math 1A is different than the pass rate for Math 1B when, in fact, the pass rates are the same.

13. b. not reject H_0

14. c. Iris

15. c. Student's t

16. b. is left-tailed.

17. c. cluster sampling

18. b. median

19. a. the probability that an outcome of the data will happen purely by chance when the null hypothesis is true.

20. d. stratified

21. b. 25

22. c. 4

23. a. (1.85, 2.32)

24. c. Both above are correct.

25. c. 5.8

26. c. 0.6321

27. a. 0.8413

28. a. (0.6030, 0.7954)

29. a. $N\left(145, \frac{14}{\sqrt{10}}\right)$

30. d. 3.66

31. b. 5.1

32. a. 13.46

33. b. There is a strong linear pattern. Therefore, it is most likely a good model to be used.

34. b. Chi^2_3.

35. d. 70

36. b. There is sufficient evidence to conclude that the choice of major and the gender of the student are not independent of each other.

37. a. Chi^2 goodness-of-fit

Practice Final Exam 2

1. A study was done to determine the proportion of teenagers that own a car. The population proportion of teenagers that own a car is the:

  a. statistic.

  b. parameter.

  c. population.

  d. variable.

Use the following information to answer the next two exercises:

value	frequency
0	1
1	4

Table B22

value	frequency
2	7
3	9
6	4

Table B22

2. The box plot for the data is:

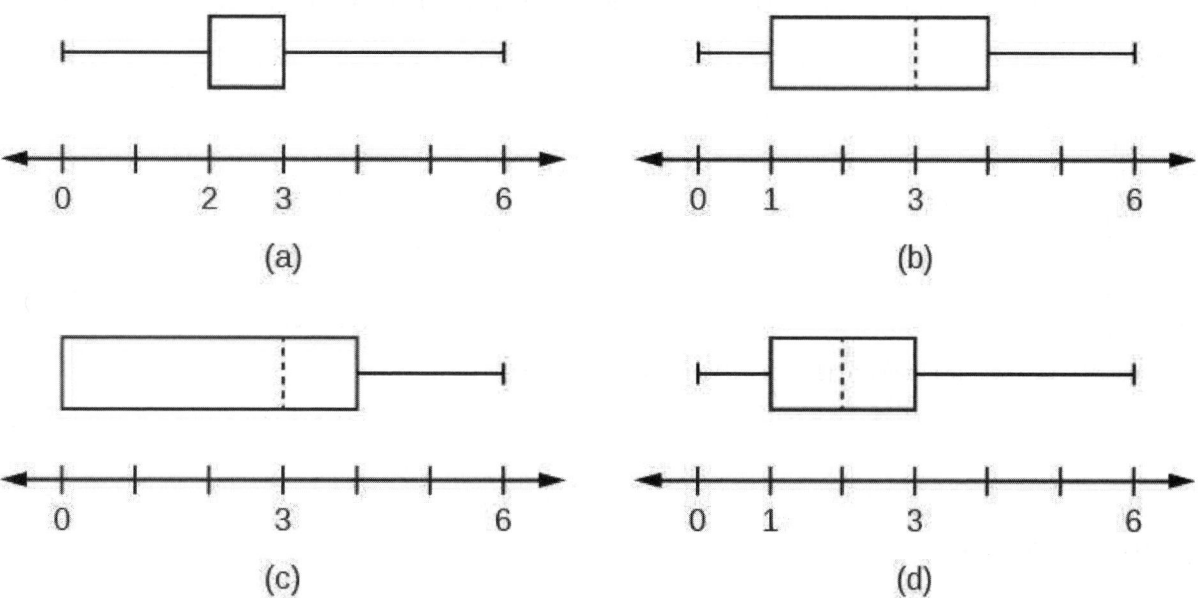

(a)

(b)

(c)

(d)

Figure B10

3. If six were added to each value of the data in the table, the 15th percentile of the new list of values is:

a. six

b. one

c. seven

d. eight

Use the following information to answer the next two exercises: Suppose that the probability of a drought in any independent year is 20%. Out of those years in which a drought occurs, the probability of water rationing is ten percent. However, in any year, the probability of water rationing is five percent.

4. What is the probability of both a drought and water rationing occurring?

a. 0.05

b. 0.01

c. 0.02

d. 0.30

5. Which of the following is true?

a. Drought and water rationing are independent events.

b. Drought and water rationing are mutually exclusive events.

c. None of the above

Use the following information to answer the next two exercises: Suppose that a survey yielded the following data:

gender	apple	pumpkin	pecan
female	40	10	30
male	20	30	10

Table B23 Favorite Pie

6. Suppose that one individual is randomly chosen. The probability that the person's favorite pie is apple or the person is male is _____.

    a. $\dfrac{40}{60}$

    b. $\dfrac{60}{140}$

    c. $\dfrac{120}{140}$

    d. $\dfrac{100}{140}$

7. Suppose H_0 is: Favorite pie and gender are independent. The *p*-value is _____.

    a. ≈ 0

    b.   1

    c.   0.05

    d.   cannot be determined

Use the following information to answer the next two exercises: Let's say that the probability that an adult watches the news at least once per week is 0.60. We randomly survey 14 people. Of interest is the number of people who watch the news at least once per week.

8. Which of the following statements is FALSE?

    a. $X \sim B(14\ 0.60)$

    b.   The values for *x* are: {1 ,2 ,3 ,... ,14}.

    c. $\mu = 8.4$

    d. $P(X = 5) = 0.0408$

9. Find the probability that at least six adults watch the news at least once per week.

    a. $\dfrac{6}{14}$

    b.   0.8499

    c.   0.9417

    d.   0.6429

10. The following histogram is most likely to be a result of sampling from which distribution?

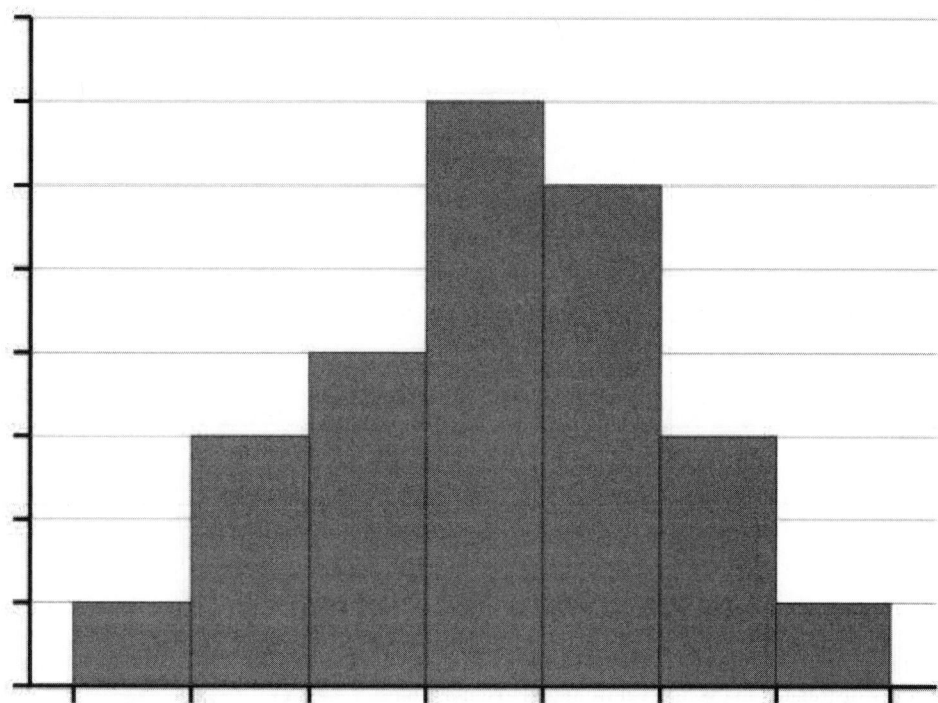

Figure B11

a. chi-square with $df = 6$

b. exponential

c. uniform

d. binomial

11. The ages of campus day and evening students is known to be normally distributed. A sample of six campus day and evening students reported their ages (in years) as: {18, 35, 27, 45, 20, 20}. What is the error bound for the 90% confidence interval of the true average age?

a. 11.2

b. 22.3

c. 17.5

d. 8.7

12. If a normally distributed random variable has $\mu = 0$ and $\sigma = 1$, then 97.5% of the population values lie above:

a. −1.96.

b. 1.96.

c. 1.

d. −1.

Use the following information to answer the next three exercises. The amount of money a customer spends in one trip to the supermarket is known to have an exponential distribution. Suppose the average amount of money a customer spends in one trip to the supermarket is $72.

13. What is the probability that one customer spends less than $72 in one trip to the supermarket?

a. 0.6321

b. 0.5000

c. 0.3714

d. 1

14. How much money altogether would you expect the next five customers to spend in one trip to the supermarket (in dollars)?

a. 72

b. $\dfrac{72^2}{5}$

c. 5184

d. 360

15. If you want to find the probability that the mean amount of money 50 customers spend in one trip to the supermarket is less than \$60, the distribution to use is:

a. $N(72, 72)$

b. $N\left(72, \dfrac{72}{\sqrt{50}}\right)$

c. $Exp(72)$

d. $Exp\left(\dfrac{1}{72}\right)$

Use the following information to answer the next three exercises: The amount of time it takes a fourth grader to carry out the trash is uniformly distributed in the interval from one to ten minutes.

16. What is the probability that a randomly chosen fourth grader takes more than seven minutes to take out the trash?

a. $\dfrac{3}{9}$

b. $\dfrac{7}{9}$

c. $\dfrac{3}{10}$

d. $\dfrac{7}{10}$

17. Which graph best shows the probability that a randomly chosen fourth grader takes more than six minutes to take out the trash given that he or she has already taken more than three minutes?

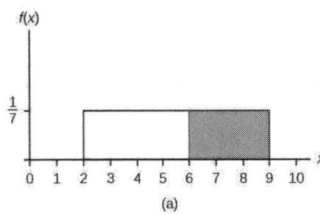

(a)

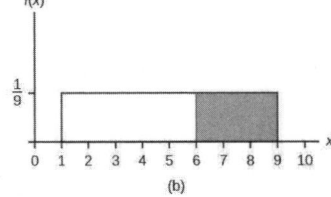

(b)

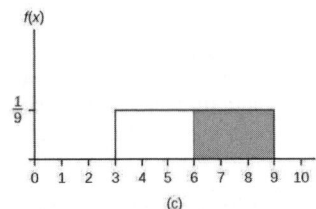

(c)

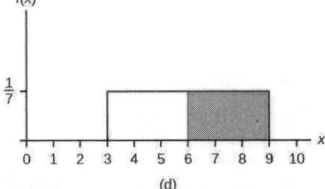

(d)

Figure B12

18. We should expect a fourth grader to take how many minutes to take out the trash?

a. 4.5

b. 5.5

c. 5

d. 10

Use the following information to answer the next three exercises: At the beginning of the quarter, the amount of time a student waits in line at the campus cafeteria is normally distributed with a mean of five minutes and a standard deviation of 1.5 minutes.

19. What is the 90th percentile of waiting times (in minutes)?

a. 1.28

b. 90

c. 7.47

d. 6.92

20. The median waiting time (in minutes) for one student is:

a. 5.

b. 50.

c. 2.5.

d. 1.5.

21. Find the probability that the average wait time for ten students is at most 5.5 minutes.

a. 0.6301

b. 0.8541

c. 0.3694

d. 0.1459

22. A sample of 80 software engineers in Silicon Valley is taken and it is found that 20% of them earn approximately $50,000 per year. A point estimate for the true proportion of engineers in Silicon Valley who earn $50,000 per year is:

a. 16.

b. 0.2.

c. 1.

d. 0.95.

23. If $P(Z < z_\alpha) = 0.1587$ where $Z \sim N(0, 1)$, then α is equal to:

a. −1.

b. 0.1587.

c. 0.8413.

d. 1.

24. A professor tested 35 students to determine their entering skills. At the end of the term, after completing the course, the same test was administered to the same 35 students to study their improvement. This would be a test of:

a. independent groups.

b. two proportions.

c. matched pairs, dependent groups.

d. exclusive groups.

A math exam was given to all the third grade children attending ABC School. Two random samples of scores were taken.

	n	$\overline{x}$	s
Boys	55	82	5
Girls	60	86	7

Table B24

25. Which of the following correctly describes the results of a hypothesis test of the claim, "There is a difference between the mean scores obtained by third grade girls and boys at the 5% level of significance"?

a. Do not reject H_0. There is insufficient evidence to conclude that there is a difference in the mean scores.

b. Do not reject H_0. There is sufficient evidence to conclude that there is a difference in the mean scores.

c. Reject H_0. There is insufficient evidence to conclude that there is no difference in the mean scores.

d. Reject H_0. There is sufficient evidence to conclude that there is a difference in the mean scores.

26. In a survey of 80 males, 45 had played an organized sport growing up. Of the 70 females surveyed, 25 had played an organized sport growing up. We are interested in whether the proportion for males is higher than the proportion for females. The correct conclusion is that:

a. there is insufficient information to conclude that the proportion for males is the same as the proportion for females.

b. there is insufficient information to conclude that the proportion for males is not the same as the proportion for females.

c. there is sufficient evidence to conclude that the proportion for males is higher than the proportion for females.

d. not enough information to make a conclusion.

27. From past experience, a statistics teacher has found that the average score on a midterm is 81 with a standard deviation of 5.2. This term, a class of 49 students had a standard deviation of 5 on the midterm. Do the data indicate that we should reject the teacher's claim that the standard deviation is 5.2? Use $\alpha = 0.05$.

a. Yes

b. No

c. Not enough information given to solve the problem

28. Three loading machines are being compared. Ten samples were taken for each machine. Machine I took an average of 31 minutes to load packages with a standard deviation of two minutes. Machine II took an average of 28 minutes to load packages with a standard deviation of 1.5 minutes. Machine III took an average of 29 minutes to load packages with a standard deviation of one minute. Find the p-value when testing that the average loading times are the same.

a. p-value is close to zero

b. p-value is close to one

c. not enough information given to solve the problem

Use the following information to answer the next three exercises: A corporation has offices in different parts of the country. It has gathered the following information concerning the number of bathrooms and the number of employees at seven sites:

Number of employees x	650	730	810	900	102	107	1150
Number of bathrooms y	40	50	54	61	82	110	121

Table B25

29. Is the correlation between the number of employees and the number of bathrooms significant?

a. Yes

b. No

c. Not enough information to answer question

30. The linear regression equation is:

   a. $\hat{y} = 0.0094 - 79.96x$

   b. $\hat{y} = 79.96 + 0.0094x$

   c. $\hat{y} = 79.96 - 0.0094x$

   d. $\hat{y} = -0.0094 + 79.96x$

31. If a site has 1,150 employees, approximately how many bathrooms should it have?

   a. 69

   b. 91

   c. 91,954

   d. We should not be estimating here.

32. Suppose that a sample of size ten was collected, with $\bar{x} = 4.4$ and $s = 1.4$. H_0: $\sigma^2 = 1.6$ vs. H_a: $\sigma^2 \neq 1.6$. Which graph best describes the results of the test?

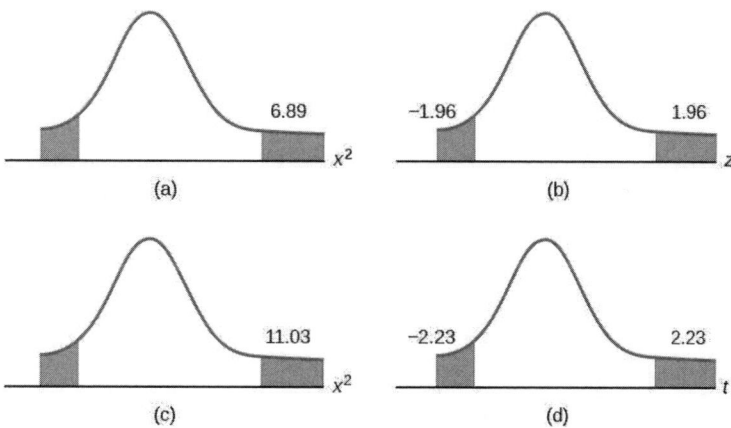

Figure B13

Sixty-four backpackers were asked the number of days since their latest backpacking trip. The number of days is given in **Table B26**:

# of days	1	2	3	4	5	6	7	8
Frequency	5	9	6	12	7	10	5	10

Table B26

33. Conduct an appropriate test to determine if the distribution is uniform.

   a. The p-value is > 0.10. There is insufficient information to conclude that the distribution is not uniform.

   b. The p-value is < 0.01. There is sufficient information to conclude the distribution is not uniform.

   c. The p-value is between 0.01 and 0.10, but without alpha (α) there is not enough information

   d. There is no such test that can be conducted.

34. Which of the following statements is true when using one-way ANOVA?

   a. The populations from which the samples are selected have different distributions.

   b. The sample sizes are large.

   c. The test is to determine if the different groups have the same means.

   d. There is a correlation between the factors of the experiment.

Practice Final Exam 2 Solutions
Solutions

1. b. parameter.

2. a.

3. c. seven

4. c. 0.02

5. c. none of the above

6. d. $\frac{100}{140}$

7. a. ≈ 0

8. b. The values for x are: $\{1, 2, 3,..., 14\}$

9. c. 0.9417.

10. d. binomial

11. d. 8.7

12. a. −1.96

13. a. 0.6321

14. d. 360

15. b. $N\left(72, \frac{72}{\sqrt{50}}\right)$

16. a. $\frac{3}{9}$

17. d.

18. b. 5.5

19. d. 6.92

20. a. 5

21. b. 0.8541

22. b. 0.2

23. a. −1.

24. c. matched pairs, dependent groups.

25. d. Reject H_0. There is sufficient evidence to conclude that there is a difference in the mean scores.

26. c. there is sufficient evidence to conclude that the proportion for males is higher than the proportion for females.

27. b. no

28. b. p-value is close to 1.

29. b. No

30. c. $\hat{y} = 79.96x - 0.0094$

31. d. We should not be estimating here.

32. a.

33. a. The p-value is > 0.10. There is insufficient information to conclude that the distribution is not uniform.

34. c. The test is to determine if the different groups have the same means.

APPENDIX C: DATA SETS

Lap Times

The following tables provide lap times from Terri Vogel's log book. Times are recorded in seconds for 2.5-mile laps completed in a series of races and practice runs.

	Lap 1	Lap 2	Lap 3	Lap 4	Lap 5	Lap 6	Lap 7
Race 1	135	130	131	132	130	131	133
Race 2	134	131	131	129	128	128	129
Race 3	129	128	127	127	130	127	129
Race 4	125	125	126	125	124	125	125
Race 5	133	132	132	132	131	130	132
Race 6	130	130	130	129	129	130	129
Race 7	132	131	133	131	134	134	131
Race 8	127	128	127	130	128	126	128
Race 9	132	130	127	128	126	127	124
Race 10	135	131	131	132	130	131	130
Race 11	132	131	132	131	130	129	129
Race 12	134	130	130	130	131	130	130
Race 13	128	127	128	128	128	129	128
Race 14	132	131	131	131	132	130	130
Race 15	136	129	129	129	129	129	129
Race 16	129	129	129	128	128	129	129
Race 17	134	131	132	131	132	132	132
Race 18	129	129	130	130	133	133	127
Race 19	130	129	129	129	129	129	128
Race 20	131	128	130	128	129	130	130

Table C1 Race Lap Times (in seconds)

	Lap 1	Lap 2	Lap 3	Lap 4	Lap 5	Lap 6	Lap 7
Practice 1	142	143	180	137	134	134	172
Practice 2	140	135	134	133	128	128	131
Practice 3	130	133	130	128	135	133	133

Table C2 Practice Lap Times (in seconds)

	Lap 1	Lap 2	Lap 3	Lap 4	Lap 5	Lap 6	Lap 7
Practice 4	141	136	137	136	136	136	145
Practice 5	140	138	136	137	135	134	134
Practice 6	142	142	139	138	129	129	127
Practice 7	139	137	135	135	137	134	135
Practice 8	143	136	134	133	134	133	132
Practice 9	135	134	133	133	132	132	133
Practice 10	131	130	128	129	127	128	127
Practice 11	143	139	139	138	138	137	138
Practice 12	132	133	131	129	128	127	126
Practice 13	149	144	144	139	138	138	137
Practice 14	133	132	137	133	134	130	131
Practice 15	138	136	133	133	132	131	131

Table C2 Practice Lap Times (in seconds)

Stock Prices

The following table lists initial public offering (IPO) stock prices for all 1999 stocks that at least doubled in value during the first day of trading.

$17.00	$23.00	$14.00	$16.00	$12.00	$26.00
$20.00	$22.00	$14.00	$15.00	$22.00	$18.00
$18.00	$21.00	$21.00	$19.00	$15.00	$21.00
$18.00	$17.00	$15.00	$25.00	$14.00	$30.00
$16.00	$10.00	$20.00	$12.00	$16.00	$17.44
$16.00	$14.00	$15.00	$20.00	$20.00	$16.00
$17.00	$16.00	$15.00	$15.00	$19.00	$48.00
$16.00	$18.00	$9.00	$18.00	$18.00	$20.00
$8.00	$20.00	$17.00	$14.00	$11.00	$16.00
$19.00	$15.00	$21.00	$12.00	$8.00	$16.00
$13.00	$14.00	$15.00	$14.00	$13.41	$28.00
$21.00	$17.00	$28.00	$17.00	$19.00	$16.00
$17.00	$19.00	$18.00	$17.00	$15.00	
$14.00	$21.00	$12.00	$18.00	$24.00	
$15.00	$23.00	$14.00	$16.00	$12.00	
$24.00	$20.00	$14.00	$14.00	$15.00	
$14.00	$19.00	$16.00	$38.00	$20.00	

Table C3 IPO Offer Prices

$24.00	$16.00	$8.00	$18.00	$17.00
$16.00	$15.00	$7.00	$19.00	$12.00
$8.00	$23.00	$12.00	$18.00	$20.00
$21.00	$34.00	$16.00	$26.00	$14.00

Table C3 IPO Offer Prices

References

Data compiled by Jay R. Ritter of University of Florida using data from *Securities Data Co.* and *Bloomberg.*

APPENDIX D: GROUP AND PARTNER PROJECTS

Univariate Data

Student Learning Objectives

- The student will design and carry out a survey.
- The student will analyze and graphically display the results of the survey.

Instructions

As you complete each task below, check it off. Answer all questions in your summary.

_____ Decide what data you are going to study.

> Here are two examples, but you may **NOT** use them: number of M&M's per bag, number of pencils students have in their backpacks.

_____ Are your data discrete or continuous? How do you know?

_____ Decide how you are going to collect the data (for instance, buy 30 bags of M&M's; collect data from the World Wide Web).

_____ Describe your sampling technique in detail. Use cluster, stratified, systematic, or simple random (using a random number generator) sampling. Do not use convenience sampling. Which method did you use? Why did you pick that method?

_____ Conduct your survey. **Your data size must be at least 30.**

_____ Summarize your data in a chart with columns showing **data value, frequency, relative frequency and cumulative relative frequency.**

Answer the following (rounded to two decimal places):

a. $\bar{x} =$ _____

b. $s =$ _____

c. First quartile = _____

d. Median = _____

e. 70th percentile = _____

_____ What value is two standard deviations above the mean?

_____ What value is 1.5 standard deviations below the mean?

_____ Construct a histogram displaying your data.

_____ In complete sentences, describe the shape of your graph.

_____ Do you notice any potential outliers? If so, what values are they? Show your work in how you used the potential outlier formula to determine whether or not the values might be outliers.

_____ Construct a box plot displaying your data.

_____ Does the middle 50% of the data appear to be concentrated together or spread apart? Explain how you determined this.

_____ Looking at both the histogram and the box plot, discuss the distribution of your data.

Assignment Checklist

You need to turn in the following typed and stapled packet, with pages in the following order:

_____ **Cover sheet**: name, class time, and name of your study

_____ **Summary page**: This should contain paragraphs written with complete sentences. It should include answers to all the questions above. It should also include statements describing the population under study, the sample, a parameter or parameters being studied, and the statistic or statistics produced.

_____ **URL** for data, if your data are from the World Wide Web

_____ **Chart of data, frequency, relative frequency, and cumulative relative frequency**

_____ **Page(s) of graphs:** histogram and box plot

Continuous Distributions and Central Limit Theorem

Student Learning Objectives

- The student will collect a sample of continuous data.

- The student will attempt to fit the data sample to various distribution models.

- The student will validate the central limit theorem.

Instructions

As you complete each task below, check it off. Answer all questions in your summary.

Part I: Sampling

_____ Decide what **continuous** data you are going to study. (Here are two examples, but you may NOT use them: the amount of money a student spent on college supplies this term, or the length of time distance telephone call lasts.)

_____ Describe your sampling technique in detail. Use cluster, stratified, systematic, or simple random (using a random number generator) sampling. Do not use convenience sampling. What method did you use? Why did you pick that method?

_____ Conduct your survey. Gather **at least 150 pieces of continuous, quantitative data**.

_____ Define (in words) the random variable for your data. $X =$ _____

_____ Create two lists of your data: (1) unordered data, (2) in order of smallest to largest.

_____ Find the sample mean and the sample standard deviation (rounded to two decimal places).

a. $\bar{x} =$ _____

b. $s =$ _____

_____ Construct a histogram of your data containing five to ten intervals of equal width. The histogram should be a representative display of your data. Label and scale it.

Part II: Possible Distributions

_____ Suppose that X followed the following theoretical distributions. Set up each distribution using the appropriate information from your data.

_____ Uniform: $X \sim U$ _____ Use the lowest and highest values as a and b.

_____ Normal: $X \sim N$ _____ Use $\bar{x}$ to estimate for μ and s to estimate for σ.

_____ **Must** your data fit one of the above distributions? Explain why or why not.

_____ **Could** the data fit two or three of the previous distributions (at the same time)? Explain.

_____ Calculate the value k(an X value) that is 1.75 standard deviations above the sample mean. $k =$ _____ (rounded to two decimal places) Note: $k = \bar{x} + (1.75)s$

_____ Determine the relative frequencies (*RF*) rounded to four decimal places.

> **NOTE**
> _____
>
> $RF = \dfrac{\text{frequency}}{\text{total number surveyed}}$

a. $RF(X < k) =$ _____

b. $RF(X > k) =$ _____

c. $RF(X = k) =$ _____

NOTE

You should have one page for the uniform distribution, one page for the exponential distribution, and one page for the normal distribution.

_____ State the distribution: $X \sim$ _____
_____ Draw a graph for each of the three theoretical distributions. Label the axes and mark them appropriately.
_____ Find the following theoretical probabilities (rounded to four decimal places).

a. $P(X < k) =$ _____

b. $P(X > k) =$ _____

c. $P(X = k) =$ _____

_____ Compare the relative frequencies to the corresponding probabilities. Are the values close?
_____ Does it appear that the data fit the distribution well? Justify your answer by comparing the probabilities to the relative frequencies, and the histograms to the theoretical graphs.

Part III: CLT Experiments

_____ From your original data (before ordering), use a random number generator to pick 40 samples of size five. For each sample, calculate the average.
_____ On a separate page, attached to the summary, include the 40 samples of size five, along with the 40 sample averages.

_____ List the 40 averages in order from smallest to largest.

_____ Define the random variable, $\bar{X}$, in words. $\bar{X}$ = _____

_____ State the approximate theoretical distribution of $\bar{X}$. $\bar{X} \sim$ _____
_____ Base this on the mean and standard deviation from your original data.
_____ Construct a histogram displaying your data. Use five to six intervals of equal width. Label and scale it.

Calculate the value k (an $\bar{X}$ value) that is 1.75 standard deviations above the sample mean. k = _____ (rounded to two decimal places)

Determine the relative frequencies (*RF*) rounded to four decimal places.

a. $RF(\bar{X} < \bar{k}) =$ _____

b. $RF(\bar{X} > \bar{k}) =$ _____

c. $RF(\bar{X} = \bar{k}) =$ _____

Find the following theoretical probabilities (rounded to four decimal places).

a. $P(\bar{X} < \bar{k}) =$ _____

b. $P(\bar{X} > \bar{k}) =$ _____

c. $P(\bar{X} = \bar{k}) =$ _____

_____ Draw the graph of the theoretical distribution of $\bar{X}$.
_____ Compare the relative frequencies to the probabilities. Are the values close?

_____ Does it appear that the data of averages fit the distribution of $\bar{X}$ well? Justify your answer by comparing the probabilities to the relative frequencies, and the histogram to the theoretical graph.

In three to five complete sentences for each, answer the following questions. Give thoughtful explanations.

_____ In summary, do your original data seem to fit the uniform, exponential, or normal distributions? Answer why or why not for each distribution. If the data do not fit any of those distributions, explain why.
_____ What happened to the shape and distribution when you averaged your data? **In theory,** what should have happened? In theory, would "it" always happen? Why or why not?

_____ Were the relative frequencies compared to the theoretical probabilities closer when comparing the X or $\bar{X}$

distributions? Explain your answer.

Assignment Checklist

You need to turn in the following typed and stapled packet, with pages in the following order:
____ **Cover sheet**: name, class time, and name of your study
____ **Summary pages**: These should contain several paragraphs written with complete sentences that describe the experiment, including what you studied and your sampling technique, as well as answers to all of the questions previously asked questions
____ **URL** for data, if your data are from the World Wide Web
____ **Pages, one for each theoretical distribution**, with the distribution stated, the graph, and the probability questions answered
____ **Pages of the data requested**
____ **All graphs required**

Hypothesis Testing-Article
Student Learning Objectives

- The student will identify a hypothesis testing problem in print.

- The student will conduct a survey to verify or dispute the results of the hypothesis test.

- The student will summarize the article, analysis, and conclusions in a report.

Instructions

As you complete each task, check it off. Answer all questions in your summary.
____**Find an article** in a newspaper, magazine, or on the internet which makes a claim about **ONE** population mean or **ONE** population proportion. The claim may be based upon a survey that the article was reporting on. Decide whether this claim is the null or alternate hypothesis.
____**Copy or print out the article** and include a copy in your project, along with the source.
____**State how you will collect your data.** (Convenience sampling is not acceptable.)
____**Conduct your survey. You must have more than 50 responses in your sample.** When you hand in your final project, attach the tally sheet or the packet of questionnaires that you used to collect data. Your data must be real.
____**State the statistics** that are a result of your data collection: sample size, sample mean, and sample standard deviation, OR sample size and number of successes.
____**Make two copies of the appropriate solution sheet.**
____**Record the hypothesis test** on the solution sheet, based on your experiment. **Do a DRAFT solution** first on one of the solution sheets and check it over carefully. Have a classmate check your solution to see if it is done correctly. Make your decision using a 5% level of significance. Include the 95% confidence interval on the solution sheet.
____**Create a graph that illustrates your data.** This may be a pie or bar graph or may be a histogram or box plot, depending on the nature of your data. Produce a graph that makes sense for your data and gives useful visual information about your data. You may need to look at several types of graphs before you decide which is the most appropriate for the type of data in your project.
____**Write your summary** (in complete sentences and paragraphs, with proper grammar and correct spelling) that describes the project. The summary **MUST** include:

a. Brief discussion of the article, including the source

b. Statement of the claim made in the article (one of the hypotheses).

c. Detailed description of how, where, and when you collected the data, including the sampling technique; did you use cluster, stratified, systematic, or simple random sampling (using a random number generator)? As previously mentioned, convenience sampling is not acceptable.

d. Conclusion about the article claim in light of your hypothesis test; this is the conclusion of your hypothesis test, stated in words, in the context of the situation in your project in sentence form, as if you were writing this conclusion for a non-statistician.

e. Sentence interpreting your confidence interval in the context of the situation in your project

Assignment Checklist

Turn in the following typed (12 point) and stapled packet for your final project:
____**Cover sheet** containing your name(s), class time, and the name of your study
____**Summary**, which includes all items listed on summary checklist

____**Solution sheet** neatly and completely filled out. The solution sheet does not need to be typed.

____**Graphic representation of your data**, created following the guidelines previously discussed; include only graphs which are appropriate and useful.

____**Raw data collected AND a table summarizing the sample data** (n, $\bar{x}$ and s; or x, n, and p', as appropriate for your hypotheses); the raw data does not need to be typed, but the summary does. Hand in the data as you collected it. (Either attach your tally sheet or an envelope containing your questionnaires.)

Bivariate Data, Linear Regression, and Univariate Data

Student Learning Objectives

- The students will collect a bivariate data sample through the use of appropriate sampling techniques.

- The student will attempt to fit the data to a linear model.

- The student will determine the appropriateness of linear fit of the model.

- The student will analyze and graph univariate data.

Instructions

1. As you complete each task below, check it off. Answer all questions in your introduction or summary.

2. Check your course calendar for intermediate and final due dates.

3. Graphs may be constructed by hand or by computer, unless your instructor informs you otherwise. All graphs must be neat and accurate.

4. All other responses must be done on the computer.

5. Neatness and quality of explanations are used to determine your final grade.

Part I: Bivariate Data

Introduction

____State the bivariate data your group is going to study.

> Here are two examples, but you may **NOT** use them: height vs. weight and age vs. running distance.

____Describe your sampling technique in detail. Use cluster, stratified, systematic, or simple random sampling (using a random number generator) sampling. Convenience sampling is **NOT** acceptable.
____Conduct your survey. Your number of pairs must be at least 30.
____Print out a copy of your data.

Analysis

____On a separate sheet of paper construct a scatter plot of the data. Label and scale both axes.
____State the least squares line and the correlation coefficient.
____On your scatter plot, in a different color, construct the least squares line.
____Is the correlation coefficient significant? Explain and show how you determined this.
____Interpret the slope of the linear regression line in the context of the data in your project. Relate the explanation to your data, and quantify what the slope tells you.
____Does the regression line seem to fit the data? Why or why not? If the data does not seem to be linear, explain if any other model seems to fit the data better.
____Are there any outliers? If so, what are they? Show your work in how you used the potential outlier formula in the Linear Regression and Correlation chapter (since you have bivariate data) to determine whether or not any pairs might be outliers.

Part II: Univariate Data

In this section, you will use the data for **ONE** variable only. Pick the variable that is more interesting to analyze. For example: if your independent variable is sequential data such as year with 30 years and one piece of data per year, your x-values might be 1971, 1972, 1973, 1974, …, 2000. This would not be interesting to analyze. In that case, choose to use the dependent variable to analyze for this part of the project.
____Summarize your data in a chart with columns showing data value, frequency, relative frequency, and cumulative

relative frequency.

_____Answer the following question, rounded to two decimal places:

a. Sample mean = _____

b. Sample standard deviation = _____

c. First quartile = _____

d. Third quartile = _____

e. Median = _____

f. 70th percentile = _____

g. Value that is 2 standard deviations above the mean = _____

h. Value that is 1.5 standard deviations below the mean = _____

_____Construct a histogram displaying your data. Group your data into six to ten intervals of equal width. Pick regularly spaced intervals that make sense in relation to your data. For example, do NOT group data by age as 20-26,27-33,34-40,41-47,48-54,55-61 . . . Instead, maybe use age groups 19.5-24.5, 24.5-29.5, . . . or 19.5-29.5, 29.5-39.5, 39.5-49.5, . . .

_____In complete sentences, describe the shape of your histogram.

_____Are there any potential outliers? Which values are they? Show your work and calculations as to how you used the potential outlier formula in **Descriptive Statistics** (since you are now using univariate data) to determine which values might be outliers.

_____Construct a box plot of your data.

_____Does the middle 50% of your data appear to be concentrated together or spread out? Explain how you determined this.

_____Looking at both the histogram AND the box plot, discuss the distribution of your data. For example: how does the spread of the middle 50% of your data compare to the spread of the rest of the data represented in the box plot; how does this correspond to your description of the shape of the histogram; how does the graphical display show any outliers you may have found; does the histogram show any gaps in the data that are not visible in the box plot; are there any interesting features of your data that you should point out.

Due Dates

- Part I, Intro: _____ (keep a copy for your records)

- Part I, Analysis: _____ (keep a copy for your records)

- Entire Project, typed and stapled: _____

    _____ Cover sheet: names, class time, and name of your study

    _____ Part I: label the sections "Intro" and "Analysis."

    _____ Part II:

    _____ Summary page containing several paragraphs written in complete sentences describing the experiment, including what you studied and how you collected your data. The summary page should also include answers to ALL the questions asked above.

    _____ All graphs requested in the project

    _____ All calculations requested to support questions in data

    _____ Description: what you learned by doing this project, what challenges you had, how you overcame the challenges

NOTE

Include answers to ALL questions asked, even if not explicitly repeated in the items above.

APPENDIX E: SOLUTION SHEETS

Hypothesis Testing with One Sample

Class Time: _____

Name: _____

a. H_0: _____

b. H_a: _____

c. In words, **CLEARLY** state what your random variable $\bar{X}$ or P' represents.

d. State the distribution to use for the test.

e. What is the test statistic?

f. What is the p-value? In one or two complete sentences, explain what the p-value means for this problem.

g. Use the previous information to sketch a picture of this situation. CLEARLY, label and scale the horizontal axis and shade the region(s) corresponding to the p-value.

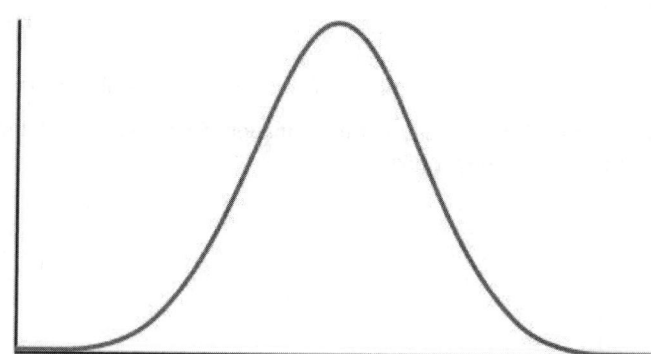

Figure E1

h. Indicate the correct decision ("reject" or "do not reject" the null hypothesis), the reason for it, and write an appropriate conclusion, using **complete sentences**.

   i. Alpha: _____

   ii. Decision: _____

   iii. Reason for decision: _____

   iv. Conclusion: _____

i. Construct a 95% confidence interval for the true mean or proportion. Include a sketch of the graph of the situation. Label the point estimate and the lower and upper bounds of the confidence interval.

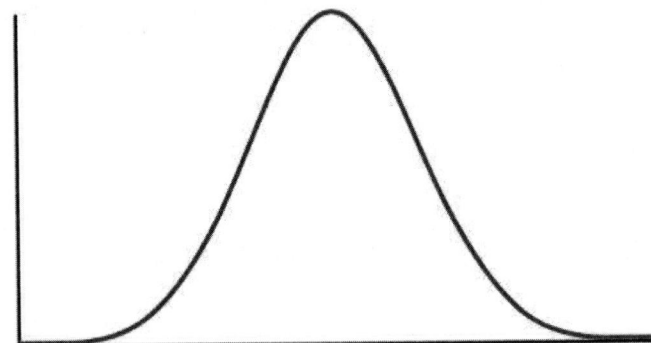

Figure E2

Hypothesis Testing with Two Samples

Class Time: _____

Name: _____

a. H_0: _____

b. H_a: _____

c. In words, **clearly** state what your random variable $\overline{X}_1 - \overline{X}_2$, $P'_1 - P'_2$ or $\overline{X}_d$ represents.

d. State the distribution to use for the test.

e. What is the test statistic?

f. What is the *p*-value? In one to two complete sentences, explain what the p-value means for this problem.

g. Use the previous information to sketch a picture of this situation. **CLEARLY** label and scale the horizontal axis and shade the region(s) corresponding to the *p*-value.

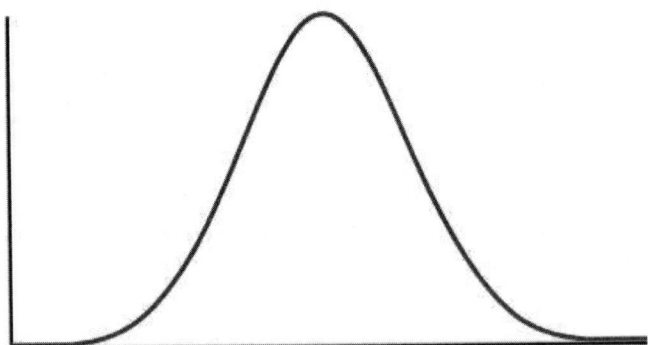

Figure E3

h. Indicate the correct decision ("reject" or "do not reject" the null hypothesis), the reason for it, and write an appropriate conclusion, using **complete sentences**.

    a. Alpha: _____

    b. Decision: _____

    c. Reason for decision: _____

    d. Conclusion: _____

i. In complete sentences, explain how you determined which distribution to use.

The Chi-Square Distribution

Class Time: _____

Name: _____

a. H_0: _____

b. H_a: _____

c. What are the degrees of freedom?

d. State the distribution to use for the test.

e. What is the test statistic?

f. What is the *p*-value? In one to two complete sentences, explain what the *p*-value means for this problem.

g. Use the previous information to sketch a picture of this situation. **Clearly** label and scale the horizontal axis and shade the region(s) corresponding to the *p*-value.

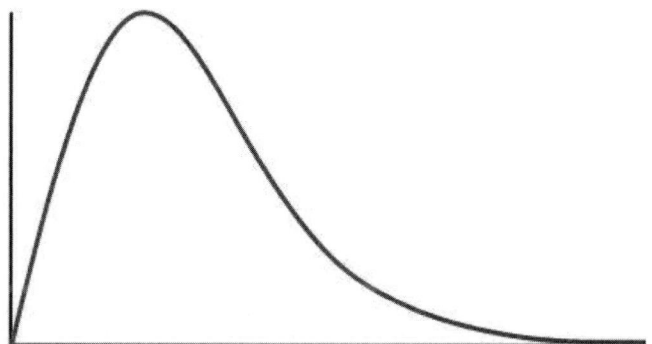

Figure E4

h. Indicate the correct decision ("reject" or "do not reject" the null hypothesis) and write appropriate conclusions, using **complete sentences.**

    i. Alpha: _____

    ii. Decision: _____

    iii. Reason for decision: _____

    iv. Conclusion: _____

F Distribution and One-Way ANOVA

Class Time: _____

Name: _____

a. H_0: _____

b. H_a: _____

c. $df(n) =$ _____ $df(d) =$ _____

d. State the distribution to use for the test.

e. What is the test statistic?

f. What is the *p*-value?

g. Use the previous information to sketch a picture of this situation. **Clearly** label and scale the horizontal axis and shade the region(s) corresponding to the *p*-value.

Figure E5

h. Indicate the correct decision ("reject" or "do not reject" the null hypothesis) and write appropriate conclusions, using **complete sentences**.

 a. Alpha: _____

 b. Decision: _____

 c. Reason for decision: _____

 d. Conclusion: _____

APPENDIX F: MATHEMATICAL PHRASES, SYMBOLS, AND FORMULAS

English Phrases Written Mathematically

When the English says:	Interpret this as:
X is at least 4.	$X \geq 4$
The minimum of X is 4.	$X \geq 4$
X is no less than 4.	$X \geq 4$
X is greater than or equal to 4.	$X \geq 4$
X is at most 4.	$X \leq 4$
The maximum of X is 4.	$X \leq 4$
X is no more than 4.	$X \leq 4$
X is less than or equal to 4.	$X \leq 4$
X does not exceed 4.	$X \leq 4$
X is greater than 4.	$X > 4$
X is more than 4.	$X > 4$
X exceeds 4.	$X > 4$
X is less than 4.	$X < 4$
There are fewer X than 4.	$X < 4$
X is 4.	$X = 4$
X is equal to 4.	$X = 4$
X is the same as 4.	$X = 4$
X is not 4.	$X \neq 4$
X is not equal to 4.	$X \neq 4$
X is not the same as 4.	$X \neq 4$
X is different than 4.	$X \neq 4$

Table F1

Formulas

Formula 1: Factorial

$$n! = n(n-1)(n-2)...(1)$$

$$0! = 1$$

Formula 2: Combinations

$$\binom{n}{r} = \frac{n!}{(n-r)!\,r!}$$

Formula 3: Binomial Distribution

$$X \sim B(n, p)$$

$$P(X = x) = \binom{n}{x}p^x q^{n-x}, \text{ for } x = 0, 1, 2, ..., n$$

Formula 4: Geometric Distribution

$$X \sim G(p)$$

$$P(X = x) = q^{x-1}p, \text{ for } x = 1, 2, 3, ...$$

Formula 5: Hypergeometric Distribution

$$X \sim H(r, b, n)$$

$$P(X = x) = \left(\frac{\binom{r}{x}\binom{b}{n-x}}{\binom{r+b}{n}} \right)$$

Formula 6: Poisson Distribution

$$X \sim P(\mu)$$

$$P(X = x) = \frac{\mu^x e^{-\mu}}{x!}$$

Formula 7: Uniform Distribution

$$X \sim U(a, b)$$

$$f(X) = \frac{1}{b-a}, \ a < x < b$$

Formula 8: Exponential Distribution

$$X \sim Exp(m)$$

$$f(x) = me^{-mx}\, m > 0, \ x \geq 0$$

Formula 9: Normal Distribution

$$X \sim N(\mu, \sigma^2)$$

$$f(x) = \frac{1}{\sigma\sqrt{2\pi}}e^{\frac{-(x-\mu)^2}{2\sigma^2}}, \ -\infty < x < \infty$$

Formula 10: Gamma Function

$$\Gamma(z) = \int_{\infty}^{0} x^{z-1} e^{-x} dx \quad z > 0$$

$$\Gamma\left(\frac{1}{2}\right) = \sqrt{\pi}$$

$\Gamma(m+1) = m!$ for m, a nonnegative integer

otherwise: $\Gamma(a+1) = a\Gamma(a)$

Formula 11: Student's *t*-distribution

$X \sim t_{df}$

$$f(x) = \frac{\left(1 + \frac{x^2}{n}\right)^{\frac{-(n+1)}{2}} \Gamma\left(\frac{n+1}{2}\right)}{\sqrt{n\pi}\Gamma\left(\frac{n}{2}\right)}$$

$$X = \frac{Z}{\sqrt{\frac{Y}{n}}}$$

$Z \sim N(0, 1), Y \sim X_{df}^2$, n = degrees of freedom

Formula 12: Chi-Square Distribution

$X \sim X_{df}^2$

$$f(x) = \frac{x^{\frac{n-2}{2}} e^{\frac{-x}{2}}}{2^{\frac{n}{2}} \Gamma\left(\frac{n}{2}\right)}, \quad x > 0 \; , \; n = \text{positive integer and degrees of freedom}$$

Formula 13: F Distribution

$X \sim F_{df(n), df(d)}$

$df(n) = $ degrees of freedom for the numerator

$df(d) = $ degrees of freedom for the denominator

$$f(x) = \frac{\Gamma\left(\frac{u+v}{2}\right)}{\Gamma\left(\frac{u}{2}\right)\Gamma\left(\frac{v}{2}\right)}\left(\frac{u}{v}\right)^{\frac{u}{2}} x^{\left(\frac{u}{2}-1\right)}[1 + \left(\frac{u}{v}\right)x^{-0.5(u+v)}]$$

$X = \frac{Y_u}{W_v}$, Y, W are chi-square

Symbols and Their Meanings

Chapter (1st used)	Symbol	Spoken	Meaning
Sampling and Data	$\sqrt{}$	The square root of	same
Sampling and Data	π	Pi	3.14159... (a specific number)
Descriptive Statistics	Q_1	Quartile one	the first quartile

Table F2 Symbols and their Meanings

Chapter (1st used)	Symbol	Spoken	Meaning
Descriptive Statistics	Q_2	Quartile two	the second quartile
Descriptive Statistics	Q_3	Quartile three	the third quartile
Descriptive Statistics	IQR	interquartile range	$Q_3 - Q_1 = IQR$
Descriptive Statistics	$\bar{x}$	x-bar	sample mean
Descriptive Statistics	μ	mu	population mean
Descriptive Statistics	$s\ s_x\ sx$	s	sample standard deviation
Descriptive Statistics	$s^2\ s_x^2$	s squared	sample variance
Descriptive Statistics	$\sigma\ \sigma_x\ \sigma x$	sigma	population standard deviation
Descriptive Statistics	$\sigma^2\ \sigma_x^2$	sigma squared	population variance
Descriptive Statistics	Σ	capital sigma	sum
Probability Topics	$\{\}$	brackets	set notation
Probability Topics	S	S	sample space
Probability Topics	A	Event A	event A
Probability Topics	$P(A)$	probability of A	probability of A occurring
Probability Topics	$P(A\vert B)$	probability of A given B	prob. of A occurring given B has occurred
Probability Topics	$P(A \text{ OR } B)$	prob. of A or B	prob. of A or B or both occurring
Probability Topics	$P(A \text{ AND } B)$	prob. of A and B	prob. of both A and B occurring (same time)
Probability Topics	A'	A-prime, complement of A	complement of A, not A
Probability Topics	$P(A')$	prob. of complement of A	same
Probability Topics	G_1	green on first pick	same
Probability Topics	$P(G_1)$	prob. of green on first pick	same
Discrete Random Variables	PDF	prob. distribution function	same
Discrete Random Variables	X	X	the random variable X
Discrete Random Variables	$X \sim$	the distribution of X	same
Discrete Random Variables	B	binomial distribution	same
Discrete Random Variables	G	geometric distribution	same
Discrete Random Variables	H	hypergeometric dist.	same
Discrete Random Variables	P	Poisson dist.	same
Discrete Random Variables	λ	Lambda	average of Poisson distribution
Discrete Random Variables	$\geq$	greater than or equal to	same
Discrete Random Variables	$\leq$	less than or equal to	same
Discrete Random Variables	$=$	equal to	same

Table F2 Symbols and their Meanings

Chapter (1st used)	Symbol	Spoken	Meaning
Discrete Random Variables	$\neq$	not equal to	same
Continuous Random Variables	$f(x)$	f of x	function of x
Continuous Random Variables	pdf	prob. density function	same
Continuous Random Variables	U	uniform distribution	same
Continuous Random Variables	Exp	exponential distribution	same
Continuous Random Variables	k	k	critical value
Continuous Random Variables	$f(x) =$	f of x equals	same
Continuous Random Variables	m	m	decay rate (for exp. dist.)
The Normal Distribution	N	normal distribution	same
The Normal Distribution	z	z-score	same
The Normal Distribution	Z	standard normal dist.	same
The Central Limit Theorem	CLT	Central Limit Theorem	same
The Central Limit Theorem	$\bar{X}$	X-bar	the random variable X-bar
The Central Limit Theorem	μ_x	mean of X	the average of X
The Central Limit Theorem	$\mu_{\bar{x}}$	mean of X-bar	the average of X-bar
The Central Limit Theorem	σ_x	standard deviation of X	same
The Central Limit Theorem	$\sigma_{\bar{x}}$	standard deviation of X-bar	same
The Central Limit Theorem	ΣX	sum of X	same
The Central Limit Theorem	Σx	sum of x	same
Confidence Intervals	CL	confidence level	same
Confidence Intervals	CI	confidence interval	same
Confidence Intervals	EBM	error bound for a mean	same
Confidence Intervals	EBP	error bound for a proportion	same
Confidence Intervals	t	Student's t-distribution	same
Confidence Intervals	df	degrees of freedom	same
Confidence Intervals	$t_{\frac{\alpha}{2}}$	student t with $a/2$ area in right tail	same
Confidence Intervals	p' ; $\hat{p}$	p-prime; p-hat	sample proportion of success
Confidence Intervals	q' ; $\hat{q}$	q-prime; q-hat	sample proportion of failure

Table F2 Symbols and their Meanings

Chapter (1st used)	Symbol	Spoken	Meaning
Hypothesis Testing	H_0	H-naught, H-sub 0	null hypothesis
Hypothesis Testing	H_a	H-a, H-sub a	alternate hypothesis
Hypothesis Testing	H_1	H-1, H-sub 1	alternate hypothesis
Hypothesis Testing	α	alpha	probability of Type I error
Hypothesis Testing	β	beta	probability of Type II error
Hypothesis Testing	$\overline{X1} - \overline{X2}$	$X1$-bar minus $X2$-bar	difference in sample means
Hypothesis Testing	$\mu_1 - \mu_2$	mu-1 minus mu-2	difference in population means
Hypothesis Testing	$P'_1 - P'_2$	$P1$-prime minus $P2$-prime	difference in sample proportions
Hypothesis Testing	$p_1 - p_2$	$p1$ minus $p2$	difference in population proportions
Chi-Square Distribution	X^2	Ky-square	Chi-square
Chi-Square Distribution	O	Observed	Observed frequency
Chi-Square Distribution	E	Expected	Expected frequency
Linear Regression and Correlation	$y = a + bx$	y equals a plus b-x	equation of a line
Linear Regression and Correlation	$\hat{y}$	y-hat	estimated value of y
Linear Regression and Correlation	r	correlation coefficient	same
Linear Regression and Correlation	ε	error	same
Linear Regression and Correlation	SSE	Sum of Squared Errors	same
Linear Regression and Correlation	$1.9s$	1.9 times s	cut-off value for outliers
F-Distribution and ANOVA	F	F-ratio	F-ratio

Table F2 Symbols and their Meanings

APPENDIX G: NOTES FOR THE TI-83, 83+, 84, 84+ CALCULATORS

Quick Tips

Legend

- 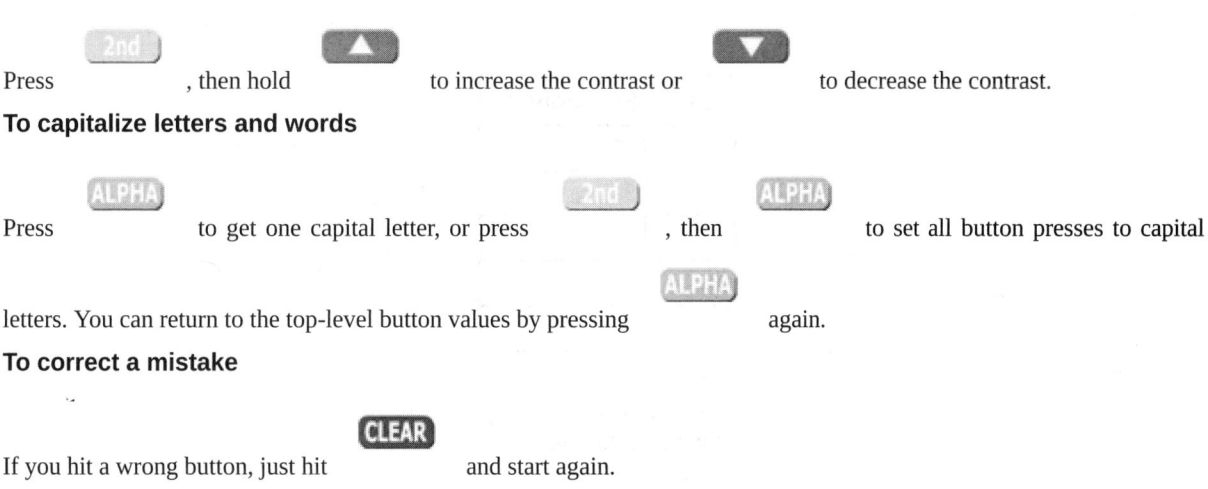 represents a button press
- [ ] represents yellow command or green letter behind a key
- < > represents items on the screen

To adjust the contrast

Press ⬛2nd, then hold ▲ to increase the contrast or ▼ to decrease the contrast.

To capitalize letters and words

Press ⬛ALPHA to get one capital letter, or press ⬛2nd, then ⬛ALPHA to set all button presses to capital

letters. You can return to the top-level button values by pressing ⬛ALPHA again.

To correct a mistake

If you hit a wrong button, just hit ⬛CLEAR and start again.

To write in scientific notation

Numbers in scientific notation are expressed on the TI-83, 83+, 84, and 84+ using E notation, such that...

- 4.321 E 4 = 4.321×10^{4}
- 4.321 E –4 = 4.321×10^{-4}

To transfer programs or equations from one calculator to another:

Both calculators: Insert your respective end of the link cable cable and press ⬛2nd, then [LINK].

Calculator receiving information:
1. Use the arrows to navigate to and select <RECEIVE>

2. Press .

Calculator sending information:
1. Press appropriate number or letter.

2.   Use up and down arrows to access the appropriate item.

ENTER

3.   Press   to select item to transfer.

4.   Press right arrow to navigate to and select **<TRANSMIT>**.

ENTER

5.   Press

Both calculators: Insert your respective end of the link cable cable Both calculators: press   **2nd** , then [QUIT] to exit when done.

Manipulating One-Variable Statistics

NOTE

These directions are for entering data with the built-in statistical program.

Data	Frequency
–2	10
–1	3
0	4
1	5
3	8

Table G1 Sample Data We are manipulating one-variable statistics.

To begin:
1.   Turn on the calculator.

 ON

2.   Access statistics mode.

 STAT

3.   Select **<4:ClrList>** to clear data from lists, if desired.

 **4**   **ENTER**

,

4.   Enter list **[L1]** to be cleared.

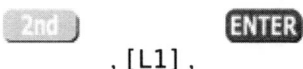

, [L1],

5. Display last instruction.

, [ENTRY]

6. Continue clearing remaining lists in the same fashion, if desired.

,   , [L2],

7. Access statistics mode.

8. Select <1:Edit . . .>

ENTER

9. Enter data. Data values go into [L1]. (You may need to arrow over to [L1]).

    ∘ Type in a data value and enter it. (For negative numbers, use the negate (-) key at the bottom of the keypad).

    ,   ,

    ∘ Continue in the same manner until all data values are entered.

10. In [L2], enter the frequencies for each data value in [L1].

    ∘ Type in a frequency and enter it. (If a data value appears only once, the frequency is "1").

    ,

    ∘ Continue in the same manner until all data values are entered.

11. Access statistics mode.

12. Navigate to <CALC>.

13. Access <1:1-var Stats>.

ENTER

14. Indicate that the data is in [L1]...

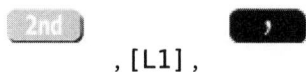

, [L1],

15. ...and indicate that the frequencies are in [L2].

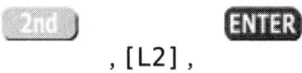

, [L2],

16. The statistics should be displayed. You may arrow down to get remaining statistics. Repeat as necessary.

Drawing Histograms

NOTE

We will assume that the data is already entered.

We will construct two histograms with the built-in STATPLOT application. The first way will use the default ZOOM. The second way will involve customizing a new graph.

1. Access graphing mode.

, [STAT PLOT]

2. Select <1:plot 1> to access plotting - first graph.

3. Use the arrows navigate go to <ON> to turn on Plot 1.

<ON>,

4. Use the arrows to go to the histogram picture and select the histogram.

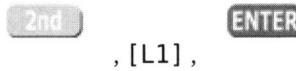

5. Use the arrows to navigate to <Xlist>.

6. If "L1" is not selected, select it.

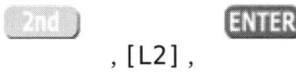
, [L1],

7. Use the arrows to navigate to <Freq>.

8. Assign the frequencies to [L2].

, [L2],

9. Go back to access other graphs.

, [STAT PLOT]

10. Use the arrows to turn off the remaining plots.

11. **Be sure to deselect or clear all equations before graphing.**

To deselect equations:

1. Access the list of equations.

2. Select each equal sign (=).

      ENTER

3. Continue, until all equations are deselected.

To clear equations:

1. Access the list of equations.

2. Use the arrow keys to navigate to the right of each equal sign (=) and clear them.

          CLEAR

3. Repeat until all equations are deleted.

To draw default histogram:
1. Access the ZOOM menu.

2. Select <9:ZoomStat>.

3. The histogram will show with a window automatically set.

To draw custom histogram:
1. Access window mode to set the graph parameters.

2.   ◦ $X_{min} = -2.5$

      ◦ $X_{max} = 3.5$

      ◦ $X_{scl} = 1$ (width of bars)

      ◦ $Y_{min} = 0$

      ◦ $Y_{max} = 10$

      ◦ $Y_{scl} = 1$ (spacing of tick marks on y-axis)

      ◦ $X_{res} = 1$

3. Access graphing mode to see the histogram.

GRAPH

To draw box plots:
1. Access graphing mode.

        , [STAT PLOT]

2. Select <1:Plot 1> to access the first graph.

3. Use the arrows to select <ON> and turn on Plot 1.

ENTER

4. Use the arrows to select the box plot picture and enable it.

5. Use the arrows to navigate to <Xlist>.

6. If "L1" is not selected, select it.

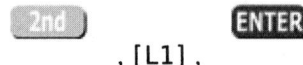
, [L1],

7. Use the arrows to navigate to <Freq>.

8. Indicate that the frequencies are in [L2].

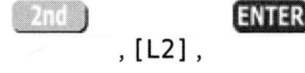
, [L2],

9. Go back to access other graphs.

, [STAT PLOT]

10. **Be sure to deselect or clear all equations before graphing** using the method mentioned above.

11. View the box plot.

, [STAT PLOT]

Linear Regression

Sample Data

The following data is real. The percent of declared ethnic minority students at De Anza College for selected years from 1970–1995 was:

Year	Student Ethnic Minority Percentage
1970	14.13
1973	12.27
1976	14.08
1979	18.16
1982	27.64
1983	28.72
1986	31.86
1989	33.14
1992	45.37
1995	53.1

Table G2 The independent variable is "Year," while the independent variable is "Student Ethnic Minority Percent."

Student Ethnic Minority Percentage

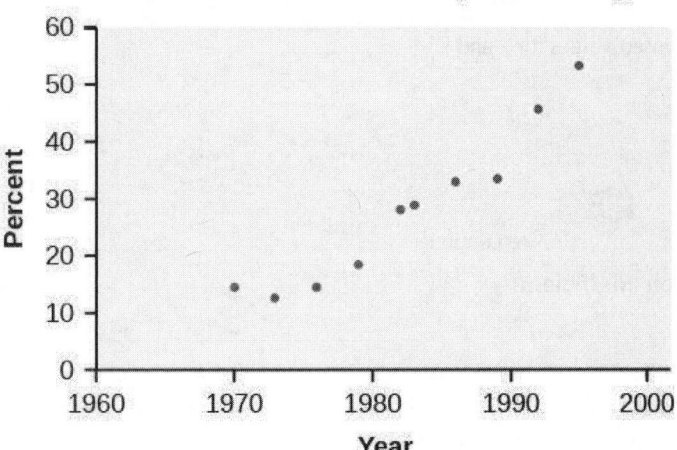

Figure G1 Student Ethnic Minority Percentage By hand, verify the scatterplot above.

NOTE

The TI-83 has a built-in linear regression feature, which allows the data to be edited. The *x*-values will be in [L1]; the *y*-values in [L2].

To enter data and do linear regression:

1. ON Turns calculator on.

2. Before accessing this program, be sure to turn off all plots.

   ◦ Access graphing mode.

   , [STAT PLOT]

   ◦ Turn off all plots.

3. Round to three decimal places. To do so:

   ◦ Access the mode menu.

   , [STAT PLOT]

   ◦ Navigate to <Float> and then to the right to <3>.

   ◦ All numbers will be rounded to three decimal places until changed.

4. Enter statistics mode and clear lists [L1] and [L2], as describe previously.

,

5.   Enter editing mode to insert values for *x* and *y*.

,

6.   Enter each value. Press   to continue.

To display the correlation coefficient:
1.   Access the catalog.

, [CATALOG]

2.   Arrow down and select `<DiagnosticOn>`

... ,   ,

3. r and r^2 will be displayed during regression calculations.

4.   Access linear regression.

5.   Select the form of $y = a + bx$.

The display will show:

LinReg
- $y = a + bx$
- $a = -3176.909$
- $b = 1.617$
- $r = 2\ 0.924$
- $r = 0.961$

This means the Line of Best Fit (Least Squares Line) is:
- $y = -3176.909 + 1.617x$
- Percent = $-3176.909 + 1.617$ (year #)

The correlation coefficient $r = 0.961$

To see the scatter plot:
1.   Access graphing mode.

, [STAT PLOT]

2.   Select `<1:plot 1>` To access plotting - first graph.

3. Navigate and select **<ON>** to turn on Plot 1.

   ENTER
   <ON>

4. Navigate to the first picture.

5. Select the scatter plot.

   ENTER

6. Navigate to **<Xlist>**.

   2nd

7. If **[L1]** is not selected, press   , **[L1]** to select it.

8. Confirm that the data values are in **[L1]**.

   ENTER
   <ON>

9. Navigate to **<Ylist>**.

10. Select that the frequencies are in **[L2]**.

    2nd   **ENTER**
               , [L2] ,

11. Go back to access other graphs.

    2nd
               , [STAT PLOT]

12. Use the arrows to turn off the remaining plots.

13. Access window mode to set the graph parameters.

    WINDOW

    ◦ $X_{min} = 1970$

    ◦ $X_{max} = 2000$

    ◦ $X_{scl} = 10$ (spacing of tick marks on *x*-axis)

    ◦ $Y_{min} = -0.05$

    ◦ $Y_{max} = 60$

    ◦ $Y_{scl} = 10$ (spacing of tick marks on *y*-axis)

    ◦ $X_{res} = 1$

14. Be sure to deselect or clear all equations before graphing, using the instructions above.

    GRAPH

15. Press the graph button to see the scatter plot.

To see the regression graph:

1. Access the equation menu. The regression equation will be put into Y1.

   Y=

2. Access the vars menu and navigate to `<5: Statistics>`.

,

3. Navigate to `<EQ>`.

4. `<1: RegEQ>` contains the regression equation which will be entered in Y1.

ENTER

5. Press the graphing mode button. The regression line will be superimposed over the scatter plot.

GRAPH

To see the residuals and use them to calculate the critical point for an outlier:

1. Access the list. RESID will be an item on the menu. Navigate to it.

, [LIST], `<RESID>`

2. Confirm twice to view the list of residuals. Use the arrows to select them.

ENTER   **ENTER**
,

3. The critical point for an outlier is: $1.9V\dfrac{\text{SSE}}{n-2}$ where:

   ◦ n = number of pairs of data

   ◦ SSE = sum of the squared errors

   ◦ $\sum\left(\text{residual}^2\right)$

4. Store the residuals in `[L3]`.

,   , [L3] ,

5. Calculate the $\dfrac{(\text{residual})^2}{n-2}$. Note that $n - 2 = 8$

, [L3] ,   ,   ,

6. Store this value in `[L4]`.

,   , [L4] ,

7. Calculate the critical value using the equation above.

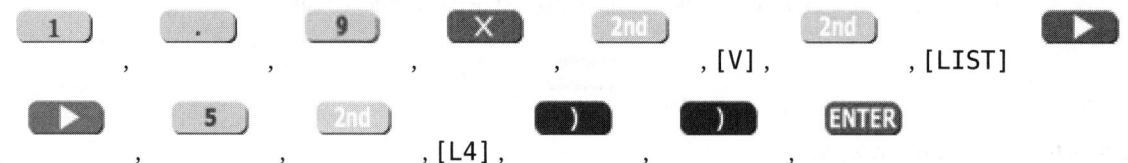
,   ,   ,   ,   , [V] ,   , [LIST]
,   ,   , [L4] ,   ,   ,

8. Verify that the calculator displays: 7.642669563. This is the critical value.

9. Compare the absolute value of each residual value in `[L3]` to 7.64. If the absolute value is greater than 7.64, then the (x, y) corresponding point is an outlier. In this case, none of the points is an outlier.

To obtain estimates of *y* for various *x*-values:

There are various ways to determine estimates for "*y*." One way is to substitute values for "*x*" in the equation. Another way

is to use the on the graph of the regression line.

TI-83, 83+, 84, 84+ instructions for distributions and tests
Distributions

Access DISTR (for "Distributions").

For technical assistance, visit the Texas Instruments website at **http://www.ti.com (http://www.ti.com)** and enter your calculator model into the "search" box.

Binomial Distribution

- binompdf(*n*,*p*,*x*) corresponds to $P(X = x)$
- binomcdf(*n*,*p*,*x*) corresponds to $P(X \leq x)$
- To see a list of all probabilities for *x*: 0, 1, . . . , *n*, leave off the "*x*" parameter.

Poisson Distribution

- poissonpdf(λ,*x*) corresponds to $P(X = x)$
- poissoncdf(λ,*x*) corresponds to $P(X \leq x)$

Continuous Distributions (general)

- $-\infty$ uses the value –1EE99 for left bound
- $+\infty$ uses the value 1EE99 for right bound

Normal Distribution

- normalpdf(*x*,μ,σ) yields a probability density function value (only useful to plot the normal curve, in which case "*x*" is the variable)
- normalcdf(left bound, right bound, μ, σ) corresponds to P(left bound < X < right bound)
- normalcdf(left bound, right bound) corresponds to P(left bound < Z < right bound) – standard normal
- invNorm(*p*,μ,σ) yields the critical value, *k*: $P(X < k) = p$
- invNorm(*p*) yields the critical value, *k*: $P(Z < k) = p$ for the standard normal

Student's *t*-Distribution

- tpdf(*x*,*df*) yields the probability density function value (only useful to plot the student-*t* curve, in which case "*x*" is the variable)
- tcdf(left bound, right bound, *df*) corresponds to P(left bound < *t* < right bound)

Chi-square Distribution

- X^2pdf(*x*,*df*) yields the probability density function value (only useful to plot the chi^2 curve, in which case "*x*" is the variable)
- X^2cdf(left bound, right bound, *df*) corresponds to P(left bound < X^2 < right bound)

F Distribution

- Fpdf(*x*,*dfnum*,*dfdenom*) yields the probability density function value (only useful to plot the *F* curve, in which case "*x*" is the variable)
- Fcdf(left bound,right bound,*dfnum*,*dfdenom*) corresponds to P(left bound < *F* < right bound)

Tests and Confidence Intervals

Access STAT and TESTS.

For the confidence intervals and hypothesis tests, you may enter the data into the appropriate lists and press DATA to have the calculator find the sample means and standard deviations. Or, you may enter the sample means and sample standard deviations directly by pressing STAT once in the appropriate tests.

Confidence Intervals

- **ZInterval** is the confidence interval for mean when σ is known.
- **TInterval** is the confidence interval for mean when σ is unknown; *s* estimates σ.
- **1-PropZInt** is the confidence interval for proportion.

NOTE

The confidence levels should be given as percents (ex. enter "**95**" or "**.95**" for a 95% confidence level).

Hypothesis Tests

- **Z-Test** is the hypothesis test for single mean when σ is known.
- **T-Test** is the hypothesis test for single mean when σ is unknown; *s* estimates σ.
- **2-SampZTest** is the hypothesis test for two independent means when both σ's are known.
- **2-SampTTest** is the hypothesis test for two independent means when both σ's are unknown.
- **1-PropZTest** is the hypothesis test for single proportion.
- **2-PropZTest** is the hypothesis test for two proportions.
- **X^2-Test** is the hypothesis test for independence.
- **X^{2}GOF-Test** is the hypothesis test for goodness-of-fit (TI-84+ only).
- **LinRegTTEST** is the hypothesis test for Linear Regression (TI-84+ only).

NOTE

Input the null hypothesis value in the row below "**Inpt**." For a test of a single mean, "μ∅" represents the null hypothesis. For a test of a single proportion, "p∅" represents the null hypothesis. Enter the alternate hypothesis on the bottom row.

APPENDIX H: TABLES

The module contains links to government site tables used in statistics.

NOTE

When you are finished with the table link, use the back button on your browser to return here.

Tables (NIST/SEMATECH e-Handbook of Statistical Methods, http://www.itl.nist.gov/div898/handbook/, January 3, 2009)

- **Student t table (http://www.itl.nist.gov/div898/handbook/eda/section3/eda3672.htm)**

- **Normal table (http://www.itl.nist.gov/div898/handbook/eda/section3/eda3671.htm)**

- **Chi-Square table (http://www.itl.nist.gov/div898/handbook/eda/section3/eda3674.htm)**

- **F-table (http://www.itl.nist.gov/div898/handbook/eda/section3/eda3673.htm)**

- All **four tables (http://www.itl.nist.gov/div898/handbook/eda/section3/eda367.htm)** can be accessed by going to

95% Critical Values of the Sample Correlation Coefficient Table
- **95% Critical Values of the Sample Correlation Coefficient**

INDEX

Symbols
α, **513**

A
absolute value of a residual, **687**
alternative hypothesis, **506**
Analysis of Variance, **762**
Area to the left, **371**
Area to the right, **371**
assumption, **511**
average, **7**
Average, **45**, **425**

B
balanced design, **753**
bar graph, **14**
Bernoulli Trial, **254**
Bernoulli Trials, **278**
binomial distribution, **416**, **460**, **511**
Binomial Distribution, **474**, **534**
Binomial Experiment, **278**
binomial probability distribution, **254**
Binomial Probability Distribution, **278**
bivariate, **680**
Blinding, **36**, **45**
Box plot, **123**
Box plots, **96**
box-and-whisker plots, **96**
box-whisker plots, **96**

C
categorical data, **10**
Categorical Variable, **45**
Categorical variables, **7**
central limit theorem, **399**, **401**, **408**, **517**
Central Limit Theorem, **425**, **534**
central limit theorem for means, **403**
central limit theorem for sums, **405**
chi-square distribution, **622**
Cluster Sampling, **45**
Coefficient of Correlation, **711**
coefficient of determination, **691**
Cohen's *d*, **574**
complement, **177**
conditional probability, **177**, **322**
Conditional Probability, **213**, **342**
confidence interval, **444**, **456**
Confidence Interval (CI), **474**, **534**
confidence intervals, **460**
Confidence intervals, **506**
confidence level, **445**, **460**
Confidence Level (CL), **474**
contingency table, **193**, **213**, **633**
Contingency Table, **651**
continuity correction factor, **416**
continuous, **10**
Continuous Random Variable, **45**
continuous random variable, **326**
control group, **36**
Control Group, **45**
Convenience Sampling, **45**
critical value, **374**
cumulative distribution function (CDF), **327**
Cumulative relative frequency, **28**
Cumulative Relative Frequency, **45**

D
data, **5**
Data, **7**, **45**
decay parameter, **342**
degrees of freedom, **456**
Degrees of Freedom (*df*), **474**, **594**
degrees of freedom (*df*), **569**
Dependent Events, **213**
descriptive statistics, **6**
discrete, **10**
Discrete Random Variable, **45**
double-blind experiment, **36**
Double-blinding, **45**

E
Empirical Rule, **368**
empirical rule, **444**
equal standard deviations, **744**
Equally likely, **176**
Equally Likely, **213**
equally likely, **317**
error bound, **460**
error bound for a population mean, **445**, **457**
Error Bound for a Population Mean (*EBM*), **474**
Error Bound for a Population Proportion (EBP), **474**
event, **176**
Event, **213**

expected value, **247**, **247**
Expected Value, **278**
expected values, **623**
experiment, **176**
Experiment, **213**
experimental unit, **35**
Experimental Unit, **45**
explanatory variable, **35**
Explanatory Variable, **45**
exponential distribution, **326**, **412**
Exponential Distribution, **342**, **425**
extrapolation, **697**

F
F distribution, **745**
F ratio, **745**
fair, **176**
first quartile, **88**
First Quartile, **123**
frequency, **28**, **77**
Frequency, **45**, **123**
Frequency Polygon, **123**
Frequency Table, **123**

G
geometric distribution, **261**
Geometric Distribution, **278**
Geometric Experiment, **278**
goodness-of-fit test, **623**

H
histogram, **77**
Histogram, **123**
hypergeometric experiment, **280**
Hypergeometric Experiment, **278**
hypergeometric probability, **263**
Hypergeometric Probability, **278**
hypotheses, **506**
Hypothesis, **534**
hypothesis test, **511**, **514**, **535**
hypothesis testing, **506**
Hypothesis Testing, **534**

I
independent, **181**, **189**
Independent Events, **213**
Independent groups, **568**
inferential statistics, **6**, **444**
Inferential Statistics, **474**
influential points, **697**
informed consent, **38**
Informed Consent, **45**
Institutional Review Board, **45**
Institutional Review Boards

(IRB), **38**
interpolation, **697**
interquartile range, **88**
Interquartile Range, **123**
Interval, **123**
interval scale, **27**

L

law of large numbers, **177, 409**
Least-Squares Line, **685**
least-squares regression line, **686**
level of measurement, **27**
Level of Significance of the Test , **534**
Line of Best Fit, **685**
linear regression, **685**
long-term relative frequency, **176**
Lurking Variable, **45**
lurking variables, **36**

M

margin of error, **444**
matched pairs, **568**
mean, **7, 7, 100, 247, 400, 403, 409**
Mean, **123, 278, 425**
Mean of a Probability Distribution, **279**
mean square, **745**
median, **88, 100**
Median, **123**
memoryless property, **342**
Midpoint, **123**
mode, **102**
Mode, **123**
multivariate, **680**
mutually exclusive, **182, 189**
Mutually Exclusive, **213**

N

nominal scale, **27**
Nonsampling Error, **45**
normal approximation to the binomial, **416**
Normal Distribution, **384, 425, 425, 474, 534**
normal distribution, **456, 461, 511**
Normal distribution, **576**
normally distributed, **401, 405, 511**
null hypothesis, **506, 511, 512, 513**
Numerical Variable, **45**
Numerical variables, **7**

O

observed values, **623**
One-Way ANOVA, **762**
ordinal scale, **27**
outcome, **176**
Outcome, **213**
outlier, **69, 89**
Outlier, **123, 711**
outliers, **697**

P

p-value, **511, 514, 534**
paired data set, **85**
Paired Data Set, **123**
parameter, **7, 444**
Parameter, **45, 474**
Pareto chart, **14**
Pearson, **6**
Percentile, **123**
percentile, **407**
percentiles, **87**
pie chart, **14**
placebo, **36**
Placebo, **45**
point estimate, **444**
Point Estimate, **474**
Poisson distribution, **342**
Poisson probability distribution, **266, 280**
Poisson Probability Distribution, **279**
Pooled Proportion, **594**
population, **7, 25**
Population, **45**
population variance, **641**
potential outlier, **701**
Probability, **6, 45, 213**
probability, **176**
probability density function, **312**
probability distribution function, **244**
Probability Distribution Function (PDF), **279**
proportion, **7**
Proportion, **46**

Q

Qualitative data, **10**
Qualitative Data, **46**
quantitative continuous data, **10**
Quantitative data, **10**
Quantitative Data, **46**
quantitative discrete data, **10**
quartiles, **87**
Quartiles, **88, 123**

R

random assignment, **36**
Random Assignment, **46**
Random Sampling, **46**
random variable, **244**
Random variable, **570**
Random Variable, **577**
Random Variable (RV), **279**
ratio scale, **27**
relative frequency, **28, 77**
Relative Frequency, **46, 123**
replacement, **181**
representative sample, **7**
Representative Sample, **46**
residual, **687**
response variable, **35**
Response Variable, **46**

S

sample, **7**
Sample, **46**
sample mean, **401**
sample size, **401, 406**
sample space, **176, 189, 199**
Sample Space, **213**
samples, **25**
sampling, **7**
Sampling Bias, **46**
sampling distribution, **103**
Sampling Distribution, **425**
Sampling Error, **46**
sampling variability of a statistic, **111**
Sampling with Replacement, **46, 213**
Sampling without Replacement, **46, 213**
simple random sample, **511**
Simple Random Sampling, **46**
single population mean, **511**
single population proportion, **511**
Skewed, **123**
standard deviation, **110, 456, 511, 511, 512, 516**
Standard Deviation, **123, 474, 534, 594**
Standard Deviation of a Probability Distribution, **279**
standard error, **568**
Standard Error of the Mean, **425**
standard error of the mean., **401**
standard normal distribution, **366**
Standard Normal Distribution, **384**

statistic, **7**
Statistic, **46**
statistics, **5**
Stratified Sampling, **46**
Student's t-distribution, **456**, **511, 511**
Student's **t**-Distribution, **474**, **534**
Sum of Squared Errors (SSE), **687**
sum of squares, **745**
Systematic Sampling, **46**

T

test for homogeneity, **638**
test of a single variance, **641**
test of independence, **633**
test statistic, **577**
The AND Event, **213**
The Complement Event, **213**
The Conditional Probability of *A* GIVEN *B*, **213**
The Conditional Probability of One Event Given Another Event, **213**
The Law of Large Numbers, **279**
The Or Event, **213**
The OR of Two Events, **213**
The standard deviation, **577**
third quartile, **88**
treatments, **35**
Treatments, **46**
tree diagram, **199**
Tree Diagram, **213**
Type 1 Error, **534**
Type 2 Error, **535**
Type I error, **508, 513**
Type II error, **508**

U

unfair, **177**
Uniform Distribution, **342, 425**
uniform distribution, **409**

V

variable, **7**
Variable, **46**
Variable (Random Variable), **594**
variance, **111**
Variance, **123, 762**
Variance between samples, **745**
Variance within samples, **745**
variances, **744**
Variation, **24**
Venn diagram, **204**
Venn Diagram, **214**

Z

z-score, **384, 456**
z-scores, **366**

Rational (Reciprocal) Function

$$f(x) = \frac{1}{x}$$

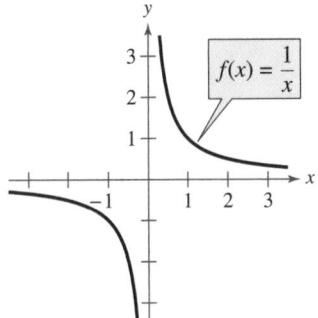

Domain: $(-\infty, 0) \cup (0, \infty)$
Range: $(-\infty, 0) \cup (0, \infty)$
No intercepts
Decreasing on $(-\infty, 0)$ and $(0, \infty)$
Odd function
Origin symmetry
Vertical asymptote: y-axis
Horizontal asymptote: x-axis

Exponential Function

$$f(x) = a^x, \ a > 0, \ a \neq 1$$

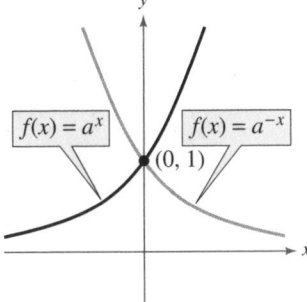

Domain: $(-\infty, \infty)$
Range: $(0, \infty)$
Intercept: $(0, 1)$
Increasing on $(-\infty, \infty)$
    for $f(x) = a^x$
Decreasing on $(-\infty, \infty)$
    for $f(x) = a^{-x}$
x-axis is a horizontal asymptote
Continuous

Logarithmic Function

$$f(x) = \log_a x, \ a > 0, \ a \neq 1$$

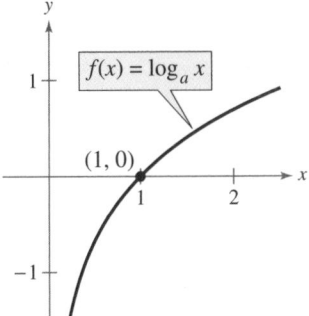

Domain: $(0, \infty)$
Range: $(-\infty, \infty)$
Intercept: $(1, 0)$
Increasing on $(0, \infty)$
y-axis is a vertical asymptote
Continuous
Reflection of graph of $f(x) = a^x$
    in the line $y = x$

Sine Function

$$f(x) = \sin x$$

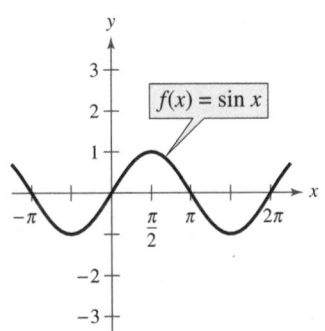

Domain: $(-\infty, \infty)$
Range: $[-1, 1]$
Period: 2π
x-intercepts: $(n\pi, 0)$
y-intercept: $(0, 0)$
Odd function
Origin symmetry

Cosine Function

$$f(x) = \cos x$$

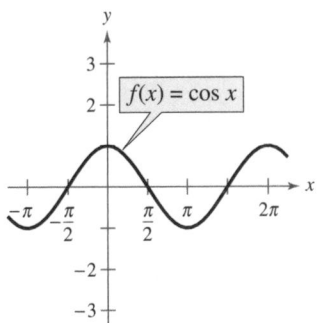

Domain: $(-\infty, \infty)$
Range: $[-1, 1]$
Period: 2π
x-intercepts: $\left(\frac{\pi}{2} + n\pi, 0\right)$
y-intercept: $(0, 1)$
Even function
y-axis symmetry

Tangent Function

$$f(x) = \tan x$$

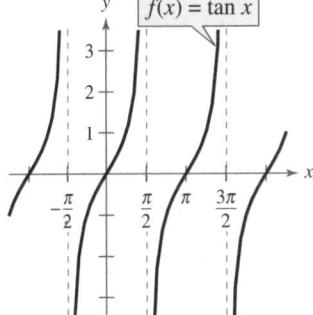

Domain: all $x \neq \dfrac{\pi}{2} + n\pi$

Range: $(-\infty, \infty)$
Period: π
x-intercepts: $(n\pi, 0)$
y-intercept: $(0, 0)$
Vertical asymptotes:

$$x = \frac{\pi}{2} + n\pi$$

Odd function
Origin symmetry

Cosecant Function

$f(x) = \csc x$

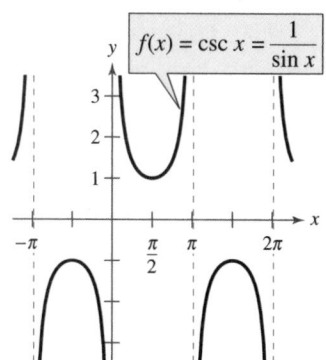

Domain: all $x \neq n\pi$
Range: $(-\infty, -1] \cup [1, \infty)$
Period: 2π
No intercepts
Vertical asymptotes: $x = n\pi$
Odd function
Origin symmetry

Secant Function

$f(x) = \sec x$

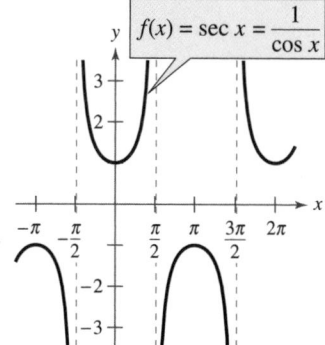

Domain: all $x \neq \dfrac{\pi}{2} + n\pi$

Range: $(-\infty, -1] \cup [1, \infty)$
Period: 2π
y-intercept: $(0, 1)$
Vertical asymptotes:

$$x = \frac{\pi}{2} + n\pi$$

Even function
y-axis symmetry

Cotangent Function

$f(x) = \cot x$

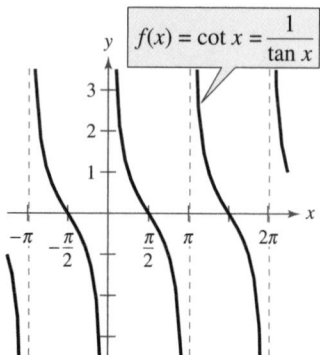

Domain: all $x \neq n\pi$
Range: $(-\infty, \infty)$
Period: π

x-intercepts: $\left(\dfrac{\pi}{2} + n\pi, 0\right)$

Vertical asymptotes: $x = n\pi$
Odd function
Origin symmetry

Inverse Sine Function

$f(x) = \arcsin x$

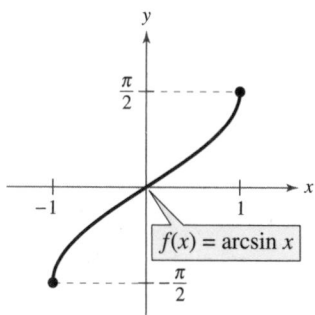

Domain: $[-1, 1]$

Range: $\left[-\dfrac{\pi}{2}, \dfrac{\pi}{2}\right]$

Intercept: $(0, 0)$
Odd function
Origin symmetry

Inverse Cosine Function

$f(x) = \arccos x$

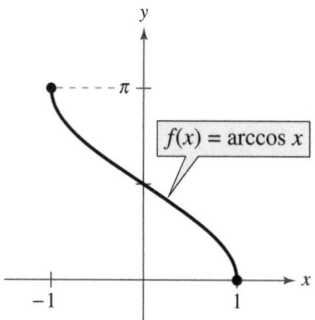

Domain: $[-1, 1]$
Range: $[0, \pi]$

y-intercept: $\left(0, \dfrac{\pi}{2}\right)$

Inverse Tangent Function

$f(x) = \arctan x$

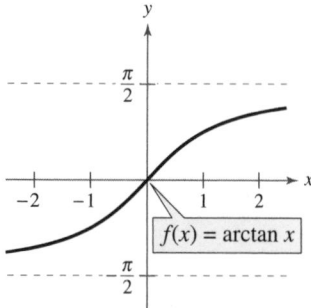

Domain: $(-\infty, \infty)$

Range: $\left(-\dfrac{\pi}{2}, \dfrac{\pi}{2}\right)$

Intercept: $(0, 0)$
Horizontal asymptotes:

$$y = \pm\frac{\pi}{2}$$

Odd function
Origin symmetry

Precalculus
A Graphing Approach

Fourth Edition

Ron Larson

Robert P. Hostetler
The Pennsylvania State University
The Behrend College

Bruce H. Edwards
The University of Florida

With the assistance of David C. Falvo
The Pennsylvania State University
The Behrend College

Houghton Mifflin Company   Boston   New York

Vice President and Publisher: Jack Shira
Associate Sponsoring Editor: Cathy Cantin
Development Manager: Maureen Ross
Assistant Editor: Lisa Pettinato
Assistant Editor: James Cohen
Supervising Editor: Karen Carter
Senior Project Editor: Patty Bergin
Editorial Assistant: Allison Seymour
Production Technology Supervisor: Gary Crespo
Executive Marketing Manager: Michael Busnach
Senior Marketing Manager: Danielle Potvin
Marketing Associate: Nicole Mollica
Senior Manufacturing Coordinator: Priscilla Bailey
Composition and Art: Meridian Creative Group
Cover Design Manager: Diana Coe

Cover photograph of Canary Wharf Tower, London, England © Ray Juno/Corbis

We have included examples and exercises that use real-life data as well as technology output from a variety of software. This would not have been possible without the help of many people and organizations. Our wholehearted thanks go to all their time and effort.

Printed in the U.S.A.

Library of Congress Catalog Card Number: 2003113991

ISBN: 0-618-39466-4

123456789–DOW–08 07 06 05 04

Contents

A Word from the Authors (Preface) vi

Features Highlights x

Chapter P **Prerequisites** 1

P.1 Real Numbers 2

P.2 Exponents and Radicals 12

P.3 Polynomials and Factoring 24

P.4 Rational Expressions 37

P.5 The Cartesian Plane 47

P.6 Exploring Data: Representing Data Graphically 58

Chapter Summary 67 **Review Exercises** 68

Chapter Test 72

Chapter 1 **Functions and Their Graphs** 73

Introduction to Library of Functions 74

1.1 Graphs of Equations 75

1.2 Lines in the Plane 86

1.3 Functions 99

1.4 Graphs of Functions 113

1.5 Shifting, Reflecting, and Stretching Graphs 125

1.6 Combinations of Functions 134

1.7 Inverse Functions 145

Chapter Summary 155 **Review Exercises** 156

Chapter Test 160

Chapter 2 **Solving Equations and Inequalities** 161

2.1 Linear Equations and Problem Solving 162

2.2 Solving Equations Graphically 172

2.3 Complex Numbers 183

2.4 Solving Equations Algebraically 191

2.5 Solving Inequalities Algebraically and Graphically 210

2.6 Exploring Data: Linear Models and Scatter Plots 222

Chapter Summary 231 **Review Exercises** 232

Chapter Test 236 **Cumulative Test: Chapters P–2** 237

Chapter 3 **Polynomial and Rational Functions** 239

3.1 Quadratic Functions 240

3.2 Polynomial Functions of Higher Degree 251

3.3 Real Zeros of Polynomial Functions 264

3.4 The Fundamental Theorem of Algebra 279

3.5 Rational Functions and Asymptotes 286

3.6 Graphs of Rational Functions 296

3.7 Exploring Data: Quadratic Models 305

Chapter Summary 312 **Review Exercises** 313

Chapter Test 318

Chapter 4   **Exponential and Logarithmic Functions**   319
  4.1   Exponential Functions and Their Graphs   320
  4.2   Logarithmic Functions and Their Graphs   332
  4.3   Properties of Logarithms   343
  4.4   Solving Exponential and Logarithmic Equations   350
  4.5   Exponential and Logarithmic Models   361
  4.6   Exploring Data: Nonlinear Models   373
         Chapter Summary   382   Review Exercises   383
         Chapter Test   388   Cumulative Test: Chapters 3–4   389

Chapter 5   **Trigonometric Functions   391**
  5.1   Angles and Their Measure   392
  5.2   Right Triangle Trigonometry   403
  5.3   Trigonometric Functions of Any Angle   414
  5.4   Graphs of Sine and Cosine Functions   427
  5.5   Graphs of Other Trigonometric Functions   438
  5.6   Inverse Trigonometric Functions   449
  5.7   Applications and Models   460
         Chapter Summary   472   Review Exercises   473
         Chapter Test   478

Chapter 6   **Analytic Trigonometry   479**
  6.1   Using Fundamental Identities   480
  6.2   Verifying Trigonometric Identities   488
  6.3   Solving Trigonometric Equations   496
  6.4   Sum and Difference Formulas   508
  6.5   Multiple-Angle and Product-to-Sum Formulas   515
         Chapter Summary   526   Review Exercises   527
         Chapter Test   530

Chapter 7   **Additional Topics in Trigonometry   531**
  7.1   Law of Sines   532
  7.2   Law of Cosines   541
  7.3   Vectors in the Plane   548
  7.4   Vectors and Dot Products   562
  7.5   Trigonometric Form of a Complex Number   572
         Chapter Summary   583   Review Exercises   584
         Chapter Test   588   Cumulative Test: Chapters 5–7   589

Chapter 8   **Linear Systems and Matrices   591**
  8.1   Solving Systems of Equations   592
  8.2   Systems of Linear Equations in Two Variables   603
  8.3   Multivariable Linear Systems   613
  8.4   Matrices and Systems of Equations   629
  8.5   Operations with Matrices   644

8.6   The Inverse of a Square Matrix   659

8.7   The Determinant of a Square Matrix   668

8.8   Applications of Matrices and Determinants   676

Chapter Summary   686   **Review Exercises**   688

Chapter Test   694

Chapter 9   **Sequences, Series, and Probability**   695

9.1   Sequences and Series   696

9.2   Arithmetic Sequences and Partial Sums   707

9.3   Geometric Sequences and Series   716

9.4   Mathematical Induction   726

9.5   The Binomial Theorem   734

9.6   Counting Principles   742

9.7   Probability   752

Chapter Summary   765   **Review Exercises**   766

Chapter Test   770

Chapter 10   **Topics in Analytic Geometry**   771

10.1 Conics   772

10.2 Translations of Conics   786

10.3 Parametric Equations   795

10.4 Polar Coordinates   803

10.5 Graphs of Polar Equations   809

10.6 Polar Equations of Conics   818

Chapter Summary   825   **Review Exercises**   826

Chapter Test   830   **Cumulative Test: Chapters 8–10**   831

Appendices   **Appendix A   Technology Support Guide**   A1

Appendix B   Proofs of Selected Theorems   A25

Appendix C   Concepts in Statistics   A38

C.1   Measures of Central Tendency and Dispersion   A38

C.2   Least Squares Regression   A47

Appendix D   Solving Linear Equations and Inequalities   A49

Appendix E   Systems of Inequalities   A52

E.1   Solving Systems of Inequalities   A52

E.2   Linear Programming   A62

Answers to Odd-Numbered Exercises and Tests   A71

Index of Applications   A211

Index   A215

A Word from the Authors

Welcome to *Precalculus: A Graphing Approach*, Fourth Edition. We are pleased to present this new edition of our textbook in which we focus on making the mathematics accessible, supporting student success, and offering instructors flexibility in how the course can be taught.

Accessible to Students

Over the years we have taken care to write this text with the student in mind. Paying careful attention to the presentation, we use precise mathematical language and a clear writing style to develop an effective learning tool. We believe that every student can learn mathematics, and we are committed to providing a text that makes the mathematics of the college algebra course accessible to all students. For the Fourth Edition, we have revised and improved many text features designed for this purpose.

Throughout the text, we present solutions to many examples from multiple perspectives—algebraic, graphic, and numeric. The side-by-side format of this pedagogical feature helps students to see that a problem can be solved in more than one way and to see that different methods yield the same result. The side-by-side format also addresses many different learning styles.

We have found that many precalculus students grasp mathematical concepts more easily when they work with them in the context of real-life situations. Students have numerous opportunities to do this throughout the Fourth Edition, in examples and exercises, including developing models to fit current real data. To reinforce the concept of functions, we have compiled all the elementary functions as a *Library of Functions*. Each function is introduced at the first point of use in the text with a definition and description of basic characteristics; all elementary functions are also presented in a summary on the front endpapers of the text for convenient reference.

We have carefully written and designed each page to make the book more readable and accessible to students. For example, to avoid unnecessary page turning and disruptions to students' thought processes, each example and corresponding solution begins and ends on the same page.

Supports Student Success

During more than thirty years of teaching and writing, we have learned many things about the teaching and learning of mathematics. We have found that students are most successful when they know what they are expected to learn and why it is important to learn it. With that in mind, we have enhanced the thematic study thread throughout the Fourth Edition.

Each chapter begins with a list of section references and a study guide, *What You Should Learn*, which is a comprehensive overview of the chapter concepts. This study guide helps students prepare to study and learn the material in the chapter.

Using the same pedagogical theme, each section begins with a set of section learning objectives—*What You Should Learn*. These are followed by an engaging real-life application—*Why You Should Learn It*—that motivates students and illustrates an area where the mathematical concepts will be applied in an example or exercise in the section. The *Chapter Summary—What Did You Learn?*—at the end of each chapter is a section-by-section overview that ties the learning objectives from the chapter to sets of *Review Exercises* at the end of each chapter.

Throughout the text, other features further improve accessibility. *Study Tips* are provided throughout the text at point-of-use to reinforce concepts and to help students learn how to study mathematics. *Explorations* have been expanded in order to reinforce mathematical concepts. Each Example with worked-out solution is followed by a *Checkpoint*, which directs the student to work a similar exercise from the exercise set. The *Section Exercises* now begin with a *Vocabulary Check*, which gives the students an opportunity to test their understanding of the important terms in the section. *Synthesis Exercises* check students' conceptual understanding of the topics in each section and *Review Exercises* provide additional practice with the concepts in the chapter or previous chapters. *Chapter Tests*, at the end of each chapter, and periodic *Cumulative Tests* offer students frequent opportunities for self-assessment and to develop strong study- and test-taking skills.

The use of technology also supports students with different learning styles, and graphing calculators are fully integrated into the text presentation. In the Fourth Edition, a robust *Technology Support Appendix* has been added to make it easier for students to use technology. *Technology Support* notes are provided throughout the text at point-of-use. These notes guide students to the *Technology Support Appendix*, where they can learn how to use specific graphing calculator features to enhance their understanding of the concepts presented in the text. These notes also direct students to the *Graphing Technology Guide*, on the textbook website, for keystroke support that is available for numerous calculator models. *Technology Tips* are provided in the text at point-of-use to call attention to the strengths and weaknesses of graphing technology, as well as to offer alternative methods for solving or checking a problem using technology. Because students are often misled by the limitations of graphing calculators, we have, where appropriate, used color to enhance the graphing calculator displays in the textbook. This enables students to visualize the mathematical concepts clearly and accurately and avoid common misunderstandings.

Numerous additional text-specific resources are available to help students succeed in the precalculus course. These include "live" online tutoring, instructional DVDs and videos, and a variety of other resources, such as tutorial support and self-assessment, which are available on CD-ROM and the Web. In addition, the *Student Success Organizer* is a note-taking guide that helps students organize their class notes and create an effective study and review tool.

Flexible Options for Instructors

From the time we first began writing textbooks in the early 1970s, we have always considered it a critical part of our role as authors to provide instructors with flexible programs. In addition to addressing a variety of learning styles, the optional features within the text allow instructors to design their courses to meet their instructional needs and the needs of their students. For example, the

Explorations throughout the text can be used as a quick introduction to concepts or as a way to reinforce student understanding.

Our goal when developing the exercise sets was to address a wide variety of learning styles and teaching preferences. New to this edition are the *Vocabulary Check* questions, which are provided at the beginning of every exercise set to help students learn proper mathematical terminology. In each exercise set we have included a variety of exercise types, including questions requiring writing and critical thinking, as well as real-data applications. The problems are carefully graded in difficulty from mastery of basic skills to more challenging exercises. Some of the more challenging exercises include the *Synthesis Exercises* that combine skills and are used to check for conceptual understanding. *Review Exercises*, placed at the end of each exercise set, reinforce previously learned skills in preparation for the next lesson. In addition, Houghton Mifflin's Eduspace® website offers instructors the option to assign homework and tests online—and also includes the ability to grade these assignments automatically.

Several other print and media resources are also available to support instructors. The *Instructor Success Organizer* includes suggested lesson plans and is an especially useful tool for larger departments that want all sections of a course to follow the same outline. The *Instructor's Edition* of the *Student Success Organizer* can be used as a lecture outline for every section of the text and includes additional examples for classroom discussion and important definitions. This is another valuable resource for schools trying to have consistent instruction and it can be used as a resource to support less experienced instructors. When used in conjunction with the *Student Success Organizer* these resources can save instructors preparation time and help students concentrate on important concepts. For a complete list of resources available with this text, see page xv.

We hope you enjoy the Fourth Edition!

Ron Larson

Robert P. Hostetler

Bruce H. Edwards

Acknowledgments

We would like to thank the many people who have helped us prepare the text and the supplements package. Their encouragement, criticisms, and suggestions have been invaluable to us.

Fourth Edition Reviewers

Tony Homayoon Akhlaghi, Bellevue Community College; Kimberly Bennekin, Georgia Perimeter College; Charles M. Biles, Humboldt State University; Phyllis Barsch Bolin, Oklahoma Christian University; Khristo Boyadzhiev, Ohio Northern University; Jennifer Dollar, Grand Rapids Community College; Susan E. Enyart, Otterbein College; Patricia K. Gramling, Trident Technical College; Rodney Holke-Farnam, Hawkeye Community College; Deborah Johnson, Cambridge South Dorchester High School; Susan Kellicut, Seminole Community College; Richard J. Maher, Loyola University; Rupa M. Patel, University of Portland; Lila F. Roberts, Georgia Southern University; Keith Schwingendorf, Purdue University North Central; Pamela K. M. Smith, Fort Lewis College; Hayat Weiss, Middlesex Community College; Fred Worth, Henderson State University.

We would like to thank the staff of Larson Texts, Inc. and the staff of Meridian Creative Group, who assisted in proofreading the manuscript, preparing and proofreading the art package, and typesetting the supplements.

On a personal level, we are grateful to our wives, Deanna Gilbert Larson, Eloise Hostetler, and Consuelo Edwards for their love, patience, and support. Also, a special thanks goes to R. Scott O'Neil.

If you have suggestions for improving this text, please feel free to write us. Over the past two decades we have received many useful comments from both instructors and students, and we value these very much.

Ron Larson
Robert P. Hostetler
Bruce H. Edwards

Features Highlights

Colleges and universities track enrollment figures in order to determine the financial outlook of the institution. The growth in student enrollment at a college or university can be modeled by a linear equation.

1 Functions and Their Graphs

What You Should Learn

1.1 Graphs of Equations
1.2 Lines in the Plane
1.3 Functions
1.4 Graphs of Functions
1.5 Shifting, Reflecting, and Stretching Graphs
1.6 Combinations of Functions
1.7 Inverse Functions

In this chapter, you will learn how to:

■ Sketch graphs of equations by point plotting or by using a graphing utility.

■ Find and use the slope of a line to write and graph linear equations.

■ Evaluate functions and find their domains.

■ Analyze graphs of functions.

■ Identify and graph shifts, reflections, and nonrigid transformations of functions.

■ Find arithmetic combinations and compositions of functions.

■ Find inverse functions graphically and algebraically.

73

● "What You Should Learn"

Each chapter begins with *What You Should Learn*, a comprehensive overview of the chapter concepts. The photograph and caption illustrate a real-life application of a key concept. Section references help students prepare for the chapter.

● "What You Should Learn" and "Why You Should Learn It"

Sections begin with *What You Should Learn*, an outline of the main concepts covered in the section, and *Why You Should Learn It*, a real-life application or mathematical reference that illustrates the relevance of the section content.

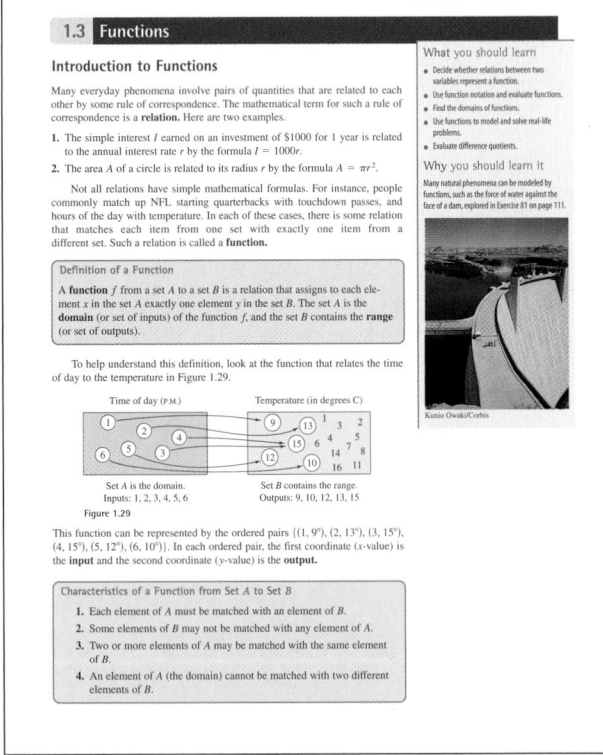

Section 1.3   Functions   99

1.3 Functions

Introduction to Functions

Many everyday phenomena involve pairs of quantities that are related to each other by some rule of correspondence. The mathematical term for such a rule of correspondence is a **relation.** Here are two examples.

1. The simple interest I earned on an investment of \$1000 for 1 year is related to the annual interest rate r by the formula $I = 1000r$.

2. The area A of a circle is related to its radius r by the formula $A = \pi r^2$.

Not all relations have simple mathematical formulas. For instance, people commonly match up NFL starting quarterbacks with touchdown passes, and hours of the day with temperature. In each of these cases, there is some relation that matches each item from one set with exactly one item from a different set. Such a relation is called a **function.**

Definition of a Function

A **function** f from a set A to a set B is a relation that assigns to each element x in the set A exactly one element y in the set B. The set A is the **domain** (or set of inputs) of the function f, and the set B contains the **range** (or set of outputs).

To help understand this definition, look at the function that relates the time of day to the temperature in Figure 1.29.

Time of day (P.M.)   Temperature (in degrees C)

Set A is the domain.   Set B contains the range.
Inputs: 1, 2, 3, 4, 5, 6   Outputs: 9, 10, 12, 13, 15
Figure 1.29

This function can be represented by the ordered pairs {(1, 9°), (2, 13°), (3, 15°), (4, 15°), (5, 12°), (6, 10°)}. In each ordered pair, the first coordinate (x-value) is the **input** and the second coordinate (y-value) is the **output.**

Characteristics of a Function from Set A to Set B

1. Each element of A must be matched with an element of B.
2. Some elements of B may not be matched with any element of A.
3. Two or more elements of A may be matched with the same element of B.
4. An element of A (the domain) cannot be matched with two different elements of B.

What you should learn
● Decide whether relations between two variables represent a function.
● Use function notation and evaluate functions.
● Find the domains of functions.
● Use functions to model and solve real-life problems.
● Evaluate difference quotients.

Why you should learn it
Many natural phenomena can be modeled by functions, such as the force of water against the face of a dam, explored in Exercise 81 on page 111.

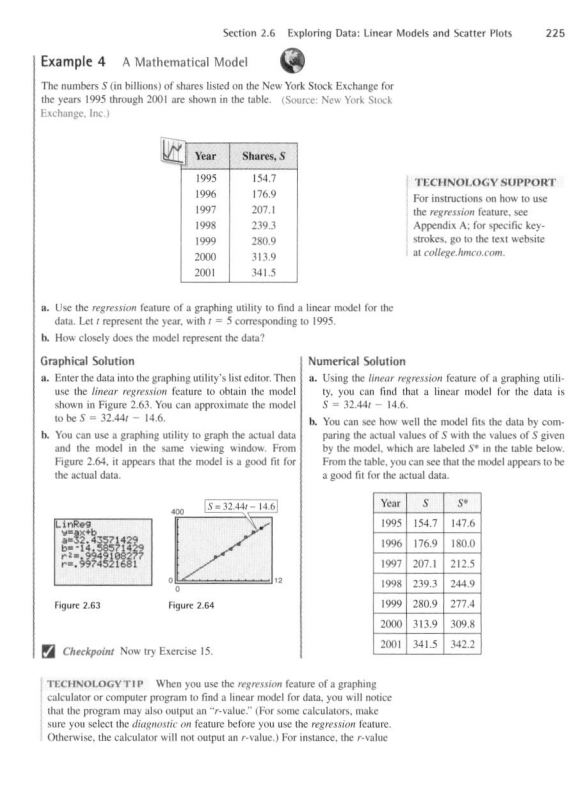

Examples

Many examples present side-by-side solutions from multiple approaches—algebraic, graphical, and numerical. This format addresses a variety of learning styles and shows students that different solution methods yield the same result.

Checkpoint

The *Checkpoint* directs students to work a similar problem in the exercise set for extra practice.

Library of Functions

The *Library of Functions* feature defines each elementary function and its characteristics at first point of use.

Explorations

The *Exploration* engages students in active discovery of mathematical concepts, strengthens critical thinking skills, and helps them to develop an intuitive understanding of theoretical concepts.

Study Tips

Study Tips reinforce concepts and help students learn how to study mathematics.

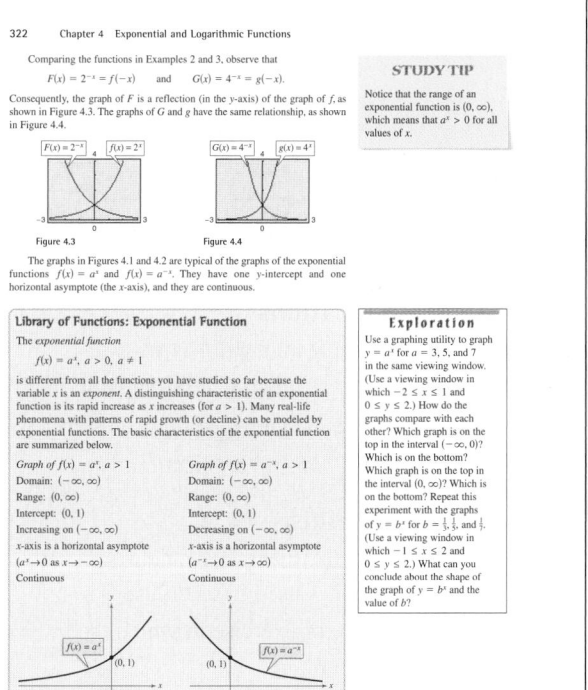

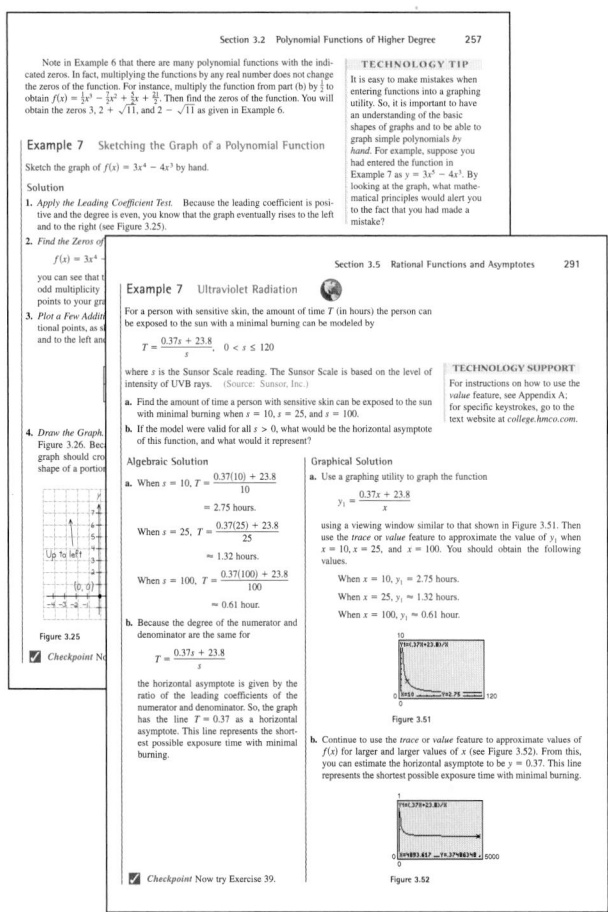

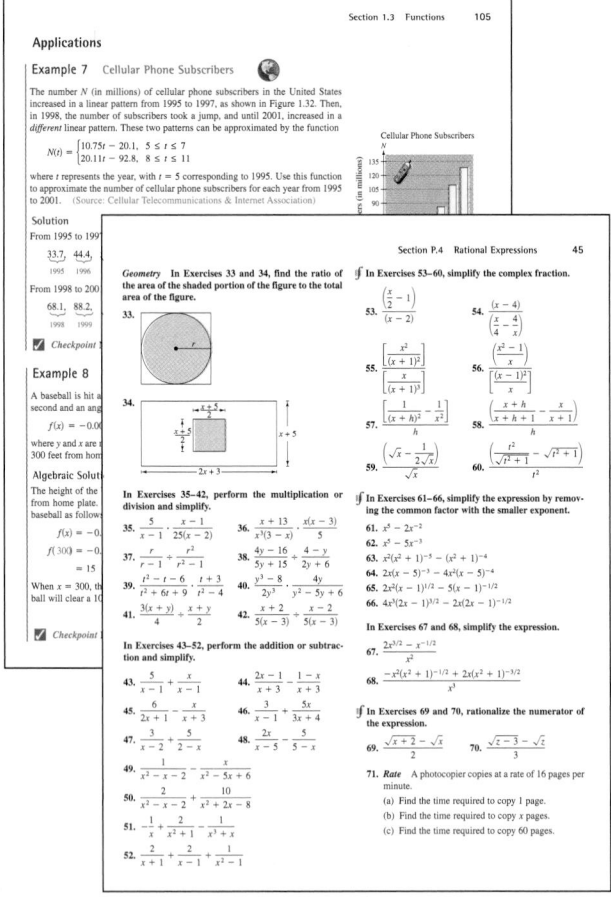

Technology Tip

Technology Tips point out the pros and cons of technology use in certain mathematical situations. *Technology Tips* also provide alternative methods of solving or checking a problem by the use of a graphing calculator.

Technology Support

The *Technology Support* feature guides students to the *Technology Support Appendix* if they need to reference a specific calculator feature. These notes also direct students to the *Graphing Technology Guide*, on the textbook website, for keystroke support that is available for numerous calculator models.

Real-Life Applications

A wide variety of real-life applications, many using current real data, are integrated throughout the examples and exercises. The 🌐 indicates an example that involves a real-life application.

Algebra of Calculus

Throughout the text, special emphasis is given to the algebraic techniques used in calculus. 𝄌 indicates an example or exercise in which the algebra of calculus is featured.

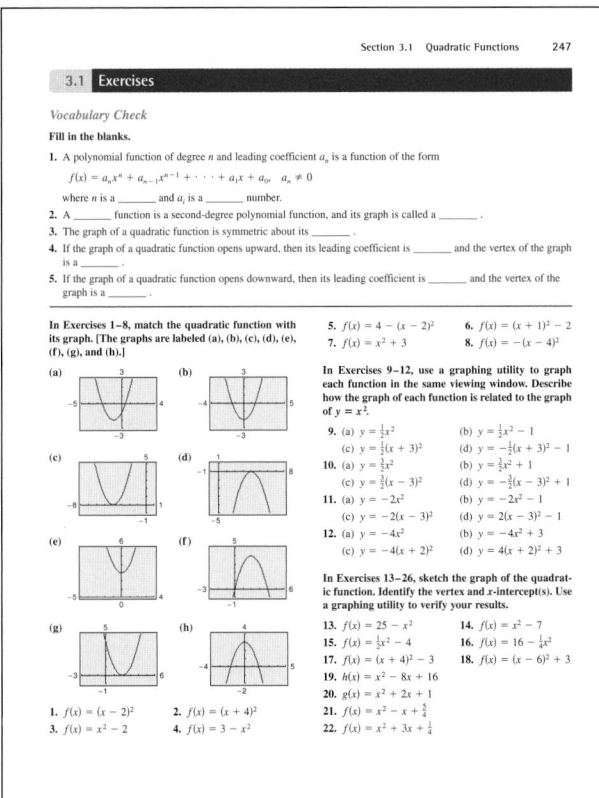

Section 3.1   Quadratic Functions   247

3.1 Exercises

Vocabulary Check

Fill in the blanks.

1. A polynomial function of degree n and leading coefficient a_n is a function of the form

$$f(x) = a_n x^n + a_{n-1} x^{n-1} + \cdots + a_1 x + a_0, \quad a_n \neq 0$$

where n is a _____ and a_i is a _____ number.

2. A _____ function is a second-degree polynomial function, and its graph is called a _____ .

3. The graph of a quadratic function is symmetric about its _____ .

4. If the graph of a quadratic function opens upward, then its leading coefficient is _____ and the vertex of the graph is a _____ .

5. If the graph of a quadratic function opens downward, then its leading coefficient is _____ and the vertex of the graph is a _____ .

In Exercises 1–8, match the quadratic function with its graph. [The graphs are labeled (a), (b), (c), (d), (e), (f), (g), and (h).]

5. $f(x) = 4 - (x - 2)^2$
6. $f(x) = (x + 1)^2 - 2$
7. $f(x) = x^2 + 3$
8. $f(x) = -(x - 4)^2$

In Exercises 9–12, use a graphing utility to graph each function in the same viewing window. Describe how the graph of each function is related to the graph of $y = x^2$.

9. (a) $y = \frac{1}{2}x^2$ (b) $y = \frac{1}{2}x^2 - 1$
   (c) $y = \frac{1}{2}(x + 3)^2$ (d) $y = -\frac{1}{2}(x + 3)^2 - 1$
10. (a) $y = \frac{3}{2}x^2$ (b) $y = \frac{3}{2}x^2 + 1$
    (c) $y = \frac{3}{2}(x - 3)^2$ (d) $y = -\frac{3}{2}(x - 3)^2 + 1$
11. (a) $y = -2x^2$ (b) $y = -2x^2 - 1$
    (c) $y = -2(x - 3)^2$ (d) $y = 2(x - 3)^2 - 1$
12. (a) $y = -4x^2$ (b) $y = -4x^2 + 3$
    (c) $y = -4(x + 2)^2$ (d) $y = 4(x + 2)^2 + 3$

In Exercises 13–26, sketch the graph of the quadratic function. Identify the vertex and x-intercept(s). Use a graphing utility to verify your results.

13. $f(x) = 25 - x^2$
14. $f(x) = x^2 - 7$
15. $f(x) = \frac{1}{2}x^2 - 4$
16. $f(x) = 16 - \frac{1}{4}x^2$
17. $f(x) = (x + 4)^2 - 3$
18. $f(x) = (x - 6)^2 + 3$
19. $h(x) = x^2 - 8x + 16$
20. $g(x) = x^2 + 2x + 1$
21. $f(x) = x^2 - x + \frac{5}{4}$
22. $f(x) = x^2 + 3x + \frac{1}{4}$

1. $f(x) = (x - 2)^2$
2. $f(x) = (x + 4)^2$
3. $f(x) = x^2 - 2$
4. $f(x) = 3 - x^2$

● Vocabulary Check

Section exercises begin with a *Vocabulary Check* that serves as a review of the important mathematical terms in each section.

● Section Exercises

The section exercise sets consist of a variety of computational, conceptual, and applied problems.

● Synthesis and Review Exercises

Each exercise set concludes with two types of exercises.

Synthesis exercises promote further exploration of mathematical concepts, critical thinking skills, and writing about mathematics. The exercises require students to show their understanding of the relationships between many concepts in the section.

Review Exercises reinforce previously learned skills and concepts.

---

278   Chapter 3   Polynomial and Rational Functions

(b) Use a graphing utility and the model to create a table of estimated values for S. Compare the estimated values with the actual data.

(c) Use the Remainder Theorem to evaluate the model for the year 2008. Even though the model is relatively accurate for estimating the given data, would you use this model to predict the sales from lottery tickets in the future? Explain.

81. *Geometry* A rectangular package sent by a delivery service can have a maximum combined length and girth (perimeter of a cross section) of 120 inches (see figure).

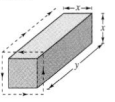

(a) Show that the volume of the package is given by the function

$$V(x) = 4x^2(30 - x).$$

(b) Use a graphing utility to graph the function and approximate the dimensions of the package that yield a maximum volume.

(c) Find values of x such that $V = 13,500$. Which of these values is a physical impossibility in the construction of the package? Explain.

82. *Automobile Emissions* The number of parts per million of nitric oxide emissions y from a car engine is approximated by the model

$$y = -5.05x^3 + 3857x - 38,411.25, \quad 13 \le x \le 18$$

where x is the air-fuel ratio.

(a) Use a graphing utility to graph the model.

(b) It is observed from the graph that two air-fuel ratios produce 2400 parts per million of nitric oxide, with one being 15. Use the graph to approximate the second air-fuel ratio.

(c) Algebraically approximate the second air-fuel ratio that produces 2400 parts per million of nitric oxide. (*Hint:* Because you know that an air-fuel ratio of 15 produces the specified nitric oxide emission, you can use synthetic division.)

Synthesis

True or False? In Exercises 83 and 84, determine whether the statement is true or false. Justify your answer.

83. If $(7x + 4)$ is a factor of some polynomial function f, then $\frac{4}{7}$ is a zero of f.

84. $(2x - 1)$ is a factor of the polynomial

$$6x^6 + x^5 - 92x^4 + 45x^3 + 184x^2 + 4x - 48.$$

Think About It In Exercises 85 and 86, perform the division by assuming that n is a positive integer.

85. $\dfrac{x^{3n} + 9x^{2n} + 27x^n + 27}{x^n + 3}$

86. $\dfrac{x^{3n} - 3x^{2n} + 5x^n - 6}{x^n - 2}$

87. *Writing* Complete each polynomial division. Write a brief description of the pattern that you obtain, and use your result to find a formula for the polynomial division $(x^n - 1)/(x - 1)$. Create a numerical example to test your formula.

(a) $\dfrac{x^2 - 1}{x - 1} = $ ▢

(b) $\dfrac{x^3 - 1}{x - 1} = $ ▢

(c) $\dfrac{x^4 - 1}{x - 1} = $ ▢

88. *Writing* Write a short paragraph explaining how you can check polynomial division. Give an example.

Review

In Exercises 89–92, use any convenient method to solve the quadratic equation.

89. $9x^2 - 25 = 0$
90. $16x^2 - 21 = 0$
91. $2x^2 + 6x + 3 = 0$
92. $8x^2 - 22x + 15 = 0$

In Exercises 93–96, find a polynomial function that has the given zeros. (There are many correct answers.)

93. $0, -12$
94. $1, -3, 8$
95. $0, -1, 2, 5$
96. $2 + \sqrt{3}, 2 - \sqrt{3}$

FEATURES

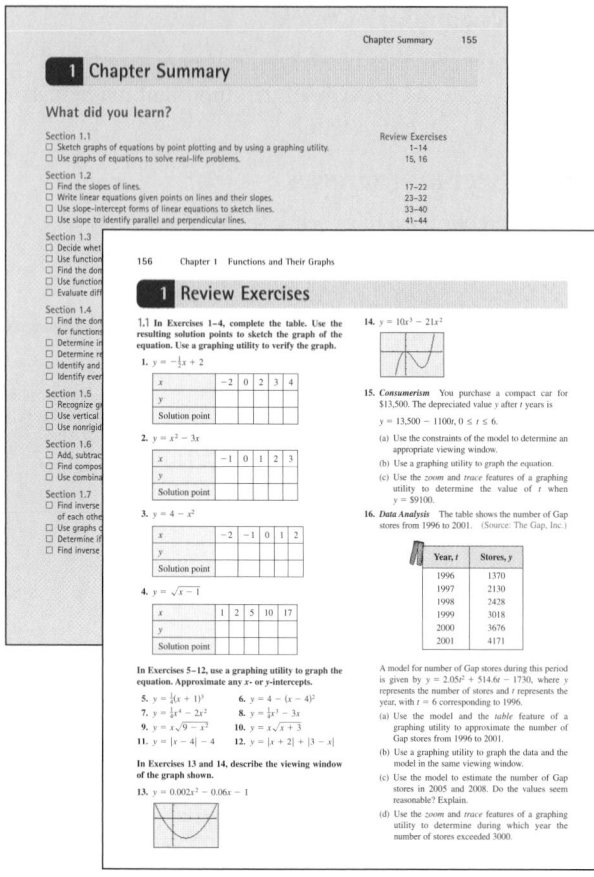

● Chapter Summary

The *Chapter Summary*, *"What Did You Learn?"* is a section-by-section overview that ties the learning objectives from the chapter to sets of Review Exercises for extra practice.

● Review Exercises

The chapter *Review Exercises* provide additional practice with the concepts in the chapter.

● Chapter Tests and Cumulative Tests

Chapter Tests, at the end of each chapter, and periodic *Cumulative Tests* offer students frequent opportunities for self-assessment and to develop strong study- and test-taking skills.

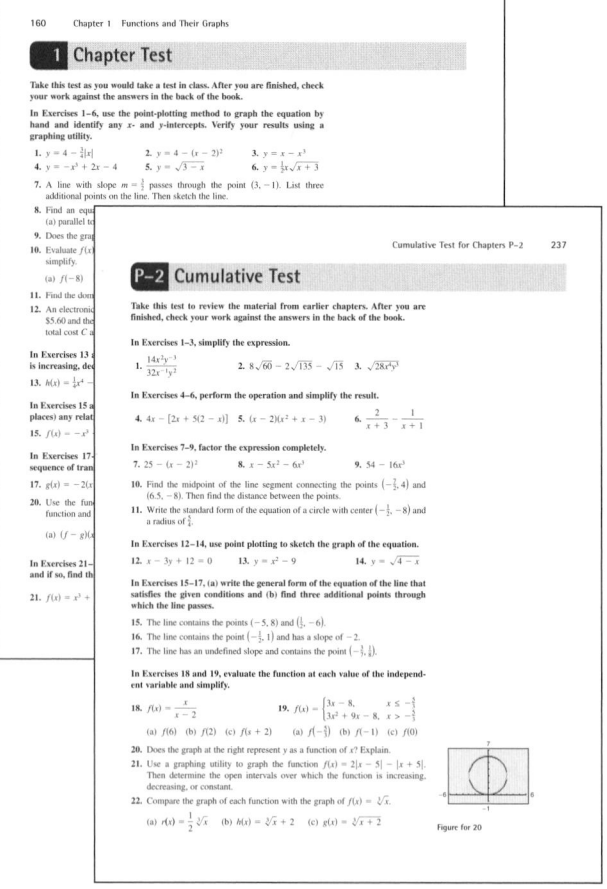

Supplements

Resources

Text website (*college.hmco.com*)
Many text-specific resources for students and instructors can be found at the Houghton Mifflin website. They include, but are not limited to, the following features for the student and instructor.

Student Website

- Student Success Organizer
- Digital Lessons
- Graphing Technology Guide
- Graphing Calculator Programs
- Chapter Projects
- Historical Notes
- Ace Quizzes

Instructor Website

- Instructor Success Organizer
- Digital Art and Tables
- Digital Lessons
- Graphing Technology Guide
- Graphing Calculator Programs
- Chapter Projects
- Answers to Chapter Projects
- Link to Student website

Additional Resources for the Student

Study and Solutions Guide by Bruce H. Edwards (University of Florida)

HM mathSpace® Tutorial CD-ROM: This new tutorial CD-ROM allows students to practice skills and review concepts as many times as necessary by using algorithmically generated exercises and step-by-step solutions for practice. The CD-ROM contains a variety of other student resources as well.

Instructional Videotapes by Dana Mosely

Instructional Videotapes for Graphing Calculators by Dana Mosely

SMARTTHINKING™ Live, On-Line Tutoring: Houghton Mifflin has partnered with SMARTTHINKING™ to provide an easy-to-use, effective, on-line tutorial service. Through state-of-the-art tools and a two-way whiteboard, students communicate in real-time with qualified e-structors who can help the students understand difficult concepts and guide them through the problem solving process while studying or completing homework. Live online tutoring support, Question submission, Pre-scheduled tutoring time, and Reviews of past online sessions are four levels of service offered to the students.

Eduspace®: Eduspace® is a text-specific online learning environment that combines algorithmic tutorials with homework capabilities. Text-specific content is available to help you understand the mathematics covered in this textbook.

Eduspace® with eSolutions: Eduspace® with eSolutions combines all the features of Eduspace® with an electronic version of the textbook exercises and the complete solutions to the odd-numbered exercises. The result is a convenient and comprehensive way to do homework and view your course materials.

Additional Resources for the Instructor

Instructor's Annotated Edition (IAE)

Instructor's Solutions Guide and Test Item File by Bruce H. Edwards (University of Florida)

HM ClassPrep with HM Testing CD-ROM: This CD-ROM is a combination of two course management tools.

- HM Testing 6.0 computerized testing software provides instructors with an array of algorithmic test items, allowing for the creation of an unlimited number of tests for each chapter, including cumulative tests and final exams. HM Testing also offers online testing via a Local Area Network (LAN) or the Internet, as well as a grade book function.
- HM ClassPrep features supplements and text-specific resources.

Eduspace®: Eduspace® is a text-specific online learning environment that combines algorithmic tutorials with homework capabilities and classroom management functions. Electronic grading and Course Management are two levels of service provided for instructors. Please contact your Houghton Mifflin sales representative for detailed information about the course content available for this text.

Eduspace® with eSolutions: Eduspace® with eSolutions combines all the features of Eduspace® with an electronic version of the textbook exercises and the complete solutions to the odd-numbered exercises, providing students with a convenient and comprehensive way to do homework and view course materials.

The stopping distance of an automobile depends on the distance traveled during the driver's reaction time and the distance traveled after the brakes are applied. The total stopping distance can be modeled by a polynomial.

David Young-Wolff/PhotoEdit

Prerequisites

P.1 Real Numbers

P.2 Exponents and Radicals

P.3 Polynomials and Factoring

P.4 Rational Expressions

P.5 The Cartesian Plane

P.6 Exploring Data: Representing Data Graphically

What You Should Learn

In this chapter, you will learn how to:

■ Represent, classify, and order real numbers and use inequalities.

■ Evaluate algebraic expressions using the basic rules of algebra.

■ Use properties of exponents and radicals to simplify and evaluate expressions.

■ Add, subtract, and multiply polynomials.

■ Factor expressions completely.

■ Determine the domains of algebraic expressions and simplify rational expressions.

■ Use algebraic techniques common in calculus.

■ Plot points in the coordinate plane and use the Distance and Midpoint Formulas.

■ Organize data and represent data graphically.

P.1   Real Numbers

Real Numbers

Real numbers are used in everyday life to describe quantities such as age, miles per gallon, and population. Real numbers are represented by symbols such as

$$-5, 9, 0, \tfrac{4}{3}, 0.666\ldots, 28.21, \sqrt{2}, \pi, \text{ and } \sqrt[3]{-32}.$$

Here are some important **subsets** (each member of subset B is also a member of set A) of the set of real numbers.

$$\{1, 2, 3, 4, \ldots\} \qquad \text{Set of natural numbers}$$

$$\{0, 1, 2, 3, 4, \ldots\} \qquad \text{Set of whole numbers}$$

$$\{\ldots, -3, -2, -1, 0, 1, 2, 3, \ldots\} \qquad \text{Set of integers}$$

A real number is **rational** if it can be written as the ratio p/q of two integers, where $q \neq 0$. For instance, the numbers

$$\frac{1}{3} = 0.3333\ldots = 0.\overline{3}, \ \frac{1}{8} = 0.125, \text{ and } \frac{125}{111} = 1.126126\ldots = 1.\overline{126}$$

are rational. The decimal representation of a rational number either *repeats* (as in $\frac{173}{55} = 3.1\overline{45}$) or *terminates* (as in $\frac{1}{2} = 0.5$). A real number that cannot be written as the ratio of two integers is called **irrational**. Irrational numbers have infinite nonrepeating decimal representations. For instance, the numbers

$$\sqrt{2} = 1.4142135\ldots \approx 1.41 \quad \text{and} \quad \pi = 3.1415925\ldots \approx 3.14$$

are irrational. (The symbol $\approx$ means "is approximately equal to.") Figure P.1 shows subsets of real numbers and their relationships to each other.

Real numbers are represented graphically by a **real number line.** The point 0 on the real number line is the **origin.** Numbers to the right of 0 are positive and numbers to the left of 0 are negative, as shown in Figure P.2. The term **nonnegative** describes a number that is either positive or zero.

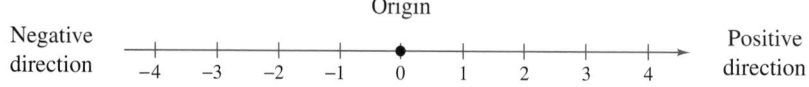

Figure P.2   The Real Number Line

There is a *one-to-one correspondence* between real numbers and points on the real number line. That is, every point on the real number line corresponds to exactly one real number, called its **coordinate,** and every real number corresponds to exactly one point on the real number line, as shown in Figure P.3.

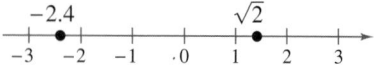

Every point on the real number line corresponds to exactly one real number.

Figure P.3   One-to-One Correspondence

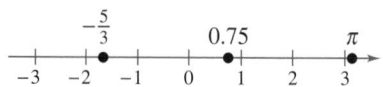

Every real number corresponds to exactly one point on the real number line.

What you should learn

- Represent and classify real numbers.
- Order real numbers and use inequalities.
- Find the absolute values of real numbers and the distance between two real numbers.
- Evaluate algebraic expressions.
- Use the basic rules and properties of algebra.

Why you should learn it

Real numbers are used in every aspect of our daily lives, such as finding the variance of a budget. See Exercises 67–70 on page 10.

SuperStock

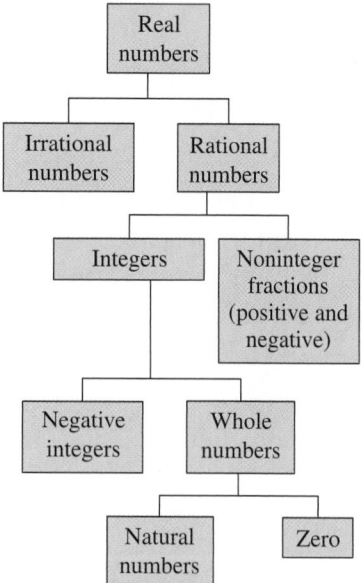

Figure P.1   Subsets of Real Numbers

Ordering Real Numbers

One important property of real numbers is that they are **ordered.**

> **Definition of Order on the Real Number Line**
>
> If a and b are real numbers, a is **less than** b if $b - a$ is positive. This order is denoted by the **inequality** $a < b$. This relationship can also be described by saying that b is **greater than** a and writing $b > a$. The inequality $a \le b$ means that a is **less than or equal to** b, and the inequality $b \ge a$ means that b is **greater than or equal to** a. The symbols $<$, $>$, $\le$, and $\ge$ are **inequality symbols.**

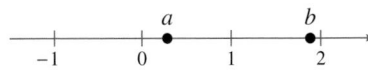

Figure P.4 $a < b$ if and only if a lies to the left of b.

Geometrically, this definition implies that $a < b$ if and only if a lies to the *left* of b on the real number line, as shown in Figure P.4.

Example 1   Interpreting Inequalities

Describe the subset of real numbers represented by each inequality.

a. $x \le 2$ **b.** $x > -1$ **c.** $-2 \le x < 3$

Solution

a. The inequality $x \le 2$ denotes all real numbers less than or equal to 2, as shown in Figure P.5.

b. The inequality $x > -1$ denotes all real numbers greater than -1, as shown in Figure P.6.

c. The inequality $-2 \le x < 3$ means that $x \ge -2$ *and* $x < 3$. The "double inequality" denotes all real numbers between -2 and 3, including -2 but not including 3, as shown in Figure P.7.

✓ *Checkpoint* Now try Exercise 31.

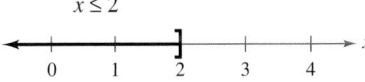

Figure P.5

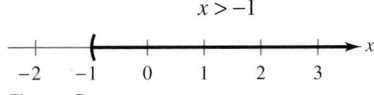

Figure P.6

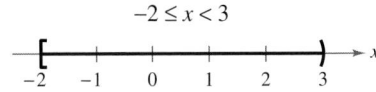

Figure P.7

Inequalities can be used to describe subsets of real numbers called **intervals.** In the bounded intervals below, the real numbers a and b are the **endpoints** of each interval.

Bounded Intervals on the Real Number Line

Notation	Interval Type	Inequality	Graph
$[a, b]$	Closed	$a \le x \le b$	
(a, b)	Open	$a < x < b$	
$[a, b)$		$a \le x < b$	
$(a, b]$		$a < x \le b$	

STUDY TIP

The endpoints of a closed interval are included in the interval. The endpoints of an open interval are *not* included in the interval.

The symbols ∞, **positive infinity,** and $-\infty$, **negative infinity,** do not represent real numbers. They are simply convenient symbols used to describe the unboundedness of an interval such as $(1, \infty)$ or $(-\infty, 3]$.

Unbounded Intervals on the Real Number Line

Notation	Interval Type	Inequality	Graph
$[a, \infty)$		$x \geq a$	
(a, ∞)	Open	$x > a$	
$(-\infty, b]$		$x \leq b$	
$(-\infty, b)$	Open	$x < b$	
$(-\infty, \infty)$	Entire real line	$-\infty < x < \infty$	

Example 2   Using Inequalities to Represent Intervals

Use inequality notation to describe each of the following.

a. c is at most 2.   **b.** All x in the interval $(-3, 5]$

Solution

a. The statement "c is at most 2" can be represented by $c \leq 2$.

b. "All x in the interval $(-3, 5]$" can be represented by $-3 < x \leq 5$.

✓ *Checkpoint* Now try Exercise 35.

Example 3   Interpreting Intervals

Give a verbal description of each interval.

a. $(-1, 0)$ **b.** $[2, \infty)$ **c.** $(-\infty, 0)$

Solution

a. This interval consists of all real numbers that are greater than -1 and less than 0.

b. This interval consists of all real numbers that are greater than or equal to 2.

c. This interval consists of all negative real numbers.

✓ *Checkpoint* Now try Exercise 41.

The **Law of Trichotomy** states that for any two real numbers a and b, precisely one of three relationships is possible:

$a = b$, $a < b$, or $a > b$.   Law of Trichotomy

Absolute Value and Distance

The **absolute value** of a real number is its *magnitude*, or the distance between the origin and the point representing the real number on the real number line.

Definition of Absolute Value

If a is a real number, the **absolute value** of a is

$$|a| = \begin{cases} a, & \text{if } a \geq 0 \\ -a, & \text{if } a < 0 \end{cases}.$$

Notice from this definition that the absolute value of a real number is never negative. For instance, if $a = -5$, then $|-5| = -(-5) = 5$. The absolute value of a real number is either positive or zero. Moreover, 0 is the only real number whose absolute value is 0. So, $|0| = 0$.

Example 4   Evaluating the Absolute Value of a Number

Evaluate $\dfrac{|x|}{x}$ for (a) $x > 0$ and (b) $x < 0$.

Solution

a. If $x > 0$, then $|x| = x$ and $\dfrac{|x|}{x} = \dfrac{x}{x} = 1$.

b. If $x < 0$, then $|x| = -x$ and $\dfrac{|x|}{x} = \dfrac{-x}{x} = -1$.

✓ *Checkpoint* Now try Exercise 47.

Properties of Absolute Value

1. $|a| \geq 0$ **2.** $|-a| = |a|$

3. $|ab| = |a||b|$ **4.** $\left|\dfrac{a}{b}\right| = \dfrac{|a|}{|b|}, \quad b \neq 0$

Absolute value can be used to define the distance between two points on the real number line. For instance, the distance between -3 and 4 is

$$|-3 - 4| = |-7| = 7$$

as shown in Figure P.8.

Distance Between Two Points on the Real Line

Let a and b be real numbers. The **distance between a and b** is

$$d(a, b) = |b - a| = |a - b|.$$

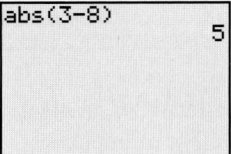
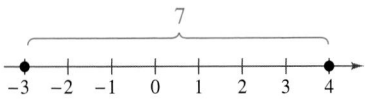

Figure P.8 The distance between -3 and 4 is 7.

Algebraic Expressions

One characteristic of algebra is the use of letters to represent numbers. The letters are **variables,** and combinations of letters and numbers are **algebraic expressions.** Here are a few examples of algebraic expressions.

$$5x, \qquad 2x - 3, \qquad \frac{4}{x^2 + 2}, \qquad 7x + y$$

Definition of an Algebraic Expression

An **algebraic expression** is a combination of letters (**variables**) and real numbers (**constants**) combined using the operations of addition, subtraction, multiplication, division, and exponentiation.

The **terms** of an algebraic expression are those parts that are separated by *addition*. For example,

$$x^2 - 5x + 8 = x^2 + (-5x) + 8$$

has three terms: x^2 and $-5x$ are the **variable terms** and 8 is the **constant term.** The numerical factor of a variable term is the **coefficient** of the variable term. For instance, the coefficient of $-5x$ is -5, and the coefficient of x^2 is 1.

To **evaluate** an algebraic expression, substitute numerical values for each of the variables in the expression. Here are two examples.

Expression	Value of Variable	Substitute	Value of Expression
$-3x + 5$	$x = 3$	$-3(3) + 5$	$-9 + 5 = -4$
$3x^2 + 2x - 1$	$x = -1$	$3(-1)^2 + 2(-1) - 1$	$3 - 2 - 1 = 0$

When an algebraic expression is evaluated, the **Substitution Principle** is used. It states, "If $a = b$, then a can be replaced by b in any expression involving a." In the first evaluation shown above, for instance, 3 is *substituted* for x in the expression $-3x + 5$.

Basic Rules of Algebra

There are four arithmetic operations with real numbers: *addition, multiplication, subtraction,* and *division,* denoted by the symbols $+$, $\times$ or $\cdot$, $-$, and $\div$ or $/$. Of these, addition and multiplication are the two primary operations. Subtraction and division are the inverse operations of addition and multiplication, respectively.

Subtraction: Add the opposite of b.   *Division: Multiply by the reciprocal of b.*

$$a - b = a + (-b) \qquad\qquad \text{If } b \neq 0, \text{ then } a/b = a\left(\frac{1}{b}\right) = \frac{a}{b}.$$

In these definitions, $-b$ is the **additive inverse** (or opposite) of b, and $1/b$ is the **multiplicative inverse** (or reciprocal) of b. In the fractional form a/b, a is the **numerator** of the fraction and b is the **denominator.**

Because the properties of real numbers below are true for variables and algebraic expressions, as well as for real numbers, they are often called the **Basic Rules of Algebra.** Try to formulate a verbal description of each property. For instance, the first property states that *the order in which two real numbers are added does not affect their sum.*

Basic Rules of Algebra

Let a, b, and c be real numbers, variables, or algebraic expressions.

	Property	Example
Commutative Property of Addition:	$a + b = b + a$	$4x + x^2 = x^2 + 4x$
Commutative Property of Multiplication:	$ab = ba$	$(1 - x)x^2 = x^2(1 - x)$
Associative Property of Addition:	$(a + b) + c = a + (b + c)$	$(x + 5) + x^2 = x + (5 + x^2)$
Associative Property of Multiplication:	$(ab)c = a(bc)$	$(2x \cdot 3y)(8) = (2x)(3y \cdot 8)$
Distributive Properties:	$a(b + c) = ab + ac$	$3x(5 + 2x) = 3x \cdot 5 + 3x \cdot 2x$
	$(a + b)c = ac + bc$	$(y + 8)y = y \cdot y + 8 \cdot y$
Additive Identity Property:	$a + 0 = a$	$5y^2 + 0 = 5y^2$
Multiplicative Identity Property:	$a \cdot 1 = a$	$(4x^2)(1) = 4x^2$
Additive Inverse Property:	$a + (-a) = 0$	$6x^3 + (-6x^3) = 0$
Multiplicative Inverse Property:	$a \cdot \dfrac{1}{a} = 1, \quad a \neq 0$	$(x^2 + 4)\left(\dfrac{1}{x^2 + 4}\right) = 1$

Because subtraction is defined as "adding the opposite," the Distributive Properties are also true for subtraction. For instance, the "subtraction form" of $a(b + c) = ab + ac$ is $a(b - c) = ab - ac$.

Properties of Negation and Equality

Let a, b, and c be real numbers, variables, or algebraic expressions.

	Property	Example
1.	$(-1)a = -a$	$(-1)7 = -7$
2.	$-(-a) = a$	$-(-6) = 6$
3.	$(-a)b = -(ab) = a(-b)$	$(-5)3 = -(5 \cdot 3) = 5(-3)$
4.	$(-a)(-b) = ab$	$(-2)(-x) = 2x$
5.	$-(a + b) = (-a) + (-b)$	$-(x + 8) = (-x) + (-8) = -x - 8$
6.	If $a = b$, then $a + c = b + c$.	$\frac{1}{2} + 3 = 0.5 + 3$
7.	If $a = b$, then $ac = bc$.	$4^2(2) = 16(2)$
8.	If $a + c = b + c$, then $a = b$.	$1.4 - 1 = \frac{7}{5} - 1$
9.	If $ac = bc$ and $c \neq 0$, then $a = b$.	$\dfrac{3}{4} = \dfrac{\sqrt{9}}{4}$

STUDY TIP

Be sure you see the difference between the *opposite of a number* and a *negative number.* If a is already negative, then its opposite, $-a$, is positive. For instance, if $a = -2$, then $-a = -(-2) = 2$.

Properties of Zero

Let a and b be real numbers, variables, or algebraic expressions.

1. $a + 0 = a$ and $a - 0 = a$ **2.** $a \cdot 0 = 0$

3. $\dfrac{0}{a} = 0, \quad a \neq 0$ **4.** $\dfrac{a}{0}$ is undefined.

5. Zero-Factor Property: If $ab = 0$, then $a = 0$ or $b = 0$.

STUDY TIP

The "or" in the Zero-Factor Property includes the possibility that either or both factors may be zero. This is an **inclusive or,** and it is the way the word "or" is generally used in mathematics.

Properties and Operations of Fractions

Let a, b, c, and d be real numbers, variables, or algebraic expressions such that $b \neq 0$ and $d \neq 0$.

1. Equivalent Fractions: $\dfrac{a}{b} = \dfrac{c}{d}$ if and only if $ad = bc$.

2. Rules of Signs: $-\dfrac{a}{b} = \dfrac{-a}{b} = \dfrac{a}{-b}$ and $\dfrac{-a}{-b} = \dfrac{a}{b}$

3. Generate Equivalent Fractions: $\dfrac{a}{b} = \dfrac{ac}{bc}, \quad c \neq 0$

4. Add or Subtract with Like Denominators: $\dfrac{a}{b} \pm \dfrac{c}{b} = \dfrac{a \pm c}{b}$

5. Add or Subtract with Unlike Denominators: $\dfrac{a}{b} \pm \dfrac{c}{d} = \dfrac{ad \pm bc}{bd}$

6. Multiply Fractions: $\dfrac{a}{b} \cdot \dfrac{c}{d} = \dfrac{ac}{bd}$

7. Divide Fractions: $\dfrac{a}{b} \div \dfrac{c}{d} = \dfrac{a}{b} \cdot \dfrac{d}{c} = \dfrac{ad}{bc}, \quad c \neq 0$

Example 5   Properties and Operations of Fractions

a. $\dfrac{x}{3} + \dfrac{2x}{5} = \dfrac{5 \cdot x + 3 \cdot 2x}{15} = \dfrac{11x}{15}$ Add fractions with unlike denominators.

b. $\dfrac{7}{x} \div \dfrac{3}{2} = \dfrac{7}{x} \cdot \dfrac{2}{3} = \dfrac{14}{3x}$ Divide fractions.

✓ *Checkpoint* Now try Exercise 101.

STUDY TIP

In Property 1 of fractions, the phrase "if and only if" implies two statements. One statement is: If $a/b = c/d$, then $ad = bc$. The other statement is: If $ad = bc$, where $b \neq 0$ and $d \neq 0$, then $a/b = c/d$.

If a, b, and c are integers such that $ab = c$, then a and b are **factors** or **divisors** of c. A **prime number** is an integer that has exactly two positive factors: itself and 1. For example, 2, 3, 5, 7, and 11 are prime numbers. The numbers 4, 6, 8, 9, and 10 are **composite** because they can be written as the product of two or more prime numbers. The number 1 is neither prime nor composite. The **Fundamental Theorem of Arithmetic** states that every positive integer greater than 1 can be written as the product of prime numbers. For instance, the **prime factorization** of 24 is $24 = 2 \cdot 2 \cdot 2 \cdot 3$.

P.1 Exercises

Vocabulary Check

Fill in the blanks.

1. A real number is _____ if it can be written as the ratio $\frac{p}{q}$ of two integers, where $q \neq 0$.

2. _____ numbers have infinite nonrepeating decimal representations.

3. The distance between a point on the real number line and the origin is the _____ of the real number.

4. Numbers that can be written as the product of two or more prime numbers are called _____ numbers.

5. Integers that have exactly two positive factors, the integer itself and 1, are called _____ numbers.

6. An algebraic expression is a combination of letters called _____ and real numbers called _____ .

7. The _____ of an algebraic expression are those parts separated by addition.

8. The numerical factor of a variable term is the _____ of the variable term.

9. The _____ states: If $ab = 0$, then $a = 0$ or $b = 0$.

In Exercises 1–6, determine which numbers are (a) natural numbers, (b) whole numbers, (c) integers, (d) rational numbers, and (e) irrational numbers.

1. $\left\{ -9, -\frac{7}{2}, 5, \frac{2}{3}, \sqrt{2}, 0, 1, -4, -1 \right\}$

2. $\left\{ \sqrt{5}, -7, -\frac{7}{3}, 0, 3.12, \frac{5}{4}, -2, -8, 3 \right\}$

3. $\{2.01, 0.666\ldots, -13, 0.010110111\ldots, 1, -10, 20\}$

4. $\{2.3030030003\ldots, 0.7575, -4.63, \sqrt{10}, -2, 0.03, -10\}$

5. $\left\{ -\pi, -\frac{1}{3}, \frac{6}{3}, \frac{1}{2}\sqrt{2}, -7.5, -2, 3, -3 \right\}$

6. $\left\{ 25, -17, -\frac{12}{5}, \sqrt{9}, 3.12, \frac{1}{2}\pi, 6, -4, 18 \right\}$

In Exercises 7–12, use a calculator to find the decimal form of the rational number. If it is a nonterminating decimal, write the repeating pattern.

7. $\frac{5}{8}$

8. $\frac{17}{4}$

9. $\frac{41}{333}$

10. $\frac{6}{11}$

11. $-\frac{100}{11}$

12. $-\frac{218}{33}$

In Exercises 13–16, use a graphing utility to rewrite the rational number as the ratio of two integers.

13. $4.\overline{6}$

14. $12.\overline{3}$

15. 6.5

16. $-1.8\overline{3}$

In Exercises 17 and 18, approximate the numbers and place the correct inequality symbol (< or >) between them.

17.

18.

In Exercises 19–24, plot the two real numbers on the real number line. Then place the correct inequality symbol (< or >) between them.

19. $-4, -8$

20. $-3.5, 1$

21. $\frac{3}{2}, 7$

22. $1, \frac{16}{3}$

23. $\frac{5}{6}, \frac{2}{3}$

24. $-\frac{8}{7}, -\frac{3}{7}$

In Exercises 25–32, (a) verbally describe the subset of real numbers represented by the inequality, (b) sketch the subset on the real number line, and (c) state whether the interval is bounded or unbounded.

25. $x \leq 5$

26. $x > 3$

27. $x < 0$

28. $x \geq 4$

29. $-2 < x < 2$

30. $0 \leq x \leq 5$

31. $-1 \leq x < 0$

32. $0 < x \leq 6$

In Exercises 33–38, use inequality and interval notation to describe the set.

33. x is negative.   **34.** z is at least 10.

35. y is nonnegative.   **36.** y is no more than 25.

37. p is less than 9 but no less than -1.

38. The annual rate of inflation r is expected to be at least 2.5%, but no more than 5%.

In Exercises 39–42, give a verbal description of the interval.

39. $(-6, \infty)$ **40.** $(-\infty, 4]$

41. $(-\infty, 2]$ **42.** $[1, \infty)$

In Exercises 43–48, evaluate the expression.

43. $|-10|$ **44.** $|0|$

45. $-3|-3|$ **46.** $|-1| - |-2|$

47. $\dfrac{|x + 2|}{x + 2}$ **48.** $\dfrac{|x - 1|}{x - 1}$

In Exercises 49–54, place the correct symbol ($<$, $>$, or $=$) between the pair of real numbers.

49. $|-3|$ ▢ $-|-3|$ **50.** $|-4|$ ▢ $|4|$

51. -5 ▢ $-|5|$ **52.** $-|-6|$ ▢ $|-6|$

53. $-|-2|$ ▢ $-|2|$ **54.** $-(-2)$ ▢ -2

In Exercises 55–60, find the distance between a and b.

55. $a = 126, b = 75$ **56.** $a = -126, b = -75$

57. $a = -\frac{5}{2}, b = 0$ **58.** $a = \frac{1}{4}, b = \frac{11}{4}$

59. $a = \frac{16}{5}, b = \frac{112}{75}$ **60.** $a = 9.34, b = -5.65$

In Exercises 61–66, use absolute value notation to describe the situation.

61. The distance between x and 5 is no more than 3.

62. The distance between x and -10 is at least 6.

63. y is at least six units from 0.

64. y is at most two units from a.

65. While traveling on the Pennsylvania Turnpike, you pass milepost 57 near Pittsburgh, then milepost 236 near Gettysburg. How many miles do you travel during that time period?

66. The temperature in Bismarck, North Dakota was $60°$ at noon, then $23°$ at midnight. What was the change in temperature over the 12-hour period?

Budget Variance   **In Exercises 67–70, the accounting department of a company is checking to determine whether the actual expenses of a department differ from the budgeted expenses by more than \$500 or by more than 5%. Fill in the missing parts of the table, and determine whether the actual expense passes the "budget variance test."**

	Budgeted Expense, b	Actual Expense, a	$|a - b|$	$0.05b$
67. Wages	\$112,700	\$113,356	▢	▢
68. Utilities	\$9400	\$9772	▢	▢
69. Taxes	\$37,640	\$37,335	▢	▢
70. Insurance	\$2575	\$2613	▢	▢

Federal Deficit   **In Exercises 71–76, use the bar graph, which shows the receipts of the federal government (in billions of dollars) for selected years from 1960 through 2002. In each exercise you are given the expenditures of the federal government. Find the magnitude of the surplus or deficit for the year.**
(Source: U.S. Office of Management and Budget)

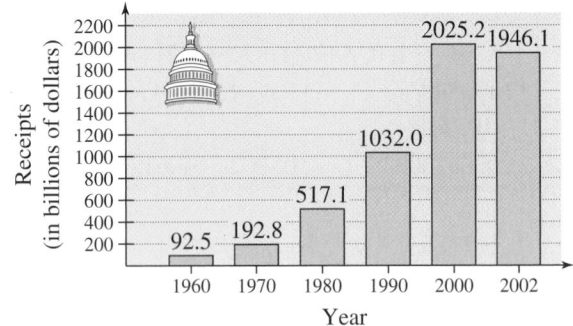

	Receipts	Expenditures	$|$Receipts $-$ Expenditures$|$
71. 1960	▢	\$92.2 billion	▢
72. 1970	▢	\$195.6 billion	▢
73. 1980	▢	\$590.9 billion	▢
74. 1990	▢	\$1253.2 billion	▢
75. 2000	▢	\$1788.8 billion	▢
76. 2002	▢	\$2052.3 billion	▢

In Exercises 77–82, identify the terms. Then identify the coefficients of the variable terms of the expression.

77. $7x + 4$ **78.** $2x - 9$

79. $\sqrt{3}x^2 - 8x - 11$ **80.** $7\sqrt{5}x^2 + 3$

81. $4x^3 + \dfrac{x}{2} - 5$

82. $3x^4 + \dfrac{2x^3}{5}$

In Exercises 83–86, evaluate the expression for each value of x. (If not possible, state the reason.)

Expression	Values

83. $4x - 6$ (a) $x = -1$ (b) $x = 0$

84. $9 - 7x$ (a) $x = -3$ (b) $x = 3$

85. $-x^2 + 5x - 4$ (a) $x = -1$ (b) $x = 1$

86. $\dfrac{x}{x + 2}$ (a) $x = 2$ (b) $x = -2$

In Exercises 87–94, identify the rule(s) of algebra illustrated by the statement.

87. $x + 9 = 9 + x$

88. $2\left(\frac{1}{2}\right) = 1$

89. $\dfrac{1}{h + 6}(h + 6) = 1, \quad h \neq -6$

90. $(x + 3) - (x + 3) = 0$

91. $2(x + 3) = 2x + 6$

92. $(z - 2) + 0 = z - 2$

93. $x + (y + 10) = (x + y) + 10$

94. $\frac{1}{7}(7 \cdot 12) = \left(\frac{1}{7} \cdot 7\right)12 = 1 \cdot 12 = 12$

In Exercises 95–104, perform the operations. (Write fractional answers in simplest form.)

95. $\frac{3}{16} + \frac{5}{16}$

96. $\frac{6}{7} - \frac{4}{7}$

97. $\frac{5}{8} - \frac{5}{12} + \frac{1}{6}$

98. $\frac{10}{11} + \frac{6}{33} - \frac{13}{66}$

99. $\dfrac{x}{6} + \dfrac{3x}{4}$

100. $\dfrac{2x}{5} + \dfrac{x}{10}$

101. $\dfrac{12}{x} \div \dfrac{1}{8}$

102. $\dfrac{11}{x} \div \dfrac{3}{4}$

103. $\left(\frac{2}{5} \div 4\right) - \left(4 \cdot \frac{3}{8}\right)$

104. $\left(\frac{3}{5} \div 3\right) - \left(6 \cdot \frac{4}{8}\right)$

In Exercises 105–110, use a calculator to evaluate the expression. (Round your answer to two decimal places.)

105. $14\left(-3 + \frac{3}{7}\right)$

106. $3\left(-\frac{5}{12} + \frac{3}{8}\right)$

107. $\dfrac{11.46 - 5.37}{3.91}$

108. $\dfrac{12.24 - 8.4}{2.5}$

109. $\dfrac{\frac{2}{3}(-2 - 6)}{-\frac{2}{5}}$

110. $\dfrac{\frac{1}{5}(-8 - 9)}{-\frac{1}{3}}$

111. (a) Use a calculator to complete the table.

n	1	0.5	0.01	0.0001	0.000001
$5/n$					

    (b) Use the result from part (a) to make a conjecture about the value of $5/n$ as n approaches 0.

112. (a) Use a calculator to complete the table.

n	1	10	100	10,000	100,000
$5/n$					

    (b) Use the result from part (a) to make a conjecture about the value of $5/n$ as n increases without bound.

Synthesis

True or False? In Exercises 113 and 114, determine whether the statement is true or false. Justify your answer.

113. Let $a > b$, then $\dfrac{1}{a} > \dfrac{1}{b}$, where $a \neq 0$ and $b \neq 0$.

114. Because $\dfrac{a + b}{c} = \dfrac{a}{c} + \dfrac{b}{c}$, then $\dfrac{c}{a + b} = \dfrac{c}{a} + \dfrac{c}{b}$.

In Exercises 115 and 116, use the real numbers A, B, and C shown on the number line. Determine the sign of each expression.

115. (a) $-A$

    (b) $B - A$

116. (a) $-C$

    (b) $A - C$

117. **Exploration** Consider $|u + v|$ and $|u| + |v|$.

    (a) Are the values of the expressions always equal? If not, under what conditions are they unequal?

    (b) If the two expressions are not equal for certain values of u and v, is one of the expressions always greater than the other? Explain.

118. **Think About It** Is there a difference between saying that a real number is positive and saying that a real number is nonnegative? Explain.

119. **Writing** Describe the differences among the sets of whole numbers, natural numbers, integers, rational numbers, and irrational numbers.

P.2   Exponents and Radicals

Integer Exponents

Repeated *multiplication* can be written in **exponential form.**

Repeated Multiplication	Exponential Form
$a \cdot a \cdot a \cdot a \cdot a$	a^5
$(-4)(-4)(-4)$	$(-4)^3$
$(2x)(2x)(2x)(2x)$	$(2x)^4$

In general, if a is a real number, variable, or algebraic expression and n is a positive integer, then

$$a^n = \underbrace{a \cdot a \cdot a \cdots a}_{n \text{ factors}}$$

where n is the **exponent** and a is the **base.** The expression a^n is read "a to the nth **power.**" An exponent can be negative as well. Property 3 below shows how to use a negative exponent.

Properties of Exponents

Let a and b be real numbers, variables, or algebraic expressions, and let m and n be integers. (All denominators and bases are nonzero.)

Property	Example
1. $a^m a^n = a^{m+n}$	$3^2 \cdot 3^4 = 3^{2+4} = 3^6 = 729$
2. $\dfrac{a^m}{a^n} = a^{m-n}$	$\dfrac{x^7}{x^4} = x^{7-4} = x^3$
3. $a^{-n} = \dfrac{1}{a^n} = \left(\dfrac{1}{a}\right)^n$	$y^{-4} = \dfrac{1}{y^4} = \left(\dfrac{1}{y}\right)^4$
4. $a^0 = 1, \quad a \neq 0$	$(x^2 + 1)^0 = 1$
5. $(ab)^m = a^m b^m$	$(5x)^3 = 5^3 x^3 = 125x^3$
6. $(a^m)^n = a^{mn}$	$(y^3)^{-4} = y^{3(-4)} = y^{-12} = \dfrac{1}{y^{12}}$
7. $\left(\dfrac{a}{b}\right)^m = \dfrac{a^m}{b^m}$	$\left(\dfrac{2}{x}\right)^3 = \dfrac{2^3}{x^3} = \dfrac{8}{x^3}$
8. $\lvert a^2 \rvert = \lvert a \rvert^2 = a^2$	$\lvert (-2)^2 \rvert = \lvert -2 \rvert^2 = 2^2 = 4$

It is important to recognize the difference between expressions such as $(-2)^4$ and -2^4. In $(-2)^4$, the parentheses indicate that the exponent applies to the negative sign as well as to the 2, but in $-2^4 = -(2^4)$, the exponent applies only to the 2. So, $(-2)^4 = 16$, whereas $-2^4 = -16$. It is also important to know when to use parentheses when evaluating exponential expressions using a graphing calculator. Figure P.9 shows that a graphing calculator follows the order of operations.

What you should learn

- Use properties of exponents.
- Use scientific notation to represent real numbers.
- Use properties of radicals.
- Simplify and combine radicals.
- Rationalize denominators and numerators.
- Use properties of rational exponents.

Why you should learn it

Real numbers and algebraic expressions are often written with exponents and radicals. For instance, in Exercise 93 on page 23, you will use an expression involving a radical to find the size of a particle that can be carried by a stream moving at a certain velocity.

SuperStock

```
(-2)^4
              16
-2^4
             -16
```

Figure P.9

The properties of exponents listed on the previous page apply to *all* integers *m* and *n*, not just positive integers. For instance, by Property 2, you can write

$$\frac{3^4}{3^{-5}} = 3^{4-(-5)} = 3^{4+5} = 3^9.$$

Example 1   Using Properties of Exponents

a. $(-3ab^4)(4ab^{-3}) = -12(a)(a)(b^4)(b^{-3}) = -12a^2b$

b. $(2xy^2)^3 = 2^3(x)^3(y^2)^3 = 8x^3y^6$

c. $3a(-4a^2)^0 = 3a(1) = 3a, \qquad a \neq 0$

✓ *Checkpoint* Now try Exercise 15.

Example 2   Rewriting with Positive Exponents

a. $x^{-1} = \dfrac{1}{x}$ Property 3

b. $\dfrac{1}{3x^{-2}} = \dfrac{1(x^2)}{3} = \dfrac{x^2}{3}$ The exponent -2 does not apply to 3.

c. $\dfrac{1}{(3x)^{-2}} = (3x)^2 = 9x^2$ The exponent -2 does apply to 3.

d. $\dfrac{12a^3b^{-4}}{4a^{-2}b} = \dfrac{12a^3 \cdot a^2}{4b \cdot b^4} = \dfrac{3a^5}{b^5}$ Properties 3 and 1

e. $\left(\dfrac{3x^2}{y}\right)^{-2} = \dfrac{3^{-2}(x^2)^{-2}}{y^{-2}}$ Properties 5 and 7

$\phantom{\left(\dfrac{3x^2}{y}\right)^{-2}} = \dfrac{3^{-2}x^{-4}}{y^{-2}}$ Property 6

$\phantom{\left(\dfrac{3x^2}{y}\right)^{-2}} = \dfrac{y^2}{3^2x^4} = \dfrac{y^2}{9x^4}$ Property 3, and simplify.

✓ *Checkpoint* Now try Exercise 19.

STUDY TIP

Rarely in algebra is there only one way to solve a problem. Don't be concerned if the steps you use to solve a problem are not exactly the same as the steps presented in this text. The important thing is to use steps that you understand *and*, of course, that are justified by the rules of algebra. For instance, you might prefer the following steps for Example 2(e).

$$\left(\frac{3x^2}{y}\right)^{-2} = \left(\frac{y}{3x^2}\right)^{2} = \frac{y^2}{9x^4}$$

Example 3   Calculators and Exponents

Expression	*Graphing Calculator Keystrokes*	*Display*
a. $3^{-2} + 4^{-1}$	3 ^ (−) 2 + 4 ^ (−) 1 ENTER	.3611111111
b. $\dfrac{3^5 + 1}{3^5 - 1}$	(3 ^ 5 + 1) ÷	
	(3 ^ 5 − 1) ENTER	1.008264463

✓ *Checkpoint* Now try Exercise 23.

TECHNOLOGY TIP   The graphing calculator keystrokes given in this text may not be the same as the keystrokes for your graphing calculator. Be sure you are familiar with the use of the keys on your own calculator.

Scientific Notation

Exponents provide an efficient way of writing and computing with very large (or very small) numbers. For instance, there are about 359 billion billion gallons of water on Earth—that is, 359 followed by 18 zeros.

359,000,000,000,000,000,000

It is convenient to write such numbers in **scientific notation.** This notation has the form $\pm c \times 10^n$, where $1 \le c < 10$ and n is an integer. So, the number of gallons of water on Earth can be written in scientific notation as

$3.59 \times 100,000,000,000,000,000,000 = 3.59 \times 10^{20}.$

The *positive* exponent 20 indicates that the number is *large* (10 or more) and that the decimal point has been moved 20 places. A *negative* exponent indicates that the number is *small* (less than 1). For instance, the mass (in grams) of one electron is approximately

$9.0 \times 10^{-28} = 0.00000000000000000000000000009.$

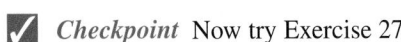

28 decimal places

Example 4   Scientific Notation

a. $1.345 \times 10^2 = 134.5$ **b.** $0.0000782 = 7.82 \times 10^{-5}$

c. $-9.36 \times 10^{-6} = -0.00000936$ **d.** $836,100,000 = 8.361 \times 10^8$

✓ *Checkpoint* Now try Exercise 27.

TECHNOLOGY TIP   Most calculators automatically switch to scientific notation when they are showing large or small numbers that exceed the display range. Try evaluating $86,500,000 \times 6000$. If your calculator follows standard conventions, its display should be

| 5.19 11 | or | 5.19 E 11 |

which is 5.19×10^{11}.

Example 5   Using Scientific Notation with a Calculator

Use a calculator to evaluate $65,000 \times 3,400,000,000$.

Solution

Because $65,000 = 6.5 \times 10^4$ and $3,400,000,000 = 3.4 \times 10^9$, you can multiply the two numbers using the following graphing calculator keystrokes.

6.5 [EE] 4 [×] 3.4 [EE] 9 [ENTER]

After entering these keystrokes, the calculator display should read [2.21 E 14].
So, the product of the two numbers is

$(6.5 \times 10^4)(3.4 \times 10^9) = 2.21 \times 10^{14} = 221,000,000,000,000.$

✓ *Checkpoint* Now try Exercise 35.

Radicals and Their Properties

A **square root** of a number is one of its two equal factors. For example, 5 is a square root of 25 because 5 is one of the two equal factors of $25 = 5 \cdot 5$. In a similar way, a **cube root** of a number is one of its three equal factors, as in $125 = 5^3$.

Definition of the *n*th Root of a Number

Let a and b be real numbers and let $n \geq 2$ be a positive integer. If

$$a = b^n$$

then b is an ***n*th root of *a*.** If $n = 2$, the root is a **square root.** If $n = 3$, the root is a **cube root.**

Some numbers have more than one *n*th root. For example, both 5 and -5 are square roots of 25. The *principal square root* of 25, written as $\sqrt{25}$, is the positive root, 5. The **principal *n*th root** of a number is defined as follows.

Principal *n*th Root of a Number

Let a be a real number that has at least one *n*th root. The **principal *n*th root of *a*** is the *n*th root that has the same sign as a. It is denoted by a **radical symbol**

$$\sqrt[n]{a}.$$ Principal *n*th root

The positive integer n is the **index** of the radical, and the number a is the **radicand.** If $n = 2$, omit the index and write $\sqrt{a}$ rather than $\sqrt[2]{a}$. (The plural of index is *indices*.)

A common misunderstanding is that the square root sign implies both negative and positive roots. This is not correct. The square root sign implies only a positive root. When a negative root is needed, you must use the negative sign with the square root sign.

Incorrect: $\sqrt{4} = \pm 2$ Correct: $-\sqrt{4} = -2$ and $\sqrt{4} = 2$

Example 6   Evaluating Expressions Involving Radicals

a. $\sqrt{36} = 6$ because $6^2 = 36$.

b. $-\sqrt{36} = -6$ because $-\left(\sqrt{36}\right) = -\left(\sqrt{6^2}\right) = -(6) = -6$.

c. $\sqrt[3]{\dfrac{125}{64}} = \dfrac{5}{4}$ because $\left(\dfrac{5}{4}\right)^3 = \dfrac{5^3}{4^3} = \dfrac{125}{64}$.

d. $\sqrt[5]{-32} = -2$ because $(-2)^5 = -32$.

e. $\sqrt[4]{-81}$ is not a real number because there is no real number that can be raised to the fourth power to produce -81.

 *Checkpoint* Now try Exercise 41.

Here are some generalizations about the *n*th roots of a real number.

Generalizations About *n*th Roots of Real Numbers

Real Number a	Integer n	Root(s) of a	Example
$a > 0$	$n > 0$, n is even.	$\sqrt[n]{a},\ -\sqrt[n]{a}$	$\sqrt[4]{81} = 3,\ -\sqrt[4]{81} = -3$
$a > 0$ or $a < 0$	n is odd.	$\sqrt[n]{a}$	$\sqrt[3]{-8} = -2$
$a < 0$	n is even.	No real roots	$\sqrt{-4}$ is not a real number.
$a = 0$	n is even or odd.	$\sqrt[n]{0} = 0$	$\sqrt[5]{0} = 0$

Integers such as 1, 4, 9, 16, 25, and 36 are called **perfect squares** because they have integer square roots. Similarly, integers such as 1, 8, 27, 64, and 125 are called **perfect cubes** because they have integer cube roots.

Properties of Radicals

Let a and b be real numbers, variables, or algebraic expressions such that the indicated roots are real numbers, and let m and n be positive integers.

Property	*Example*
1. $\sqrt[n]{a^m} = \left(\sqrt[n]{a}\right)^m$	$\sqrt[3]{8^2} = \left(\sqrt[3]{8}\right)^2 = (2)^2 = 4$
2. $\sqrt[n]{a} \cdot \sqrt[n]{b} = \sqrt[n]{ab}$	$\sqrt{5} \cdot \sqrt{7} = \sqrt{5 \cdot 7} = \sqrt{35}$
3. $\dfrac{\sqrt[n]{a}}{\sqrt[n]{b}} = \sqrt[n]{\dfrac{a}{b}}, \ b \neq 0$	$\dfrac{\sqrt[4]{27}}{\sqrt[4]{9}} = \sqrt[4]{\dfrac{27}{9}} = \sqrt[4]{3}$
4. $\sqrt[m]{\sqrt[n]{a}} = \sqrt[mn]{a}$	$\sqrt[3]{\sqrt{10}} = \sqrt[6]{10}$
5. $\left(\sqrt[n]{a}\right)^n = a$	$\left(\sqrt{3}\right)^2 = 3$
6. For n even, $\sqrt[n]{a^n} = |a|$.	$\sqrt{(-12)^2} = |-12| = 12$
For n odd, $\sqrt[n]{a^n} = a$.	$\sqrt[3]{(-12)^3} = -12$

Example 7   Using Properties of Radicals

Use the properties of radicals to simplify each expression.

a. $\sqrt{8} \cdot \sqrt{2}$ **b.** $\left(\sqrt[3]{5}\right)^3$ **c.** $\sqrt[3]{x^3}$ **d.** $\sqrt[6]{y^6}$

Solution

a. $\sqrt{8} \cdot \sqrt{2} = \sqrt{8 \cdot 2} = \sqrt{16} = 4$
b. $\left(\sqrt[3]{5}\right)^3 = 5$
c. $\sqrt[3]{x^3} = x$
d. $\sqrt[6]{y^6} = |y|$

✓ *Checkpoint* Now try Exercise 55.

TECHNOLOGY TIP

There are four methods of evaluating radicals on most graphing calculators. For square roots, you can use the *square root key* ☑. For cube roots, you can use the *cube root key* ∛ (or menu choice). For other roots, you can first convert the radical to exponential form and then use the *exponential key* ⌃ or you can use the *xth root key* ⌃ (or menu choice). For example, the screens below show you how to evaluate $\sqrt{36}$, $\sqrt[3]{-8}$, $\sqrt{16}$, and $\sqrt[5]{32}$ using one of the four methods described.

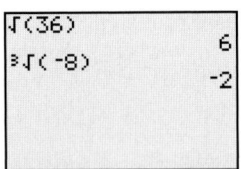

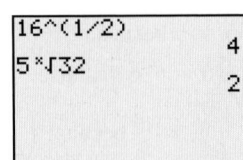

Simplifying Radicals

An expression involving radicals is in **simplest form** when the following conditions are satisfied.

1. All possible factors have been removed from the radical.

2. All fractions have radical-free denominators (accomplished by a process called *rationalizing the denominator*).

3. The index of the radical is reduced.

To simplify a radical, factor the radicand into factors whose exponents are multiples of the index. The roots of these factors are written outside the radical, and the "leftover" factors make up the new radicand.

Example 8   Simplifying Even Roots

Perfect   Leftover
4th power   factor

a. $\sqrt[4]{48} = \sqrt[4]{16 \cdot 3} = \sqrt[4]{2^4 \cdot 3} = 2\sqrt[4]{3}$

Perfect   Leftover
square   factor

b. $\sqrt{75x^3} = \sqrt{25x^2 \cdot 3x}$ Find largest square factor.

$= \sqrt{(5x)^2 \cdot 3x}$

$= 5x\sqrt{3x}$ Find root of perfect square.

c. $\sqrt[4]{(5x)^4} = |5x| = 5|x|$

✓ *Checkpoint* Now try Exercise 57(a).

> ### STUDY TIP
>
> When you simplify a radical, it is important that both expressions are defined for the same values of the variable. For instance, in Example 8(b), $\sqrt{75x^3}$ and $5x\sqrt{3x}$ are both defined only for nonnegative values of x. Similarly, in Example 8(c), $\sqrt[4]{(5x)^4}$ and $5|x|$ are both defined for all real values of x.

Example 9   Simplifying Odd Roots

Perfect   Leftover
cube   factor

a. $\sqrt[3]{24} = \sqrt[3]{8 \cdot 3} = \sqrt[3]{2^3 \cdot 3} = 2\sqrt[3]{3}$

Perfect   Leftover
cube   factor

b. $\sqrt[3]{-40x^6} = \sqrt[3]{(-8x^6) \cdot 5}$ Find largest cube factor.

$= \sqrt[3]{(-2x^2)^3 \cdot 5}$

$= -2x^2\sqrt[3]{5}$ Find root of perfect cube.

✓ *Checkpoint* Now try Exercise 57(b).

Radical expressions can be combined (added or subtracted) if they are **like radicals**—that is, if they have the same index and radicand. For instance, $\sqrt{2}$, $3\sqrt{2}$, and $\frac{1}{2}\sqrt{2}$ are like radicals, but $\sqrt{3}$ and $\sqrt{2}$ are unlike radicals. To determine whether two radicals can be combined, you should first simplify each radical.

Example 10 Combining Radicals

a. $2\sqrt{48} - 3\sqrt{27} = 2\sqrt{16 \cdot 3} - 3\sqrt{9 \cdot 3}$ Find square factors.

$\qquad\qquad\qquad = 8\sqrt{3} - 9\sqrt{3}$ Find square roots and multiply by coefficients.

$\qquad\qquad\qquad = (8 - 9)\sqrt{3}$ Combine like terms.

$\qquad\qquad\qquad = -\sqrt{3}$ Simplify.

b. $\sqrt[3]{16x} - \sqrt[3]{54x^4} = \sqrt[3]{8 \cdot 2x} - \sqrt[3]{27 \cdot x^3 \cdot 2x}$ Find cube factors.

$\qquad\qquad\qquad = 2\sqrt[3]{2x} - 3x\sqrt[3]{2x}$ Find cube roots.

$\qquad\qquad\qquad = (2 - 3x)\sqrt[3]{2x}$ Combine like terms.

✓ *Checkpoint* Now try Exercise 61.

Try using your calculator to check the result of Example 10(a). You should obtain -1.732050808, which is the same as the calculator's approximation for $-\sqrt{3}$.

Rationalizing Denominators and Numerators

To rationalize a denominator or numerator of the form $a - b\sqrt{m}$ or $a + b\sqrt{m}$, multiply both numerator and denominator by a **conjugate**: $a + b\sqrt{m}$ and $a - b\sqrt{m}$ are conjugates of each other. If $a = 0$, then the rationalizing factor for $\sqrt{m}$ is itself, $\sqrt{m}$.

Example 11 Rationalizing Denominators

Rationalize the denominator of each expression.

a. $\dfrac{5}{2\sqrt{3}}$ **b.** $\dfrac{2}{\sqrt[3]{5}}$

Solution

a. $\dfrac{5}{2\sqrt{3}} = \dfrac{5}{2\sqrt{3}} \cdot \dfrac{\sqrt{3}}{\sqrt{3}}$ $\sqrt{3}$ is rationalizing factor.

$\qquad = \dfrac{5\sqrt{3}}{2(3)}$ Multiply.

$\qquad = \dfrac{5\sqrt{3}}{6}$ Simplify.

b. $\dfrac{2}{\sqrt[3]{5}} = \dfrac{2}{\sqrt[3]{5}} \cdot \dfrac{\sqrt[3]{5^2}}{\sqrt[3]{5^2}}$ $\sqrt[3]{5^2}$ is rationalizing factor.

$\qquad = \dfrac{2\sqrt[3]{5^2}}{\sqrt[3]{5^3}} = \dfrac{2\sqrt[3]{25}}{5}$ Multiply and simplify.

✓ *Checkpoint* Now try Exercise 67.

STUDY TIP

Notice in Example 11(b) that the numerator and denominator are multiplied by $\sqrt[3]{5^2}$ to produce a perfect cube radicand.

Example 12   Rationalizing a Denominator with Two Terms

Rationalize the denominator of $\dfrac{2}{3 + \sqrt{7}}$.

Solution

$$\frac{2}{3 + \sqrt{7}} = \frac{2}{3 + \sqrt{7}} \cdot \frac{3 - \sqrt{7}}{3 - \sqrt{7}}$$

Multiply numerator and denominator by conjugate of denominator.

$$= \frac{2(3 - \sqrt{7})}{(3)^2 - (\sqrt{7})^2}$$

Find products. In denominator,
$(a + b)(a - b) = a^2 - ab + ab - b^2$
$= a^2 - b^2$.

$$= \frac{2(3 - \sqrt{7})}{2} = 3 - \sqrt{7}$$

Simplify and divide out common
factors.

✓ *Checkpoint* Now try Exercise 69.

Sometimes it is necessary to rationalize the numerator of expressions from calculus.

Example 13   Rationalizing a Numerator

Rationalize the numerator of $\dfrac{\sqrt{5} - \sqrt{7}}{2}$.

Solution

$$\frac{\sqrt{5} - \sqrt{7}}{2} = \frac{\sqrt{5} - \sqrt{7}}{2} \cdot \frac{\sqrt{5} + \sqrt{7}}{\sqrt{5} + \sqrt{7}}$$

Multiply numerator and denominator by conjugate of numerator.

$$= \frac{(\sqrt{5})^2 - (\sqrt{7})^2}{2(\sqrt{5} + \sqrt{7})}$$

Find products. In numerator,
$(a + b)(a - b) = a^2 - ab + ab - b^2$
$= a^2 - b^2$.

$$= \frac{-2}{2(\sqrt{5} + \sqrt{7})} = \frac{-1}{\sqrt{5} + \sqrt{7}}$$

Simplify and divide out common
factors.

✓ *Checkpoint* Now try Exercise 73.

STUDY TIP

Do not confuse the expression
$\sqrt{5} + \sqrt{7}$ with the expression
$\sqrt{5 + 7}$. In general, $\sqrt{x + y}$
does not equal $\sqrt{x} + \sqrt{y}$.
Similarly, $\sqrt{x^2 + y^2}$ does not
equal $x + y$.

Rational Exponents

Definition of Rational Exponents

If a is a real number and n is a positive integer such that the principal nth root of a exists, then $a^{1/n}$ is defined as

$a^{1/n} = \sqrt[n]{a}$ where $1/n$ is the **rational exponent** of a.

Moreover, if m is a positive integer that has no common factor with n, then

$a^{m/n} = (a^{1/n})^m = (\sqrt[n]{a})^m$ and $a^{m/n} = (a^m)^{1/n} = \sqrt[n]{a^m}$.

The symbol ∫ indicates an example or exercise that highlights algebraic techniques specifically used in calculus.

The numerator of a rational exponent denotes the *power* to which the base is raised, and the denominator denotes the *index* or the *root* to be taken.

$$b^{m/n} = \left(\sqrt[n]{b}\right)^m = \sqrt[n]{b^m}$$

Power

Index

When you are working with rational exponents, the properties of integer exponents still apply. For instance,

$$2^{1/2}2^{1/3} = 2^{(1/2)+(1/3)} = 2^{5/6}.$$

Example 14   Changing from Radical to Exponential Form

a. $\sqrt{3} = 3^{1/2}$

b. $\sqrt{(3xy)^5} = \sqrt[2]{(3xy)^5} = (3xy)^{(5/2)}$

c. $2x\sqrt[4]{x^3} = (2x)(x^{3/4}) = 2x^{1+(3/4)} = 2x^{7/4}$

✓ *Checkpoint* Now try Exercise 75.

Example 15   Changing from Exponential to Radical Form

a. $(x^2 + y^2)^{3/2} = \left(\sqrt{x^2 + y^2}\right)^3 = \sqrt{(x^2 + y^2)^3}$

b. $2y^{3/4}z^{1/4} = 2(y^3z)^{1/4} = 2\sqrt[4]{y^3z}$

c. $a^{-3/2} = \dfrac{1}{a^{3/2}} = \dfrac{1}{\sqrt{a^3}}$

d. $x^{0.2} = x^{1/5} = \sqrt[5]{x}$

✓ *Checkpoint* Now try Exercise 77.

Rational exponents are useful for evaluating roots of numbers on a calculator, reducing the index of a radical, and simplifying calculus expressions.

Example 16   Simplifying with Rational Exponents

a. $(-32)^{-4/5} = \left(\sqrt[5]{-32}\right)^{-4} = (-2)^{-4} = \dfrac{1}{(-2)^4} = \dfrac{1}{16}$

b. $(-5x^{5/3})(3x^{-3/4}) = -15x^{(5/3)-(3/4)} = -15x^{11/12}, \qquad x \neq 0$

c. $\sqrt[9]{a^3} = a^{3/9} = a^{1/3} = \sqrt[3]{a}$ Reduce index.

d. $\sqrt[3]{\sqrt{125}} = \sqrt[6]{125} = \sqrt[6]{(5)^3} = 5^{3/6} = 5^{1/2} = \sqrt{5}$

e. $(2x - 1)^{4/3}(2x - 1)^{-1/3} = (2x - 1)^{(4/3)-(1/3)} = 2x - 1, \qquad x \neq \dfrac{1}{2}$

✓ *Checkpoint* Now try Exercise 83.

P.2   Exercises

Vocabulary Check

Fill in the blanks.

1. In the exponential form a^n, n is the _____ and a is the _____ .

2. A convenient way of writing very large or very small numbers is called _____ .

3. One of the two equal factors of a number is called a _____ of the number.

4. The _____ of a number is the nth root that has the same sign as a, and is denoted by $\sqrt[n]{a}$.

5. In the radical form $\sqrt[n]{a}$, the positive integer n is called the _____ of the radical and the number a is called the _____ .

6. When an expression involving radicals has all possible factors removed, radical-free denominators, and a reduced index, it is in _____ .

7. The expressions $a + b\sqrt{m}$ and $a - b\sqrt{m}$ are _____ of each other.

8. The process used to create a radical-free denominator is known as _____ the denominator.

9. In the expression $b^{m/n}$, m denotes the _____ to which the base is raised and n denotes the _____ or root to be taken.

In Exercises 1–8, evaluate each expression.

1. (a) $4^2 \cdot 3$ (b) $3 \cdot 3^3$

2. (a) $\dfrac{5^5}{5^2}$ (b) $\dfrac{3^2}{3^4}$

3. (a) $(3^3)^2$ (b) -3^2

4. (a) $(2^3 \cdot 3^2)^2$ (b) $\left(-\frac{3}{5}\right)^3\left(\frac{5}{3}\right)^2$

5. (a) $\dfrac{3}{3^{-4}}$ (b) $24(-2)^{-5}$

6. (a) $\dfrac{4 \cdot 3^{-2}}{2^{-2} \cdot 3^{-1}}$ (b) $(-2)^0$

7. (a) $2^{-1} + 3^{-1}$ (b) $(2^{-1})^{-2}$

8. (a) $3^{-1} + 2^{-2}$ (b) $(3^{-2})^2$

In Exercises 9–14, evaluate the expression for the value of x.

Expression	Value
9. $7x^{-2}$	2
10. $6x^0 - (6x)^0$	7
11. $2x^3$	-3
12. $-3x^4$	-2
13. $4x^2$	$-\frac{1}{2}$
14. $5(-x)^3$	$\frac{1}{3}$

In Exercises 15–20, simplify each expression.

15. (a) $(-5z)^3$ (b) $5x^4(x^2)$

16. (a) $(3x)^2$ (b) $(4x^3)^2$

17. (a) $\dfrac{7x^2}{x^3}$ (b) $\dfrac{12(x + y)^3}{9(x + y)}$

18. (a) $\dfrac{r^4}{r^6}$ (b) $\left(\dfrac{4}{y}\right)^3\left(\dfrac{3}{y}\right)^4$

19. (a) $\left[(x^2y^{-2})^{-1}\right]^{-1}$ (b) $\left(\dfrac{a^{-2}}{b^{-2}}\right)\left(\dfrac{b}{a}\right)^3$

20. (a) $(2x^5)^0, \quad x \neq 0$ (b) $(5x^2z^6)^3(5x^2z^6)^{-3}$

In Exercises 21–24, use a calculator to evaluate the expression. (Round your answer to three decimal places.)

21. $(-4)^3(5^2)$ 22. $(8^{-4})(10^3)$

23. $\dfrac{3^6}{7^3}$ 24. $\dfrac{4^3}{3^{-4}}$

In Exercises 25–28, write the number in scientific notation.

25. Land area of Earth: 57,300,000 square miles

26. Light year: 9,460,000,000,000 kilometers

27. Relative density of hydrogen: 0.0000899 gram per cubic centimeter

28. One micron (millionth of a meter): 0.00003937 inch

In Exercises 29–32, write the number in decimal notation.

29. Worldwide Coca-Cola products daily consumption: 5.64×10^8 drinks   (Source: The Coca-Cola Company)

30. Interior temperature of sun: 1.5×10^7 degrees Celsius

31. Charge of electron: 1.6022×10^{-19} coulomb

32. Width of human hair: 9.0×10^{-5} meter

In Exercises 33 and 34, evaluate the expression without using a calculator.

33. $\sqrt{25 \times 10^8}$

34. $\sqrt[3]{8 \times 10^{15}}$

In Exercises 35–38, use a calculator to evaluate each expression. (Round your answer to three decimal places.)

35. (a) $(9.3 \times 10^6)^3 (6.1 \times 10^{-4})$

(b) $\dfrac{(2.414 \times 10^4)^6}{(1.68 \times 10^5)^5}$

36. (a) $750\left(1 + \dfrac{0.11}{365}\right)^{800}$

(b) $\dfrac{67,000,000 + 93,000,000}{0.0052}$

37. (a) $\sqrt{4.5 \times 10^9}$

(b) $\sqrt[3]{6.3 \times 10^4}$

38. (a) $(2.65 \times 10^{-4})^{1/3}$

(b) $\sqrt{9 \times 10^{-4}}$

In Exercises 39–48, evaluate the expression without using a calculator.

39. $\sqrt{121}$

40. $\sqrt{16}$

41. $-\sqrt[3]{-27}$

42. $\dfrac{\sqrt[4]{81}}{3}$

43. $\left(\sqrt[3]{-125}\right)^3$

44. $\sqrt[4]{562^4}$

45. $32^{-3/5}$

46. $\left(\frac{9}{4}\right)^{-1/2}$

47. $\left(-\dfrac{1}{64}\right)^{-1/3}$

48. $-\left(\dfrac{1}{125}\right)^{-4/3}$

In Exercises 49–54, use a calculator to approximate the number. (Round your answer to three decimal places.)

49. $\sqrt[5]{-27^3}$

50. $\sqrt[3]{45^2}$

51. $(3.4)^{2.5}$

52. $(6.1)^{-2.9}$

53. $(1.2^{-2})\sqrt{75} + 3\sqrt{8}$

54. $\dfrac{-5 + \sqrt{33}}{5}$

In Exercises 55 and 56, use the properties of radicals to simplify each expression.

55. (a) $\left(\sqrt[4]{3}\right)^4$ (b) $\sqrt[5]{96x^5}$

56. (a) $\sqrt{12} \cdot \sqrt{3}$ (b) $\sqrt[4]{x^4}$

In Exercises 57–62, simplify each expression.

57. (a) $\sqrt{54xy^4}$

(b) $\sqrt[3]{\dfrac{32a^2}{b^2}}$

58. (a) $\sqrt[3]{54}$

(b) $\sqrt{32x^3y^4}$

59. (a) $2\sqrt{50} + 12\sqrt{8}$

(b) $10\sqrt{32} - 6\sqrt{18}$

60. (a) $5\sqrt{x} - 3\sqrt{x}$

(b) $-2\sqrt{9y} + 10\sqrt{y}$

61. (a) $3\sqrt{x+1} + 10\sqrt{x+1}$

(b) $7\sqrt{80x} - 2\sqrt{125x}$

62. (a) $5\sqrt{10x^2} - \sqrt{90x^2}$

(b) $8\sqrt[3]{27x} - \frac{1}{2}\sqrt[3]{64x}$

In Exercises 63–66, complete the statement with <, =, or >.

63. $\sqrt{5} + \sqrt{3}$ ▢ $\sqrt{5 + 3}$

64. $\sqrt{\dfrac{3}{11}}$ ▢ $\dfrac{\sqrt{3}}{\sqrt{11}}$

65. 5 ▢ $\sqrt{3^2 + 2^2}$

66. 5 ▢ $\sqrt{3^2 + 4^2}$

In Exercises 67–70, rationalize the denominator of the expression. Then simplify your answer.

67. $\dfrac{1}{\sqrt{3}}$

68. $\dfrac{8}{\sqrt[3]{2}}$

69. $\dfrac{5}{\sqrt{14} - 2}$

70. $\dfrac{3}{\sqrt{5} + \sqrt{6}}$

f In Exercises 71–74, rationalize the numerator of the expression and simplify your answer.

71. $\dfrac{\sqrt{8}}{2}$

72. $\dfrac{\sqrt{2}}{3}$

73. $\dfrac{\sqrt{5} + \sqrt{3}}{3}$

74. $\dfrac{\sqrt{7} - 3}{4}$

In Exercises 75–82, fill in the missing form of the expression.

Radical Form	Rational Exponent Form
75. $\sqrt[3]{64}$	
76.	$-(144^{1/2})$
77.	$32^{1/5}$
78. $\sqrt[3]{614.125}$	
79. $\sqrt[3]{-216}$	
80.	$(-243)^{1/5}$
81. $\sqrt[4]{81^3}$	
82.	$16^{5/4}$

In Exercises 83–86, perform the operations and simplify.

83. $\dfrac{(2x^2)^{3/2}}{2^{1/2}x^4}$

84. $\dfrac{x^{4/3}y^{2/3}}{(xy)^{1/3}}$

85. $\dfrac{x^{-3} \cdot x^{1/2}}{x^{3/2} \cdot x^{-1}}$

86. $\dfrac{5^{-1/2} \cdot 5x^{5/2}}{(5x)^{3/2}}$

In Exercises 87 and 88, reduce the index of each radical and rewrite in radical form.

87. (a) $\sqrt[4]{3^2}$ (b) $\sqrt[6]{(x + 1)^4}$

88. (a) $\sqrt[6]{x^3}$ (b) $\sqrt[4]{(3x^2)^4}$

In Exercises 89 and 90, write each expression as a single radical. Then simplify your answer.

89. (a) $\sqrt{\sqrt{32}}$ (b) $\sqrt{\sqrt[4]{2x}}$

90. (a) $\sqrt{\sqrt{243(x + 1)}}$ (b) $\sqrt{\sqrt[3]{10a^7b}}$

91. *Period of a Pendulum* The period T (in seconds) of a pendulum is given by $T = 2\pi\sqrt{L/32}$, where L is the length of the pendulum (in feet). Find the period of a pendulum whose length is 2 feet.

92. *Mathematical Modeling* A funnel is filled with water to a height of h centimeters. The formula

$$t = 0.03[12^{5/2} - (12 - h)^{5/2}], \quad 0 \le h \le 12$$

represents the amount of time t (in seconds) it will take for the funnel to empty. Find t for $h = 7$ centimeters.

93. *Erosion* A stream of water moving at the rate of v feet per second can carry particles of size $0.03\sqrt{v}$ inches. Find the size of the particle that can be carried by a stream flowing at the rate of $\frac{3}{4}$ foot per second.

94. *Environment* There were 2.319×10^8 tons of municipal waste generated in 2000. Find the number of tons for each of the categories in the graph. (Source: Franklin Associates, Ltd.)

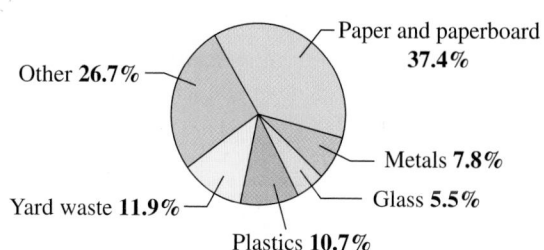

Synthesis

True or False? In Exercises 95 and 96, determine whether the statement is true or false. Justify your answer.

95. $\dfrac{x^{k+1}}{x} = x^k$

96. $(a^n)^k = a^{(n^k)}$

97. *Think About It* Verify that $a^0 = 1, a \ne 0$. (*Hint:* Use the property of exponents $a^m/a^n = a^{m-n}$.)

98. *Think About It* Is the real number 52.7×10^5 written in scientific notation? Explain.

99. *Exploration* List all possible digits that occur in the units place of the square of a positive integer. Use that list to determine whether $\sqrt{5233}$ is an integer.

100. *Think About It* Square the real number $2/\sqrt{5}$ and note that the radical is eliminated from the denominator. Is this equivalent to rationalizing the denominator? Why or why not?

The symbol f indicates an example or exercise that highlights algebraic techniques specifically used in calculus.

P.3 Polynomials and Factoring

Polynomials

An algebraic expression is a collection of variables and real numbers. The most common type of algebraic expression is the **polynomial.** Some examples are

$$2x + 5, \quad 3x^4 - 7x^2 + 2x + 4, \quad \text{and} \quad 5x^2y^2 - xy + 3.$$

The first two are *polynomials in x* and the third is a *polynomial in x and y.* The terms of a polynomial in x have the form ax^k, where a is the **coefficient** and k is the **degree** of the term. For instance, the polynomial

$$2x^3 - 5x^2 + 1 = 2x^3 + (-5)x^2 + (0)x + 1$$

has coefficients 2, -5, 0, and 1.

Definition of a Polynomial in x

Let $a_0, a_1, a_2, \ldots, a_n$ be *real numbers* and let n be a *nonnegative integer.* A **polynomial in x** is an expression of the form

$$a_n x^n + a_{n-1} x^{n-1} + \cdots + a_1 x + a_0$$

where $a_n \neq 0$. The polynomial is of **degree** n, a_n is the **leading coefficient**, and a_0 is the **constant term.**

In **standard form,** a polynomial in x is written with descending powers of x. Polynomials with one, two, and three terms are called **monomials, binomials,** and **trinomials,** respectively.

A polynomial that has all zero coefficients is called the **zero polynomial,** denoted by 0. No degree is assigned to this particular polynomial. For polynomials in more than one variable, the degree of a *term* is the sum of the exponents of the variables in the term. The degree of the *polynomial* is the highest degree of its terms. For instance, the degree of the polynomial $-2x^3y^6 + 4xy - x^7y^4$ is 11 because the sum of the exponents in the last term is the greatest. Expressions such as the following are not polynomials.

$$x^3 - \sqrt{3x} = x^3 - (3x)^{1/2} \qquad \text{The exponent 1/2 is not an integer.}$$

$$x^2 + 5x^{-1} \qquad \text{The exponent } -1 \text{ is not a nonnegative integer.}$$

Example 1 Writing Polynomials in Standard Form

	Polynomial	Standard Form	Degree
a.	$4x^2 - 5x^7 - 2 + 3x$	$-5x^7 + 4x^2 + 3x - 2$	7
b.	$4 - 9x^2$	$-9x^2 + 4$	2
c.	8	$8 \ (8 = 8x^0)$	0

✓ *Checkpoint* Now try Exercise 15.

Operations with Polynomials

You can add and subtract polynomials in much the same way you add and subtract real numbers. Simply add or subtract the *like terms* (terms having the same variables to the same powers) by adding their coefficients. For instance, $-3xy^2$ and $5xy^2$ are like terms and their sum is

$$-3xy^2 + 5xy^2 = (-3 + 5)xy^2 = 2xy^2.$$

Example 2   Sums and Differences of Polynomials

Perform the indicated operation.

a. $(5x^3 - 7x^2 - 3) + (x^3 + 2x^2 - x + 8)$

b. $(7x^4 - x^2 - 4x + 2) - (3x^4 - 4x^2 + 3x)$

Solution

a. $(5x^3 - 7x^2 - 3) + (x^3 + 2x^2 - x + 8)$

$\qquad = (5x^3 + x^3) + (-7x^2 + 2x^2) - x + (-3 + 8)$ Group like terms.

$\qquad = 6x^3 - 5x^2 - x + 5$ Combine like terms.

b. $(7x^4 - x^2 - 4x + 2) - (3x^4 - 4x^2 + 3x)$

$\qquad = 7x^4 - x^2 - 4x + 2 - 3x^4 + 4x^2 - 3x$ Distributive Property

$\qquad = (7x^4 - 3x^4) + (-x^2 + 4x^2) + (-4x - 3x) + 2$ Group like terms.

$\qquad = 4x^4 + 3x^2 - 7x + 2$ Combine like terms.

✓ *Checkpoint* Now try Exercise 23.

> **STUDY TIP**
>
> When a negative sign precedes an expression within parentheses, remember to distribute the negative sign to each term inside the parentheses.
>
> $-(x^2 - x + 3) = -x^2 + x - 3$

To find the product of two polynomials, use the left and right Distributive Properties.

Example 3   Multiplying Polynomials: The FOIL Method

$(3x - 2)(5x + 7) = 3x(5x + 7) - 2(5x + 7)$

$\qquad = (3x)(5x) + (3x)(7) - (2)(5x) - (2)(7)$

$\qquad = 15x^2 + 21x - 10x - 14$

Product of	Product of	Product of	Product of
First terms	**Outer terms**	**Inner terms**	**Last terms**

$\qquad = 15x^2 + 11x - 14$

Note that when using the **FOIL Method** (which can only be used to multiply two binomials), the outer (O) and inner (I) terms are like terms and can be combined into one term.

✓ *Checkpoint* Now try Exercise 39.

Example 4   The Product of Two Trinomials

Find the product of $4x^2 + x - 2$ and $-x^2 + 3x + 5$.

Solution

When multiplying two polynomials, be sure to multiply *each* term of one polynomial by *each* term of the other. A vertical format is helpful.

$$
\begin{array}{r}
4x^2 + x - 2 \\
\times \quad\quad\quad -x^2 + 3x + 5 \\
\hline
20x^2 + 5x - 10 \\
12x^3 + 3x^2 - 6x \\
-4x^4 - x^3 + 2x^2 \\
\hline
-4x^4 + 11x^3 + 25x^2 - x - 10
\end{array}
$$

Write in standard form.

Write in standard form.

$5(4x^2 + x - 2)$

$3x(4x^2 + x - 2)$

$-x^2(4x^2 + x - 2)$

Combine like terms.

✓ *Checkpoint* Now try Exercise 59.

Special Products

Special Products

Let u and v be real numbers, variables, or algebraic expressions.

Special Product	*Example*
Sum and Difference of Same Terms	
$(u + v)(u - v) = u^2 - v^2$	$(x + 4)(x - 4) = x^2 - 4^2 = x^2 - 16$
Square of a Binomial	
$(u + v)^2 = u^2 + 2uv + v^2$	$(x + 3)^2 = x^2 + 2(x)(3) + 3^2 = x^2 + 6x + 9$
$(u - v)^2 = u^2 - 2uv + v^2$	$(3x - 2)^2 = (3x)^2 - 2(3x)(2) + 2^2 = 9x^2 - 12x + 4$
Cube of a Binomial	
$(u + v)^3 = u^3 + 3u^2v + 3uv^2 + v^3$	$(x + 2)^3 = x^3 + 3x^2(2) + 3x(2^2) + 2^3 = x^3 + 6x^2 + 12x + 8$
$(u - v)^3 = u^3 - 3u^2v + 3uv^2 - v^3$	$(x - 1)^3 = x^3 - 3x^2(1) + 3x(1^2) - 1^3 = x^3 - 3x^2 + 3x - 1$

Example 5   The Product of Two Trinomials

Find the product of $x + y - 2$ and $x + y + 2$.

Solution

By grouping $x + y$ in parentheses, you can write the product of the trinomials as a special product.

$$
\begin{aligned}
(x + y - 2)(x + y + 2) &= [(x + y) - 2][(x + y) + 2] \\
&= (x + y)^2 - 2^2 = x^2 + 2xy + y^2 - 4
\end{aligned}
$$

✓ *Checkpoint* Now try Exercise 61.

Factoring

The process of writing a polynomial as a product is called **factoring.** It is an important tool for solving equations and for simplifying rational expressions.

Unless noted otherwise, when you are asked to factor a polynomial, you can assume that you are looking for factors with integer coefficients. If a polynomial cannot be factored using integer coefficients, it is **prime** or **irreducible over the integers.** For instance, the polynomial $x^2 - 3$ is irreducible over the integers. Over the real numbers, this polynomial can be factored as

$$x^2 - 3 = (x + \sqrt{3})(x - \sqrt{3}).$$

A polynomial is **completely factored** when each of its factors is prime. So,

$$x^3 - x^2 + 4x - 4 = (x - 1)(x^2 + 4) \qquad \text{Completely factored}$$

is completely factored, but

$$x^3 - x^2 - 4x + 4 = (x - 1)(x^2 - 4) \qquad \text{Not completely factored}$$

is not completely factored. Its complete factorization is

$$x^3 - x^2 - 4x + 4 = (x - 1)(x + 2)(x - 2).$$

The simplest type of factoring involves a polynomial that can be written as the product of a monomial and another polynomial. The technique used here is the Distributive Property, $a(b + c) = ab + ac$, in the *reverse* direction. For instance, the polynomial $5x^2 + 15x$ can be factored as follows.

$$5x^2 + 15x = 5x(x) + 5x(3) \qquad 5x \text{ is a common factor.}$$
$$= 5x(x + 3)$$

The first step in completely factoring a polynomial is to remove (factor out) any common factors, as shown in the next example.

Example 6   Removing Common Factors

Factor each expression.

a. $6x^3 - 4x$ **b.** $3x^4 + 9x^3 + 6x^2$ **c.** $(x - 2)(2x) + (x - 2)(3)$

Solution

a. $6x^3 - 4x = 2x(3x^2) - 2x(2) = 2x(3x^2 - 2)$ $2x$ is a common factor.

b. $3x^4 + 9x^3 + 6x^2 = 3x^2(x^2) + 3x^2(3x) + 3x^2(2)$ $3x^2$ is a common factor.

$$= 3x^2(x^2 + 3x + 2)$$

c. $(x - 2)(2x) + (x - 2)(3) = (x - 2)(2x + 3)$ $x - 2$ is a common factor.

✓ *Checkpoint* Now try Exercise 73.

Factoring Special Polynomial Forms

Some polynomials have special forms that arise from the special product forms on page 26. You should learn to recognize these forms so that you can factor such polynomials easily.

Factoring Special Polynomial Forms

Factored Form	*Example*

Difference of Two Squares

$u^2 - v^2 = (u + v)(u - v)$ $9x^2 - 4 = (3x)^2 - 2^2 = (3x + 2)(3x - 2)$

Perfect Square Trinomial

$u^2 + 2uv + v^2 = (u + v)^2$ $x^2 + 6x + 9 = x^2 + 2(x)(3) + 3^2 = (x + 3)^2$

$u^2 - 2uv + v^2 = (u - v)^2$ $x^2 - 6x + 9 = x^2 - 2(x)(3) + 3^2 = (x - 3)^2$

Sum or Difference of Two Cubes

$u^3 + v^3 = (u + v)(u^2 - uv + v^2)$ $x^3 + 8 = x^3 + 2^3 = (x + 2)(x^2 - 2x + 4)$

$u^3 - v^3 = (u - v)(u^2 + uv + v^2)$ $27x^3 - 1 = (3x)^3 - 1^3 = (3x - 1)(9x^2 + 3x + 1)$

One of the easiest special polynomial forms to factor is the difference of two squares. Think of this form as follows.

$$u^2 - v^2 = (u + v)(u - v)$$

Difference   Opposite signs

To recognize perfect square terms, look for coefficients that are squares of integers and variables raised to *even powers*.

Example 7   Removing a Common Factor First

$3 - 12x^2 = 3(1 - 4x^2)$ 3 is a common factor.

$\quad\quad\quad = 3[1^2 - (2x)^2]$ Difference of two squares

$\quad\quad\quad = 3(1 + 2x)(1 - 2x)$ Factored form

✓ *Checkpoint* Now try Exercise 77.

STUDY TIP

In Example 7, note that the first step in factoring a polynomial is to check for a common factor. Once the common factor is removed, it is often possible to recognize patterns that were not immediately obvious.

Example 8   Factoring the Difference of Two Squares

a. $(x + 2)^2 - y^2 = [(x + 2) + y][(x + 2) - y]$

$\quad\quad\quad\quad\quad\quad = (x + 2 + y)(x + 2 - y)$

b. $16x^4 - 81 = (4x^2)^2 - 9^2$ Difference of two squares

$\quad\quad\quad\quad = (4x^2 + 9)(4x^2 - 9)$

$\quad\quad\quad\quad = (4x^2 + 9)[(2x)^2 - 3^2]$ Difference of two squares

$\quad\quad\quad\quad = (4x^2 + 9)(2x + 3)(2x - 3)$ Factored form

✓ *Checkpoint* Now try Exercise 81.

A perfect square trinomial is the square of a binomial, as shown below.

$$u^2 + 2uv + v^2 = (u + v)^2 \quad \text{or} \quad u^2 - 2uv + v^2 = (u - v)^2$$

Like signs   Like signs

Note that the first and last terms are squares and the middle term is twice the product of u and v.

Example 9   Factoring Perfect Square Trinomials

Factor each trinomial.

a. $x^2 - 10x + 25$ **b.** $16x^2 + 8x + 1$

Solution

a. $x^2 - 10x + 25 = x^2 - 2(x)(5) + 5^2$ Rewrite in $u^2 - 2uv + v^2$ form.

$\qquad\qquad\qquad = (x - 5)^2$

b. $16x^2 + 8x + 1 = (4x)^2 + 2(4x)(1) + 1^2$ Rewrite in $u^2 + 2uv + v^2$ form.

$\qquad\qquad\qquad = (4x + 1)^2$

✓ *Checkpoint* Now try Exercise 87.

The next two formulas show the sums and differences of cubes. Pay special attention to the signs of the terms.

Like signs   Like signs

$$u^3 + v^3 = (u + v)(u^2 - uv + v^2) \quad u^3 - v^3 = (u - v)(u^2 + uv + v^2)$$

Unlike signs   Unlike signs

Exploration

Rewrite $u^6 - v^6$ as the difference of two squares. Then find a formula for completely factoring $u^6 - v^6$. Use your formula to completely factor $x^6 - 1$ and $x^6 - 64$.

Example 10   Factoring the Difference of Cubes

Factor $x^3 - 27$.

Solution

$\qquad x^3 - 27 = x^3 - 3^3$ Rewrite 27 as 3^3.

$\qquad\qquad\quad = (x - 3)(x^2 + 3x + 9)$ Factor.

✓ *Checkpoint* Now try Exercise 91.

Example 11   Factoring the Sum of Cubes

$3x^3 + 192 = 3(x^3 + 64)$ 3 is a common factor.

$\qquad\qquad = 3(x^3 + 4^3)$ Rewrite 64 as 4^3.

$\qquad\qquad = 3(x + 4)(x^2 - 4x + 16)$ Factor.

✓ *Checkpoint* Now try Exercise 93.

Trinomials with Binomial Factors

To factor a trinomial of the form $ax^2 + bx + c$, use the following pattern.

Factors of a

$$ax^2 + bx + c = (x +)(x +)$$

Factors of c

The goal is to find a combination of factors of a and c so that the outer and inner products add up to the middle term bx. For instance, in the trinomial $6x^2 + 17x + 5$, you can write all possible factorizations and determine which one has outer and inner products that add up to $17x$.

$(6x + 5)(x + 1),\ (6x + 1)(x + 5),\ (2x + 1)(3x + 5),\ (2x + 5)(3x + 1)$

You can see that $(2x + 5)(3x + 1)$ is the correct factorization because the outer (O) and inner (I) products add up to $17x$.

$$\overset{F}{}\quad\overset{O}{}\quad\overset{I}{}\quad\overset{L}{}\qquad\overset{O + I}{}$$

$$(2x + 5)(3x + 1) = 6x^2 + 2x + 15x + 5 = 6x^2 + 17x + 5.$$

Example 12   Factoring a Trinomial: Leading Coefficient Is 1

Factor $x^2 - 7x + 12$.

Solution

The possible factorizations are

$(x - 2)(x - 6),\quad (x - 1)(x - 12),\quad$ and $\quad (x - 3)(x - 4).$

Testing the middle term, you will find the correct factorization to be

$$x^2 - 7x + 12 = (x - 3)(x - 4). \qquad \text{O + I} = -4x + (-3x) = -7x$$

✓ *Checkpoint* Now try Exercise 103.

STUDY TIP

Factoring a trinomial can involve trial and error. However, once you have produced the factored form, it is an easy matter to check your answer. For instance, you can verify the factorization in Example 12 by multiplying out the expression $(x - 3)(x - 4)$ to see that you obtain the original trinomial, $x^2 - 7x + 12$.

Example 13   Factoring a Trinomial: Leading Coefficient Is Not 1

Factor $2x^2 + x - 15$.

Solution

The eight possible factorizations are as follows.

$(2x - 1)(x + 15),\ (2x + 1)(x - 15),\ (2x - 3)(x + 5),\ (2x + 3)(x - 5),$

$(2x - 5)(x + 3),\ (2x + 5)(x - 3),\ (2x - 15)(x + 1),\ (2x + 15)(x - 1)$

Testing the middle term, you will find the correct factorization to be

$$2x^2 + x - 15 = (2x - 5)(x + 3). \qquad \text{O + I} = 6x - 5x = x$$

✓ *Checkpoint* Now try Exercise 111.

Factoring by Grouping

Sometimes polynomials with more than three terms can be factored by a method called **factoring by grouping.**

Example 14   Factoring by Grouping

Use factoring by grouping to factor $x^3 - 2x^2 - 3x + 6$.

Solution

$$x^3 - 2x^2 - 3x + 6 = (x^3 - 2x^2) - (3x - 6) \quad \text{Group terms.}$$
$$= x^2(x - 2) - 3(x - 2) \quad \text{Factor groups.}$$
$$= (x - 2)(x^2 - 3) \quad (x - 2) \text{ is a common factor.}$$

✓ *Checkpoint* Now try Exercise 115.

Factoring a trinomial can involve quite a bit of trial and error. Some of this trial and error can be lessened by using factoring by grouping. The key to this method of factoring is knowing how to rewrite the middle term. In general, to factor a trinomial $ax^2 + bx + c$ by grouping, choose factors of the product ac that add up to b and use these factors to rewrite the middle term.

Example 15   Factoring a Trinomial by Grouping

Use factoring by grouping to factor $2x^2 + 5x - 3$.

Solution

In the trinomial $2x^2 + 5x - 3$, $a = 2$ and $c = -3$, which implies that the product ac is -6. Now, because -6 factors as $(6)(-1)$ and $6 - 1 = 5 = b$, rewrite the middle term as $5x = 6x - x$. This produces the following.

$$2x^2 + 5x - 3 = 2x^2 + 6x - x - 3 \quad \text{Rewrite middle term.}$$
$$= (2x^2 + 6x) - (x + 3) \quad \text{Group terms.}$$
$$= 2x(x + 3) - (x + 3) \quad \text{Factor groups.}$$
$$= (x + 3)(2x - 1) \quad (x + 3) \text{ is a common factor.}$$

So, the trinomial factors as $2x^2 + 5x - 3 = (x + 3)(2x - 1)$.

✓ *Checkpoint* Now try Exercise 117.

Guidelines for Factoring Polynomials

1. Factor out any common factors using the Distributive Property.

2. Factor according to one of the special polynomial forms.

3. Factor as $ax^2 + bx + c = (mx + r)(nx + s)$.

4. Factor by grouping.

P.3 Exercises

Vocabulary Check

Fill in the blanks.

1. For the polynomial $a_nx^n + a_{n-1}x^{n-1} + \cdots + a_1x + a_0$, the degree is _____ and the leading coefficient is _____ .

2. A polynomial that has all zero coefficients is called the _____ .

3. A polynomial with one term is called a _____ .

4. The letters in "FOIL" stand for the following.
   F _____ O _____ I _____ L _____

5. If a polynomial cannot be factored using integer coefficients, it is called _____ .

6. The polynomial $u^2 + 2uv + v^2$ is called a _____ .

In Exercises 1–6, match the polynomial with its description. [The polynomials are labeled (a), (b), (c), (d), (e), and (f).]

(a) $6x$ (b) $1 - 4x^3$

(c) $x^3 + 2x^2 - 4x + 1$ (d) 7

(e) $-3x^5 + 2x^3 + x$ (f) $\frac{3}{4}x^4 + x^2 + 14$

1. A polynomial of degree zero

2. A trinomial of degree five

3. A binomial with leading coefficient -4

4. A monomial of positive degree

5. A trinomial with leading coefficient $\frac{3}{4}$

6. A third-degree polynomial with leading coefficient 1

In Exercises 7–10, write a polynomial that fits the description. (There are many correct answers.)

7. A third-degree polynomial with leading coefficient -2

8. A fifth-degree polynomial with leading coefficient 8

9. A fourth-degree polynomial with a negative leading coefficient

10. A third-degree trinomial with an even leading coefficient

In Exercises 11–16, write the polynomial in standard form. Then identify the degree and leading coefficient of the polynomial.

11. $3x + 4x^2 + 2$ 12. $x^2 - 4 - 3x^4$

13. $1 + x^7$ 14. $-21x$

15. $1 - x + 6x^4 - 2x^5$ 16. $7 + 8x$

In Exercises 17–20, determine whether the expression is a polynomial. If so, write the polynomial in standard form.

17. $7x - 2x^3 + 10$ 18. $4x^3 + x - x^{-1}$

19. $\sqrt{x^2 - x^4}$ 20. $\dfrac{x^2 + 2x - 3}{6}$

In Exercises 21–36, perform the operations and write the result in standard form.

21. $(6x + 5) - (8x + 15)$

22. $(2x^2 + 1) - (x^2 - 2x + 1)$

23. $-(x^3 - 2) + (4x^3 - 2x)$

24. $-(5x^2 - 1) - (-3x^2 + 5)$

25. $(15x^2 - 6) - (-8.1x^3 - 14.7x^2 - 17)$

26. $(15.6x^4 - 18x - 19.4) - (13.9x^4 - 9.2x + 15)$

27. $3x(x^2 - 2x + 1)$ 28. $y^2(4y^2 + 2y - 3)$

29. $-5z(3z - 1)$ 30. $(-3x)(5x + 2)$

31. $(1 - x^3)(4x)$ 32. $-4x(3 - x^3)$

33. $(2.5x^2 + 5)(-3x)$ 34. $(2 - 3.5y)(4y^3)$

35. $-2x\left(\frac{1}{8}x + 3\right)$ 36. $6y\left(4 - \frac{3}{8}y\right)$

In Exercises 37–68, multiply or find the special product.

37. $(x + 3)(x + 4)$ 38. $(x - 5)(x + 10)$

39. $(3x - 5)(2x + 1)$ 40. $(7x - 2)(4x - 3)$

41. $(2x - 5y)^2$ 42. $(5 - 8x)^2$

43. $(x + 10)(x - 10)$ 44. $(2x + 3)(2x - 3)$

45. $(x + 2y)(x - 2y)$ 46. $(2x + 3y)(2x - 3y)$

47. $(2r^2 - 5)(2r^2 + 5)$

48. $(3a^3 - 4b^2)(3a^3 + 4b^2)$

49. $(x + 1)^3$ **50.** $(x - 2)^3$

51. $(2x - y)^3$ **52.** $(3x + 2y)^3$

53. $\left(\frac{1}{2}x - 5\right)^2$ **54.** $\left(\frac{3}{5}t + 4\right)^2$

55. $\left(\frac{1}{4}x - 3\right)\left(\frac{1}{4}x + 3\right)$ **56.** $\left(2x + \frac{1}{6}\right)\left(2x - \frac{1}{6}\right)$

57. $(2.4x + 3)^2$ **58.** $(1.8y - 5)^2$

59. $(-x^2 + x - 5)(3x^2 + 4x + 1)$

60. $(x^2 + 3x + 2)(2x^2 - x + 4)$

61. $[(m - 3) + n][(m - 3) - n]$

62. $[(x + y) + 1][(x + y) - 1]$

63. $[(x - 3) + y]^2$ **64.** $[(x + 1) - y]^2$

65. $5x(x + 1) - 3x(x + 1)$

66. $(2x - 1)(x + 3) + 3(x + 3)$

67. $(u + 2)(u - 2)(u^2 + 4)$

68. $(x + y)(x - y)(x^2 + y^2)$

In Exercises 69–74, factor out the common factor.

69. $2x + 8$ **70.** $5y - 30$

71. $2x^3 - 6x$ **72.** $4x^3 - 6x^2 + 12x$

73. $3x(x - 5) + 8(x - 5)$

74. $(5x - 4)^2 + (5x - 4)$

In Exercises 75–82, factor the difference of two squares.

75. $x^2 - 64$ **76.** $x^2 - 81$

77. $32y^2 - 18$ **78.** $4 - 36y^2$

79. $4x^2 - \frac{1}{9}$ **80.** $\frac{25}{36}y^2 - 49$

81. $(x - 1)^2 - 4$ **82.** $25 - (z + 5)^2$

In Exercises 83–90, factor the perfect square trinomial.

83. $x^2 - 4x + 4$ **84.** $x^2 + 10x + 25$

85. $x^2 + x + \frac{1}{4}$ **86.** $x^2 - \frac{4}{3}x + \frac{4}{9}$

87. $4t^2 + 4t + 1$ **88.** $9x^2 - 12x + 4$

89. $9t^2 + \frac{3}{2}t + \frac{1}{16}$ **90.** $4t^2 + \frac{8}{5}t + \frac{4}{25}$

In Exercises 91–100, factor the sum or difference of cubes.

91. $x^3 - 8$ **92.** $x^3 + 27$

93. $y^3 + 216$ **94.** $z^3 - 125$

95. $x^3 - \frac{8}{27}$ **96.** $x^3 + \frac{8}{125}$

97. $8x^3 - 1$ **98.** $27x^3 + 8$

99. $\frac{1}{8}x^3 + 1$ **100.** $\frac{27}{64}x^3 - 1$

In Exercises 101–114, factor the trinomial.

101. $x^2 + x - 2$ **102.** $x^2 + 5x + 6$

103. $s^2 - 5s + 6$ **104.** $t^2 - t - 6$

105. $20 - y - y^2$ **106.** $24 + 5z - z^2$

107. $3x^2 - 5x + 2$ **108.** $3x^2 + 13x - 10$

109. $2x^2 - x - 1$ **110.** $2x^2 - x - 21$

111. $5x^2 + 26x + 5$ **112.** $8x^2 - 45x - 18$

113. $-5u^2 - 13u + 6$ **114.** $-6x^2 + 23x + 4$

In Exercises 115–118, factor by grouping.

115. $x^3 - x^2 + 2x - 2$

116. $x^3 + 5x^2 - 5x - 25$

117. $6x^2 + x - 2$

118. $3x^2 + 10x + 8$

In Exercises 119–150, completely factor the expression.

119. $x^3 - 16x$ **120.** $12x^2 - 48$

121. $x^3 - x^2$ **122.** $6x^2 - 54$

123. $x^2 - 2x + 1$ **124.** $9x^2 - 6x + 1$

125. $1 - 4x + 4x^2$ **126.** $16 - 6x - x^2$

127. $2x^2 + 4x - 2x^3$ **128.** $7y^2 + 15y - 2y^3$

129. $9x^2 + 10x + 1$ **130.** $13x + 6 + 5x^2$

131. $\frac{1}{8}x^2 - \frac{1}{96}x - \frac{1}{16}$ **132.** $\frac{1}{81}x^2 + \frac{2}{9}x - 8$

133. $3x^3 + x^2 + 15x + 5$

134. $5 - x + 5x^2 - x^3$

135. $3u - 2u^2 + 6 - u^3$

136. $x^4 - 4x^3 + x^2 - 4x$

137. $25 - (z + 5)^2$ **138.** $(t - 1)^2 - 49$

139. $(x^2 + 1)^2 - 4x^2$ **140.** $(x^2 + 8)^2 - 36x^2$

141. $2t^3 - 16$ **142.** $5x^3 + 40$

143. $4x(2x - 1) + 2(2x - 1)^2$

144. $5(3 - 4x)^2 - 8(3 - 4x)(5x - 1)$

145. $2(x + 1)(x - 3)^2 - 3(x + 1)^2(x - 3)$

146. $7(3x + 2)^2(1 - x)^2 + (3x + 2)(1 - x)^3$

147. $7x(2)(x^2 + 1)(2x) - (x^2 + 1)^2(7)$

148. $3(x - 2)^2(x + 1)^4 + (x - 2)^3(4)(x + 1)^3$

149. $2x(x - 5)^4 - x^2(4)(x - 5)^3$

150. $5(x^6 + 1)^4(6x^5)(3x + 2)^3 + 3(3x + 2)^2(3)(x^6 + 1)^5$

151. *Compound Interest* After 2 years, an investment of \$500 compounded annually at an interest rate r will yield an amount of $500(1 + r)^2$.

(a) Write this polynomial in standard form.

(b) Use a calculator to evaluate the polynomial for the values of r shown in the table.

r	$2\frac{1}{2}\%$	3%	4%	$4\frac{1}{2}\%$	5%
$500(1 + r)^2$					

(c) What conclusion can you make from the table?

152. *Compound Interest* After 3 years, an investment of \$1200 compounded annually at an interest rate r will yield an amount of $1200(1 + r)^3$.

(a) Write this polynomial in standard form.

(b) Use a calculator to evaluate the polynomial for the values of r shown in the table.

r	2%	3%	$3\frac{1}{2}\%$	4%	$4\frac{1}{2}\%$
$1200(1 + r)^3$					

(c) What conclusion can you make from the table?

153. *Geometry* An overnight shipping company is designing a closed box by cutting along the solid lines and folding along the broken lines on the rectangular piece of corrugated cardboard shown in the figure. The length and width of the rectangle are 45 centimeters and 15 centimeters, respectively. Find the volume of the box in terms of x. Find the volume when $x = 3$, $x = 5$, and $x = 7$.

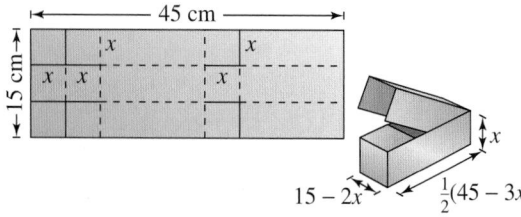

154. *Geometry* A take-out fast food restaurant is constructing an open box made by cutting squares out of the corners of a piece of cardboard that is 18 centimeters by 26 centimeters. The edge of each cut-out square is x inches. Find the volume of the box in terms of x. Find the volume when $x = 1$, $x = 2$, and $x = 3$.

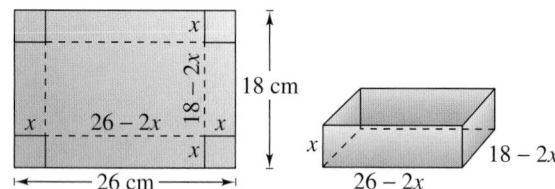

Figure for 154

155. *Stopping Distance* The stopping distance of an automobile is the distance traveled during the driver's reaction time plus the distance traveled after the brakes are applied. In an experiment, these distances were measured (in feet) when the automobile was traveling at a speed of x miles per hour on dry, level pavement, as shown in the bar graph. The distance traveled during the reaction time R was $R = 1.1x$, and the braking distance B was

$$B = 0.0475x^2 - 0.001x + 0.23.$$

(a) Determine the polynomial that represents the total stopping distance T.

(b) Use the result of part (a) to estimate the total stopping distance when $x = 30$, $x = 40$, and $x = 55$.

(c) Use the bar graph to make a statement about the total stopping distance required for increasing speeds.

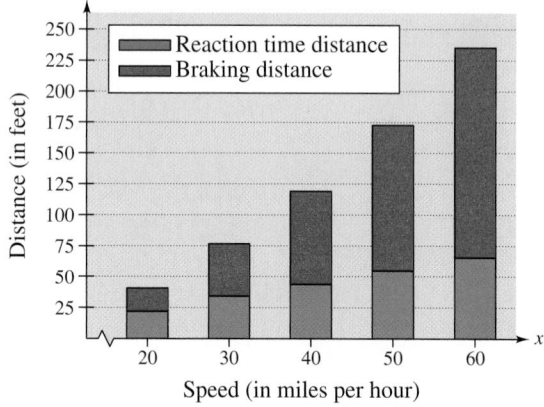

156. *Engineering* A uniformly distributed load is placed on a one-inch-wide steel beam. When the span of the beam is x feet and its depth is 6 inches, the safe load S (in pounds) is approximated by

$$S_6 = (0.06x^2 - 2.42x + 38.71)^2.$$

When the depth is 8 inches, the safe load is approximated by

$$S_8 = (0.08x^2 - 3.30x + 51.93)^2.$$

(a) Use the bar graph to estimate the difference in the safe loads for these two beams when the span is 12 feet.

(b) How does the difference in safe load change as the span increases?

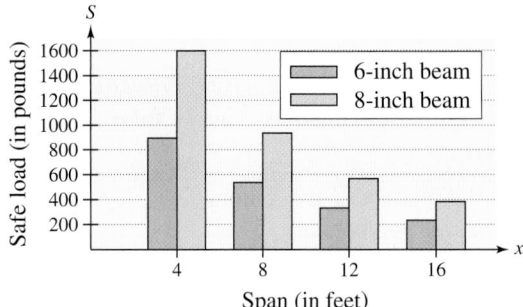

(b)

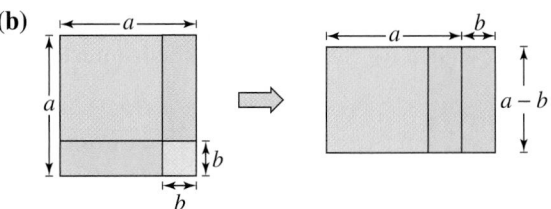

(c)

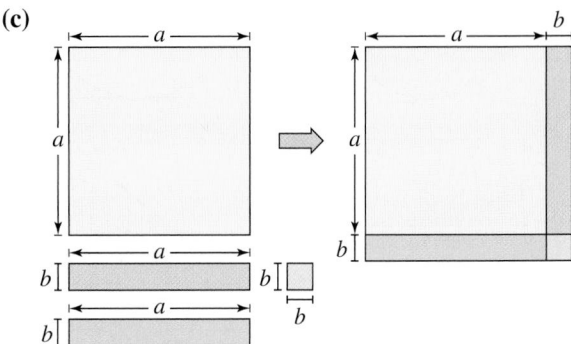

Geometric Modeling **In Exercises 157–160, match the factoring formula with the correct geometric factoring model. [The models are labeled (a), (b), (c), and (d).] For instance, a factoring model for**

$$2x^2 + 3x + 1 = (2x + 1)(x + 1)$$

is shown in the figure.

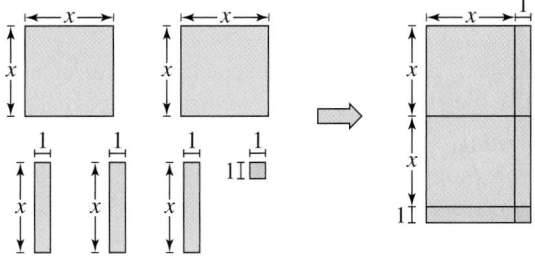

(a)

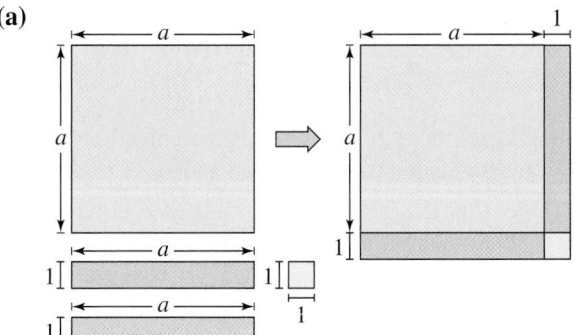

(d)

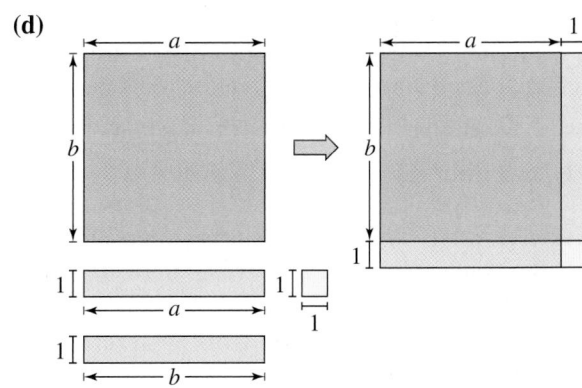

157. $a^2 - b^2 = (a + b)(a - b)$

158. $a^2 + 2ab + b^2 = (a + b)^2$

159. $a^2 + 2a + 1 = (a + 1)^2$

160. $ab + a + b + 1 = (a + 1)(b + 1)$

Geometric Modeling **In Exercises 161–164, draw a geometric factoring model to represent the factorization.**

161. $3x^2 + 7x + 2 = (3x + 1)(x + 2)$

162. $x^2 + 4x + 3 = (x + 3)(x + 1)$

163. $2x^2 + 7x + 3 = (2x + 1)(x + 3)$

164. $x^2 + 3x + 2 = (x + 2)(x + 1)$

Geometry In Exercises 165–168, write an expression in factored form for the area of the shaded portion of the figure.

165.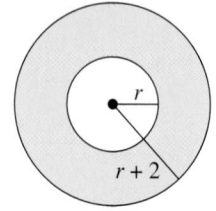

166.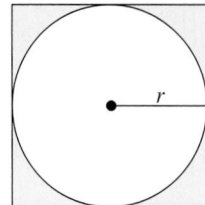

167.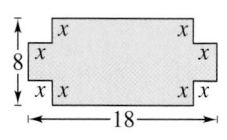

168.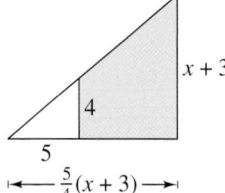

In Exercises 169–172, find all values of b for which the trinomial can be factored with integer coefficients.

169. $x^2 + bx - 15$

170. $x^2 + bx - 12$

171. $x^2 + bx + 50$

172. $x^2 + bx + 24$

In Exercises 173–176, find two integer values of c such that the trinomial can be factored. (There are many correct answers.)

173. $2x^2 + 5x + c$

174. $3x^2 - x + c$

175. $3x^2 - 10x + c$

176. $2x^2 + 9x + c$

177. *Geometry* The cylindrical shell shown in the figure has a volume of $V = \pi R^2 h - \pi r^2 h$.

(a) Factor the expression for the volume.

(b) From the result of part (a), show that the volume is

2π (average radius)(thickness of the shell)h.

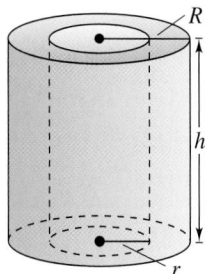

178. *Chemical Reaction* The rate of change of an autocatalytic chemical reaction is $kQx - kx^2$, where Q is the amount of the original substance, x is the amount of substance formed, and k is a constant of proportionality. Factor the expression.

Synthesis

True or False? In Exercises 179–181, determine whether the statement is true or false. Justify your answer.

179. The product of two binomials is always a second-degree polynomial.

180. The difference of two perfect squares can be factored as the product of conjugate pairs.

181. The sum of two perfect squares can be factored as the binomial sum squared.

182. *Exploration* Find the degree of the product of two polynomials of degrees m and n.

183. *Exploration* Find the degree of the sum of two polynomials of degrees m and n if $m < n$.

184. *Writing* A student's homework paper included the following.

$(x - 3)^2 = x^2 + 9$

Write a paragraph fully explaining the error and give the correct method for squaring a binomial.

185. *Writing* Explain what is meant when it is said that a polynomial is in factored form.

186. *Think About It* Is $(3x - 6)(x + 1)$ completely factored? Explain.

187. *Error Analysis* Describe the error.

$9x^2 - 9x - 54 = (3x + 6)(3x - 9)$
$= 3(x + 2)(x - 3)$

188. *Think About It* A third-degree polynomial and a fourth-degree polynomial are added.

(a) Can the sum be a fourth-degree polynomial? Explain or give an example.

(b) Can the sum be a second-degree polynomial? Explain or give an example.

(c) Can the sum be a seventh-degree polynomial? Explain or give an example.

189. *Think About It* Must the sum of two second-degree polynomials be a second-degree polynomial? If not, give an example.

P.4 Rational Expressions

Domain of an Algebraic Expression

The set of real numbers for which an algebraic expression is defined is the **domain** of the expression. Two algebraic expressions are **equivalent** if they have the same domain and yield the same values for all numbers in their domain. For instance, the expressions $(x + 1) + (x + 2)$ and $2x + 3$ are equivalent because

$$(x + 1) + (x + 2) = x + 1 + x + 2 = x + x + 1 + 2 = 2x + 3.$$

Example 1   Finding the Domain of an Algebraic Expression

a. The domain of the polynomial

$$2x^3 + 3x + 4$$

is the set of all real numbers. In fact, the domain of any polynomial is the set of all real numbers, unless the domain is specifically restricted.

b. The domain of the radical expression

$$\sqrt{x - 2}$$

is the set of real numbers greater than or equal to 2, because the square root of a negative number is not a real number.

c. The domain of the expression

$$\frac{x + 2}{x - 3}$$

is the set of all real numbers except $x = 3$, which would result in division by zero, which is undefined.

 Checkpoint Now try Exercise 5.

The quotient of two algebraic expressions is a **fractional expression.** Moreover, the quotient of two *polynomials* such as

$$\frac{1}{x}, \qquad \frac{2x - 1}{x + 1}, \qquad \text{or} \qquad \frac{x^2 - 1}{x^2 + 1}$$

is a **rational expression.**

Simplifying Rational Expressions

Recall that a fraction is in simplest form if its numerator and denominator have no factors in common aside from ± 1. To write a fraction in simplest form, divide out common factors.

$$\frac{a \cdot \cancel{c}}{b \cdot \cancel{c}} = \frac{a}{b}, \qquad c \neq 0.$$

The key to success in simplifying rational expressions lies in your ability to *factor* polynomials. When simplifying rational expressions, be sure to factor each polynomial completely before concluding that the numerator and denominator have no factors in common.

Example 2   Simplifying a Rational Expression

Write $\dfrac{x^2 + 4x - 12}{3x - 6}$ in simplest form.

Solution

$$\frac{x^2 + 4x - 12}{3x - 6} = \frac{(x + 6)(x - 2)}{3(x - 2)} \qquad \text{Factor completely.}$$

$$= \frac{x + 6}{3}, \qquad x \neq 2 \qquad \text{Divide out common factors.}$$

Note that the original expression is undefined when $x = 2$ (because division by zero is undefined). To make sure that the simplified expression is *equivalent* to the original expression, you must restrict the domain of the simplified expression by excluding the value $x = 2$.

✓ *Checkpoint* Now try Exercise 15.

It may sometimes be necessary to change the sign of a factor to simplify a rational expression, as shown in Example 3.

Example 3   Simplifying Rational Expressions

Write $\dfrac{12 + x - x^2}{2x^2 - 9x + 4}$ in simplest form.

Solution

$$\frac{12 + x - x^2}{2x^2 - 9x + 4} = \frac{(4 - x)(3 + x)}{(2x - 1)(x - 4)} \qquad \text{Factor completely.}$$

$$= \frac{-(x - 4)(3 + x)}{(2x - 1)(x - 4)} \qquad (4 - x) = -(x - 4)$$

$$= -\frac{3 + x}{2x - 1}, \qquad x \neq 4 \qquad \text{Divide out common factors.}$$

✓ *Checkpoint* Now try Exercise 23.

Operations with Rational Expressions

To multiply or divide rational expressions, you can use the properties of fractions discussed in Section P.1. Recall that to divide fractions you invert the divisor and multiply.

STUDY TIP

In this text, when a rational expression is written, the domain is usually not listed with the expression. It is *implied* that the real numbers that make the denominator zero are excluded from the expression. Also, when performing operations with rational expressions, this text follows the convention of listing *beside the simplified expression* all values of x that must be specifically excluded from the domain in order to make the domains of the simplified and original expressions agree. In Example 3, for instance, the restriction $x \neq 4$ is listed beside the simplified expression to make the two domains agree. Note that the value $x = \frac{1}{2}$ is excluded from *both* domains, so it is not necessary to list this value.

Example 4   Multiplying Rational Expressions

$$\frac{2x^2 + x - 6}{x^2 + 4x - 5} \cdot \frac{x^3 - 3x^2 + 2x}{4x^2 - 6x} = \frac{(2x - 3)(x + 2)}{(x + 5)(x - 1)} \cdot \frac{x(x - 2)(x - 1)}{2x(2x - 3)}$$

$$= \frac{(x + 2)(x - 2)}{2(x + 5)}, \quad x \neq 0, x \neq 1, x \neq \frac{3}{2}$$

✓ *Checkpoint* Now try Exercise 39.

Example 5   Dividing Rational Expressions

Divide $\dfrac{x^3 - 8}{x^2 - 4}$ by $\dfrac{x^2 + 2x + 4}{x^3 + 8}$.

Solution

$$\frac{x^3 - 8}{x^2 - 4} \div \frac{x^2 + 2x + 4}{x^3 + 8} = \frac{x^3 - 8}{x^2 - 4} \cdot \frac{x^3 + 8}{x^2 + 2x + 4} \qquad \text{Invert and multiply.}$$

$$= \frac{(x - 2)(x^2 + 2x + 4)}{(x + 2)(x - 2)} \cdot \frac{(x + 2)(x^2 - 2x + 4)}{(x^2 + 2x + 4)}$$

$$= x^2 - 2x + 4, \quad x \neq \pm 2 \qquad \begin{array}{l}\text{Divide out common} \\ \text{factors.}\end{array}$$

✓ *Checkpoint* Now try Exercise 41.

To add or subtract rational expressions, you can use the LCD (least common denominator) method or the basic definition

$$\frac{a}{b} \pm \frac{c}{d} = \frac{ad \pm bc}{bd}, \qquad b \neq 0 \text{ and } d \neq 0. \qquad \text{Basic definition}$$

This definition provides an efficient way of adding or subtracting *two* fractions that have no common factors in their denominators.

Example 6   Subtracting Rational Expressions

Subtract $\dfrac{2}{3x + 4}$ from $\dfrac{x}{x - 3}$.

Solution

$$\frac{x}{x - 3} - \frac{2}{3x + 4} = \frac{x(3x + 4) - 2(x - 3)}{(x - 3)(3x + 4)} \qquad \text{Basic definition}$$

$$= \frac{3x^2 + 4x - 2x + 6}{(x - 3)(3x + 4)} \qquad \text{Distributive Property}$$

$$= \frac{3x^2 + 2x + 6}{(x - 3)(3x + 4)} \qquad \text{Combine like terms.}$$

✓ *Checkpoint* Now try Exercise 45.

STUDY TIP

When subtracting rational expressions, remember to distribute the negative sign to *all* the terms in the quantity that is being subtracted.

For three or more fractions, or for fractions with a repeated factor in the denominators, the LCD method works well. Recall that the least common denominator of several fractions consists of the product of all prime factors in the denominators, with each factor given the highest power of its occurrence in any denominator. Here is a numerical example.

$$\frac{1}{6} + \frac{3}{4} - \frac{2}{3} = \frac{1 \cdot 2}{6 \cdot 2} + \frac{3 \cdot 3}{4 \cdot 3} - \frac{2 \cdot 4}{3 \cdot 4}$$ The LCD is 12.

$$= \frac{2}{12} + \frac{9}{12} - \frac{8}{12}$$

$$= \frac{3}{12} = \frac{1}{4}$$

Sometimes the numerator of the answer has a factor in common with the denominator. In such cases the answer should be simplified. For instance, in the example above, $\frac{3}{12}$ was simplified to $\frac{1}{4}$.

Example 7 Combining Rational Expressions: The LCD Method

Perform the operations and simplify.

$$\frac{3}{x-1} - \frac{2}{x} + \frac{x+3}{x^2-1}$$

Solution

Using the factored denominators $(x - 1)$, x, and $(x + 1)(x - 1)$, you can see that the LCD is $x(x + 1)(x - 1)$.

$$\frac{3}{x-1} - \frac{2}{x} + \frac{x+3}{(x+1)(x-1)}$$

$$= \frac{3(x)(x+1)}{x(x+1)(x-1)} - \frac{2(x+1)(x-1)}{x(x+1)(x-1)} + \frac{(x+3)(x)}{x(x+1)(x-1)}$$

$$= \frac{3(x)(x+1) - 2(x+1)(x-1) + (x+3)(x)}{x(x+1)(x-1)}$$

$$= \frac{3x^2 + 3x - 2x^2 + 2 + x^2 + 3x}{x(x+1)(x-1)}$$ Distributive Property

$$= \frac{(3x^2 - 2x^2 + x^2) + (3x + 3x) + 2}{x(x+1)(x-1)}$$ Group like terms.

$$= \frac{2x^2 + 6x + 2}{x(x+1)(x-1)}$$ Combine like terms.

$$= \frac{2(x^2 + 3x + 1)}{x(x+1)(x-1)}$$ Factor.

✓ *Checkpoint* Now try Exercise 51.

Complex Fractions

Fractional expressions with separate fractions in the numerator, denominator, or both are called **complex fractions.** Here are two examples.

$$\frac{\left(\dfrac{1}{x}\right)}{x^2 + 1} \quad \text{and} \quad \frac{\left(\dfrac{1}{x}\right)}{\left(\dfrac{1}{x^2 + 1}\right)}$$

A complex fraction can be simplified by combining the fractions in its numerator into a single fraction and then combining the fractions in its denominator into a single fraction. Then invert the denominator and multiply.

Example 8   Simplifying a Complex Fraction

$$\frac{\left(\dfrac{2}{x} - 3\right)}{\left(1 - \dfrac{1}{x - 1}\right)} = \frac{\left[\dfrac{2 - 3(x)}{x}\right]}{\left[\dfrac{1(x - 1) - 1}{x - 1}\right]} \qquad \text{Combine fractions.}$$

$$= \frac{\left(\dfrac{2 - 3x}{x}\right)}{\left(\dfrac{x - 2}{x - 1}\right)} \qquad \text{Simplify.}$$

$$= \frac{2 - 3x}{x} \cdot \frac{x - 1}{x - 2} \qquad \text{Invert and multiply.}$$

$$= \frac{(2 - 3x)(x - 1)}{x(x - 2)}, \quad x \neq 1$$

✓ *Checkpoint* Now try Exercise 57.

In Example 8, the restriction $x \neq 1$ is added to the final expression to make its domain agree with the domain of the original expression.

Another way to simplify a complex fraction is to multiply each term in its numerator and denominator by the LCD of all fractions in its numerator and denominator. This method is applied to the fraction in Example 8 as follows.

$$\frac{\left(\dfrac{2}{x} - 3\right)}{\left(1 - \dfrac{1}{x - 1}\right)} = \frac{\left(\dfrac{2}{x} - 3\right)}{\left(1 - \dfrac{1}{x - 1}\right)} \cdot \frac{x(x - 1)}{x(x - 1)} \qquad \text{LCD is } x(x - 1).$$

$$= \frac{\left(\dfrac{2 - 3x}{x}\right) \cdot x(x - 1)}{\left(\dfrac{x - 2}{x - 1}\right) \cdot x(x - 1)} \qquad \text{Combine fractions.}$$

$$= \frac{(2 - 3x)(x - 1)}{x(x - 2)}, \quad x \neq 1 \qquad \text{Simplify.}$$

The next four examples illustrate some methods for simplifying rational expressions involving negative exponents and radicals. These types of expressions occur frequently in calculus.

To simplify an expression with negative exponents, one method is to begin by factoring out the common factor with the smaller exponent. Remember that when factoring, you subtract exponents. For instance, in $3x^{-5/2} + 2x^{-3/2}$ the smaller exponent is $-\frac{5}{2}$ and the common factor is $x^{-5/2}$.

$$3x^{-5/2} + 2x^{-3/2} = x^{-5/2}[3(1) + 2x^{-3/2-(-5/2)}]$$

$$= x^{-5/2}(3 + 2x^1) = \frac{3 + 2x}{x^{5/2}}$$

Example 9 Simplifying an Expression with Negative Exponents

Simplify $x(1 - 2x)^{-3/2} + (1 - 2x)^{-1/2}$.

Solution

Begin by factoring out the common factor with the smaller exponent.

$$x(1 - 2x)^{-3/2} + (1 - 2x)^{-1/2} = (1 - 2x)^{-3/2}[x + (1 - 2x)^{(-1/2)-(-3/2)}]$$

$$= (1 - 2x)^{-3/2}[x + (1 - 2x)^1]$$

$$= \frac{1 - x}{(1 - 2x)^{3/2}}$$

✓ *Checkpoint* Now try Exercise 63.

A second method for simplifying this type of expression involves multiplying the numerator and denominator by a term to eliminate the negative exponent.

Example 10 Simplifying an Expression with Negative Exponents

Simplify $\dfrac{(4 - x^2)^{1/2} + x^2(4 - x^2)^{-1/2}}{4 - x^2}$.

Solution

$$\frac{(4 - x^2)^{1/2} + x^2(4 - x^2)^{-1/2}}{4 - x^2}$$

$$= \frac{(4 - x^2)^{1/2} + x^2(4 - x^2)^{-1/2}}{4 - x^2} \cdot \frac{(4 - x^2)^{1/2}}{(4 - x^2)^{1/2}}$$

$$= \frac{(4 - x^2)^1 + x^2(4 - x^2)^0}{(4 - x^2)^{3/2}}$$

$$= \frac{4 - x^2 + x^2}{(4 - x^2)^{3/2}} = \frac{4}{(4 - x^2)^{3/2}}$$

✓ *Checkpoint* Now try Exercise 67.

Example 11   Rewriting a Difference Quotient

The following expression from calculus is an example of a *difference quotient*.

$$\frac{\sqrt{x+h}-\sqrt{x}}{h}$$

Rewrite this expression by rationalizing its numerator.

Solution

$$\frac{\sqrt{x+h}-\sqrt{x}}{h} = \frac{\sqrt{x+h}-\sqrt{x}}{h} \cdot \frac{\sqrt{x+h}+\sqrt{x}}{\sqrt{x+h}+\sqrt{x}}$$

$$= \frac{\left(\sqrt{x+h}\right)^2 - \left(\sqrt{x}\right)^2}{h\left(\sqrt{x+h}+\sqrt{x}\right)}$$

$$= \frac{h}{h\left(\sqrt{x+h}+\sqrt{x}\right)}$$

$$= \frac{1}{\sqrt{x+h}+\sqrt{x}}, \qquad h \neq 0$$

Notice that the original expression is undefined when $h = 0$. So, you must exclude $h = 0$ from the domain of the simplified expression so that the expressions are equivalent.

✓ *Checkpoint* Now try Exercise 69.

Difference quotients, like that in Example 11, occur frequently in calculus. Often, they need to be rewritten in an equivalent form that can be evaluated when $h = 0$. Note that the equivalent form is not simpler than the original form, but it has the advantage in that it is defined when $h = 0$.

Example 12   Rewriting a Difference Quotient

Rewrite the expression by rationalizing its numerator.

$$\frac{\sqrt{x-4}-\sqrt{x}}{4}$$

Solution

$$\frac{\sqrt{x-4}-\sqrt{x}}{4} = \frac{\sqrt{x-4}-\sqrt{x}}{4} \cdot \frac{\sqrt{x-4}+\sqrt{x}}{\sqrt{x-4}+\sqrt{x}}$$

$$= \frac{\left(\sqrt{x-4}\right)^2 - \left(\sqrt{x}\right)^2}{4\left(\sqrt{x-4}+\sqrt{x}\right)}$$

$$= \frac{-4}{4\left(\sqrt{x-4}+\sqrt{x}\right)}$$

$$= -\frac{1}{\sqrt{x-4}+\sqrt{x}}$$

✓ *Checkpoint* Now try Exercise 70.

P.4 Exercises

Vocabulary Check

Fill in the blanks.

1. The set of real numbers for which an algebraic expression is defined is the _____ of the expression.

2. The quotient of two algebraic expressions is a fractional expression and the quotient of two polynomials is a _____ .

3. Fractional expressions with separate fractions in the numerator, denominator, or both are called _____ .

4. To simplify an expression with negative exponents, it is possible to begin by factoring out the common factor with the _____ exponent.

5. Two algebraic expressions that have the same domain and yield the same values for all numbers in their domains are called _____ .

In Exercises 1–8, find the domain of the expression.

1. $3x^2 - 4x + 7$

2. $2x^2 + 5x - 2$

3. $4x^3 + 3, \quad x \geq 0$

4. $6x^2 - 9, \quad x > 0$

5. $\dfrac{1}{3 - x}$

6. $\dfrac{x + 6}{3x + 2}$

7. $\sqrt{x + 7}$

8. $\sqrt{4 - x}$

In Exercises 9 and 10, find the missing factor in the numerator so that the two fractions are equivalent.

9. $\dfrac{5}{2x} = \dfrac{5(\quad)}{6x^2}$

10. $\dfrac{3}{4} = \dfrac{3(\quad)}{4(x + 1)}$

In Exercises 11–28, write the rational expression in simplest form.

11. $\dfrac{15x^2}{10x}$

12. $\dfrac{18y^2}{60y^5}$

13. $\dfrac{3xy}{xy + x}$

14. $\dfrac{2x^2y}{xy - y}$

15. $\dfrac{4y - 8y^2}{10y - 5}$

16. $\dfrac{9x^2 + 9x}{2x + 2}$

17. $\dfrac{x - 5}{10 - 2x}$

18. $\dfrac{12 - 4x}{x - 3}$

19. $\dfrac{y^2 - 16}{y + 4}$

20. $\dfrac{x^2 - 25}{5 - x}$

21. $\dfrac{x^3 + 5x^2 + 6x}{x^2 - 4}$

22. $\dfrac{x^2 + 8x - 20}{x^2 + 11x + 10}$

23. $\dfrac{y^2 - 7y + 12}{y^2 + 3y - 18}$

24. $\dfrac{3 - x}{x^2 + 11x + 10}$

25. $\dfrac{2 - x + 2x^2 - x^3}{x - 2}$

26. $\dfrac{x^2 - 9}{x^3 + x^2 - 9x - 9}$

27. $\dfrac{z^3 - 8}{z^2 + 2z + 4}$

28. $\dfrac{y^3 - 2y^2 - 3y}{y^3 + 1}$

In Exercises 29 and 30, complete the table. What can you conclude?

29.

x	0	1	2	3	4	5	6
$\dfrac{x^2 - 2x - 3}{x - 3}$							
$x + 1$							

30.

x	0	1	2	3	4	5	6
$\dfrac{x - 3}{x^2 - x - 6}$							
$\dfrac{1}{x + 2}$							

31. **Error Analysis** Describe the error.

$$\frac{5x^3}{2x^3 + 4} = \frac{5x^3}{2x^3 + 4} = \frac{5}{2 + 4} = \frac{5}{6}$$

32. **Error Analysis** Describe the error.

$$\frac{x^3 + 25x}{x^2 - 2x - 15} = \frac{x(x^2 + 25)}{(x - 5)(x + 3)}$$
$$= \frac{x(x - 5)(x + 5)}{(x - 5)(x + 3)} = \frac{x(x + 5)}{x + 3}$$

Geometry   In Exercises 33 and 34, find the ratio of the area of the shaded portion of the figure to the total area of the figure.

33.

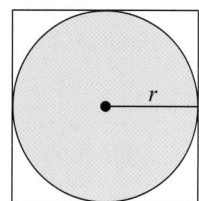

34.

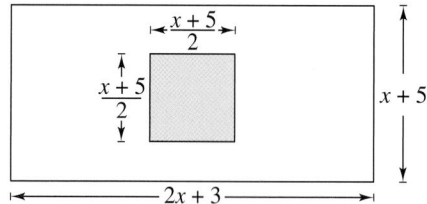

In Exercises 35–42, perform the multiplication or division and simplify.

35. $\dfrac{5}{x-1} \cdot \dfrac{x-1}{25(x-2)}$

36. $\dfrac{x+13}{x^3(3-x)} \cdot \dfrac{x(x-3)}{5}$

37. $\dfrac{r}{r-1} \div \dfrac{r^2}{r^2-1}$

38. $\dfrac{4y-16}{5y+15} \div \dfrac{4-y}{2y+6}$

39. $\dfrac{t^2-t-6}{t^2+6t+9} \cdot \dfrac{t+3}{t^2-4}$

40. $\dfrac{y^3-8}{2y^3} \cdot \dfrac{4y}{y^2-5y+6}$

41. $\dfrac{3(x+y)}{4} \div \dfrac{x+y}{2}$

42. $\dfrac{x+2}{5(x-3)} \div \dfrac{x-2}{5(x-3)}$

In Exercises 43–52, perform the addition or subtraction and simplify.

43. $\dfrac{5}{x-1} + \dfrac{x}{x-1}$

44. $\dfrac{2x-1}{x+3} - \dfrac{1-x}{x+3}$

45. $\dfrac{6}{2x+1} - \dfrac{x}{x+3}$

46. $\dfrac{3}{x-1} + \dfrac{5x}{3x+4}$

47. $\dfrac{3}{x-2} + \dfrac{5}{2-x}$

48. $\dfrac{2x}{x-5} - \dfrac{5}{5-x}$

49. $\dfrac{1}{x^2-x-2} - \dfrac{x}{x^2-5x+6}$

50. $\dfrac{2}{x^2-x-2} + \dfrac{10}{x^2+2x-8}$

51. $-\dfrac{1}{x} + \dfrac{2}{x^2+1} - \dfrac{1}{x^3+x}$

52. $\dfrac{2}{x+1} + \dfrac{2}{x-1} + \dfrac{1}{x^2-1}$

In Exercises 53–60, simplify the complex fraction.

53. $\dfrac{\left(\dfrac{x}{2}-1\right)}{(x-2)}$

54. $\dfrac{(x-4)}{\left(\dfrac{x}{4}-\dfrac{4}{x}\right)}$

55. $\dfrac{\left[\dfrac{x^2}{(x+1)^2}\right]}{\left[\dfrac{x}{(x+1)^3}\right]}$

56. $\dfrac{\left(\dfrac{x^2-1}{x}\right)}{\left[\dfrac{(x-1)^2}{x}\right]}$

57. $\dfrac{\left[\dfrac{1}{(x+h)^2}-\dfrac{1}{x^2}\right]}{h}$

58. $\dfrac{\left(\dfrac{x+h}{x+h+1}-\dfrac{x}{x+1}\right)}{h}$

59. $\dfrac{\left(\sqrt{x}-\dfrac{1}{2\sqrt{x}}\right)}{\sqrt{x}}$

60. $\dfrac{\left(\dfrac{t^2}{\sqrt{t^2+1}}-\sqrt{t^2+1}\right)}{t^2}$

In Exercises 61–66, simplify the expression by removing the common factor with the smaller exponent.

61. $x^5 - 2x^{-2}$

62. $x^5 - 5x^{-3}$

63. $x^2(x^2+1)^{-5} - (x^2+1)^{-4}$

64. $2x(x-5)^{-3} - 4x^2(x-5)^{-4}$

65. $2x^2(x-1)^{1/2} - 5(x-1)^{-1/2}$

66. $4x^3(2x-1)^{3/2} - 2x(2x-1)^{-1/2}$

In Exercises 67 and 68, simplify the expression.

67. $\dfrac{2x^{3/2} - x^{-1/2}}{x^2}$

68. $\dfrac{-x^2(x^2+1)^{-1/2} + 2x(x^2+1)^{-3/2}}{x^3}$

In Exercises 69 and 70, rationalize the numerator of the expression.

69. $\dfrac{\sqrt{x+2}-\sqrt{x}}{2}$

70. $\dfrac{\sqrt{z-3}-\sqrt{z}}{3}$

71. **Rate**   A photocopier copies at a rate of 16 pages per minute.

(a) Find the time required to copy 1 page.

(b) Find the time required to copy x pages.

(c) Find the time required to copy 60 pages.

72. *Monthly Payment* The formula that approximates the annual interest rate r of a monthly installment loan is given by

$$r = \frac{\left[\dfrac{24(NM - P)}{N}\right]}{\left(P + \dfrac{NM}{12}\right)}$$

where N is the total number of payments, M is the monthly payment, and P is the amount financed.

(a) Approximate the annual interest rate for a five-year car loan of $20,000 that has monthly payments of $400.

(b) Simplify the expression for the annual interest rate r, and then rework part (a).

Probability **In Exercises 73 and 74, consider an experiment in which a marble is tossed into a box whose base is shown in the figure. The probability that the marble will come to rest in the shaded portion of the box is equal to the ratio of the shaded area to the total area of the figure. Find the probability.**

73.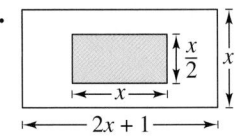

74.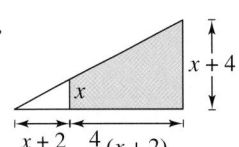

75. *Refrigeration* When food (at room temperature) is placed in a refrigerator, the time required for the food to cool depends on the amount of food, the air circulation in the refrigerator, the original temperature of the food, and the temperature of the refrigerator. Consider the model that gives the temperature of food that is at 75°F and is placed in a 40°F refrigerator as

$$T = 10\left(\frac{4t^2 + 16t + 75}{t^2 + 4t + 10}\right)$$

where T is the temperature (in degrees Fahrenheit) and t is the time (in hours).

(a) Complete the table.

t	0	2	4	6	8	10
T						

t	12	14	16	18	20	22
T						

(b) What value of T does the mathematical model appear to be approaching?

76. *Plants* The table shows the numbers of endangered and threatened plant species in the United States for the years 1996 through 2002. (Source: U.S. Fish and Wildlife Service)

Year	Endangered	Threatened
1996	513	101
1997	553	115
1998	567	135
1999	581	140
2000	593	142
2001	595	145
2002	598	147

Mathematical models for this data are

$$\text{Endangered plants} = \frac{-141.341t + 663.9}{-0.227t + 1.0}$$

and

$$\text{Threatened plants} = -1.80t^2 + 39.7t - 72$$

where t represents the year, with $t = 6$ corresponding to 1996.

(a) Using the models, create a table to estimate the number of endangered plant species and the number of threatened plant species for the given years. Compare these estimates with the actual data.

(b) Determine a model for the ratio of the number of threatened plant species to the number of endangered plant species. Use the model to find this ratio for the given years.

Synthesis

True or False? **In Exercises 77 and 78, determine whether the statement is true or false. Justify your answer.**

77. $\dfrac{x^{2n} - 1^{2n}}{x^n - 1^n} = x^n + 1^n$ **78.** $\dfrac{x^{2n} - n^2}{x^n - n} = x^n + n$

79. *Think About It* How do you determine whether a rational expression is in simplest form?

80. *Think About It* Is the following statement true for all nonzero real numbers a and b? Explain.

$$\frac{ax - b}{b - ax} = -1$$

P.5 The Cartesian Plane

The Cartesian Plane

Just as you can represent real numbers by points on a real number line, you can represent ordered pairs of real numbers by points in a plane called the **rectangular coordinate system,** or the **Cartesian plane,** after the French mathematician René Descartes (1596–1650).

The Cartesian plane is formed by using two real number lines intersecting at right angles, as shown in Figure P.10. The horizontal real number line is usually called the **x-axis,** and the vertical real number line is usually called the **y-axis.** The point of intersection of these two axes is the **origin,** and the two axes divide the plane into four parts called **quadrants.**

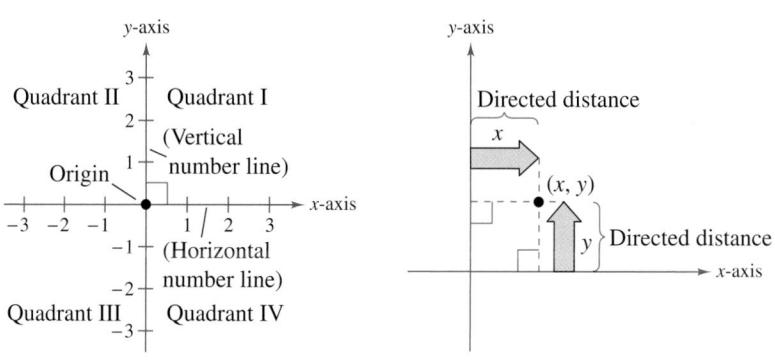

Figure P.10   The Cartesian Plane   **Figure P.11**   Ordered Pair (x, y)

Each point in the plane corresponds to an **ordered pair** (x, y) of real numbers x and y, called **coordinates** of the point. The **x-coordinate** represents the directed distance from the y-axis to the point, and the **y-coordinate** represents the directed distance from the x-axis to the point, as shown in Figure P.11.

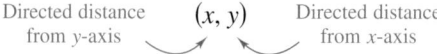

The notation (x, y) denotes both a point in the plane and an open interval on the real number line. The context will tell you which meaning is intended.

Example 1   Plotting Points in the Cartesian Plane

Plot the points (−1, 2), (3, 4), (0, 0), (3, 0), and (−2, −3).

Solution

To plot the point (−1, 2), imagine a vertical line through −1 on the x-axis and a horizontal line through 2 on the y-axis. The intersection of these two lines is the point (−1, 2). This point is one unit to the left of the y-axis and two units up from the x-axis. The other four points can be plotted in a similar way (see Figure P.12).

☑ *Checkpoint* Now try Exercise 3.

Figure P.12

What you should learn

- Plot points in the Cartesian plane and sketch scatter plots.
- Use the Distance Formula to find the distance between two points.
- Use the Midpoint Formula to find the midpoint of a line segment.
- Find the equation of a circle.
- Translate points in the plane.

Why you should learn it

The Cartesian plane can be used to represent relationships between two variables. For instance, Exercise 75 on page 57 shows how to graphically represent the number of recording artists inducted to the Rock and Roll Hall of Fame from 1986 to 2003.

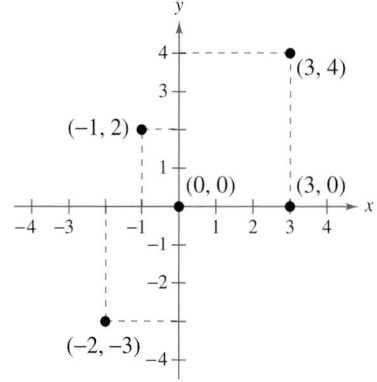

Alex Bartel/Getty Images

The beauty of a rectangular coordinate system is that it enables you to see relationships between two variables. It would be difficult to overestimate the importance of Descartes's introduction of coordinates to the plane. Today, his ideas are in common use in virtually every scientific and business-related field.

In the next example, data is represented graphically by points plotted on a rectangular coordinate system. This type of graph is called a **scatter plot.**

Example 2   Sketching a Scatter Plot

From 1996 through 2001, the amount *A* (in millions of dollars) spent on archery equipment in the United States is shown in the table, where *t* represents the year. Sketch a scatter plot of the data by hand.   (Source: National Sporting Goods Association)

Year, *t*	Amount, *A*
1996	276
1997	270
1998	255
1999	262
2000	254
2001	262

Solution

Before you sketch the scatter plot, it is helpful to represent each pair of values by an ordered pair (t, A), as follows.

(1996, 276), (1997, 270), (1998, 255), (1999, 262), (2000, 254), (2001, 262)

To sketch a scatter plot of the data shown in the table, first draw a vertical axis to represent the amount (in millions of dollars) and a horizontal axis to represent the year. Then plot the resulting points, as shown in Figure P.13. Note that the break in the *t*-axis indicates that the numbers between 0 and 1996 have been omitted.

STUDY TIP

In Example 2, you could have let $t = 1$ represent the year 1996. In that case, the horizontal axis of the graph would not have been broken, and the tick marks would have been labeled 1 through 6 (instead of 1996 through 2001).

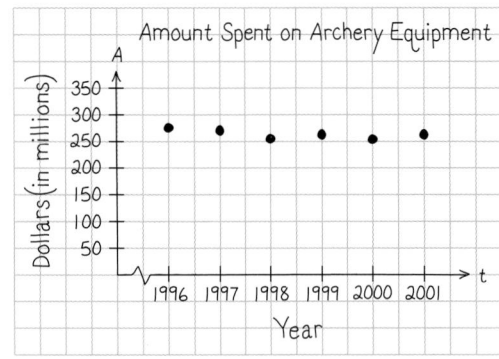

Figure P.13

✓ *Checkpoint* Now try Exercise 21.

TECHNOLOGY TIP   You can use a graphing utility to graph the scatter plot in Example 2. First, enter the data into the graphing utility's *list editor* as shown in Figure P.14. Then use the *statistical plotting* feature to set up the scatter plot, as shown in Figure P.15. Finally, display the scatter plot (use a viewing window in which $1995 \le x \le 2002$ and $0 \le y \le 300$) as shown in Figure P.16.

TECHNOLOGY SUPPORT

For instructions on how to use the *list editor*, see Appendix A; for specific keystrokes, go to the text website at *college.hmco.com*.

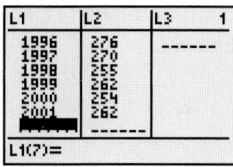

Figure P.14

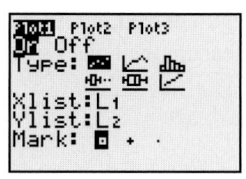

Figure P.15

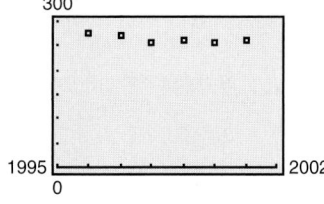

Figure P.16

Some graphing utilities have a *ZoomStat* feature, as shown in Figure P.17. This feature automatically selects an appropriate viewing window that displays all the data in the list editor, as shown in Figure P.18.

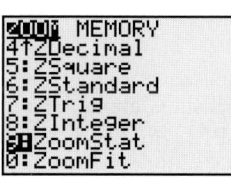

Figure P.17

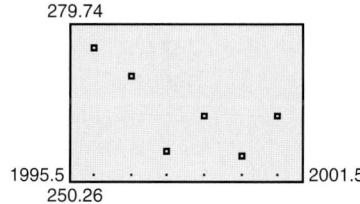

Figure P.18

The Distance Formula

Recall from the Pythagorean Theorem that, for a right triangle with hypotenuse of length c and sides of lengths a and b, you have $a^2 + b^2 = c^2$ as shown in Figure P.19. (The converse is also true. That is, if $a^2 + b^2 = c^2$, then the triangle is a right triangle.)

Suppose you want to determine the distance d between two points (x_1, y_1) and (x_2, y_2) in the plane. With these two points, a right triangle can be formed, as shown in Figure P.20. The length of the vertical side of the triangle is $|y_2 - y_1|$, and the length of the horizontal side is $|x_2 - x_1|$. By the Pythagorean Theorem,

$$d^2 = |x_2 - x_1|^2 + |y_2 - y_1|^2$$
$$d = \sqrt{|x_2 - x_1|^2 + |y_2 - y_1|^2}$$
$$d = \sqrt{(x_2 - x_1)^2 + (y_2 - y_1)^2}.$$

This result is called the **Distance Formula.**

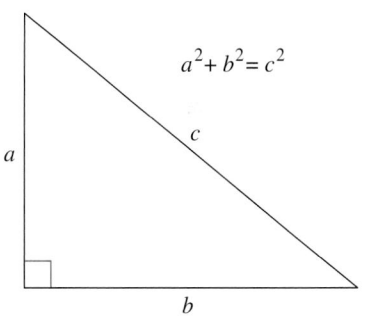

Figure P.19

> The Distance Formula
>
> The distance d between the points (x_1, y_1) and (x_2, y_2) in the plane is
> $$d = \sqrt{(x_2 - x_1)^2 + (y_2 - y_1)^2}.$$

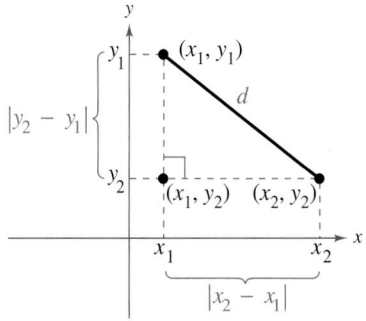

Figure P.20

Example 3   Finding a Distance

Find the distance between the points $(-2, 1)$ and $(3, 4)$.

Algebraic Solution

Let $(x_1, y_1) = (-2, 1)$ and $(x_2, y_2) = (3, 4)$. Then apply the Distance Formula as follows.

$$d = \sqrt{(x_2 - x_1)^2 + (y_2 - y_1)^2} \qquad \text{Distance Formula}$$

$$= \sqrt{[3 - (-2)]^2 + (4 - 1)^2} \qquad \begin{array}{l}\text{Substitute for}\\ x_1, y_1, x_2, \text{ and } y_2.\end{array}$$

$$= \sqrt{(5)^2 + (3)^2} \qquad \text{Simplify.}$$

$$= \sqrt{34} \approx 5.83 \qquad \text{Simplify.}$$

So, the distance between the points is about 5.83 units.

You can use the Pythagorean Theorem to check that the distance is correct.

$$d^2 \overset{?}{=} 3^2 + 5^2 \qquad \text{Pythagorean Theorem}$$

$$\left(\sqrt{34}\right)^2 \overset{?}{=} 3^2 + 5^2 \qquad \text{Substitute for } d.$$

$$34 = 34 \qquad \text{Distance checks. } \checkmark$$

✓ **Checkpoint** Now try Exercise 23.

Graphical Solution

Use centimeter graph paper to plot the points $A(-2, 1)$ and $B(3, 4)$. Carefully sketch the line segment from A to B. Then use a centimeter ruler to measure the length of the segment.

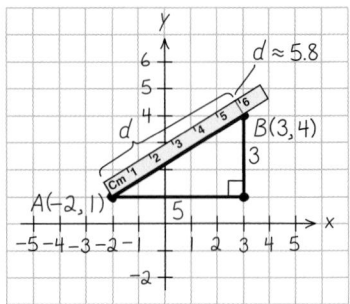

Figure P.21

The line segment measures about 5.8 centimeters, as shown in Figure P.21. So, the distance between the points is about 5.8 units.

Example 4   Verifying a Right Triangle

Show that the points $(2, 1)$, $(4, 0)$, and $(5, 7)$ are the vertices of a right triangle.

Solution

The three points are plotted in Figure P.22. Using the Distance Formula, you can find the lengths of the three sides as follows.

$$d_1 = \sqrt{(5 - 2)^2 + (7 - 1)^2} = \sqrt{9 + 36} = \sqrt{45}$$

$$d_2 = \sqrt{(4 - 2)^2 + (0 - 1)^2} = \sqrt{4 + 1} = \sqrt{5}$$

$$d_3 = \sqrt{(5 - 4)^2 + (7 - 0)^2} = \sqrt{1 + 49} = \sqrt{50}$$

Because $(d_1)^2 + (d_2)^2 = 45 + 5 = 50 = (d_3)^2$, you can conclude that the triangle must be a right triangle.

✓ **Checkpoint** Now try Exercise 37.

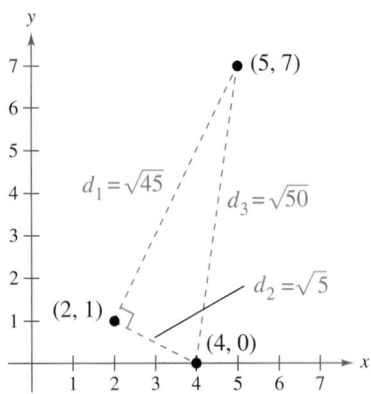

Figure P.22

The Midpoint Formula

To find the **midpoint** of the line segment that joins two points in a coordinate plane, find the average values of the respective coordinates of the two endpoints using the **Midpoint Formula**. See Appendix B for a proof of the Midpoint Formula.

> **The Midpoint Formula**
>
> The midpoint of the line segment joining the points (x_1, y_1) and (x_2, y_2) is given by the Midpoint Formula
>
> $$\text{Midpoint} = \left(\frac{x_1 + x_2}{2}, \frac{y_1 + y_2}{2} \right).$$

Example 5 Finding a Line Segment's Midpoint

Find the midpoint of the line segment joining the points $(-5, -3)$ and $(9, 3)$.

Solution

Let $(x_1, y_1) = (-5, -3)$ and $(x_2, y_2) = (9, 3)$.

$$\text{Midpoint} = \left(\frac{x_1 + x_2}{2}, \frac{y_1 + y_2}{2} \right) \qquad \text{Midpoint Formula}$$

$$= \left(\frac{-5 + 9}{2}, \frac{-3 + 3}{2} \right) \qquad \text{Substitute for } x_1, y_1, x_2, \text{ and } y_2.$$

$$= (2, 0) \qquad \text{Simplify.}$$

The midpoint of the line segment is $(2, 0)$, as shown in Figure P.23.

✓ *Checkpoint* Now try Exercise 43.

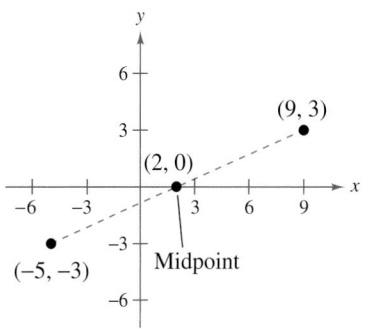

Figure P.23

Example 6 Estimating Annual Sales

The Wm. Wrigley Jr. Company had annual sales of \$2.15 billion in 2000 and \$2.75 billion in 2002. Without knowing any additional information, what would you estimate the 2001 sales to have been?   (Source: Wm. Wrigley Jr. Company)

Solution

One solution to the problem is to assume that sales followed a *linear* pattern. With this assumption, you can estimate the 2001 sales by finding the midpoint of the line segment connecting the points $(2000, 2.15)$ and $(2002, 2.75)$.

$$\text{Midpoint} = \left(\frac{2000 + 2002}{2}, \frac{2.15 + 2.75}{2} \right)$$

$$= (2001, 2.45)$$

So, you would estimate the 2001 sales to have been about \$2.45 billion, as shown in Figure P.24. (The actual 2001 sales were \$2.43 billion.)

✓ *Checkpoint* Now try Exercise 51.

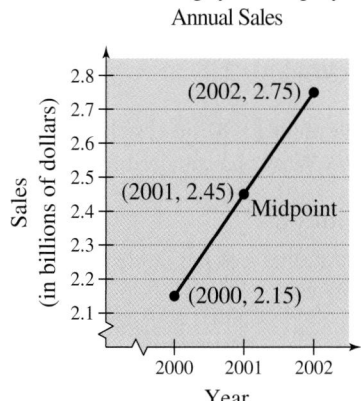

Figure P.24

The Equation of a Circle

The Distance Formula provides a convenient way to define circles. A **circle of radius r** with center at the point (h, k) is shown in Figure P.25. The point (x, y) is on this circle if and only if its distance from the center (h, k) is r. This means that a **circle** in the plane consists of all points (x, y) that are a given positive distance r from a fixed point (h, k). Using the Distance Formula, you can express this relationship by saying that the point (x, y) lies on the circle if and only if

$$\sqrt{(x - h)^2 + (y - k)^2} = r.$$

By squaring each side of this equation, you obtain the **standard form of the equation of a circle.**

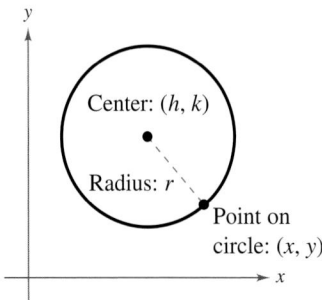

Figure P.25

Standard Form of the Equation of a Circle

The **standard form of the equation of a circle** is

$$(x - h)^2 + (y - k)^2 = r^2.$$

The point (h, k) is the **center** of the circle, and the positive number r is the **radius** of the circle. The standard form of the equation of a circle whose center is the origin, $(h, k) = (0, 0)$, is $x^2 + y^2 = r^2$.

Example 7   Writing the Equation of a Circle

The point $(3, 4)$ lies on a circle whose center is at $(-1, 2)$, as shown in Figure P.26. Write the standard form of the equation of this circle.

Solution

The radius r of the circle is the distance between $(-1, 2)$ and $(3, 4)$.

$$r = \sqrt{[3 - (-1)]^2 + (4 - 2)^2} \qquad \text{Substitute for } x, y, h, \text{ and } k.$$

$$= \sqrt{16 + 4} \qquad \text{Simplify.}$$

$$= \sqrt{20} \qquad \text{Radius.}$$

Using $(h, k) = (-1, 2)$ and $r = \sqrt{20}$, the equation of the circle is

$$(x - h)^2 + (y - k)^2 = r^2 \qquad \text{Equation of circle}$$

$$[x - (-1)]^2 + (y - 2)^2 = \left(\sqrt{20}\right)^2 \qquad \text{Substitute for } h, k, \text{ and } r.$$

$$(x + 1)^2 + (y - 2)^2 = 20. \qquad \text{Standard form}$$

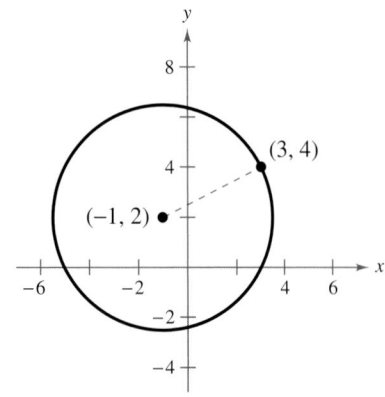

Figure P.26

✓ *Checkpoint* Now try Exercise 57.

Example 8   Translating Points in the Plane

The triangle in Figure P.27 has vertices at the points $(-1, 2)$, $(1, -4)$, and $(2, 3)$. Shift the triangle three units to the right and two units upward and find the vertices of the shifted triangle, as shown in Figure P.28.

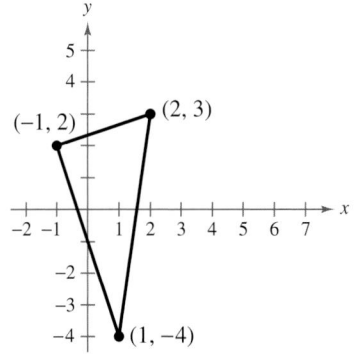

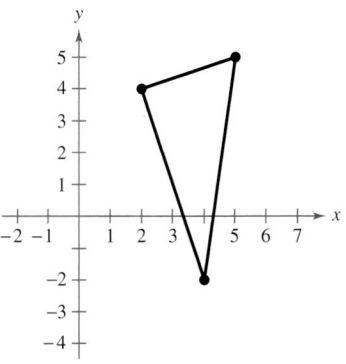

Figure P.27   **Figure P.28**

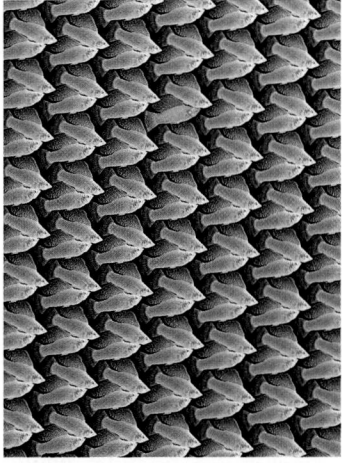

Much of computer graphics, including this computer-generated goldfish tessellation, consists of transformations of points in a coordinate plane. One type of transformation, a translation, is illustrated in Example 8. Other types of transformations include reflections, rotations, and stretches.

Solution

To shift the vertices three units to the right, add 3 to each of the x-coordinates. To shift the vertices two units upward, add 2 to each of the y-coordinates.

Original Point	Translated Point
$(-1, 2)$	$(-1 + 3, 2 + 2) = (2, 4)$
$(1, -4)$	$(1 + 3, -4 + 2) = (4, -2)$
$(2, 3)$	$(2 + 3, 3 + 2) = (5, 5)$

Plotting the translated points and sketching the line segments between them produces the shifted triangle shown in Figure P.28.

 *Checkpoint*   Now try Exercise 69.

Example 8 shows how to translate points in a coordinate plane. The following transformed points are related to the original points as follows.

Original Point	Transformed Point	
(x, y)	$(-x, y)$	$(-x, y)$ is a reflection of the original point in the y-axis.
(x, y)	$(x, -y)$	$(x, -y)$ is a reflection of the original point in the x-axis.
(x, y)	$(-x, -y)$	$(-x, -y)$ is a reflection of the original point through the origin.

The figure provided with Example 8 was not really essential to the solution. Nevertheless, it is strongly recommended that you develop the habit of including sketches with your solutions, even if they are not required, because they serve as useful problem-solving tools.

P.5 | Exercises

Vocabulary Check

1. Match each term with its definition.

  (a) *x*-axis   (i) point of intersection of vertical axis and horizontal axis

  (b) *y*-axis   (ii) directed distance from the *x*-axis

  (c) origin   (iii) horizontal real number line

  (d) quadrants   (iv) four regions of the coordinate plane

  (e) *x*-coordinate   (v) directed distance from the *y*-axis

  (f) *y*-coordinate   (vi) vertical real number line

In Exercises 2–5, fill in the blanks.

2. An ordered pair of real numbers can be represented in a plane called the rectangular coordinate system or the _____ plane.

3. The _____ is a result derived from the Pythagorean Theorem.

4. Finding the average values of the respective coordinates of the two endpoints of a line segment in a coordinate plane is also known as using the _____ .

5. The standard form of the equation of a circle is _____ , where the point (h, k) is the _____ of the circle and the positive number r is the _____ of the circle.

In Exercises 1 and 2, approximate the coordinates of the points.

1.   **2.**

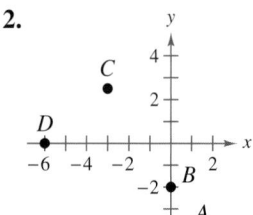

In Exercises 3–6, plot the points in the Cartesian plane.

3. $(-4, 2), (-3, -6), (0, 5), (1, -4)$

4. $(4, -2), (0, 0), (-4, 0), (-5, -5)$

5. $(3, 8), (0.5, -1), (5, -6), (-2, -2.5)$

6. $\left(1, -\frac{1}{2}\right), \left(-\frac{3}{4}, 2\right), (3, -3), \left(\frac{3}{2}, \frac{4}{3}\right)$

In Exercises 7–10, find the coordinates of the point.

7. The point is located five units to the left of the *y*-axis and four units above the *x*-axis.

8. The point is located three units below the *x*-axis and two units to the right of the *y*-axis.

9. The point is located six units below the *x*-axis and the coordinates of the point are equal.

10. The point is on the *x*-axis and 10 units to the left of the *y*-axis.

In Exercises 11–20, determine the quadrant(s) in which (x, y) is located so that the condition(s) is (are) satisfied.

11. $x > 0$ and $y < 0$

12. $x < 0$ and $y < 0$

13. $x = -4$ and $y > 0$

14. $x > 2$ and $y = 3$

15. $y < -5$

16. $x > 4$

17. $x < 0$ and $-y > 0$

18. $-x > 0$ and $y < 0$

19. $xy > 0$

20. $xy < 0$

In Exercises 21 and 22, sketch a scatter plot of the data shown in the table.

21. *Meteorology*   The table shows the lowest temperature on record y (in degrees Fahrenheit) in Duluth, Minnesota, for each month x, where $x = 1$ represents January.   (Source: NOAA)

Month, x	Temperature, y
1	-39
2	-39
3	-29
4	-5
5	17
6	27
7	35
8	32
9	22
10	8
11	-23
12	-34

22. *Number of Stores*   The table shows the number y of Wal-Mart stores for each year x from 1994 through 2001.   (Source: Wal-Mart Stores, Inc.)

Year	Number of stores, y
1994	2759
1995	2943
1996	3054
1997	3406
1998	3599
1999	3985
2000	4189
2001	4414

In Exercises 23–32, find the distance between the points algebraically and verify graphically by using centimeter graph paper and a centimeter ruler.

23. $(6, -3), (6, 5)$ **24.** $(1, 4), (8, 4)$

25. $(-3, -1), (2, -1)$ **26.** $(-3, -4), (-3, 6)$

27. $(-2, 6), (3, -6)$ **28.** $(8, 5), (0, 20)$

29. $\left(\frac{1}{2}, \frac{4}{3}\right), (2, -1)$

30. $\left(-\frac{2}{3}, 3\right), \left(-1, \frac{5}{4}\right)$

31. $(-4.2, 3.1), (-12.5, 4.8)$

32. $(9.5, -2.6), (-3.9, 8.2)$

In Exercises 33–36, (a) find the length of each side of the right triangle and (b) show that these lengths satisfy the Pythagorean Theorem.

33.
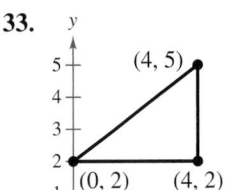

34.
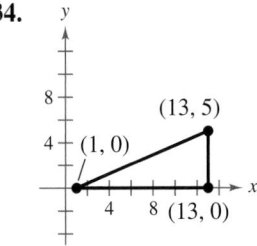

35.
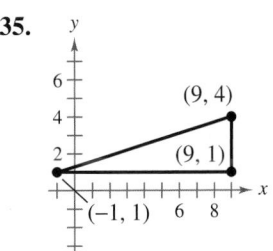

36.
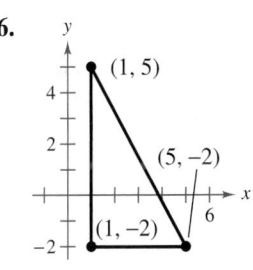

In Exercises 37–40, show that the points form the vertices of the polygon.

37. Right triangle: $(4, 0), (2, 1), (-1, -5)$

38. Isosceles triangle: $(1, -3), (3, 2), (-2, 4)$

39. Parallelogram: $(2, 5), (0, 9), (-2, 0), (0, -4)$

40. Parallelogram: $(0, 1), (3, 7), (4, 4), (1, -2)$

In Exercises 41–50, (a) plot the points, (b) find the distance between the points, and (c) find the midpoint of the line segment joining the points.

41. $(1, 1), (9, 7)$

42. $(1, 12), (6, 0)$

43. $(-4, 10), (4, -5)$

44. $(-7, -4), (2, 8)$

45. $(-1, 2), (5, 4)$

46. $(2, 10), (10, 2)$

47. $\left(\frac{1}{2}, 1\right), \left(-\frac{5}{2}, \frac{4}{3}\right)$

48. $\left(-\frac{1}{3}, -\frac{1}{3}\right), \left(-\frac{1}{6}, -\frac{1}{2}\right)$

49. $(6.2, 5.4), (-3.7, 1.8)$

50. $(-16.8, 12.3), (5.6, 4.9)$

Sales **In Exercises 51 and 52, use the Midpoint Formula to estimate the sales of PETCO Animal Supplies, Inc. and PetsMART, Inc. in 2000. The sales for the two companies in 1998 and 2002 are shown in the tables. Assume that the sales followed a linear pattern.**

51. PETCO

Year	Sales (in millions)
1998	$839.6
2002	$1480.0

(Source: PETCO Animal Supplies, Inc.)

52. PetsMART

Year	Sales (in millions)
1998	$2109.3
2002	$2750.0

(Source: PetsMART, Inc.)

53. *Exploration*   A line segment has (x_1, y_1) as one endpoint and (x_m, y_m) as its midpoint. Find the other endpoint (x_2, y_2) of the line segment in terms of $x_1, y_1, x_m,$ and y_m. Use the result to find the coordinates of the endpoint of a line segment if the coordinates of the other endpoint and midpoint are, respectively,

(a) $(1, -2), (4, -1)$

(b) $(-5, 11), (2, 4)$

54. *Exploration*   Use the Midpoint Formula three times to find the three points that divide the line segment joining (x_1, y_1) and (x_2, y_2) into four parts. Use the result to find the points that divide the line segment joining the given points into four equal parts.

(a) $(1, -2), (4, -1)$

(b) $(-2, -3), (0, 0)$

In Exercises 55–62, write the standard form of the equation of the specified circle.

55. Center: $(0, 0)$; radius: 3

56. Center: $(0, 0)$; radius: 6

57. Center: $(2, -1)$; radius: 4

58. Center: $\left(0, \frac{1}{3}\right)$; radius: $\frac{1}{3}$

59. Center: $(-1, 2)$; solution point: $(0, 0)$

60. Center: $(3, -2)$; solution point: $(-1, 1)$

61. Endpoints of a diameter: $(0, 0), (6, 8)$

62. Endpoints of a diameter: $(-4, -1), (4, 1)$

In Exercises 63–68, find the center and radius, and sketch the circle.

63. $x^2 + y^2 = 25$

64. $x^2 + y^2 = 16$

65. $(x - 1)^2 + (y + 3)^2 = 4$

66. $x^2 + (y - 1)^2 = 49$

67. $\left(x - \frac{1}{2}\right)^2 + \left(y - \frac{1}{2}\right)^2 = \frac{9}{4}$

68. $\left(x - \frac{2}{3}\right)^2 + \left(y + \frac{1}{4}\right)^2 = \frac{25}{9}$

In Exercises 69–72, the polygon is shifted to a new position in the plane. Find the coordinates of the vertices of the polygon in the new position.

69.

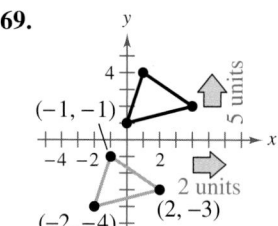

70.

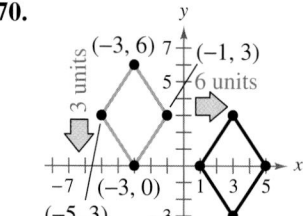

71. Original coordinates of vertices:

$(0, 2), (3, 5), (5, 2), (2, -1)$

Shift: three units upward, one unit to the left

72. Original coordinates of vertices:

$(1, -1), (3, 2), (1, -2)$

Shift: two units downward, three units to the left

Analyzing Data **In Exercises 73 and 74, refer to the scatter plot, which shows the mathematics entrance test scores *x* and the final examination scores *y* in an algebra course for a sample of 10 students.**

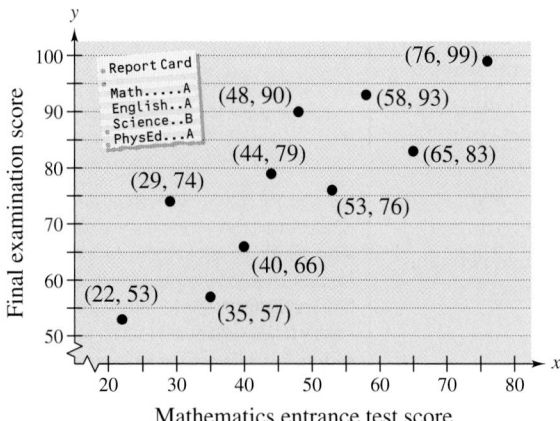

Mathematics entrance test score

73. Find the entrance exam score of any student with a final exam score in the 80s.

74. Does a higher entrance exam score necessarily imply a higher final exam score? Explain.

75. *Rock and Roll Hall of Fame* The graph shows the numbers of recording artists inducted to the Rock and Roll Hall of Fame from 1986 to 2003.

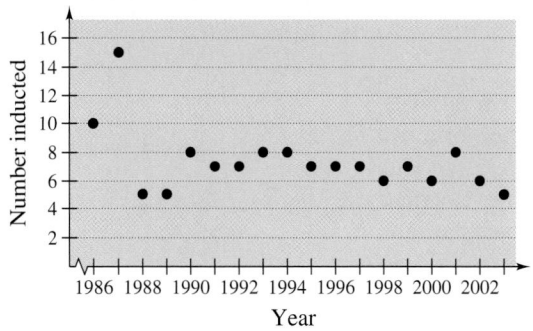

Year

(a) Describe any trends in the data. From these trends, predict the number of artists that will be elected in 2005.

(b) Why do you think the numbers elected in 1986 and 1987 were greater than in other years?

76. *Flying Distance* A jet plane flies from Naples, Italy in a straight line to Rome, Italy, which is 120 kilometers west and 150 kilometers north of Naples. How far does the plane fly?

77. *Sports* In a football game, a quarterback throws a pass from the 15-yard line, 10 yards from the sideline as shown in the figure. The pass is caught on the 40-yard line, 45 yards from the same sideline. How long is the pass?

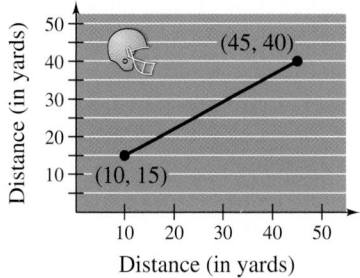

Distance (in yards)

78. *Make a Conjecture* Plot the points $(2, 1)$, $(-3, 5)$, and $(7, -3)$ on a rectangular coordinate system. Then change the sign of the indicated coordinate(s) of each point and plot the three new points on the same rectangular coordinate system. Make a conjecture about the location of a point when each of the following occurs.

(a) The sign of the *x*-coordinate is changed.

(b) The sign of the *y*-coordinate is changed.

(c) The signs of both the *x*- and *y*-coordinates are changed.

Synthesis

True or False? **In Exercises 79–81, determine whether the statement is true or false. Justify your answer.**

79. In order to divide a line segment into 16 equal parts, you would have to use the Midpoint Formula 16 times.

80. The points $(-8, 4)$, $(2, 11)$, and $(-5, 1)$ represent the vertices of an isosceles triangle.

81. If four points represent the vertices of a polygon, and the four sides are equal, then the polygon must be a square.

82. *Think About It* What is the *y*-coordinate of any point on the *x*-axis? What is the *x*-coordinate of any point on the *y*-axis?

83. *Think About It* When plotting points on the rectangular coordinate system, is it true that the scales on the *x*- and *y*-axes must be the same? Explain.

P.6 Exploring Data: Representing Data Graphically

Line Plots

Statistics is the branch of mathematics that studies techniques for collecting, organizing, and interpreting data. In this section, you will study several ways to organize data. The first is a **line plot,** which uses a portion of a real number line to order numbers. Line plots are especially useful for ordering small sets of numbers (about 50 or less) by hand.

Many statistical measures can be obtained from a line plot. Two such measures are the *frequency* and *range* of the data. The **frequency** measures the number of times a value occurs in a data set. The **range** is the difference between the greatest and least data values. For example, consider the data values

    20, 21, 21, 25, 32.

The frequency of 21 in the data set is 2 because 21 occurs twice. The range is 12 because the difference between the greatest and least data values is $32 - 20 = 12$.

Example 1   Constructing a Line Plot

Use a line plot to organize the following test scores. Which score occurs with the greatest frequency? What is the range of scores?

    93, 70, 76, 67, 86, 93, 82, 78, 83, 86, 64, 78, 76, 66, 83
    83, 96, 74, 69, 76, 64, 74, 79, 76, 88, 76, 81, 82, 74, 70

Solution

Begin by scanning the data to find the smallest and largest numbers. For this data, the smallest number is 64 and the largest is 96. Next, draw a portion of a real number line that includes the interval $[64, 96]$. To create the line plot, start with the first number, 93, and enter an $\times$ above 93 on the number line. Continue recording $\times$'s for each number in the list until you obtain the line plot shown in Figure P.29. From the line plot, you can see that 76 occurs with the greatest frequency. Because the range is the difference between the greatest and least data values, the range of scores is $96 - 64 = 32$.

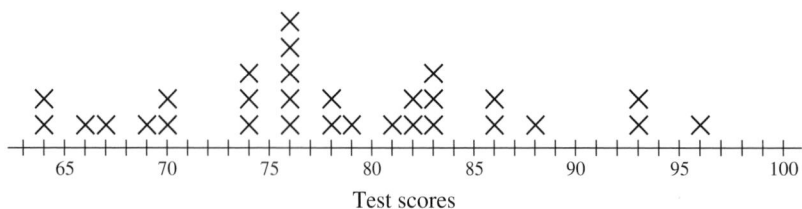

Test scores

Figure P.29

 Checkpoint Now try Exercise 1.

Histograms and Frequency Distributions

When you want to organize large sets of data, it is useful to group the data into intervals and plot the frequency of the data in each interval. A **frequency distribution** can be used to construct a **histogram.** A histogram uses a portion of a real number line as its horizontal axis. The bars of a histogram are not separated by spaces.

Example 2   Constructing a Histogram

The table at the right shows the percent of the resident population of each state and the District of Columbia that was at least 65 years old in 2000. Construct a frequency distribution and a histogram for the data.   (Source: U.S. Census Bureau)

AK	5.7	MT	13.4
AL	13.0	NC	12.0
AR	14.0	ND	14.7
AZ	13.0	NE	13.6
CA	10.6	NH	12.0
CO	9.7	NJ	13.2
CT	13.8	NM	11.7
DC	12.2	NV	11.0
DE	13.0	NY	12.9
FL	17.6	OH	13.3
GA	9.6	OK	13.2
HI	13.3	OR	12.8
IA	14.9	PA	15.6
ID	11.3	RI	14.5
IL	12.1	SC	12.1
IN	12.4	SD	14.3
KS	13.3	TN	12.4
KY	12.5	TX	9.9
LA	11.6	UT	8.5
MA	13.5	VA	11.2
MD	11.3	VT	12.7
ME	14.4	WA	11.2
MI	12.3	WI	13.1
MN	12.1	WV	15.3
MO	13.5	WY	11.7
MS	12.1		

Solution

To begin constructing a frequency distribution, you must first decide on the number of intervals. There are several ways to group this data. However, because the smallest number is 5.7 and the largest is 17.6, it seems that seven intervals would be appropriate. The first would be the interval $[5, 7)$, the second would be $[7, 9)$, and so on. By tallying the data into the seven intervals, you obtain the frequency distribution shown below. You can construct the histogram by drawing a vertical axis to represent the number of states and a horizontal axis to represent the percent of the population 65 and older. Then, for each interval, draw a vertical bar whose height is the total tally, as shown in Figure P.30.

Interval	*Tally*
$[5, 7)$	|
$[7, 9)$	|
$[9, 11)$	||||
$[11, 13)$	⊬⊬⊬ ⊬⊬⊬ ⊬⊬⊬ ⊬⊬⊬ ||
$[13, 15)$	⊬⊬⊬ ⊬⊬⊬ ⊬⊬⊬ ⊬⊬⊬
$[15, 17)$	||
$[17, 19)$	|

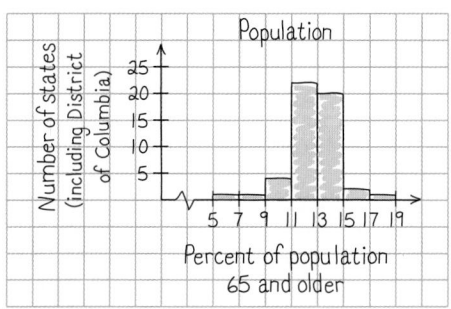

Figure P.30

☑ *Checkpoint* Now try Exercise 5.

Example 3   Constructing a Histogram

A company has 48 sales representatives who sold the following numbers of units during the first quarter of 2005. Construct a frequency distribution for this data.

107	162	184	170	177	102	145	141
105	193	167	149	195	127	193	191
150	153	164	167	171	163	141	129
109	171	150	138	100	164	147	153
171	163	118	142	107	144	100	132
153	107	124	162	192	134	187	177

Interval	Tally
100–109	⦀⦀ |||
110–119		
120–129	|||
130–139	|||
140–149	⦀⦀ ||
150–159	⦀⦀
160–169	⦀⦀ |||
170–179	⦀⦀	
180–189	||
190–199	⦀⦀

Solution

To begin constructing a frequency distribution, you must first decide on the number of intervals. There are several ways to group this data. However, because the smallest number is 100 and the largest is 195, it seems that 10 intervals would be appropriate. The first interval would be 100–109, the second would be 110–119, and so on. By tallying the data into the 10 intervals, you obtain the distribution shown at the right above. A histogram for the distribution is shown in Figure P.31.

✓ *Checkpoint*   Now try Exercise 6.

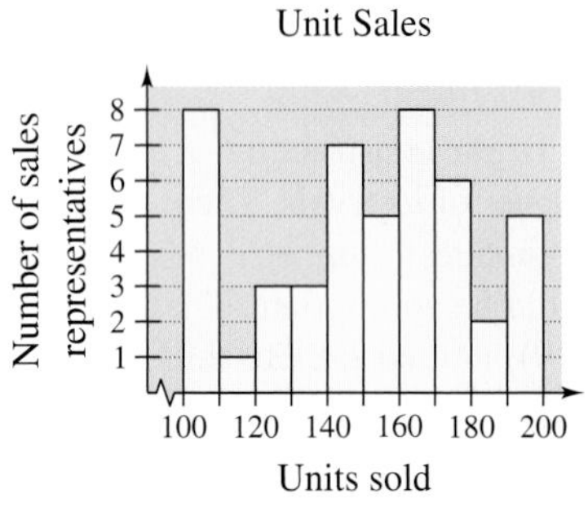

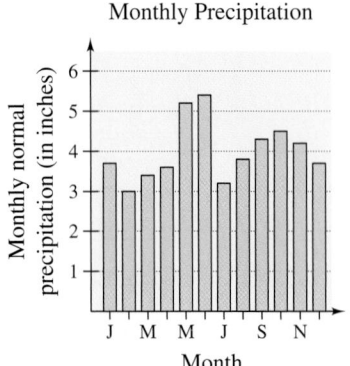

Figure P.31

Bar Graphs

A **bar graph** is similar to a histogram, except that the bars can be either horizontal or vertical and the labels of the bars are not necessarily numbers. Another difference between a bar graph and a histogram is that the bars in a bar graph are usually separated by spaces.

Example 4   Constructing a Bar Graph

The data below shows the monthly normal precipitation (in inches) in Houston, Texas. Construct a bar graph for this data. What can you conclude?   (Source: National Climatic Data Center)

January	3.7	February	3.0	March	3.4
April	3.6	May	5.2	June	5.4
July	3.2	August	3.8	September	4.3
October	4.5	November	4.2	December	3.7

Solution

To create a bar graph, begin by drawing a vertical axis to represent the precipitation and a horizontal axis to represent the month. The bar graph is shown in Figure P.32. From the graph, you can see that Houston receives a fairly consistent amount of rain throughout the year—the driest month tends to be February and the wettest month tends to be June.

✓ *Checkpoint*   Now try Exercise 9.

Figure P.32

Example 5   Constructing a Double Bar Graph

The table shows the percents of bachelor's degrees awarded to males and females for selected fields of study in the United States in 2000. Construct a double bar graph for this data.   (Source: U.S. National Center for Education Statistics)

Field of study	% Female	% Male
Agriculture and Natural Resources	42.9	57.1
Biological Sciences/Life Sciences	58.3	41.7
Business and Management	49.7	50.3
Education	75.8	24.2
Engineering	18.5	81.5
Law and Legal Studies	73.0	27.0
Liberal/General Studies	66.1	33.9
Mathematics	47.1	52.9
Physical Sciences	40.3	59.7
Social Sciences	51.2	48.8

Solution

For this data, a horizontal bar graph seems to be appropriate. This makes it easier to label the bars. Such a graph is shown in Figure P.33.

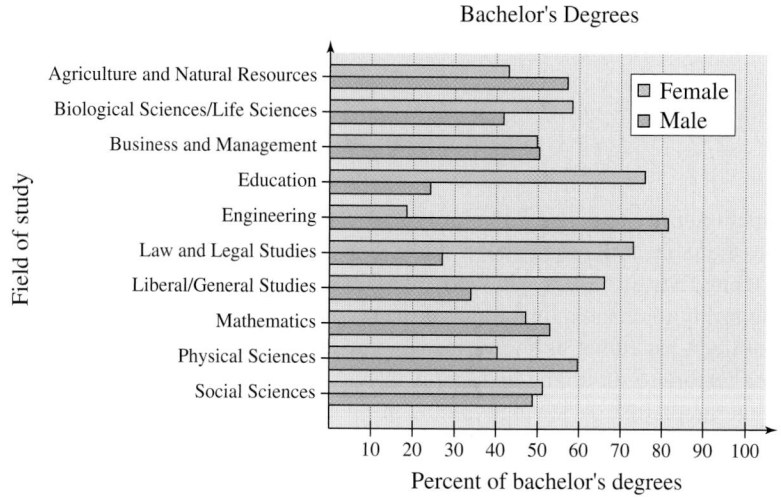

Figure P.33

✓ *Checkpoint* Now try Exercise 10.

Line Graphs

A **line graph** is similar to a standard coordinate graph. Line graphs are usually used to show trends over periods of time.

Example 6 Constructing a Line Graph

The table at the right shows the number of immigrants (in thousands) entering the United States for each decade from 1901 to 2000. Construct a line graph for this data. What can you conclude? (Source: U.S. Immigration and Naturalization Service)

Decade	Number
1901–1910	8795
1911–1920	5736
1921–1930	4107
1931–1940	528
1941–1950	1035
1951–1960	2515
1961–1970	3322
1971–1980	4493
1981–1990	7338
1991–2000	9095

Solution

Begin by drawing a vertical axis to represent the number of immigrants in thousands. Then label the horizontal axis with decades and plot the points shown in the table. Finally, connect the points with line segments, as shown in Figure P.34. From the line graph, you can see that the number of immigrants hit a low point during the depression of the 1930s. Since then the number has steadily increased.

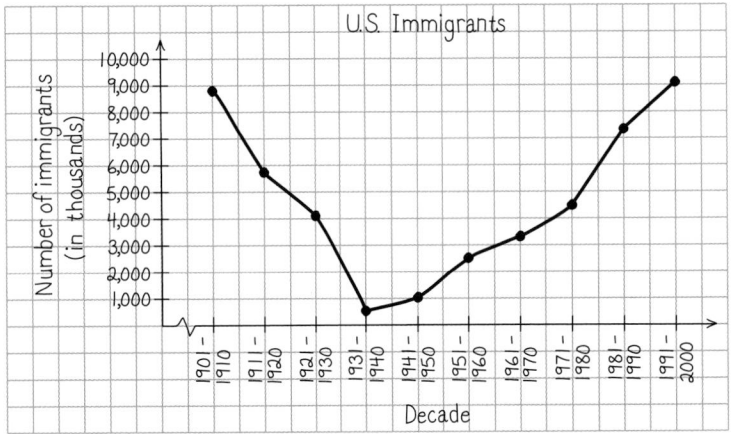

Figure P.34

✓ *Checkpoint* Now try Exercise 15.

TECHNOLOGY TIP You can use a graphing utility to create different types of graphs, such as line graphs. For instance, the table at the right shows the number N of women on active duty in the United States military (in thousands) for selected years. To use a graphing utility to create a line graph of the data, first enter the data into the graphing utility's list editor, as shown in Figure P.35. Then use the *statistical plotting* feature to set up the line graph, as shown in Figure P.36. Finally, display the line graph (use a viewing window in which 1970 ≤ x ≤ 2005 and 0 ≤ y ≤ 250) as shown in Figure P.37. (Source: U.S. Department of Defense)

Year	Number
1975	97
1980	171
1985	212
1990	227
1995	196
2000	203

Figure P.35

Figure P.36

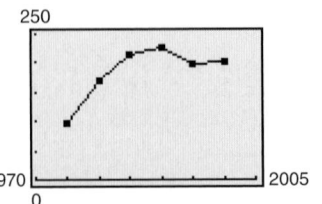

Figure P.37

P.6   Exercises

Vocabulary Check

Fill in the blanks.

1. _____ is the branch of mathematics that studies techniques for collecting, organizing, and interpreting data.

2. _____ are useful for ordering small sets of numbers by hand.

3. A _____ has a portion of a real number line as its horizontal axis, and the bars are not separated by spaces.

4. You use a _____ to construct a histogram.

5. The bars on a _____ can be either vertical or horizontal.

6. _____ show trends over periods of time.

---

1. **Consumer Awareness**   The line plot shows a sample of prices of unleaded regular gasoline from 25 different cities.

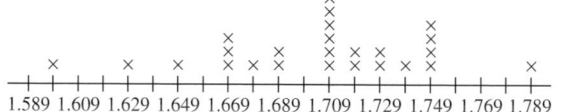

1.589 1.609 1.629 1.649 1.669 1.689 1.709 1.729 1.749 1.769 1.789

   (a) What price occurred with the greatest frequency?

   (b) What is the range of prices?

2. **Agriculture**   The line plot shows the weights (to the nearest hundred pounds) of 30 head of cattle sold by a rancher.

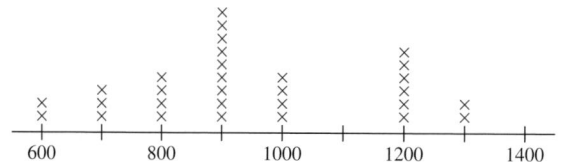

   600   800   1000   1200   1400

   (a) What weight occurred with the greatest frequency?

   (b) What is the range of weights?

Quiz and Exam Scores   **In Exercises 3 and 4, use the following scores from an algebra class of 30 students. The scores are for one 25-point quiz and one 100-point exam.**

Quiz   **20, 15, 14, 20, 16, 19, 10, 21, 24, 15, 15, 14, 15, 21, 19, 15, 20, 18, 18, 22, 18, 16, 18, 19, 21, 19, 16, 20, 14, 12**

Exam   **77, 100, 77, 70, 83, 89, 87, 85, 81, 84, 81, 78, 89, 78, 88, 85, 90, 92, 75, 81, 85, 100, 98, 81, 78, 75, 85, 89, 82, 75**

3. Construct a line plot for the quiz. Which score(s) occurred with the greatest frequency?

4. Construct a line plot for the exam. Which score(s) occurred with the greatest frequency?

5. **Education**   The list shows the per capita expenditures for public elementary and secondary education in the 50 states and the District of Columbia in 2001. Use a frequency distribution and a histogram to organize the data. (Source: National Education Association)

AK 2165	AL 1056	AR 1102	AZ 1078
CA 1374	CO 1339	CT 1907	D.C. 1786
DE 1555	FL 1171	GA 1506	HI 1164
IA 1231	ID 1203	IL 1621	IN 1495
KS 1276	KY 1193	LA 1159	MA 1511
MD 1412	ME 1427	MI 1487	MN 1718
MO 1233	MS 1041	MT 1233	NC 1163
ND 859	NE 1194	NH 1262	NJ 1669
NM 1222	NV 1316	NY 1783	OH 1295
OK 1181	OR 1347	PA 1223	RI 1399
SC 1264	SD 1176	TN 973	TX 1602
UT 1151	VA 1177	VT 1672	WA 1436
WI 1593	WV 1347	WY 1549	

6. Agriculture The list shows the number of farms (in thousands) in the 50 states in 2001. Use a frequency distribution and a histogram to organize the data. (Source: U.S. Department of Agriculture)

AK 0.6	AL 47.0	AR 48.0	AZ 7.3
CA 88.0	CO 30.0	CT 3.9	DE 2.5
FL 44.0	GA 50.0	HI 5.3	IA 93.5
ID 24.0	IL 76.0	IN 63.0	KS 63.0
KY 88.0	LA 29.0	MA 6.0	MD 12.4
ME 6.7	MI 52.0	MN 79.0	MO 108.0
MS 42.0	MT 26.6	NC 56.0	ND 30.3
NE 53.0	NH 3.1	NJ 9.6	NM 15.0
NV 3.0	NY 37.5	OH 78.0	OK 86.0
OR 40.0	PA 59.0	RI 0.7	SC 24.0
SD 32.5	TN 91.0	TX 227.0	UT 15.0
VA 49.0	VT 6.6	WA 39.0	WI 77.0
WV 20.5	WY 9.2		

7. Entertainment The bar graph shows the number (in millions) of CDs sold for the years 1997 through 2001. Determine the percent increase in sales from 1997 to 2000. Determine the percent decrease in sales from 2000 to 2001. (Source: Recording Industry Association of America)

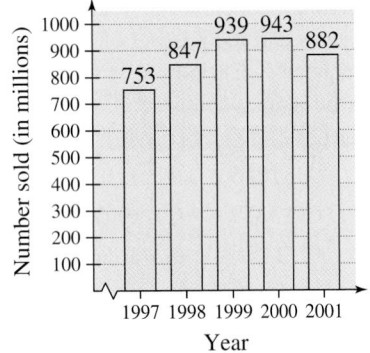

8. Agriculture The double bar graph shows the production and exports (in millions of metric tons) of corn, soybeans, and wheat for the year 2001. Approximate the percent of each product that is exported. (Source: U.S. Department of Agriculture)

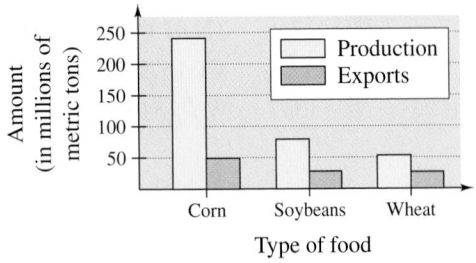

9. Sports The table shows the number of people (in millions) over the age of seven who participated in popular sports activities in 2000 in the United States. Construct a bar graph for the data. (Source: National Sporting Goods Association)

Activity	Participants
Exercise walking	86.3
Swimming	60.8
Bicycling	43.1
Camping	49.9
Bowling	43.1
Basketball	27.1
Running	22.8
Aerobic exercising	28.6

10. Population The table shows the population (in millions) in the coastal regions of the United States in 1970 and 2000. Construct a double bar graph for the data. (Source: U.S. Census Bureau)

Region	1970 population	2000 population
Atlantic	51.5	65.2
Gulf of Mexico	10.0	18.0
Great Lakes	26.0	27.3
Pacific	22.8	37.8

Retail Price In Exercises 11 and 12, use the line graph, which shows the average retail price of one pound of chicken breast from 1994 to 2001. (Source: U.S. Bureau of Labor Statistics)

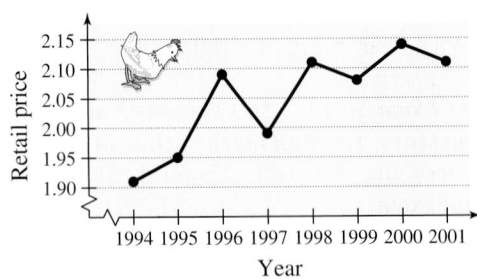

11. Approximate the highest price of one pound of chicken breast shown in the graph. When did this price occur?

12. Approximate the difference in the price of one pound of chicken breast from the highest price shown in the graph to the price in 1994.

Advertising **In Exercises 13 and 14, use the line graph, which shows the cost of a 30-second television spot (in thousands of dollars) during the Super Bowl from 1995 to 2002.** (Source: The Associated Press)

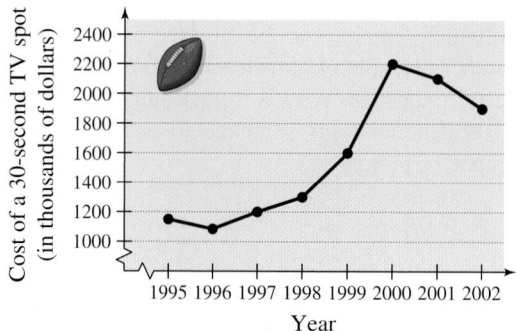

13. Approximate the percent increase in the cost of a 30-second spot from Super Bowl XXX in 1996 to Super Bowl XXXVI in 2002.

14. Estimate the increase or decrease in the cost of a 30-second spot from (a) Super Bowl XXIV in 1995 to Super Bowl XXXIII in 1999, and (b) Super Bowl XXXIV in 2000 to Super Bowl XXXVI in 2002.

15. *Oil Imports* The table shows the amount of crude oil imported into the United States (in millions of barrels) for the years 1995 through 2001. Construct a line graph for the data and state what information the graph reveals. (Source: U.S. Energy Information Administration)

Year	Imports
1995	2693
1996	2740
1997	3002
1998	3178
1999	3187
2000	3260
2001	3405

16. *Entertainment* The table shows the percent of U.S. households owning televisions that owned more than one television set for selected years from 1960 to 2000. Construct a line graph for the data and state what information the graph reveals. (Source: Nielsen Media Research)

Year	Percent
1960	12
1965	22
1970	35
1975	43
1980	50
1985	57
1990	65
1995	71
2000	76

17. *Government* The table shows the number of U.S. representatives from the state of New York for selected years from 1930 to 2000. Use a graphing utility to construct a line graph for the data. (Source: U.S. Census Bureau)

Year	Representatives
1930	45
1940	45
1950	43
1960	41
1970	39
1980	34
1990	31
2000	29

18. **Personal Savings**   The table shows the amount (in billions of dollars) of personal savings in the United States from 1995 to 2001. Use a graphing utility to construct a line graph for the data.   (Source: Bureau of Economic Analysis)

Year	Personal savings
1995	179.8
1996	158.5
1997	121.0
1998	265.4
1999	160.9
2000	201.5
2001	169.7

19. **Travel**   The table shows the places of origin and numbers of travelers (in millions) to the United States in 2000. Choose an appropriate display to organize the data.   (Source: U.S. Department of Commerce)

Place of origin	Travelers
Canada	14.6
Caribbean	1.3
Europe	11.6
Far East	7.6
Mexico	10.3
South America	2.9

20. **Education**   The table shows the number of college degrees (in thousands) awarded in the United States from 1996 to 2002. Choose an appropriate display to organize the data.   (Source: U.S. Department of Education)

Year	Degrees
1996	1692
1997	1717
1998	1739
1999	1763
2000	1820
2001	1766
2002	1786

Synthesis

21. **Writing**   Describe the differences between a bar graph and a histogram.

22. **Think About It**   How can you decide which type of graph to use when you are organizing data?

23. **Graphical Interpretation**   The graphs shown below represent the same data points. Which of the two graphs is misleading, and why? Discuss other ways in which graphs can be misleading. Try to find another example of a misleading graph in a newspaper or magazine. Why is it misleading? Why would it be beneficial for someone to use a misleading graph?

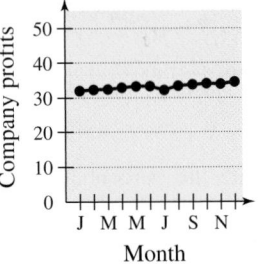

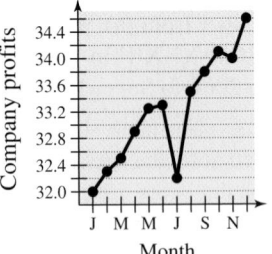

P Chapter Summary

What did you learn?

Section P.1	Review Exercises
☐ Represent and classify real numbers.	1, 2
☐ Order real numbers and use inequalities.	3–6
☐ Find the absolute values of real numbers and the distance between two real numbers.	7–12
☐ Evaluate algebraic expressions.	13–16
☐ Use the basic rules and properties of algebra.	17–26

Section P.2
☐ Use properties of exponents.	27–30
☐ Use scientific notation to represent real numbers.	31–34
☐ Use properties of radicals.	35, 36
☐ Simplify and combine radicals.	37–50
☐ Rationalize denominators and numerators.	51–54
☐ Use properties of rational exponents.	55–58

Section P.3
☐ Write polynomials in standard form.	59, 60
☐ Add, subtract, and multiply polynomials.	61–68
☐ Use special products to multiply polynomials.	69–76
☐ Remove common factors from polynomials.	77–84
☐ Factor special polynomial forms.	85–88
☐ Factor trinomials as the product of two binomials.	89–92
☐ Factor by grouping.	93–96

Section P.4
☐ Find domains of algebraic expressions.	97–100
☐ Simplify rational expressions.	101–104
☐ Add, subtract, multiply, and divide rational expressions.	105–112
☐ Simplify complex fractions.	113, 114

Section P.5
☐ Plot points in the Cartesian plane and sketch scatter plots.	115–122
☐ Use the Distance Formula to find the distance between two points.	123, 124
☐ Use the Midpoint Formula to find the midpoint of a line segment.	125, 126
☐ Find the equation of a circle.	127, 128
☐ Translate points in the plane.	129, 130

Section P.6
☐ Use line plots to order and analyze data.	131
☐ Use histograms to represent frequency distributions.	132
☐ Use bar graphs and line graphs to represent and analyze data.	133, 134

P Review Exercises

P.1 In Exercises 1 and 2, determine which numbers are (a) natural numbers, (b) whole numbers, (c) integers, (d) rational numbers, and (e) irrational numbers.

1. $\left\{ 11, -14, -\frac{8}{9}, \frac{5}{2}, \sqrt{6}, 0.4 \right\}$

2. $\left\{ \sqrt{15}, -22, -\frac{10}{3}, 0, 5.2, \frac{3}{7} \right\}$

In Exercises 3 and 4, use a calculator to find the decimal form of each rational number. If it is a nonterminating decimal, write the repeating pattern. Then plot the numbers on a real number line and place the correct inequality symbol ($<$ or $>$) between them.

3. (a) $\frac{5}{6}$ (b) $\frac{7}{8}$ 4. (a) $\frac{1}{3}$ (b) $\frac{9}{25}$

In Exercises 5 and 6, verbally describe the subset of real numbers represented by the inequality. Then sketch the subset on the real number line.

5. $x \le 7$ 6. $x > 1$

In Exercises 7 and 8, find the distance between a and b.

7. $a = -74,\ \ b = 48$ 8. $a = -123,\ \ b = -9$

In Exercises 9–12, use absolute value notation to describe the situation.

9. The distance between x and 8 is at least 3.

10. The distance between x and 25 is no more than 10.

11. The distance between y and -30 is less than 5.

12. The distance between y and -16 is greater than 8.

In Exercises 13–16, evaluate the expression for each value of x. (If not possible, state the reason.)

Expression	*Values*	
13. $10x - 3$	(a) $x = -1$	(b) $x = 3$
14. $x^2 - 11x + 24$	(a) $x = -2$	(b) $x = 2$
15. $-2x^2 - x + 3$	(a) $x = 3$	(b) $x = -3$
16. $\dfrac{4x}{x - 1}$	(a) $x = -1$	(b) $x = 1$

In Exercises 17–20, identify the rule of algebra illustrated by the statement.

17. $2x + (3x - 10) = (2x + 3x) - 10$

18. $\dfrac{2}{y + 4} \cdot \dfrac{y + 4}{2} = 1, \ \ y \ne -4$

19. $(t + 4)(2t) = (2t)(t + 4)$

20. $0 + (a - 5) = a - 5$

In Exercises 21–26, perform the operations. (Write fractional answers in simplest form.)

21. $\frac{2}{3} + \frac{8}{9}$ 22. $\frac{3}{4} - \frac{1}{6} + \frac{1}{8}$

23. $\frac{3}{16} \div \frac{9}{2}$ 24. $\frac{5}{8} \cdot \frac{2}{3}$

25. $\dfrac{x}{5} + \dfrac{7x}{12}$ 26. $\dfrac{9}{x} \div \dfrac{1}{6}$

P.2 In Exercises 27–30, simplify each expression.

27. (a) $(-2z)^3$ (b) $(a^2 b^4)(3ab^{-2})$

28. (a) $\dfrac{(8y)^0}{y^2}$ (b) $\dfrac{40(b - 3)^5}{75(b - 3)^2}$

29. (a) $\dfrac{6^2 u^3 v^{-3}}{12u^{-2}v}$ (b) $\dfrac{3^{-4} m^{-1} n^{-3}}{9^{-2} mn^{-3}}$

30. (a) $(x + y^{-1})^{-1}$ (b) $\left(\dfrac{x^{-3}}{y} \right)\left(\dfrac{x}{y} \right)^{-1}$

In Exercises 31 and 32, write the number in scientific notation.

31. *Revenues of Target Corporation in 2002:*
    $43,800,000,000   (Source: Target Corporation)

32. *Number of meters in one foot:* 0.3048

In Exercises 33 and 34, write the number in decimal notation.

33. *Distance between the Sun and Jupiter:*
    4.836×10^8 miles

34. *Ratio of day to year:* 2.74×10^{-3}

In Exercises 35 and 36, use the properties of radicals to simplify the expression.

35. $\left(\sqrt[4]{78} \right)^4$ 36. $\sqrt[3]{9} \cdot \sqrt[3]{3}$

In Exercises 37–42, simplify by removing all possible factors from the radical.

37. $\sqrt{4x^4}$ 38. $\sqrt[5]{64x^6}$

39. $\sqrt{\dfrac{81}{144}}$ 40. $\sqrt[3]{\dfrac{125}{216}}$

41. $\sqrt[3]{\dfrac{2x^3}{27}}$ **42.** $\sqrt{\dfrac{75x^2}{y^4}}$

In Exercises 43–48, simplify the expression.

43. $\sqrt{50} - \sqrt{18}$ **44.** $3\sqrt{32} + 4\sqrt{98}$

45. $8\sqrt{3x} - 5\sqrt{3x}$ **46.** $-11\sqrt{36y} - 6\sqrt{y}$

47. $\sqrt{8x^3} + \sqrt{2x}$ **48.** $3\sqrt{14x^2} - \sqrt{56x^2}$

Strength of a Wooden Beam **In Exercises 49 and 50, use the figure, which shows the rectangular cross section of a wooden beam cut from a log of diameter 24 inches.**

49. Find the area of the cross section when $w = 12\sqrt{2}$ inches and $h = \sqrt{24^2 - \left(12\sqrt{2}\right)^2}$ inches. What is the shape of the cross section? Explain.

50. The rectangular cross section will have a maximum strength when $w = 8\sqrt{3}$ inches and $h = \sqrt{24^2 - \left(8\sqrt{3}\right)^2}$ inches. Find the area of the cross section.

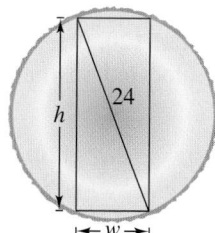

In Exercises 51 and 52, rationalize the denominator of the expression. Then simplify your answer.

51. $\dfrac{1}{2 - \sqrt{3}}$ **52.** $\dfrac{1}{\sqrt{x} - 1}$

In Exercises 53 and 54, rationalize the numerator of the expression. Then simplify your answer.

53. $\dfrac{\sqrt{20}}{4}$ **54.** $\dfrac{\sqrt{2} - \sqrt{11}}{3}$

In Exercises 55–58, simplify the expression.

55. $81^{3/2}$ **56.** $64^{-2/3}$

57. $\left(-3x^{2/5}\right)\left(-2x^{1/2}\right)$ **58.** $(x - 1)^{1/3}(x - 1)^{-1/4}$

P.3 In Exercises 59 and 60, write the polynomial in standard form. Then identify the degree and leading coefficient of the polynomial.

59. $15x^2 - 2x^5 + 3x^3 + 5 - x^4$

60. $-2x^4 + x^2 - 10 - x + x^3$

In Exercises 61–68, perform the operations and write the result in standard form.

61. $-(3x^2 + 2x) + (1 - 5x)$

62. $8y - [2y^2 - (3y - 8)]$

63. $(2x^3 - 5x^2 + 10x - 7) + (4x^2 - 7x - 2)$

64. $(6x^4 - 4x^3 - x + 3 - 20x^2) - (16 + 9x^4 - 11x^2)$

65. $(x^2 - 2x + 1)(x^3 - 1)$

66. $(x^3 - 3x)(2x^2 + 3x + 5)$

67. $(y^2 - y)(y^2 + 1)(y^2 + y + 1)$

68. $\left(x - \dfrac{1}{x}\right)(x + 2)$

In Exercises 69–74, find the special product.

69. $(x + 8)(x - 8)$ **70.** $(7x + 4)(7x - 4)$

71. $(x - 4)^3$ **72.** $(2x - 1)^3$

73. $(m - 4 + n)(m - 4 - n)$

74. $(x - y - 6)(x - y + 6)$

75. ***Geometry*** Use the area model to write two different expressions for the area. Then equate the two expressions and name the algebraic property that is illustrated.

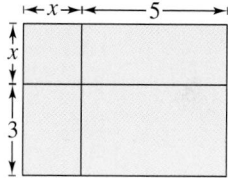

76. ***Compound Interest*** After 2 years, an investment of $2500 compounded annually at an interest rate r will yield an amount of $2500(1 + r)^2$. Write this polynomial in standard form.

In Exercises 77–82, factor out the common factor.

77. $7x + 35$ **78.** $10x - 2$

79. $x^3 - x$ **80.** $x(x - 3) + 4(x - 3)$

81. $2x^3 + 18x^2 - 4x$ **82.** $-6x^4 - 3x^3 + 12x$

83. ***Geometry*** The surface area of a right circular cylinder is $S = 2\pi r^2 + 2\pi rh$.

(a) Draw a right circular cylinder of radius r and height h. Use the figure to explain how the surface area formula is obtained.

(b) Factor the expression for surface area.

84. *Business*   The revenue for selling x units of a product at a price of p dollars per unit is $R = xp$. For a flat panel television the revenue is

$$R = 1600x - 0.50x^2.$$

Factor the expression and determine an expression that gives the price in terms of x.

In Exercises 85–92, factor the expression.

85. $x^2 - 169$

86. $9x^2 - \frac{1}{25}$

87. $x^3 + 216$

88. $64x^3 - 27$

89. $x^2 - 6x - 27$

90. $x^2 - 9x + 14$

91. $2x^2 + 21x + 10$

92. $3x^2 + 14x + 8$

In Exercises 93–96, factor by grouping.

93. $x^3 - 4x^2 - 3x + 12$ **94.** $x^3 - 6x^2 - x + 6$

95. $2x^2 - x - 15$ **96.** $6x^2 + x - 12$

P.4 In Exercises 97–100, find the domain of the expression.

97. $-5x^2 - x - 1$

98. $9x^4 + 7, \quad x > 0$

99. $\dfrac{4}{2x - 3}$

100. $\sqrt{x + 12}$

In Exercises 101–104, write the rational expression in simplest form.

101. $\dfrac{4x^2}{4x^3 + 28x}$

102. $\dfrac{6xy}{xy + 2x}$

103. $\dfrac{x^2 - x - 30}{x^2 - 25}$

104. $\dfrac{x^2 - 9x + 18}{8x - 48}$

In Exercises 105–112, perform the operation and simplify your answer.

105. $\dfrac{x^2 - 4}{x^4 - 2x^2 - 8} \cdot \dfrac{x^2 + 2}{x^2}$

106. $\dfrac{2x - 1}{x + 1} \cdot \dfrac{x^2 - 1}{2x^2 - 7x + 3}$

107. $\dfrac{x^2(5x - 6)}{2x + 3} \div \dfrac{5x}{2x + 3}$

108. $\dfrac{4x - 6}{(x - 1)^2} \div \dfrac{2x^2 - 3x}{x^2 + 2x - 3}$

109. $x - 1 + \dfrac{1}{x + 2} + \dfrac{1}{x - 1}$

110. $2x + \dfrac{3}{2(x - 4)} - \dfrac{1}{2(x + 2)}$

111. $\dfrac{1}{x} - \dfrac{x - 1}{x^2 + 1}$

112. $\dfrac{1}{x - 1} + \dfrac{1 - x}{x^2 + x + 1}$

In Exercises 113 and 114, simplify the complex fraction.

113. $\dfrac{\left(\dfrac{1}{x} - \dfrac{1}{y}\right)}{(x^2 - y^2)}$

114. $\dfrac{\left(\dfrac{1}{2x - 3} - \dfrac{1}{2x + 3}\right)}{\left(\dfrac{1}{2x} - \dfrac{1}{2x + 3}\right)}$

P.5 In Exercises 115–118, plot the point in the Cartesian plane and determine the quadrant in which it is located.

115. $(8, -3)$

116. $(-4, -9)$

117. $\left(-\frac{5}{2}, 10\right)$

118. $(-6.5, -0.5)$

In Exercises 119 and 120, determine the quadrant(s) in which (x, y) is located so that the conditions are satisfied.

119. $x > 0$ and $y = -2$ **120.** $xy = 4$

Patents   **In Exercises 121 and 122, use the table, which shows the number of patents P (in thousands) issued in the United States from 1994 through 2001.** (Source: U.S. Patent and Trademark Office)

Year	Patents, P
1994	113.6
1995	113.8
1996	121.7
1997	124.1
1998	163.1
1999	169.1
2000	176.0
2001	184.0

121. Sketch a scatter plot of the data.

122. What statement can be made about the number of patents issued in the United States?

In Exercises 123 and 124, plot the points and find the distance between the points.

123. $(-3, 8), (1, 5)$ **124.** $(5.6, 0), (0, 8.2)$

In Exercises 125 and 126, plot the points and find the midpoint of the line segment joining the points.

125. $(-12, 5), (4, -7)$

126. $(1.8, 7.4), (-0.6, -14.5)$

In Exercises 127 and 128, write the standard form of the equation of the specified circle.

127. Center: $(3, -1)$; solution point: $(-5, 1)$

128. Endpoints of a diameter: $(-4, 6), (10, -2)$

In Exercises 129 and 130, the polygon is shifted to a new position in the plane. Find the coordinates of the vertices of the polygon in the new position.

129. Original coordinates of vertices:

$(4, 8), (6, 8), (4, 3), (6, 3)$

Shift: three units downward, two units to the left

130. Original coordinates of vertices:

$(0, 1), (3, 3), (0, 5), (-3, 3)$

Shift: five units upward, four units to the right

P.6

131. ***Consumer Awareness***   Use a line plot to organize the following sample of prices (in dollars) of running shoes. Which price occurred with the greatest frequency?

100, 65, 67, 88, 69, 60, 100, 100, 88, 79, 99, 75, 65, 89, 68, 74, 100, 66, 81, 95, 75, 69, 85, 91, 71

132. ***Sports***   The list shows the free-throw percentages for the players in the 2002 WNBA playoffs. Use a frequency distribution and a histogram to organize the data.   (Source: WNBA)

82, 50, 60, 100, 67, 71, 100, 50, 50, 17, 100, 100, 70, 71, 75, 88, 100, 83, 40, 86, 75, 50, 50, 73, 60, 93, 100, 67, 100, 80, 50, 80, 70, 88, 88, 100, 73, 69, 94, 90, 84, 36, 75, 100, 100, 68, 71, 68, 87, 88, 50, 50, 100, 91, 71, 100, 50

133. ***Meteorology***   The normal daily maximum and minimum temperatures (in °F) for each month for the city of Chicago are shown in the table. Construct a double bar graph for the data. (Source: National Climatic Data Center)

Month	Max.	Min.
Jan.	29.6	14.3
Feb.	34.7	19.2
Mar.	46.1	28.5
Apr.	58.0	37.6
May	69.9	47.5
Jun.	79.2	57.2
Jul.	83.5	63.2
Aug.	81.2	62.2
Sep.	73.9	53.7
Oct.	62.1	42.1
Nov.	47.1	31.6
Dec.	34.4	20.4

Table for 133

134. ***Travel***   The table shows the numbers (in millions) of automobile trips taken by U.S. residents from 1995 to 2001. Construct a line graph for the data and state what information the graph reveals. (Source: Travel Industry Association of America)

Year	Trips
1995	396.2
1996	400.7
1997	402.7
1998	410.5
1999	387.7
2000	386.3
2001	396.1

Synthesis

True or False?   **In Exercises 135 and 136, determine whether the statement is true or false. Justify your answer.**

135. $\dfrac{x^3 - 1}{x - 1} = x^2 + x + 1$ for all values of x.

136. A binomial sum squared is equal to the sum of the terms squared.

Error Analysis   **In Exercises 137 and 138, describe the error.**

137. $(2x)^4 = 2x^4$ **138.** $\sqrt{3^2 + 4^2} = 3 + 4$

139. ***Writing***   Explain why $\sqrt{5u} + \sqrt{3u} \neq 2\sqrt{2u}$.

P Chapter Test

Take this test as you would take a test in class. After you are finished, check your work against the answers in the back of the book.

1. Place the correct symbol ($<$ or $>$) between $-\frac{10}{3}$ and $-|-4|$.

2. Find the distance between the real numbers -17 and 39.

3. Identify the rule of algebra illustrated by $(5 - x) + 0 = 5 - x$.

In Exercises 4 and 5, evaluate each expression without using a calculator.

4. (a) $27\left(-\frac{2}{3}\right)$ (b) $\frac{5}{18} \div \frac{15}{8}$ (c) $\left(-\frac{2}{7}\right)^3$ (d) $\left(\frac{3^2}{2}\right)^{-3}$

5. (a) $\sqrt{5} \cdot \sqrt{125}$ (b) $\frac{\sqrt{72}}{\sqrt{2}}$ (c) $\frac{5.4 \times 10^8}{3 \times 10^3}$ (d) $(3 \times 10^4)^3$

In Exercises 6 and 7, simplify each expression.

6. (a) $3z^2(2z^3)^2$ (b) $(u - 2)^{-4}(u - 2)^{-3}$ (c) $\left(\frac{x^{-2}y^2}{3}\right)^{-1}$

7. (a) $9z\sqrt{8z} - 3\sqrt{2z^3}$ (b) $-5\sqrt{16y} + 10\sqrt{y}$ (c) $\sqrt[3]{\frac{16}{v^5}}$

8. Write the polynomial $3 - 2x^5 + 3x^3 - x^4$ in standard form. Identify the degree and leading coefficient.

In Exercises 9–12, perform the operations and simplify.

9. $(x^2 + 3) - [3x + (8 - x^2)]$ 10. $(x + \sqrt{5})(x - \sqrt{5})$

11. $\frac{8x}{x - 3} + \frac{24}{3 - x}$ 12. $\frac{\left(\dfrac{2}{x} - \dfrac{2}{x + 1}\right)}{\left(\dfrac{4}{x^2 - 1}\right)}$

In Exercises 13–15, factor the expression completely.

13. $2x^4 - 3x^3 - 2x^2$ 14. $x^3 + 2x^2 - 4x - 8$ 15. $8x^3 - 27$

16. Rationalize each denominator: (a) $\frac{16}{\sqrt[3]{16}}$ and (b) $\frac{6}{1 - \sqrt{3}}$.

17. Write an expression for the area of the shaded region in the figure at the right and simplify the result.

18. Plot the points $(-2, 5)$ and $(6, 0)$. Find the coordinates of the midpoint of the line segment joining the points and the distance between the points.

19. The numbers (in millions) of votes cast for the Democratic candidates for president in 1980, 1984, 1988, 1992, 1996, and 2000 were 35.5, 37.6, 41.8, 44.9, 47.4, and 51.0, respectively. Construct a bar graph for this data. (Source: Congressional Quarterly, Inc.)

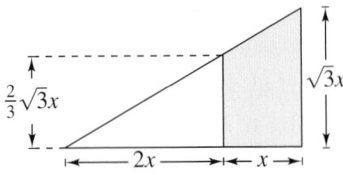

Figure for 17

Colleges and universities track enrollment figures in order to determine the financial outlook of the institution. The growth in student enrollment at a college or university can be modeled by a linear equation.

David Young-Wolff/PhotoEdit

1 Functions and Their Graphs

1.1 Graphs of Equations
1.2 Lines in the Plane
1.3 Functions
1.4 Graphs of Functions
1.5 Shifting, Reflecting, and Stretching Graphs
1.6 Combinations of Functions
1.7 Inverse Functions

What You Should Learn

In this chapter, you will learn how to:

■ Sketch graphs of equations by point plotting or by using a graphing utility.

■ Find and use the slope of a line to write and graph linear equations.

■ Evaluate functions and find their domains.

■ Analyze graphs of functions.

■ Identify and graph shifts, reflections, and nonrigid transformations of functions.

■ Find arithmetic combinations and compositions of functions.

■ Find inverse functions graphically and algebraically.

Introduction to Library of Functions

In Chapter 1, you will be introduced to the concept of a *function*. As you proceed through the text, you will see that functions play a primary role in modeling real-life situations.

There are three basic types of functions that have proven to be the most important in modeling real-life situations. These functions are algebraic functions, exponential and logarithmic functions, and trigonometric and inverse trigonometric functions. These three types of functions are referred to as the *elementary functions*, though they are often placed in the two categories of *algebraic functions* and *transcendental functions*. Each time a new type of function is studied in detail in this text, it will be highlighted in a box similar to this one. The graphs of many of these functions are shown on the inside front cover of this text.

Algebraic Functions

These functions are formed by applying algebraic operations to the identity function $f(x) = x$.

Name	Function	Location
Linear	$f(x) = ax + b$	Section 1.2
Quadratic	$f(x) = ax^2 + bx + c$	Section 3.1
Cubic	$f(x) = ax^3 + bx^2 + cx + d$	Section 3.2
Polynomial	$P(x) = a_n x^n + a_{n-1} x^{n-1} + \cdots + a_2 x^2 + a_1 x + a_0$	Section 3.2
Rational	$f(x) = \dfrac{N(x)}{D(x)}$, $N(x)$ and $D(x)$ are polynomial functions	Section 3.5
Radical	$f(x) = \sqrt[n]{P(x)}$	Section 1.3

Transcendental Functions

These functions cannot be formed from the identity function by using algebraic operations.

Name	Function	Location
Exponential	$f(x) = a^x, a > 0, a \neq 1$	Section 4.1
Logarithmic	$f(x) = \log_a x, x > 0, a > 0, a \neq 1$	Section 4.2
Trigonometric	$f(x) = \sin x, f(x) = \cos x, f(x) = \tan x,$	
	$f(x) = \csc x, f(x) = \sec x, f(x) = \cot x$	Section 5.3
Inverse Trigonometric	$f(x) = \arcsin x, f(x) = \arccos x, f(x) = \arctan x$	Section 5.7

Nonelementary Functions

Some useful nonelementary functions include the following.

Name	Function	Location
Absolute value	$f(x) = |g(x)|$, $g(x)$ is an elementary function	Section 1.3
Piecewise-defined	$f(x) = \begin{cases} 3x + 2, & x \geq 1 \\ -2x + 4, & x < 1 \end{cases}$	Section 1.3
Greatest integer	$f(x) = [\![g(x)]\!]$, $g(x)$ is an elementary function	Section 1.4
Data defined	Formula for temperature: $F = \dfrac{9}{5}C + 32$	Section 1.3

1.1 Graphs of Equations

The Graph of an Equation

News magazines often show graphs comparing the rate of inflation, the federal deficit, or the unemployment rate to the time of year. Businesses use graphs to report monthly sales statistics. Such graphs provide geometric pictures of the way one quantity changes with respect to another. Frequently, the relationship between two quantities is expressed as an **equation.** This section introduces the basic procedure for determining the geometric picture associated with an equation.

For an equation in the variables x and y, a point (a, b) is a **solution point** if the substitution of $x = a$ and $y = b$ satisfies the equation. Most equations have *infinitely many* solution points. For example, the equation $3x + y = 5$ has solution points $(0, 5)$, $(1, 2)$, $(2, -1)$, $(3, -4)$, and so on. The set of all solution points of an equation is the **graph of the equation.**

What you should learn
- Sketch graphs of equations by point plotting.
- Graph equations using a graphing utility.
- Use graphs of equations to solve real-life problems.

Why you should learn it
The graph of an equation can help you see relationships between real-life quantities. For example, Exercise 71 on page 85 shows how a graph can be used to understand the relationship between life expectancy and the year a child is born.

Bruce Avres/Getty Images

Example 1   Determining Solution Points

Determine whether (a) $(2, 13)$ and (b) $(-1, -3)$ lie on the graph of $y = 10x - 7$.

Solution

a. $y = 10x - 7$ Write original equation.

$13 \overset{?}{=} 10(2) - 7$ Substitute 2 for x and 13 for y.

$13 = 13$ $(2, 13)$ is a solution. ✓

The point $(2, 13)$ *does* lie on the graph of $y = 10x - 7$ because it is a solution point of the equation.

b. $y = 10x - 7$ Write original equation.

$-3 \overset{?}{=} 10(-1) - 7$ Substitute -1 for x and -3 for y.

$-3 \neq -17$ $(-1, -3)$ is not a solution.

The point $(-1, -3)$ *does not* lie on the graph of $y = 10x - 7$ because it is not a solution point of the equation.

✓ *Checkpoint* Now try Exercise 3.

The basic technique used for sketching the graph of an equation is the point-plotting method.

Sketching the Graph of an Equation by Point Plotting

  1. If possible, rewrite the equation so that one of the variables is isolated on one side of the equation.

  2. Make a table of values showing several solution points.

  3. Plot these points on a rectangular coordinate system.

  4. Connect the points with a smooth curve or line.

Example 2   Sketching a Graph by Point Plotting

Use point plotting and graph paper to sketch the graph of $3x + y = 6$.

Solution

In this case you can isolate the variable y.

$y = 6 - 3x$ Solve equation for y.

Using negative, zero, and positive values for x, you can obtain the following table of values (solution points).

x	-1	0	1	2	3
$y = 6 - 3x$	9	6	3	0	-3
Solution point	$(-1, 9)$	$(0, 6)$	$(1, 3)$	$(2, 0)$	$(3, -3)$

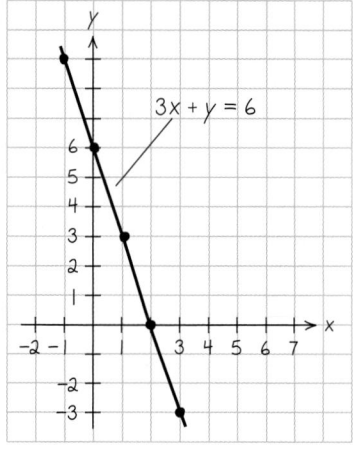

Figure 1.1

Next, plot these points and connect them, as shown in Figure 1.1. It appears that the graph is a straight line. You will study lines extensively in Section 1.2.

 Checkpoint Now try Exercise 7.

The points at which a graph touches or crosses an axis are called the **intercepts** of the graph. For instance, in Example 2 the point $(0, 6)$ is the y-intercept of the graph because the graph crosses the y-axis at that point. The point $(2, 0)$ is the x-intercept of the graph because the graph crosses the x-axis at that point.

Example 3   Sketching a Graph by Point Plotting

Use point plotting and graph paper to sketch the graph of $y = x^2 - 2$.

Solution

Because the equation is already solved for y, make a table of values by choosing several convenient values of x and calculating the corresponding values of y.

x	-2	-1	0	1	2	3
$y = x^2 - 2$	2	-1	-2	-1	2	7
Solution point	$(-2, 2)$	$(-1, -1)$	$(0, -2)$	$(1, -1)$	$(2, 2)$	$(3, 7)$

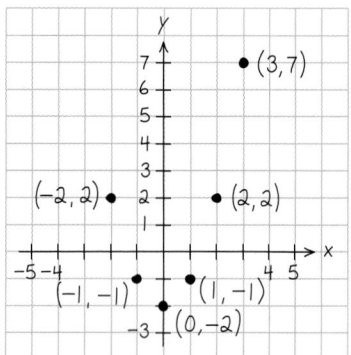

(a)

Next, plot the corresponding solution points, as shown in Figure 1.2(a). Finally, connect the points with a smooth curve, as shown in Figure 1.2(b). This graph is called a *parabola*. You will study parabolas in Section 3.1.

 Checkpoint Now try Exercise 9.

In this text, you will study two basic ways to create graphs: *by hand* and *using a graphing utility*. For instance, the graphs in Figures 1.1 and 1.2 were sketched by hand and the graph in Figure 1.6 was created using a graphing utility.

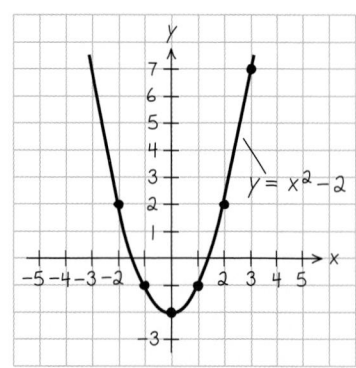

(b)

Figure 1.2

Using a Graphing Utility

One of the disadvantages of the point-plotting method is that to get a good idea about the shape of a graph, you need to plot *many* points. With only a few points, you could badly misrepresent the graph. For instance, consider the equation

$$y = \frac{1}{30}x(x^4 - 10x^2 + 39).$$

Suppose you plotted only five points: $(-3, -3), (-1, -1), (0, 0), (1, 1)$, and $(3, 3)$, as shown in Figure 1.3(a). From these five points, you might assume that the graph of the equation is a line. That, however, is not correct. By plotting several more points and connecting the points with a smooth curve, you can see that the actual graph is not a line at all, as shown in Figure 1.3(b).

TECHNOLOGY TIP

This section presents a brief overview of how to use a graphing utility to graph an equation. For more extensive coverage of this topic, see Appendix A and the *Graphing Technology Guide* on the text website at *college.hmco.com*.

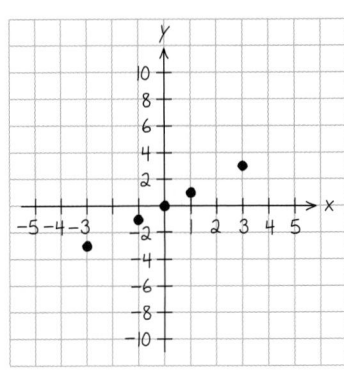

(a)

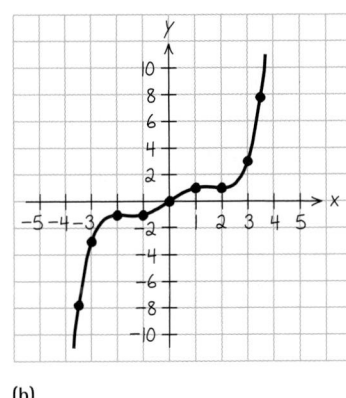

(b)

Figure 1.3

From this, you can see that the point-plotting method leaves you with a dilemma. The method can be very inaccurate if only a few points are plotted and it is very time-consuming to plot a dozen (or more) points. Technology can help solve this dilemma. Plotting several (even several hundred) points on a rectangular coordinate system is something that a computer or calculator can do easily.

TECHNOLOGY TIP The point-plotting method is the method used by *all* graphing utilities. Each computer or calculator screen is made up of a grid of hundreds or thousands of small areas called *pixels*. Screens that have many pixels per square inch are said to have a higher *resolution* than screens with fewer pixels.

Using a Graphing Utility to Graph an Equation

To graph an equation involving x and y on a graphing utility, use the following procedure.

1. Rewrite the equation so that y is isolated on the left side.

2. Enter the equation into the graphing utility.

3. Determine a *viewing window* that shows all important features of the graph.

4. Graph the equation.

Example 4   Using a Graphing Utility to Graph an Equation

Use a graphing utility to graph $2y + x^3 = 4x$.

Solution

To begin, solve the equation for y in terms of x.

$2y + x^3 = 4x$ Write original equation.

$2y = -x^3 + 4x$ Subtract x^3 from each side.

$y = -\dfrac{1}{2}x^3 + 2x$ Divide each side by 2.

Enter this equation into a graphing utility (see Figure 1.4). Using a standard viewing window (see Figure 1.5), you can obtain the graph shown in Figure 1.6.

TECHNOLOGY TIP

Many graphing utilities are capable of creating a table of values such as the following, which shows some points of the graph in Figure 1.6. For instructions on how to use the *table* feature, see Appendix A; for specific keystrokes, go to the text website at *college.hmco.com*.

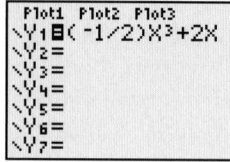

Figure 1.4

Figure 1.5

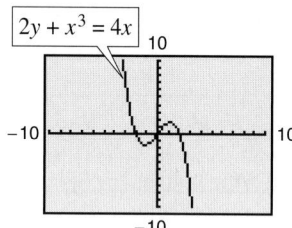

Figure 1.6

✓ *Checkpoint* Now try Exercise 39.

TECHNOLOGY TIP   By choosing different viewing windows for a graph, it is possible to obtain very different impressions of the graph's shape. For instance, Figure 1.7 shows three different viewing windows for the graph of the equation in Example 4. However, none of these views show *all* of the important features of the graph as does Figure 1.6. For instructions on how to set up a viewing window, see Appendix A; for specific keystrokes, go to the text website at *college.hmco.com*.

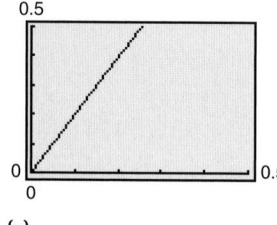

(a)

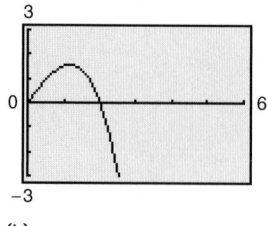

(b)

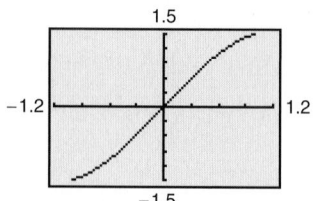

(c)

Figure 1.7

TECHNOLOGY TIP   The standard viewing window on many graphing utilities does not give a true geometric perspective because the screen is rectangular, which distorts the image. That is, perpendicular lines will not appear to be perpendicular and circles will not appear to be circular. To overcome this, you can use a *square setting*, as demonstrated in Example 5.

Example 5   Using a Graphing Utility to Graph a Circle

Use a graphing utility to graph $x^2 + y^2 = 9$.

Solution

The graph of $x^2 + y^2 = 9$ is a circle whose center is the origin and whose radius is 3. (See Section P.5.) To graph the equation, begin by solving the equation for y.

$$x^2 + y^2 = 9 \qquad \text{Write original equation.}$$

$$y^2 = 9 - x^2 \qquad \text{Subtract } x^2 \text{ from each side.}$$

$$y = \pm\sqrt{9 - x^2} \qquad \text{Take square root of each side.}$$

Remember that when you take the square root of a variable expression, you must account for both the positive and negative solutions. The graph of

$$y = \sqrt{9 - x^2} \qquad \text{Upper semicircle}$$

is the upper semicircle. The graph of

$$y = -\sqrt{9 - x^2} \qquad \text{Lower semicircle}$$

is the lower semicircle. Enter *both* equations in your graphing utility and generate the resulting graphs. In Figure 1.8, note that if you use a standard viewing window, the two graphs do not appear to form a circle. You can overcome this problem by using a *square setting*, in which the horizontal and vertical tick marks have equal spacing, as shown in Figure 1.9. On many graphing utilities, a square setting can be obtained by using a y to x ratio of 2 to 3. For instance, in Figure 1.9, the y to x ratio is

$$\frac{Y_{max} - Y_{min}}{X_{max} - X_{min}} = \frac{4 - (-4)}{6 - (-6)} = \frac{8}{12} = \frac{2}{3}.$$

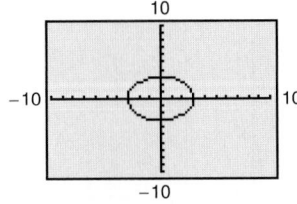

Figure 1.8

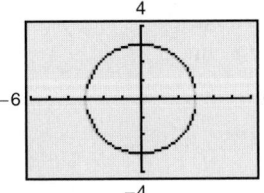

Figure 1.9

✓ *Checkpoint*   Now try Exercise 55.

TECHNOLOGY TIP

Notice that when you graph a circle by graphing two separate equations for y, your graphing utility may not connect the two semicircles. This is because some graphing utilities are limited in their resolution. So, in this text, a blue curve is placed behind the graphing utility's display to indicate where the graph should appear.

Applications

Throughout this course, you will learn that there are many ways to approach a problem. Two of the three common approaches are illustrated in Example 6.

A Numerical Approach: Construct and use a table.

An Algebraic Approach: Use the rules of algebra.

A Graphical Approach: Draw and use a graph.

You should develop the habit of using at least two approaches to solve every problem in order to build your intuition and to check that your answer is reasonable.

The following two applications show how to develop mathematical models to represent real-world situations. You will see that both a graphing utility and algebra can be used to understand and solve the problems posed.

Example 6 Running a Marathon

A runner runs at a constant rate of 4.9 miles per hour. The verbal model and algebraic equation relating distance run and elapsed time are as follows.

Verbal Model: $\boxed{\text{Distance}} = \boxed{\text{Rate}} \cdot \boxed{\text{Time}}$ *Equation:* $d = 4.9t$

a. Determine how far the runner can run in 3.1 hours.

b. Determine how long it will take to run a 26.2-mile marathon.

TECHNOLOGY SUPPORT

For instructions on how to use the *value* feature, the *zoom* and *trace* features, and the *table* feature, see Appendix A; for specific keystrokes, go to the text website at *college.hmco.com*.

Algebraic Solution

a. To begin, find how far the runner can run in 3.1 hours by substituting 3.1 for t in the equation.

$d = 4.9t$ Write original equation.

$ = 4.9(3.1)$ Substitute 3.1 for t.

$ \approx 15.2$ Use a calculator.

So, the runner can run about 15.2 miles in 3.1 hours. Use estimation to check your answer. Because 4.9 is about 5 and 3.1 is about 3, the distance is about $5(3) = 15$. So, 15.2 is reasonable.

b. You can find how long it will take to run a 26.2-mile marathon as follows. (For help with solving linear equations, see Appendix D.)

$d = 4.9t$ Write original equation.

$26.2 = 4.9t$ Substitute 26.2 for d.

$\dfrac{26.2}{4.9} = t$ Divide each side by 4.9.

$5.3 \approx t$ Use a calculator.

So, it will take about 5.3 hours to run 26.2 miles.

✓ *Checkpoint* Now try Exercise 67.

Graphical Solution

a. Use a graphing utility to graph the equation $d = 4.9t$. (Represent d by y and t by x.) Be sure to use a viewing window that shows the graph when $x = 3.1$. Then use the *value* feature or the *zoom* and *trace* features of the graphing utility to estimate that when $x = 3.1$, the distance is $y \approx 15.2$ miles, as shown in Figure 1.10(a).

b. Adjust the viewing window so that it shows the graph when $y = 26.2$. Use the *zoom* and *trace* features to estimate that when $y = 26.2$, the time is $x \approx 5.4$ hours, as shown in Figure 1.10(b).

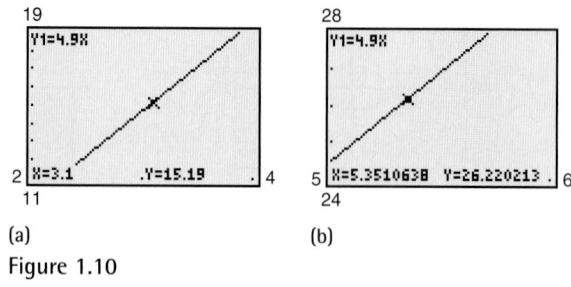

(a)   (b)

Figure 1.10

Note that the viewing window on your graphing utility may differ slightly from those shown in Figure 1.10.

Example 7   Monthly Wage

You receive a monthly salary of $2000 plus a commission of 10% of sales. The verbal model and algebraic equations relating the wages, the salary, and the commission are as follows.

Verbal Model: Wages = Salary + Commission on sales

Equation: $y = 2000 + 0.1x$

a. Sales are $x = 1480$ in August. What are your wages for that month?

b. You receive $2225 for September. What are your sales for that month?

Numerical Solution

a. To find the wages in August, evaluate the equation when $x = 1480$.

$$y = 2000 + 0.1x \qquad \text{Write original equation.}$$

$$= 2000 + 0.1(1480) \qquad \text{Substitute 1480 for } x.$$

$$= 2148 \qquad \text{Simplify.}$$

So, the wages in August are $2148.

b. You can use the *table* feature of a graphing utility to create a table that shows the wages for different sales amounts. First enter the equation in the graphing utility. Then set up a table, as shown in Figure 1.11. The graphing utility produces the table shown in Figure 1.12.

Figure 1.11   Figure 1.12

From the table, you can see that wages of $2225 result from sales between $2200 and $2300. You can improve this estimate by setting up the table shown in Figure 1.13. The graphing utility produces the table shown in Figure 1.14.

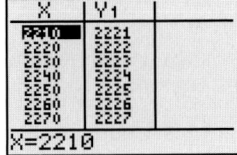

Figure 1.13   Figure 1.14

From the table, you can see that wages of $2225 result from sales of $2250.

 Checkpoint Now try Exercise 72.

Graphical Solution

a. You can use a graphing utility to graph $y = 2000 + 0.1x$ and then estimate the wages when $x = 1480$. Be sure to use a viewing window that shows the graph when $x \geq 0$ and $y > 2000$. Then, by using the *value* feature or the *zoom* and *trace* features near $x = 1480$, you can estimate that the wages are about $2148, as shown in Figure 1.15(a).

b. Use the graphing utility to find the value along the x-axis (sales) that corresponds to a y-value of 2225 (wages). Using the *zoom* and *trace* features, you can estimate the sales to be about $2250, as shown in Figure 1.15(b).

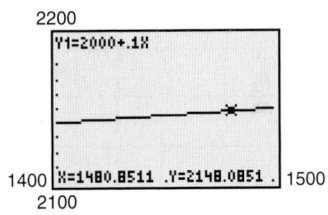

(a) Zoom near $x = 1480$

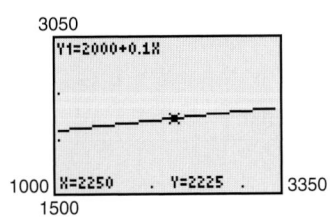

(b) Zoom near $y = 2225$

Figure 1.15

1.1   Exercises

Vocabulary Check

Fill in the blanks.

1. For an equation in x and y, if the substitution of $x = a$ and $y = b$ satisfies the equation, then the point (a, b) is a _____ .

2. The set of all solution points of an equation is the _____ of the equation.

3. The points at which a graph touches or crosses an axis are called the _____ of the graph.

In Exercises 1–6, determine whether each point lies on the graph of the equation.

	Equation		Points	
1.	$y = \sqrt{x + 4}$	(a) $(0, 2)$	(b) $(5, 3)$	
2.	$y = x^2 - 3x + 2$	(a) $(2, 0)$	(b) $(-2, 8)$	
3.	$y = 4 - |x - 2|$	(a) $(1, 5)$	(b) $(1.2, 3.2)$	
4.	$2x - y - 3 = 0$	(a) $(1, 2)$	(b) $(1, -1)$	
5.	$x^2 + y^2 = 20$	(a) $(3, -2)$	(b) $(-4, 2)$	
6.	$y = \frac{1}{3}x^3 - 2x^2$	(a) $\left(2, -\frac{16}{3}\right)$	(b) $(-3, 9)$	

In Exercises 7–10, complete the table. Use the resulting solution points to sketch the graph of the equation. Use a graphing utility to verify the graph.

7. $y = -2x + 3$

x	-1	0	1	$\frac{3}{2}$	2
y					
Solution point					

8. $y = \frac{3}{2}x - 1$

x	-2	0	$\frac{2}{3}$	1	2
y					
Solution point					

9. $y = x^2 - 2x$

x	-1	0	1	2	3
y					
Solution point					

10. $y = 3 - |x - 2|$

x	0	1	2	3	4
y					
Solution point					

11. *Exploration*

(a) Complete the table for the equation $y = \frac{1}{4}x - 3$.

x	-2	-1	0	1	2
y					

(b) Use the solution points to sketch the graph. Then use a graphing utility to verify the graph.

(c) Repeat parts (a) and (b) for the equation $y = -\frac{1}{4}x - 3$. Use the result to describe any differences between the graphs.

12. *Exploration*

(a) Complete the table for the equation

$$y = \frac{6x}{x^{-2} + 1}.$$

x	-2	-1	0	1	2
y					

(b) Use the solution points to sketch the graph. Then use a graphing utility to verify the graph.

(c) Continue the table in part (a) for x-values of 5, 10, 20, and 40. What is the value of y approaching? Can y be negative for positive values of x? Explain.

In Exercises 13–18, match the equation with its graph. [The graphs are labeled (a), (b), (c), (d), (e), and (f).]

(a)
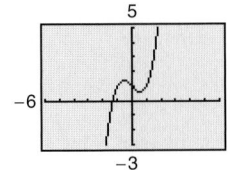

(b)
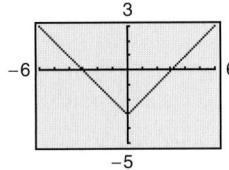

(c)
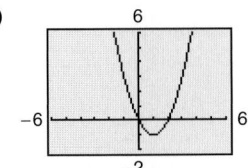

(d)
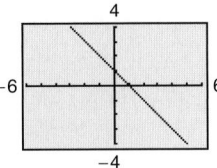

(e)
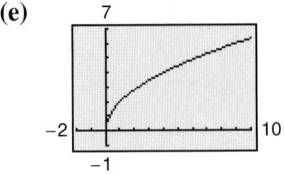

(f)
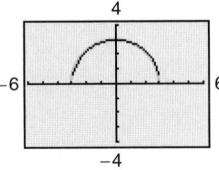

13. $y = 1 - x$

14. $y = x^2 - 2x$

15. $y = \sqrt{9 - x^2}$

16. $y = 2\sqrt{x}$

17. $y = x^3 - x + 1$

18. $y = |x| - 3$

In Exercises 19–32, sketch the graph of the equation.

19. $y = -4x + 1$

20. $y = 2x - 3$

21. $y = 2 - x^2$

22. $y = x^2 - 1$

23. $y = x^2 - 3x$

24. $y = -x^2 - 4x$

25. $y = x^3 + 2$

26. $y = x^3 - 3$

27. $y = \sqrt{x - 3}$

28. $y = \sqrt{1 - x}$

29. $y = |x - 2|$

30. $y = 5 - |x|$

31. $x = y^2 - 1$

32. $x = y^2 - 4$

In Exercises 33–46, use a graphing utility to graph the equation. Use a standard viewing window. Approximate any x- or y-intercepts of the graph.

33. $y = x - 7$

34. $y = x + 1$

35. $y = 3 - \frac{1}{2}x$

36. $y = \frac{2}{3}x - 1$

37. $y = x^2 - 4x + 3$

38. $y = \frac{1}{2}(x + 4)(x - 2)$

39. $y = x(x - 2)^2$

40. $y = -x^3 + 1$

41. $y = \dfrac{2x}{x - 1}$

42. $y = \dfrac{4}{x}$

43. $y = x\sqrt{x + 3}$

44. $y = (6 - x)\sqrt{x}$

45. $y = \sqrt[3]{x}$

46. $y = \sqrt[3]{x + 1}$

In Exercises 47–50, use a graphing utility to graph the equation. Begin by using a standard viewing window. Then graph the equation a second time using the specified viewing window. Which viewing window is better? Explain.

47. $y = \frac{5}{2}x + 5$

48. $y = -3x + 50$

Xmin = 0
Xmax = 6
Xscl = 1
Ymin = 0
Ymax = 10
Yscl = 1

Xmin = -1
Xmax = 4
Xscl = 1
Ymin = -5
Ymax = 60
Yscl = 5

49. $y = -x^2 + 10x - 5$

50. $y = 4(x + 5)\sqrt{4 - x}$

Xmin = -1
Xmax = 11
Xscl = 1
Ymin = -5
Ymax = 25
Yscl = 5

Xmin = -6
Xmax = 6
Xscl = 1
Ymin = -5
Ymax = 50
Yscl = 5

In Exercises 51–54, describe the viewing window of the graph shown.

51. $y = 4x^2 - 25$

52. $y = x^3 - 3x^2 + 4$

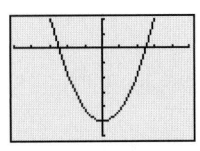

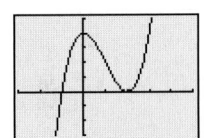

53. $y = |x| + |x - 10|$

54. $y = 8\sqrt[3]{x - 6}$

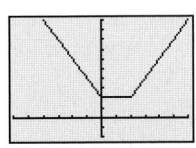

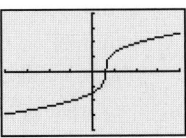

In Exercises 55–58, solve for y and use a graphing utility to graph each of the resulting equations in the same viewing window. (Adjust the viewing window so that the circle appears circular.)

55. $x^2 + y^2 = 64$

56. $x^2 + y^2 = 49$

57. $(x - 1)^2 + (y - 2)^2 = 16$

58. $(x - 3)^2 + (y - 1)^2 = 25$

In Exercises 59–62, explain how to use a graphing utility to verify that $y_1 = y_2$. Identify the rule of algebra that is illustrated.

59. $y_1 = \frac{1}{4}(x^2 - 8)$

     $y_2 = \frac{1}{4}x^2 - 2$

60. $y_1 = \frac{1}{2}x + (x + 1)$

     $y_2 = \frac{3}{2}x + 1$

61. $y_1 = \frac{1}{5}[10(x^2 - 1)]$

     $y_2 = 2(x^2 - 1)$

62. $y_1 = (x - 3) \cdot \dfrac{1}{x - 3}$

     $y_2 = 1$

In Exercises 63–66, use a graphing utility to graph the equation. Use the *trace* feature of the graphing utility to approximate the unknown coordinate of each solution point accurate to two decimal places. (*Hint:* You may need to use the *zoom* feature of the graphing utility to obtain the required accuracy.)

63. $y = \sqrt{5 - x}$

   (a) $(2, y)$

   (b) $(x, 3)$

64. $y = x^3(x - 3)$

   (a) $(2.25, y)$

   (b) $(x, 20)$

65. $y = x^5 - 5x$

   (a) $(-0.5, y)$

   (b) $(x, -4)$

66. $y = |x^2 - 6x + 5|$

   (a) $(2, y)$

   (b) $(x, 1.5)$

67. *Depreciation* A manufacturing plant purchases a new molding machine for $225,000. The depreciated value (drop in value) y after t years is

$$y = 225{,}000 - 20{,}000t, \quad 0 \le t \le 8.$$

(a) Use the constraints of the model to determine an appropriate viewing window.

(b) Use a graphing utility to graph the equation.

(c) Use the *value* feature or the *zoom* and *trace* features of a graphing utility to determine the value of y when $t = 5.8$. Verify your answer algebraically.

(d) Use the *value* feature or the *zoom* and *trace* features of a graphing utility to determine the value of y when $t = 2.35$. Verify your answer algebraically.

68. *Consumerism* You purchase a personal watercraft for $8100. The depreciated value y after t years is

$$y = 8100 - 929t, \quad 0 \le t \le 6.$$

(a) Use the constraints of the model to determine an appropriate viewing window.

(b) Use a graphing utility to graph the equation.

(c) Use the *zoom* and *trace* features of a graphing utility to determine the value of t when $y = 5545.25$. Verify your answer algebraically.

(d) Use the *value* feature or the *zoom* and *trace* features of a graphing utility to determine the value of y when $t = 5.5$. Verify your answer algebraically.

69. *Geometry* A rectangle of length x and width w has a perimeter of 12 meters.

(a) Draw a diagram to represent the rectangle. Use the specified variables to label its sides.

(b) Show that the width of the rectangle is $w = 6 - x$ and its area is $A = x(6 - x)$.

(c) Use a graphing utility to graph the area equation.

(d) Use the *zoom* and *trace* features of a graphing utility to determine the value of A when $w = 4.9$ meters. Verify your answer algebraically.

(e) From the graph in part (c), estimate the dimensions of the rectangle that yield a maximum area.

70. *Data Analysis* The table shows the median (middle) sales prices (in thousands of dollars) of new one-family homes in the United States from 1996 to 2001. (Sources: U.S. Census Bureau and U.S. Department of Housing and Urban Development)

Year	Median sales price, y
1996	140
1997	146
1998	153
1999	161
2000	169
2001	175

A model for the median sales price during this period is given by

$$y = -0.167t^3 + 4.32t^2 - 29.3t + 196, \quad 6 \le t \le 11$$

where y represents the sales price and t represents the year, with $t = 6$ corresponding to 1996.

(a) Use the model and the *table* feature of a graphing utility to find the median sales prices from 1996 to 2001.

(b) Use a graphing utility to graph the data from the table above and the model in the same viewing window.

(c) Use the model to estimate the median sales prices in 2005 and 2010. Do the values seem reasonable? Explain.

(d) Use the *zoom* and *trace* features of a graphing utility to determine during which year(s) the median sales price exceeded $160,000.

71. Population Statistics   The table shows the life expectancy of a child (at birth) in the United States for selected years from 1930 to 2000.   (Source: U.S. National Center for Health Statistics)

Year	Life expectancy, y
1930	59.7
1940	62.9
1950	68.2
1960	69.7
1970	70.8
1980	73.7
1990	75.4
2000	76.9

A model for the life expectancy during this period is given by

$$y = \frac{59.97 + 0.98t}{1 + 0.01t}, \quad 0 \le t \le 70$$

where y represents the life expectancy and t is the time in years, with $t = 0$ corresponding to 1930.

(a) What does the y-intercept of the graph of the model represent?

(b) Use the *zoom* and *trace* features of a graphing utility to determine the year when the life expectancy was 73.2. Verify your answer algebraically.

(c) Determine the life expectancy in 1948 both graphically and algebraically.

(d) Use the model to estimate the life expectancy of a child born in 2010.

72. Electronics   The resistance y (in ohms) of 1000 feet of solid copper wire at 68 degrees Fahrenheit can be approximated by the mathematical model

$$y = \frac{10{,}770}{x^2} - 0.37, \quad 5 \le x \le 100$$

where x is the diameter of the wire in mils (0.001 inch).   (Source: American Wire Gage)

(a) Complete the table.

x	10	20	30	40	50
y					

x	60	70	80	90	100
y					

(b) Use your table to approximate the value of x when the resistance is 4.8 ohms. Then determine the answer algebraically.

(c) Use the *value* feature or the *zoom* and *trace* features of a graphing utility to determine the resistance when $x = 85.5$.

(d) What can you conclude in general about the relationship between the diameter of the copper wire and the resistance?

Synthesis

True or False?   **In Exercises 73 and 74, determine whether the statement is true or false. Justify your answer.**

73. A parabola can have only one x-intercept.

74. The graph of a linear equation can have either no x-intercepts or only one x-intercept.

75. Writing   Explain how to find an appropriate viewing window for the graph of an equation.

76. Writing   Your employer offers you a choice of wage scales: a monthly salary of $3000 plus commission of 7% of sales or a salary of $3400 plus a 5% commission. Write a short paragraph discussing how you would choose your option. At what sales level would the options yield the same salary?

Review

In Exercises 77–80, perform the operations and simplify.

77. $7\sqrt{72} - 5\sqrt{18}$

78. $-10\sqrt{25y} - \sqrt{y}$

79. $7^{3/2} \cdot 7^{11/2}$

80. $\dfrac{10^{17/4}}{10^{5/4}}$

In Exercises 81 and 82, perform the operation and write the result in standard form.

81. $(9x - 4) + (2x^2 - x + 15)$

82. $(3x^2 - 5)(-x^2 + 1)$

1.2 Lines in the Plane

The Slope of a Line

In this section, you will study lines and their equations. The **slope** of a nonvertical line represents the number of units the line rises or falls vertically for each unit of horizontal change from left to right. For instance, consider the two points (x_1, y_1) and (x_2, y_2) on the line shown in Figure 1.16. As you move from left to right along this line, a change of $(y_2 - y_1)$ units in the vertical direction corresponds to a change of $(x_2 - x_1)$ units in the horizontal direction. That is,

$$y_2 - y_1 = \text{the change in } y$$

and

$$x_2 - x_1 = \text{the change in } x.$$

The slope of the line is given by the ratio of these two changes.

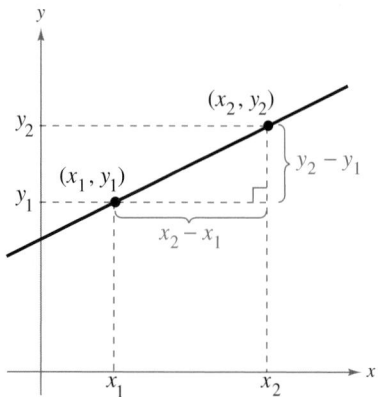

Figure 1.16

What you should learn

- Find the slopes of lines.
- Write linear equations given points on lines and their slopes.
- Use slope-intercept forms of linear equations to sketch lines.
- Use slope to identify parallel and perpendicular lines.

Why you should learn it

The slope of a line can be used to solve real-life problems. For instance, Exercise 68 on page 96 shows how to use slope to determine the years in which the earnings per share of stock for Harley-Davidson, Inc. showed the greatest and smallest increase.

Dwayne Newton/PhotoEdit

Definition of the Slope of a Line

The **slope** m of the nonvertical line through (x_1, y_1) and (x_2, y_2) is

$$m = \frac{y_2 - y_1}{x_2 - x_1} = \frac{\text{change in } y}{\text{change in } x}$$

where $x_1 \neq x_2$.

When this formula for slope is used, the *order of subtraction* is important. Given two points on a line, you are free to label either one of them as (x_1, y_1) and the other as (x_2, y_2). However, once you have done this, you must form the numerator and denominator using the same order of subtraction.

$$\underbrace{m = \frac{y_2 - y_1}{x_2 - x_1}}_{\text{Correct}} \qquad \underbrace{m = \frac{y_1 - y_2}{x_1 - x_2}}_{\text{Correct}} \qquad \underbrace{m = \frac{y_2 - y_1}{x_1 - x_2}}_{\text{Incorrect}}$$

Throughout this text, the term *line* always means a *straight* line.

Example 1   Finding the Slope of a Line

Find the slope of the line passing through each pair of points.

a. $(-2, 0)$ and $(3, 1)$ **b.** $(-1, 2)$ and $(2, 2)$ **c.** $(0, 4)$ and $(1, -1)$

Solution

Difference in y-values

a. $m = \dfrac{\overbrace{y_2 - y_1}}{\underbrace{x_2 - x_1}} = \dfrac{1 - 0}{3 - (-2)} = \dfrac{1}{3 + 2} = \dfrac{1}{5}$

Difference in x-values

b. $m = \dfrac{2 - 2}{2 - (-1)} = \dfrac{0}{3} = 0$

c. $m = \dfrac{-1 - 4}{1 - 0} = \dfrac{-5}{1} = -5$

The graphs of the three lines are shown in Figure 1.17. Note that the square setting gives the correct "steepness" of the lines.

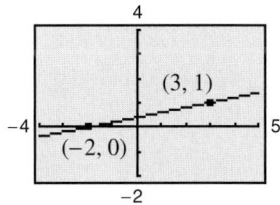

(a)

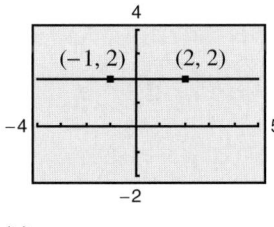

(b)

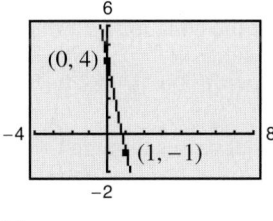

(c)

Figure 1.17

✓ *Checkpoint* Now try Exercise 9.

Exploration

Use a graphing utility to compare the slopes of the lines $y = 0.5x$, $y = x$, $y = 2x$, and $y = 4x$. What do you observe about these lines? Compare the slopes of the lines $y = -0.5x$, $y = -x$, $y = -2x$, and $y = -4x$. What do you observe about these lines? (*Hint:* Use a square setting to guarantee a true geometric perspective.)

The definition of slope does not apply to vertical lines. For instance, consider the points $(3, 4)$ and $(3, 1)$ on the vertical line shown in Figure 1.18. Applying the formula for slope, you obtain

$m = \dfrac{4 - 1}{3 - 3} = \dfrac{3}{0}$.   Undefined

Because division by zero is undefined, the slope of a vertical line is undefined.

From the slopes of the lines shown in Figures 1.17 and 1.18, you can make the following generalizations about the slope of a line.

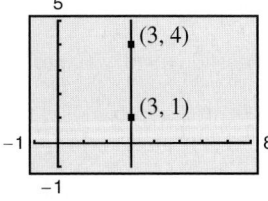

Figure 1.18

The Slope of a Line

1. A line with positive slope $(m > 0)$ *rises* from left to right.

2. A line with negative slope $(m < 0)$ *falls* from left to right.

3. A line with zero slope $(m = 0)$ is *horizontal*.

4. A line with undefined slope is *vertical*.

The Point–Slope Form of the Equation of a Line

If you know the slope of a line *and* you also know the coordinates of one point on the line, you can find an equation for the line. For instance, in Figure 1.19, let (x_1, y_1) be a point on the line whose slope is m. If (x, y) is any *other* point on the line, it follows that

$$\frac{y - y_1}{x - x_1} = m.$$

This equation in the variables x and y can be rewritten in the **point-slope form** of the equation of a line.

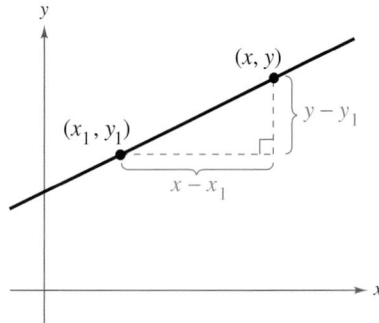

Figure 1.19

Point-Slope Form of the Equation of a Line

The **point-slope form** of the equation of the line that passes through the point (x_1, y_1) and has a slope of m is

$$y - y_1 = m(x - x_1).$$

The point-slope form is most useful for finding the equation of a line if you know at least one point that the line passes through and the slope of the line. You should remember this form of the equation of a line.

Example 2   The Point-Slope Form of the Equation of a Line

Find an equation of the line that passes through the point $(1, -2)$ and has a slope of 3.

Solution

$$y - y_1 = m(x - x_1) \qquad \text{Point-slope form}$$

$$y - (-2) = 3(x - 1) \qquad \text{Substitute for } y_1, m, \text{ and } x_1.$$

$$y + 2 = 3x - 3 \qquad \text{Simplify.}$$

$$y = 3x - 5 \qquad \text{Solve for } y.$$

The line is shown in Figure 1.20.

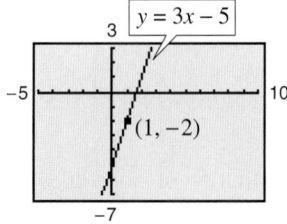

Figure 1.20

☑ *Checkpoint* Now try Exercise 25.

The point-slope form can be used to find an equation of a nonvertical line passing through two points (x_1, y_1) and (x_2, y_2). First, find the slope of the line.

$$m = \frac{y_2 - y_1}{x_2 - x_1}, \ x_1 \ne x_2$$

Then use the point-slope form to obtain the equation

$$y - y_1 = \frac{y_2 - y_1}{x_2 - x_1}(x - x_1).$$

This is sometimes called the **two-point form** of the equation of a line.

STUDY TIP

When you find an equation of the line that passes through two given points, you need to substitute the coordinates of only one of the points into the point-slope form. It does not matter which point you choose because both points will yield the same result.

Example 3   A Linear Model for Sales Prediction

During 2000, Nike's net sales were \$9.0 billion, and in 2001 net sales were \$9.5 billion. Write a linear equation giving the net sales y in terms of the year x. Then use the equation to predict the net sales for 2002.   (Source: Nike, Inc.)

Solution

Let $x = 0$ represent 2000. In Figure 1.21, let $(0, 9.0)$ and $(1, 9.5)$ be two points on the line representing the net sales. The slope of this line is

$$m = \frac{9.5 - 9.0}{1 - 0} = 0.5. \qquad m = \frac{y_2 - y_1}{x_2 - x_1}$$

By the point-slope form, the equation of the line is as follows.

$$y - 9.0 = 0.5(x - 0) \qquad \text{Write in point-slope form.}$$

$$y = 0.5x + 9.0 \qquad \text{Simplify.}$$

Now, using this equation, you can predict the 2002 net sales $(x = 2)$ to be

$$y = 0.5(2) + 9.0 = 1 + 9.0 = \$10.0 \text{ billion.}$$

 Checkpoint Now try Exercise 43.

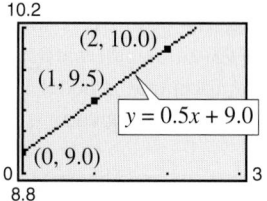

Figure 1.21

Library of Functions: Linear Function

In the next section, you will be introduced to the precise meaning of the term *function*. The simplest type of function is a *linear function* of the form

$$f(x) = mx + b.$$

As its name implies, the graph of a linear function is a line that has a slope of m and a y-intercept at $(0, b)$. The basic characteristics of a linear function are summarized below. (Note that some of the terms below will be defined later in the text.)

Graph of $f(x) = mx + b, m > 0$
Domain: $(-\infty, \infty)$
Range: $(-\infty, \infty)$
x-intercept: $(-b/m, 0)$
y-intercept: $(0, b)$
Increasing

Graph of $f(x) = mx + b, m < 0$
Domain: $(-\infty, \infty)$
Range: $(-\infty, \infty)$
x-intercept: $(-b/m, 0)$
y-intercept: $(0, b)$
Decreasing

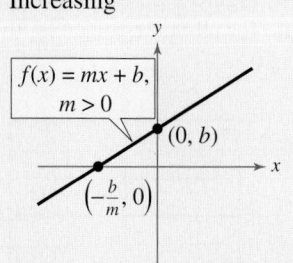

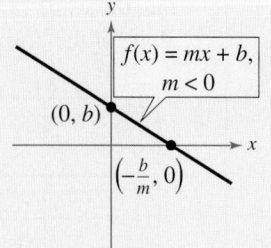

When $m = 0$, the function $f(x) = b$ is called a *constant function* and its graph is a horizontal line.

STUDY TIP

The prediction method illustrated in Example 3 is called **linear extrapolation.** Note in the top figure below that an extrapolated point does not lie between the given points. When the estimated point lies between two given points, as shown in the bottom figure, the procedure used to predict the point is called **linear interpolation.**

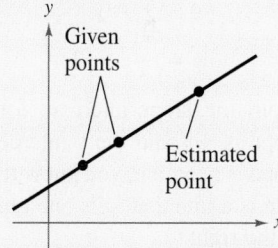

Linear Extrapolation

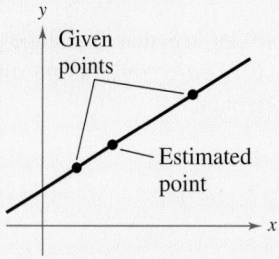

Linear Interpolation

Sketching Graphs of Lines

Many problems in coordinate geometry can be classified as follows.

1. Given a graph (or parts of it), find its equation.

2. Given an equation, sketch its graph.

For lines, the first problem is solved easily by using the point-slope form. This formula, however, is not particularly useful for solving the second type of problem. The form that is better suited to graphing linear equations is the **slope-intercept form** of the equation of a line, $y = mx + b$.

Slope-Intercept Form of the Equation of a Line

The graph of the equation

$$y = mx + b$$

is a line whose slope is m and whose y-intercept is $(0, b)$.

Example 4   Using the Slope-Intercept Form

Determine the slope and y-intercept of each linear equation. Then describe its graph.

a. $x + y = 2$ **b.** $y = 2$

Algebraic Solution

a. Begin by writing the equation in slope-intercept form.

$x + y = 2$	Write original equation.
$y = 2 - x$	Subtract x from each side.
$y = -x + 2$	Write in slope-intercept form.

From the slope-intercept form of the equation, the slope is -1 and the y-intercept is $(0, 2)$. Because the slope is negative, you know that the graph of the equation is a line that falls one unit for every unit it moves to the right.

b. By writing the equation $y = 2$ in slope-intercept form

$$y = (0)x + 2$$

you can see that the slope is 0 and the y-intercept is $(0, 2)$. A zero slope implies that the line is horizontal.

✓ *Checkpoint* Now try Exercise 45.

Graphical Solution

a. Solve the equation for y to obtain $y = 2 - x$. Enter this equation in your graphing utility. Use a decimal viewing window to graph the equation. To find the y-intercept, use the *value* or *trace* feature. When $x = 0$, $y = 2$, as shown in Figure 1.22(a). So, the y-intercept is $(0, 2)$. To find the slope, continue to use the *trace* feature. Move the cursor along the line until $x = 1$. At this point, $y = 1$. So the graph falls 1 unit for every unit it moves to the right, and the slope is -1.

b. Enter the equation $y = 2$ in your graphing utility and graph the equation. Use the *trace* feature to verify the y-intercept $(0, 2)$ as shown in Figure 1.22(b), and to see that the value of y is the same for all values of x. So, the slope of the horizontal line is 0.

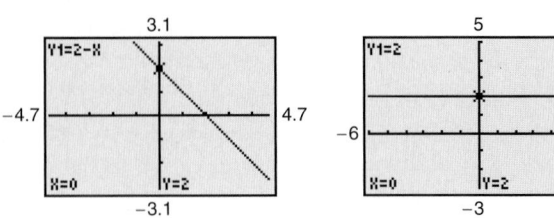

(a)   (b)

Figure 1.22

From the slope-intercept form of the equation of a line, you can see that a horizontal line ($m = 0$) has an equation of the form $y = b$. This is consistent with the fact that each point on a horizontal line through $(0, b)$ has a y-coordinate of b. Similarly, each point on a vertical line through $(a, 0)$ has an x-coordinate of a. So, a vertical line has an equation of the form $x = a$. This equation cannot be written in slope-intercept form because the slope of a vertical line is undefined. However, *every* line has an equation that can be written in the **general form**

$$Ax + By + C = 0 \qquad \text{General form of the equation of a line}$$

where A and B are not *both* zero.

Summary of Equations of Lines

1. General form: $Ax + By + C = 0$

2. Vertical line: $x = a$

3. Horizontal line: $y = b$

4. Slope-intercept form: $y = mx + b$

5. Point-slope form: $y - y_1 = m(x - x_1)$

> **Exploration**
>
> Graph the lines $y_1 = 2x + 1$, $y_2 = \frac{1}{2}x + 1$, and $y_3 = -2x + 1$ in the same viewing window. What do you observe?
>
> Graph the lines $y_1 = 2x + 1$, $y_2 = 2x$, and $y_3 = 2x - 1$ in the same viewing window. What do you observe?

Example 5   Different Viewing Windows

The graphs of the two lines

$$y = -x - 1 \qquad \text{and} \qquad y = -10x - 1$$

are shown in Figure 1.23. Even though the slopes of these lines are quite different (-1 and -10, respectively), the graphs seem misleadingly similar because the viewing windows are different.

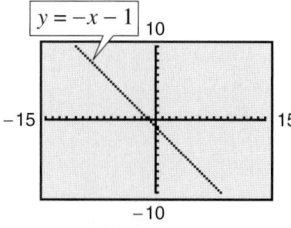

Figure 1.23

✓ *Checkpoint* Now try Exercise 49.

TECHNOLOGY TIP   When a graphing utility is used to graph a line, it is important to realize that the graph of the line may not visually appear to have the slope indicated by its equation. This occurs because of the viewing window used for the graph. For instance, Figure 1.24 shows graphs of $y = 2x + 1$ produced on a graphing utility using three different viewing windows. Notice that the slopes in Figures 1.24(a) and (b) do not visually appear to be equal to 2. However, if you use a *square setting*, as in Figure 1.24(c), the slope visually appears to be 2.

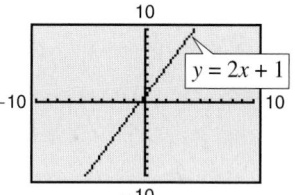

(a)

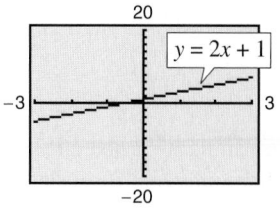

(b)

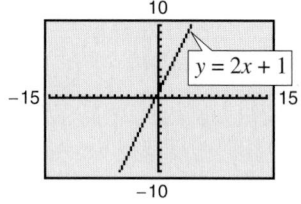

(c)
Figure 1.24

Parallel and Perpendicular Lines

The slope of a line is a convenient tool for determining whether two lines are parallel or perpendicular.

> **Parallel Lines**
>
> Two distinct nonvertical lines are **parallel** if and only if their slopes are equal. That is,
> $$m_1 = m_2.$$

Example 6   Equations of Parallel Lines

Find the slope-intercept form of the equation of the line that passes through the point $(2, -1)$ and is parallel to the line $2x - 3y = 5$.

Solution

Begin by writing the equation of the given line in slope-intercept form.

$$2x - 3y = 5 \qquad \text{Write original equation.}$$
$$-2x + 3y = -5 \qquad \text{Multiply by } -1.$$
$$3y = 2x - 5 \qquad \text{Add } 2x \text{ to each side.}$$
$$y = \frac{2}{3}x - \frac{5}{3} \qquad \text{Write in slope-intercept form.}$$

Therefore, the given line has a slope of $m = \frac{2}{3}$. Any line parallel to the given line must also have a slope of $\frac{2}{3}$. So, the line through $(2, -1)$ has the following equation.

$$y - (-1) = \frac{2}{3}(x - 2) \qquad \text{Write in point-slope form.}$$
$$y + 1 = \frac{2}{3}x - \frac{4}{3} \qquad \text{Simplify.}$$
$$y = \frac{2}{3}x - \frac{7}{3} \qquad \text{Write in slope-intercept form.}$$

Notice the similarity between the slope-intercept form of the original equation and the slope-intercept form of the parallel equation. The graphs of both equations are shown in Figure 1.25.

✓ *Checkpoint*   Now try Exercise 55(a).

> **Perpendicular Lines**
>
> Two nonvertical lines are **perpendicular** if and only if their slopes are negative reciprocals of each other. That is,
> $$m_1 = -\frac{1}{m_2}.$$

TECHNOLOGY TIP

Be careful when you graph equations such as $y = \frac{2}{3}x - \frac{7}{3}$ on your graphing utility. A common mistake is to type in the equation as

Y1 = 2/3X − 7/3,

which may not be interpreted by your graphing utility as the original equation. You should use one of the following formulas.

Y1 = 2X/3 − 7/3

Y1 = (2/3)X − 7/3

Do you see why?

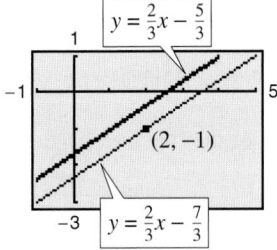

Figure 1.25

Example 7   Equations of Perpendicular Lines

Find the slope-intercept form of the equation of the line that passes through the point $(2, -1)$ and is perpendicular to the line $2x - 3y = 5$.

Solution

From Example 6, you know that the equation can be written in the slope-intercept form $y = \frac{2}{3}x - \frac{5}{3}$. You can see that the line has a slope of $\frac{2}{3}$. So, any line perpendicular to this line must have a slope of $-\frac{3}{2}$ (because $-\frac{3}{2}$ is the negative reciprocal of $\frac{2}{3}$). So, the line through the point $(2, -1)$ has the following equation.

$$y - (-1) = -\tfrac{3}{2}(x - 2) \qquad \text{Write in point-slope form.}$$

$$y + 1 = -\tfrac{3}{2}x + 3 \qquad \text{Simplify.}$$

$$y = -\tfrac{3}{2}x + 2 \qquad \text{Write in slope-intercept form.}$$

The graphs of both equations are shown in Figure 1.26.

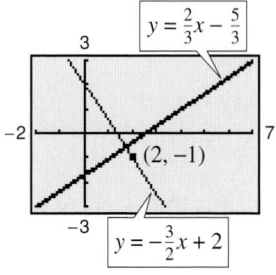

Figure 1.26

✓ *Checkpoint* Now try Exercise 55(b).

Example 8   Graphs of Perpendicular Lines

Use a graphing utility to graph the lines

$$y = x + 1$$

and

$$y = -x + 3$$

in the same viewing window. The lines are supposed to be perpendicular (they have slopes of $m_1 = 1$ and $m_2 = -1$). Do they appear to be perpendicular on the display?

Solution

If the viewing window is nonsquare, as in Figure 1.27, the two lines will not appear perpendicular. If, however, the viewing window is square, as in Figure 1.28, the lines will appear perpendicular.

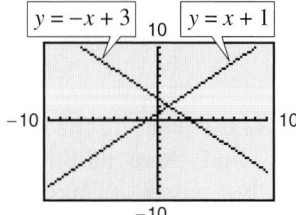

Figure 1.27   Figure 1.28

✓ *Checkpoint* Now try Exercise 61.

1.2 Exercises

Vocabulary Check

1. Match each equation with its form.

(a) $Ax + By + C = 0$ (i)   vertical line

(b) $x = a$ (ii) slope-intercept form

(c) $y = b$ (iii) general form

(d) $y = mx + b$ (iv) point-slope form

(e) $y - y_1 = m(x - x_1)$ (v)   horizontal line

In Exercises 2–5, fill in the blanks.

2. For a line, the ratio of the change in y to the change in x is called the _____ of the line.

3. Two lines are _____ if and only if their slopes are equal.

4. Two lines are _____ if and only if their slopes are negative reciprocals of each other.

5. The prediction method _____ is the method used to estimate a point on a line that does not lie between the given points.

In Exercises 1 and 2, identify the line that has the indicated slope.

1. (a) $m = \frac{2}{3}$ (b) m is undefined.   (c) $m = -2$

2. (a) $m = 0$ (b) $m = -\frac{3}{4}$ (c) $m = 1$

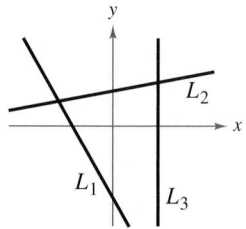

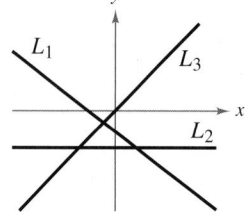

Figure for 1   Figure for 2

In Exercises 3 and 4, sketch the lines through the point with the indicated slopes on the same set of coordinate axes.

Point	Slopes	
3. $(2, 3)$	(a) 0	(b) 1
	(c) 2	(d) -3
4. $(-4, 1)$	(a) 3	(b) -3
	(c) $\frac{1}{2}$	(d) Undefined

In Exercises 5 and 6, estimate the slope of the line.

5.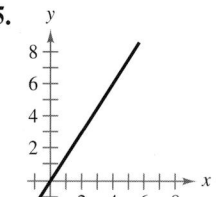

6.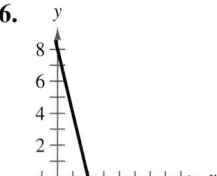

In Exercises 7–10, use a graphing utility to plot the points and use the *draw* feature to graph the line segment connecting the two points. (Use a square setting.) Then find the slope of the line passing through the pair of points.

7. $(0, -10), (-4, 0)$ **8.** $(2, 4), (4, -4)$

9. $(-6, -1), (-6, 4)$ **10.** $(-3, -2), (1, 6)$

In Exercises 11–18, use the point on the line and the slope of the line to find three additional points through which the line passes. (There are many correct answers.)

Point	Slope
11. $(2, 1)$	$m = 0$
12. $(3, -2)$	$m = 0$
13. $(1, 5)$	m is undefined.
14. $(-4, 1)$	m is undefined.

Point	Slope
15. $(0, -9)$	$m = -2$
16. $(-5, 4)$	$m = 2$
17. $(7, -2)$	$m = \frac{1}{2}$
18. $(-1, -6)$	$m = -\frac{1}{2}$

In Exercises 19–24, (a) find the slope and *y*-intercept (if possible) of the equation of the line algebraically, (b) sketch the line by hand, and (c) use a graphing utility to verify your answers to parts (a) and (b).

19. $5x - y + 3 = 0$ **20.** $2x + 3y - 9 = 0$

21. $5x - 2 = 0$ **22.** $3x + 7 = 0$

23. $3y + 5 = 0$ **24.** $-11 - 8y = 0$

In Exercises 25–32, find the general form of the equation of the line that passes through the given point and has the indicated slope. Sketch the line by hand. Use a graphing utility to verify your sketch, if possible.

Point	Slope
25. $(0, -2)$	$m = 3$
26. $(-3, 6)$	$m = -2$
27. $(0, 0)$	$m = 4$
28. $(-2, -5)$	$m = \frac{3}{4}$
29. $(6, -1)$	m is undefined.
30. $(-10, 4)$	m is undefined.
31. $\left(-\frac{1}{2}, \frac{3}{2}\right)$	$m = 0$
32. $(2.3, -8.5)$	$m = 0$

In Exercises 33–42, find the slope-intercept form of the equation of the line that passes through the points. Use a graphing utility to graph the line.

33. $(5, -1), (-5, 5)$ **34.** $(4, 3), (-4, -4)$

35. $(-8, 1), (-8, 7)$ **36.** $(-1, 4), (6, 4)$

37. $\left(2, \frac{1}{2}\right), \left(\frac{1}{2}, \frac{5}{4}\right)$ **38.** $(1, 1), \left(6, -\frac{2}{3}\right)$

39. $\left(-\frac{1}{10}, -\frac{3}{5}\right), \left(\frac{9}{10}, -\frac{9}{5}\right)$ **40.** $\left(\frac{3}{4}, \frac{3}{2}\right), \left(-\frac{4}{3}, \frac{7}{4}\right)$

41. $(1, 0.6), (-2, -0.6)$ **42.** $(-8, 0.6), (2, -2.4)$

43. *Annual Salary*   A jeweler's salary was \$28,500 in 2000 and \$32,900 in 2002. The jeweler's salary follows a linear growth pattern. What will the jeweler's salary be in 2006?

44. *Annual Salary*   A librarian's salary was \$25,000 in 2000 and \$27,500 in 2002. The librarian's salary follows a linear growth pattern. What will the librarian's salary be in 2006?

In Exercises 45–48, determine the slope and *y*-intercept of the linear equation. Then describe its graph.

45. $x - 2y = 4$ **46.** $3x + 4y = 1$

47. $x = -6$ **48.** $y = 12$

In Exercises 49 and 50, use a graphing utility to graph the equation using each of the suggested viewing windows. Describe the difference between the two graphs.

49. $y = 0.5x - 3$

Xmin = -5
Xmax = 10
Xscl = 1
Ymin = -1
Ymax = 10
Yscl = 1

Xmin = -2
Xmax = 10
Xscl = 1
Ymin = -4
Ymax = 1
Yscl = 1

50. $y = -8x + 5$

Xmin = -5
Xmax = 5
Xscl = 1
Ymin = -10
Ymax = 10
Yscl = 1

Xmin = -5
Xmax = 10
Xscl = 1
Ymin = -80
Ymax = 80
Yscl = 20

In Exercises 51–54, determine whether the lines L_1 and L_2 passing through the pairs of points are parallel, perpendicular, or neither.

51. L_1: $(0, -1), (5, 9)$ **52.** L_1: $(-2, -1), (1, 5)$
   L_2: $(0, 3), (4, 1)$ L_2: $(1, 3), (5, -5)$

53. L_1: $(3, 6), (-6, 0)$ **54.** L_1: $(4, 8), (-4, 2)$
   L_2: $(0, -1), \left(5, \frac{7}{3}\right)$ L_2: $(3, -5), \left(-1, \frac{1}{3}\right)$

In Exercises 55–60, write the slope-intercept forms of the equations of the lines through the given point (a) parallel to the given line and (b) perpendicular to the given line.

Point	Line
55. $(2, 1)$	$4x - 2y = 3$
56. $(-3, 2)$	$x + y = 7$
57. $\left(-\frac{2}{3}, \frac{7}{8}\right)$	$3x + 4y = 7$
58. $(-3.9, -1.4)$	$6x + 2y = 9$
59. $(3, -2)$	$x - 4 = 0$
60. $(-4, 1)$	$y + 2 = 0$

Graphical Analysis   **In Exercises 61–64, identify any relationships that exist among the lines, and then use a graphing utility to graph the three equations in the same viewing window. Adjust the viewing window so that each slope appears visually correct. Use the slopes of the lines to verify your results.**

61. (a) $y = 2x$ (b) $y = -2x$ (c) $y = \frac{1}{2}x$

62. (a) $y = \frac{2}{3}x$ (b) $y = -\frac{3}{2}x$ (c) $y = \frac{2}{3}x + 2$

63. (a) $y = -\frac{1}{2}x$ (b) $y = -\frac{1}{2}x + 3$ (c) $y = 2x - 4$

64. (a) $y = x - 8$ (b) $y = x + 1$ (c) $y = -x + 3$

65. *Sales*   The following are the slopes of lines representing annual sales y in terms of time x in years. Use each slope to interpret any change in annual sales for a one-year increase in time.

(a) The line has a slope of $m = 135$.

(b) The line has a slope of $m = 0$.

(c) The line has a slope of $m = -40$.

66. *Revenue*   The following are the slopes of lines representing daily revenues y in terms of time x in days. Use each slope to interpret any change in daily revenues for a one-day increase in time.

(a) The line has a slope of $m = 400$.

(b) The line has a slope of $m = 100$.

(c) The line has a slope of $m = 0$.

67. *Earnings per Share*   The graph shows the earnings per share of stock for Circuit City for the years 1992 through 2002.   (Source: Circuit City Stores, Inc.)

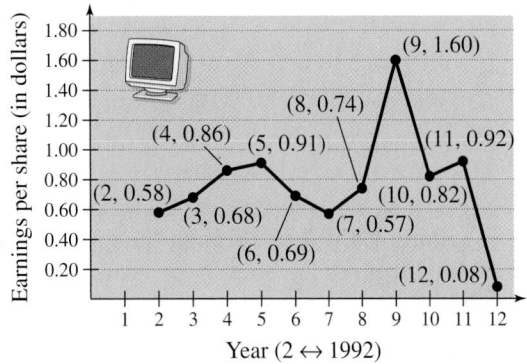

(a) Use the slopes to determine the year(s) in which the earnings per share of stock showed the greatest increase and decrease.

(b) Find the equation of the line between the years 1992 and 2002.

(c) Interpret the meaning of the slope of the equation from part (b) in the context of the problem.

(d) Use the equation from part (b) to estimate the earnings per share of stock for the year 2006. Do you think this is an accurate estimation? Explain.

68. *Earnings per Share*   The graph shows the earnings per share of stock for Harley-Davidson, Inc. for the years 1992 through 2002. (Source: Harley-Davidson, Inc.)

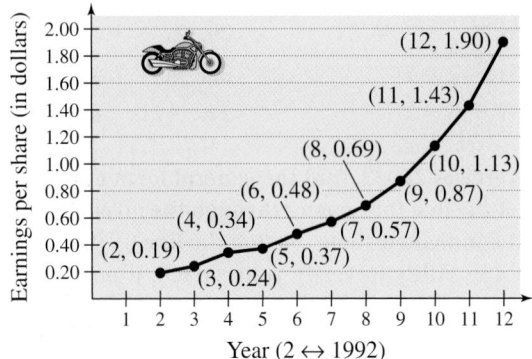

(a) Use the slopes to determine the years in which the earnings per share of stock showed the greatest increase and the smallest increase.

(b) Find the equation of the line between the years 1992 and 2002.

(c) Interpret the meaning of the slope of the equation from part (b) in the context of the problem.

(d) Use the equation from part (b) to estimate the earnings per share of stock for the year 2006. Do you think this is an accurate estimation? Explain.

69. *Height*   The "rise to run" ratio of the roof of a house determines the steepness of the roof. The rise to run ratio of a roof is 3 to 4. Determine the maximum height in the attic of the house if the house is 32 feet wide.

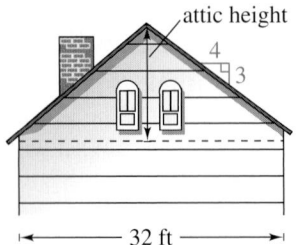

70. *Road Grade* When driving down a mountain road, you notice warning signs indicating that it is a "12% grade." This means that the slope of the road is $-\frac{12}{100}$. Approximate the amount of horizontal change in your position if you note from elevation markers that you have descended 2000 feet vertically.

Rate of Change **In Exercises 71–74, you are given the dollar value of a product in 2004 and the rate at which the value of the product is expected to change during the next 5 years. Write a linear equation that gives the dollar value *V* of the product in terms of the year *t*. (Let *t* = 4 represent 2004.)**

	2004 Value	*Rate*
71.	$2540	$125 increase per year
72.	$156	$4.50 increase per year
73.	$20,400	$2000 decrease per year
74.	$245,000	$5600 decrease per year

Graphical Interpretation **In Exercises 75–78, match the description with its graph. Determine the slope of each graph and how it is interpreted in the given context. [The graphs are labeled (a), (b), (c), and (d).]**

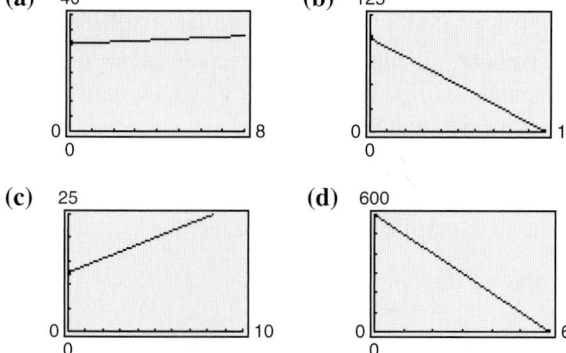

(a) 40, 0, 0, 8   **(b)** 125, 0, 0, 10   **(c)** 25, 0, 0, 10   **(d)** 600, 0, 0, 6

75. You are paying $10 per week to repay a $100 loan.

76. An employee is paid $12.50 per hour plus $1.50 for each unit produced per hour.

77. A sales representative receives $30 per day for food plus $0.35 for each mile traveled.

78. A word processor that was purchased for $600 depreciates $100 per year.

79. *Meteorology* Find the equation of the line that shows the relationship between the temperature in degrees Celsius *C* and degrees Fahrenheit *F*. Remember that water freezes at 0°C (32°F) and boils at 100°C (212°F).

80. *Meteorology* Use the result of Exercise 79 to complete the table.

C		−10°	10°			177°
F	0°			68°	90°	

81. *Depreciation* A pizza shop purchases a used pizza oven for $875. After 5 years, the oven will have to be replaced.

   (a) Write a linear equation giving the value *V* of the oven during the 5 years it will be used.

   (b) Use a graphing utility to graph the linear equation representing the depreciation of the oven, and use the *value* or *trace* feature to complete the table.

t	0	1	2	3	4	5
V						

   (c) Verify your answers in part (b) algebraically by using the equation you found in part (a).

82. *Depreciation* A school district purchases a high-volume printer, copier, and scanner for $25,000. After 10 years, the equipment will have to be replaced. Its value at that time is expected to be $2000.

   (a) Write a linear equation giving the value *V* of the equipment during the 10 years it will be used.

   (b) Use a graphing utility to graph the linear equation representing the depreciation of the equipment, and use the *value* or *trace* feature to complete the table.

t	0	1	2	3	4	5	6	7	8	9	10
V											

   (c) Verify your answers in part (b) algebraically by using the equation you found in part (a).

83. *Cost, Revenue, and Profit* A contractor purchases a bulldozer for $36,500. The bulldozer requires an average expenditure of $5.25 per hour for fuel and maintenance, and the operator is paid $11.50 per hour.

   (a) Write a linear equation giving the total cost *C* of operating the bulldozer for *t* hours. (Include the purchase cost of the bulldozer.)

(b) Assuming that customers are charged $27 per hour of bulldozer use, write an equation for the revenue R derived from t hours of use.

(c) Use the profit formula $(P = R - C)$ to write an equation for the profit derived from t hours of use.

(d) Use the result of part (c) to find the break-even point (the number of hours the bulldozer must be used to yield a profit of 0 dollars).

84. **Rental Demand**   A real estate office handles an apartment complex with 50 units. When the rent per unit is $580 per month, all 50 units are occupied. However, when the rent is $625 per month, the average number of occupied units drops to 47. Assume that the relationship between the monthly rent p and the demand x is linear.

(a) Write the equation of the line giving the demand x in terms of the rent p.

(b) Use a graphing utility to graph the demand equation and use the *trace* feature to estimate the number of units occupied when the rent is $655. Verify your answer algebraically.

(c) Use the demand equation to predict the number of units occupied when the rent is lowered to $595. Verify your answer graphically.

85. **Education**   In 1990, Penn State University had an enrollment of 75,365 students. By 2002, the enrollment had increased to 83,038.   (Source: Penn State Fact Book)

(a) What was the average annual change in enrollment from 1990 to 2002?

(b) Use the average annual change in enrollment to estimate the enrollments in 1984, 1997, and 2000.

(c) Write the equation of a line that represents the given data. What is its slope? Interpret the slope in the context of the problem.

86. **Writing**   Using the results from Exercise 85, write a short paragraph discussing the concepts of *slope* and *average rate of change*.

Synthesis

True or False?   In Exercises 87 and 88, determine whether the statement is true or false. Justify your answer.

87. The line through $(-8, 2)$ and $(-1, 4)$ and the line through $(0, -4)$ and $(-7, 7)$ are parallel.

88. If the points $(10, -3)$ and $(2, -9)$ lie on the same line, then the point $\left(-12, -\frac{37}{2}\right)$ also lies on that line.

Exploration   In Exercises 89 and 90, use the values of a and b and a graphing utility to graph the equation of the line

$$\frac{x}{a} + \frac{y}{b} = 1, \qquad a \neq 0, b \neq 0.$$

Use the graphs to make a conjecture about what a and b represent. Verify your conjecture.

89. $a = 5, \quad b = -3$ 90. $a = -6, \quad b = 2$

In Exercises 91–94, use the results of Exercises 89 and 90 to write an equation of the line that passes through the points.

91. x-intercept: $(2, 0)$ 92. x-intercept: $(-5, 0)$
     y-intercept: $(0, 3)$ y-intercept: $(0, -4)$

93. x-intercept: $\left(-\frac{1}{6}, 0\right)$ 94. x-intercept: $\left(\frac{3}{4}, 0\right)$
     y-intercept: $\left(0, -\frac{2}{3}\right)$ y-intercept: $\left(0, \frac{4}{5}\right)$

95. **Think About It**   The slopes of two lines are -3 and $\frac{5}{2}$. Which is steeper?

96. **Think About It**   Is it possible for two lines with positive slopes to be perpendicular? Explain.

97. **Writing**   Explain how you could show that the points $A(2, 3)$, $B(2, 9)$, and $C(7, 3)$ are the vertices of a right triangle.

98. **Writing**   Write a brief paragraph explaining whether or not any pair of points on a line can be used to calculate the slope of the line.

Review

In Exercises 99–104, determine whether the expression is a polynomial. If it is, write the polynomial in standard form.

99. $x + 20$ 100. $3x - 10x^2 + 1$

101. $4x^2 + x^{-1} - 3$ 102. $2x^2 - 2x^4 - x^3 + 2$

103. $\dfrac{x^2 + 3x + 4}{x^2 - 9}$ 104. $\sqrt{x^2 + 7x + 6}$

In Exercises 105–108, factor the trinomial.

105. $x^2 - 6x - 27$ 106. $x^2 - 11x + 28$

107. $2x^2 + 11x - 40$ 108. $3x^2 - 16x + 5$

1.3   Functions

Introduction to Functions

Many everyday phenomena involve pairs of quantities that are related to each other by some rule of correspondence. The mathematical term for such a rule of correspondence is a **relation.** Here are two examples.

1. The simple interest I earned on an investment of $1000 for 1 year is related to the annual interest rate r by the formula $I = 1000r$.

2. The area A of a circle is related to its radius r by the formula $A = \pi r^2$.

Not all relations have simple mathematical formulas. For instance, people commonly match up NFL starting quarterbacks with touchdown passes, and hours of the day with temperature. In each of these cases, there is some relation that matches each item from one set with exactly one item from a different set. Such a relation is called a **function.**

Definition of a Function

A **function** f from a set A to a set B is a relation that assigns to each element x in the set A exactly one element y in the set B. The set A is the **domain** (or set of inputs) of the function f, and the set B contains the **range** (or set of outputs).

To help understand this definition, look at the function that relates the time of day to the temperature in Figure 1.29.

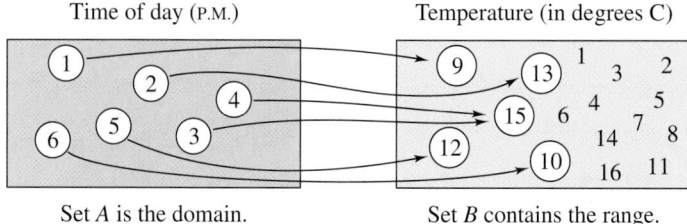

Time of day (P.M.)   Temperature (in degrees C)

Set A is the domain.   Set B contains the range.
Inputs: 1, 2, 3, 4, 5, 6   Outputs: 9, 10, 12, 13, 15

Figure 1.29

This function can be represented by the ordered pairs $\{(1, 9°), (2, 13°), (3, 15°), (4, 15°), (5, 12°), (6, 10°)\}$. In each ordered pair, the first coordinate (x-value) is the **input** and the second coordinate (y-value) is the **output.**

Characteristics of a Function from Set A to Set B

1. Each element of A must be matched with an element of B.

2. Some elements of B may not be matched with any element of A.

3. Two or more elements of A may be matched with the same element of B.

4. An element of A (the domain) cannot be matched with two different elements of B.

What you should learn

- Decide whether relations between two variables represent a function.
- Use function notation and evaluate functions.
- Find the domains of functions.
- Use functions to model and solve real-life problems.
- Evaluate difference quotients.

Why you should learn it

Many natural phenomena can be modeled by functions, such as the force of water against the face of a dam, explored in Exercise 81 on page 111.

Kunio Owaki/Corbis

Library of Functions: Data Defined Function

Many functions do not have simple mathematical formulas, but are defined by real-life data. Such functions arise when you are using collections of data to model real-life applications. Functions can be represented in four ways.

1. *Verbally* by a sentence that describes how the input variable is related to the output variable

   Example: The input value x is the election year from 1952 to 2004 and the output value y is the elected president of the United States.

2. *Numerically* by a table or a list of ordered pairs that matches input values with output values

   Example: In the set of ordered pairs $\{(2, 34), (4, 40), (6, 45), (8, 50), (10, 54)\}$, the input value is the age of a male child in years and the output value is the height of the child in inches.

3. *Graphically* by points on a graph in a coordinate plane in which the input values are represented by the horizontal axis and the output values are represented by the vertical axis

   Example: See Figure 1.30.

4. *Algebraically* by an equation in two variables

   Example: The formula for temperature, $F = \frac{9}{5}C + 32$, where F is the temperature in degrees Fahrenheit and C is the temperature in degrees Celsius, is an equation that represents a function. You will see that it is often convenient to approximate data using a mathematical model or formula.

Example 1   Testing for Functions

Decide whether the relation represents y as a function of x.

a.

Input x	2	2	3	4	5
Output y	11	10	8	5	1

b.

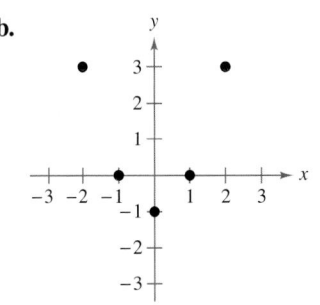

Figure 1.30

Solution

a. This table *does not* describe y as a function of x. The input value 2 is matched with two different y-values.

b. The graph in Figure 1.30 *does* describe y as a function of x. Each input value is matched with exactly one output value.

✓ *Checkpoint* Now try Exercise 5.

In algebra, it is common to represent functions by equations or formulas involving two variables. For instance, the equation $y = x^2$ represents the variable y as a function of the variable x. In this equation, x is the **independent variable** and y is the **dependent variable.** The domain of the function is the set of all values taken on by the independent variable x, and the range of the function is the set of all values taken on by the dependent variable y.

Example 2   Testing for Functions Represented Algebraically

Which of the equations represent(s) y as a function of x?

a. $x^2 + y = 1$ **b.** $-x + y^2 = 1$

Solution

To determine whether y is a function of x, try to solve for y in terms of x.

a. Solving for y yields

$$x^2 + y = 1 \qquad \text{Write original equation.}$$

$$y = 1 - x^2. \qquad \text{Solve for } y.$$

Each value of x corresponds to exactly one value of y. So, y is a function of x.

b. Solving for y yields

$$-x + y^2 = 1 \qquad \text{Write original equation.}$$

$$y^2 = 1 + x \qquad \text{Add } x \text{ to each side.}$$

$$y = \pm\sqrt{1 + x}. \qquad \text{Solve for } y.$$

The $\pm$ indicates that for a given value of x there correspond two values of y. For instance, when $x = 3$, $y = 2$ or $y = -2$. So, y is not a function of x.

✓ *Checkpoint* Now try Exercise 19.

Function Notation

When an equation is used to represent a function, it is convenient to name the function so that it can be referenced easily. For example, you know that the equation $y = 1 - x^2$ describes y as a function of x. Suppose you give this function the name "f." Then you can use the following **function notation.**

Input	*Output*	*Equation*
x	$f(x)$	$f(x) = 1 - x^2$

The symbol $f(x)$ is read as the *value of f at x* or simply *f of x*. The symbol $f(x)$ corresponds to the y-value for a given x. So, you can write $y = f(x)$. Keep in mind that f is the *name* of the function, whereas $f(x)$ is the *output value* of the function at the *input value* x. In function notation, the *input* is the independent variable and the *output* is the dependent variable. For instance, the function $f(x) = 3 - 2x$ has *function values* denoted by $f(-1), f(0)$, and so on. To find these values, substitute the specified input values into the given equation.

For $x = -1$, $f(-1) = 3 - 2(-1) = 3 + 2 = 5.$

For $x = 0$, $f(0) = 3 - 2(0) = 3 - 0 = 3.$

Exploration

Use a graphing utility to graph $x^2 + y = 1$. Then use the graph to write a convincing argument that each x-value has at most one y-value.

Use a graphing utility to graph $-x + y^2 = 1$. (*Hint:* You will need to use two equations.) Does the graph represent y as a function of x? Explain.

TECHNOLOGY TIP

You can use a graphing utility to evaluate a function. Use the Evaluating an Algebraic Expression Program found on the website *college.hmco.com*. The program will prompt you for a value of x, and then evaluate the expression in the equation editor for that value of x. Try using the program to evaluate several different functions of x.

Although f is often used as a convenient function name and x is often used as the independent variable, you can use other letters. For instance,

$$f(x) = x^2 - 4x + 7, \quad f(t) = t^2 - 4t + 7, \quad \text{and} \quad g(s) = s^2 - 4s + 7$$

all define the same function. In fact, the role of the independent variable is that of a "placeholder." Consequently, the function could be described by

$$f(\quad) = (\quad)^2 - 4(\quad) + 7.$$

Example 3   Evaluating a Function

Let $g(x) = -x^2 + 4x + 1$. Find (a) $g(2)$, (b) $g(t)$, and (c) $g(x + 2)$.

Solution

a. Replacing x with 2 in $g(x) = -x^2 + 4x + 1$ yields the following.

$$g(2) = -(2)^2 + 4(2) + 1 = -4 + 8 + 1 = 5$$

b. Replacing x with t yields the following.

$$g(t) = -(t)^2 + 4(t) + 1 = -t^2 + 4t + 1$$

c. Replacing x with $x + 2$ yields the following.

$$
\begin{aligned}
g(x + 2) &= -(x + 2)^2 + 4(x + 2) + 1 && \text{Substitute } x + 2 \text{ for } x. \\
&= -(x^2 + 4x + 4) + 4x + 8 + 1 && \text{Multiply.} \\
&= -x^2 - 4x - 4 + 4x + 8 + 1 && \text{Distributive Property} \\
&= -x^2 + 5 && \text{Simplify.}
\end{aligned}
$$

✓ *Checkpoint* Now try Exercise 33.

In Example 3, note that $g(x + 2)$ is not equal to $g(x) + g(2)$. In general, $g(u + v) \neq g(u) + g(v)$.

Library of Functions: Piecewise-Defined Function

A *piecewise-defined function* is a function that is defined by two or more equations over a specified domain. The *absolute value function* given by $f(x) = |x|$ can be written as a piecewise-defined function. The basic characteristics of the absolute value function are summarized below.

Graph of $f(x) = |x| = \begin{cases} x, & x \geq 0 \\ -x, & x < 0 \end{cases}$

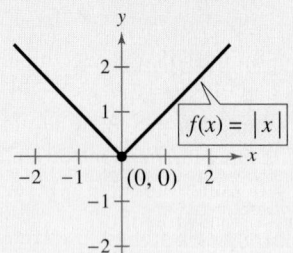

Domain: $(-\infty, \infty)$
Range: $[0, \infty)$
Intercept: $(0, 0)$
Decreasing on $(-\infty, 0)$
Increasing on $(0, \infty)$

An illustration of a piecewise-defined function is given in Example 4.

Example 4   A Piecewise–Defined Function

Evaluate the function when $x = -1$ and 0.

$$f(x) = \begin{cases} x^2 + 1, & x < 0 \\ x - 1, & x \geq 0 \end{cases}$$

Solution

Because $x = -1$ is less than 0, use $f(x) = x^2 + 1$ to obtain

$$f(-1) = (-1)^2 + 1 = 2.$$

For $x = 0$, use $f(x) = x - 1$ to obtain

$$f(0) = (0) - 1 = -1.$$

☑ *Checkpoint* Now try Exercise 37.

TECHNOLOGY TIP

Most graphing utilities can graph piecewise-defined functions. For instructions on how to enter a piecewise-defined function into your graphing utility, consult your user's manual. You may find it helpful to set your graphing utility to *dot mode* before graphing.

The Domain of a Function

The domain of a function can be described explicitly or it can be *implied* by the expression used to define the function. The **implied domain** is the set of all real numbers for which the expression is defined. For instance, the function

$$f(x) = \frac{1}{x^2 - 4} \qquad \text{Domain excludes } x\text{-values that result in division by zero.}$$

has an implied domain that consists of all real x other than $x = \pm 2$. These two values are excluded from the domain because division by zero is undefined. Another common type of implied domain is that used to avoid even roots of negative numbers. For example, the function

$$f(x) = \sqrt{x} \qquad \text{Domain excludes } x\text{-values that result in even roots of negative numbers.}$$

is defined only for $x \geq 0$. So, its implied domain is the interval $[0, \infty)$. In general, the domain of a function *excludes* values that would cause division by zero *or* result in the even root of a negative number.

Exploration

Use a graphing utility to graph $y = \sqrt{4 - x^2}$. What is the domain of this function? Then graph $y = \sqrt{x^2 - 4}$. What is the domain of this function? Do the domains of these two functions overlap? If so, for what values?

Library of Functions: Radical Function

Radical functions arise from the use of rational exponents. The most common radical function is the *square root function* given by $f(x) = \sqrt{x}$. The basic characteristics of the square root function are summarized below.

Graph of $f(x) = \sqrt{x}$

Domain: $[0, \infty)$
Range: $[0, \infty)$
Intercept: $(0, 0)$
Increasing on $(0, \infty)$

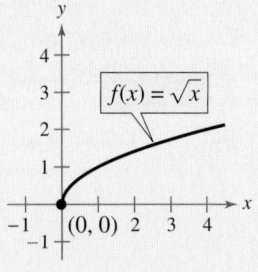

STUDY TIP

Because the square root function is not defined for $x < 0$, you must be careful when analyzing the domains of complicated functions involving the square root symbol.

Example 5   Finding the Domain of a Function

Find the domain of each function.

a. $f: \{(-3, 0), (-1, 4), (0, 2), (2, 2), (4, -1)\}$

b. $g(x) = -3x^2 + 4x + 5$ **c.** $h(x) = \dfrac{1}{x + 5}$

d. Volume of a sphere: $V = \frac{4}{3}\pi r^3$ **e.** $k(x) = \sqrt{4 - 3x}$

STUDY TIP

In Example 5(e), $4 - 3x \geq 0$ is a *linear inequality*. For help with solving linear inequalities, see Appendix D. You will study more about inequalities in Section 2.5.

Solution

a. The domain of f consists of all first coordinates in the set of ordered pairs.

$$\text{Domain} = \{-3, -1, 0, 2, 4\}$$

b. The domain of g is the set of all *real* numbers.

c. Excluding x-values that yield zero in the denominator, the domain of h is the set of all real numbers $x \neq -5$.

d. Because this function represents the volume of a sphere, the values of the radius r must be positive. So, the domain is the set of all real numbers r such that $r > 0$.

e. This function is defined only for x-values for which $4 - 3x \geq 0$. By solving this inequality, you will find that the domain of k is all real numbers that are less than or equal to $\frac{4}{3}$.

✓ *Checkpoint* Now try Exercise 51.

In Example 5(d), note that the *domain of a function may be implied by the physical context*. For instance, from the equation $V = \frac{4}{3}\pi r^3$, you would have no reason to restrict r to positive values, but the physical context implies that a sphere cannot have a negative or zero radius.

For some functions, it may be easier to find the domain and range of the function by examining its graph.

Example 6   Finding the Domain and Range of a Function

Use a graphing utility to find the domain and range of the function

$$f(x) = \sqrt{9 - x^2}.$$

Solution

Graph the function as $y = \sqrt{9 - x^2}$, as shown in Figure 1.31. Using the *trace* feature of a graphing utility, you can determine that the x-values extend from -3 to 3 and the y-values extend from 0 to 3. So, the domain of the function f is all real numbers such that $-3 \leq x \leq 3$ and the range of f is all real numbers such that $0 \leq y \leq 3$.

✓ *Checkpoint* Now try Exercise 61.

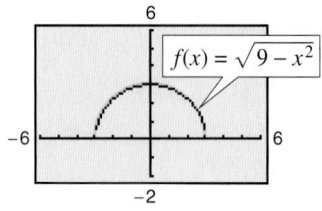

Figure 1.31

Applications

Example 7   Cellular Phone Subscribers

The number N (in millions) of cellular phone subscribers in the United States increased in a linear pattern from 1995 to 1997, as shown in Figure 1.32. Then, in 1998, the number of subscribers took a jump, and until 2001, increased in a *different* linear pattern. These two patterns can be approximated by the function

$$N(t) = \begin{cases} 10.75t - 20.1, & 5 \le t \le 7 \\ 20.11t - 92.8, & 8 \le t \le 11 \end{cases}$$

where t represents the year, with $t = 5$ corresponding to 1995. Use this function to approximate the number of cellular phone subscribers for each year from 1995 to 2001.   (Source: Cellular Telecommunications & Internet Association)

Solution

From 1995 to 1997, use $N(t) = 10.75t - 20.1$

$$\underbrace{33.7}_{1995}, \quad \underbrace{44.4}_{1996}, \quad \underbrace{55.2}_{1997}$$

From 1998 to 2001, use $N(t) = 20.11t - 92.8$.

$$\underbrace{68.1}_{1998}, \quad \underbrace{88.2}_{1999}, \quad \underbrace{108.3}_{2000}, \quad \underbrace{128.4}_{2001}$$

 Checkpoint Now try Exercise 79.

Cellular Phone Subscribers

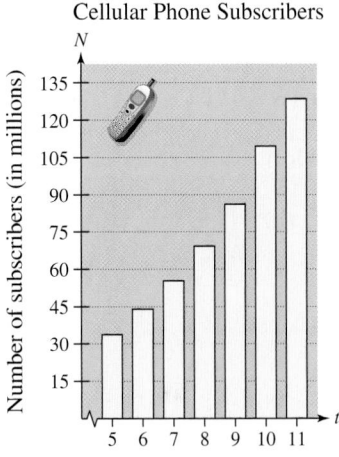

Figure 1.32

Example 8   The Path of a Baseball

A baseball is hit at a point 3 feet above the ground at a velocity of 100 feet per second and an angle of 45°. The path of the baseball is given by the function

$$f(x) = -0.0032x^2 + x + 3$$

where y and x are measured in feet. Will the baseball clear a 10-foot fence located 300 feet from home plate?

Algebraic Solution

The height of the baseball is a function of the horizontal distance from home plate. When $x = 300$, you can find the height of the baseball as follows.

$$f(x) = -0.0032x^2 + x + 3 \qquad \text{Write original function.}$$

$$f(300) = -0.0032(300)^2 + 300 + 3 \qquad \text{Substitute 300 for } x.$$

$$= 15 \qquad \text{Simplify.}$$

When $x = 300$, the height of the baseball is 15 feet, so the base-ball will clear a 10-foot fence.

 Checkpoint Now try Exercise 81.

Graphical Solution

Use a graphing utility to graph the function $y = -0.0032x^2 + x + 3$. Use the *value* feature or the *zoom* and *trace* features of the graphing utility to estimate that $y = 15$ when $x = 300$, as shown in Figure 1.33. So, the ball will clear a 10-foot fence.

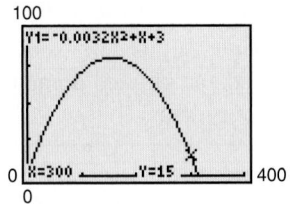

Figure 1.33

Difference Quotients

One of the basic definitions in calculus employs the ratio

$$\frac{f(x + h) - f(x)}{h}, \quad h \neq 0.$$

This ratio is called a **difference quotient,** as illustrated in Example 9.

Example 9   Evaluating a Difference Quotient

For $f(x) = x^2 - 4x + 7$, find $\dfrac{f(x + h) - f(x)}{h}$.

Solution

$$\frac{f(x + h) - f(x)}{h} = \frac{[(x + h)^2 - 4(x + h) + 7] - (x^2 - 4x + 7)}{h}$$

$$= \frac{x^2 + 2xh + h^2 - 4x - 4h + 7 - x^2 + 4x - 7}{h}$$

$$= \frac{2xh + h^2 - 4h}{h}$$

$$= \frac{h(2x + h - 4)}{h} = 2x + h - 4, \; h \neq 0$$

✓ *Checkpoint* Now try Exercise 85.

Summary of Function Terminology

Function: A **function** is a relationship between two variables such that to each value of the independent variable there corresponds exactly one value of the dependent variable.

Function Notation: $y = f(x)$

   f is the *name* of the function.
   y is the **dependent variable,** or output value.
   x is the **independent variable,** or input value.
   $f(x)$ is the *value of the function at x.*

Domain: The **domain** of a function is the set of all values (inputs) of the independent variable for which the function is defined. If x is in the domain of f, f is said to be *defined* at x. If x is not in the domain of f, f is said to be *undefined* at x.

Range: The **range** of a function is the set of all values (outputs) assumed by the dependent variable (that is, the set of all function values).

Implied Domain: If f is defined by an algebraic expression and the domain is not specified, the **implied domain** consists of all real numbers for which the expression is defined.

The symbol ∫ indicates an example or exercise that highlights algebraic techniques specifically used in calculus.

1.3   Exercises

Vocabulary Check

Fill in the blanks.

1. A relation that assigns to each element x from a set of inputs, or _____ , exactly one element y in a set of outputs, or _____ , is called a _____ .

2. For an equation that represents y as a function of x, the _____ variable is the set of all x in the domain, and the _____ variable is the set of all y in the range.

3. The function $f(x) = \begin{cases} x^2 - 4, x \le 0 \\ 2x + 1, x > 0 \end{cases}$ is an example of a _____ function.

4. If the domain of the function f is not given, then the set of values of the independent variable for which the expression is defined is called the _____ .

5. In calculus, one of the basic definitions is that of a _____ , given by $\dfrac{f(x + h) - f(x)}{h}, h \ne 0$.

In Exercises 1–4, does the relationship describe a function? Explain your reasoning.

1. Domain   Range   2. Domain   Range

   -2 ——→ 5   -2 ——→ 3
   -1 ↘ 6   -1 ——→ 4
   0 ↗ 7   0 ——→ 5
   1 ↗ 8   1 ↗
   2   2 ↗

3. Domain   Range   4. Domain   Range

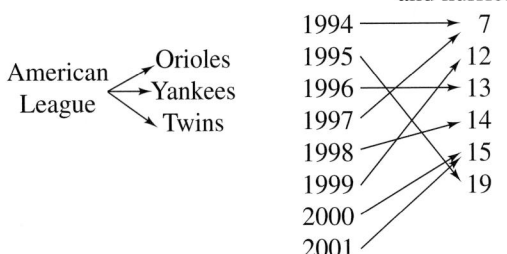

National League → Cubs, Pirates, Dodgers

American League → Orioles, Yankees, Twins

(Year)   (Number of North Atlantic tropical storms and hurricanes)

1994 ——→ 7
1995 ↘ 12
1996 ——→ 13
1997 ↗ 14
1998 ↗ 15
1999 ↗ 19
2000
2001

In Exercises 5–8, does the table describe a function? Explain your reasoning.

5.

Input Value	-2	-1	0	1	2
Output Value	-8	-1	0	1	8

6.

Input Value	0	1	2	1	0
Output Value	-4	-2	0	2	4

7.

Input Value	10	7	4	7	10
Output Value	3	6	9	12	15

8.

Input Value	0	3	9	12	15
Output Value	3	3	3	3	3

In Exercises 9 and 10, which sets of ordered pairs represent functions from A to B? Explain.

9. $A = \{0, 1, 2, 3\}$ and $B = \{-2, -1, 0, 1, 2\}$
   (a) $\{(0, 1), (1, -2), (2, 0), (3, 2)\}$
   (b) $\{(0, -1), (2, 2), (1, -2), (3, 0), (1, 1)\}$
   (c) $\{(0, 0), (1, 0), (2, 0), (3, 0)\}$
   (d) $\{(0, 2), (3, 0), (1, 1)\}$

10. $A = \{a, b, c\}$ and $B = \{0, 1, 2, 3\}$
    (a) $\{(a, 1), (c, 2), (c, 3), (b, 3)\}$
    (b) $\{(a, 1), (b, 2), (c, 3)\}$
    (c) $\{(1, a), (0, a), (2, c), (3, b)\}$
    (d) $\{(c, 0), (b, 0), (a, 3)\}$

Circulation of Newspapers **In Exercises 11 and 12, use the graph, which shows the circulation (in millions) of daily newspapers in the United States.** (Source: Editor & Publisher Company)

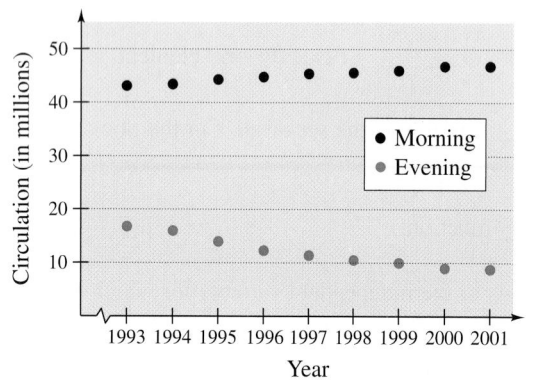

Year

11. Is the circulation of morning newspapers a function of the year? Is the circulation of evening newspapers a function of the year? Explain.

12. Let $f(x)$ represent the circulation of evening newspapers in year x. Find $f(2000)$.

In Exercises 13–24, determine whether the equation represents y as a function of x.

13. $x^2 + y^2 = 4$

14. $x = y^2$

15. $x^2 + y = -1$

16. $y = \sqrt{x + 5}$

17. $2x + 3y = 4$

18. $x = -y + 5$

19. $y^2 = x^2 - 1$

20. $x + y^2 = 3$

21. $y = |4 - x|$

22. $|y| = 4 - x$

23. $x = -7$

24. $y = 8$

In Exercises 25 and 26, fill in the blanks using the specified function and the given values of the independent variable. Simplify the result.

25. $f(x) = \dfrac{1}{x + 1}$

   (a) $f(4) = \dfrac{1}{() + 1}$

   (b) $f(0) = \dfrac{1}{() + 1}$

   (c) $f(4t) = \dfrac{1}{() + 1}$

   (d) $f(x + c) = \dfrac{1}{() + 1}$

26. $g(x) = x^2 - 2x$

   (a) $g(2) = ()^2 - 2()$

   (b) $g(-3) = ()^2 - 2()$

   (c) $g(t + 1) = ()^2 - 2()$

   (d) $g(x + c) = ()^2 - 2()$

In Exercises 27–38, evaluate the function at each specified value of the independent variable and simplify.

27. $f(x) = 2x - 3$

   (a) $f(1)$ (b) $f(-3)$ (c) $f(x - 1)$

28. $g(y) = 7 - 3y$

   (a) $g(0)$ (b) $g\left(\frac{7}{3}\right)$ (c) $g(s + 2)$

29. $h(t) = t^2 - 2t$

   (a) $h(2)$ (b) $h(1.5)$ (c) $h(x + 2)$

30. $V(r) = \frac{4}{3}\pi r^3$

   (a) $V(3)$ (b) $V\left(\frac{3}{2}\right)$ (c) $V(2r)$

31. $f(y) = 3 - \sqrt{y}$

   (a) $f(4)$ (b) $f(0.25)$ (c) $f(4x^2)$

32. $f(x) = \sqrt{x + 8} + 2$

   (a) $f(-8)$ (b) $f(1)$ (c) $f(x - 8)$

33. $q(x) = \dfrac{1}{x^2 - 9}$

   (a) $q(0)$ (b) $q(3)$ (c) $q(y + 3)$

34. $q(t) = \dfrac{2t^2 + 3}{t^2}$

   (a) $q(2)$ (b) $q(0)$ (c) $q(-x)$

35. $f(x) = \dfrac{|x|}{x}$

   (a) $f(2)$ (b) $f(-2)$ (c) $f(x^2)$

36. $f(x) = |x| + 4$

   (a) $f(2)$ (b) $f(-2)$ (c) $f(x^2)$

37. $f(x) = \begin{cases} 2x + 1, & x < 0 \\ 2x + 2, & x \geq 0 \end{cases}$

   (a) $f(-1)$ (b) $f(0)$ (c) $f(2)$

38. $f(x) = \begin{cases} x^2 + 2, & x \leq 1 \\ 2x^2 + 2, & x > 1 \end{cases}$

   (a) $f(-2)$ (b) $f(1)$ (c) $f(2)$

In Exercises 39–42, complete the table.

39. $h(t) = \frac{1}{2}|t + 3|$

t	-5	-4	-3	-2	-1
$h(t)$					

40. $f(s) = \dfrac{|s - 2|}{s - 2}$

s	0	1	$\frac{3}{2}$	$\frac{5}{2}$	4
$f(s)$					

41. $f(x) = \begin{cases} -\frac{1}{2}x + 4, & x \le 0 \\ (x - 2)^2, & x > 0 \end{cases}$

x	-2	-1	0	1	2
$f(x)$					

42. $h(x) = \begin{cases} 9 - x^2, & x < 3 \\ x - 3, & x \ge 3 \end{cases}$

x	1	2	3	4	5
$h(x)$					

In Exercises 43–46, find all real values of x such that $f(x) = 0$.

43. $f(x) = 15 - 3x$

44. $f(x) = 5x + 1$

45. $f(x) = \dfrac{3x - 4}{5}$

46. $f(x) = \dfrac{12 - x^2}{5}$

In Exercises 47 and 48, find the value(s) of x for which $f(x) = g(x)$.

47. $f(x) = x^2$, $\quad g(x) = x + 2$

48. $f(x) = x^2 + 2x + 1$, $\quad g(x) = 3x + 3$

In Exercises 49–58, find the domain of the function.

49. $f(x) = 5x^2 + 2x - 1$

50. $g(x) = 1 - 2x^2$

51. $h(t) = \dfrac{4}{t}$

52. $s(y) = \dfrac{3y}{y + 5}$

53. $f(x) = \sqrt[3]{x - 4}$

54. $f(x) = \sqrt[4]{x^2 + 3x}$

55. $g(x) = \dfrac{1}{x} - \dfrac{3}{x + 2}$

56. $h(x) = \dfrac{10}{x^2 - 2x}$

57. $g(y) = \dfrac{y + 2}{\sqrt{y - 10}}$

58. $f(x) = \dfrac{\sqrt{x + 6}}{6 + x}$

In Exercises 59–62, use a graphing utility to graph the function. Find the domain and range of the function.

59. $f(x) = \sqrt{4 - x^2}$

60. $f(x) = \sqrt{x^2 + 1}$

61. $g(x) = |2x + 3|$

62. $g(x) = |x - 5|$

In Exercises 63–66, assume that the domain of f is the set $A = \{-2, -1, 0, 1, 2\}$. Determine the set of ordered pairs representing the function f.

63. $f(x) = x^2$

64. $f(x) = x^2 - 3$

65. $f(x) = |x| + 2$

66. $f(x) = |x + 1|$

67. *Geometry*   Write the area A of a circle as a function of its circumference C.

68. *Geometry*   Write the area A of an equilateral triangle as a function of the length s of its sides.

69. *Exploration*   The cost per unit to produce a radio model is \$60. The manufacturer charges \$90 per unit for orders of 100 or less. To encourage large orders, the manufacturer reduces the charge by \$0.15 per radio for each unit ordered in excess of 100 (for example, there would be a charge of \$87 per radio for an order size of 120).

(a) The table shows the profit P (in dollars) for various numbers of units ordered, x. Use the table to estimate the maximum profit.

Units, x	Profit, P
110	3135
120	3240
130	3315
140	3360
150	3375
160	3360
170	3315

(b) Plot the points (x, P) from the table in part (a). Does the relation defined by the ordered pairs represent P as a function of x?

(c) If P is a function of x, write the function and determine its domain.

70. *Exploration*   An open box of maximum volume is to be made from a square piece of material, 24 centimeters on a side, by cutting equal squares from the corners and turning up the sides (see figure).

(a) The table shows the volume V (in cubic centimeters) of the box for various heights x (in centimeters). Use the table to estimate the maximum volume.

Height, x	Volume, V
1	484
2	800
3	972
4	1024
5	980
6	864

(b) Plot the points (x, V) from the table in part (a). Does the relation defined by the ordered pairs represent V as a function of x?

(c) If V is a function of x, write the function and determine its domain.

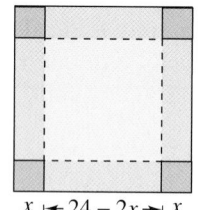 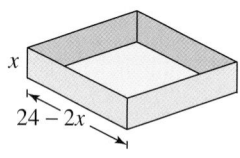

71. *Geometry*   A right triangle is formed in the first quadrant by the x- and y-axes and a line through the point $(2, 1)$ (see figure). Write the area A of the triangle as a function of x, and determine the domain of the function.

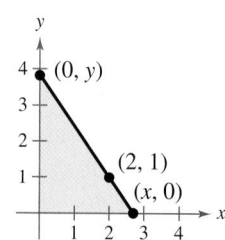

72. *Geometry*   A rectangle is bounded by the x-axis and the semicircle $y = \sqrt{36 - x^2}$ (see figure). Write the area A of the rectangle as a function of x, and determine the domain of the function.

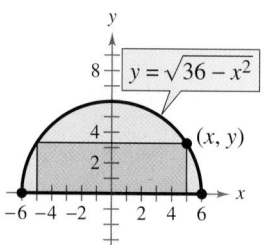

73. *Postal Regulations*   A rectangular package to be sent by the U.S. Postal Service can have a maximum combined length and girth (perimeter of a cross section) of 108 inches (see figure).

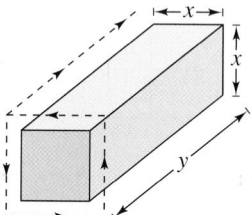

(a) Write the volume V of the package as a function of x.

(b) What is the domain of the function?

(c) Use a graphing utility to graph the function. Be sure to use the appropriate viewing window.

(d) What dimensions will maximize the volume of the package? Explain.

74. *Cost, Revenue, and Profit*   A company produces a toy for which the variable cost is $12.30 per unit and the fixed costs are $98,000. The toy sells for $17.98. Let x be the number of units produced and sold.

(a) The total cost for a business is the sum of the variable cost and the fixed costs. Write the total cost C as a function of the number of units produced.

(b) Write the revenue R as a function of the number of units sold.

(c) Write the profit P as a function of the number of units sold. (*Note:* $P = R - C$.)

Revenue   In Exercises 75–78, use the table, which shows the monthly revenue *y* (in thousands of dollars) of a landscaping business for each month of 2003, with $x = 1$ representing January.

Month, x	Revenue, y
1	5.2
2	5.6
3	6.6
4	8.3
5	11.5
6	15.8
7	12.8
8	10.1
9	8.6
10	6.9
11	4.5
12	2.7

A mathematical model that represents this data is

$$f(x) = \begin{cases} -1.97x + 26.3 \\ 0.505x^2 - 1.47x + 6.3 \end{cases}$$

75. What is the domain of each part of the piecewise-defined function? Explain your reasoning.

76. Use the mathematical model to find $f(5)$. Interpret your results in the context of the problem.

77. Use the mathematical model to find $f(11)$. Interpret your results in the context of the problem.

78. How do the values obtained from the model in Exercises 76 and 77 compare with the actual data values?

79. *Motor Vehicles*   The number *n* (in billions) of miles traveled by vans, pickup trucks, and sport utility vehicles in the United States from 1990 to 2000 can be approximated by the model

$$n(t) = \begin{cases} -9.2t^2 + 84.5t + 575, & 0 \le t \le 4 \\ 26.8t + 657, & 5 \le t \le 10 \end{cases}$$

where *t* represents the year, with $t = 0$ corresponding to 1990. Use the *table* feature of a graphing utility to approximate the number of miles traveled by vans, pickup trucks, and sport utility vehicles for each year from 1990 to 2000. (Source: U.S. Federal Highway Administration)

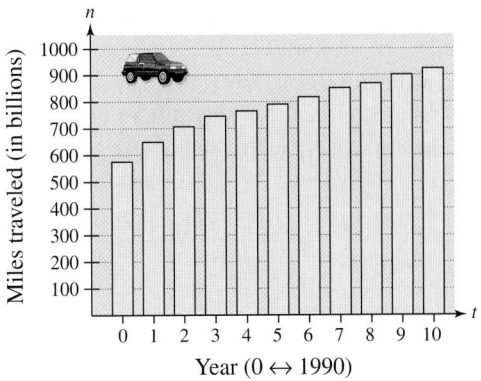

Figure for 79

80. *Transportation*   For groups of 80 or more people, a charter bus company determines the rate per person according to the formula

$$\text{Rate} = 8 - 0.05(n - 80), \quad n \ge 80$$

where the rate is given in dollars and *n* is the number of people.

(a) Write the revenue *R* of the bus company as a function of *n*.

(b) Use the function from part (a) to complete the table. What can you conclude?

n	90	100	110	120	130	140	150
R(n)							

(c) Use a graphing utility to graph *R* and determine the number of people that will produce a maximum revenue. Compare the result with your conclusion from part (b).

81. *Physics*   The force *F* (in tons) of water against the face of a dam is estimated by the function $F(y) = 149.76\sqrt{10}y^{5/2}$, where *y* is the depth of the water in feet.

(a) Complete the table. What can you conclude from the table?

y	5	10	20	30	40
F(y)					

(b) Use a graphing utility to graph the function. Describe your viewing window.

(c) Use the table to approximate the depth at which the force against the dam is 1,000,000 tons. How could you find a better estimate?

(d) Verify your answer in part (c) graphically.

82. *Data Analysis*   The graph shows the retail sales (in billions of dollars) of prescription drugs in the United States from 1995 through 2001. Let $f(x)$ represent the retail sales in year x. (Source: National Association of Chain Drug Stores)

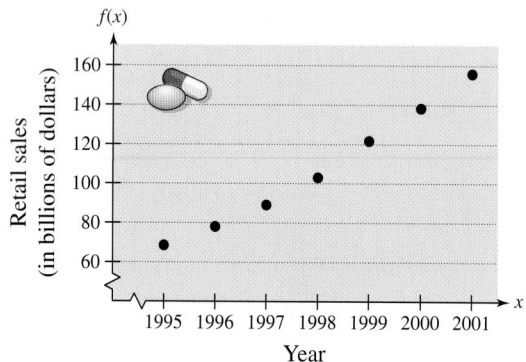

(a) Find $f(1998)$.

(b) Find $\dfrac{f(2001) - f(1995)}{2001 - 1995}$

and interpret the result in the context of the problem.

(c) An approximate model for the function is

$$P(t) = -0.1556t^3 + 4.657t^2 - 28.75t + 115.7,$$
$$5 \le t \le 11$$

where P is the retail sales (in billions of dollars) and t represents the year, with $t = 5$ corresponding to 1995. Complete the table and compare the results with the data.

t	5	6	7	8	9	10	11
$P(t)$							

(d) Use a graphing utility to graph the model and data in the same viewing window. Comment on the validity of the model.

In Exercises 83–88, find the difference quotient and simplify your answer.

83. $f(x) = 2x$, $\dfrac{f(x + c) - f(x)}{c}$, $c \neq 0$

84. $g(x) = 3x - 1$, $\dfrac{g(x + h) - g(x)}{h}$, $h \neq 0$

85. $f(x) = x^2 - x + 1$, $\dfrac{f(2 + h) - f(2)}{h}$, $h \neq 0$

86. $f(x) = x^3 + x$, $\dfrac{f(x + h) - f(x)}{h}$, $h \neq 0$

87. $f(t) = \dfrac{1}{t}$, $\dfrac{f(t) - f(1)}{t - 1}$, $t \neq 1$

88. $f(x) = \dfrac{4}{x + 1}$, $\dfrac{f(x) - f(7)}{x - 7}$, $x \neq 7$

Synthesis

True or False?   **In Exercises 89 and 90, determine whether the statement is true or false. Justify your answer.**

89. The domain of the function $f(x) = x^4 - 1$ is $(-\infty, \infty)$, and the range of $f(x)$ is $(0, \infty)$.

90. The set of ordered pairs $\{(-8, -2), (-6, 0), (-4, 0), (-2, 2), (0, 4), (2, -2)\}$ represents a function.

Exploration   **In Exercises 91 and 92, match the data with one of the functions $g(x) = cx^2$ or $r(x) = c/x$ and determine the value of the constant c such that the function fits the data given in the table.**

91.

x	-4	-1	0	1	4
y	-8	-32	Undef.	32	8

92.

x	-4	-1	0	1	4
y	-32	-2	0	-2	-32

93. *Writing*   In your own words, explain the meanings of *domain* and *range*.

94. *Think About It*   Describe an advantage of function notation.

Review

In Exercises 95–98, perform the operations and simplify.

95. $12 - \dfrac{4}{x + 2}$

96. $\dfrac{3}{x^2 + x - 20} + \dfrac{x}{x^2 + 4x - 5}$

97. $\dfrac{2x^3 + 11x^2 - 6x}{5x} \cdot \dfrac{x + 10}{2x^2 + 5x - 3}$

98. $\dfrac{x + 7}{2(x - 9)} \div \dfrac{x - 7}{2(x - 9)}$

The symbol ∫ indicates an example or exercise that highlights algebraic techniques specifically used in calculus.

1.4   Graphs of Functions

The Graph of a Function

In Section 1.3, functions were represented graphically by points on a graph in a coordinate plane in which the input values are represented by the horizontal axis and the output values are represented by the vertical axis. The **graph of a function** f is the collection of ordered pairs $(x, f(x))$ such that x is in the domain of f. As you study this section, remember the geometric interpretations of x and $f(x)$.

x = the directed distance from the y-axis

$f(x)$ = the directed distance from the x-axis

Example 1 shows how to use the graph of a function to find the domain and range of the function.

What you should learn

● Find the domains and ranges of functions and use the Vertical Line Test for functions.
● Determine intervals on which functions are increasing, decreasing, or constant.
● Determine relative maximum and relative minimum values of functions.
● Identify and graph step functions and other piecewise-defined functions.
● Identify even and odd functions.

Why you should learn it

Graphs of functions provide a visual relationship between two variables. Exercise 81 on page 123 shows how the graph of a step function can represent the cost of a telephone call.

Example 1   Finding the Domain and Range of a Function

Use the graph of the function f shown in Figure 1.34 to find (a) the domain of f, (b) the function values $f(-1)$ and $f(2)$, and (c) the range of f.

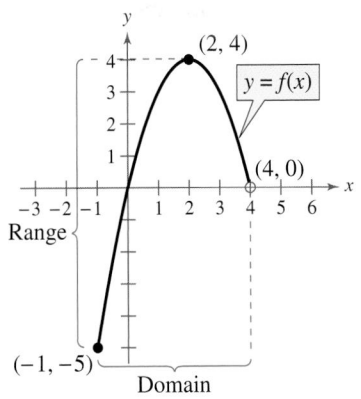

Figure 1.34

Jeff Greenberg/Peter Arnold, Inc.

Solution

a. The closed dot at $(-1, -5)$ indicates that $x = -1$ is in the domain of f, whereas the open dot at $(4, 0)$ indicates that $x = 4$ is not in the domain. So, the domain of f is all x in the interval $[-1, 4)$.

b. Because $(-1, -5)$ is a point on the graph of f, it follows that

$$f(-1) = -5.$$

Similarly, because $(2, 4)$ is a point on the graph of f, it follows that

$$f(2) = 4.$$

c. Because the graph does not extend below $f(-1) = -5$ or above $f(2) = 4$, the range of f is the interval $[-5, 4]$.

✓ *Checkpoint* Now try Exercise 3.

STUDY TIP

The use of dots (open or closed) at the extreme left and right points of a graph indicates that the graph does not extend beyond these points. If no such dots are shown, assume that the graph extends beyond these points.

Example 2   Finding the Domain and Range of a Function

Find the domain and range of

$$f(x) = \sqrt{x - 4}.$$

Algebraic Solution

Because the expression under a radical cannot be negative, the domain of $f(x) = \sqrt{x - 4}$ is the set of all real numbers such that $x - 4 \geq 0$. Solve this linear inequality for x as follows. (For help with solving linear inequalities, see Appendix D.)

$x - 4 \geq 0$ Write original inequality.

$x \geq 4$ Add 4 to each side.

So, the domain is the set of all real numbers greater than or equal to 4. Because the value of a radical expression is never negative, the range of $f(x) = \sqrt{x - 4}$ is the set of all nonnegative real numbers.

✅ *Checkpoint* Now try Exercise 7.

Graphical Solution

Use a graphing utility to graph the equation $y = \sqrt{x - 4}$, as shown in Figure 1.35. Use the *trace* feature to determine that the x-coordinates of points on the graph extend from 4 to the right. When x is greater than or equal to 4, the expression under the radical is nonnegative. So, you can conclude that the domain is the set of all real numbers greater than or equal to 4. From the graph, you can see that the y-coordinates of points on the graph extend from 0 upwards. So you can estimate the range to be the set of all nonnegative real numbers.

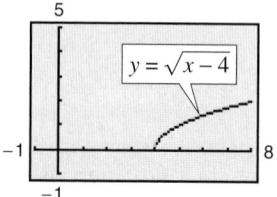

Figure 1.35

By the definition of a function, at most one y-value corresponds to a given x-value. It follows, then, that a vertical line can intersect the graph of a function at most once. This leads to the **Vertical Line Test** for functions.

> **Vertical Line Test for Functions**
>
> A set of points in a coordinate plane is the graph of y as a function of x if and only if no vertical line intersects the graph at more than one point.

Example 3   Vertical Line Test for Functions

Use the Vertical Line Test to decide whether the graphs in Figure 1.36 represent y as a function of x.

Solution

a. This is *not* a graph of y as a function of x because you can find a vertical line that intersects the graph twice.

b. This *is* a graph of y as a function of x because every vertical line intersects the graph at most once.

✅ *Checkpoint* Now try Exercise 13.

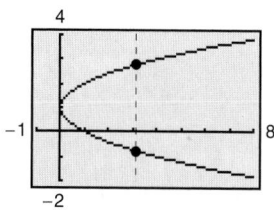

(a)

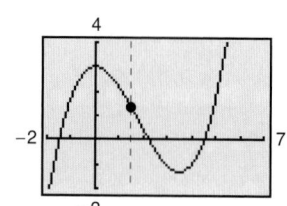

(b)

Figure 1.36

Increasing and Decreasing Functions

The more you know about the graph of a function, the more you know about the function itself. Consider the graph shown in Figure 1.37. Moving from *left to right*, this graph falls from $x = -2$ to $x = 0$, is constant from $x = 0$ to $x = 2$, and rises from $x = 2$ to $x = 4$.

Increasing, Decreasing, and Constant Functions

A function f is **increasing** on an interval if, for any x_1 and x_2 in the interval,

$$x_1 < x_2 \text{ implies } f(x_1) < f(x_2).$$

A function f is **decreasing** on an interval if, for any x_1 and x_2 in the interval,

$$x_1 < x_2 \text{ implies } f(x_1) > f(x_2).$$

A function f is **constant** on an interval if, for any x_1 and x_2 in the interval,

$$f(x_1) = f(x_2).$$

Example 4   Increasing and Decreasing Functions

In Figure 1.38, determine the open intervals on which each function is increasing, decreasing, or constant.

Solution

a. Although it might appear that there is an interval in which this function is constant, you can see that if $x_1 < x_2$, then $(x_1)^3 < (x_2)^3$, which implies that $f(x_1) < f(x_2)$. So, the function is increasing over the entire real line.

b. This function is increasing on the interval $(-\infty, -1)$, decreasing on the interval $(-1, 1)$, and increasing on the interval $(1, \infty)$.

c. This function is increasing on the interval $(-\infty, 0)$, constant on the interval $[0, 2]$, and decreasing on the interval $(2, \infty)$.

TECHNOLOGY TIP

Most graphing utilities are designed to graph functions of x more easily than other types of equations. For instance, the graph shown in Figure 1.36(a) represents the equation $x - (y - 1)^2 = 0$. To use a graphing utility to duplicate this graph you must first solve the equation for y to obtain $y = 1 \pm \sqrt{x}$, and then graph the two equations $y_1 = 1 + \sqrt{x}$ and $y_2 = 1 - \sqrt{x}$ in the same viewing window.

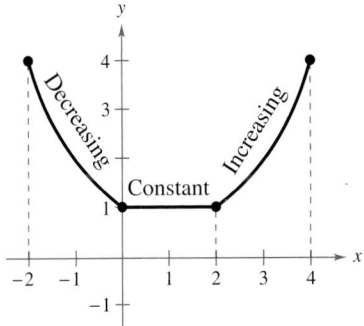

Figure 1.37

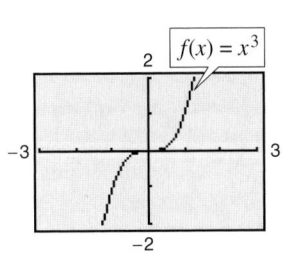

(a)

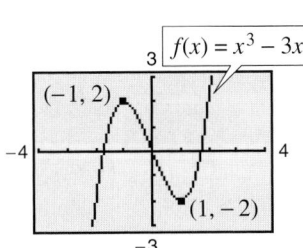

(b)

$$f(x) = \begin{cases} x + 1, & x < 0 \\ 1, & 0 \le x \le 2 \\ -x + 3 & x > 2 \end{cases}$$

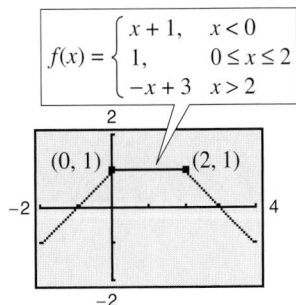

(c)

Figure 1.38

✓ *Checkpoint* Now try Exercise 19.

Relative Minimum and Maximum Values

The points at which a function changes its increasing, decreasing, or constant behavior are helpful in determining the relative maximum or relative minimum values of the function.

Definition of Relative Minimum and Relative Maximum

A function value $f(a)$ is called a **relative minimum** of f if there exists an interval (x_1, x_2) that contains a such that

$$x_1 < x < x_2 \quad \text{implies} \quad f(a) \le f(x).$$

A function value $f(a)$ is called a **relative maximum** of f if there exists an interval (x_1, x_2) that contains a such that

$$x_1 < x < x_2 \quad \text{implies} \quad f(a) \ge f(x).$$

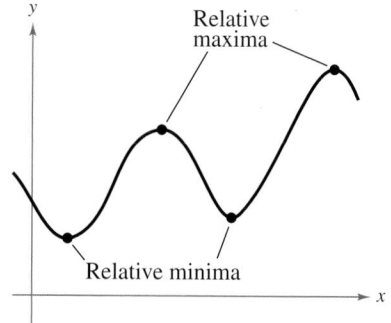

Figure 1.39

Figure 1.39 shows several different examples of relative minima and relative maxima. In Section 3.1, you will study a technique for finding the *exact points* at which a second-degree polynomial function has a relative minimum or relative maximum. For the time being, however, you can use a graphing utility to find reasonable approximations of these points.

Example 5 Approximating a Relative Minimum

Use a graphing utility to approximate the relative minimum of the function given by $f(x) = 3x^2 - 4x - 2$.

Solution

The graph of f is shown in Figure 1.40. By using the *zoom* and *trace* features of a graphing utility, you can estimate that the function has a relative minimum at the point

$(0.67, -3.33)$.   See Figure 1.41.

Later, in Section 3.1, you will be able to determine that the exact point at which the relative minimum occurs is $\left(\frac{2}{3}, -\frac{10}{3}\right)$.

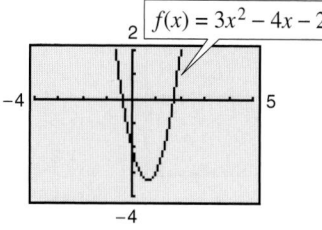

Figure 1.40

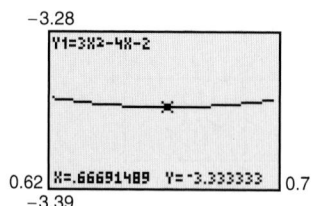

Figure 1.41

☑ *Checkpoint* Now try Exercise 29.

TECHNOLOGY TIP

When you use a graphing utility to estimate the x- and y-values of a relative minimum or relative maximum, the *zoom* feature will often produce graphs that are nearly flat, as shown in Figure 1.41. To overcome this problem, you can manually change the vertical setting of the viewing window. The graph will vertically stretch if the values of Ymin and Ymax are closer together.

TECHNOLOGY TIP   Some graphing utilities have built-in programs that will find minimum or maximum values. These features are demonstrated in Example 6.

Example 6   Approximating Relative Minima and Maxima

Use a graphing utility to approximate the relative minimum and relative maximum of the function given by $f(x) = -x^3 + x$.

Solution

The graph of f is shown in Figure 1.42. By using the *zoom* and *trace* features or the *minimum* and *maximum* features of the graphing utility, you can estimate that the function has a relative minimum at the point

$(-0.58, -0.38)$ See Figure 1.43.

and a relative maximum at the point

$(0.58, 0.38)$.   See Figure 1.44.

If you take a course in calculus, you will learn a technique for finding the exact points at which this function has a relative minimum and a relative maximum.

 Checkpoint Now try Exercise 31.

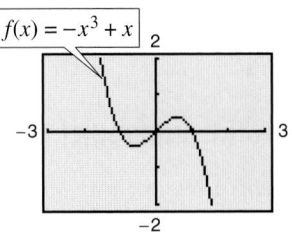

Figure 1.42

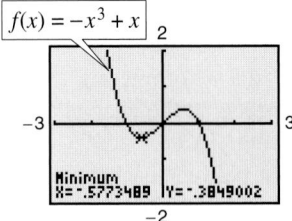

Figure 1.43

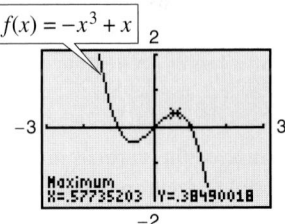

Figure 1.44

Example 7   Temperature

During a 24-hour period, the temperature y (in degrees Fahrenheit) of a certain city can be approximated by the model

$$y = 0.026x^3 - 1.03x^2 + 10.2x + 34, \qquad 0 \le x \le 24$$

where x represents the time of day, with $x = 0$ corresponding to 6 A.M. Approximate the maximum and minimum temperatures during this 24-hour period.

Solution

To solve this problem, graph the function as shown in Figure 1.45. Using the *zoom* and *trace* features or the *maximum* feature of a graphing utility, you can determine that the maximum temperature during the 24-hour period was approximately 64°F. This temperature occurred at about 12:36 P.M. $(x \approx 6.6)$, as shown in Figure 1.46. Using the *zoom* and *trace* features or the *minimum* feature, you can determine that the minimum temperature during the 24-hour period was approximately 34°F, which occurred at about 1:48 A.M. $(x \approx 19.8)$, as shown in Figure 1.47.

TECHNOLOGY SUPPORT

For instructions on how to use the *minimum* and *maximum* features, see Appendix A; for specific keystrokes, go to the text website at *college.hmco.com*.

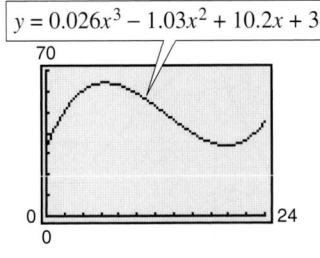

Figure 1.45

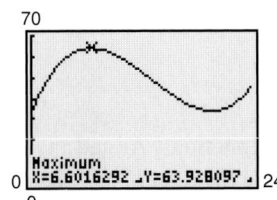

Figure 1.46

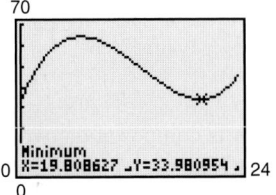

Figure 1.47

 Checkpoint Now try Exercise 87.

Graphing Step Functions and Piecewise-Defined Functions

Library of Functions: Greatest Integer Function

The *greatest integer function*, denoted by $[\![x]\!]$ and defined as the greatest integer less than or equal to x, has an infinite number of breaks or steps—one at each integer value in its domain. The basic characteristics of the greatest integer function are summarized below.

Graph of $f(x) = [\![x]\!]$

Domain: $(-\infty, \infty)$
Range: the set of integers
x-intercepts: in the interval $[0, 1)$
y-intercept: $(0, 0)$
Constant between each pair of consecutive integers
Jumps vertically one unit at each integer value

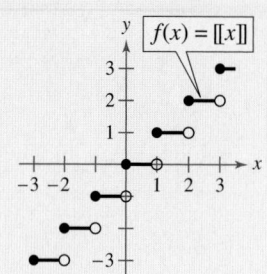

Could you describe the greatest integer function using a piecewise-defined function? How does the graph of the greatest integer function differ from the graph of a line with a slope of zero?

TECHNOLOGY TIP

Most graphing utilities display graphs in *connected mode*, which means that the graph has no breaks. When you are sketching graphs that do have breaks, it is better to use *dot mode*. Graph the greatest integer function [often called Int (x)] in connected and dot modes, and compare the two results.

Because of the vertical jumps described above, the greatest integer function is an example of a **step function** whose graph resembles a set of stairsteps. Some values of the greatest integer function are as follows.

$$[\![-1]\!] = (\text{greatest integer} \le -1) = -1$$

$$\left[\!\!\left[\tfrac{1}{10}\right]\!\!\right] = \left(\text{greatest integer} \le \tfrac{1}{10}\right) = 0$$

$$[\![1.5]\!] = (\text{greatest integer} \le 1.5) = 1$$

In Section 1.3, you learned that a piecewise-defined function is a function that is defined by two or more equations over a specified domain. To sketch the graph of a piecewise-defined function, you need to sketch the graph of each equation on the appropriate portion of the domain.

Example 8   Graphing a Piecewise-Defined Function

Sketch the graph of $f(x) = \begin{cases} 2x + 3, & x \le 1 \\ -x + 4, & x > 1 \end{cases}$ by hand.

Solution

This piecewise-defined function is composed of two linear functions. At and to the left of $x = 1$, the graph is the line given by $y = 2x + 3$. To the right of $x = 1$, the graph is the line given by $y = -x + 4$ (see Figure 1.48). Notice that the point $(1, 5)$ is a solid dot and the point $(1, 3)$ is an open dot. This is because $f(1) = 5$.

✓ *Checkpoint* Now try Exercise 41.

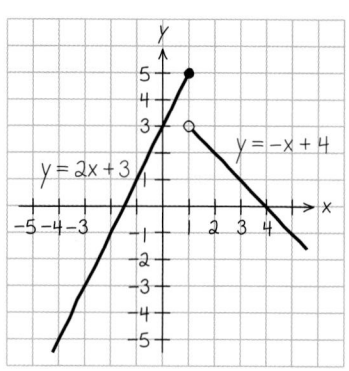

Figure 1.48

Even and Odd Functions

A graph has *symmetry with respect to the y-axis* if whenever (x, y) is on the graph, so is the point $(-x, y)$. A graph has *symmetry with respect to the origin* if whenever (x, y) is on the graph, so is the point $(-x, -y)$. A graph has *symmetry with respect to the x-axis* if whenever (x, y) is on the graph, so is the point $(x, -y)$. A function whose graph is symmetric with respect to the y-axis is an **even** function. A function whose graph is symmetric with respect to the origin is an **odd** function. A graph that is symmetric with respect to the x-axis is not the graph of a function (except for the graph of $y = 0$). These three types of symmetry are illustrated in Figure 1.49.

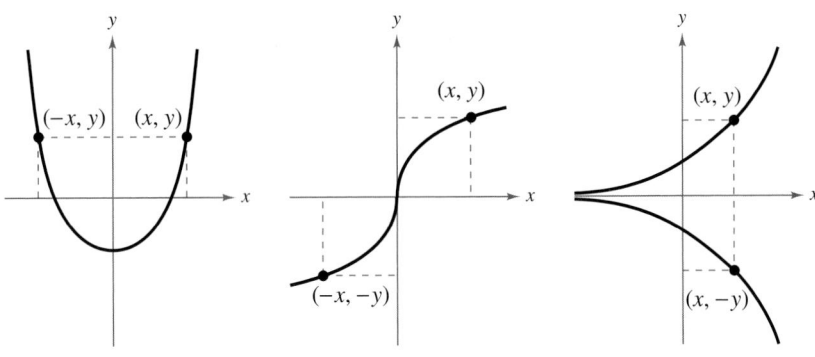

Symmetric to y-axis
Even function

Symmetric to origin
Odd function

Symmetric to x-axis
Not a function

Figure 1.49

Test for Even and Odd Functions

A function f is **even** if, for each x in the domain of f, $f(-x) = f(x)$.
A function f is **odd** if, for each x in the domain of f, $f(-x) = -f(x)$.

Example 9   Testing for Evenness and Oddness

Is the function given by $f(x) = |x|$ even, odd, or neither?

Algebraic Solution

This function is even because

$$f(-x) = |-x|$$
$$= |x|$$
$$= f(x).$$

Graphical Solution

Use a graphing utility to enter $y = |x|$ in the equation editor, as shown in Figure 1.50. Then graph the function using a standard viewing window, as shown in Figure 1.51. You can see that the graph appears to be symmetric about the y-axis. So, the function is even.

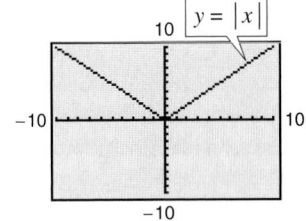

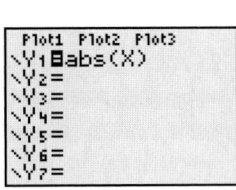

✓ *Checkpoint* Now try Exercise 49.

Figure 1.50

Figure 1.51

Example 10   Even and Odd Functions

Determine whether each function is even, odd, or neither.

a. $g(x) = x^3 - x$

b. $h(x) = x^2 + 1$

c. $f(x) = x^3 - 1$

Algebraic Solution

a. This function is odd because

$$g(-x) = (-x)^3 - (-x)$$
$$= -x^3 + x$$
$$= -(x^3 - x)$$
$$= -g(x).$$

b. This function is even because

$$h(-x) = (-x)^2 + 1$$
$$= x^2 + 1$$
$$= h(x).$$

c. Substituting $-x$ for x produces

$$f(-x) = (-x)^3 - 1$$
$$= -x^3 - 1.$$

Because $f(x) = x^3 - 1$ and $-f(x) = -x^3 + 1$, you can conclude that $f(-x) \neq f(x)$ and $f(-x) \neq -f(x)$. So, the function is neither even nor odd.

✓ *Checkpoint* Now try Exercise 51.

Graphical Solution

a. In Figure 1.52, the graph is symmetric with respect to the origin. So, this function is odd.

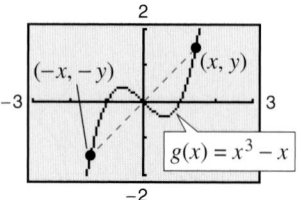

Figure 1.52

b. In Figure 1.53, the graph is symmetric with respect to the y-axis. So, this function is even.

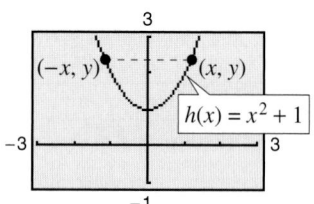

Figure 1.53

c. In Figure 1.54, the graph is neither symmetric with respect to the origin nor with respect to the y-axis. So, this function is neither even nor odd.

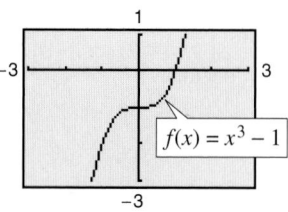

Figure 1.54

To help visualize symmetry with respect to the origin, place a pin at the origin of a graph and rotate the graph 180°. If the result after rotation coincides with the original graph, the graph is symmetric with respect to the origin.

1.4   Exercises

Vocabulary Check

Fill in the blanks.

1. The graph of a function f is a collection of _____ (x, y) such that x is in the domain of f.
2. The _____ is used to determine whether the graph of an equation is a function of y in terms of x.
3. A function f is _____ on an interval if, for any x_1 and x_2 in the interval, $x_1 < x_2$ implies $f(x_1) > f(x_2)$.
4. A function value $f(a)$ is a relative _____ of f if there exists an interval (x_1, x_2) containing a such that $x_1 < x < x_2$ implies $f(a) \leq f(x)$.
5. The function $f(x) = [\![x]\!]$ is called the _____ function, and is an example of a step function.
6. A function f is _____ if, for each x in the domain of f, $f(-x) = f(x)$.

In Exercises 1–4, use the graph of the function to find the domain and range of f. Then find $f(0)$.

1.
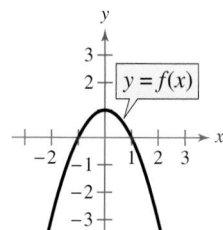

2.
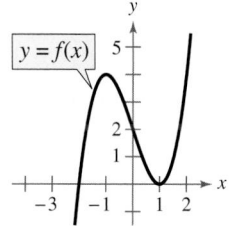

3.
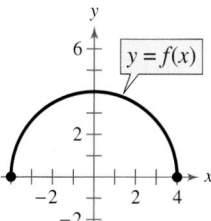

4.
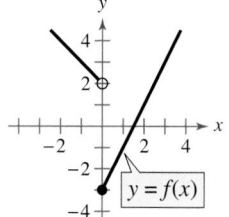

In Exercises 5–10, use a graphing utility to graph the function and estimate its domain and range. Then find the domain and range algebraically.

5. $f(x) = 2x^2 + 3$
6. $f(x) = -x^2 - 1$
7. $f(x) = \sqrt{x - 1}$
8. $h(t) = \sqrt{4 - t^2}$
9. $f(x) = |x + 3|$
10. $f(x) = -\frac{1}{4}|x - 5|$

In Exercises 11–16, use the Vertical Line Test to determine whether y is a function of x. Describe how you can use a graphing utility to produce the given graph.

11. $y = \frac{1}{2}x^2$
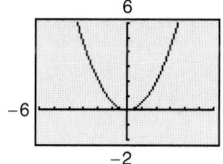

12. $y = \frac{1}{4}x^3$
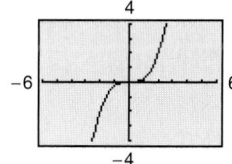

13. $x - y^2 = 1$
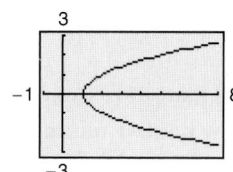

14. $x^2 + y^2 = 25$
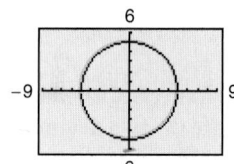

15. $x^2 = 2xy - 1$
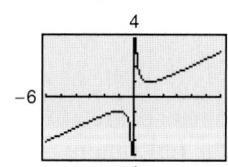

16. $x = |y + 2|$
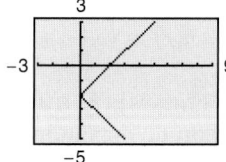

In Exercises 17–20, determine the intervals over which the function is increasing, decreasing, or constant.

17. $f(x) = \frac{3}{2}x$

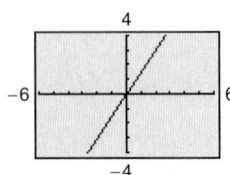

18. $f(x) = x^2 - 4x$

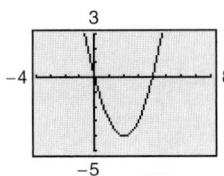

19. $f(x) = x^3 - 3x^2 + 2$

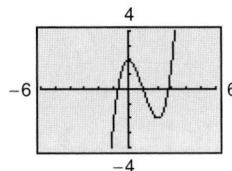

20. $f(x) = \sqrt{x^2 - 1}$

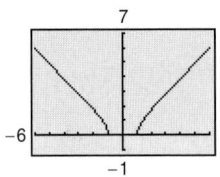

In Exercises 21–28, (a) use a graphing utility to graph the function and (b) determine the open intervals on which the function is increasing, decreasing, or constant.

21. $f(x) = 3$

22. $f(x) = x$

23. $f(x) = x^{2/3}$

24. $f(x) = -x^{3/4}$

25. $f(x) = x\sqrt{x + 3}$

26. $f(x) = \sqrt{1 - x}$

27. $f(x) = |x + 1| + |x - 1|$

28. $f(x) = -|x + 4| - |x + 1|$

In Exercises 29–34, use a graphing utility to approximate (to two decimal places) any relative minimum or maximum values of the function.

29. $f(x) = x^2 - 6x$

30. $f(x) = 3x^2 - 2x - 5$

31. $y = 2x^3 + 3x^2 - 12x$

32. $y = x^3 - 6x^2 + 15$

33. $h(x) = (x - 1)\sqrt{x}$

34. $g(x) = x\sqrt{4 - x}$

In Exercises 35–40, (a) approximate the relative minimum or maximum values of the function by sketching its graph using the point-plotting method, (b) use a graphing utility to approximate (to two decimal places) any relative minimum or maximum values, and (c) compare your answers from parts (a) and (b).

35. $f(x) = x^2 - 4x - 5$

36. $f(x) = 3x^2 - 12$

37. $f(x) = x^3 - 8x$

38. $f(x) = -x^3 + 7x$

39. $f(x) = (x - 4)^{2/3}$

40. $f(x) = \sqrt{4x^2 + 1}$

In Exercises 41–48, sketch the graph of the piecewise-defined function by hand.

41. $f(x) = \begin{cases} 2x + 3, & x < 0 \\ 3 - x, & x \geq 0 \end{cases}$

42. $f(x) = \begin{cases} x + 6, & x \leq -4 \\ 2x - 4, & x > -4 \end{cases}$

43. $f(x) = \begin{cases} \sqrt{4 + x}, & x < 0 \\ \sqrt{4 - x}, & x \geq 0 \end{cases}$

44. $f(x) = \begin{cases} 1 - (x - 1)^2, & x \leq 2 \\ \sqrt{x - 2}, & x > 2 \end{cases}$

45. $f(x) = \begin{cases} x + 3, & x \leq 0 \\ 3, & 0 < x \leq 2 \\ 2x - 1, & x > 2 \end{cases}$

46. $g(x) = \begin{cases} x + 5, & x \leq -3 \\ -2, & -3 < x < 1 \\ 5x - 4, & x \geq 1 \end{cases}$

47. $f(x) = \begin{cases} 2x + 1, & x \leq -1 \\ x^2 - 2, & x > -1 \end{cases}$

48. $h(x) = \begin{cases} 3 + x, & x < 0 \\ x^2 + 1, & x \geq 0 \end{cases}$

In Exercises 49–56, algebraically determine whether the function is even, odd, or neither. Verify your answer using a graphing utility.

49. $f(t) = t^2 + 2t - 3$

50. $f(x) = x^6 - 2x^2 + 3$

51. $g(x) = x^3 - 5x$

52. $h(x) = x^3 - 5$

53. $f(x) = x\sqrt{1 - x^2}$

54. $f(x) = x\sqrt{x + 5}$

55. $g(s) = 4s^{2/3}$

56. $f(s) = 4s^{3/2}$

Think About It   In Exercises 57–62, find the coordinates of a second point on the graph of a function f if the given point is on the graph and the function is (a) even and (b) odd.

57. $\left(-\frac{3}{2}, 4\right)$

58. $\left(-\frac{5}{3}, -7\right)$

59. $(4, 9)$

60. $(5, -1)$

61. $(x, -y)$

62. $(2a, 2c)$

In Exercises 63–72, use a graphing utility to graph the function and determine whether it is even, odd, or neither. Verify your answer algebraically.

63. $f(x) = 5$

64. $f(x) = -9$

65. $f(x) = 3x - 2$

66. $f(x) = 5 - 3x$

67. $h(x) = x^2 - 4$

68. $f(x) = -x^2 - 8$

69. $f(x) = \sqrt{1 - x}$ **70.** $g(t) = \sqrt[3]{t - 1}$

71. $f(x) = |x + 2|$ **72.** $f(x) = -|x - 5|$

In Exercises 73–76, graph the function and determine the interval(s) (if any) on the real axis for which $f(x) \geq 0$. Use a graphing utility to verify your results.

73. $f(x) = 4 - x$ **74.** $f(x) = 4x + 2$

75. $f(x) = x^2 - 9$ **76.** $f(x) = x^2 - 4x$

In Exercises 77 and 78, use a graphing utility to graph the function. State the domain and range of the function. Describe the pattern of the graph.

77. $s(x) = 2\left(\frac{1}{4}x - \left[\!\left[\frac{1}{4}x\right]\!\right]\right)$ **78.** $g(x) = 2\left(\frac{1}{4}x - \left[\!\left[\frac{1}{4}x\right]\!\right]\right)^2$

79. *Geometry* The perimeter of a rectangle is 100 meters.

(a) Show that the area of the rectangle is given by $A = x(50 - x)$, where x is its length.

(b) Use a graphing utility to graph the area function.

(c) Use a graphing utility to approximate the maximum area of the rectangle and the dimensions that yield the maximum area.

80. *Cost, Revenue, and Profit* The marketing department of a company estimates that the demand for a color scanner is $p = 100 - 0.0001x$, where p is the price per scanner and x is the number of scanners. The cost of producing x scanners is $C = 350,000 + 30x$ and the profit for producing and selling x scanners is

$$P = R - C = xp - C.$$

Use a graphing utility to graph the profit function and estimate the number of scanners that would produce a maximum profit.

81. *Communications* The cost of using a telephone calling card is $1.05 for the first minute and $0.38 for each additional minute or portion of a minute.

(a) A customer needs a model for the cost C of using the calling card for a call lasting t minutes. Which of the following is the appropriate model?

$$C_1(t) = 1.05 + 0.38[\![t - 1]\!]$$

$$C_2(t) = 1.05 - 0.38[\![-(t - 1)]\!]$$

(b) Use a graphing utility to graph the appropriate model. Use the *value* feature or the *zoom* and *trace* features to estimate the cost of a call lasting 18 minutes and 45 seconds.

82. *Delivery Charges* The cost of sending an overnight package from New York to Atlanta is $9.80 for a package weighing up to but not including 1 pound and $2.50 for each additional pound or portion of a pound. Use the greatest integer function to create a model for the cost C of overnight delivery of a package weighing x pounds, where $x > 0$. Sketch the graph of the function.

 In Exercises 83 and 84, write the height h of the rectangle as a function of x.

83.

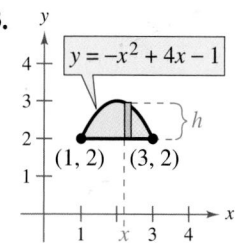

84.

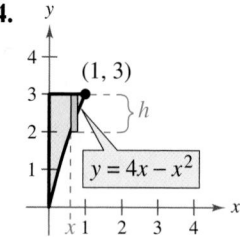

 In Exercises 85 and 86, write the length L of the rectangle as a function of y.

85.

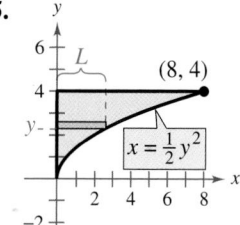

86.

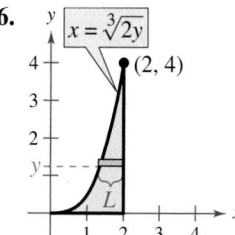

87. *Population* During a seven-year period, the population P (in thousands) of North Dakota increased and then decreased according to the model

$$P = -0.76t^2 + 9.9t + 618, \quad 5 \leq t \leq 11$$

where t represents the year, with $t = 5$ corresponding to 1995. (Source: U.S. Census Bureau)

(a) Use a graphing utility to graph the model over the appropriate domain.

(b) Use the graph from part (a) to determine during which years the population was increasing. During which years was the population decreasing?

(c) Use the *zoom* and *trace* features or the *maximum* feature of a graphing utility to approximate the maximum population between 1995 and 2001.

88. *Fluid Flow* The intake pipe of a 100-gallon tank has a flow rate of 10 gallons per minute, and two drain pipes have a flow rate of 5 gallons per minute each. The graph shows the volume V of fluid in the tank as a function of time t. Determine in which pipes the fluid is flowing in specific subintervals of the one-hour interval of time shown on the graph. (There are many correct answers.)

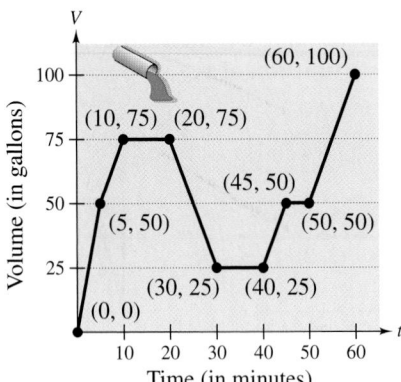

Synthesis

True or False? **In Exercises 89 and 90, determine whether the statement is true or false. Justify your answer.**

89. A function with a square root cannot have a domain that is the set of all real numbers.

90. It is possible for an odd function to have the interval $[0, \infty)$ as its domain.

91. *Proof* Prove that a function of the following form is odd.

$$y = a_{2n+1}x^{2n+1} + a_{2n-1}x^{2n-1} + \cdots + a_3x^3 + a_1x$$

92. *Proof* Prove that a function of the following form is even.

$$y = a_{2n}x^{2n} + a_{2n-2}x^{2n-2} + \cdots + a_2x^2 + a_0$$

93. If f is an even function, determine if g is even, odd, or neither. Explain.

(a) $g(x) = -f(x)$ (b) $g(x) = f(-x)$

(c) $g(x) = f(x) - 2$ (d) $g(x) = -f(x - 2)$

94. *Think About It* Does the graph in Exercise 13 represent x as a function of y? Explain.

95. *Think About It* Does the graph in Exercise 14 represent x as a function of y? Explain.

96. *Writing* Write a short paragraph describing three different functions that represent the behaviors of quantities between 1990 and 2004. Describe one quantity that decreased during this time, one that increased, and one that was constant. Present your results graphically.

Review

In Exercises 97–100, identify the terms. Then identify the coefficients of the variable terms of the expression.

97. $-2x^2 + 8x$

98. $10 + 3x$

99. $\dfrac{x}{3} - 5x^2 + x^3$

100. $7x^4 + \sqrt{2}x^2$

In Exercises 101–104, find (a) the distance between the two points and (b) the midpoint of the line segment joining the points.

101. $(-2, 7), (6, 3)$

102. $(-5, 0), (3, 6)$

103. $\left(\frac{5}{2}, -1\right), \left(-\frac{3}{2}, 4\right)$

104. $\left(-6, \frac{2}{3}\right), \left(\frac{3}{4}, \frac{1}{6}\right)$

In Exercises 105–108, evaluate the function at each specified value of the independent variable and simplify.

105. $f(x) = 5x - 1$

(a) $f(6)$ (b) $f(-1)$ (c) $f(x - 3)$

106. $f(x) = -x^2 - x + 3$

(a) $f(4)$ (b) $f(-2)$ (c) $f(x - 2)$

107. $f(x) = x\sqrt{x - 3}$

(a) $f(3)$ (b) $f(12)$ (c) $f(6)$

108. $f(x) = -\frac{1}{2}x|x + 1|$

(a) $f(-4)$ (b) $f(10)$ (c) $f\left(-\frac{2}{3}\right)$

In Exercises 109 and 110, find the difference quotient and simplify your answer.

109. $f(x) = x^2 - 2x + 9, \ \dfrac{f(3 + h) - f(3)}{h}, h \neq 0$

110. $f(x) = 5 + 6x - x^2, \ \dfrac{f(6 + h) - f(6)}{h}, h \neq 0$

1.5 Shifting, Reflecting, and Stretching Graphs

Summary of Graphs of Common Functions

One of the goals of this text is to enable you to build your intuition for the basic shapes of the graphs of different types of functions. For instance, from your study of lines in Section 1.2, you can determine the basic shape of the graph of the linear function $f(x) = mx + b$. Specifically, you know that the graph of this function is a line whose slope is m and whose y-intercept is $(0, b)$.

The six graphs shown in Figure 1.55 represent the most commonly used functions in algebra. Familiarity with the basic characteristics of these simple graphs will help you analyze the shapes of more complicated graphs.

What you should learn

- Recognize graphs of common functions.
- Use vertical and horizontal shifts and reflections to graph functions.
- Use nonrigid transformations to graph functions.

Why you should learn it

Recognizing the graphs of common functions and knowing how to shift, reflect, and stretch graphs of functions can help you sketch a wide variety of simple functions by hand. This skill is useful in sketching graphs of functions that model real-life data. For example, in Exercise 67 on page 133, you are asked to sketch a function that models the amount of fuel used by trucks from 1980 through 2000.

Index Stock

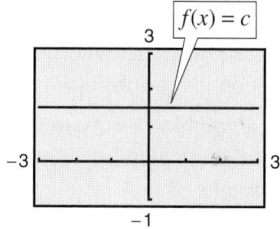

(a) Constant Function

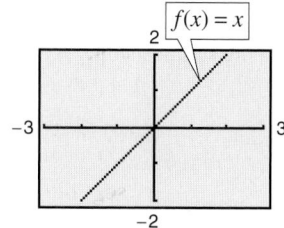

(b) Identity Function

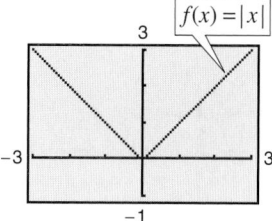

(c) Absolute Value Function

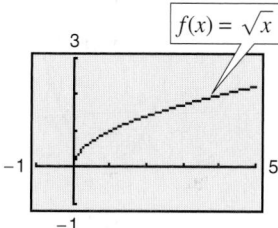

(d) Square Root Function

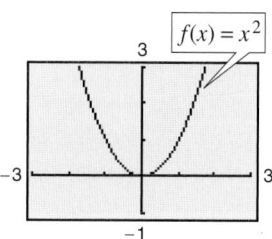

(e) Quadratic Function

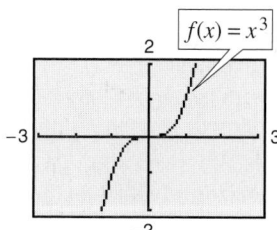

(f) Cubic Function

Figure 1.55

Throughout this section, you will discover how many complicated graphs are derived by shifting, stretching, shrinking, or reflecting the common graphs shown above. Shifts, stretches, shrinks, and reflections are called *transformations*. Many graphs of functions can be created from a combination of these transformations.

Vertical and Horizontal Shifts

Many functions have graphs that are simple transformations of the common graphs summarized in Figure 1.55. For example, you can obtain the graph of

$$h(x) = x^2 + 2$$

by shifting the graph of $f(x) = x^2$ *upward* two units, as shown in Figure 1.56. In function notation, h and f are related as follows.

$$h(x) = x^2 + 2$$
$$= f(x) + 2 \qquad \text{Upward shift of two units}$$

Similarly, you can obtain the graph of

$$g(x) = (x - 2)^2$$

by shifting the graph of $f(x) = x^2$ to the *right* two units, as shown in Figure 1.57. In this case, the functions g and f have the following relationship.

$$g(x) = (x - 2)^2$$
$$= f(x - 2) \qquad \text{Right shift of two units}$$

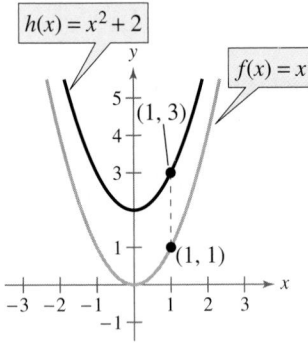

Figure 1.56 Vertical shift upward: two units

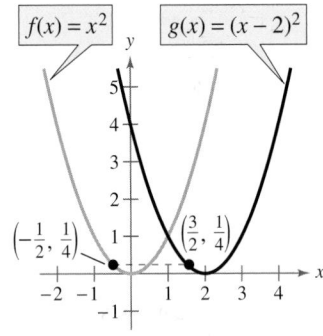

Figure 1.57 Horizontal shift to the right: two units

> ### Exploration
>
> Use a graphing utility to display (in the same viewing window) the graphs of $y = x^2 + c$, where $c = -2, 0, 2$, and 4. Use the result to describe the effect that c has on the graph.
>
> Use a graphing utility to display (in the same viewing window) the graphs of $y = (x + c)^2$, where $c = -2, 0, 2$, and 4. Use the result to describe the effect that c has on the graph.

The following list summarizes horizontal and vertical shifts.

Vertical and Horizontal Shifts

Let c be a positive real number. **Vertical and horizontal shifts** in the graph of $y = f(x)$ are represented as follows.

   1. Vertical shift c units *upward*: $h(x) = f(x) + c$

   2. Vertical shift c units *downward*: $h(x) = f(x) - c$

   3. Horizontal shift c units to the *right*: $h(x) = f(x - c)$

   4. Horizontal shift c units to the *left*: $h(x) = f(x + c)$

In items 3 and 4, be sure you see that $h(x) = f(x - c)$ corresponds to a *right* shift and $h(x) = f(x + c)$ corresponds to a *left* shift for $c > 0$.

Example 1   Shifts in the Graph of a Function

Compare the graph of each function with the graph of $f(x) = x^3$.

a. $g(x) = x^3 - 1$ **b.** $h(x) = (x - 1)^3$ **c.** $k(x) = (x + 2)^3 + 1$

Solution

a. Graph $f(x) = x^3$ and $g(x) = x^3 - 1$ [see Figure 1.58(a)]. You can obtain the graph of g by shifting the graph of f one unit downward.

b. Graph $f(x) = x^3$ and $h(x) = (x - 1)^3$ [see Figure 1.58(b)]. You can obtain the graph of h by shifting the graph of f one unit to the right.

c. Graph $f(x) = x^3$ and $k(x) = (x + 2)^3 + 1$ [see Figure 1.58(c)]. You can obtain the graph of k by shifting the graph of f two units to the left and then one unit upward.

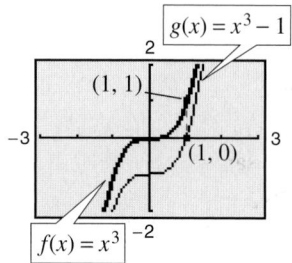
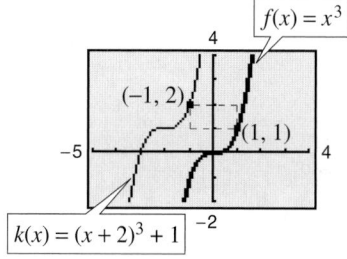

(a) Vertical shift: one unit downward   (b) Horizontal shift: one unit right   (c) Two units left and one unit upward

Figure 1.58

 Checkpoint Now try Exercise 3.

Example 2   Finding Equations from Graphs

The graph of $f(x) = x^2$ is shown in Figure 1.59. Each of the graphs in Figure 1.60 is a transformation of the graph of f. Find an equation for each function.

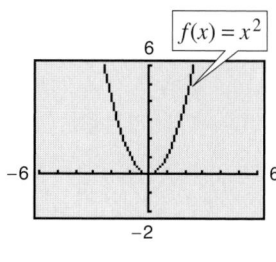
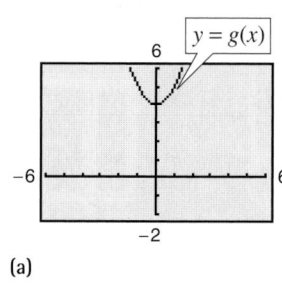
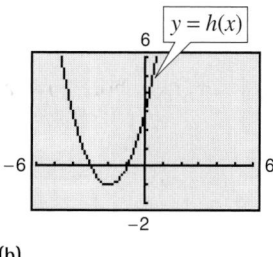

(a)   (b)

Figure 1.59   **Figure 1.60**

Solution

a. The graph of g is a vertical shift of four units upward of the graph of $f(x) = x^2$. So, the equation for g is $g(x) = x^2 + 4$.

b. The graph of h is a horizontal shift of two units to the left, and a vertical shift of one unit downward, of the graph of $f(x) = x^2$. So, the equation for h is $h(x) = (x + 2)^2 - 1$.

 Checkpoint Now try Exercise 21.

Reflecting Graphs

The second common type of transformation is called a **reflection**. For instance, if you consider the x-axis to be a mirror, the graph of $h(x) = -x^2$ is the mirror image (or reflection) of the graph of $f(x) = x^2$ (see Figure 1.61).

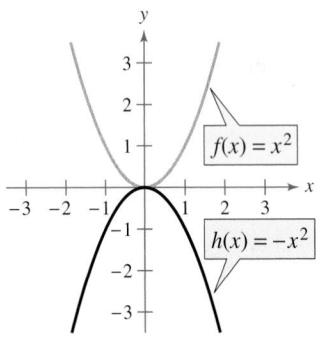

Figure 1.61

Reflections in the Coordinate Axes

Reflections in the coordinate axes of the graph of $y = f(x)$ are represented as follows.

1. Reflection in the x-axis: $h(x) = -f(x)$

2. Reflection in the y-axis: $h(x) = f(-x)$

Example 3   Finding Equations from Graphs

The graph of $f(x) = x^4$ is shown in Figure 1.62. Each of the graphs in Figure 1.63 is a transformation of the graph of f. Find an equation for each function.

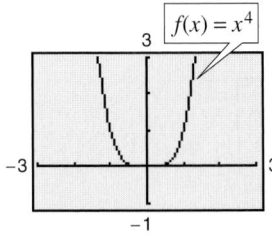

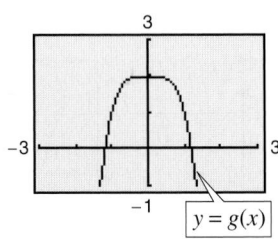

(a)

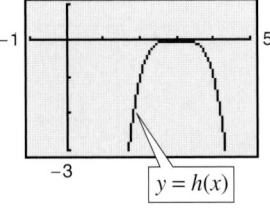

(b)

Figure 1.62   Figure 1.63

Solution

a. The graph of g is a reflection in the x-axis *followed by* an upward shift of two units of the graph of $f(x) = x^4$. So, the equation for g is $g(x) = -x^4 + 2$.

b. The graph of h is a horizontal shift of three units to the right *followed by* a reflection in the x-axis of the graph of $f(x) = x^4$. So, the equation for h is $h(x) = -(x - 3)^4$.

✓ *Checkpoint* Now try Exercise 25.

Example 4   Reflections and Shifts

Compare the graph of each function with the graph of $f(x) = \sqrt{x}$.

a. $g(x) = -\sqrt{x}$ **b.** $h(x) = \sqrt{-x}$ **c.** $k(x) = -\sqrt{x+2}$

Algebraic Solution

a. Relative to the graph of $f(x) = \sqrt{x}$, the graph of g is a reflection in the x-axis because

$$g(x) = -\sqrt{x}$$

$$= -f(x).$$

b. The graph of h is a reflection of the graph of $f(x) = \sqrt{x}$ in the y-axis because

$$h(x) = \sqrt{-x}$$

$$= f(-x).$$

c. From the equation

$$k(x) = -\sqrt{x+2}$$

$$= -f(x+2)$$

you can conclude that the graph of k is a left shift of two units, followed by a reflection in the x-axis, of the graph of $f(x) = \sqrt{x}$.

Graphical Solution

a. Use a graphing utility to graph f and g in the same viewing window. From the graph in Figure 1.64, you can see that the graph of g is a reflection of the graph of f in the x-axis.

b. Use a graphing utility to graph f and h in the same viewing window. From the graph in Figure 1.65, you can see that the graph of h is a reflection of the graph of f in the y-axis.

c. Use a graphing utility to graph f and k in the same viewing window. From the graph in Figure 1.66, you can see that the graph of k is a left shift of two units of the graph of f, followed by a reflection in the x-axis.

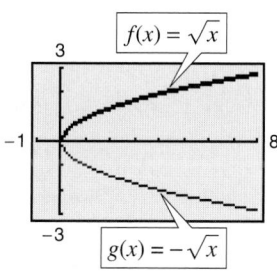

Figure 1.64

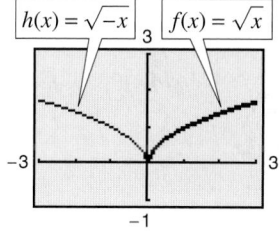

Figure 1.65

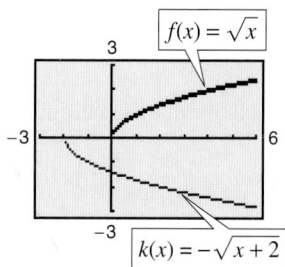

Figure 1.66

✓ *Checkpoint* Now try Exercise 27.

When graphing functions involving square roots, remember that the domain must be restricted to exclude negative numbers inside the radical. For instance, here are the domains of the functions in Example 4.

Domain of $g(x) = -\sqrt{x}$: $x \geq 0$

Domain of $h(x) = \sqrt{-x}$: $x \leq 0$

Domain of $k(x) = -\sqrt{x+2}$: $x \geq -2$

Nonrigid Transformations

Horizontal shifts, vertical shifts, and reflections are called **rigid transformations** because the basic shape of the graph is unchanged. These transformations change only the *position* of the graph in the coordinate plane. **Nonrigid transformations** are those that cause a *distortion*—a change in the shape of the original graph. For instance, a nonrigid transformation of the graph of $y = f(x)$ is represented by $y = cf(x)$ (each y-value is multiplied by c), where the transformation is a **vertical stretch** if $c > 1$ and a **vertical shrink** if $0 < c < 1$. Another nonrigid transformation of the graph of $y = f(x)$ is represented by $h(x) = f(cx)$ (each x-value is multiplied by $1/c$), where the transformation is a **horizontal shrink** if $c > 1$ and a **horizontal stretch** if $0 < c < 1$.

Example 5   Nonrigid Transformations

Compare the graph of each function with the graph of $f(x) = |x|$.

a. $h(x) = 3|x|$ **b.** $g(x) = \frac{1}{3}|x|$

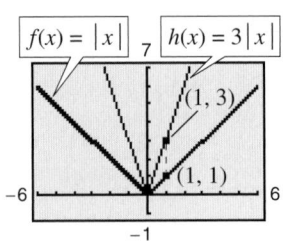

Figure 1.67

Solution

a. Relative to the graph of $f(x) = |x|$, the graph of

$$h(x) = 3|x|$$
$$= 3f(x)$$

is a vertical stretch (each y-value is multiplied by 3) of the graph of f. (See Figure 1.67.)

b. Similarly, the graph of

$$g(x) = \frac{1}{3}|x|$$
$$= \frac{1}{3}f(x)$$

is a vertical shrink $\left(\text{each } y\text{-value is multiplied by } \frac{1}{3}\right)$ of the graph of f. (See Figure 1.68.)

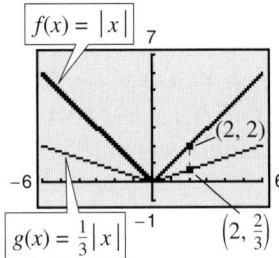

Figure 1.68

☑ *Checkpoint* Now try Exercise 37.

Example 6   Nonrigid Transformations

Compare the graph of $h(x) = f\left(\frac{1}{2}x\right)$ with the graph of $f(x) = 2 - x^3$.

Solution

Relative to the graph of $f(x) = 2 - x^3$, the graph of

$$h(x) = f\left(\tfrac{1}{2}x\right) = 2 - \left(\tfrac{1}{2}x\right)^3 = 2 - \tfrac{1}{8}x^3$$

is a horizontal stretch (each x-value is multiplied by 2) of the graph of f. (See Figure 1.69.)

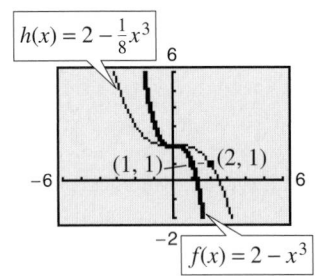

Figure 1.69

☑ *Checkpoint* Now try Exercise 43.

1.5   Exercises

Vocabulary Check

In Exercises 1–5, fill in the blanks.

1. The graph of a _____ is U-shaped.

2. The graph of an _____ is V-shaped.

3. Horizontal shifts, vertical shifts, and reflections are called _____ .

4. A reflection in the x-axis of $y = f(x)$ is represented by $h(x) =$ _____ , while a reflection in the y-axis of $y = f(x)$ is represented by $h(x) =$ _____ .

5. A nonrigid transformation of $y = f(x)$ represented by $cf(x)$ is a vertical stretch if _____ and a vertical shrink if _____ .

6. Match the rigid transformation of $y = f(x)$ with the correct representation, where $c > 0$.

 (a) $h(x) = f(x) + c$ (i) horizontal shift c units to the left

 (b) $h(x) = f(x) - c$ (ii) vertical shift c units upward

 (c) $h(x) = f(x - c)$ (iii) horizontal shift c units to the right

 (d) $h(x) = f(x + c)$ (iv) vertical shift c units downward

In Exercises 1–12, sketch the graphs of the three functions by hand on the same rectangular coordinate system. Verify your result with a graphing utility.

1. $f(x) = x$
$g(x) = x - 4$
$h(x) = 3x$

2. $f(x) = \frac{1}{2}x$
$g(x) = \frac{1}{2}x + 2$
$h(x) = \frac{1}{2}(x - 2)$

3. $f(x) = x^2$
$g(x) = x^2 + 2$
$h(x) = (x - 2)^2$

4. $f(x) = x^2$
$g(x) = x^2 - 4$
$h(x) = (x + 2)^2 + 1$

5. $f(x) = -x^2$
$g(x) = -x^2 + 1$
$h(x) = -(x - 2)^2$

6. $f(x) = (x - 2)^2$
$g(x) = (x - 2)^2 + 2$
$h(x) = -(x - 2)^2 + 4$

7. $f(x) = x^2$
$g(x) = \frac{1}{2}x^2$
$h(x) = (2x)^2$

8. $f(x) = x^2$
$g(x) = \frac{1}{4}x^2 + 2$
$h(x) = -\frac{1}{4}x^2$

9. $f(x) = |x|$
$g(x) = |x| - 1$
$h(x) = |x - 3|$

10. $f(x) = |x|$
$g(x) = |2x|$
$h(x) = -2|x + 2| - 1$

11. $f(x) = \sqrt{x}$
$g(x) = \sqrt{x + 1}$
$h(x) = \sqrt{x - 2} + 1$

12. $f(x) = \sqrt{x}$
$g(x) = \frac{1}{2}\sqrt{x}$
$h(x) = -\frac{1}{2}\sqrt{x + 4}$

13. Use the graph of f to sketch each graph. To print an enlarged copy of the graph, go to the website *www.mathgraphs.com.*

 (a) $y = f(x) + 2$

 (b) $y = -f(x)$

 (c) $y = f(x - 2)$

 (d) $y = f(x + 3)$

 (e) $y = 2f(x)$

 (f) $y = f(-x)$

 (g) $y = f\left(\frac{1}{2}x\right)$

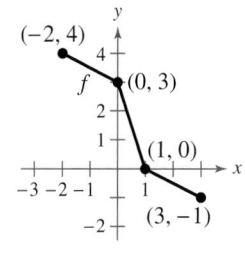

14. Use the graph of f to sketch each graph. To print an enlarged copy of the graph, go to the website *www.mathgraphs.com.*

 (a) $y = f(x) - 1$

 (b) $y = f(x + 1)$

 (c) $y = f(x - 1)$

 (d) $y = -f(x - 2)$

 (e) $y = f(-x)$

 (f) $y = \frac{1}{2}f(x)$

 (g) $y = f(2x)$

In Exercises 15–26, identify the common function and describe the transformation shown in the graph. Write an equation for the graphed function.

15.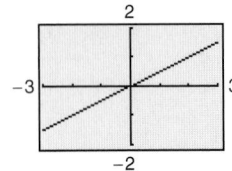

16.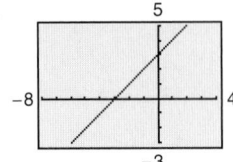

17.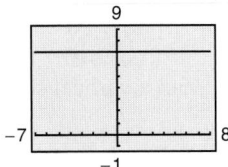

18.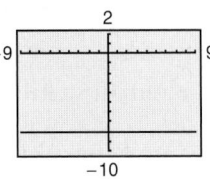

19.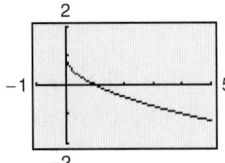

20.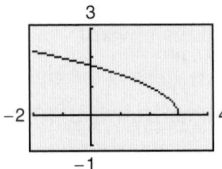

21.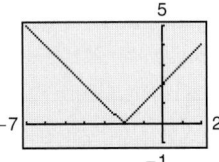

22.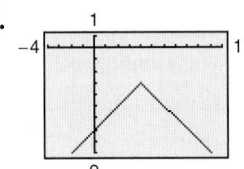

23.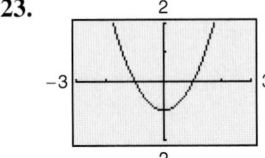

24.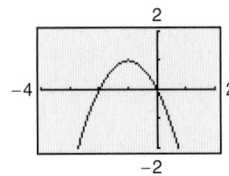

25.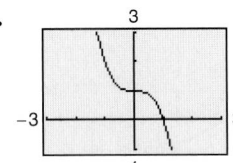

26.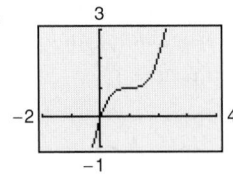

In Exercises 27–32, compare the graph of the function with the graph of $f(x) = \sqrt{x}$.

27. $y = -\sqrt{x} - 1$ **28.** $y = \sqrt{x} + 2$

29. $y = \sqrt{x - 2}$ **30.** $y = \sqrt{x + 4}$

31. $y = \sqrt{2x}$ **32.** $y = \sqrt{-x + 3}$

In Exercises 33–38, compare the graph of the function with the graph of $f(x) = |x|$.

33. $y = |x + 5|$ **34.** $y = |x| - 3$

35. $y = -|x|$ **36.** $y = |-x|$

37. $y = 4|x|$ **38.** $y = |\frac{1}{2}x|$

In Exercises 39–44, compare the graph of the function with the graph of $f(x) = x^3$.

39. $g(x) = 4 - x^3$ **40.** $g(x) = -(x - 1)^3$

41. $h(x) = \frac{1}{4}(x + 2)^3$ **42.** $h(x) = -2(x - 1)^3 + 3$

43. $p(x) = \left(\frac{1}{3}x\right)^3 + 2$ **44.** $p(x) = [3(x - 2)]^3$

In Exercises 45–48, use a graphing utility to graph the three functions in the same viewing window. Describe the graphs of g and h relative to the graph of f.

45. $f(x) = x^3 - 3x^2$
    $g(x) = f(x + 2)$
    $h(x) = \frac{1}{2}f(x)$

46. $f(x) = x^3 - 3x^2 + 2$
    $g(x) = f(x - 1)$
    $h(x) = f(3x)$

47. $f(x) = x^3 - 3x^2$
    $g(x) = -\frac{1}{3}f(x)$
    $h(x) = f(-x)$

48. $f(x) = x^3 - 3x^2 + 2$
    $g(x) = -f(x)$
    $h(x) = f(2x)$

In Exercises 49 and 50, use the graph of $f(x) = x^3 - 3x^2$ (see Exercise 45) to write a formula for the function g shown in the graph.

49.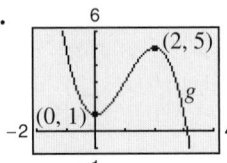

50.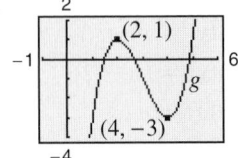

In Exercises 51–64, g is related to one of the six common functions on page 125. (a) Identify the common function f. (b) Describe the sequence of transformations from f to g. (c) Sketch the graph of g by hand. (d) Use function notation to write g in terms of the common function f.

51. $g(x) = 2 - (x + 5)^2$

52. $g(x) = -(x + 10)^2 + 5$

53. $g(x) = 3 + 2(x - 4)^2$

54. $g(x) = -\frac{1}{4}(x + 2)^2 - 2$

55. $g(x) = 3(x - 2)^3$ **56.** $g(x) = -\frac{1}{2}(x + 1)^3$

57. $g(x) = (x - 1)^3 + 2$

58. $g(x) = -(x + 3)^3 - 10$

59. $g(x) = |x + 4| + 8$

60. $g(x) = |x + 3| + 9$

61. $g(x) = -2|x - 1| - 4$

62. $g(x) = \frac{1}{2}|x - 2| - 3$

63. $g(x) = -\frac{1}{2}\sqrt{x + 3} - 1$

64. $g(x) = -\sqrt{x + 1} - 6$

65. *Profit*   The profit P per week on a case of soda pop is given by the model

$$P(x) = 80 + 20x - 0.5x^2, \qquad 0 \leq x \leq 20$$

where x is the amount spent on advertising. In this model, x and P are both measured in hundreds of dollars.

(a) Use a graphing utility to graph the profit function.

(b) The business estimates that taxes and operating costs will increase by an average of $2500 per week during the next year. Rewrite the profit function to reflect this expected decrease in profits. Describe the transformation applied to the graph of the function.

(c) Rewrite the profit function so that x measures advertising expenditures in dollars. $\left[\text{Find } P\!\left(\frac{x}{100}\right).\right]$ Describe the transformation applied to the graph of the profit function.

66. *Automobile Aerodynamics*   The number of horse-power H required to overcome wind drag on an automobile is approximated by the model

$$H(x) = 0.002x^2 + 0.005x - 0.029, \quad 10 \leq x \leq 100$$

where x is the speed of the car in miles per hour.

(a) Use a graphing utility to graph the function.

(b) Rewrite the function so that x represents the speed in kilometers per hour. [Find $H(x/1.6)$.] Describe the transformation applied to the graph of the function.

67. *Fuel Use*   The amount of fuel F (in billions of gallons) used by trucks from 1980 through 2000 can be approximated by the function $F(t) = 0.036t^2 + 20.1$, where $t = 0$ represents 1980. (Source: U.S. Federal Highway Administration)

(a) Describe the transformation of the common function $f(t) = t^2$. Then sketch the graph over the interval $0 \leq t \leq 20$.

(b) Rewrite the function so that $t = 0$ represents 1990. Explain how you got your answer.

68. *Finance*   The amount M (in billions of dollars) of mortgage debt outstanding in the United States from 1990 through 2001 can be approximated by the function $M(t) = 29.9t^2 + 3892$, where $t = 0$ represents 1990. (Source: Board of Governors of the Federal Reserve System)

(a) Describe the transformation of the common function $f(t) = t^2$. Then sketch the graph over the interval $0 \leq t \leq 11$.

(b) Rewrite the function so that $t = 0$ represents 2000. Explain how you got your answer.

Synthesis

True or False?   **In Exercises 69 and 70, determine whether the statement is true or false. Justify your answer.**

69. The graphs of $f(x) = |x| - 5$ and $g(x) = |-x| - 5$ are identical.

70. Relative to the graph of $f(x) = \sqrt{x}$, the graph of the function $h(x) = -\sqrt{x + 9} - 13$ is shifted 9 units to the left and 13 units downward, then reflected in the x-axis.

71. *Exploration*   Use a graphing utility to graph each function. Describe any similarities and differences you observe among the graphs.

(a) $y = x$ (b) $y = x^2$ (c) $y = x^3$

(d) $y = x^4$ (e) $y = x^5$ (f) $y = x^6$

72. *Conjecture*   Use the results of Exercise 71.

(a) Make a conjecture about the shapes of the graphs of $y = x^7$ and $y = x^8$. Use a graphing utility to verify your conjecture.

(b) Sketch the graphs of $y = (x - 3)^3$ and $y = (x + 1)^2$ by hand. Use a graphing utility to verify your graphs.

Review

In Exercises 73 and 74, determine whether the lines L_1 and L_2 passing through the pairs of points are parallel, perpendicular, or neither.

73. L_1: $(-2, -2), (2, 10)$ **74.** L_1: $(-1, -7), (4, 3)$
    L_2: $(-1, 3), (3, 9)$ L_2: $(1, 5), (-2, -7)$

In Exercises 75–78, find the domain of the function.

75. $f(x) = \dfrac{4}{9 - x}$

76. $f(x) = \dfrac{\sqrt{x - 5}}{x - 7}$

77. $f(x) = \sqrt{100 - x^2}$

78. $f(x) = \sqrt[3]{16 - x^2}$

1.6 Combinations of Functions

Arithmetic Combinations of Functions

Just as two real numbers can be combined by the operations of addition, subtraction, multiplication, and division to form other real numbers, two *functions* can be combined to create new functions. If $f(x) = 2x - 3$ and $g(x) = x^2 - 1$, you can form the sum, difference, product, and quotient of f and g as follows.

$$f(x) + g(x) = (2x - 3) + (x^2 - 1)$$
$$= x^2 + 2x - 4 \qquad \text{Sum}$$
$$f(x) - g(x) = (2x - 3) - (x^2 - 1)$$
$$= -x^2 + 2x - 2 \qquad \text{Difference}$$
$$f(x) \cdot g(x) = (2x - 3)(x^2 - 1)$$
$$= 2x^3 - 3x^2 - 2x + 3 \qquad \text{Product}$$
$$\frac{f(x)}{g(x)} = \frac{2x - 3}{x^2 - 1}, \qquad x \neq \pm 1 \qquad \text{Quotient}$$

The domain of an **arithmetic combination** of functions f and g consists of all real numbers that are common to the domains of f and g. In the case of the quotient $f(x)/g(x)$, there is the further restriction that $g(x) \neq 0$.

What you should learn

- Add, subtract, multiply, and divide functions.
- Find compositions of one function with another function.
- Use combinations of functions to model and solve real-life problems.

Why you should learn it

Combining functions can sometimes help you better understand the big picture. For instance, Exercises 75 and 76 on page 143 illustrate how to use combinations of functions to analyze U.S. health expenditures.

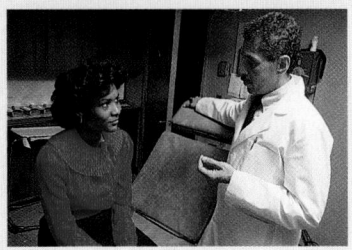

SuperStock

Sum, Difference, Product, and Quotient of Functions

Let f and g be two functions with overlapping domains. Then, for all x common to both domains, the sum, difference, product, and quotient of f and g are defined as follows.

1. **Sum:** $(f + g)(x) = f(x) + g(x)$

2. **Difference:** $(f - g)(x) = f(x) - g(x)$

3. **Product:** $(fg)(x) = f(x) \cdot g(x)$

4. **Quotient:** $\left(\dfrac{f}{g}\right)(x) = \dfrac{f(x)}{g(x)}, \quad g(x) \neq 0$

Example 1 Finding the Sum of Two Functions

Given $f(x) = 2x + 1$ and $g(x) = x^2 + 2x - 1$, find $(f + g)(x)$. Then evaluate the sum when $x = 2$.

Solution

$$(f + g)(x) = f(x) + g(x) = (2x + 1) + (x^2 + 2x - 1) = x^2 + 4x$$

When $x = 2$, the value of this sum is $(f + g)(2) = 2^2 + 4(2) = 12$.

✓ *Checkpoint* Now try Exercise 13.

Example 2   Finding the Difference of Two Functions

Given $f(x) = 2x + 1$ and $g(x) = x^2 + 2x - 1$, find $(f - g)(x)$. Then evaluate the difference when $x = 2$.

Algebraic Solution

The difference of the functions f and g is

$$(f - g)(x) = f(x) - g(x)$$

$$= (2x + 1) - (x^2 + 2x - 1)$$

$$= -x^2 + 2.$$

When $x = 2$, the value of this difference is

$$(f - g)(2) = -(2)^2 + 2$$

$$= -2.$$

Note that $(f - g)(2)$ can also be evaluated as follows.

$$(f - g)(2) = f(2) - g(2)$$

$$= [2(2) + 1] - [2^2 + 2(2) - 1]$$

$$= 5 - 7$$

$$= -2$$

✓ *Checkpoint* Now try Exercise 15.

Graphical Solution

You can use a graphing utility to graph the difference of two functions. Enter the functions as follows (see Figure 1.70).

$$y_1 = 2x + 1$$

$$y_2 = x^2 + 2x - 1$$

$$y_3 = y_1 - y_2$$

Graph y_3 as shown in Figure 1.71. Then use the *value* feature or the *zoom* and *trace* features to estimate that the value of the difference when $x = 2$ is -2.

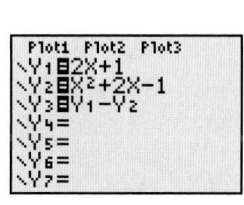

Figure 1.70

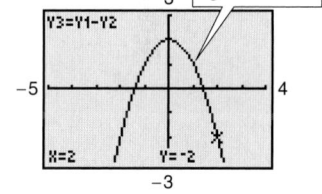

Figure 1.71

In Examples 1 and 2, both f and g have domains that consist of all real numbers. So, the domain of both $(f + g)$ and $(f - g)$ is also the set of all real numbers. Remember that any restrictions on the domains of f or g must be considered when forming the sum, difference, product, or quotient of f and g. For instance, the domain of $f(x) = 1/x$ is all $x \neq 0$, and the domain of $g(x) = \sqrt{x}$ is $[0, \infty)$. This implies that the domain of $(f + g)$ is $(0, \infty)$.

Example 3   Finding the Product of Two Functions

Given $f(x) = x^2$ and $g(x) = x - 3$, find $(fg)(x)$. Then evaluate the product when $x = 4$.

Solution

$$(fg)(x) = f(x)g(x)$$

$$= (x^2)(x - 3)$$

$$= x^3 - 3x^2$$

When $x = 4$, the value of this product is

$$(fg)(4) = 4^3 - 3(4)^2 = 16.$$

✓ *Checkpoint* Now try Exercise 17.

Example 4   Finding the Quotient of Two Functions

Find $(f/g)(x)$ and $(g/f)(x)$ for the functions given by $f(x) = \sqrt{x}$ and $g(x) = \sqrt{4 - x^2}$. Then find the domains of f/g and g/f.

Solution

The quotient of f and g is

$$\left(\frac{f}{g}\right)(x) = \frac{f(x)}{g(x)} = \frac{\sqrt{x}}{\sqrt{4 - x^2}},$$

and the quotient of g and f is

$$\left(\frac{g}{f}\right)(x) = \frac{g(x)}{f(x)} = \frac{\sqrt{4 - x^2}}{\sqrt{x}}.$$

The domain of f is $[0, \infty)$ and the domain of g is $[-2, 2]$. The intersection of these domains is $[0, 2]$. So, the domains for f/g and g/f are as follows.

Domain of (f/g): $[0, 2)$ Domain of (g/f): $(0, 2]$

 Checkpoint Now try Exercise 19.

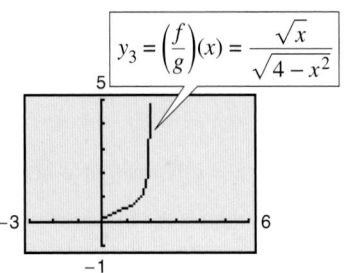

Figure 1.72

TECHNOLOGY TIP   You can confirm the domain of f/g in Example 4 with your graphing utility by entering the three functions $y_1 = \sqrt{x}$, $y_2 = \sqrt{4 - x^2}$, and $y_3 = y_1/y_2$, and graphing y_3 as shown in Figure 1.72. Use the *trace* feature to determine that the x-coordinates of points on the graph extend from 0 to 2 but do not include 2. So, you can estimate the domain of f/g to be $[0, 2)$. You can confirm the domain of g/f in Example 4 by entering $y_4 = y_2/y_1$ and graphing y_4 as shown in Figure 1.73. Use the *trace* feature to determine that the x-coordinates of points on the graph extend from 0 to 2 but do not include 0. So, you can estimate the domain of g/f to be $(0, 2]$.

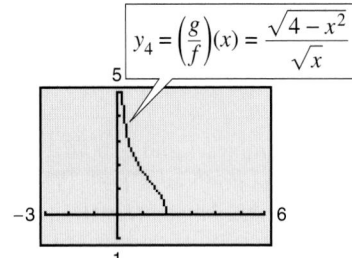

Figure 1.73

Compositions of Functions

Another way of combining two functions is to form the **composition** of one with the other. For instance, if $f(x) = x^2$ and $g(x) = x + 1$, the composition of f with g is

$$f(g(x)) = f(x + 1) = (x + 1)^2.$$

This composition is denoted as $f \circ g$ and read as "f of g."

Definition of Composition of Two Functions

The **composition** of the function f with the function g is

$$(f \circ g)(x) = f(g(x)).$$

The domain of $f \circ g$ is the set of all x in the domain of g such that $g(x)$ is in the domain of f. (See Figure 1.74.)

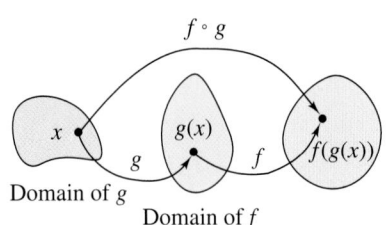

Figure 1.74

Example 5   Forming the Composition of f with g

Find $(f \circ g)(x)$ for $f(x) = \sqrt{x},\, x \geq 0$, and $g(x) = x - 1,\, x \geq 1$. If possible, find $(f \circ g)(2)$ and $(f \circ g)(0)$.

Solution

$$
\begin{aligned}
(f \circ g)(x) &= f(g(x)) & &\text{Definition of } f \circ g \\
&= f(x - 1) & &\text{Definition of } g(x) \\
&= \sqrt{x - 1}, \quad x \geq 1 & &\text{Definition of } f(x)
\end{aligned}
$$

The domain of $f \circ g$ is $[1, \infty)$. So, $(f \circ g)(2) = \sqrt{2 - 1} = 1$ is defined, but $(f \circ g)(0)$ is not defined because 0 is not in the domain of $f \circ g$.

✓ *Checkpoint*   Now try Exercise 35.

The composition of f with g is generally not the same as the composition of g with f. This is illustrated in Example 6.

> ### Exploration
>
> Let $f(x) = x + 2$ and $g(x) = 4 - x^2$. Are the compositions $f \circ g$ and $g \circ f$ equal? You can use your graphing utility to answer this question by entering and graphing the following functions.
>
> $$y_1 = (4 - x^2) + 2$$
> $$y_2 = 4 - (x + 2)^2$$
>
> What do you observe? Which function represents $f \circ g$ and which represents $g \circ f$?

Example 6   Compositions of Functions

Given $f(x) = x + 2$ and $g(x) = 4 - x^2$, evaluate (a) $(f \circ g)(x)$ and (b) $(g \circ f)(x)$ when $x = 0, 1, 2,$ and 3.

Algebraic Solution

a.
$$
\begin{aligned}
(f \circ g)(x) &= f(g(x)) & &\text{Definition of } f \circ g \\
&= f(4 - x^2) & &\text{Definition of } g(x) \\
&= (4 - x^2) + 2 & &\text{Definition of } f(x) \\
&= -x^2 + 6
\end{aligned}
$$
$$
\begin{aligned}
(f \circ g)(0) &= -0^2 + 6 = 6 \\
(f \circ g)(1) &= -1^2 + 6 = 5 \\
(f \circ g)(2) &= -2^2 + 6 = 2 \\
(f \circ g)(3) &= -3^2 + 6 = -3
\end{aligned}
$$

b.
$$
\begin{aligned}
(g \circ f)(x) &= g(f(x)) & &\text{Definition of } g \circ f \\
&= g(x + 2) & &\text{Definition of } f(x) \\
&= 4 - (x + 2)^2 & &\text{Definition of } g(x) \\
&= 4 - (x^2 + 4x + 4) \\
&= -x^2 - 4x
\end{aligned}
$$
$$
\begin{aligned}
(g \circ f)(0) &= -0^2 - 4(0) = 0 \\
(g \circ f)(1) &= -1^2 - 4(1) = -5 \\
(g \circ f)(2) &= -2^2 - 4(2) = -12 \\
(g \circ f)(3) &= -3^2 - 4(3) = -21
\end{aligned}
$$

Note that $f \circ g \neq g \circ f$.

✓ *Checkpoint*   Now try Exercise 37.

Numerical Solution

a. You can use the *table* feature of a graphing utility to evaluate $f \circ g$ when $x = 0, 1, 2,$ and 3. Enter $y_1 = g(x)$ and $y_2 = f(g(x))$ in the equation editor (see Figure 1.75). Then set the table to *ask* mode to find the desired function values (see Figure 1.76). Finally, display the table, as shown in Figure 1.77.

b. You can evaluate $g \circ f$ when $x = 0, 1, 2,$ and 3 by using a procedure similar to that of part (a). You should obtain the table shown in Figure 1.78.

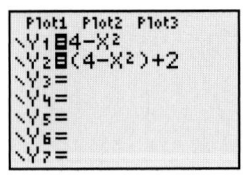

Figure 1.75

Figure 1.76

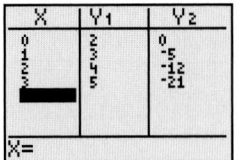

Figure 1.77   **Figure 1.78**

From the tables you can see that $f \circ g \neq g \circ f$.

To determine the domain of a composite function $f \circ g$, you need to restrict the outputs of g so that they are in the domain of f. For instance, to find the domain of $f \circ g$ given that $f(x) = 1/x$ and $g(x) = x + 1$, consider the outputs of g. These can be any real number. However, the domain of f is restricted to all real numbers except 0. So, the outputs of g must be restricted to all real numbers except 0. This means that $g(x) \neq 0$, or $x \neq -1$. So, the domain of $f \circ g$ is all real numbers except $x = -1$.

Example 7   Finding the Domain of a Composite Function

Find the domain of the composition $(f \circ g)(x)$ for the functions given by

$$f(x) = x^2 - 9 \quad \text{and} \quad g(x) = \sqrt{9 - x^2}.$$

Algebraic Solution

The composition of the functions is as follows.

$$(f \circ g)(x) = f(g(x))$$
$$= f\left(\sqrt{9 - x^2}\right)$$
$$= \left(\sqrt{9 - x^2}\right)^2 - 9$$
$$= 9 - x^2 - 9$$
$$= -x^2$$

From this, it might appear that the domain of the composition is the set of all real numbers. This, however, is not true. Because the domain of f is the set of all real numbers and the domain of g is $[-3, 3]$, the domain of $(f \circ g)$ is $[-3, 3]$.

✓ *Checkpoint* Now try Exercise 39.

Graphical Solution

You can use a graphing utility to graph the composition of the functions $(f \circ g)(x)$ as $y = \left(\sqrt{9 - x^2}\right)^2 - 9$. Enter the functions as follows.

$$y_1 = \sqrt{9 - x^2} \qquad y_2 = y_1^2 - 9$$

Graph y_2 as shown in Figure 1.79. Use the *trace* feature to determine that the x-coordinates of points on the graph extend from -3 to 3. So, you can graphically estimate the domain of $(f \circ g)(x)$ to be $[-3, 3]$.

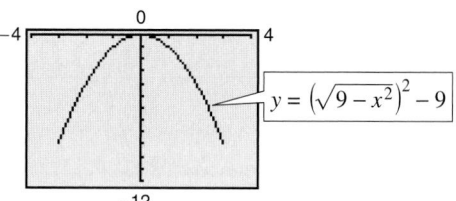

$$y = \left(\sqrt{9 - x^2}\right)^2 - 9$$

Figure 1.79

Example 8   A Case in Which $f \circ g = g \circ f$

Given $f(x) = 2x + 3$ and $g(x) = \frac{1}{2}(x - 3)$, find each composition.

a. $(f \circ g)(x)$ **b.** $(g \circ f)(x)$

Solution

a. $(f \circ g)(x) = f(g(x))$

$$= f\left(\frac{1}{2}(x - 3)\right)$$

$$= 2\left[\frac{1}{2}(x - 3)\right] + 3$$

$$= x - 3 + 3 = x$$

b. $(g \circ f)(x) = g(f(x))$

$$= g(2x + 3)$$

$$= \frac{1}{2}\left[(2x + 3) - 3\right]$$

$$= \frac{1}{2}(2x) = x$$

✓ *Checkpoint* Now try Exercise 43.

STUDY TIP

In Example 8, note that the two composite functions $f \circ g$ and $g \circ f$ are equal, and both represent the identity function. That is, $(f \circ g)(x) = x$ and $(g \circ f)(x) = x$. You will study this special case in the next section.

In Examples 5, 6, 7, and 8 you formed the composition of two given functions. In calculus, it is also important to be able to identify two functions that make up a given composite function. Basically, to "decompose" a composite function, look for an "inner" and an "outer" function.

Example 9   Identifying a Composite Function

Write the function $h(x) = (3x - 5)^3$ as a composition of two functions.

Solution

One way to write h as a composition of two functions is to take the inner function to be $g(x) = 3x - 5$ and the outer function to be $f(x) = x^3$. Then you can write

$$h(x) = (3x - 5)^3$$
$$= f(3x - 5)$$
$$= f(g(x)).$$

✓ *Checkpoint* Now try Exercise 55.

Example 10   Identifying a Composite Function

Write the function

$$h(x) = \frac{1}{(x - 2)^2}$$

as a composition of two functions.

Solution

One way to write h as a composition of two functions is to take the inner function to be $g(x) = x - 2$ and the outer function to be

$$f(x) = \frac{1}{x^2}$$
$$= x^{-2}.$$

Then you can write

$$h(x) = \frac{1}{(x - 2)^2}$$
$$= (x - 2)^{-2}$$
$$= f(x - 2)$$
$$= f(g(x)).$$

✓ *Checkpoint* Now try Exercise 59.

Exploration

The function in Example 10 can be decomposed in other ways. For which of the following pairs of functions is $h(x)$ equal to $f(g(x))$?

a. $g(x) = \dfrac{1}{x - 2}$ and

   $f(x) = x^2$

b. $g(x) = x^2$ and

   $f(x) = \dfrac{1}{x - 2}$

c. $g(x) = \dfrac{1}{x}$ and

   $f(x) = (x - 2)^2$

Example 11   Bacteria Count

The number N of bacteria in a refrigerated food is given by

$$N(T) = 20T^2 - 80T + 500, \qquad 2 \le T \le 14$$

where T is the temperature of the food in degrees Celsius. When the food is removed from refrigeration, the temperature of the food is given by

$$T(t) = 4t + 2, \qquad 0 \le t \le 3$$

where t is the time (in hours).

a. Find the composition $N(T(t))$ and interpret its meaning in context.

b. Find the number of bacteria in the food when $t = 2$ hours.

c. Find the time when the bacterial count reaches 2000.

Solution

a. $N(T(t)) = 20(4t + 2)^2 - 80(4t + 2) + 500$

$= 20(16t^2 + 16t + 4) - 320t - 160 + 500$

$= 320t^2 + 320t + 80 - 320t - 160 + 500$

$= 320t^2 + 420$

The composite function $N(T(t))$ represents the number of bacteria as a function of the amount of time the food has been out of refrigeration.

b. When $t = 2$, the number of bacteria is

$N = 320(2)^2 + 420$

$= 1280 + 420$

$= 1700.$

c. The bacterial count will reach $N = 2000$ when $320t^2 + 420 = 2000$. You can solve this equation for t algebraically as follows.

$320t^2 + 420 = 2000$

$320t^2 = 1580$

$t^2 = \dfrac{79}{16}$

$t = \dfrac{\sqrt{79}}{4}$

$t \approx 2.22$ hours

So, the count will reach 2000 when $t \approx 2.22$ hours. When you solve this equation, note that the negative value is rejected because it is not in the domain of the composite function. You can use a graphing utility to confirm your solution. First graph the equation $N = 320t^2 + 420$, as shown in Figure 1.80. Then use the *zoom* and *trace* features to approximate $N = 2000$ when $t \approx 2.22$, as shown in Figure 1.81.

✓ *Checkpoint* Now try Exercise 79.

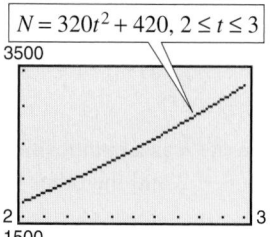

Figure 1.80

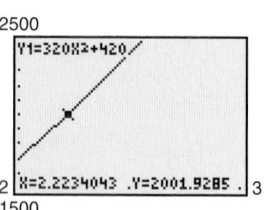

Figure 1.81

1.6 Exercises

Vocabulary Check

Fill in the blanks.

1. Two functions f and g can be combined by the arithmetic operations of _____ , _____ , _____ , and _____ to create new functions.

2. The _____ of the function f with g is $(f \circ g)(x) = f(g(x))$.

3. The domain of $f \circ g$ is the set of all x in the domain of g such that _____ is in the domain of f.

4. To decompose a composite function, look for an _____ and _____ function.

In Exercises 1–4, use the graphs of f and g to graph $h(x) = (f + g)(x)$. To print an enlarged copy of the graph, go to the website *www.mathgraphs.com*.

1.
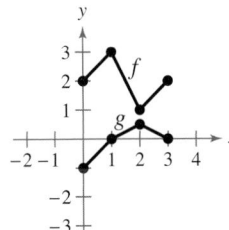

2.
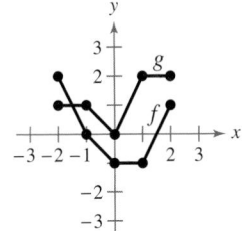

3.
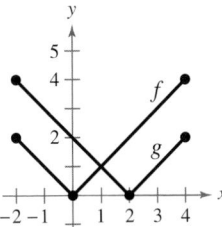

4.
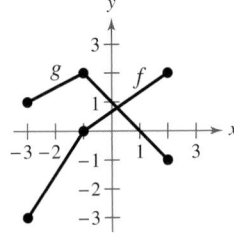

In Exercises 5–12, find (a) $(f + g)(x)$, (b) $(f - g)(x)$, (c) $(fg)(x)$, and (d) $(f/g)(x)$. What is the domain of f/g?

5. $f(x) = x + 3$, $g(x) = x - 3$

6. $f(x) = 2x - 5$, $g(x) = 1 - x$

7. $f(x) = x^2$, $g(x) = 1 - x$

8. $f(x) = 2x - 5$, $g(x) = 4$

9. $f(x) = x^2 + 5$, $g(x) = \sqrt{1 - x}$

10. $f(x) = \sqrt{x^2 - 4}$, $g(x) = \dfrac{x^2}{x^2 + 1}$

11. $f(x) = \dfrac{1}{x}$, $g(x) = \dfrac{1}{x^2}$

12. $f(x) = \dfrac{x}{x + 1}$, $g(x) = x^3$

In Exercises 13–26, evaluate the indicated function for $f(x) = x^2 + 1$ and $g(x) = x - 4$ algebraically. If possible, use a graphing utility to verify your answer.

13. $(f + g)(3)$

14. $(f - g)(-2)$

15. $(f - g)(0)$

16. $(f + g)(1)$

17. $(fg)(4)$

18. $(fg)(-6)$

19. $\left(\dfrac{f}{g}\right)(-5)$

20. $\left(\dfrac{f}{g}\right)(0)$

21. $(f - g)(2t)$

22. $(f + g)(t - 4)$

23. $(fg)(-5t)$

24. $(fg)(3t^2)$

25. $\left(\dfrac{f}{g}\right)(-t)$

26. $\left(\dfrac{f}{g}\right)(t + 2)$

In Exercises 27–30, use a graphing utility to graph the functions f, g, and $f + g$ in the same viewing window.

27. $f(x) = \frac{1}{2}x$, $g(x) = x - 1$

28. $f(x) = \frac{1}{3}x$, $g(x) = -x + 4$

29. $f(x) = x^2$, $g(x) = -2x$

30. $f(x) = 4 - x^2$, $g(x) = x$

In Exercises 31–34, use a graphing utility to graph f, g, and $f + g$ in the same viewing window. Which function contributes most to the magnitude of the sum when $0 \le x \le 2$? Which function contributes most to the magnitude of the sum when $x > 6$?

31. $f(x) = 3x$, $g(x) = -\dfrac{x^3}{10}$

32. $f(x) = \dfrac{x}{2}$, $g(x) = \sqrt{x}$

33. $f(x) = 3x + 2$, $g(x) = -\sqrt{x + 5}$

34. $f(x) = x^2 - \frac{1}{2}$, $g(x) = -3x^2 - 1$

In Exercises 35–38, find (a) $f \circ g$, **(b)** $g \circ f$, **and, if possible, (c)** $(f \circ g)(0)$.

35. $f(x) = x^2$, $g(x) = x - 1$

36. $f(x) = \sqrt[3]{x - 1}$, $g(x) = x^3 + 1$

37. $f(x) = 3x + 5$, $g(x) = 5 - x$

38. $f(x) = x^3$, $g(x) = \dfrac{1}{x}$

In Exercises 39–44, (a) find $f \circ g$, $g \circ f$, **and the domain of** $f \circ g$. **(b) Use a graphing utility to graph** $f \circ g$ **and** $g \circ f$. **Determine whether** $f \circ g = g \circ f$.

39. $f(x) = \sqrt{x + 4}$, $g(x) = x^2$

40. $f(x) = \sqrt[3]{x + 1}$, $g(x) = x^3 - 1$

41. $f(x) = \frac{1}{3}x - 3$, $g(x) = 3x + 1$

42. $f(x) = \sqrt{x}$, $g(x) = \sqrt{x}$

43. $f(x) = x^{2/3}$, $g(x) = x^6$

44. $f(x) = |x|$, $g(x) = x + 6$

In Exercises 45–50, (a) find $(f \circ g)(x)$ **and** $(g \circ f)(x)$, **(b) determine algebraically whether** $(f \circ g)(x) = (g \circ f)(x)$, **and (c) verify your answer to part (b) by comparing a table of values for each composition.**

45. $f(x) = 5x + 4$, $g(x) = 4 - x$

46. $f(x) = \frac{1}{4}(x - 1)$, $g(x) = 4x + 1$

47. $f(x) = \sqrt{x + 6}$, $g(x) = x^2 - 5$

48. $f(x) = x^3 - 4$, $g(x) = \sqrt[3]{x + 10}$

49. $f(x) = |x + 3|$, $g(x) = 2x - 1$

50. $f(x) = \dfrac{6}{3x - 5}$, $g(x) = -x$

In Exercises 51–54, use the graphs of f **and** g **to evaluate the functions.**

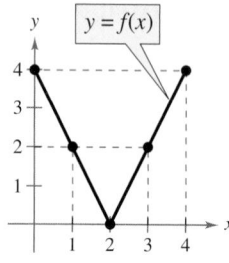
$y = f(x)$

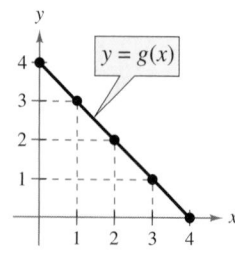
$y = g(x)$

51. (a) $(f + g)(3)$ (b) $(f/g)(2)$

52. (a) $(f - g)(1)$ (b) $(fg)(4)$

53. (a) $(f \circ g)(2)$ (b) $(g \circ f)(2)$

54. (a) $(f \circ g)(1)$ (b) $(g \circ f)(3)$

In Exercises 55–62, find two functions f **and** g **such that** $(f \circ g)(x) = h(x)$. **(There are many correct answers.)**

55. $h(x) = (2x + 1)^2$

56. $h(x) = (1 - x)^3$

57. $h(x) = \sqrt[3]{x^2 - 4}$

58. $h(x) = \sqrt{9 - x}$

59. $h(x) = \dfrac{1}{x + 2}$

60. $h(x) = \dfrac{4}{(5x + 2)^2}$

61. $h(x) = (x + 4)^2 + 2(x + 4)$

62. $h(x) = (x + 3)^{3/2} + 4(x + 3)^{1/2}$

In Exercises 63–72, determine the domains of (a) f, **(b)** g, **and (c)** $f \circ g$. **Use a graphing utility to verify your results.**

63. $f(x) = \sqrt{x + 4}$, $g(x) = x^2$

64. $f(x) = \sqrt{x + 3}$, $g(x) = \dfrac{x}{2}$

65. $f(x) = x^2 + 1$, $g(x) = \sqrt{x}$

66. $f(x) = x^{1/4}$, $g(x) = x^4$

67. $f(x) = \dfrac{1}{x}$, $g(x) = x + 3$

68. $f(x) = \dfrac{1}{x}$, $g(x) = \dfrac{1}{2x}$

69. $f(x) = |x - 4|$, $g(x) = 3 - x$

70. $f(x) = \dfrac{2}{|x|}$, $g(x) = x - 1$

71. $f(x) = x + 2$, $g(x) = \dfrac{1}{x^2 - 4}$

72. $f(x) = \dfrac{3}{x^2 - 1}$, $g(x) = x + 1$

73. *Stopping Distance* The research and development department of an automobile manufacturer has determined that when required to stop quickly to avoid an accident, the distance (in feet) a car travels during the driver's reaction time is given by $R(x) = \frac{3}{4}x$, where x is the speed of the car in miles per hour. The distance (in feet) traveled while the driver is braking is given by $B(x) = \frac{1}{15}x^2$.

(a) Find the function that represents the total stopping distance T.

(b) Use a graphing utility to graph the functions R, B, and T in the same viewing window for $0 \le x \le 60$.

(c) Which function contributes most to the magnitude of the sum at higher speeds? Explain.

74. Sales   From 2000 to 2005, the sales R_1 (in thousands of dollars) for one of two restaurants owned by the same parent company can be modeled by

$$R_1 = 480 - 8t - 0.8t^2, \qquad t = 0, 1, 2, 3, 4, 5$$

where $t = 0$ represents 2000. During the same six-year period, the sales R_2 (in thousands of dollars) for the second restaurant can be modeled by

$$R_2 = 254 + 0.78t, \qquad t = 0, 1, 2, 3, 4, 5.$$

(a) Write a function R_3 that represents the total sales for the two restaurants.

(b) Use a graphing utility to graph R_1, R_2, and R_3 (the total sales function) in the same viewing window.

Data Analysis   **In Exercises 75 and 76, use the table, which shows the total amount spent (in billions of dollars) on health services and supplies in the United States and Puerto Rico for the years 1994 through 2000. The variables $y_1, y_2,$ and y_3 represent out-of-pocket payments, insurance premiums, and other types of payments, respectively.** (Source: U.S. Centers for Medicare and Medicaid Services)

Year	y_1	y_2	y_3
1994	143.9	312.1	40.7
1995	146.5	330.1	44.9
1996	152.1	344.8	48.2
1997	162.3	359.4	52.1
1998	174.5	383.2	55.6
1999	184.4	409.4	57.3
2000	194.5	443.9	57.2

Models for the data are $y_1 = 8.93t + 103.0$, $y_2 = 1.886t^2 - 5.24t + 305.7$, and $y_3 = -0.361t^2 + 7.97t + 14.2$, where t represents the year, with $t = 4$ corresponding to 1994.

75. Use the models and the *table* feature of a graphing utility to create tables showing the values for $y_1, y_2,$ and y_3 for each year from 1994 to 2000. Compare these values with the original data.

76. Use a graphing utility to graph $y_1, y_2, y_3,$ and $y_1 + y_2 + y_3$ in the same viewing window. Use the model $y_1 + y_2 + y_3$ to estimate the total amount spent on health services and supplies for the years 2005 and 2010.

77. Ripples   A pebble is dropped into a calm pond, causing ripples in the form of concentric circles (see figure). The radius (in feet) of the outer ripple is given by $r(t) = 0.6t$, where t is the time (in seconds) after the pebble strikes the water. The area of the circle is given by $A(r) = \pi r^2$. Find and interpret $(A \circ r)(t)$.

78. Geometry   A square concrete foundation was prepared as a base for a large cylindrical gasoline tank (see figure).

(a) Write the radius r of the tank as a function of the length x of the sides of the square.

(b) Write the area A of the circular base of the tank as a function of the radius r.

(c) Find and interpret $(A \circ r)(x)$.

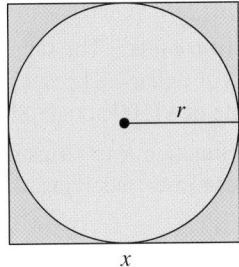

79. Cost   The weekly cost C of producing x units in a manufacturing process is given by

$$C(x) = 60x + 750.$$

The number of units x produced in t hours is $x(t) = 50t$.

(a) Find and interpret $(C \circ x)(t)$.

(b) Use a graphing utility to graph the cost as a function of time. Use the *trace* feature to estimate (to two-decimal-place accuracy) the time that must elapse until the cost increases to $15,000.

80. Air Traffic Control An air traffic controller spots two planes at the same altitude flying toward each other. Their flight paths form a right angle at point P. One plane is 150 miles from point P and is moving at 450 miles per hour. The other plane is 200 miles from point P and is moving at 450 miles per hour. Write the distance s between the planes as a function of time t.

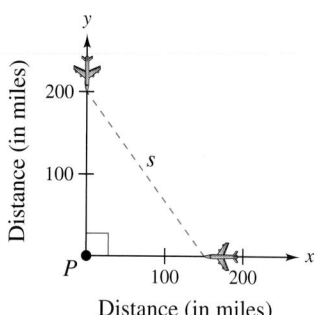

Distance (in miles)

81. Salary You are a sales representative for an automobile manufacturer. You are paid an annual salary plus a bonus of 3% of your sales over $500,000. Consider the two functions

$$f(x) = x - 500{,}000 \quad \text{and} \quad g(x) = 0.03x.$$

If x is greater than $500,000, which of the following represents your bonus? Explain.

(a) $f(g(x))$ (b) $g(f(x))$

82. Consumer Awareness The suggested retail price of a new car is p dollars. The dealership advertised a factory rebate of $1200 and an 8% discount.

(a) Write a function R in terms of p giving the cost of the car after receiving the rebate from the factory.

(b) Write a function S in terms of p giving the cost of the car after receiving the dealership discount.

(c) Form the composite functions $(R \circ S)(p)$ and $(S \circ R)(p)$ and interpret each.

(d) Find $(R \circ S)(18{,}400)$ and $(S \circ R)(18{,}400)$. Which yields the lower cost for the car? Explain.

Synthesis

True or False? In Exercises 83 and 84, determine whether the statement is true or false. Justify your answer.

83. If $f(x) = x + 1$ and $g(x) = 6x$, then

$$(f \circ g)(x) = (g \circ f)(x).$$

84. If you are given two functions $f(x)$ and $g(x)$, you can calculate $(f \circ g)(x)$ if and only if the range of g is a subset of the domain of f.

85. Proof Prove that the product of two odd functions is an even function, and that the product of two even functions is an even function.

86. Conjecture Use examples to hypothesize whether the product of an odd function and an even function is even or odd. Then prove your hypothesis.

87. Proof Given a function f, prove that $g(x)$ is even and $h(x)$ is odd, where $g(x) = \frac{1}{2}[f(x) + f(-x)]$ and $h(x) = \frac{1}{2}[f(x) - f(-x)]$.

88. (a) Use the result of Exercise 87 to prove that any function can be written as a sum of even and odd functions. (*Hint:* Add the two equations in Exercise 87.)

(b) Use the result of part (a) to write each function as a sum of even and odd functions.

$$f(x) = x^2 - 2x + 1, \quad g(x) = \frac{1}{x + 1}$$

Review

In Exercises 89–92, find three points that lie on the graph of the equation.

89. $y = -x^2 + x - 5$

90. $y = \frac{1}{5}x^3 - 4x^2 + 1$

91. $x^2 + y^2 = 24$

92. $y = \dfrac{x}{x^2 - 5}$

In Exercises 93–96, find an equation of the line that passes through the two points.

93. $(-4, -2), (-3, 8)$

94. $(1, 5), (-8, 2)$

95. $\left(\frac{3}{2}, -1\right), \left(-\frac{1}{3}, 4\right)$

96. $(0, 1.1), (-4, 3.1)$

In Exercises 97–102, use the graph of f to sketch the graph of the specified function. To print an enlarged copy of the graph, go to the website *www.mathgraphs.com*.

97. $f(x - 4)$

98. $f(x + 2)$

99. $f(x) + 4$

100. $f(x) - 1$

101. $2f(x)$

102. $f\left(\frac{1}{2}x\right)$

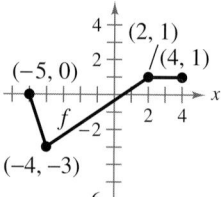

1.7 Inverse Functions

Inverse Functions

Recall from Section 1.3 that a function can be represented by a set of ordered pairs. For instance, the function $f(x) = x + 4$ from the set $A = \{1, 2, 3, 4\}$ to the set $B = \{5, 6, 7, 8\}$ can be written as follows.

$$f(x) = x + 4: \ \{(1, 5), (2, 6), (3, 7), (4, 8)\}$$

In this case, by interchanging the first and second coordinates of each of these ordered pairs, you can form the **inverse function** of f, which is denoted by f^{-1}. It is a function from the set B to the set A, and can be written as follows.

$$f^{-1}(x) = x - 4: \ \{(5, 1), (6, 2), (7, 3), (8, 4)\}$$

Note that the domain of f is equal to the range of f^{-1}, and vice versa, as shown in Figure 1.82. Also note that the functions f and f^{-1} have the effect of "undoing" each other. In other words, when you form the composition of f with f^{-1} or the composition of f^{-1} with f, you obtain the identity function.

$$f(f^{-1}(x)) = f(x - 4) = (x - 4) + 4 = x$$

$$f^{-1}(f(x)) = f^{-1}(x + 4) = (x + 4) - 4 = x$$

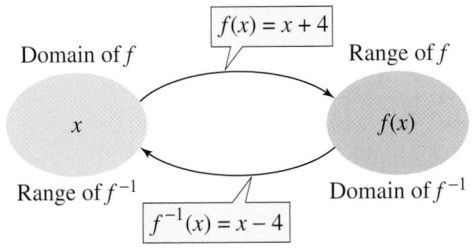

Domain of f $f(x) = x + 4$ Range of f

x ⟶ $f(x)$

Range of f^{-1} $f^{-1}(x) = x - 4$ Domain of f^{-1}

Figure 1.82

What you should learn

- Find inverse functions informally and verify that two functions are inverse functions of each other.
- Use graphs of functions to decide whether functions have inverse functions.
- Determine if functions are one-to-one.
- Find inverse functions algebraically.

Why you should learn it

Inverse functions can be helpful in further exploring how two variables relate to each other. Exercise 84 on page 154 investigates the relationship between the hourly wage and the number of units produced.

Example 1   Finding Inverse Functions Informally

Find the inverse function of $f(x) = 4x$. Then verify that both $f(f^{-1}(x))$ and $f^{-1}(f(x))$ are equal to the identity function.

Solution

The function f *multiplies* each input by 4. To "undo" this function, you need to *divide* each input by 4. So, the inverse function of $f(x) = 4x$ is given by

$$f^{-1}(x) = \frac{x}{4}.$$

You can verify that both $f(f^{-1}(x))$ and $f^{-1}(f(x))$ are equal to the identity function as follows.

$$f(f^{-1}(x)) = f\left(\frac{x}{4}\right) = 4\left(\frac{x}{4}\right) = x \qquad f^{-1}(f(x)) = f^{-1}(4x) = \frac{4x}{4} = x$$

✓ *Checkpoint* Now try Exercise 1.

STUDY TIP

Don't be confused by the use of -1 to denote the inverse function f^{-1}. In this text, whenever f^{-1} is written, it always refers to the inverse function of the function f and not to the reciprocal of $f(x)$, which is given by

$$\frac{1}{f(x)}.$$

Example 2   Finding Inverse Functions Informally

Find the inverse function of $f(x) = x - 6$. Then verify that both $f(f^{-1}(x))$ and $f^{-1}(f(x))$ are equal to the identity function.

Solution

The function f *subtracts* 6 from each input. To "undo" this function, you need to *add* 6 to each input. So, the inverse function of $f(x) = x - 6$ is given by

$$f^{-1}(x) = x + 6.$$

You can verify that both $f(f^{-1}(x))$ and $f^{-1}(f(x))$ are equal to the identity function as follows.

$$f(f^{-1}(x)) = f(x + 6) = (x + 6) - 6 = x$$
$$f^{-1}(f(x)) = f^{-1}(x - 6) = (x - 6) + 6 = x$$

✓ *Checkpoint* Now try Exercise 3.

A table of values can help you understand inverse functions. For instance, the following table shows several values of the function in Example 2. Interchange the rows of this table to obtain values of the inverse function.

x	-2	-1	0	1	2
$f(x)$	-8	-7	-6	-5	-4

x	-8	-7	-6	-5	-4
$f^{-1}(x)$	-2	-1	0	1	2

In the table at the left, each output is 6 less than the input, and in the table at the right, each output is 6 more than the input.

The formal definition of an inverse function is as follows.

Definition of Inverse Function

Let f and g be two functions such that

$$f(g(x)) = x \quad \text{for every } x \text{ in the domain of } g$$

and

$$g(f(x)) = x \quad \text{for every } x \text{ in the domain of } f.$$

Under these conditions, the function g is the **inverse function** of the function f. The function g is denoted by f^{-1} (read "f-inverse"). So,

$$f(f^{-1}(x)) = x \quad \text{and} \quad f^{-1}(f(x)) = x.$$

The domain of f must be equal to the range of f^{-1}, and the range of f must be equal to the domain of f^{-1}.

If the function g is the inverse function of the function f, it must also be true that the function f is the inverse function of the function g. For this reason, you can say that the functions f and g are *inverse functions of each other*.

Example 3   Verifying Inverse Functions Algebraically

Show that the functions are inverse functions of each other.

$$f(x) = 2x^3 - 1 \quad \text{and} \quad g(x) = \sqrt[3]{\frac{x+1}{2}}$$

Solution

$$f(g(x)) = f\left(\sqrt[3]{\frac{x+1}{2}}\right) = 2\left(\sqrt[3]{\frac{x+1}{2}}\right)^3 - 1$$

$$= 2\left(\frac{x+1}{2}\right) - 1$$

$$= x + 1 - 1$$

$$= x$$

$$g(f(x)) = g(2x^3 - 1) = \sqrt[3]{\frac{(2x^3 - 1) + 1}{2}}$$

$$= \sqrt[3]{\frac{2x^3}{2}}$$

$$= \sqrt[3]{x^3}$$

$$= x$$

✓ *Checkpoint* Now try Exercise 15.

Example 4   Verifying Inverse Functions Algebraically

Which of the functions is the inverse function of $f(x) = \dfrac{5}{x-2}$?

$$g(x) = \frac{x-2}{5} \quad \text{or} \quad h(x) = \frac{5}{x} + 2$$

Solution

By forming the composition of f with g, you have

$$f(g(x)) = f\left(\frac{x-2}{5}\right) = \frac{5}{\left(\dfrac{x-2}{5}\right) - 2} = \frac{25}{x - 12} \neq x.$$

Because this composition is not equal to the identity function x, it follows that g *is not* the inverse function of f. By forming the composition of f with h, you have

$$f(h(x)) = f\left(\frac{5}{x} + 2\right) = \frac{5}{\left(\dfrac{5}{x} + 2\right) - 2} = \frac{5}{\left(\dfrac{5}{x}\right)} = x.$$

So, it appears that h is the inverse function of f. You can confirm this by showing that the composition of h with f is also equal to the identity function.

✓ *Checkpoint* Now try Exercise 19.

TECHNOLOGY TIP

Most graphing utilities can graph $y = x^{1/3}$ in two ways:

$$y_1 = x \wedge (1/3) \quad \text{or}$$

$$y_1 = \sqrt[3]{x}.$$

However, you may not be able to obtain the complete graph of $y = x^{2/3}$ by entering $y_1 = x \wedge (2/3)$. If not, you should use

$$y_1 = (x \wedge (1/3))^2 \quad \text{or}$$

$$y_1 = \sqrt[3]{x^2}.$$

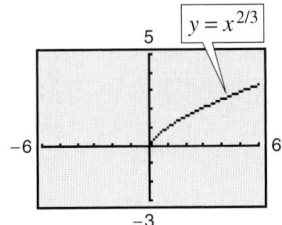

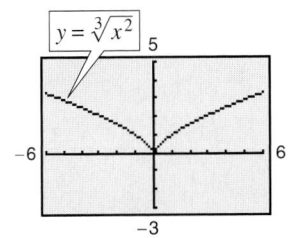

The Graph of an Inverse Function

The graphs of a function f and its inverse function f^{-1} are related to each other in the following way. If the point (a, b) lies on the graph of f, then the point (b, a) must lie on the graph of f^{-1}, and vice versa. This means that the graph of f^{-1} is a *reflection* of the graph of f in the line $y = x$, as shown in Figure 1.83.

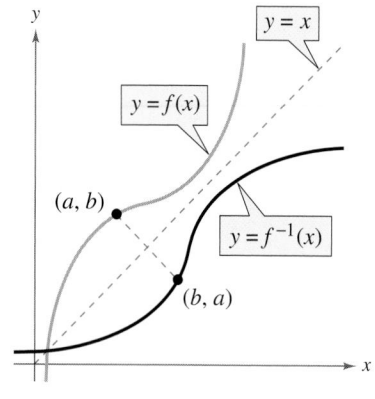

Figure 1.83

> **TECHNOLOGY TIP**
>
> In Examples 3 and 4, inverse functions were verified algebraically. A graphing utility can also be helpful in checking whether one function is the inverse function of another function. Use the Graph Reflection Program found on the website *college.hmco.com* to verify Example 4 graphically.

Example 5   Verifying Inverse Functions Graphically and Numerically

Verify that the functions f and g from Example 3 are inverse functions of each other graphically and numerically.

Graphical Solution

You can *graphically* verify that f and g are inverse functions of each other by using a graphing utility to graph f and g in the same viewing window. (Be sure to use a square setting.) From the graph in Figure 1.84, you can verify that the graph of g is the reflection of the graph of f in the line $y = x$.

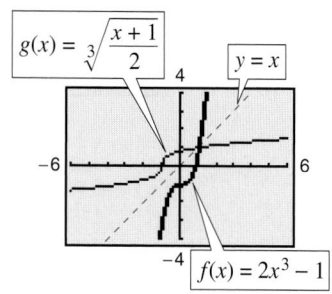

Figure 1.84

✓ *Checkpoint* Now try Exercise 25.

Numerical Solution

You can *numerically* verify that f and g are inverse functions of each other. Begin by entering the compositions $f(g(x))$ and $g(f(x))$ into a graphing utility as follows.

$$y_1 = f(g(x)) = 2\left(\sqrt[3]{\frac{x+1}{2}}\right)^3 - 1$$

$$y_2 = g(f(x)) = \sqrt[3]{\frac{(2x^3 - 1) + 1}{2}}$$

Then use the *table* feature of the graphing utility to create a table, as shown in Figure 1.85. Note that the entries for x, y_1, and y_2 are the same. So, $f(g(x)) = x$ and $g(f(x)) = x$. You can now conclude that f and g are inverse functions of each other.

X	Y1	Y2
-3	-3	-3
-2	-2	-2
-1	-1	-1
0	0	0
1	1	1
2	2	2
3	3	3

X=-3

Figure 1.85

The Existence of an Inverse Function

Consider the function $f(x) = x^2$. The first table at the right is a table of values for $f(x) = x^2$. The second table was created by interchanging the rows of the first table. The second table does not represent a function because the input $x = 4$ is matched with two different outputs: $y = -2$ and $y = 2$. So, $f(x) = x^2$ does not have an inverse function.

x	-2	-1	0	1	2
$f(x)$	4	1	0	1	4

x	4	1	0	1	4
$g(x)$	-2	-1	0	1	2

To have an inverse function, a function must be **one-to-one,** which means that no two elements in the domain of f correspond to the same element in the range of f.

> **Definition of a One-to-One Function**
>
> A function f is **one-to-one** if, for a and b in its domain, $f(a) = f(b)$ implies that $a = b$.

> **Existence of an Inverse Function**
>
> A function f has an inverse function f^{-1} if and only if f is one-to-one.

From its graph, it is easy to tell whether a function of x is one-to-one. Simply check to see that every horizontal line intersects the graph of the function at most once. This is called the **Horizontal Line Test.** For instance, Figure 1.86 shows the graph of $y = x^4$. On the graph, you can find a horizontal line that intersects the graph twice.

Two special types of functions that pass the Horizontal Line Test are those that are increasing or decreasing on their entire domains.

1. If f is *increasing* on its entire domain, then f is one-to-one.

2. If f is *decreasing* on its entire domain, then f is one-to-one.

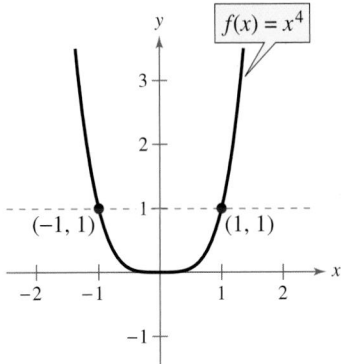

Figure 1.86 $f(x) = x^4$ is not one-to-one.

Example 6   Testing for One-to-One Functions

Is the function $f(x) = \sqrt{x} + 1$ one-to-one?

Algebraic Solution

Let a and b be nonnegative real numbers with $f(a) = f(b)$.

$$\sqrt{a} + 1 = \sqrt{b} + 1 \qquad \text{Set } f(a) = f(b).$$

$$\sqrt{a} = \sqrt{b}$$

$$a = b$$

So, $f(a) = f(b)$ implies that $a = b$. We can conclude that f *is* one-to-one and *does* have an inverse function.

Graphical Solution

Use a graphing utility to graph the function $y = \sqrt{x} + 1$. From Figure 1.87, you can see that a horizontal line will intersect the graph at most once and the function is increasing. So, f *is* one-to-one and *does* have an inverse function.

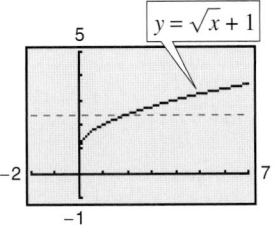

Figure 1.87

✓ *Checkpoint* Now try Exercise 33.

Finding Inverse Functions Algebraically

For simple functions you can find inverse functions by inspection. For more complicated functions, however, it is best to use the following guidelines.

Finding an Inverse Function

1. Use the Horizontal Line Test to decide whether f has an inverse function.

2. In the equation for $f(x)$, replace $f(x)$ by y.

3. Interchange the roles of x and y, and solve for y.

4. Replace y by $f^{-1}(x)$ in the new equation.

5. Verify that f and f^{-1} are inverse functions of each other by showing that the domain of f is equal to the range of f^{-1}, the range of f is equal to the domain of f^{-1}, and $f(f^{-1}(x)) = x$ and $f^{-1}(f(x)) = x$.

It is important to note that in Step 1 above, the domain of f is assumed to be the entire real line. However, the domain of f may be restricted so that f does have an inverse function. For instance, if the domain of $f(x) = x^2$ is restricted to the nonnegative real numbers, then f does have an inverse function.

Example 7   Finding an Inverse Function Algebraically

Find the inverse function of $f(x) = \dfrac{5 - 3x}{2}$.

Solution

The graph of f in Figure 1.88 passes the Horizontal Line Test. So you know that f is one-to-one and has an inverse function.

$$f(x) = \frac{5 - 3x}{2} \qquad \text{Write original equation.}$$

$$y = \frac{5 - 3x}{2} \qquad \text{Replace } f(x) \text{ by } y.$$

$$x = \frac{5 - 3y}{2} \qquad \text{Interchange } x \text{ and } y.$$

$$2x = 5 - 3y \qquad \text{Multiply each side by 2.}$$

$$3y = 5 - 2x \qquad \text{Isolate the } y\text{-term.}$$

$$y = \frac{5 - 2x}{3} \qquad \text{Solve for } y.$$

$$f^{-1}(x) = \frac{5 - 2x}{3} \qquad \text{Replace } y \text{ by } f^{-1}(x).$$

The domain and range of both f and f^{-1} consist of all real numbers. Verify that $f(f^{-1}(x)) = x$ and $f^{-1}(f(x)) = x$.

✓ *Checkpoint* Now try Exercise 53.

TECHNOLOGY TIP

Many graphing utilities have a built-in feature to draw an inverse function. To see how this works, consider the function $f(x) = \sqrt{x}$. The inverse function of f is given by $f^{-1}(x) = x^2$, $x \geq 0$. Enter the function $y_1 = \sqrt{x}$. Then graph it in the standard viewing window and use the *draw inverse* feature. You should obtain the figure below, which shows both f and its inverse function f^{-1}. For instructions on how to use the *draw inverse* feature, see Appendix A; for specific keystrokes, go to the text website at *college.hmco.com*.

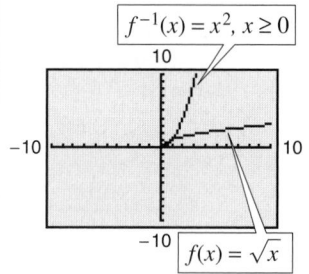

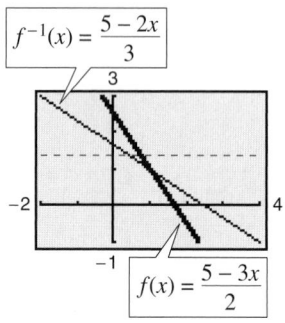

Figure 1.88

Example 8   Finding an Inverse Function Algebraically

Find the inverse function of $f(x) = x^3 - 4$ and use a graphing utility to graph f and f^{-1} in the same viewing window.

Solution

$$f(x) = x^3 - 4 \qquad \text{Write original function.}$$

$$y = x^3 - 4 \qquad \text{Replace } f(x) \text{ by } y.$$

$$x = y^3 - 4 \qquad \text{Interchange } x \text{ and } y.$$

$$y^3 = x + 4 \qquad \text{Isolate } y.$$

$$y = \sqrt[3]{x + 4} \qquad \text{Solve for } y.$$

$$f^{-1}(x) = \sqrt[3]{x + 4} \qquad \text{Replace } y \text{ by } f^{-1}(x).$$

The graph of f in Figure 1.89 passes the Horizontal Line Test. So, you know that f is one-to-one and has an inverse function. The graph of f^{-1} in Figure 1.89 is the reflection of the graph of f in the line $y = x$.

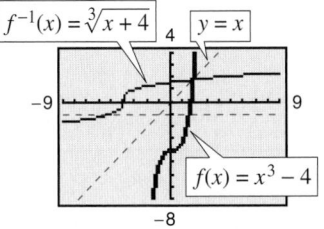

Figure 1.89

✓ *Checkpoint* Now try Exercise 55.

Example 9   Finding an Inverse Function Algebraically

Find the inverse function of $f(x) = \sqrt{2x - 3}$ and use a graphing utility to graph f and f^{-1} in the same viewing window.

Solution

$$f(x) = \sqrt{2x - 3} \qquad \text{Write original equation.}$$

$$y = \sqrt{2x - 3} \qquad \text{Replace } f(x) \text{ by } y.$$

$$x = \sqrt{2y - 3} \qquad \text{Interchange } x \text{ and } y.$$

$$x^2 = 2y - 3 \qquad \text{Square each side.}$$

$$2y = x^2 + 3 \qquad \text{Isolate } y.$$

$$y = \frac{x^2 + 3}{2} \qquad \text{Solve for } y.$$

$$f^{-1}(x) = \frac{x^2 + 3}{2}, \quad x \geq 0 \qquad \text{Replace } y \text{ by } f^{-1}(x).$$

The graph of f in Figure 1.90 passes the Horizontal Line Test. So you know that f is one-to-one and has an inverse function. The graph of f^{-1} in Figure 1.90 is the reflection of the graph of f in the line $y = x$. Note that the range of f is the interval $[0, \infty)$, which implies that the domain of f^{-1} is the interval $[0, \infty)$. Moreover, the domain of f is the interval $\left[\frac{3}{2}, \infty\right)$, which implies that the range of f^{-1} is the interval $\left[\frac{3}{2}, \infty\right)$.

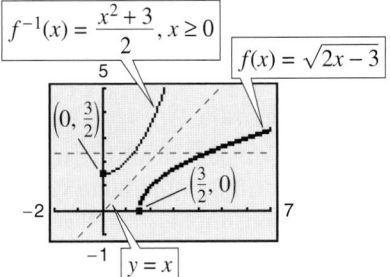

Figure 1.90

✓ *Checkpoint* Now try Exercise 59.

1.7 Exercises

Vocabulary Check

Fill in the blanks.

1. If the composite functions $f(g(x)) = x$ and $g(f(x)) = x$, then the function g is the _____ function of f, and is denoted by _____ .

2. The domain of f is the _____ of f^{-1}, and the _____ of f^{-1} is the range of f.

3. The graphs of f and f^{-1} are reflections of each other in the line _____ .

4. To have an inverse function, a function f must be _____ ; that is, $f(a) = f(b)$ implies $a = b$.

5. A graphical test for the existence of an inverse function is called the _____ Line Test.

In Exercises 1–8, find the inverse function of f informally. Verify that $f(f^{-1}(x)) = x$ and $f^{-1}(f(x)) = x$.

1. $f(x) = 6x$
2. $f(x) = \frac{1}{3}x$
3. $f(x) = x + 7$
4. $f(x) = x - 3$
5. $f(x) = 2x + 1$
6. $f(x) = \dfrac{x - 1}{4}$
7. $f(x) = \sqrt[3]{x}$
8. $f(x) = x^5$

In Exercises 9–14, (a) show that f and g are inverse functions algebraically and (b) verify that f and g are inverse functions numerically by creating a table of values for each function.

9. $f(x) = -\dfrac{7}{2}x - 3$, $g(x) = -\dfrac{2x + 6}{7}$

10. $f(x) = \dfrac{x - 9}{4}$, $g(x) = 4x + 9$

11. $f(x) = x^3 + 5$, $g(x) = \sqrt[3]{x - 5}$

12. $f(x) = \dfrac{x^3}{2}$, $g(x) = \sqrt[3]{2x}$

13. $f(x) = -\sqrt{x - 8}$; $g(x) = 8 + x^2$, $x \le 0$

14. $f(x) = \sqrt[3]{3x - 10}$, $g(x) = \dfrac{x^3 + 10}{3}$

In Exercises 15–20, show that f and g are inverse functions algebraically. Use a graphing utility to graph f and g in the same viewing window. Describe the relationship between the graphs.

15. $f(x) = x^3$, $g(x) = \sqrt[3]{x}$

16. $f(x) = \dfrac{1}{x}$, $g(x) = \dfrac{1}{x}$

17. $f(x) = \sqrt{x - 4}$; $g(x) = x^2 + 4$, $x \ge 0$

18. $f(x) = 9 - x^2$, $x \ge 0$; $g(x) = \sqrt{9 - x}$

19. $f(x) = 1 - x^3$, $g(x) = \sqrt[3]{1 - x}$

20. $f(x) = \dfrac{1}{1 + x}$, $x \ge 0$; $g(x) = \dfrac{1 - x}{x}$, $0 < x \le 1$

In Exercises 21–24, match the graph of the function with the graph of its inverse function. [The graphs of the inverse functions are labeled (a), (b), (c), and (d).]

(a) 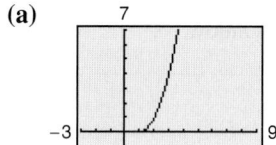   (b)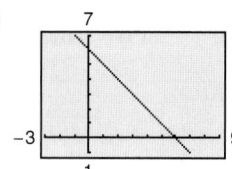

(c) 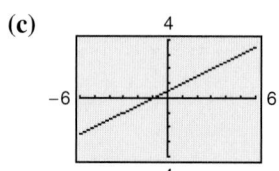   (d)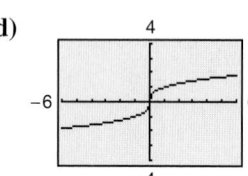

21. 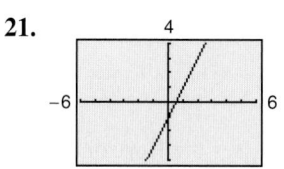   22.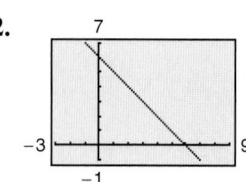

23. 24.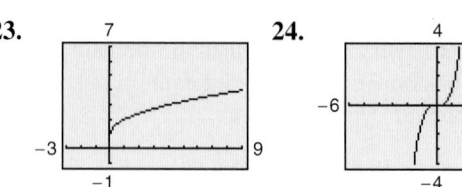

In Exercises 25–28, show that f and g are inverse functions (a) graphically and (b) numerically.

25. $f(x) = 2x$, $g(x) = \dfrac{x}{2}$

26. $f(x) = x - 5$, $g(x) = x + 5$

27. $f(x) = \dfrac{x - 1}{x + 5}$, $g(x) = -\dfrac{5x + 1}{x - 1}$

28. $f(x) = \dfrac{x + 3}{x - 2}$, $g(x) = \dfrac{2x + 3}{x - 1}$

In Exercises 29–40, use a graphing utility to graph the function and use the Horizontal Line Test to determine whether the function is one-to-one and so has an inverse function.

29. $f(x) = 3 - \frac{1}{2}x$

30. $f(x) = \frac{1}{4}(x + 2)^2 - 1$

31. $h(x) = \dfrac{x^2}{x^2 + 1}$

32. $g(x) = \dfrac{4 - x}{6x^2}$

33. $h(x) = \sqrt{16 - x^2}$

34. $f(x) = -2x\sqrt{16 - x^2}$

35. $f(x) = 10$

36. $f(x) = -0.65$

37. $g(x) = (x + 5)^3$

38. $f(x) = x^5 - 7$

39. $h(x) = |x + 4| - |x - 4|$

40. $f(x) = -\dfrac{|x - 6|}{|x + 6|}$

In Exercises 41–52, determine algebraically whether the function is one-to-one. If it is, find its inverse function. Verify your answer graphically.

41. $f(x) = x^4$

42. $g(x) = x^2 - x^4$

43. $f(x) = \dfrac{3x + 4}{5}$

44. $f(x) = 3x + 5$

45. $f(x) = \dfrac{1}{x^2}$

46. $h(x) = \dfrac{4}{x^2}$

47. $f(x) = (x + 3)^2$, $x \geq -3$

48. $q(x) = (x - 5)^2$, $x \leq 5$

49. $f(x) = \sqrt{2x + 3}$

50. $f(x) = \sqrt{x - 2}$

51. $f(x) = |x - 2|$, $x \leq 2$

52. $f(x) = \dfrac{x^2}{x^2 + 1}$

In Exercises 53–62, find the inverse function of f. Use a graphing utility to graph both f and f^{-1} in the same viewing window. Describe the relationship between the graphs.

53. $f(x) = 2x - 3$

54. $f(x) = 3x$

55. $f(x) = x^5$

56. $f(x) = x^3 + 1$

57. $f(x) = x^{3/5}$

58. $f(x) = x^2$, $x \geq 0$

59. $f(x) = \sqrt{4 - x^2}$, $0 \leq x \leq 2$

60. $f(x) = \sqrt{16 - x^2}$, $-4 \leq x \leq 0$

61. $f(x) = \dfrac{4}{x}$

62. $f(x) = \dfrac{6}{\sqrt{x}}$

Think About It   In Exercises 63–66, delete part of the graph of the function so that the part that remains is one-to-one. Find the inverse function of the remaining part and give the domain of the inverse function. (There are many correct answers.)

63. $f(x) = (x - 2)^2$

64. $f(x) = 1 - x^4$

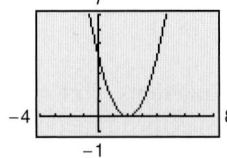

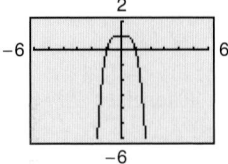

65. $f(x) = |x + 2|$

66. $f(x) = |x - 2|$

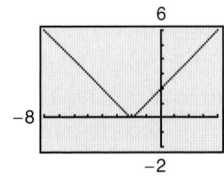

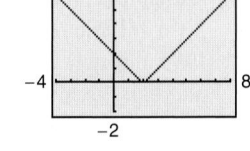

In Exercises 67 and 68, use the graph of the function f to complete the table and sketch the graph of f^{-1}.

67.

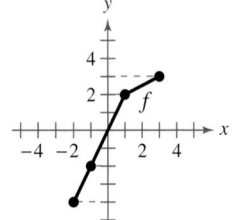

x	$f^{-1}(x)$
-4	
-2	
2	
3	

68.

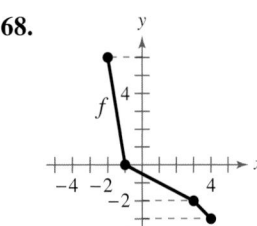

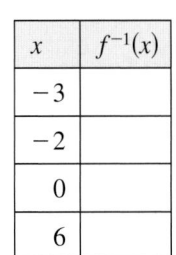

x	$f^{-1}(x)$
-3	
-2	
0	
6	

Graphical Reasoning   In Exercises 69–72, (a) use a graphing utility to graph the function, (b) use the *draw inverse* feature of the graphing utility to draw the inverse of the function, and (c) determine whether the graph of the inverse relation is an inverse function, explaining your reasoning.

69. $f(x) = x^3 + x + 1$

70. $h(x) = x\sqrt{4 - x^2}$

71. $g(x) = \dfrac{3x^2}{x^2 + 1}$

72. $f(x) = \dfrac{4x}{\sqrt{x^2 + 15}}$

In Exercises 73–78, use the functions $f(x) = \frac{1}{8}x - 3$ and $g(x) = x^3$ to find the indicated value or function.

73. $(f^{-1} \circ g^{-1})(1)$

74. $(g^{-1} \circ f^{-1})(-3)$

75. $(f^{-1} \circ f^{-1})(6)$

76. $(g^{-1} \circ g^{-1})(-4)$

77. $(f \circ g)^{-1}$

78. $g^{-1} \circ f^{-1}$

In Exercises 79–82, use the functions $f(x) = x + 4$ and $g(x) = 2x - 5$ to find the specified function.

79. $g^{-1} \circ f^{-1}$

80. $f^{-1} \circ g^{-1}$

81. $(f \circ g)^{-1}$

82. $(g \circ f)^{-1}$

83. *Transportation*   The total value of new car sales f (in billions of dollars) in the United States from 1995 through 2001 is shown in the table. The time (in years) is given by t, with $t = 5$ corresponding to 1995.   (Source: National Automobile Dealers Association)

Year, t	Sales, $f(t)$
5	456.2
6	490.0
7	507.5
8	546.3
9	606.5
10	650.3
11	690.4

(a) Does f^{-1} exist?

(b) If f^{-1} exists, what does it mean in the context of the problem?

(c) If f^{-1} exists, find $f^{-1}(650.3)$.

(d) If the table above were extended to 2002 and if the total value of new car sales for that year were $546.3 billion, would f^{-1} exist? Explain.

84. *Hourly Wage*   Your wage is $8.00 per hour plus $0.75 for each unit produced per hour. So, your hourly wage y in terms of the number of units produced is $y = 8 + 0.75x$.

(a) Find the inverse function. What does each variable in the inverse function represent?

(b) Use a graphing utility to graph the function and its inverse function.

(c) Use the *trace* feature of a graphing utility to find the hourly wage when 10 units are produced per hour.

(d) Use the *trace* feature of a graphing utility to find the number of units produced when your hourly wage is $22.25.

Synthesis

True or False?   In Exercises 85 and 86, determine whether the statement is true or false. Justify your answer.

85. If f is an even function, f^{-1} exists.

86. If the inverse function of f exists, and the graph of f has a y-intercept, the y-intercept of f is an x-intercept of f^{-1}.

87. *Proof*   Prove that if f and g are one-to-one functions, $(f \circ g)^{-1}(x) = (g^{-1} \circ f^{-1})(x)$.

88. *Proof*   Prove that if f is a one-to-one odd function, f^{-1} is an odd function.

Review

In Exercises 89–92, write the rational expression in simplest form.

89. $\dfrac{27x^3}{3x^2}$

90. $\dfrac{5x^2y}{xy + 5x}$

91. $\dfrac{x^2 - 36}{6 - x}$

92. $\dfrac{x^2 + 3x - 40}{x^2 - 3x - 10}$

In Exercises 93–98, determine whether the equation represents y as a function of x.

93. $4x - y = 3$

94. $x = 5$

95. $x^2 + y^2 = 9$

96. $x^2 + y = 8$

97. $y = \sqrt{x + 2}$

98. $x - y^2 = 0$

1 Chapter Summary

What did you learn?

Section 1.1   Review Exercises
☐ Sketch graphs of equations by point plotting and by using a graphing utility.   1–14
☐ Use graphs of equations to solve real-life problems.   15, 16

Section 1.2
☐ Find the slopes of lines.   17–22
☐ Write linear equations given points on lines and their slopes.   23–32
☐ Use slope-intercept forms of linear equations to sketch lines.   33–40
☐ Use slope to identify parallel and perpendicular lines.   41–44

Section 1.3
☐ Decide whether relations between two variables represent a function.   45–50
☐ Use function notation and evaluate functions.   51–54
☐ Find the domains of functions.   55–60
☐ Use functions to model and solve real-life problems.   61, 62
☐ Evaluate difference quotients.   63, 64

Section 1.4
☐ Find the domains and ranges of functions and use the Vertical Line Test
   for functions.   65–72
☐ Determine intervals on which functions are increasing, decreasing, or constant. 73–76
☐ Determine relative maximum and relative minimum values of functions.   77–80
☐ Identify and graph step functions and other piecewise-defined functions.   81, 82
☐ Identify even and odd functions.   83, 84

Section 1.5
☐ Recognize graphs of common functions.   85–88
☐ Use vertical and horizontal shifts and reflections to graph functions.   89–96
☐ Use nonrigid transformations to graph functions.   97–100

Section 1.6
☐ Add, subtract, multiply, and divide functions.   101–106
☐ Find compositions of one function with another function.   107–110
☐ Use combinations of functions to model and solve real-life problems.   111, 112

Section 1.7
☐ Find inverse functions informally and verify that two functions are inverse functions
   of each other.   113, 114
☐ Use graphs of functions to decide whether functions have inverse functions.   115, 116
☐ Determine if functions are one-to-one.   117–120
☐ Find inverse functions algebraically.   121–126

1 | Review Exercises

1.1 **In Exercises 1–4, complete the table. Use the resulting solution points to sketch the graph of the equation. Use a graphing utility to verify the graph.**

1. $y = -\frac{1}{2}x + 2$

x	-2	0	2	3	4
y					
Solution point					

2. $y = x^2 - 3x$

x	-1	0	1	2	3
y					
Solution point					

3. $y = 4 - x^2$

x	-2	-1	0	1	2
y					
Solution point					

4. $y = \sqrt{x - 1}$

x	1	2	5	10	17
y					
Solution point					

In Exercises 5–12, use a graphing utility to graph the equation. Approximate any x- or y-intercepts.

5. $y = \frac{1}{4}(x + 1)^3$ **6.** $y = 4 - (x - 4)^2$

7. $y = \frac{1}{4}x^4 - 2x^2$ **8.** $y = \frac{1}{4}x^3 - 3x$

9. $y = x\sqrt{9 - x^2}$ **10.** $y = x\sqrt{x + 3}$

11. $y = |x - 4| - 4$ **12.** $y = |x + 2| + |3 - x|$

In Exercises 13 and 14, describe the viewing window of the graph shown.

13. $y = 0.002x^2 - 0.06x - 1$

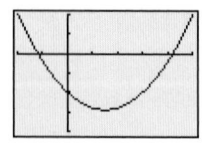

14. $y = 10x^3 - 21x^2$

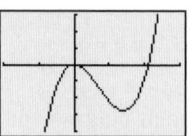

15. ***Consumerism***   You purchase a compact car for $13,500. The depreciated value y after t years is

$$y = 13{,}500 - 1100t, \quad 0 \le t \le 6.$$

(a) Use the constraints of the model to determine an appropriate viewing window.

(b) Use a graphing utility to graph the equation.

(c) Use the *zoom* and *trace* features of a graphing utility to determine the value of t when $y = \$9100$.

16. ***Data Analysis***   The table shows the number of Gap stores from 1996 to 2001.   (Source: The Gap, Inc.)

Year, t	Stores, y
1996	1370
1997	2130
1998	2428
1999	3018
2000	3676
2001	4171

A model for number of Gap stores during this period is given by $y = 2.05t^2 + 514.6t - 1730$, where y represents the number of stores and t represents the year, with $t = 6$ corresponding to 1996.

(a) Use the model and the *table* feature of a graphing utility to approximate the number of Gap stores from 1996 to 2001.

(b) Use a graphing utility to graph the data and the model in the same viewing window.

(c) Use the model to estimate the number of Gap stores in 2005 and 2008. Do the values seem reasonable? Explain.

(d) Use the *zoom* and *trace* features of a graphing utility to determine during which year the number of stores exceeded 3000.

1.2 In Exercises 17–22, plot the two points and find the slope of the line passing through the pair of points.

17. $(-3, 2), (8, 2)$

18. $(7, -1), (7, 12)$

19. $\left(\frac{3}{2}, 1\right), \left(5, \frac{5}{2}\right)$

20. $\left(-\frac{3}{4}, \frac{5}{6}\right), \left(\frac{1}{2}, -\frac{5}{2}\right)$

21. $(-4.5, 6), (2.1, 3)$

22. $(-2.7, -6.3), (-1, -1.2)$

In Exercises 23–32, use the point on the line and the slope of the line to find the general form of the equation of the line, and find three additional points through which the line passes. (There are many correct answers.)

	Point	Slope
23.	$(2, -1)$	$m = \frac{1}{4}$
24.	$(-3, 5)$	$m = -\frac{3}{2}$
25.	$(0, -5)$	$m = \frac{3}{2}$
26.	$(3, 0)$	$m = -\frac{2}{3}$
27.	$\left(\frac{1}{5}, -5\right)$	$m = -1$
28.	$\left(0, \frac{7}{8}\right)$	$m = -\frac{4}{5}$
29.	$(-2, 6)$	$m = 0$
30.	$(-8, 8)$	$m = 0$
31.	$(10, -6)$	m is undefined.
32.	$(5, 4)$	m is undefined.

In Exercises 33–36, find the slope-intercept form of the equation of the line that passes through the points. Use a graphing utility to graph the line.

33. $(2, -1), (4, -1)$

34. $(0, 0), (0, 10)$

35. $(-1, 0), (6, 2)$

36. $(1, 6), (4, 2)$

Rate of Change In Exercises 37 and 38, you are given the dollar value of a product in 2005 *and* the rate at which the value of the item is expected to change during the 5 years following. Use this information to write a linear equation that gives the dollar value V of the product in terms of the year t. (Let $t = 5$ represent 2005.)

	2005 Value	Rate
37.	$12,500	$850 increase per year
38.	$72.95	$5.15 decrease per year

39. *Sales* During the second and third quarters of the year, an e-commerce business had sales of $160,000 and $185,000, respectively. The growth of sales follows a linear pattern. Estimate sales during the fourth quarter.

40. *Depreciation* The dollar value of a VCR in 2004 is $85, and the product will decrease in value at an expected rate of $10.75 per year.

(a) Write a linear equation that gives the dollar value V of the VCR in terms of the year t. (Let $t = 4$ represent 2004.)

(b) Use a graphing utility to graph the equation found in part (a).

(c) Use the *value* or *trace* feature of your graphing utility to estimate the dollar value of the VCR in 2008.

In Exercises 41–44, write the slope-intercept forms of the equations of the lines through the given point (a) parallel to the given line and (b) perpendicular to the given line. Verify your result with a graphing utility (use a square setting).

	Point	Line
41.	$(3, -2)$	$5x - 4y = 8$
42.	$(-8, 3)$	$2x + 3y = 5$
43.	$(-6, 2)$	$x = 4$
44.	$(3, -4)$	$y = 2$

1.3 In Exercises 45 and 46, which sets of ordered pairs represent functions from A to B? Explain.

45. $A = \{10, 20, 30, 40\}$ and $B = \{0, 2, 4, 6\}$

(a) $\{(20, 4), (40, 0), (20, 6), (30, 2)\}$

(b) $\{(10, 4), (20, 4), (30, 4), (40, 4)\}$

(c) $\{(40, 0), (30, 2), (20, 4), (10, 6)\}$

(d) $\{(20, 2), (10, 0), (40, 4)\}$

46. $A = \{u, v, w\}$ and $B = \{-2, -1, 0, 1, 2\}$

(a) $\{(v, -1), (u, 2), (w, 0), (u, -2)\}$

(b) $\{(u, -2), (v, 2), (w, 1)\}$

(c) $\{(u, 2), (v, 2), (w, 1), (w, 1)\}$

(d) $\{(w, -2), (v, 0), (w, 2)\}$

In Exercises 47–50, determine whether the equation represents y as a function of x.

47. $16x - y^4 = 0$

48. $2x - y - 3 = 0$

49. $y = \sqrt{1 - x}$

50. $|y| = x + 2$

In Exercises 51–54, evaluate the function at each value of the independent variable and simplify.

51. $f(x) = x^2 + 1$

   (a) $f(2)$ (b) $f(-4)$

   (c) $f(t^2)$ (d) $-f(x)$

52. $g(x) = x^{4/3}$

   (a) $g(8)$ (b) $g(t + 1)$

   (c) $g(-27)$ (d) $g(-x)$

53. $h(x) = \begin{cases} 2x + 1, & x \le -1 \\ x^2 + 2, & x > -1 \end{cases}$

   (a) $h(-2)$ (b) $h(-1)$

   (c) $h(0)$ (d) $h(2)$

54. $f(x) = \dfrac{3}{2x - 5}$

   (a) $f(1)$ (b) $f(-2)$

   (c) $f(t)$ (d) $f(10)$

In Exercises 55–60, find the domain of the function.

55. $f(x) = (x - 1)(x + 2)$

56. $f(x) = x^2 - 4x - 32$

57. $f(x) = \sqrt{25 - x^2}$ **58.** $f(x) = \sqrt{x^2 + 8x}$

59. $g(s) = \dfrac{5}{3s - 9}$ **60.** $f(x) = \dfrac{2}{3x + 4}$

61. *Cost*   A hand tool manufacturer produces a product for which the variable cost is \$5.35 per unit and the fixed costs are \$16,000. The company sells the product for \$8.20 and can sell all that it produces.

   (a) Write the total cost C as a function of x, the number of units produced.

   (b) Write the profit P as a function of x.

62. *Consumerism*   The retail sales R (in billions of dollars) of lawn care products and services in the United States from 1994 to 2001 can be approximated by the model

$$R(t) = \begin{cases} -0.67t + 11.0, & 4 \le t \le 7 \\ 0.600t^2 - 10.06t + 50.7, & 8 \le t \le 11 \end{cases}$$

where t represents the year, with $t = 4$ corresponding to 1994. Use the *table* feature of a graphing utility to approximate the retail sales of lawn care products and services for each year from 1994 to 2001. (Source: The National Gardening Association)

In Exercises 63 and 64, find the difference quotient and simplify your answer.

63. $f(x) = 2x^2 + 3x - 1$, $\dfrac{f(x + h) - f(x)}{h}$, $h \ne 0$

64. $f(x) = x^3 - 5x^2 + x$, $\dfrac{f(x + h) - f(x)}{h}$, $h \ne 0$

1.4 **In Exercises 65–68, use a graphing utility to graph the function and estimate its domain and range. Then find the domain and range algebraically.**

65. $f(x) = 3 - 2x^2$ **66.** $f(x) = \sqrt{2x^2 - 1}$

67. $h(x) = \sqrt{36 - x^2}$ **68.** $g(x) = |x + 5|$

In Exercises 69–72, (a) use a graphing utility to graph the equation and (b) use the Vertical Line Test to determine whether y is a function of x.

69. $y = \dfrac{x^2 + 3x}{6}$ **70.** $y = -\dfrac{2}{3}|x + 5|$

71. $3x + y^2 = 2$ **72.** $x^2 + y^2 = 49$

In Exercises 73–76, (a) use a graphing utility to graph the function and (b) determine the open intervals on which the function is increasing, decreasing, or constant.

73. $f(x) = x^3 - 3x$ **74.** $f(x) = \sqrt{x^2 - 9}$

75. $f(x) = x\sqrt{x - 6}$ **76.** $f(x) = \dfrac{|x + 8|}{2}$

In Exercises 77–80, use a graphing utility to approximate (to two decimal places) any relative minimum or maximum values of the function.

77. $f(x) = (x^2 - 4)^2$ **78.** $f(x) = x^2 - x - 1$

79. $h(x) = 4x^3 - x^4$ **80.** $f(x) = x^3 - 4x^2 - 1$

In Exercises 81 and 82, sketch the graph of the piecewise-defined function by hand.

81. $f(x) = \begin{cases} 3x + 5, & x < 0 \\ x - 4, & x \ge 0 \end{cases}$

82. $f(x) = \begin{cases} x^2 + 7, & x < 1 \\ x^2 - 5x + 6, & x \ge 1 \end{cases}$

In Exercises 83 and 84, algebraically determine whether the function is even, odd, or neither. Verify your answer using a graphing utility.

83. $f(x) = (x^2 - 8)^2$ **84.** $f(x) = 2x^3 - x^2$

1.5 In Exercises 85–88, identify the common function and describe the transformation shown in the graph. Write an equation for the graphed function.

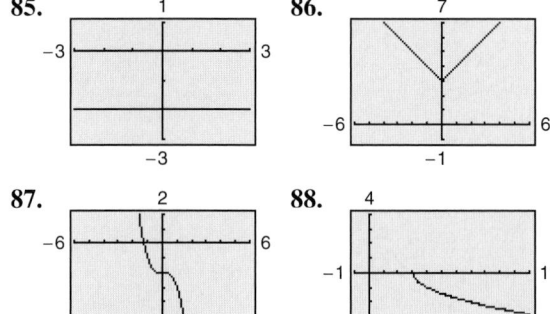

85.

86.

87.

88.

In Exercises 89–100, h is related to one of the six common functions on page 125. (a) Identify the common function f. (b) Describe the sequence of transformations from f to h. (c) Sketch the graph of h by hand. (d) Use function notation to write h in terms of the common function f.

89. $h(x) = x^2 - 6$
90. $h(x) = (x - 3)^2 - 2$
91. $h(x) = (x - 1)^3 + 7$
92. $h(x) = (x + 2)^3 + 5$
93. $h(x) = \sqrt{x} - 5$
94. $h(x) = |x + 8| - 1$
95. $h(x) = -x^2 - 3$
96. $h(x) = -(x - 2)^2 - 8$
97. $h(x) = -2x^2 + 3$
98. $h(x) = \frac{1}{2}(x - 3)^2 + 6$
99. $h(x) = -\frac{1}{2}|x| + 9$
100. $h(x) = \sqrt{3x} - 5$

1.6 In Exercises 101–110, let $f(x) = 3 - 2x$, $g(x) = \sqrt{x}$, and $h(x) = 3x^2 + 2$, and find the indicated values.

101. $(f - g)(4)$
102. $(f + h)(5)$
103. $(f + g)(25)$
104. $(g - h)(1)$
105. $(fh)(1)$
106. $\left(\dfrac{g}{h}\right)(1)$
107. $(h \circ g)(7)$
108. $(g \circ f)(-2)$
109. $(f \circ h)(-4)$
110. $(g \circ h)(6)$

Data Analysis In Exercises 111 and 112, the numbers (in thousands) of students taking the SAT (y_1) and ACT (y_2) for the years 1996 through 2001 can be modeled by $y_1 = -2.75t^2 + 86.8t + 659$ and $y_2 = -1.88t^2 + 62.4t + 616$, where t represents the year, with $t = 6$ corresponding to 1996.   (Source: College Entrance Examination Board and ACT, Inc.)

111. Use a graphing utility to graph y_1, y_2, and $y_1 + y_2$ in the same viewing window.

112. Use the model $y_1 + y_2$ to estimate the total number of students taking the SAT and ACT in 2006.

1.7 In Exercises 113 and 114, find the inverse function of f informally. Verify that $f(f^{-1}(x)) = x$ and $f^{-1}(f(x)) = x$.

113. $f(x) = 6x$
114. $f(x) = x + 5$

In Exercises 115 and 116, show that f and g are inverse functions (a) graphically and (b) numerically.

115. $f(x) = 3 - 4x$, $g(x) = \dfrac{3 - x}{4}$

116. $f(x) = \sqrt{x + 1}$, $g(x) = x^2 - 1, x \geq 0$

In Exercises 117–120, use a graphing utility to graph the function and use the Horizontal Line Test to determine whether the function is one-to-one and so has an inverse function.

117. $f(x) = \frac{1}{2}x - 3$
118. $f(x) = (x - 1)^2$
119. $h(t) = \dfrac{2}{t - 3}$
120. $g(x) = \sqrt{x + 6}$

In Exercises 121–126, find the inverse function of f algebraically.

121. $f(x) = \dfrac{x}{12}$
122. $f(x) = \dfrac{7x + 3}{8}$
123. $f(x) = 4x^3 - 3$
124. $f(x) = x^3 - 2$
125. $f(x) = \sqrt{x + 10}$
126. $f(x) = 4\sqrt{6 - x}$

Synthesis

True or False? In Exercises 127–129, determine whether the statement is true or false. Justify your answer.

127. If the graph of the common function $f(x) = x^2$ is moved six units to the right, moved three units upward, and reflected in the x-axis, then the point $(-1, 28)$ will lie on the graph of the transformation.

128. If $f(x) = x^n$ where n is odd, f^{-1} exists.

129. There exists no function f such that $f = f^{-1}$.

1 Chapter Test

Take this test as you would take a test in class. After you are finished, check your work against the answers in the back of the book.

In Exercises 1–6, use the point-plotting method to graph the equation by hand and identify any x- and y-intercepts. Verify your results using a graphing utility.

1. $y = 4 - \frac{3}{4}|x|$

2. $y = 4 - (x - 2)^2$

3. $y = x - x^3$

4. $y = -x^3 + 2x - 4$

5. $y = \sqrt{3 - x}$

6. $y = \frac{1}{2}x\sqrt{x + 3}$

7. A line with slope $m = \frac{3}{2}$ passes through the point $(3, -1)$. List three additional points on the line. Then sketch the line.

8. Find an equation of the line that passes through the point $(0, 4)$ and is (a) parallel to and (b) perpendicular to the line $5x + 2y = 3$.

9. Does the graph at the right represent y as a function of x? Explain.

10. Evaluate $f(x) = |x + 2| - 15$ at each value of the independent variable and simplify.

    (a) $f(-8)$ (b) $f(14)$ (c) $f(t - 6)$

11. Find the domain of $f(x) = 10 - \sqrt{3 - x}$.

12. An electronics company produces a car stereo for which the variable cost is $5.60 and the fixed costs are $24,000. The product sells for $99.50. Write the total cost C as a function of x. Write the profit P as a function of x.

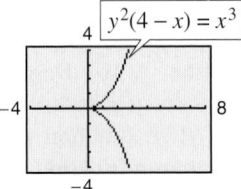

Figure for 9

In Exercises 13 and 14, determine the open intervals on which the function is increasing, decreasing, or constant.

13. $h(x) = \frac{1}{4}x^4 - 2x^2$

14. $g(t) = |t + 2| - |t - 2|$

In Exercises 15 and 16, use a graphing utility to approximate (to two decimal places) any relative minimum or maximum values of the function.

15. $f(x) = -x^3 - 5x^2 + 12$

16. $f(x) = x^5 - x^3 + 2$

In Exercises 17–19, (a) identify the common function f, (b) describe the sequence of transformations from f to g, and (c) sketch the graph of g.

17. $g(x) = -2(x - 5)^3 + 3$

18. $g(x) = \sqrt{-x - 7}$

19. $g(x) = 4|-x| - 7$

20. Use the functions $f(x) = x^2$ and $g(x) = \sqrt{2 - x}$ to find the specified function and its domain.

    (a) $(f - g)(x)$ (b) $\left(\dfrac{f}{g}\right)(x)$ (c) $(f \circ g)(x)$ (d) $(g \circ f)(x)$

In Exercises 21–23, determine whether the function has an inverse function, and if so, find the inverse function.

21. $f(x) = x^3 + 8$

22. $f(x) = x^2 + 6$

23. $f(x) = \dfrac{3x\sqrt{x}}{8}$

A quadratic equation can be used to model the number of hours spent annually per person using the internet in the United States.

Royalty Free/Corbis

2 Solving Equations and Inequalities

2.1 Linear Equations and Problem Solving

2.2 Solving Equations Graphically

2.3 Complex Numbers

2.4 Solving Equations Algebraically

2.5 Solving Inequalities Algebraically and Graphically

2.6 Exploring Data: Linear Models and Scatter Plots

What You Should Learn

In this chapter, you will learn how to:

- Solve and use linear equations, including those involving fractions.

- Write and use mathematical models to solve real-life problems.

- Find intercepts, zeros, and solutions of equations graphically.

- Perform operations with complex numbers and plot complex numbers in the complex plane.

- Solve quadratic equations, polynomial equations, and equations involving radicals, fractions, and absolute values.

- Solve linear inequalities, inequalities involving absolute values, polynomial inequalities, and rational inequalities.

- Use scatter plots and a graphing utility to find linear models for data.

161

2.1 Linear Equations and Problem Solving

Equations and Solutions of Equations

An **equation** in x is a statement that two algebraic expressions are equal. For example, $3x - 5 = 7$, $x^2 - x - 6 = 0$, and $\sqrt{2x} = 4$ are equations. To **solve** an equation in x means to find all values of x for which the equation is true. Such values are **solutions.** For instance, $x = 4$ is a solution of the equation $3x - 5 = 7$, because $3(4) - 5 = 7$ is a true statement.

The solutions of an equation depend on the kinds of numbers being considered. For instance, in the set of rational numbers, $x^2 = 10$ has no solution because there is no rational number whose square is 10. However, in the set of real numbers the equation has the two solutions $\sqrt{10}$ and $-\sqrt{10}$.

An equation that is true for *every* real number in the domain of the variable is called an **identity.** For example, $x^2 - 9 = (x + 3)(x - 3)$ is an identity because it is a true statement for any real value of x, and $x/(3x^2) = 1/(3x)$, where $x \neq 0$, is an identity because it is true for any nonzero real value of x.

An equation that is true for just *some* (or even none) of the real numbers in the domain of the variable is called a **conditional equation.** For example, the equation $x^2 - 9 = 0$ is conditional because $x = 3$ and $x = -3$ are the only values in the domain that satisfy the equation. The equation $2x + 1 = 2x - 3$ is also conditional because there are no real values of x for which the equation is true. Learning to solve conditional equations is the primary focus of this chapter.

A **linear equation in one variable x** is an equation that can be written in the standard form $ax + b = 0$, where a and b are real numbers, with $a \neq 0$. For a review of solving one- and two-step linear equations, see Appendix D.

To solve an equation involving fractional expressions, find the least common denominator (LCD) of all terms in the equation and multiply every term by this LCD. This procedure clears the equation of fractions as demonstrated in Example 1.

Example 1   Solving an Equation Involving Fractions

Solve $\dfrac{x}{3} + \dfrac{3x}{4} = 2$.

Solution

$$\frac{x}{3} + \frac{3x}{4} = 2 \qquad \text{Write original equation.}$$

$$(12)\frac{x}{3} + (12)\frac{3x}{4} = (12)2 \qquad \text{Multiply each term by the LCD of 12.}$$

$$4x + 9x = 24 \qquad \text{Divide out and multiply.}$$

$$13x = 24 \qquad \text{Combine like terms.}$$

$$x = \frac{24}{13} \qquad \text{Divide each side by 13.}$$

✓ *Checkpoint* Now try Exercise 15.

What you should learn

- Solve equations involving fractional expressions.
- Write and use mathematical models to solve real-life problems.
- Use common formulas to solve real-life problems.

Why you should learn it

Linear equations are useful for modeling situations in which you need to find missing information. For instance, Exercise 43 on page 169 shows how to use a linear equation to determine the score you must get on a test in order to get an A for the course.

PhotoEdit

STUDY TIP

After solving an equation, you should check each solution in the original equation. For instance, you can check the solution to Example 1 as follows.

$$\frac{x}{3} + \frac{3x}{4} = 2$$

$$\frac{\frac{24}{13}}{3} + \frac{3\left(\frac{24}{13}\right)}{4} \overset{?}{=} 2$$

$$\frac{8}{13} + \frac{18}{13} \overset{?}{=} 2$$

$$2 = 2 \checkmark$$

When multiplying or dividing an equation by a *variable* expression, it is possible to introduce an **extraneous solution**—one that does not satisfy the original equation. The next example demonstrates the importance of checking your solution when you have multiplied or divided by a variable expression.

Example 2   An Equation with an Extraneous Solution

Solve $\dfrac{1}{x-2} = \dfrac{3}{x+2} - \dfrac{6x}{x^2-4}$.

Algebraic Solution

The LCD is

$$x^2 - 4 = (x+2)(x-2).$$

Multiplying each term by the LCD and simplifying produces the following.

$$\frac{1}{x-2}(x+2)(x-2)$$

$$= \frac{3}{x+2}(x+2)(x-2) - \frac{6x}{x^2-4}(x+2)(x-2)$$

$$x + 2 = 3(x-2) - 6x, \quad x \neq \pm 2$$

$$x + 2 = 3x - 6 - 6x$$

$$4x = -8$$

$$x = -2 \qquad \text{Extraneous solution}$$

A check of $x = -2$ in the original equation shows that it yields a denominator of zero. So, $x = -2$ is an extraneous solution, and the original equation has *no solution*.

 Checkpoint   Now try Exercise 29.

Graphical Solution

Use a graphing utility (in *dot* mode) to graph the left and right sides of the equation

$$y_1 = \frac{1}{x-2} \quad \text{and} \quad y_2 = \frac{3}{x+2} - \frac{6x}{x^2-4}$$

in the same viewing window, as shown in Figure 2.1. The graphs of the equations do not appear to intersect. This means that there is no point for which the left side of the equation y_1 is equal to the right side of the equation y_2. So, the equation appears to have *no solution*.

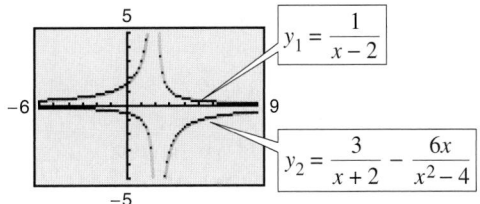

Figure 2.1

Using Mathematical Models to Solve Problems

One of the primary goals of this text is to learn how algebra can be used to solve problems that occur in real-life situations. This procedure is called **mathematical modeling.**

A good approach to mathematical modeling is to use two stages. Begin by using the verbal description of the problem to form a *verbal model*. Then, after assigning labels to the quantities in the verbal model, form a *mathematical model* or an *algebraic equation*.

Verbal Description ⟹ Verbal Model ⟹ Algebraic Equation

When you are trying to construct a verbal model, it is helpful to look for a *hidden equality*—a statement that two algebraic expressions are equal. These two expressions might be explicitly stated as being equal, or they might be known to be equal (based on prior knowledge or experience).

TECHNOLOGY TIP

Notice in Figure 2.1 that the equations were graphed using the *dot* mode of a graphing utility. In this text, a blue or light red curve is placed behind the graphing utility's display to indicate where the graph should appear. You will learn more about how graphing utilities graph these types of equations in Section 3.6.

Example 3 Finding the Dimensions of a Room

A rectangular family room is twice as long as it is wide, and its perimeter is 84 feet. Find the dimensions of the family room.

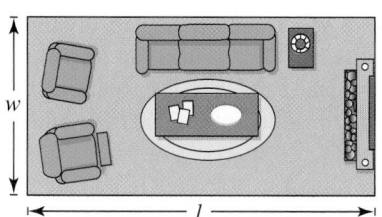

Figure 2.2

Solution

For this problem, it helps to draw a diagram, as shown in Figure 2.2.

Verbal Model: $2 \cdot \boxed{\text{Length}} + 2 \cdot \boxed{\text{Width}} = \boxed{\text{Perimeter}}$

Labels:

Perimeter = 84	(feet)
Width = w	(feet)
Length = $l = 2w$	(feet)

Equation:

$$2(2w) + 2w = 84 \qquad \text{Original equation}$$
$$6w = 84 \qquad \text{Group like terms.}$$
$$w = 14 \qquad \text{Divide each side by 6.}$$

Because the length is twice the width, you have

$$l = 2w \qquad \text{Length is twice width.}$$
$$= 2(14) \qquad \text{Substitute 14 for } w.$$
$$= 28. \qquad \text{Simplify.}$$

So, the dimensions of the room are 14 feet by 28 feet.

 Checkpoint Now try Exercise 41.

Example 4 A Distance Problem

A plane is flying nonstop from New York to San Francisco, a distance of about 2900 miles, as shown in Figure 2.3. After $1\frac{1}{2}$ hours in the air, the plane flies over Chicago (a distance of about 800 miles from New York). Estimate the time it will take the plane to fly from New York to San Francisco.

Solution

Verbal Model: $\boxed{\text{Distance}} = \boxed{\text{Rate}} \cdot \boxed{\text{Time}}$

Labels:

Distance = 2900	(miles)
Time = t	(hours)
Rate = $\dfrac{\text{Distance to Chicago}}{\text{Time to Chicago}} = \dfrac{800}{1.5}$	(miles per hour)

Equation:

$$2900 = \frac{800}{1.5}t$$
$$5.44 \approx t$$

The trip will take about 5.44 hours, or about 5 hours and 27 minutes.

 Checkpoint Now try Exercise 45.

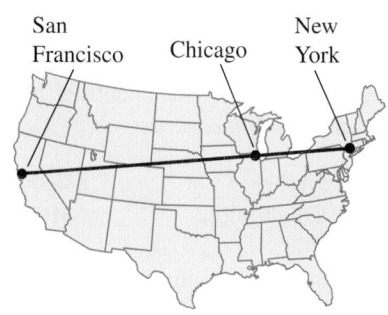

Figure 2.3

Example 5   Height of a Building

To determine the height of the Aon Center Building (in Chicago), you measure the shadow cast by the building and find it to be 142 feet long, as shown in Figure 2.4. Then you measure the shadow cast by a 48-inch post and find it to be 6 inches long. Estimate the building's height.

Solution

To solve this problem, you use a result from geometry that states that the ratios of corresponding sides of similar triangles are equal.

Verbal Model: $\dfrac{\text{Height of building}}{\text{Length of building's shadow}} = \dfrac{\text{Height of post}}{\text{Length of post's shadow}}$

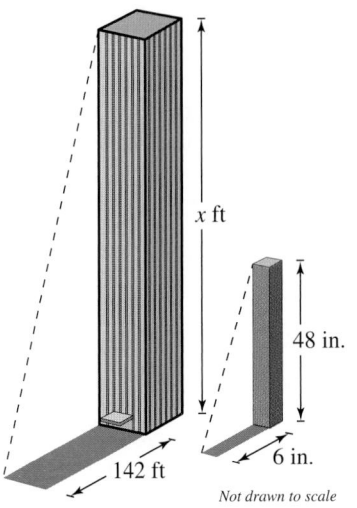

Figure 2.4

Labels: Height of building $= x$ (feet)

Length of building's shadow $= 142$ (feet)

Height of post $= 48$ (inches)

Length of post's shadow $= 6$ (inches)

Equation: $\dfrac{x}{142} = \dfrac{48}{6}$ ⟹ $x = 1136$

So, the Aon Center Building is about 1136 feet high.

 Checkpoint Now try Exercise 51.

Example 6   An Inventory Problem

A store has $30,000 of inventory in 13-inch and 19-inch color televisions. The profit on a 13-inch set is 22% and the profit on a 19-inch set is 40%. The profit for the entire stock is 35%. How much was invested in each type of television?

Solution

Verbal Model: Profit from 13-inch sets + Profit from 19-inch sets = Total profit

Labels: Inventory of 13-inch sets $= x$ (dollars)

Inventory of 19-inch sets $= 30{,}000 - x$ (dollars)

Profit from 13-inch sets $= 0.22x$ (dollars)

Profit from 19-inch sets $= 0.40(30{,}000 - x)$ (dollars)

Total profit $= 0.35(30{,}000) = 10{,}500$ (dollars)

Equation: $0.22x + 0.40(30{,}000 - x) = 10{,}500$

$$-0.18x = -1500$$

$$x \approx 8333.33$$

So, $8333.33 was invested in 13-inch sets and $30{,}000 - x$, or $21,666.67, was invested in 19-inch sets.

 Checkpoint Now try Exercise 55.

Common Formulas

Many common types of geometric, scientific, and investment problems use ready-made equations called **formulas.** Knowing these formulas will help you translate and solve a wide variety of real-life applications.

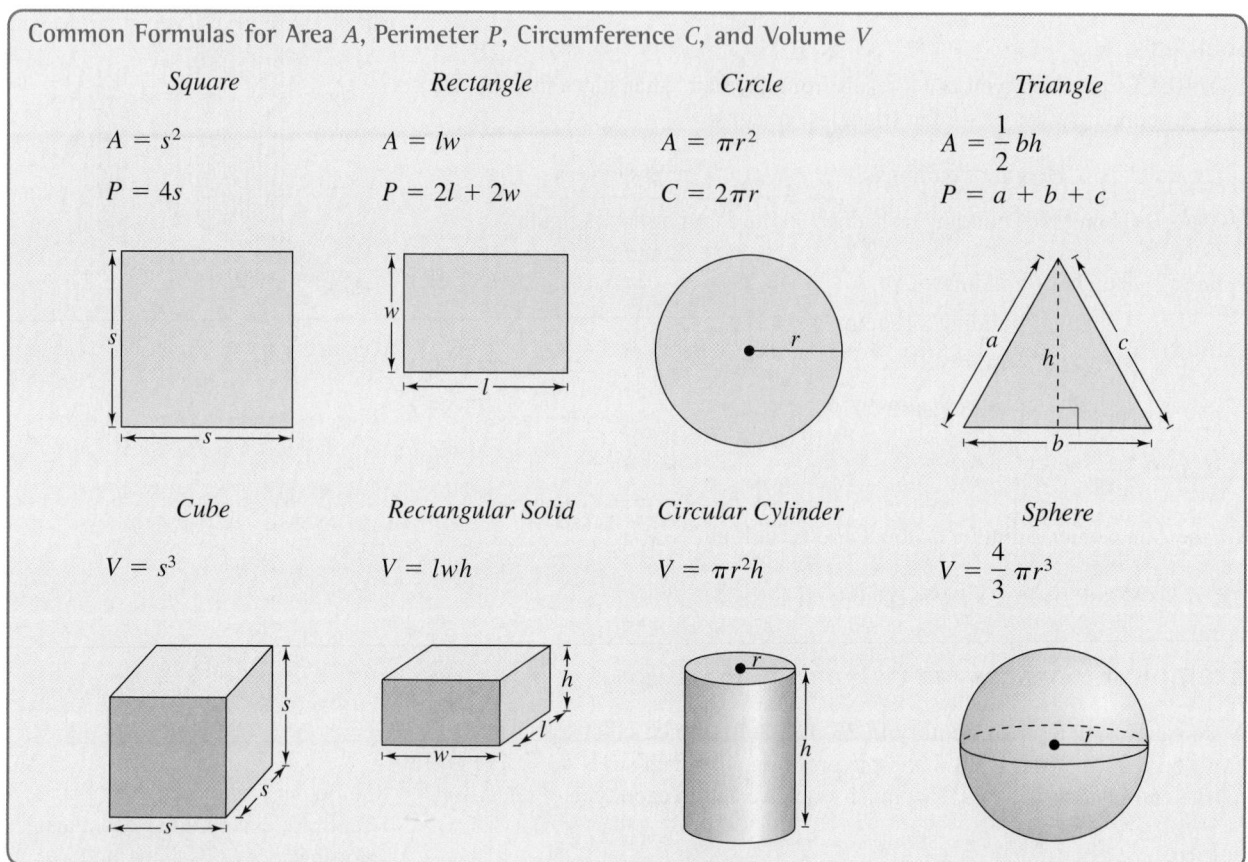

Common Formulas for Area A, Perimeter P, Circumference C, and Volume V

Square

$A = s^2$

$P = 4s$

Rectangle

$A = lw$

$P = 2l + 2w$

Circle

$A = \pi r^2$

$C = 2\pi r$

Triangle

$A = \dfrac{1}{2}bh$

$P = a + b + c$

Cube

$V = s^3$

Rectangular Solid

$V = lwh$

Circular Cylinder

$V = \pi r^2 h$

Sphere

$V = \dfrac{4}{3}\pi r^3$

Miscellaneous Common Formulas

Temperature: $F = \dfrac{9}{5}C + 32$ F = degrees Fahrenheit, C = degrees Celsius

Simple Interest: $I = Prt$ I = interest, P = principal (original deposit),
r = annual interest rate, t = time in years

Compound Interest: $A = P\left(1 + \dfrac{r}{n}\right)^{nt}$ A = balance, P = principal (original deposit),
r = annual interest rate, n = compoundings (number of times interest is calculated) per year, t = time in years

Distance: $d = rt$ d = distance traveled, r = rate, t = time

When working with applied problems, you often need to rewrite one of the common formulas. For instance, the formula for the perimeter of a rectangle, $P = 2l + 2w$, can be solved for w as $w = \frac{1}{2}(P - 2l)$.

Example 7   Using a Formula

A cylindrical can has a volume of 600 cubic centimeters and a radius of 4 centimeters, as shown in Figure 2.5. Find the height of the can.

Solution

The formula for the volume of a cylinder is $V = \pi r^2 h$. To find the height of the can, solve for h as

$$h = \frac{V}{\pi r^2}.$$

Then, using $V = 600$ and $r = 4$, find the height.

$$h = \frac{600}{\pi(4)^2} = \frac{600}{16\pi} \approx 11.94$$

You can use unit analysis to check that your answer is reasonable.

$$\frac{600 \text{ cm}^3}{16\pi \text{ cm}^2} \approx 11.94 \text{ cm}$$

✓ *Checkpoint* Now try Exercise 57.

Figure 2.5

Example 8   Using a Formula

The average daily temperature in San Diego, California is 64.4°F. What is San Diego's average daily temperature in degrees Celsius? (Source: U.S. National Oceanic and Atmospheric Administration)

Solution

Use $F = 64.4$ in the formula for temperature to find the temperature in degrees Celsius.

$$F = \frac{9}{5}C + 32 \qquad \text{Formula for temperature}$$

$$64.4 = \frac{9}{5}C + 32 \qquad \text{Substitute 64.4 for } F.$$

$$32.4 = \frac{9}{5}C \qquad \text{Subtract 32 from each side.}$$

$$18 = C \qquad \text{Simplify.}$$

The average daily temperature in San Diego is 18°C.

✓ *Checkpoint* Now try Exercise 60.

2.1 Exercises

Vocabulary Check

Fill in the blanks.

1. A(n) _____ is a statement that equates two algebraic expressions.
2. To find all values that satisfy an equation is to _____ the equation.
3. There are two types of equations, _____ and _____ .
4. A linear equation in one variable is an equation that can be written in the standard form _____ .
5. When solving an equation, it is possible to introduce an _____ solution, which is a value that does not satisfy the original equation.
6. _____ is a procedure used in algebra to solve problems that occur in real-life situations.
7. Many real-life problems can be solved using ready-made equations called _____ .

In Exercises 1–6, determine whether each value of x is a solution of the equation.

	Equation		Values	
1.	$\dfrac{5}{2x} - \dfrac{4}{x} = 3$	(a) $x = -\tfrac{1}{2}$	(b) $x = 4$	
		(c) $x = 0$	(d) $x = \tfrac{1}{4}$	
2.	$\dfrac{x}{2} + \dfrac{6x}{7} = \dfrac{19}{14}$	(a) $x = -2$	(b) $x = 1$	
		(c) $x = \dfrac{1}{2}$	(d) $x = 7$	
3.	$3 + \dfrac{1}{x + 2} = 4$	(a) $x = -1$	(b) $x = -2$	
		(c) $x = 0$	(d) $x = 5$	
4.	$\dfrac{(x + 5)(x - 3)}{2} = 24$	(a) $x = -3$	(b) $x = -2$	
		(c) $x = 7$	(d) $x = 9$	
5.	$\dfrac{\sqrt{x + 4}}{6} + 3 = 4$	(a) $x = -3$	(b) $x = 0$	
		(c) $x = 21$	(d) $x = 32$	
6.	$\dfrac{\sqrt[3]{x - 8}}{3} = -\dfrac{2}{3}$	(a) $x = -16$	(b) $x = 0$	
		(c) $x = 9$	(d) $x = 16$	

In Exercises 7–12, determine whether the equation is an identity or a conditional equation.

7. $2(x - 1) = 2x - 2$

8. $-7(x - 3) + 4x = 3(7 - x)$

9. $x^2 - 8x + 5 = (x - 4)^2 - 11$

10. $x^2 + 2(3x - 2) = x^2 + 6x - 4$

11. $3 + \dfrac{1}{x + 1} = \dfrac{4x}{x + 1}$

12. $\dfrac{5}{x} + \dfrac{3}{x} = 24$

In Exercises 13 and 14, solve the equation using two methods. Then explain which method is easier.

13. $\dfrac{3x}{8} - \dfrac{4x}{3} = 4$

14. $\dfrac{3z}{8} - \dfrac{z}{10} = 6$

In Exercises 15–30, solve the equation (if possible). Then use a graphing utility to verify your solution.

15. $\dfrac{x}{5} - \dfrac{x}{2} = 3$

16. $\dfrac{5x}{4} + \dfrac{1}{2} = x - \dfrac{1}{2}$

17. $\tfrac{3}{2}(z + 5) - \tfrac{1}{4}(z + 24) = 0$

18. $\dfrac{3x}{2} + \dfrac{1}{4}(x - 2) = 10$

19. $\dfrac{100 - 4u}{3} = \dfrac{5u + 6}{4} + 6$

20. $\dfrac{17 + y}{y} + \dfrac{32 + y}{y} = 100$

21. $\dfrac{5x - 4}{5x + 4} = \dfrac{2}{3}$

22. $\dfrac{10x + 3}{5x + 6} = \dfrac{1}{2}$

23. $\dfrac{1}{x - 3} + \dfrac{1}{x + 3} = \dfrac{10}{x^2 - 9}$

24. $\dfrac{1}{x - 2} + \dfrac{3}{x + 3} = \dfrac{4}{x^2 + x - 6}$

25. $\dfrac{7}{2x + 1} - \dfrac{8x}{2x - 1} = -4$

26. $\dfrac{x}{x + 4} + \dfrac{4}{x + 4} + 2 = 0$

27. $\dfrac{1}{x} + \dfrac{2}{x - 5} = 0$ 28. $3 = 2 + \dfrac{2}{z + 2}$

29. $\dfrac{3}{x^2 - 3x} + \dfrac{4}{x} = \dfrac{1}{x - 3}$

30. $\dfrac{6}{x} - \dfrac{2}{x + 3} = \dfrac{3(x + 5)}{x(x + 3)}$

In Exercises 31–38, solve for the indicated variable.

31. *Area of a Triangle*

Solve for h: $A = \frac{1}{2}bh$

32. *Area of a Trapezoid*

Solve for b: $A = \frac{1}{2}(a + b)h$

33. *Investment at Compound Interest*

Solve for P: $A = P\left(1 + \dfrac{r}{n}\right)^{nt}$

34. *Investment at Simple Interest*

Solve for r: $A = P + Prt$

35. *Geometric Progression*

Solve for r: $S = \dfrac{rL - a}{r - 1}$

36. *Arithmetic Progression*

Solve for n: $L = a + (n - 1)d$

37. *Volume of an Oblate Spheroid*

Solve for b: $V = \dfrac{4}{3}\pi a^2 b$

38. *Volume of a Spherical Segment*

Solve for r: $V = \dfrac{1}{3}\pi h^2(3r - h)$

Anthropology **In Exercises 39 and 40, use the following information. The relationship between the length of an adult's femur (thigh bone) and the height of the adult can be approximated by the linear equations**

$y = 0.432x - 10.44$ **Female**

$y = 0.449x - 12.15$ **Male**

where y is the length of the femur in inches and x is the height of the adult in inches (see figure).

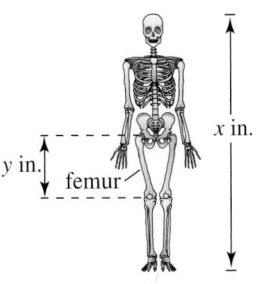

Figure for 39 and 40

39. An anthropologist discovers a femur belonging to an adult human female. The bone is 16 inches long. Estimate the height of the female.

40. From the foot bones of an adult human male, an anthropologist estimates that the person's height was 69 inches. A few feet away from the site where the foot bones were discovered, the anthropologist discovers a male adult femur that is 19 inches long. Is it likely that both the foot bones and the thigh bone came from the same person?

41. *Geometry*   A room is 1.5 times as long as it is wide, and its perimeter is 25 meters.

(a) Draw a diagram that gives a visual representation of the problem. Identify the length as l and the width as w.

(b) Write l in terms of w and write an equation for the perimeter in terms of w.

(c) Find the dimensions of the room.

42. *Geometry*   A picture frame has a total perimeter of 3 meters. The height of the frame is $\frac{2}{3}$ times its width.

(a) Draw a diagram that gives a visual representation of the problem. Identify the width as w and the height as h.

(b) Write h in terms of w and write an equation for the perimeter in terms of w.

(c) Find the dimensions of the picture frame.

43. *Course Grade*   To get an A in a course, you must have an average of at least 90 on four tests of 100 points each. The scores on your first three tests were 87, 92, and 84.

(a) Write a verbal model for the test average for the course.

(b) What must you score on the fourth test to get an A for the course?

44. *Course Grade* You are taking a course that has four tests. The first three tests are 100 points each and the fourth test is 200 points. To get an A in the course, you must have an average of at least 90% on the four tests. Your scores on the first three tests were 87, 92, and 84. What must you score on the fourth test to get an A for the course?

45. *Travel Time* You are driving on a Canadian freeway to a town that is 300 kilometers from your home. After 30 minutes you pass a freeway exit that you know is 50 kilometers from your home. Assuming that you continue at the same constant speed, how long will it take for the entire trip?

46. *Travel Time* On the first part of a 317-mile trip, a salesperson averaged 58 miles per hour. The salesperson averaged only 52 miles per hour on the last part of the trip because of an increased volume of traffic. The total time of the trip was 5 hours and 45 minutes. Find the amount of time at each of the two speeds.

47. *Average Speed* A truck driver traveled at an average speed of 55 miles per hour on a 200-mile trip to pick up a load of freight. On the return trip (with the truck fully loaded), the average speed was 40 miles per hour. Find the average speed for the round trip.

48. *Wind Speed* An executive flew in the corporate jet to a meeting in a city 1500 kilometers away. After traveling the same amount of time on the return flight, the pilot mentioned that they still had 300 kilometers to go. The air speed of the plane was 600 kilometers per hour. How fast was the wind blowing? (Assume that the wind direction was parallel to the flight path and constant all day.)

49. *Speed of Light* Light travels at the speed of 3.0×10^8 meters per second. Find the time in minutes required for light to travel from the sun to Earth (a distance of 1.5×10^{11} meters).

50. *Radio Waves* Radio waves travel at the same speed as light, 3.0×10^8 meters per second. Find the time required for a radio wave to travel from Mission Control in Houston to NASA astronauts on the surface of the moon 3.84×10^8 meters away.

51. *Height* To obtain the height of a barn silo, you measure the silo's shadow and find that it is 80 feet long. You also measure the shadow of a four-foot stake and find that it is $3\frac{1}{2}$ feet long.

(a) Draw a diagram that illustrates the problem. Let *h* represent the height of the silo.

(b) Find the height of the silo.

52. *Height* A person who is 6 feet tall walks away from a flagpole toward the tip of the shadow of the flagpole. When the person is 30 feet from the flagpole, the tips of the person's shadow and the shadow cast by the flagpole coincide at a point 5 feet in front of the person.

(a) Draw a diagram that illustrates the problem. Let *h* represent the height of the flagpole.

(b) Find the height of the flagpole.

53. *Investment* You plan to invest $12,000 in two funds paying $4\frac{1}{2}\%$ and 5% simple interest. (There is more risk in the 5% fund.) Your goal is to obtain a total annual interest income of $560 from the investments. What is the smallest amount you can invest in the 5% fund in order to meet your objective?

54. *Investment* You plan to invest $25,000 in two funds paying 3% and $4\frac{1}{2}\%$ simple interest. (There is more risk in the $4\frac{1}{2}\%$ fund.) Your goal is to obtain a total annual interest income of $1000 from the investments. What is the smallest amount you can invest in the $4\frac{1}{2}\%$ fund in order to meet your objective?

55. *Mixture Problem* A grocer mixes peanuts that cost $2.49 per pound and walnuts that cost $3.89 per pound to make 100 pounds of a mixture that costs $3.19 per pound. How much of each kind of nut is put into the mixture?

56. *Mixture Problem* A forester mixes gasoline and oil to make 2 gallons of mixture for his two-cycle chainsaw engine. This mixture is 32 parts gasoline and 1 part two-cycle oil. How much gasoline must be added to bring the mixture to 40 parts gasoline and 1 part oil?

57. *Height* A triangular sail has an area of 182.25 square feet. The sail has a base of 13.5 feet. Find the height of the sail.

58. *Geometry* The volume of a rectangular package is 2304 cubic inches. The length of the package is 3 times its width, and the height is one and a half times its width.

(a) Draw a diagram that illustrates the problem. Label the height, width, and length accordingly.

(b) Find the dimensions of the package.

59. *Geometry* The volume of a globe is about 47,712.94 cubic centimeters. Use a graphing utility to find the radius of the globe. Round your result to two decimal places.

60. *Meteorology*   The line graph shows the temperatures (in degrees Fahrenheit) on a summer day in Buffalo, New York from 10:00 A.M. to 6:00 P.M. Create a new line graph showing the temperatures throughout the day in degrees Celsius.

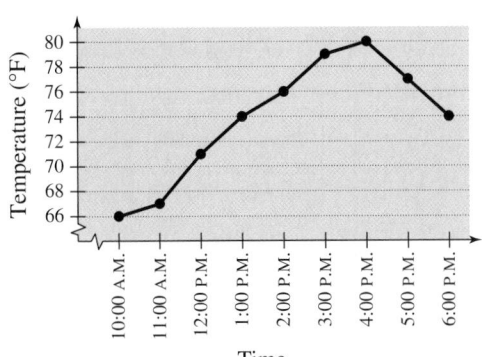

Statics   **In Exercises 61 and 62, you have a uniform beam of length L with a fulcrum x feet from one end (see figure). Objects with weights W_1 and W_2 are placed at opposite ends of the beam. The beam will balance when**

$$W_1 x = W_2(L - x).$$

Find x such that the beam will balance.

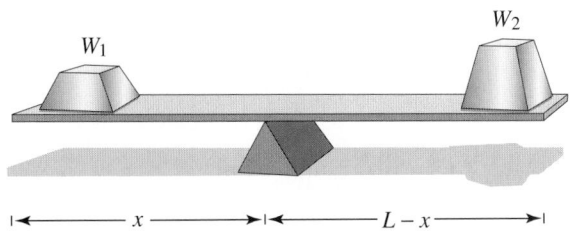

61. Two children weighing 50 pounds and 75 pounds are going to play on a seesaw that is 10 feet long.

62. A person weighing 200 pounds is attempting to move a 550-pound rock with a bar that is 5 feet long.

Synthesis

True or False?   **In Exercises 63 and 64, determine whether the statement is true or false. Justify your answer.**

63. The equation

$$x(3 - x) = 10$$

is a linear equation.

64. The volume of a cube with a side length of 9.5 inches is greater than the volume of a sphere with a radius of 5.9 inches.

In Exercises 65 and 66, write a linear equation that has the given solution. (There are many correct answers.)

65. $x = -3$

66. $x = \frac{1}{4}$

67. *Think About It*   What is meant by *equivalent equations*? Give an example of two equivalent equations.

68. *Writing*   In your own words, describe how to clear an equation of fractions.

Review

In Exercises 69–74, sketch the graph of the equation by hand. Verify using a graphing utility.

69. $y = \frac{5}{8}x - 2$

70. $y = \dfrac{3x - 5}{2} + 2$

71. $y = (x - 3)^2 + 7$

72. $y = \frac{1}{3}x^2 - 4$

73. $y = -\frac{1}{2}|x + 4| - 1$

74. $y = |x - 2| + 10$

In Exercises 75–80, evaluate the combination of functions for $f(x) = -x^2 + 4$ and $g(x) = 6x - 5$.

75. $(f + g)(-3)$

76. $(g - f)(-1)$

77. $(fg)(8)$

78. $\left(\dfrac{f}{g}\right)\left(\dfrac{1}{2}\right)$

79. $(f \circ g)(4)$

80. $(g \circ f)(2)$

2.2 Solving Equations Graphically

Intercepts, Zeros, and Solutions

In Section 1.1, you learned that the intercepts of a graph are the points at which the graph intersects the x- or y-axis.

> **Definition of Intercepts**
>
> 1. The point $(a, 0)$ is called an **x-intercept** of the graph of an equation if it is a solution point of the equation. To find the x-intercept(s), set y equal to 0 and solve the equation for x.
>
> 2. The point $(0, b)$ is called a **y-intercept** of the graph of an equation if it is a solution point of the equation. To find the y-intercept(s), set x equal to 0 and solve the equation for y.

Sometimes it is convenient to denote the x-intercept as simply the x-coordinate of the point $(a, 0)$ rather than the point itself. Unless it is necessary to make a distinction, "intercept" will be used to mean either the point or the coordinate.

It is possible for a graph to have no intercepts, one intercept, or several intercepts. For instance, consider the four graphs shown in Figure 2.6.

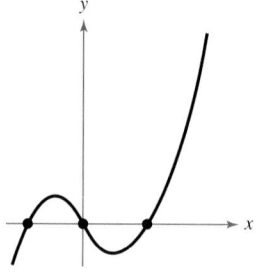

Three x-Intercepts
One y-Intercept

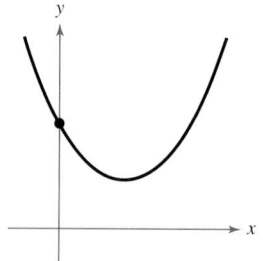

No x-Intercepts
One y-Intercept

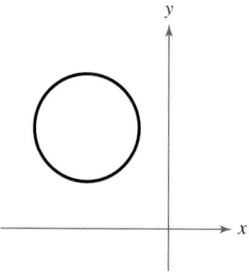

No Intercepts

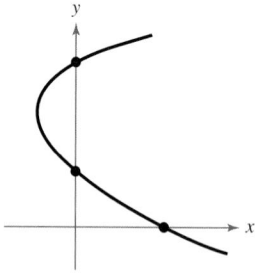

One x-Intercept
Two y-Intercepts

Figure 2.6

As you study this section, you will see the connection between intercepts, zeros, and solutions of functions.

What you should learn

- Find x- and y-intercepts of graphs of equations.
- Find solutions of equations graphically.
- Find the points of intersection of two graphs.

Why you should learn it

Because some real-life problems involve equations that are difficult to solve algebraically, it is helpful to use a graphing utility to approximate the solutions of such equations. For instance, you can use a graphing utility to find the intersection point of the equations in Example 7 on page 178 to determine the year during which the number of morning newspapers in the United States exceeded the number of evening newspapers.

Simon Bottomley/Getty Images

Example 1   Finding *x*- and *y*-Intercepts

Find the *x*- and *y*-intercepts of the graph of $2x + 3y = 5$.

Solution

To find the *x*-intercept, let $y = 0$ and solve for *x*. This produces

$$2x = 5 \implies x = \tfrac{5}{2}$$

which implies that the graph has one *x*-intercept: $\left(\tfrac{5}{2}, 0\right)$. To find the *y*-intercept, let $x = 0$ and solve for *y*. This produces

$$3y = 5 \implies y = \tfrac{5}{3}$$

which implies that the graph has one *y*-intercept: $\left(0, \tfrac{5}{3}\right)$. See Figure 2.7.

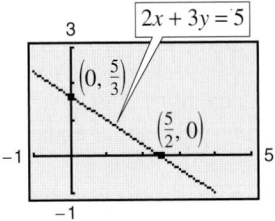

Figure 2.7

✓ *Checkpoint*   Now try Exercise 1.

A **zero** of a function $y = f(x)$ is a number *a* such that $f(a) = 0$. So, to find the zeros of a function, you must solve the equation $f(x) = 0$.

The concepts of *x*-intercepts, zeros of functions, and solutions of equations are closely related. In fact, the following statements are equivalent.

1. The point $(a, 0)$ is an *x-intercept* of the graph of $y = f(x)$.
2. The number *a* is a *zero* of the function *f*.
3. The number *a* is a *solution* of the equation $f(x) = 0$.

Example 2   Verifying Zeros of Functions

Verify that the real numbers -2 and 3 are zeros of the function $f(x) = x^2 - x - 6$.

Algebraic Solution

To verify that -2 is a zero of *f*, check that $f(-2) = 0$.

$f(x) = x^2 - x - 6$ Write original function.

$f(-2) = (-2)^2 - (-2) - 6$ Substitute -2 for *x*.

$ = 4 + 2 - 6 = 0$ -2 is a solution. ✓

To verify that 3 is a zero of *f*, check that $f(3) = 0$.

$f(x) = x^2 - x - 6$ Write original function.

$f(3) = (3)^2 - (3) - 6$ Substitute 3 for *x*.

$ = 9 - 3 - 6 = 0$ 3 is a solution. ✓

✓ *Checkpoint*   Now try Exercise 15.

Graphical Solution

Use a graphing utility to graph $y = x^2 - x - 6$. From the graph in Figure 2.8, it appears that the function has *x*-intercepts (where *y* is zero) at $x = -2$ and at $x = 3$. Use the *zero* or *root* feature to confirm this. So, you can approximate the zeros of the function to be -2 and 3.

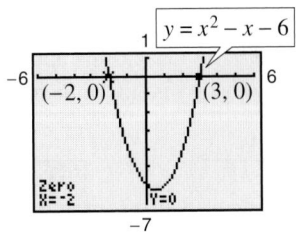

Figure 2.8

Note that the graph of $y = x^2 - x - 6$ in Figure 2.8 has *x*-intercepts of $(3, 0)$ and $(-2, 0)$ because the equation $0 = x^2 - x - 6$ has the *solutions* $x = 3$ and $x = -2$.

The close connection among x-intercepts, zeros, and solutions is crucial to your study of algebra. You can take advantage of this connection in two ways. Use your algebraic "equation-solving skills" to find the x-intercepts of a graph and your "graphing skills" to approximate the solutions of an equation.

Finding Solutions Graphically

Polynomial equations of degree 1 or 2 can be solved in relatively straightforward ways. Solving polynomial equations of a higher degree can, however, be quite difficult, especially if you rely only on algebraic techniques. For such equations, a graphing utility can be very helpful.

> **Graphical Approximations of Solutions of an Equation**
>
> 1. Write the equation in *general form*, $f(x) = 0$, with the nonzero terms on one side of the equation and zero on the other side.
>
> 2. Use a graphing utility to graph the function $y = f(x)$. Be sure the viewing window shows all the relevant features of the graph.
>
> 3. Use the *zero* or *root* feature or the *zoom* and *trace* features of the graphing utility to approximate the x-intercepts of the graph of f.

In Chapter 3 you will learn techniques for determining the number of solutions of a polynomial equation. For now, you should know that a polynomial equation of degree n cannot have more than n different solutions.

Example 3 Finding Solutions of an Equation Graphically

Use a graphing utility to approximate the solutions of $2x^3 - 3x + 2 = 0$.

Solution

Graph the function $y = 2x^3 - 3x + 2$. You can see from the graph that there is one x-intercept. It lies between -2 and -1 and is approximately -1.5. By using the *zero* or *root* feature of a graphing utility, you can improve the approximation. Choose a left bound of $x = -2$ (see Figure 2.9) and a right bound of $x = -1$ (see Figure 2.10). To three-decimal-place accuracy, the solution is $x \approx -1.476$, as shown in Figure 2.11. Check this approximation on your calculator. You will find that the value of y is $y = 2(-1.476)^3 - 3(-1.476) + 2 \approx -0.003$.

Exploration

In Chapter 3 you will learn that a cubic equation such as

$$24x^3 - 36x + 17 = 0$$

can have up to three real solutions. Use a graphing utility to graph

$$y = 24x^3 - 36x + 17.$$

Describe a viewing window that enables you to determine the number of real solutions of the equation

$$24x^3 - 36x + 17 = 0.$$

Use the same technique to determine the number of real solutions of

$$97x^3 - 102x^2 - 200x - 63 = 0.$$

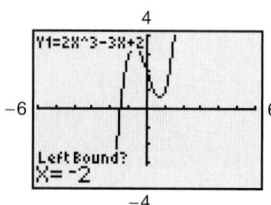

Figure 2.9

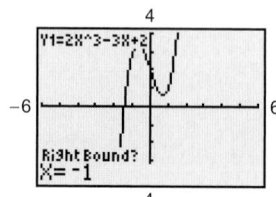

Figure 2.10

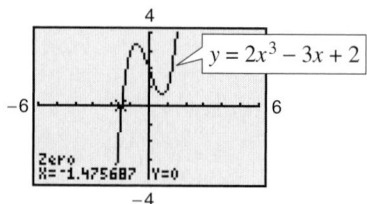

Figure 2.11

✓ *Checkpoint* Now try Exercise 39.

TECHNOLOGY TIP   You can also use a graphing calculator's *zoom* and *trace* features to approximate the solution of an equation. Here are some suggestions for using the *zoom-in* feature of a graphing utility.

1. With each successive zoom-in, adjust the *x*-scale (if necessary) so that the resulting viewing window shows at least the two scale marks between which the solution lies.

2. The accuracy of the approximation will always be such that the error is less than the distance between two scale marks.

3. If you have a *trace* feature on your graphing utility, you can generally add one more decimal place of accuracy without changing the viewing window.

Unless stated otherwise, this book will approximate all real solutions with an error of *at most* 0.01.

Example 4   Approximating Solutions of an Equation Graphically

Use a graphing utility to approximate the solutions of $x^2 + 3 = 5x$.

Solution

In general form, this equation is

$$x^2 - 5x + 3 = 0. \qquad \text{Equation in general form}$$

So, you can begin by graphing

$$y = x^2 - 5x + 3 \qquad \text{Function to be graphed}$$

as shown in Figure 2.12. This graph has two *x*-intercepts, and by using the *zoom* and *trace* features you can approximate the corresponding solutions to be $x \approx 0.70$ and $x \approx 4.30$, as shown in Figures 2.13 and 2.14.

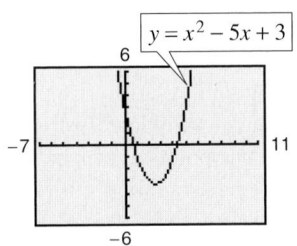

Figure 2.12

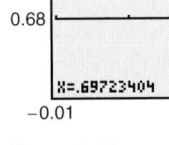

Figure 2.13

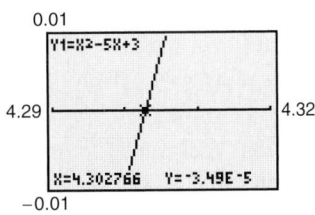

Figure 2.14

✅ *Checkpoint* Now try Exercise 43.

TECHNOLOGY TIP   Remember from Example 3 that the built-in *zero* or *root* features of a graphing utility will approximate solutions of equations or *x*-intercepts of graphs. If your graphing utility has such features, try using them to approximate the solutions in Example 4.

TECHNOLOGY SUPPORT

For instructions on how to use the *zoom* and *trace* features, see Appendix A; for specific keystrokes, go to the text website at *college.hmco.com*.

TECHNOLOGY TIP

Remember that the more decimal places in the solution, the more accurate the solution is. You can reach the desired accuracy when zooming in as follows.

• To approximate the zero to the nearest hundredth, set the *x*-scale to 0.01.

• To approximate the zero to the nearest thousandth, set the *x*-scale to 0.001.

Points of Intersection of Two Graphs

An ordered pair that is a solution of two different equations is called a **point of intersection** of the graphs of the two equations. For instance, in Figure 2.15 you can see that the graphs of the following equations have two points of intersection.

$y = x + 2$ Equation 1

$y = x^2 - 2x - 2$ Equation 2

The point $(-1, 1)$ is a solution of both equations, and the point $(4, 6)$ is a solution of both equations. To check this algebraically, substitute $x = -1$ and $x = 4$ into each equation.

> *Check that $(-1, 1)$ is a solution.*
>
> Equation 1: $y = -1 + 2 = 1$ Solution checks. ✓
>
> Equation 2: $y = (-1)^2 - 2(-1) - 2 = 1$ Solution checks. ✓
>
> *Check that $(4, 6)$ is a solution.*
>
> Equation 1: $y = 4 + 2 = 6$ Solution checks. ✓
>
> Equation 2: $y = (4)^2 - 2(4) - 2 = 6$ Solution checks. ✓

To find the points of intersection of the graphs of two equations, solve each equation for y (or x) and set the two results equal to each other. The resulting equation will be an equation in one variable, which can be solved using standard procedures, as shown in Example 5.

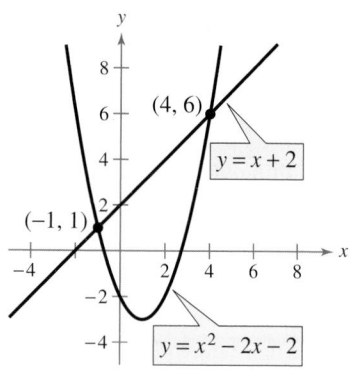

Figure 2.15

Example 5   Finding Points of Intersection

Find the points of intersection of the graphs of $2x - 3y = -2$ and $4x - y = 6$.

Algebraic Solution

To begin, solve each equation for y to obtain

$$y = \frac{2}{3}x + \frac{2}{3} \quad \text{and} \quad y = 4x - 6.$$

Next, set the two expressions for y equal to each other and solve the resulting equation for x, as follows.

$$\frac{2}{3}x + \frac{2}{3} = 4x - 6 \qquad \text{Equate expressions for } y.$$

$$2x + 2 = 12x - 18 \qquad \text{Multiply each side by 3.}$$

$$-10x = -20 \qquad \text{Subtract } 12x \text{ and 2 from each side.}$$

$$x = 2 \qquad \text{Divide each side by } -10.$$

When $x = 2$, the y-value of each of the original equations is 2. So, the point of intersection is $(2, 2)$.

 Checkpoint Now try Exercise 59.

Graphical Solution

To begin, solve each equation for y to obtain $y_1 = \frac{2}{3}x + \frac{2}{3}$ and $y_2 = 4x - 6$. Then use a graphing utility to graph both equations in the same viewing window. In Figure 2.16, the graphs appear to have one point of intersection. Use the *intersect* feature of the graphing utility to approximate the point of intersection to be $(2, 2)$.

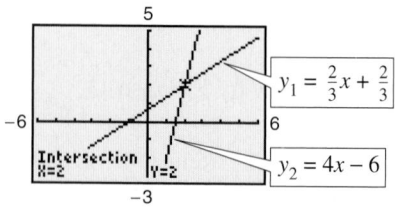

Figure 2.16

TECHNOLOGY TIP   Another way to approximate the points of intersection of two graphs is to graph both equations with a graphing utility and use the *zoom* and *trace* features to find the point or points at which the two graphs intersect.

Example 6   Approximating Points of Intersection Graphically

Approximate the point(s) of intersection of the graphs of the following equations.

$$y = x^2 - 3x - 4 \qquad \text{Equation 1 (quadratic function)}$$

$$y = x^3 + 3x^2 - 2x - 1 \qquad \text{Equation 2 (cubic function)}$$

Solution

Begin by using a graphing utility to graph both functions, as shown in Figure 2.17. From this display, you can see that the two graphs have only one point of intersection. Then, using the *zoom* and *trace* features, approximate the point of intersection to be $(-2.17, 7.25)$, as shown in Figure 2.18.

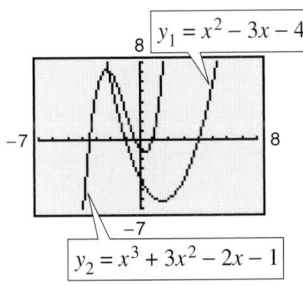

Figure 2.17

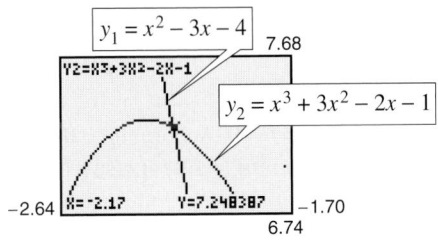

Figure 2.18

To test the reasonableness of this approximation, you can evaluate both functions at $x = -2.17$.

Quadratic Function:

$$y = (-2.17)^2 - 3(-2.17) - 4$$

$$\approx 7.22$$

Cubic Function:

$$y = (-2.17)^3 + 3(-2.17)^2 - 2(-2.17) - 1$$

$$\approx 7.25$$

Because both functions yield approximately the same y-value, you can conclude that the approximate coordinates of the point of intersection are $x \approx -2.17$ and $y \approx 7.25$.

☑ *Checkpoint*   Now try Exercise 63.

TECHNOLOGY TIP   If you choose to use the *intersect* feature of your graphing utility to find the point of intersection of the graphs in Example 6, you will see that it yields the same result.

TECHNOLOGY TIP

The table shows some points on the graphs of the equations in Example 5. Find the points of intersection of the graphs by finding the value(s) of x for which y_1 and y_2 are equal.

X	Y1	Y2
-1	0	-10
0	.66667	-6
1	1.3333	-2
2	2	2
3	2.6667	6
4	3.3333	10
5	4	14

X=2

The method shown in Example 6 gives a nice graphical picture of the points of intersection of two graphs. However, for actual approximation purposes, it is better to use the algebraic procedure described in Example 5. That is, the point of intersection of $y = x^2 - 3x - 4$ and $y = x^3 + 3x^2 - 2x - 1$ coincides with the solution of the equation

$$x^3 + 3x^2 - 2x - 1 = x^2 - 3x - 4 \qquad \text{Equate } y\text{-values.}$$

$$x^3 + 2x^2 + x + 3 = 0. \qquad \text{Write in general form.}$$

By graphing $y = x^3 + 2x^2 + x + 3$ on a graphing utility and using the *zoom* and *trace* features (or the *zero* or *root* feature), you can approximate the solution of this equation to be $x \approx -2.17$. The corresponding y-value for *both* of the functions given in Example 6 is $y \approx 7.25$.

Example 7   A Historical Look at Newspapers

Between 1990 and 2001, the number of morning newspapers in the United States was *increasing* and the number of evening newspapers was *decreasing*. Two models that approximate the numbers of newspapers are

$$M = 20.5t + 557, \quad 0 \le t \le 11 \qquad \text{Morning newspapers}$$

$$E = -34.4t + 1070, \quad 0 \le t \le 11 \qquad \text{Evening newspapers}$$

where t represents the year, with $t = 0$ corresponding to 1990. According to these two models, when would you expect the number of morning newspapers to have exceeded the number of evening newspapers?   (Source: Editor & Publisher Co.)

Algebraic Solution

Set the two expressions equal to each other and solve the resulting equation for t, as follows.

$$20.5t + 557 = -34.4t + 1070 \qquad \text{Equate expressions.}$$

$$54.9t + 557 = 1070 \qquad \text{Add } 34.4t \text{ to each side.}$$

$$54.9t = 513 \qquad \text{Subtract 557 from each side.}$$

$$t = \frac{513}{54.9} \qquad \text{Divide each side by 54.9.}$$

$$t \approx 9.34 \qquad \text{Use a calculator.}$$

So, from the given models, you would expect that the number of morning newspapers exceeded the number of evening newspapers sometime during 1999.

✓ *Checkpoint* Now try Exercise 76.

Graphical Solution

Use a graphing utility to graph both equations in the same viewing window. From Figure 2.19, the graphs appear to have one point of intersection. Use the *intersect* feature of the graphing utility to approximate the point of intersection to be (9.34, 748.56). So, you would expect that the number of morning newspapers exceeded the number of evening newspapers sometime during 1999.

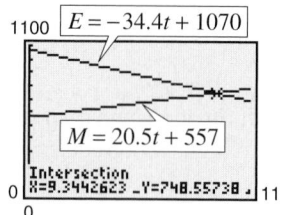

Figure 2.19

TECHNOLOGY TIP   If you choose to use the *zoom* and *trace* features of your graphing utility to find the point of intersection of the graphs in Example 7, you will see that these features yield the same result.

2.2   Exercises

Vocabulary Check

Fill in the blanks.

1. The points $(a, 0)$ and $(0, b)$ are called the _____ and _____ , respectively, of the graph of an equation.

2. A _____ of a function is a number a such that $f(a) = 0$.

3. An ordered pair that is a solution of two different equations is called a _____ of the graphs of the two equations.

In Exercises 1–12, find the x- and y-intercepts of the graph of the equation.

1. $y = x - 5$

2. $y = -\frac{3}{4}x - 3$

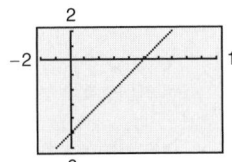 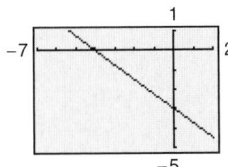

3. $y = x^2 + x - 2$

4. $y = 4 - x^2$

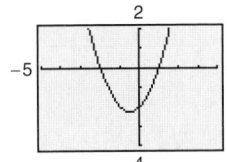 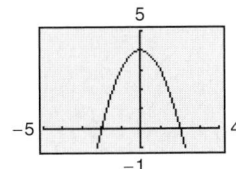

5. $y = x\sqrt{x + 2}$

6. $y = -\frac{1}{2}x\sqrt{x + 3} + 1$

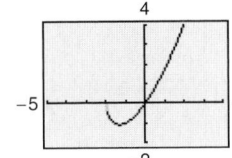 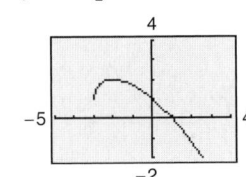

7. $xy = 4$

8. $4xy = 3x - 1$

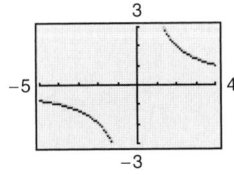 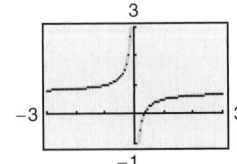

9. $y = |x - 2| - 4$

10. $y = 3 - \frac{1}{2}|x + 1|$

11. $xy - 2y - x + 1 = 0$

12. $x^2y - x^2 + 4y = 0$

In Exercises 13–18, the zero(s) of the function are given. Verify the zero(s) both algebraically and graphically.

	Function	*Zero(s)*
13.	$f(x) = 5(4 - x)$	$x = 4$
14.	$f(x) = 3(x - 5) + 9$	$x = 2$
15.	$f(x) = x^3 - 6x^2 + 5x$	$x = 0, 5, 1$
16.	$f(x) = x^3 - 9x^2 + 18x$	$x = 0, 3, 6$
17.	$f(x) = \dfrac{x + 2}{3} - \dfrac{x - 1}{5} - 1$	$x = 1$
18.	$f(x) = x - 3 - \dfrac{10}{x}$	$x = -2, 5$

Graphical Analysis   In Exercises 19–22, use a graphing utility to graph the equation and approximate any x-intercepts. Set $y = 0$ and solve the resulting equation. Compare the results with the x-intercepts of the graph.

19. $y = 2(x - 1) - 4$ 20. $y = 4(x + 3) - 2$

21. $y = 20 - (3x - 10)$ 22. $y = 10 + 2(x - 2)$

In Exercises 23–36, solve the equation algebraically. Then write the equation in the form $f(x) = 0$ and use a graphing utility to verify the algebraic solution.

23. $2.7x - 0.4x = 1.2$ 24. $3.5x - 8 = 0.5x$

25. $25(x - 3) = 12(x + 2) - 10$

26. $1200 = 300 + 2(x - 500)$

27. $\dfrac{3x}{2} + \dfrac{1}{4}(x - 2) = 10$

28. $\dfrac{2x}{3} + \dfrac{1}{2}(x - 5) = 6$

29. $0.60x + 0.40(100 - x) = 1.2$

30. $0.75x + 0.2(80 - x) = 20$

31. $\dfrac{2x}{3} = 10 - \dfrac{24}{x}$

32. $\dfrac{x-3}{25} = \dfrac{x-5}{12}$

33. $\dfrac{3}{x+2} - \dfrac{4}{x-2} = 5$

34. $\dfrac{6}{x} + \dfrac{8}{x+5} = 3$

35. $(x+2)^2 = x^2 - 6x + 1$

36. $(x+1)^2 + 2(x-2) = (x+1)(x-2)$

In Exercises 37–50, use a graphing utility to approximate any solutions (accurate to three decimal places) of the equation. [Remember to write the equation in the form $f(x) = 0$.]

37. $\frac{1}{4}(x^2 - 10x + 17) = 0$

38. $-\frac{1}{2}(x^2 - 6x + 6) = 0$

39. $x^3 + x + 4 = 0$

40. $\frac{1}{9}x^3 + x + 4 = 0$

41. $2x^3 - x^2 - 18x + 9 = 0$

42. $4x^3 + 12x^2 - 26x - 24 = 0$

43. $x^4 = 2x^3 + 1$

44. $x^5 = 3 + 2x^3$

45. $\dfrac{2}{x+2} = 3$

46. $\dfrac{5}{x} = 1 + \dfrac{3}{x+2}$

47. $|x - 3| = 4$

48. $|x + 1| = 6$

49. $\sqrt{x-2} = 3$

50. $\sqrt{x-4} = 8$

51. *Exploration*

(a) Use a graphing utility to complete the table.

x	-1	0	1	2	3	4
$3.2x - 5.8$						

(b) Use the table in part (a) to determine the interval in which the solution to the equation $3.2x - 5.8 = 0$ is located. Explain your reasoning.

(c) Use a graphing utility to complete the table.

x	1.5	1.6	1.7	1.8	1.9	2
$3.2x - 5.8$						

(d) Use the table in part (c) to determine the interval in which the solution to the equation $3.2x - 5.8 = 0$ is located. Explain how this process can be used to approximate the solution to any desired degree of accuracy.

(e) Use a graphing utility to verify graphically the solution to $3.2x - 5.8 = 0$ found in part (d).

52. *Exploration* Use the procedure from Exercise 51 to approximate the solution of the equation $0.3(x - 1.5) - 2 = 0$ accurate to two decimal places.

In Exercises 53–58, determine any point(s) of intersection algebraically. Then verify your result numerically by creating a table of values for each function.

53. $y = 2 - x$
$y = 2x - 1$

54. $y = 7 - x$
$y = \frac{3}{2} - \frac{11}{2}x$

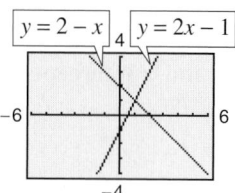

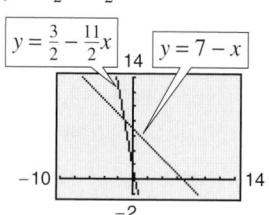

55. $2x + y = 6$
$-x + y = 0$

56. $x - y = -4$
$x + 2y = 5$

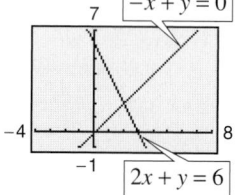

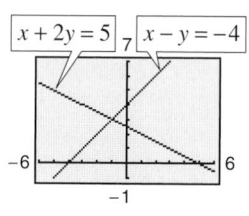

57. $x - y = -4$
$x^2 - y = -2$

58. $3x + y = 2$
$x^3 + y = 0$

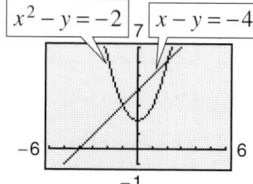

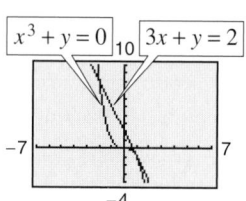

In Exercises 59–64, use a graphing utility to approximate any points of intersection (accurate to three decimal places) of the graphs of the equations. Verify your results algebraically.

59. $y = 9 - 2x$
$y = x - 3$

60. $y = \frac{1}{3}x + 2$
$y = \frac{5}{2}x - 11$

61. $y = 4 - x^2$
$y = 2x - 1$

62. $y = x^3 - 3$
$y = 5 - 2x$

63. $y = 2x^2$
$y = x^4 - 2x^2$

64. $y = -x$
$y = 2x - x^2$

In Exercises 65 and 66, evaluate the expression in two ways. **(a) Calculate entirely on your calculator by storing intermediate results and then rounding the final answer to two decimal places. (b) Round both the numerator and denominator to two decimal places before dividing, and then round the final answer to two decimal places. Does the method in part (b) decrease the accuracy? Explain.**

65. $\dfrac{1 + 0.73205}{1 - 0.73205}$ **66.** $\dfrac{1 + 0.86603}{1 - 0.86603}$

67. *Travel Time* On the first part of a 280-mile trip, a salesperson averaged 63 miles per hour. The salesperson averaged only 54 miles per hour on the last part of the trip because of an increased volume of traffic.

(a) Write the total time t for the trip as a function of the distance x traveled at an average speed of 63 miles per hour.

(b) Use a graphing utility to graph the time function. What is the domain of the function?

(c) Approximate the number of miles traveled at 63 miles per hour when the total time is 4 hours and 45 minutes.

68. *Production* An electronics company has fixed costs of $25,000 per month and a variable cost of $18.65 per 13-inch TV/VCR combination manufactured. (*Fixed costs* are those that occur regardless of the level of production.)

(a) Write the total monthly costs C as a function of the number of units x produced.

(b) Use a graphing utility to graph the cost function.

(c) Use the graph from part (b) to approximate the number of units that can be produced per month if total costs cannot exceed $200,000. Verify algebraically. Is this problem better solved algebraically or graphically? Explain.

69. *Mixture Problem* A 55-gallon barrel contains a mixture with a concentration of 33% sodium chloride. You remove x gallons of this mixture and replace it with 100% sodium chloride.

(a) Write the amount A of sodium chloride in the final mixture as a function of x.

(b) Use a graphing utility to graph the concentration function. What is the domain of the function?

(c) Approximate (accurate to one decimal place) the value of x when the final mixture is 60% sodium chloride.

70. *Geometry* A rectangular horse corral with a perimeter of 230 meters has a length of x.

(a) Draw a diagram that gives a visual representation of the problem.

(b) Write the corral's area A as a function of x.

(c) Use a graphing utility to graph the area function. What is the domain of the function?

(d) Approximate (accurate to one decimal place) the dimensions of the corral when its area is 2000 square meters.

Geometry **In Exercises 71 and 72, (a) write a function for the area of the region, (b) use a graphing utility to graph the function, and (c) approximate the value of x when the area of the region is 200 square units.**

71. 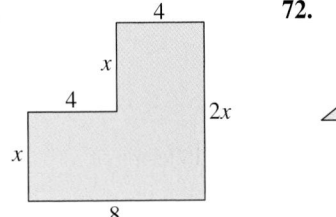   **72.**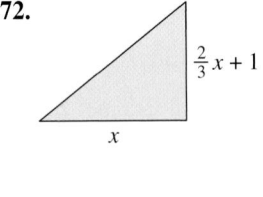

73. *Geometry* Consider the swimming pool in the figure. (When finding its volume, use the fact that the volume is the area of the region on the vertical sidewall times the width of the pool.)

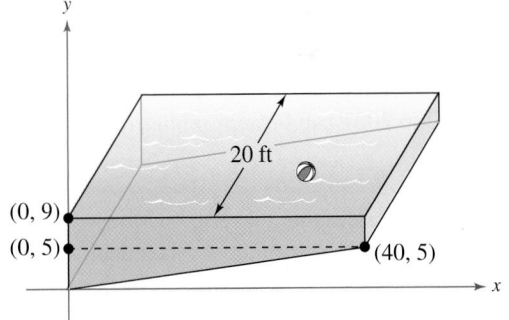

(a) Find the volume of the pool.

(b) Find an equation of the line representing the base of the pool.

(c) The depth of the water at the deep end of the pool is d feet. Show that the volume of water is

$$V(d) = \begin{cases} 80d^2, & 0 \le d \le 5 \\ 800d - 2000, & 5 < d \le 9 \end{cases}.$$

(d) Graph the volume function.

(e) Use a graphing utility to complete the table.

d	3	5	7	9
V				

(f) Approximate the depth of the water at the deep end when the volume is 4800 cubic feet.

(g) How many gallons of water are in the pool? (There are 7.48 gallons of water in 1 cubic foot.)

74. *Income Tax* The following information describes a possible negative income tax for a family consisting of two adults and two children. The plan would guarantee the poor a minimum income while encouraging a family to increase its private income ($0 \leq x \leq 20,000$). (A *subsidy* is a grant of money.)

Family's earned income: $I = x$

Subsidy: $S = 10,000 - \frac{1}{2}x$

Total income: $T = I + S$

(a) Write the total income T in terms of x.

(b) Use a graphing utility to find the earned income x when the subsidy is $6600. Verify your answer algebraically.

(c) Use a graphing utility to find the earned income x when the total income is $13,800. Verify your answer algebraically.

(d) Find the subsidy S graphically when the total income is $12,500.

75. *Labor Force* The number y (in millions) of women in the civilian labor force in the United States from 1990 to 2001 can be approximated by the model

$$y = 0.91t + 56.4, \quad 0 \leq t \leq 11$$

where t represents the year, with $t = 0$ corresponding to 1990. According to this model, during which year did the number of women in the civilian labor force reach 60 million? Explain how to answer the question graphically and algebraically. (Source: U.S. Bureau of Labor Statistics)

76. *Population* The population (in thousands) of Arizona A, and Minnesota M, from 1995 to 2001 can be modeled by

$$A = 142.9t + 3729, \quad 5 \leq t \leq 11$$

$$M = 52.1t + 4400, \quad 5 \leq t \leq 11$$

where t represents the year, with $t = 5$ corresponding to 1995. (Source: U.S. Census Bureau)

(a) Use a graphing utility to graph each model in the same viewing window over the appropriate domain. Approximate the point of intersection.

(b) Find the point of intersection algebraically. What does the point of intersection represent?

(c) Use the models to estimate the population of each state in 2006.

Synthesis

True or False? **In Exercises 77–79, determine whether the statement is true or false. Justify your answer.**

77. To find the y-intercept of a graph, let $x = 0$ and solve the equation for y.

78. Every linear equation has at least one y-intercept or x-intercept.

79. Two linear equations can have either one point of intersection or no points of intersection.

80. *Writing* You are solving the equation

$$\frac{x}{x-1} - \frac{99}{100} = 0$$

for x, and you obtain $x = -99.1$ as your solution. Substituting this value back into the equation produces

$$\frac{-99.1}{-99.1 - 1} - \frac{99}{100} = 0.00000999$$

$$= 9.99 \times 10^{-6} \approx 0.$$

Does this mean that -99.1 is a good approximation of the solution? Write a short paragraph explaining why or why not.

Review

In Exercises 81–84, rationalize the denominator.

81. $\dfrac{12}{5\sqrt{3}}$

82. $\dfrac{4}{\sqrt{10} - 2}$

83. $\dfrac{3}{8 + \sqrt{11}}$

84. $\dfrac{14}{3\sqrt{10} - 1}$

In Exercises 85–88, find the product.

85. $(x + 6)(3x - 5)$

86. $(3x + 13)(4x - 7)$

87. $(2x - 9)(2x + 9)$

88. $(4x + 1)^2$

2.3   Complex Numbers

The Imaginary Unit *i*

What you should learn

- Use the imaginary unit *i* to write complex numbers.
- Add, subtract, and multiply complex numbers.
- Use complex conjugates to write the quotient of two complex numbers in standard form.
- Plot complex numbers in the complex plane.

Why you should learn it

Complex numbers are used to model numerous aspects of the natural world, such as the impedance of an electrical circuit, as shown in Exercises 77 and 78 on page 190.

Some quadratic equations have no real solutions. For instance, the quadratic equation $x^2 + 1 = 0$ has no real solution because there is no real number x that can be squared to produce -1. To overcome this deficiency, mathematicians created an expanded system of numbers using the **imaginary unit *i*,** defined as

$$i = \sqrt{-1} \qquad \text{Imaginary unit}$$

where $i^2 = -1$. By adding real numbers to real multiples of this imaginary unit, you obtain the set of **complex numbers.** Each complex number can be written in the **standard form $a + bi$.** For instance, the standard form of the complex number $\sqrt{-9} - 5$ is $-5 + 3i$ because

$$\sqrt{-9} - 5 = \sqrt{3^2(-1)} - 5 = 3\sqrt{-1} - 5 = 3i - 5 = -5 + 3i.$$

In the standard form $a + bi$, the real number a is called the **real part** of the **complex number $a + bi$,** and the number bi (where b is a real number) is called the **imaginary part** of the complex number.

> **Definition of a Complex Number**
>
> If a and b are real numbers, the number $a + bi$ is a **complex number,** and it is said to be written in **standard form.** If $b = 0$, the number $a + bi = a$ is a real number. If $b \neq 0$, the number $a + bi$ is called an **imaginary number.** A number of the form bi, where $b \neq 0$, is called a **pure imaginary number.**

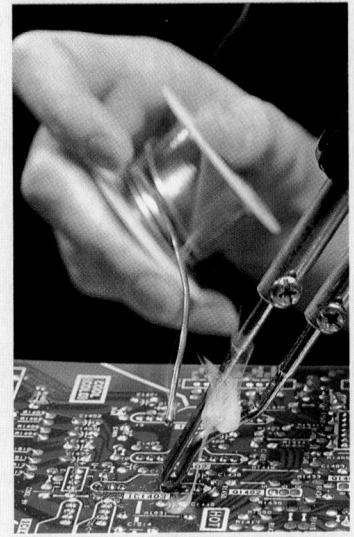

Phil Degginger/Getty Images

The set of real numbers is a subset of the set of complex numbers, as shown in Figure 2.20. This is true because every real number a can be written as a complex number using $b = 0$. That is, for every real number a, you can write $a = a + 0i$.

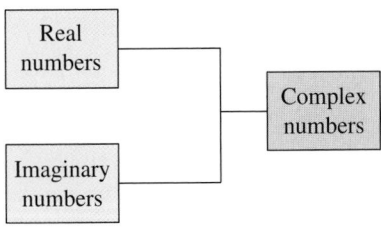

Figure 2.20

> **Equality of Complex Numbers**
>
> Two complex numbers $a + bi$ and $c + di$, written in standard form, are equal to each other
>
> $$a + bi = c + di \qquad \text{Equality of two complex numbers}$$
>
> if and only if $a = c$ and $b = d$.

Operations with Complex Numbers

To add (or subtract) two complex numbers, you add (or subtract) the real and imaginary parts of the numbers separately.

Addition and Subtraction of Complex Numbers

If $a + bi$ and $c + di$ are two complex numbers written in standard form, their sum and difference are defined as follows.

Sum: $(a + bi) + (c + di) = (a + c) + (b + d)i$

Difference: $(a + bi) - (c + di) = (a - c) + (b - d)i$

The **additive identity** in the complex number system is zero (the same as in the real number system). Furthermore, the **additive inverse** of the complex number $a + bi$ is

$-(a + bi) = -a - bi.$ Additive inverse

So, you have $(a + bi) + (-a - bi) = 0 + 0i = 0.$

Example 1   Adding and Subtracting Complex Numbers

a. $(3 - i) + (2 + 3i) = 3 - i + 2 + 3i$ Remove parentheses.

$\qquad\qquad\qquad = 3 + 2 - i + 3i$ Group like terms.

$\qquad\qquad\qquad = (3 + 2) + (-1 + 3)i$

$\qquad\qquad\qquad = 5 + 2i$ Write in standard form.

b. $2i + (-4 - 2i) = 2i - 4 - 2i$ Remove parentheses.

$\qquad\qquad\qquad = -4 + 2i - 2i$ Group like terms.

$\qquad\qquad\qquad = -4$ Write in standard form.

c. $3 - (-2 + 3i) + (-5 + i) = 3 + 2 - 3i - 5 + i$

$\qquad\qquad\qquad\qquad = 3 + 2 - 5 - 3i + i$

$\qquad\qquad\qquad\qquad = 0 - 2i$

$\qquad\qquad\qquad\qquad = -2i$

d. $(3 + 2i) + (4 - i) - (7 + i) = 3 + 2i + 4 - i - 7 - i$

$\qquad\qquad\qquad\qquad = 3 + 4 - 7 + 2i - i - i$

$\qquad\qquad\qquad\qquad = 0 + 0i$

$\qquad\qquad\qquad\qquad = 0$

✓ *Checkpoint* Now try Exercise 19.

In Examples 1(b) and 1(d), note that the sum of complex numbers can be a real number.

Many of the properties of real numbers are valid for complex numbers as well. Here are some examples.

Associative Property of Addition and Multiplication
Commutative Property of Addition and Multiplication
Distributive Property of Multiplication over Addition

Notice how these properties are used when two complex numbers are multiplied.

$$(a + bi)(c + di) = a(c + di) + bi(c + di) \qquad \text{Distributive Property}$$

$$= ac + (ad)i + (bc)i + (bd)i^2 \qquad \text{Distributive Property}$$

$$= ac + (ad)i + (bc)i + (bd)(-1) \qquad i^2 = -1$$

$$= ac - bd + (ad)i + (bc)i \qquad \text{Commutative Property}$$

$$= (ac - bd) + (ad + bc)i \qquad \text{Associative Property}$$

The procedure above is similar to multiplying two polynomials and combining like terms, as in the FOIL method shown in Section P.3.

> ### Exploration
>
> Complete the following:
>
> | | |
> |---|---|
> | $i^1 = i$ | $i^7 =$ |
> | $i^2 = -1$ | $i^8 =$ |
> | $i^3 = -i$ | $i^9 =$ |
> | $i^4 = 1$ | $i^{10} =$ |
> | $i^5 =$ | $i^{11} =$ |
> | $i^6 =$ | $i^{12} =$ |
>
> What pattern do you see? Write a brief description of how you would find i raised to any positive integer power.

Example 2 Multiplying Complex Numbers

a. $\sqrt{-4} \cdot \sqrt{-16} = (2i)(4i)$ Write each factor in i-form.

$= 8i^2$ Multiply.

$= 8(-1)$ $i^2 = -1$

$= -8$ Simplify.

b. $(2 - i)(4 + 3i) = 8 + 6i - 4i - 3i^2$ Product of binomials

$= 8 + 6i - 4i - 3(-1)$ $i^2 = -1$

$= 8 + 3 + 6i - 4i$ Group like terms.

$= 11 + 2i$ Write in standard form.

c. $(3 + 2i)(3 - 2i) = 9 - 6i + 6i - 4i^2$ Product of binomials

$= 9 - 4(-1)$ $i^2 = -1$

$= 9 + 4$ Simplify.

$= 13$ Write in standard form.

d. $4i(-1 + 5i) = 4i(-1) + 4i(5i)$ Distributive Property

$= -4i + 20i^2$ Simplify.

$= -4i + 20(-1)$ $i^2 = -1$

$= -20 - 4i$ Write in standard form.

e. $(3 + 2i)^2 = 9 + 6i + 6i + 4i^2$ Product of binomials

$= 9 + 12i + 4(-1)$ $i^2 = -1$

$= 9 - 4 + 12i$ Group like terms.

$= 5 + 12i$ Write in standard form.

> ### STUDY TIP
>
> Before you perform operations with complex numbers, be sure to rewrite the terms or factors in i-form first and then procede with the operations, as shown in Example 2(a).

✓ *Checkpoint* Now try Exercise 29.

Complex Conjugates

Notice in Example 2(c) that the product of two complex numbers can be a real number. This occurs with pairs of complex numbers of the forms $a + bi$ and $a - bi$, called **complex conjugates.**

$$(a + bi)(a - bi) = a^2 - abi + abi - b^2i^2 = a^2 - b^2(-1) = a^2 + b^2$$

Example 3 Multiplying Conjugates

Multiply $3 - 5i$ by its complex conjugate.

Solution

The complex conjugate of $3 - 5i$ is $3 + 5i$.

$$(3 - 5i)(3 + 5i) = 3^2 - (5i)^2 = 9 - 25i^2 = 9 - 25(-1) = 34$$

✓ *Checkpoint* Now try Exercise 37.

To write the quotient of $a + bi$ and $c + di$ in standard form, where c and d are not both zero, multiply the numerator and denominator by the complex conjugate of the *denominator* to obtain

$$\frac{a + bi}{c + di} = \frac{a + bi}{c + di}\left(\frac{c - di}{c - di}\right)$$
Multiply numerator and denominator by complex conjugate of denominator.

$$= \frac{(ac + bd) + (bc - ad)i}{c^2 + d^2}.$$
Standard form

Example 4 Writing a Quotient of Complex Numbers in Standard Form

Write the quotient $\dfrac{2 + 3i}{4 - 2i}$ in standard form.

Solution

$$\frac{2 + 3i}{4 - 2i} = \frac{2 + 3i}{4 - 2i}\left(\frac{4 + 2i}{4 + 2i}\right)$$
Multiply numerator and denominator by complex conjugate of denominator.

$$= \frac{8 + 4i + 12i + 6i^2}{16 - 4i^2}$$
Expand.

$$= \frac{8 - 6 + 16i}{16 + 4}$$
$i^2 = -1$

$$= \frac{2 + 16i}{20}$$
Simplify.

$$= \frac{1}{10} + \frac{4}{5}i$$
Write in standard form.

✓ *Checkpoint* Now try Exercise 49.

TECHNOLOGY TIP

Some graphing utilities can perform operations with complex numbers. For instance, on some graphing utilities, to divide $2 + 3i$ by $4 - 2i$, use the following keystrokes.

(2 + 3 *i*) ÷

(4 − 2 *i*) ENTER

The display will be as follows.

$$.1 + .8i \quad \text{or} \quad \frac{1}{10} + \frac{4}{5}i$$

Fractals and the Mandelbrot Set

Most applications involving complex numbers are either theoretical or very technical, and are therefore not appropriate for inclusion in this text. However, to give you some idea of how complex numbers can be used in applications, a general description of their use in **fractal geometry** is presented.

To begin, consider a coordinate system called the **complex plane.** Just as every real number corresponds to a point on the real number line, every complex number corresponds to a point in the complex plane, as shown in Figure 2.21. In this figure, note that the vertical axis is called the **imaginary axis** and the horizontal axis is called the **real axis.** The point that corresponds to the complex number $a + bi$ is (a, b).

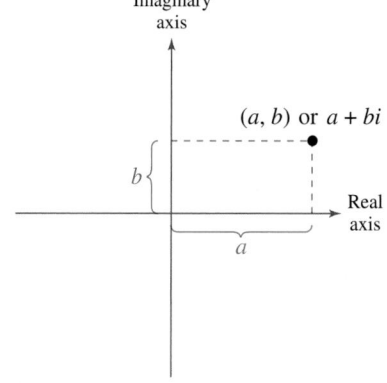

Figure 2.21

Example 5   Plotting Complex Numbers

Plot each complex number in the complex plane.

a. $2 + 3i$ **b.** $-1 + 2i$ **c.** 4 **d.** $-3i$

Solution

a. To plot the complex number $2 + 3i$, move (from the origin) two units to the right on the real axis and then three units upward, as shown in Figure 2.22. In other words, plotting the complex number $2 + 3i$ in the complex plane is comparable to plotting the point $(2, 3)$ in the Cartesian plane. (Note that in Figure 2.22, i is called the imaginary unit because it is located one unit from the origin on the imaginary axis of the complex plane.)

b. The complex number $-1 + 2i$ corresponds to the point $(-1, 2)$, as shown in Figure 2.22.

c. The complex number 4 corresponds to the point $(4, 0)$, as shown in Figure 2.22.

d. The complex number $-3i$ corresponds to the point $(0, -3)$, as shown in Figure 2.22.

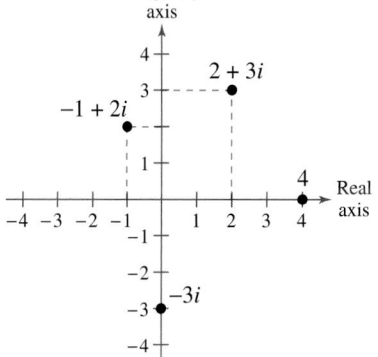

Figure 2.22

✓ *Checkpoint* Now try Exercise 67.

In the hands of a person who understands fractal geometry, the complex plane can become an easel on which stunning pictures, called **fractals,** can be drawn. The most famous such picture is called the **Mandelbrot Set,** named after the Polish-born mathematician Benoit Mandelbrot. To draw the Mandelbrot Set, consider the following sequence of numbers.

$$c, c^2 + c, (c^2 + c)^2 + c, [(c^2 + c)^2 + c]^2 + c, \ldots$$

The behavior of this sequence depends on the value of the complex number c. For some values of c this sequence is **bounded,** which means that the absolute value of each number $\left(|a + bi| = \sqrt{a^2 + b^2}\right)$ in the sequence is less than some fixed number N. For other values of c, the sequence is **unbounded,** which means that the absolute values of the terms of the sequence become infinitely large. If the sequence is bounded, the complex number c is in the Mandelbrot Set; if the sequence is unbounded, the complex number c is not in the Mandelbrot Set.

Example 6   Members of the Mandelbrot Set

a. The complex number -2 is in the Mandelbrot Set because for $c = -2$, the corresponding Mandelbrot sequence is $-2, 2, 2, 2, 2, 2, \ldots$, which is bounded.

b. The complex number i is also in the Mandelbrot Set because for $c = i$, the corresponding Mandelbrot sequence is

$$i, \quad -1 + i, \quad -i, \quad -1 + i, \quad -i, \quad -1 + i, \quad \ldots$$

which is bounded.

c. The complex number $1 + i$ is not in the Mandelbrot Set because for $c = 1 + i$, the corresponding Mandelbrot sequence is

$$1 + i, \quad 1 + 3i, \quad -7 + 7i, \quad 1 - 97i, \quad -9407 - 193i,$$

$$88{,}454{,}401 + 3{,}631{,}103i, \quad \ldots$$

which is unbounded.

✓ *Checkpoint* Now try Exercise 73.

With this definition, a picture of the Mandelbrot Set would have only two colors: one color for points that are in the set (the sequence is bounded), and one for points that are outside the set (the sequence is unbounded). Figure 2.23 shows a black and yellow picture of the Mandelbrot Set. The points that are black are in the Mandelbrot Set and the points that are yellow are not.

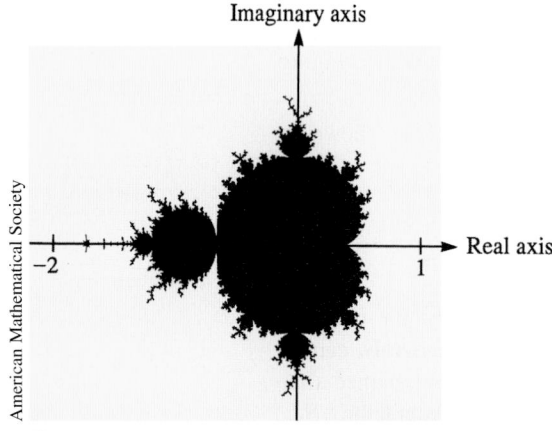

Figure 2.23

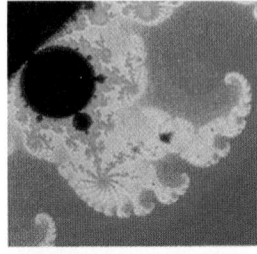

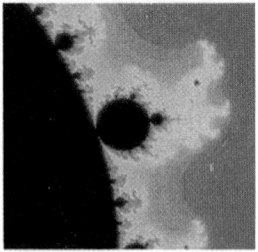

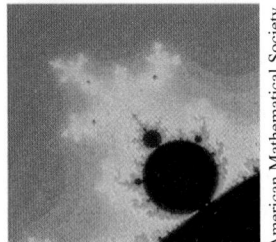

Figure 2.24

To add more interest to the picture, computer scientists discovered that the points that are not in the Mandelbrot Set can be assigned a variety of colors, depending on "how quickly" their sequences diverge (become infinitely large). Figure 2.24 shows three different appendages of the Mandelbrot Set. (The black portions of the picture represent points that are in the Mandelbrot Set.)

Figure 2.25 shows another type of fractal. From this picture, you can see why fractals have fascinated people since their discovery (around 1980). The fractal shown was produced on a graphing calculator. The problem for creating the fractal fern is available on the website *college.hmco.com.*

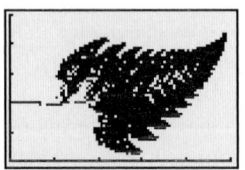

Figure 2.25   A Fractal Fern

2.3   Exercises

Vocabulary Check

1. Match the type of complex number with its definition.

   (a) real number   (i) $a + bi, a = 0, b \neq 0$

   (b) imaginary number   (ii) $a + bi, b = 0$

   (c) pure imaginary number   (iii) $a + bi, a \neq 0, b \neq 0$

In Exercises 2–5, fill in the blanks.

2. The imaginary unit i is defined as $i = $ _____ , where $i^2 = $ _____ .

3. The set of real multiples of the imaginary unit i combined with the set of real numbers is called the set of _____ numbers, which are written in the standard form _____ .

4. Complex numbers can be plotted in the complex plane, where the horizontal axis is the _____ axis and the vertical axis is the _____ axis.

5. The most famous fractal is called the _____ .

In Exercises 1–4, find real numbers a and b such that the equation is true.

1. $a + bi = -9 + 4i$
2. $a + bi = 12 + 5i$
3. $(a - 1) + (b + 3)i = 5 + 8i$
4. $(a + 6) + 2bi = 6 - 5i$

In Exercises 5–14, write the complex number in standard form.

5. $4 + \sqrt{-25}$ 6. $3 + \sqrt{-9}$
7. 7 8. 42
9. $-5i + i^2$ 10. $-3i^2 + i$
11. $\left(\sqrt{-75}\right)^2$ 12. $\left(\sqrt{-4}\right)^2 - 7$
13. $\sqrt{-0.09}$ 14. $\sqrt{-0.0004}$

In Exercises 15–24, perform the addition or subtraction and write the result in standard form.

15. $(4 + i) + (7 - 2i)$ 16. $(11 - 2i) + (-3 + 6i)$
17. $\left(-1 + \sqrt{-8}\right) + \left(8 - \sqrt{-50}\right)$
18. $\left(7 + \sqrt{-18}\right) - \left(3 + 3\sqrt{2}i\right)$
19. $13i - (14 - 7i)$ 20. $22 + (-5 + 8i) + 10i$
21. $\left(\frac{3}{2} + \frac{5}{2}i\right) + \left(\frac{5}{3} + \frac{11}{3}i\right)$ 22. $-\left(\frac{3}{4} + \frac{7}{5}i\right) - \left(\frac{5}{6} - \frac{1}{6}i\right)$
23. $(1.6 + 3.2i) + (-5.8 + 4.3i)$
24. $-(-3.7 - 12.8i) - \left(6.1 - \sqrt{-24.5}\right)$

In Exercises 25–36, perform the operation and write the result in standard form.

25. $\sqrt{-6} \cdot \sqrt{-2}$ 26. $\sqrt{-5} \cdot \sqrt{-10}$
27. $\left(\sqrt{-10}\right)^2$ 28. $\left(\sqrt{-75}\right)^2$
29. $(1 + i)(3 - 2i)$ 30. $(6 - 2i)(2 - 3i)$
31. $4i(8 + 5i)$ 32. $-3i(6 - i)$
33. $\left(\sqrt{14} + \sqrt{10}i\right)\left(\sqrt{14} - \sqrt{10}i\right)$
34. $\left(3 + \sqrt{-5}\right)\left(7 - \sqrt{-10}\right)$
35. $(4 + 5i)^2 - (4 - 5i)^2$ 36. $(1 - 2i)^2 - (1 + 2i)^2$

In Exercises 37–44, write the complex conjugate of the complex number. Then multiply the number by its complex conjugate.

37. $4 + 3i$ 38. $7 - 5i$
39. $-6 - \sqrt{5}i$ 40. $-3 + \sqrt{2}i$
41. $\sqrt{-20}$ 42. $\sqrt{-13}$
43. $3 - \sqrt{-2}$ 44. $1 + \sqrt{-8}$

In Exercises 45–52, write the quotient in standard form.

45. $\dfrac{6}{i}$ 46. $-\dfrac{5}{2i}$

47. $\dfrac{2}{4 - 5i}$ 48. $\dfrac{3}{1 - i}$

49. $\dfrac{2+i}{2-i}$

50. $\dfrac{8-7i}{1-2i}$

51. $\dfrac{i}{(4-5i)^2}$

52. $\dfrac{5i}{(2+3i)^2}$

In Exercises 53–56, perform the operation and write the result in standard form.

53. $\dfrac{2}{1+i}-\dfrac{3}{1-i}$

54. $\dfrac{2i}{2+i}+\dfrac{5}{2-i}$

55. $\dfrac{i}{3-2i}+\dfrac{2i}{3+8i}$

56. $\dfrac{1+i}{i}-\dfrac{3}{4-i}$

In Exercises 57–62, simplify the complex number and write it in standard form.

57. $-6i^3+i^2$

58. $4i^2-2i^3$

59. $\left(\sqrt{-75}\right)^3$

60. $\left(\sqrt{-2}\right)^6$

61. $\dfrac{1}{i^3}$

62. $\dfrac{1}{(2i)^3}$

63. Cube each complex number. What do you notice?

  (a) 2 (b) $-1+\sqrt{3}i$ (c) $-1-\sqrt{3}i$

64. Raise each complex number to the fourth power and simplify.

  (a) 2 (b) -2 (c) $2i$ (d) $-2i$

In Exercises 65 and 66, determine the complex number shown in the complex plane.

65.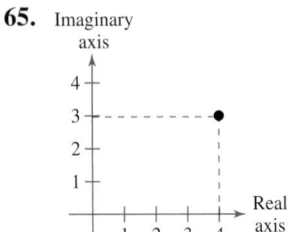

66.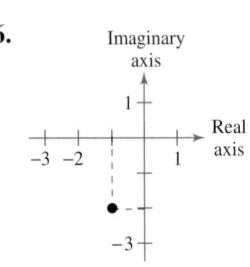

In Exercises 67–72, plot the complex number in the complex plane.

67. $4-5i$

68. $-7+2i$

69. $3i$

70. $-5i$

71. 1

72. -6

Fractals   In Exercises 73–76, find the first six terms of the sequence given on page 187. From the terms, do you think the given complex number is in the Mandelbrot Set? Explain your reasoning.

73. $c=\tfrac{1}{2}i$

74. $c=2$

75. $c=1$

76. $c=-i$

Impedance   In Exercises 77 and 78, use the following information. The opposition to current in an electrical circuit is called its impedance. The impedance z in a parallel circuit with two pathways satisfies the equation $1/z = 1/z_1 + 1/z_2$, where z_1 is the impedance (in ohms) of pathway 1 and z_2 is the impedance (in ohms) of pathway 2. Use the table to determine the impedance of the parallel circuit. (*Hint:* You can find the impedance of each pathway in a parallel circuit by adding the impedances of all components in the pathway.)

	Resistor	Inductor	Capacitor
	─⌇⌇⌇─	─⟋⟋⟋⟋⟋⟋─	─┤├─
Symbol	$a\ \Omega$	$b\ \Omega$	$c\ \Omega$
Impedance	a	bi	$-ci$

77.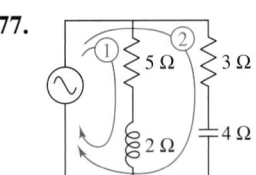

78.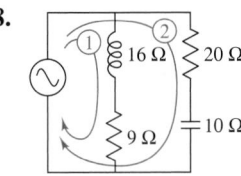

Synthesis

True or False?   In Exercises 79 and 80, determine whether the statement is true or false. Justify your answer.

79. There is no complex number that is equal to its conjugate.

80. $i^{44}+i^{150}-i^{74}-i^{109}+i^{61}=-1$

Review

In Exercises 81–84, perform the operation and write the result in standard form.

81. $(4x-5)(4x+5)$

82. $(x+2)^3$

83. $\left(3x-\tfrac{1}{2}\right)(x+4)$

84. $(2x-5)^2$

2.4 Solving Equations Algebraically

Quadratic Equations

A **quadratic equation in x** is an equation that can be written in the general form

$$ax^2 + bx + c = 0$$

where a, b, and c are real numbers with $a \neq 0$. A quadratic equation in x is also known as a **second-degree polynomial equation in x.** You should be familiar with the following four methods for solving quadratic equations.

Solving a Quadratic Equation

Factoring: If $ab = 0$, then $a = 0$ or $b = 0$.   Zero-Factor Property

Example: $x^2 - x - 6 = 0$

$$(x - 3)(x + 2) = 0$$

$$x - 3 = 0 \implies x = 3$$

$$x + 2 = 0 \implies x = -2$$

Extracting Square Roots: If $u^2 = c$, where $c > 0$, then $u = \pm\sqrt{c}$.

Example: $(x + 3)^2 = 16$

$$x + 3 = \pm 4$$

$$x = -3 \pm 4$$

$$x = 1 \quad \text{or} \quad x = -7$$

Completing the Square: If $x^2 + bx = c$, then

$$x^2 + bx + \left(\frac{b}{2}\right)^2 = c + \left(\frac{b}{2}\right)^2$$

$$\left(x + \frac{b}{2}\right)^2 = c + \frac{b^2}{4}.$$

Example: $x^2 + 6x = 5$

$$x^2 + 6x + 3^2 = 5 + 3^2$$

$$(x + 3)^2 = 14$$

$$x + 3 = \pm\sqrt{14}$$

$$x = -3 \pm \sqrt{14}$$

Quadratic Formula: If $ax^2 + bx + c = 0$, then $x = \dfrac{-b \pm \sqrt{b^2 - 4ac}}{2a}$.

Example: $2x^2 + 3x - 1 = 0$

$$x = \frac{-3 \pm \sqrt{3^2 - 4(2)(-1)}}{2(2)} = \frac{-3 \pm \sqrt{17}}{4}$$

What you should learn

- Solve quadratic equations by factoring, extracting square roots, completing the square, and using the Quadratic Formula.
- Solve polynomial equations of degree three or greater.
- Solve equations involving radicals.
- Solve equations involving fractions or absolute values.
- Use quadratic equations to model and solve real-life problems.

Why you should learn it

Knowing how to solve quadratic and other types of equations algebraically can help you solve real-life problems, such as Exercise 131 on page 208, where you determine the greatest distance a car can travel on a tank of fuel.

Paul Souders/Getty Images

Example 1 Solving a Quadratic Equation by Factoring

Solve each quadratic equation by factoring.

a. $6x^2 = 3x$ **b.** $9x^2 - 6x + 1 = 0$

Solution

a.
$$6x^2 = 3x$$ Write original equation.

$$6x^2 - 3x = 0$$ Write in general form.

$$3x(2x - 1) = 0$$ Factor.

$$3x = 0 \implies x = 0$$ Set 1st factor equal to 0.

$$2x - 1 = 0 \implies x = \tfrac{1}{2}$$ Set 2nd factor equal to 0.

b. $9x^2 - 6x + 1 = 0$ Write original equation.

$$(3x - 1)^2 = 0$$ Factor.

$$3x - 1 = 0 \implies x = \tfrac{1}{3}$$ Set repeated factor equal to 0.

Throughout the text, when solving equations, be sure to check your solutions either *algebraically* by substituting in the original equation or *graphically*.

Check

a. $6x^2 = 3x$ Write original equation.

$$6(0)^2 \overset{?}{=} 3(0)$$ Substitute 0 for x.

$$0 = 0$$ Solution checks. ✓

$$6\left(\tfrac{1}{2}\right)^2 \overset{?}{=} 3\left(\tfrac{1}{2}\right)$$ Substitute $\tfrac{1}{2}$ for x.

$$\tfrac{6}{4} = \tfrac{3}{2}$$ Solution checks. ✓

b. $9x^2 - 6x + 1 = 0$ Write original equation.

$$9\left(\tfrac{1}{3}\right)^2 - 6\left(\tfrac{1}{3}\right) + 1 \overset{?}{=} 0$$ Substitute $\tfrac{1}{3}$ for x.

$$1 - 2 + 1 \overset{?}{=} 0$$ Simplify.

$$0 = 0$$ Solution checks. ✓

Similarly, you can graphically check your solutions using the graphs in Figure 2.26.

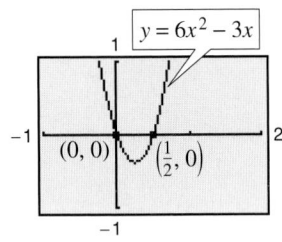

(a)

(b)

Figure 2.26

✓ *Checkpoint* Now try Exercise 7.

STUDY TIP

Quadratic equations always have two solutions. From the graph in Figure 2.26(b), it looks like there is only one solution to the equation $9x^2 - 6x + 1 = 0$.

Because the equation is a perfect square trinomial, its two factors are identical. As a result, the equation has two *repeated* solutions.

Solving a quadratic equation by extracting square roots is an efficient method to use when the quadratic equation can be written in the form $ax^2 + c = 0$, as shown in Example 2.

Example 2   Extracting Square Roots

Solve each quadratic equation.

a. $4x^2 = 12$ **b.** $(x - 3)^2 = 7$

Solution

a. $4x^2 = 12$ Write original equation.

$\quad\ x^2 = 3$ Divide each side by 4.

$\quad\ \ x = \pm\sqrt{3}$ Take square root of each side.

This equation has two solutions: $x = \sqrt{3}$ and $x = -\sqrt{3}$.

b. $(x - 3)^2 = 7$ Write original equation.

$\quad x - 3 = \pm\sqrt{7}$ Take square root of each side.

$\quad\quad\ \ x = 3 \pm \sqrt{7}$ Add 3 to each side.

This equation has two solutions: $x = 3 + \sqrt{7}$ and $x = 3 - \sqrt{7}$.

The graphs of $y = 4x^2 - 12$ and $y = (x - 3)^2 - 7$, shown in Figure 2.27, verify the solutions.

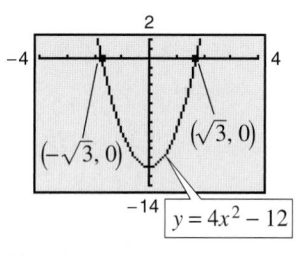

(a)

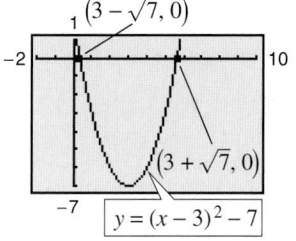

(b)

Figure 2.27

✓ *Checkpoint* Now try Exercise 19.

TECHNOLOGY TIP   Note that the solutions shown in Example 2 are listed in *exact* form. Most graphing utilities produce decimal approximations of solutions rather than exact forms. For instance, if you solve the equations in Example 2 using a graphing utility, you will obtain $x \approx \pm 1.732$ in part (a) and $x \approx 5.646$ and $x \approx 0.354$ in part (b). Some graphing utilities have symbolic algebra programs that *can* list the exact form of a solution.

Completing the square can be used to solve any quadratic equation, but it is best suited for quadratic equations in general form $ax^2 + bx + c = 0$ with $a = 1$ and b an even number (see page 191). If the leading coefficient of the quadratic is not 1, divide each side of the equation by this coefficient *before* completing the square, as shown in Example 4.

Example 3   Completing the Square: Leading Coefficient Is 1

Solve $x^2 + 2x - 6 = 0$ by completing the square.

Solution

$$x^2 + 2x - 6 = 0 \qquad \text{Write original equation.}$$

$$x^2 + 2x = 6 \qquad \text{Add 6 to each side.}$$

$$x^2 + 2x + 1^2 = 6 + 1^2 \qquad \text{Add } 1^2 \text{ to each side.}$$

$$\underbrace{\qquad}_{(\text{Half of 2})^2}$$

$$(x + 1)^2 = 7 \qquad \text{Simplify.}$$

$$x + 1 = \pm\sqrt{7} \qquad \text{Take square root of each side.}$$

$$x = -1 \pm \sqrt{7} \qquad \text{Solutions}$$

Using a calculator, the two solutions are $x \approx 1.646$ and $x \approx -3.646$, which agree with the graphical solutions shown in Figure 2.28.

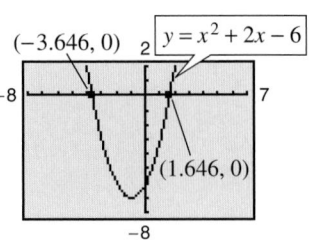

Figure 2.28

✓ **Checkpoint** Now try Exercise 23.

Example 4   Completing the Square: Leading Coefficient Is Not 1

Solve $2x^2 + 8x + 3 = 0$ by completing the square.

Solution

$$2x^2 + 8x + 3 = 0 \qquad \text{Write original equation.}$$

$$2x^2 + 8x = -3 \qquad \text{Subtract 3 from each side.}$$

$$x^2 + 4x = -\frac{3}{2} \qquad \text{Divide each side by 2.}$$

$$x^2 + 4x + 2^2 = -\frac{3}{2} + 2^2 \qquad \text{Add } 2^2 \text{ to each side.}$$

$$\underbrace{\qquad}_{(\text{Half of 4})^2}$$

$$(x + 2)^2 = \frac{5}{2} \qquad \text{Simplify.}$$

$$x + 2 = \pm\sqrt{\frac{5}{2}} \qquad \text{Take square root of each side.}$$

$$x + 2 = \pm\frac{\sqrt{10}}{2} \qquad \text{Rationalize denominator.}$$

$$x = -2 \pm \frac{\sqrt{10}}{2} \qquad \text{Solutions}$$

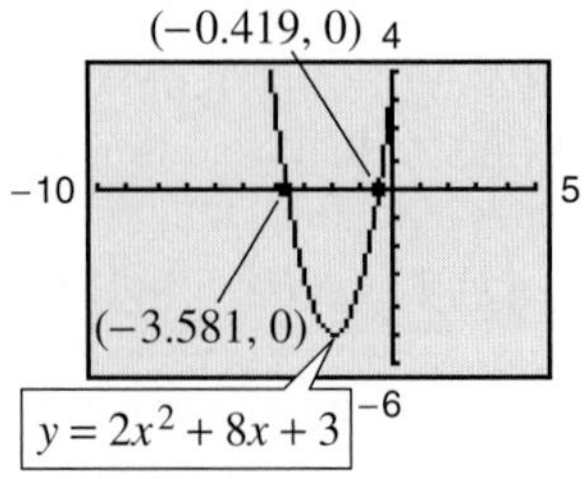

Using a calculator, the two solutions are $x \approx -0.419$ and $x \approx -3.581$, which agree with the graphical solutions shown in Figure 2.29.

Figure 2.29

✓ **Checkpoint** Now try Exercise 27.

Example 5   Completing the Square: Leading Coefficient Is Not 1

Solve $3x^2 - 4x - 5 = 0$ by completing the square.

Solution

$$3x^2 - 4x - 5 = 0 \qquad\qquad \text{Write original equation.}$$

$$3x^2 - 4x = 5 \qquad\qquad \text{Add 5 to each side.}$$

$$x^2 - \frac{4}{3}x = \frac{5}{3} \qquad\qquad \text{Divide each side by 3.}$$

$$x^2 - \frac{4}{3}x + \left(-\frac{2}{3}\right)^2 = \frac{5}{3} + \left(-\frac{2}{3}\right)^2 \qquad\qquad \text{Add } \left(-\tfrac{2}{3}\right)^2 \text{ to each side.}$$

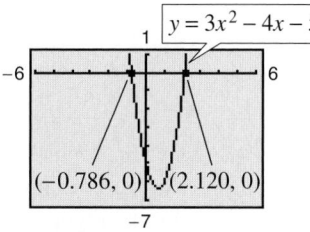

$$\left(\text{Half of } -\frac{4}{3}\right)^2$$

$$\left(x - \frac{2}{3}\right)^2 = \frac{19}{9} \qquad\qquad \text{Simplify.}$$

$$x - \frac{2}{3} = \pm\frac{\sqrt{19}}{3} \qquad\qquad \text{Take square root of each side.}$$

$$x = \frac{2}{3} \pm \frac{\sqrt{19}}{3} \qquad\qquad \text{Solutions}$$

Using a calculator, the two solutions are $x \approx 2.120$ and $x \approx -0.786$, which agree with the graphical solutions shown in Figure 2.30.

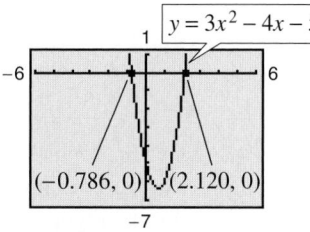

Figure 2.30

✓ *Checkpoint* Now try Exercise 31.

Often in mathematics you are taught the long way of solving a problem first. Then, the longer method is used to develop shorter techniques. The long way stresses understanding and the short way stresses efficiency.

For instance, you can think of completing the square as a "long way" of solving a quadratic equation. When you use the method of completing the square to solve a quadratic equation, you must complete the square for *each* equation separately. In the derivation on the following page, you complete the square *once* in a general setting to obtain the Quadratic Formula, which is a shortcut for solving a quadratic equation.

$$ax^2 + bx + c = 0$$

Quadratic equation in general form, $a \neq 0$

$$ax^2 + bx = -c$$

Subtract c from each side.

$$x^2 + \frac{b}{a}x = -\frac{c}{a}$$

Divide each side by a.

$$x^2 + \frac{b}{a}x + \left(\frac{b}{2a}\right)^2 = -\frac{c}{a} + \left(\frac{b}{2a}\right)^2$$

Complete the square.

$$\underbrace{\left(\text{half of } \frac{b}{a}\right)^2}$$

$$\left(x + \frac{b}{2a}\right)^2 = \frac{b^2 - 4ac}{4a^2}$$

Simplify.

$$x + \frac{b}{2a} = \pm\sqrt{\frac{b^2 - 4ac}{4a^2}}$$

Extract square roots.

$$x = -\frac{b}{2a} \pm \frac{\sqrt{b^2 - 4ac}}{2|a|}$$

Solutions

Note that because $\pm 2|a|$ represents the same numbers as $\pm 2a$, you can omit the absolute value sign. So, the formula simplifies to

$$x = \frac{-b \pm \sqrt{b^2 - 4ac}}{2a}.$$

> ### Exploration
>
> Use a graphing utility to graph the three quadratic equations
>
> $$y_1 = x^2 - 2x$$
> $$y_2 = x^2 - 2x + 1$$
> $$y_3 = x^2 - 2x + 2$$
>
> in the same viewing window. Compute the *discriminant* $\sqrt{b^2 - 4ac}$ for each and discuss the relationship between the discriminant and the number of zeros of the quadratic function.

Example 6 Quadratic Formula: Two Distinct Solutions

Solve $x^2 + 3x = 9$ using the Quadratic Formula.

Algebraic Solution

$$x^2 + 3x = 9$$

Write original equation.

$$x^2 + 3x - 9 = 0$$

Write in general form.

$$x = \frac{-b \pm \sqrt{b^2 - 4ac}}{2a}$$

Quadratic Formula

$$x = \frac{-3 \pm \sqrt{3^2 - 4(1)(-9)}}{2(1)}$$

Substitute 3 for b, 1 for a, and -9 for c.

$$x = \frac{-3 \pm \sqrt{45}}{2}$$

Simplify.

$$x = \frac{-3 \pm 3\sqrt{5}}{2}$$

Simplify radical.

$$x \approx 1.85 \text{ or } -4.85$$

Solutions

The equation has two solutions: $x \approx 1.85$ and $x \approx -4.85$. Check these solutions in the original equation.

 Checkpoint Now try Exercise 47.

Graphical Solution

Use a graphing utility to graph $y_1 = x^2 + 3x$ and $y_2 = 9$ in the same viewing window. Use the *intersect* feature of the graphing utility to approximate the points where the graphs intersect. From Figure 2.31, it appears that the graphs intersect at $x \approx 1.85$ and $x \approx -4.85$. These x-coordinates of the intersection points are the solutions of the equation $x^2 + 3x = 9$.

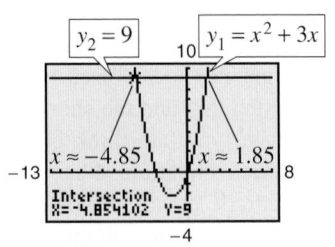

Figure 2.31

Example 7   Quadratic Formula: One Repeated Solution

Solve $8x^2 - 24x + 18 = 0$.

Algebraic Solution

This equation has a common factor of 2. You can simplify the equation by dividing each side of the equation by 2.

$$8x^2 - 24x + 18 = 0 \qquad \text{Write original equation.}$$

$$4x^2 - 12x + 9 = 0 \qquad \text{Divide each side by 2.}$$

$$x = \frac{-b \pm \sqrt{b^2 - 4ac}}{2a} \qquad \text{Quadratic Formula}$$

$$x = \frac{-(-12) \pm \sqrt{(-12)^2 - 4(4)(9)}}{2(4)}$$

$$x = \frac{12 \pm \sqrt{0}}{8} = \frac{3}{2} \qquad \text{Repeated solution}$$

This quadratic equation has only one solution: $x = \frac{3}{2}$. Check this solution in the original equation.

 Checkpoint Now try Exercise 49.

Graphical Solution

Use a graphing utility to graph

$$y = 8x^2 - 24x + 18.$$

Use the *zero* feature of the graphing utility to approximate the value(s) of x for which the function is equal to zero. From the graph in Figure 2.32, it appears that the function is equal to zero when $x = 1.5 = \frac{3}{2}$. This is the only solution of the equation $8x^2 - 24x + 18 = 0$.

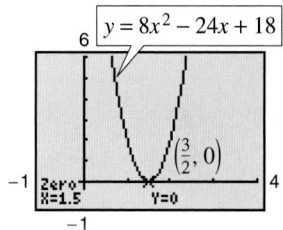

Figure 2.32

Example 8   Complex Solutions of a Quadratic Equation

Solve $3x^2 - 2x + 5 = 0$.

Algebraic Solution

By the Quadratic Formula, you can write the solutions as follows.

$$3x^2 - 2x + 5 = 0 \qquad \text{Write original equation.}$$

$$x = \frac{-b \pm \sqrt{b^2 - 4ac}}{2a} \qquad \text{Quadratic Formula}$$

$$= \frac{-(-2) \pm \sqrt{(-2)^2 - 4(3)(5)}}{2(3)} \qquad \begin{array}{l}\text{Substitute } -2 \text{ for } b,\\ 3 \text{ for } a, \text{ and } 5 \text{ for } c.\end{array}$$

$$= \frac{2 \pm \sqrt{-56}}{6} \qquad \text{Simplify.}$$

$$= \frac{2 \pm 2\sqrt{14}\,i}{6} \qquad \text{Simplify radical.}$$

$$= \frac{1}{3} \pm \frac{\sqrt{14}}{3}\,i \qquad \text{Solutions}$$

The equation has no real solution, but it has two complex solutions:
$x = \frac{1}{3}\left(1 + \sqrt{14}\,i\right)$ and $x = \frac{1}{3}\left(1 - \sqrt{14}\,i\right)$.

 Checkpoint Now try Exercise 51.

Graphical Solution

Use a graphing utility to graph

$$y = 3x^2 - 2x + 5.$$

Note in Figure 2.33 that the graph of the function appears to have no x-intercepts. From this you can conclude that the equation $3x^2 - 2x + 5 = 0$ has no real solution. You can solve the equation algebraically to find the complex solutions.

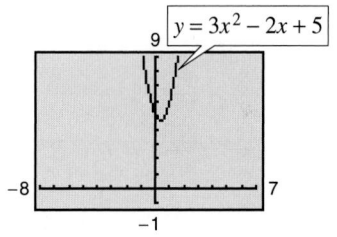

Figure 2.33

Polynomial Equations of Higher Degree

The methods used to solve quadratic equations can sometimes be extended to polynomial equations of higher degree, as shown in the next two examples.

Example 9 Solving an Equation of Quadratic Type

Solve $x^4 - 3x^2 + 2 = 0$.

Solution

The expression $x^4 - 3x^2 + 2$ is said to be in *quadratic form* because it is written in the form $au^2 + bu + c$, where u is any expression in x, namely x^2. You can use factoring to solve the equation as follows.

$$x^4 - 3x^2 + 2 = 0 \qquad \text{Write original equation.}$$
$$(x^2)^2 - 3(x^2) + 2 = 0 \qquad \text{Write in quadratic form.}$$
$$(x^2 - 1)(x^2 - 2) = 0 \qquad \text{Partially factor.}$$
$$(x + 1)(x - 1)(x^2 - 2) = 0 \qquad \text{Factor completely.}$$
$$x + 1 = 0 \implies x = -1 \qquad \text{Set 1st factor equal to 0.}$$
$$x - 1 = 0 \implies x = 1 \qquad \text{Set 2nd factor equal to 0.}$$
$$x^2 - 2 = 0 \implies x = \pm\sqrt{2} \qquad \text{Set 3rd factor equal to 0.}$$

The equation has four solutions: $x = -1$, $x = 1$, $x = \sqrt{2}$, and $x = -\sqrt{2}$. Check these solutions in the original equation. Figure 2.34 verifies the solutions graphically.

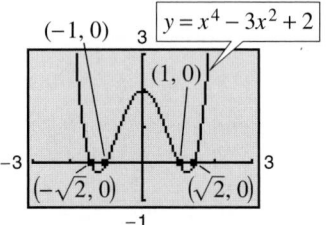

Figure 2.34

✓ *Checkpoint* Now try Exercise 63.

Example 10 Solving a Polynomial Equation by Factoring

Solve $2x^3 - 6x^2 - 6x + 18 = 0$.

Solution

This equation has a common factor of 2. You can simplify the equation by first dividing each side of the equation by 2.

$$2x^3 - 6x^2 - 6x + 18 = 0 \qquad \text{Write original equation.}$$
$$x^3 - 3x^2 - 3x + 9 = 0 \qquad \text{Divide each side by 2.}$$
$$x^2(x - 3) - 3(x - 3) = 0 \qquad \text{Group terms.}$$
$$(x - 3)(x^2 - 3) = 0 \qquad \text{Factor by grouping.}$$
$$x - 3 = 0 \implies x = 3 \qquad \text{Set 1st factor equal to 0.}$$
$$x^2 - 3 = 0 \implies x = \pm\sqrt{3} \qquad \text{Set 2nd factor equal to 0.}$$

The equation has three solutions: $x = 3$, $x = \sqrt{3}$, and $x = -\sqrt{3}$. Check these solutions in the original equation. Figure 2.35 verifies the solutions graphically.

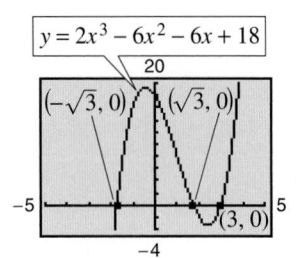

Figure 2.35

✓ *Checkpoint* Now try Exercise 67.

Equations Involving Radicals

An equation involving a radical expression can often be cleared of radicals by raising each side of the equation to an appropriate power. When using this procedure, remember to check for extraneous solutions.

Example 11   Solving an Equation Involving a Radical

Solve $\sqrt{2x + 7} - x = 2$.

Algebraic Solution

$\sqrt{2x + 7} - x = 2$	Write original equation.
$\sqrt{2x + 7} = x + 2$	Isolate radical.
$2x + 7 = x^2 + 4x + 4$	Square each side.
$x^2 + 2x - 3 = 0$	Write in general form.
$(x + 3)(x - 1) = 0$	Factor.
$x + 3 = 0 \implies x = -3$	Set 1st factor equal to 0.
$x - 1 = 0 \implies x = 1$	Set 2nd factor equal to 0.

By substituting into the original equation, you can determine that $x = -3$ is extraneous, whereas $x = 1$ is valid. So, the equation has only one real solution: $x = 1$.

 Checkpoint Now try Exercise 83.

Graphical Solution

First rewrite the equation as $\sqrt{2x + 7} - x - 2 = 0$. Then use a graphing utility to graph $y = \sqrt{2x + 7} - x - 2$, as shown in Figure 2.36. Notice that the domain is $x \geq -\frac{7}{2}$ because the expression under the radical cannot be negative. There appears to be one solution near $x = 1$. Use the *zoom* and *trace* features, as shown in Figure 2.37, to approximate the only solution to be $x = 1$.

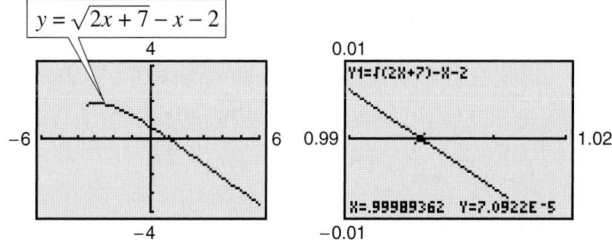

Figure 2.36   Figure 2.37

Example 12   Solving an Equation Involving Two Radicals

$\sqrt{2x + 6} - \sqrt{x + 4} = 1$	Original equation
$\sqrt{2x + 6} = 1 + \sqrt{x + 4}$	Isolate $\sqrt{2x + 6}$.
$2x + 6 = 1 + 2\sqrt{x + 4} + (x + 4)$	Square each side.
$x + 1 = 2\sqrt{x + 4}$	Isolate $2\sqrt{x + 4}$.
$x^2 + 2x + 1 = 4(x + 4)$	Square each side.
$x^2 - 2x - 15 = 0$	Write in general form.
$(x - 5)(x + 3) = 0$	Factor.
$x - 5 = 0 \implies x = 5$	Set 1st factor equal to 0.
$x + 3 = 0 \implies x = -3$	Set 2nd factor equal to 0.

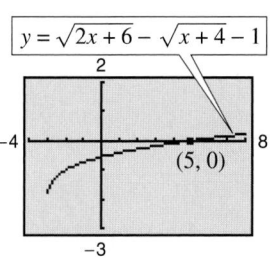

Figure 2.38

By substituting into the original equation, you can determine that $x = -3$ is extraneous, whereas $x = 5$ is valid. Figure 2.38 verifies that $x = 5$ is the only solution.

 Checkpoint Now try Exercise 89.

Example 13 Solving an Equation with Rational Exponents

Solve $(x + 1)^{2/3} = 4$.

Algebraic Solution	
$(x + 1)^{2/3} = 4$	Write original equation.
$\sqrt[3]{(x + 1)^2} = 4$	Rewrite in radical form.
$(x + 1)^2 = 64$	Cube each side.
$x + 1 = \pm 8$	Take square root of each side.
$x = 7, x = -9$	Subtract 1 from each side.

Substitute $x = 7$ and $x = -9$ into the original equation to determine that both are valid solutions.

Graphical Solution

Use a graphing utility to graph $y_1 = \sqrt[3]{(x + 1)^2}$ and $y_2 = 4$ in the same viewing window. Use the *intersect* feature of the graphing utility to approximate the solutions to be $x = -9$ and $x = 7$, as shown in Figure 2.39.

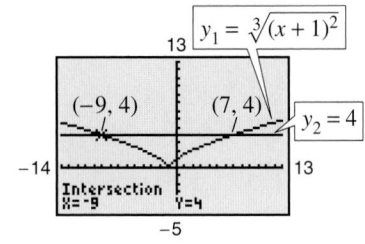

Figure 2.39

✓ *Checkpoint* Now try Exercise 91.

Equations Involving Fractions or Absolute Values

As demonstrated in Section 2.1, you can algebraically solve an equation involving fractions by multiplying each side of the equation by the least common denominator of all terms in the equation to clear the equation of fractions.

Example 14 Solving an Equation Involving Fractions

Solve $\dfrac{2}{x} = \dfrac{3}{x - 2} - 1$.

Solution

For this equation, the least common denominator of the three terms is $x(x - 2)$, so you can begin by multiplying each term of the equation by this expression.

$$\frac{2}{x} = \frac{3}{x - 2} - 1 \qquad \text{Write original equation.}$$

$$x(x - 2)\frac{2}{x} = x(x - 2)\frac{3}{x - 2} - x(x - 2)(1) \qquad \text{Multiply each term by the LCD.}$$

$$2(x - 2) = 3x - x(x - 2), \quad x \neq 0, 2 \qquad \text{Simplify.}$$

$$x^2 - 3x - 4 = 0 \qquad \text{Write in general form.}$$

$$(x - 4)(x + 1) = 0 \qquad \text{Factor.}$$

$$x - 4 = 0 \quad \Longrightarrow \quad x = 4 \qquad \text{Set 1st factor equal to 0.}$$

$$x + 1 = 0 \quad \Longrightarrow \quad x = -1 \qquad \text{Set 2nd factor equal to 0.}$$

The equation has two solutions: $x = 4$ and $x = -1$. Check these solutions in the original equation. Use a graphing utility to verify these solutions graphically.

✓ *Checkpoint* Now try Exercise 101.

Exploration

Using *dot* mode, graph the equations

$$y_1 = \frac{2}{x}$$

and

$$y_2 = \frac{3}{x - 2} - 1$$

in the same viewing window. How many times do the graphs of the equations intersect? What does this tell you about the solution to Example 14?

TECHNOLOGY TIP

Graphs of functions involving variable denominators can be tricky because of the way graphing utilities skip over points at which the denominator is zero. You will study graphs of such functions in Sections 3.5 and 3.6.

Example 15   Solving an Equation Involving Absolute Value

Solve $|x^2 - 3x| = -4x + 6$.

Solution

Begin by writing the equation as $|x^2 - 3x| + 4x - 6 = 0$. From the graph of $y = |x^2 - 3x| + 4x - 6$ in Figure 2.40, you can estimate the solutions to be $x = -3$ and $x = 1$. These can be verified by substitution into the equation. To solve *algebraically* an equation involving an absolute value, you must consider the fact that the expression inside the absolute value symbols can be positive or negative. This results in *two* separate equations, each of which must be solved.

First Equation:

$x^2 - 3x = -4x + 6$	Use positive expression.
$x^2 + x - 6 = 0$	Write in general form.
$(x + 3)(x - 2) = 0$	Factor.
$x + 3 = 0 \quad\Longrightarrow\quad x = -3$	Set 1st factor equal to 0.
$x - 2 = 0 \quad\Longrightarrow\quad x = 2$	Set 2nd factor equal to 0.

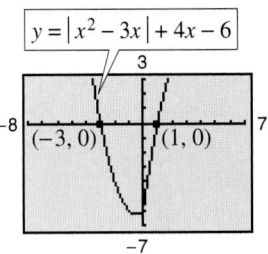

$y = |x^2 - 3x| + 4x - 6$

Figure 2.40

Second Equation:

$-(x^2 - 3x) = -4x + 6$	Use negative expression.
$x^2 - 7x + 6 = 0$	Write in general form.
$(x - 1)(x - 6) = 0$	Factor.
$x - 1 = 0 \quad\Longrightarrow\quad x = 1$	Set 1st factor equal to 0.
$x - 6 = 0 \quad\Longrightarrow\quad x = 6$	Set 2nd factor equal to 0.

Check

$|(-3)^2 - 3(-3)| \overset{?}{=} -4(-3) + 6$	Substitute -3 for x.
$18 = 18$	-3 checks. ✓
$|2^2 - 3(2)| \overset{?}{=} -4(2) + 6$	Substitute 2 for x.
$2 \neq -2$	2 does not check.
$|1^2 - 3(1)| \overset{?}{=} -4(1) + 6$	Substitute 1 for x.
$2 = 2$	1 checks. ✓
$|6^2 - 3(6)| \overset{?}{=} -4(6) + 6$	Substitute 6 for x.
$18 \neq -18$	6 does not check.

The equation has only two solutions: $x = -3$ and $x = 1$, just as you obtained by graphing.

✓ *Checkpoint* Now try Exercise 107.

> **Exploration**
>
> In Figure 2.40, the graph of $y = |x^2 - 3x| + 4x - 6$ appears to be a straight line to the right of the y-axis. Is it? Explain how you decided.

Applications

A common application of quadratic equations involves an object that is falling (or projected into the air). The general equation that gives the height of such an object is called a **position equation,** and on *Earth's* surface it has the form

$$s = -16t^2 + v_0 t + s_0.$$

In this equation, s represents the height of the object (in feet), v_0 represents the initial velocity of the object (in feet per second), s_0 represents the initial height of the object (in feet), and t represents the time (in seconds). Note that this position equation ignores air resistance.

Example 16   Falling Time

A construction worker on the 24th floor of a building project (see Figure 2.41) accidentally drops a wrench and yells, "Look out below!" Could a person at ground level hear this warning in time to get out of the way?

Solution

Assume that each floor of the building is 10 feet high, so that the wrench is dropped from a height of 235 feet (the construction worker's hand is 5 feet below the ceiling of the 24th floor). Because sound travels at about 1100 feet per second, it follows that a person at ground level hears the warning within 1 second of the time the wrench is dropped. To set up a mathematical model for the height of the wrench, use the position equation

$$s = -16t^2 + v_0 t + s_0. \qquad \text{Position equation}$$

Because the object is dropped rather than thrown, the initial velocity is $v_0 = 0$ feet per second. So, with an initial height of $s_0 = 235$ feet, you have the model

$$s = -16t^2 + (0)t + 235 = -16t^2 + 235.$$

After falling for 1 second, the height of the wrench is $-16(1)^2 + 235 = 219$. After falling for 2 seconds, the height of the wrench is $-16(2)^2 + 235 = 171$. To find the number of seconds it takes the wrench to hit the ground, let the height s be zero and solve the equation for t.

$s = -16t^2 + 235$	Write position equation.
$0 = -16t^2 + 235$	Substitute 0 for s.
$16t^2 = 235$	Add $16t^2$ to each side.
$t^2 = \dfrac{235}{16}$	Divide each side by 16.
$t = \dfrac{\sqrt{235}}{4} \approx 3.83$	Extract positive square root.

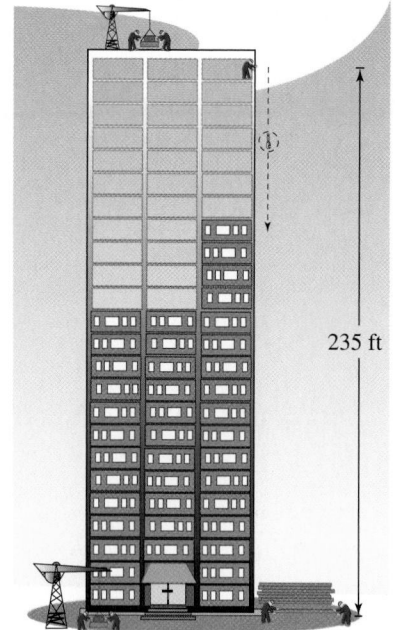

235 ft

Figure 2.41

The wrench will take about 3.83 seconds to hit the ground. If the person hears the warning 1 second after the wrench is dropped, the person still has almost 3 more seconds to get out of the way.

✓ *Checkpoint* Now try Exercise 125.

Example 17   Quadratic Modeling: Internet Use

From 1996 to 2001, the number of hours h spent annually per person using the Internet in the United States closely followed the quadratic model

$$h = -0.05t^2 + 29.6t - 168$$

where t represents the year, with $t = 6$ corresponding to 1996. The number of hours per year is shown graphically in Figure 2.42. According to this model, in which year will the number of hours spent per person reach or surpass 300? (Source: Veronis Suhler Stevenson)

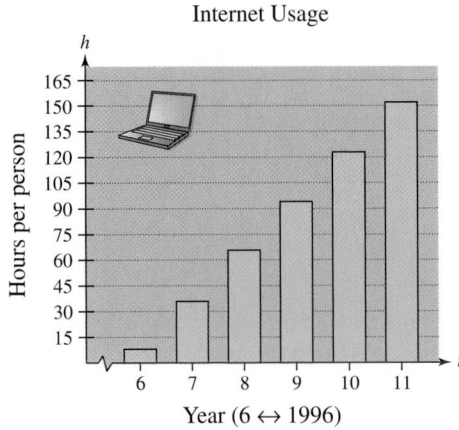

Internet Usage

Figure 2.42

Solution

To find when the number of hours spent per person will reach 300, you need to solve the equation

$$-0.05t^2 + 29.6t - 168 = 300.$$

To begin, write the equation in general form.

$$-0.05t^2 + 29.6t - 468 = 0$$

Then apply the Quadratic Formula.

$$t = \frac{-29.6 \pm \sqrt{(29.6)^2 - 4(-0.05)(-468)}}{2(-0.05)}$$

$$\approx 16.3 \text{ or } 575.7$$

Choose the smaller value $t = 16.3$. Because $t = 6$ corresponds to 1996, it follows that $t = 16.3$ must correspond to some time in 2006. So, the number of hours spent annually per person using the Internet should reach 300 during 2006.

✅ *Checkpoint* Now try Exercise 129.

TECHNOLOGY TIP   You can solve Example 17 with your graphing utility by graphing the two functions $y_1 = -0.05t^2 + 29.6t - 168$ and $y_2 = 300$ in the same viewing window and finding their point of intersection. You should obtain $x \approx 16.3$, which verifies the answer obtained algebraically.

Another type of application that often involves a quadratic equation is one dealing with the hypotenuse of a right triangle. These types of applications often use the Pythagorean Theorem, which states that

$$a^2 + b^2 = c^2 \qquad \text{Pythagorean Theorem}$$

where a and b are the legs of a right triangle and c is the hypotenuse, as indicated in Figure 2.43.

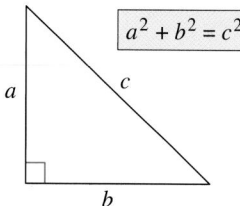

Figure 2.43

Example 18　An Application Involving the Pythagorean Theorem

An L-shaped sidewalk from the athletic center to the library on a college campus is shown in Figure 2.44. The sidewalk was constructed so that the length of one sidewalk forming the L is twice as long as the other. The length of the diagonal sidewalk that cuts across the grounds between the two buildings is 102 feet. How many feet does a person save by walking on the diagonal sidewalk?

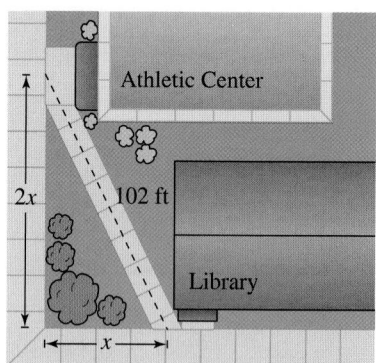

Figure 2.44

Solution

Using the Pythagorean Theorem, you have

$$
\begin{aligned}
a^2 + b^2 &= c^2 && \text{Pythagorean Theorem} \\
x^2 + (2x)^2 &= 102^2 && \text{Substitute for } a, b, \text{ and } c. \\
5x^2 &= 10{,}404 && \text{Combine like terms.} \\
x^2 &= 2080.8 && \text{Divide each side by 5.} \\
x &= \pm\sqrt{2080.8} && \text{Take the square root of each side.} \\
x &= \sqrt{2080.8} && \text{Extract positive square root.}
\end{aligned}
$$

The total distance covered by walking on the L-shaped sidewalk is

$$
\begin{aligned}
x + 2x &= 3x \\
&= 3\sqrt{2080.8} \\
&\approx 136.8 \text{ feet.}
\end{aligned}
$$

Walking on the diagonal sidewalk saves a person about $136.8 - 102 = 34.8$ feet.

✓ *Checkpoint*　Now try Exercise 135.

2.4 Exercises

Vocabulary Check

Fill in the blanks.

1. An equation of the form $ax^2 + bx + c = 0$, where a, b, and c are real numbers and $a \neq 0$, is a _____ , or a second-degree polynomial equation in x.

2. The four methods that can be used to solve a quadratic equation are _____ , _____ , _____ , and the _____ .

3. The part of the Quadratic Formula $\sqrt{b^2 - 4ac}$, known as the _____ , determines the type of solutions of a quadratic equation.

4. The general equation that gives the height of an object (in feet) in terms of the time t (in seconds) is called the _____ equation, and has the form $s =$ _____ , where v_0 represents the _____ and s_0 represents the _____ .

In Exercises 1–4, write the quadratic equation in general form. Do not solve the equation.

1. $2x^2 = 3 - 5x$
2. $x^2 = 25x + 26$
3. $\frac{1}{5}(3x^2 - 10) = 12x$
4. $x(x + 2) = 3x^2 + 1$

In Exercises 5–14, solve the quadratic equation by factoring. Check your solutions in the original equation.

5. $6x^2 + 3x = 0$
6. $9x^2 - 1 = 0$
7. $x^2 - 2x - 8 = 0$
8. $x^2 - 10x + 9 = 0$
9. $3 + 5x - 2x^2 = 0$
10. $2x^2 = 19x + 33$
11. $x^2 + 4x = 12$
12. $-x^2 + 8x = 12$
13. $(x + a)^2 - b^2 = 0$
14. $x^2 + 2ax + a^2 = 0$

In Exercises 15–22, solve the equation by extracting square roots. List both the exact solutions and the decimal solutions rounded to two decimal places.

15. $x^2 = 49$
16. $x^2 = 144$
17. $(x - 12)^2 = 16$
18. $(x - 5)^2 = 25$
19. $(2x - 1)^2 = 12$
20. $(4x + 7)^2 = 44$
21. $(x - 7)^2 = (x + 3)^2$
22. $(x + 5)^2 = (x + 4)^2$

In Exercises 23–32, solve the quadratic equation by completing the square. Verify your answer graphically.

23. $x^2 + 4x - 32 = 0$
24. $x^2 - 2x - 3 = 0$
25. $x^2 + 6x + 2 = 0$
26. $x^2 + 8x + 14 = 0$
27. $9x^2 - 18x + 3 = 0$
28. $4x^2 - 4x - 99 = 0$
29. $8 + 4x - x^2 = 0$
30. $-x^2 + x - 1 = 0$

31. $2x^2 + 5x - 8 = 0$
32. $9x^2 - 12x - 14 = 0$

Graphical Reasoning **In Exercises 33–38, (a) use a graphing utility to graph the equation, (b) use the graph to approximate any x-intercepts of the graph, (c) set $y = 0$ and solve the resulting equation, and (d) compare the result of part (c) with the x-intercepts of the graph.**

33. $y = (x + 3)^2 - 4$
34. $y = 1 - (x - 2)^2$
35. $y = -4x^2 + 4x + 3$
36. $y = x^2 + 3x - 4$
37. $y = \frac{1}{4}(4x^2 - 20x + 25)$
38. $y = -\frac{1}{4}(x^2 - 2x + 9)$

In Exercises 39–44, use a graphing utility to determine the number of real solutions of the quadratic equation.

39. $2x^2 - 5x + 5 = 0$
40. $2x^2 - x - 1 = 0$
41. $\frac{4}{7}x^2 - 8x + 28 = 0$
42. $\frac{1}{3}x^2 - 5x + 25 = 0$
43. $-0.2x^2 + 1.2x - 8 = 0$
44. $9 + 2.4x - 8.3x^2 = 0$

In Exercises 45–52, use the Quadratic Formula to solve the equation. Use a graphing utility to verify your solutions graphically.

45. $2 + 2x - x^2 = 0$
46. $x^2 - 10x + 22 = 0$
47. $x^2 + 8x - 4 = 0$
48. $4x^2 - 4x - 4 = 0$
49. $28x - 49x^2 = 4$
50. $9x^2 + 24x + 16 = 0$
51. $4x^2 + 16x + 17 = 0$
52. $9x^2 - 6x + 37 = 0$

In Exercises 53–60, solve the equation using any convenient method.

53. $x^2 - 2x - 1 = 0$

54. $11x^2 + 33x = 0$

55. $(x + 3)^2 = 81$

56. $x^2 - 14x + 49 = 0$

57. $x^2 - x - \frac{11}{4} = 0$

58. $x^2 + 3x - \frac{3}{4} = 0$

59. $(x + 1)^2 = x^2$

60. $a^2x^2 - b^2 = 0, a \neq 0$

In Exercises 61–78, find all solutions of the equation algebraically. Use a graphing utility to verify the solutions graphically.

61. $4x^4 - 18x^2 = 0$

62. $20x^3 - 125x = 0$

63. $x^4 - 4x^2 + 3 = 0$

64. $x^4 + 5x^2 - 36 = 0$

65. $5x^3 + 30x^2 + 45x = 0$

66. $9x^4 - 24x^3 + 16x^2 = 0$

67. $x^3 - 3x^2 - x + 3 = 0$

68. $x^4 + 2x^3 - 8x - 16 = 0$

69. $4x^4 - 65x^2 + 16 = 0$ 70. $36t^4 + 29t^2 - 7 = 0$

71. $\frac{1}{t^2} + \frac{8}{t} + 15 = 0$ 72. $6 - \frac{1}{x} - \frac{1}{x^2} = 0$

73. $6\left(\frac{s}{s+1}\right)^2 + 5\left(\frac{s}{s+1}\right) - 6 = 0$

74. $8\left(\frac{t}{t-1}\right)^2 - 2\left(\frac{t}{t-1}\right) - 3 = 0$

75. $2x + 9\sqrt{x} - 5 = 0$ 76. $6x - 7\sqrt{x} - 3 = 0$

77. $3x^{1/3} + 2x^{2/3} = 5$

78. $9t^{2/3} + 24t^{1/3} + 16 = 0$

Graphical Analysis **In Exercises 79–82, (a) use a graphing utility to graph the equation, (b) use the graph to approximate any x-intercepts of the graph, (c) set y = 0 and solve the resulting equation, and (d) compare the result of part (c) with the x-intercepts of the graph.**

79. $y = x^3 - 2x^2 - 3x$

80. $y = 2x^4 - 15x^3 + 18x^2$

81. $y = x^4 - 10x^2 + 9$

82. $y = x^4 - 29x^2 + 100$

In Exercises 83–94, find all solutions of the equation algebraically. Check your solutions both algebraically and graphically.

83. $\sqrt{x - 10} - 4 = 0$ 84. $\sqrt{2x + 5} + 3 = 0$

85. $\sqrt{x + 1} - 3x = 1$ 86. $\sqrt{x + 5} - 2x = 3$

87. $\sqrt[3]{2x + 1} + 8 = 0$ 88. $\sqrt[3]{4x - 3} + 2 = 0$

89. $\sqrt{x} - \sqrt{x - 5} = 1$ 90. $\sqrt{x} + \sqrt{x - 20} = 10$

91. $(x - 5)^{2/3} = 16$

92. $(x^2 - x - 22)^{4/3} = 16$

93. $3x(x - 1)^{1/2} + 2(x - 1)^{3/2} = 0$

94. $4x^2(x - 1)^{1/3} + 6x(x - 1)^{4/3} = 0$

Graphical Analysis **In Exercises 95–98, (a) use a graphing utility to graph the equation, (b) use the graph to approximate any x-intercepts of the graph, (c) set y = 0 and solve the resulting equation, and (d) compare the result of part (c) with the x-intercepts of the graph.**

95. $y = \sqrt{11x - 30} - x$ 96. $y = 2x - \sqrt{15 - 4x}$

97. $y = \sqrt{7x + 36} - \sqrt{5x + 16} - 2$

98. $y = 3\sqrt{x} - \dfrac{4}{\sqrt{x}} - 4$

In Exercises 99–108, find all solutions of the equation. Use a graphing utility to verify your solutions graphically.

99. $\dfrac{20 - x}{x} = x$ 100. $\dfrac{4}{x} - \dfrac{5}{3} = \dfrac{x}{6}$

101. $\dfrac{1}{x} - \dfrac{1}{x + 1} = 3$ 102. $\dfrac{x}{x^2 - 4} + \dfrac{1}{x + 2} = 3$

103. $x = \dfrac{3}{x} + \dfrac{1}{2}$ 104. $4x + 1 = \dfrac{3}{x}$

105. $|2x - 1| = 5$ 106. $|3x + 2| = 7$

107. $|x| = x^2 + x - 3$ 108. $|x - 10| = x^2 - 10x$

Graphical Analysis **In Exercises 109–112, (a) use a graphing utility to graph the equation, (b) use the graph to approximate any x-intercepts of the graph, (c) set y = 0 and solve the resulting equation, and (d) compare the result of part (c) with the x-intercepts of the graph.**

109. $y = \dfrac{1}{x} - \dfrac{4}{x - 1} - 1$ 110. $y = x + \dfrac{9}{x + 1} - 5$

111. $y = |x + 1| - 2$ 112. $y = |x - 2| - 3$

Think About It **In Exercises 113–118, find an equation having the given solutions. (There are many correct answers.)**

113. $-6, 5$ 114. $-\frac{7}{3}, \frac{6}{7}$

115. $\sqrt{2}, -\sqrt{2}, 4$

116. $2, \sqrt{5}, -\sqrt{5}$

117. $-2, 2, i, -i$

118. $4i, -4i, 6, -6$

Think About It   **In Exercises 119 and 120, find x such that the distance between the points is 13.**

119. $(1, 2), (x, -10)$

120. $(-8, 0), (x, 5)$

121. ***Geometry***   The floor of a one-story building is 14 feet longer than it is wide. The building has 1632 square feet of floor space.

    (a) Draw a diagram that gives a visual representation of the floor space. Represent the width as w and show the length in terms of w.

    (b) Write a quadratic equation in terms of w.

    (c) Find the length and width of the building floor.

122. ***Geometry***   An above-ground swimming pool with a square base is to be constructed such that the surface area of the pool is 576 square feet. The height of the pool is to be 4 feet. What should the dimensions of the base be? (*Hint:* The surface area is $S = x^2 + 4xh$.)

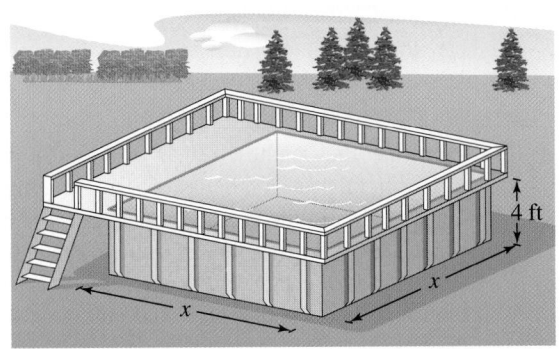

123. ***Packaging***   An open gift box is to be made from a square piece of material by cutting two-centimeter squares from each corner and turning up the sides (see figure). The volume of the finished gift box is to be 200 cubic centimeters. Find the size of the original piece of material.

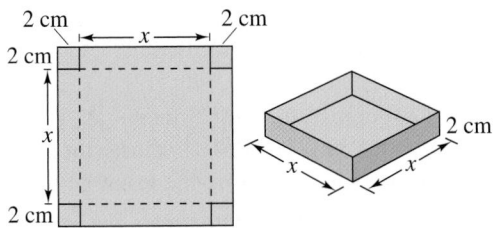

124. ***Exploration***   A rancher has 100 meters of fencing to enclose two adjacent rectangular corrals as shown in the figure.

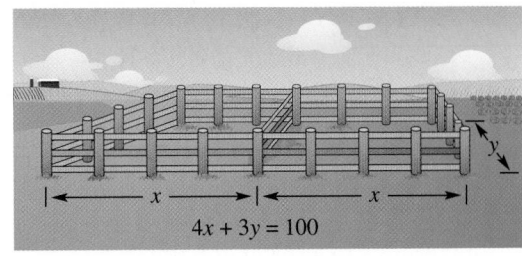

$$4x + 3y = 100$$

    (a) Write the area of the enclosed region as a function of x.

    (b) Use a graphing utility to generate additional rows of the table. Use the table to estimate the dimensions that will produce a maximum area.

x	y	Area
2	$\frac{92}{3}$	$\frac{368}{3} \approx 123$
4	28	224

    (c) Use a graphing utility to graph the area function, and use the graph to estimate the dimensions that will produce a maximum area.

    (d) Use the graph to approximate the dimensions such that the enclosed area is 350 square meters.

    (e) Find the required dimensions of part (d) algebraically.

In Exercises 125–127, use the position equation given on page 202 as the model for the problem.

125. ***CN Tower***   At 1815 feet tall, the CN Tower in Toronto, Ontario is the world's tallest self-supporting structure. An object is dropped from the top of the tower.

    (a) Find the position equation

$$s = -16t^2 + v_0t + s_0.$$

    (b) Complete the table.

t	0	2	4	6	8	10	12
s							

    (c) From the table in part (b), determine the time interval during which the object reaches the ground. Find the time algebraically.

126. Military   A cargo plane flying at 8000 feet over level terrain drops a 500-pound supply package.

(a) How long will it take the package to strike the ground?

(b) The plane is flying at 600 miles per hour. How far will the package travel horizontally during its descent?

127. Sports   You throw a baseball straight up into the air at a velocity of 45 feet per second. You release the baseball at a height of 5.5 feet and catch it when it falls back to a height of 6 feet.

(a) Use the position equation to write a mathematical model for the height of the baseball.

(b) Find the height of the baseball after 0.5 second.

(c) How many seconds is the baseball in the air?

(d) Use a graphing utility to verify your answer in part (c).

128. Transportation   The total number y of electric-powered vehicles in the United States from 1992 through 2001 can be approximated by the model

$$y = 75.76t^2 + 912, \quad 2 \le t \le 11$$

where t represents the year, with $t = 2$ corresponding to 1992.   (Source: Energy Information Administration)

(a) Determine algebraically when the number of electric-powered vehicles reached 7000.

(b) Verify your answer to part (a) by creating a table of values for the model.

(c) Use a graphing utility to graph the model.

(d) Use the *zoom* and *trace* features of a graphing utility to find the year in which the total number of electric-powered vehicles reached 9000.

(e) Verify your answer to part (d) algebraically.

129. Agriculture   The total number S (in millions) of sheep and lambs on farms in the United States from 1995 through 2002 can be approximated by the model $S = 0.032t^2 - 0.87t + 12.6$, $5 \le t \le 12$, where t represents the year, with $t = 5$ corresponding to 1995.   (Source: U.S. Department of Agriculture)

(a) Use a graphing utility to graph the model.

(b) Extend the model past 2002. Does the model predict that the number of sheep and lambs will eventually increase? If so, estimate when the number of sheep and lambs will once again reach 8 million.

130. Biology   The metabolic rate of an ectothermic organism increases with increasing temperature within a certain range. Experimental data for oxygen consumption C (in microliters per gram per hour) of a beetle at certain temperatures yielded the model $C = 0.45x^2 - 1.65x + 50.75$, $10 \le x \le 25$, where x is the air temperature in degrees Celsius.

(a) Use a graphing utility to graph the consumption model over the specified domain.

(b) Use the graph to approximate the air temperature resulting in oxygen consumption of 150 microliters per gram per hour.

(c) The temperature is increased from 10°C to 20°C. The oxygen consumption is increased by approximately what factor?

131. Fuel Efficiency   The distance d (in miles) a car can travel on one tank of fuel is approximated by $d = -0.024s^2 + 1.455s + 431.5$, $0 < s \le 75$, where s is the average speed of the car in miles per hour.

(a) Use a graphing utility to graph the function over the specified domain.

(b) Use the graph to determine the greatest distance that can be traveled on a tank of fuel. How long will the trip take?

(c) Determine the greatest distance that can be traveled in this car in 8 hours with no refueling. How fast should the car be driven? [*Hint:* The distance traveled in 8 hours is $8s$. Graph this expression in the same viewing window as the graph in part (a) and approximate the point of intersection.]

132. Saturated Steam   The temperature T (in degrees Fahrenheit) of saturated steam increases as pressure increases. This relationship is approximated by the model

$$T = 75.82 - 2.11x + 43.51\sqrt{x}, \quad 5 \le x \le 40$$

where x is the absolute pressure in pounds per square inch.

(a) Use a graphing utility to graph the function over the specified domain.

(b) The temperature of steam at sea level ($x = 14.696$) is 212°F. Evaluate the model at this pressure and verify the result graphically.

(c) Use the model to approximate the pressure for a steam temperature of 240°F.

133. *Meteorology*   A meteorologist is positioned 100 feet from the point at which a weather balloon is launched. When the balloon is at height h, the distance d (in feet) between the meteorologist and the balloon is $d = \sqrt{100^2 + h^2}$.

(a) Use a graphing utility to graph the equation. Use the *trace* feature to approximate the value of h when $d = 200$.

(b) Complete the table. Use the table to approximate the value of h when $d = 200$.

h	160	165	170	175	180	185
d						

(c) Find h algebraically when $d = 200$.

(d) Compare the results of each method. In each case, what information did you gain that wasn't revealed by another solution method?

134. *Geometry*   An equilateral triangle has a height of 10 inches. How long is each of its sides? (*Hint:* Use the height of the triangle to partition the triangle into two congruent right triangles.)

135. *Flying Speed*   Two planes leave simultaneously from Chicago's O'Hare Airport, one flying due north and the other due east. The northbound plane is flying 50 miles per hour faster than the eastbound plane. After 3 hours the planes are 2440 miles apart. Find the speed of each plane. (*Hint:* draw a diagram.)

136. *Flying Distance*   A chartered airplane flies to three cities whose locations form the vertices of a right triangle (see figure). The total flight distance (from Indianapolis to Peoria to Springfield and back to Indianapolis) is approximately 448 miles. It is 195 miles between Indianapolis and Peoria. Approximate the other two distances.

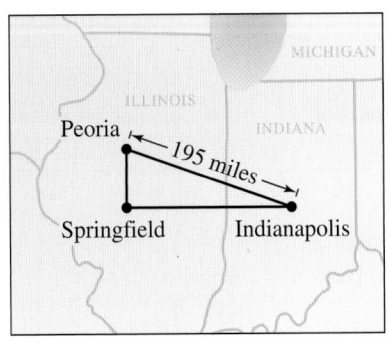

Synthesis

True or False?   **In Exercises 137–139, determine whether the statement is true or false. Justify your answer.**

137. The quadratic equation $-3x^2 - x = 10$ has two real solutions.

138. If $(2x - 3)(x + 5) = 8$, then $2x - 3 = 8$ or $x + 5 = 8$.

139. An equation can never have more than one extraneous solution.

140. *Exploration*   Solve $3(x + 4)^2 + (x + 4) - 2 = 0$ in two ways.

(a) Let $u = x + 4$, and solve the resulting equation for u. Then find the corresponding values of x that are the solutions of the original equation.

(b) Expand and collect like terms in the original equation, and solve the resulting equation for x.

(c) Which method is easier? Explain.

141. *Exploration*   Given that a and b are nonzero real numbers, determine the solutions of the equations.

(a) $ax^2 + bx = 0$ (b) $ax^2 - ax = 0$

142. *Writing*   On a graphing utility, store the value 5 in A, -2 in B, and 1 in C. Use the graphing utility to graph $y = C(x - A)(x - B)$. Explain how the values of A and B can be determined from the graph. Now store any other nonzero value in C. Does the value of C affect the x-intercepts of the graph? Explain. Find values of A, B, and C such that the graph opens downward and has x-intercepts at $(-5, 0)$ and $(0, 0)$. Summarize your findings.

Review

In Exercises 143–146, completely factor the expression over the real numbers.

143. $x^5 - 27x^2$

144. $x^3 - 5x^2 - 14x$

145. $x^3 + 5x^2 - 2x - 10$

146. $5(x + 5)x^{1/3} + 4x^{4/3}$

In Exercises 147–152, determine whether y is a function of x.

147. $5x + 8y = -1$

148. $-x^2 + y^2 = 2$

149. $x + y^2 = 10$

150. $-2y = \sqrt{x + 6}$

151. $y = |x - 3|$

152. $|y| = 1 - x$

2.5 Solving Inequalities Algebraically and Graphically

Properties of Inequalities

Simple inequalities were reviewed in Section P.1. There, the inequality symbols $<$, $\leq$, $>$, and $\geq$ were used to compare two numbers and to denote subsets of real numbers. For instance, the simple inequality $x \geq 3$ denotes all real numbers x that are greater than or equal to 3.

In this section you will study inequalities that contain more involved statements such as

$$5x - 7 > 3x + 9 \qquad \text{and} \qquad -3 \leq 6x - 1 < 3.$$

As with an equation, you **solve an inequality** in the variable x by finding all values of x for which the inequality is true. These values are **solutions** of the inequality and are said to **satisfy** the inequality. For instance, the number 9 is a solution of the first inequality listed above because

$$5(9) - 7 > 3(9) + 9$$

$$38 > 36.$$

On the other hand, the number 7 is not a solution because

$$5(7) - 7 \not> 3(7) + 9$$

$$28 \not> 30.$$

The set of all real numbers that are solutions of an inequality is the **solution set** of the inequality.

The set of all points on the real number line that represent the solution set is the **graph of the inequality**. Graphs of many types of inequalities consist of intervals on the real number line.

The procedures for solving linear inequalities in one variable are much like those for solving linear equations. To isolate the variable, you can make use of the **properties of inequalities**. These properties are similar to the properties of equality, but there are two important exceptions. When each side of an inequality is multiplied or divided by a negative number, *the direction of the inequality symbol must be reversed* in order to maintain a true statement. Here is an example.

$$-2 < 5 \qquad \text{Original inequality}$$

$$(-3)(-2) > (-3)(5) \qquad \text{Multiply each side by } -3 \text{ and reverse inequality.}$$

$$6 > -15 \qquad \text{Simplify.}$$

Two inequalities that have the same solution set are **equivalent inequalities**. For instance, the inequalities

$$x + 2 < 5 \qquad \text{and} \qquad x < 3$$

are equivalent. To obtain the second inequality from the first, you can subtract 2 from each side of the inequality. The properties listed at the top of the next page describe operations that can be used to create equivalent inequalities.

Properties of Inequalities

Let a, b, c, and d be real numbers.

1. *Transitive Property*

$$a < b \text{ and } b < c \quad \Longrightarrow \quad a < c$$

2. *Addition of Inequalities*

$$a < b \text{ and } c < d \quad \Longrightarrow \quad a + c < b + d$$

3. *Addition of a Constant*

$$a < b \quad \Longrightarrow \quad a + c < b + c$$

4. *Multiplying by a Constant*

For $c > 0$, $a < b \quad \Longrightarrow \quad ac < bc$

For $c < 0$, $a < b \quad \Longrightarrow \quad ac > bc$

> **Exploration**
>
> Use a graphing utility to graph $f(x) = 5x - 7$ and $g(x) = 3x + 9$ in the same viewing window. (Use $-1 \leq x \leq 15$ and $-5 \leq y \leq 50$.) For which values of x does the graph of f lie above the graph of g? Explain how the answer to this question can be used to solve the inequality in Example 1.

Each of the properties above is true if the symbol $<$ is replaced by $\leq$ and $>$ is replaced by $\geq$. For instance, another form of Property 3 is as follows.

$$a \leq b \quad \Longrightarrow \quad a + c \leq b + c$$

Solving a Linear Inequality

The simplest type of inequality to solve is a **linear inequality** in one variable, such as $2x + 3 > 4$. (See Appendix D for help with solving one-step linear inequalities.)

Example 1 Solving a Linear Inequality

Solve $5x - 7 > 3x + 9$.

Solution

$5x - 7 > 3x + 9$	Write original inequality.
$2x - 7 > 9$	Subtract $3x$ from each side.
$2x > 16$	Add 7 to each side.
$x > 8$	Divide each side by 2.

So, the solution set is all real numbers that are greater than 8. The interval notation for this solution set is $(8, \infty)$. The number line graph of this solution set is shown in Figure 2.45. Note that a parenthesis at 8 on the number line indicates that 8 *is not* part of the solution set.

✓ *Checkpoint* Now try Exercise 11.

> **STUDY TIP**
>
> Checking the solution set of an inequality is not as simple as checking the solution(s) of an equation because there are simply too many x-values to substitute into the original inequality. However, you can get an indication of the validity of the solution set by substituting a few convenient values of x. For instance, in Example 1, try substituting $x = 5$ and $x = 10$ into the original inequality.

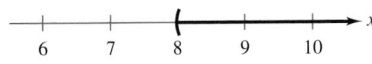

Figure 2.45 Solution interval: $(8, \infty)$

Note that the four inequalities forming the solution steps of Example 1 are all *equivalent* in the sense that each has the same solution set.

Example 2   Solving an Inequality

Solve $1 - \frac{3}{2}x \geq x - 4$.

Algebraic Solution

$$1 - \frac{3}{2}x \geq x - 4 \qquad \text{Write original inequality.}$$

$$2 - 3x \geq 2x - 8 \qquad \text{Multiply each side by the LCD.}$$

$$2 - 5x \geq -8 \qquad \text{Subtract } 2x \text{ from each side.}$$

$$-5x \geq -10 \qquad \text{Subtract 2 from each side.}$$

$$x \leq 2 \qquad \text{Divide each side by } -5 \text{ and reverse inequality.}$$

The solution set is all real numbers that are less than or equal to 2. The interval notation for this solution set is $(-\infty, 2]$. The number line graph of this solution set is shown in Figure 2.46. Note that a bracket at 2 on the number line indicates that 2 *is* part of the solution set.

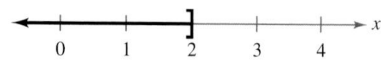

Figure 2.46   Solution interval: $(-\infty, 2]$

Graphical Solution

Use a graphing utility to graph $y_1 = 1 - \frac{3}{2}x$ and $y_2 = x - 4$ in the same viewing window. In Figure 2.47, you can see that the graphs appear to intersect at the point $(2, -2)$. Use the *intersect* feature of the graphing utility to confirm this. The graph of y_1 lies above the graph of y_2 to the left of their point of intersection, which implies that $y_1 \geq y_2$ for all $x \leq 2$.

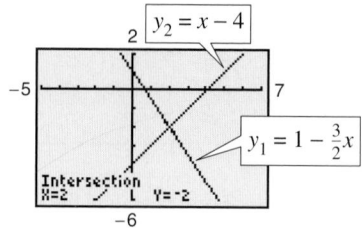

Figure 2.47

✓ *Checkpoint* Now try Exercise 13.

Sometimes it is possible to write two inequalities as a **double inequality,** as demonstrated in Example 3.

Example 3   Solving a Double Inequality

Solve $-3 \leq 6x - 1$ and $6x - 1 < 3$.

Algebraic Solution

$$-3 \leq 6x - 1 < 3 \qquad \text{Write as a double inequality.}$$

$$-2 \leq 6x < 4 \qquad \text{Add 1 to each part.}$$

$$-\frac{1}{3} \leq x < \frac{2}{3} \qquad \text{Divide by 6 and simplify.}$$

The solution set is all real numbers that are greater than or equal to $-\frac{1}{3}$ *and* less than $\frac{2}{3}$. The interval notation for this solution set is $\left[-\frac{1}{3}, \frac{2}{3}\right)$. The number line graph of this solution set is shown in Figure 2.48.

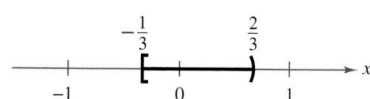

Figure 2.48   Solution interval $\left[-\frac{1}{3}, \frac{2}{3}\right)$

Graphical Solution

Use a graphing utility to graph $y_1 = 6x - 1$, $y_2 = -3$, and $y_3 = 3$ in the same viewing window. In Figure 2.49, you can see that the graphs appear to intersect at the points $\left(-\frac{1}{3}, -3\right)$ and $\left(\frac{2}{3}, 3\right)$. Use the *intersect* feature of the graphing utility to confirm this. The graph of y_1 lies above the graph of y_2 to the right of $\left(-\frac{1}{3}, -3\right)$ *and* the graph of y_1 lies below the graph of y_3 to the left of $\left(\frac{2}{3}, 3\right)$. This implies that $y_2 \leq y_1 < y_3$ when $-\frac{1}{3} \leq x < \frac{2}{3}$.

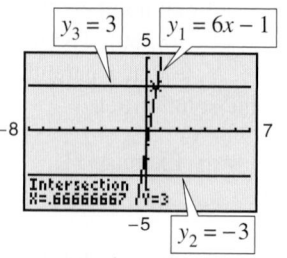

Figure 2.49

✓ *Checkpoint* Now try Exercise 15.

Inequalities Involving Absolute Value

> **Solving an Absolute Value Inequality**
>
> Let x be a variable or an algebraic expression and let a be a real number such that $a \geq 0$.
>
> **1.** The solutions of $|x| < a$ are all values of x that lie between $-a$ and a.
>
> $$|x| < a \quad \text{if and only if} \quad -a < x < a. \qquad \text{Double inequality}$$
>
> **2.** The solutions of $|x| > a$ are all values of x that are less than $-a$ or greater than a.
>
> $$|x| > a \quad \text{if and only if} \quad x < -a \quad \text{or} \quad x > a. \qquad \text{Compound inequality}$$
>
> These rules are also valid if $<$ is replaced by $\leq$ and $>$ is replaced by $\geq$.

Example 4   Solving Absolute Value Inequalities

Solve each inequality.

a. $|x - 5| < 2$ **b.** $|x - 5| > 2$

Algebraic Solution

a.
$|x - 5| < 2$	Write original inequality.
$-2 < x - 5 < 2$	Write double inequality.
$3 < x < 7$	Add 5 to each part.

The solution set is all real numbers that are greater than 3 *and* less than 7. The interval notation for this solution set is $(3, 7)$. The number line graph of this solution set is shown in Figure 2.50.

b. The absolute value inequality $|x - 5| > 2$ is equivalent to the following compound inequality: $x - 5 < -2$ *or* $x - 5 > 2$.

Solve first inequality:	$x - 5 < -2$	Write first inequality.
	$x < 3$	Add 5 to each side.

Solve second inequality:	$x - 5 > 2$	Write second inequality.
	$x > 7$	Add 5 to each side.

The solution set is all real numbers that are less than 3 *or* greater than 7. The interval notation for this solution set is $(-\infty, 3) \cup (7, \infty)$. The symbol $\cup$ is called a *union* symbol and is used to denote the combining of two sets. The number line graph of this solution set is shown in Figure 2.51.

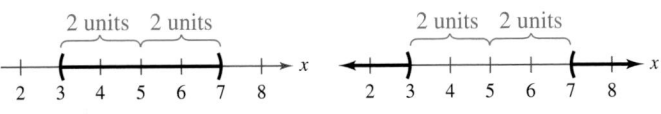

Figure 2.50   Figure 2.51

☑ *Checkpoint* Now try Exercise 29.

Graphical Solution

a. Use a graphing utility to graph $y_1 = |x - 5|$ and $y_2 = 2$ in the same viewing window. In Figure 2.52, you can see that the graphs appear to intersect at the points $(3, 2)$ and $(7, 2)$. Use the *intersect* feature of the graphing utility to confirm this. The graph of y_1 lies below the graph of y_2 when $3 < x < 7$. So, you can approximate the solution set to be all real numbers greater than 3 *and* less than 7.

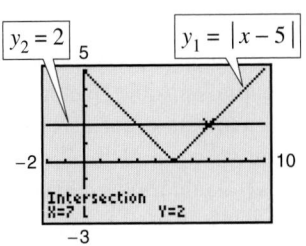

Figure 2.52

b. In Figure 2.52, you can see that the graph of y_1 lies above the graph of y_2 when $x < 3$ or when $x > 7$. So, you can approximate the solution set to be all real numbers that are less than 3 *or* greater than 7.

Polynomial Inequalities

To solve a polynomial inequality such as $x^2 - 2x - 3 < 0$, use the fact that a polynomial can change signs only at its zeros (the x-values that make the polynomial equal to zero). Between two consecutive zeros, a polynomial must be entirely positive or entirely negative. This means that when the real zeros of a polynomial are put in order, they divide the real number line into intervals in which the polynomial has no sign changes. These zeros are the **critical numbers** of the inequality, and the resulting open intervals are the **test intervals** for the inequality. For instance, the polynomial above factors as

$$x^2 - 2x - 3 = (x + 1)(x - 3)$$

and has two zeros, $x = -1$ and $x = 3$, which divide the real number line into three test intervals: $(-\infty, -1)$, $(-1, 3)$, and $(3, \infty)$. To solve the inequality $x^2 - 2x - 3 < 0$, you need to test only one value from each test interval.

TECHNOLOGY TIP

Some graphing utilities will produce graphs of inequalities. For instance, you can graph $2x^2 + 5x > 12$ by setting the graphing utility to *dot* mode and entering $y = 2x^2 + 5x > 12$. Using the settings $-10 \le x \le 10$ and $-4 \le y \le 4$, your graph should look like the graph shown below. Solve the problem algebraically to verify that the solution is $(-\infty, -4) \cup \left(\frac{3}{2}, \infty\right)$.

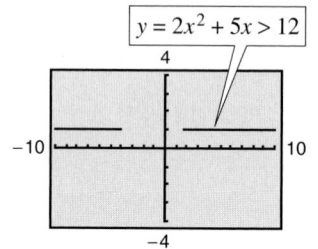

> **Finding Test Intervals for a Polynomial**
>
> To determine the intervals on which the values of a polynomial are entirely negative or entirely positive, use the following steps.
>
> **1.** Find all real zeros of the polynomial, and arrange the zeros in increasing order. The zeros of a polynomial are its critical numbers.
>
> **2.** Use the critical numbers to determine the test intervals.
>
> **3.** Choose one representative x-value in each test interval and evaluate the polynomial at that value. If the value of the polynomial is negative, the polynomial will have negative values for *every* x-value in the interval. If the value of the polynomial is positive, the polynomial will have positive values for every x-value in the interval.

Example 5   Investigating Polynomial Behavior

To determine the intervals on which $x^2 - x - 6$ is entirely negative and those on which it is entirely positive, factor the quadratic as $x^2 - x - 6 = (x + 2)(x - 3)$. The critical numbers occur at $x = -2$ and $x = 3$. So, the test intervals for the quadratic are $(-\infty, -2)$, $(-2, 3)$, and $(3, \infty)$. In each test interval, choose a representative x-value and evaluate the polynomial, as shown in the table.

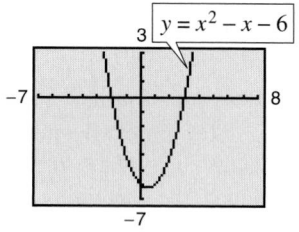

Figure 2.53

Interval	x-Value	Value of Polynomial	Sign of Polynomial
$(-\infty, -2)$	$x = -3$	$(-3)^2 - (-3) - 6 = 6$	Positive
$(-2, 3)$	$x = 0$	$(0)^2 - (0) - 6 = -6$	Negative
$(3, \infty)$	$x = 5$	$(5)^2 - (5) - 6 = 14$	Positive

The polynomial has negative values for every x in the interval $(-2, 3)$ and positive values for every x in the intervals $(-\infty, -2)$ and $(3, \infty)$. This result is shown graphically in Figure 2.53.

✓ *Checkpoint* Now try Exercise 43.

To determine the test intervals for a polynomial inequality, the inequality must first be written in general form with the polynomial on one side.

Example 6   Solving a Polynomial Inequality

Solve $2x^2 + 5x > 12$.

Algebraic Solution

$$2x^2 + 5x - 12 > 0 \qquad \text{Write inequality in general form.}$$

$$(x + 4)(2x - 3) > 0 \qquad \text{Factor.}$$

Critical Numbers: $x = -4, x = \frac{3}{2}$

Test Intervals: $(-\infty, -4), \left(-4, \frac{3}{2}\right), \left(\frac{3}{2}, \infty\right)$

Test: Is $(x + 4)(2x - 3) > 0$?

After testing these intervals, you can see that the polynomial $2x^2 + 5x - 12$ is positive on the open intervals $(-\infty, -4)$ and $\left(\frac{3}{2}, \infty\right)$. Therefore, the solution set of the inequality is

$$(-\infty, -4) \cup \left(\frac{3}{2}, \infty\right).$$

✓ *Checkpoint* Now try Exercise 47.

Graphical Solution

First write the polynomial inequality $2x^2 + 5x > 12$ as $2x^2 + 5x - 12 > 0$. Then use a graphing utility to graph $y = 2x^2 + 5x - 12$. In Figure 2.54, you can see that the graph is *above* the x-axis when x is less than -4 *or* when x is greater than $\frac{3}{2}$. So, you can graphically approximate the solution set to be $(-\infty, -4) \cup \left(\frac{3}{2}, \infty\right)$.

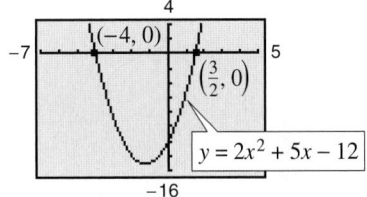

Figure 2.54

Example 7   Solving a Polynomial Inequality

Solve $2x^3 - 3x^2 - 32x > -48$.

Solution

$$2x^3 - 3x^2 - 32x + 48 > 0 \qquad \text{Write inequality in general form.}$$

$$x^2(2x - 3) - 16(2x - 3) > 0 \qquad \text{Factor by grouping.}$$

$$(x^2 - 16)(2x - 3) > 0 \qquad \text{Distributive Property}$$

$$(x - 4)(x + 4)(2x - 3) > 0 \qquad \text{Factor difference of two squares.}$$

The critical numbers are $x = -4, x = \frac{3}{2}$, and $x = 4$; and the test intervals are $(-\infty, -4), \left(-4, \frac{3}{2}\right), \left(\frac{3}{2}, 4\right)$, and $(4, \infty)$.

Interval	x-Value	Polynomial Value	Conclusion
$(-\infty, -4)$	$x = -5$	$2(-5)^3 - 3(-5)^2 - 32(-5) + 48 = -117$	Negative
$\left(-4, \frac{3}{2}\right)$	$x = 0$	$2(0)^3 - 3(0)^2 - 32(0) + 48 = 48$	Positive
$\left(\frac{3}{2}, 4\right)$	$x = 2$	$2(2)^3 - 3(2)^2 - 32(2) + 48 = -12$	Negative
$(4, \infty)$	$x = 5$	$2(5)^3 - 3(5)^2 - 32(5) + 48 = 63$	Positive

From this you can conclude that the polynomial is positive on the open intervals $\left(-4, \frac{3}{2}\right)$ and $(4, \infty)$. So, the solution set is $\left(-4, \frac{3}{2}\right) \cup (4, \infty)$.

✓ *Checkpoint* Now try Exercise 49.

STUDY TIP

When solving a quadratic inequality, be sure you have accounted for the particular type of inequality symbol given in the inequality. For instance, in Example 7, note that the original inequality contained a "greater than" symbol and the solution consisted of two open intervals. If the original inequality had been

$$2x^3 - 3x^2 - 32x \geq -48,$$

the solution would have consisted of the closed interval $\left[-4, \frac{3}{2}\right]$ and the interval $[4, \infty)$.

Example 8 Unusual Solution Sets

a. The solution set of

$$x^2 + 2x + 4 > 0$$

consists of the entire set of real numbers, $(-\infty, \infty)$. In other words, the value of the quadratic $x^2 + 2x + 4$ is positive for every real value of x, as indicated in Figure 2.55(a). (Note that this quadratic inequality has *no* critical numbers. In such a case, there is only one test interval—the entire real number line.)

b. The solution set of

$$x^2 + 2x + 1 \leq 0$$

consists of the single real number $\{-1\}$, because the quadratic $x^2 + 2x + 1$ has one critical number, $x = -1$, and it is the only value that satisfies the inequality, as indicated in Figure 2.55(b).

c. The solution set of

$$x^2 + 3x + 5 < 0$$

is empty. In other words, the quadratic $x^2 + 3x + 5$ is not less than zero for any value of x, as indicated in Figure 2.55(c).

d. The solution set of

$$x^2 - 4x + 4 > 0$$

consists of all real numbers *except* the number 2. In interval notation, this solution set can be written as $(-\infty, 2) \cup (2, \infty)$. The graph of $x^2 - 4x + 4$ lies above the x-axis except at $x = 2$, where it touches it, as indicated in Figure 2.55(d).

TECHNOLOGY TIP

One of the advantages of technology is that you can solve complicated polynomial inequalities that might be difficult, or even impossible, to factor. For instance, you could use a graphing utility to approximate the solution to the inequality

$$x^3 - 0.2x^2 - 3.16x + 1.4 < 0.$$

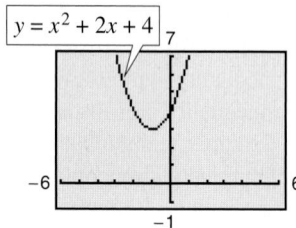

(a)

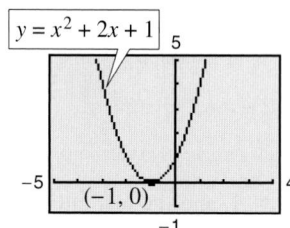

(b)

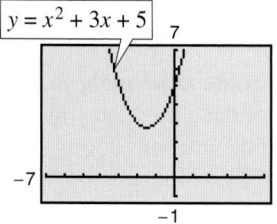

(c)

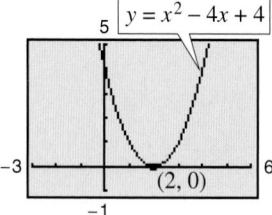

(d)

Figure 2.55

Rational Inequalities

The concepts of critical numbers and test intervals can be extended to inequalities involving rational expressions. To do this, use the fact that the value of a rational expression can change sign only at its *zeros* (the *x*-values for which its numerator is zero) and its *undefined values* (the *x*-values for which its denominator is zero). These two types of numbers make up the *critical numbers* of a rational inequality.

Example 9 Solving a Rational Inequality

Solve $\dfrac{2x - 7}{x - 5} \le 3$.

Algebraic Solution

$$\frac{2x - 7}{x - 5} \le 3 \qquad \text{Write original inequality.}$$

$$\frac{2x - 7}{x - 5} - 3 \le 0 \qquad \text{Write in general form.}$$

$$\frac{2x - 7 - 3x + 15}{x - 5} \le 0 \qquad \text{Write as single fraction.}$$

$$\frac{-x + 8}{x - 5} \le 0 \qquad \text{Simplify.}$$

Now, in standard form you can see that the critical numbers are $x = 5$ and $x = 8$, and you can proceed as follows.

Critical Numbers: $x = 5, x = 8$

Test Intervals: $(-\infty, 5), (5, 8), (8, \infty)$

Test: Is $\dfrac{-x + 8}{x - 5} \le 0$?

Interval	*x*-Value	Polynomial Value	Conclusion
$(-\infty, 5)$	$x = 0$	$\dfrac{-0 + 8}{0 - 5} = -\dfrac{8}{5}$	Negative
$(5, 8)$	$x = 6$	$\dfrac{-6 + 8}{6 - 5} = 2$	Positive
$(8, \infty)$	$x = 9$	$\dfrac{-9 + 8}{9 - 5} = -\dfrac{1}{4}$	Negative

By testing these intervals, you can determine that the rational expression $(-x + 8)/(x - 5)$ is negative in the open intervals $(-\infty, 5)$ and $(8, \infty)$. Moreover, because $(-x + 8)/(x - 5) = 0$ when $x = 8$, you can conclude that the solution set of the inequality is $(-\infty, 5) \cup [8, \infty)$.

✓ *Checkpoint* Now try Exercise 55.

Graphical Solution

Use a graphing utility to graph

$$y_1 = \frac{2x - 7}{x - 5} \text{ and } y_2 = 3$$

in the same viewing window. In Figure 2.56, you can see that the graphs appear to intersect at the point $(8, 3)$. Use the *intersect* feature of the graphing utility to confirm this. The graph of y_1 lies below the graph of y_2 in the intervals $(-\infty, 5)$ and $[8, \infty)$. So, you can graphically approximate the solution set to be all real numbers less than 5 *or* greater than or equal to 8.

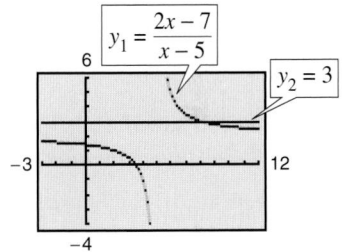

Figure 2.56

Note in Example 9 that $x = 5$ is not included in the solution set because the inequality is undefined when $x = 5$.

Application

In Section 1.3 you studied the *implied domain* of a function, the set of all x-values for which the function is defined. A common type of implied domain is used to avoid even roots of negative numbers, as shown in Example 10.

Example 10 Finding the Domain of an Expression

Find the domain of $\sqrt{64 - 4x^2}$.

Solution

Because $\sqrt{64 - 4x^2}$ is defined only if $64 - 4x^2$ is nonnegative, the domain is given by $64 - 4x^2 \geq 0$.

$$64 - 4x^2 \geq 0 \qquad \text{Write in general form.}$$

$$16 - x^2 \geq 0 \qquad \text{Divide each side by 4.}$$

$$(4 - x)(4 + x) \geq 0 \qquad \text{Factor.}$$

The inequality has two critical numbers: $x = -4$ and $x = 4$. A test shows that $64 - 4x^2 \geq 0$ in the *closed interval* $[-4, 4]$. The graph of $y = \sqrt{64 - 4x^2}$, shown in Figure 2.57, confirms that the domain is $[-4, 4]$.

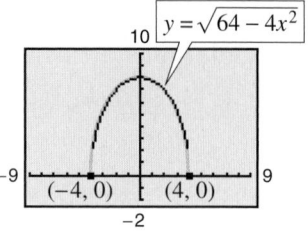

Figure 2.57

 Checkpoint Now try Exercise 63.

Example 11 Height of a Projectile

A projectile is fired straight upward from ground level with an initial velocity of 384 feet per second. During what time period will its height exceed 2000 feet?

Solution

In Section 2.4 you saw that the position of an object moving vertically can be modeled by the *position equation*

$$s = -16t^2 + v_0 t + s_0$$

where s is the height in feet and t is the time in seconds. In this case, $s_0 = 0$ and $v_0 = 384$. So, you need to solve the inequality $-16t^2 + 384t > 2000$. Using a graphing utility, graph $y_1 = -16t^2 + 384t$ and $y_2 = 2000$, as shown in Figure 2.58. From the graph, you can determine that $-16t^2 + 384t > 2000$ for t between approximately 7.6 and 16.4. You can verify this result algebraically.

$$-16t^2 + 384t > 2000 \qquad \text{Write original inequality.}$$

$$t^2 - 24t < -125 \qquad \text{Divide by } -16 \text{ and reverse inequality.}$$

$$t^2 - 24t + 125 < 0 \qquad \text{Write in general form.}$$

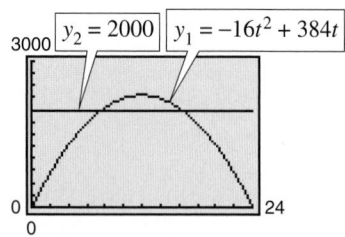

Figure 2.58

By the Quadratic Formula the critical numbers are $t = 12 - \sqrt{19}$ and $t = 12 + \sqrt{19}$, or approximately 7.64 and 16.36. A test will verify that the height of the projectile will exceed 2000 feet when $7.64 < t < 16.36$; that is, during the time interval $(7.64, 16.36)$ seconds.

 Checkpoint Now try Exercise 65.

2.5   Exercises

Vocabulary Check

Fill in the blanks.

1. To solve a linear inequality in one variable, you can use the properties of inequalities, which are identical to those used to solve an equation, with the exception of multiplying or dividing each side by a _____ constant.

2. It is sometimes possible to write two inequalities as one inequality, called a _____ inequality.

3. The solutions to $|x| \le a$ are those values of x such that _____ .

4. The solutions to $|x| \ge a$ are those values of x such that _____ or _____ .

5. The critical numbers of a rational expression are its _____ and its _____ .

In Exercises 1–4, match the inequality with its graph. [The graphs are labeled (a), (b), (c), and (d).]

(a)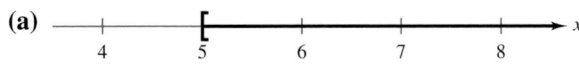

(b)

(c)

(d)

1. $x < 3$

2. $x \ge 5$

3. $-3 < x \le 4$

4. $0 \le x \le \frac{9}{2}$

In Exercises 5–8, determine whether each value of x is a solution of the inequality.

Inequality	Values	
5. $5x - 12 > 0$	(a) $x = 3$	(b) $x = -3$
	(c) $x = \frac{5}{2}$	(d) $x = \frac{3}{2}$
6. $-5 < 2x - 1 \le 1$	(a) $x = -\frac{1}{2}$	(b) $x = -\frac{5}{2}$
	(c) $x = \frac{4}{3}$	(d) $x = 0$
7. $-1 < \dfrac{3 - x}{2} \le 1$	(a) $x = 0$	(b) $x = \sqrt{5}$
	(c) $x = 1$	(d) $x = 5$
8. $|x - 10| \ge 3$	(a) $x = 13$	(b) $x = -1$
	(c) $x = 14$	(d) $x = 9$

In Exercises 9–18, solve the inequality and sketch the solution on the real number line. Use a graphing utility to verify your solution graphically.

9. $-10x < 40$

10. $6x > 15$

11. $4(x + 1) < 2x + 3$

12. $2x + 7 < 3(x - 4)$

13. $\frac{3}{4}x - 6 \le x - 7$

14. $3 + \frac{2}{7}x > x - 2$

15. $-8 \le 1 - 3(x - 2) < 13$

16. $0 \le 2 - 3(x + 1) < 20$

17. $-4 < \dfrac{2x - 3}{3} < 4$

18. $0 \le \dfrac{x + 3}{2} < 5$

Graphical Analysis **In Exercises 19–22, use a graphing utility to approximate the solution.**

19. $5 - 2x \ge 1$

20. $20 < 6x - 1$

21. $3(x + 1) < x + 7$

22. $4(x - 3) \le 8 - x$

In Exercises 23–26, use a graphing utility to graph the equation and graphically approximate the values of x that satisfy the specified inequalities. Then solve each inequality algebraically.

Equation	Inequalities	
23. $y = 2x - 3$	(a) $y \ge 1$	(b) $y \le 0$
24. $y = -3x + 8$	(a) $-1 \le y \le 3$	(b) $y \le 0$
25. $y = -\frac{1}{2}x + 2$	(a) $0 \le y \le 3$	(b) $y \ge 0$
26. $y = \frac{2}{3}x + 1$	(a) $y \le 5$	(b) $y \ge 0$

In Exercises 27–34, solve the inequality and sketch the solution on the real number line.

27. $|5x| > 10$

28. $\left|\dfrac{x}{2}\right| \le 1$

29. $|x - 7| < 6$

30. $|x - 20| \ge 4$

31. $|x + 14| + 3 > 17$

32. $\left|\dfrac{x - 3}{2}\right| \ge 5$

33. $10|1 - 2x| < 5$

34. $3|4 - 5x| \le 9$

In Exercises 35 and 36, use a graphing utility to graph the equation and graphically approximate the values of x that satisfy the specified inequalities. Then solve each inequality algebraically.

Equation	Inequalities	
35. $y = |x - 3|$	(a) $y \le 2$	(b) $y \ge 4$
36. $y = \left|\frac{1}{2}x + 1\right|$	(a) $y \le 4$	(b) $y \ge 1$

In Exercises 37–42, use absolute value notation to define the interval (or pair of intervals) on the real number line.

37.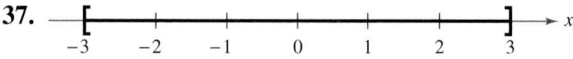

38. ![number line from -7 to 3 with bracket at -5 and bracket at 3]

39. ![number line from -3 to 3 with parenthesis at -3 and parenthesis at 3]

40. ![number line from 4 to 14 with bracket at 4 and bracket at 10]

41. All real numbers within 10 units of 7

42. All real numbers no more than 8 units from -5

In Exercises 43 and 44, determine the intervals on which the polynomial is entirely negative and those on which it is entirely positive.

43. $x^2 - 4x - 5$

44. $2x^2 - 4x - 3$

In Exercises 45–50, solve the inequality and graph the solution on the real number line. Use a graphing utility to verify your solution graphically.

45. $(x + 2)^2 < 25$ **46.** $(x - 3)^2 \ge 1$

47. $x^2 + 4x + 4 \ge 9$ **48.** $x^2 - 6x + 9 < 16$

49. $x^3 - 4x \ge 0$ **50.** $x^4(x - 3) \le 0$

In Exercises 51 and 52, use a graphing utility to graph the equation and graphically approximate the values of x that satisfy the specified inequalities. Then solve each inequality algebraically.

Equation	Inequalities	
51. $y = -x^2 + 2x + 3$	(a) $y \le 0$	(b) $y \ge 3$
52. $y = x^3 - x^2 - 16x + 16$	(a) $y \le 0$	(b) $y \ge 36$

In Exercises 53–56, solve the inequality and graph the solution on the real number line. Use a graphing utility to verify your solution graphically.

53. $\dfrac{1}{x} - x > 0$ **54.** $\dfrac{1}{x} - 4 < 0$

55. $\dfrac{x + 6}{x + 1} - 2 < 0$ **56.** $\dfrac{x + 12}{x + 2} - 3 \ge 0$

In Exercises 57 and 58, use a graphing utility to graph the equation and graphically approximate the values of x that satisfy the specified inequalities. Then solve each inequality algebraically.

Equation	Inequalities	
57. $y = \dfrac{3x}{x - 2}$	(a) $y \le 0$	(b) $y \ge 6$
58. $y = \dfrac{5x}{x^2 + 4}$	(a) $y \ge 1$	(b) $y \le 0$

In Exercises 59–64, find the domain of x in the expression.

59. $\sqrt{x - 5}$ **60.** $\sqrt[4]{6x + 15}$

61. $\sqrt[3]{6 - x}$ **62.** $\sqrt[3]{2x^2 - 8}$

63. $\sqrt{x^2 - 4}$ **64.** $\sqrt[4]{4 - x^2}$

65. *Data Analysis* You want to determine whether there is a relationship between an athlete's weight x (in pounds) and the athlete's maximum bench-press weight y (in pounds). The table shows a sample of data from 12 athletes.

Athlete's weight, x	Bench-press weight, y
165	170
184	185
150	200
210	255
196	205
240	295
202	190
170	175
185	195
190	185
230	250
160	150

(a) Use a graphing utility to plot the data.

(b) A model for this data is $y = 1.3x - 36$. Use a graphing utility to graph the equation in the same viewing window used in part (a).

(c) Use the graph to estimate the values of x that predict a maximum bench-press weight of at least 200 pounds.

(d) Use the graph to write a statement about the accuracy of the model. If you think the graph indicates that an athlete's weight is not a good indicator of the athlete's maximum bench-press weight, list other factors that might influence an individual's maximum bench-press weight.

66. *Education* The number D (in thousands) of earned bachelor's degrees conferred annually in the United States for selected years from 1975 to 2000 is approximated by the model $D = 0.42t^2 - 1.3t + 911$, where t represents the year, with $t = 5$ corresponding to 1975. (Source: U.S. National Center for Education Statistics)

(a) Use a graphing utility to graph the model.

(b) According to this model, estimate when the number of degrees will exceed 1,400,000.

Music In Exercises 67–70, use the following information. Michael Kasha of Florida State University used physics and mathematics to design a new classical guitar. He used the model for the frequency of the vibrations on a circular plate

$$v = \frac{2.6t}{d^2} \sqrt{\frac{E}{\rho}}$$

where v is the frequency (in vibrations per second), t is the plate thickness (in millimeters), d is the diameter of the plate, E is the elasticity of the plate material, and ρ is the density of the plate material. For fixed values of d, E, and ρ, the graph of the equation is a line, as shown in the figure.

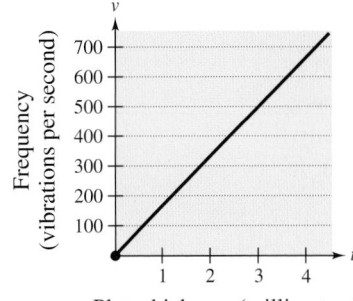

Plate thickness (millimeters)

67. Estimate the frequency when the plate thickness is 2 millimeters.

68. Estimate the plate thickness when the frequency is 600 vibrations per second.

69. Approximate the interval for the plate thickness when the frequency is between 200 and 400 vibrations per second.

70. Approximate the interval for the frequency when the plate thickness is less than 3 millimeters.

Synthesis

True or False? **In Exercises 71 and 72, determine whether the statement is true or false. Justify your answer.**

71. If $-10 \le x \le 8$, then $-10 \ge -x$ and $-x \ge -8$.

72. The solution set of the inequality $\frac{3}{2}x^2 + 3x + 6 \ge 0$ is the entire set of real numbers.

In Exercises 73 and 74, consider the polynomial $(x - a)(x - b)$ and the real number line (see figure).

73. Identify the points on the line where the polynomial is zero.

74. In each of the three subintervals of the line, write the sign of each factor and the sign of the product. For which x-values does the polynomial possibly change signs?

Review

In Exercises 75–78, find the distance between each pair of points. Then find the midpoint of the line segment joining the points.

75. $(-4, 2), (1, 12)$ 76. $(1, -2), (10, 3)$

77. $(3, 6), (-5, -8)$ 78. $(0, -3), (-6, 9)$

In Exercises 79–82, sketch a graph of the function.

79. $f(x) = -x^2 + 6$ 80. $f(x) = \frac{1}{3}(x - 5)^2$

81. $f(x) = -|x + 5| - 6$ 82. $f(x) = \frac{1}{2}|-x| - 4$

In Exercises 83–86, find the inverse function.

83. $y = 12x$ 84. $y = 5x + 8$

85. $y = x^3 + 7$ 86. $y = \sqrt[3]{x - 7}$

2.6 Exploring Data: Linear Models and Scatter Plots

Scatter Plots and Correlation

Many real-life situations involve finding relationships between two variables, such as the year and the number of people in the labor force. In a typical situation, data is collected and written as a set of ordered pairs. The graph of such a set, called a *scatter plot*, was discussed briefly in Section P.5.

Example 1   Constructing a Scatter Plot

The data in the table shows the number P (in millions) of people in the United States who were part of the labor force from 1995 through 2001. Construct a scatter plot of the data.   (Source: U.S. Bureau of Labor Statistics)

Year	People, P
1995	132
1996	134
1997	136
1998	138
1999	139
2000	141
2001	142

Solution

Begin by representing the data with a set of ordered pairs. Let t represent the year, with $t = 5$ corresponding to 1995.

$(5, 132), (6, 134), (7, 136), (8, 138), (9, 139), (10, 141), (11, 142)$

Then plot each point in a coordinate plane, as shown in Figure 2.59.

✓ *Checkpoint* Now try Exercise 1.

From the scatter plot in Figure 2.59, it appears that the points describe a relationship that is nearly linear. The relationship is not *exactly* linear because the labor force did not increase by precisely the same amount each year.

A mathematical equation that approximates the relationship between t and P is a *mathematical model*. When developing a mathematical model to describe a set of data, you strive for two (often conflicting) goals—accuracy and simplicity. For the data above, a linear model of the form $P = at + b$ appears to be best. It is simple and relatively accurate.

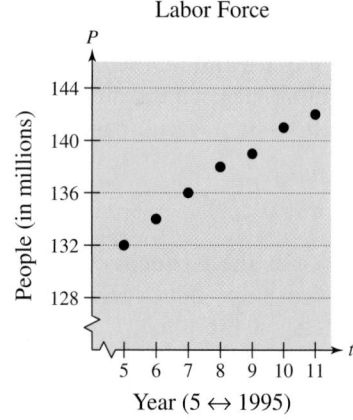

Figure 2.59

Consider a collection of ordered pairs of the form (x, y). If y tends to increase as x increases, the collection is said to have a **positive correlation.** If y tends to decrease as x increases, the collection is said to have a **negative correlation.** Figure 2.60 shows three examples: one with a positive correlation, one with a negative correlation, and one with no (discernible) correlation.

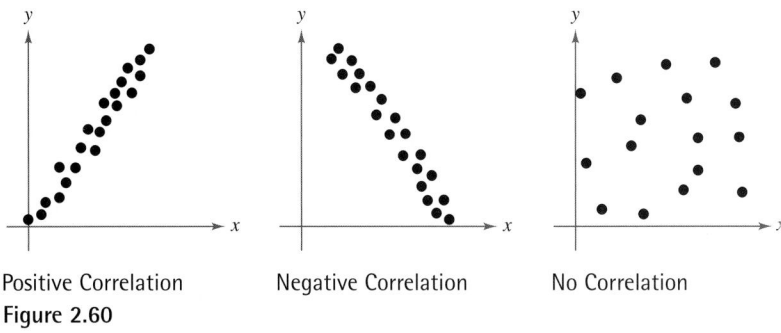

Positive Correlation   Negative Correlation   No Correlation

Figure 2.60

Example 2   Interpreting Correlation

On a Friday, 22 students in a class were asked to record the number of hours they spent studying for a test on Monday and the number of hours they spent watching television. The results are shown below. (The first coordinate is the number of hours and the second coordinate is the score obtained on the test.)

Study Hours: $(0, 40)$, $(1, 41)$, $(2, 51)$, $(3, 58)$, $(3, 49)$, $(4, 48)$, $(4, 64)$, $(5, 55)$, $(5, 69)$, $(5, 58)$, $(5, 75)$, $(6, 68)$, $(6, 63)$, $(6, 93)$, $(7, 84)$, $(7, 67)$, $(8, 90)$, $(8, 76)$, $(9, 95)$, $(9, 72)$, $(9, 85)$, $(10, 98)$

TV Hours: $(0, 98)$, $(1, 85)$, $(2, 72)$, $(2, 90)$, $(3, 67)$, $(3, 93)$, $(3, 95)$, $(4, 68)$, $(4, 84)$, $(5, 76)$, $(7, 75)$, $(7, 58)$, $(9, 63)$, $(9, 69)$, $(11, 55)$, $(12, 58)$, $(14, 64)$, $(16, 48)$, $(17, 51)$, $(18, 41)$, $(19, 49)$, $(20, 40)$

a. Construct a scatter plot for each set of data.

b. Determine whether the points are positively correlated, are negatively correlated, or have no discernable correlation. What can you conclude?

Solution

a. Scatter plots for the two sets of data are shown in Figure 2.61.

b. The scatter plot relating study hours and test scores has a positive correlation. This means that the more a student studied, the higher his or her score tended to be. The scatter plot relating television hours and test scores has a negative correlation. This means that the more time a student spent watching television, the lower his or her score tended to be.

 Checkpoint Now try Exercise 3.

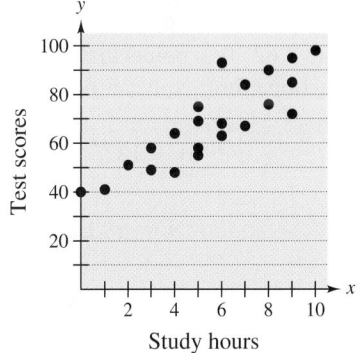

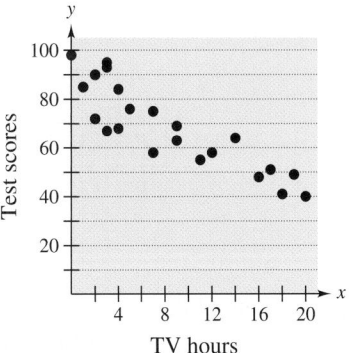

Figure 2.61

Fitting a Line to Data

Finding a linear model to represent the relationship described by a scatter plot is called **fitting a line to data.** You can do this graphically by simply sketching the line that appears to fit the points, finding two points on the line, and then finding the equation of the line that passes through the two points.

Example 3   Fitting a Line to Data

Find a linear model that relates the year to the number of people in the United
States labor force. (See Example 1.)

Year	People, P
1995	132
1996	134
1997	136
1998	138
1999	139
2000	141
2001	142

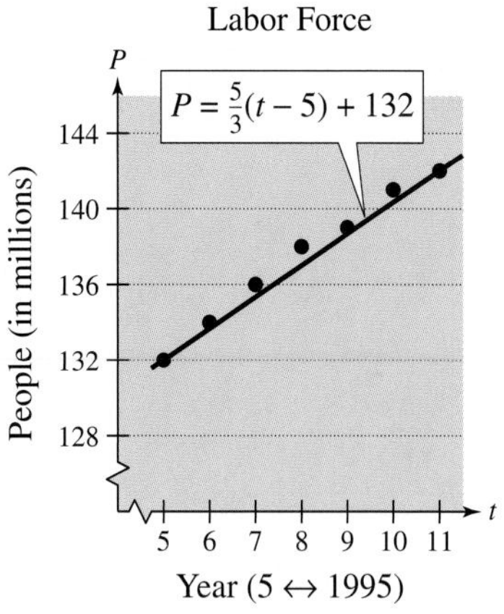

Labor Force

People (in millions)

$P = \frac{5}{3}(t-5) + 132$

Year (5 ↔ 1995)

Figure 2.62

Solution

Let t represent the year, with $t = 5$ corresponding to 1995. After plotting the data
in the table, draw the line that you think best represents the data, as shown in
Figure 2.62. Two points that lie on this line are $(5, 132)$ and $(11, 142)$. Using the
point-slope form, you can find the equation of the line to be

$$P = \frac{5}{3}(t - 5) + 132. \qquad \text{Linear model}$$

☑ *Checkpoint* Now try Exercise 11(a) and (b).

Once you have found a model, you can measure how well the model fits the
data by comparing the actual values with the values given by the model, as shown
in the following table.

t	5	6	7	8	9	10	11
Actual ⇨ P	132	134	136	138	139	141	142
Model ⇨ P	132	133.7	135.3	137	138.7	140.3	142

The sum of the squares of the differences between the actual values and the
model values is the **sum of the squared differences.** The model that has the least
sum is the **least squares regression line** for the data. For the model in Example
3, the sum of the squared differences is 2.16. The least squares regression line for
the data is

$$P = 1.7t + 124. \qquad \text{Best-fitting linear model}$$

Its sum of squared differences is 1.04. See Appendix C for more on the least
squares regression line.

Example 4   A Mathematical Model

The numbers S (in billions) of shares listed on the New York Stock Exchange for the years 1995 through 2001 are shown in the table.   (Source: New York Stock Exchange, Inc.)

Year	Shares, S
1995	154.7
1996	176.9
1997	207.1
1998	239.3
1999	280.9
2000	313.9
2001	341.5

TECHNOLOGY SUPPORT

For instructions on how to use the *regression* feature, see Appendix A; for specific keystrokes, go to the text website at *college.hmco.com*.

a. Use the *regression* feature of a graphing utility to find a linear model for the data. Let t represent the year, with $t = 5$ corresponding to 1995.

b. How closely does the model represent the data?

Graphical Solution

a. Enter the data into the graphing utility's list editor. Then use the *linear regression* feature to obtain the model shown in Figure 2.63. You can approximate the model to be $S = 32.44t - 14.6$.

b. You can use a graphing utility to graph the actual data and the model in the same viewing window. From Figure 2.64, it appears that the model is a good fit for the actual data.

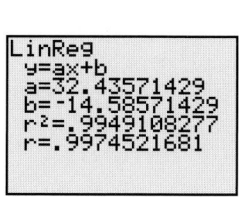

Figure 2.63   Figure 2.64

Numerical Solution

a. Using the *linear regression* feature of a graphing utility, you can find that a linear model for the data is $S = 32.44t - 14.6$.

b. You can see how well the model fits the data by comparing the actual values of S with the values of S given by the model, which are labeled S^* in the table below. From the table, you can see that the model appears to be a good fit for the actual data.

Year	S	S^*
1995	154.7	147.6
1996	176.9	180.0
1997	207.1	212.5
1998	239.3	244.9
1999	280.9	277.4
2000	313.9	309.8
2001	341.5	342.2

✓ *Checkpoint* Now try Exercise 15.

TECHNOLOGY TIP   When you use the *regression* feature of a graphing calculator or computer program to find a linear model for data, you will notice that the program may also output an "*r*-value." (For some calculators, make sure you select the *diagnostic on* feature before you use the *regression* feature. Otherwise, the calculator will not output an *r*-value.) For instance, the *r*-value from Example 4 was $r \approx 0.997$. This r-value is the **correlation coefficient** of the data and gives a measure of how well the model fits the data. Correlation coefficients vary between -1 and 1. Basically, the closer $|r|$ is to 1, the better the points can be described by a line. Three examples are shown in Figure 2.65.

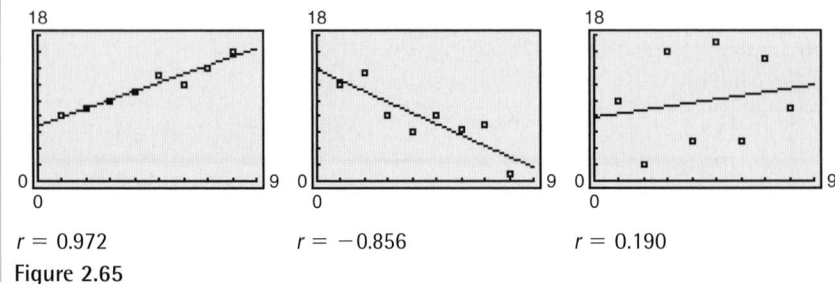

$r = 0.972$ $r = -0.856$ $r = 0.190$

Figure 2.65

Example 5   Finding a Least Squares Regression Line

The following ordered pairs (w, h) represent the shoe sizes w and the heights h (in inches) of 25 men. Use the *regression* feature of a graphing utility to find the least squares regression line for the data.

(10.0, 70.5)	(10.5, 71.0)	(9.5, 69.0)	(11.0, 72.0)	(12.0, 74.0)
(8.5, 67.0)	(9.0, 68.5)	(13.0, 76.0)	(10.5, 71.5)	(10.5, 70.5)
(10.0, 71.0)	(9.5, 70.0)	(10.0, 71.0)	(10.5, 71.0)	(11.0, 71.5)
(12.0, 73.5)	(12.5, 75.0)	(11.0, 72.0)	(9.0, 68.0)	(10.0, 70.0)
(13.0, 75.5)	(10.5, 72.0)	(10.5, 71.0)	(11.0, 73.0)	(8.5, 67.5)

Solution

After entering the data into a graphing utility (see Figure 2.66), you obtain the model shown in Figure 2.67. So, the least squares regression line for the data is

$$h = 1.84w + 51.9.$$

In Figure 2.68, this line is plotted with the data. Note that the plot does not have 25 points because some of the ordered pairs graph as the same point. The correlation coefficient for this model is $r \approx 0.981$, which implies that the model is a good fit for the data.

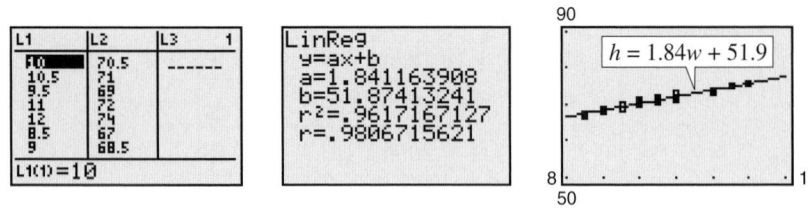

Figure 2.66   **Figure 2.67**   **Figure 2.68**

 Checkpoint Now try Exercise 17.

2.6   Exercises

Vocabulary Check

Fill in the blanks.

1. Consider a collection of ordered pairs of the form (x, y). If y tends to increase as x increases, then the collection is said to have a _____ correlation.

2. Consider a collection of ordered pairs of the form (x, y). If y tends to decrease as x increases, then the collection is said to have a _____ correlation.

3. The process of finding a linear model for a set of data is called _____ .

4. Correlation coefficients vary between _____ and _____ .

---

1. *Sales*   The following ordered pairs give the years of experience x for 15 sales representatives and the monthly sales y (in thousands of dollars).

   (1.5, 41.7), (1.0, 32.4), (0.3, 19.2), (3.0, 48.4),
   (4.0, 51.2), (0.5, 28.5), (2.5, 50.4), (1.8, 35.5),
   (2.0, 36.0), (1.5, 40.0), (3.5, 50.3), (4.0, 55.2),
   (0.5, 29.1), (2.2, 43.2), (2.0, 41.6)

   (a) Create a scatter plot of the data.

   (b) Does the relationship between x and y appear to be approximately linear? Explain.

2. *Quiz Scores*   The following ordered pairs give the scores on two consecutive 15-point quizzes for a class of 18 students.

   (7, 13), (9, 7), (14, 14), (15, 15), (10, 15), (9, 7),
   (14, 11), (14, 15), (8, 10), (9, 10), (15, 9), (10, 11),
   (11, 14), (7, 14), (11, 10), (14, 11), (10, 15), (9, 6)

   (a) Create a scatter plot for the data.

   (b) Does the relationship between consecutive quiz scores appear to be approximately linear? If not, give some possible explanations.

In Exercises 3–6, the scatter plots of sets of data are shown. Determine whether there is positive correlation, negative correlation, or no discernable correlation between the variables.

3.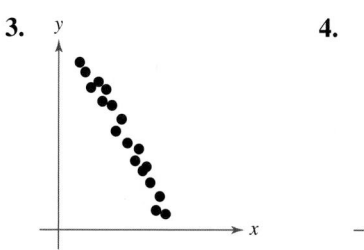

4.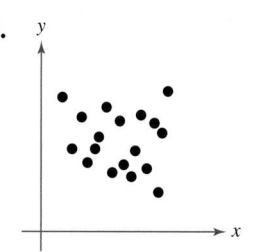

5.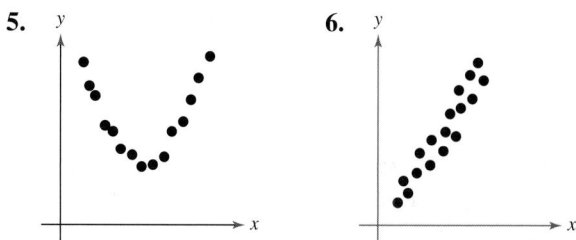

6.

In Exercises 7–10, (a) for the data points given, draw a line of best fit through two of the points and find the equation of the line through the points, (b) use the *regression* feature of a graphing utility to find a linear model for the data, (c) graph the data points and the lines obtained in parts (a) and (b) in the same viewing window, and (d) comment on the validity of both models. To print an enlarged copy of the graph, go to the website *www.mathgraphs.com*.

7.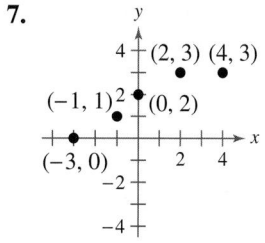

8.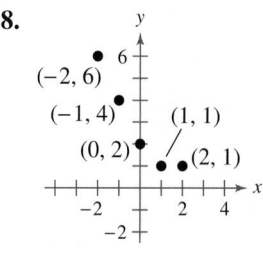

9.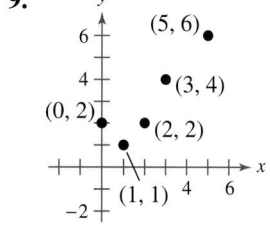

10.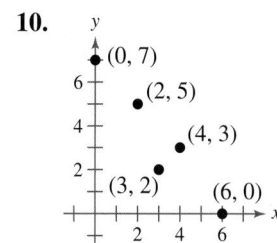

11. *Hooke's Law*   Hooke's Law states that the force F required to compress or stretch a spring (within its elastic limits) is proportional to the distance d that the spring is compressed or stretched from its original length. That is, $F = kd$, where k is the measure of the stiffness of the spring and is called the *spring constant*. The table shows the elongation d in centimeters of a spring when a force of F kilograms is applied.

Force, F	Elongation, d
20	1.4
40	2.5
60	4.0
80	5.3
100	6.6

(a) Sketch a scatter plot of the data.

(b) Find the equation of the line that seems to best fit the data.

(c) Use the *regression* feature of a graphing utility to find a linear model for the data. Compare this model with the model from part (b).

(d) Use the model from part (c) to estimate the elongation of the spring when a force of 55 kilograms is applied.

12. *Radio*   The number R of U.S. radio stations for selected years from 1970 through 2000 is shown in the table.   (Source: M Street Corporation)

Year	Radio stations, R
1970	6,760
1975	7,744
1980	8,566
1985	10,359
1990	10,788
1995	11,834
2000	13,058

(a) Use the *regression* feature of a graphing utility to find a linear model for the data. Let t represent the year, with $t = 0$ corresponding to 1970.

(b) Use a graphing utility to plot the data and graph the model in the same viewing window.

(c) Interpret the slope of the model in the context of the problem.

(d) Use the model to predict the number of radio stations in 2010.

13. *Sports*   The average salary S (in millions of dollars) for professional baseball players from 1996 through 2002 is shown in the table.   (Source: Associated Press and Major League Baseball)

Year	Salary, S
1996	1.1
1997	1.3
1998	1.4
1999	1.6
2000	1.8
2001	2.1
2002	2.3

(a) Use the *regression* feature of a graphing utility to find a linear model for the data. Let t represent the year, with $t = 6$ corresponding to 1996.

(b) Use a graphing utility to plot the data and graph the model in the same viewing window.

(c) Interpret the slope of the model in the context of the problem.

(d) Use the model to predict the average salary for a professional baseball player in 2006.

14. *Number of Stores*   The table shows the number T of Target stores from 1997 to 2002.   (Source: Target Corp.)

Year	Number of stores, T
1997	1130
1998	1182
1999	1243
2000	1307
2001	1381
2002	1476

(a) Use the *regression* feature of a graphing utility to find a linear model for the data. Let t represent the year, with $t = 7$ corresponding to 1997.

(b) Use a graphing utility to plot the data and graph the model in the same viewing window.

(c) Interpret the slope of the model in the context of the problem.

(d) Use the model to find the year in which the number of Target stores will exceed 1800.

(e) Create a table showing the actual values of T and the values of T given by the model. How closely does the model represent the data?

15. Communications   The table shows the average monthly spending S (in dollars) on paging and messaging services in the United States from 1997 to 2002.   (Source: The Strategis Group)

Year	Spending, S
1997	8.30
1998	8.50
1999	8.65
2000	8.80
2001	9.00
2002	9.25

(a) Use the *regression* feature of a graphing utility to find a linear model for the data. Let t represent the year, with $t = 7$ corresponding to 1997.

(b) Use a graphing utility to plot the data and graph the model in the same viewing window.

(c) Interpret the slope of the model in the context of the problem.

(d) Use the model to estimate the average monthly spending on paging and messaging services in 2008.

(e) Create a table showing the actual values of S and the values of S given by the model. How closely does the model represent the data?

16. Advertising and Sales   The table shows the advertising expenditures x and sales volume y for a company for seven randomly selected months. Both are measured in thousands of dollars.

Month	Advertising expenditures, x	Sales volume, y
1	2.4	202
2	1.6	184
3	2.0	220
4	2.6	240
5	1.4	180
6	1.6	164
7	2.0	186

Table for 16

(a) Use the *regression* feature of a graphing utility to find a linear model for the data.

(b) Use a graphing utility to plot the data and graph the model in the same viewing window.

(c) Interpret the slope of the model in the context of the problem.

(d) Use the model to estimate sales for advertising expenditures of $1500.

17. Sports   The following ordered pairs (x, y) represent the Olympic year x and the winning time y (in minutes) in the women's 400-meter freestyle swimming event.   (Source: The New York Times Almanac 2003)

(1948, 5.30)	(1976, 4.16)
(1952, 5.20)	(1980, 4.15)
(1956, 4.91)	(1984, 4.12)
(1960, 4.84)	(1988, 4.06)
(1964, 4.72)	(1992, 4.12)
(1968, 4.53)	(1996, 4.12)
(1972, 4.32)	(2000, 4.10)

(a) Use the *regression* feature of a graphing utility to find a linear model for the data. Let x represent the year, with $x = 0$ corresponding to 1950.

(b) What information is given by the sign of the slope of the model?

(c) Use a graphing utility to plot the data and graph the model in the same viewing window.

(d) How closely does the model fit the data?

(e) Can the model be used to estimate the winning times in the future? Explain.

18. **Elections** The data shows the percent x of the voting-age population that was registered to vote and the percent y that actually voted by state in 2000. (Source: U.S. Census Bureau)

AK (72.5, 65.6)   AL (73.6, 59.6)   AR (59.4, 49.4)
AZ (53.3, 46.7)   CA (52.8, 46.4)   CO (64.1, 53.6)
CT (62.5, 55.2)   D.C. (72.4, 65.6)   DE (67.9, 62.2)
FL (60.5, 51.6)   GA (61.1, 49.0)   HI (47.0, 39.7)
IA (72.2, 64.1)   ID (61.4, 53.9)   IL (66.7, 56.8)
IN (68.5, 58.5)   KS (67.7, 60.2)   KY (69.7, 54.9)
LA (75.4, 64.6)   MA (70.3, 60.1)   MD (65.6, 57.1)
ME (80.3, 69.2)   MI (69.1, 60.1)   MN (76.7, 67.8)
MO (74.3, 65.4)   MS (72.2, 59.8)   MT (70.0, 62.2)
NC (66.1, 53.2)   ND (91.1, 69.8)   NE (71.8, 58.9)
NH (69.6, 63.3)   NJ (63.2, 55.2)   NM (59.5, 51.3)
NV (52.3, 46.5)   NY (58.6, 51.0)   OH (67.0, 58.1)
OK (68.3, 58.3)   OR (68.2, 60.8)   PA (65.3, 55.7)
RI (69.7, 60.1)   SC (68.0, 58.9)   SD (70.9, 58.7)
TN (62.1, 52.3)   TX (61.4, 48.2)   UT (64.7, 56.3)
VA (64.1, 57.2)   VT (72.0, 63.3)   WA (66.1, 58.6)
WI (76.5, 67.8)   WV (63.1, 52.1)   WY (68.6, 62.5)

(a) Use the *regression* feature of a graphing utility to find a linear model for the data.

(b) Use a graphing utility to plot the data and graph the model in the same viewing window.

(c) Interpret the graph in part (b). Use the graph to identify any states that appear to differ substantially from most of the others.

(d) Interpret the slope of the model in the context of the problem.

Synthesis

True or False? **In Exercises 19 and 20, determine whether the statement is true or false. Justify your answer.**

19. A linear regression model with a positive correlation will have a slope that is greater than 0.

20. If the correlation coefficient for a linear regression model is close to -1, the regression line cannot be used to describe the data.

21. **Writing** A linear mathematical model for predicting prize winnings at a race is based on data for 3 years. Write a paragraph discussing the potential accuracy or inaccuracy of such a model.

22. **Research Project** Use your school's library, the Internet, or some other reference source to locate data that you think describes a linear relationship. Create a scatter plot of the data and find the least squares regression line that represents the points. Interpret the slope and y-intercept in the context of the data. Write a summary of your findings.

Review

In Exercises 23–26, use inequality and interval notation to describe the set.

23. P is no more than 2.

24. x is positive.

25. z is at least -3 and at most 10.

26. W is less than 7 but no less than -6.

In Exercises 27 and 28, simplify the complex fraction.

27. $\dfrac{x^2 - 4}{\left(\dfrac{x + 2}{5}\right)}$

28. $\dfrac{\left(\dfrac{x}{x^2 + 3x - 10}\right)}{\left(\dfrac{x^2 + 3x}{x^2 + 6x + 5}\right)}$

In Exercises 29–32, evaluate the function at each value of the independent variable and simplify.

29. $f(x) = 2x^2 - 3x + 5$
    (a) $f(-1)$ (b) $f(w + 2)$

30. $g(x) = 5x^2 - 6x + 1$
    (a) $g(-2)$ (b) $g(z - 2)$

31. $h(x) = \begin{cases} 1 - x^2, & x \le 0 \\ 2x + 3, & x > 0 \end{cases}$
    (a) $h(1)$ (b) $h(0)$

32. $k(x) = \begin{cases} 5 - 2x, & x < -1 \\ x^2 + 4, & x \ge -1 \end{cases}$
    (a) $k(-3)$ (b) $k(-1)$

In Exercises 33–38, solve the equation algebraically. Check your solution graphically.

33. $6x + 1 = -9x - 8$

34. $3(x - 3) = 7x + 2$

35. $8x^2 - 10x - 3 = 0$

36. $10x^2 - 23x - 5 = 0$

37. $2x^2 - 7x + 4 = 0$

38. $2x^2 - 8x + 5 = 0$

2 Chapter Summary

What did you learn?

Section 2.1	Review Exercises
☐ Solve equations involving fractional expressions.	1–8
☐ Write and use mathematical models to solve real-life problems.	9–14
☐ Use common formulas to solve real-life problems.	15, 16

Section 2.2
☐ Find x- and y-intercepts of graphs of equations.   17–22
☐ Find solutions of equations graphically.   23–28
☐ Find the points of intersection of two graphs.   29–32

Section 2.3
☐ Use the imaginary unit i to write complex numbers.   33–36
☐ Add, subtract, and multiply complex numbers.   37–44
☐ Use complex conjugates to write the quotient of two complex numbers in standard form.   45–48
☐ Plot complex numbers in the complex plane.   49–54

Section 2.4
☐ Solve quadratic equations by factoring, extracting square roots, completing the square,
and using the Quadratic Formula.   55–64
☐ Solve polynomial equations of degree three or greater.   65–68
☐ Solve equations involving radicals.   69–78
☐ Solve equations involving fractions or absolute values.   79–86
☐ Use quadratic equations to model and solve real-life problems.   87, 88

Section 2.5
☐ Use properties of inequalities to solve linear inequalities.   89–94
☐ Solve inequalities involving absolute values.   95–100
☐ Solve polynomial inequalities.   101–106
☐ Solve rational inequalities.   107–110
☐ Use inequalities to model and solve real-life problems.   111, 112

Section 2.6
☐ Construct scatter plots and interpret correlation.   113, 114
☐ Use scatter plots and a graphing utility to find linear models for data.   115–118

2 Review Exercises

2.1 **In Exercises 1 and 2, determine whether each value of x is a solution of the equation.**

Equation	Values

1. $6 + \dfrac{3}{x - 4} = 5$ (a) $x = 5$ (b) $x = 0$
(c) $x = -2$ (d) $x = 1$

2. $6 + \dfrac{2}{x + 3} = \dfrac{6x + 1}{3}$ (a) $x = -3$ (b) $x = 3$
(c) $x = 0$ (d) $x = -\frac{2}{3}$

In Exercises 3–8, solve the equation (if possible). Then use a graphing utility to verify your solution.

3. $\dfrac{18}{x} = \dfrac{10}{x - 4}$

4. $\dfrac{5}{x - 2} = \dfrac{13}{2x - 3}$

5. $14 + \dfrac{2}{x - 1} = 10$

6. $6 - \dfrac{11}{x} = 3 + \dfrac{7}{x}$

7. $\dfrac{9x}{3x - 1} - \dfrac{4}{3x + 1} = 3$

8. $\dfrac{5}{x - 5} + \dfrac{1}{x + 5} = \dfrac{2}{x^2 - 25}$

9. *Profit*   In October, a greeting card company's total profit was 12% more than it was in September. The total profit for the two months was $689,000. Find the profit for each month.

10. *Cost Sharing*   A group of farmers agree to share equally in the cost of a $48,000 piece of machinery. If they can find two more farmers to join the group, each person's share of the cost will decrease by $4000. How many farmers are presently in the group?

11. *Mixture Problem*   A car radiator contains 10 liters of a 30% antifreeze solution. How many liters will have to be replaced with pure antifreeze if the resulting solution is to be 50% antifreeze?

12. *Average Speed*   You drove 56 miles one way on a service call. On the return trip, your average speed was 8 miles per hour greater and the trip took 10 fewer minutes. What was your average speed on the return trip?

13. *Height*   To obtain the height of a tree, you measure the tree's shadow and find that it is 8 meters long. You also measure the shadow of a two-meter lamppost and find that it is 75 centimeters long.

   (a) Draw a diagram that illustrates the problem. Let h represent the height of the tree.

   (b) Find the height of the tree in meters.

14. *Investment*   You invest $12,000 in a fund paying $2\frac{1}{2}\%$ simple interest and $10,000 in a fund with a variable interest rate. At the end of the year, you were notified that the total interest for both funds was $870. Find the equivalent simple interest rate on the variable–rate fund.

15. *Meteorology*   The average daily temperature for the month of January in Juneau, Alaska is 25.7° F. What is Juneau's average daily temperature for the month of January in degrees Celsius?   (Source: U.S. National Oceanic and Atmospheric Administration)

16. *Geometry*   A basketball and a baseball have circumferences of 30 inches and $9\frac{1}{4}$ inches, respectively. Find the volume of each.

2.2 **In Exercises 17–22, find the x- and y-intercepts of the graph of the equation.**

17. $-x + y = 3$ **18.** $x - 5y = 20$

19. $y = x^2 - 9x + 8$ **20.** $y = 25 - x^2$

21. $y = -|x + 5| - 2$ **22.** $y = 6 - 2|x - 3|$

In Exercises 23–28, use a graphing utility to approximate any solutions (accurate to three decimal places) of the equation. [Remember to write the equation in the form $f(x) = 0$.]

23. $5(x - 2) - 1 = 0$ **24.** $12 - 5(x - 7) = 0$

25. $3x^3 - 2x + 4 = 0$ **26.** $\frac{1}{3}x^3 - x + 4 = 0$

27. $x^4 - 3x + 1 = 0$ **28.** $6 - \frac{1}{2}x^2 + \frac{5}{6}x^4 = 0$

In Exercises 29–32, determine any point(s) of intersection algebraically. Use a graphing utility to verify your answer(s).

29. $3x + 5y = -7$ **30.** $x - y = 3$
  $-x - 2y = 3$ $2x + y = 12$

31. $x^2 + 2y = 14$ **32.** $y = -x + 7$
  $3x + 4y = 1$ $y = 2x^3 - x + 9$

2.3 In Exercises 33–36, write the complex number in standard form.

33. $6 + \sqrt{-25}$

34. $-\sqrt{-12} + 3$

35. $-2i^2 + 7i$

36. $-i^2 - 4i$

In Exercises 37–44, perform the operations and write the result in standard form.

37. $(7 + 5i) + (-4 + 2i)$

38. $\left(\dfrac{\sqrt{2}}{2} - \dfrac{\sqrt{2}}{2}i\right) - \left(\dfrac{\sqrt{2}}{2} + \dfrac{\sqrt{2}}{2}i\right)$

39. $5i(13 - 8i)$

40. $(1 + 6i)(5 - 2i)$

41. $(10 - 8i)(2 - 3i)$

42. $i(6 + i)(3 - 2i)$

43. $(3 + 7i)^2 + (3 - 7i)^2$

44. $(4 - i)^2 - (4 + i)^2$

In Exercises 45–48, write the quotient in standard form.

45. $\dfrac{6 + i}{i}$

46. $\dfrac{4}{-3i}$

47. $\dfrac{3 + 2i}{5 + i}$

48. $\dfrac{1 - 7i}{2 + 3i}$

In Exercises 49–54, plot the complex number in the complex plane.

49. $2 - 5i$

50. $-1 + 4i$

51. $-6i$

52. $7i$

53. 3

54. -2

2.4 In Exercises 55–64, solve the equation using any convenient method. Use a graphing utility to verify your solution(s).

55. $6x = 3x^2$

56. $15 + x - 2x^2 = 0$

57. $(x + 4)^2 = 18$

58. $16x^2 = 25$

59. $x^2 - 12x + 30 = 0$

60. $x^2 + 6x - 3 = 0$

61. $2x^2 + 9x - 5 = 0$

62. $-x^2 - x + 15 = 0$

63. $x^2 + 4x + 10 = 0$

64. $2x^2 - 6x + 21 = 0$

In Exercises 65–86, find all real solutions of the equation algebraically. Use a graphing utility to verify the solutions graphically.

65. $3x^3 - 26x^2 + 16x = 0$

66. $216x^4 - x = 0$

67. $5x^4 - 12x^3 = 0$

68. $4x^3 - 6x^2 = 0$

69. $\sqrt{x + 4} = 3$

70. $\sqrt{x - 2} - 8 = 0$

71. $2\sqrt{x} - 5 = 0$

72. $\sqrt{3x - 2} = 4 - x$

73. $\sqrt{2x + 3} + \sqrt{x - 2} = 2$

74. $5\sqrt{x} - \sqrt{x - 1} = 6$

75. $(x - 1)^{2/3} - 25 = 0$

76. $(x + 2)^{3/4} = 27$

77. $(x + 4)^{1/2} + 5x(x + 4)^{3/2} = 0$

78. $8x^2(x^2 - 4)^{1/3} + (x^2 - 4)^{4/3} = 0$

79. $3\left(1 - \dfrac{1}{5t}\right) = 0$

80. $\dfrac{1}{x - 2} = 3$

81. $\dfrac{4}{(x - 4)^2} = 1$

82. $\dfrac{1}{(t + 1)^2} = 1$

83. $|x - 5| = 10$

84. $|2x + 3| = 7$

85. $|x^2 - 3| = 2x$

86. $|x^2 - 6| = x$

87. *Population*   The population P of South Dakota (in thousands) from 1995 through 2001 can be approximated by the model

$$P = 0.11t^2 + 1.5t + 728, \quad 5 \le t \le 11$$

where t represents the year, with $t = 5$ corresponding to 1995.   (Source: U.S. Census Bureau)

(a) Use the model to approximate algebraically when the population reached 750,000.

(b) Verify your answer to part (a) by creating a table of values for the model.

(c) Use a graphing utility to graph the model.

(d) Use the *zoom* and *trace* features of a graphing utility to determine when the population exceeded 740,000.

(e) Verify your answer to part (d) algebraically.

88. *Life Insurance*   The value y (in trillions of dollars) of life insurance policies in the United States from 1992 through 2000 can be approximated by the model

$$y = 0.045t^2 + 0.20t + 9.8, \quad 2 \le t \le 10$$

where t represents the year, with $t = 2$ corresponding to 1992.   (Source: American Council of Life Insurers)

(a) Use a graphing utility to graph the model.

(b) Use the graph to determine the year in which the value of life insurance policies was $15 trillion.

(c) Is this model accurate for predicting the value of life insurance policies in the future? Explain.

2.5 **In Exercises 89–110, solve the inequality and sketch the solution on the real number line. Use a graphing utility to verify your solution graphically.**

89. $8x - 3 < 6x + 15$

90. $9x - 8 \le 7x + 16$

91. $\frac{1}{2}(3 - x) > \frac{1}{3}(2 - 3x)$

92. $4(5 - 2x) \ge \frac{1}{2}(8 - x)$

93. $-2 < -x + 7 \le 10$

94. $-6 \le 3 - 2(x - 5) < 14$

95. $|x - 2| < 1$ **96.** $|x| \le 4$

97. $\left|x - \frac{3}{2}\right| \ge \frac{3}{2}$ **98.** $|x - 3| > 4$

99. $4|3 - 2x| \le 16$ **100.** $|x + 9| + 7 > 19$

101. $x^2 - 2x \ge 3$

102. $x^2 - 6x - 27 < 0$

103. $4x^2 - 23x \le 6$ **104.** $6x^2 + 5x < 4$

105. $x^3 - 16x \ge 0$ **106.** $12x^3 - 20x^2 < 0$

107. $\dfrac{x - 5}{3 - x} < 0$ **108.** $\dfrac{2}{x + 1} \le \dfrac{3}{x - 1}$

109. $\dfrac{3x + 8}{x - 3} \le 4$ **110.** $\dfrac{x + 8}{x + 5} - 2 < 0$

111. *Accuracy of Measurement*   The side of a square is measured as 20.8 inches with a possible error of $\frac{1}{16}$ inch. Using these measurements, determine the interval containing the area of the square.

112. *Meteorology*   An electronic device is to be operated in an environment with relative humidity h in the interval defined by

$$|h - 50| \le 30.$$

What are the minimum and maximum relative humidities for the operation of this device?

2.6

113. *Education*   The following ordered pairs give the entrance exam scores x and the grade-point averages y after 1 year of college for 10 students.

(75, 2.3), (82, 3.0), (90, 3.6), (65, 2.0), (70, 2.1), (88, 3.5), (93, 3.9), (69, 2.0), (80, 2.8), (85, 3.3)

(a) Create a scatter plot for the data.

(b) Does the relationship between x and y appear to be approximately linear? Explain.

114. *Stress Test*   A machine part was tested by bending it x centimeters 10 times per minute until it failed (y equals the time to failure in hours). The results

are given as the following ordered pairs.

(3, 61), (6, 56), (9, 53), (12, 55), (15, 48), (18, 35), (21, 36), (24, 33), (27, 44), (30, 23)

(a) Create a scatter plot for the data.

(b) Does the relationship between x and y appear to be approximately linear? If not, give some possible explanations.

115. *Falling Object*   In an experiment, students measured the speed s (in meters per second) of a ball t seconds after it was released. The results are shown in the table.

Time, t	Speed, s
0	0
1	11.0
2	19.4
3	29.2
4	39.4

(a) Sketch a scatter plot of the data.

(b) Find the equation of the line that seems to best fit the data.

(c) Use the *regression* feature of a graphing utility to find a linear model for the data. Compare with the model from part (b).

(d) Use the model from part (c) to estimate the speed of the ball after 2.5 seconds.

116. *Sales*   The table shows the sales S (in millions of dollars) for Timberland from 1995 to 2002. (Source: The Timberland Co.)

Year	Sales, S
1995	655.1
1996	690.0
1997	796.5
1998	862.2
1999	917.2
2000	1091.5
2001	1183.6
2002	1190.9

(a) Use the *regression* feature of a graphing utility to find a linear model for the data. Let t represent the year, with $t = 5$ corresponding to 1995.

(b) Use a graphing utility to plot the data and graph the model in the same viewing window.

(c) Interpret the slope of the model in the context of the problem.

(d) Use the model to find the year in which the sales will exceed $1300 million.

(e) Create a table showing the actual values of S and the values of S given by the model. How closely does the model represent the data?

117. **Height**   The following ordered pairs (x, y) represent the percent y of women between the ages of 20 and 29 who are under a certain height x (in feet). (Source: U.S. National Center for Health Statistics)

(4.67, 0.6)   (5.42, 62.7)
(4.75, 0.7)   (5.50, 74.0)
(4.83, 1.2)   (5.58, 84.7)
(4.92, 3.1)   (5.67, 92.4)
(5.00, 6.0)   (5.75, 96.2)
(5.08, 11.5)   (5.83, 98.6)
(5.17, 21.8)   (5.92, 99.5)
(5.25, 34.3)   (6.00, 100.0)
(5.33, 48.9)

(a) Use the *regression* feature of a graphing utility to find a linear model for the data.

(b) Use a graphing utility to plot the data and graph the model in the same viewing window.

(c) How closely does the model fit the data?

(d) Can the model be used to estimate the percent of women who are under a height of greater than 6 feet?

118. **Sports**   The following ordered pairs (x, y) represent the Olympic year x and the winning time y (in minutes) in the men's 1500-meter speed skating event. (Source: The New York Times Almanac 2003)

(1964, 2.17)   (1988, 1.87)
(1968, 2.06)   (1992, 1.91)
(1972, 2.05)   (1994, 1.85)
(1976, 1.99)   (1998, 1.80)
(1980, 1.92)   (2002, 1.73)
(1984, 1.97)

(a) Use the *regression* feature of a graphing utility to find a linear model for the data. Let x represent the year, with $x = 4$ corresponding to 1964.

(b) What information is given by the sign of the slope of the model?

(c) Use a graphing utility to plot the data and graph the model in the same viewing window.

(d) How closely does the model fit the data?

(e) Can the model be used to estimate the winning times in the future? Explain.

Synthesis

True or False?   In Exercises 119–121, determine whether the statement is true or false. Justify your answer.

119. The graph of a function may have two distinct y-intercepts.

120. The sum of two complex numbers cannot be a real number.

121. The sign of the slope of a regression line is always positive.

122. **Writing**   In your own words, explain the difference between an identity and a conditional equation.

123. **Writing**   Describe the relationship among the x-intercepts of a graph, the zeros of a function, and the solutions of an equation.

124. Consider the linear equation $ax + b = 0$.

(a) What is the sign of the solution if $ab > 0$?

(b) What is the sign of the solution if $ab < 0$?

125. **Error Analysis**   Describe the error.

$$\sqrt{-6}\sqrt{-6} = \sqrt{(-6)(-6)} = \sqrt{36} = 6$$

126. **Error Analysis**   Describe the error.

$$-i\left(\sqrt{-4} - 1\right) = -i(4i - 1)$$
$$= -4i^2 - i$$
$$= 4 - i$$

127. Write each of the powers of i as i, $-i$, 1, or -1.

(a) i^{40} (b) i^{25} (c) i^{50} (d) i^{67}

2 | Chapter Test

Take this test as you would take a test in class. After you are finished, check your work against the answers given in the back of the book.

In Exercises 1 and 2, solve the equation (if possible). Then use a graphing utility to verify your solution.

1. $\dfrac{12}{x} - 7 = -\dfrac{27}{x} + 6$

2. $\dfrac{4}{3x - 2} - \dfrac{9x}{3x + 2} = -3$

In Exercises 3–8, perform the operations and write the result in standard form.

3. $(-8 - 3i) + (-1 - 15i)$

4. $\left(10 + \sqrt{-20}\right) - \left(4 - \sqrt{-14}\right)$

5. $(2 + i)(6 - i)$

6. $(4 + 3i)^2 - (5 + i)^2$

In Exercises 7 and 8, write the quotient in standard form.

7. $\dfrac{8 + 5i}{6 - i}$

8. $\dfrac{5i}{2 + i}$

In Exercises 9–12, use a graphing utility to graph the equation and approximate any x-intercepts. Set $y = 0$ and solve the resulting equation. Compare the results with the x-intercepts of the graph.

9. $y = 3x^2 + 1$

10. $y = 2 + 8x^{-2}$

11. $y = x^3 - 4x^2 + 5x$

12. $y = x^3 + x$

In Exercises 13–16, solve the equation using any convenient method. Use a graphing utility to verify the solutions graphically.

13. $x^2 - 10x + 9 = 0$

14. $x^2 + 12x - 2 = 0$

15. $4x^2 - 81 = 0$

16. $5x^2 + 14x - 3 = 0$

In Exercises 17–20, find all solutions of the equation algebraically. Use a graphing utility to verify the solutions graphically.

17. $3x^3 - 4x^2 - 12x + 16 = 0$

18. $x + \sqrt{22 - 3x} = 6$

19. $(x^2 + 6)^{2/3} = 16$

20. $|8x - 1| = 21$

In Exercises 21–23, solve the inequality and sketch the solution on the real number line. Use a graphing utility to verify your solution graphically.

21. $-\dfrac{5}{6} < x - 2 < \dfrac{1}{8}$

22. $2|x - 8| < 10$

23. $\dfrac{3 - 5x}{2 + 3x} < -2$

24. The table shows the number of local telephone access lines L (in millions) in the United States from 1994 through 2000, where t represents the year, with $t = 4$ corresponding to 1994. Use the *regression* feature of a graphing utility to find a linear model for the data. Use the model to find the year in which the number of local telephone access lines will exceed 300 million. (Source: U.S. Federal Communications Commission)

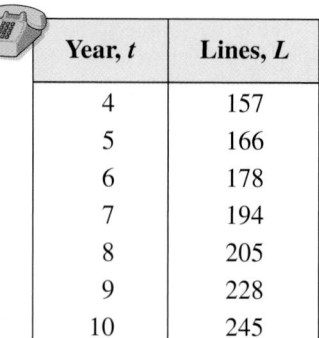

Year, t	Lines, L
4	157
5	166
6	178
7	194
8	205
9	228
10	245

Table for 24

P–2 | Cumulative Test

Take this test to review the material from earlier chapters. After you are finished, check your work against the answers in the back of the book.

In Exercises 1–3, simplify the expression.

1. $\dfrac{14x^2y^{-3}}{32x^{-1}y^2}$

2. $8\sqrt{60} - 2\sqrt{135} - \sqrt{15}$

3. $\sqrt{28x^4y^3}$

In Exercises 4–6, perform the operation and simplify the result.

4. $4x - [2x + 5(2 - x)]$ **5.** $(x - 2)(x^2 + x - 3)$ **6.** $\dfrac{2}{x + 3} - \dfrac{1}{x + 1}$

In Exercises 7–9, factor the expression completely.

7. $25 - (x - 2)^2$ **8.** $x - 5x^2 - 6x^3$ **9.** $54 - 16x^3$

10. Find the midpoint of the line segment connecting the points $\left(-\frac{7}{2}, 4\right)$ and $(6.5, -8)$. Then find the distance between the points.

11. Write the standard form of the equation of a circle with center $\left(-\frac{1}{2}, -8\right)$ and a radius of $\frac{5}{4}$.

In Exercises 12–14, use point plotting to sketch the graph of the equation.

12. $x - 3y + 12 = 0$ **13.** $y = x^2 - 9$ **14.** $y = \sqrt{4 - x}$

In Exercises 15–17, (a) write the general form of the equation of the line that satisfies the given conditions and (b) find three additional points through which the line passes.

15. The line contains the points $(-5, 8)$ and $\left(\frac{1}{2}, -6\right)$.

16. The line contains the point $\left(-\frac{1}{2}, 1\right)$ and has a slope of -2.

17. The line has an undefined slope and contains the point $\left(-\frac{3}{7}, \frac{1}{8}\right)$.

In Exercises 18 and 19, evaluate the function at each value of the independent variable and simplify.

18. $f(x) = \dfrac{x}{x - 2}$ **19.** $f(x) = \begin{cases} 3x - 8, & x \le -\frac{5}{3} \\ 3x^2 + 9x - 8, & x > -\frac{5}{3} \end{cases}$

     (a) $f(6)$ (b) $f(2)$ (c) $f(s + 2)$ (a) $f\left(-\frac{5}{3}\right)$ (b) $f(-1)$ (c) $f(0)$

20. Does the graph at the right represent y as a function of x? Explain.

21. Use a graphing utility to graph the function $f(x) = 2|x - 5| - |x + 5|$. Then determine the open intervals over which the function is increasing, decreasing, or constant.

22. Compare the graph of each function with the graph of $f(x) = \sqrt[3]{x}$.

     (a) $r(x) = \dfrac{1}{2}\sqrt[3]{x}$ (b) $h(x) = \sqrt[3]{x} + 2$ (c) $g(x) = \sqrt[3]{x + 2}$

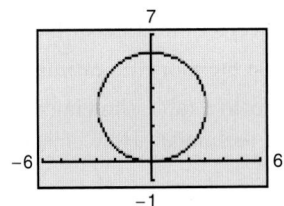

Figure for 20

In Exercises 23–26, evaluate the indicated function for

$f(x) = -x^2 + 3x - 10$ and $g(x) = 4x + 1.$

23. $(f + g)(-4)$ **24.** $(g - f)\left(\frac{3}{4}\right)$ **25.** $(g \circ f)(-2)$ **26.** $(fg)(-1)$

27. Determine whether $h(x) = 5x - 2$ has an inverse function. If so, find it.

28. Plot the complex number $-5 + 4i$ in the complex plane.

In Exercises 29–32, use a graphing utility to graph the equation and approximate any x-intercepts of the graph. Set $y = 0$ and solve the resulting equation. Compare the results with the x-intercepts of the graph.

29. $y = 4x^3 - 12x^2 + 8x$ **30.** $y = 12x^3 - 84x^2 + 120x$

31. $y = |2x - 3| - 5$ **32.** $y = \sqrt{x^2 + 1} + x - 9$

In Exercises 33 and 34, solve the equation for the indicated variable.

33. Solve for X: $Z = \sqrt{R^2 - X^2}$ **34.** Solve for p: $L = \dfrac{k}{3\pi r^2 p}$

In Exercises 35–38, solve the inequality and graph the solution on the real number line. Use a graphing utility to verify your solution graphically.

35. $\dfrac{x}{5} - 6 \le -\dfrac{x}{2} + 6$ **36.** $2x^2 + x \ge 15$

37. $|7 + 8x| > 5$ **38.** $\dfrac{2(x - 2)}{x + 1} \le 0$

39. A soccer ball has a volume of about 370.7 cubic inches. Find the radius of the soccer ball (accurate to three decimal places).

40. A rectangular plot of land with a perimeter of 546 feet has a width of x.

    (a) Write the area A of the plot as a function of x.

    (b) Use a graphing utility to graph the area function. What is the domain of the function?

    (c) Approximate the dimensions of the plot when the area is 15,000 square feet.

41. The total revenues R (in millions of dollars) for Papa John's from 1995 through 2001 are shown in the table.   (Source: Papa John's International)

    (a) Use the *regression* feature of a graphing utility to find a linear model for the data. Let t represent the year, with $t = 5$ corresponding to 1995.

    (b) Use a graphing utility to plot the data and graph the model in the same viewing window.

    (c) Interpret the slope of the model in the context of the problem.

    (d) Use the model to estimate the revenues for Papa John's in 2007.

    (e) Create a table showing the actual values of R and the values of R given by the model. How closely does the model represent the data?

Year	Revenues, R
1995	253.4
1996	360.1
1997	508.8
1998	669.8
1999	805.3
2000	944.7
2001	971.2

Table for 41

The average monthly rate for basic cable television service in the United States has increased from 1995 to 2001. You can use a cubic polynomial to model this growth and predict future cable rates.

Jose Luis Pelaez, Inc./Corbis

3 Polynomial and Rational Functions

3.1 **Quadratic Functions**

3.2 **Polynomial Functions of Higher Degree**

3.3 **Real Zeros of Polynomial Functions**

3.4 **The Fundamental Theorem of Algebra**

3.5 **Rational Functions and Asymptotes**

3.6 **Graphs of Rational Functions**

3.7 **Exploring Data: Quadratic Models**

What You Should Learn

In this chapter, you will learn how to:

■ Sketch and analyze graphs of quadratic and polynomial functions.

■ Use long division and synthetic division to divide polynomials by other polynomials.

■ Determine the numbers of rational and real zeros of polynomial functions, and find the zeros.

■ Determine the domains, find the asymptotes, and sketch the graphs of rational functions.

■ Classify scatter plots and use a graphing utility to find quadratic models for data.

3.1 Quadratic Functions

The Graph of a Quadratic Function

In this and the next section, you will study the graphs of polynomial functions.

> **Definition of Polynomial Function**
>
> Let n be a nonnegative integer and let $a_n, a_{n-1}, \ldots, a_2, a_1, a_0$ be real numbers with $a_n \neq 0$. The function given by
>
> $$f(x) = a_n x^n + a_{n-1} x^{n-1} + \cdots + a_2 x^2 + a_1 x + a_0$$
>
> is called a **polynomial function of x with degree n.**

Polynomial functions are classified by degree. For instance, the polynomial function

$$f(x) = a, \quad a \neq 0 \qquad \text{Constant function}$$

has degree 0 and is called a **constant function.** In Chapter 1, you learned that the graph of this type of function is a horizontal line. The polynomial function

$$f(x) = mx + b, \quad m \neq 0 \qquad \text{Linear function}$$

has degree 1 and is called a **linear function.** You also learned in Chapter 1 that the graph of the linear function $f(x) = mx + b$ is a line whose slope is m and whose y-intercept is $(0, b)$. In this section you will study second-degree polynomial functions, which are called **quadratic functions.**

> **Definition of Quadratic Function**
>
> Let a, b, and c be real numbers with $a \neq 0$. The function given by
>
> $$f(x) = ax^2 + bx + c \qquad \text{Quadratic function}$$
>
> is called a **quadratic function.**

Often real-life data can be modeled by quadratic functions. For instance, the table at the right shows the height h (in feet) of a projectile fired from a height of 6 feet with an initial velocity of 256 feet per second at any time t (in seconds). A quadratic model for the data in the table is $h(t) = -16t^2 + 256t + 6$ for $0 \leq t \leq 16$.

The graph of a quadratic function is a special type of U-shaped curve called a **parabola.** Parabolas occur in many real-life applications, especially those involving reflective properties, such as satellite dishes or flashlight reflectors. You will study these properties in a later chapter.

All parabolas are symmetric with respect to a line called the **axis of symmetry,** or simply the **axis** of the parabola. The point where the axis intersects the parabola is called the **vertex** of the parabola.

What you should learn

- Analyze graphs of quadratic functions.
- Write quadratic functions in standard form and use the results to sketch graphs of functions.
- Find minimum and maximum values of functions in real-life applications.

Why you should learn it

Quadratic functions can be used to model data to analyze consumer behavior. For instance, Exercise 68 on page 250 shows how a quadratic function can model VCR usage in the United States.

Mary K. Kenny/PhotoEdit

t	h
0	6
2	454
4	774
6	966
8	1030
10	966
12	774
13	454
16	6

Library of Functions: Quadratic Function

The simplest type of *quadratic function* is $f(x) = ax^2$, also known as the *squaring function*. The basic characteristics of the squaring function are summarized below.

Graph of $f(x) = ax^2$, $a > 0$

Domain: $(-\infty, \infty)$
Range: $[0, \infty)$
Intercept: $(0, 0)$
Decreasing on $(-\infty, 0)$
Increasing on $(0, \infty)$
Even function
y-Axis symmetry
Relative minimum or vertex: $(0, 0)$

Graph of $f(x) = ax^2$, $a < 0$

Domain: $(-\infty, \infty)$
Range: $(-\infty, 0]$
Intercept: $(0, 0)$
Increasing on $(-\infty, 0)$
Decreasing on $(0, \infty)$
Even function
y-Axis symmetry
Relative maximum or vertex: $(0, 0)$

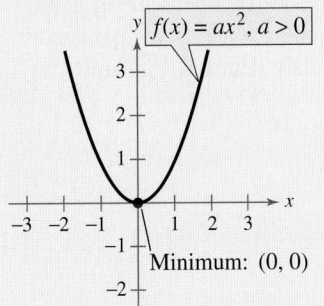

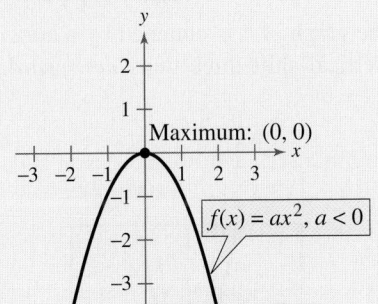

For the general quadratic form $f(x) = ax^2 + bx + c$, if the leading coefficient a is positive, the parabola opens upward; and if the leading coefficient a is negative, the parabola opens downward. Later in this section you will learn ways to find the coordinates of the vertex of a parabola.

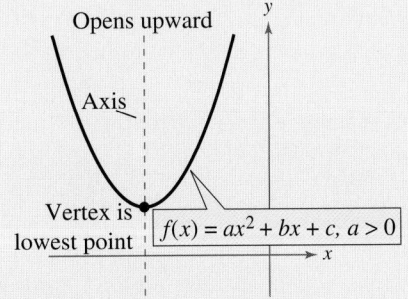

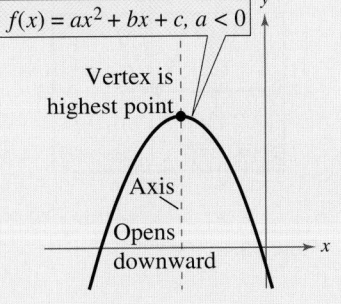

Exploration

Use a graphing utility to graph the parabola

$$y = x^2 + c$$

for $c = -3, -2, -1, 1, 2,$ and 3. What can you conclude about the parabola when $c < 0$? When $c > 0$?

When sketching the graph of $f(x) = ax^2$, it is helpful to use the graph of $y = x^2$ as a reference, as discussed in Section 1.5. There you saw that when $a > 1$, the graph of $y = af(x)$ is a vertical stretch of the graph of $y = f(x)$. When $0 < a < 1$, the graph of $y = af(x)$ is a vertical shrink of the graph of $y = f(x)$. This is demonstrated again in Example 1.

Example 1   Graphing Simple Quadratic Functions

Describe how the graph of each function is related to the graph of $y = x^2$.

a. $f(x) = \dfrac{1}{3}x^2$ **b.** $g(x) = 2x^2$

c. $h(x) = -x^2 + 1$ **d.** $k(x) = (x + 2)^2 - 3$

Solution

a. Compared with $y = x^2$, each output of f "shrinks" by a factor of $\frac{1}{3}$. The result is a parabola that opens upward and is broader than the parabola represented by $y = x^2$, as shown in Figure 3.1.

b. Compared with $y = x^2$, each output of g "stretches" by a factor of 2, creating a narrower parabola, as shown in Figure 3.2.

c. With respect to the graph of $y = x^2$, the graph of h is obtained by a *reflection* in the x-axis and a vertical shift one unit *upward*, as shown in Figure 3.3.

d. With respect to the graph of $y = x^2$, the graph of k is obtained by a horizontal shift two units *to the left* and a vertical shift three units *downward*, as shown in Figure 3.4.

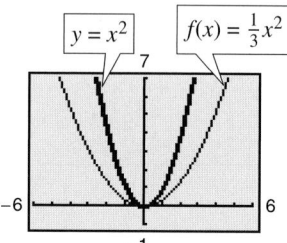

Figure 3.1

Figure 3.2

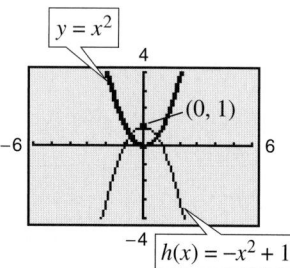

Figure 3.3

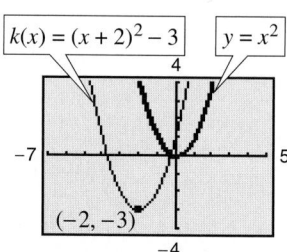

Figure 3.4

✓ *Checkpoint* Now try Exercise 9.

Recall from Section 1.5 that the graphs of $y = f(x \pm c)$, $y = f(x) \pm c$, $y = -f(x)$, and $y = f(-x)$ are rigid transformations of the graph of $y = f(x)$.

$y = f(x \pm c)$	Horizontal shift	$y = -f(x)$	Reflection in x-axis
$y = f(x) \pm c$	Vertical shift	$y = f(-x)$	Reflection in y-axis

The Standard Form of a Quadratic Function

The equation in Example 1(d) is written in the **standard form**

$$f(x) = a(x - h)^2 + k.$$

This form is especially convenient for sketching a parabola because it identifies the vertex of the parabola as (h, k).

Standard Form of a Quadratic Equation

The quadratic function given by

$$f(x) = a(x - h)^2 + k, \qquad a \neq 0$$

is in **standard form**. The graph of f is a parabola whose axis is the vertical line $x = h$ and whose vertex is the point (h, k). If $a > 0$, the parabola opens upward, and if $a < 0$, the parabola opens downward.

Example 2   Identifying the Vertex of a Quadratic Function

Describe the graph of $f(x) = 2x^2 + 8x + 7$ and identify the vertex.

Solution

Write the quadratic function in standard form by completing the square. Recall that the first step is to factor out any coefficient of x^2 that is not 1.

$f(x) = 2x^2 + 8x + 7$	Write original function.
$= 2(x^2 + 4x) + 7$	Factor 2 out of x-terms.
$= 2(x^2 + 4x + 4 - 4) + 7$	Because $b = 4$, add and subtract $(4/2)^2 = 4$ within parentheses.

$$\left(\frac{4}{2}\right)^2$$

$= 2(x^2 + 4x + 4) - 2(4) + 7$	Regroup terms.
$= 2(x + 2)^2 - 1$	Write in standard form.

From the standard form, you can see that the graph of f is a parabola that opens upward with vertex $(-2, -1)$, as shown in Figure 3.5. This corresponds to a left shift of two units and a downward shift of one unit relative to the graph of $y = 2x^2$.

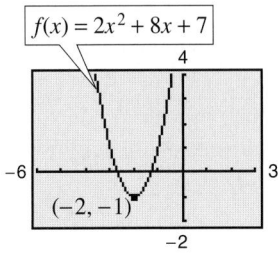

$f(x) = 2x^2 + 8x + 7$

$(-2, -1)$

Figure 3.5

 *Checkpoint* Now try Exercise 19.

To find the x-intercepts of the graph of $f(x) = ax^2 + bx + c$, solve the equation $ax^2 + bx + c = 0$. If $ax^2 + bx + c$ does not factor, you can use the Quadratic Formula to find the x-intercepts, or a graphing utility to approximate the x-intercepts. Remember, however, that a parabola may not have x-intercepts.

Example 3 Identifying *x*-Intercepts of a Quadratic Function

Describe the graph of $f(x) = -x^2 + 6x - 8$ and identify any *x*-intercepts.

Solution

$$f(x) = -x^2 + 6x - 8 \qquad \text{Write original function.}$$

$$= -(x^2 - 6x) - 8 \qquad \text{Factor } -1 \text{ out of } x\text{-terms.}$$

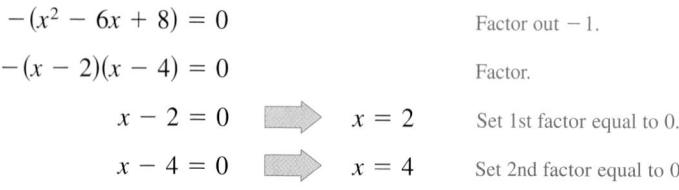
$$= -(x^2 - 6x + 9 - 9) - 8 \qquad \begin{array}{l}\text{Because } b = 6, \text{ add and subtract} \\ (6/2)^2 = 9 \text{ within parentheses.}\end{array}$$

$$= -(x^2 - 6x + 9) - (-9) - 8 \qquad \text{Regroup terms.}$$

$$= -(x - 3)^2 + 1 \qquad \text{Write in standard form.}$$

The graph of *f* is a parabola that opens downward with vertex $(3, 1)$, as shown in Figure 3.6. The *x*-intercepts are determined as follows.

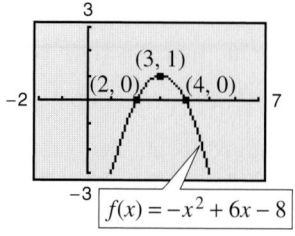

Figure 3.6

$$-(x^2 - 6x + 8) = 0 \qquad \text{Factor out } -1.$$

$$-(x - 2)(x - 4) = 0 \qquad \text{Factor.}$$

$$x - 2 = 0 \qquad x = 2 \qquad \text{Set 1st factor equal to 0.}$$

$$x - 4 = 0 \qquad x = 4 \qquad \text{Set 2nd factor equal to 0.}$$

So, the *x*-intercepts are $(2, 0)$ and $(4, 0)$, as shown in Figure 3.6.

 *Checkpoint* Now try Exercise 23.

Example 4 Writing the Equation of a Parabola in Standard Form

Write the standard form of the equation of the parabola whose vertex is $(1, 2)$ and that passes through the point $(3, -6)$, as shown in Figure 3.7.

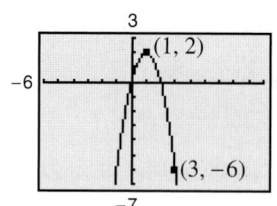

Figure 3.7

Solution

Because the vertex of the parabola is $(h, k) = (1, 2)$, the equation has the form

$$f(x) = a(x - 1)^2 + 2. \qquad \text{Substitute for } h \text{ and } k \text{ in standard form.}$$

Because the parabola passes through the point $(3, -6)$, it follows that $f(3) = -6$. So, you obtain

$$-6 = a(3 - 1)^2 + 2$$

$$-6 = 4a + 2$$

$$-2 = a.$$

The equation in standard form is $f(x) = -2(x - 1)^2 + 2$. Try graphing $f(x) = -2(x - 1)^2 + 2$ with a graphing utility to confirm that its vertex is $(1, 2)$ and that it passes through the point $(3, -6)$.

 *Checkpoint* Now try Exercise 35.

STUDY TIP

In Example 4, there are infinitely many different parabolas that have a vertex at $(1, 2)$. Of these, however, the only one that passes through the point $(3, -6)$ is the one given by

$$f(x) = -2(x - 1)^2 + 2.$$

Finding Minimum and Maximum Values

Many applications involve finding the maximum or minimum value of a quadratic function. By writing the quadratic function $f(x) = ax^2 + bx + c$ in standard form,

$$f(x) = a\left(x + \frac{b}{2a}\right)^2 + \left(c - \frac{b^2}{4a}\right)$$

you can see that the vertex occurs at $x = -b/(2a)$, which implies the following.

Minimum and Maximum Values of Quadratic Functions

1. If $a > 0$, f has a *minimum* at $x = -\dfrac{b}{2a}$.

2. If $a < 0$, f has a *maximum* at $x = -\dfrac{b}{2a}$.

Example 5   The Maximum Height of a Baseball

A baseball is hit at a point 3 feet above the ground at a velocity of 100 feet per second and at an angle of 45° with respect to the ground. The path of the baseball is given by the function $f(x) = -0.0032x^2 + x + 3$, where $f(x)$ is the height of the baseball (in feet) and x is the horizontal distance from home plate (in feet). What is the maximum height reached by the baseball?

Algebraic Solution

For this quadratic function, you have

$$f(x) = ax^2 + bx + c = -0.0032x^2 + x + 3$$

which implies that $a = -0.0032$ and $b = 1$. Because the function has a maximum when $x = -b/(2a)$, you can conclude that the baseball reaches its maximum height when it is x feet from home plate, where x is

$$x = -\frac{b}{2a}$$

$$= -\frac{1}{2(-0.0032)} = 156.25 \text{ feet.}$$

At this distance, the maximum height is

$$f(156.25) = -0.0032(156.25)^2 + 156.25 + 3$$

$$= 81.125 \text{ feet.}$$

 Checkpoint Now try Exercise 63.

Graphical Solution

Use a graphing utility to graph $y = -0.0032x^2 + x + 3$ so that you can see the important features of the parabola. Use the *maximum* feature (see Figure 3.8) or the *zoom* and *trace* features (see Figure 3.9) of the graphing utility to approximate the maximum height on the graph to be $y \approx 81.125$ feet at $x \approx 156.25$. Note that when using the *zoom* and *trace* features, you might have to change the y-scale in order to avoid a graph that is "too flat."

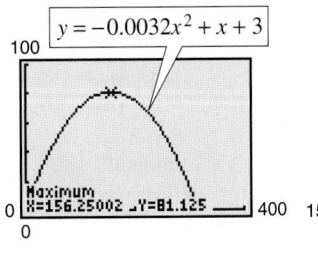

Figure 3.8

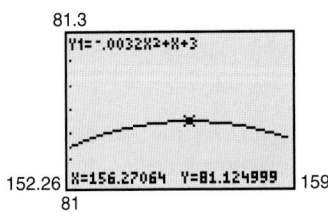

Figure 3.9

TECHNOLOGY SUPPORT   For instructions on how to use the *maximum*, the *minimum*, the *table*, and the *zoom* and *trace* features, see Appendix A; for specific keystrokes, go to the text website at *college.hmco.com*.

Example 6 Cost

A soft-drink manufacturer has daily production costs of

$$C = 70{,}000 - 120x + 0.055x^2$$

where C is the total cost (in dollars) and x is the number of units produced. Estimate numerically the number of units that should be produced each day to yield a minimum cost.

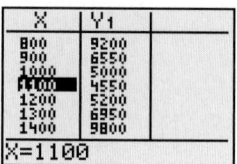

Solution

Enter the function $y = 70{,}000 - 120x + 0.055x^2$ into your graphing utility. Then use the *table* feature of the graphing utility to create a table. Set the table to start at $x = 0$ and set the table step to 100. By scrolling through the table you can see that the minimum cost is between 1000 units and 1200 units, as shown in Figure 3.10. You can improve this estimate by starting the table at $x = 1000$ and setting the table step to 10. From the table in Figure 3.11, you can see that approximately 1090 units should be produced to yield a minimum cost of \$4545.50.

X	Y1
800	9200
900	6550
1000	5000
1100	4550
1200	5200
1300	6950
1400	9800

X=1100

Figure 3.10

X	Y1
1060	4598
1070	4569.5
1080	4552
1090	4545.5
1100	4550
1110	4565.5
1120	4592

X=1090

Figure 3.11

✓ *Checkpoint* Now try Exercise 65.

Example 7 Hairdressers and Cosmetologists

The number h (in thousands) of hairdressers and cosmetologists in the United States from 1994 to 2001 can be approximated by the model

$$h = 4.17t^2 - 48.1t + 881, \qquad 4 \le t \le 11$$

where t represents the year, with $t = 4$ corresponding to 1994. Using this model, determine the year in which the number of hairdressers and cosmetologists was the least. (Source: U.S. Bureau of Labor Statistics)

Algebraic Solution

Use the fact that the minimum point of the parabola occurs when $t = -b/(2a)$. For this function, you have $a = 4.17$ and $b = -48.1$. So,

$$t = -\frac{b}{2a}$$

$$= -\frac{-48.1}{2(4.17)}$$

$$\approx 5.8$$

From this t-value and the fact that $t = 4$ represents 1994, you can conclude that the least number of hairdressers and cosmetologists occurred sometime during 1995.

✓ *Checkpoint* Now try Exercise 67.

Graphical Solution

Use a graphing utility to graph

$$y = 4.17x^2 - 48.1x + 881$$

for $4 \le x \le 11$, as shown in Figure 3.12. Use the *minimum* feature (see Figure 3.12) or the *zoom* and *trace* features (see Figure 3.13) of the graphing utility to approximate the minimum point of the parabola to be $x \approx 5.8$. So, you can conclude that the least number of hairdressers and cosmetologists occurred sometime during 1995.

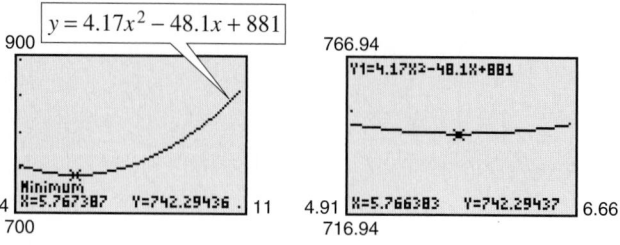

Figure 3.12

Figure 3.13

3.1   Exercises

Vocabulary Check

Fill in the blanks.

1. A polynomial function of degree n and leading coefficient a_n is a function of the form

   $$f(x) = a_n x^n + a_{n-1} x^{n-1} + \cdots + a_1 x + a_0, \quad a_n \neq 0$$

   where n is a _____ and a_i is a _____ number.

2. A _____ function is a second-degree polynomial function, and its graph is called a _____ .

3. The graph of a quadratic function is symmetric about its _____ .

4. If the graph of a quadratic function opens upward, then its leading coefficient is _____ and the vertex of the graph is a _____ .

5. If the graph of a quadratic function opens downward, then its leading coefficient is _____ and the vertex of the graph is a _____ .

In Exercises 1–8, match the quadratic function with its graph. [The graphs are labeled (a), (b), (c), (d), (e), (f), (g), and (h).]

(a)
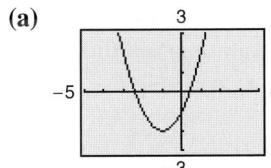

(b)
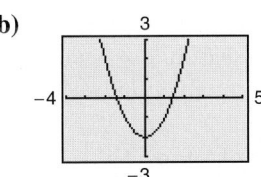

(c)
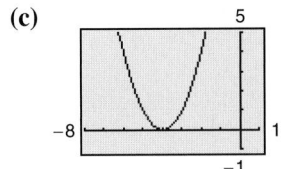

(d)
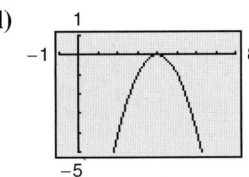

(e)
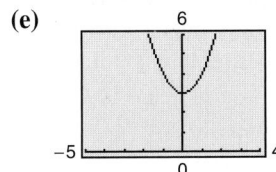

(f)
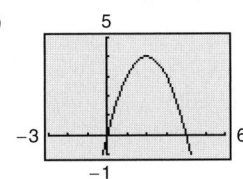

(g)
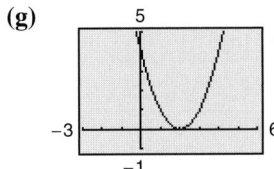

(h)
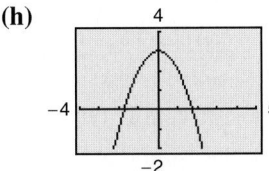

1. $f(x) = (x - 2)^2$
2. $f(x) = (x + 4)^2$
3. $f(x) = x^2 - 2$
4. $f(x) = 3 - x^2$
5. $f(x) = 4 - (x - 2)^2$
6. $f(x) = (x + 1)^2 - 2$
7. $f(x) = x^2 + 3$
8. $f(x) = -(x - 4)^2$

In Exercises 9–12, use a graphing utility to graph each function in the same viewing window. Describe how the graph of each function is related to the graph of $y = x^2$.

9. (a) $y = \frac{1}{2}x^2$ (b) $y = \frac{1}{2}x^2 - 1$
   (c) $y = \frac{1}{2}(x + 3)^2$ (d) $y = -\frac{1}{2}(x + 3)^2 - 1$

10. (a) $y = \frac{3}{2}x^2$ (b) $y = \frac{3}{2}x^2 + 1$
    (c) $y = \frac{3}{2}(x - 3)^2$ (d) $y = -\frac{3}{2}(x - 3)^2 + 1$

11. (a) $y = -2x^2$ (b) $y = -2x^2 - 1$
    (c) $y = -2(x - 3)^2$ (d) $y = 2(x - 3)^2 - 1$

12. (a) $y = -4x^2$ (b) $y = -4x^2 + 3$
    (c) $y = -4(x + 2)^2$ (d) $y = 4(x + 2)^2 + 3$

In Exercises 13–26, sketch the graph of the quadratic function. Identify the vertex and x-intercept(s). Use a graphing utility to verify your results.

13. $f(x) = 25 - x^2$ 14. $f(x) = x^2 - 7$
15. $f(x) = \frac{1}{2}x^2 - 4$ 16. $f(x) = 16 - \frac{1}{4}x^2$
17. $f(x) = (x + 4)^2 - 3$ 18. $f(x) = (x - 6)^2 + 3$
19. $h(x) = x^2 - 8x + 16$
20. $g(x) = x^2 + 2x + 1$
21. $f(x) = x^2 - x + \frac{5}{4}$
22. $f(x) = x^2 + 3x + \frac{1}{4}$

23. $f(x) = -x^2 + 2x + 5$

24. $f(x) = -x^2 - 4x + 1$

25. $h(x) = 4x^2 - 4x + 21$

26. $f(x) = 2x^2 - x + 1$

In Exercises 27–34, use a graphing utility to graph the quadratic function. Identify the vertex and x-intercept(s). Then check your results algebraically by writing the quadratic function in standard form.

27. $f(x) = -(x^2 + 2x - 3)$

28. $f(x) = -(x^2 + x - 30)$

29. $g(x) = x^2 + 8x + 11$

30. $f(x) = x^2 + 10x + 14$

31. $f(x) = -2x^2 + 16x - 31$

32. $f(x) = -4x^2 + 24x - 41$

33. $g(x) = \frac{1}{2}(x^2 + 4x - 2)$

34. $f(x) = \frac{3}{5}(x^2 + 6x - 5)$

In Exercises 35–38, write an equation for the parabola in standard form. Use a graphing utility to graph the equation and verify your result.

35. 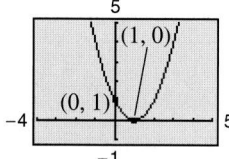   **36.**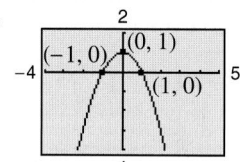

37. 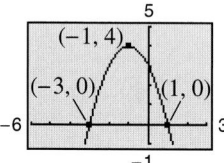   **38.**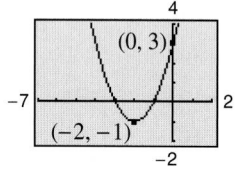

In Exercises 39–42, write the standard form of the quadratic function that has the indicated vertex and whose graph passes through the given point. Verify your result with a graphing utility.

39. Vertex: $(-2, 5)$;   Point: $(0, 9)$

40. Vertex: $(4, -1)$;   Point: $(2, 3)$

41. Vertex: $\left(\frac{5}{2}, -\frac{3}{4}\right)$;   Point: $(-2, 4)$

42. Vertex: $\left(-\frac{5}{2}, 0\right)$;   Point: $\left(-\frac{7}{2}, -\frac{16}{3}\right)$

Graphical Reasoning In Exercises 43–46, determine the x-intercept(s) of the graph visually. How do the x-intercepts correspond to the solutions of the quadratic equation when $y = 0$?

43. 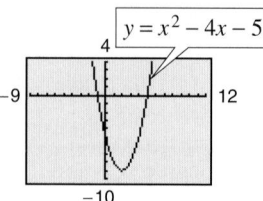   **44.**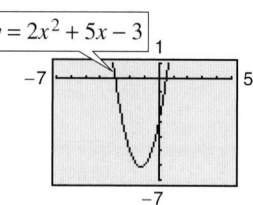

45. 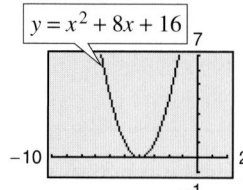   **46.**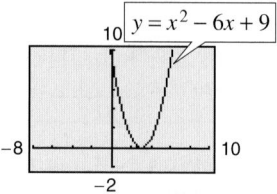

In Exercises 47–52, use a graphing utility to graph the quadratic function. Find the x-intercepts of the graph and compare them with the solutions of the corresponding quadratic equation when $y = 0$.

47. $y = x^2 - 4x$

48. $y = -2x^2 + 10x$

49. $y = 2x^2 - 7x - 30$

50. $y = 4x^2 + 25x - 21$

51. $y = -\frac{1}{2}(x^2 - 6x - 7)$

52. $y = \frac{7}{10}(x^2 + 12x - 45)$

In Exercises 53–56, find two quadratic functions, one that opens upward and one that opens downward, whose graphs have the given x-intercepts. (There are many correct answers.)

53. $(-1, 0), (3, 0)$ **54.** $(0, 0), (10, 0)$

55. $(-3, 0), \left(-\frac{1}{2}, 0\right)$ **56.** $\left(-\frac{5}{2}, 0\right), (2, 0)$

In Exercises 57–60, find two positive real numbers whose product is a maximum.

57. The sum is 110.

58. The sum is S.

59. The sum of the first and twice the second is 24.

60. The sum of the first and three times the second is 42.

61. *Geometry*   An indoor physical fitness room consists of a rectangular region with a semicircle on each end. The perimeter of the room is to be a 200-meter single-lane running track.

(a) Draw a diagram that illustrates the problem. Let x and y represent the length and width of the rectangular region, respectively.

(b) Determine the radius of the semicircular ends of the track. Determine the distance, in terms of y, around the inside edge of the two semicircular parts of the track.

(c) Use the result of part (b) to write an equation, in terms of x and y, for the distance traveled in one lap around the track. Solve for y.

(d) Use the result of part (c) to write the area A of the rectangular region as a function of x.

(e) Use a graphing utility to graph the area function from part (d). Use the graph to approximate the dimensions that will produce a rectangle of maximum area.

62. *Numerical, Graphical, and Analytical Analysis*   A rancher has 200 feet of fencing to enclose two adjacent rectangular corrals (see figure). Use the following methods to determine the dimensions that will produce a maximum enclosed area.

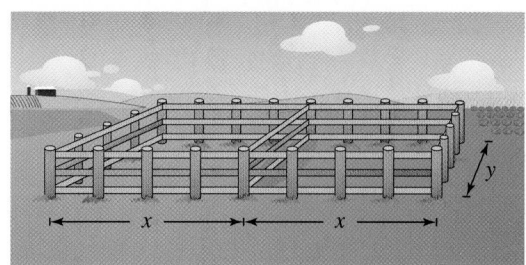

(a) Write the area A of the corral as a function of x.

(b) Use the *table* feature of a graphing utility to create a table showing possible values of x and the corresponding areas of the corral. Use the table to estimate the dimensions that will produce the maximum enclosed area.

(c) Use a graphing utility to graph the area function. Use the graph to approximate the dimensions that will produce the maximum enclosed area.

(d) Write the area function in standard form to find algebraically the dimensions that will produce the maximum area.

(e) Compare your results from parts (b), (c), and (d).

63. *Height of a Ball*   The height y (in feet) of a ball thrown by a child is given by

$$y = -\tfrac{1}{12}x^2 + 2x + 4$$

where x is the horizontal distance (in feet) from where the ball is thrown (see figure).

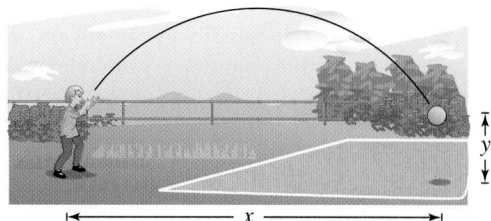

(a) Use a graphing utility to graph the path of the ball.

(b) How high is the ball when it leaves the child's hand? (*Hint:* Find y when $x = 0$.)

(c) What is the maximum height of the ball?

(d) How far from the child does the ball strike the ground?

64. *Path of a Diver*   The path of a diver is given by

$$y = -\tfrac{4}{9}x^2 + \tfrac{24}{9}x + 12$$

where y is the height (in feet) and x is the horizontal distance (in feet) from the end of the diving board (see figure). What is the maximum height of the diver? Verify your answer using a graphing utility.

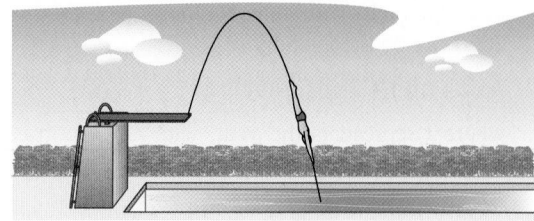

65. *Cost*   A manufacturer of lighting fixtures has daily production costs of

$$C = 800 - 10x + 0.25x^2$$

where C is the total cost (in dollars) and x is the number of units produced. Use the *table* feature of a graphing utility to determine how many fixtures should be produced each day to yield a minimum cost.

66. *Automobile Aerodynamics* The number of horsepower y required to overcome wind drag on a certain automobile is approximated by

$$y = 0.002s^2 + 0.005s - 0.029, \quad 0 \le s \le 100$$

where s is the speed of the car (in miles per hour).

(a) Use a graphing utility to graph the function.

(b) Graphically estimate the maximum speed of the car if the power required to overcome wind drag is not to exceed 10 horsepower. Verify your result algebraically.

67. *Graphical Analysis* From 1960 to 2001, the average annual per capita consumption C of cigarettes by Americans (age 18 and older) can be modeled by $C = 4274 + 3.4t - 1.52t^2, 0 \le t \le 41$, where t is the year, with $t = 0$ corresponding to 1960. (Source: Tobacco Situation and Outlook Yearbook)

(a) Use a graphing utility to graph the model.

(b) Use the graph of the model to approximate the maximum average annual consumption. Beginning in 1966, all cigarette packages were required by law to carry a health warning. Do you think the warning had any effect? Explain.

(c) In 2000, the U.S. population (age 18 and over) was 209,128,000. Of these, about 48,300,000 were smokers. What was the average annual cigarette consumption *per smoker* in 2000? What was the average daily cigarette consumption *per smoker*?

68. *Data Analysis* The number y (in millions) of VCRs in use in the United States for the years 1994 through 2000 can be modeled by

$$y = -0.17t^2 + 4.3t + 60, \quad 4 \le t \le 10$$

where t represents the year, with $t = 4$ corresponding to 1994. (Source: Television Bureau of Advertising, Inc.)

(a) Use a graphing utility to graph the model.

(b) Do you think the model can be used to estimate VCR use in the year 2008? Explain.

Synthesis

True or False? **In Exercises 69 and 70, determine whether the statement is true or false. Justify your answer.**

69. The function $f(x) = -12x^2 - 1$ has no x-intercepts.

70. The graphs of $f(x) = -4x^2 - 10x + 7$ and $g(x) = 12x^2 + 30x + 1$ have the same axis of symmetry.

71. *Profit* The profit P (in millions of dollars) for a recreational vehicle retailer is modeled by a quadratic function of the form $P = at^2 + bt + c$, where t represents the year. If you were president of the company, which of the following models would you prefer? Explain your reasoning.

(a) a is positive and $t \ge -b/(2a)$.

(b) a is positive and $t \le -b/(2a)$.

(c) a is negative and $t \ge -b/(2a)$.

(d) a is negative and $t \le -b/(2a)$.

72. *Writing* The parabola in the figure below has an equation of the form

$$y = ax^2 + bx - 4.$$

Find the equation of this parabola in two different ways, by hand and with technology (graphing utility or computer software). Write a paragraph describing the methods you used and comparing the results of the two methods.

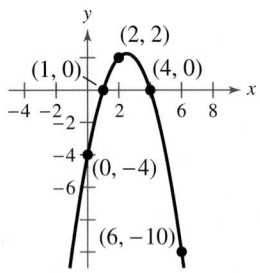

Review

In Exercises 73–76, determine algebraically any points of intersection of the graphs of the equations. Verify your results using the *intersect* feature of a graphing utility.

73. $x + y = 8$
$-\frac{2}{3}x + y = 6$

74. $y = 3x - 10$
$y = \frac{1}{4}x + 1$

75. $y = 9 - x^2$
$y = x + 3$

76. $y = x^3 + 2x - 1$
$y = -2x + 15$

In Exercises 77–80, perform the operation and write the result in standard form.

77. $(6 - i) - (2i + 11)$

78. $(2i + 5)^2 - 21$

79. $(3i + 7)(-4i + 1)$

80. $(4 - i)^3$

3.2 Polynomial Functions of Higher Degree

Graphs of Polynomial Functions

You should be able to sketch accurate graphs of polynomial functions of degrees 0, 1, and 2. The graphs of polynomial functions of degree greater than 2 are more difficult to sketch by hand. However, in this section you will learn how to recognize some of the basic features of the graphs of polynomial functions. Using these features along with point plotting, intercepts, and symmetry, you should be able to make reasonably accurate sketches *by hand.*

The graph of a polynomial function is **continuous.** Essentially, this means that the graph of a polynomial function has no breaks, holes, or gaps, as shown in Figure 3.14.

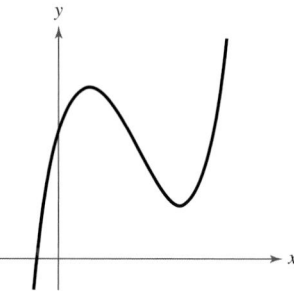

(a) Polynomial functions have continuous graphs.

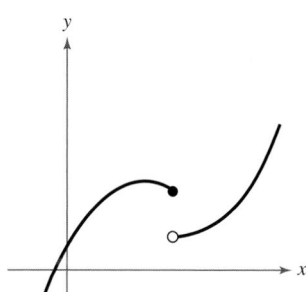

(b) Functions with graphs that are not continuous are not polynomial functions.

Figure 3.14

Another feature of the graph of a polynomial function is that it has only smooth, rounded turns, as shown in Figure 3.15(a). It cannot have a sharp turn such as the one shown in Figure 3.15(b).

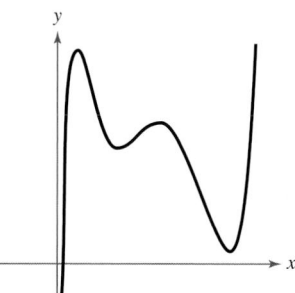

(a) Polynomial functions have graphs with smooth, rounded turns.

Figure 3.15

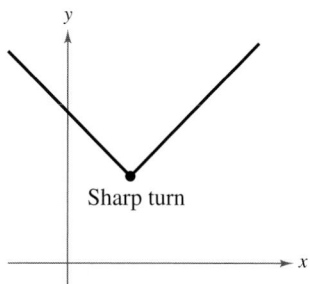

Sharp turn

(b) Graphs of polynomial functions cannot have sharp turns.

Informally, you can say that a function is continuous if its graph can be drawn with a pencil without lifting the pencil from the paper.

What you should learn

- Use transformations to sketch graphs of polynomial functions.
- Use the Leading Coefficient Test to determine the end behavior of graphs of polynomial functions.
- Find and use zeros of polynomial functions as sketching aids.
- Use the Intermediate Value Theorem to help locate zeros of polynomial functions.

Why you should learn it

You can use polynomial functions to model various aspects of nature, such as the growth of a red oak tree, as shown in Exercise 88 on page 262.

Leonard Lee Rue III/Earth Scenes

Library of Functions: Polynomial Function

The graphs of polynomial functions of degree 1 are lines, and those of functions of degree 2 are parabolas. The graphs of polynomial functions of higher degree are smooth and continuous. A polynomial function of degree n has the form

$$f(x) = a_n x^n + a_{n-1} x^{n-1} + \cdots + a_2 x^2 + a_1 x + a_0$$

where n is a positive integer and $a_n \neq 0$. The polynomial functions that have the simplest graphs are monomials of the form $f(x) = x^n$, where n is an integer greater than zero. If n is even, the graph is similar to the graph of $f(x) = x^2$ and touches the axis at the x-intercept. If n is odd, the graph is similar to the graph of $f(x) = x^3$ and crosses the axis at the x-intercept. The greater the value of n, the flatter the graph near the origin. The basic characteristics of the *cubic function* $f(x) = x^3$ are summarized below.

Graph of $f(x) = x^3$

Domain: $(-\infty, \infty)$
Range: $(-\infty, \infty)$
Intercept: $(0, 0)$
Increasing on $(-\infty, \infty)$
Odd function
Origin symmetry

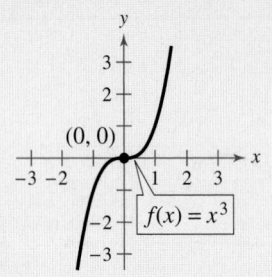

Exploration

Use a graphing utility to graph $y = x^n$ for $n = 2, 4,$ and 8. (Use the viewing window $-1.5 \leq x \leq 1.5$ and $-1 \leq y \leq 6$.) Compare the graphs. In the interval $(-1, 1)$, which graph is on the bottom? Outside the interval $(-1, 1)$, which graph is on the bottom?

Use a graphing utility to graph $y = x^n$ for $n = 3, 5,$ and 7. (Use the viewing window $-1.5 \leq x \leq 1.5$ and $-4 \leq y \leq 4$.) Compare the graphs. In the intervals $(-\infty, -1)$ and $(0, 1)$, which graph is on the bottom? In the intervals $(-1, 0)$ and $(1, \infty)$, which graph is on the bottom?

Example 1 Transformations of Monomial Functions

Sketch the graph of each function.

a. $f(x) = -x^5$ **b.** $g(x) = x^4 + 1$ **c.** $h(x) = (x + 1)^4$

Solution

a. Because the degree of $f(x) = -x^5$ is odd, the graph is similar to the graph of $y = x^3$. Moreover, the negative coefficient reflects the graph in the x-axis, as shown in Figure 3.16.

b. The graph of $g(x) = x^4 + 1$ is an upward shift of one unit of the graph of $y = x^4$, as shown in Figure 3.17.

c. The graph of $h(x) = (x + 1)^4$ is a left shift of one unit of the graph of $y = x^4$, as shown in Figure 3.18.

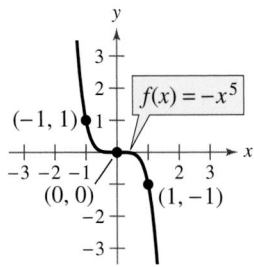

Figure 3.16

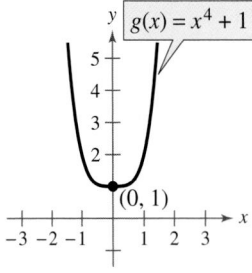

Figure 3.17

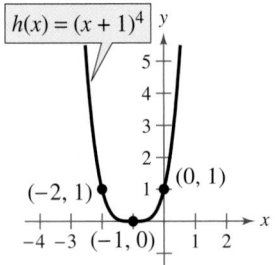

Figure 3.18

✓ *Checkpoint* Now try Exercise 9.

The Leading Coefficient Test

In Example 1, note that all three graphs eventually rise or fall without bound as x moves to the right. Whether the graph of a polynomial eventually rises or falls can be determined by the function's degree (even or odd) and by its leading coefficient, as indicated in the **Leading Coefficient Test.**

Leading Coefficient Test

As x moves without bound to the left or to the right, the graph of the polynomial function $f(x) = a_n x^n + \cdots + a_1 x + a_0$, $a_n \neq 0$, eventually rises or falls in the following manner.

1. When n is odd:

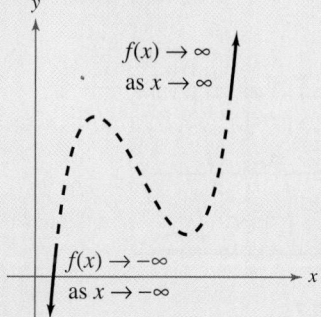

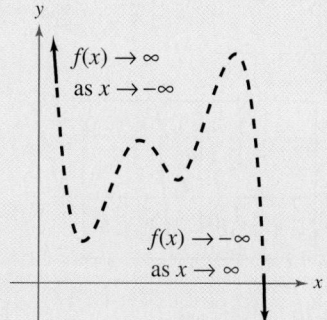

If the leading coefficient is positive $(a_n > 0)$, the graph falls to the left and rises to the right.

If the leading coefficient is negative $(a_n < 0)$, the graph rises to the left and falls to the right.

2. When n is even:

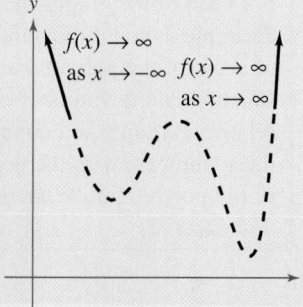

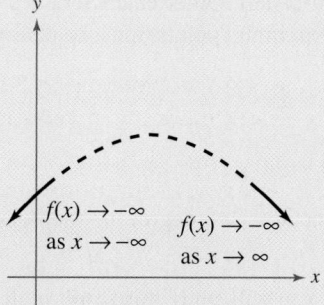

If the leading coefficient is positive $(a_n > 0)$, the graph rises to the left and right.

If the leading coefficient is negative $(a_n < 0)$, the graph falls to the left and right.

Note that the dashed portions of the graphs indicate that the test determines only the right-hand and left-hand behavior of the graph.

As you continue to study polynomial functions and their graphs, you will notice that the degree of a polynomial plays an important role in determining other characteristics of the polynomial and its graph.

Example 2   Applying the Leading Coefficient Test

Use the Leading Coefficient Test to describe the right-hand and left-hand behavior of the graph of each polynomial function.

a. $f(x) = -x^3 + 4x$ **b.** $f(x) = x^4 - 5x^2 + 4$ **c.** $f(x) = x^5 - x$

Solution

a. Because the degree is odd and the leading coefficient is negative, the graph rises to the left and falls to the right, as shown in Figure 3.19.

b. Because the degree is even and the leading coefficient is positive, the graph rises to the left and right, as shown in Figure 3.20.

c. Because the degree is odd and the leading coefficient is positive, the graph falls to the left and rises to the right, as shown in Figure 3.21.

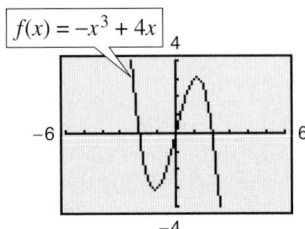

Figure 3.19

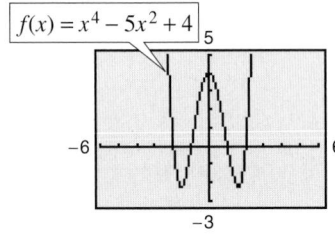

Figure 3.20

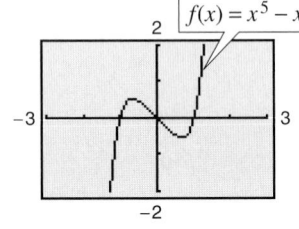

Figure 3.21

 Checkpoint Now try Exercise 17.

In Example 2, note that the Leading Coefficient Test only tells you whether the graph *eventually* rises or falls to the right or left. Other characteristics of the graph, such as intercepts and minimum and maximum points, must be determined by other tests.

Zeros of Polynomial Functions

It can be shown that for a polynomial function f of degree n, the following statements are true.

1. The function f has at most n real zeros. (You will study this result in detail in Section 3.4 on the Fundamental Theorem of Algebra.)

2. The graph of f has at most $n - 1$ relative **extrema** (relative **minima** or **maxima**).

Recall that a **zero** of a function f is a number x for which $f(x) = 0$. Finding the zeros of polynomial functions is one of the most important problems in algebra. You have already seen that there is a strong interplay between graphical and algebraic approaches to this problem. Sometimes you can use information about the graph of a function to help find its zeros. In other cases, you can use information about the zeros of a function to find a good viewing window.

> **Exploration**
>
> For each of the graphs in Example 2, count the number of zeros of the polynomial function and the number of relative extrema, and compare these numbers with the degree of the polynomial. What do you observe?

> **Real Zeros of Polynomial Functions**
>
> If f is a polynomial function and a is a real number, the following statements are equivalent.
>
> 1. $x = a$ is a *zero* of the function f.
> 2. $x = a$ is a *solution* of the polynomial equation $f(x) = 0$.
> 3. $(x - a)$ is a *factor* of the polynomial $f(x)$.
> 4. $(a, 0)$ is an *x*-intercept of the graph of f.

TECHNOLOGY SUPPORT

For instructions on how to use the *zero* or *root* feature, see Appendix A; for specific keystrokes, go to the text website at *college.hmco.com*.

Finding zeros of polynomial functions is closely related to factoring and finding *x*-intercepts, as demonstrated in Examples 3, 4, and 5.

Example 3   Finding Zeros of a Polynomial Function

Find all real zeros of $f(x) = x^3 - x^2 - 2x$.

Algebraic Solution

$$f(x) = x^3 - x^2 - 2x \qquad \text{Write original function.}$$
$$0 = x^3 - x^2 - 2x \qquad \text{Substitute 0 for } f(x).$$
$$0 = x(x^2 - x - 2) \qquad \text{Remove common monomial factor.}$$
$$0 = x(x - 2)(x + 1) \qquad \text{Factor completely.}$$

So, the real zeros are $x = 0$, $x = 2$, and $x = -1$, and the corresponding *x*-intercepts are $(0, 0)$, $(2, 0)$, and $(-1, 0)$.

Check

$$(0)^3 - (0)^2 - 2(0) = 0 \qquad x = 0 \text{ is a zero. } ✓$$
$$(2)^3 - (2)^2 - 2(2) = 0 \qquad x = 2 \text{ is a zero. } ✓$$
$$(-1)^3 - (-1)^2 - 2(-1) = 0 \qquad x = -1 \text{ is a zero. } ✓$$

✓ *Checkpoint* Now try Exercise 35.

Graphical Solution

Use a graphing utility to graph $y = x^3 - x^2 - 2x$. In Figure 3.22, the graph appears to have the *x*-intercepts $(0, 0)$, $(2, 0)$, and $(-1, 0)$. Use the *zero* or *root* feature, or the *zoom* and *trace* features, of the graphing utility to verify these intercepts. Note that this third-degree polynomial has two relative extrema, at $(-0.5486, 0.6311)$ and $(1.2152, -2.1126)$.

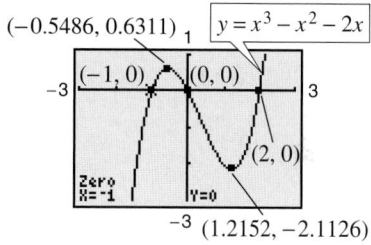

Figure 3.22

Example 4   Analyzing a Polynomial Function

Find all real zeros and relative extrema of $f(x) = -2x^4 + 2x^2$.

Solution

$$0 = -2x^4 + 2x^2 \qquad \text{Substitute 0 for } f(x).$$
$$0 = -2x^2(x^2 - 1) \qquad \text{Remove common monomial factor.}$$
$$0 = -2x^2(x - 1)(x + 1) \qquad \text{Factor completely.}$$

So, the real zeros are $x = 0$, $x = 1$, and $x = -1$, and the corresponding *x*-intercepts are $(0, 0)$, $(1, 0)$, and $(-1, 0)$, as shown in Figure 3.23. Using the *minimum* and *maximum* features of a graphing utility, you can approximate the three relative extrema to be $(-0.7071, 0.5)$, $(0, 0)$, and $(0.7071, 0.5)$.

✓ *Checkpoint* Now try Exercise 47.

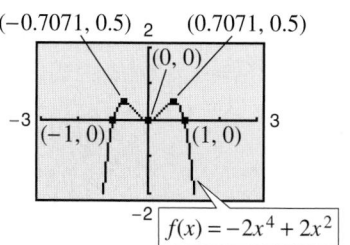

Figure 3.23

Repeated Zeros

For a polynomial function, a factor of $(x - a)^k$, $k > 1$, yields a **repeated zero** $x = a$ of **multiplicity** k.

1. If k is odd, the graph *crosses* the x-axis at $x = a$.

2. If k is even, the graph *touches* the x-axis (but does not cross the x-axis) at $x = a$.

STUDY TIP

In Example 4, note that because k is even, the factor $-2x^2$ yields the repeated zero $x = 0$. The graph touches (but does not cross) the x-axis at $x = 0$, as shown in Figure 3.23.

Example 5 Finding Zeros of a Polynomial Function

Find all real zeros of $f(x) = x^5 - 3x^3 - x^2 - 4x - 1$.

Solution

Use a graphing utility to obtain the graph shown in Figure 3.24. From the graph, you can see that there are three zeros. Using the *zero* or *root* feature, you can determine that the zeros are approximately $x \approx -1.861$, $x \approx -0.254$, and $x \approx 2.115$. It should be noted that this fifth-degree polynomial factors as

$$f(x) = x^5 - 3x^3 - x^2 - 4x - 1 = (x^2 + 1)(x^3 - 4x - 1).$$

The three zeros obtained above are the zeros of the cubic factor $x^3 - 4x - 1$ (the quadratic factor $x^2 + 1$ has two complex zeros and so no *real* zeros).

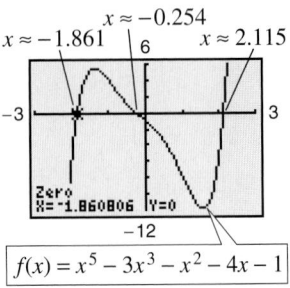

Figure 3.24

✓ *Checkpoint* Now try Exercise 49.

Example 6 Finding a Polynomial Function with Given Zeros

Find polynomial functions with the following zeros. (There are many correct solutions.)

a. $-\dfrac{1}{2}, 3, 3$ **b.** $3, 2 + \sqrt{11}, 2 - \sqrt{11}$

Solution

a. Note that the zero $x = -\frac{1}{2}$ corresponds to either $\left(x + \frac{1}{2}\right)$ or $(2x + 1)$. To avoid fractions, choose the second factor and write

$$f(x) = (2x + 1)(x - 3)^2$$
$$= (2x + 1)(x^2 - 6x + 9) = 2x^3 - 11x^2 + 12x + 9.$$

b. For each of the given zeros, form a corresponding factor and write

$$f(x) = (x - 3)\left[x - \left(2 + \sqrt{11}\right)\right]\left[x - \left(2 - \sqrt{11}\right)\right]$$
$$= (x - 3)\left[(x - 2) - \sqrt{11}\right]\left[(x - 2) + \sqrt{11}\right]$$
$$= (x - 3)\left[(x - 2)^2 - \left(\sqrt{11}\right)^2\right]$$
$$= (x - 3)(x^2 - 4x + 4 - 11)$$
$$= (x - 3)(x^2 - 4x - 7) = x^3 - 7x^2 + 5x + 21.$$

✓ *Checkpoint* Now try Exercise 57.

Exploration

Use a graphing utility to graph

$$y_1 = x + 2$$
$$y_2 = (x + 2)(x - 1).$$

Predict the shape of the curve $y = (x + 2)(x - 1)(x - 3)$, and verify your answer with a graphing utility.

Note in Example 6 that there are many polynomial functions with the indicated zeros. In fact, multiplying the functions by any real number does not change the zeros of the function. For instance, multiply the function from part (b) by $\frac{1}{2}$ to obtain $f(x) = \frac{1}{2}x^3 - \frac{7}{2}x^2 + \frac{5}{2}x + \frac{21}{2}$. Then find the zeros of the function. You will obtain the zeros 3, $2 + \sqrt{11}$, and $2 - \sqrt{11}$ as given in Example 6.

Example 7   Sketching the Graph of a Polynomial Function

Sketch the graph of $f(x) = 3x^4 - 4x^3$ by hand.

Solution

1. *Apply the Leading Coefficient Test.*   Because the leading coefficient is positive and the degree is even, you know that the graph eventually rises to the left and to the right (see Figure 3.25).

2. *Find the Zeros of the Polynomial.*   By factoring

$$f(x) = 3x^4 - 4x^3 = x^3(3x - 4)$$

you can see that the zeros of f are $x = 0$ (of odd multiplicity 3) and $x = \frac{4}{3}$ (of odd multiplicity 1). So, the x-intercepts occur at $(0, 0)$ and $\left(\frac{4}{3}, 0\right)$. Add these points to your graph, as shown in Figure 3.25.

3. *Plot a Few Additional Points.*   To sketch the graph by hand, find a few additional points, as shown in the table. Be sure to choose points between the zeros and to the left and right of the zeros. Then plot the points (see Figure 3.26).

x	-1	0.5	1	1.5
$f(x)$	7	-0.3125	-1	1.6875

4. *Draw the Graph.*   Draw a continuous curve through the points, as shown in Figure 3.26. Because both zeros are of odd multiplicity, you know that the graph should cross the x-axis at $x = 0$ and $x = \frac{4}{3}$. If you are unsure of the shape of a portion of the graph, plot some additional points.

TECHNOLOGY TIP

It is easy to make mistakes when entering functions into a graphing utility. So, it is important to have an understanding of the basic shapes of graphs and to be able to graph simple polynomials *by hand*. For example, suppose you had entered the function in Example 7 as $y = 3x^5 - 4x^3$. By looking at the graph, what mathematical principles would alert you to the fact that you had made a mistake?

Exploration

Partner Activity   Multiply three, four, or five distinct linear factors to obtain the equation of a polynomial function of degree 3, 4, or 5. Exchange equations with your partner and sketch, *by hand*, the graph of the equation that your partner wrote. When you are finished, use a graphing utility to check each other's work.

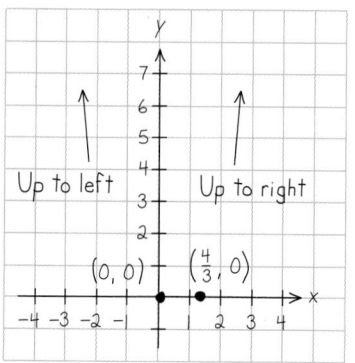

Figure 3.25

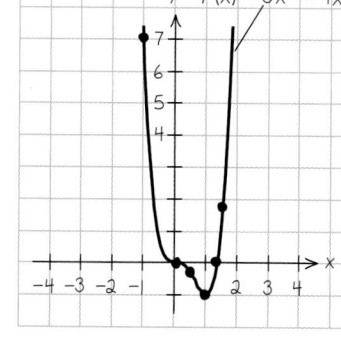

Figure 3.26

✓ *Checkpoint*   Now try Exercise 65.

Example 8   Sketching the Graph of a Polynomial Function

Sketch the graph of $f(x) = -2x^3 + 6x^2 - \frac{9}{2}x$.

Solution

1. *Apply the Leading Coefficient Test.*   Because the leading coefficient is negative and the degree is odd, you know that the graph eventually rises to the left and falls to the right (see Figure 3.27).

2. *Find the Zeros of the Polynomial.*   By factoring

$$f(x) = -2x^3 + 6x^2 - \frac{9}{2}x$$

$$= -\frac{1}{2}x(4x^2 - 12x + 9)$$

$$= -\frac{1}{2}x(2x - 3)^2$$

you can see that the zeros of f are $x = 0$ (of odd multiplicity 1) and $x = \frac{3}{2}$ (of even multiplicity 2). So, the x-intercepts occur at $(0, 0)$ and $\left(\frac{3}{2}, 0\right)$. Add these points to your graph, as shown in Figure 3.27.

3. *Plot a Few Additional Points.*   To sketch the graph by hand, find a few additional points, as shown in the table. Then plot the points (see Figure 3.28.)

x	-0.5	0.5	1	2
$f(x)$	4	-1	-0.5	-1

4. *Draw the Graph.*   Draw a continuous curve through the points, as shown in Figure 3.28. As indicated by the multiplicities of the zeros, the graph crosses the x-axis at $(0, 0)$ and touches (but does not cross) the x-axis at $\left(\frac{3}{2}, 0\right)$.

$$f(x) = -2x^3 + 6x^2 - \frac{9}{2}x$$

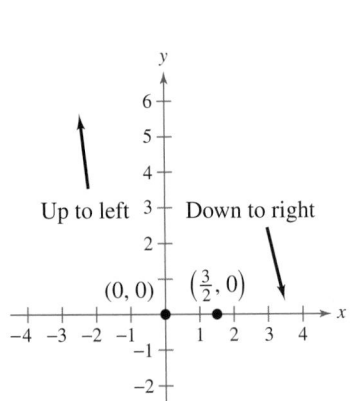

Figure 3.27

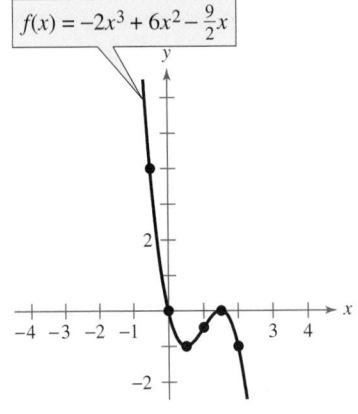

Figure 3.28

✓ *Checkpoint*   Now try Exercise 67.

TECHNOLOGY TIP   Remember that when using a graphing utility to verify your graphs, you may need to adjust your viewing window in order to see all the features of the graph.

STUDY TIP

Observe in Example 8 that the sign of $f(x)$ is positive to the left of and negative to the right of the zero $x = 0$. Similarly, the sign of $f(x)$ is negative to the left and to the right of the zero $x = \frac{3}{2}$. This suggests that if a zero of a polynomial function is of *odd* multiplicity, then the sign of $f(x)$ changes from one side of the zero to the other side. If a zero is of *even* multiplicity, then the sign of $f(x)$ does not change from one side of the zero to the other side. The following table helps to illustrate this result.

x	-0.5	0	0.5
$f(x)$	4	0	-1
Sign	$+$		$-$

x	1	$\frac{3}{2}$	2
$f(x)$	-0.5	0	-1
Sign	$-$		$-$

This sign analysis may be helpful in graphing polynomial functions.

The Intermediate Value Theorem

The **Intermediate Value Theorem** concerns the existence of real zeros of polynomial functions. The theorem states that if $(a, f(a))$ and $(b, f(b))$ are two points on the graph of a polynomial function such that $f(a) \neq f(b)$, then for any number d between $f(a)$ and $f(b)$ there must be a number c between a and b such that $f(c) = d$. (See Figure 3.29.)

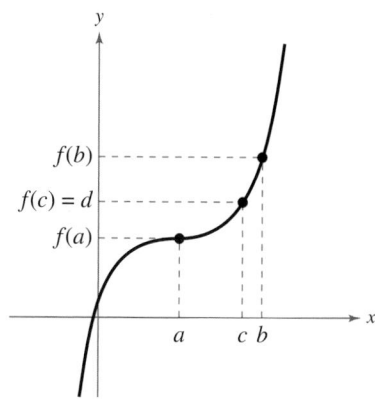

> **Intermediate Value Theorem**
>
> Let a and b be real numbers such that $a < b$. If f is a polynomial function such that $f(a) \neq f(b)$, then in the interval $[a, b]$, f takes on every value between $f(a)$ and $f(b)$.

Figure 3.29

This theorem helps you locate the real zeros of a polynomial function in the following way. If you can find a value $x = a$ at which a polynomial function is positive, and another value $x = b$ at which it is negative, you can conclude that the function has at least one real zero between these two values. For example, the function $f(x) = x^3 + x^2 + 1$ is negative when $x = -2$ and positive when $x = -1$. Therefore, it follows from the Intermediate Value Theorem that f must have a real zero somewhere between -2 and -1.

Example 9   Approximating the Zeros of a Function

Find three intervals of length 1 in which the polynomial $f(x) = 12x^3 - 32x^2 + 3x + 5$ is guaranteed to have a zero.

Graphical Solution

Use a graphing utility to graph

$$y = 12x^3 - 32x^2 + 3x + 5$$

as shown in Figure 3.30.

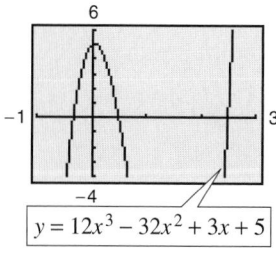

$$y = 12x^3 - 32x^2 + 3x + 5$$

Figure 3.30

From the figure, you can see that the graph crosses the x-axis three times—between -1 and 0, between 0 and 1, and between 2 and 3. So, you can conclude that the function has zeros in the intervals $(-1, 0)$, $(0, 1)$, and $(2, 3)$.

✓ *Checkpoint* Now try Exercise 73.

Numerical Solution

Use the *table* feature of a graphing utility to create a table of function values. Scroll through the table looking for consecutive function values that differ in sign. For instance, from the table in Figure 3.31 you can see that $f(-1)$ and $f(0)$ differ in sign. So, you can conclude from the Intermediate Value Theorem that the function has a zero between -1 and 0. Similarly, $f(0)$ and $f(1)$ differ in sign, so the function has a zero between 0 and 1. Likewise, $f(2)$ and $f(3)$ differ in sign, so the function has a zero between 2 and 3. So, you can conclude that the function has zeros in the intervals $(-1, 0)$, $(0, 1)$, and $(2, 3)$.

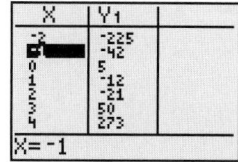

Figure 3.31

3.2 Exercises

Vocabulary Check

Fill in the blanks.

1. The graphs of all polynomial functions are _____ , which means that the graphs have no breaks, holes, or gaps.

2. The _____ is used to determine the left-hand and right-hand behavior of the graph of a polynomial function.

3. A polynomial function of degree n has at most _____ real zeros and at most _____ turning points, called _____ .

4. If $x = a$ is a zero of a polynomial function f, then the following statements are true.
   (a) $x = a$ is a _____ of the polynomial equation $f(x) = 0$.
   (b) _____ is a factor of the polynomial $f(x)$.
   (c) $(a, 0)$ is an _____ of the graph of f.

5. If a zero of a polynomial function is of even multiplicity, then the graph of f _____ the x-axis, and if the zero is of odd multiplicity, then the graph of f _____ the x-axis.

6. The _____ Theorem states that if f is a polynomial function such that $f(a) \neq f(b)$, then in the interval $[a, b]$, f takes on every value between $f(a)$ and $f(b)$.

In Exercises 1–8, match the polynomial function with its graph. [The graphs are labeled (a) through (h).]

(a)

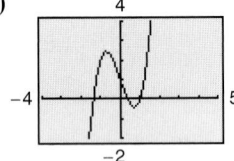

(b)

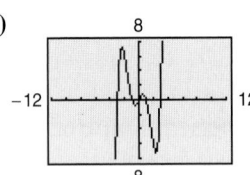

(c)

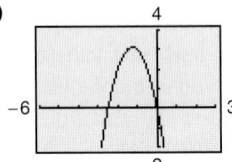

(d)

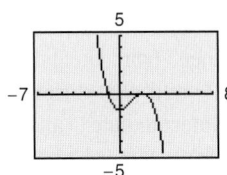

(e)

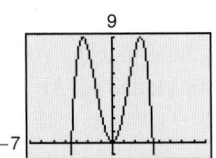

(f)

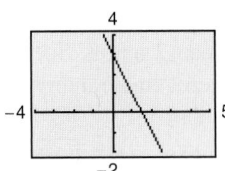

(g)

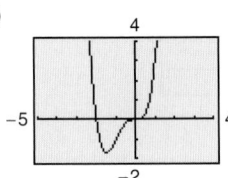

(h)

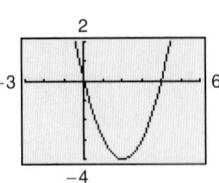

1. $f(x) = -2x + 3$
2. $f(x) = x^2 - 4x$
3. $f(x) = -2x^2 - 5x$
4. $f(x) = 2x^3 - 3x + 1$
5. $f(x) = -\frac{1}{4}x^4 + 3x^2$
6. $f(x) = -\frac{1}{3}x^3 + x^2 - \frac{4}{3}$
7. $f(x) = x^4 + 2x^3$
8. $f(x) = \frac{1}{5}x^5 - 2x^3 + \frac{9}{5}x$

In Exercises 9–12, sketch the graph of $y = x^n$ and each specified transformation.

9. $y = x^3$
   (a) $f(x) = (x - 2)^3$
   (b) $f(x) = x^3 - 2$
   (c) $f(x) = -\frac{1}{2}x^3$
   (d) $f(x) = (x - 2)^3 - 2$

10. $y = x^5$
    (a) $f(x) = (x + 3)^5$
    (b) $f(x) = x^5 + 3$
    (c) $f(x) = 1 - \frac{1}{2}x^5$
    (d) $f(x) = -\frac{1}{2}(x + 1)^5$

11. $y = x^4$
    (a) $f(x) = (x + 5)^4$
    (b) $f(x) = x^4 - 5$
    (c) $f(x) = 4 - x^4$
    (d) $f(x) = \frac{1}{2}(x - 1)^4$

12. $y = x^6$
    (a) $f(x) = -\frac{1}{8}x^6$
    (b) $f(x) = x^6 - 4$
    (c) $f(x) = -\frac{1}{4}x^6 + 1$
    (d) $f(x) = (x + 2)^6 - 4$

Graphical Analysis **In Exercises 13–16, use a graphing utility to graph the functions f and g in the same viewing window. Zoom out far enough so that the right-hand and left-hand behaviors of f and g appear identical. Show both graphs.**

13. $f(x) = 3x^3 - 9x + 1$, $g(x) = 3x^3$

14. $f(x) = -\frac{1}{3}(x^3 - 3x + 2)$, $g(x) = -\frac{1}{3}x^3$

15. $f(x) = -(x^4 - 4x^3 + 16x)$, $g(x) = -x^4$

16. $f(x) = 3x^4 - 6x^2$, $g(x) = 3x^4$

In Exercises 17–24, use the Leading Coefficient Test to determine the right-hand and left-hand behavior of the graph of the polynomial function. Use a graphing utility to verify your result.

17. $f(x) = 2x^4 - 3x + 1$ **18.** $f(x) = \frac{1}{3}x^3 + 5x$

19. $g(x) = 5 - \frac{7}{2}x - 3x^2$ **20.** $h(x) = 1 - x^6$

21. $f(x) = \dfrac{6 - 2x + 4x^2 - 5x^3}{3}$

22. $f(x) = \dfrac{3x^4 - 2x + 5}{4}$

23. $h(t) = -\frac{2}{3}(t^2 - 5t + 3)$

24. $f(s) = -\frac{7}{8}(s^3 + 5s^2 - 7s + 1)$

In Exercises 25–34, find all the real zeros of the polynomial function. Determine the multiplicity of each zero. Use a graphing utility to verify your result.

25. $f(x) = x^2 - 25$ **26.** $f(x) = 49 - x^2$

27. $h(t) = t^2 - 6t + 9$ **28.** $f(x) = x^2 + 10x + 25$

29. $f(x) = x^2 + x - 2$ **30.** $f(x) = 2x^2 - 14x + 24$

31. $f(t) = t^3 - 4t^2 + 4t$ **32.** $f(x) = x^4 - x^3 - 20x^2$

33. $f(x) = \frac{1}{2}x^2 + \frac{5}{2}x - \frac{3}{2}$ **34.** $f(x) = \frac{5}{3}x^2 + \frac{8}{3}x - \frac{4}{3}$

Graphical Analysis **In Exercises 35–46, (a) use a graphing utility to graph the function, (b) use the graph to approximate any zeros (accurate to three decimal places), and (c) find the zeros algebraically.**

35. $f(x) = 3x^2 - 12x + 3$

36. $g(x) = 5x^2 - 10x - 5$

37. $g(t) = \frac{1}{2}t^4 - \frac{1}{2}$ **38.** $y = \frac{1}{4}x^3(x^2 - 9)$

39. $f(x) = x^5 + x^3 - 6x$ **40.** $g(t) = t^5 - 6t^3 + 9t$

41. $f(x) = 2x^4 - 2x^2 - 40$

42. $f(x) = 5x^4 + 15x^2 + 10$

43. $f(x) = x^3 - 4x^2 - 25x + 100$

44. $y = 4x^3 + 4x^2 - 7x + 2$

45. $y = 4x^3 - 20x^2 + 25x$

46. $y = x^5 - 5x^3 + 4x$

In Exercises 47–50, use a graphing utility to graph the function and approximate (accurate to three decimal places) any real zeros and relative extrema.

47. $f(x) = 2x^4 - 6x^2 + 1$

48. $f(x) = -\frac{3}{8}x^4 - x^3 + 2x^2 + 5$

49. $f(x) = x^5 + 3x^3 - x + 6$

50. $f(x) = -3x^3 - 4x^2 + x - 3$

In Exercises 51–60, find a polynomial function that has the given zeros. (There are many correct answers.)

51. $0, 4$ **52.** $-7, 2$

53. $0, -2, -3$ **54.** $0, 2, 5$

55. $4, -3, 3, 0$ **56.** $-2, -1, 0, 1, 2$

57. $1 + \sqrt{3}, 1 - \sqrt{3}$ **58.** $6 + \sqrt{3}, 6 - \sqrt{3}$

59. $2, 4 + \sqrt{5}, 4 - \sqrt{5}$ **60.** $4, 2 + \sqrt{7}, 2 - \sqrt{7}$

In Exercises 61–72, sketch the graph of the function by (a) applying the Leading Coefficient Test, (b) finding the zeros of the polynomial, (c) plotting sufficient solution points, and (d) drawing a continuous curve through the points.

61. $f(x) = x^3 - 9x$ **62.** $g(x) = x^4 - 4x^2$

63. $f(t) = \frac{1}{4}(t^2 - 2t + 15)$

64. $g(x) = -x^2 + 10x - 16$

65. $f(x) = x^3 - 3x^2$ **66.** $f(x) = 3x^3 - 24x^2$

67. $f(x) = -x^3 - 5x^2$ **68.** $f(x) = 3x^4 - 48x^2$

69. $f(x) = x^2(x - 4)$ **70.** $h(x) = \frac{1}{3}x^3(x - 4)^2$

71. $g(t) = -\frac{1}{4}(t - 2)^2(t + 2)^2$

72. $g(x) = \frac{1}{10}(x + 1)^2(x - 3)^2$

In Exercises 73–76, (a) use the Intermediate Value Theorem and a graphing utility to find intervals of length 1 in which the polynomial function is guaranteed to have a zero, (b) use the *root* or *zero* feature of the graphing utility to approximate the zeros of the function, and (c) verify your answers in part (a) by using the *table* feature of the graphing utility.

73. $f(x) = x^3 - 3x^2 + 3$

74. $f(x) = 0.11x^3 - 2.07x^2 + 9.81x - 6.88$

75. $g(x) = 3x^4 + 4x^3 - 3$

76. $h(x) = x^4 - 10x^2 + 2$

In Exercises 77–84, use a graphing utility to graph the function. Identify any symmetry with respect to the x-axis, y-axis, or origin. Determine the number of x-intercepts of the graph.

77. $f(x) = x^2(x + 6)$ **78.** $h(x) = x^3(x - 4)^2$

79. $g(t) = -\frac{1}{2}(t - 4)^2(t + 4)^2$

80. $g(x) = \frac{1}{8}(x + 1)^2(x - 3)^3$

81. $f(x) = x^3 - 4x$ **82.** $f(x) = x^4 - 2x^2$

83. $g(x) = \frac{1}{5}(x + 1)^2(x - 3)(2x - 9)$

84. $h(x) = \frac{1}{5}(x + 2)^2(3x - 5)^2$

85. *Numerical and Graphical Analysis* An open box is to be made from a square piece of material 36 centimeters on a side by cutting equal squares with sides of length x from the corners and turning up the sides (see figure).

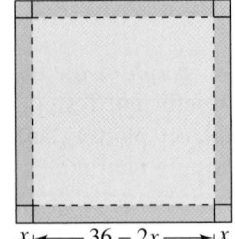 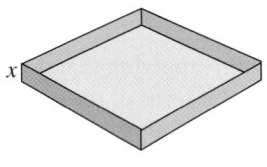

$x \,\vert\!\!\longleftarrow 36 - 2x \longrightarrow\!\!\vert\, x$

(a) Verify that the volume of the box is given by the function $V(x) = x(36 - 2x)^2$.

(b) Determine the domain of the function V.

(c) Use the *table* feature of a graphing utility to create a table that shows various box heights x and the corresponding volumes V. Use the table to estimate a range of dimensions within which the maximum volume is produced.

(d) Use a graphing utility to graph V and use the range of dimensions from part (c) to find the x-value for which $V(x)$ is maximum.

86. *Geometry* An open box with locking tabs is to be made from a square piece of material 24 inches on a side. This is done by cutting equal squares from the corners and folding along the dashed lines, as shown in the figure.

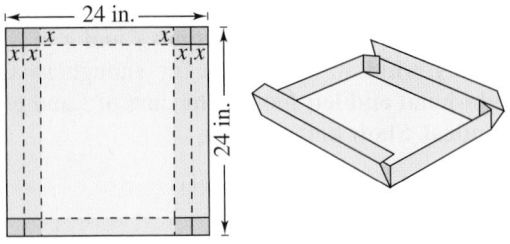

Figure for 86

(a) Verify that the volume of the box is given by the function $V(x) = 8x(6 - x)(12 - x)$.

(b) Determine the domain of the function V.

(c) Sketch the graph of the function and estimate the value of x for which $V(x)$ is maximum.

87. *Revenue* The total revenue R (in millions of dollars) for a company is related to its advertising expense by the function $R = 0.00001(-x^3 + 600x^2)$, $0 \le x \le 400$, where x is the amount spent on advertising (in tens of thousands of dollars). Use the graph of the function shown in the figure to estimate the point on the graph at which the function is increasing most rapidly. This point is called the **point of diminishing returns** because any expense above this amount will yield less return per dollar invested in advertising.

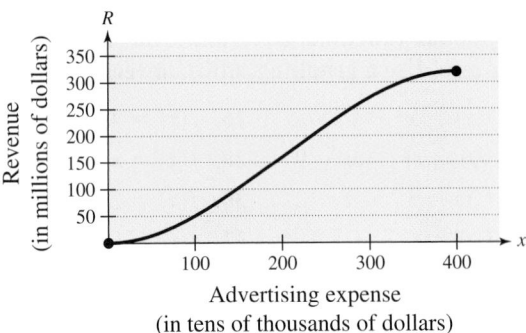

88. *Environment* The growth of a red oak tree is approximated by the function

$$G = -0.003t^3 + 0.137t^2 + 0.458t - 0.839$$

where G is the height of the tree (in feet) and t ($2 \le t \le 34$) is its age (in years). Use a graphing utility to graph the function and estimate the age of the tree when it is growing most rapidly. This point is called the **point of diminishing returns** because the increase in growth will be less with each additional year. (*Hint:* Use a viewing window in which $0 \le x \le 35$ and $0 \le y \le 60$.)

Data Analysis   In Exercises 89–92, use the table, which shows the median prices (in thousands of dollars) of new privately owned U.S. homes in the Northeast y_1 and in the South y_2 for the years 1995 through 2001. The data can be approximated by the following models.

$y_1 = 0.1250t^3 - 1.446t^2 + 9.07t + 155.5$

$y_2 = -0.2000t^3 + 5.155t^2 - 37.23t + 206.8$

In the models, t represents the year, with $t = 5$ corresponding to 1995. (Sources: U.S. Census Bureau; U.S. Department of Housing and Urban Development)

Year, t	y_1	y_2
5	180.0	124.5
6	186.0	126.2
7	190.0	129.6
8	200.0	135.8
9	210.5	145.9
10	227.4	148.0
11	246.4	155.4

89. Use a graphing utility to plot the data and graph the model for y_1 in the same viewing window. How closely does the model represent the data?

90. Use a graphing utility to plot the data and graph the model for y_2 in the same viewing window. How closely does the model represent the data?

91. Use the models to predict the median price of a new privately-owned home in both regions in 2007. Do your answers seem reasonable? Explain.

92. Use the graphs of the models in Exercises 89 and 90 to write a short paragraph about the relationship between the median prices of homes in the two regions.

Synthesis

True or False?   In Exercises 93 and 94, determine whether the statement is true or false. Justify your answer.

93. A sixth-degree polynomial can have six turning points.

94. The graph of the function

$$f(x) = 2 + x - x^2 + x^3 - x^4 + x^5 + x^6 - x^7$$

rises to the left and falls to the right.

Writing   In Exercises 95–98, match the graph of each cubic function with one of the basic shapes and write a short paragraph describing how you reached your conclusion. Is it possible for a polynomial of odd degree to have no real zeros? Explain.

(a) 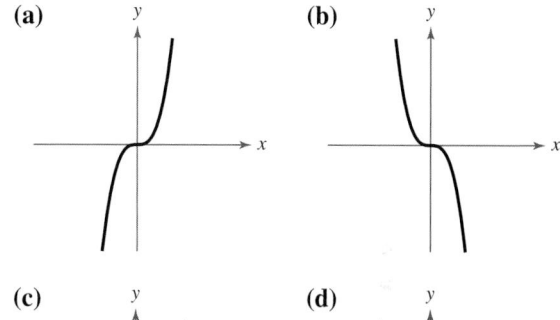   (b)

(c) 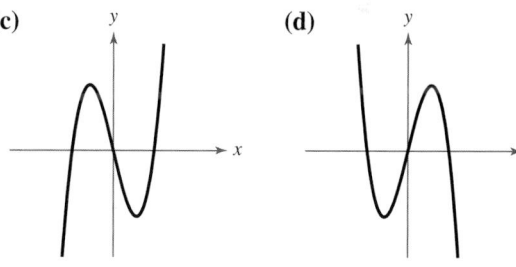   (d)

95. $f(x) = -x^3$ 96. $f(x) = -x^3 + 4x$

97. $f(x) = x^3$ 98. $f(x) = x^3 - 4x$

Review

In Exercises 99–104, let $f(x) = 14x - 3$ and $g(x) = 8x^2$. Find the indicated value.

99. $(f + g)(-4)$ 100. $(g - f)(3)$

101. $(fg)\left(-\dfrac{4}{7}\right)$ 102. $\left(\dfrac{f}{g}\right)(-1.5)$

103. $(f \circ g)(-1)$ 104. $(g \circ f)(0)$

In Exercises 105–108, solve the inequality and sketch the solution on the real number line. Use a graphing utility to verify your solution graphically.

105. $3(x - 5) < 4x - 7$ 106. $2x^2 - x \geq 1$

107. $\dfrac{5x - 2}{x - 7} \leq 4$ 108. $|x + 8| - 1 \geq 15$

3.3 Real Zeros of Polynomial Functions

Long Division of Polynomials

Consider the graph of

$$f(x) = 6x^3 - 19x^2 + 16x - 4.$$

Notice in Figure 3.32 that $x = 2$ appears to be a zero of f. Because $f(2) = 0$, you know that $x = 2$ is a zero of the polynomial function f, and that $(x - 2)$ is a factor of $f(x)$. This means that there exists a second-degree polynomial $q(x)$ such that $f(x) = (x - 2) \cdot q(x)$. To find $q(x)$, you can use **long division of polynomials.**

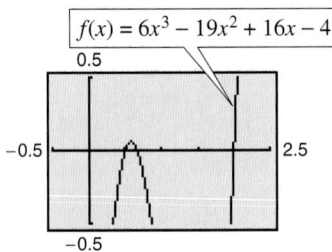

Figure 3.32

What you should learn

- Use long division to divide polynomials by other polynomials.
- Use synthetic division to divide polynomials by binomials of the form $(x - k)$.
- Use the Remainder and Factor Theorems.
- Use the Rational Zero Test to determine possible rational zeros of polynomial functions.
- Use Descartes's Rule of Signs and the Upper and Lower Bound Rules to find zeros of polynomials.

Why you should learn it

Polynomial division can help you rewrite polynomials that are used to model real-life problems. For instance, Exercise 80 on page 277 shows how polynomial division can be used to model the sales from lottery tickets in the United States from 1995 through 2001.

Reuters NewMedia, Inc./Corbis

Example 1 Long Division of Polynomials

Divide $6x^3 - 19x^2 + 16x - 4$ by $x - 2$, and use the result to factor the polynomial completely.

Solution

Partial quotients

$$
\begin{array}{r}
6x^2 - 7x + 2 \\
x - 2\overline{)6x^3 - 19x^2 + 16x - 4} \\
\underline{6x^3 - 12x^2} \\
-7x^2 + 16x \\
\underline{-7x^2 + 14x} \\
2x - 4 \\
\underline{2x - 4} \\
0
\end{array}
$$

Multiply: $6x^2(x - 2)$.
Subtract.
Multiply: $-7x(x - 2)$.
Subtract.
Multiply: $2(x - 2)$.
Subtract.

You can see that

$$6x^3 - 19x^2 + 16x - 4 = (x - 2)(6x^2 - 7x + 2)$$

$$= (x - 2)(2x - 1)(3x - 2).$$

Note that this factorization agrees with the graph of f (see Figure 3.32) in that the three x-intercepts occur at $x = 2$, $x = \frac{1}{2}$, and $x = \frac{2}{3}$.

✓ *Checkpoint* Now try Exercise 1.

STUDY TIP

Note that in Example 1, the division process requires $-7x^2 + 14x$ to be subtracted from $-7x^2 + 16x$. Therefore it is implied that

$$\frac{-7x^2 + 16x}{-(-7x^2 + 14x)} = \frac{-7x^2 + 16x}{7x^2 - 14x}$$

and instead is written simply as

$$\begin{array}{r} -7x^2 + 16x \\ -7x^2 + 14x. \\ \hline 2x \end{array}$$

In Example 1, $x - 2$ is a factor of the polynomial $6x^3 - 19x^2 + 16x - 4$, and the long division process produces a remainder of zero. Often, long division will produce a nonzero remainder. For instance, if you divide $x^2 + 3x + 5$ by $x + 1$, you obtain the following.

$$
\begin{array}{r}
x + 2 \qquad \text{Quotient} \\
x + 1 \overline{)\, x^2 + 3x + 5} \qquad \text{Dividend} \\
\underline{x^2 +\ x} \qquad\qquad \\
2x + 5 \qquad\quad \\
\underline{2x + 2} \qquad\quad \\
3 \qquad \text{Remainder}
\end{array}
$$

Divisor ⟹

In fractional form, you can write this result as follows.

$$
\underbrace{\frac{\overbrace{x^2 + 3x + 5}^{\text{Dividend}}}{\underbrace{x + 1}_{\text{Divisor}}}}= \overbrace{x + 2}^{\text{Quotient}} + \overset{\text{Remainder}}{\frac{3}{\underbrace{x + 1}_{\text{Divisor}}}}
$$

This implies that

$$x^2 + 3x + 5 = (x + 1)(x + 2) + 3 \qquad \text{Multiply each side by } (x + 1).$$

which illustrates the following theorem, called the **Division Algorithm.**

The Division Algorithm

If $f(x)$ and $d(x)$ are polynomials such that $d(x) \neq 0$, and the degree of $d(x)$ is less than or equal to the degree of $f(x)$, there exist unique polynomials $q(x)$ and $r(x)$ such that

$$f(x) = d(x)q(x) + r(x)$$

Dividend Divisor Quotient Remainder

where $r(x) = 0$ *or* the degree of $r(x)$ is less than the degree of $d(x)$. If the remainder $r(x)$ is zero, $d(x)$ *divides evenly* into $f(x)$.

The Division Algorithm can also be written as

$$\frac{f(x)}{d(x)} = q(x) + \frac{r(x)}{d(x)}.$$

In the Division Algorithm, the rational expression $f(x)/d(x)$ is **improper** because the degree of $f(x)$ is greater than or equal to the degree of $d(x)$. On the other hand, the rational expression $r(x)/d(x)$ is **proper** because the degree of $r(x)$ is less than the degree of $d(x)$.

Before you apply the Division Algorithm, follow these steps.

1. Write the dividend and divisor in descending powers of the variable.
2. Insert placeholders with zero coefficients for missing powers of the variable.

Example 2 Long Division of Polynomials

Divide $x^3 - 1$ by $x - 1$.

Solution

Because there is no x^2-term or x-term in the dividend, you need to line up the subtraction by using zero coefficients (or leaving spaces) for the missing terms.

$$
\begin{array}{r}
x^2 + x + 1 \\
x - 1 \overline{\smash{)}\, x^3 + 0x^2 + 0x - 1} \\
\underline{x^3 - x^2} \\
x^2 + 0x \\
\underline{x^2 - x} \\
x - 1 \\
\underline{x - 1} \\
0
\end{array}
$$

So, $x - 1$ divides evenly into $x^3 - 1$, and you can write

$$
\frac{x^3 - 1}{x - 1} = x^2 + x + 1, \qquad x \neq 1.
$$

✓ *Checkpoint* Now try Exercise 7.

You can check the result of Example 2 by multiplying.

$$
(x - 1)(x^2 + x + 1) = x^3 + x^2 + x - x^2 - x - 1
$$
$$
= x^3 - 1
$$

Example 3 Long Division of Polynomials

Divide $2x^4 + 4x^3 - 5x^2 + 3x - 2$ by $x^2 + 2x - 3$.

Solution

$$
\begin{array}{r}
2x^2 + 1 \\
x^2 + 2x - 3 \overline{\smash{)}\, 2x^4 + 4x^3 - 5x^2 + 3x - 2} \\
\underline{2x^4 + 4x^3 - 6x^2} \\
x^2 + 3x - 2 \\
\underline{x^2 + 2x - 3} \\
x + 1
\end{array}
$$

Note that the first subtraction eliminated two terms from the dividend. When this happens, the quotient skips a term. You can write the result as

$$
\frac{2x^4 + 4x^3 - 5x^2 + 3x - 2}{x^2 + 2x - 3} = 2x^2 + 1 + \frac{x + 1}{x^2 + 2x - 3}.
$$

✓ *Checkpoint* Now try Exercise 9.

Synthetic Division

There is a nice shortcut for long division of polynomials when dividing by divisors of the form $x - k$. The shortcut is called **synthetic division.** The pattern for synthetic division of a cubic polynomial is summarized as follows. (The pattern for higher-degree polynomials is similar.)

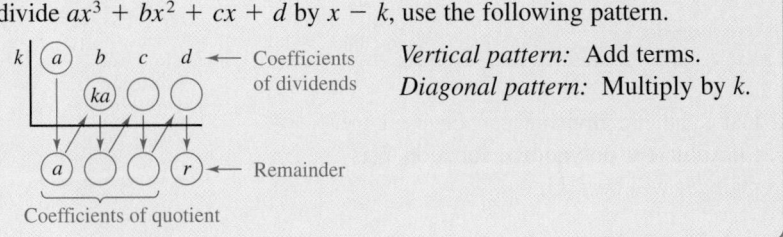

Synthetic Division (of a Cubic Polynomial)

To divide $ax^3 + bx^2 + cx + d$ by $x - k$, use the following pattern.

Vertical pattern: Add terms.
Diagonal pattern: Multiply by k.

Synthetic division works *only* for divisors of the form $x - k$. [Remember that $x + k = x - (-k)$.] You cannot use synthetic division to divide a polynomial by a quadratic such as $x^2 - 3$.

Example 4   Using Synthetic Division

Use synthetic division to divide $x^4 - 10x^2 - 2x + 4$ by $x + 3$.

Solution

You should set up the array as follows. Note that a zero is included for each missing term in the dividend.

$$-3 \,\big|\; 1 \quad 0 \;-10 \;-2 \quad 4$$

Then, use the synthetic division pattern by adding terms in columns and multiplying the results by -3.

Divisor: $x + 3$ Dividend: $x^4 - 10x^2 - 2x + 4$

$$
\begin{array}{r|rrrrr}
-3 & 1 & 0 & -10 & -2 & 4 \\
   &   & -3 & 9 & 3 & -3 \\
\hline
   & 1 & -3 & -1 & 1 & 1 \\
\end{array}
$$

Remainder: 1

Quotient: $x^3 - 3x^2 - x + 1$

So, you have

$$\frac{x^4 - 10x^2 - 2x + 4}{x + 3} = x^3 - 3x^2 - x + 1 + \frac{1}{x + 3}.$$

✓ *Checkpoint* Now try Exercise 19.

Exploration

Evaluate the polynomial $x^4 - 10x^2 - 2x + 4$ at $x = -3$. What do you observe?

The Remainder and Factor Theorems

The remainder obtained in the synthetic division process has an important interpretation, as described in the **Remainder Theorem.** See Appendix B for a proof of the Remainder Theorem.

> **The Remainder Theorem**
>
> If a polynomial $f(x)$ is divided by $x - k$, the remainder is
>
> $\quad r = f(k).$

The Remainder Theorem tells you that synthetic division can be used to evaluate a polynomial function. That is, to evaluate a polynomial function $f(x)$ when $x = k$, divide $f(x)$ by $x - k$. The remainder will be $f(k)$.

Example 5   Using the Remainder Theorem

Use the Remainder Theorem to evaluate the following function at $x = -2$.

$\quad f(x) = 3x^3 + 8x^2 + 5x - 7$

Solution

Using synthetic division, you obtain the following.

$$
\begin{array}{r|rrrr}
-2 & 3 & 8 & 5 & -7 \\
   &   & -6 & -4 & -2 \\
\hline
   & 3 & 2 & 1 & -9
\end{array}
$$

Because the remainder is $r = -9$, you can conclude that

$\quad f(-2) = -9. \qquad {\scriptstyle r = f(k)}$

This means that $(-2, -9)$ is a point on the graph of f. You can check this by substituting $x = -2$ in the original function.

Check

$$
\begin{aligned}
f(-2) &= 3(-2)^3 + 8(-2)^2 + 5(-2) - 7 \\
&= 3(-8) + 8(4) - 10 - 7 \\
&= -24 + 32 - 10 - 7 = -9
\end{aligned}
$$

☑ *Checkpoint* Now try Exercise 31.

Another important theorem is the **Factor Theorem.** This theorem states that you can test whether a polynomial has $(x - k)$ as a factor by evaluating the polynomial at $x = k$. If the result is 0, $(x - k)$ is a factor. See Appendix B for a proof of the Factor Theorem.

> **The Factor Theorem**
>
> A polynomial $f(x)$ has a factor $(x - k)$ if and only if $f(k) = 0$.

Example 6   Factoring a Polynomial: Repeated Division

Show that $(x - 2)$ and $(x + 3)$ are factors of

$$f(x) = 2x^4 + 7x^3 - 4x^2 - 27x - 18.$$

Then find the remaining factors of $f(x)$.

Algebraic Solution

Using synthetic division with the factor $(x - 2)$, you obtain the following.

$$
\begin{array}{r|rrrrr}
2 & 2 & 7 & -4 & -27 & -18 \\
  &   & 4 & 22 & 36 & 18 \\
\hline
  & 2 & 11 & 18 & 9 & 0
\end{array}
$$

0 remainder; $(x - 2)$ is a factor.

Take the result of this division and perform synthetic division again using the factor $(x + 3)$.

$$
\begin{array}{r|rrrr}
-3 & 2 & 11 & 18 & 9 \\
   &   & -6 & -15 & -9 \\
\hline
   & 2 & 5 & 3 & 0
\end{array}
$$

0 remainder; $(x + 3)$ is a factor.

$\underbrace{2x^2 + 5x + 3}$

Because the resulting quadratic factors as

$$2x^2 + 5x + 3 = (2x + 3)(x + 1)$$

the complete factorization of $f(x)$ is

$$f(x) = (x - 2)(x + 3)(2x + 3)(x + 1).$$

 Checkpoint   Now try Exercise 39.

Graphical Solution

The graph of a polynomial with factors of $(x - 2)$ and $(x + 3)$ has x-intercepts at $x = 2$ and $x = -3$. Use a graphing utility to graph

$$y = 2x^4 + 7x^3 - 4x^2 - 27x - 18.$$

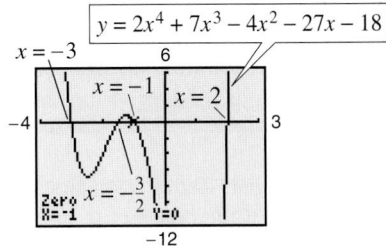

Figure 3.33

From Figure 3.33, you can see that the graph appears to cross the x-axis in two other places, near $x = -1$ and $x = -\frac{3}{2}$. Use the *zero* or *root* feature or the *zoom* and *trace* features to approximate the other two intercepts to be $x = -1$ and $x = -\frac{3}{2}$. So, the factors of f are $(x - 2)$, $(x + 3)$, $\left(x + \frac{3}{2}\right)$, and $(x + 1)$. You can rewrite the factor $\left(x + \frac{3}{2}\right)$ as $(2x + 3)$, so the complete factorization of f is $f(x) = (x - 2)(x + 3)(2x + 3)(x + 1)$.

Using the Remainder in Synthetic Division

In summary, the remainder r, obtained in the synthetic division of $f(x)$ by $x - k$, provides the following information.

1. The remainder r gives the value of f at $x = k$. That is, $r = f(k)$.

2. If $r = 0$, $(x - k)$ is a factor of $f(x)$.

3. If $r = 0$, $(k, 0)$ is an x-intercept of the graph of f.

Throughout this text, the importance of developing several problem-solving strategies is emphasized. In the exercises for this section, try using more than one strategy to solve several of the exercises. For instance, if you find that $x - k$ divides evenly into $f(x)$, try sketching the graph of f. You should find that $(k, 0)$ is an x-intercept of the graph.

The Rational Zero Test

The **Rational Zero Test** relates the possible rational zeros of a polynomial (having integer coefficients) to the leading coefficient and to the constant term of the polynomial.

> **The Rational Zero Test**
>
> If the polynomial
>
> $$f(x) = a_n x^n + a_{n-1} x^{n-1} + \cdots + a_2 x^2 + a_1 x + a_0$$
>
> has integer coefficients, every rational zero of f has the form
>
> $$\text{Rational zero} = \frac{p}{q}$$
>
> where p and q have no common factors other than 1, p is a factor of the constant term a_0, and q is a factor of the leading coefficient a_n.

To use the Rational Zero Test, first list all rational numbers whose numerators are factors of the constant term and whose denominators are factors of the leading coefficient.

$$\text{Possible rational zeros} = \frac{\text{factors of constant term}}{\text{factors of leading coefficient}}$$

Now that you have formed this list of *possible rational zeros*, use a trial-and-error method to determine which, if any, are actual zeros of the polynomial. Note that when the leading coefficient is 1, the possible rational zeros are simply the factors of the constant term. This case is illustrated in Example 7.

STUDY TIP

Graph the polynomial
$y = x^3 - 53x^2 + 103x - 51$
in the standard viewing window. From the graph alone, it appears that there is only one zero. From the Leading Coefficient Test, you know that because the degree of the polynomial is odd and the leading coefficient is positive, the graph falls to the left and rises to the right. So, the function must have another zero. From the Rational Zero Test, you know that ± 51 might be zeros of the function. If you zoom out several times, you will see a more complete picture of the graph. Your graph should confirm that $x = 51$ is a zero of f.

Example 7   Rational Zero Test with Leading Coefficient of 1

Find the rational zeros of $f(x) = x^3 + x + 1$.

Solution

Because the leading coefficient is 1, the possible rational zeros are simply the factors of the constant term.

Possible rational zeros: ± 1

By testing these possible zeros, you can see that neither works.

$$f(1) = (1)^3 + 1 + 1 = 3$$

$$f(-1) = (-1)^3 + (-1) + 1 = -1$$

So, you can conclude that the polynomial has *no* rational zeros. Note from the graph of f in Figure 3.34 that f does have one real zero between -1 and 0. However, by the Rational Zero Test, you know that this real zero is *not* a rational number.

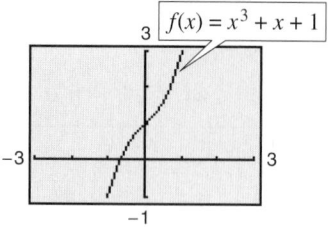

Figure 3.34

✓ *Checkpoint* Now try Exercise 45.

If the leading coefficient of a polynomial is not 1, the list of possible rational zeros can increase dramatically. In such cases the search can be shortened in several ways.

1. A programmable calculator can be used to speed up the calculations.
2. A graphing utility can give a good estimate of the locations of the zeros.
3. The Intermediate Value Theorem, along with a table generated by a graphing utility, can give approximations of zeros.
4. The Factor Theorem and synthetic division can be used to test the possible rational zeros.

Finding the first zero is often the most difficult part. After that, the search is simplified by working with the lower-degree polynomial obtained in synthetic division.

Example 8   Using the Rational Zero Test

Find the rational zeros of $f(x) = 2x^3 + 3x^2 - 8x + 3$.

Solution

The leading coefficient is 2 and the constant term is 3.

Possible rational zeros:

$$\frac{\text{Factors of 3}}{\text{Factors of 2}} = \frac{\pm 1, \pm 3}{\pm 1, \pm 2} = \pm 1, \pm 3, \pm \frac{1}{2}, \pm \frac{3}{2}$$

By synthetic division, you can determine that $x = 1$ is a rational zero.

$$\begin{array}{r|rrrr}
1 & 2 & 3 & -8 & 3 \\
  &   & 2 & 5 & -3 \\
\hline
  & 2 & 5 & -3 & 0
\end{array}$$

So, $f(x)$ factors as

$$f(x) = (x - 1)(2x^2 + 5x - 3) = (x - 1)(2x - 1)(x + 3)$$

and you can conclude that the rational zeros of f are $x = 1$, $x = \frac{1}{2}$, and $x = -3$, as shown in Figure 3.35.

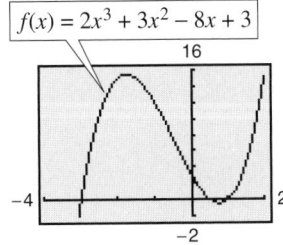

Figure 3.35

✓ *Checkpoint* Now try Exercise 47.

A graphing utility can help you determine which possible rational zeros to test, as demonstrated in Example 9.

Example 9   Finding Real Zeros of a Polynomial Function

Find all the real zeros of $f(x) = 10x^3 - 15x^2 - 16x + 12$.

Solution

Because the leading coefficient is 10 and the constant term is 12, there is a long list of possible rational zeros.

Possible rational zeros:

$$\frac{\text{Factors of 12}}{\text{Factors of 10}} = \frac{\pm 1, \pm 2, \pm 3, \pm 4, \pm 6, \pm 12}{\pm 1, \pm 2, \pm 5, \pm 10}$$

With so many possibilities (32, in fact), it is worth your time to use a graphing utility to focus on just a few. By using the *trace* feature of a graphing utility, it looks like three reasonable choices are $x = -\frac{6}{5}$, $x = \frac{1}{2}$, and $x = 2$ (see Figure 3.36). Synthetic division shows that only $x = 2$ works. (You could also use the Factor Theorem to test these choices.)

$$
\begin{array}{r|rrrr}
2 & 10 & -15 & -16 & 12 \\
  &   & 20 & 10 & -12 \\
\hline
  & 10 & 5   & -6 & 0 \\
\end{array}
$$

So, $x = 2$ is one zero and you have

$$f(x) = (x - 2)(10x^2 + 5x - 6).$$

Using the Quadratic Formula, you find that the two additional zeros are irrational numbers.

$$x = \frac{-5 + \sqrt{265}}{20} \approx 0.5639 \quad \text{and} \quad x = \frac{-5 - \sqrt{265}}{20} \approx -1.0639$$

 Checkpoint   Now try Exercise 51.

TECHNOLOGY TIP

You can use the *table* feature of a graphing utility to test the possible rational zeros of the function in Example 9, as shown below. Set the table to start at $x = -12$ and set the table step to 0.1. Look through the table to determine the values of x for which y_1 is 0.

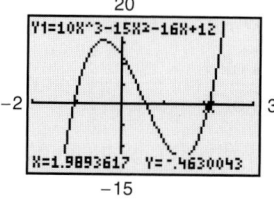

Figure 3.36

Other Tests for Zeros of Polynomials

You know that an nth-degree polynomial function can have *at most* n real zeros. Of course, many nth-degree polynomials do not have that many real zeros. For instance, $f(x) = x^2 + 1$ has no real zeros, and $f(x) = x^3 + 1$ has only one real zero. The following theorem, called **Descartes's Rule of Signs,** sheds more light on the number of real zeros of a polynomial.

Descartes's Rule of Signs

Let $f(x) = a_n x^n + a_{n-1} x^{n-1} + \cdots + a_2 x^2 + a_1 x + a_0$ be a polynomial with real coefficients and $a_0 \neq 0$.

1. The number of *positive real zeros* of f is either equal to the number of variations in sign of $f(x)$ or less than that number by an even integer.

2. The number of *negative real zeros* of f is either equal to the number of variations in sign of $f(-x)$ or less than that number by an even integer.

A **variation in sign** means that two consecutive (nonzero) coefficients have opposite signs.

When using Descartes's Rule of Signs, a zero of multiplicity k should be counted as k zeros. For instance, the polynomial $x^3 - 3x + 2$ has two variations in sign, and so has either two positive or no positive real zeros. Because

$$x^3 - 3x + 2 = (x - 1)(x - 1)(x + 2)$$

you can see that the two positive real zeros are $x = 1$ of multiplicity 2.

Example 10   Using Descartes's Rule of Signs

Describe the possible real zeros of $f(x) = 3x^3 - 5x^2 + 6x - 4$.

Solution

The original polynomial has *three* variations in sign.

$$\overset{\displaystyle +\text{ to }-\qquad\quad +\text{ to }-}{f(x) = 3x^3 - 5x^2 + 6x - 4}$$

$$\underset{-\text{ to }+}{}$$

The polynomial

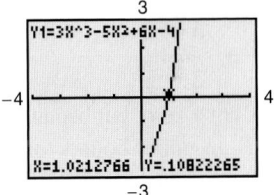

Figure 3.37

$$f(-x) = 3(-x)^3 - 5(-x)^2 + 6(-x) - 4 = -3x^3 - 5x^2 - 6x - 4$$

has no variations in sign. So, from Descartes's Rule of Signs, the polynomial $f(x) = 3x^3 - 5x^2 + 6x - 4$ has either three positive real zeros or one positive real zero, and has no negative real zeros. By using the *trace* feature of a graphing utility, you can see that the function has only one real zero (it is a positive number near $x = 1$), as shown in Figure 3.37.

✓ *Checkpoint* Now try Exercise 57.

Another test for zeros of a polynomial function is related to the sign pattern in the last row of the synthetic division array. This test can give you an upper or lower bound of the real zeros of f, which can help you eliminate possible real zeros. A real number b is an **upper bound** for the real zeros of f if no zeros are greater than b. Similarly, b is a **lower bound** if no real zeros of f are less than b.

Upper and Lower Bound Rules

Let $f(x)$ be a polynomial with real coefficients and a positive leading coefficient. Suppose $f(x)$ is divided by $x - c$, using synthetic division.

1. If $c > 0$ and each number in the last row is either positive or zero, c is an **upper bound** for the real zeros of f.

2. If $c < 0$ and the numbers in the last row are alternately positive and negative (zero entries count as positive or negative), c is a **lower bound** for the real zeros of f.

Example 11 Finding the Zeros of a Polynomial Function

Find the real zeros of $f(x) = 6x^3 - 4x^2 + 3x - 2$.

Solution

The possible real zeros are as follows.

$$\frac{\text{Factors of 2}}{\text{Factors of 6}} = \frac{\pm 1, \pm 2}{\pm 1, \pm 2, \pm 3, \pm 6} = \pm 1, \pm\frac{1}{2}, \pm\frac{1}{3}, \pm\frac{1}{6}, \pm\frac{2}{3}, \pm 2$$

The original polynomial $f(x)$ has three variations in sign. The polynomial

$$f(-x) = 6(-x)^3 - 4(-x)^2 + 3(-x) - 2$$

$$= -6x^3 - 4x^2 - 3x - 2$$

has no variations in sign. As a result of these two findings, you can apply Descartes's Rule of Signs to conclude that there are three positive real zeros or one positive real zero, and no negative zeros. Trying $x = 1$ produces the following.

$$\begin{array}{r|rrrr} 1 & 6 & -4 & 3 & -2 \\ & & 6 & 2 & 5 \\ \hline & 6 & 2 & 5 & 3 \end{array}$$

So, $x = 1$ is not a zero, but because the last row has all positive entries, you know that $x = 1$ is an upper bound for the real zeros. Therefore, you can restrict the search to zeros between 0 and 1. By trial and error, you can determine that $x = \frac{2}{3}$ is a zero. So,

$$f(x) = \left(x - \frac{2}{3}\right)(6x^2 + 3).$$

Because $6x^2 + 3$ has no real zeros, it follows that $x = \frac{2}{3}$ is the only real zero.

☑ *Checkpoint* Now try Exercise 67.

Before concluding this section, here are two additional hints that can help you find the real zeros of a polynomial.

1. If the terms of $f(x)$ have a common monomial factor, it should be factored out before applying the tests in this section. For instance, by writing

$$f(x) = x^4 - 5x^3 + 3x^2 + x = x(x^3 - 5x^2 + 3x + 1)$$

you can see that $x = 0$ is a zero of f and that the remaining zeros can be obtained by analyzing the cubic factor.

2. If you are able to find all but two zeros of $f(x)$, you can always use the Quadratic Formula on the remaining quadratic factor. For instance, if you succeeded in writing

$$f(x) = x^4 - 5x^3 + 3x^2 + x = x(x - 1)(x^2 - 4x - 1)$$

you can apply the Quadratic Formula to $x^2 - 4x - 1$ to conclude that the two remaining zeros are $x = 2 + \sqrt{5}$ and $x = 2 - \sqrt{5}$.

Exploration

Use a graphing utility to graph

$$y_1 = 6x^3 - 4x^2 + 3x - 2.$$

Notice that the graph intersects the x-axis at the point $\left(\frac{2}{3}, 0\right)$. How does this information relate to the real zero found in Example 11? Use a graphing utility to graph

$$y_2 = x^4 - 5x^3 + 3x^2 + x.$$

How many times does the graph intersect the x-axis? How many real zeros does y_2 have?

Exploration

Use a graphing utility to graph

$$y = x^3 + 4.9x^2 - 126x + 382.5$$

in the standard viewing window. From the graph, what do the real zeros appear to be? Discuss how the mathematical tools of this section might help you realize that the graph does not show all the important features of the polynomial function. Now use the *zoom* feature to find all the zeros of this function.

3.3   Exercises

Vocabulary Check

1. Two forms of the Division Algorithm are shown below. Identify and label each part.

   $$f(x) = d(x)q(x) + r(x) \qquad \frac{f(x)}{d(x)} = q(x) + \frac{r(x)}{d(x)}$$

In Exercises 2–7, fill in the blanks.

2. The rational expression $p(x)/q(x)$ is called _____ if the degree of the numerator is greater than or equal to that of the denominator, and is called _____ if the degree of the numerator is less than that of the denominator.

3. An alternative method to long division of polynomials is called _____ , in which the divisor must be of the form $x - k$.

4. The test that gives a list of the possible rational zeros of a polynomial function is known as the _____ Test.

5. The theorem that can be used to determine the possible numbers of positive real zeros and negative real zeros of a function is called _____ of _____ .

6. The _____ states that if a polynomial $f(x)$ is divided by $x - k$, then the remainder is $r = f(k)$.

7. A real number b is an _____ for the real zeros of f if no zeros are greater than b, and is a _____ if no real zeros of f are less than b.

In Exercises 1–12, use long division to divide.

1. Divide $2x^2 + 10x + 12$ by $x + 3$.

2. Divide $5x^2 - 17x - 12$ by $x - 4$.

3. Divide $4x^3 - 7x^2 - 11x + 5$ by $4x + 5$.

4. Divide $x^4 + 5x^3 + 6x^2 - x - 2$ by $x + 2$.

5. Divide $7x + 3$ by $x + 2$.

6. Divide $8x - 5$ by $2x + 1$.

7. $(6x^3 + 10x^2 + x + 8) \div (2x^2 + 1)$

8. $(x^4 + 3x^2 + 1) \div (x^2 - 2x + 3)$

9. $(x^3 - 9) \div (x^2 + 1)$ 10. $(x^5 + 7) \div (x^3 - 1)$

11. $\dfrac{2x^3 - 4x^2 - 15x + 5}{(x - 1)^2}$ 12. $\dfrac{x^4}{(x - 1)^3}$

In Exercises 13–22, use synthetic division to divide.

13. $(3x^3 - 17x^2 + 15x - 25) \div (x - 5)$

14. $(5x^3 + 18x^2 + 7x - 6) \div (x + 3)$

15. $(6x^3 + 7x^2 - x + 26) \div (x - 3)$

16. $(2x^3 + 14x^2 - 20x + 7) \div (x + 6)$

17. $(9x^3 - 18x^2 - 16x + 32) \div (x - 2)$

18. $(5x^3 + 6x + 8) \div (x + 2)$

19. $(x^3 + 512) \div (x + 8)$

20. $(x^3 - 729) \div (x - 9)$

21. $\dfrac{4x^3 + 16x^2 - 23x - 15}{x + \frac{1}{2}}$ 22. $\dfrac{3x^3 - 4x^2 + 5}{x - \frac{3}{2}}$

Graphical Analysis **In Exercises 23 and 24, use a graphing utility to graph the two equations in the same viewing window. Use the graphs to verify that the expressions are equivalent. Verify the results algebraically.**

23. $y_1 = \dfrac{x^2}{x + 2}$, $y_2 = x - 2 + \dfrac{4}{x + 2}$

24. $y_1 = \dfrac{x^4 - 3x^2 - 1}{x^2 + 5}$, $y_2 = x^2 - 8 + \dfrac{39}{x^2 + 5}$

In Exercises 25–30, write the function in the form $f(x) = (x - k)q(x) + r(x)$ for the given value of k. Use a graphing utility to demonstrate that $f(k) = r$.

Function	*Value of k*
25. $f(x) = x^3 - x^2 - 14x + 11$	$k = 4$

Function   *Value of k*

26. $f(x) = 15x^4 + 10x^3 - 6x^2 + 14$ $k = -\frac{2}{3}$

27. $f(x) = x^3 + 3x^2 - 2x - 14$ $k = \sqrt{2}$

28. $f(x) = x^3 + 2x^2 - 5x - 4$ $k = -\sqrt{5}$

29. $f(x) = 4x^3 - 6x^2 - 12x - 4$ $k = 1 - \sqrt{3}$

30. $f(x) = -3x^3 + 8x^2 + 10x - 8$ $k = 2 + \sqrt{2}$

In Exercises 31–34, use synthetic division to find each function value. Use a graphing utility to verify your results.

31. $f(x) = 4x^3 - 13x + 10$

     (a) $f(1)$ (b) $f(-2)$ (c) $f\left(\frac{1}{2}\right)$ (d) $f(8)$

32. $g(x) = x^6 - 4x^4 + 3x^2 + 2$

     (a) $g(2)$ (b) $g(-4)$ (c) $g(3)$ (d) $g(-1)$

33. $h(x) = 3x^3 + 5x^2 - 10x + 1$

     (a) $h(3)$ (b) $h\left(\frac{1}{3}\right)$ (c) $h(-2)$ (d) $h(-5)$

34. $f(x) = 0.4x^4 - 1.6x^3 + 0.7x^2 - 2$

     (a) $f(1)$ (b) $f(-2)$ (c) $f(5)$ (d) $f(-10)$

In Exercises 35–38, use synthetic division to show that x is a solution of the third-degree polynomial equation, and use the result to factor the polynomial completely. List all the real zeros of the function.

Polynomial Equation   *Value of x*

35. $x^3 - 7x + 6 = 0$ $x = 2$

36. $x^3 - 28x - 48 = 0$ $x = -4$

37. $2x^3 - 15x^2 + 27x - 10 = 0$ $x = \frac{1}{2}$

38. $48x^3 - 80x^2 + 41x - 6 = 0$ $x = \frac{2}{3}$

In Exercises 39–44, (a) verify the given factors of the function f, (b) find the remaining factors of f, (c) use your results to write the complete factorization of f, (d) list all real zeros of f, and (e) confirm your results by using a graphing utility to graph the function.

Function   *Factors*

39. $f(x) = 2x^3 + x^2 - 5x + 2$ $(x + 2), (x - 1)$

40. $f(x) = 3x^3 + 2x^2 - 19x + 6$ $(x + 3), (x - 2)$

41. $f(x) = x^4 - 4x^3 - 15x^2$

     $+ 58x - 40$ $(x - 5), (x + 4)$

42. $f(x) = 8x^4 - 14x^3 - 71x^2$

     $- 10x + 24$ $(x + 2), (x - 4)$

43. $f(x) = 6x^3 + 41x^2 - 9x - 14$ $(2x + 1), (3x - 2)$

44. $f(x) = 2x^3 - x^2 - 10x + 5$ $(2x - 1), \left(x + \sqrt{5}\right)$

In Exercises 45–48, use the Rational Zero Test to list all possible rational zeros of f. Use a graphing utility to verify that the zeros of f are contained in the list.

45. $f(x) = x^3 + 3x^2 - x - 3$

46. $f(x) = x^3 - 4x^2 - 4x + 16$

47. $f(x) = 2x^4 - 17x^3 + 35x^2 + 9x - 45$

48. $f(x) = 4x^5 - 8x^4 - 5x^3 + 10x^2 + x - 2$

In Exercises 49–52, find all real solutions of the polynomial equation.

49. $z^4 - z^3 - 2z - 4 = 0$

50. $x^4 - x^3 - 29x^2 - x - 30 = 0$

51. $2y^4 + 7y^3 - 26y^2 + 23y - 6 = 0$

52. $x^5 - x^4 - 3x^3 + 5x^2 - 2x = 0$

Graphical Analysis **In Exercises 53–56, (a) use the *zero* or *root* feature of a graphing utility to approximate (accurate to three decimal places) the zeros of the function, (b) determine one of the exact zeros and use synthetic division to verify your result, and (c) factor the polynomial completely.**

53. $h(t) = t^3 - 2t^2 - 7t + 2$

54. $f(s) = s^3 - 12s^2 + 40s - 24$

55. $h(x) = x^5 - 7x^4 + 10x^3 + 14x^2 - 24x$

56. $g(x) = 6x^4 - 11x^3 - 51x^2 + 99x - 27$

In Exercises 57–60, use Descartes's Rule of Signs to determine the possible numbers of positive and negative real zeros of the function.

57. $f(x) = 2x^4 - x^3 + 6x^2 - x + 5$

58. $f(x) = 3x^4 + 5x^3 - 6x^2 + 8x - 3$

59. $g(x) = 4x^3 - 5x + 8$

60. $g(x) = 2x^3 - 4x^2 - 5$

In Exercises 61–66, (a) use Descartes's Rule of Signs to determine the possible numbers of positive and negative real zeros of f, (b) list the possible rational zeros of f, (c) use a graphing utility to graph f so that some of the possible zeros in parts (a) and (b) can be disregarded, and (d) determine all the real zeros of f.

61. $f(x) = x^3 + x^2 - 4x - 4$

62. $f(x) = -3x^3 + 20x^2 - 36x + 16$

63. $f(x) = -2x^4 + 13x^3 - 21x^2 + 2x + 8$

64. $f(x) = 4x^4 - 17x^2 + 4$

65. $f(x) = 32x^3 - 52x^2 + 17x + 3$

66. $f(x) = 4x^3 + 7x^2 - 11x - 18$

In Exercises 67–70, use synthetic division to verify the upper and lower bounds of the real zeros of f.

67. $f(x) = x^4 - 4x^3 + 15$

Upper bound: $x = 4$;   Lower bound: $x = -1$

68. $f(x) = 2x^3 - 3x^2 - 12x + 8$

Upper bound: $x = 4$;   Lower bound: $x = -3$

69. $f(x) = x^4 - 4x^3 + 16x - 16$

Upper bound: $x = 5$;   Lower bound: $x = -3$

70. $f(x) = 2x^4 - 8x + 3$

Upper bound: $x = 3$;   Lower bound: $x = -4$

In Exercises 71–74, find the rational zeros of the polynomial function.

71. $P(x) = x^4 - \frac{25}{4}x^2 + 9 = \frac{1}{4}(4x^4 - 25x^2 + 36)$

72. $f(x) = x^3 - \frac{3}{2}x^2 - \frac{23}{2}x + 6 = \frac{1}{2}(2x^3 - 3x^2 - 23x + 12)$

73. $f(x) = x^3 - \frac{1}{4}x^2 - x + \frac{1}{4} = \frac{1}{4}(4x^3 - x^2 - 4x + 1)$

74. $f(z) = z^3 + \frac{11}{6}z^2 - \frac{1}{2}z - \frac{1}{3}$
$= \frac{1}{6}(6z^3 + 11z^2 - 3z - 2)$

In Exercises 75–78, match the cubic function with the correct number of rational and irrational zeros.

(a) Rational zeros: 0;   Irrational zeros: 1

(b) Rational zeros: 3;   Irrational zeros: 0

(c) Rational zeros: 1;   Irrational zeros: 2

(d) Rational zeros: 1;   Irrational zeros: 0

75. $f(x) = x^3 - 1$

76. $f(x) = x^3 - 2$

77. $f(x) = x^3 - x$

78. $f(x) = x^3 - 2x$

79. *Data Analysis*   The average monthly rate R for basic cable television in the United States for the years 1995 through 2001 is shown in the table. The data can be approximated by the model

$R = 0.03889t^3 - 0.9064t^2 + 8.327t - 0.92$

where t represents the year, with $t = 5$ corresponding to 1995.   (Source: Kagan World Media)

Year	Rate, R
1995	23.07
1996	24.41
1997	26.48
1998	27.81
1999	28.92
2000	30.37
2001	32.87

Table for 79

(a) Use a graphing utility to plot the data and graph the model in the same viewing window. How closely does the model represent the data?

(b) Use a graphing utility and the model to create a table of estimated values for R. Compare the estimated values with the actual data.

(c) Use the Remainder Theorem to evaluate the model for the year 2008. Even though the model is relatively accurate for estimating the given data, do you think it is accurate for predicting future cable rates? Explain.

80. *Data Analysis*   The table shows the sales S (in billions of dollars) from lottery tickets in the United States from 1995 to 2001. The data can be approximated by the model

$S = 0.0778t^3 - 1.931t^2 + 16.36t - 11.4$

where t represents the year, with $t = 5$ corresponding to 1995.   (Source: TLF Publications, Inc.)

Year	Sales, S
1995	31.9
1996	34.0
1997	35.5
1998	35.6
1999	36.0
2000	37.2
2001	38.4

(a) Use a graphing utility to plot the data and graph the model in the same viewing window. How closely does the model represent the data?

(b) Use a graphing utility and the model to create a table of estimated values for S. Compare the estimated values with the actual data.

(c) Use the Remainder Theorem to evaluate the model for the year 2008. Even though the model is relatively accurate for estimating the given data, would you use this model to predict the sales from lottery tickets in the future? Explain.

81. Geometry A rectangular package sent by a delivery service can have a maximum combined length and girth (perimeter of a cross section) of 120 inches (see figure).

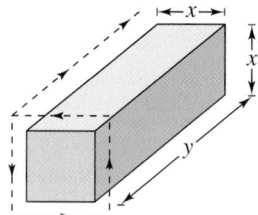

(a) Show that the volume of the package is given by the function

$$V(x) = 4x^2(30 - x).$$

(b) Use a graphing utility to graph the function and approximate the dimensions of the package that yield a maximum volume.

(c) Find values of x such that $V = 13,500$. Which of these values is a physical impossibility in the construction of the package? Explain.

82. Automobile Emissions The number of parts per million of nitric oxide emissions y from a car engine is approximated by the model

$$y = -5.05x^3 + 3857x - 38,411.25, \quad 13 \le x \le 18$$

where x is the air-fuel ratio.

(a) Use a graphing utility to graph the model.

(b) It is observed from the graph that two air-fuel ratios produce 2400 parts per million of nitric oxide, with one being 15. Use the graph to approximate the second air-fuel ratio.

(c) Algebraically approximate the second air-fuel ratio that produces 2400 parts per million of nitric oxide. (*Hint:* Because you know that an air-fuel ratio of 15 produces the specified nitric oxide emission, you can use synthetic division.)

Synthesis

True or False? **In Exercises 83 and 84, determine whether the statement is true or false. Justify your answer.**

83. If $(7x + 4)$ is a factor of some polynomial function f, then $\frac{4}{7}$ is a zero of f.

84. $(2x - 1)$ is a factor of the polynomial

$$6x^6 + x^5 - 92x^4 + 45x^3 + 184x^2 + 4x - 48.$$

Think About It **In Exercises 85 and 86, perform the division by assuming that n is a positive integer.**

85. $\dfrac{x^{3n} + 9x^{2n} + 27x^n + 27}{x^n + 3}$

86. $\dfrac{x^{3n} - 3x^{2n} + 5x^n - 6}{x^n - 2}$

87. Writing Complete each polynomial division. Write a brief description of the pattern that you obtain, and use your result to find a formula for the polynomial division $(x^n - 1)/(x - 1)$. Create a numerical example to test your formula.

(a) $\dfrac{x^2 - 1}{x - 1} = $

(b) $\dfrac{x^3 - 1}{x - 1} = $

(c) $\dfrac{x^4 - 1}{x - 1} = $

88. Writing Write a short paragraph explaining how you can check polynomial division. Give an example.

Review

In Exercises 89–92, use any convenient method to solve the quadratic equation.

89. $9x^2 - 25 = 0$

90. $16x^2 - 21 = 0$

91. $2x^2 + 6x + 3 = 0$

92. $8x^2 - 22x + 15 = 0$

In Exercises 93–96, find a polynomial function that has the given zeros. (There are many correct answers.)

93. $0, -12$

94. $1, -3, 8$

95. $0, -1, 2, 5$

96. $2 + \sqrt{3}, 2 - \sqrt{3}$

3.4 The Fundamental Theorem of Algebra

The Fundamental Theorem of Algebra

You know that an nth-degree polynomial can have at most n real zeros. In the complex number system, this statement can be improved. That is, in the complex number system, every nth-degree polynomial function has *precisely n zeros*. This important result is derived from the **Fundamental Theorem of Algebra,** first proved by the German mathematician Carl Friedrich Gauss (1777–1855).

> **The Fundamental Theorem of Algebra**
>
> If $f(x)$ is a polynomial of degree n, where $n > 0$, then f has at least one zero in the complex number system.

Using the Fundamental Theorem of Algebra and the equivalence of zeros and factors, you obtain the **Linear Factorization Theorem.** See Appendix B for a proof of the Linear Factorization Theorem.

> **Linear Factorization Theorem**
>
> If $f(x)$ is a polynomial of degree n where $n > 0$, f has precisely n linear factors
>
> $$f(x) = a_n(x - c_1)(x - c_2) \cdots (x - c_n)$$
>
> where $c_1, c_2, \ldots, c_n$ are complex numbers.

Note that neither the Fundamental Theorem of Algebra nor the Linear Factorization Theorem tells you *how* to find the zeros or factors of a polynomial. Such theorems are called *existence theorems*. To find the zeros of a polynomial function, you still must rely on other techniques.

Remember that the n zeros of a polynomial function can be real or complex, and they may be repeated. Examples 1 and 2 illustrate several cases.

Example 1   Real Zeros of a Polynomial Function

Counting multiplicity, justify that the second-degree polynomial function

$$f(x) = x^2 - 6x + 9 = (x - 3)(x - 3)$$

has exactly *two* zeros: $x = 3$ and $x = 3$.

Solution

$$(x - 3)(x - 3) = (x - 3)^2 = 0$$

$$x - 3 = 0 \implies x = 3 \qquad \text{Repeated solution}$$

The graph in Figure 3.38 touches the x-axis at $x = 3$.

✓ *Checkpoint* Now try Exercise 1.

What you should learn

● Use the Fundamental Theorem of Algebra to determine the number of zeros of a polynomial function.

● Find all zeros of polynomial functions, including complex zeros.

● Find conjugate pairs of complex zeros.

● Find zeros of polynomials by factoring.

Why you should learn it

Being able to find zeros of polynomial functions is an important part of modeling real-life problems. For instance, Exercise 57 on page 285 shows how to determine whether a ball thrown with a given velocity can reach a certain height.

Jed Jacobsohn/Getty Images

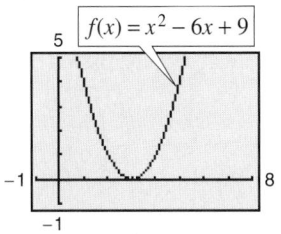

Figure 3.38

Example 2 Real and Complex Zeros of a Polynomial Function

Justify that the third-degree polynomial function

$$f(x) = x^3 + 4x = x(x^2 + 4)$$

has exactly three zeros: $x = 0$, $x = 2i$, and $x = -2i$.

Solution

Factor the polynomial completely as $x(x - 2i)(x + 2i)$. So, the zeros are

$$x(x - 2i)(x + 2i) = 0$$

$$x = 0$$

$$x - 2i = 0 \implies x = 2i$$

$$x + 2i = 0 \implies x = -2i.$$

In the graph in Figure 3.39, only the real zero $x = 0$ appears as an intercept.

✓ *Checkpoint* Now try Exercise 3.

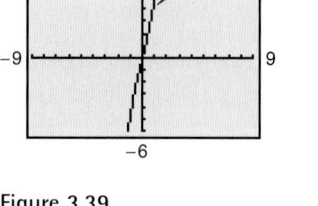

Figure 3.39

Example 3 shows how to use the methods described in Sections 3.2 and 3.3 (the Rational Zero Test, synthetic division, and factoring) to find all the zeros of a polynomial function, including complex zeros.

Example 3 Finding the Zeros of a Polynomial Function

Write $f(x) = x^5 + x^3 + 2x^2 - 12x + 8$ as the product of linear factors, and list all the zeros of f.

Solution

The possible rational zeros are $\pm 1, \pm 2, \pm 4$, and ± 8. The graph shown in Figure 3.40 indicates that 1 and -2 are likely zeros, and that 1 is possibly a repeated zero because it appears that the graph touches (but does not cross) the x-axis at this point. Using synthetic division, you can determine that -2 is a zero and 1 is a repeated zero of f. So, you have

$$f(x) = x^5 + x^3 + 2x^2 - 12x + 8 = (x - 1)(x - 1)(x + 2)(x^2 + 4).$$

By factoring $x^2 + 4$ as

$$x^2 - (-4) = \left(x - \sqrt{-4}\right)\left(x + \sqrt{-4}\right) = (x - 2i)(x + 2i)$$

you obtain

$$f(x) = (x - 1)(x - 1)(x + 2)(x - 2i)(x + 2i)$$

which gives the following five zeros of f.

$$x = 1, x = 1, x = -2, x = 2i, \text{ and } x = -2i$$

Note from the graph of f shown in Figure 3.40 that the *real* zeros are the only ones that appear as x-intercepts.

✓ *Checkpoint* Now try Exercise 25.

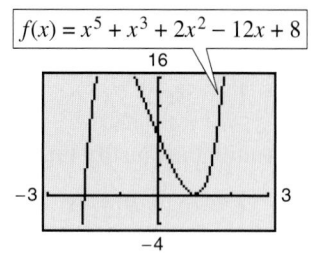

Figure 3.40

Conjugate Pairs

In Example 3, note that the two complex zeros are **conjugates.** That is, they are of the forms $a + bi$ and $a - bi$.

Complex Zeros Occur in Conjugate Pairs

Let $f(x)$ be a polynomial function that has *real coefficients*. If $a + bi$, where $b \neq 0$, is a zero of the function, the conjugate $a - bi$ is also a zero of the function.

Be sure you see that this result is true only if the polynomial function has *real coefficients*. For instance, the result applies to the function $f(x) = x^2 + 1$, but not to the function $g(x) = x - i$.

Example 4 Finding a Polynomial with Given Zeros

Find a *fourth-degree* polynomial function with real coefficients that has -1, -1, and $3i$ as zeros.

Solution

Because $3i$ is a zero *and* the polynomial is stated to have real coefficients, you know that the conjugate $-3i$ must also be a zero. So, from the Linear Factorization Theorem, $f(x)$ can be written as

$$f(x) = a(x + 1)(x + 1)(x - 3i)(x + 3i).$$

For simplicity, let $a = 1$ to obtain

$$f(x) = (x^2 + 2x + 1)(x^2 + 9) = x^4 + 2x^3 + 10x^2 + 18x + 9.$$

✓ *Checkpoint* Now try Exercise 37.

Factoring a Polynomial

The Linear Factorization Theorem states that you can write any nth-degree polynomial as the product of n linear factors.

$$f(x) = a(x - c_1)(x - c_2)(x - c_3) \cdots (x - c_n)$$

However, this result includes the possibility that some of the values of c_i are complex. The following theorem states that even if you do not want to get involved with "complex factors," you can still write $f(x)$ as the product of linear and/or quadratic factors. See Appendix B for a proof of this theorem.

Factors of a Polynomial

Every polynomial of degree $n > 0$ with real coefficients can be written as the product of linear and quadratic factors with real coefficients, where the quadratic factors have no real zeros.

A quadratic factor with no real zeros is said to be **prime** or **irreducible over the reals.** Be sure you see that this is not the same as being *irreducible over the rationals.* For example, the quadratic

$$x^2 + 1 = (x - i)(x + i)$$

is irreducible over the reals (and therefore over the rationals). On the other hand, the quadratic

$$x^2 - 2 = \left(x - \sqrt{2}\right)\left(x + \sqrt{2}\right)$$

is irreducible over the rationals, but *reducible* over the reals.

> **STUDY TIP**
>
> Recall that irrational and rational numbers are subsets of the set of real numbers, and the real numbers are a subset of the set of complex numbers.

Example 5   Factoring a Polynomial

Write the polynomial

$$f(x) = x^4 - x^2 - 20$$

a. as the product of factors that are irreducible over the *rationals*,

b. as the product of linear factors and quadratic factors that are irreducible over the *reals*, and

c. in completely factored form.

Solution

a. Begin by factoring the polynomial into the product of two quadratic polynomials.

$$x^4 - x^2 - 20 = (x^2 - 5)(x^2 + 4)$$

Both of these factors are irreducible over the rationals.

b. By factoring over the reals, you have

$$x^4 - x^2 - 20 = \left(x + \sqrt{5}\right)\left(x - \sqrt{5}\right)(x^2 + 4)$$

where the quadratic factor is irreducible over the reals.

c. In completely factored form, you have

$$x^4 - x^2 - 20 = \left(x + \sqrt{5}\right)\left(x - \sqrt{5}\right)(x - 2i)(x + 2i).$$

✓ *Checkpoint* Now try Exercise 41.

In Example 5, notice from the completely factored form that the fourth-degree polynomial has four zeros.

Throughout this chapter, the results and theorems have been stated in terms of zeros of polynomial functions. Be sure you see that the same results could have been stated in terms of solutions of polynomial equations. This is true because the zeros of the polynomial function

$$f(x) = a_n x^n + a_{n-1} x^{n-1} + \cdots + a_2 x^2 + a_1 x + a_0$$

are precisely the solutions of the polynomial equation

$$a_n x^n + a_{n-1} x^{n-1} + \cdots + a_2 x^2 + a_1 x + a_0 = 0.$$

Example 6   Finding the Zeros of a Polynomial Function

Find all the zeros of

$$f(x) = x^4 - 3x^3 + 6x^2 + 2x - 60$$

given that $1 + 3i$ is a zero of f.

Algebraic Solution

Because complex zeros occur in conjugate pairs, you know that $1 - 3i$ is also a zero of f. This means that both

$$x - (1 + 3i) \quad \text{and} \quad x - (1 - 3i)$$

are factors of f. Multiplying these two factors produces

$$[x - (1 + 3i)][x - (1 - 3i)] = [(x - 1) - 3i][(x - 1) + 3i]$$
$$= (x - 1)^2 - 9i^2$$
$$= x^2 - 2x + 10.$$

Using long division, you can divide $x^2 - 2x + 10$ into f to obtain the following.

$$
\begin{array}{r}
x^2 - x - 6 \\
x^2 - 2x + 10 \overline{)\, x^4 - 3x^3 + 6x^2 + 2x - 60} \\
\underline{x^4 - 2x^3 + 10x^2} \\
-x^3 - 4x^2 + 2x \\
\underline{-x^3 + 2x^2 - 10x} \\
-6x^2 + 12x - 60 \\
\underline{-6x^2 + 12x - 60} \\
0
\end{array}
$$

So, you have

$$f(x) = (x^2 - 2x + 10)(x^2 - x - 6)$$
$$= (x^2 - 2x + 10)(x - 3)(x + 2)$$

and you can conclude that the zeros of f are $x = 1 + 3i$, $x = 1 - 3i$, $x = 3$, and $x = -2$.

✅ *Checkpoint* Now try Exercise 47.

Graphical Solution

Because complex zeros always occur in conjugate pairs, you know that $1 - 3i$ is also a zero of f. Because the polynomial is a fourth-degree polynomial, you know that there are at most two other zeros of the function. Use a graphing utility to graph

$$y = x^4 - 3x^3 + 6x^2 + 2x - 60$$

as shown in Figure 3.41.

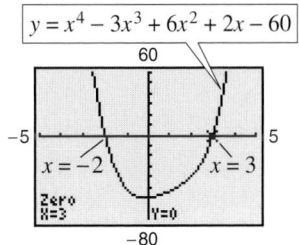

Figure 3.41

You can see that -2 and 3 appear to be x-intercepts of the graph of the function. Use the *zero* or *root* feature or the *zoom* and *trace* features of the graphing utility to confirm that $x = -2$ and $x = 3$ are x-intercepts of the graph. So, you can conclude that the zeros of f are

$$x = 1 + 3i, \ x = 1 - 3i, \ x = 3, \text{ and}$$
$$x = -2.$$

In Example 6, if you were not told that $1 + 3i$ is a zero of f, you could still find all zeros of the function by using synthetic division to find the real zeros -2 and 3. Then, you could factor the polynomial as $(x + 2)(x - 3)(x^2 - 2x + 10)$. Finally, by using the Quadratic Formula, you could determine that the zeros are $x = 1 + 3i$, $x = 1 - 3i$, $x = 3$, and $x = -2$.

3.4 Exercises

Vocabulary Check

Fill in the blanks.

1. The _____ of _____ states that if $f(x)$ is a polynomial function of degree n ($n > 0$), then f has at least one zero in the complex number system.

2. The _____ states that if $f(x)$ is a polynomial of degree n, then f has precisely n linear factors

   $$f(x) = a_n(x - c_1)(x - c_2) \cdots (x - c_n)$$

   where $c_1, c_2, \cdots, c_n$ are complex numbers.

3. A quadratic factor that cannot be factored further as a product of linear factors containing real numbers is said to be _____ over the _____ .

4. If $a + bi$ is a complex zero of a polynomial with real coefficients, then so is its _____ .

In Exercises 1–4, find all the zeros of the function.

1. $f(x) = x^2(x + 3)$

2. $g(x) = (x - 2)(x + 4)^3$

3. $f(x) = (x + 9)(x + 2i)(x - 2i)$

4. $h(t) = (t - 3)(t - 2)(t - 3i)(t + 3i)$

Graphical and Analytical Analysis **In Exercises 5–8, find all the zeros of the function. Is there a relationship between the number of real zeros and the number of x-intercepts of the graph? Explain.**

5. $f(x) = x^3 - 4x^2$
   $+ x - 4$

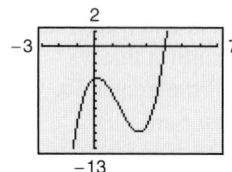

6. $f(x) = x^3 - 4x^2$
   $- 4x + 16$

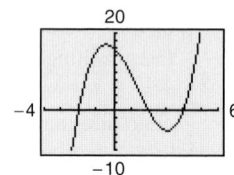

7. $f(x) = x^4 + 4x^2 + 4$

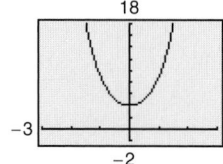

8. $f(x) = x^4 - 3x^2 - 4$

In Exercises 9–26, find all the zeros of the function and write the polynomial as a product of linear factors. Use a graphing utility to graph the function to verify your results graphically. (If possible, use your graphing utility to verify the complex zeros.)

9. $h(x) = x^2 - 4x + 1$

10. $g(x) = x^2 + 10x + 23$

11. $f(x) = x^2 - 12x + 26$

12. $f(x) = x^2 + 6x - 2$

13. $f(x) = x^2 + 25$

14. $f(x) = x^2 + 36$

15. $f(x) = x^4 - 81$

16. $f(y) = y^4 - 625$

17. $f(z) = z^2 - z + 56$

18. $h(x) = x^2 - 4x - 3$

19. $f(t) = t^3 - 3t^2 - 15t + 125$

20. $f(x) = x^3 + 11x^2 + 39x + 29$

21. $f(x) = 5x^3 - 9x^2 + 28x + 6$

22. $f(s) = 3s^3 - 4s^2 + 8s + 8$

23. $f(x) = x^4 + 10x^2 + 9$

24. $f(x) = x^4 + 29x^2 + 100$

25. $g(x) = x^4 - 4x^3 + 8x^2 - 16x + 16$

26. $h(x) = x^4 + 6x^3 + 10x^2 + 6x + 9$

In Exercises 27–34, (a) find all zeros of the function, (b) write the polynomial as a product of linear factors, (c) use your factorization to determine the x-intercepts of the graph of the function, and (d) use a graphing utility to verify that the real zeros are the only x-intercepts.

27. $f(x) = x^2 - 14x + 46$

28. $f(x) = x^2 - 12x + 34$

29. $f(x) = x^2 + 14x + 44$

30. $f(x) = x^2 - 16x + 62$

31. $f(x) = x^3 - 11x + 150$

32. $f(x) = x^3 + 10x^2 + 33x + 34$

33. $f(x) = x^4 + 25x^2 + 144$

34. $f(x) = x^4 - 8x^3 + 17x^2 - 8x + 16$

In Exercises 35–40, find a polynomial function with real coefficients that has the given zeros. (There are many correct answers.)

35. $3, i, -i$

36. $4, 3i, -3i$

37. $2, -4 + i, -4 - i$

38. $-1, 6 + 5i, 6 - 5i$

39. $-5, -5, 1 + \sqrt{3}i$

40. $0, 0, 4, 1 + \sqrt{2}i$

In Exercises 41–44, write the polynomial (a) as the product of factors that are irreducible over the *rationals*, (b) as the product of linear and quadratic factors that are irreducible over the *reals*, and (c) in completely factored form.

41. $f(x) = x^4 - 6x^2 - 7$ 42. $f(x) = x^4 + 6x^2 - 27$

43. $f(x) = x^4 - 2x^3 - 3x^2 + 12x - 18$
    (*Hint:* One factor is $x^2 - 6$.)

44. $f(x) = x^4 - 3x^3 - x^2 - 12x - 20$
    (*Hint:* One factor is $x^2 + 4$.)

In Exercises 45–52, use the given zero to find all the zeros of the function.

Function	Zero
45. $f(x) = 2x^3 + 3x^2 + 50x + 75$	$5i$
46. $f(x) = x^3 + x^2 + 9x + 9$	$3i$
47. $g(x) = x^3 - 7x^2 - x + 87$	$5 + 2i$
48. $g(x) = 4x^3 + 23x^2 + 34x - 10$	$-3 + i$
49. $h(x) = 3x^3 - 4x^2 + 8x + 8$	$1 - \sqrt{3}i$
50. $f(x) = x^3 + 4x^2 + 14x + 20$	$-1 - 3i$
51. $h(x) = 8x^3 - 14x^2 + 18x - 9$	$\frac{1}{2}(1 - \sqrt{5}i)$
52. $f(x) = 25x^3 - 55x^2 - 54x - 18$	$\frac{1}{5}(-2 + \sqrt{2}i)$

Graphical Analysis   **In Exercises 53–56, (a) use the *zero* or *root* feature of a graphing utility to approximate the zeros of the function accurate to three decimal places and (b) find the exact values of the remaining zeros.**

53. $f(x) = x^4 + 3x^3 - 5x^2 - 21x + 22$

54. $f(x) = x^3 + 4x^2 + 14x + 20$

55. $h(x) = 8x^3 - 14x^2 + 18x - 9$

56. $f(x) = 25x^3 - 55x^2 - 54x - 18$

57. *Height*   A baseball is thrown upward from ground level with an initial velocity of 48 feet per second, and its height h (in feet) is given by

$$h(t) = -16t^2 + 48t, \quad 0 \le t \le 3$$

where t is the time (in seconds). You are told that the ball reaches a height of 64 feet. Is this possible? Explain.

58. *Profit*   The demand equation for a microwave is $p = 140 - 0.0001x$, where p is the unit price (in dollars) of the microwave and x is the number of units produced and sold. The cost equation for the microwave is $C = 80x + 150,000$, where C is the total cost (in dollars) and x is the number of units produced. The total profit obtained by producing and selling x units is given by

$$P = R - C = xp - C.$$

You are working in the marketing department that produces this microwave, and you are asked to determine a price p that would yield a profit of \$9 million. Is this possible? Explain.

Synthesis

True or False?   **In Exercises 59 and 60, decide whether the statement is true or false. Justify your answer.**

59. It is possible for a third-degree polynomial function with integer coefficients to have no real zeros.

60. If $x = 4 + 3i$ is a zero of the function $f(x) = x^4 - 7x^3 - 13x^2 + 265x - 750$, then $x = -3i + 4$ must also be a zero of f.

61. *Exploration*   Use a graphing utility to graph the function $f(x) = x^4 - 4x^2 + k$ for different values of k. Find values of k such that the zeros of f satisfy the specified characteristics. (Some parts have many correct answers.)

(a) Two real zeros, each of multiplicity 2

(b) Two real zeros and two complex zeros

62. *Writing*   Compile a list of all the various techniques for factoring a polynomial that have been covered so far in the text. Give an example illustrating each technique, and write a paragraph discussing when the use of each technique is appropriate.

Review

In Exercises 63–66, sketch the graph of the quadratic function. Identify the vertex and any intercepts. Use a graphing utility to verify your results.

63. $f(x) = x^2 - 7x - 8$ 64. $f(x) = -x^2 + x + 6$

65. $f(x) = 6x^2 + 5x - 6$ 66. $f(x) = 4x^2 + 2x - 12$

Introduction to Rational Functions

A **rational function** can be written in the form

$$f(x) = \frac{N(x)}{D(x)}$$

where $N(x)$ and $D(x)$ are polynomials and $D(x)$ is not the zero polynomial.

In general, the *domain* of a rational function of x includes all real numbers except x-values that make the denominator zero. Much of the discussion of rational functions will focus on their graphical behavior near these x-values.

Example 1   Finding the Domain of a Rational Function

Find the domain of $f(x) = 1/x$ and discuss the behavior of f near any excluded x-values.

Solution

Because the denominator is zero when $x = 0$, the domain of f is all real numbers except $x = 0$. To determine the behavior of f near this excluded value, evaluate $f(x)$ to the left and right of $x = 0$, as indicated in the following tables.

x	-1	-0.5	-0.1	-0.01	-0.001	$\to 0$
$f(x)$	-1	-2	-10	-100	-1000	$\to -\infty$

x	$0 \leftarrow$	0.001	0.01	0.1	0.5	1
$f(x)$	$\infty \leftarrow$	1000	100	10	2	1

Note that as x approaches 0 *from the left*, $f(x)$ decreases without bound. In contrast, as x approaches 0 *from the right*, $f(x)$ increases without bound. The graph of f is shown in Figure 3.42.

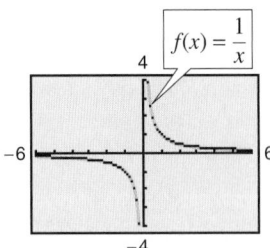

Figure 3.42

Library of Functions: Rational Function

A *rational function* $f(x)$ is the quotient of two polynomials,

$$f(x) = \frac{N(x)}{D(x)}.$$

A rational function is not defined at values of x for which $D(x) = 0$. Near these values the graph of the rational function may increase or decrease without bound. The simplest type of rational function is the *reciprocal function* $f(x) = 1/x$. The basic characteristics of the reciprocal function are summarized below.

Graph of $f(x) = \dfrac{1}{x}$

Domain: $(-\infty, 0) \cup (0, \infty)$

Range: $(-\infty, 0) \cup (0, \infty)$

No intercepts

Decreasing on $(-\infty, 0)$ and $(0, \infty)$

Odd function

Origin symmetry

Vertical asymptote: y-axis

Horizontal asymptote: x-axis

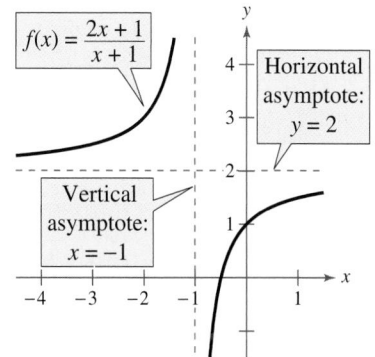

Horizontal and Vertical Asymptotes

In Example 1, the behavior of f near $x = 0$ is denoted as follows.

$f(x) \to -\infty$ as $x \to 0^{-}$

$f(x)$ decreases without bound as x approaches 0 from the left.

$f(x) \to \infty$ as $x \to 0^{+}$

$f(x)$ increases without bound as x approaches 0 from the right.

The line $x = 0$ is a **vertical asymptote** of the graph of f, as shown in the figure above. The graph of f also has a **horizontal asymptote**—the line $y = 0$. This means the values of $f(x) = 1/x$ approach zero as x increases or decreases without bound.

$f(x) \to 0$ as $x \to -\infty$

$f(x)$ approaches 0 as x decreases without bound.

$f(x) \to 0$ as $x \to \infty$

$f(x)$ approaches 0 as x increases without bound.

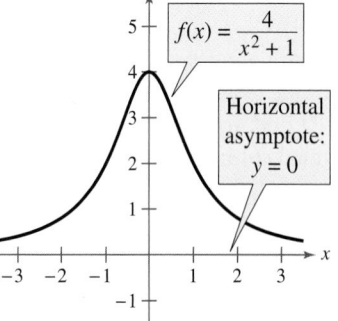

Definition of Vertical and Horizontal Asymptotes

1. The line $x = a$ is a **vertical asymptote** of the graph of f if $f(x) \to \infty$ or $f(x) \to -\infty$ as $x \to a$, either from the right or from the left.

2. The line $y = b$ is a **horizontal asymptote** of the graph of f if $f(x) \to b$ as $x \to \infty$ or $x \to -\infty$.

Figure 3.43 shows the horizontal and vertical asymptotes of the graphs of three rational functions.

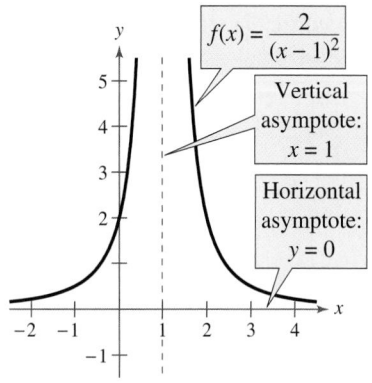

Figure 3.43

Asymptotes of a Rational Function

Let f be the rational function

$$f(x) = \frac{N(x)}{D(x)} = \frac{a_n x^n + a_{n-1} x^{n-1} + \cdots + a_1 x + a_0}{b_m x^m + b_{m-1} x^{m-1} + \cdots + b_1 x + b_0}$$

where $N(x)$ and $D(x)$ have no common factors.

1. The graph of f has *vertical* asymptotes at the zeros of $D(x)$.

2. The graph of f has at most one *horizontal* asymptote determined by comparing the degrees of $N(x)$ and $D(x)$.

   a. If $n < m$, the graph of f has the line $y = 0$ (the x-axis) as a horizontal asymptote.

   b. If $n = m$, the graph of f has the line $y = a_n/b_m$ as a horizontal asymptote, where a_n is the leading coefficient of the numerator and b_m is the leading coefficient of the denominator.

   c. If $n > m$, the graph of f has no horizontal asymptote.

Example 2   Finding Horizontal and Vertical Asymptotes

Find all horizontal and vertical asymptotes of the graph of each rational function.

a. $f(x) = \dfrac{2x}{3x^2 + 1}$ **b.** $f(x) = \dfrac{2x^2}{x^2 - 1}$

Solution

a. For this rational function, the degree of the numerator is *less than* the degree of the denominator, so the graph has the line $y = 0$ as a horizontal asymptote. To find any vertical asymptotes, set the denominator equal to zero and solve the resulting equation for x.

$$3x^2 + 1 = 0 \qquad \text{Set denominator equal to zero.}$$

Because this equation has no real solutions, you can conclude that the graph has no vertical asymptote. The graph of the function is shown in Figure 3.44.

b. For this rational function, the degree of the numerator is *equal to* the degree of the denominator. The leading coefficient of the numerator is 2 and the leading coefficient of the denominator is 1, so the graph has the line $y = 2$ as a horizontal asymptote. To find any vertical asymptotes, set the denominator equal to zero and solve the resulting equation for x.

$$x^2 - 1 = 0 \qquad \text{Set denominator equal to zero.}$$

$$(x + 1)(x - 1) = 0 \qquad \text{Factor.}$$

$$x + 1 = 0 \ \Longrightarrow \ x = -1 \qquad \text{Set 1st factor equal to 0.}$$

$$x - 1 = 0 \ \Longrightarrow \ x = 1 \qquad \text{Set 2nd factor equal to 0.}$$

This equation has two real solutions, $x = -1$ and $x = 1$, so the graph has the lines $x = -1$ and $x = 1$ as vertical asymptotes, as shown in Figure 3.45.

✓ *Checkpoint* Now try Exercise 13.

Exploration

Use a graphing utility to compare the graphs of y_1 and y_2.

$$y_1 = \frac{3x^3 - 5x^2 + 4x - 5}{2x^2 - 6x + 7}$$

$$y_2 = \frac{3x^3}{2x^2}$$

Start with a viewing window in which $-5 \le x \le 5$ and $-10 \le y \le 10$, then zoom out. Write a convincing argument that the shape of the graph of a rational function eventually behaves like the graph of $y = a_n x^n / b_m x^m$, where $a_n x^n$ is the leading term of the numerator and $b_m x^m$ is the leading term of the denominator.

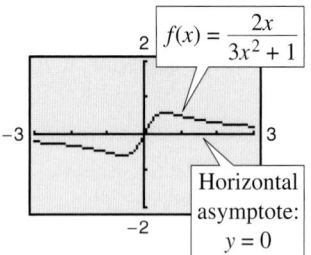

Figure 3.44

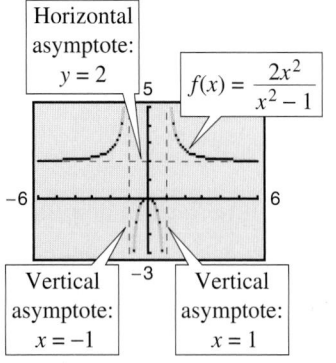

Figure 3.45

Example 3   Finding Horizontal and Vertical Asymptotes

Find all horizontal and vertical asymptotes of the graph of $f(x) = \dfrac{x^2 + x - 2}{x^2 - x - 6}$.

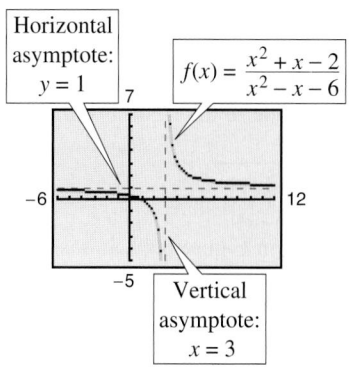

Figure 3.46

Solution

For this rational function the degree of the numerator is *equal to* the degree of the denominator. The leading coefficient of both the numerator and denominator is 1, so the graph has the line $y = 1$ as a horizontal asymptote. To find any vertical asymptotes, first factor the numerator and denominator as follows.

$$f(x) = \frac{x^2 + x - 2}{x^2 - x - 6} = \frac{(x - 1)(x + 2)}{(x + 2)(x - 3)} = \frac{x - 1}{x - 3}, \quad x \neq -2$$

By setting the denominator $x - 3$ (of the simplified function) equal to zero, you can determine that the graph has the line $x = 3$ as a vertical asymptote, as shown in Figure 3.46. Notice in the graph that the function appears to be defined at $x = -2$. Because the domain of the function is all real numbers except $x = -2$ and $x = 3$, you know this is not true. Graphing utilities are limited in their resolution and therefore may not show a break or hole in the graph. Using the *table* feature of a graphing utility, you can verify that the function is not defined at $x = -2$, as shown in Figure 3.47.

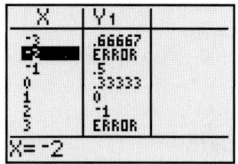

Figure 3.47

 Checkpoint   Now try Exercise 17.

Example 4   Finding a Function's Domain and Asymptotes

For the function f, find (a) the domain of f, (b) the vertical asymptote of f, and (c) the horizontal asymptote of f.

$$f(x) = \frac{3x^3 + 7x^2 + 2}{-4x^3 + 5}$$

Algebraic Solution

a. Because the denominator is zero when $-4x^3 + 5 = 0$, solve this equation to determine that the domain of f is all real numbers except $x = \sqrt[3]{\frac{5}{4}}$.

b. Because the denominator of f has a zero at $x = \sqrt[3]{\frac{5}{4}}$, and $\sqrt[3]{\frac{5}{4}}$ is not a zero of the numerator, the graph of f has the vertical asymptote $x = \sqrt[3]{\frac{5}{4}} \approx 1.08$.

c. Because the degrees of the numerator and denominator are the same, the horizontal asymptote is given by the ratio of the leading coefficients.

$$y = \frac{\text{leading coefficient of numerator}}{\text{leading coefficient of denominator}} = -\frac{3}{4}$$

The horizontal asymptote of f is $y = -\frac{3}{4}$.

Use a graphing utility to verify the vertical and horizontal asymptotes.

 Checkpoint   Now try Exercise 19.

Numerical Solution

a. See *Algebraic Solution* part (a).

b. See *Algebraic Solution* part (b).

c. You can use the table feature of a graphing utility to create tables like those shown in Figure 3.48. From the tables you can estimate that the graph of f has a horizontal asymptote at $y = -\frac{3}{4}$ because the values of $f(x)$ become closer and closer to $-\frac{3}{4}$ as x becomes increasingly large or small.

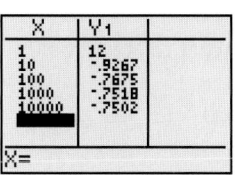   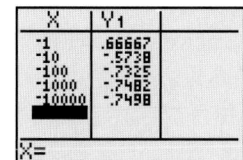

x Increases without Bound   *x* Decreases without Bound

Figure 3.48

Example 5   A Graph with Two Horizontal Asymptotes

A function that is not rational can have two horizontal asymptotes—one to the left and one to the right. For instance, the graph of

$$f(x) = \frac{x + 10}{|x| + 2}$$

is shown in Figure 3.49. It has the line $y = -1$ as a horizontal asymptote to the left and the line $y = 1$ as a horizontal asymptote to the right. You can confirm this by rewriting the function as follows.

$$f(x) = \begin{cases} \dfrac{x + 10}{-x + 2}, & x < 0 \qquad |x| = -x \text{ for } x < 0 \\ \dfrac{x + 10}{x + 2}, & x \geq 0 \qquad |x| = x \text{ for } x \geq 0 \end{cases}$$

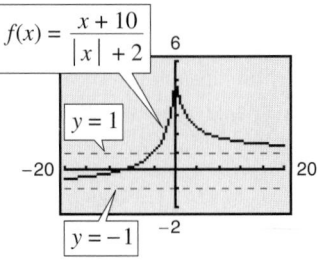

Figure 3.49

 Checkpoint Now try Exercise 21.

Applications

There are many examples of asymptotic behavior in real life. For instance, Example 6 shows how a vertical asymptote can be used to analyze the cost of removing pollutants from smokestack emissions.

Example 6   Cost-Benefit Model

A utility company burns coal to generate electricity. The cost C (in dollars) of removing $p\%$ of the smokestack pollutants is given by $C = 80{,}000p/(100 - p)$ for $0 \leq p < 100$. Use a graphing utility to graph this function. You are a member of a state legislature that is considering a law that would require utility companies to remove 90% of the pollutants from their smokestack emissions. The current law requires 85% removal. How much additional cost would there be to the utility company because of the new law?

Solution

The graph of this function is shown in Figure 3.50. Note that the graph has a vertical asymptote at $p = 100$. Because the current law requires 85% removal, the current cost to the utility company is

$$C = \frac{80{,}000(85)}{100 - 85} \approx \$453{,}333. \qquad \text{Evaluate } C \text{ when } p = 85.$$

If the new law increases the percent removal to 90%, the cost will be

$$C = \frac{80{,}000(90)}{100 - 90} = \$720{,}000. \qquad \text{Evaluate } C \text{ when } p = 90.$$

So, the new law would require the utility company to spend an additional

$$720{,}000 - 453{,}333 = \$266{,}667. \qquad \text{Subtract 85\% removal cost from 90\% removal cost.}$$

 Checkpoint Now try Exercise 35.

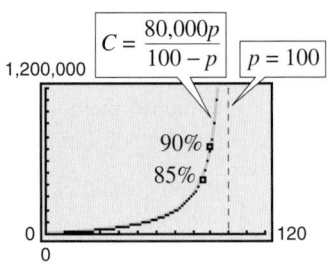

Figure 3.50

Exploration

The *table* feature of a graphing utility can be used to estimate vertical and horizontal asymptotes of rational functions. Use the *table* feature to find any horizontal or vertical asymptotes of

$$f(x) = \frac{2x}{x + 1}.$$

Write a statement explaining how you found the asymptote(s) using the table.

Example 7   Ultraviolet Radiation

For a person with sensitive skin, the amount of time T (in hours) the person can be exposed to the sun with a minimal burning can be modeled by

$$T = \frac{0.37s + 23.8}{s}, \quad 0 < s \leq 120$$

where s is the Sunsor Scale reading. The Sunsor Scale is based on the level of intensity of UVB rays.   (Source: Sunsor, Inc.)

a. Find the amount of time a person with sensitive skin can be exposed to the sun with minimal burning when $s = 10$, $s = 25$, and $s = 100$.

b. If the model were valid for all $s > 0$, what would be the horizontal asymptote of this function, and what would it represent?

TECHNOLOGY SUPPORT

For instructions on how to use the *value* feature, see Appendix A; for specific keystrokes, go to the text website at *college.hmco.com*.

Algebraic Solution

a. When $s = 10$, $T = \dfrac{0.37(10) + 23.8}{10}$

$$= 2.75 \text{ hours.}$$

When $s = 25$, $T = \dfrac{0.37(25) + 23.8}{25}$

$$\approx 1.32 \text{ hours.}$$

When $s = 100$, $T = \dfrac{0.37(100) + 23.8}{100}$

$$\approx 0.61 \text{ hour.}$$

b. Because the degree of the numerator and denominator are the same for

$$T = \frac{0.37s + 23.8}{s}$$

the horizontal asymptote is given by the ratio of the leading coefficients of the numerator and denominator. So, the graph has the line $T = 0.37$ as a horizontal asymptote. This line represents the shortest possible exposure time with minimal burning.

Graphical Solution

a. Use a graphing utility to graph the function

$$y_1 = \frac{0.37x + 23.8}{x}$$

using a viewing window similar to that shown in Figure 3.51. Then use the *trace* or *value* feature to approximate the value of y_1 when $x = 10$, $x = 25$, and $x = 100$. You should obtain the following values.

When $x = 10$, $y_1 = 2.75$ hours.

When $x = 25$, $y_1 \approx 1.32$ hours.

When $x = 100$, $y_1 \approx 0.61$ hour.

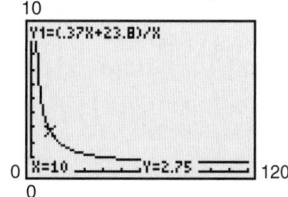

Figure 3.51

b. Continue to use the *trace* or *value* feature to approximate values of $f(x)$ for larger and larger values of x (see Figure 3.52). From this, you can estimate the horizontal asymptote to be $y = 0.37$. This line represents the shortest possible exposure time with minimal burning.

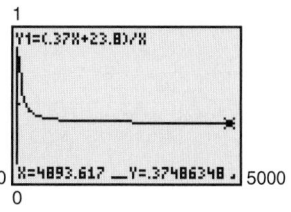

Figure 3.52

✓ *Checkpoint* Now try Exercise 39.

3.5 | Exercises

Vocabulary Check

Fill in the blanks.

1. Functions of the form $f(x) = N(x)/D(x)$, where $N(x)$ and $D(x)$ are polynomials and $D(x)$ is not the zero polynomial, are called _____ .

2. If $f(x) \to \pm\infty$ as $x \to a$ from the left (or right), then $x = a$ is a _____ of the graph of f.

3. If $f(x) \to b$ as $x \to \pm\infty$, then $y = b$ is a _____ of the graph of f.

In Exercises 1–6, (a) complete each table, (b) determine the vertical and horizontal asymptotes of the function, and (c) find the domain of the function.

x	$f(x)$
0.5	
0.9	
0.99	
0.999	

x	$f(x)$
1.5	
1.1	
1.01	
1.001	

x	$f(x)$
5	
10	
100	
1000	

x	$f(x)$
-5	
-10	
-100	
-1000	

1. $f(x) = \dfrac{1}{x-1}$

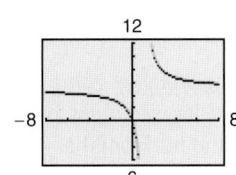

2. $f(x) = \dfrac{5x}{x-1}$

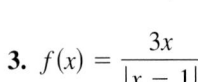

3. $f(x) = \dfrac{3x}{|x-1|}$

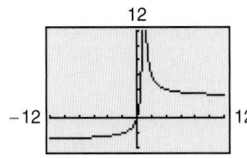

4. $f(x) = \dfrac{3}{|x-1|}$

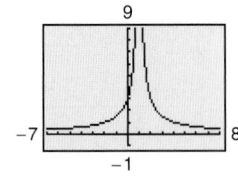

5. $f(x) = \dfrac{3x^2}{x^2-1}$

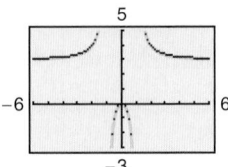

6. $f(x) = \dfrac{4x}{x^2-1}$

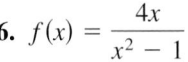

In Exercises 7–12, match the function with its graph. [The graphs are labeled (a), (b), (c), (d), (e), and (f).]

(a)

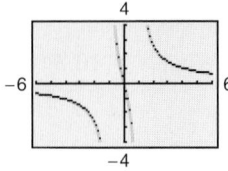

(b)

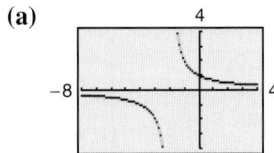

(c)

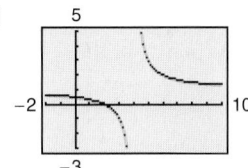

(d)

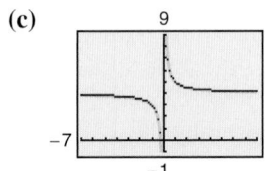

(e)

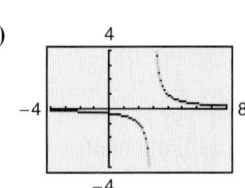

(f)

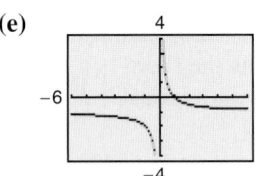

7. $f(x) = \dfrac{2}{x+2}$

8. $f(x) = \dfrac{1}{x-3}$

9. $f(x) = \dfrac{4x+1}{x}$

10. $f(x) = \dfrac{1-x}{x}$

11. $f(x) = \dfrac{x-2}{x-4}$

12. $f(x) = -\dfrac{x+2}{x+4}$

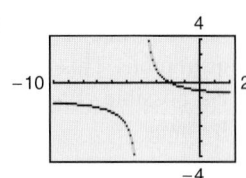

In Exercises 13–22, (a) find the domain of the function, (b) identify any horizontal and vertical asymptotes, and (c) verify your answer to part (a) both graphically by using a graphing utility and numerically by creating a table of values.

13. $f(x) = \dfrac{1}{x^2}$

14. $f(x) = \dfrac{3}{(x-2)^3}$

15. $f(x) = \dfrac{2+x}{2-x}$

16. $f(x) = \dfrac{1-5x}{1+2x}$

17. $f(x) = \dfrac{x^2+2x}{2x^2-x}$

18. $f(x) = \dfrac{x^2-25}{x^2+5x}$

19. $f(x) = \dfrac{3x^2+x-5}{x^2+1}$

20. $f(x) = \dfrac{3x^2+1}{x^2+x+9}$

21. $f(x) = \dfrac{x-3}{|x|}$

22. $f(x) = \dfrac{x+1}{|x|+1}$

Analytical and Numerical Explanation   In Exercises 23–26, (a) determine the domains of f and g, (b) simplify f and find any vertical asymptotes of f, (c) complete the table, and (d) explain how the two functions differ.

23. $f(x) = \dfrac{x^2-4}{x+2}$, $g(x) = x-2$

x	-4	-3	-2.5	-2	-1.5	-1	0
$f(x)$							
$g(x)$							

24. $f(x) = \dfrac{x^2(x-3)}{x^2-3x}$, $g(x) = x$

x	-1	0	1	2	3	3.5	4
$f(x)$							
$g(x)$							

25. $f(x) = \dfrac{x-3}{x^2-3x}$, $g(x) = \dfrac{1}{x}$

x	-1	-0.5	0	0.5	2	3	4
$f(x)$							
$g(x)$							

26. $f(x) = \dfrac{2x-8}{x^2-9x+20}$, $g(x) = \dfrac{2}{x-5}$

x	0	1	2	3	4	5	6
$f(x)$							
$g(x)$							

Exploration   In Exercises 27–30, determine the value that the function f approaches as the magnitude of x increases. Is $f(x)$ greater than or less than this functional value when x is positive and large in magnitude? What about when x is negative and large in magnitude?

27. $f(x) = 4 - \dfrac{1}{x}$

28. $f(x) = 2 + \dfrac{1}{x-3}$

29. $f(x) = \dfrac{2x-1}{x-3}$

30. $f(x) = \dfrac{2x-1}{x^2+1}$

In Exercises 31–34, find the zeros (if any) of the rational function. Use a graphing utility to verify your answer.

31. $g(x) = \dfrac{x^2-4}{x+3}$

32. $g(x) = \dfrac{x^3-8}{x^2+4}$

33. $f(x) = 1 - \dfrac{2}{x-5}$

34. $h(x) = 5 + \dfrac{3}{x^2+1}$

35. *Environment*   The cost C (in millions of dollars) of removing $p\%$ of the industrial and municipal pollutants discharged into a river is given by

$$C = \dfrac{255p}{100-p}, \quad 0 \le p < 100.$$

(a) Find the cost of removing 10% of the pollutants.

(b) Find the cost of removing 40% of the pollutants.

(c) Find the cost of removing 75% of the pollutants.

(d) Use a graphing utility to graph the cost function. Be sure to choose an appropriate viewing window. Explain why you chose the values that you used in your viewing window.

(e) According to this model, would it be possible to remove 100% of the pollutants? Explain.

36. *Environment* In a pilot project, a rural township is given recycling bins for separating and storing recyclable products. The cost C (in dollars) for supplying bins to $p\%$ of the population is given by

$$C = \frac{25{,}000p}{100 - p}, \quad 0 \le p < 100.$$

(a) Find the cost of supplying bins to 15% of the population.

(b) Find the cost of supplying bins to 50% of the population.

(c) Find the cost of supplying bins to 90% of the population.

(d) Use a graphing utility to graph the cost function. Be sure to choose an appropriate viewing window. Explain why you chose the values that you used in your viewing window.

(e) According to this model, would it be possible to supply bins to 100% of the residents? Explain.

37. *Data Analysis* The endpoints of the interval over which distinct vision is possible are called the *near point* and *far point* of the eye (see figure). With increasing age these points normally change. The table shows the approximate near points y (in inches) for various ages x (in years).

Object blurry   Object clear   Object blurry

Near point

Far point

Age, x	Near point, y
16	3.0
32	4.7
44	9.8
50	19.7
60	39.4

(a) Find a rational model for the data. Take the reciprocals of the near points to generate the points $(x, 1/y)$. Use the *regression* feature of a graphing utility to find a linear model for the data. The resulting line has the form

$$\frac{1}{y} = ax + b.$$

Solve for y.

(b) Use the *table* feature of a graphing utility to create a table showing the predicted near point based on the model for each of the ages in the original table.

(c) Do you think the model can be used to predict the near point for a person who is 70 years old? Explain.

38. *Data Analysis* Consider a physics laboratory experiment designed to determine an unknown mass. A flexible metal meter stick is clamped to a table with 50 centimeters overhanging the edge (see figure). Known masses M ranging from 200 grams to 2000 grams are attached to the end of the meter stick. For each mass, the meter stick is displaced vertically and then allowed to oscillate. The average time t (in seconds) of one oscillation for each mass is recorded in the table.

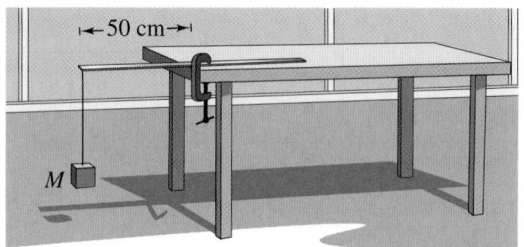

Mass, M	Time, t
200	0.450
400	0.597
600	0.721
800	0.831
1000	0.906
1200	1.003
1400	1.088
1600	1.168
1800	1.218
2000	1.338

A model for the data is given by

$$t = \frac{38M + 16,965}{10(M + 5000)}.$$

(a) Use the *table* feature of a graphing utility to create a table showing the estimated time based on the model for each of the masses shown in the table. What can you conclude?

(b) Use the model to approximate the mass of an object when the average time for one oscillation is 1.056 seconds.

39. Wildlife   The game commission introduces 100 deer into newly acquired state game lands. The population N of the herd is given by

$$N = \frac{20(5 + 3t)}{1 + 0.04t}, \quad t \geq 0$$

where t is the time in years.

(a) Use a graphing utility to graph the model.

(b) Find the population when $t = 5$, $t = 10$, and $t = 25$.

(c) What is the limiting size of the herd as time increases? Explain.

40. Wildlife   The table shows the number N of threatened and endangered species in the United States from 1993 to 2002. The data can be approximated by the model

$$N = \frac{42.58t^2 + 690}{0.03t^2 + 1}$$

where t represents the year, with $t = 3$ corresponding to 1993. (Source: U.S. Fish and Wildlife Service)

Year	Number, N
1993	813
1994	941
1995	962
1996	1053
1997	1132
1998	1194
1999	1205
2000	1244
2001	1254
2002	1262

(a) Use a graphing utility to plot the data and graph the model in the same viewing window. How closely does the model represent the data?

(b) Use the model to estimate the number of threatened and endangered species in 2006.

(c) Would this model be useful for estimating the number of threatened and endangered species in future years? Explain.

Synthesis

True or False?   In Exercises 41 and 42, determine whether the statement is true or false. Justify your answer.

41. A rational function can have infinitely many vertical asymptotes.

42. $f(x) = x^3 - 2x^2 - 5x + 6$ is a rational function.

Think About It   In Exercises 43–46, write a rational function f having the specified characteristics. (There are many correct answers.)

43. Vertical asymptotes: $x = -2$, $x = 1$

44. Vertical asymptote: None

Horizontal asymptote: $y = 0$

45. Vertical asymptote: None

Horizontal asymptote: $y = 2$

46. Vertical asymptotes: $x = 0$, $x = \frac{5}{2}$

Horizontal asymptote: $y = -3$

Review

In Exercises 47–50, write the general form of the equation of the line that passes through the points.

47. $(3, 2), (0, -1)$ **48.** $(-6, 1), (4, -5)$

49. $(2, 7), (3, 10)$ **50.** $(0, 0), (-9, 4)$

In Exercises 52–54, divide using long division.

51. $(x^2 + 5x + 6) \div (x - 4)$

52. $(x^2 - 10x + 15) \div (x - 3)$

53. $(2x^2 + x - 11) \div (x + 5)$

54. $(4x^2 + 3x - 10) \div (x + 6)$

3.6 Graphs of Rational Functions

The Graph of a Rational Function

To sketch the graph of a rational function, use the following guidelines.

> **Guidelines for Graphing Rational Functions**
>
> Let $f(x) = N(x)/D(x)$, where $N(x)$ and $D(x)$ are polynomials.
>
> 1. Simplify f, if possible.
>
> 2. Find and plot the y-intercept (if any) by evaluating $f(0)$.
>
> 3. Find the zeros of the numerator (if any) by solving the equation $N(x) = 0$. Then plot the corresponding x-intercepts.
>
> 4. Find the zeros of the denominator (if any) by solving the equation $D(x) = 0$. Then sketch the corresponding vertical asymptotes using dashed vertical lines.
>
> 5. Find and sketch the horizontal asymptote (if any) of the graph using a dashed horizontal line.
>
> 6. Plot at least one point *between* and one point *beyond* each x-intercept and vertical asymptote.
>
> 7. Use smooth curves to complete the graph between and beyond the vertical asymptotes.

What you should learn

- Analyze and sketch graphs of rational functions.
- Sketch graphs of rational functions that have slant asymptotes.
- Use rational functions to model and solve real-life problems.

Why you should learn it

The graph of a rational function provides a good indication of the future behavior of a mathematical model. Exercise 72 on page 304 models the average room rate for hotels in the U.S. and enables you to estimate the average room rate in the coming years.

Michael Keller/Corbis

TECHNOLOGY TIP   Some graphing utilities have difficulty graphing rational functions that have vertical asymptotes. Often, the utility will connect parts of the graph that are not supposed to be connected. For instance, notice that the graph in Figure 3.53(a) should consist of two *unconnected* portions—one to the left of $x = 2$ and the other to the right of $x = 2$. To eliminate this problem, you can try changing the *mode* of the graphing utility to *dot mode* [see Figure 3.53(b)]. The problem with this mode is that the graph is then represented as a collection of dots rather than as a smooth curve, as shown in Figure 3.53(c). In this text, a blue curve is placed behind the graphing utility's display to indicate where the graph should appear. [See Figure 3.53(c).]

TECHNOLOGY SUPPORT

For instructions on how to use the *connected* mode and the *dot* mode, see Appendix A; for specific keystrokes, go to the text website at *college.hmco.com*.

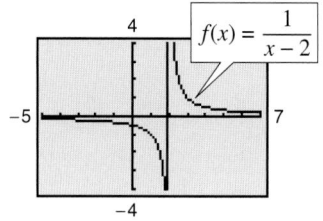

(a) Connected mode

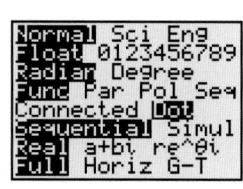

(b) Mode screen

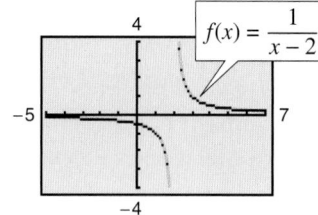

(c) Dot mode

Figure 3.53

Example 1   Sketching the Graph of a Rational Function

Sketch the graph of $g(x) = \dfrac{3}{x - 2}$ by hand.

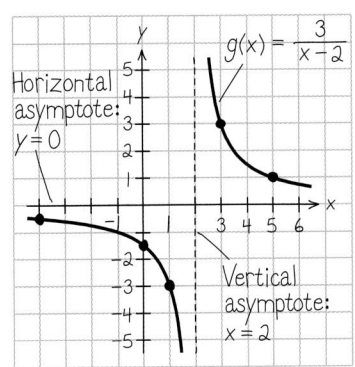

Figure 3.54

Solution

y-Intercept: $\left(0, -\frac{3}{2}\right)$, because $g(0) = -\frac{3}{2}$

x-Intercept: None, because $3 \neq 0$

Vertical Asymptote: $x = 2$, zero of denominator

Horizontal Asymptote: $y = 0$, because degree of $N(x) <$ degree of $D(x)$

Additional Points:

x	-4	1	2	3	5
$g(x)$	-0.5	-3	Undefined	3	1

By plotting the intercept, asymptotes, and a few additional points, you can obtain the graph shown in Figure 3.54. Confirm this with a graphing utility.

 Checkpoint Now try Exercise 9.

STUDY TIP

Note in the examples in this section that the vertical asymptotes are included in the table of additional points. This is done to emphasize numerically the behavior of the graph of the function.

Note that the graph of g in Example 1 is a vertical stretch and a right shift of the graph of

$$f(x) = \frac{1}{x}$$

because

$$g(x) = \frac{3}{x - 2} = 3\left(\frac{1}{x - 2}\right) = 3f(x - 2).$$

Example 2   Sketching the Graph of a Rational Function

Sketch the graph of $f(x) = \dfrac{2x - 1}{x}$ by hand.

Solution

y-Intercept: None, because $x = 0$ is not in the domain

x-Intercept: $\left(\frac{1}{2}, 0\right)$, because $2x - 1 = 0$

Vertical Asymptote: $x = 0$, zero of denominator

Horizontal Asymptote: $y = 2$, because degree of $N(x) =$ degree of $D(x)$

Additional Points:

x	-4	-1	0	$\frac{1}{4}$	4
$f(x)$	2.25	3	Undefined	-2	1.75

By plotting the intercept, asymptotes, and a few additional points, you can obtain the graph shown in Figure 3.55. Confirm this with a graphing utility.

 Checkpoint Now try Exercise 13.

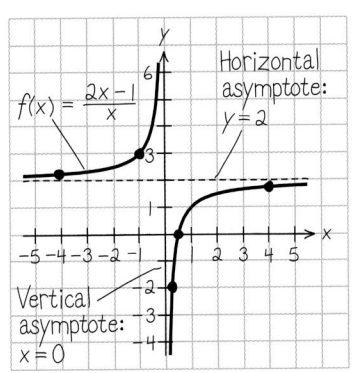

Figure 3.55

Example 3   Sketching the Graph of a Rational Function

Sketch the graph of $f(x) = \dfrac{x}{x^2 - x - 2}$.

Solution

Factor the denominator to determine more easily the zeros of the denominator.

$$f(x) = \frac{x}{x^2 - x - 2} = \frac{x}{(x + 1)(x - 2)}.$$

y-Intercept: $(0, 0)$, because $f(0) = 0$

x-Intercept: $(0, 0)$

Vertical Asymptotes: $x = -1$, $x = 2$, zeros of denominator

Horizontal Asymptote: $y = 0$, because degree of $N(x) <$ degree of $D(x)$

Additional Points:

x	-3	-1	-0.5	1	2	3
$f(x)$	-0.3	Undefined	0.4	-0.5	Undefined	0.75

The graph is shown in Figure 3.56.

 Checkpoint Now try Exercise 21.

Example 4   Sketching the Graph of a Rational Function

Sketch the graph of $f(x) = \dfrac{x^2 - 9}{x^2 - 2x - 3}$.

Solution

By factoring the numerator and denominator, you have

$$f(x) = \frac{x^2 - 9}{x^2 - 2x - 3} = \frac{(x - 3)(x + 3)}{(x - 3)(x + 1)} = \frac{x + 3}{x + 1}, \quad x \neq 3.$$

y-Intercept: $(0, 3)$, because $f(0) = 3$

x-Intercept: $(-3, 0)$

Vertical Asymptote: $x = -1$, zero of (simplified) denominator

Horizontal Asymptote: $y = 1$, because degree of $N(x) =$ degree of $D(x)$

Additional Points:

x	-5	-2	-1	1	-0.5	3	4
$f(x)$	0.5	-1	Undefined	2	5	Undefined	1.4

The graph is shown in Figure 3.57. Notice there is a hole in the graph at $x = 3$. This is because the function is not defined when $x = 3$.

 Checkpoint Now try Exercise 23.

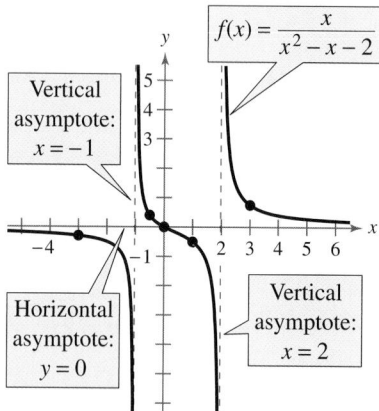

Figure 3.56

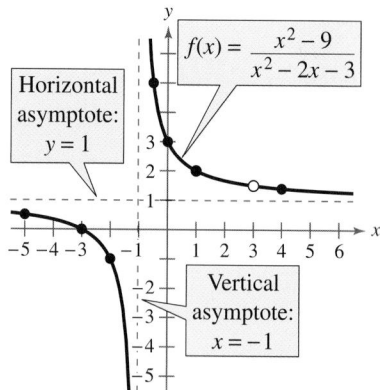

Figure 3.57   Hole at $x = 3$

Slant Asymptotes

Consider a rational function whose denominator is of degree 1 or greater. If the degree of the numerator is exactly *one more* than the degree of the denominator, the graph of the function has a **slant** (or **oblique**) **asymptote.** For example, the graph of

$$f(x) = \frac{x^2 - x}{x + 1}$$

has a slant asymptote, as shown in Figure 3.58. To find the equation of a slant asymptote, use long division. For instance, by dividing $x + 1$ into $x^2 - x$, you have

$$f(x) = \frac{x^2 - x}{x + 1} = \underbrace{x - 2}_{\substack{\text{Slant asymptote} \\ (y = x - 2)}} + \frac{2}{x + 1}.$$

As x increases or decreases without bound, the remainder term $2/(x + 1)$ approaches 0, so the graph of f approaches the line $y = x - 2$, as shown in Figure 3.58.

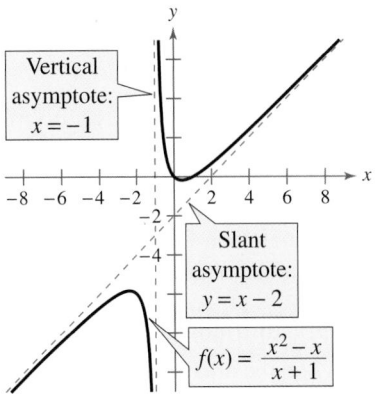

Figure 3.58

Example 5   A Rational Function with a Slant Asymptote

Sketch the graph of $f(x) = \dfrac{x^2 - x - 2}{x - 1}$.

Solution

First write $f(x)$ in two different ways. Factoring the numerator

$$f(x) = \frac{x^2 - x - 2}{x - 1} = \frac{(x - 2)(x + 1)}{x - 1}$$

enables you to recognize the x-intercepts. Long division

$$f(x) = \frac{x^2 - x - 2}{x - 1} = x - \frac{2}{x - 1}$$

enables you to recognize that the line $y = x$ is a slant asymptote of the graph.

y-Intercept:	$(0, 2)$, because $f(0) = 2$
x-Intercepts:	$(-1, 0)$ and $(2, 0)$
Vertical Asymptote:	$x = 1$, zero of denominator
Horizontal Asymptote:	None, because degree of $N(x) >$ degree of $D(x)$
Slant Asymptote:	$y = x$
Additional Points:	

x	-2	0.5	1	1.5	3
$f(x)$	-1.33	4.5	Undefined	-2.5	2

The graph is shown in Figure 3.59.

✓ *Checkpoint* Now try Exercise 45.

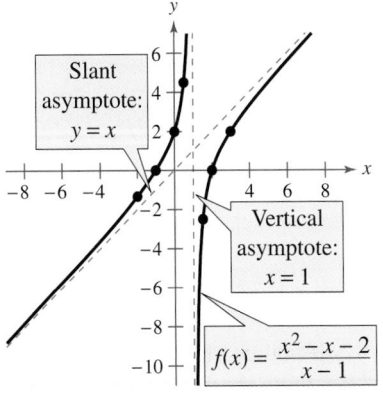

Figure 3.59

Application

Example 6 Finding a Minimum Area

A rectangular page is designed to contain 48 square inches of print. The margins on each side of the page are $1\frac{1}{2}$ inches wide. The margins at the top and bottom are each 1 inch deep. What should the dimensions of the page be so that the minimum amount of paper is used?

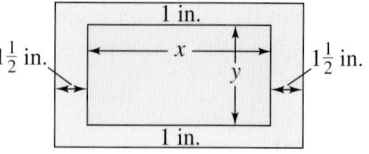

Figure 3.60

Graphical Solution

Let A be the area to be minimized. From Figure 3.60, you can write

$$A = (x + 3)(y + 2).$$

The printed area inside the margins is modeled by $48 = xy$ or $y = 48/x$. To find the minimum area, rewrite the equation for A in terms of just one variable by substituting $48/x$ for y.

$$A = (x + 3)\left(\frac{48}{x} + 2\right) = \frac{(x + 3)(48 + 2x)}{x}, \quad x > 0$$

The graph of this rational function is shown in Figure 3.61. Because x represents the width of the printed area, you need consider only the portion of the graph for which x is positive. Using the *minimum* feature or the *zoom* and *trace* features of a graphing utility, you can approximate the minimum value of A to occur when $x \approx 8.5$ inches. The corresponding value of y is $48/8.5 \approx 5.6$ inches. So, the dimensions should be

$$x + 3 \approx 11.5 \text{ inches by } y + 2 \approx 7.6 \text{ inches.}$$

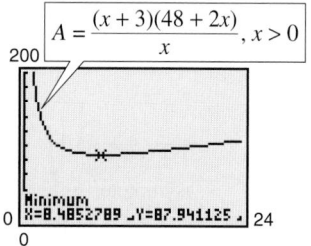

Figure 3.61

✓ *Checkpoint* Now try Exercise 65.

Numerical Solution

Let A be the area to be minimized. From Figure 3.60, you can write

$$A = (x + 3)(y + 2).$$

The printed area inside the margins is modeled by $48 = xy$ or $y = 48/x$. To find the minimum area, rewrite the equation for A in terms of just one variable by substituting $48/x$ for y.

$$A = (x + 3)\left(\frac{48}{x} + 2\right) = \frac{(x + 3)(48 + 2x)}{x}, \quad x > 0$$

Use the *table* feature of a graphing utility to create a table of values for the function

$$y_1 = \frac{(x + 3)(48 + 2x)}{x}$$

beginning at $x = 1$. From the table, you can see that the minimum value of y_1 occurs when x is somewhere between 8 and 9, as shown in Figure 3.62. To approximate the minimum value of y_1 to one decimal place, change the table to begin at $x = 8$ and set the table step to 0.1. The minimum value of y_1 occurs when $x \approx 8.5$, as shown in Figure 3.63. The corresponding value of y is $48/8.5 \approx 5.6$ inches. So, the dimensions should be $x + 3 \approx 11.5$ inches by $y + 2 \approx 7.6$ inches.

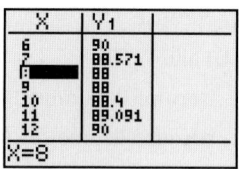

Figure 3.62

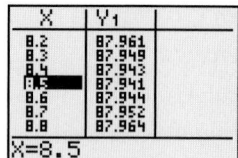

Figure 3.63

If you go on to take a course in calculus, you will learn an analytic technique for finding the exact value of x that produces a minimum area in Example 6. In this case, that value is $x = 6\sqrt{2} \approx 8.485$.

3.6   Exercises

Vocabulary Check

Fill in the blanks.

1. For the rational function $f(x) = N(x)/D(x)$, if the degree of $N(x)$ is exactly one more than the degree of $D(x)$, then the graph of f has a _____ (or oblique) _____ .
2. The graph of $f(x) = 1/x$ has a _____ asymptote at $x = 0$.

In Exercises 1–4, use a graphing utility to graph $f(x) = 2/x$ and the function g in the same viewing window. Describe the relationship between the two graphs.

1. $g(x) = f(x) + 1$
2. $g(x) = f(x - 1)$
3. $g(x) = -f(x)$
4. $g(x) = \frac{1}{2}f(x + 2)$

In Exercises 5–8, use a graphing utility to graph $f(x) = 2/x^2$ and the function g in the same viewing window. Describe the relationship between the two graphs.

5. $g(x) = f(x) - 2$
6. $g(x) = -f(x)$
7. $g(x) = f(x - 2)$
8. $g(x) = \frac{1}{4}f(x)$

In Exercises 9–26, sketch the graph of the rational function by hand. As sketching aids, check for intercepts, vertical asymptotes, and horizontal asymptotes. Use a graphing utility to verify your graph.

9. $f(x) = \dfrac{1}{x + 2}$
10. $f(x) = \dfrac{1}{x - 6}$

11. $C(x) = \dfrac{5 + 2x}{1 + x}$
12. $P(x) = \dfrac{1 - 3x}{1 - x}$

13. $f(t) = \dfrac{1 - 2t}{t}$
14. $g(x) = \dfrac{1}{x + 2} + 2$

15. $f(x) = \dfrac{x^2}{x^2 - 4}$
16. $g(x) = \dfrac{x}{x^2 - 9}$

17. $f(x) = \dfrac{x}{x^2 - 1}$
18. $f(x) = -\dfrac{1}{(x - 2)^2}$

19. $g(x) = \dfrac{4(x + 1)}{x(x - 4)}$
20. $h(x) = \dfrac{2}{x^2(x - 3)}$

21. $f(x) = \dfrac{3x}{x^2 - x - 2}$
22. $f(x) = \dfrac{2x}{x^2 + x - 2}$

23. $f(x) = \dfrac{x^2 + 3x}{x^2 + x - 6}$
24. $g(x) = \dfrac{5(x + 4)}{x^2 + x - 12}$

25. $f(x) = \dfrac{x^2 - 1}{x + 1}$
26. $f(x) = \dfrac{x^2 - 16}{x - 4}$

In Exercises 27–36, use a graphing utility to graph the function. Determine its domain and identify any vertical or horizontal asymptotes.

27. $f(x) = \dfrac{2 + x}{1 - x}$
28. $f(x) = \dfrac{3 - x}{2 - x}$

29. $f(t) = \dfrac{3t + 1}{t}$
30. $h(x) = \dfrac{x - 2}{x - 3}$

31. $h(t) = \dfrac{4}{t^2 + 1}$
32. $g(x) = -\dfrac{x}{(x - 2)^2}$

33. $f(x) = \dfrac{x + 1}{x^2 - x - 6}$
34. $f(x) = \dfrac{x + 4}{x^2 + x - 6}$

35. $f(x) = \dfrac{20x}{x^2 + 1} - \dfrac{1}{x}$

36. $f(x) = 5\left(\dfrac{1}{x - 4} - \dfrac{1}{x + 2}\right)$

Exploration **In Exercises 37–42, use a graphing utility to graph the function. What do you observe about its asymptotes?**

37. $h(x) = \dfrac{6x}{\sqrt{x^2 + 1}}$
38. $f(x) = -\dfrac{x}{\sqrt{9 + x^2}}$

39. $g(x) = \dfrac{4|x - 2|}{x + 1}$
40. $f(x) = -\dfrac{8|3 + x|}{x - 2}$

41. $f(x) = \dfrac{4(x - 1)^2}{x^2 - 4x + 5}$
42. $g(x) = \dfrac{3x^4 - 5x + 3}{x^4 + 1}$

In Exercises 43–50, sketch the graph of the rational function by hand. As sketching aids, check for intercepts, vertical asymptotes, and slant asymptotes.

43. $f(x) = \dfrac{2x^2 + 1}{x}$
44. $g(x) = \dfrac{1 - x^2}{x}$

45. $h(x) = \dfrac{x^2}{x-1}$

46. $f(x) = \dfrac{x^3}{x^2-1}$

47. $g(x) = \dfrac{x^3}{2x^2-8}$

48. $f(x) = \dfrac{x^2-1}{x^2+4}$

49. $f(x) = \dfrac{x^3+2x^2+4}{2x^2+1}$

50. $f(x) = \dfrac{2x^2-5x+5}{x-2}$

Graphical Reasoning　In Exercises 51–54, (a) use the graph to estimate any x-intercepts of the rational function and (b) set $y = 0$ and solve the resulting equation to confirm your result in part (a).

51. $y = \dfrac{x+1}{x-3}$

52. $y = \dfrac{2x}{x-3}$

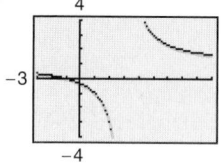

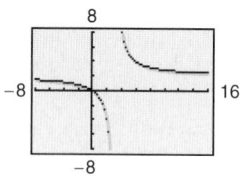

53. $y = \dfrac{1}{x} - x$

54. $y = x - 3 + \dfrac{2}{x}$

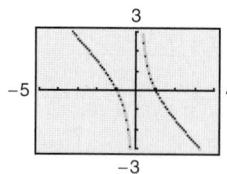

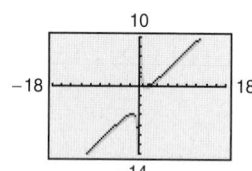

In Exercises 55–58, use a graphing utility to graph the rational function. Determine the domain of the function and identify any asymptotes.

55. $y = \dfrac{2x^2+x}{x+1}$

56. $y = \dfrac{x^2+5x+8}{x+3}$

57. $y = \dfrac{1+3x^2-x^3}{x^2}$

58. $y = \dfrac{12-2x-x^2}{2(4+x)}$

Graphical Reasoning　In Exercises 59–62, (a) use a graphing utility to graph the function and determine any x-intercepts, and (b) set $y = 0$ and solve the resulting equation to confirm your result in part (a).

59. $y = \dfrac{1}{x+5} + \dfrac{4}{x}$

60. $y = 20\left(\dfrac{2}{x+1} - \dfrac{3}{x}\right)$

61. $y = x - \dfrac{6}{x-1}$

62. $y = x - \dfrac{9}{x}$

63. *Concentration of a Mixture*　A 1000-liter tank contains 50 liters of a 25% brine solution. You add x liters of a 75% brine solution to the tank.

(a) Show that the concentration C, the proportion of brine to the total solution, of the final mixture is given by

$$C = \dfrac{3x+50}{4(x+50)}.$$

(b) Determine the domain of the function based on the physical constraints of the problem.

(c) Use a graphing utility to graph the function. As the tank is filled, what happens to the rate at which the concentration of brine increases? What percent does the concentration of brine appear to approach?

64. *Geometry*　A rectangular region of length x and width y has an area of 500 square meters.

(a) Write the width y as a function of x.

(b) Determine the domain of the function based on the physical constraints of the problem.

(c) Sketch a graph of the function and determine the width of the rectangle when $x = 30$ meters.

65. *Page Design*　A page that is x inches wide and y inches high contains 30 square inches of print. The margins at the top and bottom are 2 inches deep and the margins on each side are 1 inch wide (see figure).

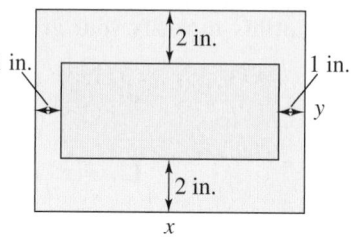

(a) Show that the total area A of the page is given by

$$A = \dfrac{2x(2x+11)}{x-2}.$$

(b) Determine the domain of the function based on the physical constraints of the problem.

(c) Use a graphing utility to graph the area function and approximate the page size such that the minimum amount of paper will be used. Verify your answer numerically using the *table* feature of a graphing utility.

66. Geometry A right triangle is formed in the first quadrant by the *x*-axis, the *y*-axis, and a line segment through the point (3, 2) (see figure).

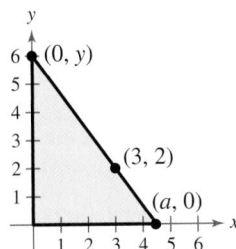

(a) Show that an equation of the line segment is given by

$$y = \frac{2(a - x)}{a - 3}, \quad 0 \le x \le a.$$

(b) Show that the area of the triangle is given by

$$A = \frac{a^2}{a - 3}.$$

(c) Use a graphing utility to graph the area function and estimate the value of *a* that yields a minimum area. Estimate the minimum area. Verify your answer numerically using the *table* feature of a graphing utility.

67. Cost The ordering and transportation cost *C* (in thousands of dollars) for the components used in manufacturing a product is given by

$$C = 100\left(\frac{200}{x^2} + \frac{x}{x + 30}\right), \quad x \ge 1$$

where *x* is the order size (in hundreds). Use a graphing utility to graph the cost function. From the graph, estimate the order size that minimizes cost.

68. Average Cost The cost *C* of producing *x* units of a product is given by $C = 0.2x^2 + 10x + 5$, and the average cost per unit is given by

$$\overline{C} = \frac{C}{x} = \frac{0.2x^2 + 10x + 5}{x}, \quad x > 0.$$

Sketch the graph of the average cost function, and estimate the number of units that should be produced to minimize the average cost per unit.

69. Medicine The concentration *C* of a chemical in the bloodstream *t* hours after injection into muscle tissue is given by

$$C = \frac{3t^2 + t}{t^3 + 50}, \quad t \ge 0.$$

(a) Determine the horizontal asymptote of the function and interpret its meaning in the context of the problem.

(b) Use a graphing utility to graph the function and approximate the time when the bloodstream concentration is greatest.

(c) Use a graphing utility to determine when the concentration is less than 0.345.

70. Numerical and Graphical Analysis A driver averaged 50 miles per hour on the round trip between Baltimore, Maryland and Philadelphia, Pennsylvania, 100 miles away. The average speeds for going and returning were *x* and miles per hour, respectively.

(a) Show that $y = (25x)/(x - 25)$.

(b) Determine the vertical and horizontal asymptotes of the function.

(c) Use a graphing utility to complete the table. What do you observe?

x	30	35	40	45	50	55	60
y							

(d) Use a graphing utility to graph the function.

(e) Is it possible to average 20 miles per hour in one direction and still average 50 miles per hour on the round trip? Explain.

71. Comparing Models The attendance *A* (in millions) at women's Division I college basketball games from 1995 to 2002 is shown in the table. (Source: NCAA)

Year	Attendance, *A*
1995	4.0
1996	4.2
1997	4.9
1998	5.4
1999	5.8
2000	6.4
2001	6.5
2002	6.9

For each of the following, let t represent the year, with $t = 5$ corresponding to 1995.

(a) Use the *regression* feature of a graphing utility to find a linear model for the data. Use a graphing utility to plot the data and graph the model in the same viewing window.

(b) Find a rational model for the data. Take the reciprocal of A to generate the points $(t, 1/A)$. Use the *regression* feature of a graphing utility to find a linear model for this data. The resulting line has the form

$$\frac{1}{A} = at + b.$$

Solve for A. Use a graphing utility to plot the data and graph the rational model in the same viewing window.

(c) Use the *table* feature of a graphing utility to create a table showing the predicted attendance based on each model for each of the years in the original table. Which model do you prefer? Why?

72. *Comparing Models* The table shows the average room rate R (in dollars) for hotels in the United States from 1995 to 2001. The data can be approximated by the model

$$R = \frac{6.245t + 44.05}{0.025t + 1.00}, \quad 5 \le t \le 11$$

where t represents the year, with $t = 5$ corresponding to 1995. (Source: American Hotel & Lodging Association)

Year	Rate, R
1995	66.65
1996	70.93
1997	75.31
1998	78.62
1999	81.33
2000	85.89
2001	88.27

(a) Use a graphing utility to plot the data and graph the model in the same viewing window.

(b) Use the *regression* feature of a graphing utility to find a linear model for the data. Then use a graphing utility to plot the data and graph the linear model in the same viewing window.

(c) Which of the two models would you recommend as a predictor of the average room rate for a hotel for the years following 2001? Explain your reasoning.

Synthesis

True or False? **In Exercises 73 and 74, determine whether the statement is true or false. Justify your answer.**

73. If the graph of a rational function f has a vertical asymptote at $x = 5$, it is possible to sketch the graph without lifting your pencil from the paper.

74. The graph of a rational function can never cross one of its asymptotes.

Think About It **In Exercises 75 and 76, use a graphing utility to graph the function. Explain why there is no vertical asymptote when a superficial examination of the function might indicate that there should be one.**

75. $h(x) = \dfrac{6 - 2x}{3 - x}$

76. $g(x) = \dfrac{x^2 + x - 2}{x - 1}$

Think About It **In Exercises 77 and 78, write a rational function satisfying the following criteria.**

77. Vertical asymptote: $x = 2$
Slant asymptote: $y = x + 1$
Zero of the function: $x = -2$

78. Vertical asymptote: $x = -4$
Slant asymptote: $y = x - 2$
Zero of the function: $x = 3$

Review

In Exercises 79–84, simplify the expression.

79. $\left(\dfrac{x}{8}\right)^{-3}$

80. $(4x^2)^{-2}$

81. $\dfrac{3x^3y^2}{15xy^4}$

82. $\dfrac{(4x^2)^{3/2}}{8x^5}$

83. $\dfrac{3^{7/6}}{3^{1/6}}$

84. $\dfrac{x^{-2} \cdot x^{1/2}}{x^{-1} \cdot x^{5/2}}$

In Exercises 85–88, use a graphing utility to graph the function and find its domain and range.

85. $f(x) = \sqrt{6 + x^2}$

86. $f(x) = \sqrt{121 - x^2}$

87. $f(x) = -|x + 9|$

88. $f(x) = -x^2 + 9$

3.7 Exploring Data: Quadratic Models

Classifying Scatter Plots

In real life, many relationships between two variables are parabolic, as in Section 3.1, Example 5. A scatter plot can be used to give you an idea of which type of model will best fit a set of data.

Example 1   Classifying Scatter Plots

Decide whether each set of data could best be modeled by a linear model, $y = ax + b$, or a quadratic model, $y = ax^2 + bx + c$.

a. $(0.9, 1.4)$, $(1.3, 1.5)$, $(1.3, 1.9)$, $(1.4, 2.1)$, $(1.6, 2.8)$, $(1.8, 2.9)$, $(2.1, 3.4)$, $(2.1, 3.4)$, $(2.5, 3.6)$, $(2.9, 3.7)$, $(3.2, 4.2)$, $(3.3, 4.3)$, $(3.6, 4.4)$, $(4.0, 4.5)$, $(4.2, 4.8)$, $(4.3, 5.0)$

b. $(0.9, 2.5)$, $(1.3, 4.03)$, $(1.3, 4.1)$, $(1.4, 4.4)$, $(1.6, 5.1)$, $(1.8, 6.05)$, $(2.1, 7.48)$, $(2.1, 7.6)$, $(2.5, 9.8)$, $(2.9, 12.4)$, $(3.2, 14.3)$, $(3.3, 15.2)$, $(3.6, 18.1)$, $(4.0, 19.9)$, $(4.2, 23.0)$, $(4.3, 23.9)$

Solution

Begin by entering the data into a graphing utility as shown in Figure 3.64.

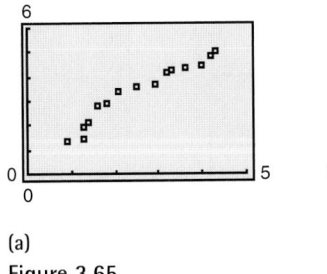

(a)

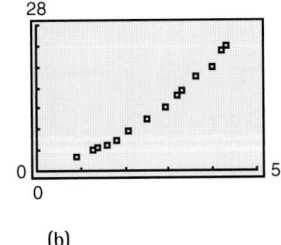

(b)

Figure 3.64

Then display the scatter plots as shown in Figure 3.65.

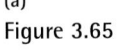

(a)   (b)

Figure 3.65

From the scatter plots, it appears that the data in part (a) follows a linear pattern. So, it can be modeled by a linear function. The data in part (b) follows a parabolic pattern. So, it can be modeled by a quadratic function.

✓ *Checkpoint* Now try Exercise 3.

What you should learn

- Classify scatter plots.
- Use scatter plots and a graphing utility to find quadratic models for data.
- Choose a model that best fits a set of data.

Why you should learn it

Many real-life situations can be modeled by quadratic equations. For instance, in Example 4 on page 308, a quadratic equation is used to model the amount spent on books and maps in the United States from 1990 to 2000.

Lee Snider/The Image Works

Fitting a Quadratic Model to Data

In Section 2.6, you created scatter plots of data and used a graphing utility to find the least squares regression lines for the data. You can use a similar procedure to find a model for nonlinear data. Once you have used a scatter plot to determine the type of model that would best fit a set of data, there are several ways that you can actually find the model. Each method is best used with a computer or calculator, rather than with hand calculations.

Example 2   Fitting a Quadratic Model to Data

A study was done to compare the speed x (in miles per hour) with the mileage y (in miles per gallon) of an automobile. The results are shown in the table. (Source: Federal Highway Administration)

Speed, x	Mileage, y
15	22.3
20	25.5
25	27.5
30	29.0
35	28.8
40	30.0
45	29.9
50	30.2
55	30.4
60	28.8
65	27.4
70	25.3
75	23.3

a. Use a graphing utility to create a scatter plot of the data.

b. Use the *regression* feature of the graphing utility to find a model that best fits the data.

c. Approximate the speed at which the mileage is the greatest.

Solution

a. Begin by entering the data into a graphing utility and displaying the scatter plot, as shown in Figure 3.66. From the scatter plot, you can see that the data has a parabolic trend.

b. Using the *regression* feature of a graphing utility, you can find the quadratic model, as shown in Figure 3.67. So, the quadratic equation that best fits the data is given by

$$y = -0.0082x^2 + 0.746x + 13.47.   \text{Quadratic model}$$

c. Graph the data and the model in the same viewing window, as shown in Figure 3.68. Use the *maximum* feature or *zoom* and *trace* features of the graphing utility to approximate the speed at which the mileage is greatest. You should obtain a maximum of approximately (47, 30), as shown in Figure 3.68. So, the speed at which the mileage is greatest is about 47 miles per hour.

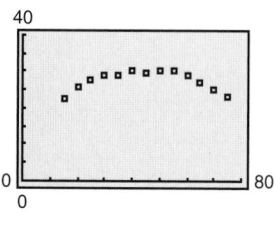

Figure 3.66

Figure 3.67

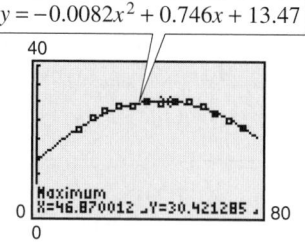

$y = -0.0082x^2 + 0.746x + 13.47$

Figure 3.68

✓ *Checkpoint*   Now try Exercise 13.

TECHNOLOGY SUPPORT   For instructions on how to use the *regression* feature, see Appendix A; for specific keystrokes, go to the text website at *college.hmco.com.*

Example 3   Fitting a Quadratic Model to Data

A basketball is dropped from a height of about 5.25 feet. The height of the bas-ketball is recorded 23 times at intervals of about 0.02 second.* The results are shown in the table. Use a graphing utility to find a model that best fits the data. Then use the model to predict the time when the basketball will hit the ground.

Time, x	Height, y
0.0	5.23594
0.02	5.20353
0.04	5.16031
0.06	5.09910
0.08	5.02707
0.099996	4.95146
0.119996	4.85062
0.139992	4.74979
0.159988	4.63096
0.179988	4.50132
0.199984	4.35728
0.219984	4.19523
0.23998	4.02958
0.25993	3.84593
0.27998	3.65507
0.299976	3.44981
0.319972	3.23375
0.339961	3.01048
0.359961	2.76921
0.379951	2.52074
0.399941	2.25786
0.419941	1.98058
0.439941	1.63488

Solution

Begin by entering the data into a graphing utility and displaying the scatter plot, as shown in Figure 3.69. From the scatter plot, you can see that the data has a par-abolic trend. So, using the *regression* feature of the graphing utility, you can find the quadratic model, as shown in Figure 3.70. The quadratic model that best fits the data is given by

$$y = -15.449x^2 - 1.30x + 5.2. \qquad \text{Quadratic model}$$

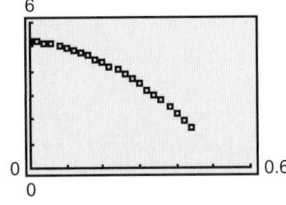

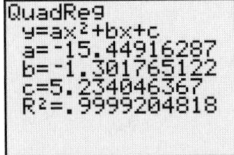

Figure 3.69   Figure 3.70

Using this model, you can predict the time when the basketball will hit the ground by substituting 0 for y and solving the resulting equation for x.

$$y = -15.449x^2 - 1.30x + 5.2 \qquad \text{Write original model.}$$

$$0 = -15.449x^2 - 1.30x + 5.2 \qquad \text{Substitute 0 for } y.$$

$$x = \frac{-b \pm \sqrt{b^2 - 4ac}}{2a} \qquad \text{Quadratic Formula}$$

$$= \frac{-(-1.30) \pm \sqrt{(-1.30)^2 - 4(-15.449)(5.2)}}{2(-15.449)} \qquad \text{Substitute for } a, b, \text{ and } c.$$

$$\approx 0.54 \qquad \text{Choose positive solution.}$$

So, the solution is about 0.54 second. In other words, the basketball will continue to fall for about $0.54 - 0.44 = 0.1$ second more before hitting the ground.

 Checkpoint   Now try Exercise 15.

Choosing a Model

Sometimes it is not easy to distinguish from a scatter plot which type of model a set of data can best be modeled by. You should first find several models for the data and then choose the model that best fits the data by comparing the y-values of each model with the actual y-values.

---

*Data was collected with a Texas Instruments CBL (Calculator-Based Laboratory) System.

Example 4   Choosing a Model

The table shows the amount y (in billions of dollars) spent on books and maps in the United States for the years 1990 to 2000. Use the *regression* feature of a graphing utility to find a linear model and a quadratic model for the data. Determine which model best fits the data.   (Source: U.S. Bureau of Economic Analysis)

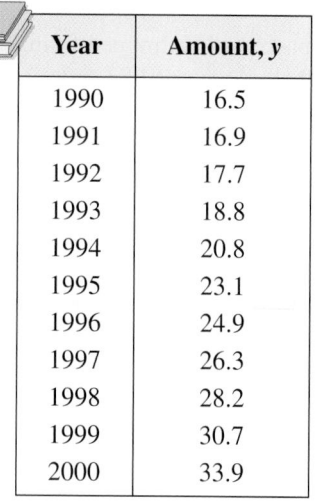

Year	Amount, y
1990	16.5
1991	16.9
1992	17.7
1993	18.8
1994	20.8
1995	23.1
1996	24.9
1997	26.3
1998	28.2
1999	30.7
2000	33.9

Solution

Let x represent the year, with $x = 0$ corresponding to 1990. Begin by entering the data into the graphing utility. Then use the *regression* feature to find a linear model (see Figure 3.71) and a quadratic model (see Figure 3.72) for the data.

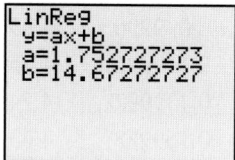

Figure 3.71   Linear model

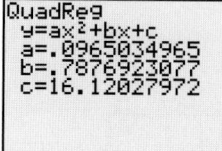

Figure 3.72   Quadratic model

So, a linear model for the data is given by

$$y = 1.75x + 14.7 \qquad \text{Linear model}$$

and a quadratic model for the data is given by

$$y = 0.097x^2 + 0.79x + 16.1. \qquad \text{Quadratic model}$$

Plot the data and the linear model in the same viewing window, as shown in Figure 3.73. Then plot the data and the quadratic model in the same viewing window, as shown in Figure 3.74. To determine which model best fits the data, compare the y-values given by each model with the actual y-values. The model whose y-values are closest to the actual values is the one that fits best. In this case, the best-fitting model is the quadratic model.

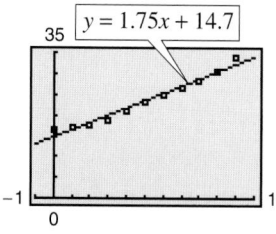

Figure 3.73

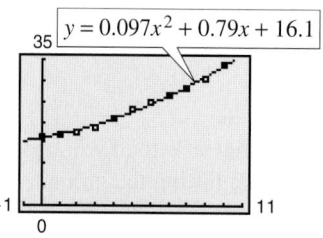

Figure 3.74

 Checkpoint   Now try Exercise 21.

TECHNOLOGY TIP   Recall from Section 2.6 that when you use the *regression* feature of a graphing utility, the program may output a correlation coefficient. The correlation coefficient for the linear model in Example 4 is $r^2 \approx 0.972$ and the correlation coefficient for the quadratic model is $r^2 \approx 0.995$. Because the correlation coefficient for the quadratic model is closer to 1, the quadratic model better fits the data.

Vocabulary Check

Fill in the blanks.

1. A scatter plot with either a positive or a negative correlation could be modeled by a _____ equation.

2. A scatter plot that appears parabolic could be modeled by a _____ equation.

In Exercises 1–6, determine whether the scatter plot could best be modeled by a linear model, a quadratic model, or neither.

1.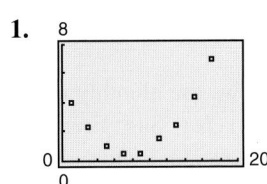

2.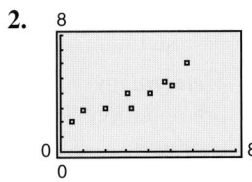

3.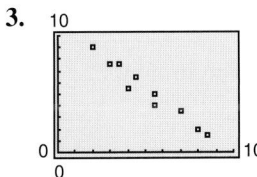

4.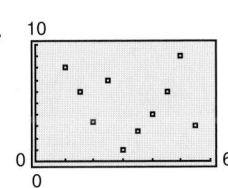

5.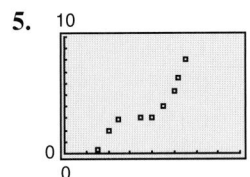

6.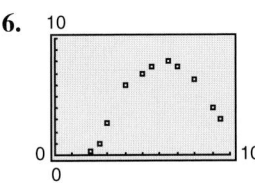

In Exercises 7–12, (a) use a graphing utility to create a scatter plot of the data, (b) determine whether the data could best be modeled by a linear model or a quadratic model, (c) use the *regression* feature of a graphing utility to find a model for the data, (d) use a graphing utility to graph the model with the scatter plot from part (a), and (e) create a table to compare the original data with the data given by the model.

7. $(0, 2.1)$, $(1, 2.4)$, $(2, 2.5)$, $(3, 2.8)$, $(4, 2.9)$, $(5, 3.0)$, $(6, 3.0)$, $(7, 3.2)$, $(8, 3.4)$, $(9, 3.5)$, $(10, 3.6)$

8. $(0, 10.0)$, $(1, 9.7)$, $(2, 9.4)$, $(3, 9.3)$, $(4, 9.1)$, $(5, 8.9)$, $(6, 8.6)$, $(7, 8.4)$, $(8, 8.4)$, $(9, 8.2)$, $(10, 8.0)$

9. $(0, 3480)$, $(5, 2235)$, $(10, 1250)$, $(15, 565)$, $(20, 150)$, $(25, 12)$, $(30, 145)$, $(35, 575)$, $(40, 1275)$, $(45, 2225)$, $(50, 3500)$, $(55, 5010)$

10. $(0, 6140)$, $(2, 6815)$, $(4, 7335)$, $(6, 7710)$, $(8, 7915)$, $(10, 7590)$, $(12, 7975)$, $(14, 7700)$, $(16, 7325)$, $(18, 6820)$, $(20, 6125)$, $(22, 5325)$

11. $(-5, 3.8)$, $(-4, 4.7)$, $(-3, 5.5)$, $(-2, 6.2)$, $(-1, 7.1)$, $(0, 7.9)$, $(1, 8.1)$, $(2, 7.7)$, $(3, 6.9)$, $(4, 6.0)$, $(5, 5.6)$, $(6, 4.4)$, $(7, 3.2)$

12. $(-9, -8.7)$, $(-8, -6.5)$, $(-7, -4.5)$, $(-6, -2.4)$, $(-5, -1.2)$, $(-4, 0.3)$, $(-3, 1.5)$, $(-2, 2.5)$, $(-1, 3.3)$, $(0, 3.9)$, $(1, 4.5)$, $(2, 4.6)$

13. ***Education***   The table shows the percent P of public schools in the United States with access to the Internet from 1994 to 2000. (Source: U.S. National Center for Education Statistics)

Year	Percent, P
1994	35
1995	50
1996	65
1997	78
1998	89
1999	95
2000	98

(a) Use a graphing utility to create a scatter plot of the data. Let t represent the year, with $t = 4$ corresponding to 1994.

(b) Use the *regression* feature of a graphing utility to find a quadratic model for the data.

(c) Use a graphing utility to graph the model with the scatter plot from part (a). Is the quadratic model a good fit for the data?

(d) Use the model to determine when 100% of public schools will have access to the Internet.

(e) Can the model be used to predict the percent of public schools with Internet access in the future? Explain.

14. ***Entertainment***   The table on the next page shows the number H of hours spent per person playing video games in the United States from 1995 to 2000. (Source: Veronis Suhler Stevenson)

Year	Hours, H
1995	24
1996	25
1997	36
1998	43
1999	61
2000	70

Table for 14

(a) Use a graphing utility to create a scatter plot of the data. Let t represent the year, with $t = 5$ corresponding to 1995.

(b) Use the *regression* feature of a graphing utility to find a quadratic model for the data.

(c) Use a graphing utility to graph the model with the scatter plot from part (a). Is the quadratic model a good fit for the data?

(d) The projected number H^* of hours spent per person playing video games for the years 2001 to 2005 is shown in the table. Use the model obtained in part (b) to predict the number of hours for the same years.

Year	2001	2002	2003	2004	2005
H^*	79	90	97	103	115

(e) Compare your predictions from part (d) with those given in the table. Explain why the values may differ.

15. **Medicine** The table shows the number H (in thousands) of hospitals in the United States for selected years from 1960 to 2000. (Source: Health Forum)

Year	Hospitals, H
1960	6876
1965	7123
1970	7123
1975	7156
1980	6965
1985	6872
1990	6649
1995	6291
2000	5810

(a) Use a graphing utility to create a scatter plot of the data. Let t represent the year, with $t = 0$ corresponding to 1960.

(b) Use the *regression* feature of a graphing utility to find a quadratic model for the data.

(c) Use a graphing utility to graph the model with the scatter plot from part (a). Is the quadratic model a good fit for the data?

(d) Use the graph from part (c) to determine in which year the number of hospitals reached a maximum.

(e) Do you think the model can be used to predict the number of hospitals in the United States in the future? Explain.

16. **Meteorology** The table shows the monthly normal precipitation P (in inches) for San Francisco, California. (Source: U.S. National Oceanic and Atmospheric Administration)

Month	Precipitation, P
January	4.45
February	4.01
March	3.26
April	1.17
May	0.38
June	0.11
July	0.03
August	0.07
September	0.20
October	1.04
November	2.49
December	2.89

(a) Use a graphing utility to create a scatter plot of the data. Let t represent the month, with $t = 1$ corresponding to January.

(b) Use the *regression* feature of a graphing utility to find a quadratic model for the data.

(c) Use a graphing utility to graph the model with the scatter plot from part (a).

(d) Use the graph from part (c) to determine in which month the normal precipitation in San Francisco is the least.

In Exercises 17–20, (a) use the *regression* feature of a graphing utility to find a linear model and a quadratic model for the data, (b) determine the correlation coefficient for each model, and (c) use the correlation coefficient to determine which model best fits the data.

17. $(1, 4.0)$, $(2, 6.5)$, $(3, 8.8)$, $(4, 10.6)$, $(5, 13.9)$, $(6, 15.0)$, $(7, 17.5)$, $(8, 20.1)$, $(9, 24.0)$, $(10, 27.1)$

18. $(1, 1.1)$, $(2, 3.0)$, $(3, 5.1)$, $(4, 7.3)$, $(5, 9.3)$, $(6, 11.5)$, $(7, 13.6)$, $(8, 15.5)$, $(9, 17.8)$, $(10, 20.0)$

19. $(-8, 7.4)$, $(-6, 5.7)$, $(-4, 3.7)$, $(-2, 2.1)$, $(0, 0.2)$, $(2, -1.6)$, $(4, -3.4)$, $(6, -5.1)$, $(8, -6.9)$, $(10, -8.6)$

20. $(-20, 805)$, $(-15, 744)$, $(-10, 704)$, $(-5, 653)$, $(0, 587)$, $(5, 551)$, $(10, 512)$, $(15, 478)$, $(20, 436)$, $(25, 430)$

21. Sales The table shows the sales S (in millions of dollars) for Guitar Center, Inc. from 1996 to 2002. (Source: Guitar Center, Inc.)

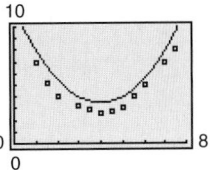

Year	Sales, S
1996	213.3
1997	296.7
1998	391.7
1999	620.1
2000	785.7
2001	938.2
2002	1101.1

(a) Use a graphing utility to create a scatter plot of the data. Let t represent the year, with $t = 6$ corresponding to 1996.

(b) Use the *regression* feature of a graphing utility to find a linear model for the data.

(c) Use a graphing utility to graph the model with the scatter plot from part (a).

(d) Use the *regression* feature of a graphing utility to find a quadratic model for the data.

(e) Use a graphing utility to graph the quadratic model with the scatter plot from part (a).

(f) Determine which model best fits the data and use the model you chose to predict the sales for Guitar Center, Inc. in 2007.

22. Writing Explain why the parabola shown in the figure is not a good fit for the data.

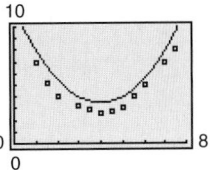

Synthesis

True or False? **In Exercises 23 and 24, determine whether the statement is true or false. Justify your answer.**

23. The graph of a quadratic model with a negative leading coefficient will have a maximum value at its vertex.

24. The graph of a quadratic model with a positive leading coefficient will have a minimum value at its vertex.

Review

In Exercises 25–28, find (a) $f \circ g$ and (b) $g \circ f$.

25. $f(x) = 2x - 1$, $g(x) = x^2 + 3$

26. $f(x) = 5x + 8$, $g(x) = 2x^2 - 1$

27. $f(x) = x^3 - 1$, $g(x) = \sqrt[3]{x + 1}$

28. $f(x) = \sqrt[3]{x + 5}$, $g(x) = x^3 - 5$

In Exercises 29–32, determine algebraically whether the function is one-to-one. If it is, find its inverse function. Verify your answer graphically.

29. $f(x) = 2x + 5$

30. $f(x) = \dfrac{x - 4}{5}$

31. $f(x) = x^2 + 5, x \ge 0$

32. $f(x) = 2x^2 - 3, x \ge 0$

In Exercises 33–36, plot the complex number in the complex plane.

33. $1 - 3i$

34. $-2 + 4i$

35. $-5i$

36. $8i$

3 Chapter Summary

What did you learn?

Section 3.1	Review Exercises
☐ Analyze graphs of quadratic functions.	1, 2
☐ Write quadratic functions in standard form and use the results to sketch graphs of functions.	3–10
☐ Find minimum and maximum values of functions in real-life applications.	11, 12

Section 3.2
☐ Use transformations to sketch graphs of polynomial functions.	13–16
☐ Use the Leading Coefficient Test to determine the end behavior of graphs of polynomial functions.	17–22
☐ Find and use zeros of polynomial functions as sketching aids.	23–28
☐ Use the Intermediate Value Theorem to help locate zeros of polynomial functions.	29–32

Section 3.3
☐ Use long division to divide polynomials by other polynomials.	35–42
☐ Use synthetic division to divide polynomials by binomials of the form $(x - k)$.	43–48
☐ Use the Remainder and Factor Theorems.	49–54
☐ Use the Rational Zero Test to determine possible rational zeros of polynomial functions.	55–60
☐ Use Descartes's Rule of Signs and the Upper and Lower Bound Rules to find zeros of polynomials.	61–64

Section 3.4
☐ Use the Fundamental Theorem of Algebra to determine the number of zeros of a polynomial function.	65–68
☐ Find all zeros of polynomial functions, including complex zeros.	69–78
☐ Find conjugate pairs of complex zeros.	79–82
☐ Find zeros of polynomials by factoring.	83–86

Section 3.5
☐ Find the domains of rational functions.	87–98
☐ Find horizontal and vertical asymptotes of graphs of rational functions.	87–98
☐ Use rational functions to model and solve real-life problems.	99, 100

Section 3.6
☐ Analyze and sketch graphs of rational functions.	101–110
☐ Sketch graphs of rational functions that have slant asymptotes.	111–114
☐ Use rational functions to model and solve real-life problems.	115, 116

Section 3.7
☐ Classify scatter plots.	117–120
☐ Use scatter plots and a graphing utility to find quadratic models for data.	121
☐ Choose a model that best fits a set of data.	122

3 Review Exercises

3.1 In Exercises 1 and 2, use a graphing utility to graph each function in the same viewing window. Describe how the graph of each function is related to the graph of $y = x^2$.

1. (a) $y = 2x^2$ (b) $y = -2x^2$
   (c) $y = x^2 + 2$ (d) $y = (x + 5)^2$
2. (a) $y = x^2 - 4$ (b) $y = 4 - x^2$
   (c) $y = (x - 1)^2$ (d) $y = \frac{1}{2}x^2 - 1$

In Exercises 3–6, sketch the graph of the quadratic function. Identify the vertex and the intercept(s).

3. $f(x) = \left(x + \frac{3}{2}\right)^2 + 1$
4. $f(x) = (x - 4)^2 - 4$
5. $f(x) = \frac{1}{3}(x^2 + 5x - 4)$
6. $f(x) = 3x^2 - 12x + 11$

In Exercises 7–10, write the standard form of the quadratic function that has the indicated vertex and whose graph passes through the given point. Verify your result with a graphing utility.

7. Vertex: $(1, -4)$;   Point: $(2, -3)$
8. Vertex: $(2, 3)$;   Point: $(0, 2)$
9. Vertex: $(-2, -2)$;   Point: $(-1, 0)$
10. Vertex: $\left(-\frac{1}{4}, \frac{3}{2}\right)$;   Point: $(-2, 0)$

11. **Numerical, Graphical, and Analytical Analysis**   A rectangle is inscribed in the region bounded by the x-axis, the y-axis, and the graph of $x + 2y - 8 = 0$, as shown in the figure.

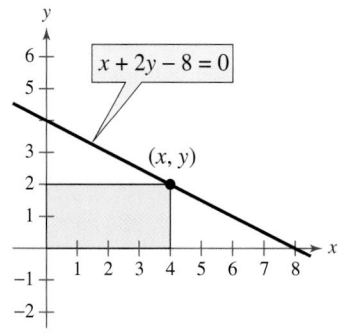

(a) Write the area A as a function of x. Determine the domain of the function in the context of the problem.

(b) Use the *table* feature of a graphing utility to create a table showing possible values of x and the corresponding areas of the rectangle. Use the table to estimate the dimensions that will produce a maximum area.

(c) Use a graphing utility to graph the area function. Use the graph to approximate the dimensions that will produce a maximum area.

(d) Write the area function in standard form to find algebraically the dimensions that will produce a maximum area.

(e) Compare your results from parts (b), (c), and (d).

12. **Cost**   A textile manufacturer has daily production costs of

$$C = 10,000 - 110x + 0.45x^2$$

where C is the total cost (in dollars) and x is the number of units produced. Use the *table* feature of a graphing utility to determine how many units should be produced each day to yield a minimum cost.

3.2 In Exercises 13–16, sketch the graph of $y = x^n$ and each specified transformation.

13. $y = x^4$
   (a) $f(x) = (x + 5)^4$ (b) $f(x) = x^4 - 4$
   (c) $f(x) = 3 + x^4$ (d) $f(x) = \frac{1}{4}(x - 2)^4$
14. $y = x^5$
   (a) $f(x) = (x + 4)^5$ (b) $f(x) = 6 + x^5$
   (c) $f(x) = 3 - \frac{1}{2}x^5$ (d) $f(x) = 2(x + 3)^5$
15. $y = x^6$
   (a) $f(x) = x^6 - 2$ (b) $f(x) = -\frac{1}{4}x^6$
   (c) $f(x) = -\frac{1}{2}x^6 - 5$ (d) $f(x) = -(x + 7)^6 - 5$
16. $y = x^3$
   (a) $f(x) = -x^3 + 4$ (b) $f(x) = (x + 2)^3 - 1$
   (c) $f(x) = -\frac{1}{3}x^3 + 1$ (d) $f(x) = -(x + 8)^3$

Graphical Analysis In Exercises 17 and 18, use a graphing utility to graph the functions f and g in the same viewing window. Zoom out far enough so that the right-hand and left-hand behaviors of f and g appear identical.

17. $f(x) = \frac{1}{2}x^3 - 2x + 1$, $\quad g(x) = \frac{1}{2}x^3$

18. $f(x) = -x^4 + 2x^3$, $\quad g(x) = -x^4$

In Exercises 19–22, use the Leading Coefficient Test to determine the right-hand and left-hand behavior of the graph of the polynomial function.

19. $f(x) = -x^2 + 6x + 9$

20. $f(x) = \frac{1}{2}x^3 + 2x$

21. $g(x) = \frac{3}{4}(x^4 + 3x^2 + 2)$

22. $h(x) = -x^5 - 7x^2 + 10x$

In Exercises 23–28, (a) use a graphing utility to graph the function, (b) use the graph to approximate any zeros, and (c) find the zeros algebraically.

23. $g(x) = x^4 - x^3 - 2x^2$

24. $h(x) = -2x^3 - x^2 + x$

25. $f(t) = t^3 - 3t$

26. $f(x) = -(x + 6)^3 - 8$

27. $f(x) = x(x + 3)^2$

28. $f(t) = t^4 - 4t^2$

In Exercises 29–32, (a) use the Intermediate Value Theorem and a graphing utility to find intervals of length 1 in which the polynomial function is guaranteed to have a zero, (b) use the *zero* or *root* feature of a graphing utility to approximate the zeros of the function, and (c) verify your results in part (a) by using the *table* feature of a graphing utility.

29. $f(x) = x^3 + 2x^2 - x - 1$

30. $f(x) = 0.24x^3 - 2.6x - 1.4$

31. $f(x) = x^4 - 6x^2 - 4$

32. $f(x) = 2x^4 + \frac{7}{2}x^3 - 2$

3.3 *Graphical Analysis* In Exercises 33 and 34, use a graphing utility to graph the two equations in the same viewing window. Use the graphs to verify that the expressions are equivalent. Verify the results algebraically.

33. $y_1 = \frac{x^2}{x - 2}$, $\quad y_2 = x + 2 + \frac{4}{x - 2}$

34. $y_1 = \frac{x^4 + 1}{x^2 + 2}$, $\quad y_2 = x^2 - 2 + \frac{5}{x^2 + 2}$

In Exercises 35–42, use long division to divide.

35. $\dfrac{24x^2 - x - 8}{3x - 2}$

36. $\dfrac{4x^2 + 7}{3x - 2}$

37. $\dfrac{x^4 - 3x^2 + 2}{x^2 - 1}$

38. $\dfrac{3x^4}{x^2 - 1}$

39. $(5x^3 - 13x^2 - x + 2) \div (x^2 - 3x + 1)$

40. $(x^4 + x^3 - x^2 + 2x) \div (x^2 + 2x)$

41. $\dfrac{6x^4 + 10x^3 + 13x^2 - 5x + 2}{2x^2 - 1}$

42. $\dfrac{x^4 - 3x^3 + 4x^2 - 6x + 3}{x^2 + 2}$

In Exercises 43–48, use synthetic division to divide.

43. $(0.25x^4 - 4x^3) \div (x + 2)$

44. $(0.1x^3 + 0.3x^2 - 0.5) \div (x - 5)$

45. $(6x^4 - 4x^3 - 27x^2 + 18x) \div \left(x - \frac{2}{3}\right)$

46. $(2x^3 + 2x^2 - x + 2) \div \left(x - \frac{1}{2}\right)$

47. $(3x^3 - 10x^2 + 12x - 22) \div (x - 4)$

48. $(2x^3 + 6x^2 - 14x + 9) \div (x - 1)$

In Exercises 49 and 50, use synthetic division to find each function value. Use a graphing utility to verify your results.

49. $f(x) = x^4 + 10x^3 - 24x^2 + 20x + 44$
    (a) $f(-3)$ (b) $f(-1)$

50. $g(t) = 2t^5 - 5t^4 - 8t + 20$
    (a) $g(-4)$ (b) $g(\sqrt{2})$

In Exercises 51–54, (a) verify the given factor(s) of the function f, (b) find the remaining factors of f, (c) use your results to write the complete factorization of f, (d) list all real zeros of f, and (e) confirm your results by using a graphing utility to graph the function.

	Function	*Factor(s)*
51.	$f(x) = x^3 + 4x^2 - 25x - 28$	$(x - 4)$
52.	$f(x) = 2x^3 + 11x^2 - 21x - 90$	$(x + 6)$
53.	$f(x) = x^4 - 4x^3 - 7x^2 + 22x + 24$	$(x + 2),$
		$(x - 3)$
54.	$f(x) = x^4 - 11x^3 + 41x^2 - 61x + 30$	$(x - 2),$
		$(x - 5)$

In Exercises 55 and 56, use the Rational Zero Test to list all possible rational zeros of f. Use a graphing utility to verify that the zeros of f are contained in the list.

55. $f(x) = 4x^3 - 11x^2 + 10x - 3$

56. $f(x) = 10x^3 + 21x^2 - x - 6$

In Exercises 57–60, find all the zeros of the function.

57. $f(x) = 6x^3 - 5x^2 + 24x - 20$

58. $f(x) = x^3 - 1.3x^2 - 1.7x + 0.6$

59. $f(x) = 6x^4 - 25x^3 + 14x^2 + 27x - 18$

60. $f(x) = 5x^4 + 126x^2 + 25$

In Exercises 61 and 62, use Descartes's Rule of Signs to determine the possible numbers of positive and negative real zeros of the function.

61. $g(x) = 5x^3 + 3x^2 - 6x + 9$

62. $h(x) = -2x^5 + 4x^3 - 2x^2 + 5$

In Exercises 63 and 64, use synthetic division to verify the upper and lower bounds of the real zeros of f.

63. $f(x) = 4x^3 - 3x^2 + 4x - 3$

Upper bound: $x = 1$; Lower bound: $x = -\frac{1}{4}$

64. $f(x) = 2x^3 - 5x^2 - 14x + 8$

Upper bound: $x = 8$; Lower bound: $x = -4$

3.4 In Exercises 65–68, find all the zeros of the function.

65. $f(x) = 3x(x - 2)^2$

66. $f(x) = (x - 4)(x + 9)^2$

67. $f(x) = (x + 4)(x - 6)(x - 2i)(x + 2i)$

68. $g(t) = (t - 8)(t - 5)^2(t - 3 + i)(t - 3 - i)$

In Exercises 69–72, find all the zeros of the function and write the polynomial as a product of linear factors. Use a graphing utility to graph the function to verify your results graphically.

69. $f(x) = 2x^4 - 5x^3 + 10x - 12$

70. $g(x) = 3x^4 - 4x^3 + 7x^2 + 10x - 4$

71. $h(x) = x^3 - 7x^2 + 18x - 24$

72. $f(x) = 2x^3 - 5x^2 - 9x + 40$

In Exercises 73–78, (a) find all the zeros of the function, (b) write the polynomial as a product of linear factors, (c) use your factorization to determine the x-intercepts of the graph of the function, and (d) use a graphing utility to verify that the real zeros are the only x-intercepts.

73. $f(x) = x^3 - 4x^2 + 6x - 4$

74. $f(x) = x^3 - 5x^2 - 7x + 51$

75. $f(x) = x^3 + 6x^2 + 11x + 12$

76. $f(x) = 2x^3 - 9x^2 + 22x - 30$

77. $f(x) = x^4 + 34x^2 + 225$

78. $f(x) = x^4 + 10x^3 + 26x^2 + 10x + 25$

In Exercises 79–82, find a polynomial function with real coefficients that has the given zeros. (There are many correct answers.)

79. $-2, -2, -5i$

80. $4, 4, 2i$

81. $1, -4, -3 + 5i$

82. $-4, -4, 1 + \sqrt{3}i$

In Exercises 83–86, write the polynomial (a) as the product of factors that are irreducible over the *rationals*, (b) as the product of linear and quadratic factors that are irreducible over the *reals*, and (c) in completely factored form.

83. $f(x) = x^4 + 2x^2 - 8$

84. $f(x) = x^4 - x^3 - x^2 + 5x - 20$

(*Hint:* One factor is $x^2 - 5$.)

85. $f(x) = x^4 - 2x^3 + 8x^2 - 18x - 9$

(*Hint:* One factor is $x^2 + 9$.)

86. $f(x) = x^4 - 4x^3 + 3x^2 + 8x - 16$

(*Hint:* One factor is $x^2 - x - 4$.)

3.5 In Exercises 87–98, (a) find the domain of the function and (b) identify any horizontal and vertical asymptotes.

87. $f(x) = \dfrac{x - 8}{1 - x}$

88. $f(x) = \dfrac{5x}{x + 12}$

89. $f(x) = \dfrac{2}{x^2 - 3x - 18}$

90. $f(x) = \dfrac{2x^2 + 3}{x^2 + x + 3}$

91. $f(x) = \dfrac{7 + x}{7 - x}$

92. $f(x) = \dfrac{6x}{x^2 - 1}$

93. $f(x) = \dfrac{4x^2}{2x^2 - 3}$

94. $f(x) = \dfrac{3x^2 - 11x - 4}{x^2 + 2}$

95. $f(x) = \dfrac{2x - 10}{x^2 - 2x - 15}$ **96.** $f(x) = \dfrac{x^3 - 4x^2}{x^2 + 3x + 2}$

97. $f(x) = \dfrac{x - 2}{|x| + 2}$ **98.** $f(x) = \dfrac{2x}{|2x - 1|}$

99. Seizure of Illegal Drugs The cost C in millions of dollars for the U.S. government to seize $p\%$ of an illegal drug as it enters the country is given by

$$C = \frac{528p}{100 - p}, \quad 0 \le p < 100.$$

(a) Find the cost of seizing 25%, 50%, and 75% of the illegal drug.

(b) Use a graphing utility to graph the function. Be sure to choose an appropriate viewing window. Explain why you chose the values you used in your viewing window.

(c) According to this model, would it be possible to seize 100% of the drug? Explain.

100. Wildlife A biology class performs an experiment comparing the quantity of food consumed by a certain kind of moth with the quantity supplied. The model for the experimental data is given by

$$y = \frac{1.568x - 0.001}{6.360x + 1}, \quad x > 0$$

where x is the quantity (in milligrams) of food supplied and y is the quantity (in milligrams) eaten (see figure). At what level of consumption will the moth become satiated?

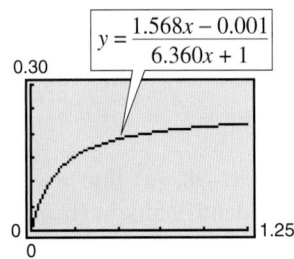

$$y = \frac{1.568x - 0.001}{6.360x + 1}$$

0.30

0

0

1.25

3.6 **In Exercises 101–110, sketch the graph of the rational function by hand. As sketching aids, check for intercepts, vertical asymptotes, and horizontal asymptotes. Use a graphing utility to verify your graph.**

101. $f(x) = \dfrac{2x - 1}{x - 5}$ **102.** $f(x) = \dfrac{x - 3}{x - 2}$

103. $f(x) = \dfrac{2x}{x^2 + 4}$ **104.** $f(x) = \dfrac{2x^2}{x^2 - 4}$

105. $f(x) = \dfrac{x^2}{x^2 + 1}$ **106.** $f(x) = \dfrac{5x}{x^2 + 1}$

107. $f(x) = \dfrac{2}{(x + 1)^2}$ **108.** $f(x) = \dfrac{4}{(x - 1)^2}$

109. $f(x) = \dfrac{2(x^2 - 16)}{x^2 + 2x - 8}$ **110.** $f(x) = \dfrac{3x^2 - 6x}{x^2 - 4}$

In Exercises 111–114, sketch the graph of the rational function by hand. As sketching aids, check for intercepts, vertical asymptotes, horizontal asymptotes, and slant asymptotes.

111. $f(x) = \dfrac{2x^3}{x^2 + 1}$ **112.** $f(x) = \dfrac{x^3}{3x^2 - 6}$

113. $f(x) = \dfrac{x^2 - x + 1}{x - 3}$ **114.** $f(x) = \dfrac{2x^2 + 7x + 3}{x + 1}$

115. Wildlife The Parks and Wildlife Commission introduces 80,000 fish into a large human-made lake. The population N of the fish in thousands is given by

$$N = \frac{20(4 + 3t)}{1 + 0.05t}, \quad t \ge 0$$

where t is time in years.

(a) Use a graphing utility to graph the function.

(b) Use the graph from part (a) to find the populations when $t = 5$, $t = 10$, and $t = 25$.

(c) What is the maximum number of fish in the lake as time increases? Explain your reasoning.

116. Page Design A page that is x inches wide and y inches high contains 30 square inches of print. The top and bottom margins are 2 inches deep and the margins on each side are 2 inches wide.

(a) Draw a diagram that illustrates the problem.

(b) Show that the total area A of the page is given by

$$A = \frac{2x(2x + 7)}{x - 4}.$$

(c) Determine the domain of the function based on the physical constraints of the problem.

(d) Use a graphing utility to graph the area function and approximate the page size such that the minimum amount of paper will be used. Verify your answer numerically using the *table* feature of a graphing utility.

3.7 In Exercises 117–120, determine whether the scatter plot could best be modeled by a linear model, a quadratic model, or neither.

117. 118.

119. 120.

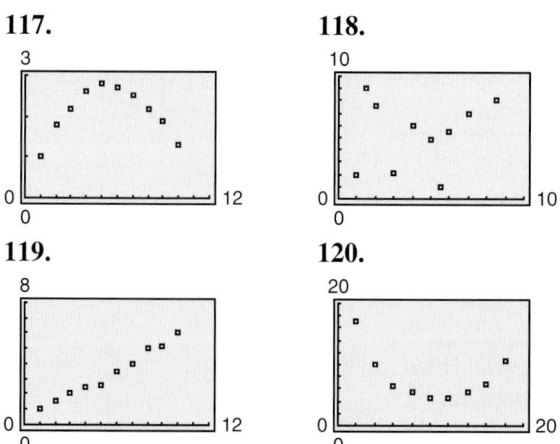

121. **Revenue** The table shows the revenue R (in millions of dollars) for OfficeMax, Inc. from 1994 to 2001. (Source: OfficeMax, Inc.)

Year	Revenue, R
1994	1841.2
1995	2542.5
1996	3179.3
1997	3765.4
1998	4337.8
1999	4842.7
2000	5156.4
2001	4636.0

(a) Use a graphing utility to create a scatter plot of the data. Let t represent the year, with $t = 4$ corresponding to 1994.

(b) Use the *regression* feature of a graphing utility to find a quadratic model for the data.

(c) Use a graphing utility to graph the model with the scatter plot from part (a). Is the quadratic model a good fit for the data?

(d) Use the graph from part (c) to determine in which year the revenue for OfficeMax, Inc. was the greatest.

(e) Do you think the model can be used to predict the revenue for OfficeMax, Inc. in the future? Explain.

122. **Consumer Awareness** The table shows the average price P (in dollars) for a personal computer from 1997 to 2002. (Source: Consumer Electronics Association)

Year	Average price, P
1997	1450
1998	1300
1999	1100
2000	1000
2001	900
2002	855

(a) Use a graphing utility to create a scatter plot of the data. Let t represent the year, with $t = 7$ corresponding to 1997.

(b) Use the *regression* feature of a graphing utility to find a linear model for the data.

(c) Use a graphing utility to graph the linear model with the scatter plot from part (a).

(d) Use the *regression* feature of a graphing utility to find a quadratic model for the data.

(e) Use a graphing utility to graph the quadratic model with the scatter plot from part (a).

(f) Determine which model best fits the data and use the model you chose to predict the average price for a personal computer in 2008. Does your answer seem reasonable? Explain.

Synthesis

True or False? **In Exercises 123 and 124, determine whether the statement is true or false. Justify your answer.**

123. The graph of $f(x) = \dfrac{2x^3}{x + 1}$ has a slant asymptote.

124. A fourth-degree polynomial with real coefficients can have -5, $-8i$, $4i$, and 5 as its zeros.

125. **Think About It** What does it mean for a divisor to divide evenly into a dividend?

126. **Writing** Write a paragraph discussing whether every rational function has a vertical asymptote.

3 Chapter Test

Take this test as you would take a test in class. After you are finished, check your work against the answers given in the back of the book.

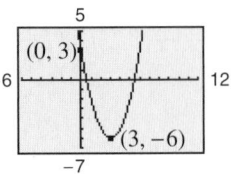

1. Describe how the graph of g differs from the graph of $f(x) = x^2$.
   (a) $g(x) = 6 - x^2$ (b) $g(x) = \left(x - \frac{3}{2}\right)^2$

2. Identify the vertex and intercepts of the graph of $y = x^2 + 4x + 3$.

3. Write an equation of the parabola shown at the right.

Figure for 3

4. The path of a ball is given by $y = -\frac{1}{20}x^2 + 3x + 5$, where y is the height (in feet) and x is the horizontal distance (in feet).

   (a) Find the maximum height of the ball.

   (b) Which term determines the height at which the ball was thrown? Does changing this term change the maximum height of the ball? Explain.

5. Divide using long division: $(3x^3 + 4x - 1) \div (x^2 + 1)$.

6. Divide using synthetic division: $(2x^4 - 5x^2 - 3) \div (x - 2)$.

In Exercises 7 and 8, list all the possible rational zeros of the function. Use a graphing utility to graph the function and find all the rational zeros.

7. $g(t) = 2t^4 - 3t^3 + 16t - 24$ 8. $h(x) = 3x^5 + 2x^4 - 3x - 2$

In Exercises 9 and 10, use the *zero* or *root* feature of a graphing utility to approximate (accurate to three decimal places) the real zeros of the function.

9. $f(x) = x^4 - x^3 - 1$ 10. $f(x) = 3x^5 + 2x^4 - 12x - 8$

In Exercises 11–13, find a polynomial function with real coefficients that has the given zeros. (There are many correct answers.)

11. $0, 3, 3 + i, 3 - i$ 12. $1 - \sqrt{3}i, 2, 2$ 13. $0, -5, 1 + i$

In Exercises 14–16, sketch the graph of the rational function. As sketching aids, check for intercepts, vertical asymptotes, horizontal asymptotes, and slant asymptotes.

14. $h(x) = \dfrac{4}{x^2} - 1$ 15. $g(x) = \dfrac{x^2 + 2}{x - 1}$ 16. $f(x) = \dfrac{2x^2 + 9}{5x^2 + 2}$

17. The table shows the number C of U.S. Supreme Court cases waiting to be tried for the years 1995 to 2000. (Source: Office of the Clerk, Supreme Court of the United States)

    (a) Use a graphing utility to create a scatter plot of the data. Let t represent the year, with $t = 5$ corresponding to 1995.

    (b) Use the *regression* feature of a graphing utility to find a quadratic model for the data.

    (c) Use a graphing utility to graph the model with the scatter plot from part (a). Is the quadratic model a good fit for the data?

    (d) Use the model to predict the year in which there will be 15,000 U.S. Supreme Court cases waiting to be tried.

Year	Cases, C
1995	7565
1996	7602
1997	7692
1998	8083
1999	8445
2000	8965

Exponential models are widely used in the financial world. The growth pattern of a savings account and the calculation of mortgage rates both require exponential functions.

Ryan McVay/Photodisc/Getty Images

HOUSE
FOR
SALE

4 Exponential and Logarithmic Functions

4.1 Exponential Functions and Their Graphs

4.2 Logarithmic Functions and Their Graphs

4.3 Properties of Logarithms

4.4 Solving Exponential and Logarithmic Equations

4.5 Exponential and Logarithmic Models

4.6 Exploring Data: Nonlinear Models

What You Should Learn

In this chapter, you will learn how to:

■ Recognize, evaluate, and graph exponential and logarithmic functions.

■ Rewrite logarithmic functions with different bases.

■ Use properties of logarithms to evaluate, rewrite, expand, or condense logarithmic expressions.

■ Solve exponential and logarithmic equations.

■ Use exponential growth models, exponential decay models, Gaussian models, logistic models, and logarithmic models to solve real-life problems.

■ Fit exponential, logarithmic, power, and logistic models to sets of data.

4.1 Exponential Functions and Their Graphs

Exponential Functions

So far, this text has dealt mainly with **algebraic functions,** which include polynomial functions and rational functions. In this chapter you will study two types of nonalgebraic functions—*exponential functions* and *logarithmic functions*. These functions are examples of **transcendental functions.**

Definition of Exponential Function

The **exponential function** f **with base** a is denoted by

$$f(x) = a^x$$

where $a > 0$, $a \neq 1$, and x is any real number.

Note that in the definition of an exponential function, the base $a = 1$ is excluded because it yields $f(x) = 1^x = 1$. This is a constant function, not an exponential function.

You have already evaluated a^x for integer and rational values of x. For example, you know that $4^3 = 64$ and $4^{1/2} = 2$. However, to evaluate 4^x for any real number x, you need to interpret forms with *irrational* exponents. For the purposes of this text, it is sufficient to think of

$$a^{\sqrt{2}} \left(\text{where } \sqrt{2} \approx 1.41421356 \right)$$

as the number that has the successively closer approximations

$$a^{1.4}, a^{1.41}, a^{1.414}, a^{1.4142}, a^{1.41421}, \ldots$$

Example 1 shows how to use a calculator to evaluate exponential functions.

Example 1 Evaluating Exponential Functions

Use a calculator to evaluate each function at the indicated value of x.

Function	Value
a. $f(x) = 2^x$	$x = -3.1$
b. $f(x) = 2^{-x}$	$x = \pi$
c. $f(x) = 0.6^x$	$x = \frac{3}{2}$

Solution

Function Value	Graphing Calculator Keystrokes	Display
a. $f(-3.1) = 2^{-3.1}$	2 ^ (−) 3.1 ENTER	0.1166291
b. $f(\pi) = 2^{-\pi}$	2 ^ (−) π ENTER	0.1133147
c. $f(\frac{3}{2}) = (0.6)^{3/2}$	.6 ^ (3 ÷ 2) ENTER	0.4647580

✓ *Checkpoint* Now try Exercise 3.

What you should learn

- Recognize and evaluate exponential functions with base a.
- Graph exponential functions.
- Recognize, evaluate, and graph exponential functions with base e.
- Use exponential functions to model and solve real-life problems.

Why you should learn it

Exponential functions are useful in modeling data that represents quantities that increase or decrease quickly. For instance, Example 11 on page 328 shows how an exponential function is used to model the number of fruit flies in a population.

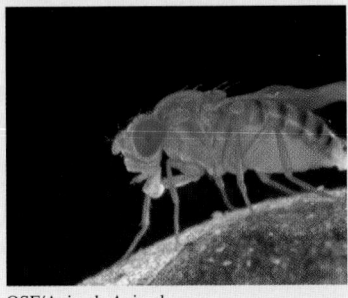

OSF/Animals Animals

TECHNOLOGY TIP

When evaluating exponential functions with a calculator, remember to enclose fractional exponents in parentheses. Because the calculator follows the order of operations, parentheses are crucial in order to obtain the correct result.

Graphs of Exponential Functions

The graphs of all exponential functions have similar characteristics, as shown in Examples 2, 3, and 4.

Example 2   Graphs of $y = a^x$

In the same coordinate plane, sketch the graph of each function by hand.

a. $f(x) = 2^x$ **b.** $g(x) = 4^x$

Solution

The table below lists some values for each function. By plotting these points and connecting them with a smooth curve, you obtain the graphs shown in Figure 4.1. Note that both graphs are increasing. Moreover, the graph of $g(x) = 4^x$ is increasing more rapidly than the graph of $f(x) = 2^x$.

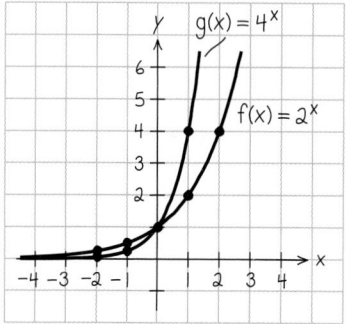

Figure 4.1

x	-2	-1	0	1	2	3
2^x	$\frac{1}{4}$	$\frac{1}{2}$	1	2	4	8
4^x	$\frac{1}{16}$	$\frac{1}{4}$	1	4	16	64

✓ *Checkpoint* Now try Exercise 7.

Example 3   Graphs of $y = a^{-x}$

In the same coordinate plane, sketch the graph of each function by hand.

a. $F(x) = 2^{-x}$ **b.** $G(x) = 4^{-x}$

Solution

The table below lists some values for each function. By plotting these points and connecting them with a smooth curve, you obtain the graphs shown in Figure 4.2. Note that both graphs are decreasing. Moreover, the graph of $G(x) = 4^{-x}$ is decreasing more rapidly than the graph of $F(x) = 2^{-x}$.

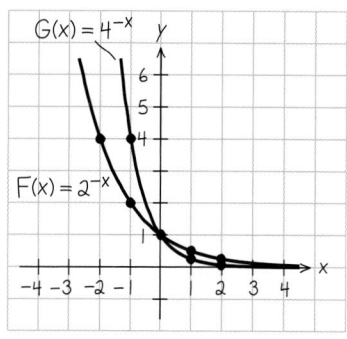

Figure 4.2

x	-3	-2	-1	0	1	2
2^{-x}	8	4	2	1	$\frac{1}{2}$	$\frac{1}{4}$
4^{-x}	64	16	4	1	$\frac{1}{4}$	$\frac{1}{16}$

✓ *Checkpoint* Now try Exercise 9.

The properties of exponents presented in Section P.2 can also be applied to real-number exponents. For review, these properties are listed below.

1. $a^x a^y = a^{x+y}$ **2.** $\dfrac{a^x}{a^y} = a^{x-y}$ **3.** $a^{-x} = \dfrac{1}{a^x} = \left(\dfrac{1}{a}\right)^x$ **4.** $a^0 = 1$

5. $(ab)^x = a^x b^x$ **6.** $(a^x)^y = a^{xy}$ **7.** $\left(\dfrac{a}{b}\right)^x = \dfrac{a^x}{b^x}$ **8.** $|a^2| = |a|^2 = a^2$

STUDY TIP

In Example 3, note that the functions $F(x) = 2^{-x}$ and $G(x) = 4^{-x}$ can be rewritten with positive exponents.

$$F(x) = 2^{-x} = \left(\frac{1}{2}\right)^x \quad \text{and}$$

$$G(x) = 4^{-x} = \left(\frac{1}{4}\right)^x$$

Comparing the functions in Examples 2 and 3, observe that

$$F(x) = 2^{-x} = f(-x) \qquad \text{and} \qquad G(x) = 4^{-x} = g(-x).$$

Consequently, the graph of F is a reflection (in the y-axis) of the graph of f, as shown in Figure 4.3. The graphs of G and g have the same relationship, as shown in Figure 4.4.

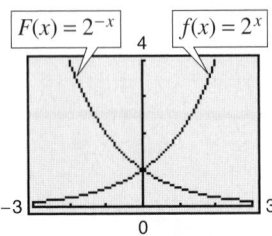

Figure 4.3

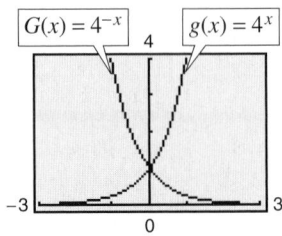

Figure 4.4

STUDY TIP

Notice that the range of an exponential function is $(0, \infty)$, which means that $a^x > 0$ for all values of x.

The graphs in Figures 4.1 and 4.2 are typical of the graphs of the exponential functions $f(x) = a^x$ and $f(x) = a^{-x}$. They have one y-intercept and one horizontal asymptote (the x-axis), and they are continuous.

Library of Functions: Exponential Function

The *exponential function*

$$f(x) = a^x, \ a > 0, \ a \neq 1$$

is different from all the functions you have studied so far because the variable x is an *exponent*. A distinguishing characteristic of an exponential function is its rapid increase as x increases (for $a > 1$). Many real-life phenomena with patterns of rapid growth (or decline) can be modeled by exponential functions. The basic characteristics of the exponential function are summarized below.

Graph of $f(x) = a^x$, $a > 1$

Domain: $(-\infty, \infty)$

Range: $(0, \infty)$

Intercept: $(0, 1)$

Increasing on $(-\infty, \infty)$

x-axis is a horizontal asymptote
$(a^x \to 0$ as $x \to -\infty)$

Continuous

Graph of $f(x) = a^{-x}$, $a > 1$

Domain: $(-\infty, \infty)$

Range: $(0, \infty)$

Intercept: $(0, 1)$

Decreasing on $(-\infty, \infty)$

x-axis is a horizontal asymptote
$(a^{-x} \to 0$ as $x \to \infty)$

Continuous

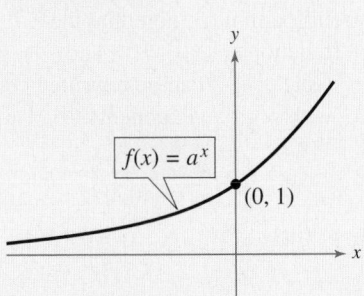

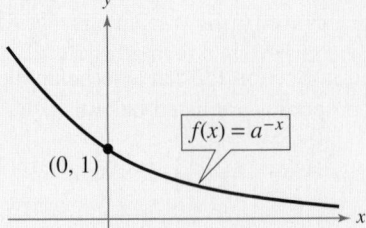

Exploration

Use a graphing utility to graph $y = a^x$ for $a = 3$, 5, and 7 in the same viewing window. (Use a viewing window in which $-2 \leq x \leq 1$ and $0 \leq y \leq 2$.) How do the graphs compare with each other? Which graph is on the top in the interval $(-\infty, 0)$? Which is on the bottom? Which graph is on the top in the interval $(0, \infty)$? Which is on the bottom? Repeat this experiment with the graphs of $y = b^x$ for $b = \frac{1}{3}, \frac{1}{5}$, and $\frac{1}{7}$. (Use a viewing window in which $-1 \leq x \leq 2$ and $0 \leq y \leq 2$.) What can you conclude about the shape of the graph of $y = b^x$ and the value of b?

In the following example, notice how the graph of $y = a^x$ can be used to sketch the graphs of functions of the form $f(x) = b \pm a^{x+c}$.

Example 4   Transformations of Graphs of Exponential Functions

Each of the following graphs is a transformation of the graph of $f(x) = 3^x$.

a. Because $g(x) = 3^{x+1} = f(x + 1)$, the graph of g can be obtained by shifting the graph of f one unit to the *left*, as shown in Figure 4.5.

b. Because $h(x) = 3^x - 2 = f(x) - 2$, the graph of h can be obtained by shifting the graph of f *downward* two units, as shown in Figure 4.6.

c. Because $k(x) = -3^x = -f(x)$, the graph of k can be obtained by *reflecting* the graph of f in the x-axis, as shown in Figure 4.7.

d. Because $j(x) = 3^{-x} = f(-x)$, the graph of j can be obtained by *reflecting* the graph of f in the y-axis, as shown in Figure 4.8.

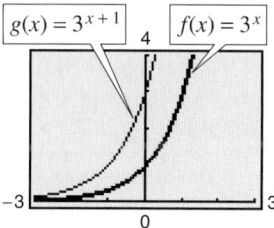

Figure 4.5

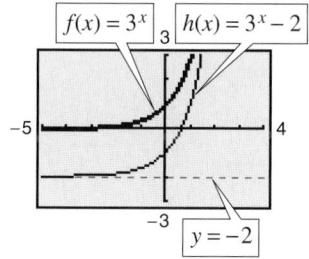

Figure 4.6

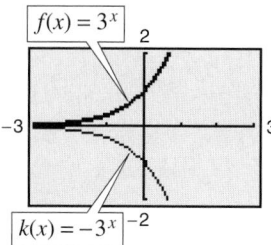

Figure 4.7

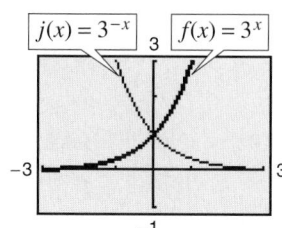

Figure 4.8

✓ *Checkpoint* Now try Exercise 19.

Notice that the transformations in Figures 4.5, 4.7, and 4.8 keep the x-axis ($y = 0$) as a horizontal asymptote, but the transformation in Figure 4.6 yields a new horizontal asymptote of $y = -2$. Also, be sure to note how the y-intercept is affected by each transformation.

The Natural Base e

For many applications, the convenient choice for a base is the irrational number

$$e \approx 2.718281828.$$

Exploration

The following table shows some points of the graphs in Figure 4.5. The functions $f(x)$ and $g(x)$ are represented by Y1 and Y2, respectively. Explain how you can use the table to describe the transformation.

X	Y1	Y2
-3	.03704	.11111
-2	.11111	.33333
-1	.33333	1
0	1	3
1	3	9
2	9	27
3	27	81

X= -3

This number is called the **natural base.** The function $f(x) = e^x$ is called the **natural exponential function** and its graph is shown in Figure 4.9. The graph of the exponential function has the same basic characteristics as the graph of the function $f(x) = a^x$ (see page 322). Be sure you see that for the exponential function $f(x) = e^x$, e is the constant $2.718281828 \ldots$, whereas x is the variable.

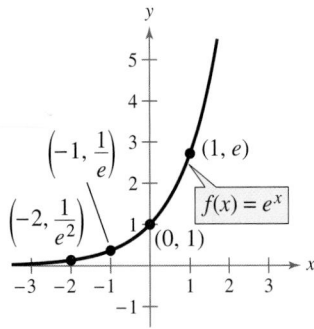

Figure 4.9   The Natural Exponential Function

Exploration

Use your graphing utility to graph the functions

$$y_1 = 2^x$$

$$y_2 = e^x$$

$$y_3 = 3^x$$

in the same viewing window. From the relative positions of these graphs, make a guess as to the value of the real number e. Then try to find a number a such that the graphs of $y_2 = e^x$ and $y_4 = a^x$ are as close as possible.

In Example 5, you will see that the number e can be approximated by the expression

$$\left(1 + \frac{1}{x}\right)^x \text{ for large values of } x.$$

TECHNOLOGY SUPPORT

For instructions on how to use the *trace* feature and the *table* feature, see Appendix A; for specific keystrokes, go to the text website at *college.hmco.com*.

Example 5   Approximation of the Number e

Evaluate the expression $[1 + (1/x)]^x$ for several large values of x to see that the values approach $e \approx 2.718281828$ as x increases without bound.

Graphical Solution

Use a graphing utility to graph

$$y_1 = [1 + (1/x)]^x \qquad \text{and} \qquad y_2 = e$$

in the same viewing window, as shown in Figure 4.10. Use the *trace* feature of the graphing utility to verify that as x increases, the graph of y_1 gets closer and closer to the line $y_2 = e$.

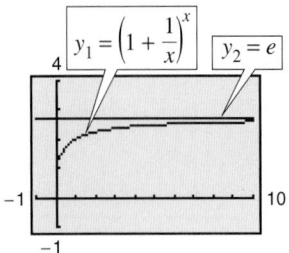

Figure 4.10

Numerical Solution

Use the *table* feature (in *ask* mode) of a graphing utility to create a table of values for the function $y = [1 + (1/x)]^x$, beginning at $x = 10$ and increasing the x-values as shown in Figure 4.11.

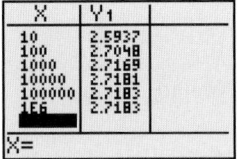

Figure 4.11

From the table, it seems reasonable to conclude that

$$\left(1 + \frac{1}{x}\right)^x \to e \text{ as } x \to \infty.$$

✓ *Checkpoint*   Now try Exercise 37.

Example 6   Evaluating the Natural Exponential Function

Use a calculator to evaluate the function $f(x) = e^x$ at each indicated value of x.

a. $x = -2$ **b.** $x = 0.25$ **c.** $x = -0.4$

Solution

Function Value	Graphing Calculator Keystrokes	Display
a. $f(-2) = e^{-2}$	[eˣ] [(-)] 2 [ENTER]	0.1353353
b. $f(0.25) = e^{0.25}$	[eˣ] .25 [ENTER]	1.2840254
c. $f(-0.4) = e^{-0.4}$	[eˣ] [(-)] .4 [ENTER]	0.6703200

✓ *Checkpoint* Now try Exercise 23.

Example 7   Graphing Natural Exponential Functions

Sketch the graph of each natural exponential function.

a. $f(x) = 2e^{0.24x}$ **b.** $g(x) = \frac{1}{2}e^{-0.58x}$

Solution

To sketch these two graphs, you can use a calculator to construct a table of values, as shown below.

x	-3	-2	-1	0	1	2	3
$f(x)$	0.974	1.238	1.573	2.000	2.542	3.232	4.109
$g(x)$	2.849	1.595	0.893	0.500	0.280	0.157	0.088

After constructing the table, plot the points and connect them with smooth curves. Note that the graph in Figure 4.12 is increasing, whereas the graph in Figure 4.13 is decreasing. Use a graphing calculator to verify these graphs.

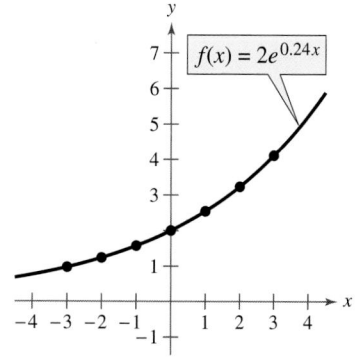

Figure 4.12

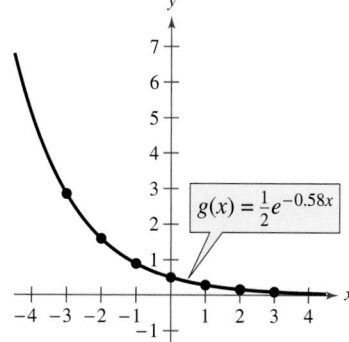

Figure 4.13

✓ *Checkpoint* Now try Exercise 35.

Applications

One of the most familiar examples of exponential growth is that of an investment earning *continuously compounded interest*. Suppose a principal P is invested at an annual interest rate r, compounded once a year. If the interest is added to the principal at the end of the year, the new balance P_1 is $P_1 = P + Pr = P(1 + r)$. This pattern of multiplying the previous principal by $1 + r$ is then repeated each successive year, as shown in the table.

Time in Years	Balance After Each Compounding
0	$P = P$
1	$P_1 = P(1 + r)$
2	$P_2 = P_1(1 + r) = P(1 + r)(1 + r) = P(1 + r)^2$
$\vdots$	$\vdots$
t	$P_t = P(1 + r)^t$

To accommodate more frequent (quarterly, monthly, or daily) compounding of interest, let n be the number of compoundings per year and let t be the number of years. (The product nt represents the total number of times the interest will be compounded.) Then the interest rate per compounding period is r/n, and the account balance after t years is

$$A = P\left(1 + \frac{r}{n}\right)^{nt}.$$ Amount (balance) with n compoundings per year

If you let the number of compoundings n increase without bound, the process approaches what is called **continuous compounding.** In the formula for n compoundings per year, let $m = n/r$. This produces

$$A = P\left(1 + \frac{r}{n}\right)^{nt} = P\left(1 + \frac{1}{m}\right)^{mrt} = P\left[\left(1 + \frac{1}{m}\right)^{m}\right]^{rt}.$$

As m increases without bound, you know from Example 5 that $\left[1 + (1/m)\right]^m$ approaches e. So, for continuous compounding, it follows that

$$P\left[\left(1 + \frac{1}{m}\right)^{m}\right]^{rt} \rightarrow P[e]^{rt}$$

and you can write $A = Pe^{rt}$. This result is part of the reason that e is the "natural" choice for a base of an exponential function.

Formulas for Compound Interest

After t years, the balance A in an account with principal P and annual interest rate r (in decimal form) is given by the following formulas.

1. For n compoundings per year: $A = P\left(1 + \dfrac{r}{n}\right)^{nt}$

2. For continuous compounding: $A = Pe^{rt}$

Exploration

Use the formula

$$A = P\left(1 + \frac{r}{n}\right)^{nt}$$

to calculate the amount in an account when $P = \$3000$, $r = 6\%$, $t = 10$ years, and the number of compoundings is (a) by the day, (b) by the hour, (c) by the minute, and (d) by the second. Does increasing the number of compoundings per year result in unlimited growth of the amount in the account? Explain.

STUDY TIP

The interest rate r in the formula for compound interest should be written as a decimal. For example, an interest rate of 7% would be written as $r = 0.07$.

Example 8   Finding the Balance for Compound Interest

A total of $9000 is invested at an annual interest rate of 2.5%, compounded annually. Find the balance in the account after 5 years.

Algebraic Solution

In this case,

$$P = 9000, \ r = 2.5\% = 0.025, \ n = 1, \ t = 5.$$

Using the formula for compound interest with n compoundings per year, you have

$$A = P\left(1 + \frac{r}{n}\right)^{nt} \qquad \text{Formula for compound interest}$$

$$= 9000\left(1 + \frac{0.025}{1}\right)^{1(5)} \qquad \text{Substitute for } P, r, n, \text{ and } t.$$

$$= 9000(1.025)^5 \qquad \text{Simplify.}$$

$$\approx \$10{,}182.67. \qquad \text{Use a calculator.}$$

So, the balance in the account after 5 years will be about $10,182.67.

Graphical Solution

Substitute the values for P, r, and n into the formula for compound interest with n compoundings per year as follows.

$$A = P\left(1 + \frac{r}{n}\right)^{nt} \qquad \text{Formula for compound interest}$$

$$= 9000\left(1 + \frac{0.025}{1}\right)^{(1)t} \qquad \text{Substitute for } P, r, \text{ and } n.$$

$$= 9000(1.025)^t \qquad \text{Simplify.}$$

Use a graphing utility to graph $y = 9000(1.025)^x$. Using the *value* feature or *zoom* and *trace* features, you can approximate the value of y when $x = 5$ to be about 10,182.67, as shown in Figure 4.14. So, the balance in the account after 5 years will be about $10,182.67.

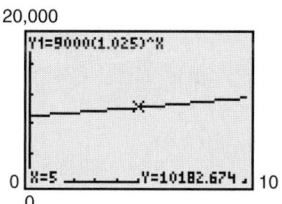

Figure 4.14

 Checkpoint Now try Exercise 55.

Example 9   Finding Compound Interest

A total of $12,000 is invested at an annual interest rate of 3%. Find the balance after 4 years if the interest is compounded (a) quarterly and (b) continuously.

Solution

a. For quarterly compoundings, $n = 4$. So, after 4 years at 3%, the balance is

$$A = P\left(1 + \frac{r}{n}\right)^{nt} = 12{,}000\left(1 + \frac{0.03}{4}\right)^{4(4)}$$

$$\approx \$13{,}523.91.$$

b. For continuous compounding, the balance is

$$A = Pe^{rt} = 12{,}000e^{0.03(4)}$$

$$\approx \$13{,}529.96.$$

Note that a continuous-compounding account yields more than a quarterly-compounding account.

 Checkpoint Now try Exercise 57.

Example 10   Radioactive Decay

Let y represent a mass of radioactive strontium (^{90}Sr), in grams, whose half-life is 28 years. The quantity of strontium present after t years is $y = 10\left(\frac{1}{2}\right)^{t/28}$.

a. What is the initial mass (when $t = 0$)?

b. How much of the initial mass is present after 80 years?

Algebraic Solution

a. $y = 10\left(\dfrac{1}{2}\right)^{t/28}$ Write original equation.

$= 10\left(\dfrac{1}{2}\right)^{0/28}$ Substitute 0 for t.

$= 10$ Simplify.

So, the initial mass is 10 grams.

b. $y = 10\left(\dfrac{1}{2}\right)^{t/28}$ Write original equation.

$= 10\left(\dfrac{1}{2}\right)^{80/28}$ Substitute 80 for t.

$\approx 10\left(\dfrac{1}{2}\right)^{2.857}$ Simplify.

≈ 1.380 Use a calculator.

So, about 1.380 grams is present after 80 years.

✅ *Checkpoint* Now try Exercise 65.

Graphical Solution

Use a graphing utility to graph $y = 10\left(\frac{1}{2}\right)^{x/28}$.

a. Use the *value* feature or the *zoom* and *trace* features of the graphing utility to determine that the value of y when $x = 0$ is 10, as shown in Figure 4.15. So, the initial mass is 10 grams.

b. Use the *value* feature or the *zoom* and *trace* features of the graphing utility to determine that the value of y when $x = 80$ is about 1.380, as shown in Figure 4.16. So, about 1.380 grams is present after 80 years.

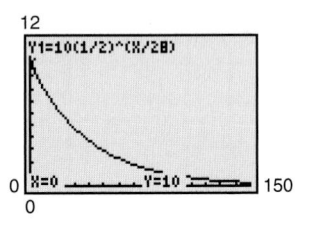

Figure 4.15   Figure 4.16

Example 11   Population Growth

The approximate number of fruit flies in an experimental population after t hours is given by $Q(t) = 20e^{0.03t}$, where $t \geq 0$.

a. Find the initial number of fruit flies in the population.

b. How large is the population of fruit flies after 72 hours?

c. Graph Q.

Solution

a. To find the initial population, evaluate $Q(t)$ at $t = 0$.

$$Q(0) = 20e^{0.03(0)} = 20e^0 = 20(1) = 20 \text{ flies}$$

b. After 72 hours, the population size is

$$Q(72) = 20e^{0.03(72)} = 20e^{2.16} \approx 173 \text{ flies}.$$

c. The graph of Q is shown in Figure 4.17.

✅ *Checkpoint* Now try Exercise 67.

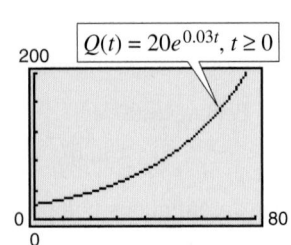

Figure 4.17

4.1   Exercises

Vocabulary Check

Fill in the blanks.

1. Polynomial and rational functions are examples of _____ functions.

2. Exponential and logarithmic functions are examples of nonalgebraic functions, also called _____ functions.

3. The exponential function $f(x) = e^x$ is called the _____ function, and the base e is called the _____ base.

4. To find the amount A in an account after t years with principal P and annual interest rate r compounded n times per year, you can use the formula _____ .

5. To find the amount A in an account after t years with principal P and annual interest rate r compounded continuously, you can use the formula _____ .

In Exercises 1–6, use a calculator to evaluate the function at the indicated value of x. Round your result to three decimal places.

Function	Value
1. $f(x) = 3.4^x$	$x = 6.8$
2. $f(x) = 1.2^x$	$x = \frac{1}{3}$
3. $g(x) = 5^x$	$x = -\pi$
4. $g(x) = 5000(2^x)$	$x = -1.5$
5. $h(x) = 17^{2x}$	$x = \sqrt{3}$
6. $h(x) = 8.6^{-3x}$	$x = -\sqrt{2}$

In Exercises 7–14, graph the exponential function by hand. Identify any asymptotes and intercepts and determine whether the graph of the function is increasing or decreasing.

7. $g(x) = 5^x$

8. $f(x) = \left(\frac{3}{2}\right)^x$

9. $f(x) = \left(\frac{1}{5}\right)^x = 5^{-x}$

10. $h(x) = \left(\frac{3}{2}\right)^{-x}$

11. $h(x) = 5^{x-2}$

12. $g(x) = \left(\frac{3}{2}\right)^{x+2}$

13. $g(x) = 5^{-x} - 3$

14. $f(x) = \left(\frac{3}{2}\right)^{-x} + 2$

In Exercises 15–18, use the graph of $y = 2^x$ to match the function with its graph. [The graphs are labeled (a), (b), (c), and (d).]

(a)

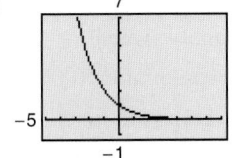

(b)

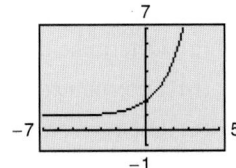

(c)

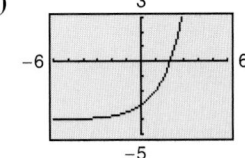

(d)

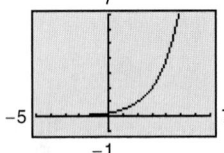

15. $f(x) = 2^{x-2}$

16. $f(x) = 2^{-x}$

17. $f(x) = 2^x - 4$

18. $f(x) = 2^x + 1$

In Exercises 19–22, use the graph of f to describe the transformation that yields the graph of g.

19. $f(x) = 3^x$, $g(x) = 3^{x-5}$

20. $f(x) = -2^x$, $g(x) = 5 - 2^x$

21. $f(x) = \left(\frac{3}{5}\right)^x$, $g(x) = -\left(\frac{3}{5}\right)^{x+4}$

22. $f(x) = 0.3^x$, $g(x) = -0.3^x + 5$

In Exercises 23–28, use a calculator to evaluate the function at the indicated value of x. Round your result to three decimal places.

Function	Value
23. $f(x) = e^x$	$x = 9.2$
24. $f(x) = e^{-x}$	$x = -\frac{3}{4}$
25. $g(x) = 50e^{4x}$	$x = 0.02$
26. $g(x) = 100e^{0.01x}$	$x = 12$
27. $h(x) = 2.5e^x$	$x = -\frac{1}{2}$
28. $h(x) = -5.5e^{-x}$	$x = 200$

In Exercises 29–38, use a graphing utility to construct a table of values for the function. Then sketch the graph of the function.

29. $f(x) = \left(\frac{5}{2}\right)^x$

30. $f(x) = \left(\frac{5}{2}\right)^{-x}$

31. $f(x) = 6^x$

32. $f(x) = 2^{x-1}$

33. $f(x) = 3^{x+2}$

34. $f(x) = e^{-x}$

35. $f(x) = 3e^{x+4}$

36. $f(x) = 2e^{-0.5x}$

37. $f(x) = 2 + e^{x-5}$

38. $f(x) = 4^{x-3} + 3$

In Exercises 39–46, use a graphing utility to graph the exponential function. Identify any asymptotes of the graph.

39. $y = 2^{-x^2}$

40. $y = 3^{-|x|}$

41. $y = 3^{x-2} + 1$

42. $y = 4^{x+1} - 2$

43. $g(x) = 2 - e^{-x}$

44. $s(t) = 3e^{-0.2t}$

45. $s(t) = 2e^{0.12t}$

46. $g(x) = 1 + e^{-x}$

In Exercises 47–50, use a graphing utility to (a) graph the function and (b) find any asymptotes numerically by creating a table of values for the function.

47. $f(x) = \dfrac{8}{1 + e^{-0.5x}}$

48. $g(x) = \dfrac{8}{1 + e^{-0.5/x}}$

49. $f(x) = -\dfrac{6}{2 - e^{0.2x}}$

50. $f(x) = \dfrac{6}{2 - e^{0.2/x}}$

In Exercises 51–54, (a) use a graphing utility to graph the function, (b) use the graph to find the open intervals on which the function is increasing and decreasing, and (c) approximate any relative maximum or minimum values.

51. $f(x) = x^2 e^{-x}$

52. $f(x) = 2x^2 e^{x+1}$

53. $f(x) = x(2^{3-x})$

54. $f(x) = -\left(\frac{1}{2}x\right)3^{x+4}$

Compound Interest **In Exercises 55–58, complete the table to determine the balance A for P dollars invested at rate r for t years and compounded n times per year.**

n	1	2	4	12	365	Continuous
A						

55. $P = \$2500, r = 2.5\%, t = 10$ years

56. $P = \$1000, r = 6\%, t = 10$ years

57. $P = \$2500, r = 4\%, t = 20$ years

58. $P = \$1000, r = 3\%, t = 40$ years

Compound Interest **In Exercises 59–62, complete the table to determine the balance A for \$12,000 invested at a rate r for t years, compounded continuously.**

t	1	10	20	30	40	50
A						

59. $r = 4\%$

60. $r = 6\%$

61. $r = 3.5\%$

62. $r = 2.5\%$

63. *Demand*   The demand function for a product is given by

$$p = 5000\left(1 - \frac{4}{4 + e^{-0.002x}}\right)$$

where p is the price and x is the number of units.

(a) Use a graphing utility to graph the demand function for $x > 0$ and $p > 0$.

(b) Find the price p for a demand of $x = 500$ units.

(c) Use the graph in part (a) to approximate the highest price that will still yield a demand of at least 600 units.

(d) Verify your answers to parts (b) and (c) numerically by creating a table of values for the function.

64. *Compound Interest*   There are three options for investing \$500. The first earns 7% compounded annually, the second earns 7% compounded quarterly, and the third earns 7% compounded continuously.

(a) Find equations that model each investment growth and use a graphing utility to graph each model in the same viewing window over a 20-year period.

(b) Use the graph from part (a) to determine which investment yields the highest return after 20 years. What is the difference in earnings between each investment?

65. *Radioactive Decay*   Let Q represent a mass of radioactive radium (^{226}Ra), in grams, whose half-life is 1620 years. The quantity of radium present after t years is given by $Q = 25\left(\frac{1}{2}\right)^{t/1620}$.

(a) Determine the initial quantity (when $t = 0$).

(b) Determine the quantity present after 1000 years.

(c) Use a graphing utility to graph the function over the interval $t = 0$ to $t = 5000$.

(d) When will the quantity of radium be 0 grams? Explain.

66. Radioactive Decay   Let Q represent a mass of carbon 14 (^{14}C), in grams, whose half-life is 5730 years. The quantity present after t years is given by $Q = 10\left(\frac{1}{2}\right)^{t/5730}$.

(a) Determine the initial quantity (when $t = 0$).

(b) Determine the quantity present after 2000 years.

(c) Sketch the graph of the function over the interval $t = 0$ to $t = 10,000$.

67. Bacteria Growth   A certain type of bacteria increases according to the model $P(t) = 100e^{0.2197t}$, where t is the time in hours.

(a) Use a graphing utility to graph the model.

(b) Use a graphing utility to approximate $P(0)$, $P(5)$, and $P(10)$.

(c) Verify your answers in part (b) algebraically.

68. Population Growth   The population of a town increases according to the model $P(t) = 2500e^{0.0293t}$, where t is the time in years, with $t = 0$ corresponding to 2000.

(a) Use a graphing utility to graph the function for the years 2000 through 2025.

(b) Use a graphing utility to approximate the population in 2015 and 2025.

(c) Verify your answers in part (b) algebraically.

69. Inflation   If the annual rate of inflation averages 4% over the next 10 years, the approximate cost C of goods or services during any year in that decade will be modeled by $C(t) = P(1.04)^t$, where t is the time (in years) and P is the present cost. The price of an oil change for your car is presently $23.95.

(a) Use a graphing utility to graph the function.

(b) Use the graph in part (a) to approximate the price of an oil change 10 years from now.

(c) Verify your answer in part (b) algebraically.

70. Depreciation   After t years, the value of a car that costs $20,000 is modeled by $V(t) = 20,000\left(\frac{3}{4}\right)^t$.

(a) Use a graphing utility to graph the function.

(b) Use a graphing utility to create a table of values that shows the value V for $t = 1$ to $t = 10$ years.

Synthesis

True or False?   **In Exercises 71 and 72, determine whether the statement is true or false. Justify your answer.**

71. $f(x) = 1^x$ is not an exponential function.

72. $e = \dfrac{271,801}{99,990}$

73. Exploration   Use a graphing utility to graph $y_1 = e^x$ and each of the functions $y_2 = x^2$, $y_3 = x^3$, $y_4 = \sqrt{x}$, and $y_5 = |x|$.

(a) Which function increases at the fastest rate for "large" values of x?

(b) Use the result of part (a) to make a conjecture about the rates of growth of $y_1 = e^x$ and $y = x^n$, where n is a natural number and x is "large."

(c) Use the results of parts (a) and (b) to describe what is implied when it is stated that a quantity is growing exponentially.

74. Exploration   Consider the functions $f(x) = 3^x$ and $g(x) = 4^x$.

(a) Use a graphing utility to complete the table, and use the table to estimate the solution of the inequality $4^x < 3^x$.

x	-1	-0.5	0	0.5	1
$f(x)$					
$g(x)$					

(b) Use a graphing utility to graph f and g in the same viewing window. Use the graphs to solve the inequalities (i) $4^x < 3^x$ and (ii) $4^x > 3^x$.

75. Graphical Analysis   Use a graphing utility to graph $f(x) = (1 + 0.5/x)^x$ and $g(x) = e^{0.5}$ in the same viewing window. What is the relationship between f and g as x increases without bound?

76. Think About It   Which functions are exponential? Explain.

(a) $3x$ (b) $3x^2$ (c) 3^x (d) 2^{-x}

Review

In Exercises 77–80, determine whether the function has an inverse function. If it does, find f^{-1}.

77. $f(x) = 5x - 7$ **78.** $f(x) = -\frac{2}{3}x + \frac{5}{2}$

79. $f(x) = \sqrt[3]{x + 8}$ **80.** $f(x) = \sqrt{x^2 + 6}$

In Exercises 81 and 82, sketch the graph of the rational function.

81. $f(x) = \dfrac{2x}{x - 7}$ **82.** $f(x) = \dfrac{x^2 + 3}{x + 1}$

4.2   Logarithmic Functions and Their Graphs

Logarithmic Functions

In Section 1.7, you studied the concept of an inverse function. There, you learned that if a function is one-to-one—that is, if the function has the property such that no horizontal line intersects its graph more than once—the function must have an inverse function. By looking back at the graphs of the exponential functions introduced in Section 4.1, you will see that every function of the form

$$f(x) = a^x, \quad a > 0, a \neq 1$$

passes the Horizontal Line Test and therefore must have an inverse function. This inverse function is called the **logarithmic function with base a.**

> **Definition of Logarithmic Function**
>
> For $x > 0$, $a > 0$, and $a \neq 1$,
>
> $$y = \log_a x \quad \text{if and only if} \quad x = a^y.$$
>
> The function given by
>
> $$f(x) = \log_a x \qquad \text{Read as "log base } a \text{ of } x\text{."}$$
>
> is called the **logarithmic function with base a.**

The equations

$$y = \log_a x \quad \text{and} \quad x = a^y$$

are equivalent. The first equation is in logarithmic form and the second is in exponential form.

When evaluating logarithms, remember that *a logarithm is an exponent.* This means that $\log_a x$ is the exponent to which a must be raised to obtain x. For instance, $\log_2 8 = 3$ because 2 must be raised to the third power to get 8.

Example 1   Evaluating Logarithms

Use the definition of logarithmic function to evaluate each logarithm at the indicated value of x.

a. $f(x) = \log_2 x, \ x = 32$ **b.** $f(x) = \log_3 x, \ x = 1$
c. $f(x) = \log_4 x, \ x = 2$ **d.** $f(x) = \log_{10} x, \ x = \frac{1}{100}$

Solution

a. $f(32) = \log_2 32 = 5$ because $2^5 = 32$.
b. $f(1) = \log_3 1 = 0$ because $3^0 = 1$.
c. $f(2) = \log_4 2 = \frac{1}{2}$ because $4^{1/2} = \sqrt{4} = 2$.
d. $f\left(\frac{1}{100}\right) = \log_{10} \frac{1}{100} = -2$ because $10^{-2} = \frac{1}{10^2} = \frac{1}{100}$.

✓ *Checkpoint* Now try Exercise 17.

What you should learn

● Recognize and evaluate logarithmic functions with base a.
● Graph logarithmic functions.
● Recognize, evaluate, and graph natural logarithmic functions.
● Use logarithmic functions to model and solve real-life problems.

Why you should learn it

Logarithmic functions are useful in modeling data that represents quantities that increase or decrease slowly. For instance, Exercise 76 on page 341 shows how to use a logarithmic function to model the minimum required ventilation rates in public school classrooms.

Mark Richards/PhotoEdit

TECHNOLOGY TIP   The logarithmic function with base 10 is called the **common logarithmic function.** On most calculators, this function is denoted by $\boxed{\text{LOG}}$. Example 2 shows how to use a calculator to evaluate common logarithmic functions. You will learn how to use a calculator to calculate logarithms to any base in the next section.

Example 2   Evaluating Common Logarithms on a Calculator

Use a calculator to evaluate the function $f(x) = \log_{10} x$ at each value of x.

a. $x = 10$ **b.** $x = 2.5$ **c.** $x = -2$ **d.** $x = \frac{1}{4}$

Solution

Function Value	Graphing Calculator Keystrokes	Display
a. $f(10) = \log_{10} 10$	$\boxed{\text{LOG}}$ 10 $\boxed{\text{ENTER}}$	1
b. $f(2.5) = \log_{10} 2.5$	$\boxed{\text{LOG}}$ 2.5 $\boxed{\text{ENTER}}$	0.3979400
c. $f(-2) = \log_{10}(-2)$	$\boxed{\text{LOG}}$ $\boxed{(-)}$ 2 $\boxed{\text{ENTER}}$	ERROR
d. $f\left(\frac{1}{4}\right) = \log_{10} \frac{1}{4}$	$\boxed{\text{LOG}}$ $\boxed{(}$ 1 $\boxed{\div}$ 4 $\boxed{)}$ $\boxed{\text{ENTER}}$	−0.6020600

Note that the calculator displays an error message when you try to evaluate $\log_{10}(-2)$. The reason for this is that the domain of every logarithmic function is the set of *positive* real numbers. In this case, there is no *real* power to which 10 can be raised to obtain -2.

 Checkpoint   Now try Exercise 21.

TECHNOLOGY TIP

Some graphing utilities do not give an error message for $\log_{10}(-2)$. Instead, the graphing utility will display a complex number. For the purpose of this text, however, it will be said that the domain of a logarithmic function is the set of positive *real* numbers.

The following properties follow directly from the definition of the logarithmic function with base a.

Properties of Logarithms

1. $\log_a 1 = 0$ because $a^0 = 1$.

2. $\log_a a = 1$ because $a^1 = a$.

3. $\log_a a^x = x$ and $a^{\log_a x} = x$.   Inverse Properties

4. If $\log_a x = \log_a y$, then $x = y$.   One-to-One Property

---

Example 3   Using Properties of Logarithms

a. Solve for x: $\log_2 x = \log_2 3$ **b.** Solve for x: $\log_4 4 = x$

c. Simplify: $\log_5 5^x$ **d.** Simplify: $7^{\log_7 14}$

Solution

a. Using the One-to-One Property (Property 4), you can conclude that $x = 3$.

b. Using Property 2, you can conclude that $x = 1$.

c. Using the Inverse Property (Property 3), it follows that $\log_5 5^x = x$.

d. Using the Inverse Property (Property 3), it follows that $7^{\log_7 14} = 14$.

 Checkpoint   Now try Exercise 25.

Graphs of Logarithmic Functions

To sketch the graph of $y = \log_a x$, you can use the fact that the graphs of inverse functions are reflections of each other in the line $y = x$.

Example 4   Graphs of Exponential and Logarithmic Functions

In the same coordinate plane, sketch the graph of each function by hand.

a. $f(x) = 2^x$ **b.** $g(x) = \log_2 x$

Solution

a. For $f(x) = 2^x$, construct a table of values. By plotting these points and connecting them with a smooth curve, you obtain the graph of f shown in Figure 4.18.

x	-2	-1	0	1	2	3
$f(x) = 2^x$	$\frac{1}{4}$	$\frac{1}{2}$	1	2	4	8

b. Because $g(x) = \log_2 x$ is the inverse function of $f(x) = 2^x$, the graph of g is obtained by plotting the points $(f(x), x)$ and connecting them with a smooth curve. The graph of g is a reflection of the graph of f in the line $y = x$, as shown in Figure 4.18.

✓ *Checkpoint* Now try Exercise 35.

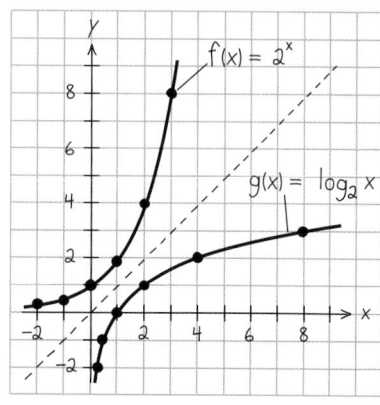

Figure 4.18

Before you can confirm the result of Example 4 using a graphing utility, you need to know how to enter $\log_2 x$. You will learn how to do this using the *change-of-base formula* discussed in Section 4.3.

Example 5   Sketching the Graph of a Logarithmic Function

Sketch the graph of the common logarithmic function $f(x) = \log_{10} x$ by hand.

Solution

Begin by constructing a table of values. Note that some of the values can be obtained without a calculator by using the Inverse Property of Logarithms. Others require a calculator. Next, plot the points and connect them with a smooth curve, as shown in Figure 4.19.

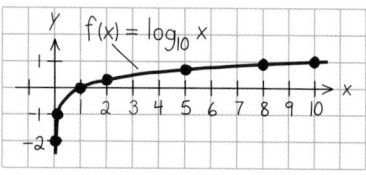

Figure 4.19

x	Without Calculator				With Calculator		
	$\frac{1}{100}$	$\frac{1}{10}$	1	10	2	5	8
$f(x) = \log_{10} x$	-2	-1	0	1	0.301	0.699	0.903

✓ *Checkpoint* Now try Exercise 41.

The nature of the graph in Figure 4.19 is typical of functions of the form $f(x) = \log_a x$, $a > 1$. They have one x-intercept and one vertical asymptote. Notice how slowly the graph rises for $x > 1$.

STUDY TIP

In Example 5, you can also sketch the graph of $f(x) = \log_{10} x$ by evaluating the inverse function of f, $g(x) = 10^x$, for several values of x. Plot the points, sketch the graph of g, and then reflect the graph in the line $y = x$ to obtain the graph of f.

Library of Functions: Logarithmic Function

The *logarithmic function*

$$f(x) = \log_a x, \quad a > 0, \ a \neq 1$$

is the inverse function of the exponential function. Its domain is the set of positive real numbers and its range is the set of all real numbers. This is the opposite of the exponential function. Moreover, the logarithmic function has the *y*-axis as a vertical asymptote, whereas the exponential function has the *x*-axis as a horizontal asymptote. Many real-life phenomena with a slow rate of growth can be modeled by logarithmic functions. The basic characteristics of the logarithmic function are summarized below.

Graph of $f(x) = \log_a x, \ a > 1$

Domain: $(0, \infty)$

Range: $(-\infty, \infty)$

Intercept: $(1, 0)$

Increasing on $(0, \infty)$

y-axis is a vertical asymptote
$(\log_a x \to -\infty \text{ as } x \to 0^+)$

Continuous

Reflection of graph of $f(x) = a^x$
in the line $y = x$

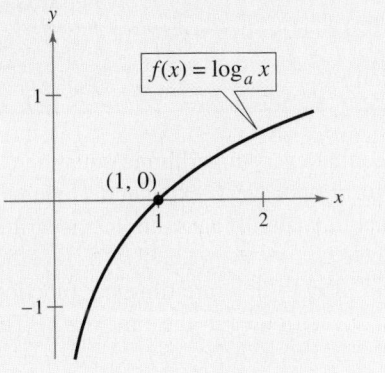

Exploration

Use a graphing utility to graph $y = \log_{10} x$ and $y = 8$ in the same viewing window. Find a viewing window that shows the point of intersection. What is the point of intersection? Use the point of intersection to complete the equation below.

$$\log_{10} \boxed{} = 8$$

Example 6 Transformations of Graphs of Logarithmic Functions

Each of the following functions is a transformation of the graph of $f(x) = \log_{10} x$.

a. Because $g(x) = \log_{10}(x - 1) = f(x - 1)$, the graph of g can be obtained by shifting the graph of f one unit to the *right*, as shown in Figure 4.20.

b. Because $h(x) = 2 + \log_{10} x = 2 + f(x)$, the graph of h can be obtained by shifting the graph of f two units *upward*, as shown in Figure 4.21.

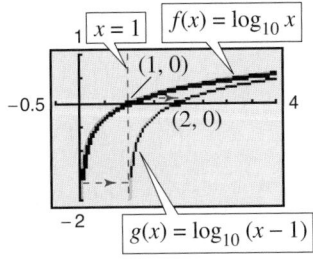

Figure 4.20

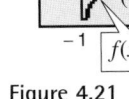

Figure 4.21

Notice that the transformation in Figure 4.21 keeps the *y*-axis as a vertical asymptote, but the transformation in Figure 4.20 yields the new vertical asymptote $x = 1$.

✓ *Checkpoint* Now try Exercise 49.

TECHNOLOGY TIP

When a graphing utility graphs a logarithmic function, it may appear that the graph has an endpoint. Recall from Section 1.1 that this is because some graphing utilities have a limited resolution. So, in this text a blue or light red curve is placed behind the graphing utility's display to indicate where the graph should appear.

The Natural Logarithmic Function

By looking back at the graph of the natural exponential function introduced in Section 4.1, you will see that $f(x) = e^x$ is one-to-one and so has an inverse function. This inverse function is called the **natural logarithmic function** and is denoted by the special symbol ln x, read as "the natural log of x" or "el en of x."

> **The Natural Logarithmic Function**
>
> For $x > 0$,
>
> $\quad y = \ln x$ if and only if $x = e^y$.
>
> The function given by
>
> $\quad f(x) = \log_e x = \ln x$
>
> is called the **natural logarithmic function.**

From the above definition, you can see that every logarithmic equation can be written in an equivalent exponential form and every exponential equation can be written in logarithmic form. Note that the natural logarithm ln x is written without a base. The base is understood to be e.

Because the functions $f(x) = e^x$ and $g(x) = \ln x$ are inverse functions of each other, their graphs are reflections of each other in the line $y = x$. This reflective property is illustrated in Figure 4.22.

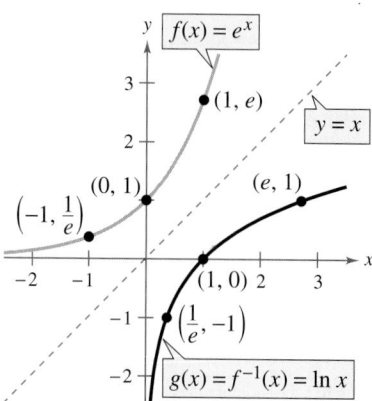

Reflection of graph of $f(x) = e^x$ in the line $y = x$

Figure 4.22

Example 7 Evaluating the Natural Logarithmic Function

Use a calculator to evaluate the function $f(x) = \ln x$ at each indicated value of x.

a. $x = 2$ **b.** $x = 0.3$ **c.** $x = -1$

Solution

Function Value	Graphing Calculator Keystrokes	Display
a. $f(2) = \ln 2$	LN 2 ENTER	0.6931472
b. $f(0.3) = \ln 0.3$	LN .3 ENTER	-1.2039728
c. $f(-1) = \ln(-1)$	LN (−) 1 ENTER	ERROR

✓ *Checkpoint* Now try Exercise 53.

The four properties of logarithms listed on page 333 are also valid for natural logarithms.

> **Properties of Natural Logarithms**
>
> **1.** $\ln 1 = 0$ because $e^0 = 1$.
>
> **2.** $\ln e = 1$ because $e^1 = e$.
>
> **3.** $\ln e^x = x$ and $e^{\ln x} = x$. Inverse Properties
>
> **4.** If $\ln x = \ln y$, then $x = y$. One-to-One Property

TECHNOLOGY TIP

On most calculators, the natural logarithm is denoted by LN, as illustrated in Example 7.

STUDY TIP

In Example 7(c), be sure you see that $\ln(-1)$ gives an error message on most calculators. This occurs because the domain of ln x is the set of *positive* real numbers (see Figure 4.22). So, $\ln(-1)$ is undefined.

Example 8   Using Properties of Natural Logarithms

Use the properties of natural logarithms to rewrite each expression.

a. $\ln \dfrac{1}{e}$ **b.** $e^{\ln 5}$ **c.** $\ln e^0$ **d.** $2 \ln e$

Solution

a. $\ln \dfrac{1}{e} = \ln e^{-1} = -1$ Inverse Property   **b.** $e^{\ln 5} = 5$ Inverse Property

c. $\ln e^0 = \ln 1 = 0$ Property 1   **d.** $2 \ln e = 2(1) = 2$ Property 2

 Checkpoint Now try Exercise 57.

Example 9   Finding the Domains of Logarithmic Functions

Find the domain of each function.

a. $f(x) = \ln(x - 2)$ **b.** $g(x) = \ln(2 - x)$ **c.** $h(x) = \ln x^2$

Algebraic Solution

a. Because $\ln(x - 2)$ is defined only if

$$x - 2 > 0,$$

it follows that the domain of f is $(2, \infty)$.

b. Because $\ln(2 - x)$ is defined only if

$$2 - x > 0,$$

it follows that the domain of g is $(-\infty, 2)$.

c. Because $\ln x^2$ is defined only if

$$x^2 > 0,$$

it follows that the domain of h is all real numbers except $x = 0$.

Graphical Solution

Use a graphing utility to graph each function using an appropriate viewing window. Then use the *trace* feature to determine the domain of each function.

a. From Figure 4.23, you can see that the x-coordinates of the points on the graph appear to extend from the right of 2 to $+\infty$. So, you can estimate the domain to be $(2, \infty)$.

b. From Figure 4.24, you can see that the x-coordinates of the points on the graph appear to extend from $-\infty$ to the left of 2. So, you can estimate the domain to be $(-\infty, 2)$.

c. From Figure 4.25, you can see that the x-coordinates of the points on the graph appear to include all real numbers except $x = 0$. So, you can estimate the domain to be all real numbers except $x = 0$.

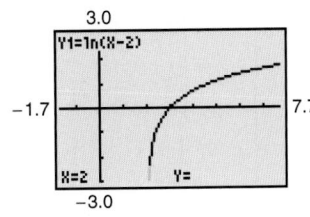

Figure 4.23

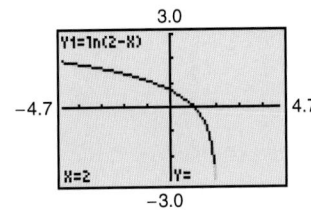

Figure 4.24

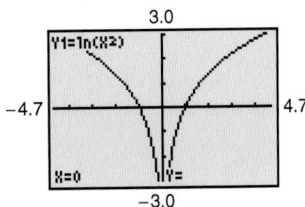

Figure 4.25

 Checkpoint Now try Exercise 61.

In Example 9, suppose you had been asked to analyze the function $h(x) = \ln|x - 2|$. How would the domain of this function compare with the domains of the functions given in parts (a) and (b) of the example?

Application

Logarithmic functions are used to model many situations in real life, as shown in the next example.

Example 10   Human Memory Model

Students participating in a psychology experiment attended several lectures on a subject and were given an exam. Every month for a year after the exam, the students were retested to see how much of the material they remembered. The average scores for the group are given by the *human memory model*

$$f(t) = 75 - 6 \ln(t + 1), \quad 0 \le t \le 12$$

where t is the time in months.

a. What was the average score on the original ($t = 0$) exam?

b. What was the average score at the end of $t = 2$ months?

c. What was the average score at the end of $t = 6$ months?

TECHNOLOGY SUPPORT

For instructions on how to use the *value* feature and the *zoom* and *trace* features, see Appendix A; for specific keystrokes, go to the text website at *college.hmco.com*.

Algebraic Solution

a. The original average score was

$$f(0) = 75 - 6 \ln(0 + 1)$$
$$= 75 - 6 \ln 1$$
$$= 75 - 6(0)$$
$$= 75.$$

b. After 2 months, the average score was

$$f(2) = 75 - 6 \ln(2 + 1)$$
$$= 75 - 6 \ln 3$$
$$\approx 75 - 6(1.0986)$$
$$\approx 68.4.$$

c. After 6 months, the average score was

$$f(6) = 75 - 6 \ln(6 + 1)$$
$$= 75 - 6 \ln 7$$
$$\approx 75 - 6(1.9459)$$
$$\approx 63.3.$$

Graphical Solution

Use a graphing utility to graph the model $y = 75 - 6 \ln(x + 1)$. Then use the *value* or *trace* feature to approximate the following.

a. When $x = 0$, $y = 75$ (see Figure 4.26). So, the original average score was 75.

b. When $x = 2$, $y \approx 68.4$ (see Figure 4.27). So, the average score after 2 months was about 68.4.

c. When $x = 6$, $y \approx 63.3$ (see Figure 4.28). So, the average score after 6 months was about 63.3.

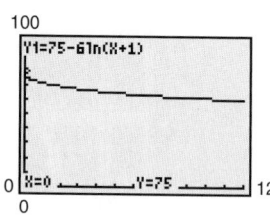

Figure 4.26

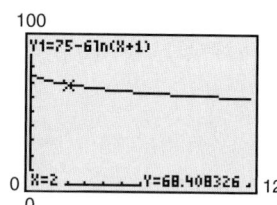

Figure 4.27

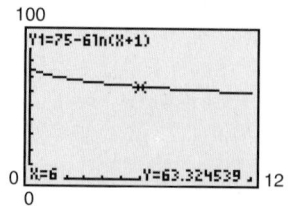

Figure 4.28

✓ *Checkpoint* Now try Exercise 69.

4.2   Exercises

Vocabulary Check

Fill in the blanks.

1. The inverse function of the exponential function $f(x) = a^x$ is called the _____ with base a.

2. The common logarithmic function has base _____ .

3. The logarithmic function $f(x) = \ln x$ is called the _____ function.

4. The inverse property of logarithms states that $\log_a a^x = x$ and _____ .

5. The one-to-one property of natural logarithms states that if $\ln x = \ln y$, then _____ .

In Exercises 1–8, write the logarithmic equation in exponential form. For example, the exponential form of $\log_5 25 = 2$ is $5^2 = 25$.

1. $\log_4 64 = 3$ 2. $\log_3 81 = 4$

3. $\log_7 \frac{1}{49} = -2$ 4. $\log_{10} \frac{1}{1000} = -3$

5. $\log_{32} 4 = \frac{2}{5}$ 6. $\log_{16} 8 = \frac{3}{4}$

7. $\ln 1 = 0$ 8. $\ln 4 = 1.386 . . .$

In Exercises 9–16, write the exponential equation in logarithmic form. For example, the logarithmic form of $2^3 = 8$ is $\log_2 8 = 3$.

9. $5^3 = 125$ 10. $8^2 = 64$

11. $81^{1/4} = 3$ 12. $9^{3/2} = 27$

13. $6^{-2} = \frac{1}{36}$ 14. $10^{-3} = 0.001$

15. $e^3 = 20.0855 . . .$ 16. $e^x = 4$

In Exercises 17–20, evaluate the function at the indicated value of x without using a calculator.

Function	*Value*
17. $f(x) = \log_2 x$	$x = 16$
18. $f(x) = \log_{16} x$	$x = \frac{1}{4}$
19. $g(x) = \log_{10} x$	$x = 0.01$
20. $g(x) = \log_{10} x$	$x = 10$

In Exercises 21–24, use a calculator to evaluate the function at the indicated value of x. Round your result to three decimal places.

Function	*Value*
21. $f(x) = \log_{10} x$	$x = 345$
22. $f(x) = \log_{10} x$	$x = \frac{4}{5}$

Function	*Value*
23. $h(x) = 6 \log_{10} x$	$x = 14.8$
24. $h(x) = 1.9 \log_{10} x$	$x = 4.3$

In Exercises 25–30, solve the equation for x.

25. $\log_7 x = \log_7 9$ 26. $\log_5 5 = x$

27. $\log_6 6^2 = x$ 28. $\log_2 2^{-1} = x$

29. $\log_8 x = \log_8 10^{-1}$ 30. $\log_3 4^3 = x$

In Exercises 31–34, describe the relationship between the graphs of f and g.

31. $f(x) = 3^x$ 32. $f(x) = 5^x$

    $g(x) = \log_3 x$ $g(x) = \log_5 x$

33. $f(x) = e^x$ 34. $f(x) = 10^x$

    $g(x) = \ln x$ $g(x) = \log_{10} x$

In Exercises 35–44, find the domain, vertical asymptote, and x-intercept of the logarithmic function, and sketch its graph by hand. Verify using a graphing utility.

35. $f(x) = \log_4 x$

36. $g(x) = \log_6 x$

37. $f(x) = \log_{10} \left(\dfrac{x}{5} \right)$

38. $g(x) = \log_2(-x)$

39. $h(x) = \log_4(x - 3)$

40. $f(x) = -\log_6(x + 2)$

41. $y = -\log_{10} x + 2$

42. $y = \log_{10}(x - 1) + 4$

43. $f(x) = 6 + \log_6(x - 3)$

44. $f(x) = -\log_3(x + 2) - 4$

In Exercises 45–48, use the graph of $y = \log_3 x$ to match the function with its graph. [The graphs are labeled (a), (b), (c), and (d).]

(a)

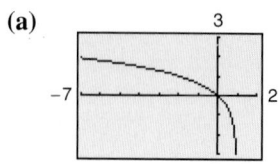

(b)

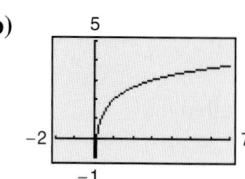

(c)

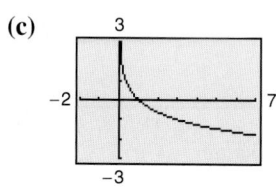

(d)

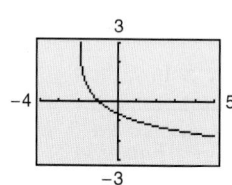

45. $f(x) = \log_3 x + 2$

46. $f(x) = -\log_3 x$

47. $f(x) = -\log_3(x + 2)$

48. $f(x) = \log_3(1 - x)$

In Exercises 49–52, use the graph of f to describe the transformation that yields the graph of g.

49. $f(x) = \log_{10} x, \quad g(x) = -\log_{10} x$

50. $f(x) = \log_{10} x, \quad g(x) = \log_{10}(x + 7)$

51. $f(x) = \log_2 x, \quad g(x) = 4 - \log_2 x$

52. $f(x) = \log_2 x, \quad g(x) = 3 + \log_2 x$

In Exercises 53–56, use a calculator to evaluate the function at the indicated value of x. Round your result to three decimal places.

Function	Value
53. $f(x) = \ln x$	$x = \sqrt{42}$
54. $f(x) = \ln x$	$x = 18.31$
55. $f(x) = -\ln x$	$x = \frac{1}{2}$
56. $f(x) = 3 \ln x$	$x = 0.75$

In Exercises 57–60, use the properties of natural logarithms to rewrite the expression.

57. $\ln e^2$

58. $-\ln e$

59. $e^{\ln 1.8}$

60. $7 \ln e^0$

In Exercises 61–64, use a graphing utility to graph the logarithmic function. Determine the domain and identify any vertical asymptote and x-intercept.

61. $f(x) = \ln(x - 1)$

62. $h(x) = \ln(x + 1)$

63. $g(x) = \ln(-x)$

64. $f(x) = \ln(3 - x)$

In Exercises 65–68, (a) use a graphing utility to graph the function, (b) find the domain, (c) use the graph to find the open intervals on which the function is increasing and decreasing, and (d) approximate any relative maximum or minimum values of the function.

65. $f(x) = \dfrac{x}{2} - \ln \dfrac{x}{4}$

66. $g(x) = \dfrac{12 \ln x}{x}$

67. $h(x) = 4x \ln x$

68. $f(x) = \dfrac{x}{\ln x}$

69. *Human Memory Model* Students in a mathematics class were given an exam and then tested monthly with an equivalent exam. The average scores for the class are given by the human memory model

$$f(t) = 80 - 17 \log_{10}(t + 1), \quad 0 \le t \le 12$$

where t is the time in months.

(a) What was the average score on the original exam $(t = 0)$?

(b) What was the average score after 4 months?

(c) What was the average score after 10 months?

(d) Verify your answers in parts (a), (b), and (c) using a graphing utility.

70. *Data Analysis* The table shows the temperatures T (in °F) at which water boils at selected pressures p (in pounds per square inch). (Source: Standard Handbook of Mechanical Engineers)

Pressure, p	Temperature, T
5	162.24°
10	193.21°
14.696 (1 atm)	212.00°
20	227.96°
30	250.33°
40	267.25°
60	292.71°
80	312.03°
100	327.81°

A model that approximates this data is given by

$$T = 87.97 + 34.96 \ln p + 7.91 \sqrt{p}.$$

(a) Use a graphing utility to plot the data and graph the model in the same viewing window. How well does the model fit the data?

(b) Use the graph to estimate the pressure required for the boiling point of water to exceed 300°F.

(c) Calculate T when the pressure is 74 pounds per square inch. Verify your answer graphically.

71. *Compound Interest*   A principal P, invested at $5\frac{1}{2}\%$ and compounded continuously, increases to an amount K times the original principal after t years, where $t = (\ln K)/0.055$.

(a) Complete the table and interpret your results.

K	1	2	4	6	8	10	12
t							

(b) Use a graphing utility to graph the function.

72. *Population*   The time t in years for the world population to double if it is increasing at a continuous rate of r is given by

$$t = \frac{\ln 2}{r}.$$

(a) Complete the table and interpret your results.

r	0.005	0.010	0.015	0.020	0.025	0.030
t						

(b) Use a graphing utility to graph the function.

73. *Sound Intensity*   The relationship between the number of decibels β and the intensity of a sound I in watts per square meter is given by

$$\beta = 10 \log_{10}\left(\frac{I}{10^{-12}}\right).$$

(a) Determine the number of decibels of a sound with an intensity of 1 watt per square meter.

(b) Determine the number of decibels of a sound with an intensity of 10^{-2} watt per square meter.

(c) The intensity of the sound in part (a) is 100 times as great as that in part (b). Is the number of decibels 100 times as great? Explain.

74. *Home Mortgage*   The model

$$t = 16.625 \ln\left(\frac{x}{x-750}\right), \quad x > 750$$

approximates the length of a home mortgage of $150,000 at 6% in terms of the monthly payment. In

the model, t is the length of the mortgage in years and x is the monthly payment in dollars.

(a) Use the model to approximate the length of a $150,000 mortgage at 6% when the monthly payment is $897.72 and when the monthly payment is $1659.24.

(b) Approximate the total amount paid over the term of the mortgage with a monthly payment of $897.72 and with a monthly payment of $1659.24. What amount of the total is interest costs for each payment?

Ventilation Rates   **In Exercises 75 and 76, use the model**

$$y = 80.4 - 11 \ln x, \quad 100 \le x \le 1500$$

which approximates the minimum required ventilation rate in terms of the air space per child in a public school classroom. In the model, x is the air space per child (in cubic feet) and y is the ventilation rate per child (in cubic feet per minute).

75. Use a graphing utility to graph the function and approximate the required ventilation rate when there is 300 cubic feet of air space per child.

76. A classroom is designed for 30 students. The air-conditioning system in the room has the capacity to move 450 cubic feet of air per minute.

(a) Determine the ventilation rate per child, assuming that the room is filled to capacity.

(b) Use the graph in Exercise 75 to estimate the air space required per child.

(c) Determine the minimum number of square feet of floor space required for the room if the ceiling height is 30 feet.

Synthesis

True or False?   **In Exercises 77 and 78, determine whether the statement is true or false. Justify your answer.**

77. You can determine the graph of $f(x) = \log_6 x$ by graphing $g(x) = 6^x$ and reflecting it about the x-axis.

78. The graph of $f(x) = \log_3 x$ contains the point $(27, 3)$.

79. *Writing*   Explain why $\log_a x$ is defined only for $0 < a < 1$ and $a > 1$.

80. *Graphical Analysis* Use a graphing utility to graph *f* and *g* in the same viewing window and determine which is increasing at the greater rate as *x* approaches $+\infty$. What can you conclude about the rate of growth of the natural logarithmic function?

(a) $f(x) = \ln x, \quad g(x) = \sqrt{x}$

(b) $f(x) = \ln x, \quad g(x) = \sqrt[4]{x}$

81. *Exploration* The following table of values was obtained by evaluating a function. Determine which of the statements may be true and which must be false.

x	1	2	8
y	0	1	3

(a) *y* is an exponential function of *x*.

(b) *y* is a logarithmic function of *x*.

(c) *x* is an exponential function of *y*.

(d) *y* is a linear function of *x*.

82. *Pattern Recognition*

(a) Use a graphing utility to compare the graph of the function $y = \ln x$ with the graph of each function.

$$y_1 = x - 1, \ y_2 = (x - 1) - \tfrac{1}{2}(x - 1)^2,$$

$$y_3 = (x - 1) - \tfrac{1}{2}(x - 1)^2 + \tfrac{1}{3}(x - 1)^3$$

(b) Identify the pattern of successive polynomials given in part (a). Extend the pattern one more term and compare the graph of the resulting polynomial function with the graph of $y = \ln x$. What do you think the pattern implies?

83. *Numerical and Graphical Analysis*

(a) Use a graphing utility to complete the table for the function

$$f(x) = \frac{\ln x}{x}.$$

x	1	5	10	10²	10⁴	10⁶
f(x)						

(b) Use the table in part (a) to determine what value $f(x)$ approaches as *x* increases without bound.

(c) Use a graphing utility to confirm the result of part (b).

84. *Writing* Use a graphing utility to determine how many months it would take for the average score in Example 10 to decrease to 60. Explain your method of solving the problem. Describe another way that you can use a graphing utility to determine the answer. Also, make a statement about the general shape of the model. Would a student forget more quickly soon after the test or as time passes? Explain your reasoning.

Review

In Exercises 85–92, factor the polynomial.

85. $x^2 + 2x - 3$

86. $2x^2 + 3x - 5$

87. $12x^2 + 5x - 3$

88. $16x^2 + 16x + 7$

89. $16x^2 - 25$

90. $36x^2 - 49$

91. $2x^3 + x^2 - 45x$

92. $3x^2 - 5x^2 - 12x$

In Exercises 93–96, evaluate the function for $f(x) = 3x + 2$ and $g(x) = x^3 - 1$.

93. $(f + g)(2)$

94. $(f - g)(-1)$

95. $(fg)(6)$

96. $\left(\dfrac{f}{g}\right)(0)$

In Exercises 97–100, solve the equation graphically.

97. $5x - 7 = x + 4$

98. $-2x + 3 = 8x$

99. $\sqrt{3x - 2} = 9$

100. $\sqrt{x - 11} = x + 2$

In Exercises 101–106, find the vertical and horizontal asymptotes of the rational function.

101. $f(x) = \dfrac{4}{-8 - x}$

102. $f(x) = \dfrac{2x^3 - 3}{x^2}$

103. $f(x) = \dfrac{x + 5}{2x^2 + x - 15}$

104. $f(x) = \dfrac{2x^2(x - 5)}{x - 7}$

105. $g(x) = \dfrac{x^2 - 4}{x^2 - 4x - 12}$

106. $g(x) = \dfrac{x^2 + 3x}{2x^2 + 3x - 2}$

4.3 Properties of Logarithms

Change of Base

What you should learn

● Rewrite logarithms with different bases.
● Use properties of logarithms to evaluate or rewrite logarithmic expressions.
● Use properties of logarithms to expand or condense logarithmic expressions.
● Use logarithmic functions to model and solve real-life problems.

Most calculators have only two types of log keys, one for common logarithms (base 10) and one for natural logarithms (base e). Although common logs and natural logs are the most frequently used, you may occasionally need to evaluate logarithms to other bases. To do this, you can use the following **change-of-base formula.**

Why you should learn it

Logarithmic functions can be used to model and solve real-life problems, such as the human memory model in Exercise 82 on page 348.

Gary Conner/PhotoEdit

Change-of-Base Formula

Let a, b, and x be positive real numbers such that $a \neq 1$ and $b \neq 1$. Then $\log_a x$ can be converted to a different base using any of the following formulas.

Base b	Base 10	Base e
$\log_a x = \dfrac{\log_b x}{\log_b a}$	$\log_a x = \dfrac{\log_{10} x}{\log_{10} a}$	$\log_a x = \dfrac{\ln x}{\ln a}$

One way to look at the change-of-base formula is that logarithms to base a are simply *constant multiples* of logarithms to base b. The constant multiplier is $1/(\log_b a)$.

Example 1   Changing Bases Using Common Logarithms

a. $\log_4 25 = \dfrac{\log_{10} 25}{\log_{10} 4}$ $\log_a x = \dfrac{\log_{10} x}{\log_{10} a}$

$\approx \dfrac{1.39794}{0.60206} \approx 2.3219$ Use a calculator.

b. $\log_2 12 = \dfrac{\log_{10} 12}{\log_{10} 2} \approx \dfrac{1.07918}{0.30103} \approx 3.5850$

✓ *Checkpoint* Now try Exercise 9.

Example 2   Changing Bases Using Natural Logarithms

a. $\log_4 25 = \dfrac{\ln 25}{\ln 4}$ $\log_a x = \dfrac{\ln x}{\ln a}$

$\approx \dfrac{3.21888}{1.38629} \approx 2.3219$ Use a calculator.

b. $\log_2 12 = \dfrac{\ln 12}{\ln 2} \approx \dfrac{2.48491}{0.69315} \approx 3.5850$

✓ *Checkpoint* Now try Exercise 11.

STUDY TIP

Notice in Examples 1 and 2 that the result is the same whether common logarithms or natural logarithms are used in the change-of-base formula.

Properties of Logarithms

You know from the previous section that the logarithmic function with base a is the *inverse function* of the exponential function with base a. So, it makes sense that the properties of exponents (see Section 4.1) should have corresponding properties involving logarithms. For instance, the exponential property $a^0 = 1$ has the corresponding logarithmic property $\log_a 1 = 0$.

Properties of Logarithms

Let a be a positive number such that $a \neq 1$, and let n be a real number. If u and v are positive real numbers, the following properties are true.

Logarithm with Base a	*Natural Logarithm*
1. $\log_a(uv) = \log_a u + \log_a v$	**1.** $\ln(uv) = \ln u + \ln v$
2. $\log_a \dfrac{u}{v} = \log_a u - \log_a v$	**2.** $\ln \dfrac{u}{v} = \ln u - \ln v$
3. $\log_a u^n = n \log_a u$	**3.** $\ln u^n = n \ln u$

STUDY TIP

There is no general property that can be used to rewrite $\log_a(u \pm v)$. Specifically, $\log_a(x + y)$ is *not* equal to $\log_a x + \log_a y$.

See Appendix B for a proof of Property 1.

Example 3   Using Properties of Logarithms

Write each logarithm in terms of $\ln 2$ and $\ln 3$.

a. $\ln 6$ **b.** $\ln \dfrac{2}{27}$

Solution

a. $\ln 6 = \ln(2 \cdot 3)$ Rewrite 6 as $2 \cdot 3$.

  $= \ln 2 + \ln 3$ Property 1

b. $\ln \dfrac{2}{27} = \ln 2 - \ln 27$ Property 2

  $= \ln 2 - \ln 3^3$ Rewrite 27 as 3^3.

  $= \ln 2 - 3 \ln 3$ Property 3

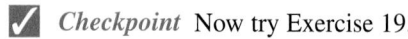 *Checkpoint* Now try Exercise 19.

Example 4   Using Properties of Logarithms

Use the properties of logarithms to verify that $-\log_{10} \frac{1}{100} = \log_{10} 100$.

Solution

$-\log_{10} \frac{1}{100} = -\log_{10}(100^{-1})$ Rewrite $\frac{1}{100}$ as 100^{-1}.

$= -(-1)\log_{10} 100 = \log_{10} 100$ Property 3 and simplify.

 Checkpoint Now try Exercise 21.

Rewriting Logarithmic Expressions

The properties of logarithms are useful for rewriting logarithmic expressions in forms that simplify the operations of algebra. This is true because they convert complicated products, quotients, and exponential forms into simpler sums, differences, and products, respectively.

Example 5   Expanding Logarithmic Expressions

Use the properties of logarithms to expand each expression.

a. $\log_4 5x^3y$ **b.** $\ln \dfrac{\sqrt{3x-5}}{7}$

Solution

a. $\log_4 5x^3y = \log_4 5 + \log_4 x^3 + \log_4 y$ Property 1

$\qquad\qquad = \log_4 5 + 3 \log_4 x + \log_4 y$ Property 3

b. $\ln \dfrac{\sqrt{3x-5}}{7} = \ln\left[\dfrac{(3x-5)^{1/2}}{7}\right]$ Rewrite rational exponent.

$\qquad\qquad = \ln(3x-5)^{1/2} - \ln 7$ Property 2

$\qquad\qquad = \tfrac{1}{2}\ln(3x-5) - \ln 7$ Property 3

✓ *Checkpoint* Now try Exercise 39.

In Example 5, the properties of logarithms were used to *expand* logarithmic expressions. In Example 6, this procedure is reversed and the properties of logarithms are used to *condense* logarithmic expressions.

> ### Exploration
>
> Use a graphing utility to graph the functions
>
> $$y = \ln x - \ln(x-3)$$
>
> and
>
> $$y = \ln \dfrac{x}{x-3}$$
>
> in the same viewing window. Does the graphing utility show the functions with the same domain? If so, should it? Explain your reasoning.

Example 6   Condensing Logarithmic Expressions

Use the properties of logarithms to condense each logarithmic expression.

a. $\tfrac{1}{2}\log_{10} x + 3 \log_{10}(x+1)$ **b.** $2 \ln(x+2) - \ln x$

c. $\tfrac{1}{3}[\log_2 x + \log_2(x-4)]$

Solution

a. $\tfrac{1}{2}\log_{10} x + 3 \log_{10}(x+1) = \log_{10} x^{1/2} + \log_{10}(x+1)^3$ Property 3

$\qquad\qquad\qquad = \log_{10}\left[\sqrt{x}(x+1)^3\right]$ Property 1

b. $2 \ln(x+2) - \ln x = \ln(x+2)^2 - \ln x$ Property 3

$\qquad\qquad = \ln \dfrac{(x+2)^2}{x}$ Property 2

c. $\tfrac{1}{3}[\log_2 x + \log_2(x-4)] = \tfrac{1}{3}\{\log_2[x(x-4)]\}$ Property 1

$\qquad\qquad = \log_2[x(x-4)]^{1/3} = \log_2 \sqrt[3]{x(x-4)}$ Property 3

✓ *Checkpoint* Now try Exercise 57.

Example 7   Finding a Mathematical Model

The table shows the mean distance from the sun x and the period (the time it takes a planet to orbit the sun) y for each of the six planets that are closest to the sun. In the table, the mean distance is given in astronomical units (where the Earth's mean distance is defined as 1.0), and the period is given in years. Find an equation that relates y and x.

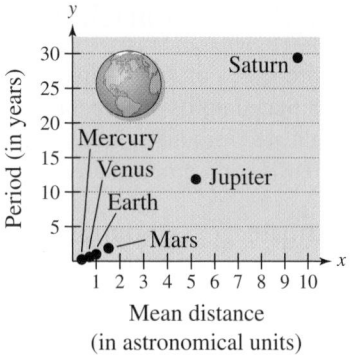

Figure 4.29

Planet	Mercury	Venus	Earth	Mars	Jupiter	Saturn
Mean distance, x	0.387	0.723	1.000	1.524	5.203	9.555
Period, y	0.241	0.615	1.000	1.881	11.860	29.420

Algebraic Solution

The points in the table are plotted in Figure 4.29. From this figure it is not clear how to find an equation that relates y and x. To solve this problem, take the natural log of each of the x- and y-values in the table. This produces the following results.

Planet	Mercury	Venus	Earth
$\ln x = X$	−0.949	−0.324	0.000
$\ln y = Y$	−1.423	−0.486	0.000

Planet	Mars	Jupiter	Saturn
$\ln x = X$	0.421	1.649	2.257
$\ln y = Y$	0.632	2.473	3.382

Now, by plotting the points in the table, you can see that all six of the points appear to lie in a line. Choose any two points to determine the slope of the line. Using the two points $(0.421, 0.632)$ and $(0, 0)$, you can determine that the slope of the line is

$$m = \frac{0.632 - 0}{0.421 - 0} \approx 1.5 = \frac{3}{2}.$$

By the point-slope form, the equation of the line is $Y = \frac{3}{2}X$, where $Y = \ln y$ and $X = \ln x$. You can therefore conclude that $\ln y = \frac{3}{2} \ln x$.

✓ *Checkpoint* Now try Exercise 83.

Graphical Solution

The points in the table are plotted in Figure 4.29. From this figure it is not clear how to find an equation that relates y and x. To solve this problem, take the natural log of each of the x- and y-values in the table. This produces the following results.

Planet	Mercury	Venus	Earth	Mars	Jupiter	Saturn
$\ln x = X$	−0.949	−0.324	0.000	0.421	1.649	2.257
$\ln y = Y$	−1.423	−0.486	0.000	0.632	2.473	3.382

Now, by plotting the points in the table, you can see that all six of the points appear to lie in a line, as shown in Figure 4.30. Using the *linear regression* feature of a graphing utility, you can find a linear model for the data, as shown in Figure 4.31. You can approximate this model to be $Y = 1.5X = \frac{3}{2}X$, where $Y = \ln y$ and $X = \ln x$. From the model, you can see that the slope of the line is $\frac{3}{2}$. So, you can conclude that $\ln y = \frac{3}{2} \ln x$.

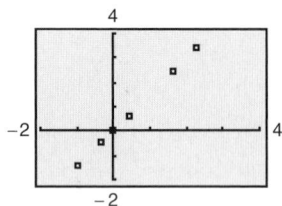

Figure 4.30

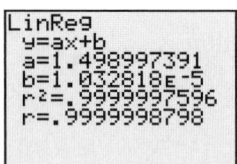

Figure 4.31

In Example 7, try to convert the final equation to $y = f(x)$ form. You will get a function of the form $y = ax^b$, which is called a *power model*.

4.3   Exercises

Vocabulary Check

Fill in the blanks.

1. To evaluate logarithms to any base, you can use the _____ formula.
2. The change-of-base formula for base e is given by $\log_a x = $ _____ .
3. _____ $= n \log_a u$
4. $\ln(uv) = $ _____

In Exercises 1–8, rewrite the logarithm as a ratio of (a) a common logarithm and (b) a natural logarithm.

1. $\log_5 x$
2. $\log_3 x$
3. $\log_{1/5} x$
4. $\log_{1/3} x$
5. $\log_a \frac{3}{10}$
6. $\log_a \frac{3}{4}$
7. $\log_{2.6} x$
8. $\log_{7.1} x$

In Exercises 9–16, evaluate the logarithm using the change-of-base formula. Round your result to three decimal places.

9. $\log_3 7$
10. $\log_7 4$
11. $\log_{1/2} 4$
12. $\log_{1/8} 64$
13. $\log_9 (0.8)$
14. $\log_3 (0.015)$
15. $\log_{15} 1460$
16. $\log_{20} 135$

In Exercises 17–20, use the properties of logarithms to rewrite and simplify the logarithmic expression.

17. $\log_4 8$
18. $\log_2 (4^2 \cdot 3^4)$
19. $\ln(5e^6)$
20. $\ln \dfrac{6}{e^2}$

In Exercises 21 and 22, use the properties of logarithms to verify the equation.

21. $\log_5 \frac{1}{250} = -3 - \log_5 2$
22. $-\ln 24 = -(3 \ln 2 + \ln 3)$

In Exercises 23–42, use the properties of logarithms to expand the expression as a sum, difference, and/or constant multiple of logarithms. (Assume all variables are positive.)

23. $\log_{10} 5x$
24. $\log_{10} 10z$
25. $\log_{10} \dfrac{5}{x}$
26. $\log_{10} \dfrac{y}{2}$
27. $\log_8 x^4$
28. $\log_6 z^{-3}$
29. $\ln \sqrt{z}$
30. $\ln \sqrt[3]{t}$
31. $\ln xyz$
32. $\ln \dfrac{xy}{z}$
33. $\ln(a^2 \sqrt{a-1}), \quad a > 1$
34. $\ln[z(z-1)^2], \quad z > 1$
35. $\ln \sqrt[3]{\dfrac{x}{y}}$
36. $\ln \sqrt{\dfrac{x^2}{y^3}}$
37. $\ln\left(\dfrac{x^2-1}{x^3}\right), \quad x > 1$
38. $\ln \dfrac{x}{\sqrt{x^2+1}}$
39. $\ln \dfrac{x^4 \sqrt{y}}{z^5}$
40. $\ln \sqrt{x^2(x+2)}$
41. $\log_b \dfrac{x^2}{y^2 z^3}$
42. $\log_b \dfrac{\sqrt{x} y^4}{z^4}$

Graphical Analysis   **In Exercises 43 and 44, (a) use a graphing utility to graph the two equations in the same viewing window and (b) use the *table* feature of the graphing utility to create a table of values for each equation. (c) What do the graphs and tables suggest? Explain your reasoning.**

43. $y_1 = \ln[x^3(x+4)], \qquad y_2 = 3 \ln x + \ln(x+4)$
44. $y_1 = \ln\left(\dfrac{\sqrt{x}}{x-2}\right), \qquad y_2 = \frac{1}{2} \ln x - \ln(x-2)$

In Exercises 45–62, condense the expression to the logarithm of a single quantity.

45. $\ln x + \ln 4$
46. $\ln y + \ln z$
47. $\log_4 z - \log_4 y$
48. $\log_5 8 - \log_5 t$
49. $2 \log_2 (x+3)$
50. $\frac{5}{2} \log_7 (z-4)$
51. $\frac{1}{3} \log_3 7x$
52. $-6 \log_6 2x$
53. $\ln x - 3 \ln(x+1)$
54. $2 \ln 8 + 5 \ln z$

55. $\ln(x - 2) - \ln(x + 2)$

56. $3 \ln x + 2 \ln y - 4 \ln z$

57. $\ln x - 2[\ln(x + 2) + \ln(x - 2)]$

58. $4[\ln z + \ln(z + 5)] - 2 \ln(z - 5)$

59. $\frac{1}{3}[2 \ln(x + 3) + \ln x - \ln(x^2 - 1)]$

60. $2[\ln x - \ln(x + 1) - \ln(x - 1)]$

61. $\frac{1}{3}[\ln y + 2 \ln(y + 4)] - \ln(y - 1)$

62. $\frac{1}{2}[\ln(x + 1) + 2 \ln(x - 1)] + 3 \ln x$

Graphical Analysis   **In Exercises 63 and 64, (a) use a graphing utility to graph the two equations in the same viewing window and (b) use the *table* feature of the graphing utility to create a table of values for each equation. (c) What do the graphs and tables suggest? Verify your conclusion algebraically.**

63. $y_1 = 2[\ln 8 - \ln(x^2 + 1)], \quad y_2 = \ln\left[\dfrac{64}{(x^2 + 1)^2}\right]$

64. $y_1 = \ln x + \frac{1}{2} \ln(x + 1), \quad y_2 = \ln(x\sqrt{x + 1})$

Think About It   **In Exercises 65 and 66, (a) use a graphing utility to graph the two equations in the same viewing window and (b) use the *table* feature of the graphing utility to create a table of values for each equation. (c) Are the expressions equivalent? Explain.**

65. $y_1 = \ln x^2, \quad y_2 = 2 \ln x$

66. $y_1 = \frac{1}{4} \ln[x^4(x^2 + 1)], \quad y_2 = \ln x + \frac{1}{4} \ln(x^2 + 1)$

In Exercises 67–80, find the exact value of the logarithm without using a calculator. If this is not possible, state the reason.

67. $\log_3 9$

68. $\log_6 \sqrt[3]{6}$

69. $\log_4 16^{3.4}$

70. $\log_5\left(\frac{1}{125}\right)$

71. $\log_2(-4)$

72. $\log_4(-16)$

73. $\log_5 75 - \log_5 3$

74. $\log_4 2 + \log_4 32$

75. $\ln e^3 - \ln e^7$

76. $\ln e^6 - 2 \ln e^5$

77. $2 \ln e^4$

78. $\ln e^{4.5}$

79. $\ln \dfrac{1}{\sqrt{e}}$

80. $\ln \sqrt[5]{e^3}$

81. *Sound Intensity*   The relationship between the number of decibels β and the intensity of a sound I in watts per square meter is given by

$$\beta = 10 \log_{10}\left(\frac{I}{10^{-12}}\right).$$

(a) Use the properties of logarithms to write the formula in a simpler form.

(b) Use a graphing utility to complete the table.

I	10^{-4}	10^{-6}	10^{-8}	10^{-10}	10^{-12}	10^{-14}
β						

(c) Verify your answers in part (b) algebraically.

82. *Human Memory Model*   Students participating in a psychology experiment attended several lectures and were given an exam. Every month for the next year, the students were retested to see how much of the material they remembered. The average scores for the group are given by the human memory model

$$f(t) = 90 - 15 \log_{10}(t + 1), \quad 0 \le t \le 12$$

where t is the time (in months).

(a) Use a graphing utility to graph the function over the specified domain.

(b) What was the average score on the original exam $(t = 0)$?

(c) What was the average score after 6 months?

(d) What was the average score after 12 months?

(e) When will the average score decrease to 75?

83. *Comparing Models*   A cup of water at an initial temperature of 78°C is placed in a room at a constant temperature of 21°C. The temperature of the water is measured every 5 minutes during a half-hour period. The results are recorded as ordered pairs of the form (t, T), where t is the time (in minutes) and T is the temperature (in degrees Celsius).

$(0, 78.0°), (5, 66.0°), (10, 57.5°), (15, 51.2°),$
$(20, 46.3°), (25, 42.5°), (30, 39.6°)$

(a) The graph of the model for the data should be asymptotic with the graph of the temperature of the room. Subtract the room temperature from each of the temperatures in the ordered pairs. Use a graphing utility to plot the data points (t, T) and $(t, T - 21)$.

(b) An exponential model for the data $(t, T - 21)$ is given by

$$T - 21 = 54.4(0.964)^t.$$

Solve for T and graph the model. Compare the result with the plot of the original data.

(c) Take the natural logarithms of the revised temperatures. Use a graphing utility to plot the points $(t, \ln(T - 21))$ and observe that the points appear linear. Use the *regression* feature of a graphing utility to fit a line to this data. The resulting line has the form

$$\ln(T - 21) = at + b.$$

Use the properties of logarithms to solve for T. Verify that the result is equivalent to the model in part (b).

(d) Fit a rational model to the data. Take the reciprocals of the y-coordinates of the revised data points to generate the points

$$\left(t, \frac{1}{T - 21}\right).$$

Use a graphing utility to plot these points and observe that they appear linear. Use the *regression* feature of a graphing utility to fit a line to this data. The resulting line has the form

$$\frac{1}{T - 21} = at + b.$$

Solve for T, and use a graphing utility to graph the rational function and the original data points.

84. *Writing*   Write a short paragraph explaining why the transformations of the data in Exercise 83 were necessary to obtain the models. Why did taking the logarithms of the temperatures lead to a linear scatter plot? Why did taking the reciprocals of the temperatures lead to a linear scatter plot?

Synthesis

True or False?   **In Exercises 85–91, determine whether the statement is true or false given that $f(x) = \ln x$. Justify your answer.**

85. $f(0) = 0$

86. $f(1) = 1$

87. $f(ax) = f(a) + f(x), \quad a > 0, x > 0$

88. $f(x - 2) = f(x) - f(2), \quad x > 2$

89. $\sqrt{f(x)} = \frac{1}{2}f(x)$

90. If $f(u) = 2f(v)$, then $v = u^2$.

91. If $f(x) < 0$, then $0 < x < 1$.

92. *Proof*   Prove that $\log_b \dfrac{u}{v} = \log_b u - \log_b v$.

93. *Proof*   Prove that $\log_b u^n = n \log_b u$.

94. *Proof*   Prove that $\dfrac{\log_a x}{\log_{a/b} x} = 1 + \log_a \dfrac{1}{b}$.

In Exercises 95–100, use the change-of-base formula to rewrite the logarithm as a ratio of logarithms. Then use a graphing utility to graph the ratio.

95. $f(x) = \log_2 x$

96. $f(x) = \log_4 x$

97. $f(x) = \log_3 \sqrt{x}$

98. $f(x) = \log_2 \sqrt[3]{x}$

99. $f(x) = \log_5 \dfrac{x}{3}$

100. $f(x) = \log_3 \dfrac{x}{5}$

101. *Think About It*   Use a graphing utility to graph

$$f(x) = \ln \frac{x}{2}, \quad g(x) = \frac{\ln x}{\ln 2}, \quad h(x) = \ln x - \ln 2$$

in the same viewing window. Which two functions have identical graphs? Explain why.

102. *Exploration*   For how many integers between 1 and 20 can the natural logarithms be approximated given that $\ln 2 \approx 0.6931$, $\ln 3 \approx 1.0986$, and $\ln 5 \approx 1.6094$? Approximate these logarithms. (Do not use a calculator.)

Review

In Exercises 103–106, simplify the expression.

103. $\dfrac{24xy^{-2}}{16x^{-3}y}$

104. $\left(\dfrac{2x^2}{3y}\right)^{-3}$

105. $(18x^3y^4)^{-3}(18x^3y^4)^3$

106. $xy(x^{-1} + y^{-1})^{-1}$

In Exercises 107–112, find all solutions of the equation. Be sure to check all your solutions.

107. $x^2 - 6x + 2 = 0$

108. $2x^3 + 20x^2 + 50x = 0$

109. $x^4 - 19x^2 + 48 = 0$

110. $9x^4 - 37x^2 + 4 = 0$

111. $x^3 - 6x^2 - 4x + 24 = 0$

112. $9x^4 - 226x^2 + 25 = 0$

4.4 Solving Exponential and Logarithmic Equations

Introduction

So far in this chapter, you have studied the definitions, graphs, and properties of exponential and logarithmic functions. In this section, you will study procedures for *solving equations* involving exponential and logarithmic functions.

There are two basic strategies for solving exponential or logarithmic equations. The first is based on the One-to-One Properties and the second is based on the Inverse Properties. For $a > 0$ and $a \neq 1$, the following properties are true for all x and y for which $\log_a x$ and $\log_a y$ are defined.

One-to-One Properties

$a^x = a^y$ if and only if $x = y$.

$\log_a x = \log_a y$ if and only if $x = y$.

Inverse Properties

$a^{\log_a x} = x$

$\log_a a^x = x$

What you should learn

- Solve simple exponential and logarithmic equations.
- Solve more complicated exponential equations.
- Solve more complicated logarithmic equations.
- Use exponential and logarithmic equations to model and solve real-life problems.

Why you should learn it

Exponential and logarithmic equations can be used to model and solve real-life problems. For instance, Exercise 115 on page 359 shows how to use an exponential function to model the average heights of men and women.

Charles Gupton/Corbis

Example 1 Solving Simple Exponential and Logarithmic Equations

	Original Equation	Rewritten Equation	Solution	Property
a.	$2^x = 32$	$2^x = 2^5$	$x = 5$	One-to-One
b.	$\ln x - \ln 3 = 0$	$\ln x = \ln 3$	$x = 3$	One-to-One
c.	$\left(\frac{1}{3}\right)^x = 9$	$3^{-x} = 3^2$	$x = -2$	One-to-One
d.	$e^x = 7$	$\ln e^x = \ln 7$	$x = \ln 7$	Inverse
e.	$\ln x = -3$	$e^{\ln x} = e^{-3}$	$x = e^{-3}$	Inverse
f.	$\log_{10} x = -1$	$10^{\log_{10} x} = 10^{-1}$	$x = 10^{-1} = \frac{1}{10}$	Inverse

✓ *Checkpoint* Now try Exercise 21.

The strategies used in Example 1 are summarized as follows.

STUDY TIP

In Example 1(d), remember that $\ln x$ has a base of e. That is, $\ln e^x = \ln_e e^x$.

Strategies for Solving Exponential and Logarithmic Equations

1. Rewrite the original equation in a form that allows the use of the One-to-One Properties of exponential or logarithmic functions.

2. Rewrite an *exponential* equation in logarithmic form and apply the Inverse Property of logarithmic functions.

3. Rewrite a *logarithmic* equation in exponential form and apply the Inverse Property of exponential functions.

Solving Exponential Equations

Example 2   Solving Exponential Equations

Solve each equation.   **a.** $e^x = 72$ **b.** $3(2^x) = 42$

Algebraic Solution

a.

$e^x = 72$	Write original equation.
$\ln e^x = \ln 72$	Take natural log of each side.
$x = \ln 72 \approx 4.277$	Inverse Property

The solution is $x = \ln 72 \approx 4.277$. Check this in the original equation.

b.

$3(2^x) = 42$	Write original equation.
$2^x = 14$	Divide each side by 3.
$\log_2 2^x = \log_2 14$	Take log (base 2) of each side.
$x = \log_2 14$	Inverse Property
$x = \dfrac{\ln 14}{\ln 2} \approx 3.807$	Change-of-base formula

The solution is $x = \log_2 14 \approx 3.807$. Check this in the original equation.

 Checkpoint   Now try Exercise 45.

Graphical Solution

a. Use a graphing utility to graph the left- and right-hand sides of the equation as $y_1 = e^x$ and $y_2 = 72$ in the same viewing window. Use the *intersect* feature or the *zoom* and *trace* features of the graphing utility to approximate the intersection point, as shown in Figure 4.32. So, the approximate solution is $x \approx 4.277$.

b. Use a graphing utility to graph $y_1 = 3(2^x)$ and $y_2 = 42$ in the same viewing window. Use the *intersect* feature or the *zoom* and *trace* features to approximate the intersection point, as shown in Figure 4.33. So, the approximate solution is $x \approx 3.807$.

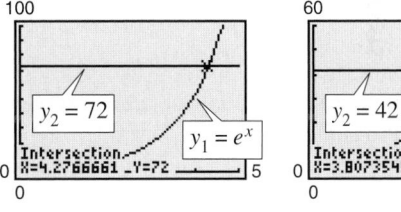

Figure 4.32   Figure 4.33

Example 3   Solving an Exponential Equation

Solve $4e^{2x} - 3 = 2$.

Algebraic Solution

$4e^{2x} - 3 = 2$	Write original equation.
$4e^{2x} = 5$	Add 3 to each side.
$e^{2x} = \frac{5}{4}$	Divide each side by 4.
$\ln e^{2x} = \ln \frac{5}{4}$	Take logarithm of each side.
$2x = \ln \frac{5}{4}$	Inverse Property
$x = \frac{1}{2} \ln \frac{5}{4} \approx 0.112$	Divide each side by 2.

The solution is $x = \frac{1}{2} \ln \frac{5}{4} \approx 0.112$. Check this in the original equation.

 Checkpoint   Now try Exercise 49.

Graphical Solution

Rather than using the procedure in Example 2, another way to graphically solve the equation is to first rewrite the equation as $4e^{2x} - 5 = 0$, then use a graphing utility to graph $y = 4e^{2x} - 5$. Use the *zero* or *root* feature or the *zoom* and *trace* features of the graphing utility to approximate the value of x for which $y = 0$. From Figure 4.34, you can see that the zero occurs at $x \approx 0.112$. So, the solution is $x \approx 0.112$.

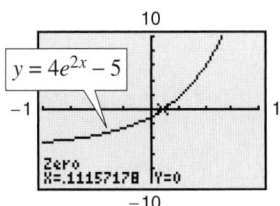

Figure 4.34

Example 4 Solving an Exponential Equation

Solve $2(3^{2t-5}) - 4 = 11$.

Solution

$$2(3^{2t-5}) - 4 = 11 \qquad \text{Write original equation.}$$
$$2(3^{2t-5}) = 15 \qquad \text{Add 4 to each side.}$$
$$3^{2t-5} = \tfrac{15}{2} \qquad \text{Divide each side by 2.}$$
$$\log_3 3^{2t-5} = \log_3 \tfrac{15}{2} \qquad \text{Take log (base 3) of each side.}$$
$$2t - 5 = \log_3 \tfrac{15}{2} \qquad \text{Inverse Property}$$
$$2t = 5 + \log_3 7.5 \qquad \text{Add 5 to each side.}$$
$$t = \tfrac{5}{2} + \tfrac{1}{2}\log_3 7.5 \qquad \text{Divide each side by 2.}$$
$$t \approx 3.417 \qquad \text{Use a calculator.}$$

The solution is $t = \tfrac{5}{2} + \tfrac{1}{2}\log_3 7.5 \approx 3.417$. Check this in the original equation.

☑ *Checkpoint* Now try Exercise 53.

> **STUDY TIP**
>
> Remember that to evaluate a logarithm such as $\log_3 7.5$, you need to use the change-of-base formula.
>
> $$\log_3 7.5 = \frac{\ln 7.5}{\ln 3} \approx 1.834$$

When an equation involves two or more exponential expressions, you can still use a procedure similar to that demonstrated in the previous three examples. However, the algebra is a bit more complicated.

Example 5 Solving an Exponential Equation in Quadratic Form

Solve $e^{2x} - 3e^x + 2 = 0$.

Algebraic Solution

$$e^{2x} - 3e^x + 2 = 0 \qquad \text{Write original equation.}$$
$$(e^x)^2 - 3e^x + 2 = 0 \qquad \text{Write in quadratic form.}$$
$$(e^x - 2)(e^x - 1) = 0 \qquad \text{Factor.}$$
$$e^x - 2 = 0 \qquad \text{Set 1st factor equal to 0.}$$
$$e^x = 2 \qquad \text{Add 2 to each side.}$$
$$x = \ln 2 \qquad \text{Solution}$$
$$e^x - 1 = 0 \qquad \text{Set 2nd factor equal to 0.}$$
$$e^x = 1 \qquad \text{Add 1 to each side.}$$
$$x = \ln 1 \qquad \text{Inverse Property}$$
$$x = 0 \qquad \text{Solution}$$

The solutions are $x = \ln 2 \approx 0.693$ and $x = 0$. Check these in the original equation.

☑ *Checkpoint* Now try Exercise 55.

Graphical Solution

Use a graphing utility to graph $y = e^{2x} - 3e^x + 2$. Use the *zero* or *root* feature or the *zoom* and *trace* features of the graphing utility to approximate the values of x for which $y = 0$. In Figure 4.35, you can see that the zeros occur at $x = 0$ and at $x \approx 0.693$. So, the solutions are $x = 0$ and $x \approx 0.693$.

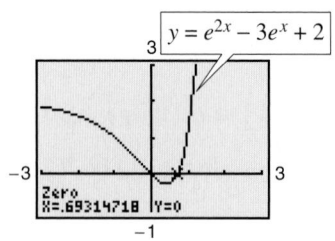

Figure 4.35

Solving Logarithmic Equations

To solve a logarithmic equation, you can write it in exponential form.

$\ln x = 3$	Logarithmic form
$e^{\ln x} = e^3$	Exponentiate each side.
$x = e^3$	Exponential form

This procedure is called *exponentiating* each side of an equation. It is applied after the logarithmic expression has been isolated.

Example 6   Solving Logarithmic Equations

Solve each logarithmic equation.

a. $\ln x = 2$ **b.** $\log_3(5x - 1) = \log_3(x + 7)$

Solution

a.

$\ln x = 2$	Write original equation.
$e^{\ln x} = e^2$	Exponentiate each side.
$x = e^2 \approx 7.389$	Inverse Property

The solution is $x = e^2 \approx 7.389$. Check this in the original equation.

b.

$\log_3(5x - 1) = \log_3(x + 7)$	Write original equation.
$5x - 1 = x + 7$	One-to-One Property
$4x = 8$	Add $-x$ and 1 to each side.
$x = 2$	Divide each side by 4.

The solution is $x = 2$. Check this in the original equation.

✓ *Checkpoint* Now try Exercise 75.

> **TECHNOLOGY SUPPORT**
>
> For instructions on how to use the *intersect* feature, the *zoom* and *trace* features, and the *zero* or *root* feature, see Appendix A; for specific keystrokes, go to the text website at *college.hmco.com*.

Example 7   Solving a Logarithmic Equation

Solve $5 + 2 \ln x = 4$.

Algebraic Solution

$5 + 2 \ln x = 4$	Write original equation.
$2 \ln x = -1$	Subtract 5 from each side.
$\ln x = -\dfrac{1}{2}$	Divide each side by 2.
$e^{\ln x} = e^{-1/2}$	Exponentiate each side.
$x = e^{-1/2}$	Inverse Property
$x \approx 0.607$	Use a calculator.

The solution is $x = e^{-1/2} \approx 0.607$. Check this in the original equation.

✓ *Checkpoint* Now try Exercise 77.

Graphical Solution

Use a graphing utility to graph $y_1 = 5 + 2 \ln x$ and $y_2 = 4$ in the same viewing window. Use the *intersect* feature or the *zoom* and *trace* features to approximate the intersection point, as shown in Figure 4.36. So, the solution is $x \approx 0.607$.

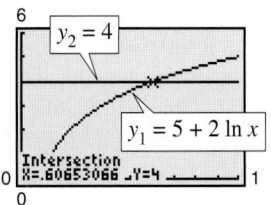

Figure 4.36

Example 8   Solving a Logarithmic Equation

Solve $2 \log_5 3x = 4$.

Solution

$$2 \log_5 3x = 4 \qquad \text{Write original equation.}$$

$$\log_5 3x = 2 \qquad \text{Divide each side by 2.}$$

$$5^{\log_5 3x} = 5^2 \qquad \text{Exponentiate each side (base 5).}$$

$$3x = 25 \qquad \text{Inverse Property}$$

$$x = \tfrac{25}{3} \qquad \text{Divide each side by 3.}$$

The solution is $x = \tfrac{25}{3}$. Check this in the original equation. Or, perform a graphical check by graphing

$$y_1 = 2 \log_5 3x = 2\left(\frac{\log_{10} 3x}{\log_{10} 5}\right) \qquad \text{and} \qquad y_2 = 4$$

in the same viewing window. The two graphs should intersect at $x = \tfrac{25}{3} \approx 8.333$ and $y = 4$, as shown in Figure 4.37.

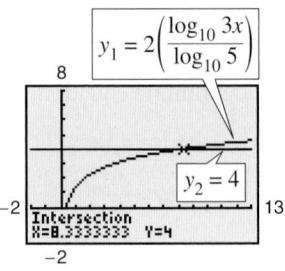

Figure 4.37

✓ *Checkpoint* Now try Exercise 81.

Because the domain of a logarithmic function generally does not include all real numbers, you should be sure to check for extraneous solutions of logarithmic equations, as shown in the next example.

Example 9   Checking for Extraneous Solutions

Solve $\ln(x - 2) + \ln(2x - 3) = 2 \ln x$.

Algebraic Solution

$$\ln(x - 2) + \ln(2x - 3) = 2 \ln x \qquad \text{Write original equation.}$$

$$\ln[(x - 2)(2x - 3)] = \ln x^2 \qquad \text{Use properties of logarithms.}$$

$$\ln(2x^2 - 7x + 6) = \ln x^2 \qquad \text{Multiply binomials.}$$

$$2x^2 - 7x + 6 = x^2 \qquad \text{One-to-One Property}$$

$$x^2 - 7x + 6 = 0 \qquad \text{Write in general form.}$$

$$(x - 6)(x - 1) = 0 \qquad \text{Factor.}$$

$$x - 6 = 0 \implies x = 6 \qquad \text{Set 1st factor equal to 0.}$$

$$x - 1 = 0 \implies x = 1 \qquad \text{Set 2nd factor equal to 0.}$$

Finally, by checking these two "solutions" in the original equation, you can conclude that $x = 1$ is not valid. This is because when $x = 1$, $\ln(x - 2) + \ln(2x - 3) = \ln(-1) + \ln(-1)$, which is invalid because -1 is not in the domain of the natural logarithmic function. So, the only solution is $x = 6$.

✓ *Checkpoint* Now try Exercise 89.

Graphical Solution

First rewrite the original equation as $\ln(x - 2) + \ln(2x - 3) - 2 \ln x = 0$. Then use a graphing utility to graph $y = \ln(x - 2) + \ln(2x - 3) - 2 \ln x$. Use the *zero* or *root* feature or the *zoom* and *trace* features of the graphing utility to determine that $x = 6$ is an approximate solution, as shown in Figure 4.38. Verify that 6 is an exact solution algebraically.

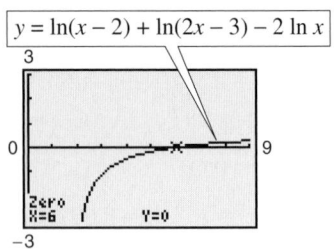

Figure 4.38

Example 10   The Change-of-Base Formula

Prove the change-of-base formula: $\log_a x = \dfrac{\log_b x}{\log_b a}$.

Solution

Begin by letting $y = \log_a x$ and writing the equivalent exponential form $a^y = x$. Now, taking the logarithms *with base b* of each side produces the following.

$$\log_b a^y = \log_b x$$

$$y \log_b a = \log_b x \qquad \text{Property of logarithms}$$

$$y = \frac{\log_b x}{\log_b a} \qquad \text{Divide each side by } \log_b a.$$

$$\log_a x = \frac{\log_b x}{\log_a a} \qquad \text{Replace } y \text{ with } \log_a x.$$

Equations that involve combinations of algebraic functions, exponential functions, and/or logarithmic functions can be very difficult to solve by algebraic procedures. Here again, you can take advantage of a graphing utility.

Example 11   Approximating the Solution of an Equation

Approximate (to three decimal places) the solution of $\ln x = x^2 - 2$.

Solution

To begin, write the equation so that all terms on one side are equal to 0.

$$\ln x - x^2 + 2 = 0$$

Then use a graphing utility to graph

$$y = -x^2 + 2 + \ln x$$

as shown in Figure 4.39. From this graph, you can see that the equation has two solutions. Next, using the *zero* or *root* feature or the *zoom* and *trace* features, you can approximate the two solutions to be $x \approx 0.138$ and $x \approx 1.564$.

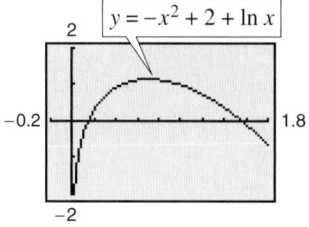

Figure 4.39

Check

$$\ln x = x^2 - 2 \qquad \text{Write original equation.}$$

$$\ln(0.138) \stackrel{?}{\approx} (0.138)^2 - 2 \qquad \text{Substitute 0.138 for } x.$$

$$-1.9805 \approx -1.9810 \qquad \text{Solution checks. } \checkmark$$

$$\ln(1.564) \stackrel{?}{\approx} (1.564)^2 - 2 \qquad \text{Substitute 1.564 for } x.$$

$$0.4472 \approx 0.4461 \qquad \text{Solution checks. } \checkmark$$

So, the two solutions $x \approx 0.138$ and $x \approx 1.564$ seem reasonable.

☑ *Checkpoint* Now try Exercise 97.

> **STUDY TIP**
>
> To solve exponential equations, it is useful to first isolate the exponential expression, then take the logarithm of each side and solve for the variable. To solve logarithmic equations, condense the logarithmic part into a single logarithm, then rewrite in exponential form and solve for the variable.

Applications

Example 12   Doubling an Investment

You have deposited $500 in an account that pays 6.75% interest, compounded continuously. How long will it take your money to double?

Solution

Using the formula for continuous compounding, you can find that the balance in the account is

$$A = Pe^{rt} = 500e^{0.0675t}.$$

To find the time required for the balance to double, let $A = 1000$, and solve the resulting equation for t.

$500e^{0.0675t} = 1000$	Substitute 1000 for A.
$e^{0.0675t} = 2$	Divide each side by 500.
$\ln e^{0.0675t} = \ln 2$	Take natural log of each side.
$0.0675t = \ln 2$	Inverse Property
$t = \dfrac{\ln 2}{0.0675} \approx 10.27$	Divide each side by 0.0675.

The balance in the account will double after approximately 10.27 years. This result is demonstrated graphically in Figure 4.40.

 Checkpoint Now try Exercise 109.

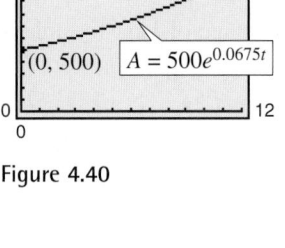

Figure 4.40

Example 13   Average Salary for Public School Teachers

For selected years from 1980 to 2000, the average salary y (in thousands of dollars) for public school teachers for the year t can be modeled by the equation

$$y = -39.2 + 23.64 \ln t, \quad 10 \le t \le 30$$

where $t = 10$ represents 1980 (see Figure 4.41). During which year did the average salary for public school teachers reach $40.0 thousand? (Source: National Education Association)

Solution

$-39.2 + 23.64 \ln t = y$	Write original equation.
$-39.2 + 23.64 \ln t = 40.0$	Substitute 40.0 for y.
$23.64 \ln t = 79.2$	Add 39.2 to each side.
$\ln t \approx 3.350$	Divide each side by 23.64.
$e^{\ln t} = e^{3.350}$	Exponentiate each side.
$t \approx 28.5$	Inverse Property

The solution is $t \approx 28.5$ years. Because $t = 10$ represents 1980, it follows that the average salary for public school teachers reached $40.0 thousand in 1998.

 Checkpoint Now try Exercise 118.

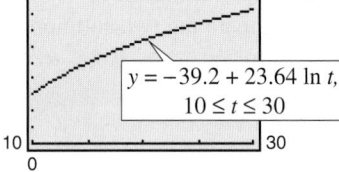

Figure 4.41

4.4   Exercises

Vocabulary Check

Fill in the blanks.

1. To _____ an equation in x means to find all values of x for which the equation is true.

2. To solve exponential and logarithmic equations, you can use the following one-to-one and inverse properties.

   (a) $a^x = a^y$ if and only if _____ .   (b) $\log_a x = \log_a y$ if and only if _____ .

   (c) $a^{\log_a x} =$ _____   (d) $\log_a a^x =$ _____

3. An _____ solution does not satisfy the original equation.

In Exercises 1–8, determine whether each x-value is a solution of the equation.

1. $4^{2x-7} = 64$

   (a) $x = 5$

   (b) $x = 2$

3. $3e^{x+2} = 75$

   (a) $x = -2 + e^{25}$

   (b) $x = -2 + \ln 25$

   (c) $x \approx 1.2189$

5. $\log_4(3x) = 3$

   (a) $x \approx 21.3560$

   (b) $x = -4$

   (c) $x = \frac{64}{3}$

7. $\ln(x - 1) = 3.8$

   (a) $x = 1 + e^{3.8}$

   (b) $x \approx 45.7012$

   (c) $x = 1 + \ln 3.8$

2. $2^{3x+1} = 32$

   (a) $x = -1$

   (b) $x = 2$

4. $4e^{x-1} = 60$

   (a) $x = 1 + \ln 15$

   (b) $x \approx 3.7081$

   (c) $x = \ln 16$

6. $\log_6\left(\frac{5}{3}x\right) = 2$

   (a) $x \approx 20.2882$

   (b) $x = \frac{108}{5}$

   (c) $x = 7.2$

8. $\ln(2 + x) = 2.5$

   (a) $x = e^{2.5} - 2$

   (b) $x \approx \frac{4073}{400}$

   (c) $x = \frac{1}{2}$

In Exercises 9–16, use a graphing utility to graph f and g in the same viewing window. Approximate the point of intersection of the graphs of f and g. Then solve the equation $f(x) = g(x)$ algebraically.

9. $f(x) = 2^x$

   $g(x) = 8$

11. $f(x) = 5^{x-2} - 15$

   $g(x) = 10$

13. $f(x) = 4 \log_3 x$

   $g(x) = 20$

15. $f(x) = \ln e^{x+1}$

   $g(x) = 2x + 5$

10. $f(x) = 27^x$

   $g(x) = 9$

12. $f(x) = 2^{-x+1} - 3$

   $g(x) = 13$

14. $f(x) = 3 \log_5 x$

   $g(x) = 6$

16. $f(x) = \ln e^{x-2}$

   $g(x) = 3x + 2$

In Exercises 17–36, solve for x.

17. $4^x = 16$

19. $5^x = \frac{1}{625}$

21. $\left(\frac{1}{8}\right)^x = 64$

23. $\left(\frac{2}{3}\right)^x = \frac{81}{16}$

25. $e^x = 4$

27. $\ln x - \ln 5 = 0$

29. $\ln x = -7$

31. $\log_x 625 = 4$

33. $\log_{10} x = -1$

35. $\ln(2x - 1) = 5$

18. $3^x = 243$

20. $7^x = \frac{1}{49}$

22. $\left(\frac{1}{2}\right)^x = 32$

24. $\left(\frac{3}{4}\right)^x = \frac{27}{64}$

26. $e^x = 0$

28. $\ln x - \ln 2 = 0$

30. $\ln x = -1$

32. $\log_x 25 = 2$

34. $\log_{10} x = -\frac{1}{2}$

36. $\ln(3x + 5) = 8$

In Exercises 37–42, simplify the expression.

37. $\ln e^{x^2}$

39. $e^{\ln(5x+2)}$

41. $e^{\ln x^2}$

38. $\ln e^{2x-1}$

40. $-1 + \ln e^{2x}$

42. $-8 + e^{\ln x^3}$

In Exercises 43–60, solve the exponential equation algebraically. Round your result to three decimal places. Use a graphing utility to verify your answer.

43. $8^{3x} = 360$

45. $2e^{5x} = 18$

47. $500e^{-x} = 300$

49. $7 - 2e^x = 5$

51. $5^{-t/2} = 0.20$

53. $2^{3-x} = 565$

55. $e^{2x} - 4e^x - 5 = 0$

57. $\dfrac{400}{1 + e^{-x}} = 350$

44. $6^{5x} = 3000$

46. $4e^{2x} = 40$

48. $1000e^{-4x} = 75$

50. $-14 + 3e^x = 11$

52. $4^{-3t} = 0.10$

54. $8^{-2-x} = 431$

56. $e^{2x} - 5e^x + 6 = 0$

58. $\dfrac{525}{1 + e^{-x}} = 275$

59. $\left(1 + \dfrac{0.10}{12}\right)^{12t} = 2$ **60.** $\left(16 + \dfrac{0.878}{26}\right)^{3t} = 30$

In Exercises 61–64, complete the table to find an interval containing the solution of the equation. Then use a graphing utility to graph both sides of the equation to estimate the solution. Round your result to three decimal places.

61. $e^{3x} = 12$

x	0.6	0.7	0.8	0.9	1.0
e^{3x}					

62. $e^{2x} = 50$

x	1.6	1.7	1.8	1.9	2.0
e^{2x}					

63. $20(100 - e^{x/2}) = 500$

x	5	6	7	8	9
$20(100 - e^{x/2})$					

64. $\dfrac{400}{1 + e^{-x}} = 350$

x	0	1	2	3	4
$\dfrac{400}{1 + e^{-x}}$					

In Exercises 65–68, use the *zero* or *root* feature or the *zoom* and *trace* features of a graphing utility to approximate the solution of the exponential equation accurate to three decimal places.

65. $\left(1 + \dfrac{0.065}{365}\right)^{365t} = 4$ **66.** $\left(4 - \dfrac{2.471}{40}\right)^{9t} = 21$

67. $\dfrac{3000}{2 + e^{2x}} = 2$ **68.** $\dfrac{119}{e^{6x} - 14} = 7$

In Exercises 69–72, use a graphing utility to graph the function and approximate its zero accurate to three decimal places.

69. $g(x) = 6e^{1-x} - 25$ **70.** $f(x) = 3e^{3x/2} - 962$

71. $g(t) = e^{0.09t} - 3$ **72.** $h(t) = e^{0.125t} - 8$

In Exercises 73–92, solve the logarithmic equation algebraically. Round the result to three decimal places. Verify your answer using a graphing utility.

73. $\ln x = -3$ **74.** $\ln x = -2$

75. $\ln 4x = 2.1$ **76.** $\ln 2x = 1.5$

77. $-2 + 2 \ln 3x = 17$ **78.** $3 + 2 \ln x = 10$

79. $\log_{10}(z - 3) = 2$ **80.** $\log_{10} x^2 = 6$

81. $7 \log_4(0.6x) = 12$ **82.** $4 \log_{10}(x - 6) = 11$

83. $\ln \sqrt{x + 2} = 1$ **84.** $\ln \sqrt{x - 8} = 5$

85. $\ln(x + 1)^2 = 2$ **86.** $\ln(x^2 + 1) = 8$

87. $\log_4 x - \log_4(x - 1) = \frac{1}{2}$

88. $\log_3 x + \log_3(x - 8) = 2$

89. $\ln(x + 5) = \ln(x - 1) - \ln(x + 1)$

90. $\ln(x + 1) - \ln(x - 2) = \ln x$

91. $\log_{10} 8x - \log_{10}\left(1 + \sqrt{x}\right) = 2$

92. $\log_{10} 4x - \log_{10}\left(12 + \sqrt{x}\right) = 2$

In Exercises 93–96, complete the table to find an interval containing the solution of the equation. Then use a graphing utility to graph both sides of the equation to estimate the solution. Round your result to three decimal places.

93. $\ln 2x = 2.4$

x	2	3	4	5	6
$\ln 2x$					

94. $3 \ln 5x = 10$

x	4	5	6	7	8
$3 \ln 5x$					

95. $6 \log_3(0.5x) = 11$

x	12	13	14	15	16
$6 \log_3(0.5x)$					

96. $5 \log_{10}(x - 2) = 11$

x	150	155	160	165	170
$5 \log_{10}(x - 2)$					

In Exercises 97–102, use the *zero* or *root* feature or the *zoom* and *trace* features of a graphing utility to approximate the solution of the logarithmic equation accurate to three decimal places.

97. $\log_{10} x = x^3 - 3$

98. $\log_{10} x^2 = 4$

99. $\log_3 x + \log_3(x - 3) = 1$

100. $\log_2 x + \log_2(x + 5) = 4$

101. $\ln(x - 3) + \ln(x + 3) = 1$

102. $\ln x + \ln(x^2 + 4) = 10$

In Exercises 103–108, use a graphing utility to approximate the point of intersection of the graphs. Round your result to three decimal places.

103. $y_1 = 7$

$y_2 = 2^{x-1} - 5$

104. $y_1 = 4$

$y_2 = 3^{x+1} - 2$

105. $y_1 = 80$

$y_2 = 4e^{-0.2x}$

106. $y_1 = 500$

$y_2 = 1500e^{-x/2}$

107. $y_1 = 3.25$

$y_2 = \frac{1}{2}\ln(x + 2)$

108. $y_1 = 1.05$

$y_2 = \ln\sqrt{x - 2}$

***Compound Interest* In Exercises 109 and 110, find the time required for a $1000 investment to (a) double at interest rate r, compounded continuously, and (b) triple at interest rate r, compounded continuously.**

109. $r = 0.085$

110. $r = 0.12$

111. *Demand* The demand equation for a camera is given by

$$p = 500 - 0.5(e^{0.004x}).$$

Find the demand x for a price of (a) $p = \$350$ and (b) $p = \$300$.

112. *Demand* The demand equation for a hand-held electronic organizer is given by

$$p = 5000\left(1 - \frac{4}{4 + e^{-0.002x}}\right).$$

Find the demand x for a price of (a) $p = \$600$ and (b) $p = \$400$.

113. *Forestry* The number of trees per acre N of a certain species is approximated by the model

$$N = 68(10^{-0.04x}), \quad 5 \le x \le 40$$

where x is the average diameter of the trees (in inches) three feet above the ground. Use the model to approximate the average diameter of the trees in a test plot for which $N = 21$.

114. *Forestry* The yield V (in millions of cubic feet per acre) for a forest at age t years is given by

$$V = 6.7e^{-48.1/t}.$$

(a) Use a graphing utility to graph the function.

(b) Determine the horizontal asymptote of the function. Interpret its meaning in the context of the problem.

(c) Find the time necessary to obtain a yield of 1.3 million cubic feet.

115. *Average Heights* The percent m of American males between the ages of 18 and 24 who are no more than x inches tall is modeled by

$$m(x) = \frac{100}{1 + e^{-0.6114(x - 69.71)}}$$

and the percent f of American females between the ages of 18 and 24 who are no more than x inches tall is modeled by

$$f(x) = \frac{100}{1 + e^{-0.66607(x - 64.51)}}.$$

(Source: U.S. National Center for Health Statistics)

(a) Use a graphing utility to graph the two functions in the same viewing window.

(b) Use the graphs in part (a) to determine the horizontal asymptotes of the functions. Interpret their meaning in the context of the problem.

(c) What is the average height for each sex?

116. *Human Memory Model* In a group project in learning theory, a mathematical model for the proportion P of correct responses after n trials was found to be

$$P = \frac{0.83}{1 + e^{-0.2n}}.$$

(a) Use a graphing utility to graph the function.

(b) Use the graph in part (a) to determine any horizontal asymptotes of the function. Interpret the meaning of the upper asymptote in the context of the problem.

(c) After how many trials will 60% of the responses be correct?

117. *Data Analysis* An object at a temperature of 160°C was removed from a furnace and placed in a room at 20°C. The temperature T of the object was measured after each hour h and recorded in the table. A model for this data is given by $T = 20[1 + 7(2^{-h})]$.

Hour, h	Temperature, T
0	160°
1	90°
2	56°
3	38°
4	29°
5	24°

(a) Use a graphing utility to plot the data and graph the model in the same viewing window.

(b) Identify the horizontal asymptote of the graph of the model and interpret the asymptote in the context of the problem.

(c) Approximate the time when the temperature of the object is 100°C.

118. *Finance* The table shows the number N (in thousands) of banks in the United States from 1995 to 2001. The data can be modeled by the logarithmic function $N = 17.02 - 3.096 \ln t$, where t represents the year, with $t = 5$ corresponding to 1995. (Source: Federal Deposit Insurance Corp.)

Year	Number, N
1995	11.97
1996	11.67
1997	10.92
1998	10.46
1999	10.22
2000	9.91
2001	9.63

(a) Use the model to determine during which year the number of banks reached 10,000.

(b) Use a graphing utility to graph the model.

(c) Use the graph from part (b) to verify your answer in part (a).

Synthesis

True or False? **In Exercises 119 and 120, determine whether the statement is true or false. Justify your answer.**

119. You can approximate the solution of the equation $\frac{2}{3}e^x = 42$ by graphing $y = \frac{2}{3}e^x - 42$ and finding its x-intercept.

120. A logarithmic equation can have at most one extraneous solution.

121. *Writing* Write two or three sentences stating the general guidelines that you follow when (a) solving exponential equations and (b) solving logarithmic equations.

122. *Graphical Analysis* Let $f(x) = \log_a x$ and $g(x) = a^x$, where $a > 1$.

(a) Let $a = 1.2$ and use a graphing utility to graph the two functions in the same viewing window. What do you observe? Approximate any points of intersection of the two graphs.

(b) Determine the value(s) of a for which the two graphs have one point of intersection.

(c) Determine the value(s) of a for which the two graphs have two points of intersection.

123. *Think About It* Is the time required for an investment to quadruple twice as long as the time required for it to double? Give a reason for your answer and verify your answer algebraically.

124. *Writing* Write a paragraph explaining whether or not the time required for an investment to double is dependent on the size of the investment.

Review

In Exercises 125–130, sketch the graph of the function.

125. $f(x) = 3x^3 - 4$

126. $f(x) = -(x + 1)^3 + 2$

127. $f(x) = |x| + 9$

128. $f(x) = |x + 2| - 8$

129. $f(x) = \begin{cases} 2x, & x < 0 \\ -x^2 + 4, & x \geq 0 \end{cases}$

130. $f(x) = \begin{cases} x - 9, & x \leq -1 \\ x^2 + 1, & x > -1 \end{cases}$

4.5 Exponential and Logarithmic Models

Introduction

The five most common types of mathematical models involving exponential functions and logarithmic functions are as follows.

1. **Exponential growth model:** $y = ae^{bx}$, $b > 0$
2. **Exponential decay model:** $y = ae^{-bx}$, $b > 0$
3. **Gaussian model:** $y = ae^{-(x-b)^2/c}$
4. **Logistic growth model:** $y = \dfrac{a}{1 + be^{-rx}}$
5. **Logarithmic models:** $y = a + b \ln x$, $y = a + b \log_{10} x$

The basic shapes of these graphs are shown in Figure 4.42.

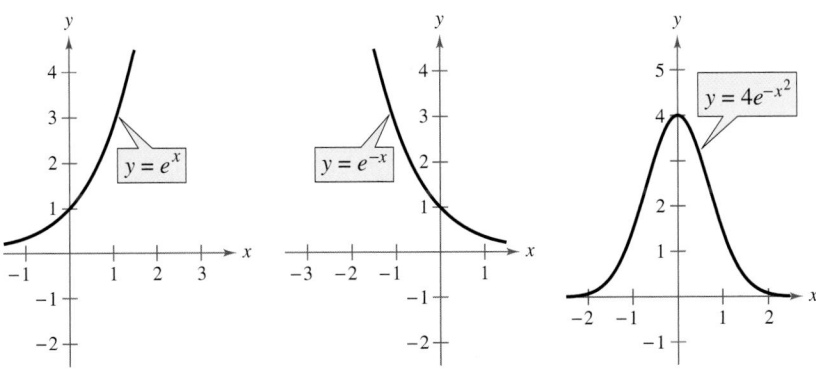

Exponential Growth Model   Exponential Decay Model   Gaussian Model

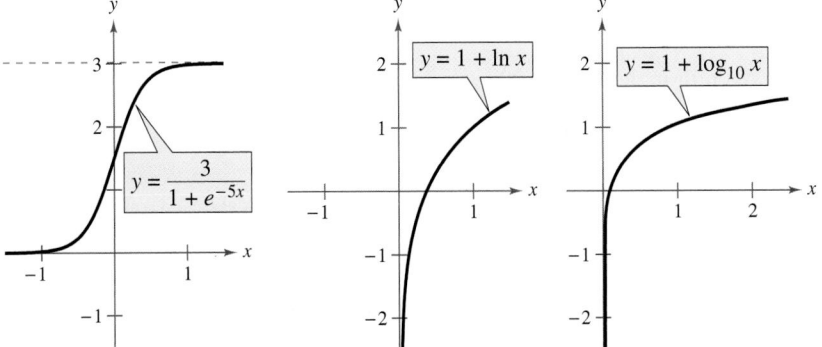

Logistic Growth Model   Natural Logarithmic Model   Common Logarithmic Model
Figure 4.42

You can often gain quite a bit of insight into a situation modeled by an exponential or logarithmic function by identifying and interpreting the function's asymptotes. Use the graphs in Figure 4.42 to identify the asymptotes of each function.

What you should learn

- Recognize the five most common types of models involving exponential or logarithmic functions.
- Use exponential growth and decay functions to model and solve real-life problems.
- Use Gaussian functions to model and solve real-life problems.
- Use logistic growth functions to model and solve real-life problems.
- Use logarithmic functions to model and solve real-life problems

Why you should learn it

Exponential and logarithmic functions can be used to model and solve a variety of business applications. In Exercise 34 on page 370, you will compare an exponential decay model and a linear model for the depreciation of a computer over 3 years.

Spencer Grant/PhotoEdit

Exponential Growth and Decay

Example 1   Population Growth

Estimates of the world population (in millions) from 1995 through 2004 are shown in the table. A scatter plot of the data is shown in Figure 4.43.   (Source: U.S. Bureau of the Census)

Year	Population, P
1995	5685
1996	5764
1997	5844
1998	5923
1999	6002

Year	Population, P
2000	6079
2001	6154
2002	6228
2003	6302
2004	6376

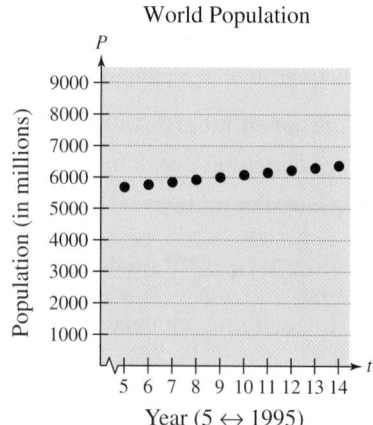

World Population

Figure 4.43

An exponential growth model that approximates this data is given by

$$P = 5344e^{0.012744t}, \qquad 5 \le t \le 14$$

where P is the population (in millions) and $t = 5$ represents 1995. Compare the values given by the model with the estimates shown in the table. According to this model, when will the world population reach 6.8 billion?

Algebraic Solution

The following table compares the two sets of population figures.

Year	1995	1996	1997	1998	1999	2000	2001	2002	2003	2004
Population	5685	5764	5844	5923	6002	6079	6154	6228	6302	6376
Model	5696	5769	5843	5918	5993	6070	6148	6227	6307	6388

To find when the world population will reach 6.8 billion, let $P = 6800$ in the model and solve for t.

$5344e^{0.012744t} = P$	Write original model.
$5344e^{0.012744t} = 6800$	Substitute 6800 for P.
$e^{0.012744t} \approx 1.27246$	Divide each side by 5344.
$\ln e^{0.012744t} \approx \ln 1.27246$	Take natural log of each side.
$0.012744t \approx 0.24095$	Inverse Property
$t \approx 18.9$	Divide each side by 0.012744.

According to the model, the world population will reach 6.8 billion in 2008.

☑ *Checkpoint* Now try Exercise 27.

Graphical Solution

Use a graphing utility to graph the model $y = 5344e^{0.012744x}$ and the data in the same viewing window. You can see in Figure 4.44 that the model appears to closely fit the data.

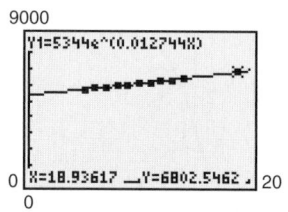

Figure 4.44

Use the *zoom* and *trace* features of the graphing utility to find that the approximate value of x for $y = 6800$ is $x \approx 18.9$. So, according to the model, the world population will reach 6.8 billion in 2008.

An exponential model increases (or decreases) by the same percent each year. What is the annual percent increase for the model in Example 1?

In Example 1, you were given the exponential growth model. Sometimes you must find such a model. One technique for doing this is shown in Example 2.

Example 2   Modeling Population Growth

In a research experiment, a population of fruit flies is increasing according to the law of exponential growth. After 2 days there are 100 flies, and after 4 days there are 300 flies. How many flies will there be after 5 days?

Solution

Let y be the number of flies at time t (in days). From the given information, you know that $y = 100$ when $t = 2$ and $y = 300$ when $t = 4$. Substituting this information into the model $y = ae^{bt}$ produces

$$100 = ae^{2b} \quad \text{and} \quad 300 = ae^{4b}.$$

To solve for b, solve for a in the first equation.

$$100 = ae^{2b} \quad\Longrightarrow\quad a = \frac{100}{e^{2b}} \qquad \text{Solve for } a \text{ in the first equation.}$$

Then substitute the result into the second equation.

$300 = ae^{4b}$	Write second equation.
$300 = \left(\dfrac{100}{e^{2b}}\right)e^{4b}$	Substitute $\dfrac{100}{e^{2b}}$ for a.
$\dfrac{300}{100} = e^{2b}$	Divide each side by 100.
$\ln \dfrac{300}{100} = \ln e^{2b}$	Take natural log of each side.
$\ln 3 = 2b$	Inverse Property
$\dfrac{1}{2}\ln 3 = b$	Solve for b.

Using $b = \frac{1}{2}\ln 3$ and the equation you found for a, you can determine that

$a = \dfrac{100}{e^{2[(1/2)\ln 3]}}$	Substitute $\frac{1}{2}\ln 3$ for b.
$= \dfrac{100}{e^{\ln 3}}$	Simplify.
$= \dfrac{100}{3} \approx 33.33.$	Inverse Property

So, with $a \approx 33.33$ and $b = \frac{1}{2}\ln 3 \approx 0.5493$, the exponential growth model is

$$y = 33.33e^{0.5493t},$$

as shown in Figure 4.45. This implies that after 5 days, the population will be

$$y = 33.33e^{0.5493(5)} \approx 520 \text{ flies.}$$

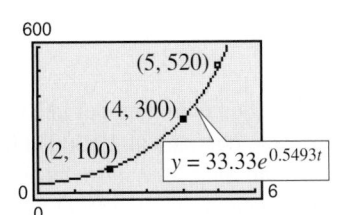

Figure 4.45

✓ *Checkpoint* Now try Exercise 29.

In living organic material, the ratio of the content of radioactive carbon isotopes (carbon 14) to the content of nonradioactive carbon isotopes (carbon 12) is about 1 to 10^{12}. When organic material dies, its carbon 12 content remains fixed, whereas its radioactive carbon 14 begins to decay with a half-life of 5730 years. To estimate the age of dead organic material, scientists use the following formula, which denotes the ratio of carbon 14 to carbon 12 present at any time t (in years).

$$R = \frac{1}{10^{12}} e^{-t/8267}$$ Carbon dating model

The graph of R is shown in Figure 4.46. Note that R decreases as t increases.

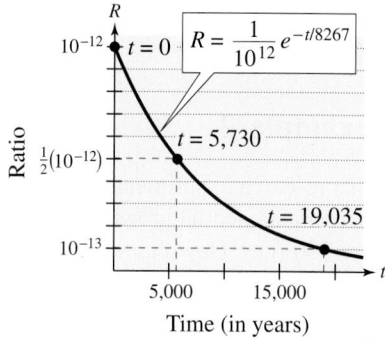

Figure 4.46

Example 3 Carbon Dating

The ratio of carbon 14 to carbon 12 in a newly discovered fossil is

$$R = \frac{1}{10^{13}}.$$

Estimate the age of the fossil.

Algebraic Solution

In the carbon dating model, substitute the given value of R to obtain the following.

$$\frac{1}{10^{12}} e^{-t/8267} = R \qquad \text{Write original model.}$$

$$\frac{e^{-t/8267}}{10^{12}} = \frac{1}{10^{13}} \qquad \text{Substitute } \frac{1}{10^{13}} \text{ for } R.$$

$$e^{-t/8267} = \frac{1}{10} \qquad \text{Multiply each side by } 10^{12}.$$

$$\ln e^{-t/8267} = \ln \frac{1}{10} \qquad \text{Take natural log of each side.}$$

$$-\frac{t}{8267} \approx -2.3026 \qquad \text{Inverse Property}$$

$$t \approx 19{,}036 \qquad \text{Multiply each side by } -8267.$$

So, to the nearest thousand years, you can estimate the age of the fossil to be 19,000 years.

✓ *Checkpoint* Now try Exercise 32.

Graphical Solution

Use a graphing utility to graph the formula for the ratio of carbon 14 to carbon 12 at any time t as

$$y_1 = \frac{1}{10^{12}} e^{-x/8267}.$$

In the same viewing window, graph $y_2 = 1/(10^{13})$. Use the *intersect* feature or the *zoom* and *trace* features of the graphing utility to estimate that $x \approx 19{,}035$ when $y = 1/(10^{13})$, as shown in Figure 4.47.

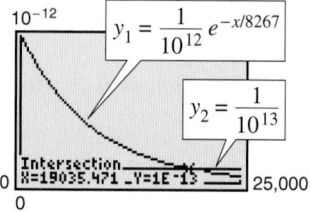

Figure 4.47

So, to the nearest thousand years, you can estimate the age of the fossil to be 19,000 years.

The carbon dating model in Example 3 assumed that the carbon 14 to carbon 12 ratio was one part in 10,000,000,000,000. Suppose an error in measurement occurred and the actual ratio was only one part in 8,000,000,000,000. The fossil age corresponding to the actual ratio would then be approximately 17,000 years. Try checking this result.

Gaussian Models

As mentioned at the beginning of this section, Gaussian models are of the form

$$y = ae^{-(x-b)^2/c}.$$

This type of model is commonly used in probability and statistics to represent populations that are **normally distributed.** For *standard* normal distributions, the model takes the form

$$y = \frac{1}{\sqrt{2\pi}}e^{-x^2/2}.$$

The graph of a Gaussian model is called a **bell-shaped curve.** Try graphing the normal distribution curve with a graphing utility. Can you see why it is called a bell-shaped curve?

The average value for a population can be found from the bell-shaped curve by observing where the maximum y-value of the function occurs. The x-value corresponding to the maximum y-value of the function represents the average value of the independent variable—in this case, x.

Example 4   SAT Scores

In 2002, the Scholastic Aptitude Test (SAT) mathematics scores for college-bound seniors roughly followed the normal distribution

$$y = 0.0035e^{-(x-516)^2/25,992}, \qquad 200 \le x \le 800$$

where x is the SAT score for mathematics. Use a graphing utility to graph this function and estimate the average SAT score.   (Source: College Board)

Solution

The graph of the function is shown in Figure 4.48. On this bell-shaped curve, the maximum value of the curve represents the average score. Using the *maximum* feature or the *zoom* and *trace* features of the graphing utility, you can see that the average mathematics score for college-bound seniors in 2002 was 516.

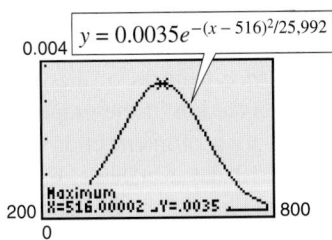

Figure 4.48

TECHNOLOGY SUPPORT

For instructions on how to use the *maximum* feature, see Appendix A; for specific keystrokes, go to the text website at *college.hmco.com*.

✓ *Checkpoint* Now try Exercise 37.

In Example 4, note that 50% of the seniors who took the test received a score lower than 516.

Logistic Growth Models

Some populations initially have rapid growth, followed by a declining rate of growth, as indicated by the graph in Figure 4.49. One model for describing this type of growth pattern is the **logistic curve** given by the function

$$y = \frac{a}{1 + be^{-rx}}$$

where y is the population size and x is the time. An example is a bacteria culture that is initially allowed to grow under ideal conditions, and then under less favorable conditions that inhibit growth. A logistic growth curve is also called a **sigmoidal curve.**

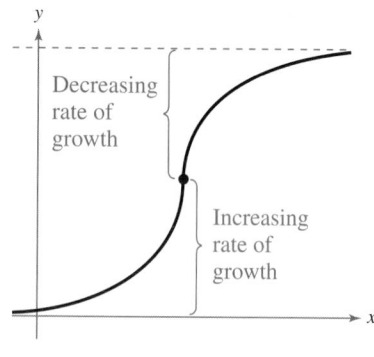

Figure 4.49 Logistic Curve

Example 5   Spread of a Virus

On a college campus of 5000 students, one student returns from vacation with a contagious flu virus. The spread of the virus is modeled by

$$y = \frac{5000}{1 + 4999e^{-0.8t}}, \qquad t \geq 0$$

where y is the total number infected after t days. The college will cancel classes when 40% or more of the students are infected. (a) How many students are infected after 5 days? (b) After how many days will the college cancel classes?

Algebraic Solution

a. After 5 days, the number of students infected is

$$y = \frac{5000}{1 + 4999e^{-0.8(5)}} = \frac{5000}{1 + 4999e^{-4}} \approx 54.$$

b. Classes are cancelled when the number of infected students is $(0.40)(5000) = 2000$.

$$2000 = \frac{5000}{1 + 4999e^{-0.8t}}$$

$$1 + 4999e^{-0.8t} = 2.5$$

$$e^{-0.8t} \approx \frac{1.5}{4999}$$

$$\ln e^{-0.8t} \approx \ln \frac{1.5}{4999}$$

$$-0.8t \approx \ln \frac{1.5}{4999}$$

$$t = -\frac{1}{0.8} \ln \frac{1.5}{4999} \approx 10.14$$

So, after about 10 days, at least 40% of the students will be infected, and classes will be canceled.

✓ *Checkpoint* Now try Exercise 39.

Graphical Solution

a. Use a graphing utility to graph $y = \dfrac{5000}{1 + 4999e^{-0.8x}}$.

Use the *value* feature or the *zoom* and *trace* features of the graphing utility to estimate that $y = 54$ when $x = 5$. So, after 5 days, about 54 students will be infected.

b. Classes are cancelled when the number of infected students is $(0.40)(5000) = 2000$. Use a graphing utility to graph

$$y_1 = \frac{5000}{1 + 4999e^{-0.8x}} \qquad \text{and} \qquad y_2 = 2000$$

in the same viewing window. Use the *intersect* feature or the *zoom* and *trace* features of the graphing utility to find the point of intersection of the graphs. In Figure 4.50, you can see that the point of intersection occurs near $x \approx 10.14$. So, after about 10 days, at least 40% of the students will be infected, and classes will be canceled.

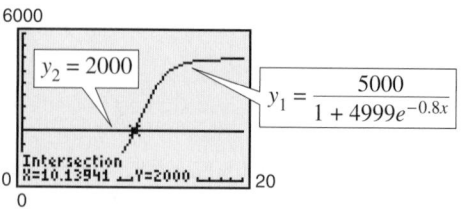

Figure 4.50

Logarithmic Models

On the Richter scale, the magnitude R of an earthquake of intensity I is given by

$$R = \log_{10} \frac{I}{I_0}$$

where $I_0 = 1$ is the minimum intensity used for comparison. Intensity is a measure of the wave energy of an earthquake.

Example 6   Magnitudes of Earthquakes

On January 22, 2003, an earthquake of magnitude 7.6 in Colima, Mexico killed at least 29 people and left 10,000 people homeless.

In 2001, the coast of Peru experienced an earthquake that measured 8.4 on the Richter scale. In 2003, Colima, Mexico experienced an earthquake that measured 7.6 on the Richter scale. Find the intensity of each earthquake and compare the two intensities.

Solution

Because $I_0 = 1$ and $R = 8.4$, you have

$$8.4 = \log_{10} \frac{I}{1} \qquad \text{Substitute 1 for } I_0 \text{ and 8.4 for } R.$$

$$10^{8.4} = 10^{\log_{10} I} \qquad \text{Exponentiate each side.}$$

$$10^{8.4} = I \qquad \text{Inverse Property}$$

$$251{,}189{,}000 \approx I. \qquad \text{Use a calculator.}$$

For $R = 7.6$, you have

$$7.6 = \log_{10} \frac{I}{1} \qquad \text{Substitute 1 for } I_0 \text{ and 7.6 for } R.$$

$$10^{7.6} = 10^{\log_{10} I} \qquad \text{Exponentiate each side.}$$

$$10^{7.6} = I \qquad \text{Inverse Property}$$

$$39{,}811{,}000 \approx I. \qquad \text{Use a calculator.}$$

Note that an increase of 0.8 unit on the Richter scale (from 7.6 to 8.4) represents an increase in intensity by a factor of

$$\frac{251{,}189{,}000}{39{,}811{,}000} \approx 6.$$

In other words, the 2001 earthquake had an intensity about 6 times greater than that of the 2003 earthquake.

✓ *Checkpoint* Now try Exercise 41.

4.5 Exercises

Vocabulary Check

Fill in the blanks.

1. An exponential growth model has the form _____ .

2. A logarithmic model has the form _____ or _____ .

3. A _____ model has the form $y = \dfrac{a}{1 + be^{-rx}}$.

4. The graph of a Gaussian model is called a _____ .

5. A logistic curve is also called a _____ curve.

**In Exercises 1–6, match the function with its graph.
[The graphs are labeled (a), (b), (c), (d), (e), and (f).]**

(a)
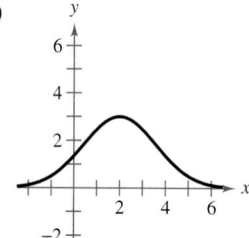

(b)
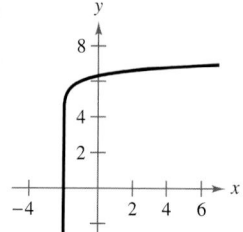

(c)
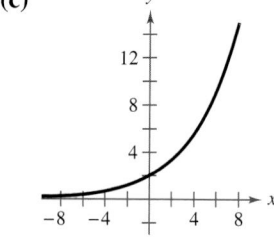

(d)
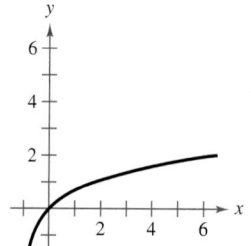

(e)
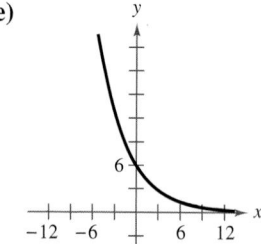

(f)
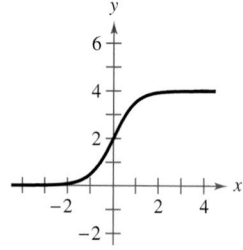

1. $y = 2e^{x/4}$

2. $y = 6e^{-x/4}$

3. $y = 6 + \log_{10}(x + 2)$

4. $y = 3e^{-(x-2)^2/5}$

5. $y = \ln(x + 1)$

6. $y = \dfrac{4}{1 + e^{-2x}}$

Compound Interest **In Exercises 7–14, complete the table for a savings account in which interest is compounded continuously.**

	Initial Investment	Annual % Rate	Time to Double	Amount After 10 Years
7.	$1000	3.5%		
8.	$20,000	$10\frac{1}{2}\%$		
9.	$750		$7\frac{3}{4}$ yr	
10.	$10,000		12 yr	
11.	$500			$1292.85
12.	$600			$1505.00
13.		4.5%		$10,000.00
14.		2%		$2000.00

15. *Compound Interest* Complete the table for the time t necessary for P dollars to triple if interest is compounded continuously at rate r. Create a scatter plot of the data.

r	2%	4%	6%	8%	10%	12%
t						

16. *Compound Interest* Complete the table for the time t necessary for P dollars to triple if interest is compounded annually at rate r. Create a scatter plot of the data.

r	2%	4%	6%	8%	10%	12%
t						

17. Comparing Investments If $1 is invested in an account over a 10-year period, the amount in the account, where t represents the time in years, is given by

$$A = 1 + 0.075[\![t]\!] \quad \text{or} \quad A = e^{0.07t}$$

depending on whether the account pays simple interest at $7\frac{1}{2}\%$ or continuous compound interest at 7%. Use a graphing utility to graph each function in the same viewing window. Which grows at a faster rate? (Remember that $[\![t]\!]$ is the greatest integer function discussed in Section 1.4.)

18. Comparing Investments If $1 is invested in an account over a 10-year period, the amount in the account, where t represents the time in years, is given by

$$A = 1 + 0.06[\![t]\!] \quad \text{or} \quad A = \left(1 + \frac{0.055}{365}\right)^{[\![365t]\!]}$$

depending on whether the account pays simple interest at 6% or compound interest at $5\frac{1}{2}\%$ compounded daily. Use a graphing utility to graph each function in the same viewing window. Which grows at a faster rate?

Radioactive Decay In Exercises 19–22, complete the table for the radioactive isotope.

Isotope	Half-Life (years)	Initial Quantity	Amount After 1000 Years
19. ^{226}Ra	1600	10 g	
20. ^{226}Ra	1600		1.5 g
21. ^{14}C	5730	3 g	
22. ^{239}Pu	24,110		0.4 g

In **Exercises 23–26, find the exponential model**
$y = ae^{bx}$ **that fits the points given in the graph or table.**

23.

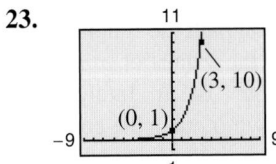

24.

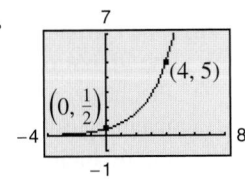

25.

x	y
0	4
5	1

26.

x	y
0	1
3	$\frac{1}{4}$

27. Population The table shows the populations (in millions) of five countries in 2000 and the projected populations (in millions) for the year 2010. (Source: U.S. Census Bureau)

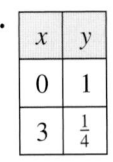

Country	2000	2010
Australia	19.2	20.9
Canada	31.3	34.3
Philippines	81.2	97.9
South Africa	43.4	41.1
Turkey	65.7	73.3

(a) Find the exponential growth or decay model, $y = ae^{bt}$ or $y = ae^{-bt}$, for the population of each country by letting $t = 0$ correspond to 2000. Use the model to predict the population of each country in 2030.

(b) You can see that the populations of Australia and Turkey are growing at different rates. What constant in the equation $y = ae^{bt}$ is determined by these different growth rates? Discuss the relationship between the different growth rates and the magnitude of the constant.

(c) You can see that the population of Canada is increasing while the population of South Africa is decreasing. What constant in the equation $y = ae^{bt}$ reflects this difference? Explain.

28. Population The population P (in thousands) of Bellevue, Washington is given by

$$P = 110e^{kt}$$

where $t = 0$ represents the year 2000. In 1980, the population was 74,000. Find the value of k and use this result to predict the population in the year 2020. (Source: U.S. Census Bureau)

29. Bacteria Growth The number N of bacteria in a culture is given by the model

$$N = 100e^{kt}$$

where t is the time (in hours). If $N = 300$ when $t = 5$, estimate the time required for the population to double in size. Verify your estimate graphically.

30. Bacteria Growth The number N of bacteria in a culture is given by the model $N = 250e^{kt}$, where t is the time (in hours). If $N = 280$ when $t = 10$, estimate the time required for the population to double in size. Verify your estimate graphically.

31. Radioactive Decay The half-life of radioactive radium (^{226}Ra) is 1620 years. What percent of a present amount of radioactive radium will remain after 100 years?

32. Carbon Dating Carbon 14 (^{14}C) dating assumes that the carbon dioxide on Earth today has the same radioactive content as it did centuries ago. If this is true, the amount of ^{14}C absorbed by a tree that grew several centuries ago should be the same as the amount of ^{14}C absorbed by a tree growing today. A piece of ancient charcoal contains only 15% as much radioactive carbon as a piece of modern charcoal. How long ago was the tree burned to make the ancient charcoal if the half-life of ^{14}C is 5730 years?

33. Depreciation A sport utility vehicle (SUV) that cost \$32,000 new has a book value of \$18,000 after 2 years.

(a) Find the linear model $V = mt + b$.

(b) Find the exponential model $V = ae^{kt}$.

(c) Use a graphing utility to graph the two models in the same viewing window. Which model depreciates faster in the first year?

(d) Use each model to find the book values of the SUV after 1 year and after 3 years.

(e) Interpret the slope of the linear model.

34. Depreciation A computer that cost \$2000 new has a book value of \$500 after 2 years.

(a) Find the linear model $V = mt + b$.

(b) Find the exponential model $V = ae^{kt}$.

(c) Use a graphing utility to graph the two models in the same viewing window. Which model depreciates faster in the first year?

(d) Use each model to find the book values of the computer after 1 year and after 3 years.

(e) Interpret the slope of the linear model.

35. Sales The sales S (in thousands of units) of a new CD burner after it has been on the market t years are given by $S = 100(1 - e^{kt})$. Fifteen thousand units of the new product were sold the first year.

(a) Complete the model by solving for k.

(b) Use a graphing utility to graph the model.

(c) Use the graph in part (b) to estimate the number of units sold after 5 years.

36. Sales The sales S (in thousands of units) of a cleaning solution after x hundred dollars is spent on advertising are given by

$$S = 10(1 - e^{kx}).$$

When \$500 is spent on advertising, 2500 units are sold.

(a) Complete the model by solving for k.

(b) Estimate the number of units that will be sold if advertising expenditures are raised to \$700.

37. IQ Scores The IQ scores for adults roughly follow the normal distribution

$$y = 0.0266e^{-(x-100)^2/450}, \quad 70 \leq x \leq 115$$

where x is the IQ score.

(a) Use a graphing utility to graph the function.

(b) From the graph in part (a), estimate the average IQ score.

38. Education The time (in hours per week) a student uses a math lab roughly follows the normal distribution

$$y = 0.7979e^{-(x-5.4)^2/0.5}, \quad 4 \leq x \leq 7$$

where x is the time spent in the lab.

(a) Use a graphing utility to graph the function.

(b) From the graph in part (a), estimate the average time a student spends per week in the math lab.

39. Wildlife A conservation organization releases 100 animals of an endangered species into a game preserve. The organization believes that the preserve has a carrying capacity of 1000 animals and that the growth of the herd will follow the logistic curve

$$p(t) = \frac{1000}{1 + 9e^{-0.1656t}}$$

where t is measured in months.

(a) Use a graphing utility to graph the function. Use the graph to determine the values of p at which the horizontal asymptotes occur. Interpret the meaning of the larger asymptote in the context of the problem.

(b) Estimate the population after 5 months.

(c) When will the population reach 500?

40. *Yeast Growth*   The amount Y of yeast in a culture is given by the model

$$Y = \frac{663}{1 + 72e^{-0.547t}}, \quad 0 \le t \le 18$$

where t represents the time (in hours).

(a) Use a graphing utility to graph the model.

(b) Use the model to predict the population for the 19th hour and the 30th hour.

(c) According to this model, what is the limiting value of the population?

(d) Why do you think the population of yeast follows a logistic growth model instead of an exponential growth model?

Geology   **In Exercises 41 and 42, use the Richter scale (see page 367) for measuring the magnitudes of earthquakes.**

41. Find the intensities I of the following earthquakes measuring R on the Richter scale (let $I_0 = 1$).

(a) Figi Islands in 2003, $R = 6.5$

(b) Central Alaska in 2002, $R = 7.9$

(c) Northern California in 2000, $R = 5.2$

42. Find the magnitudes R of the following earthquakes of intensity I (let $I_0 = 1$).

(a) $I = 39,811,000$ (b) $I = 12,589,000$

(c) $I = 251,200$

Sound Intensity   **In Exercises 43–46, use the following information for determining sound intensity. The level of sound β (in decibels) with an intensity I is $\beta = 10 \log_{10}(I/I_0)$, where I_0 is an intensity of 10^{-12} watt per square meter, corresponding roughly to the faintest sound that can be heard by the human ear. In Exercises 43 and 44, find the level of sound β.**

43. (a) $I = 10^{-10}$ watt per m² (quiet room)

(b) $I = 10^{-5}$ watt per m² (busy street corner)

(c) $I \approx 10^0$ watt per m² (threshold of pain)

44. (a) $I = 10^{-4}$ watt per m² (door slamming)

(b) $I = 10^{-3}$ watt per m² (loud car horn)

(c) $I = 10^{-2}$ watt per m² (siren at 30 meters)

45. As a result of the installation of a muffler, the noise level of an engine was reduced from 88 to 72 decibels. Find the percent decrease in the intensity level of the noise due to the installation of the muffler.

46. As a result of the installation of noise suppression materials, the noise level in an auditorium was reduced from 93 to 80 decibels. Find the percent decrease in the intensity level of the noise due to the installation of these materials.

pH Levels   **In Exercises 47–50, use the acidity model given by $pH = -\log_{10}[H^+]$, where acidity (pH) is a measure of the hydrogen ion concentration $[H^+]$ (measured in moles of hydrogen per liter) of a solution.**

47. Find the pH if $[H^+] = 2.3 \times 10^{-5}$.

48. Compute $[H^+]$ for a solution for which pH $= 5.8$.

49. A grape has a pH of 3.5, and milk of magnesia has a pH of 10.5. The hydrogen ion concentration of the grape is how many times that of the milk of magnesia?

50. The pH of a solution is decreased by one unit. The hydrogen ion concentration is increased by what factor?

51. *Home Mortgage*   A \$120,000 home mortgage for 30 years at $7\frac{1}{2}\%$ has a monthly payment of \$839.06. Part of the monthly payment goes toward the interest charge on the unpaid balance, and the remainder of the payment is used to reduce the principal. The amount that goes toward the interest is given by

$$u = M - \left(M - \frac{Pr}{12}\right)\left(1 + \frac{r}{12}\right)^{12t}$$

and the amount that goes toward reduction of the principal is given by

$$v = \left(M - \frac{Pr}{12}\right)\left(1 + \frac{r}{12}\right)^{12t}.$$

In these formulas, P is the size of the mortgage, r is the interest rate, M is the monthly payment, and t is the time (in years).

(a) Use a graphing utility to graph each function in the same viewing window. (The viewing window should show all 30 years of mortgage payments.)

(b) In the early years of the mortgage, the larger part of the monthly payment goes for what purpose? Approximate the time when the monthly payment is evenly divided between interest and principal reduction.

(c) Repeat parts (a) and (b) for a repayment period of 20 years ($M = \$966.71$). What can you conclude?

52. *Home Mortgage* The total interest u paid on a home mortgage of P dollars at interest rate r for t years is given by

$$u = P\left[\dfrac{rt}{1 - \left(\dfrac{1}{1 + r/12}\right)^{12t}} - 1\right].$$

Consider a $120,000 home mortgage at $7\frac{1}{2}\%$.

(a) Use a graphing utility to graph the total interest function.

(b) Approximate the length of the mortgage when the total interest paid is the same as the size of the mortgage. Is it possible that a person could pay twice as much in interest charges as the size of his or her mortgage?

53. *Newton's Law of Cooling* At 8:30 A.M., a coroner was called to the home of a person who had died during the night. In order to estimate the time of death, the coroner took the person's temperature twice. At 9:00 A.M. the temperature was $85.7°$F, and at 11:00 A.M. the temperature was $82.8°$F. From these two temperatures the coroner was able to determine that the time elapsed since death and the body temperature were related by the formula

$$t = -10 \ln \dfrac{T - 70}{98.6 - 70}$$

where t is the time (in hours elapsed since the person died) and T is the temperature (in degrees Fahrenheit) of the person's body. Assume that the person had a normal body temperature of $98.6°$F at death and that the room temperature was a constant $70°$F. Use the formula to estimate the time of death of the person. (This formula is derived from a general cooling principle called Newton's Law of Cooling.)

54. *Newton's Law of Cooling* You take a five-pound package of steaks out of a freezer at 11 A.M. and place it in the refrigerator. Will the steaks be thawed in time to be grilled at 6 P.M.? Assume that the refrigerator temperature is $40°$F and the freezer temperature is $0°$F. Use the formula for Newton's Law of Cooling

$$t = -5.05 \ln \dfrac{T - 40}{0 - 40}$$

where t is the time in hours (with $t = 0$ corresponding to 11 A.M.) and T is the temperature of the package of steaks (in degrees Fahrenheit).

Synthesis

True or False? In Exercises 55–58, determine whether the statement is true or false. Justify your answer.

55. The domain of a logistic growth function cannot be the set of real numbers.

56. The graph of a logistic growth function will always have an x-intercept.

57. The graph of a Gaussian model will never have an x-intercept.

58. The graph of a Gaussian model will always have a maximum point.

Review

In Exercises 59–62, match the equation with its graph, and identify any intercepts. [The graphs are labeled (a), (b), (c), and (d).]

(a)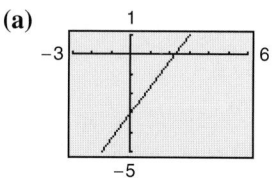

(b)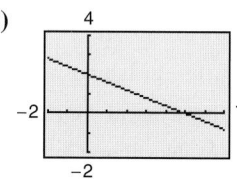

(c)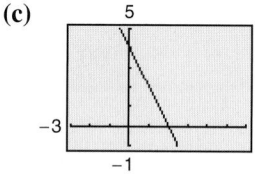

(d)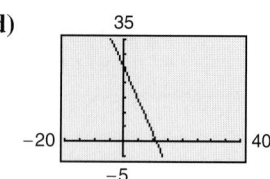

59. $4x - 3y - 9 = 0$

60. $2x + 5y - 10 = 0$

61. $y = 25 - 2.25x$

62. $\dfrac{x}{2} + \dfrac{y}{4} = 1$

In Exercises 63–66, use the Leading Coefficient Test to determine the right-hand and left-hand behavior of the graph of the polynomial function.

63. $f(x) = 2x^3 - 3x^2 + x - 1$

64. $f(x) = 5 - x^2 - 4x^4$

65. $g(x) = -1.6x^5 + 4x^2 - 2$

66. $g(x) = 7x^6 + 9.1x^5 - 3.2x^4 + 25x^3$

In Exercises 67 and 68, divide using synthetic division.

67. $(2x^3 - 8x^2 + 3x - 9) \div (x - 4)$

68. $(x^4 - 3x + 1) \div (x + 5)$

4.6 Exploring Data: Nonlinear Models

Classifying Scatter Plots

In Section 2.6, you saw how to fit linear models to data and in Section 3.7, you saw how to fit quadratic models to data. In real life, many relationships between two variables are represented by different types of growth patterns. A scatter plot can be used to give you an idea of which type of model will best fit a set of data.

Example 1   Classifying Scatter Plots

Decide whether each set of data could best be modeled by an exponential model $y = ab^x$ or a logarithmic model $y = a + b \ln x$.

a. (2, 1), (2.5, 1.2), (3, 1.3), (3.5, 1.5), (4, 1.8), (4.5, 2), (5, 2.4), (5.5, 2.5), (6, 3.1), (6.5, 3.8), (7, 4.5), (7.5, 5), (8, 6.5), (8.5, 7.8), (9, 9), (9.5, 10)

b. (2, 2), (2.5, 3.1), (3, 3.8), (3.5, 4.3), (4, 4.6), (4.5, 5.3), (5, 5.6), (5.5, 5.9), (6, 6.2), (6.5, 6.4), (7, 6.9), (7.5, 7.2), (8, 7.6), (8.5, 7.9), (9, 8), (9.5, 8.2)

Solution

Begin by entering the data into a graphing utility. You should obtain the scatter plots shown in Figure 4.51.

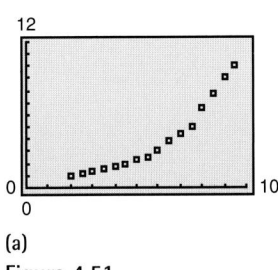
(a)

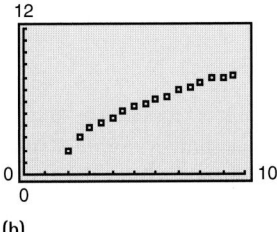
(b)

Figure 4.51

From the scatter plots, it appears that the data in part (a) can be modeled by an exponential function and the data in part (b) can be modeled by a logarithmic function.

✓ *Checkpoint* Now try Exercise 9.

You can change an exponential model of the form $y = ab^x$ to one of the form $y = ae^{cx}$ by rewriting b in the form

$$b = e^{\ln b}.$$

For instance, $y = 3(2^x)$ can be written as

$$y = 3(2^x) = 3e^{(\ln 2)x} \approx 3e^{0.693x}.$$

Fitting Nonlinear Models to Data

Once you have used a scatter plot to determine the type of model that would best fit a set of data, there are several ways that you can actually find the model. Each method is best used with a computer or calculator, rather than with hand calculations.

From Example 1(a), you already know that the data can be modeled by an exponential function. In the next example you will determine whether an exponential model best fits the data.

Example 2   Fitting a Model to Data

Fit the following data from Example 1(a) to a quadratic model, an exponential model, and a power model. Determine which model best fits the data.

(2, 1), (2.5, 1.2), (3, 1.3), (3.5, 1.5), (4, 1.8), (4.5, 2), (5, 2.4), (5.5, 2.5), (6, 3.1), (6.5, 3.8), (7, 4.5), (7.5, 5), (8, 6.5), (8.5, 7.8), (9, 9), (9.5, 10)

Solution

Begin by entering the data into a graphing utility. Then use the *regression* feature of the graphing utility to find quadratic, exponential, and power models for the data, as shown in Figure 4.52.

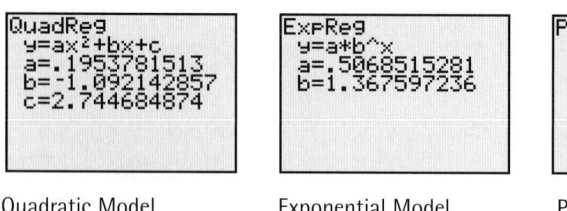

Quadratic Model

Exponential Model

Power Model

Figure 4.52

TECHNOLOGY SUPPORT

For instructions on how to use the *regression* feature, see Appendix A; for specific keystrokes, go to the text website at *college.hmco.com*.

So, a quadratic model for the data is $y = 0.195x^2 - 1.09x + 2.7$; an exponential model for the data is $y = 0.507(1.368)^x$; and a power model for the data is $y = 0.249x^{1.518}$. Plot the data and each model in the same viewing window, as shown in Figure 4.53. To determine which model best fits the data, compare the y-values given by each model with the actual y-values. The model whose y-values are closest to the actual values is the one that fits best. In this case, the best-fitting model is the exponential model.

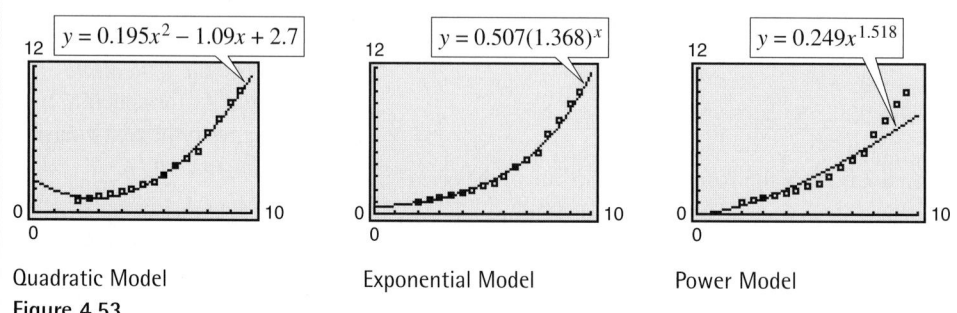

Quadratic Model

Exponential Model

Power Model

Figure 4.53

✓ *Checkpoint* Now try Exercise 27.

Deciding which model best fits a set of data is a question that is studied in detail in statistics. Recall from Section 2.6 that the model that best fits a set of data is the one whose *sum of squared differences* is the least. In Example 2, the sums of squared differences are 0.89 for the quadratic model, 0.85 for the exponential model, and 14.39 for the power model.

Example 3   Fitting a Model to Data

The table shows the yield y (in milligrams) of a chemical reaction after x minutes. Use a graphing utility to find a logarithmic model and a linear model for the data. Determine which model best fits the data.

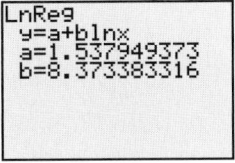

Minutes, x	Yield, y
1	1.5
2	7.4
3	10.2
4	13.4
5	15.8
6	16.3
7	18.2
8	18.3

Solution

Begin by entering the data into a graphing utility. Then use the *regression* feature of the graphing utility to find logarithmic and linear models for the data, as shown in Figure 4.54.

```
LnReg
y=a+blnx
a=1.537949373
b=8.373383316
```

Logarithmic Model

```
LinReg
y=ax+b
a=2.289285714
b=2.335714286
```

Linear Model

Figure 4.54

So, a logarithmic model for the data is $y = 1.538 + 8.373 \ln x$ and a linear model for the data is $y = 2.29x + 2.3$. Plot the data and each model in the same viewing window, as shown in Figure 4.55. To determine which model best fits the data, compare the y-values given by each model with the actual y-values. The model whose y-values are closest to the actual values is the one that fits best. In this case, the best-fitting model is the logarithmic model.

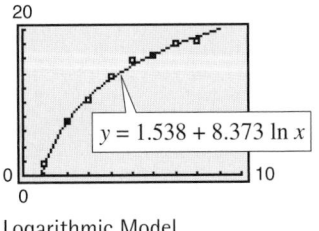

$y = 1.538 + 8.373 \ln x$

Logarithmic Model

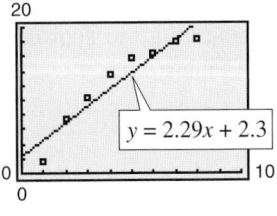

$y = 2.29x + 2.3$

Linear Model

Figure 4.55

> ### Exploration
>
> Use a graphing utility to find a quadratic model for the data in Example 3. Do you think this model fits the data better than the logarithmic model from Example 3? Explain your reasoning.

✓ *Checkpoint* Now try Exercise 29.

In Example 3, the sum of the squared differences for the logarithmic model is 1.55 and the sum of the squared differences for the linear model is 23.86.

Modeling With Exponential and Logistic Functions

Example 4   Fitting an Exponential Model to Data

The table at the right shows the revenue R (in billions of dollars) collected by the Internal Revenue Service (IRS) for selected years from 1960 to 2000. Use a graphing utility to find a model for the data. Then use the model to estimate the revenue collected in 2008.   (Source: Internal Revenue Service)

Year	Revenue, R
1960	91.8
1965	114.4
1970	195.7
1975	293.8
1980	519.4
1985	742.9
1990	1056.4
1995	1375.7
2000	2096.9

Solution

Let x represent the year, with $x = 0$ corresponding to 1960. Begin by entering the data into a graphing utility and displaying the scatter plot, as shown in Figure 4.56.

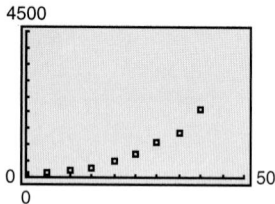

Figure 4.56

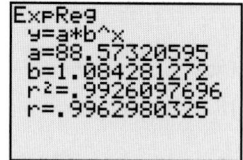

Figure 4.57

From the scatter plot, it appears that an exponential model is a good fit. Use the *regression* feature of the graphing utility to find the exponential model, as shown in Figure 4.57. Change the model to a natural exponential model, as follows.

$$R = 88.57(1.084)^x \qquad \text{Write original model.}$$

$$= 88.57e^{(\ln 1.084)x} \qquad b = e^{\ln b}$$

$$\approx 88.57e^{0.0807x} \qquad \text{Simplify.}$$

Graph the data and the model in the same viewing window, as shown in Figure 4.58. From the model, you can see that the revenue collected by the IRS from 1960 to 2000 had an average annual increase of 8%. From this model, you can estimate the 2008 revenue to be

$$R = 88.57e^{0.0807x} \qquad \text{Write original model.}$$

$$= 88.57e^{0.0807(48)} \approx \$4261.6 \text{ billion} \qquad \text{Substitute 48 for } x.$$

which is more than twice the amount collected in 2000. You can also use the *value* feature or the *zoom* and *trace* features of a graphing utility to approximate the revenue in 2008 to be $4261.6 billion, as shown in Figure 4.58.

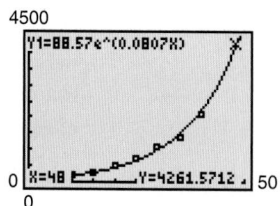

Figure 4.58

 Checkpoint Now try Exercise 33.

The next example demonstrates how to use a graphing utility to fit a logistic model to data.

Example 5   Fitting a Logistic Model to Data

To estimate the amount of defoliation caused by the gypsy moth during a given year, a forester counts the number x of egg masses on $\frac{1}{40}$ of an acre (circle of radius 18.6 feet) in the fall. The percent of defoliation y the next spring is shown in the table.   (Source: USDA, Forest Service)

Egg masses, x	Percent of defoliation, y
0	12
25	44
50	81
75	96
100	99

a. Use the *regression* feature of a graphing utility to find a logistic model for the data.

b. How closely does the model represent the data?

Graphical Solution

a. Enter the data into the graphing utility. Using the *regression* feature of the graphing utility, you can find the logistic model, as shown in Figure 4.59. You can approximate this model to be

$$y = \frac{100}{1 + 7e^{-0.069x}}.$$

b. You can use a graphing utility to graph the actual data and the model in the same viewing window. From Figure 4.60, it appears that the model is a good fit for the actual data.

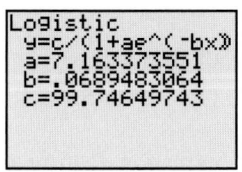

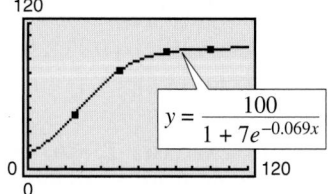

Figure 4.59   Figure 4.60

Numerical Solution

a. Enter the data into the graphing utility. Using the *regression* feature of the graphing utility, you can approximate the logistic model to be

$$y = \frac{100}{1 + 7e^{-0.069x}}.$$

b. You can see how well the model fits the data by comparing the actual values of y with the values of y given by the model, which are labeled y^* in the table below.

x	0	25	50	75	100
y	12	44	81	96	99
y*	12.5	44.5	81.8	96.2	99.3

From the table, you can see that the model appears to be a good fit for the actual data.

✓ *Checkpoint* Now try Exercise 34.

4.6 Exercises

Vocabulary Check

Fill in the blanks.

1. A linear model has the form _____ .

2. A _____ model has the form $y = ax^2 + bx + c$.

3. A power model has the form _____ .

4. One way of determining which model best fits a set of data is to compare the _____ of _____ .

5. An exponential model has the form _____ or _____ .

In Exercises 1–8, determine whether the scatter plot could best be modeled by a linear model, a quadratic model, an exponential model, a logarithmic model, or a logistic model.

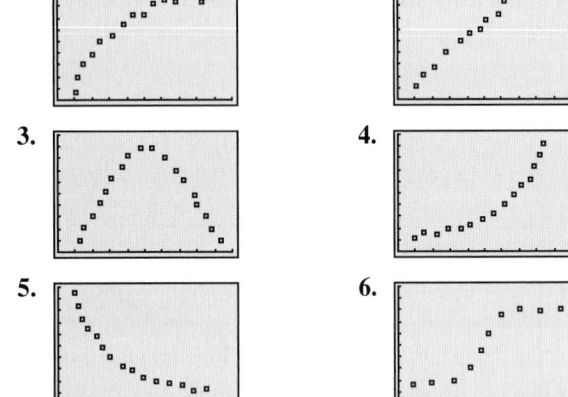

In Exercises 9–14, use a graphing utility to create a scatter plot of the data. Decide whether the data could best be modeled by a linear model, an exponential model, or a logarithmic model.

9. $(1, 2.0), (1.5, 3.5), (2, 4.0), (4, 5.8), (6, 7.0), (8, 7.8)$

10. $(1, 5.8), (1.5, 6.0), (2, 6.5), (4, 7.6), (6, 8.9),$
    $(8, 10.0)$

11. $(1, 4.4), (1.5, 4.7), (2, 5.5), (4, 9.9), (6, 18.1),$
    $(8, 33.0)$

12. $(1, 11.0), (1.5, 9.6), (2, 8.2), (4, 4.5), (6, 2.5),$
    $(8, 1.4)$

13. $(1, 7.5), (1.5, 7.0), (2, 6.8), (4, 5.0), (6, 3.5), (8, 2.0)$

14. $(1, 5.0), (1.5, 6.0), (2, 6.4), (4, 7.8), (6, 8.6), (8, 9.0)$

In Exercises 15–18, use the *regression* feature of a graphing utility to find an exponential model $y = ab^x$ for the data. Use the graphing utility to plot the data and graph the model in the same viewing window.

15. $(0, 4), (1, 5), (2, 6), (3, 8), (4, 12)$

16. $(0, 6.0), (2, 8.9), (4, 20.0), (6, 34.3), (8, 61.1),$
    $(10, 120.5)$

17. $(0, 10.0), (1, 6.1), (2, 4.2), (3, 3.8), (4, 3.6)$

18. $(-3, 120.2), (0, 80.5), (3, 64.8), (6, 58.2),$
    $(10, 55.0)$

In Exercises 19–22, use the *regression* feature of a graphing utility to find a logarithmic model $y = a + b \ln x$ for the data. Use the graphing utility to plot the data and graph the model in the same viewing window.

19. $(1, 2.0), (2, 3.0), (3, 3.5), (4, 4.0), (5, 4.1), (6, 4.2),$
    $(7, 4.5)$

20. $(1, 8.5), (2, 11.4), (4, 12.8), (6, 13.6), (8, 14.2),$
    $(10, 14.6)$

21. $(1, 10), (2, 6), (3, 6), (4, 5), (5, 3), (6, 2)$

22. $(3, 14.6), (6, 11.0), (9, 9.0), (12, 7.6), (15, 6.5)$

In Exercises 23–26, use the *regression* feature of a graphing utility to find a power model $y = ax^b$ for the data. Use the graphing utility to plot the data and graph the model in the same viewing window.

23. $(1, 2.0), (2, 3.4), (5, 6.7), (6, 7.3), (10, 12.0)$

24. $(0.5, 1.0), (2, 12.5), (4, 33.2), (6, 65.7), (8, 98.5),$
    $(10, 150.0)$

25. (1, 10.0), (2, 4.0), (3, 0.7), (4, 0.1)

26. (2, 450), (4, 385), (6, 345), (8, 332), (10, 312)

27. *Elections* The table shows the number R (in millions) of registered voters in the United States for presidential election years from 1972 to 2000. (Source: Federal Election Commission)

Year	Number of voters, R
1972	97.3
1976	105.0
1980	113.0
1984	124.2
1988	126.4
1992	133.8
1996	146.2
2000	156.4

(a) Use the *regression* feature of a graphing utility to find a quadratic model, an exponential model, and a power model for the data. Let x represent the year, with $x = 2$ corresponding to 1972.

(b) Use a graphing utility to graph each model with the original data.

(c) Determine which model best fits the data.

(d) Use the model you chose in part (c) to predict the number of registered voters in 2004.

28. *Consumer Awareness* The table shows the retail price P (in dollars) of a half-gallon package of ice cream for each year from 1995 to 2001. (Source: U.S. Bureau of Labor Statistics)

Year	Retail price, P
1995	2.68
1996	2.94
1997	3.02
1998	3.30
1999	3.40
2000	3.66
2001	3.84

(a) Use the *regression* feature of a graphing utility to find a quadratic model, an exponential model, and a power model for the data. Let x represent the year, with $x = 5$ corresponding to 1995.

(b) Use a graphing utility to graph each model with the original data.

(c) Determine which model best fits the data.

(d) Use the model you chose in part (c) to predict the price of a half-gallon package of ice cream in 2007.

29. *Population* The population y (in millions) of the United States for the years 1992 through 2001 is shown in the table, where x represents the year, with $x = 2$ corresponding to 1992. (Source: U.S. Census Bureau)

Year, x	Population, y
2	257
3	260
4	263
5	267
6	270
7	273
8	276
9	279
10	282
11	285

(a) Use the *regression* feature of a graphing utility to find a linear model for the data.

(b) Use the *regression* feature of a graphing utility to find an exponential model for the data.

(c) Population growth is often exponential. For the 10 years of data given, is the exponential model a better fit than the linear model? Explain.

(d) Use each model to predict the population in the year 2008.

30. *Atmospheric Pressure* The atmospheric pressure decreases with increasing altitude. At sea level, the average air pressure is approximately 1.03323 kilograms per square centimeter, and this pressure is called one atmosphere. Variations in weather conditions cause changes in the atmospheric pressure of up to ± 5 percent. The table shows the pressures p (in atmospheres) for different altitudes h (in kilometers).

Altitude, h	Pressure, p
0	1
5	0.55
10	0.25
15	0.12
20	0.06
25	0.02

Table for 30

(a) Use the *regression* feature of a graphing utility to attempt to find the logarithmic model $p = a + b \ln h$ for the data. Explain why the result is an error message.

(b) Use the *regression* feature of a graphing utility to find the logarithmic model $h = a + b \ln p$ for the data.

(c) Use a graphing utility to plot the data and graph the logarithmic model in the same viewing window.

(d) Use the model to estimate the altitude at which the pressure is 0.75 atmosphere.

(e) Use the graph in part (c) to estimate the pressure at an altitude of 13 kilometers.

31. **Data Analysis** A cup of water at an initial temperature of 78°C is placed in a room at a constant temperature of 21°C. The temperature of the water is measured every 5 minutes for a period of $\frac{1}{2}$ hour. The results are recorded in the table, where t is the time (in minutes) and T is the temperature (in degrees Celsius).

Time, t	Temperature, T
0	78.0°
5	66.0°
10	57.5°
15	51.2°
20	46.3°
25	42.5°
30	39.6°

(a) Use the *regression* feature of a graphing utility to find a linear model for the data. Use the graphing utility to plot the data and graph the model in the same viewing window. Does the data appear linear? Explain.

(b) Use the *regression* feature of a graphing utility to find a quadratic model for the data. Use the graphing utility to plot the data and graph the model in the same viewing window. Does the data appear quadratic? Even though the quadratic model appears to be a good fit, explain why it might not be a good model for predicting the temperature of the water when $t = 60$.

(c) The graph of the model should be asymptotic with the graph of the temperature of the room. Subtract the room temperature from each of the temperatures in the table. Use the *regression* feature of a graphing utility to find an exponential model for the revised data. Add the room temperature to this model. Use a graphing utility to plot the original data and graph the model in the same viewing window.

(d) Explain why the procedure in part (c) was necessary for finding the exponential model.

32. **Sales** The table shows the sales S (in billions of dollars) for Home Depot, Inc. from 1996 to 2001. (Source: The Home Depot, Inc.)

Year	Sales, S
1996	19.5
1997	24.2
1998	30.2
1999	38.4
2000	45.7
2001	53.6

(a) Use the *regression* feature of a graphing utility to find an exponential model for the data. Let x represent the year, with $x = 6$ corresponding to 1996.

(b) Use the graphing utility to graph the model with the original data.

(c) How closely does the model represent the data?

(d) Use the model to estimate the sales for Home Depot, Inc. in 2007.

33. **Sales** The table on the next page shows the sales S (in millions of dollars) for Carnival Corporation from 1996 to 2001. (Source: Carnival Corporation)

Year	Sales, S
1996	2212.6
1997	2447.5
1998	3009.3
1999	3497.5
2000	3778.5
2001	4535.8

Table for 33

(a) Use the *regression* feature of a graphing utility to find an exponential model for the data. Let x represent the year, with $x = 6$ corresponding to 1996.

(b) Use the graphing utility to graph the model with the original data.

(c) How closely does the model represent the data?

(d) Use the model to estimate the sales for Carnival Corporation in 2007.

34. Vital Statistics The table shows the percent P of men who have never been married for different age groups (in years).   (Source: U.S. Census Bureau)

Age Group	Percent, P
18–19	98.3
20–24	83.7
25–29	51.7
30–34	30.0
35–39	20.3
40–44	15.7
45–54	9.5
55–64	5.5
65–74	4.3
75 and over	4.1

(a) Use the *regression* feature of a graphing utility to find a logistic model for the data. Let x represent the age group, with $x = 1$ corresponding to the 18–19 age group.

(b) Use the graphing utility to graph the model with the original data.

(c) How closely does the model represent the data?

35. Comparing Models The amounts y (in billions of dollars) donated to charity (by individuals, foundations, corporations, and charitable bequests) in the United States from 1996 to 2001 are shown in the table, where x represents the year, with $x = 6$ corresponding to 1996.   (Source: AAFRC Trust for Philanthropy)

Year, x	Amount, y
6	138.6
7	157.1
8	174.8
9	199.0
10	210.9
11	212.0

Table for 35

(a) Use the *regression* feature of a graphing utility to find a linear model, a logarithmic model, a quadratic model, an exponential model, and a power model for the data.

(b) Use the graphing utility to graph each model with the original data. Use the graphs to choose the model that you think best fits the data.

(c) For each model, find the sum of the squared differences. Use the results to choose the model that best fits the data.

(d) For each model, find the r^2-value determined by the graphing utility. Use the results to choose the model that best fits the data.

(e) Compare your results from parts (b), (c), and (d).

Synthesis

36. Writing In your own words, explain how to fit a model to a set of data using a graphing utility.

True or False? In Exercises 37 and 38, determine whether the statement is true or false. Justify your answer.

37. The exponential model $y = ae^{bx}$ represents a growth model if $b > 0$.

38. To change an exponential model of the form $y = ab^x$ to one of the form $y = ae^{cx}$, rewrite b as $b = \ln e^b$.

Review

In Exercises 39–42, find the slope and y-intercept of the equation of the line. Then sketch the line by hand.

39. $2x + 5y = 10$

40. $3x - 2y = 9$

41. $1.2x + 3.5y = 10.5$

42. $0.4x - 2.5y = 12.0$

4 Chapter Summary

What did you learn?

Section 4.1	Review Exercises
☐ Recognize and evaluate exponential functions with base a.	1–4
☐ Graph exponential functions.	5–12
☐ Recognize, evaluate, and graph exponential functions with base e.	13–28
☐ Use exponential functions to model and solve real-life problems.	29–32

Section 4.2	
☐ Recognize and evaluate logarithmic functions with base a.	33–40
☐ Graph logarithmic functions.	41–44
☐ Recognize, evaluate, and graph natural logarithmic functions.	45–54
☐ Use logarithmic functions to model and solve real-life problems.	55, 56

Section 4.3	
☐ Rewrite logarithms with different bases.	57–60
☐ Use properties of logarithms to evaluate or rewrite logarithmic expressions.	61–64
☐ Use properties of logarithms to expand or condense logarithmic expressions.	65–76
☐ Use logarithmic functions to model and solve real-life problems.	77, 78

Section 4.4	
☐ Solve simple exponential and logarithmic equations.	79–86
☐ Solve more complicated exponential equations.	87–96
☐ Solve more complicated logarithmic equations.	97–108
☐ Use exponential and logarithmic equations to model and solve real-life problems.	109, 110

Section 4.5	
☐ Recognize the five most common types of models involving exponential or logarithmic functions.	111–116
☐ Use exponential growth and decay functions to model and solve real-life problems.	117–123
☐ Use Gaussian functions to model and solve real-life problems.	124
☐ Use logistic growth functions to model and solve real-life problems.	125
☐ Use logarithmic functions to model and solve real-life problems.	126

Section 4.6	
☐ Classify scatter plots.	127–130
☐ Use scatter plots and a graphing utility to find models for data and choose a model that best fits a set of data.	131
☐ Use a graphing utility to find exponential and logistic models for data.	132, 133

4 Review Exercises

4.1 In Exercises 1–4, use a calculator to evaluate the function at the indicated value of x. Round your result to four decimal places.

Function	Value
1. $f(x) = 1.45^x$	$x = 2\pi$
2. $f(x) = 7^x$	$x = -\sqrt{11}$
3. $g(x) = 60^{2x}$	$x = -1.1$
4. $g(x) = 25^{-3x}$	$x = \frac{3}{2}$

In Exercises 5–8, match the function with its graph. [The graphs are labeled (a), (b), (c), and (d).]

(a)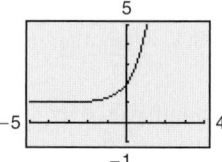

(b)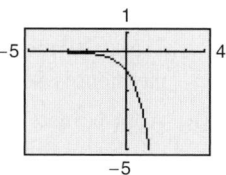

(c)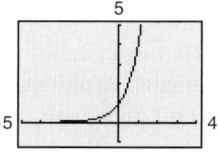

(d)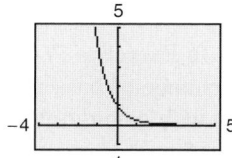

5. $f(x) = 4^x$

6. $f(x) = 4^{-x}$

7. $f(x) = -4^x$

8. $f(x) = 4^x + 1$

In Exercises 9–12, graph the exponential function by hand. Identify any asymptotes and intercepts and determine whether the graph of the function is increasing or decreasing.

9. $f(x) = 6^x$

10. $f(x) = 0.3^{x+1}$

11. $g(x) = 1 + 6^{-x}$

12. $g(x) = 0.3^{-x}$

In Exercises 13–16, use a calculator to evaluate the function $f(x) = e^x$ for the indicated value of x. Round your result to three decimal places.

13. $x = 8$

14. $x = \sqrt{5}$

15. $x = -2.1$

16. $x = -\frac{3}{5}$

In Exercises 17–22, use a graphing utility to construct a table of values for the function. Then sketch the graph of the function.

17. $h(x) = e^{x-1}$

18. $f(x) = e^{x+2}$

19. $h(x) = -e^x$

20. $f(x) = 3 - e^{-x}$

21. $f(x) = 4e^{-0.5x}$

22. $f(x) = 2 + e^{x+3}$

In Exercises 23–28, use a graphing utility to graph the exponential function. Identify any asymptotes of the graph.

23. $g(t) = 8 - 0.5e^{-t/4}$

24. $h(x) = 12(1 + e^{-x/2})$

25. $g(x) = 200e^{4/x}$

26. $f(x) = -8e^{-4/x}$

27. $f(x) = \dfrac{10}{1 + 2^{-0.05x}}$

28. $f(x) = -\dfrac{12}{1 + 4^{-x}}$

Compound Interest In Exercises 29 and 30, complete the table to determine the balance A for $10,000 invested at rate r for t years, compounded continuously.

t	1	10	20	30	40	50
A						

29. $r = 8\%$

30. $r = 3\%$

31. ***Depreciation*** After t years, the value of a car that costs $26,000 is modeled by

$$V(t) = 26{,}000\left(\frac{3}{4}\right)^t.$$

(a) Use a graphing utility to graph the function.

(b) Find the value of the car 2 years after it was purchased.

(c) According to the model, when does the car depreciate most rapidly? Is this realistic? Explain.

32. ***Radioactive Decay*** Let Q represent a mass of plutonium 241 (^{241}Pu), in grams whose half-life is 14 years. The quantity of plutonium present after t years is given by

$$Q = 100\left(\tfrac{1}{2}\right)^{t/14}.$$

(a) Determine the initial quantity (when $t = 0$).

(b) Determine the quantity present after 10 years.

(c) Use a graphing utility to graph the function over the interval $t = 0$ to $t = 100$.

4.2 In Exercises 33–36, write the exponential equation in logarithmic form.

33. $4^3 = 64$

34. $3^5 = 243$

35. $25^{3/2} = 125$

36. $12^{-1} = \frac{1}{12}$

In Exercises 37–40, evaluate the function at the indicated value of x without using a calculator.

Function	Value
37. $f(x) = \log_6 x$	$x = 216$
38. $f(x) = \log_7 x$	$x = 1$
39. $f(x) = \log_4 x$	$x = \frac{1}{4}$
40. $f(x) = \log_{10} x$	$x = 0.001$

In Exercises 41–44, find the domain, vertical asymptote, and x-intercept of the logarithmic function, and sketch its graph by hand. Verify using a graphing utility.

41. $g(x) = -\log_2 x + 5$

42. $g(x) = \log_5(x - 3)$

43. $f(x) = \log_2(x - 1) + 6$

44. $f(x) = \log_5(x + 2) - 3$

In Exercises 45–50, use a calculator to evaluate the function $f(x) = \ln x$ at the indicated value of x. Round your result to three decimal places, if necessary.

45. $x = 21.5$

46. $x = 0.98$

47. $x = e^7$

48. $x = e^{-1/2}$

49. $x = \sqrt{6}$

50. $x = \frac{2}{5}$

In Exercises 51–54, use a graphing utility to graph the logarithmic function. Determine the domain and identify any vertical asymptote and x-intercept.

51. $f(x) = \ln x + 3$

52. $f(x) = \ln(x - 3)$

53. $h(x) = \frac{1}{2} \ln x$

54. $f(x) = \frac{1}{4} \ln x$

55. *Climb Rate* The time t (in minutes) for a small plane to climb to an altitude of h feet is given by

$$t = 50 \log_{10} \frac{18{,}000}{18{,}000 - h}$$

where 18,000 feet is the plane's absolute ceiling.

(a) Determine the domain of the function appropriate for the context of the problem.

(b) Use a graphing utility to graph the function and identify any asymptotes.

(c) As the plane approaches its absolute ceiling, what can be said about the time required to further increase its altitude?

(d) Find the amount of time it will take for the plane to climb to an altitude of 4000 feet.

56. *Home Mortgage* The model

$$t = 12.542 \ln\left(\frac{x}{x - 1000}\right), \quad x > 1000$$

approximates the length of a home mortgage of $150,000 at 8% in terms of the monthly payment. In the model, t is the length of the mortgage in years and x is the monthly payment in dollars.

(a) Use the model to approximate the length of a $150,000 mortgage at 8% when the monthly payment is $1254.68.

(b) Approximate the total amount paid over the term of the mortgage with a monthly payment of $1254.68. What amount of the total is interest costs?

4.3 In Exercises 57–60, evaluate the logarithm using the change-of-base formula. Do each problem twice, once with common logarithms and once with natural logarithms. Round your results to three decimal places.

57. $\log_4 9$

58. $\log_{1/2} 5$

59. $\log_{12} 200$

60. $\log_3 0.28$

In Exercises 61–64, use the properties of logarithms to rewrite and simplify the logarithmic expression.

61. $\ln 20$

62. $\ln(3e^{-4})$

63. $\log_5\left(\frac{1}{15}\right)$

64. $\log_{10} \frac{9}{300}$

In Exercises 65–70, use the properties of logarithms to expand the expression as a sum, difference, and/or constant multiple of logarithms. (Assume all variables are positive.)

65. $\log_5 5x^2$

66. $\log_4 3xy^2$

67. $\log_{10} \frac{5\sqrt{y}}{x^2}$

68. $\ln \frac{\sqrt{x}}{4}$

69. $\ln\left(\frac{x + 3}{xy}\right)$

70. $\ln \frac{xy^5}{\sqrt{z}}$

In Exercises 71–76, condense the expression to the logarithm of a single quantity.

71. $\log_2 5 + \log_2 x$ **72.** $\log_6 y - 2\log_6 z$

73. $\frac{1}{2}\ln(2x - 1) - 2\ln(x + 1)$

74. $5\ln(x - 2) - \ln(x + 2) - 3\ln(x)$

75. $\ln 3 + \frac{1}{3}\ln(4 - x^2) - \ln x$

76. $3[\ln x - 2\ln(x^2 + 1)] + 2\ln 5$

77. Snow Removal The number of miles s of roads cleared of snow is approximated by the model

$$s = 25 - \frac{13\ln(h/12)}{\ln 3}, \quad 2 \leq h \leq 15$$

where h is the depth of the snow (in inches).

(a) Use a graphing utility to graph the function.

(b) Complete the table.

h	4	6	8	10	12	14
s						

(c) Using the graph of the function and the table, what conclusion can you make about the miles of roads cleared as the depth of the snow increases?

78. Human Memory Model Students in a sociology class were given an exam and then retested monthly with an equivalent exam. The average scores for the class are given by the human memory model $f(t) = 85 - 14\log_{10}(t + 1)$, where t is the time in months and $0 \leq t \leq 10$. When will the average score decrease to 71?

4.4 In Exercises 79–86, solve for x.

79. $8^x = 512$ **80.** $3^x = 729$

81. $6^x = \frac{1}{216}$ **82.** $6^{x-2} = 1296$

83. $\log_7 x = 4$ **84.** $\log_x 243 = 5$

85. $\ln x = 4$ **86.** $\ln x = -3$

In Exercises 87–96, solve the exponential equation algebraically. Round your result to three decimal places.

87. $e^x = 12$ **88.** $e^{3x} = 25$

89. $3e^{-5x} = 132$ **90.** $14e^{3x+2} = 560$

91. $2^x + 13 = 35$ **92.** $6^x - 28 = -8$

93. $-4(5^x) = -68$ **94.** $2(12^x) = 190$

95. $e^{2x} - 7e^x + 10 = 0$ **96.** $e^{2x} - 6e^x + 8 = 0$

In Exercises 97–108, solve the logarithmic equation algebraically. Round your result to three decimal places.

97. $\ln 3x = 8.2$ **98.** $\ln 5x = 7.2$

99. $2\ln 4x = 15$ **100.** $4\ln 3x = 15$

101. $\ln x - \ln 3 = 2$ **102.** $\ln\sqrt{x + 8} = 3$

103. $\ln\sqrt{x + 1} = 2$ **104.** $\ln x - \ln 5 = 4$

105. $\log_{10}(x - 1) = \log_{10}(x - 2) - \log_{10}(x + 2)$

106. $\log_{10}(x + 2) - \log_{10} x = \log_{10}(x + 5)$

107. $\log_{10}(1 - x) = -1$ **108.** $\log_{10}(-x - 4) = 2$

109. Compound Interest You deposit $7550 into an account that pays 7.25% interest, compounded continuously. How long will it take for the money to triple?

110. Demand The demand equation for a 32-inch television is modeled by $p = 500 - 0.5e^{0.004x}$. Find the demand x for a price of (a) $p = \$450$ and (b) $p = \$400$.

4.5 In Exercises 111–116, match the function with its graph. [The graphs are labeled (a), (b), (c), (d), (e), and (f).]

(a)
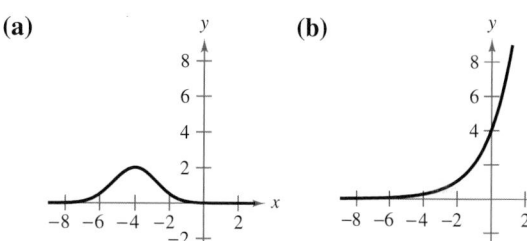

(b)

(c)
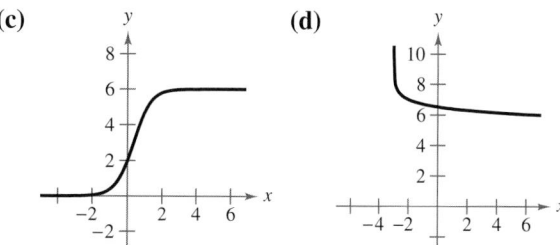

(d)

(e)
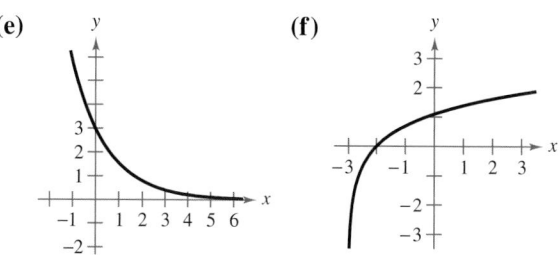

(f)

111. $y = 3e^{-2x/3}$ **112.** $y = 4e^{2x/3}$

113. $y = \ln(x + 3)$ **114.** $y = 7 - \log_{10}(x + 3)$

115. $y = 2e^{-(x+4)^2/3}$ **116.** $y = \dfrac{6}{1 + 2e^{-2x}}$

In Exercises 117–120, find the exponential model $y = ae^{bx}$ that fits the two points.

117. $(0, 2), (4, 3)$ **118.** $(0, 2), (5, 1)$

119. $\left(0, \frac{1}{2}\right), (5, 5)$ **120.** $(0, 4), \left(5, \frac{1}{2}\right)$

121. Population   The population P (in thousands) of Colorado Springs, Colorado is given by

$$P = 361e^{kt}$$

where $t = 0$ represents the year 2000. In 1980, the population was 215,000. Find the value of k and use this result to predict the population in the year 2020.   (Source: U.S. Census Bureau)

122. Radioactive Decay   The half-life of radioactive uranium II (^{234}U) is 245,500 years. What percent of the present amount of radioactive uranium II will remain after 5000 years?

123. Compound Interest   A deposit of $10,000 is made in a savings account for which the interest is compounded continuously. The balance will double in 12 years.

(a) What is the annual interest rate for this account?

(b) Find the balance after 1 year.

124. Test Scores   The test scores for a biology test follow a normal distribution modeled by

$$y = 0.0499e^{-(x-71)^2/128}$$

where x is the test score.

(a) Use a graphing utility to graph the function.

(b) From the graph in part (a), estimate the average test score.

125. Typing Speed   In a typing class, the average number of words per minute N typed after t weeks of lessons was found to be modeled by

$$N = \frac{157}{1 + 5.4e^{-0.12t}}.$$

Find the number of weeks necessary to type (a) 50 words per minute and (b) 75 words per minute.

126. Geology   On the Richter scale, the magnitude R of an earthquake of intensity I is modeled by

$$R = \log_{10}\frac{I}{I_0}$$

where $I_0 = 1$ is the minimum intensity used for comparison. Find the intensities I of the following earthquakes measuring R on the Richter scale.

(a) $R = 8.4$ (b) $R = 6.85$ (c) $R = 9.1$

4.6 **In Exercises 127–130, determine whether the scatter plot could best be modeled by a linear model, a quadratic model, an exponential model, a logarithmic model, or a logistic model.**

127.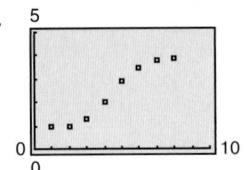

128.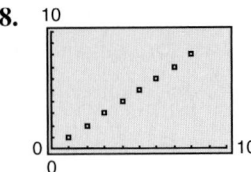

129.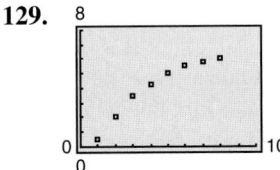

130.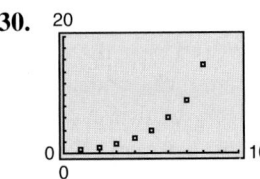

131. Entertainment   The table shows the number M (in thousands) of movie theater screens in the United States for selected years from 1975 to 2000. (Source: Motion Picture Association of America)

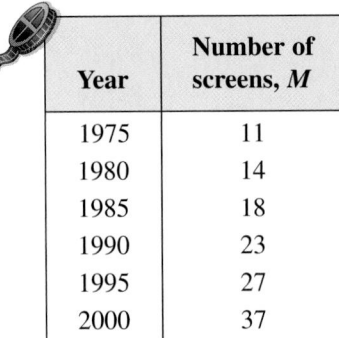

Year	Number of screens, M
1975	11
1980	14
1985	18
1990	23
1995	27
2000	37

(a) Use the *regression* feature of a graphing utility to find a quadratic model, an exponential model, and a power model for the data. Let x represent the year, with $x = 5$ corresponding to 1975.

(b) Use a graphing utility to graph each model with the original data.

(c) Determine which model best fits the data.

(d) Use the model you chose in part (c) to predict the number of movie theater screens in 2007.

132. *Sports*   The table shows the number G of municipal golf facilities in the United States for selected years from 1975 to 2000.   (Source: National Golf Foundation)

Year	Number of facilities, G
1975	1586
1980	1794
1985	1912
1990	2012
1995	2259
2000	2438

(a) Use the *regression* feature of a graphing utility to find an exponential model for the data. Let x represent the year, with $x = 5$ corresponding to 1975.

(b) Use a graphing utility to graph the model with the original data.

(c) How closely does the model represent the data?

(d) Use the model to estimate the number of municipal golf facilities in 2010.

133. *Wildlife*   A lake is stocked with 500 fish, and the fish population P increases every month. The local fish commission records this increase as shown in the table.

Month, x	Population, P
0	500
6	1488
12	3672
18	6583
24	8650
30	9550
36	9860

(a) Use the *regression* feature of a graphing utility to find a logistic model for the data. Let x represent the month.

(b) Use a graphing utility to graph the model with the original data.

(c) How closely does the model represent the data?

(d) What is the limiting size of the population?

Synthesis

134. *Think About It*   Without using a calculator, explain why you know that $2^{\sqrt{2}}$ is greater than 2, but less than 4.

True or False?   **In Exercises 135–140, determine whether the equation or statement is true or false. Justify your answer.**

135. $\log_b b^{2x} = 2x$ **136.** $e^{x-1} = \dfrac{e^x}{e}$

137. $\ln(x + y) = \ln x + \ln y$

138. $\ln(x + y) = \ln(xy)$

139. The domain of the function $f(x) = \ln x$ is the set of all real numbers.

140. The logarithm of the quotient of two numbers is equal to the difference of the logarithms of the numbers.

141. *Pattern Recognition*

(a) Use a graphing utility to compare the graph of the function $y = e^x$ with the graph of each function. [$n!$ (read as "n factorial") is defined as $n! = 1 \cdot 2 \cdot 3 \cdot \; \cdots (n - 1) \cdot n$.]

$$y_1 = 1 + \frac{x}{1!}, \quad y_2 = 1 + \frac{x}{1!} + \frac{x^2}{2!},$$

$$y_3 = 1 + \frac{x}{1!} + \frac{x^2}{2!} + \frac{x^3}{3!}$$

(b) Identify the pattern of successive polynomials given in part (a). Extend the pattern one more term and compare the graph of the resulting polynomial function with the graph of $y = e^x$. What do you think this pattern implies?

4 | Chapter Test

Take this test as you would take a test in class. After you are finished, check your work against the answers given in the back of the book.

In Exercises 1–4, evaluate the expression. Round your result to three decimal places.

1. $12.4^{2.79}$ **2.** $4^{3\pi/2}$ **3.** $e^{-7/10}$ **4.** $e^{3.1}$

In Exercises 5–7, use a graphing utility to construct a table of values for the function. Then sketch a graph of the function.

5. $f(x) = 10^{-x}$ **6.** $f(x) = -6^{x-2}$ **7.** $f(x) = 1 - e^{2x}$

8. Evaluate (a) $\log_7 7^{-0.89}$ and (b) $4.6 \ln e^2$.

In Exercises 9–11, use a graphing utility to graph the function. Determine the domain and identify any vertical asymptote and x-intercept.

9. $f(x) = -\log_{10} x - 6$ **10.** $f(x) = \ln(x - 4)$ **11.** $f(x) = 1 + \ln(x + 6)$

In Exercises 12–14, evaluate the logarithm using the change-of-base formula. Round your result to three decimal places.

12. $\log_7 44$ **13.** $\log_{2/5} 0.9$ **14.** $\log_{24} 68$

In Exercises 15 and 16, use the properties of logarithms to expand the expression as a sum, difference, and/or multiple of logarithms.

15. $\log_2 3a^4$ **16.** $\ln \dfrac{5\sqrt{x}}{6}$

In Exercises 17 and 18, condense the expression to the logarithm of a single quantity.

17. $\log_3 13 + \log_3 y$ **18.** $4 \ln x - 4 \ln y$

In Exercises 19 and 20, solve the equation algebraically. Round your result to three decimal places.

19. $\dfrac{1025}{8 + e^{4x}} = 5$ **20.** $\log_{10} x - \log_{10}(8 - 5x) = 2$

21. The half-life of radioactive actinium (^{227}Ac) is 22 years. What percent of a present amount of radioactive actinium will remain after 19 years?

22. The table at the right shows the mail revenues R (in billions of dollars) for the U.S. Postal Service from 1995 to 2001.   (Source: U.S. Postal Service)

(a) Use the *regression* feature of a graphing utility to find a quadratic model, an exponential model, and a power model for the data. Let x represent the year, with $x = 5$ corresponding to 1995.

(b) Use a graphing utility to graph each model with the original data.

(c) Determine which model best fits the data.

(d) Use the model you chose in part (c) to predict the mail revenues in 2007.

Year	Revenues, R
1995	52.5
1996	54.5
1997	56.3
1998	58.0
1999	60.4
2000	62.3
2001	63.4

3–4 Cumulative Test

Take this test to review the material from earlier chapters. After you are finished, check your work against the answers given in the back of the book.

In Exercises 1–3, sketch the graph of the function. Use a graphing utility to verify the graph.

1. $f(x) = -\frac{1}{2}(x^2 + 4x)$

2. $f(x) = \frac{1}{4}x(x - 2)^2$

3. $f(x) = x^3 + 2x^2 - 9x - 18$

4. Find all the zeros of $f(x) = x^3 + 2x^2 + 4x + 8$.

5. Use a graphing utility to approximate any real zeros of $g(x) = x^3 + 4x^2 - 11$ accurate to three decimal places.

6. Divide $(4x^2 + 14x - 9)$ by $(x + 3)$ using long division.

7. Divide $(2x^3 - 5x^2 + 6x - 20)$ by $(x - 6)$ using synthetic division.

8. Find a polynomial function with real coefficients that has the zeros $0, -3$, and $1 + \sqrt{5}i$.

In Exercises 9–11, sketch the graph of the rational function. Identify any asymptotes. Use a graphing utility to verify the graph.

9. $f(x) = \dfrac{2x}{x - 3}$

10. $f(x) = \dfrac{5x}{x^2 + x - 6}$

11. $f(x) = \dfrac{x^2 - 3x + 8}{x - 2}$

12. Write a rational function whose graph has no vertical asymptotes and has a horizontal asymptote at $y = 4$.

In Exercises 13–16, evaluate the expression without using a calculator.

13. $\log_2 64$

14. $\log_2\left(\dfrac{1}{16}\right)$

15. $\ln e^{10}$

16. $\ln \dfrac{1}{e^3}$

In Exercises 17–20, use a calculator to evaluate the expression. Round your answer to three decimal places.

17. $(1.85)^{3.1}$

18. $58^{\sqrt{5}}$

19. $e^{-20/11}$

20. $4e^{2.56}$

In Exercises 21–24, sketch the graph of the function by hand. Use a graphing utility to verify the graph.

21. $f(x) = -3^{x+4} - 5$

22. $f(x) = -\left(\frac{1}{2}\right)^{-x} - 3$

23. $f(x) = 4 + \log_{10}(x - 3)$

24. $f(x) = \ln(4 - x)$

In Exercises 25–28, evaluate the logarithm using the change-of-base formula. Round your result to three decimal places.

25. $\log_5 21$

26. $\log_9 6.8$

27. $\log_{3/4}(8.61)$

28. $\log_{7/8}\left(\frac{3}{2}\right)$

29. Write $2\ln x - \frac{1}{2}\ln(x + 5)$ as a logarithm of a single quantity.

30. Use the properties of logarithms to expand $\ln\left(x\sqrt[3]{x - 5}\right)$.

In Exercises 31–36, solve the equation algebraically. Round your result to three decimal places and verify your result graphically.

31. $6e^{2x} = 72$ **32.** $4e^{x-3} + 21 = 30$ **33.** $e^{2x} - 11e^x + 24 = 0$

34. $-3 + \ln 4x = 0$ **35.** $\ln \sqrt{x + 2} = 3$ **36.** $\log_2 x + \log_2 5 = 6$

37. The profit P (in thousands of dollars) of an office supply company is given by

$$P = 230 + 20x - \tfrac{1}{2}x^2$$

where x is the amount (in hundreds of dollars) the company spends on advertising. What amount will yield a maximum profit?

38. The average cost $\overline{C}$ (in dollars) of recycling a waste product x (in pounds) is given by

$$\overline{C}(x) = \frac{450{,}000 + 5x}{x}, \quad x > 0.$$

Find the average cost $\overline{C}$ of recycling $x = 10{,}000$ pounds, $x = 100{,}000$ pounds, and $x = 1{,}000{,}000$ pounds. According to this model, what is the limiting average cost as the number of pounds increases?

39. You deposit $2500 in an account earning 7.5% interest, compounded continuously. Find the balance after 25 years.

40. If the inflation rate averages 4.5% over the next 10 years, the approximate cost C of goods or services t years from now is given by $C(t) = P(1.045)^t$, where P is the present cost. If the price of a tire is presently $69.95, estimate the price 10 years from now.

41. The population P (in thousands) of Baton Rouge, Louisiana is given by $P = 228e^{kt}$, where t represents the year, with $t = 0$ corresponding to 2000. In 1970, the population was 166,000. Find the value of k, and use this result to predict the population in the year 2010.   (Source: U.S. Census Bureau)

42. The population p of a species t years after it is introduced into a new habitat is given by $p(t) = 1200/(1 + 3e^{-t/5})$.

(a) Determine the population size that was introduced into the habitat.

(b) Determine the population after 5 years.

(c) After how many years will the population be 800?

43. The table at the right shows the numbers y (in thousands) of pilots and copilots in the U.S. scheduled airline industry from 1994 to 2000.   (Source: Air Transport Association of America)

(a) Use the *regression* feature of a graphing utility to find a quadratic model, an exponential model, and a power model for the data. Let x represent the year, with $x = 4$ corresponding to 1994.

(b) Use a graphing utility to graph each model with the original data.

(c) Determine which model best fits the data.

(d) Use the model you chose in part (c) to predict the number of pilots and copilots in 2006.

Year	Number of pilots and copilots, y
1994	52.9
1995	55.4
1996	57.6
1997	60.4
1998	64.1
1999	67.2
2000	72.6

Trigonometric functions are used in medicine to calculate the pressure against the walls of blood vessels. One cycle of the trigonometric model corresponds to one heartbeat.

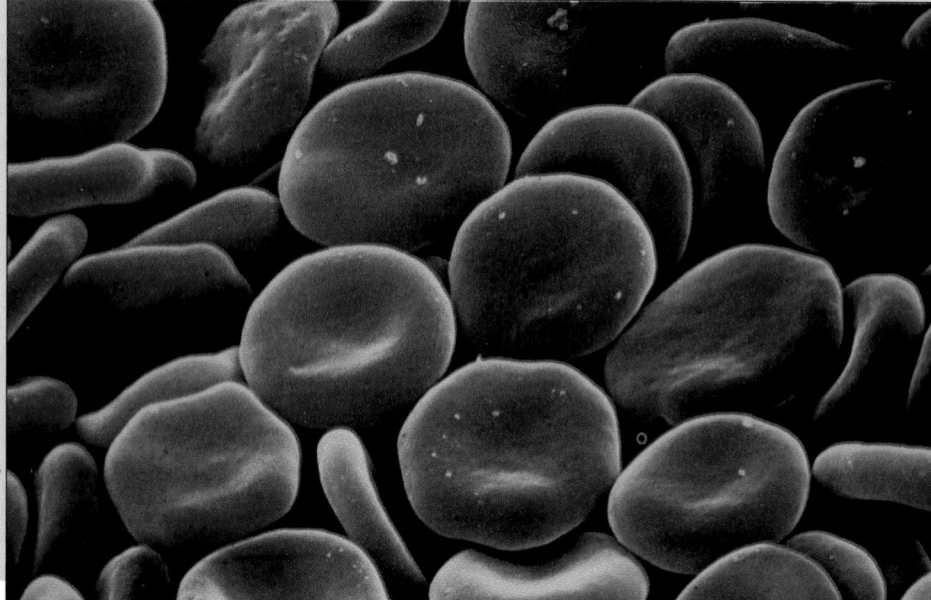

David Phillips/Visuals Unlimited

5 Trigonometric Functions

5.1 Angles and Their Measure

5.2 Right Triangle Trigonometry

5.3 Trigonometric Functions of Any Angle

5.4 Graphs of Sine and Cosine Functions

5.5 Graphs of Other Trigonometric Functions

5.6 Inverse Trigonometric Functions

5.7 Applications and Models

What You Should Learn

In this chapter, you will learn how to:

■ Describe an angle and convert between degree and radian measures.

■ Evaluate trigonometric functions of any angle.

■ Use fundamental trigonometric identities.

■ Sketch graphs of trigonometric functions.

■ Evaluate inverse trigonometric functions.

■ Evaluate the composition of trigonometric functions.

■ Use trigonometric functions to model and solve real-life problems.

391

5.1   Angles and Their Measure

Angles

As derived from the Greek language, the word **trigonometry** means "measurement of triangles." Initially, trigonometry dealt with relationships among the sides and angles of triangles and was used in the development of astronomy, navigation, and surveying. With the development of calculus and the physical sciences in the 17th century, a different perspective arose—one that viewed the classic trigonometric relationships as *functions* having the set of real numbers as their domains. Consequently, the applications of trigonometry expanded to include a vast number of physical phenomena involving rotations and vibrations, including sound waves, light rays, planetary orbits, vibrating strings, pendulums, and orbits of atomic particles.

This text incorporates *both* perspectives, starting with angles and their measure.

What you should learn

- Describe angles.
- Use degree measure.
- Use radian measure.
- Convert between degree and radian measures.
- Use angles to model and solve real-life problems.

Why you should learn it

Radian measures of angles are involved in numerous aspects of our daily lives. For instance, in Exercise 89 on page 402, you are asked to determine measures of angles of figure-skating jumps.

Reuters NewMedia, Inc./Corbis

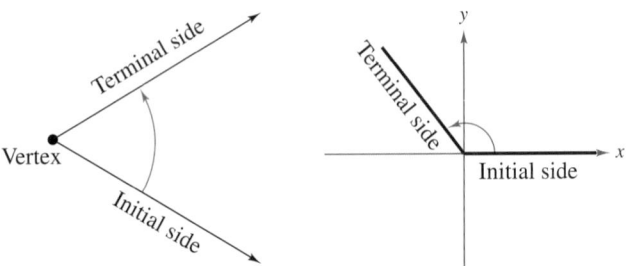

Figure 5.1   Figure 5.2

An **angle** is determined by rotating a ray (half-line) about its endpoint. The starting position of the ray is the **initial side** of the angle, and the position after rotation is the **terminal side,** as shown in Figure 5.1. The endpoint of the ray is the **vertex** of the angle. This perception of an angle fits a coordinate system in which the origin is the vertex and the initial side coincides with the positive *x*-axis. Such an angle is in **standard position,** as shown in Figure 5.2. **Positive angles** are generated by counterclockwise rotation, and **negative angles** by clockwise rotation, as shown in Figure 5.3. Angles are labeled with Greek letters such as α (alpha), β (beta), and θ (theta), as well as uppercase letters such as A, B, and C. In Figure 5.4, note that angles α and β have the same initial and terminal sides. Such angles are **coterminal.**

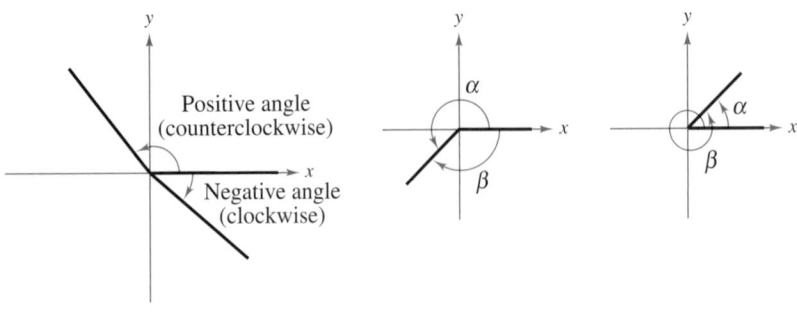

Figure 5.3   Figure 5.4

Degree Measure

The measure of an angle is determined by the amount of rotation from the initial side to the terminal side. The most common unit of angle measure is the **degree,** denoted by the symbol °. A measure of one degree (1°) is equivalent to a rotation of $\frac{1}{360}$ of a complete revolution about the vertex. To measure angles, it is convenient to mark degrees on the circumference of a circle, as shown in Figure 5.5. So, a full revolution (counterclockwise) corresponds to 360°, a half revolution to 180°, a quarter revolution to 90°, and so on.

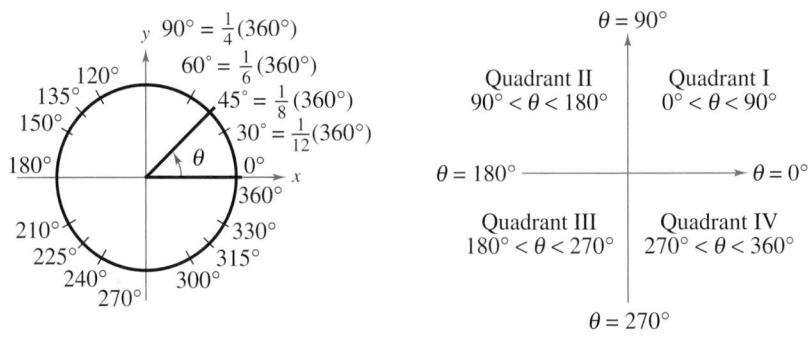

Figure 5.5   Figure 5.6

Recall that the four quadrants in a coordinate system are numbered I, II, III, and IV. Figure 5.6 shows which angles between 0° and 360° lie in each of the four quadrants. Figure 5.7 shows several common angles with their degree measures. Note that angles between 0° and 90° are **acute** and angles between 90° and 180° are **obtuse.**

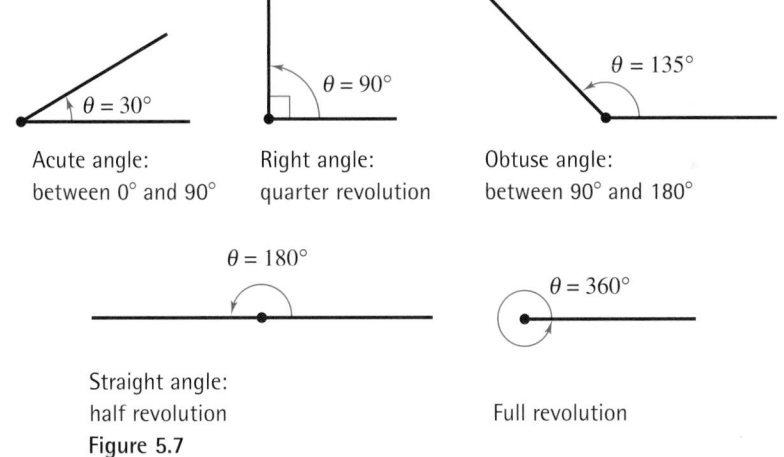

Figure 5.7

Two angles are coterminal if they have the same initial and terminal sides. For instance, the angles 0° and 360° are coterminal, as are the angles 30° and 390°. You can find an angle that is coterminal to a given angle θ by adding or subtracting 360° (one revolution), as demonstrated in Example 1. A given angle θ has infinitely many coterminal angles. For instance, θ = 30° is coterminal with

$$30° + n(360°)$$

where n is an integer.

Example 1   Sketching and Finding Coterminal Angles

Find two coterminal angles (one positive and one negative) for (a) $\theta = 390°$ and (b) $\theta = -120°$.

Solution

a. For the positive angle $\theta = 390°$, subtract $360°$ to obtain a positive coterminal angle.

$$390° - 360° = 30° \qquad \text{See Figure 5.8.}$$

Subtract $2(360°) = 720°$ to obtain a negative coterminal angle.

$$390° - 720° = -330°$$

b. For the negative angle $\theta = -120°$, add $360°$ to obtain a positive coterminal angle.

$$-120° + 360° = 240° \qquad \text{See Figure 5.9.}$$

Subtract $360°$ to obtain a negative coterminal angle.

$$-120° - 360° = -480°$$

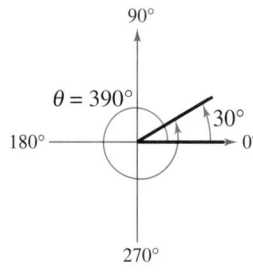

Figure 5.8   **Figure 5.9**

✓ *Checkpoint* Now try Exercise 15.

Two positive angles α and β are **complementary** (complements of each other) if their sum is $90°$. Two positive angles are **supplementary** (supplements of each other) if their sum is $180°$. See Figure 5.10.

Example 2   Complementary and Supplementary Angles

If possible, find the complement and the supplement of (a) $72°$ and (b) $148°$.

Solution

a. The complement of $72°$ is $90° - 72° = 18°$. The supplement of $72°$ is $180° - 72° = 108°$.

b. Because $148°$ is greater than $90°$, $148°$ has no complement. (Remember that complements are *positive* angles.) The supplement is

$$180° - 148° = 32°.$$

✓ *Checkpoint* Now try Exercise 29.

TECHNOLOGY TIP

With calculators, it is convenient to use *decimal* degrees to denote fractional parts of degrees. Historically, however, fractional parts of degrees were expressed in *minutes* and *seconds*, using the prime ($'$) and double prime ($''$) notations, respectively. That is,

$$1' = \text{one minute} = \tfrac{1}{60}(1°)$$

$$1'' = \text{one second} = \tfrac{1}{3600}(1°).$$

Consequently, an angle of 64 degrees, 32 minutes, and 47 seconds is represented by $\theta = 64°\,32'\,47''$.

Many calculators have special keys for converting angles in degrees, minutes, and seconds ($D°\,M'\,S''$) to decimal degree form, and vice versa.

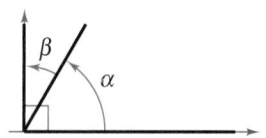

Complementary angles

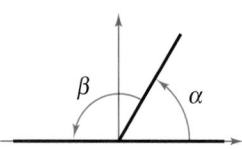

Supplementary angles
Figure 5.10

Radian Measure

A second way to measure angles is in radians. This type of measure is especially useful in calculus. To define a radian, you can use a **central angle** of a circle, one whose vertex is the center of the circle, as shown in Figure 5.11.

> **Definition of a Radian**
>
> One **radian** is the measure of a central angle θ that intercepts an arc s equal in length to the radius r of the circle. See Figure 5.11.

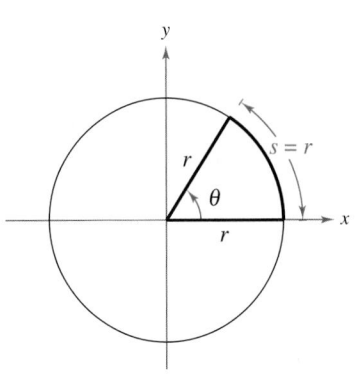

Arc length = radius when θ = 1 radian

Figure 5.11

Because the circumference of a circle is $2\pi r$ units, it follows that a central angle of one full revolution (counterclockwise) corresponds to an arc length of $s = 2\pi r$. Moreover, because $2\pi \approx 6.28$, there are just over six radius lengths in a full circle, as shown in Figure 5.12. In general, the radian measure of a central angle θ is obtained by dividing the arc length s by r. That is, $s/r = \theta$, where θ is *measured in radians*. Because the units of measure for s and r are the same, this ratio has no units—it is simply a real number.

Example 3   Finding Angles

Find each angle.

a. The complement of $\theta = \pi/12$ **b.** The supplement of $\theta = 5\pi/6$

c. A coterminal angle to $\theta = 17\pi/6$

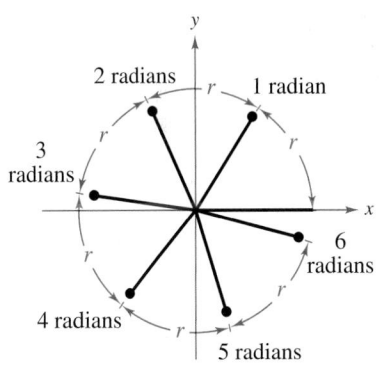

Figure 5.12

Solution

a. In radian measure, the complement of an angle is found by subtracting the angle from $\pi/2$ ($\pi/2 = 90°$). So, the complement of $\theta = \pi/12$ is $\pi/2 - \theta$, which is

$$\pi/2 - \pi/12 = 6\pi/12 - \pi/12 = 5\pi/12. \qquad \text{See Figure 5.13.}$$

b. In radian measure, the supplement of an angle is found by subtracting the angle from π ($\pi = 180°$). So, the supplement of $\theta = 5\pi/6$ is $\pi - \theta$, which is

$$\pi - 5\pi/6 = 6\pi/6 - 5\pi/6 = \pi/6. \qquad \text{See Figure 5.14.}$$

c. In radian measure, a coterminal angle is found by adding or subtracting 2π. For $\theta = 17\pi/6$, subtract 2π to obtain a coterminal angle.

$$17\pi/6 - 2\pi = 17\pi/6 - 12\pi/6 = 5\pi/6 \qquad \text{See Figure 5.15.}$$

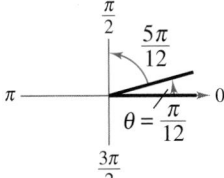

Figure 5.13

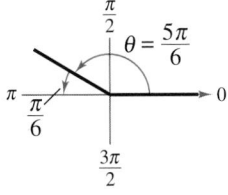

Figure 5.14

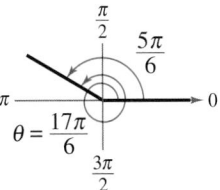

Figure 5.15

✓ *Checkpoint* Now try Exercise 49.

Conversion of Angle Measure

Because 2π radians corresponds to one complete revolution, degrees and radians are related by the equations

$$360° = 2\pi \text{ rad} \qquad \text{and} \qquad 180° = \pi \text{ rad}.$$

From the second equation, you obtain

$$1° = \frac{\pi}{180} \text{ rad} \qquad \text{and} \qquad 1 \text{ rad} = \left(\frac{180}{\pi}\right)°$$

which lead to the following conversion rules.

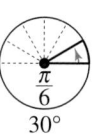
30°

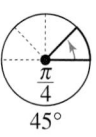
45°

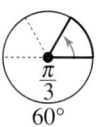
60°

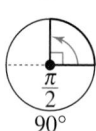
90°

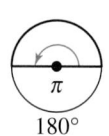
180°

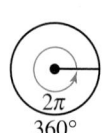
360°

Figure 5.16

Conversions Between Degrees and Radians

1. To convert degrees to radians, multiply degrees by $\dfrac{\pi \text{ rad}}{180°}$.

2. To convert radians to degrees, multiply radians by $\dfrac{180°}{\pi \text{ rad}}$.

To apply these two conversion rules, use the basic relationship $\pi \text{ rad} = 180°$. (See Figure 5.16.)

Example 4   Converting from Degrees to Radians

a. $135° = (135 \text{ deg})\left(\dfrac{\pi \text{ rad}}{180 \text{ deg}}\right) = \dfrac{3\pi}{4}$ radians   Multiply by $\frac{\pi}{180}$.

b. $-270° = (-270 \text{ deg})\left(\dfrac{\pi \text{ rad}}{180 \text{ deg}}\right) = -\dfrac{3\pi}{2}$ radians   Multiply by $\frac{\pi}{180}$.

✓ *Checkpoint* Now try Exercise 51.

Example 5   Converting from Radians to Degrees

a. $-\dfrac{\pi}{2} \text{ rad} = \left(-\dfrac{\pi}{2} \text{ rad}\right)\left(\dfrac{180 \text{ deg}}{\pi \text{ rad}}\right) = -90°$ Multiply by $\frac{180}{\pi}$.

b. $2 \text{ rad} = (2 \text{ rad})\left(\dfrac{180 \text{ deg}}{\pi \text{ rad}}\right) = \dfrac{360}{\pi} \approx 114.59°$ Multiply by $\frac{180}{\pi}$.

✓ *Checkpoint* Now try Exercise 55.

> **STUDY TIP**
>
> Note that when no units of angle measure are specified, *radian measure is implied*. For instance, if you write $\theta = \pi$ or $\theta = 2$, you imply that $\theta = \pi$ radians or $\theta = 2$ radians.

Linear and Angular Speed

The *radian measure* formula $\theta = s/r$ can be used to measure arc length along a circle. Specifically, for a circle of radius r, a central angle θ (θ is measured in radians) intercepts an arc of length s given by

$$s = r\theta. \qquad \text{Length of circular arc}$$

Example 6   Finding Arc Length

A circle has a radius of 4 inches. Find the length of the arc intercepted by a central angle of 240°, as shown in Figure 5.17.

Solution

To use the formula $s = r\theta$, first convert 240° to radian measure.

$$240° = (240 \text{ deg})\left(\frac{\pi \text{ rad}}{180 \text{ deg}}\right) \qquad \text{Convert from degrees to radians.}$$

$$= \frac{4\pi}{3} \text{ radians} \qquad \text{Simplify.}$$

Then, using a radius of $r = 4$ inches, you can find the arc length to be

$$s = r\theta \qquad \text{Length of circular arc}$$

$$= 4\left(\frac{4\pi}{3}\right) \qquad \text{Substitute for } r \text{ and } \theta.$$

$$= \frac{16\pi}{3} \qquad \text{Simplify.}$$

$$\approx 16.76 \text{ inches} \qquad \text{Use a calculator.}$$

Note that the units for $r\theta$ are determined by the units for r because θ is given in radian measure and therefore has no units.

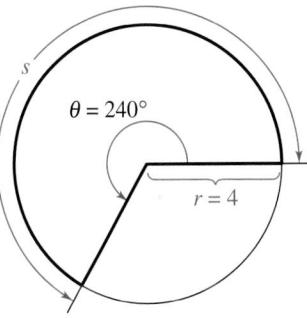

Figure 5.17

 Checkpoint Now try Exercise 79.

The formula for the length of a circular arc can be used to analyze the motion of a particle moving at a constant speed along a circular path.

Linear and Angular Speed

Consider a particle moving at a constant speed along a circular arc of radius r. If s is the length of the arc traveled in time t, then the **linear speed** of the particle is

$$\text{Linear speed} = \frac{\text{arc length}}{\text{time}} = \frac{s}{t}.$$

Moreover, if θ is the angle (in radian measure) corresponding to the arc length s, then the **angular speed** of the particle is

$$\text{Angular speed} = \frac{\text{central angle}}{\text{time}} = \frac{\theta}{t}.$$

Linear speed measures how fast the particle moves, and angular speed measures how fast the angle changes.

Example 7 Finding Linear Speed

The second hand of a clock is 10.2 centimeters long, as shown in Figure 5.18. Find the linear speed of the tip of this second hand.

Solution

In one revolution, the arc length traveled is

$$s = 2\pi r$$

$$= 2\pi(10.2) \qquad \text{Substitute for } r.$$

$$= 20.4\pi \text{ centimeters.}$$

The time required for the second hand to travel this distance is

$$t = 1 \text{ minute} = 60 \text{ seconds.}$$

So, the linear speed of the tip of the second hand is

$$\text{Linear speed} = \frac{s}{t}$$

$$= \frac{20.4\pi \text{ centimeters}}{60 \text{ seconds}} \approx 1.068 \text{ centimeters per second.}$$

 *Checkpoint* Now try Exercise 91.

Figure 5.18

Example 8 Finding Angular and Linear Speed

A lawn roller with a 10-inch radius makes 1.2 revolutions per second (see Figure 5.19).

a. Find the angular speed of the roller in radians per second.

b. Find the speed of the tractor that is pulling the roller.

Solution

a. Because each revolution generates 2π radians, it follows that the roller turns $(1.2)(2\pi) = 2.4\pi$ radians per second. In other words, the angular speed is

$$\text{Angular speed} = \frac{\theta}{t}$$

$$= \frac{2.4\pi \text{ radians}}{1 \text{ second}} = 2.4\pi \text{ radians per second.}$$

b. The linear speed is

$$\text{Linear speed} = \frac{s}{t} = \frac{r\theta}{t}$$

$$= \frac{10(2.4\pi) \text{ inches}}{1 \text{ second}} \approx 75.4 \text{ inches per second.}$$

 *Checkpoint* Now try Exercise 92.

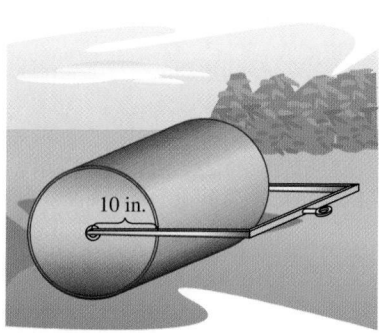

Figure 5.19

5.1   Exercises

Vocabulary Check

Fill in the blanks.

1. _____ means "measurement of triangles."

2. An _____ is determined by rotating a ray about its endpoint.

3. An angle whose initial side coincides with the positive x-axis and that has the origin as its vertex is said to be in _____ .

4. Two angles that have the same initial and terminal sides are _____ .

5. The angle measure that is equivalent to $\frac{1}{360}$ of a complete revolution about an angle's vertex is one _____ .

6. Two positive angles that have a sum of $90°$ are _____ angles.

7. Two positive angles that have a sum of $180°$ are _____ angles.

8. One _____ is the measure of a central angle that intercepts an arc equal to the radius of the circle.

9. The _____ speed of a particle is the ratio of the arc length traveled to the time traveled.

10. The _____ speed of a particle is the ratio of the change in the central angle to time.

In Exercises 1–4, estimate the number of degrees in the angle.

1.
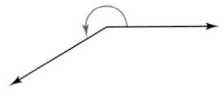

2.
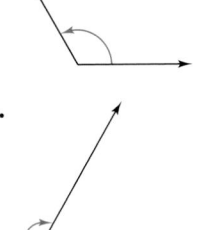

3.

4.

In Exercises 5–8, determine the quadrant in which each angle lies.

5. (a) $150°$ (b) $282°$

6. (a) $7.9°$ (b) $257.5°$

7. (a) $-132° \, 50'$ (b) $-336° \, 30'$

8. (a) $-260.25°$ (b) $-2.4°$

In Exercises 9–12, sketch each angle in standard position.

9. (a) $30°$ (b) $150°$

10. (a) $-270°$ (b) $-120°$

11. (a) $405°$ (b) $780°$

12. (a) $-450°$ (b) $-600°$

In Exercises 13–16, determine two coterminal angles in degree measure (one positive and one negative) for each angle.

13. (a) $\theta = 52°$ (b) $\theta = -36°$
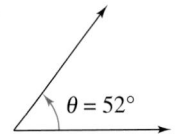
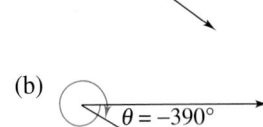

14. (a) $\theta = 114°$ (b) $\theta = -390°$
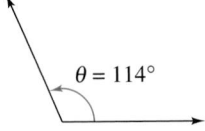

15. (a) $-495°$ (b) $230°$

16. (a) $100°$ (b) $-740°$

In Exercises 17–22, use the angle conversion capabilities of a graphing utility to convert the angle measure to decimal degree form. Round your answer to three decimal places, if necessary.

17. $64° \, 45'$ 18. $-124° \, 30'$

19. $85° \, 18' \, 30''$ 20. $-408° \, 16' \, 25''$

21. $-125° \, 36''$ 22. $330° \, 25''$

In Exercises 23–28, use the angle conversion capabilities of a graphing utility to convert the angle measure to D° M' S'' form.

23. $280.6°$ 24. $-115.8°$

25. $-345.12°$

26. $310.75°$

27. -0.355

28. 0.7865

In Exercises 29 and 30, find (if possible) the complement and supplement of each angle.

29. (a) $24°$ (b) $126°$

30. (a) $87°$ (b) $167°$

In Exercises 31–34, estimate the angle to the nearest one-half radian.

31.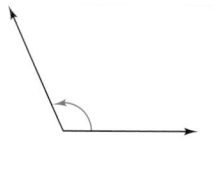

32.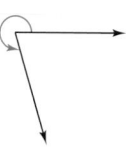

33.

34.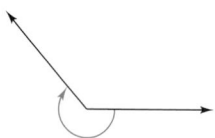

In Exercises 35–40, determine the quadrant in which each angle lies. (The angle is given in radians.)

35. (a) $\dfrac{\pi}{5}$ (b) $\dfrac{7\pi}{5}$ **36.** (a) $\dfrac{7\pi}{4}$ (b) $\dfrac{11\pi}{4}$

37. (a) $-\dfrac{\pi}{12}$ (b) $-\dfrac{11\pi}{9}$ **38.** (a) -1 (b) -2

39. (a) 3.5 (b) 2.25 **40.** (a) 5.63 (b) -2.25

In Exercises 41–44, sketch each angle in standard position.

41. (a) $\dfrac{3\pi}{4}$ (b) $\dfrac{5\pi}{6}$ **42.** (a) $-\dfrac{7\pi}{4}$ (b) $-\dfrac{7\pi}{2}$

43. (a) $\dfrac{11\pi}{6}$ (b) -3 **44.** (a) 4 (b) 5π

In Exercises 45–48, determine two coterminal angles in radian measure (one positive and one negative) for each angle.

45. (a)   (b)

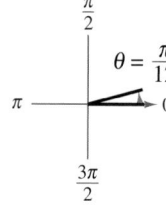
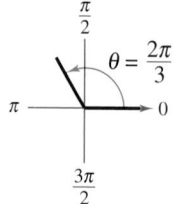

46. (a)   (b)

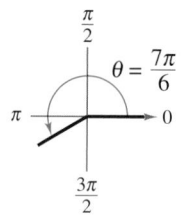
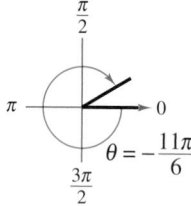

47. (a) $-\dfrac{9\pi}{4}$ (b) $-\dfrac{2\pi}{15}$

48. (a) $\dfrac{7\pi}{8}$ (b) $\dfrac{8\pi}{45}$

In Exercises 49 and 50, find (if possible) the complement and supplement of each angle.

49. (a) $\dfrac{\pi}{3}$ (b) $\dfrac{3\pi}{4}$

50. (a) 1 (b) 2

In Exercises 51–54, rewrite each angle in radian measure as a multiple of π. (Do not use a calculator.)

51. (a) $30°$ (b) $150°$

52. (a) $315°$ (b) $120°$

53. (a) $-20°$ (b) $-240°$

54. (a) $-270°$ (b) $144°$

In Exercises 55–58, rewrite each angle in degree measure. (Do not use a calculator.)

55. (a) $\dfrac{3\pi}{2}$ (b) $-\dfrac{7\pi}{6}$

56. (a) $-\dfrac{7\pi}{12}$ (b) $\dfrac{\pi}{9}$

57. (a) $\dfrac{7\pi}{3}$ (b) $-\dfrac{13\pi}{60}$

58. (a) $\dfrac{15\pi}{6}$ (b) $\dfrac{28\pi}{15}$

In Exercises 59–64, convert the angle measure from degrees to radians. Round your answer to three decimal places.

59. $126°$ **60.** $83.7°$

61. $-216.35°$ **62.** $-46.52°$

63. $-0.78°$ **64.** $383°$

In Exercises 65–70, convert the angle measure from radians to degrees. Round your answer to three decimal places.

65. $\dfrac{\pi}{7}$

66. $\dfrac{2\pi}{11}$

67. $\dfrac{13\pi}{8}$

68. 6.5π

69. -2

70. -0.39

In Exercises 71–74, find the angle in radians.

71.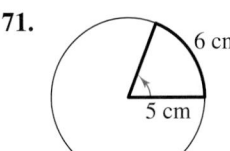

72.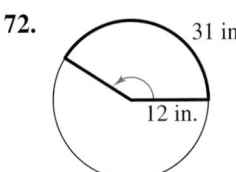

73.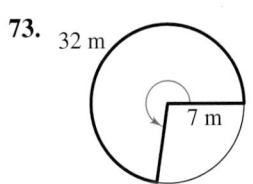

74.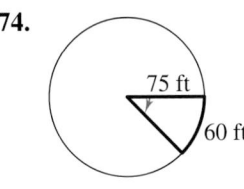

In Exercises 75–78, find the radian measure of the central angle of a circle of radius r that intercepts an arc of length s.

	Radius r	Arc Length s
75.	29 inches	8 inches
76.	14 feet	8 feet
77.	14.5 centimeters	35 centimeters
78.	80 kilometers	160 kilometers

In Exercises 79–82, find the length of the arc on a circle of radius r intercepted by a central angle θ.

	Radius r	Central Angle θ
79.	15 inches	$180°$
80.	9 feet	$60°$
81.	2 meters	1 radian
82.	40 centimeters	$\dfrac{3\pi}{4}$ radians

Distance In Exercises 83 and 84, find the distance between the cities. Assume that Earth is a sphere of radius 4000 miles and that the cities are on the same longitude (one city is due north of the other).

	City	Latitude
83.	Miami	$25°\,46'\,26''$N
	Erie	$42°\,7'\,45''$N
84.	Johannesburg, South Africa	$26°\,11'$S
	Jerusalem, Israel	$31°\,47'$N

85. *Difference in Latitudes* Assuming that Earth is a sphere of radius 6378 kilometers, what is the difference in latitudes of Syracuse, New York and Annapolis, Maryland, where Syracuse is 450 kilometers due north of Annapolis?

86. *Difference in Latitudes* Assuming that Earth is a sphere of radius 6378 kilometers, what is the difference in latitudes of Lynchburg, Virginia and Myrtle Beach, South Carolina, where Lynchburg is 400 kilometers due north of Myrtle Beach?

87. *Instrumentation* A voltmeter's pointer is 6 centimeters in length (see figure). Find the angle through which it rotates when it moves 2.5 centimeters on the scale.

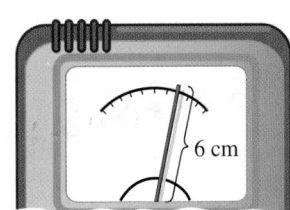

88. *Electric Hoist* An electric hoist is used to lift a beam 2 feet (see figure). The diameter of the drum on the hoist is 10 inches. Find the number of degrees through which the drum must rotate.

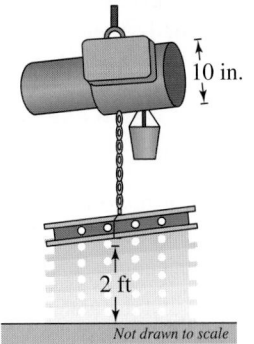

89. Sports   The number of revolutions made by a figure skater for each type of axel jump is given. Determine the measure of the angle generated as the skater performs each jump. Give the answer in both degrees and radians.

(a) Single axel: $1\frac{1}{2}$ (b) Double axel: $2\frac{1}{2}$

(c) Triple axel: $3\frac{1}{2}$

90. Angular Speed   A car is moving at a rate of 65 miles per hour, and the diameter of its wheels is 2.5 feet.

(a) Find the number of revolutions per minute the wheels are rotating.

(b) Find the angular speed of the wheels in radians per minute.

91. Floppy Disk   The radius of the magnetic disk in a 3.5-inch diskette is 1.68 inches. Find the linear speed of a point on the circumference of the disk if it is rotating at a speed of 360 revolutions per minute.

92. Construction   The circular blade on a saw has a diameter of 7.5 inches and rotates at 2400 revolutions per minute (see figure).

(a) Find the angular speed in radians per second.

(b) Find the linear speed of the saw teeth (in feet per second) as they contact the wood being cut.

— 7.5 in.—

Synthesis

True or False?   **In Exercises 93 and 94, determine whether the statement is true or false. Justify your answer.**

93. A degree is a larger unit of measure than a radian.

94. An angle that measures $-1260°$ lies in Quadrant III.

95. Writing   In your own words, explain the meanings of (a) an angle in standard position, (b) a negative angle, (c) coterminal angles, and (d) an obtuse angle.

96. Geometry   Show that the area of a circular sector of radius r with central angle θ is $A = \frac{1}{2}r^2\theta$, where θ is measured in radians.

Geometry   **In Exercises 97 and 98, use the result of Exercise 96 to find the area of the sector.**

97.

$\frac{\pi}{3}$ 10 m

98.   12 ft

15 ft

99. Graphical Reasoning   The formulas for the area of a circular sector and arc length are $A = \frac{1}{2}r^2\theta$ and $s = r\theta$, respectively. (r is the radius and θ is the angle measured in radians.)

(a) If $\theta = 0.8$, write the area and arc length as functions of r. What is the domain of each function? Use a graphing utility to graph the functions. Use the graphs to determine which function changes more rapidly as r increases. Explain.

(b) If $r = 10$ centimeters, write the area and arc length as functions of θ. What is the domain of each function? Use a graphing utility to graph and identify the functions.

100. Writing   A fan motor turns at a given angular speed. How does the speed of the tips of the blades change if a fan of greater diameter is installed on the motor? Explain.

Review

In Exercises 101 and 102, use the regression feature of a graphing utility to find a linear model that approximates the set of data.

101.

x	2	3	4	5	6	7
y	25	31	33	40	45	47

102.

x	−3	−2	−1	0	1	2
y	58.3	49.9	45.0	38.1	33.2	23.6

In Exercises 103–106, find all the real zeros of the polynomial function.

103. $f(x) = x^2 + 11x + 28$

104. $f(x) = 54x^2 - 6x^4$

105. $f(x) = x^3 + 3x^2 - 10x$

106. $f(x) = 4x^4 + 44x^3 + 96x^2$

5.2   Right Triangle Trigonometry

The Six Trigonometric Functions

Our first look at the trigonometric functions is from a *right triangle* perspective. Consider a right triangle with one acute angle labeled θ, as shown in Figure 5.20. Relative to the angle θ, the three sides of the triangle are the **hypotenuse,** the **opposite side** (the side opposite the angle θ), and the **adjacent side** (the side adjacent to the angle θ).

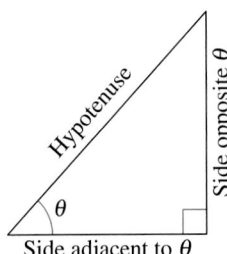

Figure 5.20

Using the lengths of these three sides, you can form six ratios that define the six trigonometric functions of the acute angle θ.

sine	**cosecant**	**cosine**	**secant**	**tangent**	**cotangent**

These six functions are normally abbreviated as sin, csc, cos, sec, tan, and cot, respectively. In the following definitions it is important to see that $0° < \theta < 90°$ (θ lies in the first quadrant) and that for such angles the value of each trigonometric function is *positive*.

Right Triangle Definitions of Trigonometric Functions

Let θ be an *acute* angle of a right triangle. Then the six trigonometric functions *of the angle* θ are defined as follows. (Note that the functions in the second row are the *reciprocals* of the corresponding functions in the first row.)

$$\sin \theta = \frac{\text{opp}}{\text{hyp}} \qquad \cos \theta = \frac{\text{adj}}{\text{hyp}} \qquad \tan \theta = \frac{\text{opp}}{\text{adj}}$$

$$\csc \theta = \frac{\text{hyp}}{\text{opp}} \qquad \sec \theta = \frac{\text{hyp}}{\text{adj}} \qquad \cot \theta = \frac{\text{adj}}{\text{opp}}$$

The abbreviations "opp," "adj," and "hyp" represent the lengths of the three sides of a right triangle.

opp = the length of the side *opposite* θ

adj = the length of the side *adjacent* to θ

hyp = the length of the *hypotenuse*

What you should learn

- Evaluate trigonometric functions of acute angles.
- Use the fundamental trigonometric identities.
- Use a calculator to evaluate trigonometric functions.
- Use trigonometric functions to model and solve real-life problems.

Why you should learn it

You can use trigonometry to analyze all aspects of a geometric figure. For instance, Exercise 62 on page 412 shows you how trigonometric functions can be used to approximate the height of the Jin Mao Building in China.

Chen Yixin/China Stock

Example 1 Evaluating Trigonometric Functions

Use the triangle in Figure 5.21 to find the exact values of the six trigonometric functions of θ.

Solution

By the Pythagorean Theorem, $(\text{hyp})^2 = (\text{opp})^2 + (\text{adj})^2$, it follows that

$$\text{hyp} = \sqrt{4^2 + 3^2} = \sqrt{25} = 5.$$

So, the six trigonometric functions of θ are

$$\sin \theta = \frac{\text{opp}}{\text{hyp}} = \frac{4}{5} \qquad \csc \theta = \frac{\text{hyp}}{\text{opp}} = \frac{5}{4}$$

$$\cos \theta = \frac{\text{adj}}{\text{hyp}} = \frac{3}{5} \qquad \sec \theta = \frac{\text{hyp}}{\text{adj}} = \frac{5}{3}$$

$$\tan \theta = \frac{\text{opp}}{\text{adj}} = \frac{4}{3} \qquad \cot \theta = \frac{\text{adj}}{\text{opp}} = \frac{3}{4}.$$

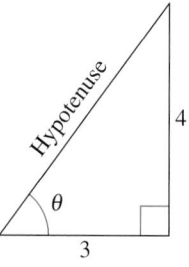

Figure 5.21

✓ *Checkpoint* Now try Exercise 3.

In Example 1, you were given the lengths of two sides of the right triangle, but not the angle θ. Often you will be asked to find the trigonometric functions for a *given* acute angle θ. To do this, construct a right triangle having θ as one of its angles.

Example 2 Evaluating Trigonometric Functions of 45°

Find the values of sin 45°, cos 45°, and tan 45°.

Solution

Construct a right triangle having 45° as one of its acute angles, as shown in Figure 5.22. Choose 1 as the length of the adjacent side. From geometry, you know that the other acute angle is also 45°. So, the triangle is isosceles, and the length of the opposite side is also 1. Using the Pythagorean Theorem, you find the length of the hypotenuse to be $\sqrt{2}$.

$$\sin 45° = \frac{\text{opp}}{\text{hyp}} = \frac{1}{\sqrt{2}} = \frac{\sqrt{2}}{2}$$

$$\cos 45° = \frac{\text{adj}}{\text{hyp}} = \frac{1}{\sqrt{2}} = \frac{\sqrt{2}}{2}$$

$$\tan 45° = \frac{\text{opp}}{\text{adj}} = \frac{1}{1} = 1$$

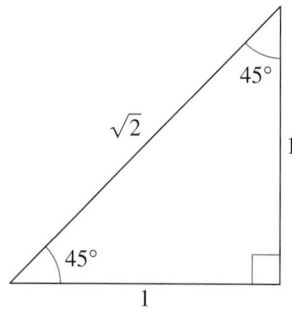

Figure 5.22

✓ *Checkpoint* Now try Exercise 17.

TECHNOLOGY TIP You can use a calculator to convert the answers in Example 2 to decimals. However, the radical form is the exact value and in most cases, the exact value is preferred.

Example 3   Evaluating Trigonometric Functions of 30° and 60°

Use the equilateral triangle shown in Figure 5.23 to find the values of sin 60°, cos 60°, sin 30°, and cos 30°.

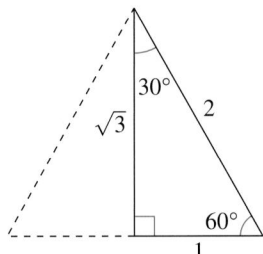

Figure 5.23

Solution

Use the Pythagorean Theorem and the equilateral triangle to verify the lengths of the sides given in Figure 5.23. For $\theta = 60°$, you have adj = 1, opp = $\sqrt{3}$, and hyp = 2. So,

$$\sin 60° = \frac{\text{opp}}{\text{hyp}} = \frac{\sqrt{3}}{2} \quad \text{and} \quad \cos 60° = \frac{\text{adj}}{\text{hyp}} = \frac{1}{2}.$$

For $\theta = 30°$, adj = $\sqrt{3}$, opp = 1, and hyp = 2. So,

$$\sin 30° = \frac{\text{opp}}{\text{hyp}} = \frac{1}{2} \quad \text{and} \quad \cos 30° = \frac{\text{adj}}{\text{hyp}} = \frac{\sqrt{3}}{2}.$$

✓ *Checkpoint* Now try Exercise 19.

Sines, Cosines, and Tangents of Special Angles

$$\sin 30° = \sin \frac{\pi}{6} = \frac{1}{2} \qquad \cos 30° = \cos \frac{\pi}{6} = \frac{\sqrt{3}}{2} \qquad \tan 30° = \tan \frac{\pi}{6} = \frac{\sqrt{3}}{3}$$

$$\sin 45° = \sin \frac{\pi}{4} = \frac{\sqrt{2}}{2} \qquad \cos 45° = \cos \frac{\pi}{4} = \frac{\sqrt{2}}{2} \qquad \tan 45° = \tan \frac{\pi}{4} = 1$$

$$\sin 60° = \sin \frac{\pi}{3} = \frac{\sqrt{3}}{2} \qquad \cos 60° = \cos \frac{\pi}{3} = \frac{1}{2} \qquad \tan 60° = \tan \frac{\pi}{3} = \sqrt{3}$$

In the box, note that $\sin 30° = \frac{1}{2} = \cos 60°$. This occurs because 30° and 60° are complementary angles, and, in general, it can be shown from the right triangle definitions that *cofunctions of complementary angles are equal.* That is, if θ is an acute angle, the following relationships are true.

$$\sin(90° - \theta) = \cos \theta \qquad \cos(90° - \theta) = \sin \theta$$

$$\tan(90° - \theta) = \cot \theta \qquad \cot(90° - \theta) = \tan \theta$$

$$\sec(90° - \theta) = \csc \theta \qquad \csc(90° - \theta) = \sec \theta$$

Trigonometric Identities

In trigonometry, a great deal of time is spent studying relationships between trigonometric functions (identities).

Fundamental Trigonometric Identities

Reciprocal Identities

$$\sin \theta = \frac{1}{\csc \theta} \qquad \cos \theta = \frac{1}{\sec \theta} \qquad \tan \theta = \frac{1}{\cot \theta}$$

$$\csc \theta = \frac{1}{\sin \theta} \qquad \sec \theta = \frac{1}{\cos \theta} \qquad \cot \theta = \frac{1}{\tan \theta}$$

Quotient Identities

$$\tan \theta = \frac{\sin \theta}{\cos \theta} \qquad \cot \theta = \frac{\cos \theta}{\sin \theta}$$

Pythagorean Identities

$$\sin^2 \theta + \cos^2 \theta = 1$$

$$1 + \tan^2 \theta = \sec^2 \theta$$

$$1 + \cot^2 \theta = \csc^2 \theta$$

Exploration

Select a number t and use your graphing utility to calculate $(\sin t)^2 + (\cos t)^2$. Repeat this experiment for other values of t and explain why the answer is always the same. Is the result true in both *radian* and *degree* modes?

Note that $\sin^2 \theta$ represents $(\sin \theta)^2$, $\cos^2 \theta$ represents $(\cos \theta)^2$, and so on.

Example 4   Applying Trigonometric Identities

Let θ be an acute angle such that $\sin \theta = 0.6$. Find the values of (a) $\cos \theta$ and (b) $\tan \theta$ using trigonometric identities.

Solution

a. To find the value of $\cos \theta$, use the Pythagorean identity

$$\sin^2 \theta + \cos^2 \theta = 1.$$

So, you have

$$(0.6)^2 + \cos^2 \theta = 1 \qquad \text{Substitute 0.6 for } \sin \theta.$$

$$\cos^2 \theta = 1 - (0.6)^2 = 0.64 \qquad \text{Subtract } (0.6)^2 \text{ from each side.}$$

$$\cos \theta = \sqrt{0.64} = 0.8. \qquad \text{Extract positive square root.}$$

b. Now, knowing the sine and cosine of θ, you can find the tangent of θ to be

$$\tan \theta = \frac{\sin \theta}{\cos \theta} = \frac{0.6}{0.8} = 0.75.$$

Use the definitions of $\cos \theta$ and $\tan \theta$ and the triangle shown in Figure 5.24 to check these results.

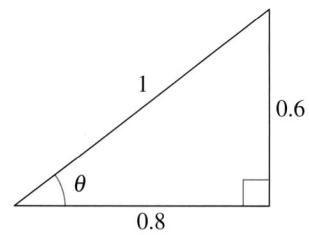

Figure 5.24

✓ *Checkpoint* Now try Exercise 31.

Example 5   Using Trigonometric Identities

Use trigonometric identities to transform one side of the equation into the other $(0 < \theta < \pi/2)$.

a. $\cos \theta \sec \theta = 1$ **b.** $(\sec \theta + \tan \theta)(\sec \theta - \tan \theta) = 1$

Solution

Simplify the expression on the left-hand side of the equation until you obtain the right-hand side.

a. $\cos \theta \sec \theta = \left(\dfrac{1}{\sec \theta}\right)\sec \theta$ Reciprocal identity

$\qquad\qquad\quad = 1$ Divide out common factor.

b. $(\sec \theta + \tan \theta)(\sec \theta - \tan \theta)$

$\qquad = \sec^2 \theta - \sec \theta \tan \theta + \sec \theta \tan \theta - \tan^2 \theta$ Distributive Property

$\qquad = \sec^2 \theta - \tan^2 \theta$ Simplify.

$\qquad = 1$ Pythagorean identity

 Checkpoint Now try Exercise 33.

Evaluating Trigonometric Functions with a Calculator

When evaluating a trigonometric function with a calculator, you need to set the calculator to the desired *mode* of measurement (degrees or radians).

Most calculators do not have keys for the cosecant, secant, and cotangent functions. To evaluate these functions, you can use the ⌊x⁻¹⌋ key with their respective reciprocal functions sine, cosine, and tangent. For example, to evaluate $\csc(\pi/8)$, use the fact that

$$\csc \frac{\pi}{8} = \frac{1}{\sin(\pi/8)}$$

and enter the following keystroke sequence in *radian* mode.

(SIN π ÷ 8)) x⁻¹ ENTER   Display 2.6131259

TECHNOLOGY TIP

The reciprocal identities for sine, cosine, and tangent can be used to evaluate the cosecant, secant, and cotangent functions with a calculator. For instance, you could use the following alternative keystroke sequence to evaluate the function in Example 6(c).

1 ÷ TAN 1.5) ENTER

You should obtain 0.0709148.

Example 6   Using a Calculator

Function	Mode	Graphing Calculator Keystrokes	Display
a. $\sin 76.4°$	Degree	SIN 76.4 ENTER	0.9719610
b. $\cos 89°$	Degree	COS 89 ENTER	0.0174524
c. $\cot 1.5$	Radian	(TAN 1.5) x⁻¹ ENTER	0.0709148

 Checkpoint Now try Exercise 41.

> **TECHNOLOGY TIP**   When evaluating trigonometric functions with a calculator, remember to enclose all fractional angle measures in parentheses. For instance, if you want to evaluate $\sin \theta$ for $\theta = \pi/6$, you should enter
>
>   [SIN] [π] [÷] 6 [)] [ENTER].
>
> These keystrokes yield the correct value of 0.5.

Applications Involving Right Triangles

Many applications of trigonometry involve a process called **solving right triangles.** In this type of application, you are usually given one side of a right triangle and one of the acute angles and asked to find one of the other sides, *or* you are given two sides and asked to find one of the acute angles. In Example 7, the angle you are given is the **angle of elevation,** which represents the angle from the horizontal upward to the object. In other applications you may be given the **angle of depression,** which represents the angle from the horizontal downward to the object.

Example 7   Using Trigonometry to Solve a Right Triangle

A surveyor is standing 50 feet from the base of a large tree, as shown in Figure 5.25. The surveyor measures the angle of elevation to the top of the tree as 71.5°. How tall is the tree?

Solution

From Figure 5.25, you can see that

$$\tan 71.5° = \frac{\text{opp}}{\text{adj}} = \frac{y}{x}$$

where $x = 50$ and y is the height of the tree. So, the height of the tree is

$$y = x \tan 71.5° \approx 50(2.9887) \approx 149.4 \text{ feet.}$$

✓ *Checkpoint* Now try Exercise 59.

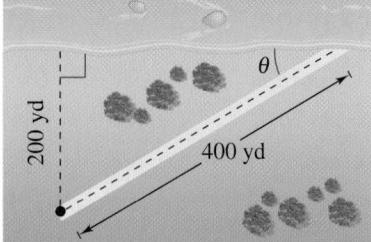

Figure 5.25

Example 8   Using Trigonometry to Solve a Right Triangle

You are 200 yards from a river. Rather than walking directly to the river, you walk 400 yards along a straight path to the river's edge. Find the acute angle θ between this path and the river's edge, as illustrated in Figure 5.26.

Solution

From Figure 5.26, you can see that the sine of the angle θ is

$$\sin \theta = \frac{\text{opp}}{\text{hyp}} = \frac{200}{400} = \frac{1}{2}.$$

Now, you should recognize that $\theta = 30°$.

✓ *Checkpoint* Now try Exercise 61.

Figure 5.26

In Example 8, you were able to recognize that $\theta = 30°$ is the acute angle that satisfies the equation $\sin \theta = \frac{1}{2}$. Suppose, however, that you were given the equation $\sin \theta = 0.6$ and were asked to find the acute angle θ. Because

$$\sin 30° = \frac{1}{2} = 0.5000$$

and

$$\sin 45° = \frac{1}{\sqrt{2}} \approx 0.7071$$

you might guess that θ lies somewhere between 30° and 45°. In a later section, you will study a method by which a more precise value of θ can be determined.

Example 9   Solving a Right Triangle

Find the length c of the skateboard ramp shown in Figure 5.27.

Figure 5.27

Solution

From Figure 5.27, you can see that

$$\sin 18.4° = \frac{\text{opp}}{\text{hyp}}$$

$$= \frac{4}{c}.$$

So, the length of the ramp is

$$c = \frac{4}{\sin 18.4°}$$

$$\approx \frac{4}{0.3156}$$

$$\approx 12.7 \text{ feet.}$$

✓ *Checkpoint* Now try Exercise 63.

TECHNOLOGY TIP

Calculators and graphing utilities have both *degree* and *radian* modes. As you progress through this chapter, be sure you use the correct mode.

5.2 Exercises

Vocabulary Check

1. Match the trigonometric function with its right triangle definition.

(a) Sine   (b) Cosine   (c) Tangent

(d) Cosecant   (e) Secant   (f) Cotangent

(i) $\dfrac{\text{hyp}}{\text{adj}}$ (ii) $\dfrac{\text{opp}}{\text{adj}}$ (iii) $\dfrac{\text{opp}}{\text{hyp}}$

(iv) $\dfrac{\text{adj}}{\text{opp}}$ (v) $\dfrac{\text{hyp}}{\text{opp}}$ (vi) $\dfrac{\text{adj}}{\text{hyp}}$

In Exercises 2 and 3, fill in the blanks.

2. Relative to the angle θ, the three sides of a right triangle are the _____ , the _____ side, and the _____ side.

3. An angle that measures from the horizontal upward to an object is called the angle of _____ , whereas an angle that measures from the horizontal downward to an object is called the angle of _____ .

In Exercises 1–4, find the exact values of the six trigonometric functions of the angle θ shown in the figure. (Use the Pythagorean Theorem to find the third side of the triangle.)

1.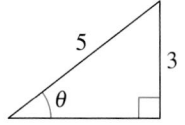

2.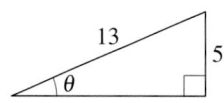

3.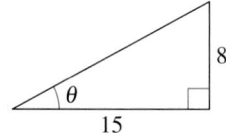

4.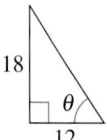

In Exercises 5–8, find the exact values of the six trigonometric functions of the angle θ for each of the triangles. Explain why the function values are the same.

5.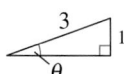

6.

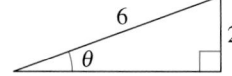

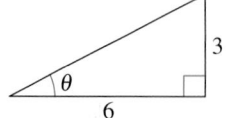

7.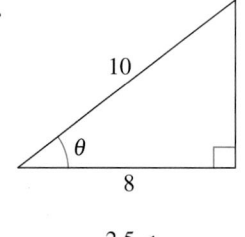

8.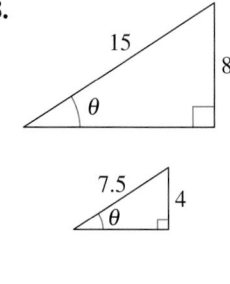

In Exercises 9–16, sketch a right triangle corresponding to the trigonometric function of the acute angle θ. Use the Pythagorean Theorem to determine the third side and then find the other five trigonometric functions of θ.

9. $\sin \theta = \frac{2}{3}$ **10.** $\cot \theta = \frac{3}{7}$

11. $\sec \theta = 4$ **12.** $\cos \theta = \frac{1}{5}$

13. $\tan \theta = 3$ **14.** $\csc \theta = 2$

15. $\cot \theta = \frac{9}{4}$ **16.** $\sin \theta = \frac{3}{8}$

In Exercises 17–26, construct an appropriate triangle to complete the table. ($0 \le \theta \le 90°$, $0 \le \theta \le \pi/2$)

Function	θ (deg)	θ (rad)	Function Value
17. sin	30°		
18. cos	45°		

Function	θ (deg)	θ (rad)	Function Value
19. tan		$\dfrac{\pi}{3}$	
20. sec		$\dfrac{\pi}{4}$	
21. cot			$\dfrac{\sqrt{3}}{3}$
22. csc			$\sqrt{2}$
23. cos		$\dfrac{\pi}{6}$	
24. sin		$\dfrac{\pi}{4}$	
25. cot			1
26. tan			$\dfrac{1}{\sqrt{3}}$

In Exercises 27–32, use the given function value(s) and trigonometric identities to find the indicated trigonometric functions.

27. $\sin 60° = \dfrac{\sqrt{3}}{2}, \quad \cos 60° = \dfrac{1}{2}$

    (a) $\tan 60°$ (b) $\sin 30°$

    (c) $\cos 30°$ (d) $\cot 60°$

28. $\sin 30° = \dfrac{1}{2}, \quad \tan 30° = \dfrac{\sqrt{3}}{3}$

    (a) $\csc 30°$ (b) $\cot 60°$

    (c) $\cos 30°$ (d) $\cot 30°$

29. $\csc \theta = 3, \quad \sec \theta = \dfrac{3\sqrt{2}}{4}$

    (a) $\sin \theta$ (b) $\cos \theta$

    (c) $\tan \theta$ (d) $\sec(90° - \theta)$

30. $\sec \theta = 5, \quad \tan \theta = 2\sqrt{6}$

    (a) $\cos \theta$ (b) $\cot \theta$

    (c) $\cot(90° - \theta)$ (d) $\sin \theta$

31. $\cos \alpha = \dfrac{1}{4}$

    (a) $\sec \alpha$ (b) $\sin \alpha$

    (c) $\cot \alpha$ (d) $\sin(90° - \alpha)$

32. $\tan \beta = 5$

    (a) $\cot \beta$ (b) $\cos \beta$

    (c) $\tan(90° - \beta)$ (d) $\csc \beta$

In Exercises 33–40, use trigonometric identities to transform one side of the equation into the other $(0 < \theta < \pi/2)$.

33. $\tan \theta \cot \theta = 1$

34. $\csc \theta \tan \theta = \sec \theta$

35. $\tan \theta \cos \theta = \sin \theta$

36. $\cot \theta \sin \theta = \cos \theta$

37. $(1 + \cos \theta)(1 - \cos \theta) = \sin^2 \theta$

38. $(1 + \sin \theta)(1 - \sin \theta) = \cos^2 \theta$

39. $\dfrac{\sin \theta}{\cos \theta} + \dfrac{\cos \theta}{\sin \theta} = \csc \theta \sec \theta$

40. $\dfrac{\tan \theta + \cot \theta}{\tan \theta} = \csc^2 \theta$

In Exercises 41–46, use a calculator to evaluate each function. Round your answers to four decimal places. (Be sure the calculator is in the correct angle mode.)

41. (a) $\sin 12°$ (b) $\cos 72°$

42. (a) $\tan 18.5°$ (b) $\cot 71.5°$

43. (a) $\sec 42° \, 12'$ (b) $\csc 48° \, 7'$

44. (a) $\cos 8° \, 50' \, 25''$ (b) $\sec 8° \, 50' \, 25''$

45. (a) $\cot \dfrac{\pi}{16}$ (b) $\tan \dfrac{\pi}{16}$

46. (a) $\sec 0.75$ (b) $\cos 0.75$

In Exercises 47–52, find each value of θ in degrees $(0° < \theta < 90°)$ and radians $(0 < \theta < \pi/2)$ without using a calculator.

47. (a) $\sin \theta = \dfrac{1}{2}$ (b) $\csc \theta = 2$

48. (a) $\cos \theta = \dfrac{\sqrt{2}}{2}$ (b) $\tan \theta = 1$

49. (a) $\sec \theta = 2$ (b) $\cot \theta = 1$

50. (a) $\tan \theta = \sqrt{3}$ (b) $\cos \theta = \dfrac{1}{2}$

51. (a) $\csc \theta = \dfrac{2\sqrt{3}}{3}$ (b) $\sin \theta = \dfrac{\sqrt{2}}{2}$

52. (a) $\cot \theta = \dfrac{\sqrt{3}}{3}$ (b) $\sec \theta = \sqrt{2}$

In Exercises 53–56, solve for *x*, *y*, or *r*, as indicated.

53. Solve for *y*.

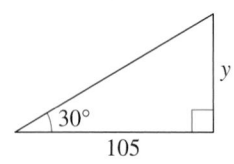

54. Solve for *x*.

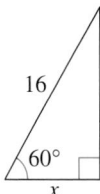

55. Solve for *x*.

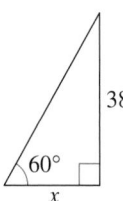

56. Solve for *r*.

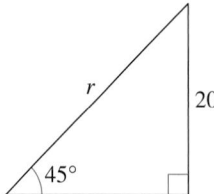

57. *Height* A six-foot person walks from the base of a streetlight directly toward the tip of the shadow cast by the streetlight. When the person is 16 feet from the streetlight and 5 feet from the tip of the streetlight's shadow, the person's shadow starts to appear beyond the streetlight's shadow.

(a) Draw a right triangle that gives a visual representation of the problem. Show the known quantities of the triangle and use a variable to indicate the height of the streetlight.

(b) Use a trigonometric function to write an equation involving the unknown quantity.

(c) What is the height of the streetlight?

58. *Height* A 30-meter line is used to tether a helium-filled balloon. Because of a breeze, the line makes an angle of approximately 75° with the ground.

(a) Draw a right triangle that gives a visual representation of the problem. Show the known quantities of the triangle and use a variable to indicate the height of the balloon.

(b) Use a trigonometric function to write an equation involving the unknown quantity.

(c) What is the height of the balloon?

59. *Width* A biologist wants to know the width *w* of a river in order to properly set instruments for studying the pollutants in the water. From point A, the biologist walks downstream 100 feet and sights to point *C*. From this sighting, it is determined that $\theta = 58°$. How wide is the river? Verify your result numerically.

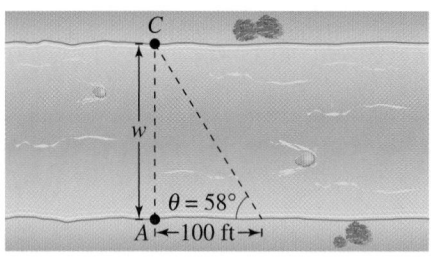

Figure for 59

60. *Height* In traveling across flat land, you notice a mountain directly in front of you. Its angle of elevation (to the peak) is 3.5°. After you drive 13 miles closer to the mountain, the angle of elevation is 9°. Approximate the height of the mountain.

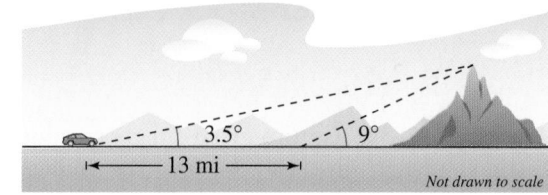

61. *Angle of Elevation* A ramp 20 feet in length rises to a loading platform that is $3\frac{1}{3}$ feet off the ground.

(a) Draw a right triangle that gives a visual representation of the problem. Show the known quantities of the triangle and use a variable to indicate the angle of elevation of the ramp.

(b) Use a trigonometric function to write an equation involving the unknown quantity.

(c) Use a graphing utility to approximate the angle of elevation numerically.

62. *Jin Mao Building* You are standing 65 meters from the base of the Jin Mao Building in Shanghai, China. You estimate that the angle of elevation to the top of the 88th floor (sightseeing level) is 80°. What is the approximate height of the building? One of your friends is on the sightseeing level. What is the distance between you and your friend?

63. *Length* A guywire is stretched from the top of a 200-foot broadcasting tower to an anchor making an angle of 58° with the ground.

(a) How long is the wire?

(b) How far is the anchor from the base of the tower?

64. *Machine Shop Calculations* A steel plate has the form of one-fourth of a circle with a radius of 60 centimeters. Two two-centimeter holes are to be drilled in the plate, positioned as shown in the figure. Find the coordinates of the center of each hole.

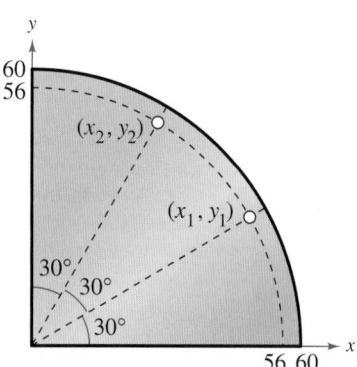

65. *Machine Shop Calculations* A tapered shaft has a diameter of 5 centimeters at the small end and is 15 centimeters long (see figure). The taper is $3°$. Find the diameter d of the large end of the shaft.

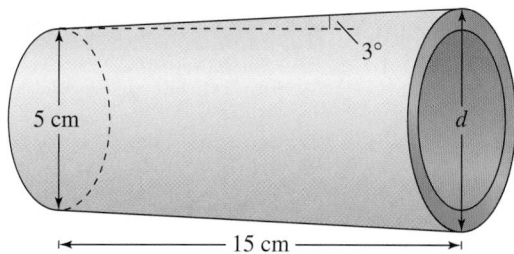

66. *Geometry* Use a compass to sketch a quarter of a circle of radius 10 centimeters. Using a protractor, construct an angle of $20°$ in standard position (see figure). Drop a perpendicular from the point of intersection of the terminal side of the angle and the arc of the circle. By actual measurement, calculate the coordinates (x, y) of the point of intersection and use these measurements to approximate the six trigonometric functions of a $20°$ angle.

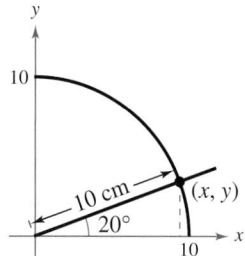

Synthesis

True or False? **In Exercises 67–70, determine whether the statement is true or false. Justify your answer.**

67. $\sin 60° \csc 60° = 1$ **68.** $\sec 30° = \csc 60°$

69. $\sin 45° + \cos 45° = 1$

70. $\cot^2 10° - \csc^2 10° = -1$

71. *Exploration*

(a) Use a graphing utility to complete the table. Round your results to four decimal places.

θ	0°	20°	40°	60°	80°
$\sin \theta$					
$\cos \theta$					
$\tan \theta$					

(b) Classify each of the three trigonometric functions as increasing or decreasing for the table values.

(c) From the values in the table, verify that the tangent function is the quotient of the sine and cosine functions.

72. *Exploration* Use a graphing utility to complete the table and make a conjecture about the relationship between $\cos \theta$ and $\sin(90° - \theta)$. What are the angles θ and $90° - \theta$ called?

θ	0°	20°	40°	60°	80°
$\cos \theta$					
$\sin (90° - \theta)$					

Review

In Exercises 73–76, sketch the graph of the equation and identify all *x*- and *y*-intercepts.

73. $y = -x - 9$ **74.** $2x + y = 10$

75. $-3x + 8y = 16$ **76.** $12x - 7y = 22$

In Exercises 77–80, use a calculator to evaluate the expression. Round your result to three decimal places.

77. $2.16^{3.8}$ **78.** $4^{2\pi}$

79. $\sqrt[3]{5286}$ **80.** $\sqrt[5]{10{,}321}$

5.3 Trigonometric Functions of Any Angle

Introduction

In Section 5.2, the definitions of trigonometric functions were restricted to acute angles. In this section, the definitions are extended to cover *any* angle. If θ is an *acute* angle, the definitions here coincide with those given in the preceding section.

What you should learn

- Evaluate trigonometric functions of any angle.
- Use reference angles to evaluate trigonometric functions.
- Evaluate trigonometric functions of real numbers.

Why you should learn it

You can use trigonometric functions to model and solve real-life problems. For instance, Exercise 107 on page 425 shows you how trigonometric functions can be used to model the monthly normal temperature in Santa Fe, New Mexico.

Definitions of Trigonometric Functions of Any Angle

Let θ be an angle in standard position with (x, y) a point on the terminal side of θ and $r = \sqrt{x^2 + y^2} \neq 0$.

$$\sin \theta = \frac{y}{r} \qquad\qquad \cos \theta = \frac{x}{r}$$

$$\tan \theta = \frac{y}{x}, \quad x \neq 0 \qquad \cot \theta = \frac{x}{y}, \quad y \neq 0$$

$$\sec \theta = \frac{r}{x}, \quad x \neq 0 \qquad \csc \theta = \frac{r}{y}, \quad y \neq 0$$

Richard Elliott/Getty Images

Because $r = \sqrt{x^2 + y^2}$ *cannot* be zero, it follows that the sine and cosine functions are defined for any real value of θ. However, if $x = 0$, the tangent and secant of θ are undefined. For example, the tangent of $90°$ is undefined. Similarly, if $y = 0$, the cotangent and cosecant of θ are undefined.

Example 1   Evaluating Trigonometric Functions

Let $(-3, 4)$ be a point on the terminal side of θ. Find the sine, cosine, and tangent of θ.

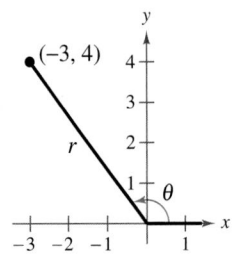

Figure 5.28

Solution

Referring to Figure 5.28, you can see that $x = -3$, $y = 4$, and

$$r = \sqrt{x^2 + y^2} = \sqrt{(-3)^2 + 4^2} = \sqrt{25} = 5.$$

So, you have $\sin \theta = \dfrac{y}{r} = \dfrac{4}{5}$, $\cos \theta = \dfrac{x}{r} = -\dfrac{3}{5}$, and $\tan \theta = \dfrac{y}{x} = -\dfrac{4}{3}$.

✓ *Checkpoint* Now try Exercise 1.

The *signs* of the trigonometric functions in the four quadrants can be determined easily from the definitions of the functions. For instance, because $\cos \theta = x/r$, it follows that $\cos \theta$ is positive wherever $x > 0$, which is in Quadrants I and IV. (Remember, r is always positive.) In a similar manner, you can verify the results shown in Figure 5.29.

Example 2   Evaluating Trigonometric Functions

Given $\tan \theta = -\frac{5}{4}$ and $\cos \theta > 0$, find $\sin \theta$ and $\sec \theta$.

Solution

Note that θ lies in Quadrant IV because that is the only quadrant in which the tangent is negative and the cosine is positive. Moreover, using

$$\tan \theta = \frac{y}{x} = -\frac{5}{4}$$

and the fact that y is negative in Quadrant IV, you can let $y = -5$ and $x = 4$. So, $r = \sqrt{16 + 25} = \sqrt{41}$, and you have the following.

$$\sin \theta = \frac{y}{r} = \frac{-5}{\sqrt{41}} \qquad \text{Exact value}$$

$$\approx -0.7809 \qquad \text{Approximate value}$$

$$\sec \theta = \frac{r}{x} = \frac{\sqrt{41}}{4} \qquad \text{Exact value}$$

$$\approx 1.6008 \qquad \text{Approximate value}$$

✓ *Checkpoint* Now try Exercise 19.

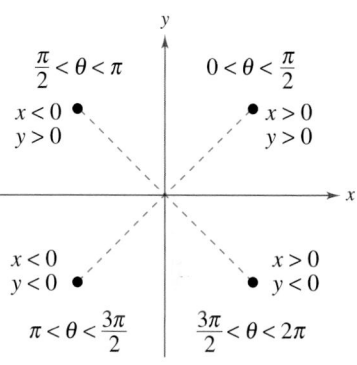

Figure 5.29

Example 3   Trigonometric Functions of Quadrant Angles

Evaluate the sine and cosine functions at the angles 0, $\frac{\pi}{2}$, π, and $\frac{3\pi}{2}$.

Solution

To begin, choose a point on the terminal side of each angle, as shown in Figure 5.30. For each of the four given points, $r = 1$, and you have the following.

$$\sin 0 = \frac{y}{r} = \frac{0}{1} = 0 \qquad \cos 0 = \frac{x}{r} = \frac{1}{1} = 1 \qquad (x, y) = (1, 0)$$

$$\sin \frac{\pi}{2} = \frac{y}{r} = \frac{1}{1} = 1 \qquad \cos \frac{\pi}{2} = \frac{x}{r} = \frac{0}{1} = 0 \qquad (x, y) = (0, 1)$$

$$\sin \pi = \frac{y}{r} = \frac{0}{1} = 0 \qquad \cos \pi = \frac{x}{r} = \frac{-1}{1} = -1 \qquad (x, y) = (-1, 0)$$

$$\sin \frac{3\pi}{2} = \frac{y}{r} = \frac{-1}{1} = -1 \qquad \cos \frac{3\pi}{2} = \frac{x}{r} = \frac{0}{1} = 0 \qquad (x, y) = (0, -1)$$

✓ *Checkpoint* Now try Exercise 29.

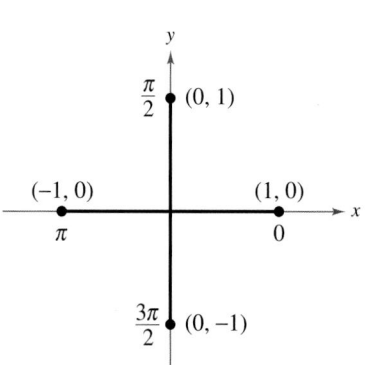

Figure 5.30

Reference Angles

The values of the trigonometric functions of angles greater than $90°$ (or less than $0°$) can be determined from their values at corresponding acute angles called **reference angles.**

> **Definition of Reference Angle**
>
> Let θ be an angle in standard position. Its **reference angle** is the acute angle θ' formed by the terminal side of θ and the horizontal axis.

Figure 5.31 shows the reference angles for θ in Quadrants II, III, and IV.

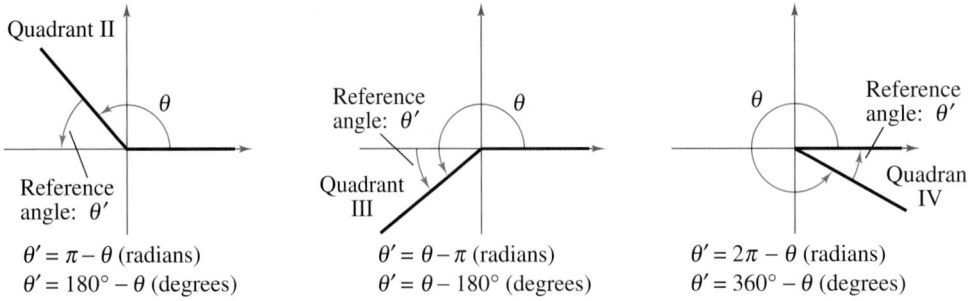

$\theta' = \pi - \theta$ (radians) $\theta' = \theta - \pi$ (radians) $\theta' = 2\pi - \theta$ (radians)
$\theta' = 180° - \theta$ (degrees) $\theta' = \theta - 180°$ (degrees) $\theta' = 360° - \theta$ (degrees)

Figure 5.31

Example 4   Finding Reference Angles

Find the reference angle θ'.

a. $\theta = 300°$ **b.** $\theta = 2.3$ **c.** $\theta = -135°$

Solution

a. Because $300°$ lies in Quadrant IV, the angle it makes with the x-axis is

$\theta' = 360° - 300° = 60°.$ Degrees

b. Because 2.3 lies between $\pi/2 \approx 1.5708$ and $\pi \approx 3.1416$, it follows that it is in Quadrant II and its reference angle is

$\theta' = \pi - 2.3 \approx 0.8416.$ Radians

c. First, determine that $-135°$ is coterminal with $225°$, which lies in Quadrant III. So, the reference angle is

$\theta' = 225° - 180° = 45°.$ Degrees

Figure 5.32 shows each angle θ and its reference angle θ'.

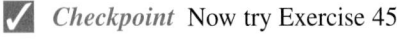 *Checkpoint* Now try Exercise 45.

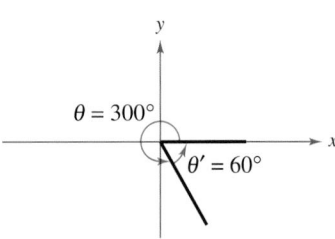

(a)

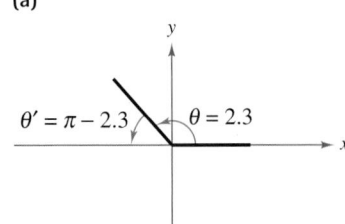

(b)

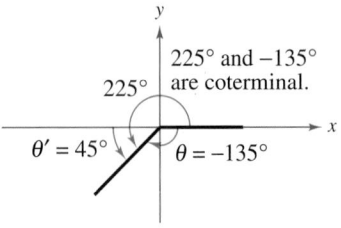

(c)
Figure 5.32

To see how a reference angle is used to evaluate a trigonometric function, consider the point (x, y) on the terminal side of θ, as shown in Figure 5.33. By definition, you know that

$$\sin \theta = \frac{y}{r} \quad \text{and} \quad \tan \theta = \frac{y}{x}.$$

For the right triangle with acute angle θ' and sides of lengths $|x|$ and $|y|$, you have

$$\sin \theta' = \frac{\text{opp}}{\text{hyp}} = \frac{|y|}{r}$$

and

$$\tan \theta' = \frac{\text{opp}}{\text{adj}} = \frac{|y|}{|x|}.$$

So, it follows that $\sin \theta$ and $\sin \theta'$ are equal, *except possibly in sign*. The same is true for $\tan \theta$ and $\tan \theta'$, and for the other four trigonometric functions. In all cases, the sign of the function value can be determined by the quadrant in which θ lies.

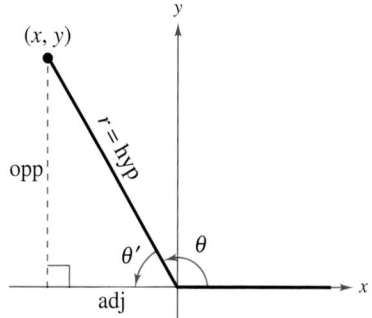

Figure 5.33

Evaluating Trigonometric Functions of Any Angle

To find the value of a trigonometric function of any angle θ:

1. Determine the function value for the associated reference angle θ'.

2. Depending on the quadrant in which θ lies, affix the appropriate sign to the function value.

By using reference angles and the special angles discussed in the preceding section, you can greatly extend the scope of *exact* trigonometric values. For instance, knowing the function values of 30° means that you know the function values of all angles for which 30° is a reference angle. For convenience, the following table shows the exact values of the trigonometric functions of special angles and quadrant angles.

Trigonometric Values of Common Angles

θ (degrees)	0°	30°	45°	60°	90°	180°	270°
θ (radians)	0	$\dfrac{\pi}{6}$	$\dfrac{\pi}{4}$	$\dfrac{\pi}{3}$	$\dfrac{\pi}{2}$	π	$\dfrac{3\pi}{2}$
$\sin \theta$	0	$\dfrac{1}{2}$	$\dfrac{\sqrt{2}}{2}$	$\dfrac{\sqrt{3}}{2}$	1	0	-1
$\cos \theta$	1	$\dfrac{\sqrt{3}}{2}$	$\dfrac{\sqrt{2}}{2}$	$\dfrac{1}{2}$	0	-1	0
$\tan \theta$	0	$\dfrac{\sqrt{3}}{3}$	1	$\sqrt{3}$	Undef.	0	Undef.

STUDY TIP

Learning the table of values at the left is worth the effort because doing so will increase both your efficiency and your confidence. Here is a pattern for the sine function that may help you remember the values.

θ	0°	30°	45°	60°	90°
$\sin \theta$	$\dfrac{\sqrt{0}}{2}$	$\dfrac{\sqrt{1}}{2}$	$\dfrac{\sqrt{2}}{2}$	$\dfrac{\sqrt{3}}{2}$	$\dfrac{\sqrt{4}}{2}$

Reverse the order to get the cosine values of the same angles.

Example 5   Trigonometric Functions of Nonacute Angles

Evaluate each trigonometric function.

a. $\cos \dfrac{4\pi}{3}$ **b.** $\tan(-210°)$ **c.** $\csc \dfrac{11\pi}{4}$

Solution

a. Because $\theta = 4\pi/3$ lies in Quadrant III, the reference angle, θ', is $(4\pi/3) - \pi = \pi/3$, as shown in Figure 5.34. Moreover, the cosine is negative in Quadrant III, so

$$\cos \frac{4\pi}{3} = (-)\cos \frac{\pi}{3} = -\frac{1}{2}.$$

b. Because $-210° + 360° = 150°$, it follows that $-210°$ is coterminal with the second-quadrant angle $150°$. Therefore, the reference angle, θ', is $180° - 150° = 30°$, as shown in Figure 5.35. Finally, because the tangent is negative in Quadrant II, you have

$$\tan(-210°) = (-)\tan 30° = -\frac{\sqrt{3}}{3}.$$

c. Because $(11\pi/4) - 2\pi = 3\pi/4$, it follows that $11\pi/4$ is coterminal with the second-quadrant angle $3\pi/4$. Therefore, the reference angle, θ', is $\pi - (3\pi/4) = \pi/4$, as shown in Figure 5.36. Because the cosecant is positive in Quadrant II, you have

$$\csc \frac{11\pi}{4} = (+)\csc \frac{\pi}{4}$$

$$= \frac{1}{\sin(\pi/4)}$$

$$= \sqrt{2}.$$

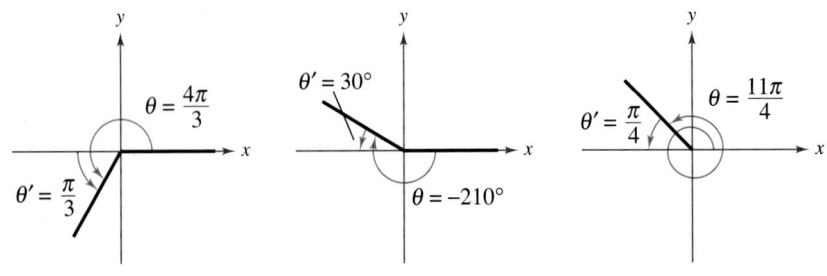

Figure 5.34   Figure 5.35   Figure 5.36

 *Checkpoint* Now try Exercise 59.

The fundamental trigonometric identities listed in the preceding section (for an acute angle θ) are also valid when θ is any angle in the domain of the function.

Example 6   Using Trigonometric Identities

Let θ be an angle in Quadrant II such that $\sin \theta = \frac{1}{3}$. Find (a) $\cos \theta$ and (b) $\tan \theta$ by using trigonometric identities.

Solution

a. Using the Pythagorean identity $\sin^2 \theta + \cos^2 \theta = 1$, you obtain

$$\left(\tfrac{1}{3}\right)^2 + \cos^2 \theta = 1$$

$$\cos^2 \theta = 1 - \frac{1}{9}$$

$$\cos^2 \theta = \frac{8}{9}$$

Because $\cos \theta < 0$ in Quadrant II, you can use the negative root to obtain

$$\cos \theta = -\frac{\sqrt{8}}{\sqrt{9}} = -\frac{2\sqrt{2}}{3}.$$

b. Using the trigonometric identity $\tan \theta = \sin \theta / \cos \theta$, you obtain

$$\tan \theta = \frac{1/3}{-2\sqrt{2}/3}$$

$$= -\frac{1}{2\sqrt{2}}$$

$$= -\frac{\sqrt{2}}{4}.$$

✓ *Checkpoint* Now try Exercise 67.

You can use a calculator to evaluate trigonometric functions, as shown in the next example.

Example 7   Using a Calculator

Use a calculator to evaluate each trigonometric function.

a. $\cot 410°$ **b.** $\sin(-7)$ **c.** $\sec \dfrac{\pi}{9}$

Solution

Function	Mode	Graphing Calculator Keystrokes	Display
a. $\cot 410°$	*Degree*	(TAN 410) x^{-1} ENTER	0.8390996
b. $\sin(-7)$	*Radian*	SIN (−) 7) ENTER	−0.6569866
c. $\sec \dfrac{\pi}{9}$	*Radian*	(COS π ÷ 9) x^{-1} ENTER	1.0641777

✓ *Checkpoint* Now try Exercise 75.

Trigonometric Functions of Real Numbers

To define a trigonometric function of a real number (rather than an angle), let t represent any real number. Then imagine that the real number line is wrapped around a *unit circle*, as shown in Figure 5.37. Note that positive numbers correspond to a counterclockwise wrapping, and negative numbers correspond to a clockwise wrapping.

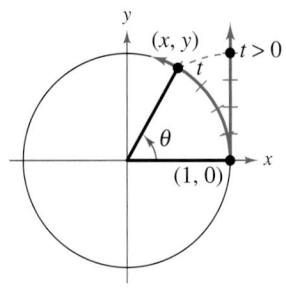 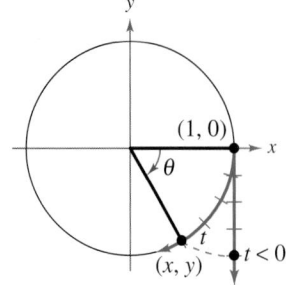

Figure 5.37

As the real number line is wrapped around the unit circle, each real number t will correspond with a central angle θ. Moreover, because the circle has a radius of 1, the arc intercepted by the angle θ will have a length of t. The point is that if θ *is measured in radians*, then $t = \theta$. So, you can define $\sin t$ as $\sin t = \sin(t \text{ radians})$. Similarly, $\cos t = \cos(t \text{ radians})$, $\tan t = \tan(t \text{ radians})$, and so on.

TECHNOLOGY SUPPORT

For instructions on how to use the *parametric* and *radian* modes and the *value* and *trace* features, see Appendix A; for specific keystrokes, go to the text website at *college.hmco.com*.

Example 8 Evaluating Trigonometric Functions

Evaluate $f(t) = \sin t$ for (a) $t = 1$ and (b) $t = 3\pi/2$.

Algebraic Solution

a. $f(1) = \sin 1$ Radian mode

≈ 0.841471

b. $f\left(\dfrac{3\pi}{2}\right) = \sin\dfrac{3\pi}{2}$ Common angle

$= -1$

Graphical Solution

Use a graphing utility set in *parametric* and *radian* modes to graph $X1T = \cos T$ and $Y1T = \sin T$ using the following settings.

Tmin $= 0$,   Tmax $= 6.3$,   Tstep $= 0.1$
Xmin $= -1.5$,   Xmax $= 1.5$,   Xscl $= 1$
Ymin $= -1$,   Ymax $= 1$,   Yscl $= 1$

a. Use the *value* or *trace* feature to estimate that $\sin 1 \approx 0.841471$, as shown in Figure 5.38.

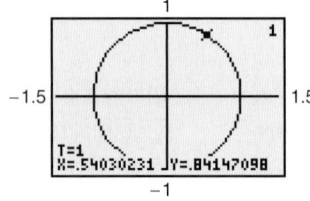

Figure 5.38

b. Use the *value* or *trace* feature to estimate that $\sin\dfrac{3\pi}{2} \approx \sin 4.7 \approx -1$.

✓ *Checkpoint* Now try Exercise 99.

The *domain* of the sine and cosine functions is the set of all real numbers. To determine the *range* of these two functions, consider the unit circle shown in Figure 5.39. Because $r = 1$, it follows that $\sin t = y$ and $\cos t = x$. Moreover, because (x, y) is on the unit circle, you know that $-1 \le y \le 1$ and $-1 \le x \le 1$. So, the values of sine and cosine also range between -1 and 1.

$$-1 \le y \quad \le 1 \qquad -1 \le x \quad \le 1$$
$$\text{and}$$
$$-1 \le \sin t \le 1 \qquad -1 \le \cos t \le 1$$

You can add 2π to each value of t in the interval $[0, 2\pi]$, completing a second revolution around the unit circle, as shown in Figure 5.40. The values of $\sin(t + 2\pi)$ and $\cos(t + 2\pi)$ correspond to those of $\sin t$ and $\cos t$. Similar results can be obtained for repeated revolutions (positive or negative) on the unit circle. This leads to the general result

$$\sin(t + 2\pi n) = \sin t \qquad \text{and} \qquad \cos(t + 2\pi n) = \cos t$$

for any integer n and real number t. Functions that behave in such a repetitive (or cyclic) manner are called **periodic.**

Exploration

With your graphing utility in *radian* mode, select a number t and calculate $\cos t$ and $\cos(t + 2\pi)$. Repeat this experiment for other values of t and explain why the answers are always the same. Perform a similar experiment with $\tan t$ and $\tan(t + \pi)$.

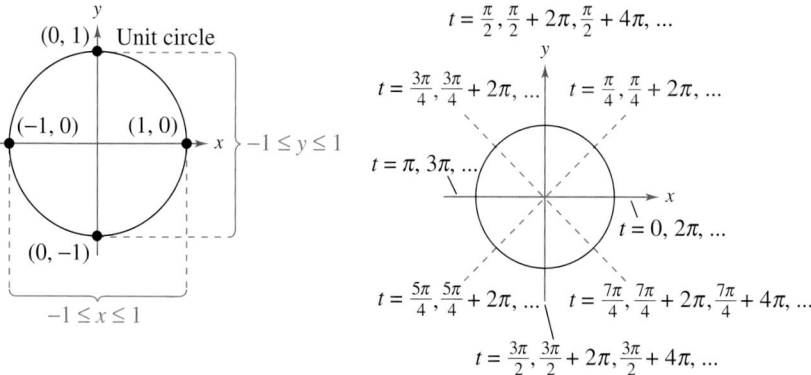

Figure 5.39 Figure 5.40

Definition of Periodic Function

A function f is **periodic** if there exists a positive real number c such that

$$f(t + c) = f(t)$$

for all t in the domain of f. The least number c for which f is periodic is called the **period** of f.

From this definition it follows that the sine and cosine functions are periodic and have a period of 2π. The other four trigonometric functions are also periodic, and more will be said about this in Section 5.5.

Recall from Section 1.4 that a function f is *even* if $f(-t) = f(t)$ and is *odd* if $f(-t) = -f(t)$.

Even and Odd Trigonometric Functions

The cosine and secant functions are *even*.

$$\cos(-t) = \cos t \qquad \sec(-t) = \sec t$$

The sine, cosecant, tangent, and cotangent functions are *odd*.

$$\sin(-t) = -\sin t \qquad \csc(-t) = -\csc t$$

$$\tan(-t) = -\tan t \qquad \cot(-t) = -\cot t$$

Exploration

Select a number t and use your graphing utility to calculate $\cos t$ and $\cos(-t)$. Repeat this experiment for other values of t and explain why the answer is always the same. Perform a similar experiment to determine the relationship between $\sin t$ and $\sin(-t)$.

Library of Functions: Trigonometric Functions

Trigonometric functions are transcendental functions. The six trigonometric functions, sine, cosine, tangent, cosecant, secant, and cotangent, have important uses in construction, surveying, and navigation. Their periodic behavior makes them useful for modeling phenomena such as business cycles, planetary orbits, pendulums, wave motion, and light rays.

The six trigonometric functions can be defined in three different ways.

1. As the ratio of two sides of a right triangle [see Figure 5.41(a)].

2. As coordinates of a point (x, y) in the plane and its distance r from the origin [see Figure 5.41(b)].

3. As functions of any real number, such as time t.

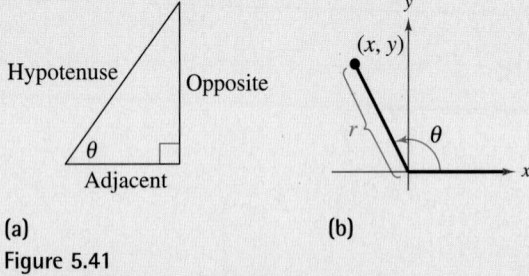

(a)   **(b)**

Figure 5.41

To be efficient in the use of trigonometric functions, you should learn the trigonometric function values of common angles, such as those listed on page 417. Because pairs of trigonometric functions are related to each other by a variety of identities, it is useful to know the fundamental identities presented in Section 5.2. Finally, trigonometric functions and their identity relationships play a prominent role in calculus.

STUDY TIP

For your convenience, a summary of basic trigonometry is included on the inside back cover of this text.

At this point, you have completed your introduction to basic trigonometry. You have measured angles in both degrees and radians. You have defined the six trigonometric functions from a right triangle perspective and as functions of real numbers. In your remaining work with trigonometry, you should continue to rely on both perspectives. For instance, in the next two sections on graphing techniques, it helps to think of the trigonometric functions as functions of real numbers. Later, in Section 5.7, you will look at applications involving angles and triangles.

5.3   Exercises

Vocabulary Check

Fill in the blanks.

1. The acute positive angle that is formed by the terminal side of the angle θ and the horizontal axis is called the _____ angle of θ and is denoted by θ'.

2. A function f is _____ if there exists a positive real number c such that $f(t + c) = f(t)$ for all t in the domain of f.

3. A function f is _____ if $f(-t) = -f(t)$.

4. A function f is _____ if $f(-t) = f(t)$.

In Exercises 1–4, determine the exact values of the six trigonometric functions of the angle θ.

1. (a)   (b)

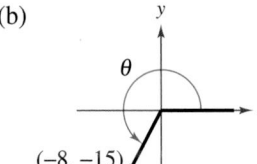

2. (a)   (b)

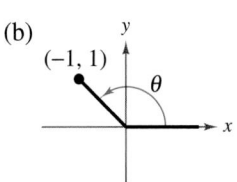

3. (a)   (b)

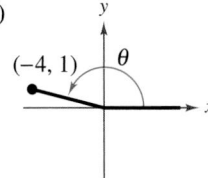

4. (a)   (b)

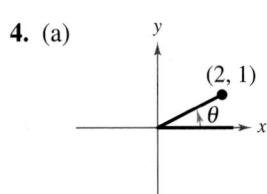
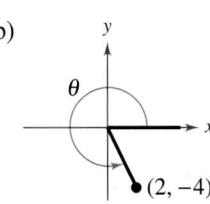

In Exercises 5–12, the point is on the terminal side of an angle in standard position. Determine the exact values of the six trigonometric functions of the angle.

5. $(7, 24)$ 6. $(8, 15)$

7. $(5, -12)$ 8. $(-24, 10)$

9. $(-4, 10)$ 10. $(-5, -2)$

11. $(-2, 9)$ 12. $(6, -14)$

In Exercises 13–16, state the quadrant in which θ lies.

13. $\sin \theta < 0$ and $\cos \theta < 0$

14. $\sin \theta > 0$ and $\cos \theta > 0$

15. $\sec \theta > 0$ and $\cot \theta < 0$

16. $\tan \theta > 0$ and $\csc \theta < 0$

In Exercises 17–24, find the values of the six trigonometric functions of θ.

Function Value	*Constraint*
17. $\sin \theta = \frac{3}{5}$	θ lies in Quadrant II.
18. $\cos \theta = -\frac{4}{5}$	θ lies in Quadrant III.
19. $\tan \theta = -\frac{15}{8}$	$\sin \theta < 0$
20. $\csc \theta = 4$	$\cot \theta < 0$
21. $\sec \theta = -2$	$0 \le \theta \le \pi$
22. $\sin \theta = 0$	$\sec \theta = -1$
23. $\cot \theta$ is undefined.	$\dfrac{\pi}{2} \le \theta \le \dfrac{3\pi}{2}$
24. $\tan \theta$ is undefined.	$\pi \le \theta \le 2\pi$

In Exercises 25–28, the terminal side of θ lies on the given line in the specified quadrant. Find the values of the six trigonometric functions of θ by finding a point on the line.

Line	*Quadrant*
25. $y = -x$	II
26. $y = \frac{1}{3}x$	III
27. $2x - y = 0$	III
28. $4x + 3y = 0$	IV

In Exercises 29–36, evaluate the trigonometric function of the quadrant angle.

29. $\sec \pi$

30. $\tan \dfrac{\pi}{2}$

31. $\cot \dfrac{3\pi}{2}$

32. $\csc \pi$

33. $\sec 0$

34. $\csc \dfrac{3\pi}{2}$

35. $\cot \pi$

36. $\csc \dfrac{\pi}{2}$

In Exercises 37–44, find the reference angle θ' for the special angle θ. Then sketch θ and θ' in standard position.

37. $\theta = 120°$

38. $\theta = 225°$

39. $\theta = -135°$

40. $\theta = -330°$

41. $\theta = \dfrac{5\pi}{3}$

42. $\theta = \dfrac{3\pi}{4}$

43. $\theta = -\dfrac{5\pi}{6}$

44. $\theta = -\dfrac{2\pi}{3}$

In Exercises 45–52, find the reference angle θ' and sketch θ and θ' in standard position.

45. $\theta = 208°$

46. $\theta = 322°$

47. $\theta = -292°$

48. $\theta = -95°$

49. $\theta = \dfrac{11\pi}{5}$

50. $\theta = \dfrac{17\pi}{7}$

51. $\theta = 3.5$

52. $\theta = -1.72$

In Exercises 53–66, evaluate the sine, cosine, and tangent of the angle without using a calculator.

53. $225°$

54. $300°$

55. $-750°$

56. $-495°$

57. $-240°$

58. $-330°$

59. $\dfrac{5\pi}{3}$

60. $\dfrac{3\pi}{4}$

61. $-\dfrac{7\pi}{6}$

62. $-\dfrac{4\pi}{3}$

63. $\dfrac{11\pi}{4}$

64. $\dfrac{10\pi}{3}$

65. $-\dfrac{17\pi}{6}$

66. $-\dfrac{20\pi}{3}$

In Exercises 67–72, find the indicated trigonometric value in the specified quadrant.

	Function	Quadrant	Trigonometric Value
67.	$\sin \theta = -\dfrac{3}{5}$	IV	$\cos \theta$
68.	$\cot \theta = -3$	II	$\sin \theta$
69.	$\tan \theta = \dfrac{3}{2}$	III	$\sec \theta$
70.	$\csc \theta = -2$	IV	$\cot \theta$
71.	$\cos \theta = \dfrac{5}{8}$	I	$\sec \theta$
72.	$\sec \theta = -\dfrac{9}{4}$	III	$\tan \theta$

In Exercises 73–88, use a calculator to evaluate the trigonometric function. Round your answer to four decimal places. (Be sure the calculator is set to the correct angle mode.)

73. $\sin 10°$

74. $\sec 235°$

75. $\tan 245°$

76. $\csc 320°$

77. $\cos(-110°)$

78. $\cot(-220°)$

79. $\sec(-280°)$

80. $\sin(-195°)$

81. $\sin 0.65$

82. $\sin(-0.65)$

83. $\cos(-1.81)$

84. $\sec 0.33$

85. $\tan \dfrac{2\pi}{9}$

86. $\tan \dfrac{11\pi}{9}$

87. $\csc\left(-\dfrac{8\pi}{9}\right)$

88. $\cos\left(-\dfrac{15\pi}{14}\right)$

In Exercises 89–94, find two solutions of the equation. Give your answers in degrees ($0° \le \theta < 360°$) and radians ($0 \le \theta < 2\pi$). Do not use a calculator.

89. (a) $\sin \theta = \dfrac{1}{2}$ (b) $\sin \theta = -\dfrac{1}{2}$

90. (a) $\cos \theta = \dfrac{\sqrt{2}}{2}$ (b) $\cos \theta = -\dfrac{\sqrt{2}}{2}$

91. (a) $\csc \theta = \dfrac{2\sqrt{3}}{3}$ (b) $\cot \theta = -1$

92. (a) $\csc \theta = -\sqrt{2}$ (b) $\csc \theta = 2$

93. (a) $\sec \theta = -\dfrac{2\sqrt{3}}{3}$ (b) $\cos \theta = \dfrac{1}{2}$

94. (a) $\cot \theta = -\sqrt{3}$ (b) $\sec \theta = \sqrt{2}$

In Exercises 95–102, find the point (x, y) on the unit circle that corresponds to the real number t. Use the result to evaluate $\sin t$, $\cos t$, and $\tan t$.

95. $t = \dfrac{\pi}{4}$ **96.** $t = \dfrac{\pi}{3}$

97. $t = \dfrac{5\pi}{6}$ **98.** $t = \dfrac{5\pi}{4}$

99. $t = \dfrac{4\pi}{3}$ **100.** $t = \dfrac{11\pi}{6}$

101. $t = \dfrac{3\pi}{2}$ **102.** $t = \pi$

Estimation   In Exercises 103 and 104, use the figure and a straightedge to approximate the value of each trigonometric function. Check your approximation using a graphing utility. To print an enlarged copy of the graph, go to the website *www.mathgraphs.com*.

103. (a) $\sin 5$ (b) $\cos 2$

104. (a) $\sin 0.75$ (b) $\cos 2.5$

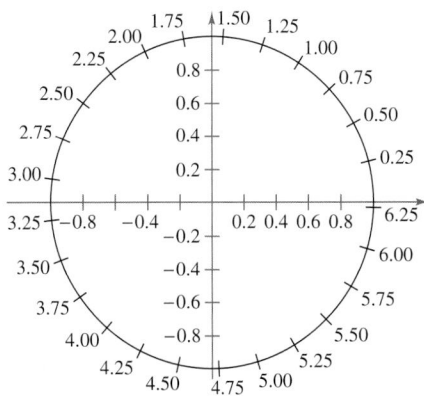

Estimation   In Exercises 105 and 106, use the figure in Exercises 103 and 104 to approximate the solution of each equation, where $0 \le t < 2\pi$. Check your approximation using a graphing utility. To print an enlarged copy of the graph, go to the website *www.mathgraphs.com*.

105. (a) $\sin t = 0.25$ (b) $\cos t = -0.25$

106. (a) $\sin t = -0.75$ (b) $\cos t = 0.75$

107. *Meteorology*   The monthly normal temperature T (in degrees Fahrenheit) for Santa Fe, New Mexico is given by

$$T = 49.5 + 20.5 \cos\left(\frac{\pi t}{6} - \frac{7\pi}{6}\right)$$

where t is the time in months, with $t = 1$ corresponding to January. Find the monthly normal temperature for each month. (Source: National Climatic Data Center)

(a) January   (b) July   (c) December

108. *Sales*   A company that produces water skis, which are seasonal products, forecasts monthly sales over a two-year period to be

$$S = 23.1 + 0.442t + 4.3 \sin \frac{\pi t}{6}$$

where S is measured in thousands of units and t is the time (in months), with $t = 1$ representing January 2004. Estimate sales for each month.

(a) January 2004   (b) February 2005

(c) May 2004   (d) June 2004

109. *Harmonic Motion*   The displacement from equilibrium of an oscillating weight suspended by a spring is given by

$$y(t) = 2e^{-t} \cos 6t$$

where y is the displacement (in centimeters) and t is the time (in seconds).

(a) What is the initial displacement $(t = 0)$?

(b) Use a graphing utility to complete the table.

t	0.50	1.02	1.54	2.07	2.59
y					

(c) The approximate times when the weight is at its maximum distance from equilibrium are shown in the table in part (b). Explain why the magnitude of the maximum displacement is decreasing. What causes this decrease in maximum displacement in the physical system? What factor in the model measures this decrease?

(d) Find the first two times that the weight is at the equilibrium point $(y = 0)$.

110. ***Harmonic Motion*** The displacement from equilibrium of an oscillating weight suspended by a spring is given by

$$y(t) = 2 \cos 6t$$

where y is the displacement (in centimeters) and t is the time (in seconds). Find the displacement when (a) $t = 0$, (b) $t = \frac{1}{4}$, and (c) $t = \frac{1}{2}$.

111. ***Electric Circuits*** The initial current and charge in an electric circuit are zero. The current when 100 volts is applied to the circuit is given by

$$I = 5e^{-2t} \sin t$$

where the resistance, inductance, and capacitance are 80 ohms, 20 henrys, and 0.01 farad, respectively. Approximate the current (in amperes) $t = 0.7$ second after the voltage is applied.

112. ***Distance*** An airplane, flying at an altitude of 6 miles, is on a flight path that passes directly over an observer (see figure). If θ is the angle of elevation from the observer to the plane, find the distance from the observer to the plane when (a) $\theta = 30°$, (b) $\theta = 90°$, and (c) $\theta = 120°$.

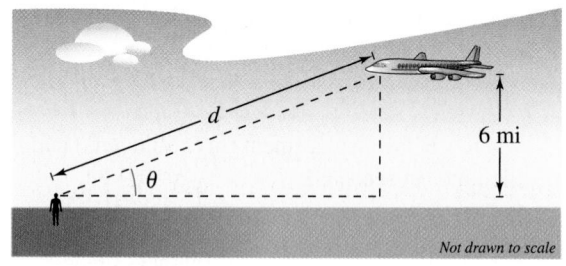

Not drawn to scale

Synthesis

True or False? **In Exercises 113–116, determine whether the statement is true or false. Justify your answer.**

113. $\sin 151° = \sin 29°$

114. $\tan 24° = \tan 156°$

115. $\csc\left(-\dfrac{7\pi}{6}\right) = \csc\left(-\dfrac{11\pi}{6}\right)$

116. $-\cot\left(\dfrac{3\pi}{4}\right) = \cot\left(-\dfrac{\pi}{4}\right)$

117. ***Conjecture***

(a) Use a graphing utility to complete the table.

θ	0°	20°	40°	60°	80°
$\sin \theta$					
$\sin(180° - \theta)$					

(b) Make a conjecture about the relationship between $\sin \theta$ and $\sin(180° - \theta)$.

118. ***Conjecture***

(a) Use a graphing utility to complete the table.

θ	0	0.3	0.6	0.9	1.2	1.5
$\cos\left(\dfrac{3\pi}{2} - \theta\right)$						
$-\sin \theta$						

(b) Make a conjecture about the relationship between $\cos\left(\dfrac{3\pi}{2} - \theta\right)$ and $-\sin \theta$.

119. ***Writing*** Create a table of the six trigonometric functions comparing their domains, ranges, evenness, oddness, periods, and zeros. Then identify and write a short paragraph describing any inherent patterns in the trigonometric functions. What can you conclude?

120. ***Think About It*** Because $f(t) = \sin t$ is an odd function and $g(t) = \cos t$ is an even function, what can be said about the function $h(t) = f(t)g(t)$?

Review

In Exercises 121–124, sketch the graph of the function. Identify any intercepts and asymptotes.

121. $y = 2^{x-1}$

122. $y = 3^{x+2}$

123. $y = \ln(x - 1)$

124. $y = \ln(x + 1)$

In Exercises 125–128, solve the equation. Round your answer to three decimal places.

125. $4^{3-x} = 726$

126. $\dfrac{4500}{4 + e^{2x}} = 50$

127. $\ln x = -6$

128. $\ln \sqrt{x + 10} = 1$

5.4 | Graphs of Sine and Cosine Functions

Basic Sine and Cosine Curves

In this section you will study techniques for sketching the graphs of the sine and cosine functions. The graph of the sine function is a **sine curve.** In Figure 5.42, the black portion of the graph represents one period of the function and is called **one cycle** of the sine curve. The gray portion of the graph indicates that the basic sine wave repeats indefinitely to the right and left. The graph of the cosine function is shown in Figure 5.43. To produce these graphs with a graphing utility, make sure you have set the graphing utility to *radian* mode.

   Recall from Section 5.3 that the domain of the sine and cosine functions is the set of all real numbers. Moreover, the range of each function is the interval $[-1, 1]$, and each function has a period of 2π. Do you see how this information is consistent with the basic graphs shown in Figures 5.42 and 5.43?

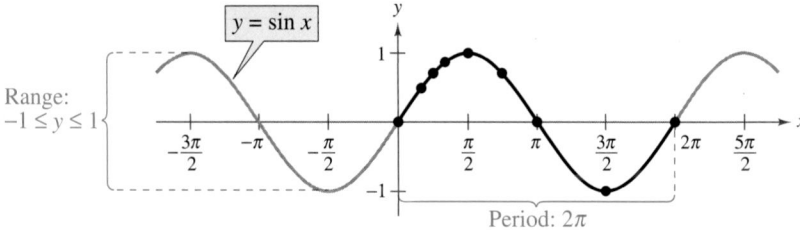

Figure 5.42

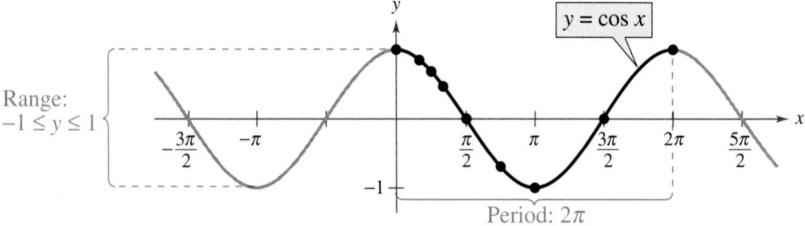

Figure 5.43

What you should learn

- Sketch the graphs of basic sine and cosine functions.
- Use amplitude and period to help sketch the graphs of sine and cosine functions.
- Sketch translations of graphs of sine and cosine functions.
- Use sine and cosine functions to model real-life data.

Why you should learn it

Sine and cosine functions are often used in scientific calculations. For instance, in Exercise 79 on page 436, you can use a trigonometric function to model the percent of the moon's face that is illuminated for any given day in 2006.

Jerry Lodriguss/Photo Researchers, Inc.

The table below lists key points on the graphs of $y = \sin x$ and $y = \cos x$.

x	0	$\dfrac{\pi}{6}$	$\dfrac{\pi}{4}$	$\dfrac{\pi}{3}$	$\dfrac{\pi}{2}$	$\dfrac{3\pi}{4}$	π	$\dfrac{3\pi}{2}$	2π
$\sin x$	0	$\dfrac{1}{2}$	$\dfrac{\sqrt{2}}{2}$	$\dfrac{\sqrt{3}}{2}$	1	$\dfrac{\sqrt{2}}{2}$	0	-1	0
$\cos x$	1	$\dfrac{\sqrt{3}}{2}$	$\dfrac{\sqrt{2}}{2}$	$\dfrac{1}{2}$	0	$-\dfrac{\sqrt{2}}{2}$	-1	0	1

   Note from Figures 5.42 and 5.43 that the sine graph is symmetric with respect to the *origin*, whereas the cosine graph is symmetric with respect to the *y-axis*. These properties of symmetry follow from the fact that the sine function is odd whereas the cosine function is even.

To sketch the graphs of the basic sine and cosine functions by hand, it helps to note five *key points* in one period of each graph: the *intercepts*, the *maximum points*, and the *minimum points*. See Figure 5.44.

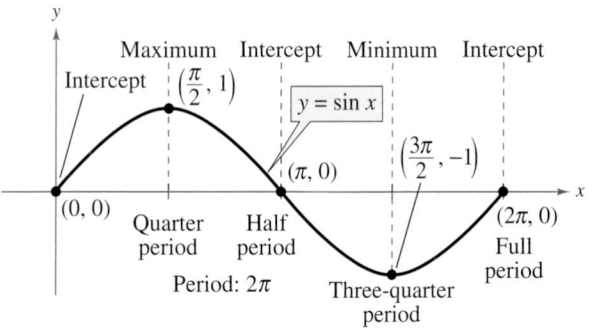
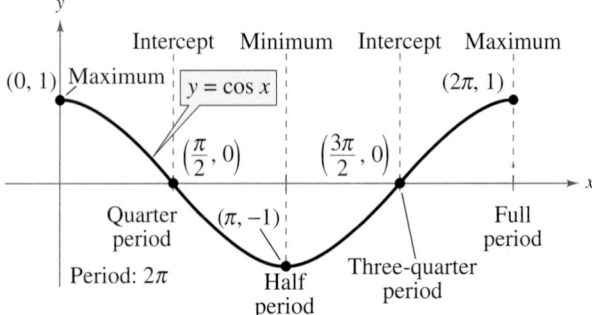

Figure 5.44

Example 1   Using Key Points to Sketch a Sine Curve

Sketch the graph of $y = 2 \sin x$ by hand on the interval $[-\pi, 4\pi]$.

Solution

Note that

$$y = 2 \sin x = 2(\sin x)$$

indicates that the y-values of the key points will have twice the magnitude of those on the graph of $y = \sin x$. Divide the period 2π into four equal parts to get the key points

Intercept	*Maximum*	*Intercept*	*Minimum*		*Intercept*
$(0, 0)$,	$\left(\dfrac{\pi}{2}, 2\right)$,	$(\pi, 0)$,	$\left(\dfrac{3\pi}{2}, -2\right)$,	and	$(2\pi, 0)$.

By connecting these key points with a smooth curve and extending the curve in both directions over the interval $[-\pi, 4\pi]$, you obtain the graph shown in Figure 5.45. Use a graphing utility to confirm this graph. Be sure to set the graphing utility to *radian* mode.

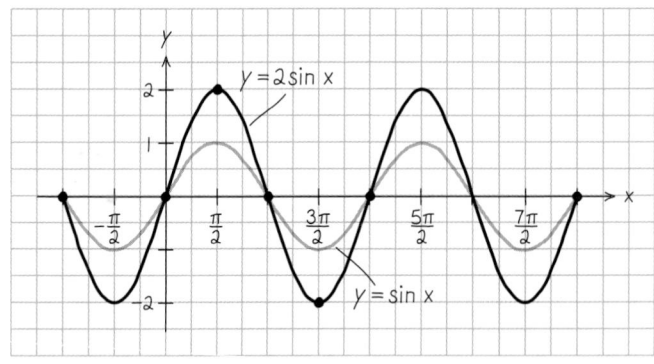

Figure 5.45

✓ *Checkpoint*   Now try Exercise 39.

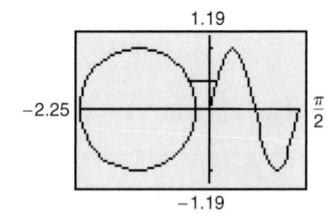

Amplitude and Period of Sine and Cosine Curves

In the rest of this section you will study the graphic effect of each of the constants a, b, c, and d in equations of the forms

$$y = d + a \sin(bx - c) \qquad \text{and} \qquad y = d + a \cos(bx - c).$$

A quick review of the transformations studied in Section 1.5 should help in this investigation.

The constant factor a in $y = a \sin x$ acts as a *scaling factor*—a *vertical stretch* or *vertical shrink* of the basic sine curve. If $|a| > 1$, the basic sine curve is stretched, and if $|a| < 1$, the basic sine curve is shrunk. The result is that the graph of $y = a \sin x$ ranges between $-a$ and a instead of between -1 and 1. The absolute value of a is the **amplitude** of the function $y = a \sin x$. The range of the function $y = a \sin x$ for $a > 0$ is $-a \leq y \leq a$.

Definition of Amplitude of Sine and Cosine Curves

The **amplitude** of $y = a \sin x$ and $y = a \cos x$ represents half the distance between the maximum and minimum values of the function and is given by

$$\text{Amplitude} = |a|.$$

Example 2   Scaling: Vertical Shrinking and Stretching

On the same set of coordinate axes, sketch the graph of each function by hand.

a. $y = \frac{1}{2} \cos x$ **b.** $y = 3 \cos x$

Solution

a. Because the amplitude of $y = \frac{1}{2} \cos x$ is $\frac{1}{2}$, the maximum value is $\frac{1}{2}$ and the minimum value is $-\frac{1}{2}$. Divide one cycle, $0 \leq x \leq 2\pi$, into four equal parts to get the key points

Maximum	Intercept	Minimum	Intercept		Maximum
$\left(0, \dfrac{1}{2}\right),$	$\left(\dfrac{\pi}{2}, 0\right),$	$\left(\pi, -\dfrac{1}{2}\right),$	$\left(\dfrac{3\pi}{2}, 0\right),$	and	$\left(2\pi, \dfrac{1}{2}\right).$

b. A similar analysis shows that the amplitude of $y = 3 \cos x$ is 3, and the key points are

Maximum	Intercept	Minimum	Intercept		Maximum
$(0, 3),$	$\left(\dfrac{\pi}{2}, 0\right),$	$(\pi, -3),$	$\left(\dfrac{3\pi}{2}, 0\right),$	and	$(2\pi, 3).$

The graphs of these two functions are shown in Figure 5.46. Notice that the graph of $y = \frac{1}{2} \cos x$ is a vertical shrink of the graph of $y = \cos x$ and the graph of $y = 3 \cos x$ is a vertical stretch of the graph of $y = \cos x$. Use a graphing utility to confirm these graphs.

✅ *Checkpoint* Now try Exercise 40.

TECHNOLOGY TIP

When using a graphing utility to graph trigonometric functions, pay special attention to the viewing window you use. For instance, try graphing $y = [\sin(10x)]/10$ in the standard viewing window in *radian* mode. What do you observe? Use the *zoom* feature to find a viewing window that displays a good view of the graph. For instructions on how to use the *zoom* feature, see Appendix A; for specific keystrokes, go to the text website at *college.hmco.com*.

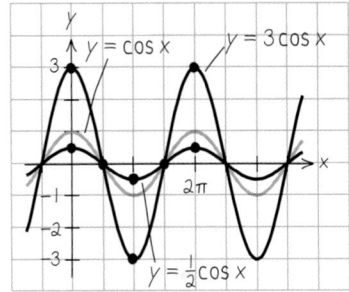

Figure 5.46

You know from Section 1.5 that the graph of $y = -f(x)$ is a *reflection* in the *x*-axis of the graph of $y = f(x)$. For instance, the graph of $y = -3 \cos x$ is a reflection of the graph of $y = 3 \cos x$, as shown in Figure 5.47.

Because $y = a \sin x$ completes one cycle from $x = 0$ to $x = 2\pi$, it follows that $y = a \sin bx$ completes one cycle from $x = 0$ to $x = 2\pi/b$.

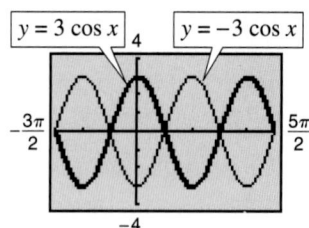

Figure 5.47

> **Period of Sine and Cosine Functions**
>
> Let b be a positive real number. The **period** of $y = a \sin bx$ and $y = a \cos bx$ is given by
>
> $$\text{Period} = \frac{2\pi}{b}.$$

Note that if $0 < b < 1$, the period of $y = a \sin bx$ is greater than 2π and represents a *horizontal stretching* of the graph of $y = a \sin x$. Similarly, if $b < 1$, the period of $y = a \sin bx$ is less than 2π and represents a *horizontal shrinking* of the graph of $y = a \sin x$. If b is negative, the identities $\sin(-x) = -\sin x$ and $\cos(-x) = \cos x$ are used to rewrite the function.

Example 3   Scaling: Horizontal Stretching

Sketch the graph of $y = \sin \dfrac{x}{2}$ by hand.

Solution

The amplitude is 1. Moreover, because $b = \frac{1}{2}$, the period is

$$\frac{2\pi}{b} = \frac{2\pi}{\frac{1}{2}} = 4\pi. \qquad \text{Substitute for } b.$$

Now, divide the period-interval $[0, 4\pi]$ into four equal parts with the values π, 2π, and 3π to obtain the key points on the graph

Intercept	Maximum	Intercept	Minimum		Intercept
$(0, 0)$,	$(\pi, 1)$,	$(2\pi, 0)$,	$(3\pi, -1)$,	and	$(4\pi, 0)$.

The graph is shown in Figure 5.48. Use a graphing utility to confirm this graph.

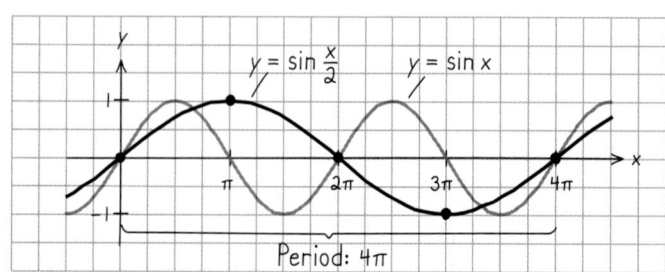

Figure 5.48

✓ *Checkpoint* Now try Exercise 41.

STUDY TIP

In general, to divide a period-interval into four equal parts, successively add "period/4," starting with the left endpoint of the interval. For instance, for the period-interval $[-\pi/6, \pi/2]$ of length $2\pi/3$, you would successively add

$$\frac{2\pi/3}{4} = \frac{\pi}{6}$$

to get $-\pi/6$, 0, $\pi/6$, $\pi/3$, and $\pi/2$ as the key points on the graph.

Translations of Sine and Cosine Curves

The constant c in the general equations

$$y = a \sin(bx - c) \qquad \text{and} \qquad y = a \cos(bx - c)$$

creates *horizontal translations* (shifts) of the basic sine and cosine curves. Comparing $y = a \sin bx$ with $y = a \sin(bx - c)$, you find that the graph of $y = a \sin(bx - c)$ completes one cycle from $bx - c = 0$ to $bx - c = 2\pi$. By solving for x, you can find the interval for one cycle to be

Left endpoint   Right endpoint

$$\frac{c}{b} \le x \le \frac{c}{b} + \frac{2\pi}{b}.$$

Period

This implies that the period of $y = a \sin(bx - c)$ is $2\pi/b$, and the graph of $y = a \sin bx$ is shifted by an amount c/b. The number c/b is the **phase shift.**

Graphs of Sine and Cosine Functions

The graphs of $y = a \sin(bx - c)$ and $y = a \cos(bx - c)$ have the following characteristics. (Assume $b > 0$.)

$$\text{Amplitude} = |a| \qquad \text{Period} = 2\pi/b$$

The left and right endpoints of a one-cycle interval can be determined by solving the equations $bx - c = 0$ and $bx - c = 2\pi$.

Example 4   Horizontal Translation

Analyze the graph of $y = \frac{1}{2} \sin(x - \pi/3)$.

Algebraic Solution

The amplitude is $\frac{1}{2}$ and the period is 2π. By solving the equations

$$x - \frac{\pi}{3} = 0 \qquad \text{and} \qquad x - \frac{\pi}{3} = 2\pi$$

$$x = \frac{\pi}{3} \qquad\qquad\qquad x = \frac{7\pi}{3}$$

you see that the interval $[\pi/3, 7\pi/3]$ corresponds to one cycle of the graph. Dividing this interval into four equal parts produces the following key points.

Intercept	Maximum	Intercept	Minimum	Intercept
$\left(\dfrac{\pi}{3}, 0\right)$,	$\left(\dfrac{5\pi}{6}, \dfrac{1}{2}\right)$,	$\left(\dfrac{4\pi}{3}, 0\right)$,	$\left(\dfrac{11\pi}{6}, -\dfrac{1}{2}\right)$,	$\left(\dfrac{7\pi}{3}, 0\right)$

☑ *Checkpoint* Now try Exercise 45.

Graphical Solution

Use a graphing utility set in *radian* mode to graph $y = (1/2) \sin(x - \pi/3)$, as shown in Figure 5.49. Use the *minimum, maximum,* and *zero* or *root* features of the graphing utility to approximate the key points $(1.047, 0)$, $(2.618, 0.5)$, $(4.189, 0)$, $(5.760, -0.5)$, and $(7.330, 0)$.

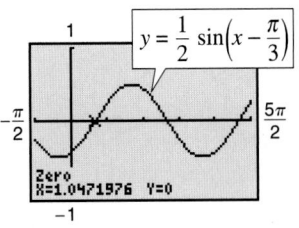

Figure 5.49

Example 5 Horizontal Translation

Use a graphing utility to analyze the graph of $y = -3 \cos(2\pi x + 4\pi)$.

Solution

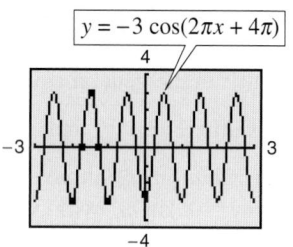

Figure 5.50

The amplitude is 3 and the period is $2\pi/2\pi = 1$. By solving the equations

$$2\pi x + 4\pi = 0 \qquad \text{and} \qquad 2\pi x + 4\pi = 2\pi$$

$$2\pi x = -4\pi \qquad\qquad\qquad 2\pi x = -2\pi$$

$$x = -2 \qquad\qquad\qquad\qquad x = -1$$

you see that the interval $[-2, -1]$ corresponds to one cycle of the graph. Dividing this interval into four equal parts produces the key points

Minimum	Intercept	Maximum	Intercept	Minimum
$(-2, -3)$,	$(-7/4, 0)$,	$(-3/2, 3)$,	$(-5/4, 0)$, and	$(-1, -3)$.

The graph is shown in Figure 5.50.

☑ *Checkpoint* Now try Exercise 47.

The final type of transformation is the *vertical translation* caused by the constant d in the equations

$$y = d + a \sin(bx - c) \qquad \text{and} \qquad y = d + a \cos(bx - c).$$

The shift is d units upward for $d > 0$ and d units downward for $d < 0$. In other words, the graph oscillates about the horizontal line $y = d$ instead of about the x-axis.

Example 6 Vertical Translation

Use a graphing utility to analyze the graph of $y = 2 + 3 \cos 2x$.

Solution

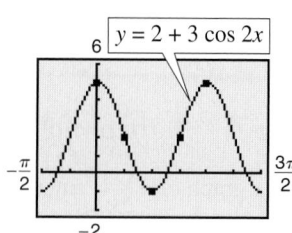

Figure 5.51

The amplitude is 3 and the period is π. The key points over the interval $[0, \pi]$ are

$$(0, 5), \qquad (\pi/4, 2), \qquad (\pi/2, -1), \qquad (3\pi/4, 2), \qquad \text{and} \qquad (\pi, 5).$$

The graph is shown in Figure 5.51. Compared with the graph of $f(x) = 3 \cos 2x$, the graph of $y = 2 + 3 \cos 2x$ is shifted upward two units.

☑ *Checkpoint* Now try Exercise 49.

Example 7 Finding an Equation for a Graph

Find the amplitude, period, and phase shift for the sine function whose graph is shown in Figure 5.52. Write an equation for this graph.

Solution

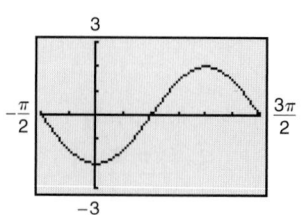

Figure 5.52

The amplitude of this sine curve is 2. The period is 2π, and there is a right phase shift of $\pi/2$. So, you can write $y = 2 \sin(x - \pi/2)$.

☑ *Checkpoint* Now try Exercise 67.

Mathematical Modeling

Sine and cosine functions can be used to model many real-life situations, including electric currents, musical tones, radio waves, tides, and weather patterns.

Example 8   Finding a Trigonometric Model

Throughout the day, the depth of the water at the end of a dock in Bangor, Washington varies with the tides. The table shows the depths (in feet) at various times during the morning.   (Source: Nautical Software, Inc.)

Time	Depth, y
Midnight	3.1
2 A.M.	7.8
4 A.M.	11.3
6 A.M.	10.9
8 A.M.	6.6
10 A.M.	1.7
Noon	0.9

a. Use a trigonometric function to model this data.

b. A boat needs at least 10 feet of water to moor at the dock. During what times in the evening can it safely dock?

Solution

a. Begin by graphing the data, as shown in Figure 5.53. You can use either a sine or cosine model. Suppose you use a cosine model of the form

$$y = a \cos(bt - c) + d.$$

The difference between the maximum height and minimum height of the graph is twice the amplitude of the function. So, the amplitude is

$$a = \tfrac{1}{2}[(\text{maximum depth}) - (\text{minimum depth})] = \tfrac{1}{2}(11.3 - 0.9) = 5.2.$$

The cosine function completes one half of a cycle between the times at which the maximum and minimum depths occur. So, the period is

$$p = 2[(\text{time of min. depth}) - (\text{time of max. depth})] = 2(12 - 4) = 16$$

which implies that $b = 2\pi/p \approx 0.393$. Because high tide occurs 4 hours after midnight, consider the left endpoint to be $c/b = 4$, so $c \approx 1.571$. Moreover, because the average depth is $\tfrac{1}{2}(11.3 + 0.9) = 6.1$, it follows that $d = 6.1$. So, you can model the depth with the function

$$y = 5.2 \cos(0.393t - 1.571) + 6.1.$$

b. Using a graphing utility, graph the model with the line $y = 10$. Using the *intersect* feature, you can determine that the depth is at least 10 feet between 6:06 P.M. ($t \approx 18.1$) and 9:48 P.M. ($t \approx 21.8$), as shown in Figure 5.54.

✓ *Checkpoint* Now try Exercise 79.

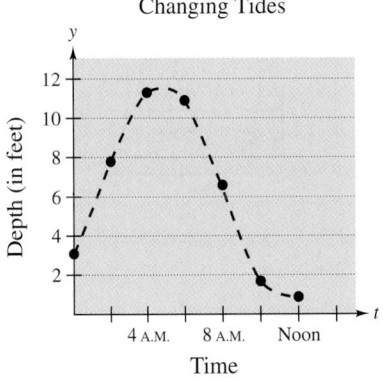

Changing Tides

Figure 5.53

TECHNOLOGY SUPPORT

For instructions on how to use the *intersect* feature, see Appendix A; for specific keystrokes, go to the text website at *college.hmco.com*.

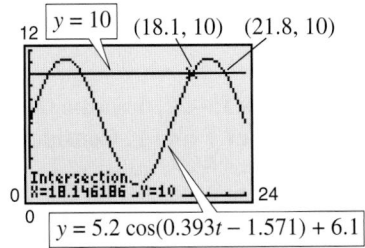

Figure 5.54

5.4   Exercises

Vocabulary Check

Fill in the blanks.

1. The _____ of a sine or cosine curve represents half the distance between the maximum and minimum values of the function.

2. One period of a sine function is called _____ of the sine curve.

3. The period of a sine or cosine function is given by _____ .

4. For the equation $y = a \sin(bx - c)$, $\dfrac{c}{b}$ is the _____ of the graph of the equation.

In Exercises 1–14, find the period and amplitude.

1. $y = 3 \sin 2x$

2. $y = 2 \cos 3x$

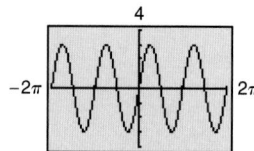

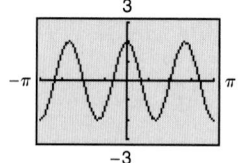

3. $y = \dfrac{5}{2} \cos \dfrac{x}{2}$

4. $y = -3 \sin \dfrac{x}{3}$

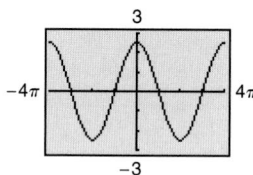

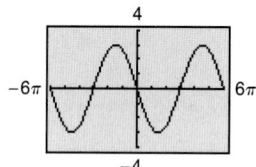

5. $y = \dfrac{2}{3} \sin \pi x$

6. $y = \dfrac{3}{2} \cos \dfrac{\pi x}{2}$

7. $y = -2 \sin x$

8. $y = -\cos \dfrac{2x}{5}$

9. $y = 3 \sin 10x$

10. $y = \dfrac{1}{3} \sin 10x$

11. $y = \dfrac{1}{4} \cos \dfrac{2x}{3}$

12. $y = \dfrac{5}{2} \cos \dfrac{x}{4}$

13. $y = \dfrac{1}{3} \sin 4\pi x$

14. $y = \dfrac{3}{4} \cos \dfrac{\pi x}{12}$

In Exercises 15–22, describe the relationship between the graphs of f and g. Consider amplitudes, periods, and shifts.

15. $f(x) = \sin x$
    $g(x) = \sin(x - \pi)$

16. $f(x) = \cos x$
    $g(x) = \cos(x + \pi)$

17. $f(x) = \cos 2x$
    $g(x) = -\cos 2x$

18. $f(x) = \sin 3x$
    $g(x) = \sin(-3x)$

19. $f(x) = \cos x$
    $g(x) = -5 \cos x$

20. $f(x) = \sin x$
    $g(x) = -\dfrac{1}{2} \sin x$

21. $f(x) = \sin 2x$
    $g(x) = 5 + \sin 2x$

22. $f(x) = \cos 4x$
    $g(x) = -6 + \cos 4x$

In Exercises 23–26, describe the relationship between the graphs of f and g. Consider amplitudes, periods, and shifts.

23.

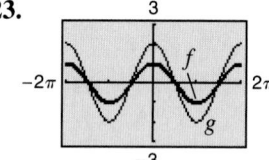

24.

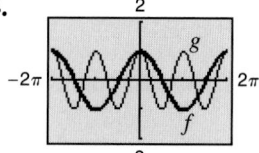

25.

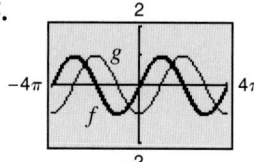

26.

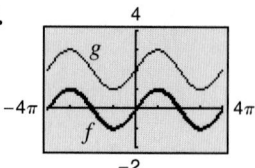

In Exercises 27–34, sketch the graphs of f and g in the same coordinate plane. (Include two full periods.)

27. $f(x) = \sin x$
    $g(x) = -4 \sin x$

28. $f(x) = \sin x$
    $g(x) = \sin \dfrac{x}{3}$

29. $f(x) = \cos x$
    $g(x) = 4 + \cos x$

30. $f(x) = 2 \cos 2x$
    $g(x) = -\cos 4x$

31. $f(x) = -\dfrac{1}{2} \sin \dfrac{x}{2}$

$g(x) = 3 - \dfrac{1}{2} \sin \dfrac{x}{2}$

32. $f(x) = 4 \sin \pi x$

$g(x) = 4 \sin \pi x - 2$

33. $f(x) = 2 \cos x$

$g(x) = 2 \cos(x + \pi)$

34. $f(x) = -\cos x$

$g(x) = -\cos\left(x - \dfrac{\pi}{2}\right)$

Conjecture In Exercises 35–38, use a graphing utility to graph f and g in the same viewing window. (Include two full periods.) Make a conjecture about the functions.

35. $f(x) = \sin x$

$g(x) = \cos\left(x - \dfrac{\pi}{2}\right)$

36. $f(x) = \sin x$

$g(x) = -\cos\left(x + \dfrac{\pi}{2}\right)$

37. $f(x) = \cos x$

$g(x) = -\sin\left(x - \dfrac{\pi}{2}\right)$

38. $f(x) = \cos x$

$g(x) = -\cos(x - \pi)$

In Exercises 39–54, sketch the graph of the function by hand. Use a graphing utility to verify your sketch. (Include two full periods.)

39. $y = 3 \sin x$

40. $y = \dfrac{1}{4} \cos x$

41. $y = \cos \dfrac{x}{2}$

42. $y = \sin 4x$

43. $y = -2 \sin \dfrac{2\pi x}{3}$

44. $y = -10 \cos \dfrac{\pi x}{6}$

45. $y = \sin\left(x - \dfrac{\pi}{4}\right)$

46. $y = \sin(x - \pi)$

47. $y = -8 \cos(x + \pi)$

48. $y = 6 \cos\left(x + \dfrac{\pi}{3}\right)$

49. $y = 1 + \dfrac{1}{2} \cos 4\pi t$

50. $y = -4 + 5 \cos \dfrac{\pi t}{12}$

51. $y = 2 - 2 \sin \dfrac{2\pi x}{3}$

52. $y = 2 \cos x - 3$

53. $y = \dfrac{2}{3} \cos\left(\dfrac{x}{2} - \dfrac{\pi}{4}\right)$

54. $y = -3 \cos(6x + \pi)$

In Exercises 55–62, use a graphing utility to graph the function. (Include two full periods.) Identify the amplitude and period of the graph.

55. $y = -2 \sin(4x + \pi)$

56. $y = -4 \sin\left(\dfrac{2}{3}x - \dfrac{\pi}{3}\right)$

57. $y = \cos\left(2\pi x - \dfrac{\pi}{2}\right) + 1$

58. $y = 3 \cos\left(\dfrac{\pi x}{2} + \dfrac{\pi}{2}\right) - 3$

59. $y = 5 \sin(\pi - 2x) + 10$

60. $y = 5 \cos(\pi - 2x) + 6$

61. $y = \dfrac{1}{100} \sin 120\pi t$ **62.** $y = -\dfrac{1}{100} \cos 50\pi t$

Graphical Reasoning In Exercises 63–66, find a and d for the function $f(x) = a \cos x + d$ such that the graph of f matches the figure.

63.

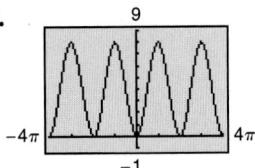

64.

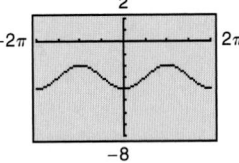

65.

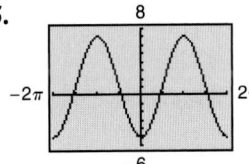

66.

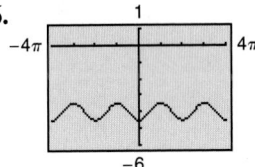

Graphical Reasoning In Exercises 67–70, find $a, b,$ and c for the function $f(x) = a \sin(bx - c)$ such that the graph of f matches the graph shown.

67.

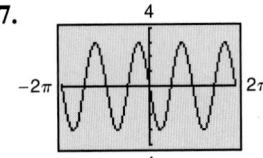

68.

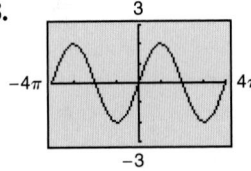

69.

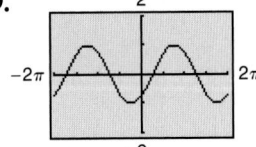

70.

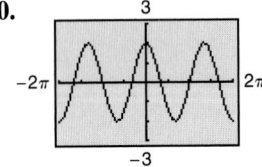

In Exercises 71 and 72, use a graphing utility to graph y_1 and y_2 for all real numbers x in the interval $[-2\pi, 2\pi]$. Use the graphs to find the real numbers x such that $y_1 = y_2$.

71. $y_1 = \sin x$

$y_2 = -\dfrac{1}{2}$

72. $y_1 = \cos x$

$y_2 = -1$

73. Health For a person at rest, the velocity v (in liters per second) of air flow during a respiratory cycle (the time from the beginning of one breath to the beginning of the next) is given by

$$v = 0.85 \sin \frac{\pi t}{3}$$

where t is the time (in seconds). (Inhalation occurs when $v > 0$, and exhalation occurs when $v < 0$.)

(a) Use a graphing utility to graph v.

(b) Find the time for one full respiratory cycle.

(c) Find the number of cycles per minute.

(d) The model is for a person at rest. How might the model change for a person who is exercising? Explain.

74. Sales A company that produces snowboards, which are seasonal products, forecasts monthly sales for 1 year to be

$$S = 74.50 + 43.75 \cos \frac{\pi t}{6}$$

where S is the sales in thousands of units and t is the time in months, with $t = 1$ corresponding to January.

(a) Use a graphing utility to graph the sales function over the one-year period.

(b) Use the graph in part (a) to determine the months of maximum and minimum sales.

75. Recreation You are riding a Ferris wheel. Your height h (in feet) above the ground at any time t (in seconds) can be modeled by

$$h = 25 \sin \frac{\pi}{15}(t - 75) + 30.$$

The Ferris wheel turns for 135 seconds before it stops to let the first passengers off.

(a) Graph the model.

(b) What are the minimum and maximum heights above the ground?

76. Health The pressure P (in millimeters of mercury) against the walls of the blood vessels of a person is modeled by

$$P = 100 - 20 \cos \frac{8\pi}{3}t$$

where t is the time (in seconds). Graph the model. One cycle is equivalent to one heartbeat. What is the person's pulse rate in heartbeats per minute?

77. Fuel Consumption The daily consumption C (in gallons) of diesel fuel on a farm is modeled by

$$C = 30.3 + 21.6 \sin\left(\frac{2\pi t}{365} + 10.9\right)$$

where t is the time in days, with $t = 1$ corresponding to January 1.

(a) What is the period of the model? Is it what you expected? Explain.

(b) What is the average daily fuel consumption? Which term of the model did you use? Explain.

(c) Use a graphing utility to graph the model. Use the graph to approximate the time of the year when consumption exceeds 40 gallons per day.

78. Data Analysis The motion of an oscillating weight suspended from a spring was measured by a motion detector. The data was collected, and the approximate maximum displacements from equilibrium ($y = 2$) are labeled in the figure. The distance y from the motion detector is measured in centimeters and the time t is measured in seconds.

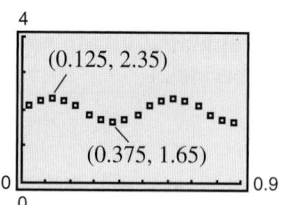

(a) Is y a function of t? Explain.

(b) Approximate the amplitude and period.

(c) Find a model for the data.

(d) Use a graphing utility to graph the model in part (c). Compare the result with the data in the figure.

79. Data Analysis The percent y of the moon's face that is illuminated on day x of the year 2006, where $x = 1$ represents January 1, is shown in the table. (Source: U.S. Naval Observatory)

Day, x	Percent, y
29	0.0
36	0.5
44	1.0
52	0.5
58	0.0
65	0.5

(a) Create a scatter plot of the data.

(b) Find a trigonometric model for the data.

(c) Add the graph of your model in part (b) to the scatter plot. How well does the model fit the data?

(d) What is the period of the model?

(e) Estimate the percent illumination of the moon on June 22, 2007.

80. _Data Analysis_ The table shows the average daily high temperatures for Nantucket, Massachusetts N and Athens, Georgia A (in degrees Fahrenheit) for month t, with $t = 1$ corresponding to January. (Source: U.S. Weather Bureau and the National Weather Service)

Month, t	Nantucket, N	Athens, A
1	40	52
2	41	56
3	42	65
4	53	73
5	62	81
6	71	87
7	78	90
8	76	88
9	70	83
10	59	74
11	48	64
12	40	55

(a) A model for the temperature in Nantucket is given by

$$N(t) = 58 + 19 \sin\left(\frac{2\pi t}{11} - \frac{21\pi}{25}\right).$$

Find a trigonometric model for Athens.

(b) Use a graphing utility to graph the data and the model for the temperatures in Nantucket in the same viewing window. How well does the model fit the data?

(c) Use a graphing utility to graph the data and the model for the temperatures in Athens in the same viewing window. How well does the model fit the data?

(d) Use the models to estimate the average daily high temperature in each city. Which term of the models did you use? Explain.

(e) What is the period of each model? Are the periods what you expected? Explain.

(f) Which city has the greater variability in temperature throughout the year? Which factor of the models determines this variability? Explain.

Synthesis

True or False? In Exercises 81–83, determine whether the statement is true or false. Justify your answer.

81. The graph of $y = 6 - \frac{3}{4} \sin \frac{3x}{10}$ has a period of $\frac{20\pi}{3}$.

82. The function $y = \frac{1}{2} \cos 2x$ has an amplitude that is twice that of the function $y = \cos x$.

83. The graph of $y = -\cos x$ is a reflection of the graph of $y = \sin(x + \pi/2)$ in the x-axis.

84. _Writing_ Use a graphing utility to graph the function

$$y = d + a \sin(bx - c)$$

for different values of a, b, c, and d. Write a paragraph describing the changes in the graph corresponding to changes in each variable.

85. _Exploration_ In Section 5.3 it was shown that $f(x) = \cos x$ is an even function and $g(x) = \sin x$ is an odd function. Use a graphing utility to graph h and use the graph to determine whether h is even, odd, or neither.

(a) $h(x) = \cos^2 x$ (b) $h(x) = \sin^2 x$

(c) $h(x) = \sin x \cos x$

86. _Conjecture_ If f is an even function and g is an odd function, use the results of Exercise 85 to make a conjecture about each of the following.

(a) $h(x) = [f(x)]^2$ (b) $h(x) = [g(x)]^2$

(c) $h(x) = f(x)g(x)$

Review

In Exercises 87 and 88, plot the points and find the slope of the line passing through the points.

87. $(0, 1), (2, 7)$ **88.** $(-1, 4), (3, -2)$

In Exercises 89 and 90, convert the angle measure from radians to degrees. Round your answer to three decimal places.

89. 8.5 **90.** -0.48

5.5   Graphs of Other Trigonometric Functions

Graph of the Tangent Function

Recall that the tangent function is odd. That is, $\tan(-x) = -\tan x$. Consequently, the graph of $y = \tan x$ is symmetric with respect to the origin. You also know from the identity $\tan x = \sin x / \cos x$ that the tangent function is undefined at values at which $\cos x = 0$. Two such values are $x = \pm \pi/2 \approx \pm 1.5708$.

x	$-\dfrac{\pi}{2}$	-1.57	-1.5	$-\dfrac{\pi}{4}$	0	$\dfrac{\pi}{4}$	1.5	1.57	$\dfrac{\pi}{2}$
$\tan x$	Undef.	-1255.8	-14.1	-1	0	1	14.1	1255.8	Undef.

$\tan x$ approaches $-\infty$ as x approaches $-\pi/2$ from the right.

$\tan x$ approaches ∞ as x approaches $\pi/2$ from the left.

As indicated in the table, $\tan x$ increases without bound as x approaches $\pi/2$ from the left, and it decreases without bound as x approaches $-\pi/2$ from the right. So, the graph of $y = \tan x$ has *vertical asymptotes* at $x = \pi/2$ and $-\pi/2$, as shown in Figure 5.55. Moreover, because the period of the tangent function is π, vertical asymptotes also occur at $x = \pi/2 + n\pi$, where n is an integer. The domain of the tangent function is the set of all real numbers other than $x = \pi/2 + n\pi$, and the range is the set of all real numbers.

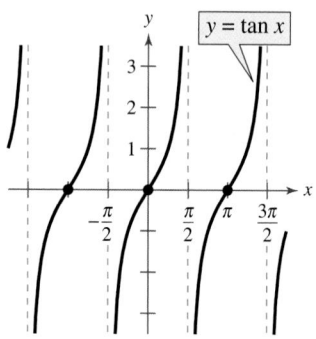

Period: π

Domain: all $x \ne \dfrac{\pi}{2} + n\pi$

Range: $(-\infty, \infty)$

Vertical asymptotes: $x = \dfrac{\pi}{2} + n\pi$

Figure 5.55

Sketching the graph of $y = a \tan(bx - c)$ is similar to sketching the graph of $y = a \sin(bx - c)$ in that you locate key points that identify the intercepts and asymptotes. Two consecutive asymptotes can be found by solving the equations $bx - c = -\pi/2$ and $bx - c = \pi/2$. The midpoint between two consecutive asymptotes is an x-intercept of the graph. The period of the function $y = a \tan(bx - c)$ is the distance between two consecutive asymptotes. The amplitude of a tangent function is not defined. After plotting the asymptotes and the x-intercept, plot a few additional points between the two asymptotes and sketch one cycle. Finally, sketch one or two additional cycles to the left and right.

Example 1   Sketching the Graph of a Tangent Function

Sketch the graph of $y = \tan \dfrac{x}{2}$ by hand.

Solution

By solving the equations $x/2 = -\pi/2$ and $x/2 = \pi/2$, you can see that two consecutive asymptotes occur at $x = -\pi$ and $x = \pi$. Between these two asymptotes, plot a few points, including the x-intercept, as shown in the table. Three cycles of the graph are shown in Figure 5.56. Use a graphing utility to confirm this graph.

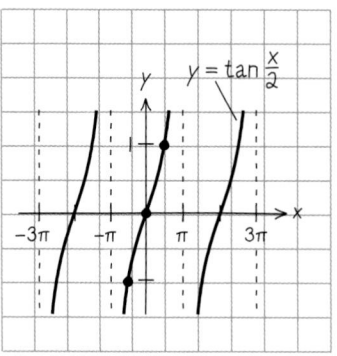

Figure 5.56

x	$-\pi$	$-\dfrac{\pi}{2}$	0	$\dfrac{\pi}{2}$	π
$\tan \dfrac{x}{2}$	Undef.	-1	0	1	Undef.

✓ *Checkpoint* Now try Exercise 7.

Example 2   Sketching the Graph of a Tangent Function

Sketch the graph of $y = -3 \tan 2x$.

Solution

By solving the equations $2x = -\pi/2$ and $2x = \pi/2$, you can see that two consecutive asymptotes occur at $x = -\pi/4$ and $x = \pi/4$. Between these two asymptotes, plot a few points, including the x-intercept, as shown in the table. Three complete cycles of the graph are shown in Figure 5.57.

x	$-\dfrac{\pi}{4}$	$-\dfrac{\pi}{8}$	0	$\dfrac{\pi}{8}$	$\dfrac{\pi}{4}$
$-3 \tan 2x$	Undef.	3	0	-3	Undef.

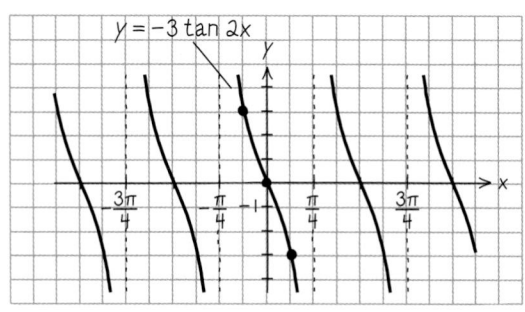

Figure 5.57

✓ *Checkpoint* Now try Exercise 9.

> **TECHNOLOGY TIP**
>
> Your graphing utility may connect parts of the graphs of tangent, cotangent, secant, and cosecant functions that are not supposed to be connected. So, in this text, these functions are graphed on a graphing utility using the *dot* mode. A blue curve is placed behind the graphing utility's display to indicate where the graph should appear. For instructions on how to use the *dot* mode, see Appendix A; for specific keystrokes, go to the text website at *college.hmco.com*.

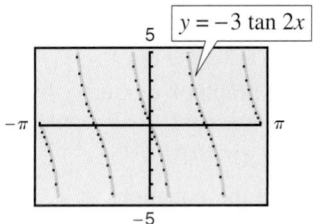

Figure 5.58

TECHNOLOGY TIP   Graphing utilities are helpful in verifying sketches of trigonometric functions. You can use a graphing utility set in *radian* and *dot* modes to graph the function $y = -3 \tan 2x$ from Example 2, as shown in Figure 5.58. You can use the *zero* or *root* feature or the *zoom* and *trace* features to approximate the key points of the graph.

By comparing the graphs in Examples 1 and 2, you can see that the graph of $y = a \tan(bx - c)$ increases between consecutive vertical asymptotes when $a > 0$ and decreases between consecutive vertical asymptotes when $a < 0$. In other words, the graph for $a < 0$ is a reflection in the x-axis of the graph for $a > 0$.

Graph of the Cotangent Function

The graph of the cotangent function is similar to the graph of the tangent function. It also has a period of π. However, from the identity

$$y = \cot x = \frac{\cos x}{\sin x}$$

you can see that the cotangent function has vertical asymptotes when $\sin x$ is zero, which occurs at $x = n\pi$, where n is an integer. The graph of the cotangent function is shown in Figure 5.59.

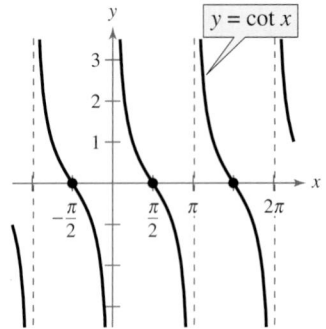

Period: π
Domain: all $x \neq n\pi$
Range: $(-\infty, \infty)$
Vertical asymptotes: $x = n\pi$
Figure 5.59

Example 3   Sketching the Graph of a Cotangent Function

Sketch the graph of $y = 2 \cot \dfrac{x}{3}$ by hand.

Solution

To locate two consecutive vertical asymptotes of the graph, solve the equations $x/3 = 0$ and $x/3 = \pi$ to see that two consecutive asymptotes occur at $x = 0$ and $x = 3\pi$. Then, between these two asymptotes, plot a few points, including the x-intercept, as shown in the table. Three cycles of the graph are shown in Figure 5.60. Use a graphing utility to confirm this graph. [Enter the function as $y = 2/\tan(x/3)$.] Note that the period is 3π, the distance between consecutive asymptotes.

x	0	$\dfrac{3\pi}{4}$	$\dfrac{3\pi}{2}$	$\dfrac{9\pi}{4}$	3π
$2 \cot \dfrac{x}{3}$	Undef.	2	0	-2	Undef.

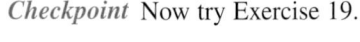 *Checkpoint* Now try Exercise 19.

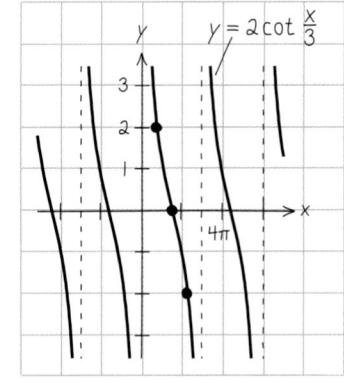

Figure 5.60

Exploration

Use a graphing utility to graph the functions $y_1 = \cos x$ and $y_2 = \sec x = 1/\cos x$ in the same viewing window. How are the graphs related? What happens to the graph of the secant function as x approaches the zeros of the cosine function?

Graphs of the Reciprocal Functions

The graphs of the two remaining trigonometric functions can be obtained from the graphs of the sine and cosine functions using the reciprocal identities

$$\csc x = \frac{1}{\sin x} \quad \text{and} \quad \sec x = \frac{1}{\cos x}.$$

For instance, at a given value of x, the y-coordinate for $\sec x$ is the reciprocal of the y-coordinate for $\cos x$. Of course, when $\cos x = 0$, the reciprocal does not exist. Near such values of x, the behavior of the secant function is similar to that of the tangent function. In other words, the graphs of

$$\tan x = \frac{\sin x}{\cos x} \quad \text{and} \quad \sec x = \frac{1}{\cos x}$$

have vertical asymptotes at $x = \pi/2 + n\pi$, where n is an integer (i.e., the values at which the cosine is zero). Similarly,

$$\cot x = \frac{\cos x}{\sin x} \quad \text{and} \quad \csc x = \frac{1}{\sin x}$$

have vertical asymptotes where $\sin x = 0$, that is, at $x = n\pi$.

To sketch the graph of a secant or cosecant function, you should first make a sketch of its reciprocal function. For instance, to sketch the graph of $y = \csc x$, first sketch the graph of $y = \sin x$. Then take the reciprocals of the y-coordinates to obtain points on the graph of $y = \csc x$. You can use this procedure to obtain the graphs shown in Figure 5.61.

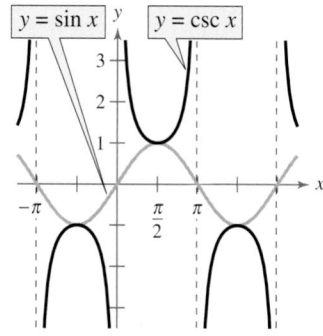

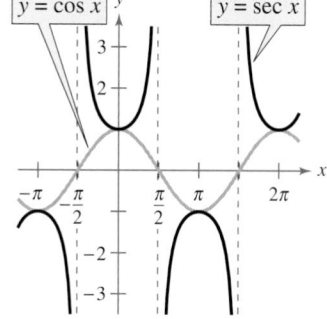

Period: 2π

Domain: all $x \neq n\pi$

Range: $(-\infty, -1] \cup [1, \infty)$

Vertical asymptotes: $x = n\pi$

Symmetry: origin

Period: 2π

Domain: all $x \neq \dfrac{\pi}{2} + n\pi$

Range: $(-\infty, -1] \cup [1, \infty)$

Vertical asymptotes: $x = \dfrac{\pi}{2} + n\pi$

Symmetry: y-axis

Figure 5.61

In comparing the graphs of the secant and cosecant functions with those of the sine and cosine functions, note that the "hills" and "valleys" are interchanged. For example, a hill (or maximum point) on the sine curve corresponds to a valley (a local minimum) on the cosecant curve, and a valley (or minimum point) on the sine curve corresponds to a hill (a local maximum) on the cosecant curve, as shown in Figure 5.62. Additionally, *x*-intercepts of the sine and cosine functions become vertical asymptotes of the cosecant and secant functions, respectively (see Figure 5.62).

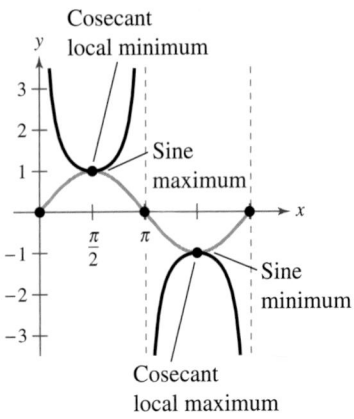

Figure 5.62

Example 4 Comparing Trigonometric Graphs

Use a graphing utility to compare the graphs of

$$y = 2 \sin\left(x + \frac{\pi}{4}\right) \quad \text{and} \quad y = 2 \csc\left(x + \frac{\pi}{4}\right).$$

Solution

The two graphs are shown in Figure 5.63. Note how the hills and valleys of the graphs are related. For the function $y = 2 \sin[x + (\pi/4)]$, the amplitude is 2 and the period is 2π. By solving the equations

$$x + \frac{\pi}{4} = 0 \quad \text{and} \quad x + \frac{\pi}{4} = 2\pi$$

you can see that one cycle of the sine function corresponds to the interval from $x = -\pi/4$ to $x = 7\pi/4$. The graph of this sine function is represented by the thick curve in Figure 5.63. Because the sine function is zero at the endpoints of this interval, the corresponding cosecant function

$$y = 2 \csc\left(x + \frac{\pi}{4}\right) = 2\left(\frac{1}{\sin[x + (\pi/4)]}\right)$$

has vertical asymptotes at $x = -\pi/4, 3\pi/4, 7\pi/4$, and so on.

✓ *Checkpoint* Now try Exercise 31.

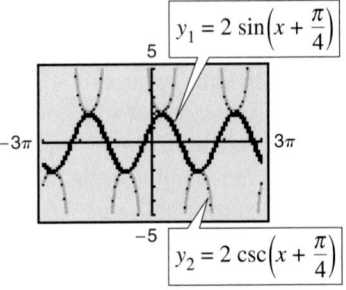

Figure 5.63

Example 5 Comparing Trigonometric Graphs

Use a graphing utility to compare the graphs of $y = \cos 2x$ and $y = \sec 2x$.

Solution

Begin by graphing $y_1 = \cos 2x$ and $y_2 = \sec 2x = 1/\cos 2x$ in the same viewing window, as shown in Figure 5.64. Note that the *x*-intercepts of $y = \cos 2x$

$$\left(-\frac{\pi}{4}, 0\right), \quad \left(\frac{\pi}{4}, 0\right), \quad \left(\frac{3\pi}{4}, 0\right), \ldots$$

correspond to the vertical asymptotes

$$x = -\frac{\pi}{4}, \quad x = \frac{\pi}{4}, \quad x = \frac{3\pi}{4}, \ldots$$

of the graph of $y = \sec 2x$. Moreover, notice that the period of $y = \cos 2x$ and $y = \sec 2x$ is π.

✓ *Checkpoint* Now try Exercise 33.

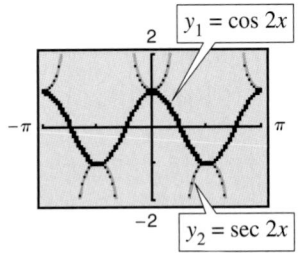

Figure 5.64

Damped Trigonometric Graphs

A *product* of two functions can be graphed using properties of the individual functions. For instance, consider the function

$$f(x) = x \sin x$$

as the product of the functions $y = x$ and $y = \sin x$. Using properties of absolute value and the fact that $|\sin x| \le 1$, you have $0 \le |x| \, |\sin x| \le |x|$. Consequently,

$$-|x| \le x \sin x \le |x|$$

which means that the graph of $f(x) = x \sin x$ lies between the lines $y = -x$ and $y = x$. Furthermore, because

$$f(x) = x \sin x = \pm x \qquad \text{at} \qquad x = \frac{\pi}{2} + n\pi$$

and

$$f(x) = x \sin x = 0 \qquad \text{at} \qquad x = n\pi$$

the graph of f touches the line $y = -x$ or the line $y = x$ at $x = \pi/2 + n\pi$ and has x-intercepts at $x = n\pi$. A sketch of f is shown in Figure 5.65. In the function $f(x) = x \sin x$, the factor x is called the **damping factor.**

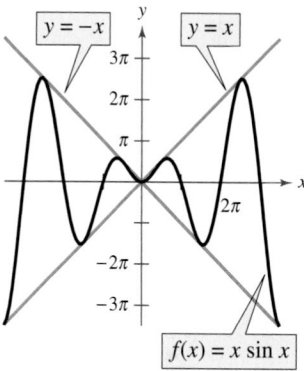

Figure 5.65

Example 6   Analyzing a Damped Sine Curve

Analyze the graph of

$$f(x) = e^{-x} \sin 3x.$$

Solution

Consider $f(x)$ as the product of the two functions

$$y = e^{-x} \qquad \text{and} \qquad y = \sin 3x$$

each of which has the set of real numbers as its domain. For any real number x, you know that $e^{-x} \ge 0$ and $|\sin 3x| \le 1$. So, $|e^{-x}| \, |\sin 3x| \le e^{-x}$, which means that

$$-e^{-x} \le e^{-x} \sin 3x \le e^{-x}.$$

Furthermore, because

$$f(x) = e^{-x} \sin 3x = \pm e^{-x} \qquad \text{at} \qquad x = \frac{\pi}{6} + \frac{n\pi}{3}$$

and

$$f(x) = e^{-x} \sin 3x = 0 \qquad \text{at} \qquad x = \frac{n\pi}{3}$$

the graph of f touches the curves $y = -e^{-x}$ and $y = e^{-x}$ at $x = \pi/6 + n\pi/3$ and has intercepts at $x = n\pi/3$. The graph is shown in Figure 5.66.

✓ *Checkpoint* Now try Exercise 57.

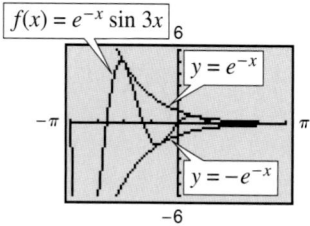

Figure 5.66

Figure 5.67 summarizes the six basic trigonometric functions.

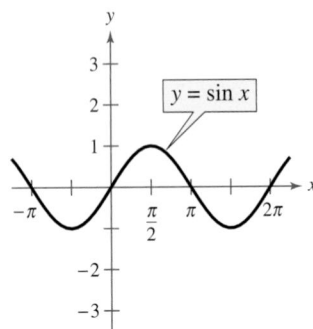

Domain: all reals
Range: $[-1, 1]$
Period: 2π

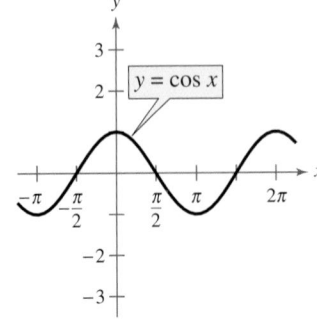

Domain: all reals
Range: $[-1, 1]$
Period: 2π

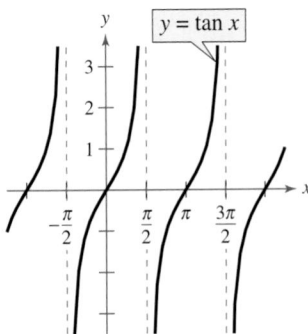

Domain: all $x \neq \dfrac{\pi}{2} + n\pi$

Range: $(-\infty, \infty)$

Period: π

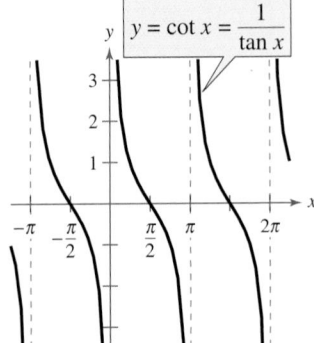

Domain: all $x \neq n\pi$
Range: $(-\infty, \infty)$
Period: π

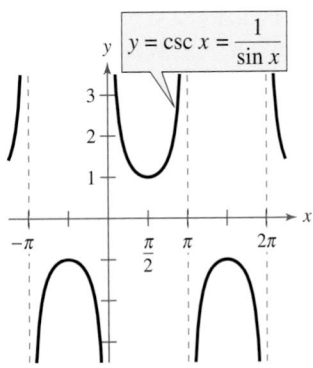

Domain: all $x \neq n\pi$
Range: $(-\infty, -1] \cup [1, \infty)$
Period: 2π

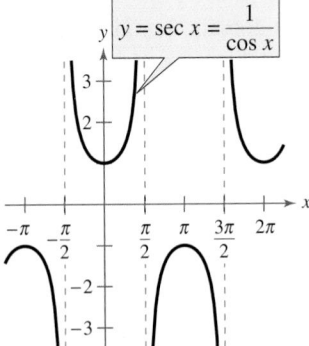

Domain: all $x \neq \dfrac{\pi}{2} + n\pi$

Range: $(-\infty, -1] \cup [1, \infty)$
Period: 2π

Figure 5.67

5.5 Exercises

Vocabulary Check

Fill in the blanks.

1. The graphs of the tangent, cotangent, secant, and cosecant functions have _____ asymptotes.
2. To sketch the graph of a secant or cosecant function, first make a sketch of its _____ function.
3. For the function $f(x) = g(x) \sin x$, $g(x)$ is called the _____ factor of the function.

In Exercises 1–6, match the function with its graph. State the period of the function. [The graphs are labeled (a), (b), (c), (d), (e), and (f).]

(a)
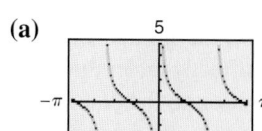

(b)
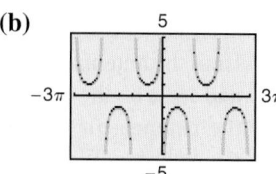

(c)
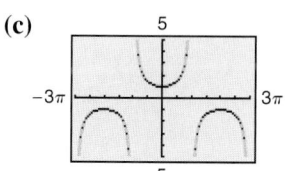

(d)
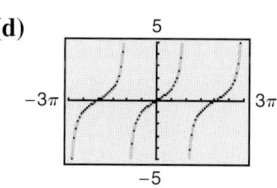

(e)
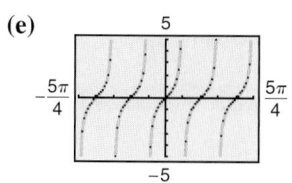

(f)
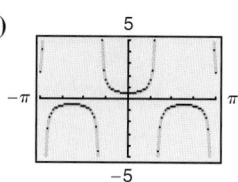

1. $y = \sec \dfrac{x}{2}$

2. $y = \tan \dfrac{x}{2}$

3. $y = \tan 2x$

4. $y = \dfrac{1}{2} \sec \dfrac{\pi x}{2}$

5. $y = \cot \dfrac{\pi x}{2}$

6. $y = -\csc x$

In Exercises 7–30, sketch the graph of the function. (Include two full periods.) Use a graphing utility to verify your result.

7. $y = \frac{1}{2} \tan x$
8. $y = \frac{1}{4} \tan x$

9. $y = -2 \tan 2x$
10. $y = -3 \tan 4x$

11. $y = -\frac{1}{2} \sec x$
12. $y = \frac{1}{4} \sec x$

13. $y = -\sec \pi x$
14. $y = 2 \sec \pi x$

15. $y = \sec \pi x - 3$
16. $y = -2 \sec 4x + 2$

17. $y = 3 \csc \dfrac{x}{2}$
18. $y = -\csc \dfrac{x}{3}$

19. $y = \dfrac{1}{2} \cot \dfrac{x}{2}$
20. $y = 3 \cot \pi x$

21. $y = 2 \tan \dfrac{\pi x}{4}$
22. $y = -\dfrac{1}{2} \tan \pi x$

23. $y = \frac{1}{2} \sec 2x$
24. $y = \sec(x + \pi)$

25. $y = \csc(\pi - x)$
26. $y = \csc(2x - \pi)$

27. $y = 2 \cot\left(x - \dfrac{\pi}{2}\right)$
28. $y = \dfrac{1}{4} \cot(x + \pi)$

29. $y = \tan\left(x - \dfrac{\pi}{4}\right)$
30. $y = \dfrac{1}{2} \tan\left(\dfrac{\pi x}{4} + \dfrac{\pi}{4}\right)$

In Exercises 31–36, use a graphing utility to graph the function. (Include two full periods.) Compare the graph of the function with the graph of the corresponding reciprocal function. Describe your viewing window.

31. $y = 2 \csc 3x$
32. $y = -\csc(4x - \pi)$

33. $y = -2 \sec 4x$
34. $y = \frac{1}{4} \sec \pi x$

35. $y = \dfrac{1}{3} \sec\left(\dfrac{\pi x}{2} + \dfrac{\pi}{2}\right)$
36. $y = \dfrac{1}{2} \csc(2x - \pi)$

In Exercises 37–40, use a graph to solve the equation on the interval $[-2\pi, 2\pi]$.

37. $\tan x = 1$
38. $\cot x = -\sqrt{3}$

39. $\sec x = -2$
40. $\csc x = \sqrt{2}$

In Exercises 41–44, use the graph of the function to determine whether the function is even, odd, or neither.

41. $f(x) = \sec x$
42. $f(x) = \tan x$

43. $f(x) = \csc 2x$
44. $f(x) = \cot 2x$

In Exercises 45–48, use a graphing utility to graph the two equations in the same viewing window. Use the graphs to determine whether the expressions are equivalent. Verify the results algebraically.

45. $y_1 = \sin x \csc x, \quad y_2 = 1$

46. $y_1 = \sin x \sec x, \quad y_2 = \tan x$

47. $y_1 = \dfrac{\cos x}{\sin x}, \quad y_2 = \cot x$

48. $y_1 = \sec^2 x - 1, \quad y_2 = \tan^2 x$

In Exercises 49–52, match the function with its graph. Describe the behavior of the function as x approaches zero. [The graphs are labeled (a), (b), (c), and (d).]

(a)
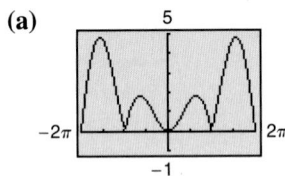

(b)
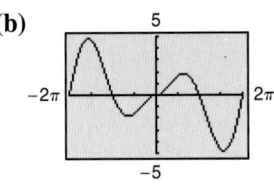

(c)
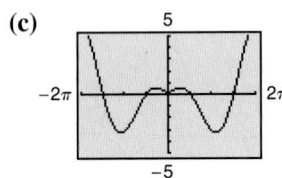

(d)
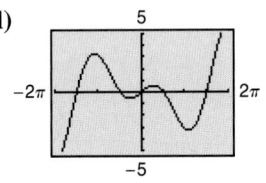

49. $f(x) = x \cos x$

50. $f(x) = |x \sin x|$

51. $g(x) = |x| \sin x$

52. $g(x) = |x| \cos x$

Conjecture In Exercises 53–56, use a graphing utility to graph the functions f and g. Use the graphs to make a conjecture about the relationship between the functions.

53. $f(x) = \sin x + \cos\left(x + \dfrac{\pi}{2}\right), \quad g(x) = 0$

54. $f(x) = \sin x - \cos\left(x + \dfrac{\pi}{2}\right), \quad g(x) = 2\sin x$

55. $f(x) = \sin^2 x, \quad g(x) = \tfrac{1}{2}(1 - \cos 2x)$

56. $f(x) = \cos^2 \dfrac{\pi x}{2}, \quad g(x) = \dfrac{1}{2}(1 + \cos \pi x)$

In Exercises 57–60, use a graphing utility to graph the function and the damping factor of the function in the same viewing window. Describe the behavior of the function as x increases without bound.

57. $f(x) = e^{-x} \cos x$

58. $f(x) = 2^{-x/4} \cos \pi x$

59. $g(x) = e^{-x^2/2} \sin x$

60. $h(x) = 2^{-x^2/4} \sin x$

Exploration In Exercises 61–66, use a graphing utility to graph the function. Describe the behavior of the function as x approaches zero.

61. $f(x) = \dfrac{6}{x} + \cos x$

62. $f(x) = \sin x - \dfrac{4}{x}$

63. $f(x) = \dfrac{\sin x}{x}$

64. $f(x) = \dfrac{1 - \cos x}{x}$

65. $f(x) = \dfrac{\tan x}{x}$

66. $f(x) = \dfrac{x}{\cot x}$

67. *Distance* A plane flying at an altitude of 5 miles over level ground will pass directly over a radar antenna (see figure). Let d be the ground distance from the antenna to the point directly under the plane and let x be the angle of elevation to the plane from the antenna. (d is positive as the plane approaches the antenna.) Write d as a function of x and graph the function over the interval $0 < x < \pi$.

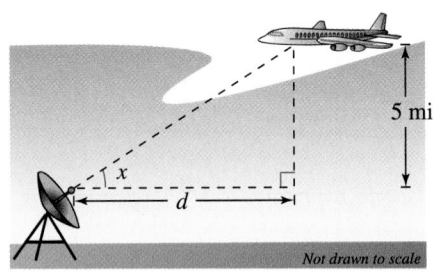

Not drawn to scale

68. *Television Coverage* A television camera is on a reviewing platform 36 meters from the street on which a parade will be passing from left to right (see figure). Write the distance d from the camera to a particular unit in the parade as a function of the angle x, and graph the function over the interval $-\pi/2 < x < \pi/2$. (Consider x as negative when a unit in the parade approaches from the left.)

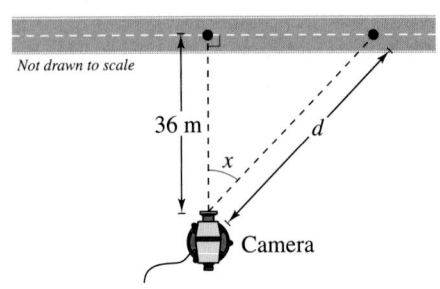

Not drawn to scale

69. Predator-Prey Model   The population of coyotes (a predator) at time t (in months) in a region is estimated to be $P = 10{,}000 + 3000 \sin{(\pi t/12)}$ and the population of rabbits (its prey) is estimated to be $p = 15{,}000 + 5000 \cos{(\pi t/12)}$. Use the graph of the models to explain the oscillations in the size of each population.

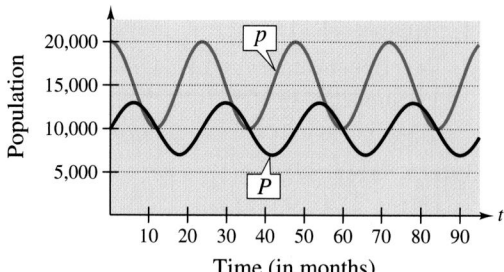

70. Meteorology   The normal monthly high temperatures in degrees Fahrenheit for Erie, Pennsylvania, are approximated by

$$H(t) = 54.33 - 20.38 \cos{\frac{\pi t}{6}} - 15.69 \sin{\frac{\pi t}{6}}$$

and the normal monthly low temperatures are approximated by

$$L(t) = 39.36 - 15.70 \cos{\frac{\pi t}{6}} - 14.16 \sin{\frac{\pi t}{6}}$$

where t is the time (in months), with $t = 1$ corresponding to January. (Source: National Oceanic and Atmospheric Association)

(a) Use a graphing utility to graph each function. What is the period of each function?

(b) During what part of the year is the difference between the normal high and normal low temperatures greatest? When is it smallest?

(c) The sun is the farthest north in the sky around June 21, but the graph shows the warmest temperatures at a later date. Approximate the lag time of the temperatures relative to the position of the sun.

71. Harmonic Motion   An object weighing W pounds is suspended from a ceiling by a steel spring (see figure). The weight is pulled downward (positive direction) from its equilibrium position and released. The resulting motion of the weight is described by the function $y = \frac{1}{2}e^{-t/4} \cos{4t}$, where y is the distance in feet and t is the time in seconds ($t > 0$).

(a) Use a graphing utility to graph the function.

(b) Describe the behavior of the displacement function for increasing values of time t.

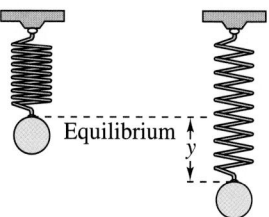

Figure for 71

72. Numerical and Graphical Reasoning   A crossed belt connects a 10-centimeter pulley on an electric motor with a 20-centimeter pulley on a saw arbor (see figure). The electric motor runs at 1700 revolutions per minute.

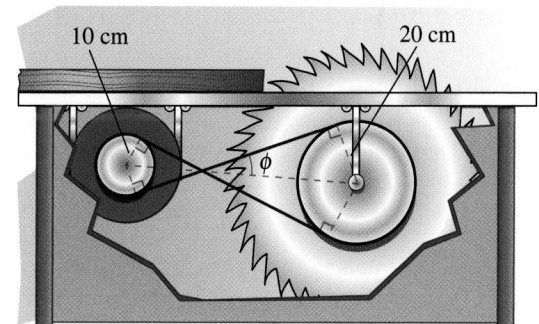

(a) Determine the number of revolutions per minute of the saw.

(b) How does crossing the belt affect the saw in relation to the motor?

(c) Let L be the total length of the belt. Write L as a function of ϕ, where ϕ is measured in radians. What is the domain of the function? (Hint: Add the lengths of the straight sections of the belt and the length of belt around each pulley.)

(d) Use a graphing utility to complete the table.

ϕ	0.3	0.6	0.9	1.2	1.5
L					

(e) As ϕ increases, do the lengths of the straight sections of the belt change faster or slower than the lengths of the belts around each pulley?

(f) Use a graphing utility to graph the function over the appropriate domain.

73. Data Analysis The motion of an oscillating weight suspended by a spring was measured by a motion detector. The data was collected, and the approximate maximum (positive and negative) displacements from equilibrium are shown in the graph. The displacement y is measured in centimeters and the time t is measured in seconds.

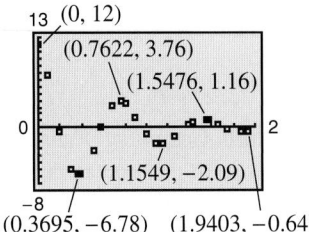

(a) Is y a function of t? Explain.

(b) Approximate the frequency of the oscillations.

(c) Fit a model of the form $y = ab^t \cos ct$ to the data. Use the result of part (b) to approximate c. Use the *regression* feature of a graphing utility to fit an exponential model to the positive maximum displacements of the weight.

(d) Rewrite the model in the form $y = ae^{kt} \cos ct$.

(e) Use a graphing utility to graph the model. Compare the result with the data in the graph above.

74. Writing Write a short paragraph describing the specified change in the physical system of Exercise 73.

(a) A spring of less stiffness is used, and so the length of time for each oscillation is greater.

(b) The effect of friction is decreased.

Synthesis

True or False? In Exercises 75 and 76, determine whether the statement is true or false. Justify your answer.

75. The graph of $y = -\dfrac{1}{8}\tan\left(\dfrac{x}{2} + \pi\right)$ has an asymptote at $x = -3\pi$.

76. For the graph of $y = 2^x \sin x$, as x approaches $-\infty$, y approaches 0.

77. Writing Describe the behavior of $f(x) = \tan x$ as x approaches $\pi/2$ from the left and from the right.

78. Writing Describe the behavior of $f(x) = \csc x$ as x approaches π from the left and from the right.

79. Graphical Reasoning Consider the functions $f(x) = 2 \sin x$ and $g(x) = \frac{1}{2}\csc x$ on the interval $(0, \pi)$.

(a) Use a graphing utility to graph f and g in the same viewing window.

(b) Approximate the interval in which $f > g$.

(c) Describe the behavior of each of the functions as x approaches π. How is the behavior of g related to the behavior of f as x approaches π?

80. Pattern Recognition

(a) Use a graphing utility to graph each function.

$$y_1 = \frac{4}{\pi}\left(\sin \pi x + \frac{1}{3}\sin 3\pi x\right)$$

$$y_2 = \frac{4}{\pi}\left(\sin \pi x + \frac{1}{3}\sin 3\pi x + \frac{1}{5}\sin 5\pi x\right)$$

(b) Identify the pattern in part (a) and find a function y_3 that continues the pattern one more term. Use a graphing utility to graph y_3.

(c) The graphs in parts (a) and (b) approximate the periodic function in the figure. Find a function y_4 that is a better approximation.

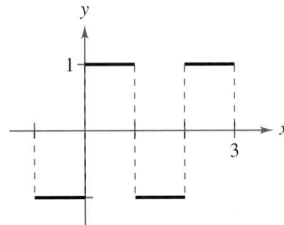

Review

In Exercises 81–84, identify the rule of algebra illustrated by the statement.

81. $5(a - 9) = 5a - 45$

82. $7\left(\frac{1}{7}\right) = 1$

83. $(3 + x) + 0 = 3 + x$

84. $(a + b) + 10 = a + (b + 10)$

In Exercises 85–88, determine whether the function is one-to-one. If it is, find its inverse function.

85. $f(x) = -10$

86. $f(x) = (x - 7)^2 + 3$

87. $f(x) = \sqrt{3x - 14}$

88. $f(x) = \sqrt[3]{x - 5}$

5.6 | Inverse Trigonometric Functions

Inverse Sine Function

Recall from Section 1.7 that for a function to have an inverse function, it must be one-to-one—that is, it must pass the Horizontal Line Test. From Figure 5.68 it is obvious that $y = \sin x$ does not pass the test because different values of x yield the same y-value.

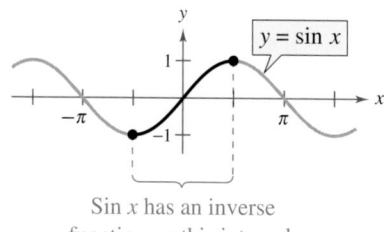

Sin x has an inverse function on this interval.

Figure 5.68

However, if you restrict the domain to the interval $-\pi/2 \le x \le \pi/2$ (corresponding to the black portion of the graph in Figure 5.68), the following properties hold.

1. On the interval $[-\pi/2, \pi/2]$, the function $y = \sin x$ is increasing.

2. On the interval $[-\pi/2, \pi/2]$, $y = \sin x$ takes on its full range of values, $-1 \le \sin x \le 1$.

3. On the interval $[-\pi/2, \pi/2]$, $y = \sin x$ is one-to-one.

So, on the restricted domain $-\pi/2 \le x \le \pi/2$, $y = \sin x$ has a unique inverse function called the **inverse sine function.** It is denoted by

$$y = \arcsin x \qquad \text{or} \qquad y = \sin^{-1} x.$$

The notation $\sin^{-1} x$ is consistent with the inverse function notation $f^{-1}(x)$. The arcsin x notation (read as "the arcsine of x") comes from the association of a central angle with its intercepted *arc length* on a unit circle. So, arcsin x means the angle (or arc) whose sine is x. Both notations, arcsin x and $\sin^{-1} x$, are commonly used in mathematics, so remember that $\sin^{-1} x$ denotes the *inverse* sine function rather than $1/\sin x$. The values of arcsin x lie in the interval $-\pi/2 \le \arcsin x \le \pi/2$. The graph of $y = \arcsin x$ is shown in Example 2.

Definition of Inverse Sine Function

The **inverse sine function** is defined by

$$y = \arcsin x \qquad \text{if and only if} \qquad \sin y = x$$

where $-1 \le x \le 1$ and $-\pi/2 \le y \le \pi/2$. The domain of $y = \arcsin x$ is $[-1, 1]$ and the range is $[-\pi/2, \pi/2]$.

When evaluating the inverse sine function, it helps to remember the phrase "the arcsine of x is the angle (or number) whose sine is x."

Example 1   Evaluating the Inverse Sine Function

If possible, find the exact value.

a. $\arcsin\left(-\dfrac{1}{2}\right)$ **b.** $\sin^{-1}\dfrac{\sqrt{3}}{2}$ **c.** $\sin^{-1} 2$

Solution

a. Because $\sin\left(-\dfrac{\pi}{6}\right) = -\dfrac{1}{2}$, and $-\dfrac{\pi}{6}$ lies in $\left[-\dfrac{\pi}{2}, \dfrac{\pi}{2}\right]$, it follows that

$$\arcsin\left(-\dfrac{1}{2}\right) = -\dfrac{\pi}{6}. \qquad \text{Angle whose sine is } -\tfrac{1}{2}$$

b. Because $\sin\left(\dfrac{\pi}{3}\right) = \dfrac{\sqrt{3}}{2}$, and $\dfrac{\pi}{3}$ lies in $\left[-\dfrac{\pi}{2}, \dfrac{\pi}{2}\right]$, it follows that

$$\sin^{-1}\dfrac{\sqrt{3}}{2} = \dfrac{\pi}{3}. \qquad \text{Angle whose sine is } \sqrt{3}/2$$

c. It is not possible to evaluate $y = \sin^{-1} x$ at $x = 2$ because there is no angle whose sine is 2. Remember that the domain of the inverse sine function is $[-1, 1]$.

✓ *Checkpoint* Now try Exercise 1.

Example 2   Graphing the Arcsine Function

Sketch a graph of $y = \arcsin x$ by hand.

Solution

By definition, the equations

$$y = \arcsin x \qquad \text{and} \qquad \sin y = x$$

are equivalent for $-\pi/2 \le y \le \pi/2$. So, their graphs are the same. For the interval $[-\pi/2, \pi/2]$, you can assign values to y in the second equation to make a table of values.

y	$-\dfrac{\pi}{2}$	$-\dfrac{\pi}{4}$	$-\dfrac{\pi}{6}$	0	$\dfrac{\pi}{6}$	$\dfrac{\pi}{4}$	$\dfrac{\pi}{2}$
$x = \sin y$	-1	$-\dfrac{\sqrt{2}}{2}$	$-\dfrac{1}{2}$	0	$\dfrac{1}{2}$	$\dfrac{\sqrt{2}}{2}$	1

Then plot the points and connect them with a smooth curve. The resulting graph of $y = \arcsin x$ is shown in Figure 5.69. Note that it is the reflection (in the line $y = x$) of the black portion of the graph in Figure 5.68. Use a graphing utility to confirm this graph. Be sure you see that Figure 5.69 shows the *entire* graph of the inverse sine function. Remember that the domain of $y = \arcsin x$ is the closed interval $[-1, 1]$ and the range is the closed interval $[-\pi/2, \pi/2]$.

✓ *Checkpoint* Now try Exercise 8.

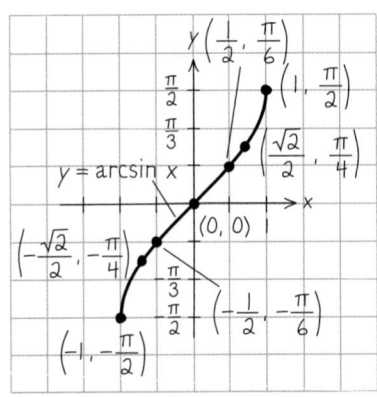

Figure 5.69

Other Inverse Trigonometric Functions

The cosine function is decreasing and one-to-one on the interval $0 \le x \le \pi$, as shown in Figure 5.70.

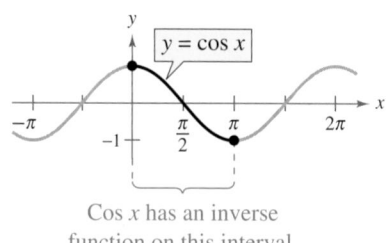

Cos *x* has an inverse function on this interval.

Figure 5.70

Consequently, on this interval the cosine function has an inverse function—the **inverse cosine function**—denoted by

$$y = \arccos x \qquad \text{or} \qquad y = \cos^{-1} x.$$

Because $y = \arccos x$ and $x = \cos y$ are equivalent for $0 \le y \le \pi$, their graphs are the same, and can be confirmed by the following table of values.

y	0	$\dfrac{\pi}{6}$	$\dfrac{\pi}{3}$	$\dfrac{\pi}{2}$	$\dfrac{2\pi}{3}$	$\dfrac{5\pi}{6}$	π
$x = \cos y$	1	$\dfrac{\sqrt{3}}{2}$	$\dfrac{1}{2}$	0	$-\dfrac{1}{2}$	$-\dfrac{\sqrt{3}}{2}$	-1

Similarly, you can define an **inverse tangent function** by restricting the domain of $y = \tan x$ to the interval $(-\pi/2, \pi/2)$. The following list summarizes the definitions of the three most common inverse trigonometric functions. The remaining three are defined in Exercises 79–81.

Definition of the Inverse Trigonometric Functions

Function	Domain	Range
$y = \arcsin x$ if and only if $\sin y = x$	$-1 \le x \le 1$	$-\dfrac{\pi}{2} \le y \le \dfrac{\pi}{2}$
$y = \arccos x$ if and only if $\cos y = x$	$-1 \le x \le 1$	$0 \le y \le \pi$
$y = \arctan x$ if and only if $\tan y = x$	$-\infty < x < \infty$	$-\dfrac{\pi}{2} < y < \dfrac{\pi}{2}$

The graphs of these three inverse trigonometric functions are shown in Figure 5.71.

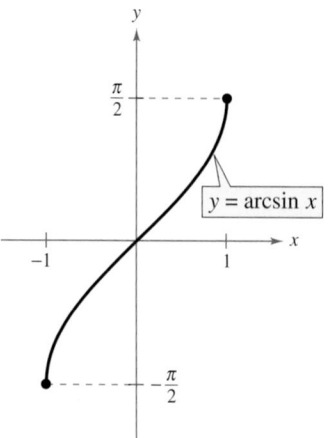

Domain: $[-1, 1]$; Range: $\left[-\dfrac{\pi}{2}, \dfrac{\pi}{2}\right]$

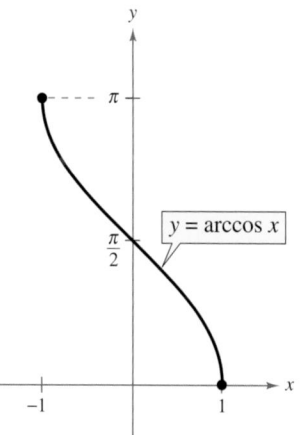

Domain: $[-1, 1]$; Range: $[0, \pi]$

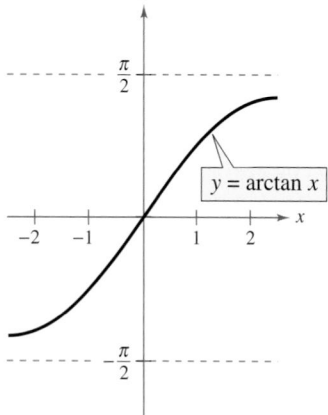

Domain: $(-\infty, \infty)$; Range: $\left(-\dfrac{\pi}{2}, \dfrac{\pi}{2}\right)$

Figure 5.71

Example 3 Evaluating Inverse Trigonometric Functions

Find the exact value.

a. $\arccos \dfrac{\sqrt{2}}{2}$ **b.** $\cos^{-1}(-1)$ **c.** $\arctan 0$ **d.** $\tan^{-1}(-1)$

Solution

a. Because $\cos(\pi/4) = \sqrt{2}/2$, and $\pi/4$ lies in $[0, \pi]$, it follows that

$$\arccos \frac{\sqrt{2}}{2} = \frac{\pi}{4}.$$ *Angle whose cosine is $\dfrac{\sqrt{2}}{2}$*

b. Because $\cos \pi = -1$, and π lies in $[0, \pi]$, it follows that

$$\cos^{-1}(-1) = \pi.$$ *Angle whose cosine is -1*

c. Because $\tan 0 = 0$, and 0 lies in $(-\pi/2, \pi/2)$, it follows that

$$\arctan 0 = 0.$$ *Angle whose tangent is 0*

d. Because $\tan(-\pi/4) = -1$ and $-\pi/4$ lies in $(-\pi/2, \pi/2)$, it follows that

$$\tan^{-1}(-1) = -\frac{\pi}{4}.$$ *Angle whose tangent is -1*

☑ *Checkpoint* Now try Exercise 3.

Example 4 Calculators and Inverse Trigonometric Functions

Use a calculator to approximate the value (if possible).

a. $\arctan(-8.45)$ **b.** $\sin^{-1} 0.2447$ **c.** $\arccos 2$

Solution

Function	*Mode*	*Graphing Calculator Keystrokes*
a. $\arctan(-8.45)$	Radian	TAN⁻¹ (−) 8.45) ENTER

From the display, it follows that $\arctan(-8.45) \approx -1.4530010$.

| **b.** $\sin^{-1} 0.2447$ | Radian | SIN⁻¹ 0.2447 ENTER |

From the display, it follows that $\sin^{-1} 0.2447 \approx 0.2472103$.

| **c.** $\arccos 2$ | Radian | COS⁻¹ 2 ENTER |

In *real number* mode, the calculator should display an *error message* because the domain of the inverse cosine function is $[-1, 1]$.

☑ *Checkpoint* Now try Exercise 13.

> **TECHNOLOGY TIP** In Example 4, if you had set the calculator to *degree* mode, the display would have been in degrees rather than in radians. This convention is peculiar to calculators. By definition, the values of inverse trigonometric functions are always in *radians*.

> **TECHNOLOGY TIP**
>
> You can use the SIN⁻¹, COS⁻¹, and TAN⁻¹ keys on your calculator to approximate values of inverse trigonometric functions. To evaluate the inverse cosecant function, the inverse secant function, or the inverse cotangent function, you can use the inverse sine, inverse cosine, and inverse tangent functions, respectively. For instance, to evaluate $\sec^{-1} 3.4$, enter the expression as shown below.
>
>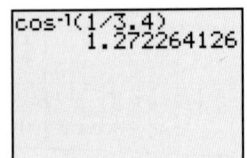

Compositions of Functions

Recall from Section 1.7 that for all x in the domains of f and f^{-1}, inverse functions have the properties

$$f(f^{-1}(x)) = x \quad \text{and} \quad f^{-1}(f(x)) = x.$$

> **Inverse Properties**
>
> If $-1 \le x \le 1$ and $-\pi/2 \le y \le \pi/2$, then
>
> $\quad \sin(\arcsin x) = x \quad$ and $\quad \arcsin(\sin y) = y.$
>
> If $-1 \le x \le 1$ and $0 \le y \le \pi$, then
>
> $\quad \cos(\arccos x) = x \quad$ and $\quad \arccos(\cos y) = y.$
>
> If x is a real number and $-\pi/2 < y < \pi/2$, then
>
> $\quad \tan(\arctan x) = x \quad$ and $\quad \arctan(\tan y) = y.$

Keep in mind that these inverse properties do not apply for arbitrary values of x and y. For instance,

$$\arcsin\left(\sin\frac{3\pi}{2}\right) = \arcsin(-1) = -\frac{\pi}{2} \ne \frac{3\pi}{2}.$$

In other words, the property $\arcsin(\sin y) = y$ is not valid for values of y outside the interval $[-\pi/2, \pi/2]$.

Example 5   Using Inverse Properties

If possible, find the exact value.

a. $\tan[\arctan(-5)]$ **b.** $\arcsin\left(\sin\dfrac{5\pi}{3}\right)$ **c.** $\cos(\cos^{-1}\pi)$

Solution

a. Because -5 lies in the domain of the arctan function, the inverse property applies, and you have $\tan[\arctan(-5)] = -5$.

b. In this case, $5\pi/3$ does not lie within the range of the arcsine function, $-\pi/2 \le y \le \pi/2$. However, $5\pi/3$ is coterminal with

$$\frac{5\pi}{3} - 2\pi = -\frac{\pi}{3}$$

which does lie in the range of the arcsine function, and you have

$$\arcsin\left(\sin\frac{5\pi}{3}\right) = \arcsin\left[\sin\left(-\frac{\pi}{3}\right)\right] = -\frac{\pi}{3}.$$

c. The expression $\cos(\cos^{-1}\pi)$ is not defined because $\cos^{-1}\pi$ is not defined. Remember that the domain of the inverse cosine function is $[-1, 1]$.

✓ *Checkpoint* Now try Exercise 33.

> **Exploration**
>
> Use a graphing utility to graph $y = \arcsin(\sin x)$. What are the domain and range of this function? Explain why $\arcsin(\sin 4)$ does not equal 4.
>
> Now graph $y = \sin(\arcsin x)$ and determine the domain and range. Explain why $\sin(\arcsin 4)$ is not defined.

Example 6 shows how to use right triangles to find exact values of compositions of inverse functions.

Example 6   Evaluating Compositions of Functions

Find the exact value.

a. $\tan\left(\arccos\dfrac{2}{3}\right)$ **b.** $\cos\left[\arcsin\left(-\dfrac{3}{5}\right)\right]$

Algebraic Solution

a. If you let $u = \arccos\frac{2}{3}$, then $\cos u = \frac{2}{3}$. Because $\cos u$ is positive, u is a first-quadrant angle. You can sketch and label angle u as shown in Figure 5.72.

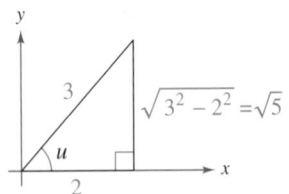

Figure 5.72

Consequently,

$$\tan\left(\arccos\dfrac{2}{3}\right) = \tan u = \dfrac{\text{opp}}{\text{adj}} = \dfrac{\sqrt{5}}{2}.$$

b. If you let $u = \arcsin\left(-\frac{3}{5}\right)$, then $\sin u = -\frac{3}{5}$. Because $\sin u$ is negative, u is a fourth-quadrant angle. You can sketch and label angle u as shown in Figure 5.73.

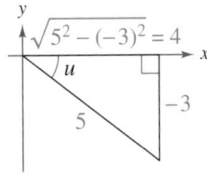

Figure 5.73

Consequently,

$$\cos\left[\arcsin\left(-\dfrac{3}{5}\right)\right] = \cos u = \dfrac{\text{adj}}{\text{hyp}} = \dfrac{4}{5}.$$

✓ *Checkpoint* Now try Exercise 41.

Graphical Solution

a. Use a graphing utility set in *radian* mode to graph $y = \tan(\arccos x)$, as shown in Figure 5.74. Use the *value* feature or the *zoom* and *trace* features of the graphing utility to find that the value of the composition of functions when $x = \frac{2}{3} \approx 0.66667$ is

$$y = 1.118 \approx \dfrac{\sqrt{5}}{2}.$$

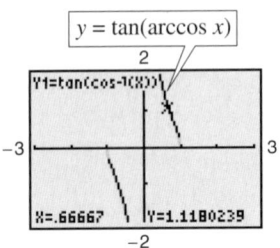

Figure 5.74

b. Use a graphing utility set in *radian* mode to graph $y = \cos(\arcsin x)$, as shown in Figure 5.75. Use the *value* feature or the *zoom* and *trace* features of the graphing utility to find that the value of the composition of functions when $x = -\frac{3}{5} = -0.6$ is

$$y = 0.8 = \dfrac{4}{5}.$$

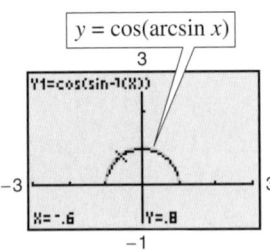

Figure 5.75

Library of Functions: Inverse Trigonometric Functions

The inverse trigonometric functions are obtained from the trigonometric functions in much the same way that the logarithmic function was developed from the exponential function. However, unlike the exponential function, the trigonometric functions are not one-to-one, and so it is necessary to restrict their domains to intervals on which they pass the Horizontal Line Test. Consequently, the inverse trigonometric functions have restricted domains and ranges, and they are not periodic.

One prominent role played by inverse trigonometric functions is in solving trigonometric equations in which the argument (angle) of the trigonometric function is the unknown quantity in the equation. You will learn how to solve such equations in the next chapter.

Inverse trigonometric functions play a unique role in calculus. There are two basic operations of calculus. One operation (called *differentiation*) transforms an inverse trigonometric function (a transcendental function) into an algebraic function. The other operation (called *integration*) produces the opposite transformation—from algebraic to transcendental.

Example 7   Some Problems from Calculus

Write each of the following as an algebraic expression in x.

a. $\sin(\arccos 3x)$, $0 \le x \le \frac{1}{3}$ **b.** $\cot(\arccos 3x)$, $0 \le x < \frac{1}{3}$

Solution

If you let $u = \arccos 3x$, then $\cos u = 3x$, where $-1 \le 3x \le 1$. Because

$$\cos u = \frac{\text{adj}}{\text{hyp}} = \frac{3x}{1}$$

you can sketch a right triangle with acute angle u, as shown in Figure 5.76. From this triangle, you can easily convert each expression to algebraic form.

a. $\sin(\arccos 3x) = \sin u = \dfrac{\text{opp}}{\text{hyp}} = \sqrt{1 - 9x^2}$, $0 \le x \le \dfrac{1}{3}$

b. $\cot(\arccos 3x) = \cot u = \dfrac{\text{adj}}{\text{opp}} = \dfrac{3x}{\sqrt{1 - 9x^2}}$, $0 \le x < \dfrac{1}{3}$

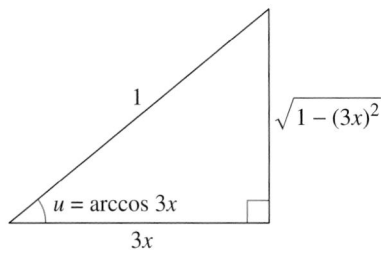

Figure 5.76

A similar argument can be made here for x-values lying in the interval $\left[-\frac{1}{3}, 0\right]$.

 Checkpoint Now try Exercise 47.

5.6 Exercises

Vocabulary Check

Fill in the blanks.

Function	Alternative Notation	Domain	Range
1. $y = \arcsin x$	_____	_____	$-\dfrac{\pi}{2} \leq y \leq \dfrac{\pi}{2}$
2. _____	$y = \cos^{-1} x$	$-1 \leq x \leq 1$	_____
3. $y = \arctan x$	_____	_____	_____

In Exercises 1–7, find the exact value of each expression without using a calculator.

1. (a) $\arcsin \frac{1}{2}$ (b) $\arcsin 0$

2. (a) $\arccos \frac{1}{2}$ (b) $\arccos 0$

3. (a) $\arctan \dfrac{\sqrt{3}}{3}$ (b) $\arctan(-1)$

4. (a) $\cos^{-1}\left(-\dfrac{\sqrt{2}}{2}\right)$ (b) $\sin^{-1}\left(-\dfrac{\sqrt{2}}{2}\right)$

5. (a) $\arctan\left(-\sqrt{3}\right)$ (b) $\arctan \sqrt{3}$

6. (a) $\arccos\left(-\dfrac{1}{2}\right)$ (b) $\arcsin \dfrac{\sqrt{2}}{2}$

7. (a) $\sin^{-1} \dfrac{\sqrt{3}}{2}$ (b) $\tan^{-1}\left(-\dfrac{\sqrt{3}}{3}\right)$

8. *Numerical and Graphical Analysis* Consider the function $y = \arcsin x$.

(a) Use a graphing utility to complete the table.

x	-1	-0.8	-0.6	-0.4	-0.2
y					

x	0	0.2	0.4	0.6	0.8	1
y						

(b) Plot the points from the table in part (a) and graph the function. (Do not use a graphing utility.)

(c) Use a graphing utility to graph the inverse sine function and compare the result with your hand-drawn graph in part (b).

(d) Determine any intercepts and symmetry of the graph.

9. *Numerical and Graphical Analysis* Consider the function $y = \arccos x$.

(a) Use a graphing utility to complete the table.

x	-1	-0.8	-0.6	-0.4	-0.2
y					

x	0	0.2	0.4	0.6	0.8	1
y						

(b) Plot the points from the table in part (a) and graph the function. (Do not use a graphing utility.)

(c) Use a graphing utility to graph the inverse cosine function and compare the result with your hand-drawn graph in part (b).

(d) Determine any intercepts and symmetry of the graph.

10. *Numerical and Graphical Analysis* Consider the function $y = \arctan x$.

(a) Use a graphing utility to complete the table.

x	-10	-8	-6	-4	-2
y					

x	0	2	4	6	8	10
y						

(b) Plot the points from the table in part (a) and graph the function. (Do not use a graphing utility.)

(c) Use a graphing utility to graph the inverse tangent function and compare the result with your hand-drawn graph in part (b).

(d) Determine the horizontal asymptotes of the graph.

In Exercises 11 and 12, determine the missing coordinates of the points on the graph of the function.

11.

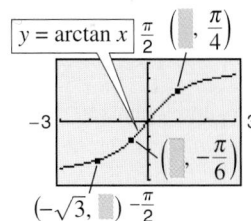

12.

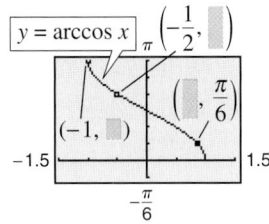

In Exercises 13–24, use a calculator to approximate the value of the expression. Round your answer to two decimal places.

13. $\cos^{-1} 0.75$

14. $\sin^{-1} 0.56$

15. $\arcsin(-0.75)$

16. $\arccos(-0.7)$

17. $\arctan(-6)$

18. $\arctan(-18)$

19. $\sin^{-1} 0.19$

20. $\cos^{-1} 0.21$

21. $\arccos(-0.51)$

22. $\arcsin(-0.125)$

23. $\tan^{-1} 1.32$

24. $\tan^{-1} 5.9$

In Exercises 25 and 26, use a graphing utility to graph $f, g,$ and $y = x$ in the same viewing window to verify geometrically that g is the inverse function of $f.$ (Be sure to properly restrict the domain of $f.$)

25. $f(x) = \tan x, \quad g(x) = \arctan x$

26. $f(x) = \sin x, \quad g(x) = \arcsin x$

In Exercises 27–30, use an inverse trigonometric function to write θ as a function of $x.$

27.

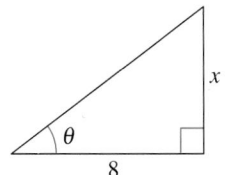

28.

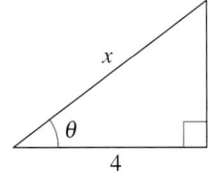

29.

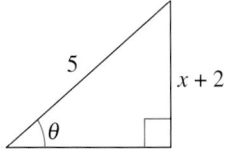

30.

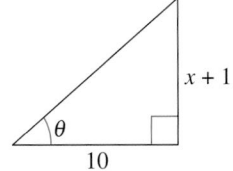

In Exercises 31–38, use the properties of inverse functions to find the exact value of the expression.

31. $\sin(\arcsin 0.7)$

32. $\tan(\arctan 35)$

33. $\cos[\arccos(-0.3)]$

34. $\sin[\arcsin(-0.1)]$

35. $\arcsin(\sin 3\pi)$

36. $\arccos\left(\cos \dfrac{7\pi}{2}\right)$

37. $\tan^{-1}\left(\tan \dfrac{11\pi}{6}\right)$

38. $\sin^{-1}\left(\sin \dfrac{7\pi}{4}\right)$

In Exercises 39–46, find the exact value of the expression. Use a graphing utility to verify your result. (*Hint:* Make a sketch of a right triangle.)

39. $\sin\left(\arctan \frac{4}{3}\right)$

40. $\sec\left(\arcsin \frac{3}{5}\right)$

41. $\cos\left(\arcsin \frac{24}{25}\right)$

42. $\csc\left[\arctan\left(-\frac{12}{5}\right)\right]$

43. $\sec\left[\arctan\left(-\frac{3}{5}\right)\right]$

44. $\tan\left[\arcsin\left(-\frac{3}{4}\right)\right]$

45. $\sin\left[\arccos\left(-\frac{2}{3}\right)\right]$

46. $\cot\left(\arctan \frac{5}{8}\right)$

In Exercises 47–54, write an algebraic expression that is equivalent to the expression. (*Hint:* Sketch a right triangle, as demonstrated in Example 7.)

47. $\cot(\arctan x)$

48. $\sin(\arctan x)$

49. $\sin[\arccos(x + 2)]$

50. $\sec[\arcsin(x - 1)]$

51. $\tan\left(\arccos \dfrac{x}{5}\right)$

52. $\cot\left(\arctan \dfrac{4}{x}\right)$

53. $\csc\left(\arctan \dfrac{x}{\sqrt{7}}\right)$

54. $\cos\left(\arcsin \dfrac{x - h}{r}\right)$

In Exercises 55 and 56, use a graphing utility to graph f and g in the same viewing window to verify that the two functions are equal. Explain why they are equal. Identify any asymptotes of the graphs.

55. $f(x) = \sin(\arctan 2x), \quad g(x) = \dfrac{2x}{\sqrt{1 + 4x^2}}$

56. $f(x) = \tan\left(\arccos \dfrac{x}{2}\right), \quad g(x) = \dfrac{\sqrt{4 - x^2}}{x}$

In Exercises 57–60, complete the equation.

57. $\arctan \dfrac{14}{x} = \arcsin(\quad), \quad x > 0$

58. $\arcsin \dfrac{\sqrt{36 - x^2}}{6} = \arccos(\quad), \quad 0 \le x \le 6$

59. $\arccos \dfrac{3}{\sqrt{x^2 - 2x + 10}} = \arcsin(\quad)$

60. $\arccos \dfrac{x - 2}{2} = \arctan(\quad), \quad 2 < x < 4$

In Exercises 61–68, use a graphing utility to graph the function.

61. $y = 2 \arccos x$

62. $y = \arcsin \dfrac{x}{2}$

63. $f(x) = \arcsin(x - 2)$

64. $g(t) = \arccos(t + 2)$

65. $f(x) = \arctan 2x$

66. $f(x) = \pi + \arctan x$

67. $h(v) = \tan(\arccos v)$

68. $f(x) = \arccos \dfrac{x}{4}$

In Exercises 69 and 70, write the function in terms of the sine function by using the identity

$$A \cos \omega t + B \sin \omega t = \sqrt{A^2 + B^2} \sin\left(\omega t + \arctan \dfrac{A}{B}\right).$$

Use a graphing utility to graph both forms of the function. What does the graph imply?

69. $f(t) = 3 \cos 2t + 3 \sin 2t$

70. $f(t) = 4 \cos \pi t + 3 \sin \pi t$

71. *Docking a Boat* A boat is pulled in by means of a winch located on a dock 10 feet above the deck of the boat (see figure). Let θ be the angle of elevation from the boat to the winch and let s be the length of the rope from the winch to the boat.

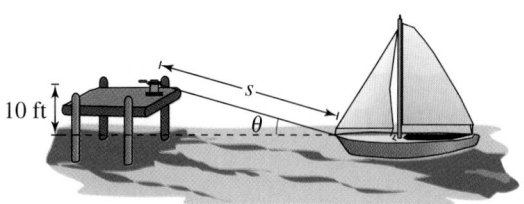

(a) Write θ as a function of s.

(b) Find θ when $s = 52$ feet and when $s = 26$ feet.

72. *Granular Angle of Repose* Different types of granular substances naturally settle at different angles when stored in cone-shaped piles. This angle θ is called the *angle of repose*. When rock salt is stored in a cone-shaped pile 11 feet high, the diameter of the pile's base is about 34 feet. (Source: Bulk-Store Structures, Inc.)

(a) Draw a diagram that gives a visual representation of the problem. Label all known and unknown quantities.

(b) Find the angle of repose for rock salt.

(c) How tall is a pile of rock salt that has a base diameter of 40 feet?

73. *Photography* A television camera at ground level is filming the lift-off of a space shuttle at a point 750 meters from the launch pad (see figure). Let θ be the angle of elevation to the shuttle and let s be the height of the shuttle.

(a) Write θ as a function of s.

(b) Find θ when $s = 400$ meters and when $s = 1600$ meters.

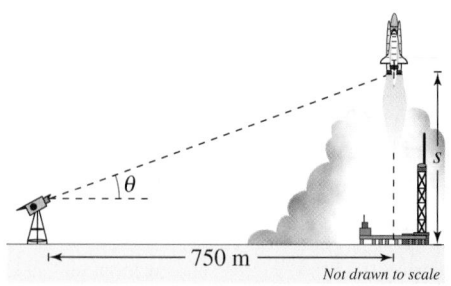

750 m

Not drawn to scale

74. *Photography* A photographer is taking a picture of a three-foot painting hung in an art gallery. The camera lens is 1 foot below the lower edge of the painting (see figure). The angle β subtended by the camera lens x feet from the painting is

$$\beta = \arctan \dfrac{3x}{x^2 + 4}, \quad x > 0.$$

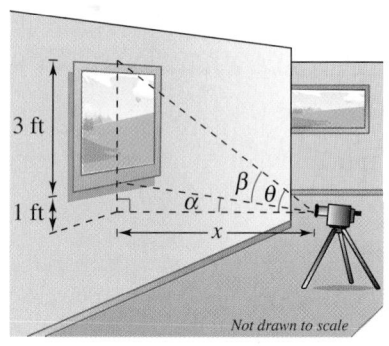

Not drawn to scale

(a) Use a graphing utility to graph β as a function of x.

(b) Move the cursor along the graph to approximate the distance from the picture when β is maximum.

(c) Identify the asymptote of the graph and discuss its meaning in the context of the problem.

75. *Angle of Elevation*   An airplane flies at an altitude of 6 miles toward a point directly over an observer. Consider θ and x as shown in the figure.

(a) Write θ as a function of x.

(b) Find θ when $x = 10$ miles and $x = 3$ miles.

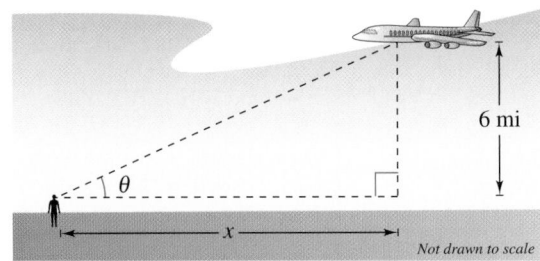

6 mi

Not drawn to scale

76. *Security Patrol*   A security car with its spotlight on is parked 20 meters from a long warehouse. Consider θ and x as shown in the figure.

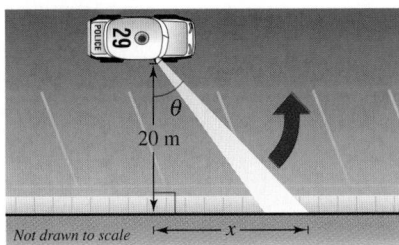

20 m

Not drawn to scale

(a) Write θ as a function of x.

(b) Find θ when $x = 5$ meters and when $x = 12$ meters.

Synthesis

True or False?   **In Exercises 77 and 78, determine whether the statement is true or false. Justify your answer.**

77. $\sin \dfrac{5\pi}{6} = \dfrac{1}{2}$ ⟹ $\arcsin \dfrac{1}{2} = \dfrac{5\pi}{6}$

78. $\arctan x = \dfrac{\arcsin x}{\arccos x}$

79. Define the inverse cotangent function by restricting the domain of the cotangent function to the interval $(0, \pi)$, and sketch the inverse function's graph.

80. Define the inverse secant function by restricting the domain of the secant function to the intervals $[0, \pi/2)$ and $(\pi/2, \pi]$, and sketch the inverse function's graph.

81. Define the inverse cosecant function by restricting the domain of the cosecant function to the intervals $[-\pi/2, 0)$ and $(0, \pi/2]$, and sketch the inverse function's graph.

82. Use the results of Exercises 79–81 to evaluate the following without using a calculator.

(a) $\operatorname{arcsec} \sqrt{2}$

(b) $\operatorname{arcsec} 1$

(c) $\operatorname{arccot}\left(-\sqrt{3}\right)$

(d) $\operatorname{arccsc} 2$

Proof   **In Exercises 83–85, prove the identity.**

83. $\arcsin(-x) = -\arcsin x$

84. $\arctan(-x) = -\arctan x$

85. $\arcsin x + \arccos x = \dfrac{\pi}{2}$

86. *Area*   In calculus, it is shown that the area of the region bounded by the graphs of $y = 0$, $y = 1/(x^2 + 1)$, $x = a$, and $x = b$ is given by

$$\text{Area} = \arctan b - \arctan a$$

(see figure). Find the areas for each value of a and b.

(a) $a = 0, b = 1$

(b) $a = -1, b = 1$

(c) $a = 0, b = 3$

(d) $a = -1, b = 3$

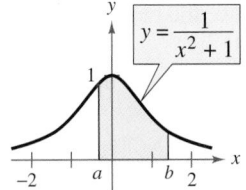

$$y = \dfrac{1}{x^2 + 1}$$

Review

In Exercises 87–90, simplify the radical expression.

87. $\dfrac{4}{4\sqrt{2}}$

88. $\dfrac{2}{\sqrt{3}}$

89. $\dfrac{2\sqrt{3}}{6}$

90. $\dfrac{5\sqrt{5}}{2\sqrt{10}}$

In Exercises 91–94, sketch a right triangle corresponding to the trigonometric function of the acute angle θ. Use the Pythagorean Theorem to determine the third side and then find the other five trigonometric functions of θ.

91. $\sin \theta = \dfrac{5}{6}$

92. $\tan \theta = 2$

93. $\sin \theta = \dfrac{3}{4}$

94. $\sec \theta = 3$

5.7 Applications and Models

Applications Involving Right Triangles

In this section, the three angles of a right triangle are denoted by the letters A, B, and C (where C is the right angle), and the lengths of the sides opposite these angles by the letters a, b, and c (where c is the hypotenuse).

Example 1   Solving a Right Triangle

Solve the right triangle shown in Figure 5.77 for all unknown sides and angles.

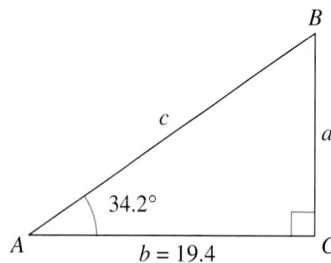

Figure 5.77

Solution

Because $C = 90°$, it follows that $A + B = 90°$ and $B = 90° - 34.2° = 55.8°$. To solve for a, use the fact that

$$\tan A = \frac{\text{opp}}{\text{adj}} = \frac{a}{b} \implies a = b \tan A.$$

So, $a = 19.4 \tan 34.2° \approx 13.18$. Similarly, to solve for c, use the fact that

$$\cos A = \frac{\text{adj}}{\text{hyp}} = \frac{b}{c} \implies c = \frac{b}{\cos A}.$$

So, $c = \dfrac{19.4}{\cos 34.2°} \approx 23.46$.

✓ *Checkpoint* Now try Exercise 1.

Recall from Section 5.2 that the term *angle of elevation* denotes the angle from the horizontal upward to an object and that the term *angle of depression* denotes the angle from the horizontal downward to an object. An angle of elevation and an angle of depression are shown in Figure 5.78.

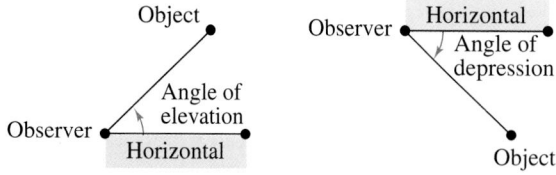

Figure 5.78

What you should learn

● Solve real-life problems involving right triangles.

● Solve real-life problems involving directional bearings.

● Solve real-life problems involving harmonic motion.

Why you should learn it

You can use trigonometric functions to model and solve real-life problems. For instance, Exercise 60 on page 470 shows you how a trigonometric function can be used to model the harmonic motion of a buoy.

Mary Kate Denny/PhotoEdit

Example 2   Finding a Side of a Right Triangle

A safety regulation states that the maximum angle of elevation for a rescue ladder is 72°. A fire department's longest ladder is 110 feet. What is the maximum safe rescue height?

Solution

A sketch is shown in Figure 5.79. From the equation $\sin A = a/c$, it follows that

$$a = c \sin A = 110 \sin 72° \approx 104.6.$$

So, the maximum safe rescue height is about 104.6 feet above the height of the fire truck.

 Checkpoint Now try Exercise 17.

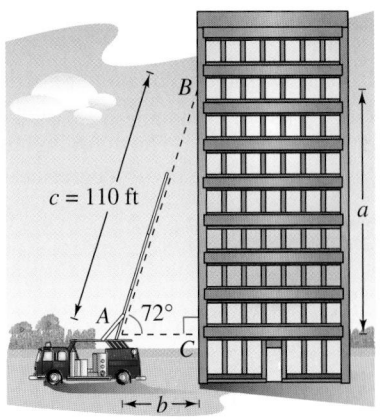

Figure 5.79

Example 3   Finding a Side of a Right Triangle

At a point 200 feet from the base of a building, the angle of elevation to the *bottom* of a smokestack is 35°, and the angle of elevation to the *top* is 53°, as shown in Figure 5.80. Find the height s of the smokestack alone.

Solution

This problem involves two right triangles. For the smaller right triangle, use the fact that $\tan 35° = a/200$ to conclude that the height of the building is

$$a = 200 \tan 35°.$$

Now, for the larger right triangle, use the equation

$$\tan 53° = \frac{a + s}{200}$$

to conclude that $s = 200 \tan 53° - a$. So, the height of the smokestack is

$$s = 200 \tan 53° - a = 200 \tan 53° - 200 \tan 35° \approx 125.4 \text{ feet.}$$

 Checkpoint Now try Exercise 19.

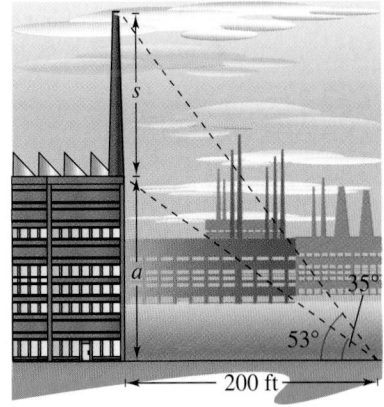

Figure 5.80

Example 4   Finding an Angle of Depression

A swimming pool is 20 meters long and 12 meters wide. The bottom of the pool is slanted so that the water depth is 1.3 meters at the shallow end and 4 meters at the deep end, as shown in Figure 5.81. Find the angle of depression of the bottom of the pool.

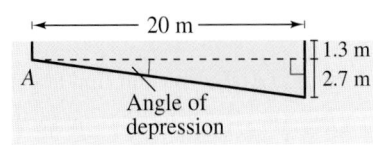

Figure 5.81

Solution

Using the tangent function, you see that

$$\tan A = \frac{\text{opp}}{\text{adj}} = \frac{2.7}{20} = 0.135.$$

So, the angle of depression is $A = \arctan 0.135 \approx 0.13419 \text{ radian} \approx 7.69°.$

 Checkpoint Now try Exercise 25.

Trigonometry and Bearings

In surveying and navigation, directions are generally given in terms of **bearings.** A bearing measures the acute angle a path or line of sight makes with a fixed north–south line, as shown in Figure 5.82. For instance, the bearing of S 35° E in Figure 5.82(a) means 35 degrees east of south.

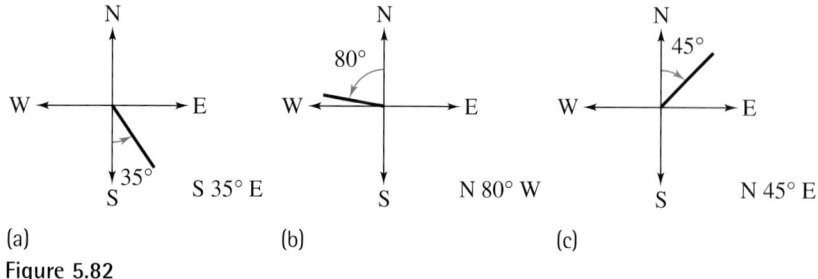

(a)   (b)   (c)

Figure 5.82

Example 5   Finding Directions in Terms of Bearings

A ship leaves port at noon and heads due west at 20 knots, or 20 nautical miles (nm) per hour. At 2 P.M. the ship changes course to N 54° W, as shown in Figure 5.83. Find the ship's bearing and distance from the port of departure at 3 P.M.

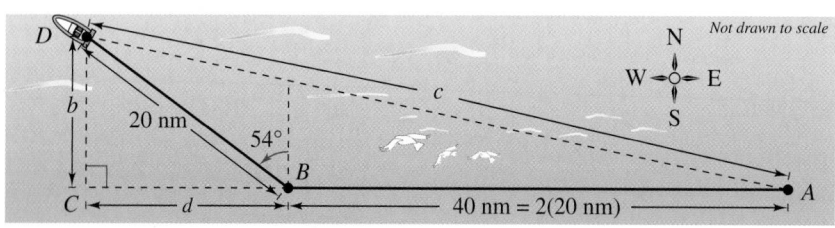

Figure 5.83

Solution

For triangle BCD, you have $B = 90° - 54° = 36°$. The two sides of this triangle can be determined to be

$$b = 20 \sin 36° \quad \text{and} \quad d = 20 \cos 36°.$$

In triangle ACD, you can find angle A as follows.

$$\tan A = \frac{b}{d + 40} = \frac{20 \sin 36°}{20 \cos 36° + 40} \approx 0.2092494$$

$$A \approx \arctan 0.2092494 \approx 0.2062732 \text{ radian} \approx 11.82°$$

The angle with the north-south line is $90° - 11.82° = 78.18°$. So, the bearing of the ship is N 78.18° W. Finally, from triangle ACD, you have $\sin A = b/c$, which yields

$$c = \frac{b}{\sin A} = \frac{20 \sin 36°}{\sin 11.82°} \approx 57.4 \text{ nautical miles.} \qquad \text{Distance from port}$$

☑ *Checkpoint* Now try Exercise 31.

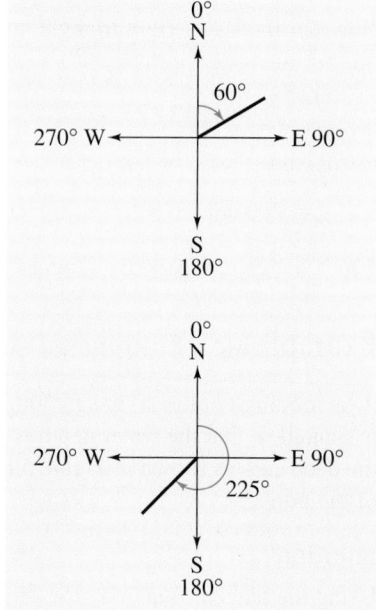

Harmonic Motion

The periodic nature of the trigonometric functions is useful for describing the motion of a point on an object that vibrates, oscillates, rotates, or is moved by wave motion.

For example, consider a ball that is bobbing up and down on the end of a spring, as shown in Figure 5.84. Suppose that 10 centimeters is the maximum distance the ball moves vertically upward or downward from its equilibrium (at-rest) position. Suppose further that the time it takes for the ball to move from its maximum displacement above zero to its maximum displacement below zero and back again is $t = 4$ seconds. Assuming the ideal conditions of perfect elasticity and no friction or air resistance, the ball would continue to move up and down in a uniform and regular manner.

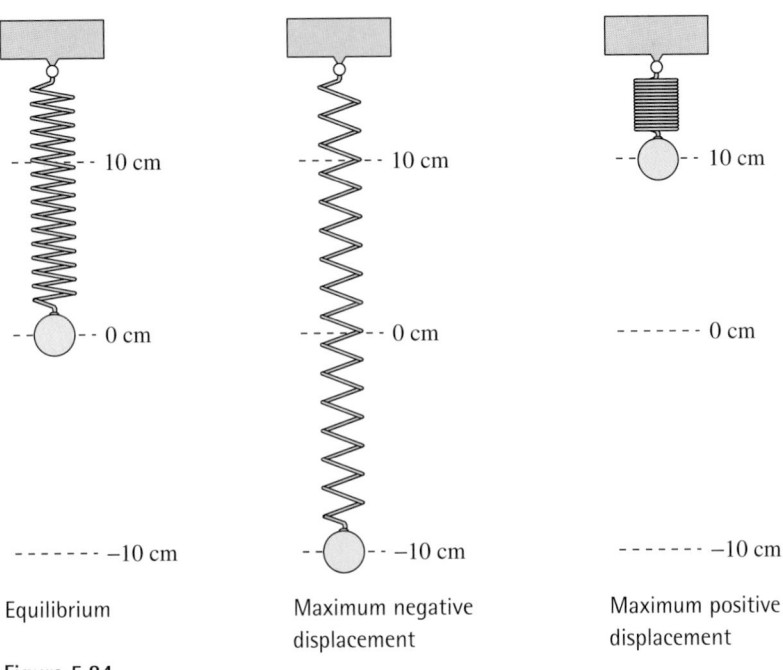

Equilibrium Maximum negative Maximum positive
displacement displacement

Figure 5.84

From this spring you can conclude that the period (time for one complete cycle) of the motion is

Period $= 4$ seconds

its amplitude (maximum displacement from equilibrium) is

Amplitude $= 10$ centimeters

and its **frequency** (number of cycles per second) is

Frequency $= \dfrac{1}{4}$ cycle per second.

Motion of this nature can be described by a sine or cosine function, and is called **simple harmonic motion.**

> **Definition of Simple Harmonic Motion**
>
> A point that moves on a coordinate line is said to be in **simple harmonic motion** if its distance d from the origin at time t is given by either
>
> $$d = a \sin \omega t \qquad \text{or} \qquad d = a \cos \omega t$$
>
> where a and ω are real numbers such that $\omega > 0$. The motion has amplitude $|a|$, period $2\pi/\omega$, and frequency $\omega/(2\pi)$.

Example 6   Simple Harmonic Motion

Write the equation for the simple harmonic motion of the ball illustrated in Figure 5.84, where the period is 4 seconds. What is the frequency of this motion?

Solution

Because the spring is at equilibrium $(d = 0)$ when $t = 0$, you use the equation

$$d = a \sin \omega t.$$

Moreover, because the maximum displacement from zero is 10 and the period is 4, you have the following.

$$\text{Amplitude} = |a| = 10$$

$$\text{Period} = \frac{2\pi}{\omega} = 4 \qquad \Longrightarrow \qquad \omega = \frac{\pi}{2}$$

Consequently, the equation of motion is

$$d = 10 \sin \frac{\pi}{2}t.$$

Note that the choice of $a = 10$ or $a = -10$ depends on whether the ball initially moves up or down. The frequency is

$$\text{Frequency} = \frac{\omega}{2\pi}$$

$$= \frac{\pi/2}{2\pi}$$

$$= \frac{1}{4} \text{ cycle per second.}$$

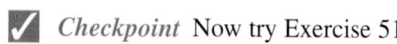 *Checkpoint* Now try Exercise 51.

One illustration of the relationship between sine waves and harmonic motion is the wave motion that results when a stone is dropped into a calm pool of water. The waves move outward in roughly the shape of sine (or cosine) waves, as shown in Figure 5.85. As an example, suppose you are fishing and your fishing bob is attached so that it does not move horizontally. As the waves move outward from the dropped stone, your fishing bob will move up and down in simple harmonic motion, as shown in Figure 5.86.

Figure 5.85

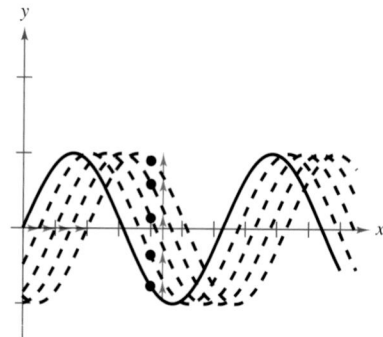

Figure 5.86

Example 7   Simple Harmonic Motion

Given the equation for simple harmonic motion

$$d = 6 \cos \frac{3\pi}{4} t$$

find (a) the maximum displacement, (b) the frequency, (c) the value of d when $t = 4$, and (d) the least positive value of t for which $d = 0$.

Algebraic Solution

The given equation has the form $d = a \cos \omega t$, with $a = 6$ and $\omega = 3\pi/4$.

a. The maximum displacement (from the point of equilibrium) is given by the amplitude. So, the maximum displacement is 6.

b. Frequency $= \dfrac{\omega}{2\pi}$

$= \dfrac{3\pi/4}{2\pi}$

$= \dfrac{3}{8}$ cycle per unit of time

c. $d = 6 \cos\left[\dfrac{3\pi}{4}(4)\right]$

$= 6 \cos 3\pi$

$= 6(-1)$

$= -6$

d. To find the least positive value of t for which $d = 0$, solve the equation

$$d = 6 \cos \frac{3\pi}{4} t = 0.$$

First divide each side by 6 to obtain

$$\cos \frac{3\pi}{4} t = 0.$$

You know that $\cos t = 0$ when

$$t = \frac{\pi}{2}, \frac{3\pi}{2}, \frac{5\pi}{2}, \ldots$$

Multiply these values by $4/(3\pi)$ to obtain

$$t = \frac{2}{3}, 2, \frac{10}{3}, \ldots$$

So, the least positive value of t is $t = \frac{2}{3}$.

✓ *Checkpoint* Now try Exercise 55.

Graphical Solution

Use a graphing utility set in *radian* mode to graph

$$y = 6 \cos \frac{3\pi}{4} x.$$

a. Use the *maximum* feature of the graphing utility to estimate that the maximum displacement from the point of equilibrium $y = 0$ is 6, as shown in Figure 5.87.

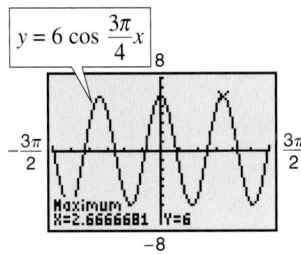

Figure 5.87

b. The period is the time for the graph to complete one cycle, which is $x \approx 2.667$. You can estimate the frequency as follows.

$$\text{Frequency} \approx \frac{1}{2.667} \approx 0.375 \text{ cycle per unit of time}$$

c. Use the *value* or *trace* feature to estimate that the value of y when $x = 4$ is $y = -6$, as shown in Figure 5.88.

d. Use the *zero* or *root* feature to estimate that the least positive value of x for which $y = 0$ is $x \approx 0.6667$, as shown in Figure 5.89.

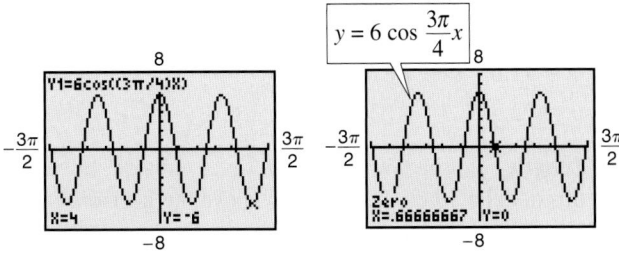

Figure 5.88   Figure 5.89

5.7 Exercises

Vocabulary Check

Fill in the blanks.

1. An angle that measures from the horizontal upward to an object is called the angle of _____ , whereas an angle that measures from the horizontal downward to an object is called the angle of _____ .

2. A _____ measures the acute angle a path or line of sight makes with a fixed north-south line.

3. A point that moves on a coordinate line is said to be in simple _____ if its distance from the origin at time t is given by either $d = a \sin \omega t$ or $d = a \cos \omega t$.

In Exercises 1–10, solve the right triangle shown in the figure. (Round your answers to two decimal places.)

1. $A = 20°$, $b = 10$
2. $B = 54°$, $c = 15$
3. $B = 71°$, $b = 24$
4. $A = 7.4°$, $a = 40.5$
5. $a = 6$, $b = 16$
6. $a = 25$, $c = 35$
7. $b = 16$, $c = 48$
8. $b = 1.32$, $c = 9.45$
9. $A = 12° 15'$, $c = 430.5$
10. $B = 65° 12'$, $a = 14.2$

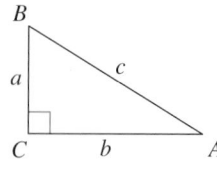   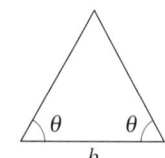

Figure for 1–10   Figure for 11–14

In Exercises 11–14, find the altitude of the isosceles triangle shown in the figure. Round your answer to two decimal places.

11. $\theta = 52°$, $b = 4$ inches
12. $\theta = 18°$, $b = 10$ meters
13. $\theta = 41.6°$, $b = 14.2$ feet
14. $\theta = 72.94°$, $b = 3.36$ centimeters

15. **Length** A shadow of length L is created by a 60-foot silo when the sun is $\theta°$ above the horizon.

    (a) Draw a right triangle that gives a visual representation of the problem. Label the known and unknown quantities.

    (b) Write L as a function of θ.

    (c) Use a graphing utility to complete the table.

θ	10°	20°	30°	40°	50°
L					

    (d) The angle measure increases in equal increments in the table. Does the length of the shadow change in equal increments? Explain.

16. **Length** A shadow of length L is created by an 850-foot building when the sun is $\theta°$ above the horizon.

    (a) Draw a right triangle that gives a visual representation of the problem. Label the known and unknown quantities.

    (b) Write L as a function of θ.

    (c) Use a graphing utility to complete the table.

θ	10°	20°	30°	40°	50°
L					

    (d) The angle measure increases in equal increments in the table. Does the length of the shadow change in equal increments? Explain.

17. **Height** A ladder 20 feet long leans against the side of a house. The angle of elevation of the ladder is 80°. Find the height from the top of the ladder to the ground.

18. **Height** The angle of elevation from the base to the top of a waterslide is 13°. The slide extends horizontally 58.2 meters. Approximate the height of the waterslide.

19. *Height*   From a point 50 feet in front of a church, the angles of elevation to the base of the steeple and the top of the steeple are 35° and 47° 40′, respectively.

(a) Draw right triangles that give a visual representation of the problem. Label the known and unknown quantities.

(b) Use a trigonometric function to write an equation involving the unknown quantity.

(c) Find the height of the steeple.

20. *Height*   From a point 100 feet in front of a public library, the angles of elevation to the base of the flagpole and the top of the flagpole are 28° and 39° 45′, respectively. The flagpole is mounted on the front of the library's roof. Find the height of the flagpole.

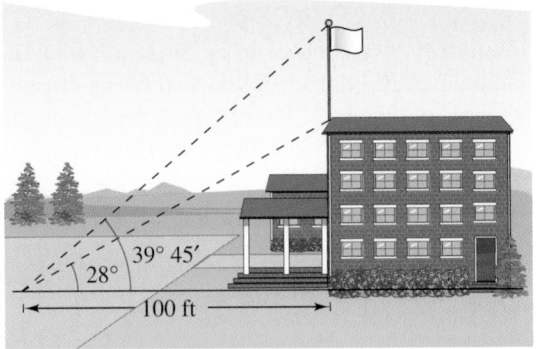

21. *Depth*   The sonar of a navy cruiser detects a submarine that is 4000 feet from the cruiser. The angle between the water level and the submarine is 31.5°. How deep is the submarine?

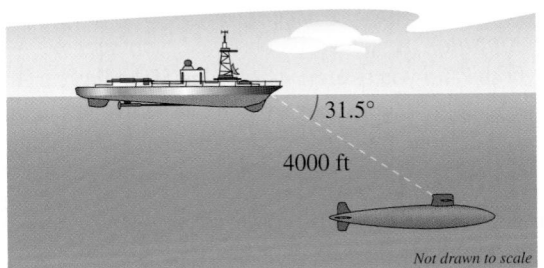

22. *Height*   A 100-foot line is attached to a kite. When the kite has pulled the line taut, the angle of elevation to the kite is approximately 50°. Approximate the height of the kite.

23. *Angle of Elevation*   An engineer erects a 75-foot vertical cellular-phone tower. Find the angle of elevation to the top of the tower from a point on level ground 95 feet from its base.

24. *Angle of Elevation*   The height of an outdoor basketball backboard is $12\frac{1}{2}$ feet, and the backboard casts a shadow $17\frac{1}{3}$ feet long.

(a) Draw a right triangle that gives a visual representation of the problem. Label the known and unknown quantities.

(b) Use a trigonometric function to write an equation involving the unknown quantity.

(c) Find the angle of elevation of the sun.

25. *Angle of Depression*   A Global Positioning System satellite orbits 12,500 miles above Earth's surface. Find the angle of depression from the satellite to the horizon. Assume the radius of Earth is 4000 miles.

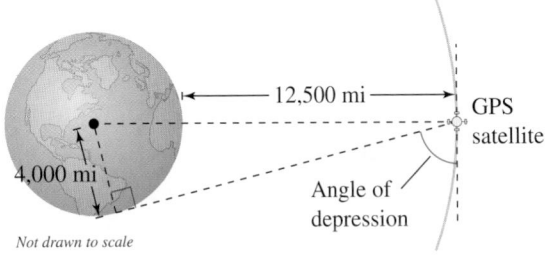

Not drawn to scale

26. *Angle of Depression*   Find the angle of depression from the top of a lighthouse 250 feet above water level to the water line of a ship $2\frac{1}{2}$ miles offshore.

27. *Airplane Ascent*   When an airplane leaves the runway, its angle of climb is 18° and its speed is 275 feet per second. Find the plane's altitude after 1 minute.

28. *Airplane Ascent*   How long will it take the plane in Exercise 27 to climb to an altitude of 10,000 feet? 16,000 feet?

29. *Mountain Descent*   A sign on the roadway at the top of a mountain indicates that for the next 4 miles the grade is 9.5° (see figure). Find the change in elevation for a car descending the mountain.

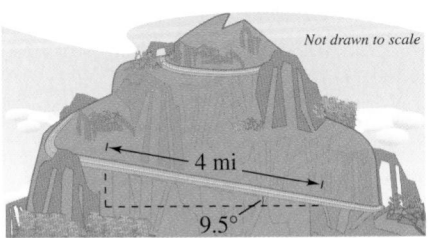

30. *Ski Slope* A ski slope on a mountain has an angle of elevation of 25.2°. The vertical height of the slope is 1808 feet. How long is the slope?

31. *Navigation* A ship leaves port at noon and has a bearing of S 29° W. The ship sails at 20 knots. How many nautical miles south and how many nautical miles west will the ship have traveled by 6:00 P.M.?

32. *Navigation* An airplane flying at 600 miles per hour has a bearing of 52°. After flying 1.5 hours, how far north and how far east has the plane traveled from its point of departure?

33. *Surveying* A surveyor wants to find the distance across a swamp. The bearing from A to B is N 32° W. The surveyor walks 50 meters from A, and at the point C the bearing to B is N 68° W. Find (a) the bearing from A to C and (b) the distance from A to B.

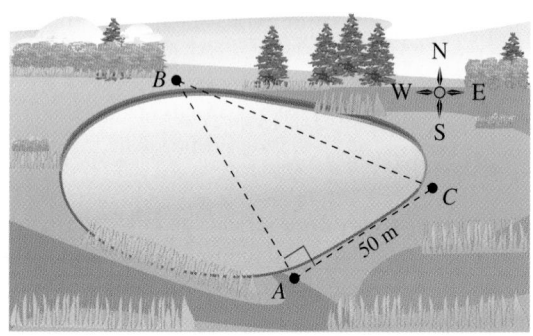

34. *Location of a Fire* Two fire towers are 30 kilometers apart, where tower A is due west of tower B. A fire is spotted from the towers, and the bearings from A and B are E 14° N and W 34° N, respectively. Find the distance d of the fire from the line segment AB.

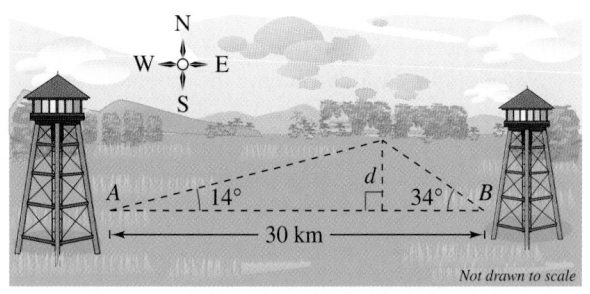

Not drawn to scale

35. *Navigation* A ship is 45 miles east and 30 miles south of port. The captain wants to sail directly to port. What bearing should be taken?

36. *Navigation* A plane is 160 miles north and 85 miles east of an airport. The pilot wants to fly directly to the airport. What bearing should be taken?

37. *Distance* An observer in a lighthouse 350 feet above sea level observes two ships directly offshore. The angles of depression to the ships are 4° and 6.5° (see figure). How far apart are the ships?

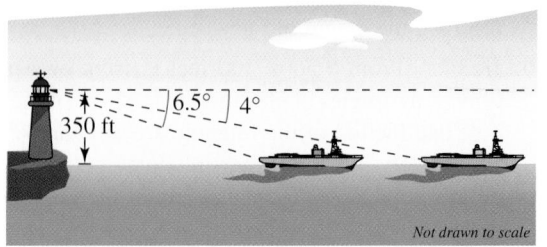

Not drawn to scale

38. *Distance* A passenger in an airplane flying at an altitude of 10 kilometers sees two towns directly to the east of the plane. The angles of depression to the towns are 28° and 55° (see figure). How far apart are the towns?

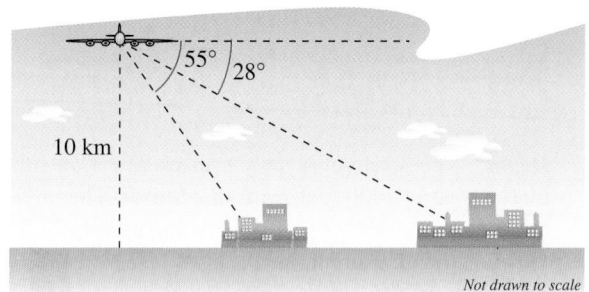

Not drawn to scale

39. *Altitude* A plane is observed approaching your home and you assume its speed is 550 miles per hour. The angle of elevation to the plane is 16° at one time and 57° one minute later. Approximate the altitude of the plane.

40. *Height* While traveling across flat land, you notice a mountain directly in front of you. The angle of elevation to the peak is 2.5°. After you drive 18 miles closer to the mountain, the angle of elevation is 10°. Approximate the height of the mountain.

Geometry   In Exercises 41 and 42, find the angle α between two nonvertical lines L_1 and L_2. The angle α satisfies the equation

$$\tan \alpha = \left| \frac{m_2 - m_1}{1 + m_2 m_1} \right|$$

where m_1 and m_2 are the slopes of L_1 and L_2, respectively. (Assume $m_1 m_2 \neq -1$.)

41. L_1: $3x - 2y = 5$
L_2: $x + y = 1$

42. L_1: $2x + y = 8$
L_2: $x - 5y = -4$

43. Geometry   Determine the angle between the diagonal of a cube and the diagonal of its base, as shown in the figure.

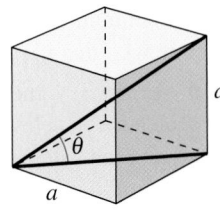

Figure for 43   Figure for 44

44. Geometry   Determine the angle between the diagonal of a cube and its edge, as shown in the figure.

45. Hardware   Write the distance y across the flat sides of a hexagonal nut as a function of r, as shown in the figure.

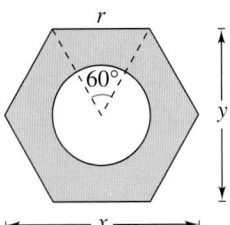

46. Hardware   The figure shows a circular piece of sheet metal of diameter 40 centimeters. The sheet contains 12 equally spaced bolt holes. Determine the straight-line distance between the centers of two consecutive bolt holes.

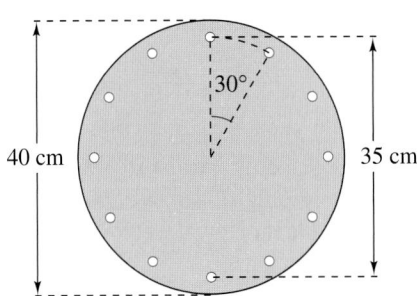

47. Geometry   A regular pentagon (a pentagon with congruent sides and angles) is inscribed in a circle of radius 25 inches. Find the length of the sides of the pentagon.

48. Geometry   A regular hexagon (a hexagon with congruent sides and angles) is inscribed in a circle of radius 25 inches. Find the length of the sides of the hexagon.

Trusses   In Exercises 49 and 50, find the lengths of all the unknown members of the truss.

49.

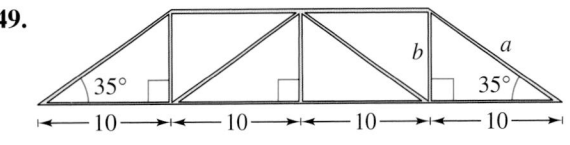

50.

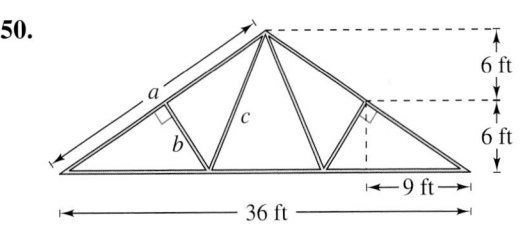

Harmonic Motion   In Exercises 51–54, find a model for simple harmonic motion satisfying the specified conditions.

Displacement ($t = 0$)	Amplitude	Period
51. 0	8 centimeters	2 seconds
52. 0	3 meters	6 seconds
53. 3 inches	3 inches	1.5 seconds
54. 2 feet	2 feet	10 seconds

Harmonic Motion   In Exercises 55–58, for the simple harmonic motion described by the trigonometric function, find (a) the maximum displacement, (b) the frequency, (c) the value of d when $t = 5$, and (d) the least positive value of t for which $d = 0$. Use a graphing utility to verify your results.

55. $d = 4 \cos 8\pi t$

56. $d = \frac{1}{2} \cos 20\pi t$

57. $d = \frac{1}{16} \sin 140\pi t$

58. $d = \frac{1}{64} \sin 792\pi t$

59. Tuning Fork   A point on the end of a tuning fork moves in the simple harmonic motion described by $d = a \sin \omega t$. Find ω given that the tuning fork for middle C has a frequency of 264 vibrations per second.

60. Wave Motion   A buoy oscillates in simple harmonic motion as waves go past. At a given time it is noted that the buoy moves a total of 3.5 feet from its low point to its high point (see figure), and that it returns to its high point every 10 seconds. Write an equation that describes the motion of the buoy if it is at its high point at time $t = 0$.

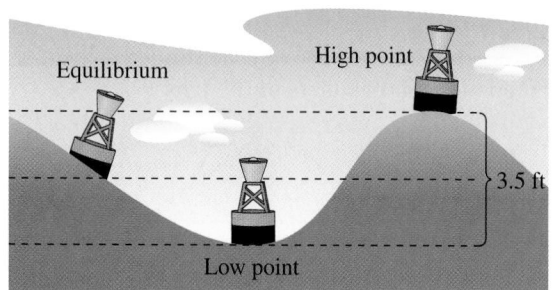

61. Springs   A ball that is bobbing up and down on the end of a spring has a maximum displacement of 3 inches. Its motion (in ideal conditions) is modeled by

$$y = \tfrac{1}{4} \cos 16t, \quad t > 0$$

where y is measured in feet and t is the time in seconds.

(a) Use a graphing utility to graph the function.

(b) What is the period of the oscillations?

(c) Determine the first time the ball passes the point of equilibrium $(y = 0)$.

62. Numerical and Graphical Analysis   A two-meter-high fence is 3 meters from the side of a grain storage bin. A grain elevator must reach from ground level outside the fence to the storage bin (see figure). The objective is to determine the shortest elevator that meets the constraints.

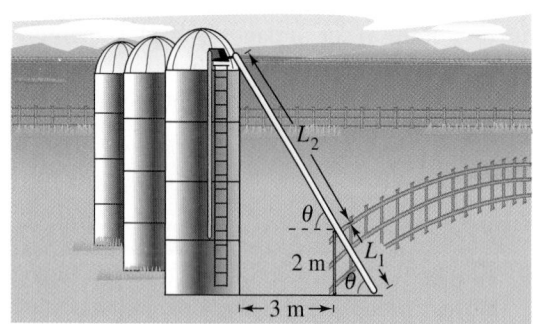

(a) Complete four rows of the table.

θ	L_1	L_2	$L_1 + L_2$
0.1	$\dfrac{2}{\sin 0.1}$	$\dfrac{3}{\cos 0.1}$	23.0
0.2	$\dfrac{2}{\sin 0.2}$	$\dfrac{3}{\cos 0.2}$	13.1

(b) Use the *table* feature of a graphing utility to generate additional rows of the table. Use the table to estimate the minimum length of the elevator.

(c) Write the length $L_1 + L_2$ as a function of θ.

(d) Use a graphing utility to graph the function. Use the graph to estimate the minimum length. How does your estimate compare with that in part (b)?

63. Numerical and Graphical Analysis   The cross sections of an irrigation canal are isosceles trapezoids, where the length of three of the sides is 8 feet (see figure). The objective is to find the angle θ that maximizes the area of the cross sections. [*Hint:* The area of a trapezoid is given by $(h/2)(b_1 + b_2)$.]

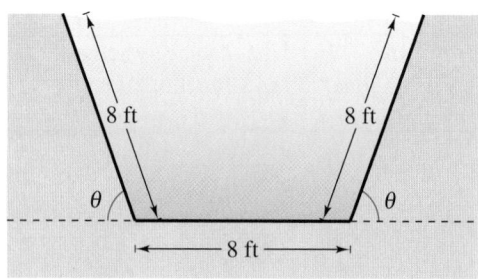

(a) Complete seven rows of the table.

Base 1	Base 2	Altitude	Area
8	$8 + 16 \cos 10°$	$8 \sin 10°$	22.1
8	$8 + 16 \cos 20°$	$8 \sin 20°$	42.5

(b) Use the *table* feature of a graphing utility to generate additional rows of the table. Use the table to estimate the maximum cross-sectional area.

(c) Write the area A as a function of θ.

(d) Use a graphing utility to graph the function. Use the graph to estimate the maximum cross-sectional area. How does your estimate compare with that in part (b)?

64. Data Analysis The times S of sunset (Greenwich Mean Time) at 40° north latitude on the 15th of each month are: 1(16:59), 2(17:35), 3(18:06), 4(18:38), 5(19:08), 6(19:30), 7(19:28), 8(18:57), 9(18:09), 10(17:21), 11(16:44), 12(16:36). The month is represented by t, with $t = 1$ corresponding to January. A model (in which minutes have been converted to the decimal parts of an hour) for this data is given by

$$S(t) = 18.09 + 1.41 \sin\left(\frac{\pi t}{6} + 4.60\right).$$

(a) Use a graphing utility to graph the data points and the model in the same viewing window.

(b) What is the period of the model? Is it what you expected? Explain.

(c) What is the amplitude of the model? What does it represent in the context of the problem? Explain.

65. Data Analysis The table shows the average sales S (in millions of dollars) of an outerwear manufacturer for each month t, where $t = 1$ represents January.

Month, t	Sales, S
1	13.46
2	11.15
3	8.00
4	4.85
5	2.54
6	1.70
7	2.54
8	4.85
9	8.00
10	11.15
11	13.46
12	14.30

(a) Create a scatter plot of the data.

(b) Find a trigonometric model that fits the data. Graph the model on your scatter plot. How well does the model fit?

(c) What is the period of the model? Do you think it is reasonable given the context? Explain your reasoning.

(d) Interpret the meaning of the model's amplitude in the context of the problem.

66. Writing Is it true that N 24° E means 24 degrees north of east? Explain.

Synthesis

True or False? **In Exercises 67 and 68, determine whether the statement is true or false. Justify your answer.**

67. In the right triangle shown below, $a = \dfrac{22.56}{\tan 41.9°}$.

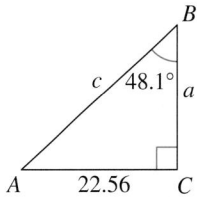

68. For the harmonic motion of a ball bobbing up and down on the end of a spring, one period can be described as the length of one coil of the spring.

Review

In Exercises 69–72, write the standard form of the equation of the line that has the specified characteristics.

69. $m = 4$, passes through $(-1, 2)$

70. $m = -\frac{1}{2}$, passes through $\left(\frac{1}{3}, 0\right)$

71. Passes through $(-2, 6)$ and $(3, 2)$

72. Passes through $\left(\frac{1}{4}, -\frac{2}{3}\right)$ and $\left(-\frac{1}{2}, \frac{1}{3}\right)$

In Exercises 73–80, find the domain of the function.

73. $f(x) = 3x + 8$ **74.** $f(x) = -x^2 - 1$

75. $g(x) = \sqrt[3]{x + 2}$ **76.** $g(x) = \sqrt{7 - x}$

77. $h(x) = \dfrac{2}{x^2 - 2x}$ **78.** $h(x) = \dfrac{x}{3x + 5}$

79. $f(x) = 4e^{-x}$ **80.** $f(x) = \ln(x - 2)$

In Exercises 81–84, solve the equation. Round your answer to three decimal places.

81. $e^{2x} = 54$ **82.** $\dfrac{300}{1 + e^{-x}} = 100$

83. $\ln(x^2 + 1) = 3.2$ **84.** $\log_8 x + \log_8(x - 1) = \frac{1}{3}$

5 Chapter Summary

What did you learn?

Section 5.1   Review Exercises
☐ Describe angles.   1, 2
☐ Use degree measure.   3–18
☐ Use radian measure.   19–26
☐ Convert between degree and radian measures.   27–34
☐ Use angles to model and solve real-life problems.   35–40

Section 5.2
☐ Evaluate trigonometric functions of acute angles.   41–44
☐ Use the fundamental trigonometric identities.   45, 46
☐ Use a calculator to evaluate trigonometric functions.   47–50
☐ Use trigonometric functions to model and solve real-life problems.   51, 52

Section 5.3
☐ Evaluate trigonometric functions of any angle.   53–62
☐ Use reference angles to evaluate trigonometric functions.   63–74
☐ Evaluate trigonometric functions of real numbers.   75–78

Section 5.4
☐ Sketch the graphs of basic sine and cosine functions.   79–82
☐ Use amplitude and period to help sketch the graphs of sine and cosine functions.   83–92
☐ Sketch translations of graphs of sine and cosine functions.   93–102
☐ Use sine and cosine functions to model real-life data.   103, 104

Section 5.5
☐ Sketch the graphs of tangent functions.   105–110
☐ Sketch the graphs of cotangent functions.   111–114
☐ Sketch the graphs of secant and cosecant functions.   115–124
☐ Sketch the graphs of damped trigonometric functions.   125–128

Section 5.6
☐ Evaluate inverse sine functions.   129, 130
☐ Evaluate other inverse trigonometric functions.   131–142
☐ Evaluate compositions of trigonometric functions.   143–146

Section 5.7
☐ Solve real-life problems involving right triangles.   147–151
☐ Solve real-life problems involving directional bearings.   152
☐ Solve real-life problems involving harmonic motion.   153, 154

5 Review Exercises

5.1 In Exercises 1 and 2, estimate the number of degrees in the angle.

1.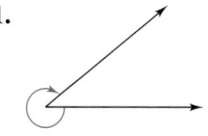

2.

In Exercises 3–6, (a) sketch the angle in standard position, (b) determine the quadrant in which the angle lies, and (c) list one positive and one negative coterminal angle.

3. $40°$ 4. $190°$

5. $-110°$ 6. $-405°$

In Exercises 7–10, find (if possible) the complement and supplement of the angle.

7. $5°$ 8. $94°$

9. $171°$ 10. $36°$

In Exercises 11–14, use the angle-conversion capabilities of a graphing utility to convert the angle measure to decimal degree form. Round your answer to three decimal places.

11. $135°\,16'\,45''$ 12. $-234°\,40''$

13. $5°\,22'\,53''$ 14. $280°\,8'\,50''$

In Exercises 15–18, use the angle-conversion capabilities of a graphing utility to convert the angle measure to D°M′S″ form.

15. $135.29°$ 16. $25.8°$

17. $-85.36°$ 18. $-327.93°$

In Exercises 19–22, (a) sketch the angle in standard position, (b) determine the quadrant in which the angle lies, and (c) list one positive and one negative coterminal angle.

19. $\dfrac{\pi}{16}$ 20. $\dfrac{40\pi}{47}$

21. $-\dfrac{9\pi}{15}$ 22. $-\dfrac{11\pi}{3}$

In Exercises 23–26, find (if possible) the complement and supplement of the angle.

23. $\dfrac{\pi}{8}$ 24. $\dfrac{\pi}{12}$

25. $\dfrac{3\pi}{10}$ 26. $\dfrac{2\pi}{21}$

In Exercises 27–30, convert the angle measure from degrees to radians. Round your answer to three decimal places.

27. $480°$ 28. $-16.5°$

29. $-33°$ 30. $84°$

In Exercises 31–34, convert the angle measure from radians to degrees. Round your answer to three decimal places.

31. $\dfrac{5\pi}{7}$ 32. $-\dfrac{3\pi}{5}$

33. -3.5 34. 1.55

35. Find the radian measure of the central angle of a circle with a radius of 12 feet that intercepts an arc of length 25 feet.

36. Find the radian measure of the central angle of a circle with a radius of 60 inches that intercepts an arc of length 245 inches.

37. Find the length of the arc on a circle with a radius of 20 meters intercepted by a central angle of $138°$.

38. Find the length of the arc on a circle with a radius of 15 centimeters intercepted by a central angle of $60°$.

39. *Music*   The radius of a compact disc is 6 centimeters. Find the linear speed of a point on the circumference of the disc if it is rotating at a speed of 500 revolutions per minute.

40. *Angular Speed*   A car is moving at a rate of 45 miles per hour, and the diameter of its wheels is about $2\frac{1}{3}$ feet.

   (a) Find the number of revolutions per minute the wheels are rotating.

   (b) Find the angular speed of the wheels in radians per minute.

5.2 In Exercises 41–44, find the exact values of the six trigonometric functions of the angle θ shown in the figure.

41.

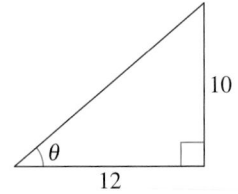

42.

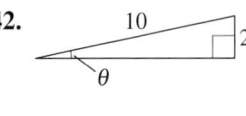

43.

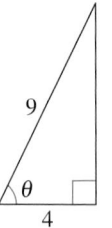

44.

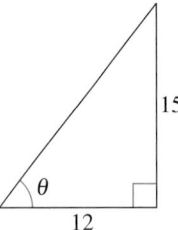

In Exercises 45 and 46, use trigonometric identities to transform one side of the equation into the other.

45. $(\csc \theta + \cot \theta)(\csc \theta - \cot \theta) = 1$

46. $\dfrac{\cot \theta + \tan \theta}{\cot \theta} = \sec^2 \theta$

In Exercises 47–50, use a calculator to evaluate each function. Round your answers to four decimal places.

47. (a) $\cos 84°$ (b) $\sin 6°$

48. (a) $\csc 52° \, 12'$ (b) $\sec 54° \, 7'$

49. (a) $\cos \dfrac{\pi}{4}$ (b) $\sec \dfrac{\pi}{4}$

50. (a) $\tan \dfrac{3\pi}{20}$ (b) $\cot \dfrac{3\pi}{20}$

51. **Width**   An engineer is trying to determine the width of a river. From point P, the engineer walks downstream 125 feet and sights to point Q. From this sighting, it is determined that $\theta = 62°$. How wide is the river?

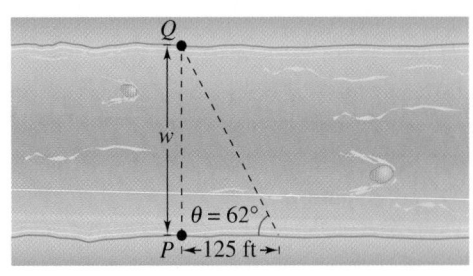

52. **Height**   An escalator 152 feet in length rises to a platform and makes a 30° angle with the ground.

(a) Draw a right triangle that gives a visual representation of the problem. Show the known quantities of the triangle and use a variable to indicate the height of the platform above the ground.

(b) Use a trigonometric function to write an equation involving the unknown quantity.

(c) Find the height of the platform above the ground.

5.3 In Exercises 53–58, the point is on the terminal side of an angle in standard position. Determine the exact values of the six trigonometric functions of the angle.

53. $(12, 16)$ 54. $(-4, -6)$

55. $(-7, 2)$ 56. $(3, -4)$

57. $\left(\dfrac{2}{3}, \dfrac{5}{2}\right)$ 58. $\left(-\dfrac{10}{3}, -\dfrac{2}{3}\right)$

In Exercises 59–62, find the values of the five trigonometric functions of θ satisfying the given condition.

59. $\sec \theta = \dfrac{6}{5}, \quad \tan \theta < 0$

60. $\tan \theta = -\dfrac{12}{5}, \quad \sin \theta > 0$

61. $\sin \theta = \dfrac{3}{8}, \quad \cos \theta < 0$

62. $\cos \theta = -\dfrac{2}{5}, \quad \sin \theta > 0$

In Exercises 63–66, find the reference angle θ′ and sketch θ and θ′ in standard position.

63. $\theta = 264°$ 64. $\theta = 635°$

65. $\theta = -\dfrac{6\pi}{5}$ 66. $\theta = \dfrac{17\pi}{3}$

In Exercises 67–74, evaluate the sine, cosine, and tangent of the angle without using a calculator.

67. $240°$ 68. $315°$

69. $-210°$ 70. $-315°$

71. $-\dfrac{9\pi}{4}$ 72. $-\dfrac{11\pi}{6}$

73. $\dfrac{\pi}{2}$ 74. $\dfrac{\pi}{3}$

In Exercises 75–78, find the point (x, y) on the unit circle that corresponds to the given real number t. Use the result to evaluate $\sin t$, $\cos t$, and $\tan t$.

75. $t = \dfrac{2\pi}{3}$

76. $t = \dfrac{7\pi}{4}$

77. $t = \dfrac{7\pi}{6}$

78. $t = \dfrac{3\pi}{4}$

5.4 In Exercises 79–82, sketch the graph of the function.

79. $f(x) = 3 \sin x$

80. $f(x) = 2 \cos x$

81. $f(x) = \frac{1}{4} \cos x$

82. $f(x) = \frac{7}{2} \sin x$

In Exercises 83–86, find the period and amplitude.

83.

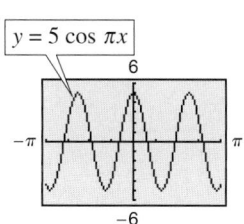

$y = 5 \cos \pi x$

84.

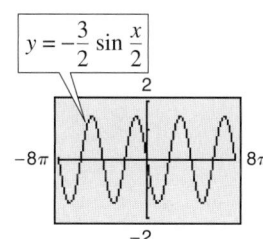

$y = -\dfrac{3}{2} \sin \dfrac{x}{2}$

85.

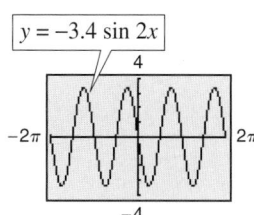

$y = -3.4 \sin 2x$

86.

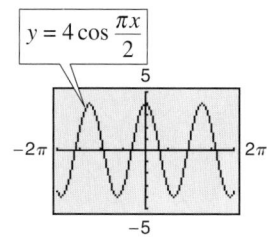

$y = 4 \cos \dfrac{\pi x}{2}$

In Exercises 87–98, sketch the graph of the function by hand. (Include two full periods.)

87. $f(x) = 3 \cos 2\pi x$

88. $f(x) = -2 \sin \pi x$

89. $f(x) = 5 \sin \dfrac{2x}{5}$

90. $f(x) = 8 \cos\left(-\dfrac{x}{4}\right)$

91. $f(x) = -\dfrac{5}{2} \cos \dfrac{x}{4}$

92. $f(x) = -\dfrac{1}{2} \sin \dfrac{\pi x}{4}$

93. $f(x) = \frac{5}{2} \sin(x - \pi)$

94. $f(x) = 3 \cos(x + \pi)$

95. $f(x) = 2 - \cos \dfrac{\pi x}{2}$

96. $f(x) = \dfrac{1}{2} \sin(\pi x) - 3$

97. $f(x) = -3 \sin\left(\dfrac{x}{2} - \dfrac{\pi}{4}\right)$

98. $f(x) = 4 - 2 \cos(4x + \pi)$

Graphical Reasoning In Exercises 99–102, find a, b, and c for the function $f(x) = a \cos(bx - c)$ such that the graph of f matches the graph shown.

99.

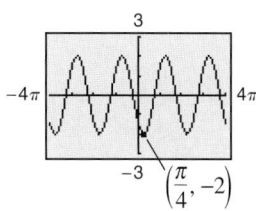

$\left(\dfrac{\pi}{4}, -2\right)$

100.

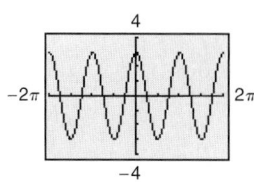

101.

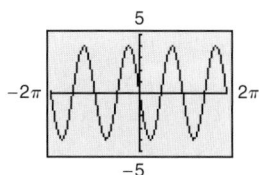

102.

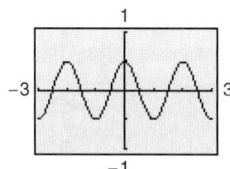

Sales In Exercises 103 and 104, use a graphing utility to graph the sales function over 1 year, where S is the sales (in thousands of units) and t is the time (in months), with $t = 1$ corresponding to January. Determine the months of maximum and minimum sales.

103. $S = 48.4 - 6.1 \cos \dfrac{\pi t}{6}$

104. $S = 56.25 + 9.50 \sin \dfrac{\pi t}{6}$

5.5 In Exercises 105–124, sketch the graph of the function. (Include two full periods.)

105. $f(x) = -\tan \dfrac{\pi x}{4}$

106. $f(x) = 4 \tan \pi x$

107. $f(x) = -\dfrac{1}{4} \tan \dfrac{\pi x}{2}$

108. $f(x) = \tan\left(x + \dfrac{\pi}{4}\right)$

109. $f(x) = \dfrac{1}{4} \tan\left(x - \dfrac{\pi}{2}\right)$

110. $f(x) = 2 + 2 \tan \dfrac{x}{3}$

111. $f(x) = 3 \cot \dfrac{x}{2}$

112. $f(x) = \dfrac{1}{2} \cot \dfrac{\pi x}{2}$

113. $f(x) = \dfrac{1}{2} \cot\left(x - \dfrac{\pi}{2}\right)$

114. $f(x) = 4 \cot\left(x + \dfrac{\pi}{4}\right)$

115. $f(x) = \frac{1}{4} \sec x$

116. $f(x) = \frac{1}{2} \csc x$

117. $f(x) = \frac{1}{4} \csc 2x$

118. $f(x) = \frac{1}{2} \sec 2\pi x$

119. $f(x) = \sec\left(x - \dfrac{\pi}{4}\right)$

120. $f(x) = \frac{1}{2} \csc(2x + \pi)$

121. $f(x) = 2 \sec(x - \pi)$

122. $f(x) = -2 \csc(x - \pi)$

123. $f(x) = \csc\left(3x - \dfrac{\pi}{2}\right)$

124. $f(x) = 3 \csc\left(2x + \dfrac{\pi}{4}\right)$

In Exercises 125–128, use a graphing utility to graph the function and the damping factor of the function in the same viewing window. Describe the behavior of the function as x increases without bound.

125. $f(x) = e^x \sin 2x$

126. $f(x) = 2x \cos x$

127. $f(x) = e^x \cos x$

128. $f(x) = x \sin \pi x$

5.6 In Exercises 129–132, find the value of each expression without using a calculator.

129. (a) $\arcsin 1$ (b) $\arcsin 4$

130. (a) $\arcsin \dfrac{\sqrt{2}}{2}$ (b) $\arcsin\left(-\dfrac{\sqrt{3}}{2}\right)$

131. (a) $\cos^{-1} \dfrac{\sqrt{2}}{2}$ (b) $\cos^{-1}\left(-\dfrac{\sqrt{3}}{2}\right)$

132. (a) $\tan^{-1}\left(-\sqrt{3}\right)$ (b) $\tan^{-1} 1$

In Exercises 133–140, use a calculator to approximate the value of the expression. Round your answer to two decimal places.

133. $\arccos 0.42$

134. $\arcsin 0.63$

135. $\sin^{-1}(-0.94)$

136. $\cos^{-1}(-0.12)$

137. $\arctan(-12)$

138. $\arctan 21$

139. $\tan^{-1} 0.81$

140. $\tan^{-1} 6.4$

In Exercises 141 and 142, use an inverse trigonometric function to write θ as a function of x.

141.

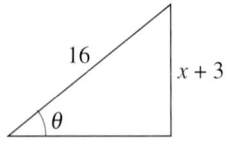

142.

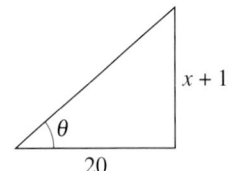

In Exercises 143–146, write an algebraic expression that is equivalent to the expression.

143. $\sec[\arcsin(x - 1)]$

144. $\tan\left(\arccos \dfrac{x}{2}\right)$

145. $\sin\left(\arccos \dfrac{x^2}{4 - x^2}\right)$

146. $\csc(\arcsin 10x)$

5.7

147. *Angle of Elevation*   The height of a radio transmission tower is 70 meters, and it casts a shadow of length 45 meters (see figure). Find the angle of elevation of the sun.

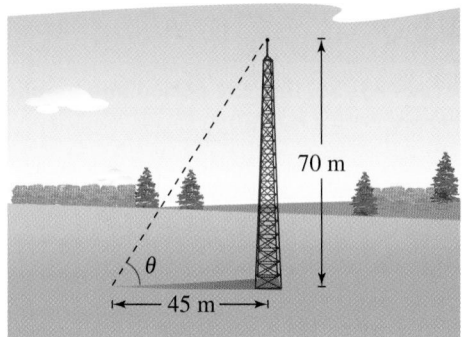

148. *Height*   An observer 2.5 miles from the launch pad of a space shuttle launch measures the angle of elevation to the base of the shuttle to be $25°$ soon after lift-off (see figure). How high is the shuttle at that instant? (Assume the shuttle is still moving vertically.)

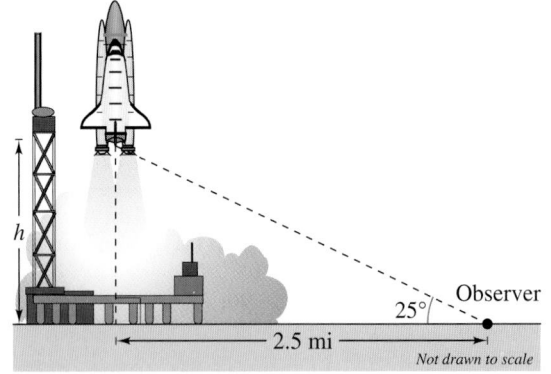

149. *Mountain Descent*   A road sign at the top of a mountain indicates that for the next 4 miles the grade is 12%. Find the angle of the grade and the change in elevation for a car descending the mountain.

150. Railroad Grade A train travels 3.5 kilometers on a straight track with a grade of 1° 10′. What is the vertical rise of the train in that distance?

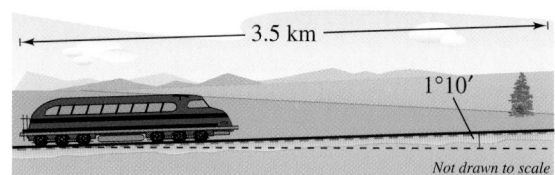

3.5 km

1°10′

Not drawn to scale

151. Distance A passenger in an airplane flying at an altitude of 37,000 feet sees two towns directly to the west of the airplane. The angles of depression to the towns are 32° and 76° (see figure). How far apart are the towns?

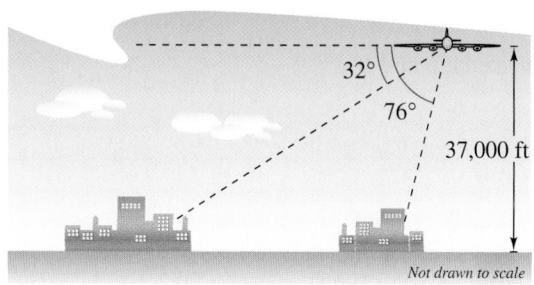

32°

76°

37,000 ft

Not drawn to scale

152. Distance From city A to city B, a plane flies 650 miles at a bearing of 48°. From city B to city C, the plane flies 810 miles at a bearing of 115°. Find the distance from A to C and the bearing from A to C.

153. Wave Motion A buoy oscillates in simple harmonic motion as waves go past. At a given time it is noted that the buoy moves a total of 6 feet from its low point to its high point (see figure), and that it returns to its high point every 15 seconds. Write an equation that describes the motion of the buoy if it is at its high point at $t = 0$.

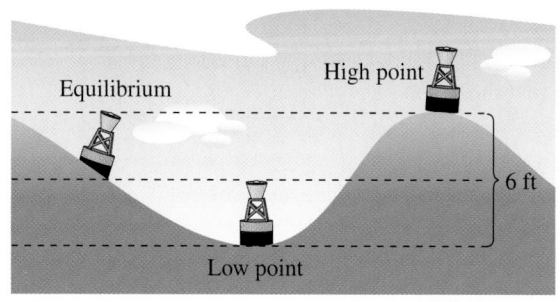

High point

Equilibrium

6 ft

Low point

154. Wave Motion Your fishing bobber oscillates in simple harmonic motion from the waves in the lake where you fish. Your bobber moves a total of 1.5 inches from its high point to its low point and returns to its high point every 3 seconds. Write an equation modeling the motion of your bobber if it is at its high point at $t = 0$.

Synthesis

True or False? **In Exercises 155 and 156, determine whether the statement is true or false. Justify your answer.**

155. $y = \sin \theta$ is not a function because $\sin 30° = \sin 150°$.

156. The tangent function is often useful for modeling simple harmonic motion.

157. Writing Consider an angle in standard position with $r = 12$ centimeters, as shown in the figure. Write a short paragraph describing the changes in the values of x, y, $\sin \theta$, $\cos \theta$, and $\tan \theta$ as θ increases continually from 0° to 90°.

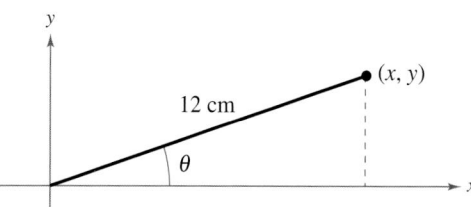

y

12 cm

(x, y)

θ

x

158. Writing Describe the behavior of $f(x) = \sec x$ at the zeros of $g(x) = \cos x$. Explain your reasoning.

159. Approximation In calculus it can be shown that the arctangent function can be approximated by the polynomial

$$\arctan x \approx x - \frac{x^3}{3} + \frac{x^5}{5} - \frac{x^7}{7}$$

where x is in radians.

(a) Use a graphing utility to graph the arctangent function and its polynomial approximation in the same viewing window. How do the graphs compare?

(b) Study the pattern in the polynomial approximation of the arctangent function and guess the next term. Then repeat part (a). How does the accuracy of the approximation change when additional terms are added?

5 Chapter Test

Take this test as you would take a test in class. After you are finished, check your work against the answers given in the back of the book.

1. Consider an angle that measures $\dfrac{5\pi}{4}$ radians.

   (a) Sketch the angle in standard position.

   (b) Determine two coterminal angles (one positive and one negative).

   (c) Convert the angle to degree measure.

2. A truck is moving at a rate of 90 kilometers per hour, and the diameter of its wheels is 1 meter. Find the angular speed of the wheels in radians per minute.

3. Find the exact values of the six trigonometric functions of the angle θ shown in the figure.

4. Given that $\tan \theta = \frac{6}{5}$, find the other five trigonometric functions of θ.

5. Determine the reference angle θ' of the angle $\theta = 255°$ and sketch θ and θ' in standard position.

6. Determine the quadrant in which θ lies if $\sec \theta < 0$ and $\tan \theta > 0$.

7. Find two exact values of θ in degrees $(0 \le \theta < 360°)$ if $\cos \theta = -\sqrt{3}/2$.

8. Use a calculator to approximate two values of θ in radians $(0 \le \theta < 2\pi)$ if $\csc \theta = 1.030$. Round your answer to two decimal places.

9. Find the five remaining trigonometric functions of θ, given that $\cos \theta = -\frac{3}{5}$ and $\sin \theta > 0$.

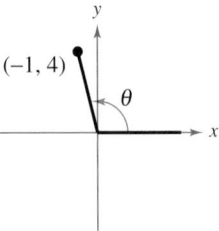

Figure for 3

In Exercises 10–15, sketch the graph of the function. (Include two full periods.)

10. $g(x) = -2 \sin\left(x - \dfrac{\pi}{4}\right)$

11. $f(\alpha) = \dfrac{1}{2} \tan 2\alpha$

12. $f(x) = \frac{1}{2} \sec(x - \pi)$

13. $f(x) = 2 \cos(\pi - 2x) + 3$

14. $f(x) = 2 \csc\left(x + \dfrac{\pi}{2}\right)$

15. $f(x) = \dfrac{1}{4} \cot\left(x - \dfrac{\pi}{2}\right)$

In Exercises 16 and 17, use a graphing utility to graph the function. If the function is periodic, find its period.

16. $y = \sin 2\pi x + 2 \cos \pi x$

17. $y = 6e^{-0.12t} \cos(0.25t), \quad 0 \le t \le 32$

18. Find a, b, and c for the function $f(x) = a \sin(bx + c)$ such that the graph of f matches the graph at the right.

19. Find the exact value of $\tan\left(\arccos \frac{2}{3}\right)$ without using a calculator.

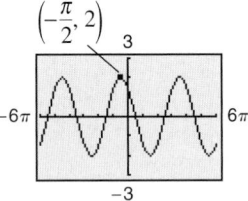

Figure for 18

In Exercises 20–22, use a graphing utility to graph the function.

20. $f(x) = 2 \arcsin\left(\dfrac{1}{2}x\right)$

21. $f(x) = 2 \arccos x$

22. $f(x) = \arctan \dfrac{x}{2}$

23. A plane is 160 miles north and 110 miles east of an airport. What bearing should be taken to fly directly to the airport?

Trigonometry can be used to model the flight of a baseball. Given the angle at which the ball leaves the bat and the initial velocity, you can determine the distance the ball will travel.

Al Bello/Getty Images

6 Analytic Trigonometry

What You Should Learn

6.1 Using Fundamental Identities

6.2 Verifying Trigonometric Identities

6.3 Solving Trigonometric Equations

6.4 Sum and Difference Formulas

6.5 Multiple-Angle and Product-to-Sum Formulas

In this chapter, you will learn how to:

■ Use fundamental trigonometric identities to evaluate trigonometric functions and simplify trigonometric expressions.

■ Verify trigonometric identities.

■ Use standard algebraic techniques and inverse trigonometric functions to solve trigonometric equations.

■ Use sum and difference formulas, multiple-angle formulas, power-reducing formulas, half-angle formulas, and product-to-sum formulas to rewrite and evaluate trigonometric functions.

6.1 Using Fundamental Identities

Introduction

In Chapter 5, you studied the basic definitions, properties, graphs, and applications of the individual trigonometric functions. In this chapter, you will learn how to use the fundamental identities to do the following.

1. Evaluate trigonometric functions.
2. Simplify trigonometric expressions.
3. Develop additional trigonometric identities.
4. Solve trigonometric equations.

Fundamental Trigonometric Identities

Reciprocal Identities

$$\sin u = \frac{1}{\csc u} \qquad \cos u = \frac{1}{\sec u} \qquad \tan u = \frac{1}{\cot u}$$

$$\csc u = \frac{1}{\sin u} \qquad \sec u = \frac{1}{\cos u} \qquad \cot u = \frac{1}{\tan u}$$

Quotient Identities

$$\tan u = \frac{\sin u}{\cos u} \qquad \cot u = \frac{\cos u}{\sin u}$$

Pythagorean Identities

$$\sin^2 u + \cos^2 u = 1 \qquad 1 + \tan^2 u = \sec^2 u \qquad 1 + \cot^2 u = \csc^2 u$$

Cofunction Identities

$$\sin\left(\frac{\pi}{2} - u\right) = \cos u \qquad \cos\left(\frac{\pi}{2} - u\right) = \sin u$$

$$\tan\left(\frac{\pi}{2} - u\right) = \cot u \qquad \cot\left(\frac{\pi}{2} - u\right) = \tan u$$

$$\sec\left(\frac{\pi}{2} - u\right) = \csc u \qquad \csc\left(\frac{\pi}{2} - u\right) = \sec u$$

Even/Odd Identities

$$\sin(-u) = -\sin u \qquad \cos(-u) = \cos u \qquad \tan(-u) = -\tan u$$

$$\csc(-u) = -\csc u \qquad \sec(-u) = \sec u \qquad \cot(-u) = -\cot u$$

Using the Fundamental Identities

One common use of trigonometric identities is to use given values of trigonometric functions to evaluate other trigonometric functions.

What you should learn

● Recognize and write the fundamental trigonometric identities.
● Use the fundamental trigonometric identities to evaluate trigonometric functions, simplify trigonometric expressions, and rewrite trigonometric expressions.

Why you should learn it

The fundamental trigonometric identities can be used to simplify trigonometric expressions. For instance, Exercise 97 on page 487 shows you how trigonometric identities can be used to simplify an expression for the rate of change of a function, a concept used in calculus.

STUDY TIP

Pythagorean identities are sometimes used in radical form such as

$$\sin u = \pm\sqrt{1 - \cos^2 u}$$

or

$$\tan u = \pm\sqrt{\sec^2 u - 1}$$

where the sign depends on the choice of u.

Example 1   Using Identities to Evaluate a Function

Use the values $\sec u = -\frac{3}{2}$ and $\tan u > 0$ to find the values of all six trigonometric functions.

Solution

Using a reciprocal identity, you have

$$\cos u = \frac{1}{\sec u} = \frac{1}{-3/2} = -\frac{2}{3}.$$

Using a Pythagorean identity, you have

$$\sin^2 u = 1 - \cos^2 u \qquad \text{Pythagorean identity}$$

$$= 1 - \left(-\frac{2}{3}\right)^2 \qquad \text{Substitute } -\frac{2}{3} \text{ for } \cos u.$$

$$= 1 - \frac{4}{9} = \frac{5}{9}. \qquad \text{Simplify.}$$

Because $\sec u < 0$ and $\tan u > 0$, it follows that u lies in Quadrant III. Moreover, because $\sin u$ is negative when u is in Quadrant III, you can choose the negative root and obtain $\sin u = -\sqrt{5}/3$. Now, knowing the values of the sine and cosine, you can find the values of all six trigonometric functions.

$$\sin u = -\frac{\sqrt{5}}{3} \qquad\qquad \csc u = \frac{1}{\sin u} = -\frac{3}{\sqrt{5}} = -\frac{3\sqrt{5}}{5}$$

$$\cos u = -\frac{2}{3} \qquad\qquad \sec u = \frac{1}{\cos u} = -\frac{3}{2}$$

$$\tan u = \frac{\sin u}{\cos u} = \frac{-\sqrt{5}/3}{-2/3} = \frac{\sqrt{5}}{2} \qquad \cot u = \frac{1}{\tan u} = \frac{2}{\sqrt{5}} = \frac{2\sqrt{5}}{5}$$

✓ *Checkpoint* Now try Exercise 11.

Example 2   Simplifying a Trigonometric Expression

Simplify $\sin x \cos^2 x - \sin x$.

Solution

First factor out a common monomial factor and then use a fundamental identity.

$$\sin x \cos^2 x - \sin x = \sin x(\cos^2 x - 1) \qquad \text{Factor out monomial factor.}$$

$$= -\sin x(1 - \cos^2 x) \qquad \text{Distributive Property}$$

$$= -\sin x(\sin^2 x) \qquad \text{Pythagorean identity}$$

$$= -\sin^3 x \qquad \text{Multiply.}$$

✓ *Checkpoint* Now try Exercise 29.

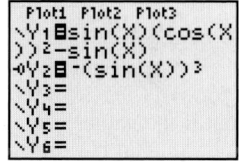
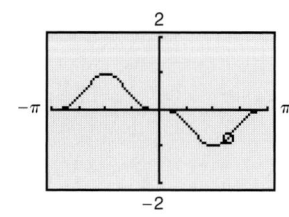

Example 3   Verifying a Trigonometric Identity

Determine whether the equation appears to be an identity.

$$\cos 3x \stackrel{?}{=} 4\cos^3 x - 3\cos x$$

Numerical Solution

Use the *table* feature of a graphing utility set in *radian* mode to create a table that shows the values of $y_1 = \cos 3x$ and $y_2 = 4\cos^3 x - 3\cos x$ for different values of x, as shown in Figure 6.1. The values of y_1 and y_2 appear to be identical, so $\cos 3x = 4\cos^3 x - 3\cos x$ appears to be an identity.

X	Y1	Y2
-.5	.07074	.07074
-.25	.73169	.73169
0	1	1
.25	.73169	.73169
.5	.07074	.07074
.75	-.6282	-.6282
1	-.99	-.99

X=1

Figure 6.1

Note that if the values of y_1 and y_2 were not identical, then the equation would not be an identity.

✓ *Checkpoint* Now try Exercise 39.

Graphical Solution

Use a graphing utility set in *radian* mode to graph $y_1 = \cos 3x$ and $y_2 = 4\cos^3 x - 3\cos x$ in the same viewing window, as shown in Figure 6.2. (Select the *line* style for y_1 and the *path* style for y_2.) Because the graphs appear to coincide, $\cos 3x = 4\cos^3 x - 3\cos x$ appears to be an identity.

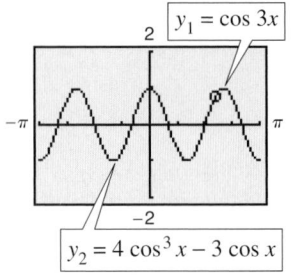

$y_1 = \cos 3x$

$y_2 = 4\cos^3 x - 3\cos x$

Figure 6.2

Note that if the graphs of y_1 and y_2 did not coincide, then the equation would not be an identity.

Example 4   Verifying a Trigonometric Identity

Verify the identity $\dfrac{\sin\theta}{1 + \cos\theta} + \dfrac{\cos\theta}{\sin\theta} = \csc\theta.$

Algebraic Solution

$$\frac{\sin\theta}{1 + \cos\theta} + \frac{\cos\theta}{\sin\theta} = \frac{(\sin\theta)(\sin\theta) + (\cos\theta)(1 + \cos\theta)}{(1 + \cos\theta)(\sin\theta)}$$

$$= \frac{\sin^2\theta + \cos^2\theta + \cos\theta}{(1 + \cos\theta)(\sin\theta)} \qquad \text{Multiply.}$$

$$= \frac{1 + \cos\theta}{(1 + \cos\theta)(\sin\theta)} \qquad \text{Pythagorean identity}$$

$$= \csc\theta \qquad \begin{array}{l}\text{Divide out common factor}\\ \text{and use reciprocal identity.}\end{array}$$

Notice how the identity is verified. You start with the left side of the equation (the more complicated side) and use the fundamental trigonometric identities to simplify it until you obtain the right side.

✓ *Checkpoint* Now try Exercise 45.

Graphical Solution

Use a graphing utility set in *radian* and *dot* modes to graph y_1 and y_2 in the same viewing window, as shown in Figure 6.3. Because the graphs appear to coincide, this equation appears to be an identity.

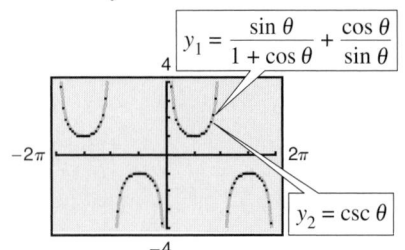

$y_1 = \dfrac{\sin\theta}{1 + \cos\theta} + \dfrac{\cos\theta}{\sin\theta}$

$y_2 = \csc\theta$

Figure 6.3

When factoring trigonometric expressions, it is helpful to find a polynomial form that fits the expression, as shown in Example 5.

Example 5   Factoring Trigonometric Expressions

Factor (a) $\sec^2 \theta - 1$ and (b) $4 \tan^2 \theta + \tan \theta - 3$.

Solution

a. Here the expression is a difference of two squares, which factors as

$$\sec^2 \theta - 1 = (\sec \theta - 1)(\sec \theta + 1).$$

b. This expression has the polynomial form $ax^2 + bx + c$ and it factors as

$$4 \tan^2 \theta + \tan \theta - 3 = (4 \tan \theta - 3)(\tan \theta + 1).$$

✔ *Checkpoint* Now try Exercise 51.

On occasion, factoring or simplifying can best be done by first rewriting the expression in terms of just *one* trigonometric function or in terms of *sine or cosine alone*. These strategies are illustrated in Examples 6 and 7.

Example 6   Factoring a Trigonometric Expression

Factor $\csc^2 x - \cot x - 3$.

Solution

Use the identity $\csc^2 x = 1 + \cot^2 x$ to rewrite the expression in terms of the cotangent.

$$
\begin{aligned}
\csc^2 x - \cot x - 3 &= (1 + \cot^2 x) - \cot x - 3 &&\text{Pythagorean identity} \\
&= \cot^2 x - \cot x - 2 &&\text{Combine like terms.} \\
&= (\cot x - 2)(\cot x + 1) &&\text{Factor.}
\end{aligned}
$$

✔ *Checkpoint* Now try Exercise 57.

Example 7   Simplifying a Trigonometric Expression

Simplify $\sin t + \cot t \cos t$.

Solution

Begin by rewriting $\cot t$ in terms of sine and cosine.

$$
\begin{aligned}
\sin t + \cot t \cos t &= \sin t + \left(\frac{\cos t}{\sin t}\right)\cos t &&\text{Quotient identity} \\
&= \frac{\sin^2 t + \cos^2 t}{\sin t} &&\text{Add fractions.} \\
&= \frac{1}{\sin t} = \csc t &&\text{Pythagorean identity and reciprocal identity}
\end{aligned}
$$

✔ *Checkpoint* Now try Exercise 67.

The last two examples in this section involve techniques for rewriting expressions into forms that are used in calculus.

Example 8   Rewriting a Trigonometric Expression

Rewrite $\dfrac{1}{1 + \sin x}$ so that it is *not* in fractional form.

Solution

From the Pythagorean identity $\cos^2 x = 1 - \sin^2 x = (1 - \sin x)(1 + \sin x)$, you can see that multiplying both the numerator and the denominator by $(1 - \sin x)$ will produce a monomial denominator.

$$\frac{1}{1 + \sin x} = \frac{1}{1 + \sin x} \cdot \frac{1 - \sin x}{1 - \sin x} \qquad \text{Multiply numerator and denominator by } (1 - \sin x).$$

$$= \frac{1 - \sin x}{1 - \sin^2 x} \qquad \text{Multiply.}$$

$$= \frac{1 - \sin x}{\cos^2 x} \qquad \text{Pythagorean identity}$$

$$= \frac{1}{\cos^2 x} - \frac{\sin x}{\cos^2 x} \qquad \text{Write as separate fractions.}$$

$$= \frac{1}{\cos^2 x} - \frac{\sin x}{\cos x} \cdot \frac{1}{\cos x} \qquad \text{Write as separate fractions.}$$

$$= \sec^2 x - \tan x \sec x \qquad \text{Reciprocal and quotient identities}$$

✓ *Checkpoint* Now try Exercise 69.

Example 9   Trigonometric Substitution

Use the substitution $x = 2 \tan \theta$, $0 < \theta < \pi/2$, to write $\sqrt{4 + x^2}$ as a trigonometric function of θ.

Solution

Begin by letting $x = 2 \tan \theta$. Then you can obtain

$$\sqrt{4 + x^2} = \sqrt{4 + (2 \tan \theta)^2} \qquad \text{Substitute } 2 \tan \theta \text{ for } x.$$

$$= \sqrt{4(1 + \tan^2 \theta)} \qquad \text{Distributive Property}$$

$$= \sqrt{4 \sec^2 \theta} \qquad \text{Pythagorean identity}$$

$$= 2 \sec \theta. \qquad \sec \theta > 0 \text{ for } 0 < \theta < \tfrac{\pi}{2}$$

✓ *Checkpoint* Now try Exercise 81.

Figure 6.4 shows the right triangle illustration of the substitution in Example 9. For $0 < \theta < \pi/2$, you have

$$\text{opp} = x, \ \text{adj} = 2, \text{ and hyp} = \sqrt{4 + x^2}.$$

Try using these expressions to obtain the result shown in Example 9.

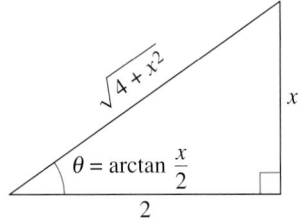

Figure 6.4

6.1   Exercises

Vocabulary Check

Fill in the blank to complete the trigonometric identity.

1. $\dfrac{1}{\cos u} = $ _____

2. $\dfrac{1}{\cot u} = $ _____

3. $\dfrac{\cos u}{\sin u} = $ _____

4. $\dfrac{1}{\sin u} = $ _____

5. $1 + $ _____ $= \csc^2 u$

6. $1 + \tan^2 u = $ _____

7. $\cos\left(\dfrac{\pi}{2} - u\right) = $ _____

8. $\sec\left(\dfrac{\pi}{2} - u\right) = $ _____

9. $\sin(-u) = $ _____

10. $\cos(-u) = $ _____

In Exercises 1–14, use the given values to evaluate (if possible) all six trigonometric functions.

1. $\sin x = \dfrac{\sqrt{3}}{2}, \quad \cos x = \dfrac{1}{2}$

2. $\csc \theta = 2, \quad \tan \theta = \dfrac{\sqrt{3}}{3}$

3. $\sec \theta = \sqrt{2}, \quad \sin \theta = -\dfrac{\sqrt{2}}{2}$

4. $\tan x = \dfrac{\sqrt{3}}{3}, \quad \cos x = -\dfrac{\sqrt{3}}{2}$

5. $\tan x = \dfrac{7}{24}, \quad \sec x = -\dfrac{25}{24}$

6. $\cot \phi = -5, \quad \sin \phi = \dfrac{\sqrt{26}}{26}$

7. $\sec \phi = -\dfrac{13}{12}, \quad \sin \phi = \dfrac{5}{13}$

8. $\cos\left(\dfrac{\pi}{2} - x\right) = \dfrac{3}{5}, \quad \cos x = \dfrac{4}{5}$

9. $\sin(-x) = -\dfrac{2}{3}, \quad \tan x = -\dfrac{2\sqrt{5}}{5}$

10. $\csc(-x) = -5, \quad \cos x = \dfrac{\sqrt{24}}{5}$

11. $\tan \theta = 2, \quad \sin \theta < 0$

12. $\sec \theta = -5, \quad \tan \theta < 0$

13. $\csc \theta$ is undefined, $\quad \cos \theta < 0$

14. $\tan \theta$ is undefined, $\quad \sin \theta > 0$

In Exercises 15–20, match the trigonometric expression with one of the following.

(a) $\sec x$ **(b)** -1 **(c)** $\cot x$

(d) 1 **(e)** $-\tan x$ **(f)** $\sin x$

15. $\sec x \cos x$

16. $\tan x \csc x$

17. $\cot^2 x - \csc^2 x$

18. $(1 - \cos^2 x)(\csc x)$

19. $\dfrac{\sin(-x)}{\cos(-x)}$

20. $\dfrac{\sin[(\pi/2) - x]}{\cos[(\pi/2) - x]}$

In Exercises 21–26, match the trigonometric expression with one of the following.

(a) $\csc x$ **(b)** $\tan x$ **(c)** $\sin^2 x$

(d) $\sin x \tan x$ **(e)** $\sec^2 x$ **(f)** $\sec^2 x + \tan^2 x$

21. $\sin x \sec x$

22. $\cos^2 x(\sec^2 x - 1)$

23. $\sec^4 x - \tan^4 x$

24. $\cot x \sec x$

25. $\dfrac{\sec^2 x - 1}{\sin^2 x}$

26. $\dfrac{\cos^2[(\pi/2) - x]}{\cos x}$

In Exercises 27–38, use the fundamental identities to simplify the expression. Use the *table* feature of a graphing utility to check your result numerically.

27. $\cot x \sin x$

28. $\cos \beta \tan \beta$

29. $\sin \phi(\csc \phi - \sin \phi)$

30. $\sec^2 x(1 - \sin^2 x)$

31. $\dfrac{\cot x}{\csc x}$

32. $\dfrac{\sec \theta}{\csc \theta}$

33. $\sec \alpha \cdot \dfrac{\sin \alpha}{\tan \alpha}$

34. $\dfrac{\tan^2 \theta}{\sec^2 \theta}$

35. $\sin\left(\dfrac{\pi}{2} - x\right)\csc x$

36. $\cot\left(\dfrac{\pi}{2} - x\right)\cos x$

37. $\dfrac{\cos^2 y}{1 - \sin y}$

38. $\dfrac{1}{\tan^2 x + 1}$

In Exercises 39–44, verify the identity algebraically. Use the *table* feature of a graphing utility to check your result numerically.

39. $\sin \theta + \cos \theta \cot \theta = \csc \theta$

40. $(\sec \theta - \tan \theta)(\csc \theta + 1) = \cot \theta$

41. $\dfrac{\cos \theta}{1 - \sin \theta} = \sec \theta + \tan \theta$

42. $\dfrac{1 + \csc \theta}{\cot \theta + \cos \theta} = \sec \theta$

43. $\dfrac{1 + \cos \theta}{\sin \theta} + \dfrac{\sin \theta}{1 + \cos \theta} = 2 \csc \theta$

44. $\dfrac{\sin \theta + \cos \theta}{\sin \theta} - \dfrac{\cos \theta - \sin \theta}{\cos \theta} = \sec \theta \csc \theta$

In Exercises 45–50, verify the identity algebraically. Use a graphing utility to check your result graphically.

45. $\csc \theta \tan \theta = \sec \theta$

46. $\cos \theta \sec \theta - \cos^2 \theta = \sin^2 \theta$

47. $1 - \dfrac{\sin^2 \theta}{1 - \cos \theta} = -\cos \theta$

48. $\dfrac{\tan \theta}{1 + \sec \theta} + \dfrac{1 + \sec \theta}{\tan \theta} = 2 \csc \theta$

49. $\dfrac{\cot(-\theta)}{\csc \theta} = -\cos \theta$

50. $\dfrac{\csc\left(\dfrac{\pi}{2} - \theta\right)}{\tan(-\theta)} = \csc \theta$

In Exercises 51–60, factor the expression and use the fundamental identities to simplify. Use a graphing utility to check your result graphically.

51. $\cot^2 x - \cot^2 x \cos^2 x$

52. $\sec^2 x \tan^2 x + \sec^2 x$

53. $\dfrac{\cos^2 x - 4}{\cos x - 2}$

54. $\dfrac{\csc^2 x - 1}{\csc x - 1}$

55. $\tan^4 x + 2 \tan^2 x + 1$

56. $1 - 2 \sin^2 x + \sin^4 x$

57. $\sin^4 x - \cos^4 x$

58. $\sec^4 x - \tan^4 x$

59. $\csc^3 x - \csc^2 x - \csc x + 1$

60. $\sec^3 x - \sec^2 x - \sec x + 1$

In Exercises 61–64, perform the multiplication and use the fundamental identities to simplify.

61. $(\sin x + \cos x)^2$

62. $(\cot x + \csc x)(\cot x - \csc x)$

63. $(\sec x + 1)(\sec x - 1)$

64. $(3 - 3 \sin x)(3 + 3 \sin x)$

In Exercises 65–68, perform the addition or subtraction and use the fundamental identities to simplify.

65. $\dfrac{1}{1 + \cos x} + \dfrac{1}{1 - \cos x}$

66. $\dfrac{1}{\sec x + 1} - \dfrac{1}{\sec x - 1}$

67. $\tan x - \dfrac{\sec^2 x}{\tan x}$

68. $\dfrac{\cos x}{1 + \sin x} + \dfrac{1 + \sin x}{\cos x}$

In Exercises 69–72, rewrite the expression so that it is *not* in fractional form.

69. $\dfrac{\sin^2 y}{1 - \cos y}$

70. $\dfrac{5}{\tan x + \sec x}$

71. $\dfrac{3}{\sec x - \tan x}$

72. $\dfrac{\tan^2 x}{\csc x + 1}$

Numerical and Graphical Analysis   **In Exercises 73–76, use a graphing utility to complete the table and graph the functions in the same viewing window. Make a conjecture about y_1 and y_2.**

x	0.2	0.4	0.6	0.8	1.0	1.2	1.4
y_1							
y_2							

73. $y_1 = \cos\left(\dfrac{\pi}{2} - x\right)$, $y_2 = \sin x$

74. $y_1 = \cos x + \sin x \tan x$, $y_2 = \sec x$

75. $y_1 = \dfrac{\cos x}{1 - \sin x}$, $y_2 = \dfrac{1 + \sin x}{\cos x}$

76. $y_1 = \sec^4 x - \sec^2 x$, $y_2 = \tan^2 x + \tan^4 x$

In Exercises 77–80, use a graphing utility to determine which of the six trigonometric functions is equal to the expression.

77. $\cos x \cot x + \sin x$ **78.** $\sin x(\cot x + \tan x)$

79. $\sec x - \dfrac{\cos x}{1 + \sin x}$

80. $\dfrac{1}{2}\left(\dfrac{1 + \sin \theta}{\cos \theta} + \dfrac{\cos \theta}{1 + \sin \theta}\right)$

In Exercises 81–84, use the trigonometric substitution to write the algebraic expression as a trigonometric function of θ, where $0 < \theta < \pi/2$.

81. $\sqrt{25 - x^2}$, $x = 5 \sin \theta$
82. $\sqrt{64 - 16x^2}$, $x = 2 \cos \theta$
83. $\sqrt{x^2 - 9}$, $x = 3 \sec \theta$
84. $\sqrt{x^2 + 100}$, $x = 10 \tan \theta$

In Exercises 85–88, use a graphing utility to solve the equation for θ, where $0 \le \theta < 2\pi$.

85. $\sin \theta = \sqrt{1 - \cos^2 \theta}$
86. $\cos \theta = -\sqrt{1 - \sin^2 \theta}$
87. $\sec \theta = \sqrt{1 + \tan^2 \theta}$
88. $\tan \theta = \sqrt{\sec^2 \theta - 1}$

In Exercises 89–92, rewrite the expression as a single logarithm and simplify the result.

89. $\ln|\cos \theta| - \ln|\sin \theta|$ **90.** $\ln|\csc \theta| + \ln|\tan \theta|$
91. $\ln(1 + \sin x) - \ln|\sec x|$
92. $\ln|\cot t| + \ln(1 + \tan^2 t)$

In Exercises 93–96, use the *table* feature of a graphing utility to demonstrate the identity for each value of θ.

93. $\csc^2 \theta - \cot^2 \theta = 1$, (a) $\theta = 132°$ (b) $\theta = \dfrac{2\pi}{7}$

94. $\tan^2 \theta + 1 = \sec^2 \theta$, (a) $\theta = 346°$ (b) $\theta = 3.1$

95. $\cos\left(\dfrac{\pi}{2} - \theta\right) = \sin \theta$, (a) $\theta = 80°$ (b) $\theta = 0.8$

96. $\sin(-\theta) = -\sin \theta$, (a) $\theta = 250°$ (b) $\theta = \frac{1}{2}$

97. *Rate of Change*   The rate of change of the function $f(x) = -\csc x - \sin x$ is given by the expression $\csc x \cot x - \cos x$. Show that this expression can also be written as $\cos x \cot^2 x$.

98. *Rate of Change*   The rate of change of the function $f(x) = \sec x + \cos x$ is given by the expression $\sec x \tan x - \sin x$. Show that this expression can also be written as $\sin x \tan^2 x$.

Synthesis

True or False? **In Exercises 99 and 100, determine whether the statement is true or false. Justify your answer.**

99. $\sin \theta \csc \theta = 1$ **100.** $\cos \theta \sec \phi = 1$

In Exercises 101–104, fill in the blanks. (*Note:* $x \to c^+$ indicates that x approaches c from the right, and $x \to c^-$ indicates that x approaches c from the left.)

101. As $x \to \dfrac{\pi}{2}^-$, $\sin x \to$ ____ and $\csc x \to$ ____ .

102. As $x \to 0^+$, $\cos x \to$ ____ and $\sec x \to$ ____ .

103. As $x \to \dfrac{\pi}{2}^-$, $\tan x \to$ ____ and $\cot x \to$ ____ .

104. As $x \to \pi^+$, $\sin x \to$ ____ and $\csc x \to$ ____ .

105. Write each of the other trigonometric functions of θ in terms of $\sin \theta$.

106. Write each of the other trigonometric functions of θ in terms of $\cos \theta$.

107. Use the definitions of sine and cosine to derive the Pythagorean identity $\sin^2 \theta + \cos^2 \theta = 1$.

108. ***Writing***   Use the Pythagorean identity $\sin^2 \theta + \cos^2 \theta = 1$ to derive the other Pythagorean identities $1 + \tan^2 \theta = \sec^2 \theta$ and $1 + \cot^2 \theta = \csc^2 \theta$. Discuss how to remember these identities and other fundamental identities.

Review

In Exercises 109–112, sketch the graph of the function. (Include two full periods.)

109. $f(x) = \dfrac{1}{2} \sin \pi x$

110. $f(x) = -2 \tan \dfrac{\pi x}{2}$

111. $f(x) = \dfrac{1}{2} \cot\left(x + \dfrac{\pi}{4}\right)$

112. $f(x) = \dfrac{3}{2} \cos(x - \pi) + 3$

6.2 Verifying Trigonometric Identities

Introduction

In this section, you will study techniques for verifying trigonometric identities. In the next section, you will study techniques for solving trigonometric equations. The key to both verifying identities *and* solving equations is your ability to use the fundamental identities and the rules of algebra to rewrite trigonometric expressions.

Remember that a *conditional equation* is an equation that is true for only some of the values in its domain. For example, the conditional equation

$$\sin x = 0 \qquad \text{Conditional equation}$$

is true only for $x = n\pi$, where n is an integer. When you find these values, you are *solving* the equation.

On the other hand, an equation that is true for all real values in the domain of the variable is an *identity*. For example, the familiar equation

$$\sin^2 x = 1 - \cos^2 x \qquad \text{Identity}$$

is true for all real numbers x. So, it is an identity.

What you should learn

● Verify trigonometric identities.

Why you should learn it

You can use trigonometric identities to rewrite trigonometric expressions. For instance, Exercise 67 on page 495 shows you how trigonometric identities can be used to solve a problem about the coefficient of friction for an object on an inclined plane.

Nancy Dudley/Stock Boston

Verifying Trigonometric Identities

Verifying that a trigonometric equation is an identity is quite different from solving an equation. There is no well-defined set of rules to follow in verifying trigonometric identities, and the process is best learned by practice.

Guidelines for Verifying Trigonometric Identities

1. Work with one side of the equation at a time. It is often better to work with the more complicated side first.

2. Look for opportunities to factor an expression, add fractions, square a binomial, or create a monomial denominator.

3. Look for opportunities to use the fundamental identities. Note which functions are in the final expression you want. Sines and cosines pair up well, as do secants and tangents, and cosecants and cotangents.

4. If the preceding guidelines do not help, try converting all terms to sines and cosines.

5. Always try *something*. Even making an attempt that leads to a dead end provides insight.

Verifying trigonometric identities is a useful process if you need to convert a trigonometric expression into a form that is more useful algebraically. When you verify an identity, you cannot assume that the two sides of the equation are equal because you are trying to verify that they are equal. As a result, when verifying identities, you cannot use operations such as adding the same quantity to each side of the equation or cross multiplication.

Example 1   Verifying a Trigonometric Identity

Verify the identity $\dfrac{\sec^2 \theta - 1}{\sec^2 \theta} = \sin^2 \theta$.

Solution

Because the left side is more complicated, start with it.

$$\dfrac{\sec^2 \theta - 1}{\sec^2 \theta} = \dfrac{(\tan^2 \theta + 1) - 1}{\sec^2 \theta} \qquad \text{Pythagorean identity}$$

$$= \dfrac{\tan^2 \theta}{\sec^2 \theta} \qquad \text{Simplify.}$$

$$= \tan^2 \theta (\cos^2 \theta) \qquad \text{Reciprocal identity}$$

$$= \dfrac{\sin^2 \theta}{\cos^2 \theta}(\cos^2 \theta) \qquad \text{Quotient identity}$$

$$= \sin^2 \theta \qquad \text{Simplify.}$$

✓ *Checkpoint* Now try Exercise 5.

> ### STUDY TIP
>
> Remember that an identity is only true for all real values in the domain of the variable. For instance, in Example 1 the identity is not true when $\theta = \pi/2$ because $\sec^2 \theta$ is not defined when $\theta = \pi/2$.

There can be more than one way to verify an identity. Here is another way to verify the identity in Example 1.

$$\dfrac{\sec^2 \theta - 1}{\sec^2 \theta} = \dfrac{\sec^2 \theta}{\sec^2 \theta} - \dfrac{1}{\sec^2 \theta} \qquad \text{Rewrite as the difference of fractions.}$$

$$= 1 - \cos^2 \theta \qquad \text{Reciprocal identity}$$

$$= \sin^2 \theta \qquad \text{Pythagorean identity}$$

Example 2   Combining Fractions Before Using Identities

Verify the identity $\dfrac{1}{1 - \sin \alpha} + \dfrac{1}{1 + \sin \alpha} = 2 \sec^2 \alpha$.

Algebraic Solution

$$\dfrac{1}{1 - \sin \alpha} + \dfrac{1}{1 + \sin \alpha} = \dfrac{1 + \sin \alpha + 1 - \sin \alpha}{(1 - \sin \alpha)(1 + \sin \alpha)} \qquad \text{Add fractions.}$$

$$= \dfrac{2}{1 - \sin^2 \alpha} \qquad \text{Simplify.}$$

$$= \dfrac{2}{\cos^2 \alpha} \qquad \text{Pythagorean identity}$$

$$= 2 \sec^2 \alpha \qquad \text{Reciprocal identity}$$

✓ *Checkpoint* Now try Exercise 31.

Numerical Solution

Use the *table* feature of a graphing utility set in *radian* mode to create a table that shows the values of $y_1 = 1/(1 - \sin x) + 1/(1 + \sin x)$ and $y_2 = 2/\cos^2 x$ for different values of x, as shown in Figure 6.5. From the table, you can see that the values appear to be identical, so $1/(1 - \sin x) + 1/(1 + \sin x) = 2 \sec^2 x$ appears to be an identity.

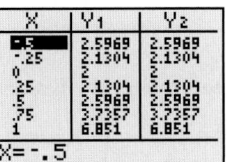

Figure 6.5

Example 3   Verifying a Trigonometric Identity

Verify the identity $(\tan^2 x + 1)(\cos^2 x - 1) = -\tan^2 x$.

Algebraic Solution

By applying identities before multiplying, you obtain the following.

$$(\tan^2 x + 1)(\cos^2 x - 1) = (\sec^2 x)(-\sin^2 x) \qquad \text{Pythagorean identities}$$

$$= -\frac{\sin^2 x}{\cos^2 x} \qquad \text{Reciprocal identity}$$

$$= -\left(\frac{\sin x}{\cos x}\right)^2 \qquad \text{Rule of exponents}$$

$$= -\tan^2 x \qquad \text{Quotient identity}$$

✓ *Checkpoint*   Now try Exercise 39.

Graphical Solution

Use a graphing utility set in *radian* mode to graph the left side of the identity $y_1 = (\tan^2 x + 1)(\cos^2 x - 1)$ and the right side of the identity $y_2 = -\tan^2 x$ in the same viewing window, as shown in Figure 6.6. (Select the *line* style for y_1 and the *path* style for y_2.) Because the graphs appear to coincide, $(\tan^2 x + 1) \cdot (\cos^2 x - 1) = -\tan^2 x$ appears to be an identity.

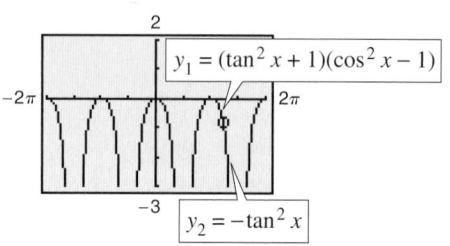

Figure 6.6

Example 4   Converting to Sines and Cosines

Verify the identity $\tan x + \cot x = \sec x \csc x$.

Solution

In this case there appear to be no fractions to add, no products to find, and no opportunities to use the Pythagorean identities. So, try converting the left side into sines and cosines.

$$\tan x + \cot x = \frac{\sin x}{\cos x} + \frac{\cos x}{\sin x} \qquad \text{Quotient identities}$$

$$= \frac{\sin^2 x + \cos^2 x}{\cos x \sin x} \qquad \text{Add fractions.}$$

$$= \frac{1}{\cos x \sin x} \qquad \text{Pythagorean identity}$$

$$= \frac{1}{\cos x} \cdot \frac{1}{\sin x} \qquad \text{Product of fractions}$$

$$= \sec x \csc x \qquad \text{Reciprocal identities}$$

✓ *Checkpoint*   Now try Exercise 41.

TECHNOLOGY TIP

Although a graphing utility can be useful in helping to verify an identity, you must use algebraic techniques to produce a valid proof. For example, graph the two functions

$$y_1 = \sin 50x$$

$$y_2 = \sin 2x$$

in a trigonometric viewing window. Although their graphs seem identical, $\sin 50x \neq \sin 2x$.

Recall from algebra that *rationalizing the denominator* using conjugates is, on occasion, a powerful simplification technique. A related form of this technique works for simplifying trigonometric expressions as well. For instance, to simplify $1/(1 - \cos x)$, multiply the numerator and the denominator by $1 + \cos x$.

$$\frac{1}{1 - \cos x} = \frac{1}{1 - \cos x}\left(\frac{1 + \cos x}{1 + \cos x}\right)$$

$$= \frac{1 + \cos x}{1 - \cos^2 x}$$

$$= \frac{1 + \cos x}{\sin^2 x}$$

$$= \csc^2 x(1 + \cos x)$$

As shown above, $\csc^2 x(1 + \cos x)$ is considered a simplified form of $1/(1 - \cos x)$ because the expression does not contain any fractions.

Example 5   Verifying a Trigonometric Identity

Verify the identity

$$\sec x + \tan x = \frac{\cos x}{1 - \sin x}.$$

Algebraic Solution

Work with the *right* side because you can create a monomial denominator by multiplying the numerator and denominator by $(1 + \sin x)$.

$$\frac{\cos x}{1 - \sin x} = \frac{\cos x}{1 - \sin x}\left(\frac{1 + \sin x}{1 + \sin x}\right) \qquad \text{Multiply numerator and denominator by } (1 + \sin x).$$

$$= \frac{\cos x + \cos x \sin x}{1 - \sin^2 x} \qquad \text{Multiply.}$$

$$= \frac{\cos x + \cos x \sin x}{\cos^2 x} \qquad \text{Pythagorean identity}$$

$$= \frac{\cos x}{\cos^2 x} + \frac{\cos x \sin x}{\cos^2 x} \qquad \text{Separate fractions.}$$

$$= \frac{1}{\cos x} + \frac{\sin x}{\cos x} \qquad \text{Simplify.}$$

$$= \sec x + \tan x \qquad \text{Identities}$$

✓ *Checkpoint* Now try Exercise 47.

TECHNOLOGY SUPPORT

For instructions on how to use the *radian* and *dot* modes, see Appendix A; for specific keystrokes, go to the text website at *college.hmco.com*.

Graphical Solution

Use a graphing utility set in *radian* and *dot* modes to graph $y_1 = \sec x + \tan x = 1/\cos x + \tan x$ and $y_2 = \cos x/(1 - \sin x)$ in the same viewing window, as shown in Figure 6.7. Because the graphs appear to coincide, $\sec x + \tan x = \cos x/(1 - \sin x)$ appears to be an identity.

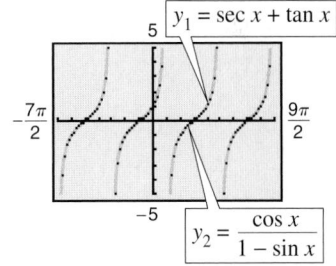

Figure 6.7

In Examples 1 through 5, you have been verifying trigonometric identities by working with one side of the equation and converting it to the form given on the other side. On occasion it is practical to work with each side *separately* to obtain one common form equivalent to both sides. This is illustrated in Example 6.

Example 6 Working with Each Side Separately

Verify the identity $\dfrac{\cot^2 \theta}{1 + \csc \theta} = \dfrac{1 - \sin \theta}{\sin \theta}$.

Solution

Working with the left side, you have

$$\frac{\cot^2 \theta}{1 + \csc \theta} = \frac{\csc^2 \theta - 1}{1 + \csc \theta} \qquad \text{Pythagorean identity}$$

$$= \frac{(\csc \theta - 1)(\cancel{\csc \theta + 1})}{\cancel{1 + \csc \theta}} \qquad \text{Factor.}$$

$$= \csc \theta - 1. \qquad \text{Simplify.}$$

Now, simplifying the right side, you have

$$\frac{1 - \sin \theta}{\sin \theta} = \frac{1}{\sin \theta} - \frac{\sin \theta}{\sin \theta} \qquad \text{Separate fractions.}$$

$$= \csc \theta - 1. \qquad \text{Reciprocal identity}$$

The identity is verified because both sides are equal to $\csc \theta - 1$.

✓ *Checkpoint* Now try Exercise 49.

In Example 7, powers of trigonometric functions are rewritten as more complicated sums of products of trigonometric functions. This is a common procedure used in calculus.

Example 7 Examples from Calculus

Verify each identity.

a. $\tan^4 x = \tan^2 x \sec^2 x - \tan^2 x$ **b.** $\sin^3 x \cos^4 x = (\cos^4 x - \cos^6 x)\sin x$

Solution

a. $\tan^4 x = (\tan^2 x)(\tan^2 x)$ — Write as separate factors.

$\qquad = \tan^2 x(\sec^2 x - 1)$ — Pythagorean identity

$\qquad = \tan^2 x \sec^2 x - \tan^2 x$ — Multiply.

b. $\sin^3 x \cos^4 x = \sin^2 x \cos^4 x \sin x$ — Write as separate factors.

$\qquad = (1 - \cos^2 x)\cos^4 x \sin x$ — Pythagorean identity

$\qquad = (\cos^4 x - \cos^6 x)\sin x$ — Multiply.

✓ *Checkpoint* Now try Exercise 63.

TECHNOLOGY TIP Remember that you can use a graphing utility to assist in verifying an identity by creating a table or by graphing.

6.2   Exercises

Vocabulary Check

In Exercises 1 and 2, fill in the blanks.

1. An equation that is true for only some values in its domain is called a _____ equation.

2. An equation that is true for all real values in its domain is called an _____ .

In Exercises 3–10, fill in the blank to complete the trigonometric identity.

3. $\dfrac{1}{\tan u} =$ _____

4. $\dfrac{1}{\csc u} =$ _____

5. $\dfrac{\sin u}{\cos u} =$ _____

6. $\dfrac{1}{\sec u} =$ _____

7. $\sin^2 u +$ _____ $= 1$

8. $\sin\left(\dfrac{\pi}{2} - u\right) =$ _____

9. $\tan(-u) =$ _____

10. $\sec(-u) =$ _____

In Exercises 1–10, verify the identity.

1. $\sin t \csc t = 1$

2. $\sec y \cos y = 1$

3. $\dfrac{\csc^2 x}{\cot x} = \csc x \sec x$

4. $\dfrac{\sin^2 t}{\tan^2 t} = \cos^2 t$

5. $\cos^2 \beta - \sin^2 \beta = 1 - 2\sin^2 \beta$

6. $\cos^2 \beta - \sin^2 \beta = 2\cos^2 \beta - 1$

7. $\tan^2 \theta + 5 = \sec^2 \theta + 4$

8. $2 - \csc^2 z = 1 - \cot^2 z$

9. $(1 + \sin x)(1 - \sin x) = \cos^2 x$

10. $\cot^2 y(\sec^2 y - 1) = 1$

Numerical, Graphical, and Algebraic Analysis   In Exercises 11–18, use a graphing utility to complete the table and graph the functions in the same viewing window. Use both the table and the graph as evidence that $y_1 = y_2$. Then verify the identity algebraically.

x	0.2	0.4	0.6	0.8	1.0	1.2	1.4
y_1							
y_2							

11. $y_1 = \dfrac{1}{\sec x \tan x}, \quad y_2 = \csc x - \sin x$

12. $y_1 = \dfrac{\csc x - 1}{1 - \sin x}, \quad y_2 = \csc x$

13. $y_1 = \csc x - \sin x, \quad y_2 = \cos x \cot x$

14. $y_1 = \sec x - \cos x, \quad y_2 = \sin x \tan x$

15. $y_1 = \sin x + \cos x \cot x, \quad y_2 = \csc x$

16. $y_1 = \cos x + \sin x \tan x, \quad y_2 = \sec x$

17. $y_1 = \dfrac{1}{\tan x} + \dfrac{1}{\cot x}, \quad y_2 = \tan x + \cot x$

18. $y_1 = \dfrac{1}{\sin x} - \dfrac{1}{\csc x}, \quad y_2 = \csc x - \sin x$

Error Analysis   **In Exercises 19 and 20, describe the error.**

19. $(1 + \tan x)[1 + \cot(-x)]$
$= (1 + \tan x)(1 + \cot x)$
$= 1 + \cot x + \tan x + \tan x \cot x$
$= 1 + \cot x + \tan x + 1$
$= 2 + \cot x + \tan x$

20. $\dfrac{1 + \sec(-\theta)}{\sin(-\theta) + \tan(-\theta)} = \dfrac{1 - \sec \theta}{\sin \theta - \tan \theta}$
$= \dfrac{1 - \sec \theta}{(\sin \theta)\left[1 - \left(\dfrac{1}{\cos \theta}\right)\right]}$
$= \dfrac{1 - \sec \theta}{\sin \theta(1 - \sec \theta)}$
$= \dfrac{1}{\sin \theta} = \csc \theta$

In Exercises 21–30, verify the identity.

21. $\sin^{1/2} x \cos x - \sin^{5/2} x \cos x = \cos^3 x \sqrt{\sin x}$

22. $\sec^6 x(\sec x \tan x) - \sec^4 x(\sec x \tan x) = \sec^5 x \tan^3 x$

23. $\tan\left(\dfrac{\pi}{2} - x\right) \sec x = \csc x$

24. $\dfrac{\cos[(\pi/2) - x]}{\sin[(\pi/2) - x]} = \tan x$

25. $\dfrac{\csc(-x)}{\sec(-x)} = -\cot x$

26. $(1 + \sin y)[1 + \sin(-y)] = \cos^2 y$

27. $\dfrac{\cos(-\theta)}{1 + \sin(-\theta)} = \sec \theta + \tan \theta$

28. $\dfrac{1 + \csc(-\theta)}{\cos(-\theta) + \cot(-\theta)} = \sec \theta$

29. $\dfrac{\sin x \cos y + \cos x \sin y}{\cos x \cos y - \sin x \sin y} = \dfrac{\tan x + \tan y}{1 - \tan x \tan y}$

30. $\dfrac{\tan x + \tan y}{1 - \tan x \tan y} = \dfrac{\cot x + \cot y}{\cot x \cot y - 1}$

In Exercises 31–38, verify the identity algebraically. Use the *table* feature of a graphing utility to check your result numerically.

31. $\dfrac{\cos x - \cos y}{\sin x + \sin y} + \dfrac{\sin x - \sin y}{\cos x + \cos y} = 0$

32. $\dfrac{\tan x + \cot y}{\tan x \cot y} = \tan y + \cot x$

33. $\sqrt{\dfrac{1 + \sin \theta}{1 - \sin \theta}} = \dfrac{1 + \sin \theta}{|\cos \theta|}$

34. $\sqrt{\dfrac{1 - \cos \theta}{1 + \cos \theta}} = \dfrac{1 - \cos \theta}{|\sin \theta|}$

35. $\cos^2 x + \cos^2\left(\dfrac{\pi}{2} - x\right) = 1$

36. $\sec^2 y - \cot^2\left(\dfrac{\pi}{2} - y\right) = 1$

37. $\sin x \csc\left(\dfrac{\pi}{2} - x\right) = \tan x$

38. $\csc^2\left(\dfrac{\pi}{2} - x\right) - 1 = \tan^2 x$

In Exercises 39–50, verify the identity algebraically. Use a graphing utility to check your result graphically.

39. $2 \sec^2 x - 2 \sec^2 x \sin^2 x - \sin^2 x - \cos^2 x = 1$

40. $\csc x(\csc x - \sin x) + \dfrac{\sin x - \cos x}{\sin x} + \cot x = \csc^2 x$

41. $\dfrac{\tan x \cot x}{\cos x} = \sec x$

42. $\dfrac{1 + \csc \theta}{\sec \theta} - \cot \theta = \cos \theta$

43. $\csc^4 x - 2 \csc^2 x + 1 = \cot^4 x$

44. $\sin x(1 - 2 \cos^2 x + \cos^4 x) = \sin^5 x$

45. $\sec^4 \theta - \tan^4 \theta = 1 + 2 \tan^2 \theta$

46. $\csc^4 \theta - \cot^4 \theta = 2 \csc^2 \theta - 1$

47. $\dfrac{\sin \beta}{1 - \cos \beta} = \dfrac{1 + \cos \beta}{\sin \beta}$

48. $\dfrac{\cot \alpha}{\csc \alpha - 1} = \dfrac{\csc \alpha + 1}{\cot \alpha}$

49. $\dfrac{\tan^3 \alpha - 1}{\tan \alpha - 1} = \tan^2 \alpha + \tan \alpha + 1$

50. $\dfrac{\sin^3 \beta + \cos^3 \beta}{\sin \beta + \cos \beta} = 1 - \sin \beta \cos \beta$

Conjecture **In Exercises 51–54, use a graphing utility to graph the trigonometric function. Use the graph to make a conjecture about a simplification of the expression. Verify the resulting identity algebraically.**

51. $y = \dfrac{1}{\cot x + 1} + \dfrac{1}{\tan x + 1}$

52. $y = \dfrac{\cos x}{1 - \tan x} + \dfrac{\sin x \cos x}{\sin x - \cos x}$

53. $y = \dfrac{1}{\sin x} - \dfrac{\cos^2 x}{\sin x}$

54. $y = \sin t + \dfrac{\cot^2 t}{\csc t}$

In Exercises 55–58, use the properties of logarithms and trigonometric identities to verify the identity.

55. $\ln|\cot \theta| = \ln|\cos \theta| - \ln|\sin \theta|$

56. $\ln|\sec \theta| = -\ln|\cos \theta|$

57. $-\ln(1 + \cos \theta) = \ln(1 - \cos \theta) - 2 \ln|\sin \theta|$

58. $-\ln|\csc \theta + \cot \theta| = \ln|\csc \theta - \cot \theta|$

In Exercises 59–62, use the cofunction identities to evaluate the expression without using a calculator.

59. $\sin^2 25° + \sin^2 65°$ **60.** $\cos^2 14° + \cos^2 76°$

61. $\cos^2 20° + \cos^2 52° + \cos^2 38° + \cos^2 70°$

62. $\sin^2 12° + \sin^2 40° + \sin^2 50° + \sin^2 78°$

ℱ **In Exercises 63–66, powers of trigonometric functions are rewritten to be useful in calculus. Verify the identity.**

63. $\tan^5 x = \tan^3 x \sec^2 x - \tan^3 x$

64. $\sec^4 x \tan^2 x = (\tan^2 x + \tan^4 x)\sec^2 x$

65. $\cos^3 x \sin^2 x = (\sin^2 x - \sin^4 x)\cos x$

66. $\sin^4 x + \cos^4 x = 1 - 2\cos^2 x + 2\cos^4 x$

67. *Friction*   The forces acting on an object weighing W units on an inclined plane positioned at an angle of θ with the horizontal (see figure) are modeled by

$$\mu W \cos \theta = W \sin \theta$$

where μ is the coefficient of friction. Solve the equation for μ and simplify the result.

68. *Shadow Length*   The length s of the shadow cast by a vertical *gnomon* (a device used to tell time) of height h when the angle of the sun above the horizon is θ can be modeled by the equation

$$s = \frac{h \sin(90° - \theta)}{\sin \theta}.$$

Show that the equation is equivalent to $s = h \cot \theta$.

Synthesis

True or False?   **In Exercises 69–72, determine whether the statement is true or false. Justify your answer.**

69. There can be more than one way to verify a trigonometric identity.

70. Of the six trigonometric functions, two are even.

71. The equation $\sin^2 \theta + \cos^2 \theta = 1 + \tan^2 \theta$ is an identity, because $\sin^2(0) + \cos^2(0) = 1$ and $1 + \tan^2(0) = 1$.

72. $\sin(x^2) = \sin^2(x)$

Think About It   **In Exercises 73 and 74, explain why the equation is not an identity and find one value of the variable for which the equation is not true.**

73. $\sqrt{\tan^2 x} = \tan x$ **74.** $\sin \theta = \sqrt{1 - \cos^2 \theta}$

75. Verify that for all integers n,

$$\cos\left[\frac{(2n + 1)\pi}{2}\right] = 0.$$

76. Verify that for all integers n,

$$\sin\left[\frac{(12n + 1)\pi}{6}\right] = \frac{1}{2}.$$

Review

In Exercises 77–80, find a polynomial function with real coefficients that has the given zeros. (There are many correct answers.)

77. $1, 8i, -8i$ **78.** $i, -i, 4i, -4i$

79. $4, 6 + i, 6 - i$ **80.** $0, 0, 2, 1 - i$

In Exercises 81–84, sketch the graph of the function by hand.

81. $f(x) = 2^x + 3$ **82.** $f(x) = -2^{x-3}$

83. $f(x) = 2^{-x} + 1$ **84.** $f(x) = 2^{x-1} + 3$

In Exercises 85–88, state the quadrant in which θ lies.

85. $\csc \theta > 0$ and $\tan \theta < 0$

86. $\cot \theta > 0$ and $\cos \theta < 0$

87. $\sec \theta > 0$ and $\sin \theta < 0$

88. $\cot \theta > 0$ and $\sec \theta < 0$

In Exercises 89–92, solve the right triangle shown in the figure. Round your answer to two decimal places.

89. $B = 80°, a = 16$ **90.** $A = 28°, c = 20$

91. $a = 14, b = 8$ **92.** $b = 6.2, c = 12.54$

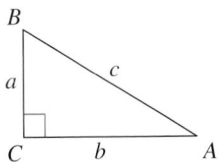

6.3 Solving Trigonometric Equations

Introduction

To solve a trigonometric equation, use standard algebraic techniques such as collecting like terms and factoring. Your preliminary goal is to isolate the trigonometric function involved in the equation.

Example 1   Solving a Trigonometric Equation

$2 \sin x - 1 = 0$	Original equation
$2 \sin x = 1$	Add 1 to each side.
$\sin x = \frac{1}{2}$	Divide each side by 2.

To solve for x, note in Figure 6.8 that the equation $\sin x = \frac{1}{2}$ has solutions $x = \pi/6$ and $x = 5\pi/6$ in the interval $[0, 2\pi)$. Moreover, because $\sin x$ has a period of 2π, there are infinitely many other solutions, which can be written as

$$x = \frac{\pi}{6} + 2n\pi \qquad \text{and} \qquad x = \frac{5\pi}{6} + 2n\pi \qquad \text{General solution}$$

where n is an integer, as shown in Figure 6.8.

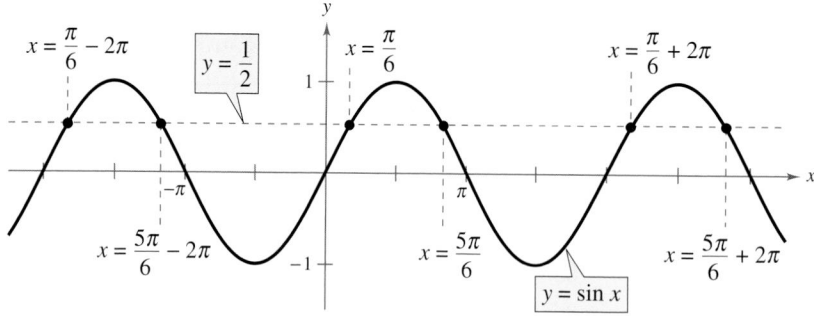

Figure 6.8

✓ *Checkpoint* Now try Exercise 7.

Figure 6.9 verifies that the equation $\sin x = \frac{1}{2}$ has infinitely many solutions. Any angles that are coterminal with $\pi/6$ or $5\pi/6$ are also solutions of the equation.

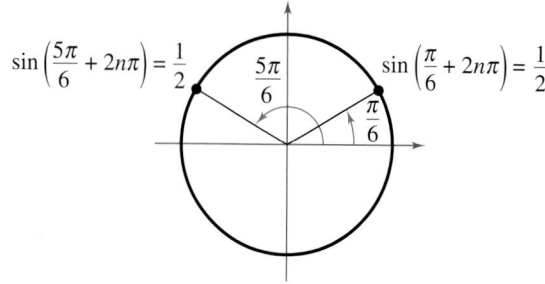

Figure 6.9

Example 2   Collecting Like Terms

Find all solutions of $\sin x + \sqrt{2} = -\sin x$ in the interval $[0, 2\pi)$.

Algebraic Solution

Rewrite the equation so that $\sin x$ is isolated on one side of the equation.

$\sin x + \sqrt{2} = -\sin x$	Write original equation.
$\sin x + \sin x = -\sqrt{2}$	Add $\sin x$ to and subtract $\sqrt{2}$ from each side.
$2\sin x = -\sqrt{2}$	Combine like terms.
$\sin x = -\dfrac{\sqrt{2}}{2}$	Divide each side by 2.

The solutions in the interval $[0, 2\pi)$ are

$$x = \frac{5\pi}{4} \quad \text{and} \quad x = \frac{7\pi}{4}.$$

✓ *Checkpoint* Now try Exercise 17.

Numerical Solution

Use the *table* feature of a graphing utility set in *radian* mode to create a table that shows the values of $y_1 = \sin x + \sqrt{2}$ and $y_2 = -\sin x$ for different values of x. Your table should go from $x = 0$ to $x = 2\pi$ using increments of $\pi/8$, as shown in Figure 6.10. From the table, you can see that the values of y_1 and y_2 appear to be identical when $x \approx 3.927 \approx 5\pi/4$ and $x \approx 5.4978 \approx 7\pi/4$. These values are the approximate solutions of $\sin x + \sqrt{2} = -\sin x$.

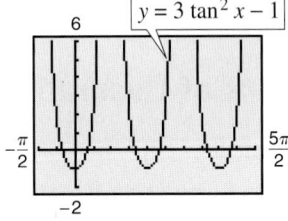

Figure 6.10

Example 3   Extracting Square Roots

Solve $3\tan^2 x - 1 = 0$.

Solution

Rewrite the equation so that $\tan x$ is isolated on one side of the equation.

$3\tan^2 x = 1$	Add 1 to each side.
$\tan^2 x = \dfrac{1}{3}$	Divide each side by 3.
$\tan x = \pm\dfrac{1}{\sqrt{3}}$	Extract square roots.

Because $\tan x$ has a period of π, first find all solutions in the interval $[0, \pi)$. These are $x = \pi/6$ and $x = 5\pi/6$. Finally, add multiples of π to each of these solutions to get the general form

$$x = \frac{\pi}{6} + n\pi \quad \text{and} \quad x = \frac{5\pi}{6} + n\pi \qquad \text{General solution}$$

where n is an integer. The graph of $y = 3\tan^2 x - 1$, shown in Figure 6.11, confirms this result.

✓ *Checkpoint* Now try Exercise 19.

> **TECHNOLOGY SUPPORT**
>
> For instructions on how to use the *table* feature, see Appendix A; for specific keystrokes, go to the text website at *college.hmco.com*.

Figure 6.11

Recall that the solutions of an equation correspond to the x-intercepts of the graph of the equation. For instance, the graph in Figure 6.11 has x-intercepts at $\pi/6$, $5\pi/6$, $7\pi/6$, and so on.

The equations in Examples 1, 2, and 3 involved only one trigonometric function. When two or more functions occur in the same equation, collect all terms on one side and try to separate the functions by factoring or by using appropriate identities. This may produce factors that yield no solutions, as illustrated in Example 4.

Example 4   Factoring

Solve $\cot x \cos^2 x = 2 \cot x$.

Solution

Begin by rewriting the equation so that all terms are collected on one side of the equation.

$$\cot x \cos^2 x = 2 \cot x \qquad \text{Write original equation.}$$

$$\cot x \cos^2 x - 2 \cot x = 0 \qquad \text{Subtract 2 cot } x \text{ from each side.}$$

$$\cot x(\cos^2 x - 2) = 0 \qquad \text{Factor.}$$

By setting each of these factors equal to zero, you obtain the following.

$$\cot x = 0 \qquad \text{and} \qquad \cos^2 x - 2 = 0$$

$$\cos^2 x = 2$$

$$\cos x = \pm\sqrt{2}$$

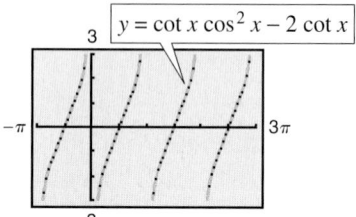

$$y = \cot x \cos^2 x - 2 \cot x$$

Figure 6.12

The equation $\cot x = 0$ has the solution $x = \pi/2$ [in the interval $(0, \pi)$]. No solution is obtained for $\cos x = \pm\sqrt{2}$ because $\pm\sqrt{2}$ are outside the range of the cosine function. Because $\cot x$ has a period of π, the general form of the solution is obtained by adding multiples of π to $x = \pi/2$, to get

$$x = \frac{\pi}{2} + n\pi \qquad \text{General solution}$$

where n is an integer. The graph of $y = \cot x \cos^2 x - 2 \cot x$ (in *dot* mode), shown in Figure 6.12, confirms this result.

 Checkpoint Now try Exercise 21.

Exploration

Using the equation from Example 4, explain what would happen if you divided each side of the equation by $\cot x$. Is this a correct method to use when solving equations?

Equations of Quadratic Type

Many trigonometric equations are of quadratic type. Here are a few examples.

Quadratic in sin x	*Quadratic in sec x*
$2 \sin^2 x - \sin x - 1 = 0$	$\sec^2 x - 3 \sec x - 2 = 0$
$2(\sin x)^2 - \sin x - 1 = 0$	$(\sec x)^2 - 3 \sec x - 2 = 0$

To solve equations of this type, factor the quadratic or, if factoring is not possible, use the Quadratic Formula.

Example 5   Factoring an Equation of Quadratic Type

Find all solutions of $2 \sin^2 x - \sin x - 1 = 0$ in the interval $[0, 2\pi)$.

Algebraic Solution

Treating the equation as quadratic in $\sin x$ and factoring produces the following.

$$2 \sin^2 x - \sin x - 1 = 0 \qquad \text{Write original equation.}$$

$$(2 \sin x + 1)(\sin x - 1) = 0 \qquad \text{Factor.}$$

Setting each factor equal to zero, you obtain the following solutions in the interval $[0, 2\pi)$.

$$2 \sin x + 1 = 0 \qquad \text{and} \qquad \sin x - 1 = 0$$

$$\sin x = -\frac{1}{2} \qquad\qquad \sin x = 1$$

$$x = \frac{7\pi}{6}, \frac{11\pi}{6} \qquad\qquad x = \frac{\pi}{2}$$

Graphical Solution

Use a graphing utility set in *radian* mode to graph $y = 2 \sin^2 x - \sin x - 1$ for $0 \le x < 2\pi$, as shown in Figure 6.13. Use the *zero* or *root* feature or the *zoom* and *trace* features to approximate the x-intercepts to be

$$x \approx 1.571 \approx \frac{\pi}{2}, \quad x \approx 3.665 \approx \frac{7\pi}{6}, \quad x \approx 5.760 \approx \frac{11\pi}{6}.$$

These values are the approximate solutions of $2 \sin^2 x - \sin x - 1 = 0$.

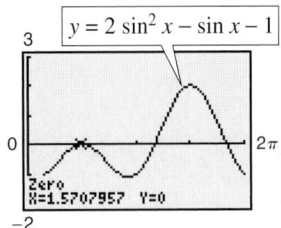

$y = 2 \sin^2 x - \sin x - 1$

Zero
X=1.5707957 Y=0

Figure 6.13

✓ *Checkpoint* Now try Exercise 31.

When working with an equation of quadratic type, be sure that the equation involves a *single* trigonometric function, as shown in the next example.

Example 6   Rewriting with a Single Trigonometric Function

Solve $2 \sin^2 x + 3 \cos x - 3 = 0$.

Solution

Begin by rewriting the equation so that it has only cosine functions.

$$2 \sin^2 x + 3 \cos x - 3 = 0 \qquad \text{Write original equation.}$$

$$2(1 - \cos^2 x) + 3 \cos x - 3 = 0 \qquad \text{Pythagorean identity}$$

$$2 \cos^2 x - 3 \cos x + 1 = 0 \qquad \begin{array}{l}\text{Combine like terms and} \\ \text{multiply each side by } -1.\end{array}$$

$$(2 \cos x - 1)(\cos x - 1) = 0 \qquad \text{Factor.}$$

By setting each factor equal to zero, you can find the solutions in the interval $[0, 2\pi)$ to be $x = 0$, $x = \pi/3$, and $x = 5\pi/3$. Because $\cos x$ has a period of 2π, the general solution is

$$x = 2n\pi, \qquad x = \frac{\pi}{3} + 2n\pi, \qquad x = \frac{5\pi}{3} + 2n\pi \qquad \text{General solution}$$

where n is an integer. The graph of $y = 2 \sin^2 x + 3 \cos x - 3$, shown in Figure 6.14, confirms this result.

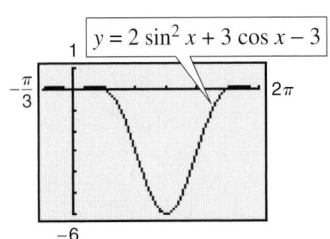

$y = 2 \sin^2 x + 3 \cos x - 3$

Figure 6.14

✓ *Checkpoint* Now try Exercise 33.

Sometimes you must square each side of an equation to obtain a quadratic. Because this procedure can introduce extraneous solutions, you should check any solutions in the original equation to see whether they are valid or extraneous.

Example 7   Squaring and Converting to Quadratic Type

Find all solutions of $\cos x + 1 = \sin x$ in the interval $[0, 2\pi)$.

Solution

It is not clear how to rewrite this equation in terms of a single trigonometric function. See what happens when you square each side of the equation.

$$\cos x + 1 = \sin x \qquad \text{Write original equation.}$$

$$\cos^2 x + 2 \cos x + 1 = \sin^2 x \qquad \text{Square each side.}$$

$$\cos^2 x + 2 \cos x + 1 = 1 - \cos^2 x \qquad \text{Pythagorean identity}$$

$$2 \cos^2 x + 2 \cos x = 0 \qquad \text{Combine like terms.}$$

$$2 \cos x(\cos x + 1) = 0 \qquad \text{Factor.}$$

Setting each factor equal to zero produces the following.

$$2 \cos x = 0 \qquad \text{and} \qquad \cos x + 1 = 0$$

$$\cos x = 0 \qquad\qquad\qquad \cos x = -1$$

$$x = \frac{\pi}{2}, \frac{3\pi}{2} \qquad\qquad\qquad x = \pi$$

Because you squared the original equation, check for extraneous solutions.

Check

$$\cos \frac{\pi}{2} + 1 \stackrel{?}{=} \sin \frac{\pi}{2} \qquad \text{Substitute } \pi/2 \text{ for } x.$$

$$0 + 1 = 1 \qquad \text{Solution checks. } \checkmark$$

$$\cos \frac{3\pi}{2} + 1 \stackrel{?}{=} \sin \frac{3\pi}{2} \qquad \text{Substitute } 3\pi/2 \text{ for } x.$$

$$0 + 1 \neq -1 \qquad \text{Solution does not check.}$$

$$\cos \pi + 1 \stackrel{?}{=} \sin \pi \qquad \text{Substitute } \pi \text{ for } x.$$

$$-1 + 1 = 0 \qquad \text{Solution checks. } \checkmark$$

Of the three possible solutions, $x = 3\pi/2$ is extraneous. So, in the interval $[0, 2\pi)$, the only solutions are $x = \pi/2$ and $x = \pi$. The graph of $y = \cos x + 1 - \sin x$, shown in Figure 6.15, confirms this result because the graph has two x-intercepts (at $x = \pi/2$ and $x = \pi$) in the interval $[0, 2\pi)$.

☑ *Checkpoint* Now try Exercise 35.

> ### Exploration
>
> Use a graphing utility to confirm the solutions found in Example 7 in two different ways. Do both methods produce the same x-values? Which method do you prefer? Why?
>
> 1. Graph both sides of the equation and find the x-coordinates of the points at which the graphs intersect.
>
>   *Left side:* $y = \cos x + 1$
>
>   *Right side:* $y = \sin x$
>
> 2. Graph the equation $y = \cos x + 1 - \sin x$ and find the x-intercepts of the graph.

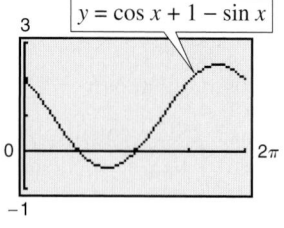

Figure 6.15

Functions Involving Multiple Angles

Example 8   Functions of Multiple Angles

Solve $2 \cos 3t - 1 = 0$.

Solution

$$2 \cos 3t - 1 = 0 \qquad \text{Write original equation.}$$

$$2 \cos 3t = 1 \qquad \text{Add 1 to each side.}$$

$$\cos 3t = \frac{1}{2} \qquad \text{Divide each side by 2.}$$

In the interval $[0, 2\pi)$, you know that $3t = \pi/3$ and $3t = 5\pi/3$ are the only solutions. So in general, you have $3t = \pi/3 + 2n\pi$ and $3t = 5\pi/3 + 2n\pi$. Dividing this result by 3, you obtain the general solution

$$t = \frac{\pi}{9} + \frac{2n\pi}{3} \qquad \text{and} \qquad t = \frac{5\pi}{9} + \frac{2n\pi}{3} \qquad \text{General solution}$$

where n is an integer. This solution is confirmed graphically in Figure 6.16.

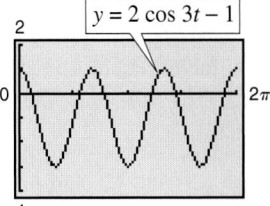

Figure 6.16

✓ *Checkpoint* Now try Exercise 39.

Example 9   Functions of Multiple Angles

Solve $3 \tan \dfrac{x}{2} + 3 = 0$.

Solution

$$3 \tan \frac{x}{2} + 3 = 0 \qquad \text{Write original equation.}$$

$$3 \tan \frac{x}{2} = -3 \qquad \text{Subtract 3 from each side.}$$

$$\tan \frac{x}{2} = -1 \qquad \text{Divide each side by 3.}$$

In the interval $[0, \pi)$, you know that $x/2 = 3\pi/4$ is the only solution. So in general, you have $x/2 = 3\pi/4 + n\pi$. Multiplying this result by 2, you obtain the general solution

$$x = \frac{3\pi}{2} + 2n\pi \qquad \text{General solution}$$

where n is an integer. This solution is confirmed graphically in Figure 6.17.

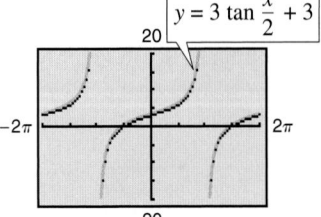

Figure 6.17

✓ *Checkpoint* Now try Exercise 45.

Using Inverse Functions

Example 10   Using Inverse Functions

Find all solutions of $\sec^2 x - 2 \tan x = 4$.

Solution

$$\sec^2 x - 2 \tan x = 4 \qquad \text{Write original equation.}$$

$$1 + \tan^2 x - 2 \tan x - 4 = 0 \qquad \text{Pythagorean identity}$$

$$\tan^2 x - 2 \tan x - 3 = 0 \qquad \text{Combine like terms.}$$

$$(\tan x - 3)(\tan x + 1) = 0 \qquad \text{Factor.}$$

Setting each factor equal to zero, you obtain two solutions in the interval $(-\pi/2, \pi/2)$. [Recall that the range of the inverse tangent function is $(-\pi/2, \pi/2)$.]

$$\tan x = 3 \qquad \text{and} \qquad \tan x = -1$$

$$x = \arctan 3 \qquad x = \arctan(-1) = -\frac{\pi}{4}$$

Finally, because $\tan x$ has a period of π, add multiples of π to obtain

$$x = \arctan 3 + n\pi \qquad \text{and} \qquad x = -\frac{\pi}{4} + n\pi \qquad \text{General solution}$$

where n is an integer. This solution is confirmed graphically in Figure 6.18.

✓ *Checkpoint*   Now try Exercise 29.

Figure 6.18

With some trigonometric equations, there is no reasonable way to find the solutions algebraically. In such cases, you can still use a graphing utility to approximate the solutions.

Example 11   Approximating Solutions

Approximate the solutions of $x = 2 \sin x$ in the interval $[-\pi, \pi]$.

Solution

Use a graphing utility to graph $y = x - 2 \sin x$ in the interval $[-\pi, \pi]$. Using the *zero* or *root* feature or the *zoom* and *trace* features, you can see that the solutions are $x \approx -1.8955$, $x = 0$, and $x \approx 1.8955$. (See Figure 6.19.)

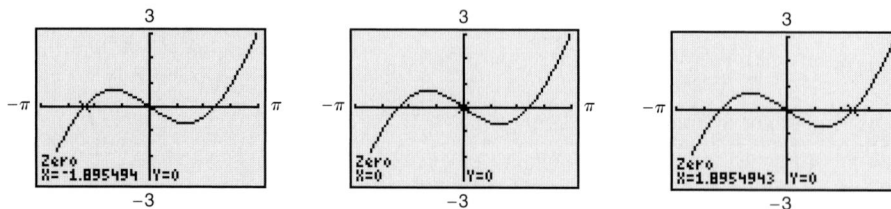

Figure 6.19 $y = x - 2 \sin x$

✓ *Checkpoint*   Now try Exercise 59.

Example 12   Surface Area of a Honeycomb

The surface area of a honeycomb is given by the equation

$$S = 6hs + \frac{3}{2}s^2\left(\frac{\sqrt{3} - \cos \theta}{\sin \theta}\right), \qquad 0 < \theta \leq 90°$$

where $h = 2.4$ inches, $s = 0.75$ inch, and θ is the angle indicated in Figure 6.20.

a. What value of θ gives a surface area of 12 square inches?

b. What value of θ gives the minimum surface area?

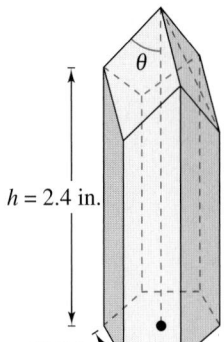

$h = 2.4$ in.

$s = 0.75$ in.

Figure 6.20

Solution

a. Let $h = 2.4$, $s = 0.75$, and $S = 12$.

$$S = 6hs + \frac{3}{2}s^2\left(\frac{\sqrt{3} - \cos \theta}{\sin \theta}\right)$$

$$12 = 6(2.4)(0.75) + \frac{3}{2}(0.75)^2\left(\frac{\sqrt{3} - \cos \theta}{\sin \theta}\right)$$

$$12 = 10.8 + 0.84375\left(\frac{\sqrt{3} - \cos \theta}{\sin \theta}\right)$$

$$0 = 0.84375\left(\frac{\sqrt{3} - \cos \theta}{\sin \theta}\right) - 1.2$$

Using a graphing utility set to *degree* mode, you can graph the function

$$y = 0.84375\left(\frac{\sqrt{3} - \cos x}{\sin x}\right) - 1.2.$$

Using the *zero* or *root* feature or the *zoom* and *trace* features, you can determine that $\theta \approx 49.9°$ and $\theta \approx 59.9°$. (See Figure 6.21.)

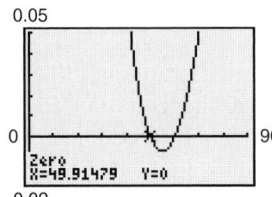

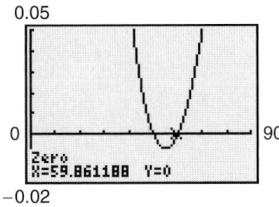

Figure 6.21 $y = 0.84375\left(\dfrac{\sqrt{3} - \cos x}{\sin x}\right) - 1.2$

> **TECHNOLOGY SUPPORT**
>
> For instructions on how to use the *degree* mode and the *minimum* feature, see Appendix A; for specific keystrokes, go to the text website at *college.hmco.com*.

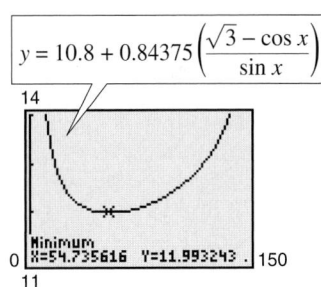

$y = 10.8 + 0.84375\left(\dfrac{\sqrt{3} - \cos x}{\sin x}\right)$

Figure 6.22

b. From part (a), let $h = 2.4$ and $s = 0.75$ to obtain

$$S = 10.8 + 0.84375\left(\frac{\sqrt{3} - \cos \theta}{\sin \theta}\right).$$

Graph this function using a graphing utility set to *degree* mode. Use the *minimum* feature or the *zoom* and *trace* features to approximate the minimum point on the graph, which occurs at $\theta \approx 54.7°$, as shown in Figure 6.22.

✓ *Checkpoint* Now try Exercise 63.

> **STUDY TIP**
>
> By using calculus, it can be shown that the exact minimum value is
>
> $$\theta = \arccos\left(\frac{1}{\sqrt{3}}\right) \approx 54.7356°.$$

6.3   Exercises

Vocabulary Check

Fill in the blanks.

1. The equation $2 \cos x - 1 = 0$ has the solutions $x = \dfrac{\pi}{3} + 2n\pi$ and $x = \dfrac{5\pi}{3} + 2n\pi$, which are called _____ solutions.

2. The equation $\tan^2 x - 5 \tan x + 6 = 0$ is an equation of _____ type.

3. A solution to an equation that does not satisfy the original equation is called an _____ solution.

In Exercises 1–6, verify that each *x*-value is a solution of the equation.

1. $2 \cos x - 1 = 0$

   (a) $x = \dfrac{\pi}{3}$ (b) $x = \dfrac{5\pi}{3}$

2. $\sec x - 2 = 0$

   (a) $x = \dfrac{\pi}{3}$ (b) $x = \dfrac{5\pi}{3}$

3. $3 \tan^2 2x - 1 = 0$

   (a) $x = \dfrac{\pi}{12}$ (b) $x = \dfrac{5\pi}{12}$

4. $4 \cos^2 2x - 2 = 0$

   (a) $x = \dfrac{\pi}{8}$ (b) $x = \dfrac{7\pi}{8}$

5. $2 \sin^2 x - \sin x - 1 = 0$

   (a) $x = \dfrac{\pi}{2}$ (b) $x = \dfrac{7\pi}{6}$

6. $\sec^4 x - 3 \sec^2 x - 4 = 0$

   (a) $x = \dfrac{2\pi}{3}$ (b) $x = \dfrac{5\pi}{3}$

In Exercises 7–16, solve the equation.

7. $2 \cos x + 1 = 0$ 8. $\sqrt{2} \sin x + 1 = 0$

9. $\sqrt{3} \sec x - 2 = 0$

10. $\cot x + 1 = 0$

11. $3 \csc^2 x - 4 = 0$

12. $3 \cot^2 x - 1 = 0$

13. $4 \cos^2 x - 1 = 0$

14. $\cos x(\cos x - 1) = 0$

15. $\sin^2 x = 3 \cos^2 x$

16. $(3 \tan^2 x - 1)(\tan^2 x - 3) = 0$

In Exercises 17–30, find all solutions of the equation in the interval $[0, 2\pi)$ algebraically. Use the *table* feature of a graphing utility to check your answers numerically.

17. $\tan x + \sqrt{3} = 0$ 18. $2 \sin x + 1 = 0$

19. $\csc^2 x - 2 = 0$ 20. $\tan^2 x - 1 = 0$

21. $3 \tan^3 x = \tan x$

22. $2 \sin^2 x = 2 + \cos x$

23. $\sec^2 x - \sec x = 2$

24. $\sec x \csc x = 2 \csc x$

25. $2 \sin x + \csc x = 0$

26. $\sec x + \tan x = 1$

27. $\cos x + \sin x \tan x = 2$

28. $\sin^2 x + \cos x + 1 = 0$

29. $\sec^2 x + \tan x = 3$

30. $2 \cos 2x + \cos x - 1 = 0$

In Exercises 31–38, use a graphing utility to approximate the solutions of the equation in the interval $[0, 2\pi)$ by setting the equation equal to 0, graphing the new equation, and using the *zero* or *root* feature to approximate the *x*-intercepts of the graph.

31. $2 \sin^2 x + 3 \sin x + 1 = 0$

32. $2 \sec^2 x + \tan^2 x - 3 = 0$

33. $4 \sin^2 x = 2 \cos x + 1$

34. $\csc^2 x = 3 \csc x + 4$

35. $\csc x + \cot x = 1$

36. $4 \sin x = \cos x - 2$

37. $\dfrac{\cos x \cot x}{1 - \sin x} = 3$

38. $\dfrac{1 + \sin x}{\cos x} + \dfrac{\cos x}{1 + \sin x} = 4$

In Exercises 39–46, solve the multiple angle equation.

39. $\sin 2x = -\dfrac{\sqrt{3}}{2}$ **40.** $\sec 4x = 2$

41. $2 \sin^2 2x = 1$ **42.** $\tan^2 3x = 3$

43. $\tan 3x(\tan x - 1) = 0$

44. $\cos 2x(2 \cos x + 1) = 0$

45. $\cos \dfrac{x}{2} = \dfrac{\sqrt{2}}{2}$ **46.** $\tan \dfrac{x}{3} = 1$

In Exercises 47–50, approximate the x-intercepts of the graph. Use a graphing utility to check your solutions.

47. $y = \sin \dfrac{\pi x}{2} + 1$ **48.** $y = \sin \pi x + \cos \pi x$

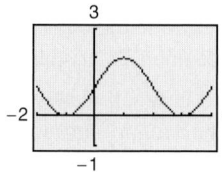
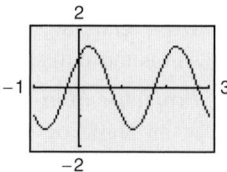

49. $y = \tan^2\left(\dfrac{\pi x}{6}\right) - 3$ **50.** $y = \sec^4\left(\dfrac{\pi x}{8}\right) - 4$

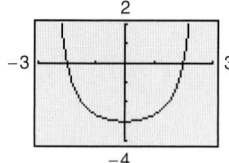
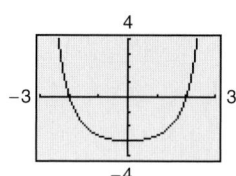

In Exercises 51–58, use a graphing utility to approximate the solutions of the equation in the interval $[0, 2\pi)$.

51. $2 \cos x - \sin x = 0$ **52.** $2 \sin x + \cos x = 0$

53. $x \tan x - 1 = 0$ **54.** $2x \sin x - 2 = 0$

55. $\sec^2 x + 0.5 \tan x = 1$

56. $\csc^2 x + 0.5 \cot x = 5$

57. $12 \sin^2 x - 13 \sin x + 3 = 0$

58. $3 \tan^2 x + 4 \tan x - 4 = 0$

In Exercises 59–62, use a graphing utility to approximate the solutions (to three decimal places) of the equation in the given interval.

59. $3 \tan^2 x + 5 \tan x - 4 = 0$, $\left[-\dfrac{\pi}{2}, \dfrac{\pi}{2}\right]$

60. $\cos^2 x - 2 \cos x - 1 = 0$, $[0, \pi]$

61. $4 \cos^2 x - 2 \sin x + 1 = 0$, $\left[-\dfrac{\pi}{2}, \dfrac{\pi}{2}\right]$

62. $2 \sec^2 x + \tan x - 6 = 0$, $\left[-\dfrac{\pi}{2}, \dfrac{\pi}{2}\right]$

In Exercises 63 and 64, (a) use a graphing utility to graph the function and approximate the maximum and minimum points of the graph in the interval $[0, 2\pi]$, and (b) solve the trigonometric equation and verify that the x-coordinates of the maximum and minimum points of f are among its solutions (the trigonometric equation is found using calculus).

	Function	*Trigonometric Equation*
63.	$f(x) = \sin x + \cos x$	$\cos x - \sin x = 0$
64.	$f(x) = 2 \sin x + \cos 2x$	$2 \cos x - 4 \sin x \cos x = 0$

Fixed Point   **In Exercises 65 and 66, find the smallest positive fixed point of the function f. [A *fixed point* of a function f is a real number c such that $f(c) = c$.]**

65. $f(x) = \tan \dfrac{\pi x}{4}$ **66.** $f(x) = \cos x$

67. *Graphical Reasoning*   Consider the function

$$f(x) = \cos \dfrac{1}{x}$$

and its graph shown in the figure.

(a) What is the domain of the function?

(b) Identify any symmetry or asymptotes of the graph.

(c) Describe the behavior of the function as $x \to 0$.

(d) How many solutions does the equation

$$\cos \dfrac{1}{x} = 0$$

have in the interval $[-1, 1]$? Find the solutions.

(e) Does the equation $\cos(1/x) = 0$ have a greatest solution? If so, approximate the solution. If not, explain.

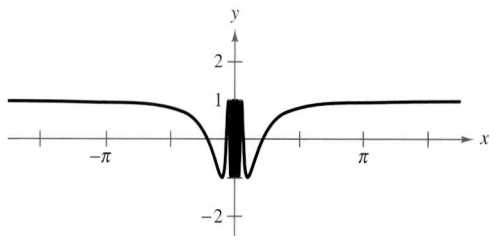

68. Graphical Reasoning   Consider the function

$$f(x) = \frac{\sin x}{x}$$

and its graph shown in the figure.

(a) What is the domain of the function?

(b) Identify any symmetry or asymptotes of the graph.

(c) Describe the behavior of the function as $x \to 0$.

(d) How many solutions does the equation

$$\frac{\sin x}{x} = 0$$

have in the interval $[-8, 8]$? Find the solutions.

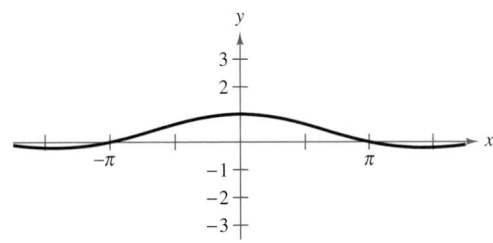

69. Harmonic Motion   A weight is oscillating on the end of a spring (see figure). The position of the weight relative to the point of equilibrium is given by

$$y = \tfrac{1}{12}(\cos 8t - 3\sin 8t)$$

where y is the displacement (in meters) and t is the time (in seconds). Find the times when the weight is at the point of equilibrium ($y = 0$) for $0 \le t \le 1$.

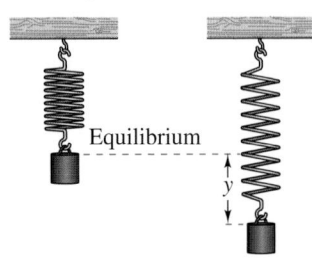

Equilibrium

70. Damped Harmonic Motion   The displacement from equilibrium of a weight oscillating on the end of a spring is given by $y = 1.56e^{-0.22t}\cos 4.9t$, where y is the displacement (in feet) and t is the time (in seconds). Use a graphing utility to graph the displacement function for $0 \le t \le 10$. Find the time beyond which the displacement does not exceed 1 foot from equilibrium.

71. Sales   The monthly sales S (in thousands of units) of lawn mowers are approximated by

$$S = 74.50 - 43.75 \cos \frac{\pi t}{6}$$

where t is the time (in months), with $t = 1$ corresponding to January. Determine the months during which sales exceed 100,000 units.

72. Position of the Sun   Cheyenne, Wyoming has a latitude of $41°$ N. At this latitude, the position of the sun at sunrise can be modeled by

$$D = 31 \sin\left(\frac{2\pi}{365}t - 1.4\right)$$

where t is the time (in days) and $t = 1$ represents January 1. In this model, D represents the number of degrees north or south of due east that the sun rises. Use a graphing utility to determine the days that the sun is more than $20°$ north of due east at sunrise.

73. Projectile Motion   A batted baseball leaves the bat at an angle of θ with the horizontal and an initial velocity of $v_0 = 100$ feet per second. The ball is caught by an outfielder 300 feet from home plate (see figure). Find θ if the range r of a projectile is given by

$$r = \tfrac{1}{32}v_0^2 \sin 2\theta.$$

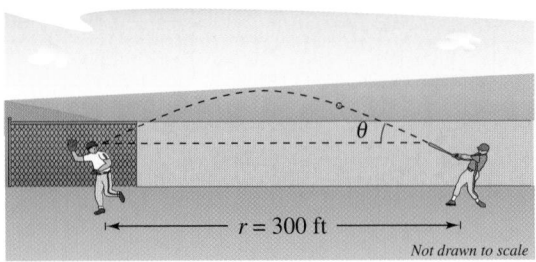

$r = 300$ ft

Not drawn to scale

74. Area   The area of a rectangle inscribed in one arch of the graph of $y = \cos x$ (see figure) is given by

$$A = 2x \cos x, \quad 0 \le x \le \frac{\pi}{2}.$$

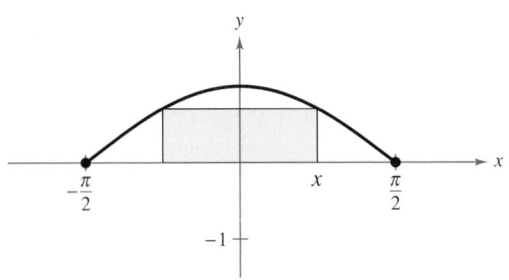

(a) Use a graphing utility to graph the area function, and approximate the area of the largest inscribed rectangle.

(b) Determine the values of x for which $A \geq 1$.

75. Data Analysis The table shows the unemployment rate r for the years 1990 through 2001 in the United States. The time t is measured in years, with $t = 0$ corresponding to 1990. (Source: U.S. Bureau of Labor Statistics)

Time, t	Rate, r
0	5.6
1	6.8
2	7.5
3	6.9
4	6.1
5	5.6
6	5.4
7	4.9
8	4.5
9	4.2
10	4.0
11	4.8

(a) Use a graphing utility to create a scatter plot of the data.

(b) A model for the data is given by $r = 1.39 \sin(0.48t + 0.42) + 5.51$. Graph the model with the scatter plot in part (a). Is the model a good fit for the original data? Explain.

(c) What term in the model gives the average unemployment rate? What is the rate?

(d) Economists study the lengths of business cycles, such as cycles in the unemployment rate. Based on this short span of time, use the model to give the length of this cycle.

(e) Use the model to estimate the next time the unemployment rate will be 6.5% or less.

76. Quadratic Approximation Consider the function

$f(x) = 3 \sin(0.6x - 2)$.

(a) Approximate the zero of the function in the interval $[0, 6]$.

(b) A quadratic approximation agreeing with f at $x = 5$ is

$g(x) = -0.45x^2 + 5.52x - 13.70$.

Use a graphing utility to graph f and g in the same viewing window. Describe the result.

(c) Use the Quadratic Formula to find the zeros of g. Compare the zero in the interval $[0, 6]$ with the result of part (a).

Synthesis

True or False? **In Exercises 77–79, determine whether the statement is true or false. Justify your answer.**

77. All trigonometric equations have either an infinite number of solutions or no solution.

78. The solutions of any trigonometric equation can always be found from its solutions in the interval $[0, 2\pi)$.

79. If you correctly solve a trigonometric equation down to the statement $\sin x = 3.4$, then you can finish solving the equation by using an inverse trigonometric function.

80. Writing Describe the difference between verifying an identity and solving an equation.

Review

In Exercises 81–84, convert the angle measure from degrees to radians. Round your answer to three decimal places.

81. $124°$

82. $486°$

83. $-0.41°$

84. $-210.55°$

In Exercises 85 and 86, solve for x.

85.

86.

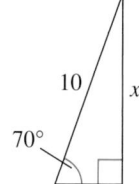

87. Distance From the 100-foot roof of a condominium on the coast, a tourist sights a cruise ship. The angle of depression is 2.5°. How far is the ship from the shoreline?

6.4 Sum and Difference Formulas

Using Sum and Difference Formulas

In this section and the following section, you will study the uses of several trigonometric identities and formulas. See Appendix B for proofs of these formulas.

Sum and Difference Formulas

$$\sin(u + v) = \sin u \cos v + \cos u \sin v \qquad \tan(u + v) = \frac{\tan u + \tan v}{1 - \tan u \tan v}$$

$$\sin(u - v) = \sin u \cos v - \cos u \sin v$$

$$\cos(u + v) = \cos u \cos v - \sin u \sin v \qquad \tan(u - v) = \frac{\tan u - \tan v}{1 + \tan u \tan v}$$

$$\cos(u - v) = \cos u \cos v + \sin u \sin v$$

Exploration

Use a graphing utility to graph $y_1 = \cos(x + 2)$ and $y_2 = \cos x + \cos 2$ in the same viewing window. What can you conclude about the graphs? Is it true that $\cos(x + 2) = \cos x + \cos 2$?

Use a graphing utility to graph $y_1 = \sin(x + 4)$ and $y_2 = \sin x + \sin 4$ in the same viewing window. What can you conclude about the graphs? Is it true that $\sin(x + 4) = \sin x + \sin 4$?

Examples 1 and 2 show how **sum and difference formulas** can be used to find exact values of trigonometric functions involving sums or differences of special angles.

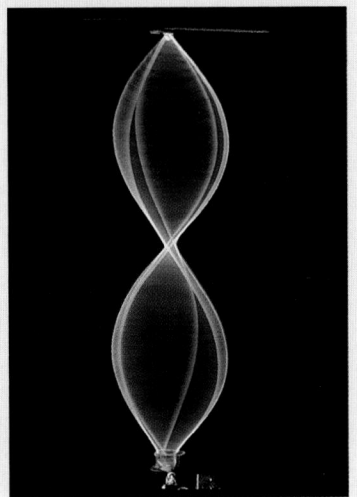

Example 1   Evaluating a Trigonometric Function

Find the exact value of $\cos 75°$.

Solution

To find the exact value of $\cos 75°$, use the fact that $75° = 30° + 45°$. Consequently, the formula for $\cos(u + v)$ yields

$$\cos 75° = \cos(30° + 45°)$$

$$= \cos 30° \cos 45° - \sin 30° \sin 45°$$

$$= \frac{\sqrt{3}}{2}\left(\frac{\sqrt{2}}{2}\right) - \frac{1}{2}\left(\frac{\sqrt{2}}{2}\right)$$

$$= \frac{\sqrt{6} - \sqrt{2}}{4}.$$

Try checking this result on your calculator. You will find that $\cos 75° \approx 0.259$.

✓ *Checkpoint* Now try Exercise 1.

Example 2   Evaluating a Trigonometric Function

Find the exact value of $\sin \dfrac{\pi}{12}$.

Solution

Using the fact that $\pi/12 = \pi/3 - \pi/4$ together with the formula for $\sin(u - v)$, you obtain

$$\sin \frac{\pi}{12} = \sin\left(\frac{\pi}{3} - \frac{\pi}{4}\right) = \sin \frac{\pi}{3} \cos \frac{\pi}{4} - \cos \frac{\pi}{3} \sin \frac{\pi}{4}$$

$$= \frac{\sqrt{3}}{2}\left(\frac{\sqrt{2}}{2}\right) - \frac{1}{2}\left(\frac{\sqrt{2}}{2}\right) = \frac{\sqrt{6} - \sqrt{2}}{4}.$$

✓ *Checkpoint* Now try Exercise 3.

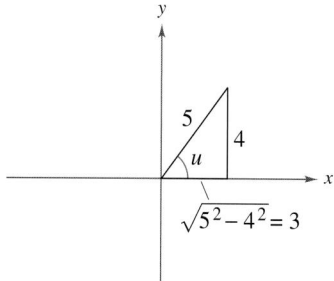

Figure 6.23

Example 3   Evaluating a Trigonometric Expression

Find the exact value of $\sin(u + v)$ given

$$\sin u = \frac{4}{5}, \text{ where } 0 < u < \frac{\pi}{2} \quad \text{and} \quad \cos v = -\frac{12}{13}, \text{ where } \frac{\pi}{2} < v < \pi.$$

Solution

Because $\sin u = 4/5$ and u is in Quadrant I, $\cos u = 3/5$, as shown in Figure 6.23. Because $\cos v = -12/13$ and v is in Quadrant II, $\sin v = 5/13$, as shown in Figure 6.24. You can find $\sin(u + v)$ as follows.

$$\sin(u + v) = \sin u \cos v + \cos u \sin v$$

$$= \left(\frac{4}{5}\right)\left(-\frac{12}{13}\right) + \left(\frac{3}{5}\right)\left(\frac{5}{13}\right) = -\frac{48}{65} + \frac{15}{65} = -\frac{33}{65}$$

✓ *Checkpoint* Now try Exercise 35.

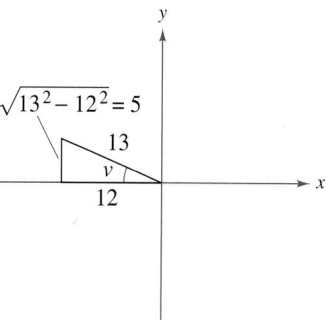

Figure 6.24

Example 4   An Application of a Sum Formula

Write $\cos(\arctan 1 + \arccos x)$ as an algebraic expression.

Solution

This expression fits the formula for $\cos(u + v)$. Angles $u = \arctan 1$ and $v = \arccos x$ are shown in Figure 6.25.

$$\cos(u + v) = \cos(\arctan 1)\cos(\arccos x) - \sin(\arctan 1)\sin(\arccos x)$$

$$= \frac{1}{\sqrt{2}} \cdot x - \frac{1}{\sqrt{2}} \cdot \sqrt{1 - x^2} = \frac{x - \sqrt{1 - x^2}}{\sqrt{2}}.$$

✓ *Checkpoint* Now try Exercise 43.

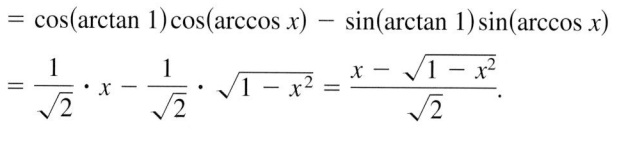
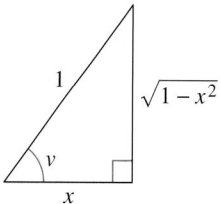

Figure 6.25

Example 5   Proving a Cofunction Identity

Prove the cofunction identity $\cos\left(\dfrac{\pi}{2} - x\right) = \sin x$.

Solution

Using the formula for $\cos(u - v)$, you have

$$\cos\left(\frac{\pi}{2} - x\right) = \cos\frac{\pi}{2}\cos x + \sin\frac{\pi}{2}\sin x$$

$$= (0)(\cos x) + (1)(\sin x)$$

$$= \sin x.$$

✓ *Checkpoint* Now try Exercise 47.

Sum and difference formulas can be used to derive **reduction formulas** involving expressions such as

$$\sin\left(\theta + \frac{n\pi}{2}\right) \quad \text{and} \quad \cos\left(\theta + \frac{n\pi}{2}\right), \text{ where } n \text{ is an integer.}$$

Example 6   Deriving Reduction Formulas

Simplify each expression.

a. $\cos\left(\theta - \dfrac{3\pi}{2}\right)$ **b.** $\tan(\theta + 3\pi)$

Solution

a. Using the formula for $\cos(u - v)$, you have

$$\cos\left(\theta - \frac{3\pi}{2}\right) = \cos\theta\cos\frac{3\pi}{2} + \sin\theta\sin\frac{3\pi}{2}$$

$$= (\cos\theta)(0) + (\sin\theta)(-1)$$

$$= -\sin\theta.$$

b. Using the formula for $\tan(u + v)$, you have

$$\tan(\theta + 3\pi) = \frac{\tan\theta + \tan 3\pi}{1 - \tan\theta\tan 3\pi}$$

$$= \frac{\tan\theta + 0}{1 - (\tan\theta)(0)}$$

$$= \tan\theta.$$

Note that the period of $\tan\theta$ is π, so the period of $\tan(\theta + 3\pi)$ is the same as the period of $\tan\theta$.

✓ *Checkpoint* Now try Exercise 51.

Example 7   Solving a Trigonometric Equation

Find all solutions of $\sin\left(x + \dfrac{\pi}{4}\right) + \sin\left(x - \dfrac{\pi}{4}\right) = -1$ in the interval $[0, 2\pi)$.

Algebraic Solution

Using sum and difference formulas, rewrite the equation as

$$\sin x \cos \frac{\pi}{4} + \cos x \sin \frac{\pi}{4} + \sin x \cos \frac{\pi}{4} - \cos x \sin \frac{\pi}{4} = -1$$

$$2 \sin x \cos \frac{\pi}{4} = -1$$

$$2(\sin x)\left(\frac{\sqrt{2}}{2}\right) = -1$$

$$\sin x = -\frac{1}{\sqrt{2}}$$

$$\sin x = -\frac{\sqrt{2}}{2}.$$

So, the only solutions in the interval $[0, 2\pi)$ are

$$x = \frac{5\pi}{4} \qquad \text{and} \qquad x = \frac{7\pi}{4}.$$

✔ *Checkpoint* Now try Exercise 55.

Graphical Solution

Use a graphing utility set in *radian* mode to

graph $\ \ y = \sin\left(x + \dfrac{\pi}{4}\right) + \sin\left(x - \dfrac{\pi}{4}\right) + 1,$

as shown in Figure 6.26. Use the *zero* or *root* feature or the *zoom* and *trace* features to approximate the *x*-intercepts in the interval $[0, 2\pi)$ to be

$$x \approx 3.927 \approx \frac{5\pi}{4} \text{ and } x \approx 5.498 \approx \frac{7\pi}{4}.$$

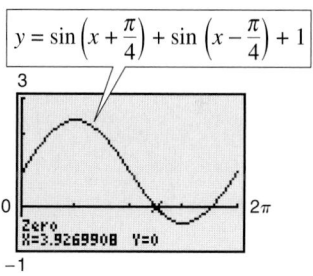

Figure 6.26

The next example was taken from calculus. It is used to derive the formula for the derivative of the sine function.

Example 8   An Application from Calculus

Verify $\dfrac{\sin(x + h) - \sin x}{h} = (\cos x)\left(\dfrac{\sin h}{h}\right) - (\sin x)\left(\dfrac{1 - \cos h}{h}\right), h \neq 0.$

Solution

Using the formula for $\sin(u + v)$, you have

$$\frac{\sin(x + h) - \sin x}{h} = \frac{\sin x \cos h + \cos x \sin h - \sin x}{h}$$

$$= \frac{\cos x \sin h - \sin x(1 - \cos h)}{h}$$

$$= (\cos x)\left(\frac{\sin h}{h}\right) - (\sin x)\left(\frac{1 - \cos h}{h}\right).$$

✔ *Checkpoint* Now try Exercise 77.

TECHNOLOGY SUPPORT

For instructions on how to use the *zero* or *root* feature and the *zoom* and *trace* features, see Appendix A; for specific keystrokes, go to the text website at *college.hmco.com*.

6.4 Exercises

Vocabulary Check

Fill in the blank to complete the trigonometric formula.

1. $\sin(u - v) = $ _____
2. $\cos(u + v) = $ _____
3. $\tan(u + v) = $ _____
4. $\sin(u + v) = $ _____
5. $\cos(u - v) = $ _____
6. $\tan(u - v) = $ _____

In Exercises 1–6, find the exact value of each expression.

1. (a) $\cos(240° - 0°)$ (b) $\cos 240° - \cos 0°$
2. (a) $\sin(390° + 120°)$ (b) $\sin 390° + \sin 120°$
3. (a) $\cos\left(\dfrac{\pi}{6} + \dfrac{\pi}{3}\right)$ (b) $\cos\dfrac{\pi}{6} + \cos\dfrac{\pi}{3}$
4. (a) $\sin\left(\dfrac{2\pi}{3} + \dfrac{3\pi}{4}\right)$ (b) $\sin\dfrac{2\pi}{3} + \sin\dfrac{3\pi}{4}$
5. (a) $\sin(315° - 60°)$ (b) $\sin 315° - \sin 60°$
6. (a) $\sin\left(\dfrac{7\pi}{6} - \dfrac{\pi}{3}\right)$ (b) $\sin\dfrac{7\pi}{6} - \sin\dfrac{\pi}{3}$

In Exercises 7–22, find the exact values of the sine, cosine, and tangent of the angle.

7. $105° = 60° + 45°$
8. $165° = 135° + 30°$
9. $195° = 225° - 30°$
10. $285° = 330° - 45°$
11. $\dfrac{11\pi}{12} = \dfrac{3\pi}{4} + \dfrac{\pi}{6}$
12. $\dfrac{17\pi}{12} = \dfrac{7\pi}{6} + \dfrac{\pi}{4}$
13. $-\dfrac{\pi}{12} = \dfrac{\pi}{6} - \dfrac{\pi}{4}$
14. $-\dfrac{19\pi}{12} = \dfrac{2\pi}{3} - \dfrac{9\pi}{4}$
15. $75°$
16. $15°$
17. $-225°$
18. $-105°$
19. $\dfrac{13\pi}{12}$
20. $\dfrac{5\pi}{12}$
21. $-\dfrac{7\pi}{12}$
22. $-\dfrac{13\pi}{12}$

In Exercises 23–30, write the expression as the sine, cosine, or tangent of an angle.

23. $\cos 60° \cos 10° - \sin 60° \sin 10°$
24. $\sin 110° \cos 80° + \cos 110° \sin 80°$
25. $\dfrac{\tan 325° - \tan 86°}{1 + \tan 325° \tan 86°}$
26. $\dfrac{\tan 152° - \tan 47°}{1 + \tan 152° \tan 47°}$
27. $\sin 3.5 \cos 1.2 - \cos 3.5 \sin 1.2$
28. $\cos 0.88 \cos 0.34 + \sin 0.88 \sin 0.34$
29. $\cos\dfrac{\pi}{7} \cos\dfrac{\pi}{5} - \sin\dfrac{\pi}{7} \sin\dfrac{\pi}{5}$
30. $\sin\dfrac{4\pi}{9} \cos\dfrac{\pi}{8} + \cos\dfrac{4\pi}{9} \sin\dfrac{\pi}{8}$

Numerical, Graphical, and Algebraic Analysis In Exercises 31–34, use a graphing utility to complete the table and graph the two functions in the same viewing window. Use both the table and the graph as evidence that $y_1 = y_2$. Then verify the identity algebraically.

x	0.2	0.4	0.6	0.8	1.0	1.2	1.4
y_1							
y_2							

31. $y_1 = \sin\left(\dfrac{\pi}{6} + x\right)$, $y_2 = \dfrac{1}{2}(\cos x + \sqrt{3}\sin x)$
32. $y_1 = \cos\left(\dfrac{5\pi}{4} - x\right)$, $y_2 = -\dfrac{\sqrt{2}}{2}(\cos x + \sin x)$
33. $y_1 = \cos(x + \pi)\cos(x - \pi)$, $y_2 = \cos^2 x$
34. $y_1 = \sin(x + \pi)\sin(x - \pi)$, $y_2 = \sin^2 x$

In Exercises 35–38, find the exact value of the trigonometric function given that $\sin u = \dfrac{5}{13}$ and $\cos v = -\dfrac{3}{5}$. (Both u and v are in Quadrant II.)

35. $\sin(u + v)$
36. $\cos(v - u)$
37. $\tan(u + v)$
38. $\sin(u - v)$

In Exercises 39–42, find the exact value of the trigonometric function given that $\sin u = -\dfrac{7}{25}$ and $\cos v = -\dfrac{4}{5}$. (Both u and v are in Quadrant III.)

39. $\cos(u + v)$
40. $\tan(u + v)$
41. $\sin(v - u)$
42. $\cos(u - v)$

In Exercises 43–46, write the trigonometric expression as an algebraic expression.

43. $\sin(\arcsin x + \arccos x)$

44. $\cos(\arccos x - \arcsin x)$

45. $\sin(\arctan 2x - \arccos x)$

46. $\cos(\arcsin x - \arctan 2x)$

In Exercises 47–54, verify the identity.

47. $\sin\left(\dfrac{\pi}{2} + x\right) = \cos x$ **48.** $\sin(3\pi - x) = \sin x$

49. $\tan(x + \pi) - \tan(\pi - x) = 2\tan x$

50. $\tan\left(\dfrac{\pi}{4} - \theta\right) = \dfrac{1 - \tan \theta}{1 + \tan \theta}$

51. $\sin(x + y) + \sin(x - y) = 2\sin x \cos y$

52. $\cos(x + y) + \cos(x - y) = 2\cos x \cos y$

53. $\cos(x + y)\cos(x - y) = \cos^2 x - \sin^2 y$

54. $\sin(x + y)\sin(x - y) = \sin^2 x - \sin^2 y$

In Exercises 55–58, find the solutions of the equation in the interval $[0, 2\pi)$. Use a graphing utility to verify your results.

55. $\sin\left(x + \dfrac{\pi}{3}\right) + \sin\left(x - \dfrac{\pi}{3}\right) = 1$

56. $\cos\left(x + \dfrac{\pi}{4}\right) - \cos\left(x - \dfrac{\pi}{4}\right) = 1$

57. $\tan(x + \pi) + 2\sin(x + \pi) = 0$

58. $2\sin\left(x + \dfrac{\pi}{2}\right) + 3\tan(\pi - x) = 0$

In Exercises 59–62, use a graphing utility to approximate the solutions of the equation in the interval $[0, 2\pi)$.

59. $\cos\left(x + \dfrac{\pi}{4}\right) + \cos\left(x - \dfrac{\pi}{4}\right) = 1$

60. $\sin\left(x + \dfrac{\pi}{2}\right) - \cos\left(x + \dfrac{3\pi}{2}\right) = 0$

61. $\tan(x + \pi) - \cos\left(x + \dfrac{\pi}{2}\right) = 0$

62. $\tan(\pi - x) + 2\cos\left(x + \dfrac{3\pi}{2}\right) = 0$

63. *Standing Waves*   The equation of a standing wave is obtained by adding the displacements of two waves traveling in opposite directions (see figure).

Assume that each of the waves has amplitude A, period T, and wavelength λ. If the models for these waves are

$$y_1 = A\cos 2\pi\left(\dfrac{t}{T} - \dfrac{x}{\lambda}\right) \text{ and } y_2 = A\cos 2\pi\left(\dfrac{t}{T} + \dfrac{x}{\lambda}\right)$$

show that

$$y_1 + y_2 = 2A\cos\dfrac{2\pi t}{T}\cos\dfrac{2\pi x}{\lambda}.$$

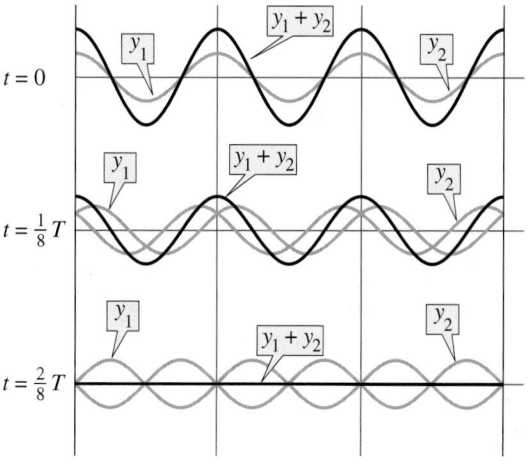

Figure for 63

64. *Harmonic Motion*   A weight is attached to a spring suspended vertically from a ceiling. When a driving force is applied to the system, the weight moves vertically from its equilibrium position, and this motion is modeled by

$$y = \tfrac{1}{3}\sin 2t + \tfrac{1}{4}\cos 2t$$

where y is the distance from equilibrium (in feet) and t is the time (in seconds).

(a) Use a graphing utility to graph the model.

(b) Use the identity

$$a\sin B\theta + b\cos B\theta = \sqrt{a^2 + b^2}\sin(B\theta + C)$$

where $C = \arctan(b/a)$, $a > 0$, to write the model in the form

$$y = \sqrt{a^2 + b^2}\sin(Bt + C).$$

Use a graphing utility to verify your result.

(c) Find the amplitude of the oscillations of the weight.

(d) Find the frequency of the oscillations of the weight.

Synthesis

True or False? In Exercises 65 and 66, determine whether the statement is true or false. Justify your answer.

65. $\cos(u \pm v) = \cos u \pm \cos v$

66. $\sin\left(x - \dfrac{11\pi}{2}\right) = \cos x$

In Exercises 67–70, verify the identity.

67. $\cos(n\pi + \theta) = (-1)^n \cos\theta$, n is an integer.

68. $\sin(n\pi + \theta) = (-1)^n \sin\theta$, n is an integer.

69. $a\sin B\theta + b\cos B\theta = \sqrt{a^2 + b^2}\,\sin(B\theta + C)$, where $C = \arctan(b/a)$ and $a > 0$.

70. $a\sin B\theta + b\cos B\theta = \sqrt{a^2 + b^2}\,\cos(B\theta - C)$, where $C = \arctan(a/b)$ and $b > 0$.

In Exercises 71–74, use the formulas given in Exercises 69 and 70 to write the expression in the following forms. Use a graphing utility to verify your results.

(a) $\sqrt{a^2 + b^2}\,\sin(B\theta + C)$

(b) $\sqrt{a^2 + b^2}\,\cos(B\theta - C)$

71. $\sin\theta + \cos\theta$ **72.** $3\sin 2\theta + 4\cos 2\theta$

73. $12\sin 3\theta + 5\cos 3\theta$ **74.** $\sin 2\theta - \cos 2\theta$

In Exercises 75 and 76, use the formulas given in Exercises 69 and 70 to write the trigonometric expression in the form $a\sin B\theta + b\cos B\theta$.

75. $2\sin\left(\theta + \dfrac{\pi}{2}\right)$

76. $5\cos\left(\theta + \dfrac{\pi}{4}\right)$

77. Verify the following identity used in calculus.

$$\frac{\cos(x + h) - \cos x}{h} = \frac{\cos x(\cos h - 1)}{h} - \frac{\sin x \sin h}{h}$$

78. *Exploration*   Let $x = \pi/6$ in the identity in Exercise 77 and define the functions f and g as follows.

$$f(h) = \frac{\cos(\pi/6 + h) - \cos(\pi/6)}{h}$$

$$g(h) = \cos\frac{\pi}{6}\left(\frac{\cos h - 1}{h}\right) - \sin\frac{\pi}{6}\left(\frac{\sin h}{h}\right)$$

(a) What are the domains of the functions f and g?

(b) Use a graphing utility to complete the table.

h	0.01	0.02	0.05	0.1	0.2	0.5
$f(h)$						
$g(h)$						

(c) Use a graphing utility to graph the functions f and g.

(d) Use the table and graph to make a conjecture about the values of the functions f and g as $h \to 0$.

79. *Conjecture*   Three squares of side s are placed side by side (see figure). Make a conjecture about the relationship between the sum $u + v$ and w. Prove your conjecture by using the identity for the tangent of the sum of two angles.

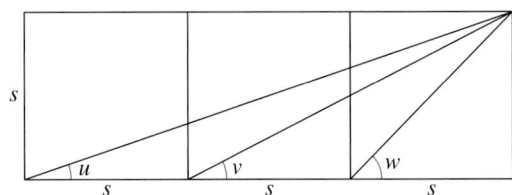

80. **(a)** Write a sum formula for $\sin(u + v + w)$.

(b) Write a sum formula for $\tan(u + v + w)$.

Review

In Exercises 81–84, find the x- and y-intercepts of the graph of the equation. Use a graphing utility to verify your results.

81. $y = -\frac{1}{2}(x - 10) + 14$

82. $y = x^2 - 3x - 40$

83. $y = |2x - 9| - 5$

84. $y = 2x\sqrt{x + 7}$

In Exercises 85–88, evaluate the expression without using a calculator.

85. $\arccos\left(\dfrac{\sqrt{3}}{2}\right)$ **86.** $\arctan\left(-\sqrt{3}\right)$

87. $\sin^{-1} 1$ **88.** $\tan^{-1} 0$

Multiple-Angle Formulas

In this section you will study four additional categories of trigonometric identities.

1. The first category involves *functions of multiple angles* such as $\sin ku$ and $\cos ku$.

2. The second category involves *squares of trigonometric functions* such as $\sin^2 u$.

3. The third category involves *functions of half-angles* such as $\sin(u/2)$.

4. The fourth category involves *products of trigonometric functions* such as $\sin u \cos v$.

You should learn the **double-angle formulas** below because they are used most often. See Appendix B for proofs of the double-angle formulas.

> **Double-Angle Formulas**
>
> $\sin 2u = 2 \sin u \cos u$ $\qquad \cos 2u = \cos^2 u - \sin^2 u$
>
> $\tan 2u = \dfrac{2 \tan u}{1 - \tan^2 u}$ $\qquad\qquad = 2 \cos^2 u - 1$
>
> $\qquad\qquad\qquad\qquad\qquad\qquad = 1 - 2 \sin^2 u$

What you should learn

- Use multiple-angle formulas to rewrite and evaluate trigonometric functions.
- Use power-reducing formulas to rewrite and evaluate trigonometric functions.
- Use half-angle formulas to rewrite and evaluate trigonometric functions.
- Use product-to-sum and sum-to-product formulas to rewrite and evaluate trigonometric functions.

Why you should learn it

You can use a variety of trigonometric formulas to rewrite trigonometric functions in more convenient forms. For instance, Exercise 115 on page 524 shows you how to use a half-angle formula to determine the apex angle of a sound wave cone caused by the speed of an airplane.

NASA-Liaison Agency

Example 1   Solving a Multiple-Angle Equation

Solve $2 \cos x + \sin 2x = 0$.

Solution

Begin by rewriting the equation so that it involves functions of x (rather than $2x$). Then factor and solve as usual.

$$2 \cos x + \sin 2x = 0 \qquad\qquad \text{Write original equation.}$$

$$2 \cos x + 2 \sin x \cos x = 0 \qquad \text{Double-angle formula}$$

$$2 \cos x(1 + \sin x) = 0 \qquad\qquad \text{Factor.}$$

$$\cos x = 0 \qquad\qquad 1 + \sin x = 0 \qquad \text{Set factors equal to zero.}$$

$$x = \frac{\pi}{2}, \frac{3\pi}{2} \qquad\qquad x = \frac{3\pi}{2} \qquad \text{Solutions in } [0, 2\pi)$$

So, the general solution is

$$x = \frac{\pi}{2} + 2n\pi \quad \text{and} \quad x = \frac{3\pi}{2} + 2n\pi \qquad \text{General solution}$$

where n is an integer. Try verifying this solution graphically.

✓ *Checkpoint* Now try Exercise 9.

Example 2 Using Double-Angle Formulas to Analyze Graphs

Analyze the graph of $y = 4\cos^2 x - 2$ in the interval $[0, 2\pi]$.

Solution

Using a double-angle formula, you can rewrite the original function as

$$y = 4\cos^2 x - 2$$
$$= 2(2\cos^2 x - 1)$$
$$= 2\cos 2x.$$

Using the techniques discussed in Section 5.4, you can recognize that the graph of this function has an amplitude of 2 and a period of π. The key points in the interval $[0, \pi]$ are as follows.

Maximum	Intercept	Minimum	Intercept	Maximum
$(0, 2)$	$\left(\dfrac{\pi}{4}, 0\right)$	$\left(\dfrac{\pi}{2}, -2\right)$	$\left(\dfrac{3\pi}{4}, 0\right)$	$(\pi, 2)$

Two cycles of the graph are shown in Figure 6.27.

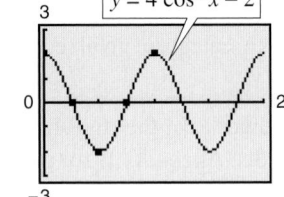

Figure 6.27

☑ *Checkpoint* Now try Exercise 13.

Example 3 Evaluating Functions Involving Double Angles

Use the following to find $\sin 2\theta$, $\cos 2\theta$, and $\tan 2\theta$.

$$\cos \theta = \frac{5}{13}, \qquad \frac{3\pi}{2} < \theta < 2\pi$$

Solution

From Figure 6.28, you can see that $\sin \theta = y/r = -12/13$. Consequently, using each of the double-angle formulas, you can write

$$\sin 2\theta = 2\sin\theta\cos\theta = 2\left(-\frac{12}{13}\right)\left(\frac{5}{13}\right) = -\frac{120}{169}$$

$$\cos 2\theta = 2\cos^2\theta - 1 = 2\left(\frac{25}{169}\right) - 1 = -\frac{119}{169}$$

$$\tan 2\theta = \frac{\sin 2\theta}{\cos 2\theta} = \frac{120}{119}.$$

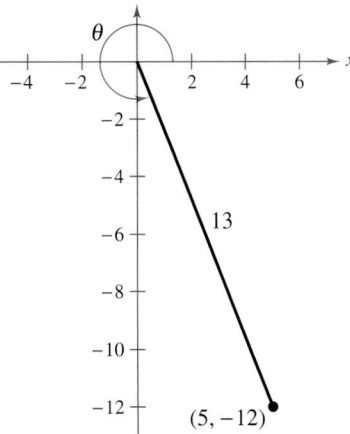

Figure 6.28

☑ *Checkpoint* Now try Exercise 17.

The double-angle formulas are not restricted to the angles 2θ and θ. Other *double* combinations, such as 4θ and 2θ or 6θ and 3θ, are also valid. Here are two examples.

$$\sin 4\theta = 2\sin 2\theta\cos 2\theta \qquad \text{and} \qquad \cos 6\theta = \cos^2 3\theta - \sin^2 3\theta$$

By using double-angle formulas together with the sum formulas derived in the preceding section, you can form other multiple-angle formulas.

Example 4   Deriving a Triple-Angle Formula

$$\sin 3x = \sin(2x + x)$$ Rewrite as sum.

$$= \sin 2x \cos x + \cos 2x \sin x$$ Sum formula

$$= 2 \sin x \cos x \cos x + (1 - 2 \sin^2 x)\sin x$$ Double-angle formula

$$= 2 \sin x \cos^2 x + \sin x - 2 \sin^3 x$$ Multiply.

$$= 2 \sin x(1 - \sin^2 x) + \sin x - 2 \sin^3 x$$ Pythagorean identity

$$= 2 \sin x - 2 \sin^3 x + \sin x - 2 \sin^3 x$$ Multiply.

$$= 3 \sin x - 4 \sin^3 x$$ Simplify.

✓ *Checkpoint* Now try Exercise 23.

Power-Reducing Formulas

The double-angle formulas can be used to obtain the following **power-reducing formulas.** See Appendix B for proofs of the power-reducing formulas.

Power-Reducing Formulas

$$\sin^2 u = \frac{1 - \cos 2u}{2} \qquad \cos^2 u = \frac{1 + \cos 2u}{2} \qquad \tan^2 u = \frac{1 - \cos 2u}{1 + \cos 2u}$$

Example 5   Reducing a Power

Rewrite $\sin^4 x$ as a sum of first powers of the cosines of multiple angles.

Solution

$$\sin^4 x = (\sin^2 x)^2$$ Property of exponents

$$= \left(\frac{1 - \cos 2x}{2}\right)^2$$ Power-reducing formula

$$= \frac{1}{4}(1 - 2 \cos 2x + \cos^2 2x)$$ Expand binomial.

$$= \frac{1}{4}\left(1 - 2 \cos 2x + \frac{1 + \cos 4x}{2}\right)$$ Power-reducing formula

$$= \frac{1}{4} - \frac{1}{2} \cos 2x + \frac{1}{8} + \frac{1}{8} \cos 4x$$ Distributive Property

$$= \frac{3}{8} - \frac{1}{2} \cos 2x + \frac{1}{8} \cos 4x$$ Simplify.

$$= \frac{1}{8}(3 - 4 \cos 2x + \cos 4x)$$ Factor.

✓ *Checkpoint* Now try Exercise 27.

STUDY TIP

Power-reducing formulas are often used in calculus. Example 5 shows a typical power reduction that is used in calculus. Note the repeated use of power-reducing formulas.

Half-Angle Formulas

You can derive some useful alternative forms of the power-reducing formulas by replacing u with $u/2$. The results are called **half-angle formulas.**

Half-Angle Formulas

$$\sin\frac{u}{2} = \pm\sqrt{\frac{1-\cos u}{2}} \qquad \cos\frac{u}{2} = \pm\sqrt{\frac{1+\cos u}{2}}$$

$$\tan\frac{u}{2} = \frac{1-\cos u}{\sin u} = \frac{\sin u}{1+\cos u}$$

The signs of $\sin\dfrac{u}{2}$ and $\cos\dfrac{u}{2}$ depend on the quadrant in which $\dfrac{u}{2}$ lies.

Example 6   Using a Half-Angle Formula

Find the exact value of $\sin 105°$.

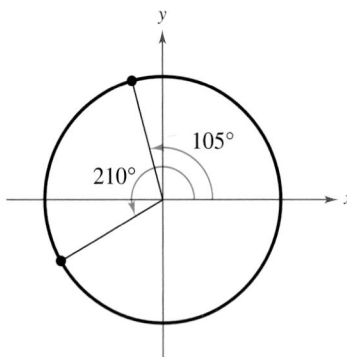

Figure 6.29

STUDY TIP

To find the exact value of a trigonometric function with an angle in D°M′S″ form using a half-angle formula, first convert the angle measure to decimal degree form. Then multiply the angle measure by 2.

Solution

Begin by noting that $105°$ is half of $210°$. Then, using the half-angle formula for $\sin(u/2)$ and the fact that $105°$ lies in Quadrant II (see Figure 6.29), you have

$$\sin 105° = \sqrt{\frac{1-\cos 210°}{2}}$$

$$= \sqrt{\frac{1-(-\cos 30°)}{2}}$$

$$= \sqrt{\frac{1+\left(\sqrt{3}/2\right)}{2}} = \frac{\sqrt{2+\sqrt{3}}}{2}.$$

The positive square root is chosen because $\sin\theta$ is positive in Quadrant II.

✓ *Checkpoint* Now try Exercise 41.

TECHNOLOGY TIP

Use your calculator to verify the result obtained in Example 6. That is, evaluate $\sin 105°$ and $\left(\sqrt{2+\sqrt{3}}\right)/2$. You will notice that both expressions yield the same result.

Example 7   Solving a Trigonometric Equation

Find all solutions of $2 - \sin^2 x = 2\cos^2 \frac{x}{2}$ in the interval $[0, 2\pi)$.

Algebraic Solution

$$2 - \sin^2 x = 2\cos^2 \frac{x}{2} \qquad \text{Write original equation.}$$

$$2 - \sin^2 x = 2\left(\pm\sqrt{\frac{1 + \cos x}{2}}\right)^2 \qquad \text{Half-angle formula}$$

$$2 - \sin^2 x = 2\left(\frac{1 + \cos x}{2}\right) \qquad \text{Simplify.}$$

$$2 - \sin^2 x = 1 + \cos x \qquad \text{Simplify.}$$

$$2 - (1 - \cos^2 x) = 1 + \cos x \qquad \text{Pythagorean identity}$$

$$\cos^2 x - \cos x = 0 \qquad \text{Simplify.}$$

$$\cos x(\cos x - 1) = 0 \qquad \text{Factor.}$$

By setting the factors $\cos x$ and $(\cos x - 1)$ equal to zero, you find that the solutions in the interval $[0, 2\pi)$ are

$$x = \frac{\pi}{2}, \quad x = \frac{3\pi}{2}, \quad \text{and} \quad x = 0.$$

☑ *Checkpoint* Now try Exercise 59.

Graphical Solution

Use a graphing utility set in *radian* mode to graph $y = 2 - \sin^2 x - 2\cos^2(x/2)$, as shown in Figure 6.30. Use the *zero* or *root* feature or the *zoom* and *trace* features to approximate the x-intercepts in the interval $[0, 2\pi)$ to be

$$x = 0, \quad x \approx 1.5708 \approx \frac{\pi}{2}, \quad \text{and} \quad x \approx 4.7124 \approx \frac{3\pi}{2}.$$

These values are the approximate solutions of $2 - \sin^2 x = 2\cos^2 \frac{x}{2}$ in the interval $[0, 2\pi)$.

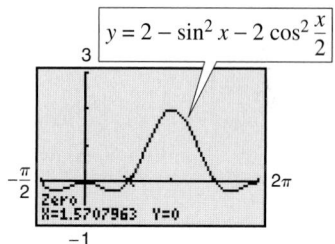

Figure 6.30

Product-to-Sum Formulas

Each of the following **product-to-sum formulas** is easily verified using the sum and difference formulas discussed in the preceding section.

> **Product-to-Sum Formulas**
>
> $$\sin u \sin v = \frac{1}{2}[\cos(u - v) - \cos(u + v)]$$
>
> $$\cos u \cos v = \frac{1}{2}[\cos(u - v) + \cos(u + v)]$$
>
> $$\sin u \cos v = \frac{1}{2}[\sin(u + v) + \sin(u - v)]$$
>
> $$\cos u \sin v = \frac{1}{2}[\sin(u + v) - \sin(u - v)]$$

Product-to-sum formulas are used in calculus to evaluate integrals involving the products of sines and cosines of two different angles.

Example 8   Writing Products as Sums

Rewrite the product as a sum or difference.

$$\cos 5x \sin 4x$$

Solution

$$\cos 5x \sin 4x = \frac{1}{2}[\sin(5x + 4x) - \sin(5x - 4x)]$$

$$= \frac{1}{2}\sin 9x - \frac{1}{2}\sin x$$

✓ *Checkpoint* Now try Exercise 65.

TECHNOLOGY TIP

You can use a graphing utility to verify the solution in Example 8. Graph $y_1 = \cos 5x \sin 4x$ and $y_2 = \frac{1}{2}\sin 9x - \frac{1}{2}\sin x$ in the same viewing window. Notice that the graphs coincide. So, you can conclude that the two expressions are equivalent.

Occasionally, it is useful to reverse the procedure and write a sum of trigonometric functions as a product. This can be accomplished with the following **sum-to-product formulas.** See Appendix B for a proof of the first formula.

Sum-to-Product Formulas

$$\sin u + \sin v = 2 \sin\left(\frac{u + v}{2}\right)\cos\left(\frac{u - v}{2}\right)$$

$$\sin u - \sin v = 2 \cos\left(\frac{u + v}{2}\right)\sin\left(\frac{u - v}{2}\right)$$

$$\cos u + \cos v = 2 \cos\left(\frac{u + v}{2}\right)\cos\left(\frac{u - v}{2}\right)$$

$$\cos u - \cos v = -2 \sin\left(\frac{u + v}{2}\right)\sin\left(\frac{u - v}{2}\right)$$

Example 9   Using a Sum-to-Product Formula

Find the exact value of $\cos 195° + \cos 105°$.

Solution

Using the appropriate sum-to-product formula, you obtain

$$\cos 195° + \cos 105° = 2 \cos\left(\frac{195° + 105°}{2}\right)\cos\left(\frac{195° - 105°}{2}\right)$$

$$= 2 \cos 150° \cos 45°$$

$$= 2\left(-\frac{\sqrt{3}}{2}\right)\left(\frac{\sqrt{2}}{2}\right)$$

$$= -\frac{\sqrt{6}}{2}.$$

✓ *Checkpoint* Now try Exercise 75.

Example 10   Solving a Trigonometric Equation

Find all solutions of $\sin 5x + \sin 3x = 0$ in the interval $[0, 2\pi)$.

Algebraic Solution

$$\sin 5x + \sin 3x = 0 \qquad \text{Write original equation.}$$

$$2 \sin\left(\frac{5x + 3x}{2}\right) \cos\left(\frac{5x - 3x}{2}\right) = 0 \qquad \text{Sum-to-product formula}$$

$$2 \sin 4x \cos x = 0 \qquad \text{Simplify.}$$

By setting the factor $\sin 4x$ equal to zero, you can find that the solutions in the interval $[0, 2\pi)$ are

$$x = 0, \frac{\pi}{4}, \frac{\pi}{2}, \frac{3\pi}{4}, \pi, \frac{5\pi}{4}, \frac{3\pi}{2}, \frac{7\pi}{4}.$$

Moreover, the equation $\cos x = 0$ yields no additional solutions.

✓ *Checkpoint* Now try Exercise 79.

Graphical Solution

Use a graphing utility set in *radian* mode to graph $y = \sin 5x + \sin 3x$, as shown in Figure 6.31. Use the *zero* or *root* feature or the *zoom* and *trace* features to approximate the *x*-intercepts in the interval $[0, 2\pi)$ to be

$$x \approx 0, \ x \approx 0.7854 \approx \frac{\pi}{4}, x \approx 1.5708 \approx \frac{\pi}{2},$$

$$x \approx 2.3562 \approx \frac{3\pi}{4}, \ x \approx 3.1416 \approx \pi, x \approx 3.9270 \approx \frac{5\pi}{4},$$

$$x \approx 4.7124 \approx \frac{3\pi}{2}, \ x \approx 5.4978 \approx \frac{7\pi}{4}.$$

These values are the approximate solutions of $\sin 5x + \sin 3x = 0$ in the interval $[0, 2\pi)$.

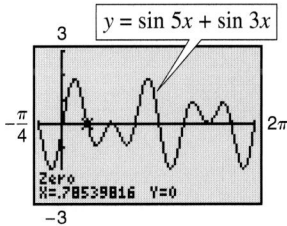

Figure 6.31

Note in Example 10 that the general solution is $x = \dfrac{n\pi}{4}$, where n is an integer.

Example 11   Verifying a Trigonometric Identity

Verify the identity $\dfrac{\sin t + \sin 3t}{\cos t + \cos 3t} = \tan 2t$.

Solution

Using appropriate sum-to-product formulas, you have

$$\frac{\sin t + \sin 3t}{\cos t + \cos 3t} = \frac{2 \sin 2t \cos(-t)}{2 \cos 2t \cos(-t)}$$

$$= \frac{\sin 2t}{\cos 2t}$$

$$= \tan 2t.$$

✓ *Checkpoint* Now try Exercise 97.

6.5 Exercises

Vocabulary Check

Fill in the blank to complete the trigonometric formula.

1. $\sin 2u = $ _____

2. $\cos^2 u = $ _____

3. _____ $= 1 - 2 \sin^2 u$

4. _____ $= \dfrac{\sin u}{1 + \cos u}$

5. $\tan 2u = $ _____

6. $\cos u \cos v = $ _____

7. _____ $= \dfrac{1 - \cos 2u}{2}$

8. _____ $= \pm\sqrt{\dfrac{1 + \cos u}{2}}$

9. $\sin u \cos v = $ _____

10. $\sin u + \sin v = $ _____

In Exercises 1–8, use the figure to find the exact value of the trigonometric function.

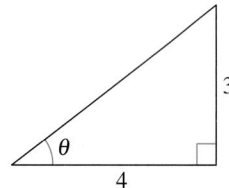

1. $\sin \theta$

2. $\cos \theta$

3. $\cos 2\theta$

4. $\sin 2\theta$

5. $\tan 2\theta$

6. $\sec 2\theta$

7. $\csc 2\theta$

8. $\cot 2\theta$

In Exercises 9–16, use a graphing utility to approximate the solutions of the equation in the interval $[0, 2\pi)$. If possible, find the exact solutions algebraically.

9. $\sin 2x - \sin x = 0$

10. $\sin 2x + \cos x = 0$

11. $4 \sin x \cos x = 1$

12. $\sin 2x \sin x = \cos x$

13. $\cos 2x - \cos x = 0$

14. $\tan 2x - \cot x = 0$

15. $\sin 4x = -2 \sin 2x$

16. $(\sin 2x + \cos 2x)^2 = 1$

In Exercises 17–22, find the exact values of $\sin 2u$, $\cos 2u$, and $\tan 2u$ using the double-angle formulas.

17. $\sin u = \frac{3}{5}$, $\quad 0 < u < \pi/2$

18. $\cos u = -\frac{2}{7}$, $\quad \pi/2 < u < \pi$

19. $\tan u = \frac{1}{2}$, $\quad \pi < u < 3\pi/2$

20. $\cot u = -6$, $\quad 3\pi/2 < u < 2\pi$

21. $\sec u = -\frac{5}{2}$, $\quad \pi/2 < u < \pi$

22. $\csc u = 3$, $\quad \pi/2 < u < \pi$

In Exercises 23–26, use a double-angle formula to rewrite the expression. Use a graphing utility to graph both expressions to verify that both forms are the same.

23. $8 \sin x \cos x$

24. $4 \sin x \cos x + 1$

25. $6 - 12 \sin^2 x$

26. $(\cos x + \sin x)(\cos x - \sin x)$

In Exercises 27–32, rewrite the expression in terms of the first power of the cosine. Use a graphing utility to graph both expressions to verify that both forms are the same.

27. $\cos^4 x$

28. $\sin^4 x$

29. $\sin^2 x \cos^2 x$

30. $\cos^6 x$

31. $\sin^2 x \cos^4 x$

32. $\sin^4 x \cos^2 x$

In Exercises 33–40, use the figure to find the exact value of the trigonometric function.

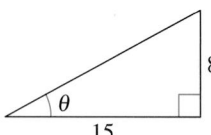

33. $\cos \dfrac{\theta}{2}$

34. $\sin \dfrac{\theta}{2}$

35. $\tan \dfrac{\theta}{2}$

36. $\sec \dfrac{\theta}{2}$

37. $\csc \dfrac{\theta}{2}$

38. $\cot \dfrac{\theta}{2}$

39. $2 \sin \dfrac{\theta}{2} \cos \dfrac{\theta}{2}$

40. $2 \cos \dfrac{\theta}{2} \tan \dfrac{\theta}{2}$

In Exercises 41–48, use the half-angle formulas to determine the exact values of the sine, cosine, and tangent of the angle.

41. $15°$

42. $165°$

43. $112° \, 30'$

44. $157° \, 30'$

45. $\dfrac{\pi}{8}$

46. $\dfrac{\pi}{12}$

47. $\dfrac{3\pi}{8}$

48. $\dfrac{7\pi}{12}$

In Exercises 49–54, find the exact values of $\sin(u/2)$, $\cos(u/2)$, and $\tan(u/2)$ using the half-angle formulas.

49. $\sin u = \frac{5}{13}, \quad \pi/2 < u < \pi$

50. $\cos u = \frac{7}{25}, \quad 0 < u < \pi/2$

51. $\tan u = -\frac{8}{5}, \quad 3\pi/2 < u < 2\pi$

52. $\cot u = 7, \quad \pi < u < 3\pi/2$

53. $\csc u = -\frac{5}{3}, \quad \pi < u < 3\pi/2$

54. $\sec u = -\frac{7}{2}, \quad \pi/2 < u < \pi$

In Exercises 55–58, use the half-angle formulas to simplify the expression.

55. $\sqrt{\dfrac{1 - \cos 6x}{2}}$

56. $\sqrt{\dfrac{1 + \cos 4x}{2}}$

57. $-\sqrt{\dfrac{1 - \cos 8x}{1 + \cos 8x}}$

58. $-\sqrt{\dfrac{1 - \cos(x - 1)}{2}}$

In Exercises 59–62, find the solutions of the equation in the interval $[0, 2\pi)$. Use a graphing utility to verify your answers.

59. $\sin \dfrac{x}{2} - \cos x = 0$

60. $\sin \dfrac{x}{2} + \cos x - 1 = 0$

61. $\cos \dfrac{x}{2} - \sin x = 0$

62. $\tan \dfrac{x}{2} - \sin x = 0$

In Exercises 63–68, use the product-to-sum formulas to write the product as a sum or difference.

63. $6 \sin \dfrac{\pi}{3} \cos \dfrac{\pi}{3}$

64. $4 \sin \dfrac{\pi}{3} \cos \dfrac{5\pi}{6}$

65. $\sin 5\theta \cos 3\theta$

66. $5 \sin 3\alpha \sin 4\alpha$

67. $5 \cos(-5\beta) \cos 3\beta$

68. $\cos 2\theta \cos 4\theta$

In Exercises 69–74, use the sum-to-product formulas to write the sum or difference as a product.

69. $\sin 5\theta - \sin \theta$

70. $\sin x + \sin 7x$

71. $\sin(\alpha + \beta) - \sin(\alpha - \beta)$

72. $\cos(\phi + 2\pi) + \cos \phi$

73. $\cos\left(\theta + \dfrac{\pi}{2}\right) - \cos\left(\theta - \dfrac{\pi}{2}\right)$

74. $\sin\left(x + \dfrac{\pi}{2}\right) + \sin\left(x - \dfrac{\pi}{2}\right)$

In Exercises 75–78, use the sum-to-product formulas to find the exact value of the expression.

75. $\sin 195° + \sin 105°$

76. $\cos 165° - \cos 75°$

77. $\cos \dfrac{5\pi}{12} + \cos \dfrac{\pi}{12}$

78. $\sin \dfrac{11\pi}{12} - \sin \dfrac{7\pi}{12}$

In Exercises 79–82, find the solutions of the equation in the interval $[0, 2\pi)$. Use a graphing utility to verify your answers.

79. $\sin 6x + \sin 2x = 0$

80. $\cos 2x - \cos 6x = 0$

81. $\dfrac{\cos 2x}{\sin 3x - \sin x} - 1 = 0$

82. $\sin^2 3x - \sin^2 x = 0$

In Exercises 83–86, use the figure and trigonometric identities to find the exact value of the trigonometric function in two ways.

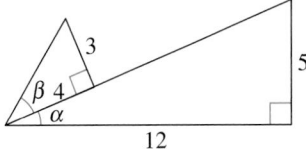

83. $\sin^2 \alpha$

84. $\cos^2 \alpha$

85. $\sin \alpha \cos \beta$

86. $\cos \alpha \sin \beta$

In Exercises 87–98, verify the identity algebraically. Use a graphing utility to check your result graphically.

87. $\csc 2\theta = \dfrac{\csc \theta}{2 \cos \theta}$

88. $\sec 2\theta = \dfrac{\sec^2 \theta}{2 - \sec^2 \theta}$

89. $\cos^2 2\alpha - \sin^2 2\alpha = \cos 4\alpha$

90. $\cos^4 x - \sin^4 x = \cos 2x$

91. $(\sin x + \cos x)^2 = 1 + \sin 2x$

92. $1 + \cos 10y = 2\cos^2 5y$

93. $\sec \dfrac{u}{2} = \pm \sqrt{\dfrac{2\tan u}{\tan u + \sin u}}$

94. $\tan \dfrac{u}{2} = \csc u - \cot u$

95. $\cos 3\beta = \cos^3 \beta - 3\sin^2 \beta \cos \beta$

96. $\sin 4\beta = 4\sin \beta \cos \beta(1 - 2\sin^2 \beta)$

97. $\dfrac{\cos 4x - \cos 2x}{2\sin 3x} = -\sin x$

98. $\dfrac{\cos 3x - \cos x}{\sin 3x - \sin x} = -\tan 2x$

In Exercises 99–102, graph the function by using the power-reducing formulas.

99. $f(x) = \sin^2 x$ **100.** $f(x) = \cos^2 x$

101. $f(x) = \cos^4 x$ **102.** $f(x) = \sin^3 x$

In Exercises 103–106, (a) use a graphing utility to graph the function and approximate the maximum and minimum points of the graph in the interval $[0, 2\pi]$, and (b) solve the trigonometric equation and verify that the x-coordinates of the maximum and minimum points of f are among its solutions (calculus is required to find the trigonometric equation).

Function	*Trigonometric Equation*

103. $f(x) = 4\sin \dfrac{x}{2} + \cos x$ $2\cos \dfrac{x}{2} - \sin x = 0$

104. $f(x) = \cos 2x - 2\sin x$ $-2\cos x(2\sin x + 1) = 0$

105. $f(x) = 2\cos \dfrac{x}{2} + \sin 2x$ $2\cos 2x - \sin \dfrac{x}{2} = 0$

106. $f(x) = 2\sin \dfrac{x}{2} - $ $10\sin\left(2x - \dfrac{\pi}{4}\right) + $

$5\cos\left(2x - \dfrac{\pi}{4}\right)$ $\cos \dfrac{x}{2} = 0$

In Exercises 107–112, write the trigonometric expression as an algebraic expression.

107. $\sin(2 \arcsin x)$ **108.** $\cos(2 \arccos x)$

109. $\cos(2 \arcsin x)$ **110.** $\sin(2 \arccos x)$

111. $\cos(2 \arctan x)$ **112.** $\sin(2 \arctan x)$

113. *Projectile Motion* The range of a projectile fired at an angle θ with the horizontal and with an initial velocity of v_0 feet per second is given by

$$r = \tfrac{1}{32}v_0^2 \sin 2\theta$$

where r is measured in feet. Rewrite the expression for the range in terms of θ.

114. *Geometry* The length of each of the two equal sides of an isosceles triangle is 10 meters (see figure). The angle between the two sides is θ.

(a) Write the area of the triangle as a function of $\theta/2$.

(b) Write the area of the triangle as a function of θ and determine the value of θ such that the area is a maximum.

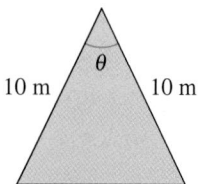

115. *Mach Number* The mach number M of an airplane is the ratio of its speed to the speed of sound. When an airplane travels faster than the speed of sound, the sound waves form a cone behind the airplane (see figure). The mach number is related to the apex angle θ of the cone by

$$\sin \frac{\theta}{2} = \frac{1}{M}.$$

(a) Find the angle θ that corresponds to a mach number of 1.

(b) Find the angle θ that corresponds to a mach number of 4.5.

(c) The speed of sound is about 760 miles per hour. Determine the speed of an object having the mach numbers in parts (a) and (b).

(d) Rewrite the equation as a trigonometric function of θ.

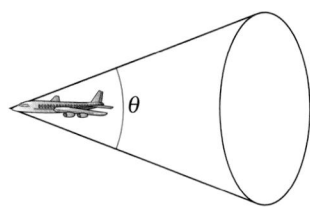

116. *Railroad Track* When two railroad tracks merge, the overlapping portions of the tracks are in the shape of a circular arc (see figure). The radius of each arc r (in feet) and the angle θ are related by

$$\frac{x}{2} = 2r \sin^2 \frac{\theta}{2}.$$

Write a formula for x in terms of $\cos \theta$.

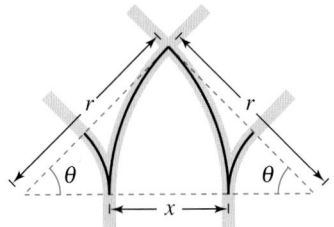

Synthesis

True or False? In Exercises 117 and 118, determine whether the statement is true or false. Justify your answer.

117. $\sin \dfrac{x}{2} = -\sqrt{\dfrac{1 - \cos x}{2}}$, $\pi \le x \le 2\pi$

118. The graph of $y = 4 - 8 \sin^2 x$ has a maximum at $(\pi, 4)$.

119. *Conjecture* Consider the function

$$f(x) = 2 \sin x \left(2 \cos^2 \frac{x}{2} - 1 \right).$$

(a) Use a graphing utility to graph the function.

(b) Make a conjecture about the function that is an identity with f.

(c) Verify your conjecture algebraically.

120. *Exploration* Consider the function

$$f(x) = \sin^4 x + \cos^4 x.$$

(a) Use the power-reducing formulas to write the function in terms of cosine to the first power.

(b) Determine another way of rewriting the function. Use a graphing utility to rule out incorrectly rewritten functions.

(c) Add a trigonometric term to the function so that it becomes a perfect square trinomial. Rewrite the function as a perfect square trinomial minus the term that you added. Use a graphing utility to rule out incorrectly rewritten functions.

(d) Rewrite the result of part (c) in terms of the sine of a double angle. Use a graphing utility to rule out incorrectly rewritten functions.

(e) When you rewrite a trigonometric expression, the result may not be the same as a friend's. Does this mean that one of you is wrong? Explain.

121. *Writing* Describe how you can use a double-angle formula or a half-angle formula to derive a formula for the area of an isosceles triangle. Use a labeled sketch to illustrate your derivation. Then write two examples that show how your formula can be used.

122. (a) Write a formula for $\cos 3\theta$.

  (b) Write a formula for $\cos 4\theta$.

Review

In Exercises 123–126, (a) plot the points, (b) find the distance between the points, and (c) find the midpoint of the line segment connecting the points.

123. $(5, 2), (-1, 4)$ **124.** $(-4, -3), (6, 10)$

125. $\left(0, \frac{1}{2}\right), \left(\frac{4}{3}, \frac{5}{2}\right)$ **126.** $\left(\frac{1}{3}, \frac{2}{3}\right), \left(-1, -\frac{3}{2}\right)$

In Exercises 127–130, find (if possible) the complement and supplement of each angle.

127. (a) $55°$ (b) $162°$

128. (a) $109°$ (b) $78°$

129. (a) $\dfrac{\pi}{18}$ (b) $\dfrac{9\pi}{20}$

130. (a) 0.95 (b) 2.76

131. Find the radian measure of the central angle of a circle with a radius of 15 inches that intercepts an arc of length 7 inches.

132. Find the length of the arc on a circle of radius 21 centimeters intercepted by a central angle of $35°$.

In Exercises 133–136, sketch a graph of the function. (Include two full periods.) Use a graphing utility to verify your graph.

133. $f(x) = \dfrac{3}{2} \cos 2x$ **134.** $f(x) = \dfrac{5}{2} \sin \dfrac{1}{2}x$

135. $f(x) = \dfrac{1}{2} \tan 2\pi x$ **136.** $f(x) = \dfrac{1}{4} \sec \dfrac{\pi x}{2}$

6 Chapter Summary

What did you learn?

Section 6.1

Review Exercises

☐ Recognize and write the fundamental trigonometric identities.   1–10

☐ Use the fundamental trigonometric identities to evaluate trigonometric functions, simplify trigonometric expressions, and rewrite trigonometric expressions.   11–24

Section 6.2

☐ Verify trigonometric identities.   25–36

Section 6.3

☐ Use standard algebraic techniques to solve trigonometric equations.   37–48

☐ Solve trigonometric equations of quadratic type.   49–52

☐ Solve trigonometric equations involving multiple angles.   53–58

☐ Use inverse trigonometric functions to solve trigonometric equations.   59–62

Section 6.4

☐ Use sum and difference formulas to evaluate trigonometric functions, verify identities, and solve trigonometric equations.   63–84

Section 6.5

☐ Use multiple-angle formulas to rewrite and evaluate trigonometric functions.   85–94

☐ Use power-reducing formulas to rewrite and evaluate trigonometric functions.   95–98

☐ Use half-angle formulas to rewrite and evaluate trigonometric functions.   99–110

☐ Use product-to-sum and sum-to-product formulas to rewrite and evaluate trigonometric functions.   111–122

6 Review Exercises

6.1 In Exercises 1–10, name the trigonometric function equivalent to the expression.

1. $\dfrac{1}{\cos x}$

2. $\dfrac{1}{\sin x}$

3. $\dfrac{1}{\sec x}$

4. $\dfrac{1}{\tan x}$

5. $\sqrt{1 - \cos^2 x}$

6. $\sqrt{1 + \tan^2 x}$

7. $\csc\left(\dfrac{\pi}{2} - x\right)$

8. $\cot\left(\dfrac{\pi}{2} - x\right)$

9. $\sec(-x)$

10. $\tan(-x)$

In Exercises 11–14, use the given values to evaluate (if possible) all six trigonometric functions of the angle.

11. $\sin x = \dfrac{4}{5}, \qquad \cos x = \dfrac{3}{5}$

12. $\tan \theta = \dfrac{2}{3}, \qquad \sec \theta = \dfrac{\sqrt{13}}{3}$

13. $\sin\left(\dfrac{\pi}{2} - x\right) = \dfrac{1}{\sqrt{2}}, \qquad \sin x = -\dfrac{1}{\sqrt{2}}$

14. $\csc\left(\dfrac{\pi}{2} - \theta\right) = 3, \qquad \sin \theta = \dfrac{2\sqrt{2}}{3}$

In Exercises 15–22, use the fundamental identities to simplify the expression. Use the *table* feature of a graphing utility to check your result numerically.

15. $\dfrac{1}{\cot^2 x + 1}$

16. $\dfrac{\sec^2 x - 1}{\sec x - 1}$

17. $\dfrac{\sin^2 \alpha - \cos^2 \alpha}{\sin^2 \alpha - \sin \alpha \cos \alpha}$

18. $\dfrac{\sin^3 \beta + \cos^3 \beta}{\sin \beta + \cos \beta}$

19. $\tan^2 \theta(\csc^2 \theta - 1)$

20. $\csc^2 x(1 - \cos^2 x)$

21. $\tan\left(\dfrac{\pi}{2} - x\right) \sec x$

22. $\dfrac{\sin(-x) \cot x}{\sin\left(\dfrac{\pi}{2} - x\right)}$

23. ***Rate of Change*** The rate of change of the function $f(x) = 2\sqrt{\sin x}$ is given by the expression $\sin^{-1/2} x \cos x$. Show that this expression can also be written as $\cot x \sqrt{\sin x}$.

24. ***Rate of Change*** The rate of change of the function $f(x) = \csc x - \cot x$ is the expression $\csc^2 x - \csc x \cot x$. Show that this expression can also be written as $(1 - \cos x)/\sin^2 x$.

6.2 In Exercises 25–36, verify the identity.

25. $\cos x(\tan^2 x + 1) = \sec x$

26. $\sec^2 x \cot x - \cot x = \tan x$

27. $\sin^3 \theta + \sin \theta \cos^2 \theta = \sin \theta$

28. $\cot^2 x - \cos^2 x = \cot^2 x \cos^2 x$

29. $\sin^5 x \cos^2 x = (\cos^2 x - 2\cos^4 x + \cos^6 x) \sin x$

30. $\cos^3 x \sin^2 x = (\sin^2 x - \sin^4 x)\cos x$

31. $\sqrt{\dfrac{1 - \sin \theta}{1 + \sin \theta}} = \dfrac{1 - \sin \theta}{|\cos \theta|}$

32. $\sqrt{1 - \cos x} = \dfrac{|\sin x|}{\sqrt{1 + \cos x}}$

33. $\dfrac{\csc(-x)}{\sec(-x)} = -\cot x$

34. $\dfrac{1 + \sec(-x)}{\sin(-x) + \tan(-x)} = -\csc x$

35. $\sin^2 x + \sin^2\left(\dfrac{\pi}{2} - x\right) = 1$

36. $\csc x \sin\left(\dfrac{\pi}{2} - x\right) = \cot x$

6.3 In Exercises 37–48, solve the equation.

37. $2 \sin x - 1 = 0$

38. $\tan x + 1 = 0$

39. $\sin x = \sqrt{3} - \sin x$

40. $4 \cos x = 1 + 2 \cos x$

41. $3\sqrt{3} \tan x = 3$

42. $\frac{1}{2} \sec x - 1 = 0$

43. $3 \csc^2 x = 4$

44. $4 \tan^2 x - 1 = \tan^2 x$

45. $4 \cos^2 x - 3 = 0$

46. $\sin x(\sin x + 1) = 0$

47. $\sin x - \tan x = 0$

48. $\csc x - 2 \cot x = 0$

In Exercises 49–58, find all solutions of the equation in the interval $[0, 2\pi)$. Use a graphing utility to check your answers.

49. $2 \cos^2 x - \cos x = 1$

50. $2 \sin^2 x - 3 \sin x = -1$

51. $\cos^2 x + \sin x = 1$

52. $\sin^2 x + 2 \cos x = 2$

53. $2 \sin 2x - \sqrt{2} = 0$

54. $\sqrt{3} \tan 3x = 0$

55. $\cos 4x(\cos x - 1) = 0$

56. $3 \csc^2 5x = -4$

57. $\cos 4x - 7 \cos 2x = 8$ **58.** $\sin 4x - \sin 2x = 0$

In Exercises 59–62, use the inverse functions where necessary to find all solutions of the equation in the interval $[0, 2\pi)$.

59. $\sin^2 x - 2 \sin x = 0$

60. $2 \cos^2 x + 3 \cos x = 0$

61. $\tan^2 \theta + \tan \theta - 12 = 0$

62. $\sec^2 x + 6 \tan x + 4 = 0$

6.4 In Exercises 63–66, find the exact values of the sine, cosine, and tangent of the angle.

63. $285° = 315° - 30°$

64. $345° = 300° + 45°$

65. $\dfrac{25\pi}{12} = \dfrac{11\pi}{6} + \dfrac{\pi}{4}$

66. $\dfrac{19\pi}{12} = \dfrac{11\pi}{6} - \dfrac{\pi}{4}$

In Exercises 67–70, write the expression as the sine, cosine, or tangent of an angle.

67. $\sin 140° \cos 50° + \cos 140° \sin 50°$

68. $\cos 45° \cos 120° - \sin 45° \sin 120°$

69. $\dfrac{\tan 25° + \tan 10°}{1 - \tan 25° \tan 10°}$

70. $\dfrac{\tan 68° - \tan 115°}{1 + \tan 68° \tan 115°}$

In Exercises 71–76, find the exact value of the trigonometric function given that $\sin u = \frac{3}{4}$ and $\cos v = -\frac{5}{13}$. (Both u and v are in Quadrant II.)

71. $\sin(u + v)$

72. $\tan(u + v)$

73. $\tan(u - v)$

74. $\sin(u - v)$

75. $\cos(u + v)$

76. $\cos(u - v)$

In Exercises 77–82, verify the identity.

77. $\cos\left(x + \dfrac{\pi}{2}\right) = -\sin x$ **78.** $\sin\left(x - \dfrac{3\pi}{2}\right) = \cos x$

79. $\cot\left(\dfrac{\pi}{2} - x\right) = \tan x$ **80.** $\sin(\pi - x) = \sin x$

81. $\cos 3x = 4 \cos^3 x - 3 \cos x$

82. $\dfrac{\sin(\alpha + \beta)}{\cos \alpha \cos \beta} = \tan \alpha + \tan \beta$

In Exercises 83 and 84, find the solutions of the equation in the interval $[0, 2\pi)$.

83. $\sin\left(x + \dfrac{\pi}{2}\right) - \sin\left(x - \dfrac{\pi}{2}\right) = \sqrt{3}$

84. $\cos\left(x + \dfrac{3\pi}{4}\right) - \cos\left(x - \dfrac{3\pi}{4}\right) = 0$

6.5 In Exercises 85–88, find the exact values of $\sin 2u$, $\cos 2u$, and $\tan 2u$ using the double-angle formulas.

85. $\sin u = -\dfrac{5}{7}$, $\pi < u < \dfrac{3\pi}{2}$

86. $\cos u = \dfrac{4}{5}$, $\dfrac{3\pi}{2} < u < 2\pi$

87. $\tan u = -\dfrac{2}{9}$, $\dfrac{\pi}{2} < u < \pi$

88. $\cos u = -\dfrac{2}{\sqrt{5}}$, $\dfrac{\pi}{2} < u < \pi$

In Exercises 89–92, use double-angle formulas to verify the identity algebraically. Use a graphing utility to check your result graphically.

89. $6 \sin x \cos x = 3 \sin 2x$

90. $4 \sin x \cos x + 2 = 2 \sin 2x + 2$

91. $1 - 4 \sin^2 x \cos^2 x = \cos^2 2x$

92. $\sin 4x = 8 \cos^3 x \sin x - 4 \cos x \sin x$

93. *Projectile Motion* A baseball leaves the hand of the first baseman at an angle of θ with the horizontal and with an initial velocity of $v_0 = 80$ feet per second. The ball is caught by the second baseman 100 feet away. Find θ if the range r of a projectile is given by $r = \frac{1}{32} v_0^2 \sin 2\theta$.

94. *Projectile Motion* Use the equation in Exercise 93 to find θ when a golf ball is hit with an initial velocity of $v_0 = 50$ feet per second and lands 77 feet away.

∫ In Exercises 95–98, use the power-reducing formulas to rewrite the expression in terms of the first power of the cosine.

95. $\sin^6 x$

96. $\cos^4 x \sin^4 x$

97. $\cos^4 2x$

98. $\sin^4 2x$

In Exercises 99–102, use the half-angle formulas to determine the exact values of the sine, cosine, and tangent of the angle.

99. $105°$

100. $67° \, 30'$

101. $\dfrac{7\pi}{8}$

102. $\dfrac{11\pi}{12}$

In Exercises 103–106, find the exact values of $\sin(u/2)$, $\cos(u/2)$, and $\tan(u/2)$ using the half-angle formulas.

103. $\sin u = \dfrac{3}{5}$, $0 < u < \dfrac{\pi}{2}$

104. $\tan u = \dfrac{5}{8}$, $\pi < u < \dfrac{3\pi}{2}$

105. $\cos u = -\dfrac{2}{7}$, $\dfrac{\pi}{2} < u < \pi$

106. $\sec u = -6$, $\dfrac{\pi}{2} < u < \pi$

In Exercises 107 and 108, use the half-angle formulas to simplify the expression.

107. $-\sqrt{\dfrac{1 + \cos 10x}{2}}$ **108.** $\dfrac{\sin 6x}{1 + \cos 6x}$

Geometry In Exercises 109 and 110, a trough for feeding cattle is 4 meters long and its cross sections are isosceles triangles with two equal sides of $\frac{1}{2}$ meter (see figure). The angle between the equal sides is θ.

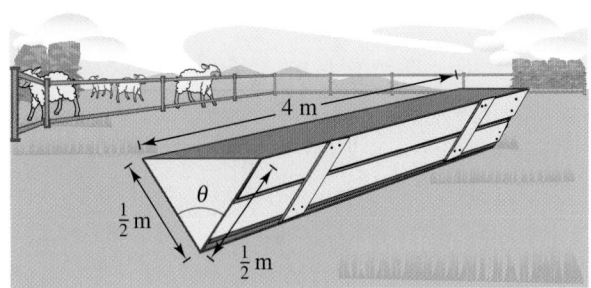

109. Write the trough's volume as a function of $\theta/2$.

110. Write the volume of the trough as a function of θ and determine the value of θ such that the volume is maximum.

In Exercises 111–114, use the product-to-sum formulas to write the product as a sum or difference.

111. $6 \sin \dfrac{\pi}{4} \cos \dfrac{\pi}{4}$ **112.** $4 \sin 15° \sin 45°$

113. $\sin 3\alpha \sin 2\alpha$ **114.** $\cos 4\theta \sin 6\theta$

In Exercises 115–118, use the sum-to-product formulas to write the sum or difference as a product.

115. $\cos 3\theta + \cos 2\theta$ **116.** $\sin 5\theta + \sin 3\theta$

117. $\sin\left(x + \dfrac{\pi}{4}\right) - \sin\left(x - \dfrac{\pi}{4}\right)$

118. $\cos\left(x + \dfrac{\pi}{6}\right) - \cos\left(x - \dfrac{\pi}{6}\right)$

Harmonic Motion In Exercises 119–122, a weight is attached to a spring suspended vertically from a ceiling. When a driving force is applied to the system, the weight moves vertically from its equilibrium position. This motion is described by the model

$$y = 1.5 \sin 8t - 0.5 \cos 8t$$

where y is the distance from equilibrium in feet and t is the time in seconds.

119. Write the model in the form
$$y = \sqrt{a^2 + b^2}\, \sin(Bt + C).$$

120. Use a graphing utility to graph the model.

121. Find the amplitude of the oscillations of the weight.

122. Find the frequency of the oscillations of the weight.

Synthesis

True or False? In Exercises 123–126, determine whether the statement is true or false. Justify your answer.

123. If $\dfrac{\pi}{2} < \theta < \pi$, then $\cos \dfrac{\theta}{2} < 0$.

124. $\sin(x + y) = \sin x + \sin y$

125. $4 \sin(-x) \cos(-x) = -2 \sin 2x$

126. $4 \sin 45° \cos 15° = 1 + \sqrt{3}$

127. List the reciprocal identities, quotient identities, and Pythagorean identities from memory.

128. Is $\cos \theta = \sqrt{1 - \sin^2 \theta}$ an identity? Explain.

In Exercises 129 and 130, use the graphs of y_1 and y_2 to determine how to change y_2 to a new function y_3 such that $y_1 = y_3$.

129. $y_1 = \sec^2\left(\dfrac{\pi}{2} - x\right)$ **130.** $y_1 = \dfrac{\cos 3x}{\cos x}$

      $y_2 = \cot^2 x$ $y_2 = (2 \sin x)^2$

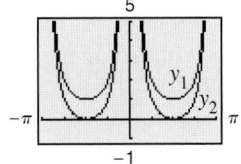   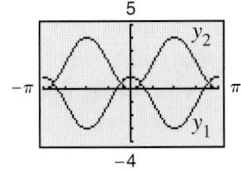

6 | Chapter Test

Take this test as you would take a test in class. After you are finished, check your work against the answers given in the back of the book.

1. If $\tan \theta = \frac{6}{5}$ and $\cos \theta < 0$, use the fundamental identities to evaluate the other five trigonometric functions of θ.

2. Use the fundamental identities to simplify $\csc^2 \beta (1 - \cos^2 \beta)$.

3. Factor and simplify $\dfrac{\sec^4 x - \tan^4 x}{\sec^2 x + \tan^2 x}$.

4. Add and simplify $\dfrac{\cos \theta}{\sin \theta} + \dfrac{\sin \theta}{\cos \theta}$.

5. Determine the values of θ, $0 \le \theta < 2\pi$, for which $\tan \theta = -\sqrt{\sec^2 \theta - 1}$ is true.

6. Use a graphing utility to graph the functions $y_1 = \cos x + \sin x \tan x$ and $y_2 = \sec x$. Make a conjecture about y_1 and y_2. Verify your result algebraically.

In Exercises 7–12, verify the identity.

7. $\sin \theta \sec \theta = \tan \theta$

8. $\sec^2 x \tan^2 x + \sec^2 x = \sec^4 x$

9. $\dfrac{\csc \alpha + \sec \alpha}{\sin \alpha + \cos \alpha} = \cot \alpha + \tan \alpha$

10. $\cos\left(x + \dfrac{\pi}{2}\right) = -\sin x$

11. $\cos(\pi - \theta) + \sin\left(\dfrac{\pi}{2} + \theta\right) = 0$

12. $(\sin x + \cos x)^2 = 1 + \sin 2x$

13. Find the exact value of $\tan 105°$.

14. Rewrite $\sin^4 x \tan^2 x$ in terms of the first power of the cosine.

15. Use a half-angle formula to simplify the expression $\dfrac{\sin 4\theta}{1 + \cos 4\theta}$.

16. Write $6 \sin 4\theta \sin 6\theta$ as a sum or difference.

17. Write $\cos 5\theta + \cos 3\theta$ as a product.

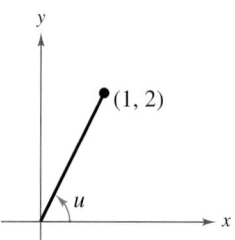

Figure for 23

In Exercises 18–21, find all solutions of the equation in the interval $[0, 2\pi)$.

18. $\tan^2 x + \tan x = 0$

19. $\sin 2\alpha - \cos \alpha = 0$

20. $4 \cos^2 x - 3 = 0$

21. $\csc^2 x - \csc x - 2 = 0$

22. Use a graphing utility to approximate the solutions of the equation $5 \cos x - x = 0$ in the interval $[0, 2\pi)$ accurate to three decimal places.

23. Use the figure at the right to find the exact values of $\sin 2u$, $\cos 2u$, and $\tan 2u$.

24. The *index of refraction* n of a transparent material is the ratio of the speed of light in a vacuum to the speed of light in the material. For the glass triangular prism in the figure at the right, $n = 1.5$ and $\alpha = 60°$. Find the angle θ for the glass prism if

$$n = \frac{\sin(\theta/2 + \alpha/2)}{\sin(\theta/2)}.$$

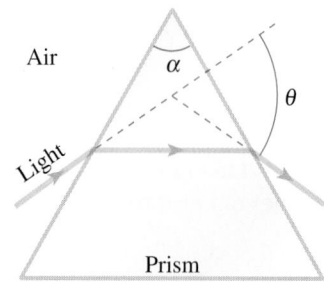

Figure for 24

The Law of Sines can be used to determine the angles and sides of triangles that occur in real-life applications. For example, you can model an airplane's glide path at landing and determine the altitude of the plane at the moment it begins its descent.

Zefa Visual Media-Germany/Index Stock

7 Additional Topics in Trigonometry

7.1 Law of Sines
7.2 Law of Cosines
7.3 Vectors in the Plane
7.4 Vectors and Dot Products
7.5 Trigonometric Form of a Complex Number

What You Should Learn

In this chapter, you will learn how to:

■ Use the Law of Sines and the Law of Cosines to solve oblique triangles.

■ Find areas of oblique triangles.

■ Represent vectors as directed line segments and perform mathematical operations on vectors.

■ Find direction angles of vectors.

■ Find the dot product of two vectors and use properties of the dot product.

■ Multiply and divide complex numbers written in trigonometric form.

■ Find powers and nth roots of complex numbers.

7.1 Law of Sines

Introduction

In Chapter 5 you looked at techniques for solving right triangles. In this section and the next, you will solve **oblique triangles**—triangles that have no right angles. As standard notation, the angles of a triangle are labeled A, B, and C, and their opposite sides are labeled a, b, and c, as shown in Figure 7.1.

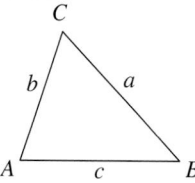

Figure 7.1

To solve an oblique triangle, you need to know the measure of at least one side and the measures of any two other parts of the triangle—two sides, two angles, or one angle and one side. This breaks down into the following four cases.

1. Two angles and any side (AAS or ASA)
2. Two sides and an angle opposite one of them (SSA)
3. Three sides (SSS)
4. Two sides and their included angle (SAS)

The first two cases can be solved using the **Law of Sines,** whereas the last two cases require the Law of Cosines (Section 7.2). See Appendix B for a proof of the Law of Sines.

Law of Sines

If ABC is a triangle with sides a, b, and c, then

$$\frac{a}{\sin A} = \frac{b}{\sin B} = \frac{c}{\sin C}.$$

Oblique Triangles

A is acute. A is obtuse.

The Law of Sines can also be written in the reciprocal form

$$\frac{\sin A}{a} = \frac{\sin B}{b} = \frac{\sin C}{c}.$$

Example 1   Given Two Angles and One Side—AAS

For the triangle in Figure 7.2, $C = 102.3°$, $B = 28.7°$, and $b = 27.4$ feet. Find the remaining angle and sides.

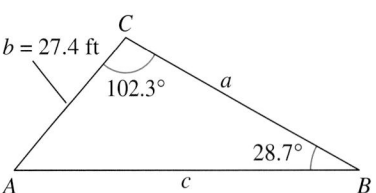

Figure 7.2

Solution

The third angle of the triangle is

$$A = 180° - B - C$$

$$= 180° - 28.7° - 102.3°$$

$$= 49.0°.$$

By the Law of Sines, you have

$$\frac{a}{\sin A} = \frac{b}{\sin B} = \frac{c}{\sin C}.$$

Using $b = 27.4$ produces

$$a = \frac{b}{\sin B}(\sin A) = \frac{27.4}{\sin 28.7°}(\sin 49.0°) \approx 43.06 \text{ feet}$$

and

$$c = \frac{b}{\sin B}(\sin C) = \frac{27.4}{\sin 28.7°}(\sin 102.3°) \approx 55.75 \text{ feet.}$$

✓ *Checkpoint* Now try Exercise 3.

Example 2   Given Two Angles and One Side—ASA

A pole tilts *toward* the sun at an 8° angle from the vertical, and it casts a 22-foot shadow. The angle of elevation from the tip of the shadow to the top of the pole is 43°. How tall is the pole?

Solution

In Figure 7.3, $A = 43°$ and $B = 90° + 8° = 98°$. So, the third angle is

$$C = 180° - A - B = 180° - 43° - 98° = 39°.$$

By the Law of Sines, you have

$$\frac{a}{\sin A} = \frac{c}{\sin C}.$$

Because $c = 22$ feet, the length of the pole is

$$a = \frac{c}{\sin C}(\sin A) = \frac{22}{\sin 39°}(\sin 43°) \approx 23.84 \text{ feet.}$$

✓ *Checkpoint* Now try Exercise 27.

For practice, try reworking Example 2 for a pole that tilts *away from* the sun under the same conditions.

> ## STUDY TIP
>
> When you are solving triangles, a careful sketch is useful as a quick test for the feasibility of an answer. Remember that the longest side lies opposite the largest angle, and the shortest side lies opposite the smallest angle.

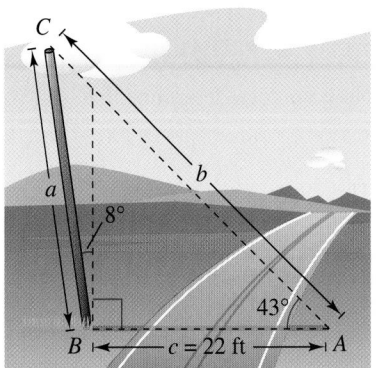

Figure 7.3

The Ambiguous Case (SSA)

In Examples 1 and 2 you saw that two angles and one side determine a unique triangle. However, if two sides and one opposite angle are given, three possible situations can occur: (1) no such triangle exists, (2) one such triangle exists, or (3) two distinct triangles satisfy the conditions.

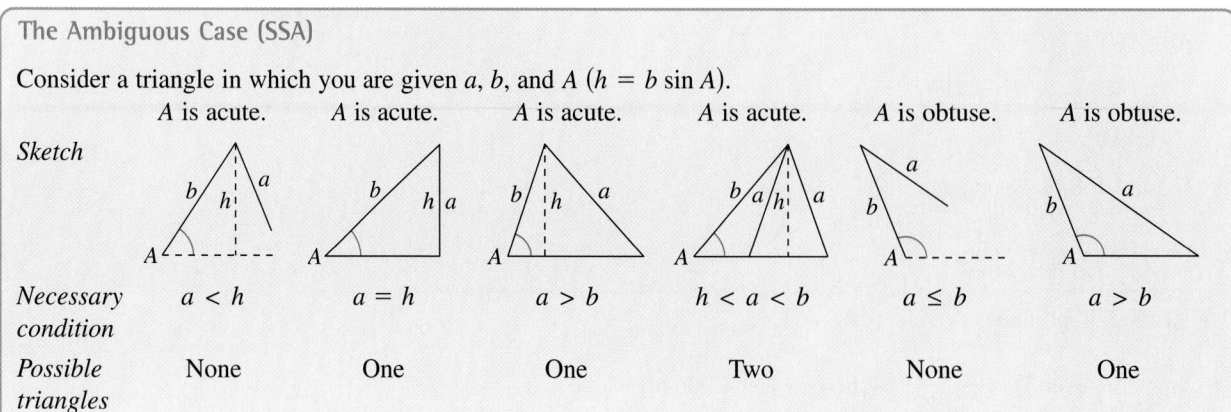

The Ambiguous Case (SSA)

Consider a triangle in which you are given a, b, and A ($h = b \sin A$).

	A is acute.	A is acute.	A is acute.	A is acute.	A is obtuse.	A is obtuse.
Necessary condition	$a < h$	$a = h$	$a > b$	$h < a < b$	$a \leq b$	$a > b$
Possible triangles	None	One	One	Two	None	One

Example 3 Single-Solution Case—SSA

For the triangle in Figure 7.4, $a = 22$ inches, $b = 12$ inches, and $A = 42°$. Find the remaining side and angles.

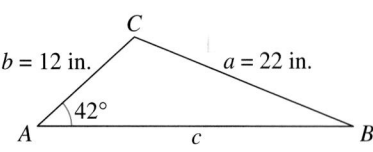

Figure 7.4 One solution: $a > b$

Solution

By the Law of Sines, you have

$$\frac{\sin B}{b} = \frac{\sin A}{a} \qquad \text{Reciprocal form}$$

$$\sin B = b\left(\frac{\sin A}{a}\right) \qquad \text{Multiply each side by } b.$$

$$\sin B = 12\left(\frac{\sin 42°}{22}\right) \qquad \text{Substitute for } A, a, \text{ and } b.$$

$$B \approx 21.41°. \qquad B \text{ is acute.}$$

Now you can determine that

$$C \approx 180° - 42° - 21.41° = 116.59°.$$

Then the remaining side is given by

$$\frac{c}{\sin C} = \frac{a}{\sin A}$$

$$c = \frac{a}{\sin A}(\sin C) = \frac{22}{\sin 42°}(\sin 116.59°) \approx 29.40 \text{ inches.}$$

✓ *Checkpoint* Now try Exercise 15.

Example 4   No-Solution Case—SSA

Show that there is no triangle for which $a = 15$, $b = 25$, and $A = 85°$.

Solution

Begin by making the sketch shown in Figure 7.5. From this figure it appears that no triangle is formed. You can verify this by using the Law of Sines.

$$\frac{\sin B}{b} = \frac{\sin A}{a} \qquad \text{Reciprocal form}$$

$$\sin B = b\left(\frac{\sin A}{a}\right) \qquad \text{Multiply each side by } b.$$

$$\sin B = 25\left(\frac{\sin 85°}{15}\right) \approx 1.660 > 1$$

This contradicts the fact that $|\sin B| \leq 1$. So, no triangle can be formed having sides $a = 15$ and $b = 25$ and an angle of $A = 85°$.

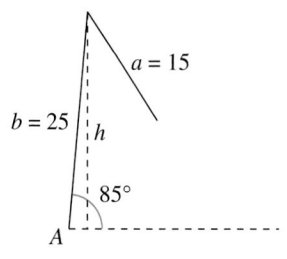

Figure 7.5   No solution: $a < h$

 Checkpoint Now try Exercise 17.

Example 5   Two-Solution Case—SSA

Find two triangles for which $a = 12$ meters, $b = 31$ meters, and $A = 20.5°$.

Solution

Because $h = b \sin A = 31(\sin 20.5°) \approx 10.86$ meters, you can conclude that there are two possible triangles (because $h < a < b$). By the Law of Sines, you have

$$\frac{\sin B}{b} = \frac{\sin A}{a} \qquad \text{Reciprocal form}$$

$$\sin B = b\left(\frac{\sin A}{a}\right) = 31\left(\frac{\sin 20.5°}{12}\right) \approx 0.9047.$$

There are two angles $B_1 \approx 64.8°$ and $B_2 \approx 180° - 64.8° = 115.2°$ between $0°$ and $180°$ whose sine is 0.9047. For $B_1 \approx 64.8°$, you obtain

$$C \approx 180° - 20.5° - 64.8° = 94.7°$$

$$c = \frac{a}{\sin A}(\sin C) = \frac{12}{\sin 20.5°}(\sin 94.7°) \approx 34.15 \text{ meters.}$$

For $B_2 \approx 115.2°$, you obtain

$$C \approx 180° - 20.5° - 115.2° = 44.3°$$

$$c = \frac{a}{\sin A}(\sin C) = \frac{12}{\sin 20.5°}(\sin 44.3°) \approx 23.93 \text{ meters.}$$

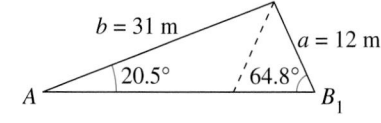

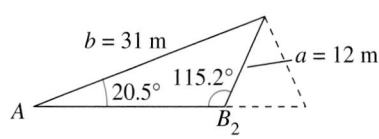

Figure 7.6   Two solutions: $h < a < b$

The resulting triangles are shown in Figure 7.6.

 Checkpoint Now try Exercise 19.

Area of an Oblique Triangle

The procedure used to prove the Law of Sines leads to a simple formula for the area of an oblique triangle. Referring to Figure 7.7, note that each triangle has a height of $h = b \sin A$. To see this when A is obtuse, substitute the reference angle $180° - A$ for A. Now the height of the triangle is given by

$$h = b \sin(180° - A).$$

Using the difference formula for sine, the height is given by

$$h = b(\sin 180° \cos A - \cos 180° \sin A) \qquad \text{\small $\sin(u - v) = \sin u \cos v - \cos u \sin v$}$$

$$= b[0 \cdot \cos A - (-1) \cdot \sin A]$$

$$= b \sin A.$$

Consequently, the area of each triangle is given by

$$\text{Area} = \frac{1}{2}(\text{base})(\text{height}) = \frac{1}{2}(c)(b \sin A) = \frac{1}{2}bc \sin A.$$

By similar arguments, you can develop the formulas

$$\text{Area} = \frac{1}{2}ab \sin C = \frac{1}{2}ac \sin B.$$

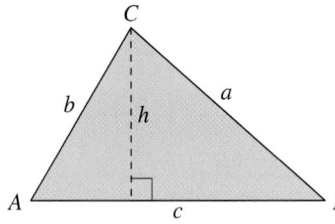

A is acute.

A is obtuse.

Figure 7.7

Area of an Oblique Triangle

The area of any triangle is one-half the product of the lengths of two sides times the sine of their included angle. That is,

$$\text{Area} = \frac{1}{2}bc \sin A = \frac{1}{2}ab \sin C = \frac{1}{2}ac \sin B.$$

Note that if angle A is 90°, the formula gives the area of a right triangle as

$$\text{Area} = \frac{1}{2}bc = \frac{1}{2}(\text{base})(\text{height}).$$

Similar results are obtained for angles C and B equal to 90°.

Example 6   Finding the Area of an Oblique Triangle

Find the area of a triangular lot having two sides of lengths 90 meters and 52 meters and an included angle of 102°.

Solution

Consider $a = 90$ meters, $b = 52$ meters, and $C = 102°$, as shown in Figure 7.8. Then the area of the triangle is

$$\text{Area} = \frac{1}{2}ab \sin C = \frac{1}{2}(90)(52)(\sin 102°) \approx 2289 \text{ square meters.}$$

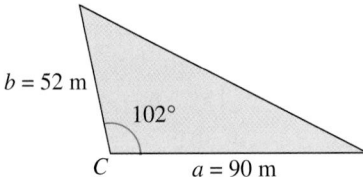

Figure 7.8

✓ *Checkpoint* Now try Exercise 21.

Example 7   An Application of the Law of Sines

The course for a boat race starts at point A and proceeds in the direction S 52° W to point B, then in the direction S 40° E to point C, and finally back to A, as shown in Figure 7.9. Point C lies 8 kilometers directly south of point A. Approximate the total distance of the race course.

Solution

Because lines BD and AC are parallel, it follows that $\angle BCA \cong \angle DBC$. Consequently, triangle ABC has the measures shown in Figure 7.10. For angle B, you have $B = 180° - 52° - 40° = 88°$. Using the Law of Sines

$$\frac{a}{\sin 52°} = \frac{b}{\sin 88°} = \frac{c}{\sin 40°}$$

you can let $b = 8$ and obtain

$$a = \frac{8}{\sin 88°}(\sin 52°) \approx 6.308$$

and

$$c = \frac{8}{\sin 88°}(\sin 40°) \approx 5.145.$$

The total length of the course is approximately

$$\text{Length} \approx 8 + 6.308 + 5.145 = 19.453 \text{ kilometers.}$$

✓ *Checkpoint* Now try Exercise 29.

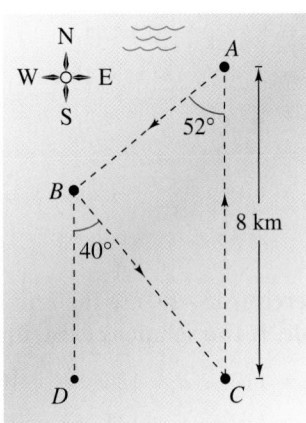

Figure 7.9

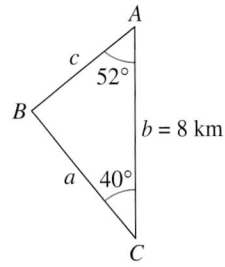

Figure 7.10

Exercises

Vocabulary Check

Fill in the blanks.

1. An _____ triangle is one that has no right angles.

2. Law of Sines: $\dfrac{a}{\sin A} =$ _____ $= \dfrac{c}{\sin C}$

3. To find the area of any triangle, use one of the following three formulas: Area = _____ , _____ , or _____ .

In Exercises 1–14, use the Law of Sines to solve the triangle.

1. $A = 30°,\quad a = 12,\quad B = 45°$
2. $C = 105°,\quad c = 20,\quad B = 40°$
3. $A = 10°,\quad a = 4.5,\quad B = 60°$
4. $C = 135°,\quad c = 45,\quad B = 10°$
5. $A = 36°,\quad a = 8,\quad b = 5$
6. $A = 60°,\quad a = 9,\quad c = 10$
7. $A = 102.4°,\quad C = 16.7°,\quad a = 21.6$
8. $A = 24.3°,\quad C = 54.6°,\quad c = 2.68$
9. $A = 83°\ 20',\quad C = 54.6°,\quad c = 18.1$
10. $A = 5°\ 40',\quad B = 8°\ 15',\quad b = 4.8$
11. $B = 15°\ 30',\quad a = 4.5,\quad b = 6.8$
12. $C = 85°\ 20',\quad a = 35,\quad c = 50$
13. $A = 110°\ 15',\quad a = 48,\quad b = 16$
14. $B = 2°\ 45',\quad b = 6.2,\quad c = 5.8$

In Exercises 15–20, use the Law of Sines to solve the triangle. If two solutions exist, find both.

15. $A = 110°,\quad a = 125,\quad b = 100$
16. $A = 110°,\quad a = 125,\quad b = 200$
17. $A = 76°,\quad a = 18,\quad b = 20$
18. $A = 76°,\quad a = 34,\quad b = 21$
19. $A = 58°,\quad a = 11.4,\quad b = 12.8$
20. $A = 58°,\quad a = 4.5,\quad b = 12.8$

In Exercises 21–26, find the area of the triangle having the indicated angle and sides.

21. $C = 110°,\quad a = 6,\quad b = 10$

22. $B = 130°,\quad a = 92,\quad c = 30$
23. $A = 38°\ 45',\quad b = 67,\quad c = 85$
24. $A = 5°\ 15',\quad b = 4.5,\quad c = 22$
25. $B = 74°\ 30',\quad a = 103,\quad c = 58$
26. $C = 84°\ 30',\quad a = 16,\quad b = 20$

27. *Height* A flagpole at a right angle to the horizontal is located on a slope that makes an angle of 14° with the horizontal. The flagpole casts a 16-meter shadow up the slope when the angle of elevation from the tip of the shadow to the sun is 20°.

    (a) Draw a triangle that represents the problem. Show the known quantities on the triangle and use a variable to indicate the height of the flagpole.

    (b) Write an equation involving the unknown quantity.

    (c) Find the height of the flagpole.

28. *Height* You are standing 40 meters from the base of a tree that is leaning 8° from vertical away from you. The angle of elevation from your feet to the top of the tree is 20° 50′.

    (a) Draw a triangle that represents the problem. Show the known quantities on the triangle and use a variable to indicate the height of the tree.

    (b) Write an equation involving the unknown height of the tree.

    (c) Find the height of the tree.

29. *Flight Path* A plane flies 500 kilometers with a bearing of 316° (clockwise from north) from Naples to Elgin (see figure on next page). The plane then flies 720 kilometers from Elgin to Canton. Find the bearing of the flight from Elgin to Canton.

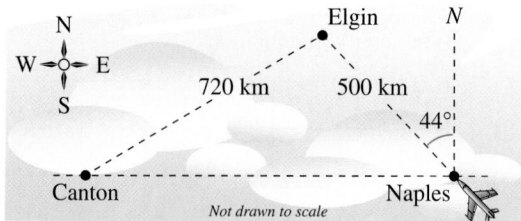

Figure for 29

30. Bridge Design A bridge is to be built across a small lake from a gazebo to a dock (see figure). The bearing from the gazebo to the dock is S 41° W. From a tree 100 meters from the gazebo, the bearings to the gazebo and the dock are S 74° E and S 28° E, respectively. Find the distance from the gazebo to the dock.

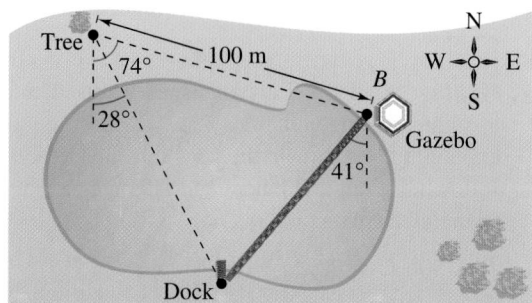

31. Railroad Track Design The circular arc of a railroad curve has a chord of length 3000 feet and a central angle of 40°.

(a) Draw a diagram that visually represents the problem. Show the known quantities on the diagram and use the variables r and s to represent the radius of the arc and the length of the arc, respectively.

(b) Find the radius r of the circular arc.

(c) Find the length s of the circular arc.

32. Glide Path A pilot has just started on the glide path for landing at an airport with a runway of length 9000 feet. The angles of depression from the plane to the ends of the runway are 17.5° and 18.8°.

(a) Draw a diagram that visually represents the problem.

(b) Find the air distance the plane must travel until touching down on the near end of the runway.

(c) Find the ground distance the plane must travel until touching down.

(d) Find the altitude of the plane when the pilot begins the descent.

33. Locating a Fire The bearing from the Pine Knob fire tower to the Colt Station fire tower is N 65° E, and the two towers are 30 kilometers apart. A fire spotted by rangers in each tower has a bearing of N 80° E from Pine Knob and S 70° E from Colt Station. Find the distance of the fire from each tower.

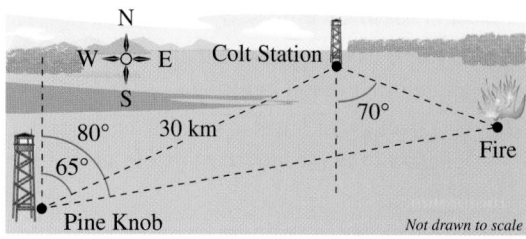

34. Distance A boat is sailing due east parallel to the shoreline at a speed of 10 miles per hour. At a given time the bearing to the lighthouse is S 70° E, and 15 minutes later the bearing is S 63° E (see figure). The lighthouse is located at the shoreline. Find the distance from the boat to the shoreline.

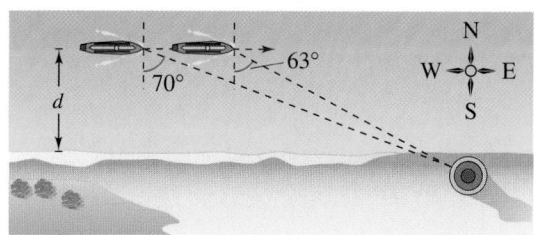

35. Angle of Elevation A 10-meter telephone pole casts a 17-meter shadow directly down a slope when the angle of elevation of the sun is 42° (see figure). Find θ, the angle of elevation of the ground.

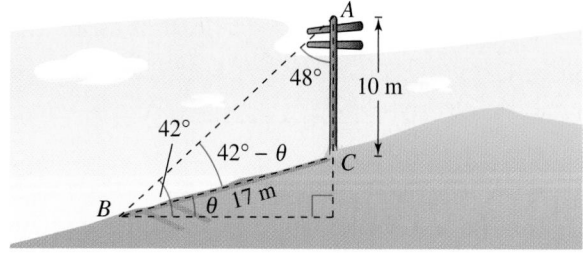

36. Distance The angles of elevation θ and ϕ to an airplane are being continuously monitored at two observation points A and B, respectively, which are 2 miles apart, and the airplane is east of both points in the same vertical plane.

(a) Draw a diagram that illustrates the problem.

(b) Write an equation giving the distance d between the plane and point B in terms of θ and ϕ.

37. Shadow Length The Leaning Tower of Pisa in Italy leans because it was built on unstable soil—a mixture of clay, sand, and water. The tower is approximately 58.36 meters tall from its foundation (see figure). The top of the tower leans about 5.45 meters off center.

(a) Find the angle of lean α of the tower.

(b) Write β as a function of d and θ, where θ is the angle of elevation to the sun.

(c) Use the Law of Sines to write an equation for the length d of the shadow cast by the tower in terms of θ.

(d) Use a graphing utility to complete the table.

θ	10°	20°	30°	40°	50°	60°
d						

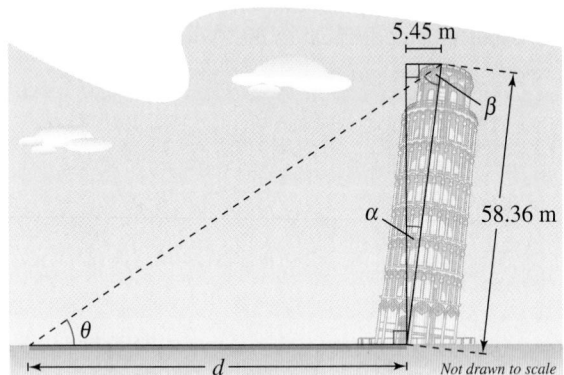

5.45 m

β

α 58.36 m

θ

d *Not drawn to scale*

38. Graphical and Numerical Analysis In the figure, α and β are positive angles.

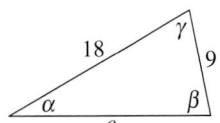

18   γ 9

α β
       c

(a) Write α as a function of β.

(b) Use a graphing utility to graph the function. Determine its domain and range.

(c) Use the result of part (b) to write c as a function of β.

(d) Use a graphing utility to graph the function in part (c). Determine its domain and range.

(e) Use a graphing utility to complete the table. What can you conclude?

β	0.4	0.8	1.2	1.6	2.0	2.4	2.8
α							
c							

Synthesis

True or False? In Exercises 39 and 40, determine whether the statement is true or false. Justify your answer.

39. If any three sides or angles of an oblique triangle are known, then the triangle can be solved.

40. If a triangle contains an obtuse angle, then it must be oblique.

41. Writing Can the Law of Sines be used to solve a right triangle? If so, write a short paragraph explaining how to use the Law of Sines to solve the following triangle. Is there an easier way to solve the triangle? Explain.

$$B = 50°, C = 90°, a = 10$$

42. Think About It Given $A = 36°$ and $a = 5$, find a value for b such that the triangle has (a) one solution, (b) two solutions, and (c) no solution.

Review

In Exercises 43–46, use the given values to find (if possible) the values of the six trigonometric functions of θ.

43. $\cos \theta = \frac{5}{13}$, $\sin \theta = -\frac{12}{13}$

44. $\tan \theta = \frac{2}{9}$, $\csc \theta = -\frac{\sqrt{85}}{2}$

45. $\sec \theta = -\frac{\sqrt{122}}{11}$, $\cot \theta = -11$

46. $\cot \theta$ is undefined, $\cos \theta < 0$

In Exercises 47–50, write the product as a sum or difference.

47. $6 \sin 8\theta \cos 3\theta$

48. $2 \cos 2\theta \cos 5\theta$

49. $3 \cos \frac{\pi}{6} \sin \frac{5\pi}{3}$

50. $\frac{5}{2} \sin \frac{3\pi}{4} \sin \frac{5\pi}{6}$

7.2 Law of Cosines

Introduction

Two cases remain in the list of conditions needed to solve an oblique triangle—SSS and SAS. To use the Law of Sines, you must know at least one side and its opposite angle. If you are given three sides (SSS), or two sides and their included angle (SAS), none of the ratios in the Law of Sines would be complete. In such cases you can use the **Law of Cosines.** See Appendix B for a proof of the Law of Cosines.

Law of Cosines

Standard Form	*Alternative Form*
$a^2 = b^2 + c^2 - 2bc \cos A$	$\cos A = \dfrac{b^2 + c^2 - a^2}{2bc}$
$b^2 = a^2 + c^2 - 2ac \cos B$	$\cos B = \dfrac{a^2 + c^2 - b^2}{2ac}$
$c^2 = a^2 + b^2 - 2ab \cos C$	$\cos C = \dfrac{a^2 + b^2 - c^2}{2ab}$

Example 1   Three Sides of a Triangle—SSS

Find the three angles of the triangle shown in Figure 7.11.

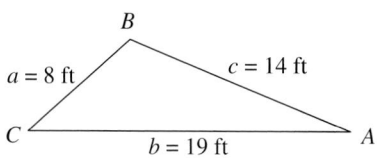

Figure 7.11

Solution

It is a good idea first to find the angle opposite the longest side—side b in this case. Using the Law of Cosines, you find that

$$\cos B = \frac{a^2 + c^2 - b^2}{2ac} = \frac{8^2 + 14^2 - 19^2}{2(8)(14)} \approx -0.45089.$$

Because $\cos B$ is negative, you know that B is an *obtuse* angle given by $B \approx 116.80°$. At this point it is simpler to use the Law of Sines to determine A.

$$\sin A = a\left(\frac{\sin B}{b}\right) \approx 8\left(\frac{\sin 116.80°}{19}\right) \approx 0.37583$$

Because B is obtuse, A must be acute, because a triangle can have at most one obtuse angle. So, $A \approx 22.08°$ and $C \approx 180° - 22.08° - 116.80° = 41.12°$.

☑ *Checkpoint* Now try Exercise 1.

Do you see why it was wise to find the largest angle *first* in Example 1? Knowing the cosine of an angle, you can determine whether the angle is acute or obtuse. That is,

$$\cos \theta > 0 \quad \text{for} \quad 0° < \theta < 90°$$ Acute

$$\cos \theta < 0 \quad \text{for} \quad 90° < \theta < 180°.$$ Obtuse

So, in Example 1, once you found that angle B was obtuse, you knew that angles A and C were both acute. Furthermore, if the largest angle is acute, the remaining two angles are also acute.

Example 2   Two Sides and the Included Angle—SAS

Find the remaining angles and the side of the triangle shown in Figure 7.12.

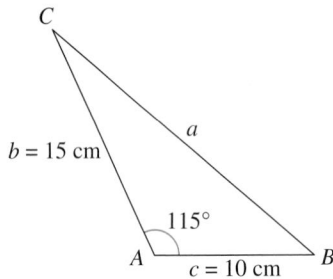

Figure 7.12

Solution

Use the Law of Cosines to find the unknown side a in the figure.

$$a^2 = b^2 + c^2 - 2bc \cos A$$

$$a^2 = 15^2 + 10^2 - 2(15)(10) \cos 115°$$

$$a^2 \approx 451.79$$

$$a \approx 21.26$$

Because $a \approx 21.26$ centimeters, you now know the ratio $\sin A/a$ and you can use the reciprocal form of the Law of Sines

$$\frac{\sin B}{b} = \frac{\sin A}{a}$$

to solve for B.

$$\sin B = b\left(\frac{\sin A}{a}\right)$$

$$= 15\left(\frac{\sin 115°}{21.26}\right)$$

$$\approx 0.63945$$

So, $B \approx \arcsin 0.63945 \approx 39.75°$, and $C \approx 180° - 115° - 39.75° = 25.25°$.

✓ *Checkpoint* Now try Exercise 3.

Applications

Example 3   An Application of the Law of Cosines

The pitcher's mound on a women's softball field is 43 feet from home plate and the distance between the bases is 60 feet, as shown in Figure 7.13. (The pitcher's mound is *not* halfway between home plate and second base.) How far is the pitcher's mound from first base?

Solution

In triangle *HPF*, $H = 45°$ (line *HP* bisects the right angle at *H*), $f = 43$, and $p = 60$. Using the Law of Cosines for this SAS case, you have

$$h^2 = f^2 + p^2 - 2fp \cos H$$

$$= 43^2 + 60^2 - 2(43)(60) \cos 45°$$

$$\approx 1800.3.$$

So, the approximate distance from the pitcher's mound to first base is

$$h \approx \sqrt{1800.3} \approx 42.43 \text{ feet.}$$

✓ *Checkpoint* Now try Exercise 25.

Figure 7.13

Example 4   An Application of the Law of Cosines

A ship travels 60 miles due east, then adjusts its course northward, as shown in Figure 7.14. After traveling 80 miles in the new direction, the ship is 139 miles from its point of departure. Describe the bearing from point *B* to point *C*.

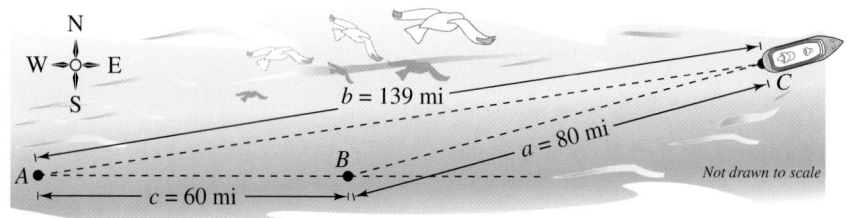

Figure 7.14

Solution

You have $a = 80$, $b = 139$, and $c = 60$; so, using the alternative form of the Law of Cosines, you have

$$\cos B = \frac{a^2 + c^2 - b^2}{2ac} = \frac{80^2 + 60^2 - 139^2}{2(80)(60)} \approx -0.97094.$$

So, $B \approx \arccos(-0.97094) \approx 166.15°$. Therefore, the bearing measured from due north from point *B* to point *C* is $166.15° - 90° = 76.15°$, or N 76.15° E.

 Checkpoint Now try Exercise 27.

Heron's Area Formula

The Law of Cosines can be used to establish the following formula for the area of a triangle. This formula is called **Heron's Area Formula** after the Greek mathematician Heron (ca. 100 B.C.). See Appendix B for a proof of Heron's Area Formula.

Heron's Area Formula

Given any triangle with sides of lengths a, b, and c, the area of the triangle is given by

$$\text{Area} = \sqrt{s(s-a)(s-b)(s-c)}$$

where $s = \dfrac{a+b+c}{2}$.

Example 5   Using Heron's Area Formula

Find the area of a triangle having sides of lengths $a = 43$ meters, $b = 53$ meters, and $c = 72$ meters.

Solution

Because $s = (a+b+c)/2 = 168/2 = 84$, Heron's Area Formula yields

$$\begin{aligned}
\text{Area} &= \sqrt{s(s-a)(s-b)(s-c)} \\
&= \sqrt{84(84-43)(84-53)(84-72)} \\
&= \sqrt{84(41)(31)(12)} \\
&\approx 1131.89 \text{ square meters.}
\end{aligned}$$

✓ *Checkpoint* Now try Exercise 35.

You have now studied three different formulas for the area of a triangle.

Formulas for Area of a Triangle

  1. Standard Formula: $\text{Area} = \frac{1}{2}bh$

  2. Oblique Triangle: $\text{Area} = \frac{1}{2}bc \sin A = \frac{1}{2}ab \sin C = \frac{1}{2}ac \sin B$

  3. Heron's Area Formula: $\text{Area} = \sqrt{s(s-a)(s-b)(s-c)}$

Exploration

Can the above formulas be used to find the area of any type of triangle? Explain the advantages and disadvantages of using one formula over another.

7.2   Exercises

Vocabulary Check

Fill in the blanks.

1. The standard form of the Law of Cosines for $\cos C = \dfrac{a^2 + b^2 - c^2}{2ab}$ is _____ .

2. _____ Formula is established by using the Law of Cosines.

3. Three different formulas for the area of a triangle are given by Area = _____ , Area = $\frac{1}{2}bc \sin A =$ $\frac{1}{2}ab \sin C = \frac{1}{2}ac \sin B$, and Area = _____ .

In Exercises 1–12, use the Law of Cosines to solve the triangle.

1. $a = 6$, $b = 8$, $c = 12$

2. $a = 9$, $b = 3$, $c = 11$

3. $A = 50°$, $b = 15$, $c = 30$

4. $C = 108°$, $a = 10$, $b = 7$

5. $a = 9$, $b = 12$, $c = 15$

6. $a = 45$, $b = 30$, $c = 72$

7. $a = 75.4$, $b = 48$, $c = 48$

8. $a = 1.42$, $b = 0.75$, $c = 1.25$

9. $B = 8° \, 15'$, $a = 26$, $c = 18$

10. $B = 10° \, 35'$, $a = 40$, $c = 30$

11. $B = 75° \, 20'$, $a = 6.2$, $c = 9.5$

12. $B = 15° \, 15'$, $a = 6.25$, $b = 2.15$

In Exercises 13–18, complete the table by solving the parallelogram shown in the figure. (The lengths of the diagonals are given by c and d.)

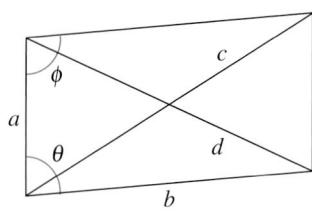

	a	b	c	d	θ	ϕ
13.	4	8			30°	
14.	25	35				120°
15.	10	14	20			
16.	40	60		80		
17.	15		25	20		
18.		25	50	35		

In Exercises 19–24, use Heron's Area Formula to find the area of the triangle.

19. $a = 5$, $b = 8$, $c = 10$

20. $a = 14$, $b = 17$, $c = 7$

21. $a = 3.5$, $b = 10.2$, $c = 9$

22. $a = 75.4$, $b = 52$, $c = 52$

23. $a = 10.59$, $b = 6.65$, $c = 12.31$

24. $a = 4.45$, $b = 1.85$, $c = 3.00$

25. **Navigation**   A plane flies 810 miles from Franklin to Centerville with a bearing of 75° (clockwise from north). Then it flies 648 miles from Centerville to Rosemont with a bearing of 32°. Draw a diagram that visually represents the problem, and find the straight-line distance and bearing from Rosemont to Franklin.

26. **Navigation**   A boat race runs along a triangular course marked by buoys A, B, and C. The race starts with the boats headed west for 3600 meters. The other two sides of the course lie to the north of the first side, and their lengths are 1500 meters and 2800 meters. Draw a diagram that visually represents the problem, and find the bearings for the last two legs of the race.

27. **Surveying**   To approximate the length of a marsh, a surveyor walks 380 meters from point A to point B. Then the surveyor turns 80° and walks 240 meters to point C (see figure). Approximate the length AC of the marsh.

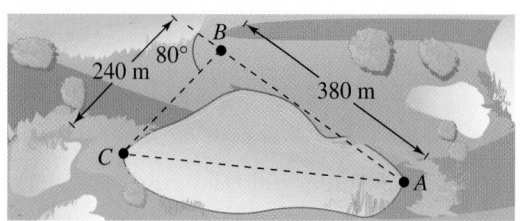

28. Streetlight Design Determine the angle θ in the design of the streetlight shown in the figure.

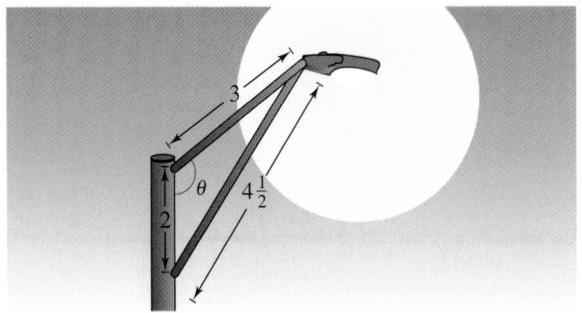

29. Distance Two ships leave a port at 9 A.M. One travels at a bearing of N 53° W at 12 miles per hour, and the other travels at a bearing of S 67° W at 16 miles per hour. Approximate how far apart the ships are at noon that day.

30. Length A 100-foot vertical tower is to be erected on the side of a hill that makes a 6° angle with the horizontal (see figure). Find the length of each of the two guy wires that will be anchored 75 feet uphill and downhill from the base of the tower.

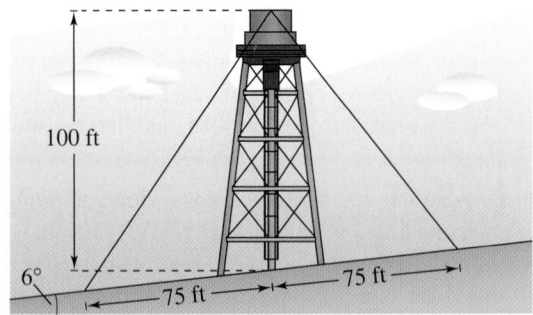

31. Navigation On a map, Orlando is 178 millimeters due south of Niagara Falls, Denver is 273 millimeters from Orlando, and Denver is 235 millimeters from Niagara Falls (see figure).

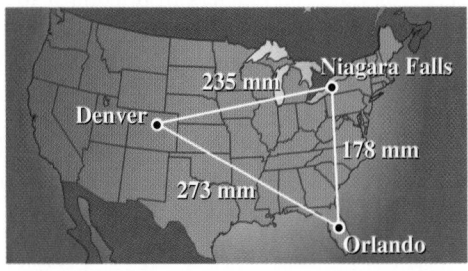

(a) Find the bearing of Denver from Orlando.

(b) Find the bearing of Denver from Niagara Falls.

32. Sports The baseball player in center field is playing approximately 330 feet from the television camera that is behind home plate. A batter hits a fly ball that goes to the wall 420 feet from the camera (see figure). The camera turns 6° to follow the play. Approximate the distance the center fielder has to run to make the catch.

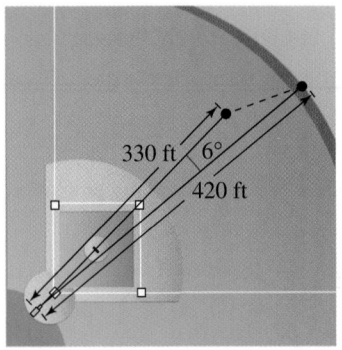

33. Trusses Q is the midpoint of the line segment $\overline{PR}$ in the truss rafter shown in the figure. What are the lengths of the line segments $\overline{PQ}$, $\overline{QS}$, and $\overline{RS}$?

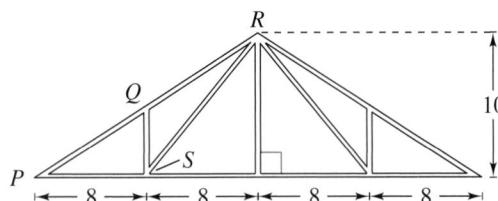

34. Awning Design A retractable awning above a patio lowers at an angle of 50° from the exterior wall at a height of 10 feet above the ground (see figure). No direct sunlight is to enter the door when the angle of elevation of the sun is greater than 70°. What is the length x of the awning?

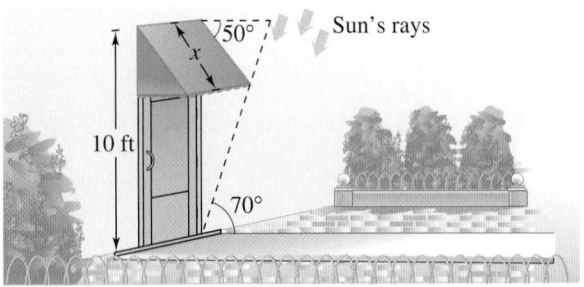

35. *Landau Building* The Landau Building in Cambridge, Massachusetts has a triangular-shaped base. The lengths of the sides of the triangular base are 145 feet, 257 feet, and 290 feet. Find the area of the base of the building.

36. *Geometry*   A parking lot has the shape of a parallelogram (see figure). The lengths of two adjacent sides are 70 meters and 100 meters. The angle between the two sides is 70°. What is the area of the parking lot?

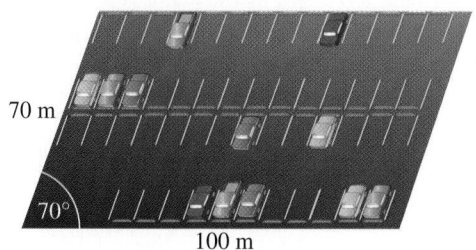

70 m
70°
100 m

37. *Engine Design*   An engine has a seven-inch connecting rod fastened to a crank (see figure).

(a) Use the Law of Cosines to write an equation giving the relationship between x and θ.

(b) Write x as a function of θ. (Select the sign that yields positive values of x.)

(c) Use a graphing utility to graph the function in part (b).

(d) Use the graph in part (c) to determine the total distance the piston moves in one cycle.

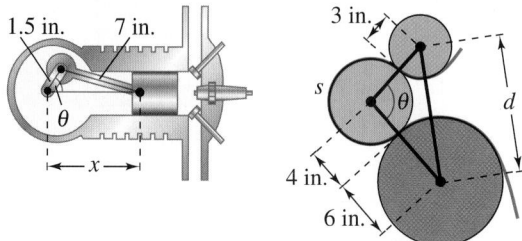

1.5 in.   7 in.
θ
x

3 in.
s
θ
d
4 in.
6 in.

Figure for 37   Figure for 38

38. *Manufacturing*   In a process with continuous paper, the paper passes across three rollers of radii 3 inches, 4 inches, and 6 inches (see figure). The centers of the three-inch and six-inch rollers are d inches apart, and the length of the arc in contact with the paper on the four-inch roller is s inches.

(a) Use the Law of Cosines to write an equation giving the relationship between d and θ.

(b) Write θ as a function of d.

(c) Write s as a function of θ.

(d) Complete the table.

d (inches)	9	10	12	13	14	15	16
θ (degrees)							
s (inches)							

Synthesis

True or False? **In Exercises 39–41, determine whether the statement is true or false. Justify your answer.**

39. A triangle with side lengths of 10 feet, 16 feet, and 5 feet can be solved using the Law of Cosines.

40. Two sides and their included angle determine a unique triangle.

41. In Heron's Area Formula, s is the average of the lengths of the three sides of the triangle.

42. *Proof*   Use the Law of Cosines to prove each of the following.

(a) $\dfrac{1}{2} bc(1 + \cos A) = \left(\dfrac{a + b + c}{2}\right)\left(\dfrac{-a + b + c}{2}\right)$

(b) $\dfrac{1}{2} bc(1 - \cos A) = \left(\dfrac{a - b + c}{2}\right)\left(\dfrac{a + b - c}{2}\right)$

Review

In Exercises 43–46, evaluate the expression without using a calculator.

43. $\arcsin(-1)$

44. $\cos^{-1} 0$

45. $\tan^{-1} \sqrt{3}$

46. $\arcsin\left(-\dfrac{\sqrt{3}}{2}\right)$

In Exercises 47 and 48, write the sum or difference as a product.

47. $\cos \dfrac{5\pi}{6} - \cos \dfrac{\pi}{3}$

48. $\sin\left(x - \dfrac{\pi}{2}\right) - \sin\left(x + \dfrac{\pi}{2}\right)$

7.3 Vectors in the Plane

Introduction

Many quantities in geometry and physics, such as area, time, and temperature, can be represented by a single real number. Other quantities, such as force and velocity, involve both *magnitude* and *direction* and cannot be completely characterized by a single real number. To represent such a quantity, you can use a **directed line segment,** as shown in Figure 7.15. The directed line segment $\overrightarrow{PQ}$ has **initial point** P and **terminal point** Q. Its **magnitude,** or **length,** is denoted by $\|\overrightarrow{PQ}\|$ and can be found by using the Distance Formula.

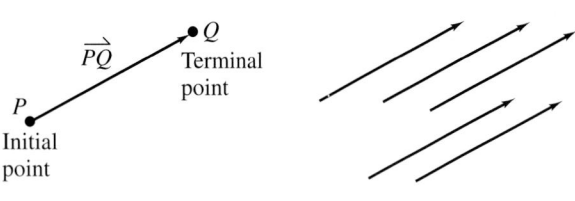

Figure 7.15   Figure 7.16

Two directed line segments that have the same magnitude and direction are *equivalent*. For example, the directed line segments in Figure 7.16 are all equivalent. The set of all directed line segments that are equivalent to a given directed line segment $\overrightarrow{PQ}$ is a **vector v in the plane,** written $\mathbf{v} = \overrightarrow{PQ}$. Vectors are denoted by lowercase, boldface letters such as $\mathbf{u}$, $\mathbf{v}$, and $\mathbf{w}$.

Example 1 Equivalent Directed Line Segments

Let $\mathbf{u}$ be represented by the directed line segment from $P = (0, 0)$ to $Q = (3, 2)$, and let $\mathbf{v}$ be represented by the directed line segment from $R = (1, 2)$ to $S = (4, 4)$, as shown in Figure 7.17. Show that $\mathbf{u} = \mathbf{v}$.

Solution

From the Distance Formula, it follows that $\overrightarrow{PQ}$ and $\overrightarrow{RS}$ have the *same magnitude*.

$$\|\overrightarrow{PQ}\| = \sqrt{(3 - 0)^2 + (2 - 0)^2} = \sqrt{13}$$
$$\|\overrightarrow{RS}\| = \sqrt{(4 - 1)^2 + (4 - 2)^2} = \sqrt{13}$$

Moreover, both line segments have the *same direction*, because they are both directed toward the upper right on lines having the same slope.

$$\text{Slope of } \overrightarrow{PQ} = \frac{2 - 0}{3 - 0} = \frac{2}{3}$$

$$\text{Slope of } \overrightarrow{RS} = \frac{4 - 2}{4 - 1} = \frac{2}{3}$$

So, $\overrightarrow{PQ}$ and $\overrightarrow{RS}$ have the same magnitude and direction, and it follows that $\mathbf{u} = \mathbf{v}$.

✓ *Checkpoint* Now try Exercise 1.

What you should learn

● Represent vectors as directed line segments.
● Write the component form of vectors.
● Perform basic vector operations and represent vectors graphically.
● Write vectors as linear combinations of unit vectors.
● Find the direction angles of vectors.
● Use vectors to model and solve real-life problems.

Why you should learn it

Vectors are used to analyze numerous aspects of everyday life. Exercise 78 on page 559 shows you how vectors can be used to determine the tension in the cables of two cranes lifting an object.

Sandra Baker/Getty Images

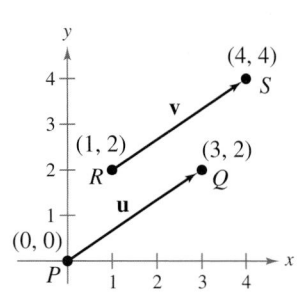

Figure 7.17

Component Form of a Vector

The directed line segment whose initial point is the origin is often the most convenient representative of a set of equivalent directed line segments. This representative of the vector **v** is in **standard position.**

A vector whose initial point is at the origin $(0, 0)$ can be uniquely represented by the coordinates of its terminal point (v_1, v_2). This is the **component form of a vector v,** written as

$$\mathbf{v} = \langle v_1, v_2 \rangle.$$

The coordinates v_1 and v_2 are the *components* of **v**. If both the initial point and the terminal point lie at the origin, **v** is the **zero vector** and is denoted by $\mathbf{0} = \langle 0, 0 \rangle$.

Component Form of a Vector

The component form of the vector with initial point $P = (p_1, p_2)$ and terminal point $Q = (q_1, q_2)$ is given by

$$\overrightarrow{PQ} = \langle q_1 - p_1, q_2 - p_2 \rangle = \langle v_1, v_2 \rangle = \mathbf{v}.$$

The **magnitude** (or length) of **v** is given by

$$\|\mathbf{v}\| = \sqrt{(q_1 - p_1)^2 + (q_2 - p_2)^2} = \sqrt{v_1^2 + v_2^2}.$$

If $\|\mathbf{v}\| = 1$, **v** is a **unit vector.** Moreover, $\|\mathbf{v}\| = 0$ if and only if **v** is the zero vector **0**.

Two vectors $\mathbf{u} = \langle u_1, u_2 \rangle$ and $\mathbf{v} = \langle v_1, v_2 \rangle$ are *equal* if and only if $u_1 = v_1$ and $u_2 = v_2$. For instance, in Example 1, the vector **u** from $P = (0, 0)$ to $Q = (3, 2)$ is

$$\mathbf{u} = \overrightarrow{PQ} = \langle 3 - 0, 2 - 0 \rangle = \langle 3, 2 \rangle$$

and the vector **v** from $R = (1, 2)$ to $S = (4, 4)$ is

$$\mathbf{v} = \overrightarrow{RS} = \langle 4 - 1, 4 - 2 \rangle = \langle 3, 2 \rangle.$$

Example 2   Finding the Component Form of a Vector

Find the component form and magnitude of the vector **v** that has initial point $(4, -7)$ and terminal point $(-1, 5)$.

Solution

Let $P = (4, -7) = (p_1, p_2)$ and $Q = (-1, 5) = (q_1, q_2)$, as shown in Figure 7.18. Then, the components of $\mathbf{v} = \langle v_1, v_2 \rangle$ are

$$v_1 = q_1 - p_1 = -1 - 4 = -5$$

$$v_2 = q_2 - p_2 = 5 - (-7) = 12.$$

So, $\mathbf{v} = \langle -5, 12 \rangle$ and the magnitude of **v** is

$$\|\mathbf{v}\| = \sqrt{(-5)^2 + 12^2} = \sqrt{169} = 13.$$

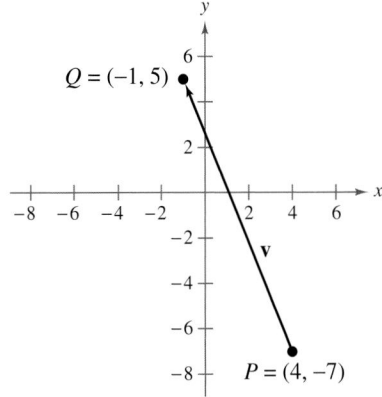

Figure 7.18

✓ *Checkpoint* Now try Exercise 11.

Vector Operations

The two basic vector operations are **scalar multiplication** and **vector addition.** Geometrically, the product of a vector **v** and a scalar k is the vector that is $|k|$ times as long as **v**. If k is positive, $k\mathbf{v}$ has the same direction as **v**, and if k is negative, $k\mathbf{v}$ has the opposite direction of **v**, as shown in Figure 7.19.

To add two vectors geometrically, position them (without changing their lengths or directions) so that the initial point of one coincides with the terminal point of the other. The sum **u** + **v** is formed by joining the initial point of the second vector **v** with the terminal point of the first vector **u**, as shown in Figure 7.20. This technique is called the **parallelogram law** for vector addition because the vector **u** + **v**, often called the **resultant** of vector addition, is the diagonal of a parallelogram having **u** and **v** as its adjacent sides.

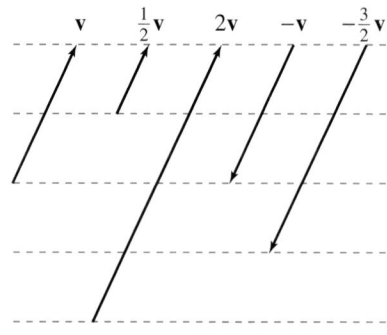

Figure 7.19

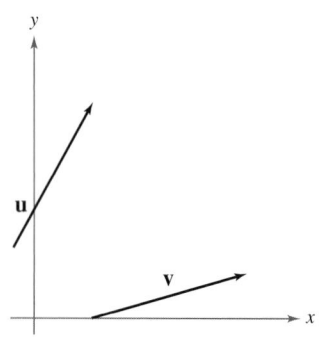
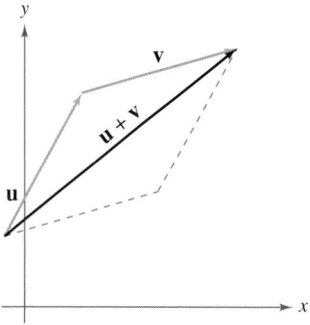

Figure 7.20

Definition of Vector Addition and Scalar Multiplication

Let $\mathbf{u} = \langle u_1, u_2 \rangle$ and $\mathbf{v} = \langle v_1, v_2 \rangle$ be vectors and let k be a scalar (a real number). Then the **sum** of **u** and **v** is the vector

$$\mathbf{u} + \mathbf{v} = \langle u_1 + v_1, u_2 + v_2 \rangle \qquad \text{Sum}$$

and the **scalar multiple** of k times **u** is the vector

$$k\mathbf{u} = k\langle u_1, u_2 \rangle = \langle ku_1, ku_2 \rangle. \qquad \text{Scalar multiple}$$

The **negative** of $\mathbf{v} = \langle v_1, v_2 \rangle$ is

$$-\mathbf{v} = (-1)\mathbf{v}$$
$$= \langle -v_1, -v_2 \rangle \qquad \text{Negative}$$

and the **difference** of **u** and **v** is

$$\mathbf{u} - \mathbf{v} = \mathbf{u} + (-\mathbf{v}) \qquad \text{Add } (-\mathbf{v}). \text{ See Figure 7.21.}$$
$$= \langle u_1 - v_1, u_2 - v_2 \rangle. \qquad \text{Difference}$$

To represent $\mathbf{u} - \mathbf{v}$ geometrically, you can use directed line segments with the *same* initial point. The difference $\mathbf{u} - \mathbf{v}$ is the vector from the terminal point of **v** to the terminal point of **u**, which is equal to $\mathbf{u} + (-\mathbf{v})$, as shown in Figure 7.21.

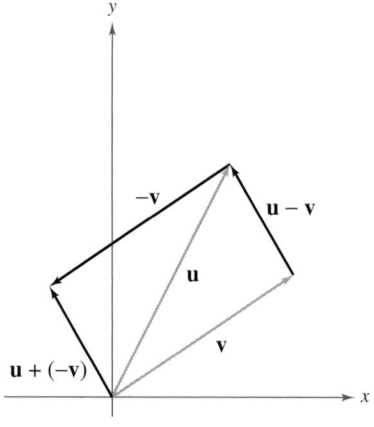

Figure 7.21

The component definitions of vector addition and scalar multiplication are illustrated in Example 3. In this example, notice that each of the vector operations can be interpreted geometrically.

Example 3   Vector Operations

Let $\mathbf{v} = \langle -2, 5 \rangle$ and $\mathbf{w} = \langle 3, 4 \rangle$, and find each of the following vectors.

a. $2\mathbf{v}$ **b.** $\mathbf{w} - \mathbf{v}$ **c.** $\mathbf{v} + 2\mathbf{w}$

Solution

a. Because $\mathbf{v} = \langle -2, 5 \rangle$, you have

$$2\mathbf{v} = 2\langle -2, 5 \rangle$$
$$= \langle 2(-2), 2(5) \rangle$$
$$= \langle -4, 10 \rangle.$$

A sketch of $2\mathbf{v}$ is shown in Figure 7.22.

b. The difference of $\mathbf{w}$ and $\mathbf{v}$ is

$$\mathbf{w} - \mathbf{v} = \langle 3 - (-2), 4 - 5 \rangle$$
$$= \langle 5, -1 \rangle.$$

A sketch of $\mathbf{w} - \mathbf{v}$ is shown in Figure 7.23.

c. The sum of $\mathbf{v}$ and $2\mathbf{w}$ is

$$\mathbf{v} + 2\mathbf{w} = \langle -2, 5 \rangle + 2\langle 3, 4 \rangle$$
$$= \langle -2, 5 \rangle + \langle 2(3), 2(4) \rangle$$
$$= \langle -2, 5 \rangle + \langle 6, 8 \rangle$$
$$= \langle -2 + 6, 5 + 8 \rangle$$
$$= \langle 4, 13 \rangle.$$

A sketch of $\mathbf{v} + 2\mathbf{w}$ is shown in Figure 7.24.

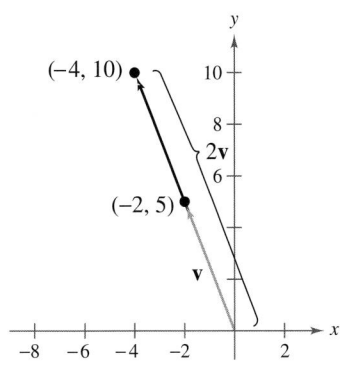

Figure 7.22

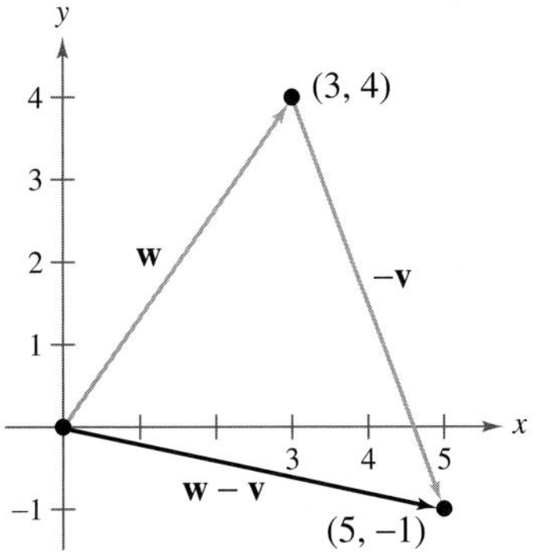

Figure 7.23

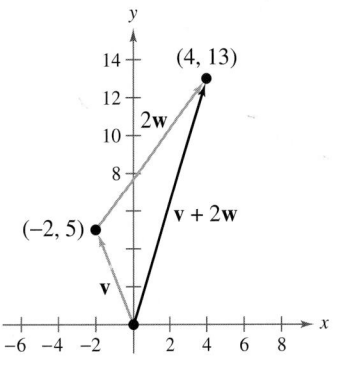

Figure 7.24

✓ *Checkpoint* Now try Exercise 19.

Note that Figure 7.23 shows the vector difference $\mathbf{w} - \mathbf{v}$ as the sum $\mathbf{w} + (-\mathbf{v})$.

Vector addition and scalar multiplication share many of the properties of ordinary arithmetic.

Properties of Vector Addition and Scalar Multiplication

Let **u**, **v**, and **w** be vectors and let c and d be scalars. Then the following properties are true.

1. $\mathbf{u} + \mathbf{v} = \mathbf{v} + \mathbf{u}$ 2. $(\mathbf{u} + \mathbf{v}) + \mathbf{w} = \mathbf{u} + (\mathbf{v} + \mathbf{w})$

3. $\mathbf{u} + \mathbf{0} = \mathbf{u}$ 4. $\mathbf{u} + (-\mathbf{u}) = \mathbf{0}$

5. $c(d\mathbf{u}) = (cd)\mathbf{u}$ 6. $(c + d)\mathbf{u} = c\mathbf{u} + d\mathbf{u}$

7. $c(\mathbf{u} + \mathbf{v}) = c\mathbf{u} + c\mathbf{v}$ 8. $1(\mathbf{u}) = \mathbf{u}, 0(\mathbf{u}) = \mathbf{0}$

9. $\|c\mathbf{v}\| = |c| \, \|\mathbf{v}\|$

STUDY TIP

Property 9 can be stated as follows: The magnitude of the vector $c\mathbf{v}$ is the absolute value of c times the magnitude of **v**.

Unit Vectors

In many applications of vectors, it is useful to find a unit vector that has the same direction as a given nonzero vector **v**. To do this, you can divide **v** by its length to obtain

$$\mathbf{u} = \text{unit vector} = \frac{\mathbf{v}}{\|\mathbf{v}\|} = \left(\frac{1}{\|\mathbf{v}\|}\right)\mathbf{v}. \qquad \text{Unit vector in direction of } \mathbf{v}$$

Note that **u** is a scalar multiple of **v**. The vector **u** has a magnitude of 1 and the same direction as **v**. The vector **u** is called a **unit vector in the direction of v.**

Example 4   Finding a Unit Vector

Find a unit vector in the direction of $\mathbf{v} = \langle -2, 5 \rangle$ and verify that the result has a magnitude of 1.

Solution

The unit vector in the direction of **v** is

$$\frac{\mathbf{v}}{\|\mathbf{v}\|} = \frac{\langle -2, 5 \rangle}{\sqrt{(-2)^2 + (5)^2}}$$

$$= \frac{1}{\sqrt{29}} \langle -2, 5 \rangle$$

$$= \left\langle \frac{-2}{\sqrt{29}}, \frac{5}{\sqrt{29}} \right\rangle.$$

This vector has a magnitude of 1 because

$$\sqrt{\left(\frac{-2}{\sqrt{29}}\right)^2 + \left(\frac{5}{\sqrt{29}}\right)^2} = \sqrt{\frac{4}{29} + \frac{25}{29}} = \sqrt{\frac{29}{29}} = 1.$$

✓ *Checkpoint* Now try Exercise 27.

The unit vectors $\langle 1, 0 \rangle$ and $\langle 0, 1 \rangle$ are called the **standard unit vectors** and are denoted by

$$\mathbf{i} = \langle 1, 0 \rangle \qquad \text{and} \qquad \mathbf{j} = \langle 0, 1 \rangle$$

as shown in Figure 7.25. (Note that the lowercase letter $\mathbf{i}$ is written in boldface to distinguish it from the imaginary number $i = \sqrt{-1}$.) These vectors can be used to represent any vector $\mathbf{v} = \langle v_1, v_2 \rangle$ as follows.

$$\begin{aligned} \mathbf{v} &= \langle v_1, v_2 \rangle \\ &= v_1 \langle 1, 0 \rangle + v_2 \langle 0, 1 \rangle \\ &= v_1 \mathbf{i} + v_2 \mathbf{j} \end{aligned}$$

The scalars v_1 and v_2 are called the **horizontal and vertical components of v**, respectively. The vector sum

$$v_1 \mathbf{i} + v_2 \mathbf{j}$$

is called a **linear combination** of the vectors $\mathbf{i}$ and $\mathbf{j}$. Any vector in the plane can be written as a linear combination of the standard unit vectors $\mathbf{i}$ and $\mathbf{j}$.

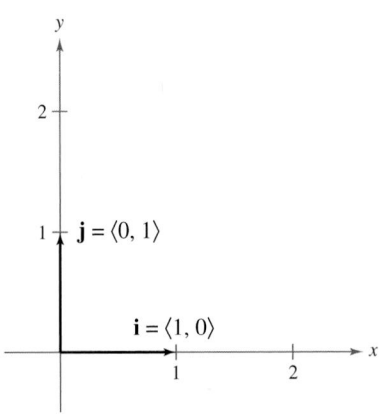

Figure 7.25

Example 5   Writing a Linear Combination of Unit Vectors

Let $\mathbf{u}$ be the vector with initial point $(2, -5)$ and terminal point $(-1, 3)$. Write $\mathbf{u}$ as a linear combination of the standard unit vectors $\mathbf{i}$ and $\mathbf{j}$.

Solution

Begin by writing the component form of the vector $\mathbf{u}$.

$$\begin{aligned} \mathbf{u} &= \langle -1 - 2, 3 - (-5) \rangle \\ &= \langle -3, 8 \rangle \\ &= -3\mathbf{i} + 8\mathbf{j} \end{aligned}$$

This result is shown graphically in Figure 7.26.

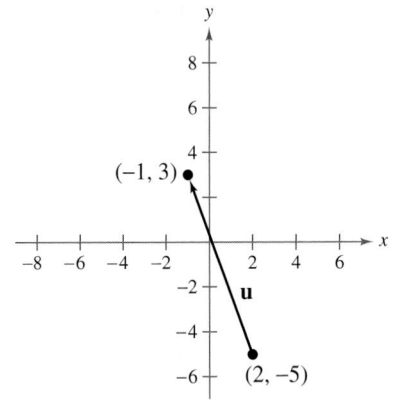

Figure 7.26

✓ *Checkpoint* Now try Exercise 41.

Example 6   Vector Operations

Let $\mathbf{u} = -3\mathbf{i} + 8\mathbf{j}$ and $\mathbf{v} = 2\mathbf{i} - \mathbf{j}$. Find $2\mathbf{u} - 3\mathbf{v}$.

Solution

You could solve this problem by converting $\mathbf{u}$ and $\mathbf{v}$ to component form. This, however, is not necessary. It is just as easy to perform the operations in unit vector form.

$$\begin{aligned} 2\mathbf{u} - 3\mathbf{v} &= 2(-3\mathbf{i} + 8\mathbf{j}) - 3(2\mathbf{i} - \mathbf{j}) \\ &= -6\mathbf{i} + 16\mathbf{j} - 6\mathbf{i} + 3\mathbf{j} \\ &= -12\mathbf{i} + 19\mathbf{j} \end{aligned}$$

✓ *Checkpoint* Now try Exercise 47.

Direction Angles

If **u** is a *unit vector* such that θ is the angle (measured counterclockwise) from the positive x-axis to **u**, the terminal point of **u** lies on the unit circle and you have

$$\mathbf{u} = \langle x, y \rangle = \langle \cos \theta, \sin \theta \rangle = (\cos \theta)\mathbf{i} + (\sin \theta)\mathbf{j}$$

as shown in Figure 7.27. The angle θ is the **direction angle** of the vector **u**.

Suppose that **u** is a unit vector with direction angle θ. If $\mathbf{v} = a\mathbf{i} + b\mathbf{j}$ is any vector that makes an angle θ with the positive x-axis, then it has the same direction as **u** and you can write

$$\mathbf{v} = \|\mathbf{v}\| \langle \cos \theta, \sin \theta \rangle$$
$$= \|\mathbf{v}\| (\cos \theta)\mathbf{i} + \|\mathbf{v}\| (\sin \theta)\mathbf{j}.$$

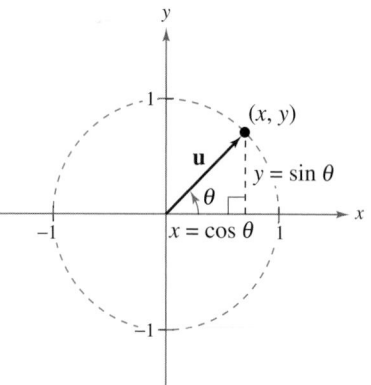

Figure 7.27

Because $\mathbf{v} = a\mathbf{i} + b\mathbf{j} = \|\mathbf{v}\| (\cos \theta)\mathbf{i} + \|\mathbf{v}\| (\sin \theta)\mathbf{j}$, it follows that the direction angle θ for **v** is determined from

$$\tan \theta = \frac{\sin \theta}{\cos \theta} \qquad \text{Quotient identity}$$

$$= \frac{\|\mathbf{v}\| \sin \theta}{\|\mathbf{v}\| \cos \theta} \qquad \text{Multiply numerator and denominator by } \|\mathbf{v}\|.$$

$$= \frac{b}{a}. \qquad \text{Simplify.}$$

Example 7 Finding Direction Angles of Vectors

Find the direction angle of each vector.

a. $\mathbf{u} = 3\mathbf{i} + 3\mathbf{j}$ **b.** $\mathbf{v} = 3\mathbf{i} - 4\mathbf{j}$

Solution

a. The direction angle is

$$\tan \theta = \frac{b}{a} = \frac{3}{3} = 1.$$

So, $\theta = 45°$, as shown in Figure 7.28.

b. The direction angle is

$$\tan \theta = \frac{b}{a} = \frac{-4}{3}.$$

Moreover, because $\mathbf{v} = 3\mathbf{i} - 4\mathbf{j}$ lies in Quadrant IV, θ lies in Quadrant IV and its reference angle is

$$\theta' = \left| \arctan\left(-\frac{4}{3}\right) \right| \approx |-53.13°| = 53.13°.$$

So, it follows that $\theta \approx 360° - 53.13° = 306.87°$, as shown in Figure 7.29.

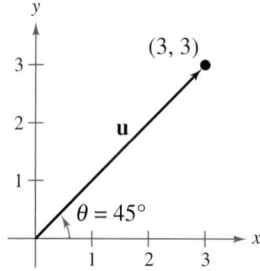

Figure 7.28

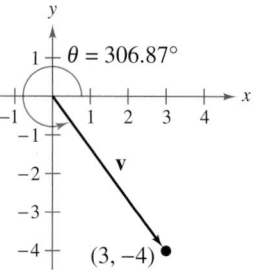

Figure 7.29

☑ *Checkpoint* Now try Exercise 55.

Applications of Vectors

Example 8   Finding the Component Form of a Vector

Find the component form of the vector that represents the velocity of an airplane descending at a speed of 100 miles per hour at an angle of 30° below the horizontal, as shown in Figure 7.30.

Solution

The velocity vector **v** has a magnitude of 100 and a direction angle of $\theta = 210°$.

$$\mathbf{v} = \|\mathbf{v}\| (\cos \theta)\mathbf{i} + \|\mathbf{v}\| (\sin \theta)\mathbf{j}$$

$$= 100(\cos 210°)\mathbf{i} + 100(\sin 210°)\mathbf{j}$$

$$= 100\left(-\frac{\sqrt{3}}{2}\right)\mathbf{i} + 100\left(-\frac{1}{2}\right)\mathbf{j}$$

$$= -50\sqrt{3}\,\mathbf{i} - 50\mathbf{j} = \langle -50\sqrt{3},\, -50 \rangle$$

You can check that **v** has a magnitude of 100 as follows.

$$\|\mathbf{v}\| = \sqrt{\left(-50\sqrt{3}\right)^2 + (-50)^2}$$

$$= \sqrt{7500 + 2500} = \sqrt{10{,}000} = 100 \qquad \text{Solution checks.} \ \checkmark$$

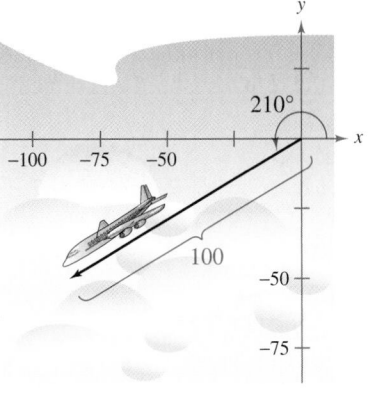

Figure 7.30

✅ *Checkpoint* Now try Exercise 75.

Example 9   Using Vectors to Determine Weight

A force of 600 pounds is required to pull a boat and trailer up a ramp inclined at 15° from the horizontal. Find the combined weight of the boat and trailer.

Solution

Based on Figure 7.31, you can make the following observations.

$\|\overrightarrow{BA}\|$ = force of gravity = combined weight of boat and trailer

$\|\overrightarrow{BC}\|$ = force against ramp

$\|\overrightarrow{AC}\|$ = force required to move boat up ramp = 600 pounds

By construction, triangles BWD and ABC are similar. So, angle ABC is 15°. In triangle ABC you have

$$\sin 15° = \frac{\|\overrightarrow{AC}\|}{\|\overrightarrow{BA}\|} = \frac{600}{\|\overrightarrow{BA}\|}$$

$$\|\overrightarrow{BA}\| = \frac{600}{\sin 15°} \approx 2318.$$

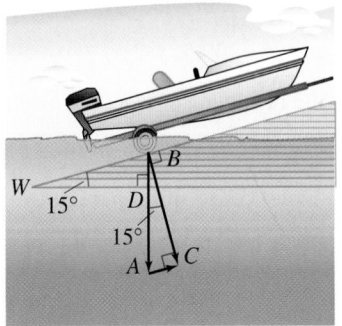

Figure 7.31

So, the combined weight is approximately 2318 pounds. (In Figure 7.31, note that $\overrightarrow{AC}$ is parallel to the ramp.)

✅ *Checkpoint* Now try Exercise 77.

Example 10 Using Vectors to Find Speed and Direction

An airplane is traveling at a speed of 500 miles per hour with a bearing of 330° at a fixed altitude with a negligible wind velocity, as shown in Figure 7.32(a). As the airplane reaches a certain point, it encounters a wind blowing with a velocity of 70 miles per hour in the direction N 45° E, as shown in Figure 7.32(b). What are the resultant speed and direction of the airplane?

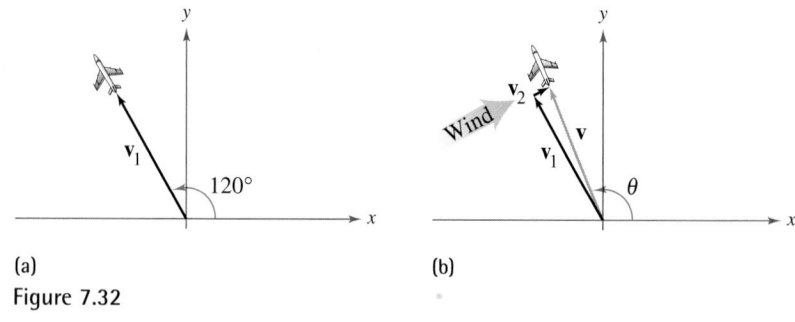

(a)   (b)

Figure 7.32

Solution

Using Figure 7.32, the velocity of the airplane (alone) is

$$\mathbf{v}_1 = 500\langle \cos 120°, \sin 120° \rangle$$
$$= \langle -250, 250\sqrt{3} \rangle$$

and the velocity of the wind is

$$\mathbf{v}_2 = 70\langle \cos 45°, \sin 45° \rangle$$
$$= \langle 35\sqrt{2}, 35\sqrt{2} \rangle.$$

So, the velocity of the airplane (in the wind) is

$$\mathbf{v} = \mathbf{v}_1 + \mathbf{v}_2$$
$$= \langle -250 + 35\sqrt{2}, 250\sqrt{3} + 35\sqrt{2} \rangle$$
$$\approx \langle -200.5, 482.5 \rangle$$

and the resultant speed of the airplane is

$$\|\mathbf{v}\| = \sqrt{(-200.5)^2 + (482.5)^2}$$
$$\approx 522.5 \text{ miles per hour.}$$

Finally, if θ is the direction angle of the flight path, you have

$$\tan \theta = \frac{482.5}{-200.5} \approx -2.4065$$

which implies that

$$\theta \approx 180° + \arctan(-2.4065) \approx 180° - 67.4° = 112.6°.$$

So, the true direction of the airplane is 337.4°.

✓ *Checkpoint* Now try Exercise 81.

7.3 Exercises

Vocabulary Check

Fill in the blanks.

1. A _____ can be used to represent a quantity that involves both magnitude and direction.
2. The directed line segment $\overrightarrow{PQ}$ has _____ point P and _____ point Q.
3. The _____ of the directed line segment $\overrightarrow{PQ}$ is denoted by $\|\overrightarrow{PQ}\|$.
4. The set of all directed line segments that are equivalent to a given directed line segment $\overrightarrow{PQ}$ is a _____ **v** in the plane.
5. The directed line segment whose initial point is the origin is said to be in _____ .
6. A vector that has a magnitude of 1 is called a _____ .
7. The two basic vector operations are scalar _____ and vector _____ .
8. The vector **u** + **v** is called the _____ of vector addition.
9. The vector sum $v_1\mathbf{i} + v_2\mathbf{j}$ is called a _____ of the vectors **i** and **j**, and the scalars v_1 and v_2 are called the _____ and _____ components of **v**, respectively.

In Exercises 1 and 2, show that u = v.

1.

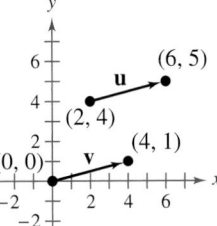

2.

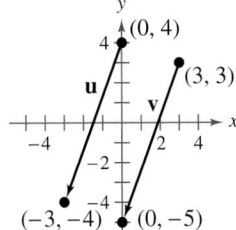

In Exercises 3–12, find the component form and the magnitude of the vector v.

3.

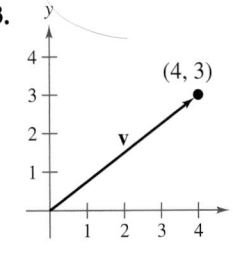

4.

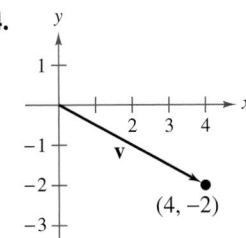

5.

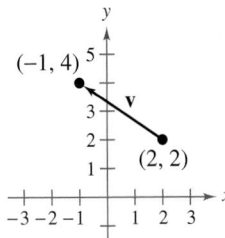

6.

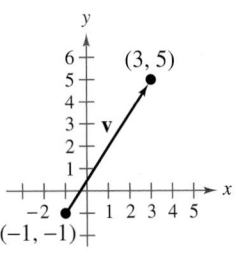

7.

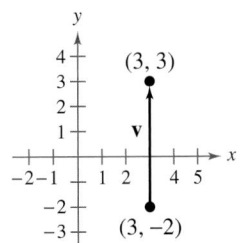

8.

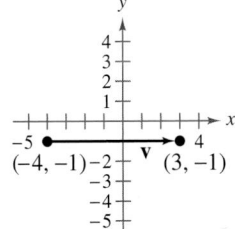

	Initial Point	Terminal Point
9.	$\left(\frac{5}{2}, 1\right)$	$\left(-2, -\frac{3}{2}\right)$
10.	$(3.4, 0)$	$(0, 5.8)$
11.	$(-3, -5)$	$(5, 1)$
12.	$(-3, 11)$	$(9, 40)$

In Exercises 13–18, use the figure to sketch a graph of the specified vector. To print an enlarged copy of the graph, go to the website *www.mathgraphs.com*.

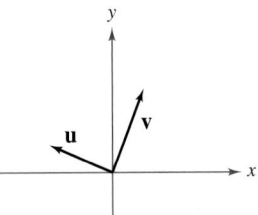

13. $-\mathbf{v}$

14. $3\mathbf{u}$

15. $\mathbf{u} + \mathbf{v}$

16. $\mathbf{u} - \mathbf{v}$

17. $\mathbf{u} + 2\mathbf{v}$

18. $\mathbf{v} - \frac{1}{2}\mathbf{u}$

In Exercises 19–24, find (a) u + v, (b) u − v, (c) 2u − 3v, and (d) v + 4u.

19. $u = \langle 4, 2 \rangle$, $v = \langle 7, 1 \rangle$

20. $u = \langle 5, 3 \rangle$, $v = \langle -4, 0 \rangle$

21. $u = \langle -6, -8 \rangle$, $v = \langle 2, 4 \rangle$

22. $u = \langle 0, -5 \rangle$, $v = \langle -3, 9 \rangle$

23. $u = i + j$, $v = 2i - 3j$

24. $u = 2i - j$, $v = -i + j$

In Exercises 25–34, find a unit vector in the direction of the given vector.

25. $u = \langle 6, 0 \rangle$ **26.** $u = \langle 0, -2 \rangle$

27. $v = \langle -1, 1 \rangle$ **28.** $v = \langle 3, -4 \rangle$

29. $v = \langle -24, -7 \rangle$ **30.** $v = \langle 8, -20 \rangle$

31. $v = 4i - 3j$ **32.** $w = i - 2j$

33. $w = 2j$ **34.** $w = -3i$

In Exercises 35–40, find the vector v with the given magnitude and the same direction as u.

Magnitude	Direction
35. $\|v\| = 8$	$u = \langle 5, 6 \rangle$
36. $\|v\| = 3$	$u = \langle 4, -4 \rangle$
37. $\|v\| = 7$	$u = 3i + 4j$
38. $\|v\| = 10$	$u = 2i - 3j$
39. $\|v\| = 8$	$u = -2i$
40. $\|v\| = 4$	$u = 5j$

In Exercises 41–44, the initial and terminal points of a vector are given. Write a linear combination of the standard unit vectors i and j.

Initial Point	Terminal Point
41. $(-3, 1)$	$(4, 5)$
42. $(0, -2)$	$(3, 6)$
43. $(-1, -5)$	$(2, 3)$
44. $(-6, 4)$	$(0, 1)$

In Exercises 45–50, find the component form of v and sketch the specified vector operations geometrically, where u = 2i − j and w = i + 2j.

45. $v = \frac{3}{2}u$ **46.** $v = \frac{2}{3}w$

47. $v = u + 2w$ **48.** $v = -u + w$

49. $v = \frac{1}{2}(3u + w)$ **50.** $v = 2u - 2w$

In Exercises 51–56, find the magnitude and direction angle of the vector v.

51. $v = 5(\cos 30°i + \sin 30°j)$

52. $v = 8(\cos 135°i + \sin 135°j)$

53. $v = 6i - 6j$ **54.** $v = -4i - 7j$

55. $v = -2i + 5j$ **56.** $v = 12i + 15j$

In Exercises 57–62, find the component form of v given its magnitude and the angle it makes with the positive x-axis. Sketch v.

Magnitude	Angle
57. $\|v\| = 3$	$\theta = 0°$
58. $\|v\| = 1$	$\theta = 45°$
59. $\|v\| = 3\sqrt{2}$	$\theta = 150°$
60. $\|v\| = 4\sqrt{3}$	$\theta = 90°$
61. $\|v\| = 2$	v in the direction $i + 3j$
62. $\|v\| = 3$	v in the direction $3i + 4j$

In Exercises 63–66, find the component form of the sum of u and v with direction angles θ_u and θ_v.

Magnitude	Angle
63. $\|u\| = 5$	$\theta_u = 60°$
$\|v\| = 5$	$\theta_v = 90°$
64. $\|u\| = 2$	$\theta_u = 30°$
$\|v\| = 2$	$\theta_v = 90°$
65. $\|u\| = 20$	$\theta_u = 45°$
$\|v\| = 50$	$\theta_v = 150°$
66. $\|u\| = 35$	$\theta_u = 25°$
$\|v\| = 50$	$\theta_v = 120°$

In Exercises 67 and 68, use the Law of Cosines to find the angle α between the vectors. (Assume $0° \leq \alpha \leq 180°$.)

67. $v = i + j$, $w = 2(i - j)$

68. $v = 3i + j$, $w = 2i - j$

In Exercises 69 and 70, graph the vectors and the resultant of the vectors. Find the magnitude and direction of the resultant.

69.   **70.**

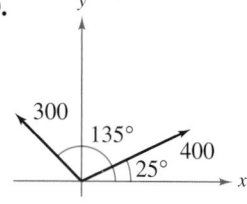

Resultant Force **In Exercises 71 and 72, find the angle between the forces given the magnitude of their resultant. (*Hint:* Write force 1 as a vector in the direction of the positive *x*-axis and force 2 as a vector at an angle θ with the positive *x*-axis.)**

	Force 1	*Force 2*	*Resultant Force*
71.	45 pounds	60 pounds	90 pounds
72.	3000 pounds	1000 pounds	3750 pounds

73. ***Resultant Force*** Forces with magnitudes of 2000 newtons and 900 newtons act on a machine part at angles of 30° and −45°, respectively, with the positive *x*-axis (see figure). Find the direction and magnitude of the resultant of these forces.

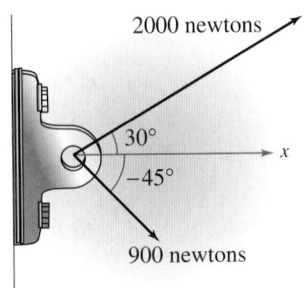

74. ***Resultant Force***

(a) Three forces with magnitudes of 70 pounds, 40 pounds, and 60 pounds act on an object at angles of −30°, 45°, and 135°, respectively, with the positive *x*-axis. Find the direction and magnitude of the resultant of these forces.

(b) Three forces with magnitudes of 75 pounds, 100 pounds, and 125 pounds act on an object at angles of 30°, 45°, and 120°, respectively, with the positive *x*-axis. Find the direction and magnitude of the resultant of these forces.

75. *Velocity* A ball is thrown with an initial velocity of 70 feet per second, at an angle of 40° with the horizontal (see figure). Find the vertical and horizontal components of the velocity.

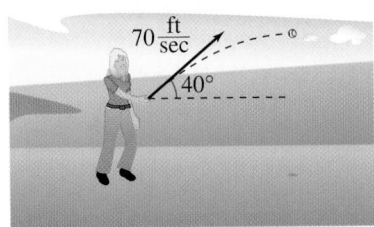

76. *Velocity* A gun with a muzzle velocity of 1200 feet per second is fired at an angle of 4° with the horizontal. Find the vertical and horizontal components of the velocity.

77. *Tension* Use the figure to determine the tension in each cable supporting the load.

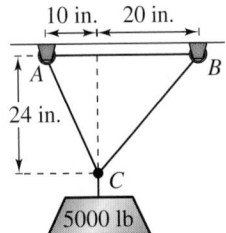

78. *Tension* The cranes shown in the figure are lifting an object that weighs 20,240 pounds. Find the tension in the cable of each crane.

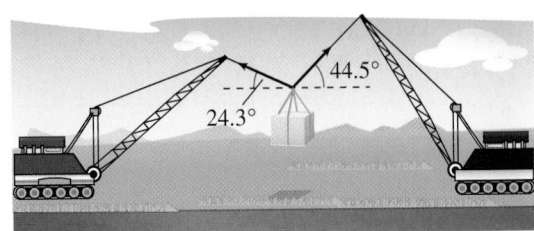

79. *Numerical and Graphical Analysis* A loaded barge is being towed by two tugboats, and the magnitude of the resultant is 6000 pounds directed along the axis of the barge (see figure). Each tow line makes an angle of θ degrees with the axis of the barge.

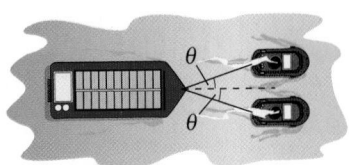

(a) Write the resultant tension *T* of each line as a function of θ. Determine the domain of the function.

(b) Use a graphing utility to complete the table.

θ	10°	20°	30°	40°	50°	60°
T						

(c) Use a graphing utility to graph the tension function.

(d) Explain why the tension increases as θ increases.

80. *Numerical and Graphical Analysis* To carry a 100-pound cylindrical weight, two people lift on the ends of short ropes that are tied to an eyelet on the top center of the cylinder. Each rope makes an angle of θ degrees with the vertical (see figure).

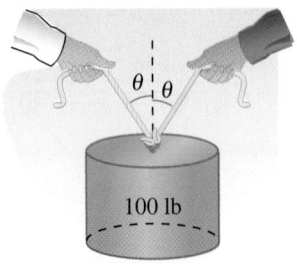

100 lb

(a) Write the tension T of each rope as a function of θ. Determine the domain of the function.

(b) Use a graphing utility to complete the table.

θ	10°	20°	30°	40°	50°	60°
T						

(c) Use a graphing utility to graph the tension function.

(d) Explain why the tension increases as θ increases.

81. *Navigation* An airplane is flying in the direction 148° with an airspeed of 860 kilometers per hour. Because of the wind, its groundspeed and direction are, respectively, 800 kilometers per hour and 140°. Find the direction and speed of the wind.

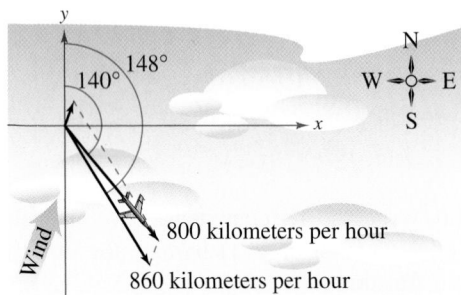

82. *Navigation* A commercial jet is flying from Miami to Seattle. The jet's velocity with respect to the air is 580 miles per hour, and its bearing is 332°. The wind, at the altitude of the plane, is blowing from the southwest with a velocity of 60 miles per hour.

(a) Draw a figure that gives a visual representation of the problem.

(b) Write the velocity of the wind as a vector in component form.

(c) Write the velocity of the jet relative to the air as a vector in component form.

(d) What is the speed of the jet with respect to the ground?

(e) What is the true direction of the jet?

83. *Numerical and Graphical Analysis* Forces with magnitudes of 150 newtons and 220 newtons act on a hook (see figure).

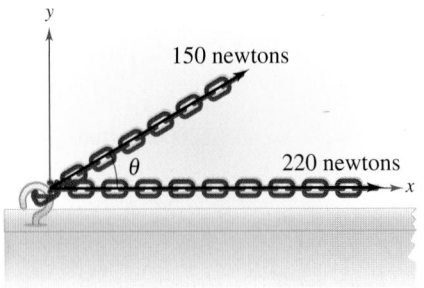

(a) Find the direction and magnitude of the resultant of the forces when $\theta = 30°$.

(b) Write the magnitude M of the resultant and the direction α of the resultant as functions of θ, where $0° \le \theta \le 180°$.

(c) Use a graphing utility to complete the table.

θ	0°	30°	60°	90°	120°	150°	180°
M							
α							

(d) Use a graphing utility to graph the two functions.

(e) Explain why one function decreases for increasing θ, whereas the other doesn't.

84. *Numerical and Graphical Analysis* A tetherball weighing 1 pound is pulled outward from the pole by a horizontal force **u** until the rope makes an angle of θ degrees with the pole (see figure).

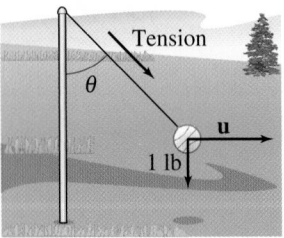

Tension

1 lb

(a) Write the tension T in the rope and the magnitude of **u** as functions of θ. Determine the domains of the functions.

(b) Use a graphing utility to complete the table.

θ	0°	10°	20°	30°	40°	50°	60°
T							
$\|\mathbf{u}\|$							

(c) Use a graphing utility to graph the two functions for $0° \le \theta \le 60°$.

(d) Compare T and $\|\mathbf{u}\|$ as θ increases.

Synthesis

True or False? **In Exercises 85–88, determine whether the statement is true or false. Justify your answer.**

85. If **u** and **v** have the same magnitude and direction, then **u** = **v**.

86. If **u** is a unit vector in the direction of **v**, then $\mathbf{v} = \|\mathbf{v}\|\,\mathbf{u}$.

87. If $\mathbf{v} = a\mathbf{i} + b\mathbf{j} = \mathbf{0}$, then $a = -b$.

88. If $\mathbf{u} = a\mathbf{i} + b\mathbf{j}$ is a unit vector, then $a^2 + b^2 = 1$.

89. ***Think About It*** Consider two forces of equal magnitude acting on a point.

(a) If the magnitude of the resultant is the sum of the magnitudes of the two forces, make a conjecture about the angle between the forces.

(b) If the resultant of the forces is **0**, make a conjecture about the angle between the forces.

(c) Can the magnitude of the resultant be greater than the sum of the magnitudes of the two forces? Explain.

90. ***Graphical Reasoning*** Consider two forces

$$\mathbf{F}_1 = \langle 10, 0 \rangle \text{ and } \mathbf{F}_2 = 5\langle \cos\theta, \sin\theta \rangle.$$

(a) Find $\|\mathbf{F}_1 + \mathbf{F}_2\|$ as a function of θ.

(b) Use a graphing utility to graph the function for $0 \le \theta < 2\pi$.

(c) Use the graph in part (b) to determine the range of the function. What is its maximum, and for what value of θ does it occur? What is its minimum, and for what value of θ does it occur?

(d) Explain why the magnitude of the resultant is never 0.

91. ***Proof*** Prove that $(\cos\theta)\mathbf{i} + (\sin\theta)\mathbf{j}$ is a unit vector for any value of θ.

92. ***Technology*** Write a program for your graphing utility that graphs two vectors and their difference given the vectors in component form.

In Exercises 93 and 94, use the program in Exercise 92 to find the difference of the vectors shown in the graph.

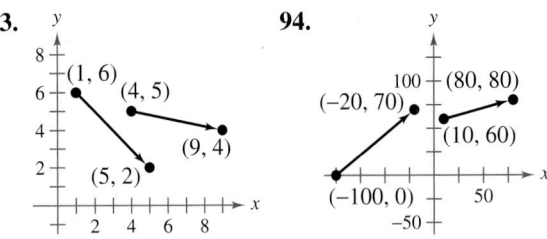

93. (1, 6), (4, 5), (9, 4), (5, 2)

94. (−20, 70), (80, 80), (10, 60), (−100, 0)

Review

In Exercises 95–100, simplify the expression.

95. $\left(\dfrac{6x^4}{7y^{-2}}\right)(14x^{-1}y^5)$

96. $(5s^5t^{-5})\left(\dfrac{3s^{-2}}{50t^{-1}}\right)$

97. $(18x)^0(4xy)^2(3x^{-1})$

98. $(5ab^2)(a^{-3}b^0)(2a^0b)^{-2}$

99. $(2.1 \times 10^9)(3.4 \times 10^{-4})$

100. $(6.5 \times 10^6)(3.8 \times 10^4)$

In Exercises 101–104, use the trigonometric substitution to write the algebraic expression as a trigonometric function of θ, where $0 < \theta < \pi/2$.

101. $\sqrt{49 - x^2}$, $x = 7\sin\theta$

102. $\sqrt{x^2 - 49}$, $x = 7\sec\theta$

103. $\sqrt{x^2 + 100}$, $x = 10\cot\theta$

104. $\sqrt{x^2 - 4}$, $x = 2\csc\theta$

In Exercises 105–108, solve the equation.

105. $\cos x(\cos x + 1) = 0$

106. $\sin x(2\sin x + \sqrt{2}) = 0$

107. $3\sec x + 4 = 10$

108. $\cos x \cot x - \cos x = 0$

7.4 Vectors and Dot Products

The Dot Product of Two Vectors

So far you have studied two vector operations—vector addition and multiplication by a scalar—each of which yields another vector. In this section you will study a third vector operation, the **dot product.** This product yields a scalar, rather than a vector.

Definition of Dot Product

The **dot product** of $\mathbf{u} = \langle u_1, u_2 \rangle$ and $\mathbf{v} = \langle v_1, v_2 \rangle$ is given by

$$\mathbf{u} \cdot \mathbf{v} = u_1 v_1 + u_2 v_2.$$

Properties of the Dot Product

Let $\mathbf{u}$, $\mathbf{v}$, and $\mathbf{w}$ be vectors in the plane or in space and let c be a scalar.

1. $\mathbf{u} \cdot \mathbf{v} = \mathbf{v} \cdot \mathbf{u}$
2. $\mathbf{0} \cdot \mathbf{v} = 0$
3. $\mathbf{u} \cdot (\mathbf{v} + \mathbf{w}) = \mathbf{u} \cdot \mathbf{v} + \mathbf{u} \cdot \mathbf{w}$
4. $\mathbf{v} \cdot \mathbf{v} = \|\mathbf{v}\|^2$
5. $c(\mathbf{u} \cdot \mathbf{v}) = c\mathbf{u} \cdot \mathbf{v} = \mathbf{u} \cdot c\mathbf{v}$

See Appendix B for proofs of the properties of the dot product.

What you should learn

- Find the dot product of two vectors and use properties of the dot product.
- Find angles between vectors and determine whether two vectors are orthogonal.
- Write vectors as sums of two vector components.
- Use vectors to find the work done by a force.

Why you should learn it

You can use the dot product of two vectors to solve real-life problems involving two vector quantities. For instance, Exercise 55 on page 570 shows you how the dot product can be used to find the force necessary to keep a truck from rolling down a hill.

Alan Thornton/Getty Images

Example 1   Finding Dot Products

Find each dot product.

a. $\langle 4, 5 \rangle \cdot \langle 2, 3 \rangle$

b. $\langle 2, -1 \rangle \cdot \langle 1, 2 \rangle$

c. $\langle 0, 3 \rangle \cdot \langle 4, -2 \rangle$

Solution

a. $\langle 4, 5 \rangle \cdot \langle 2, 3 \rangle = 4(2) + 5(3) = 8 + 15 = 23$

b. $\langle 2, -1 \rangle \cdot \langle 1, 2 \rangle = 2(1) + (-1)(2) = 2 - 2 = 0$

c. $\langle 0, 3 \rangle \cdot \langle 4, -2 \rangle = 0(4) + 3(-2) = 0 - 6 = -6$

✓ *Checkpoint* Now try Exercise 1.

In Example 1, be sure you see that the dot product of two vectors is a scalar (a real number), not a vector. Moreover, notice that the dot product can be positive, zero, or negative.

Example 2   Using Properties of Dot Products

Let $\mathbf{u} = \langle -1, 3 \rangle$, $\mathbf{v} = \langle 2, -4 \rangle$, and $\mathbf{w} = \langle 1, -2 \rangle$. Find each dot product.

a. $(\mathbf{u} \cdot \mathbf{v})\mathbf{w}$ **b.** $\mathbf{u} \cdot 2\mathbf{v}$

Solution

Begin by finding the dot product of $\mathbf{u}$ and $\mathbf{v}$.

$$\begin{aligned}
\mathbf{u} \cdot \mathbf{v} &= \langle -1, 3 \rangle \cdot \langle 2, -4 \rangle \\
&= (-1)(2) + 3(-4) \\
&= -14
\end{aligned}$$

a. $\begin{aligned}[t] (\mathbf{u} \cdot \mathbf{v})\mathbf{w} &= -14\langle 1, -2 \rangle \\ &= \langle -14, 28 \rangle \end{aligned}$

b. $\begin{aligned}[t] \mathbf{u} \cdot 2\mathbf{v} &= 2(\mathbf{u} \cdot \mathbf{v}) \\ &= 2(-14) \\ &= -28 \end{aligned}$

Notice that the product in part (a) is a vector, whereas the product in part (b) is a scalar. Can you see why?

✓ *Checkpoint* Now try Exercise 7.

Example 3   Dot Product and Magnitude

The dot product of $\mathbf{u}$ with itself is 5. What is the magnitude of $\mathbf{u}$?

Solution

Because $\|\mathbf{u}\|^2 = \mathbf{u} \cdot \mathbf{u} = 5$, it follows that

$$\begin{aligned}
\|\mathbf{u}\| &= \sqrt{\mathbf{u} \cdot \mathbf{u}} \\
&= \sqrt{5}.
\end{aligned}$$

✓ *Checkpoint* Now try Exercise 11.

The Angle Between Two Vectors

The **angle between two nonzero vectors** is the angle θ, $0 \leq \theta \leq \pi$, between their respective standard position vectors, as shown in Figure 7.33. This angle can be found using the dot product. (Note that the angle between the zero vector and another vector is not defined.) See Appendix B for a proof.

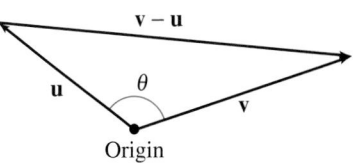

Figure 7.33

> **Angle Between Two Vectors**
>
> If θ is the angle between two nonzero vectors $\mathbf{u}$ and $\mathbf{v}$, then
>
> $$\cos \theta = \frac{\mathbf{u} \cdot \mathbf{v}}{\|\mathbf{u}\| \, \|\mathbf{v}\|}.$$

Example 4 Finding the Angle Between Two Vectors

Find the angle between $\mathbf{u} = \langle 4, 3 \rangle$ and $\mathbf{v} = \langle 3, 5 \rangle$.

Solution

$$\cos \theta = \frac{\mathbf{u} \cdot \mathbf{v}}{\|\mathbf{u}\| \|\mathbf{v}\|}$$

$$= \frac{\langle 4, 3 \rangle \cdot \langle 3, 5 \rangle}{\|\langle 4, 3 \rangle\| \|\langle 3, 5 \rangle\|}$$

$$= \frac{27}{5\sqrt{34}}$$

This implies that the angle between the two vectors is

$$\theta = \arccos \frac{27}{5\sqrt{34}} \approx 22.2°,$$

as shown in Figure 7.34.

✓ *Checkpoint* Now try Exercise 17.

Rewriting the expression for the angle between two vectors in the form

$$\mathbf{u} \cdot \mathbf{v} = \|\mathbf{u}\| \|\mathbf{v}\| \cos \theta \qquad \text{Alternative form of dot product}$$

produces an alternative way to calculate the dot product. From this form, you can see that because $\|\mathbf{u}\|$ and $\|\mathbf{v}\|$ are always positive, $\mathbf{u} \cdot \mathbf{v}$ and $\cos \theta$ will always have the same sign. Figure 7.35 shows the five possible orientations of two vectors.

TECHNOLOGY TIP

The graphing utility program Finding the Angle Between Two Vectors, found on our website *college.hmco.com*, graphs two vectors $\mathbf{u} = \langle a, b \rangle$ and $\mathbf{v} = \langle c, d \rangle$ in standard position and finds the measure of the angle between them. Use the program to verify Example 4.

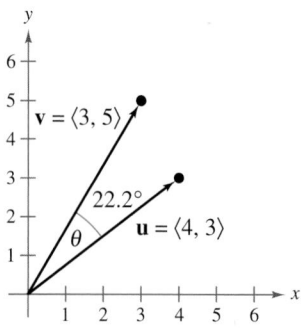

Figure 7.34

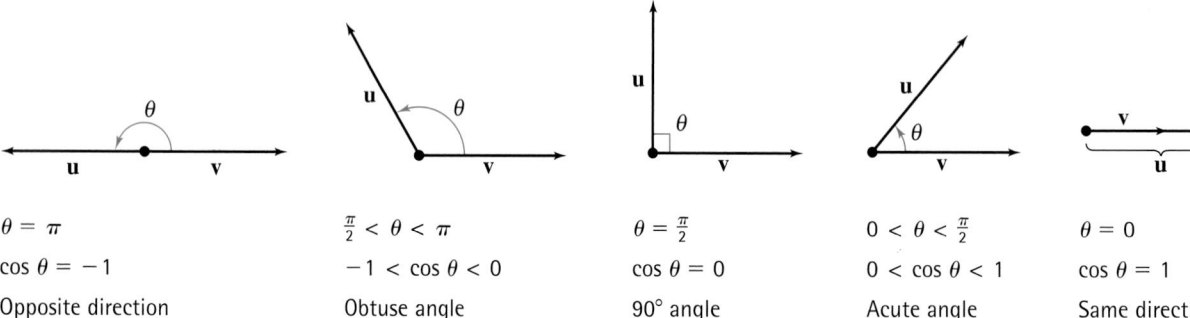

$\theta = \pi$	$\frac{\pi}{2} < \theta < \pi$	$\theta = \frac{\pi}{2}$	$0 < \theta < \frac{\pi}{2}$	$\theta = 0$
$\cos \theta = -1$	$-1 < \cos \theta < 0$	$\cos \theta = 0$	$0 < \cos \theta < 1$	$\cos \theta = 1$
Opposite direction	Obtuse angle	90° angle	Acute angle	Same direction

Figure 7.35

> **Definition of Orthogonal Vectors**
>
> The vectors $\mathbf{u}$ and $\mathbf{v}$ are **orthogonal** if $\mathbf{u} \cdot \mathbf{v} = 0$.

The terms *orthogonal* and *perpendicular* mean essentially the same thing—meeting at right angles. Even though the angle between the zero vector and another vector is not defined, it is convenient to extend the definition of orthogonality to include the zero vector. In other words, the zero vector is orthogonal to every vector $\mathbf{u}$ because $\mathbf{0} \cdot \mathbf{u} = 0$.

Example 5   Determining Orthogonal Vectors

Are the vectors $\mathbf{u} = \langle 2, -3 \rangle$ and $\mathbf{v} = \langle 6, 4 \rangle$ orthogonal?

Solution

Begin by finding the dot product of the two vectors.

$$\mathbf{u} \cdot \mathbf{v} = \langle 2, -3 \rangle \cdot \langle 6, 4 \rangle = 2(6) + (-3)(4) = 0$$

Because the dot product is 0, the two vectors are orthogonal, as shown in Figure 7.36.

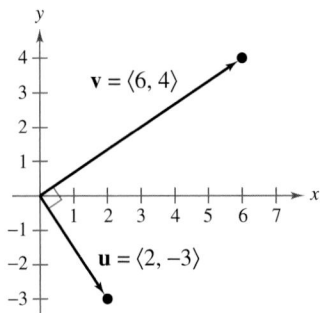

Figure 7.36

☑ *Checkpoint* Now try Exercise 35.

Finding Vector Components

You have already seen applications in which two vectors are added to produce a resultant vector. Many applications in physics and engineering pose the reverse problem—decomposing a given vector into the sum of two **vector components.**

Consider a boat on an inclined ramp, as shown in Figure 7.37. The force $\mathbf{F}$ due to gravity pulls the boat *down* the ramp and *against* the ramp. These two orthogonal forces, $\mathbf{w}_1$ and $\mathbf{w}_2$, are vector components of $\mathbf{F}$. That is,

$$\mathbf{F} = \mathbf{w}_1 + \mathbf{w}_2. \qquad \text{Vector components of } \mathbf{F}$$

The negative of component $\mathbf{w}_1$ represents the force needed to keep the boat from rolling down the ramp, and $\mathbf{w}_2$ represents the force that the tires must withstand against the ramp. A procedure for finding $\mathbf{w}_1$ and $\mathbf{w}_2$ is shown on the next page.

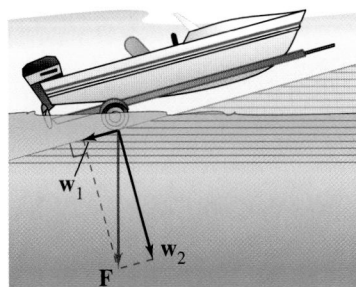

Figure 7.37

Definition of Vector Components

Let **u** and **v** be nonzero vectors such that

$$\mathbf{u} = \mathbf{w}_1 + \mathbf{w}_2$$

where $\mathbf{w}_1$ and $\mathbf{w}_2$ are orthogonal and $\mathbf{w}_1$ is parallel to (or a scalar multiple of) **v**, as shown in Figure 7.38. The vectors $\mathbf{w}_1$ and $\mathbf{w}_2$ are called **vector components** of **u**. The vector $\mathbf{w}_1$ is the **projection** of **u** onto **v** and is denoted by

$$\mathbf{w}_1 = \text{proj}_{\mathbf{v}}\mathbf{u}.$$

The vector $\mathbf{w}_2$ is given by $\mathbf{w}_2 = \mathbf{u} - \mathbf{w}_1$.

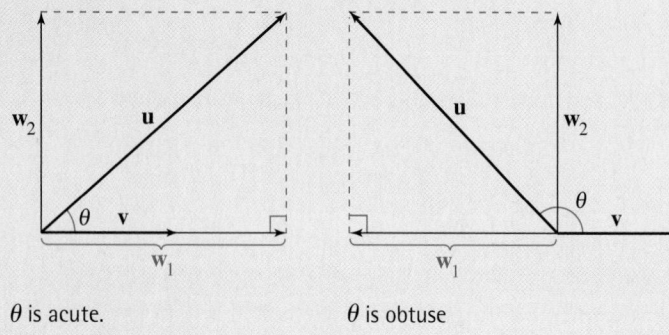

θ is acute. θ is obtuse

Figure 7.38

From the definition of vector components, you can see that it is easy to find the component $\mathbf{w}_2$ once you have found the projection of **u** onto **v**. To find the projection, you can use the dot product, as follows.

$$\mathbf{u} = \mathbf{w}_1 + \mathbf{w}_2 = c\mathbf{v} + \mathbf{w}_2 \qquad \text{$\mathbf{w}_1$ is a scalar multiple of $\mathbf{v}$.}$$

$$\mathbf{u} \cdot \mathbf{v} = (c\mathbf{v} + \mathbf{w}_2) \cdot \mathbf{v} \qquad \text{Take dot product of each side with $\mathbf{v}$.}$$

$$= c\mathbf{v} \cdot \mathbf{v} + \mathbf{w}_2 \cdot \mathbf{v}$$

$$= c\|\mathbf{v}\|^2 + 0 \qquad \text{$\mathbf{w}_2$ and $\mathbf{v}$ are orthogonal.}$$

So,

$$c = \frac{\mathbf{u} \cdot \mathbf{v}}{\|\mathbf{v}\|^2}$$

and

$$\mathbf{w}_1 = \text{proj}_{\mathbf{v}}\mathbf{u} = c\mathbf{v} = \frac{\mathbf{u} \cdot \mathbf{v}}{\|\mathbf{v}\|^2}\mathbf{v}.$$

Projection of u onto v

Let **u** and **v** be nonzero vectors. The projection of **u** onto **v** is given by

$$\text{proj}_{\mathbf{v}}\mathbf{u} = \left(\frac{\mathbf{u} \cdot \mathbf{v}}{\|\mathbf{v}\|^2}\right)\mathbf{v}.$$

Example 6   Decomposing a Vector into Components

Find the projection of $\mathbf{u} = \langle 3, -5 \rangle$ onto $\mathbf{v} = \langle 6, 2 \rangle$. Then write $\mathbf{u}$ as the sum of two orthogonal vectors, one of which is $\text{proj}_{\mathbf{v}}\mathbf{u}$.

Solution

The projection of $\mathbf{u}$ onto $\mathbf{v}$ is

$$\mathbf{w}_1 = \text{proj}_{\mathbf{v}}\mathbf{u} = \left(\frac{\mathbf{u} \cdot \mathbf{v}}{\|\mathbf{v}\|^2}\right)\mathbf{v} = \left(\frac{8}{40}\right)\langle 6, 2 \rangle = \left\langle \frac{6}{5}, \frac{2}{5} \right\rangle$$

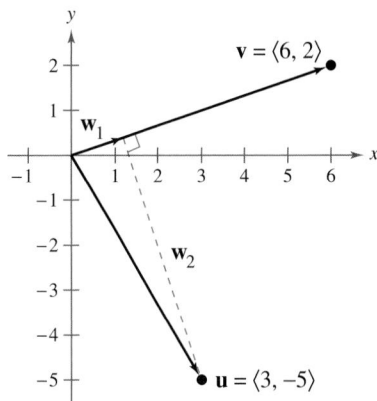

Figure 7.39

as shown in Figure 7.39. The other component, $\mathbf{w}_2$, is

$$\mathbf{w}_2 = \mathbf{u} - \mathbf{w}_1 = \langle 3, -5 \rangle - \left\langle \frac{6}{5}, \frac{2}{5} \right\rangle = \left\langle \frac{9}{5}, -\frac{27}{5} \right\rangle.$$

So, $\mathbf{u} = \mathbf{w}_1 + \mathbf{w}_2 = \left\langle \frac{6}{5}, \frac{2}{5} \right\rangle + \left\langle \frac{9}{5}, -\frac{27}{5} \right\rangle = \langle 3, -5 \rangle.$

 Checkpoint Now try Exercise 39.

Example 7   Finding a Force

A 200-pound cart sits on a ramp inclined at 30°, as shown in Figure 7.40. What force is required to keep the cart from rolling down the ramp?

Solution

Because the force due to gravity is vertical and downward, you can represent the gravitational force by the vector

$$\mathbf{F} = -200\mathbf{j}. \qquad \text{Force due to gravity}$$

To find the force required to keep the cart from rolling down the ramp, project $\mathbf{F}$ onto a unit vector $\mathbf{v}$ in the direction of the ramp, as follows.

$$\mathbf{v} = (\cos 30°)\mathbf{i} + (\sin 30°)\mathbf{j} = \frac{\sqrt{3}}{2}\mathbf{i} + \frac{1}{2}\mathbf{j} \qquad \text{Unit vector along ramp}$$

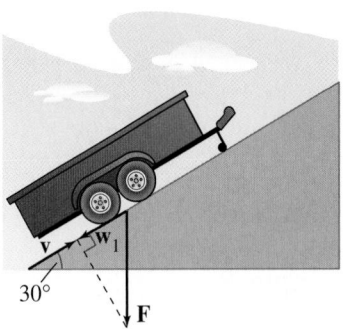

Figure 7.40

Therefore, the projection of $\mathbf{F}$ onto $\mathbf{v}$ is

$$\mathbf{w}_1 = \text{proj}_{\mathbf{v}}\mathbf{F} = \left(\frac{\mathbf{F} \cdot \mathbf{v}}{\|\mathbf{v}\|^2}\right)\mathbf{v}$$

$$= (\mathbf{F} \cdot \mathbf{v})\mathbf{v}$$

$$= (-200)\left(\frac{1}{2}\right)\mathbf{v}$$

$$= -100\left(\frac{\sqrt{3}}{2}\mathbf{i} + \frac{1}{2}\mathbf{j}\right).$$

The magnitude of this force is 100, and therefore a force of 100 pounds is required to keep the cart from rolling down the ramp.

 Checkpoint Now try Exercise 55.

Work

The work W done by a constant force $\mathbf{F}$ acting along the line of motion of an object is given by

$$W = (\text{magnitude of force})(\text{distance}) = \|\mathbf{F}\| \|\overrightarrow{PQ}\|$$

as shown in Figure 7.41. If the constant force $\mathbf{F}$ is not directed along the line of motion (see Figure 7.42), the work W done by the force is given by

$$\begin{aligned}
W &= \|\text{proj}_{\overrightarrow{PQ}} \mathbf{F}\| \|\overrightarrow{PQ}\| & \text{Projection form for work} \\
&= (\cos \theta) \|\mathbf{F}\| \|\overrightarrow{PQ}\| & \|\text{proj}_{\overrightarrow{PQ}} \mathbf{F}\| = (\cos \theta) \|\mathbf{F}\| \\
&= \mathbf{F} \cdot \overrightarrow{PQ}. & \text{Dot product form for work}
\end{aligned}$$

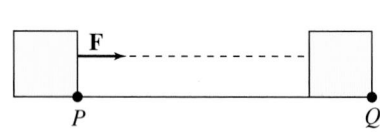

Force acts along the line of motion.

Figure 7.41

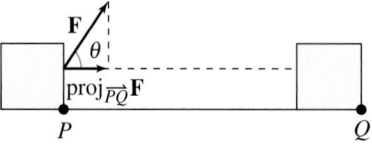

Force acts at angle θ with the line of motion.

Figure 7.42

This notion of work is summarized in the following definition.

Definition of Work

The **work** W done by a constant force $\mathbf{F}$ as its point of application moves along the vector $\overrightarrow{PQ}$ is given by either of the following.

1. $W = \|\text{proj}_{\overrightarrow{PQ}} \mathbf{F}\| \|\overrightarrow{PQ}\|$ Projection form

2. $W = \mathbf{F} \cdot \overrightarrow{PQ}$ Dot product form

---

Example 8   Finding Work

To close a barn's sliding door, a person pulls on a rope with a constant force of 50 pounds at a constant angle of 60°, as shown in Figure 7.43. Find the work done in moving the door 12 feet to its closed position.

Solution

Using a projection, you can calculate the work as follows.

$$\begin{aligned}
W &= \|\text{proj}_{\overrightarrow{PQ}} \mathbf{F}\| \|\overrightarrow{PQ}\| & \text{Projection form for work} \\
&= (\cos 60°) \|\mathbf{F}\| \|\overrightarrow{PQ}\| \\
&= \frac{1}{2}(50)(12) = 300 \text{ foot-pounds}
\end{aligned}$$

So, the work done is 300 foot-pounds. You can verify this result by finding the vectors $\mathbf{F}$ and $\overrightarrow{PQ}$ and calculating their dot product.

Figure 7.43

 Checkpoint Now try Exercise 57.

7.4   Exercises

Vocabulary Check

Fill in the blanks.

1. The _____ of two vectors yields a scalar, rather than a vector.
2. If θ is the angle between two nonzero vectors **u** and **v**, then $\cos\theta =$ _____ .
3. The vectors **u** and **v** are _____ if $\mathbf{u} \cdot \mathbf{v} = 0$.
4. The projection of **u** onto **v** is given by $\text{proj}_\mathbf{v}\mathbf{u} =$ _____ .
5. The work W done by a constant force **F** as its point of application moves along the vector $\overrightarrow{PQ}$ is given by either $W =$ _____ or $W =$ _____ .

In Exercises 1–4, find the dot product of u and v.

1. $\mathbf{u} = \langle 6, 3 \rangle$
   $\mathbf{v} = \langle 2, -4 \rangle$
2. $\mathbf{u} = \langle 1, 8 \rangle$
   $\mathbf{v} = \langle -3, 2 \rangle$
3. $\mathbf{u} = 5\mathbf{i} + \mathbf{j}$
   $\mathbf{v} = 3\mathbf{i} - \mathbf{j}$
4. $\mathbf{u} = 8\mathbf{i} - 2\mathbf{j}$
   $\mathbf{v} = 4\mathbf{i} - 3\mathbf{j}$

In Exercises 5–10, use the vectors $\mathbf{u} = \langle 2, 2 \rangle$, $\mathbf{v} = \langle -3, 4 \rangle$, and $\mathbf{w} = \langle 1, -4 \rangle$ to find the indicated quantity. State whether the result is a vector or a scalar.

5. $\mathbf{u} \cdot \mathbf{u}$
6. $\|\mathbf{u}\| - 2$
7. $(\mathbf{u} \cdot \mathbf{v})\mathbf{w}$
8. $(\mathbf{w} \cdot \mathbf{u})\mathbf{v}$
9. $\mathbf{u} \cdot 2\mathbf{v}$
10. $4\mathbf{u} \cdot \mathbf{v}$

In Exercises 11–16, use the dot product to find the magnitude of u.

11. $\mathbf{u} = \langle -5, 12 \rangle$
12. $\mathbf{u} = \langle 2, -4 \rangle$
13. $\mathbf{u} = 20\mathbf{i} + 25\mathbf{j}$
14. $\mathbf{u} = 6\mathbf{i} - 10\mathbf{j}$
15. $\mathbf{u} = -4\mathbf{j}$
16. $\mathbf{u} = 9\mathbf{i}$

In Exercises 17–24, find the angle θ between the vectors.

17. $\mathbf{u} = \langle -1, 0 \rangle$
    $\mathbf{v} = \langle 0, 2 \rangle$
18. $\mathbf{u} = \langle 4, 4 \rangle$
    $\mathbf{v} = \langle -2, 0 \rangle$
19. $\mathbf{u} = 3\mathbf{i} + 4\mathbf{j}$
    $\mathbf{v} = -2\mathbf{i} + 3\mathbf{j}$
20. $\mathbf{u} = 2\mathbf{i} - 3\mathbf{j}$
    $\mathbf{v} = \mathbf{i} - 2\mathbf{j}$
21. $\mathbf{u} = 2\mathbf{i}$
    $\mathbf{v} = -3\mathbf{j}$
22. $\mathbf{u} = 4\mathbf{j}$
    $\mathbf{v} = -3\mathbf{i}$

23. $\mathbf{u} = \cos\left(\dfrac{\pi}{3}\right)\mathbf{i} + \sin\left(\dfrac{\pi}{3}\right)\mathbf{j}$
    $\mathbf{v} = \cos\left(\dfrac{3\pi}{4}\right)\mathbf{i} + \sin\left(\dfrac{3\pi}{4}\right)\mathbf{j}$
24. $\mathbf{u} = \cos\left(\dfrac{\pi}{4}\right)\mathbf{i} + \sin\left(\dfrac{\pi}{4}\right)\mathbf{j}$
    $\mathbf{v} = \cos\left(\dfrac{2\pi}{3}\right)\mathbf{i} + \sin\left(\dfrac{2\pi}{3}\right)\mathbf{j}$

In Exercises 25–28, graph the vectors and find the degree measure of the angle between the vectors.

25. $\mathbf{u} = 3\mathbf{i} + 4\mathbf{j}$
    $\mathbf{v} = -7\mathbf{i} + 5\mathbf{j}$
26. $\mathbf{u} = -6\mathbf{i} - 3\mathbf{j}$
    $\mathbf{v} = -8\mathbf{i} + 4\mathbf{j}$
27. $\mathbf{u} = 5\mathbf{i} + 5\mathbf{j}$
    $\mathbf{v} = -8\mathbf{i} + 8\mathbf{j}$
28. $\mathbf{u} = 2\mathbf{i} - 3\mathbf{j}$
    $\mathbf{v} = 4\mathbf{i} + 3\mathbf{j}$

In Exercises 29 and 30, use vectors to find the interior angles of the triangle with the given vertices.

29. $(1, 2), (3, 4), (2, 5)$
30. $(-3, 0), (2, 2), (0, 6)$

In Exercises 31 and 32, find $\mathbf{u} \cdot \mathbf{v}$, where θ is the angle between u and v.

31. $\|\mathbf{u}\| = 4, \|\mathbf{v}\| = 10, \theta = \dfrac{2\pi}{3}$

32. $\|\mathbf{u}\| = 100, \|\mathbf{v}\| = 250, \theta = \dfrac{\pi}{6}$

In Exercises 33–38, determine whether u and v are orthogonal, parallel, or neither.

33. $u = \langle -12, 30 \rangle$
    $v = \langle \frac{1}{2}, -\frac{5}{4} \rangle$

34. $u = \langle 15, 45 \rangle$
    $v = \langle -5, 12 \rangle$

35. $u = \frac{1}{4}(3i - j)$
    $v = 5i + 6j$

36. $u = j$
    $v = i - 2j$

37. $u = 2i - 2j$
    $v = -i - j$

38. $u = 8i + 4j$
    $v = -2i - j$

In Exercises 39–42, find the projection of u onto v. Then write u as the sum of two orthogonal vectors, one of which is proj$_v$ u.

39. $u = \langle 3, 4 \rangle$
    $v = \langle 8, 2 \rangle$

40. $u = \langle 4, 2 \rangle$
    $v = \langle 1, -2 \rangle$

41. $u = \langle 0, 3 \rangle$
    $v = \langle 2, 15 \rangle$

42. $u = \langle -5, -1 \rangle$
    $v = \langle -1, 1 \rangle$

In Exercises 43–46, use the graph to mentally determine the projection of u onto v. (The coordinates of the terminal points of the vectors in standard position are given.) Use the formula for the projection of u onto v to verify your result.

43.

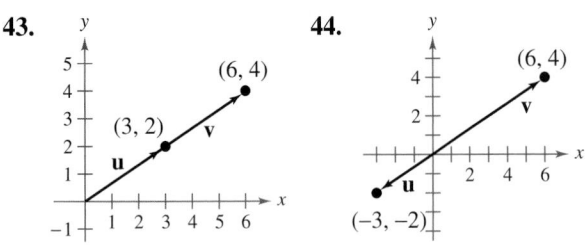

44.

45.

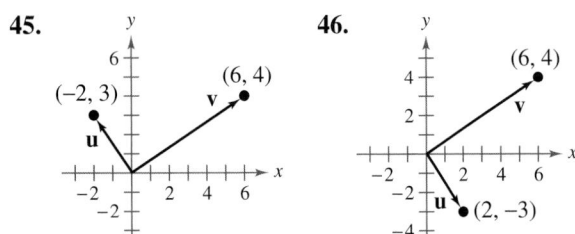

46.

In Exercises 47–50, find two vectors in opposite directions that are orthogonal to the vector u. (There are many correct answers.)

47. $u = \langle 2, 6 \rangle$

48. $u = \langle -7, 5 \rangle$

49. $u = \frac{1}{2}i - \frac{3}{4}j$

50. $u = -\frac{5}{2}i - 3j$

Work   **In Exercises 51 and 52, find the work done in moving a particle from *P* to *Q* if the magnitude and direction of the force are given by v.**

51. $P = (0, 0)$, $Q = (4, 7)$, $v = \langle 1, 4 \rangle$

52. $P = (1, 3)$, $Q = (-3, 5)$, $v = -2i + 3j$

53. ***Revenue***   The vector $u = \langle 1245, 2600 \rangle$ gives the numbers of units of two types of picture frames produced by a company. The vector $v = \langle 12.20, 8.50 \rangle$ gives the price (in dollars) of each frame, respectively. Find the dot product $u \cdot v$ and explain what information it gives.

54. ***Revenue***   Repeat Exercise 53 after increasing the prices by 5%. Identify the vector operation used to increase the prices by 5%.

55. ***Braking Load***   A truck with a gross weight of 30,000 pounds is parked on a slope of $d°$ (see figure). Assume that the only force to overcome is the force of gravity.

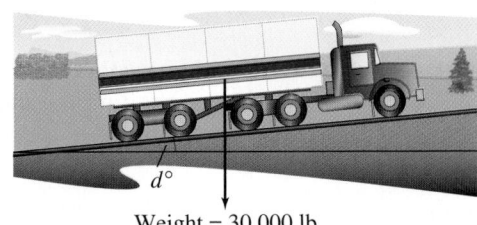

Weight = 30,000 lb

(a) Find the force required to keep the truck from rolling down the hill in terms of the slope *d*.

(b) Use a graphing utility to complete the table.

d	0°	1°	2°	3°	4°	5°
Force						

d	6°	7°	8°	9°	10°
Force					

(c) Find the force perpendicular to the hill when $d = 5°$.

56. ***Braking Load***   A sport utility vehicle with a gross weight of 5400 pounds is parked on a slope of 10°. Assume that the only force to overcome is the force of gravity. Find the force required to keep the vehicle from rolling down the hill. Find the force perpendicular to the hill.

57. Work   A tractor pulls a log d meters and the tension in the cable connecting the tractor and log is approximately 1600 kilograms (15,691 newtons). The direction of the force is $30°$ above the horizontal (see figure).

(a) Find the work done in terms of the distance d.

(b) Use a graphing utility to complete the table.

d	0	200	400	800
Work				

58. Work   A force of 45 pounds in the direction of $30°$ above the horizontal is required to slide a table across a floor. Find the work done if the table is dragged 20 feet.

59. Work   A toy wagon is pulled by exerting a force of 20 pounds on a handle that makes a $25°$ angle with the horizontal. Find the work done in pulling the wagon 40 feet.

60. Work   A mover exerts a horizontal force of 25 pounds on a crate as it is pushed up a ramp that is 12 feet long and inclined at an angle of $20°$ above the horizontal. Find the work done on the crate.

Synthesis

True or False?   **In Exercises 61 and 62, determine whether the statement is true or false. Justify your answer.**

61. The vectors $\mathbf{u} = \langle 0, 0 \rangle$ and $\mathbf{v} = \langle -12, 6 \rangle$ are orthogonal.

62. The work W done by a constant force $\mathbf{F}$ acting along the line of motion of an object is represented by a vector.

63. If $\mathbf{u} = \langle \cos \theta, \sin \theta \rangle$ and $\mathbf{v} = \langle \sin \theta, -\cos \theta \rangle$, are $\mathbf{u}$ and $\mathbf{v}$ orthogonal, parallel, or neither? Explain.

64. Think About It   What is known about θ, the angle between two nonzero vectors $\mathbf{u}$ and $\mathbf{v}$, if each of the following is true?

(a) $\mathbf{u} \cdot \mathbf{v} = 0$ (b) $\mathbf{u} \cdot \mathbf{v} > 0$ (c) $\mathbf{u} \cdot \mathbf{v} < 0$

65. Think About It   What can be said about the vectors $\mathbf{u}$ and $\mathbf{v}$ under each condition?

(a) The projection of $\mathbf{u}$ onto $\mathbf{v}$ equals $\mathbf{u}$.

(b) The projection of $\mathbf{u}$ onto $\mathbf{v}$ equals $\mathbf{0}$.

66. Proof   Use vectors to prove that the diagonals of a rhombus are perpendicular.

67. Proof   Prove the following.

$$\|\mathbf{u} - \mathbf{v}\|^2 = \|\mathbf{u}\|^2 + \|\mathbf{v}\|^2 - 2\mathbf{u} \cdot \mathbf{v}$$

68. Proof   Prove that if $\mathbf{u}$ is orthogonal to $\mathbf{v}$ and $\mathbf{w}$, then $\mathbf{u}$ is orthogonal to $c\mathbf{v} + d\mathbf{w}$ for any scalars c and d.

Review

In Exercises 69–72, describe how the graph of g is related to the graph of f.

69. $g(x) = f(x - 4)$

70. $g(x) = -f(x)$

71. $g(x) = f(x) + 6$

72. $g(x) = f(2x)$

In Exercises 73–80, perform the operation and write the result in standard form.

73. $\sqrt{-4} - 1$

74. $\sqrt{-8} + 5$

75. $3i(4 - 5i)$

76. $-2i(1 + 6i)$

77. $(1 + 3i)(1 - 3i)$

78. $(7 - 4i)(7 + 4i)$

79. $\dfrac{3}{1 + i} + \dfrac{2}{2 - 3i}$

80. $\dfrac{6}{4 - i} - \dfrac{3}{1 + i}$

In Exercises 81–84, plot the complex number in the complex plane.

81. $-2i$

82. $3i$

83. $1 + 8i$

84. $9 - 7i$

85. Partnership Costs   A group of people agree to share equally in the cost of a \$250,000 endowment to a college. If they could find two more people to join the group, each person's share of the cost would decrease by \$6250. How many people are presently in the group?

86. Current Speed   A boat travels at a speed of 18 miles per hour in still water. It travels 35 miles upstream and then returns to the starting point in a total of 4 hours. Find the speed of the current.

The Complex Plane

Recall from Section 2.3 that you can represent a complex number $z = a + bi$ as the point (a, b) in a coordinate plane (the complex plane). The horizontal axis is called the real axis and the vertical axis is called the imaginary axis, as shown in Figure 7.44.

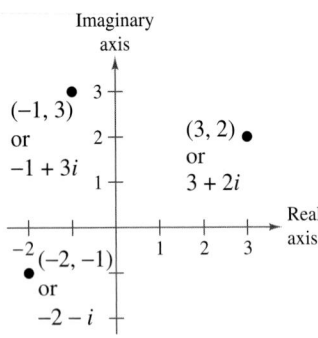

Figure 7.44

What you should learn

- Find absolute values of complex numbers.
- Write trigonometric forms of complex numbers.
- Multiply and divide complex numbers written in trigonometric form.
- Use DeMoivre's Theorem to find powers of complex numbers.
- Find *n*th roots of complex numbers.

Why you should learn it

You can use the trigonometric form of a complex number to perform operations with complex numbers. For instance, in Exercises 109–116 on page 582, you can use the trigonometric form of a complex number to help you solve polynomial equations.

The **absolute value of a complex number** $a + bi$ is defined as the distance between the origin $(0, 0)$ and the point (a, b).

> **Definition of the Absolute Value of a Complex Number**
>
> The **absolute value** of the complex number $z = a + bi$ is given by
>
> $$|a + bi| = \sqrt{a^2 + b^2}.$$

If the complex number $a + bi$ is a real number (that is, if $b = 0$), then this definition agrees with that given for the absolute value of a real number

$$|a + 0i| = \sqrt{a^2 + 0^2} = |a|.$$

Example 1 Finding the Absolute Value of a Complex Number

Plot $z = -2 + 5i$ and find its absolute value.

Solution

The number is plotted in Figure 7.45. It has an absolute value of

$$|z| = \sqrt{(-2)^2 + 5^2}$$

$$= \sqrt{29}.$$

✓ *Checkpoint* Now try Exercise 5.

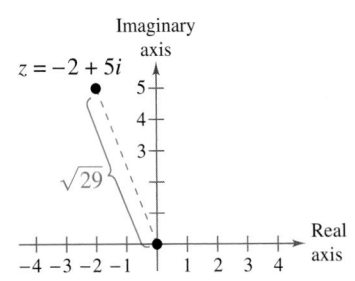

Figure 7.45

Trigonometric Form of a Complex Number

In Section 2.3 you learned how to add, subtract, multiply, and divide complex numbers. To work effectively with *powers* and *roots* of complex numbers, it is helpful to write complex numbers in trigonometric form. In Figure 7.46, consider the nonzero complex number $a + bi$. By letting θ be the angle from the positive real axis (measured counterclockwise) to the line segment connecting the origin and the point (a, b), you can write

$$a = r \cos \theta \quad \text{and} \quad b = r \sin \theta$$

where $r = \sqrt{a^2 + b^2}$. Consequently, you have

$$a + bi = (r \cos \theta) + (r \sin \theta)i$$

from which you can obtain the **trigonometric form of a complex number.**

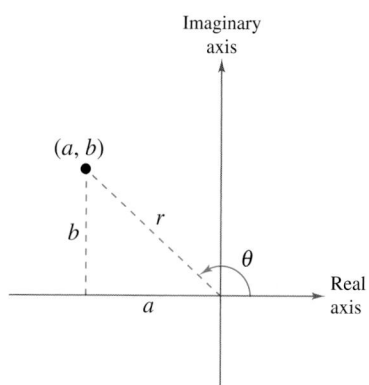

Figure 7.46

Trigonometric Form of a Complex Number

The **trigonometric form** of the complex number $z = a + bi$ is given by

$$z = r(\cos \theta + i \sin \theta)$$

where $a = r \cos \theta$, $b = r \sin \theta$, $r = \sqrt{a^2 + b^2}$, and $\tan \theta = b/a$.
The number r is the **modulus** of z, and θ is called an **argument** of z.

The trigonometric form of a complex number is also called the *polar form*. Because there are infinitely many choices for θ, the trigonometric form of a complex number is not unique. Normally, θ is restricted to the interval $0 \le \theta < 2\pi$, although on occasion it is convenient to use $\theta < 0$.

Example 2   Writing a Complex Number in Trigonometric Form

Write the complex number $z = -2 - 2\sqrt{3}i$ in trigonometric form.

Solution

The absolute value of z is

$$r = \left| -2 - 2\sqrt{3}i \right| = \sqrt{(-2)^2 + \left(-2\sqrt{3}\right)^2} = \sqrt{16} = 4$$

and the angle θ is given by

$$\tan \theta = \frac{b}{a} = \frac{-2\sqrt{3}}{-2} = \sqrt{3}.$$

Because $\tan(\pi/3) = \sqrt{3}$ and $z = -2 - 2\sqrt{3}i$ lies in Quadrant III, choose θ to be $\theta = \pi + \pi/3 = 4\pi/3$. So, the trigonometric form is

$$z = r(\cos \theta + i \sin \theta) = 4\left(\cos \frac{4\pi}{3} + i \sin \frac{4\pi}{3} \right).$$

See Figure 7.47.

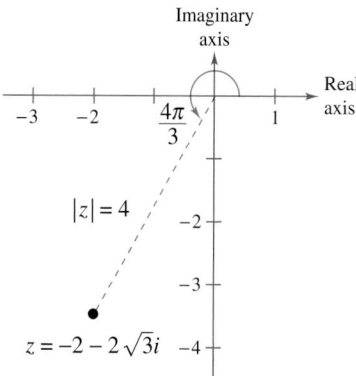

Figure 7.47

✓ *Checkpoint* Now try Exercise 15.

Example 3   Writing a Complex Number in Standard Form

Write the complex number in standard form $a + bi$.

$$z = \sqrt{8}\left[\cos\left(-\frac{\pi}{3}\right) + i\sin\left(-\frac{\pi}{3}\right)\right]$$

Solution

Because $\cos(-\pi/3) = 1/2$ and $\sin(-\pi/3) = -\sqrt{3}/2$, you can write

$$z = \sqrt{8}\left[\cos\left(-\frac{\pi}{3}\right) + i\sin\left(-\frac{\pi}{3}\right)\right]$$

$$= \sqrt{8}\left[\frac{1}{2} - \frac{\sqrt{3}}{2}i\right]$$

$$= 2\sqrt{2}\left[\frac{1}{2} - \frac{\sqrt{3}}{2}i\right] = \sqrt{2} - \sqrt{6}i.$$

✓ *Checkpoint* Now try Exercise 33.

TECHNOLOGY TIP

A graphing utility can be used to convert a complex number in trigonometric form to standard form. For instance, enter the complex number $\sqrt{2}(\cos \pi/4 + i \sin \pi/4)$ into your graphing utility and press ENTER. You should obtain the standard form $1 + i$, as shown below.

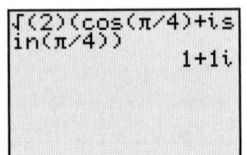

Multiplication and Division of Complex Numbers

The trigonometric form adapts nicely to multiplication and division of complex numbers. Suppose you are given two complex numbers

$$z_1 = r_1(\cos\theta_1 + i\sin\theta_1) \qquad \text{and} \qquad z_2 = r_2(\cos\theta_2 + i\sin\theta_2).$$

The product of z_1 and z_2 is

$$z_1 z_2 = r_1 r_2(\cos\theta_1 + i\sin\theta_1)(\cos\theta_2 + i\sin\theta_2)$$

$$= r_1 r_2[(\cos\theta_1\cos\theta_2 - \sin\theta_1\sin\theta_2) + i(\sin\theta_1\cos\theta_2 + \cos\theta_1\sin\theta_2)].$$

Using the sum and difference formulas for cosine and sine, you can rewrite this equation as

$$z_1 z_2 = r_1 r_2[\cos(\theta_1 + \theta_2) + i\sin(\theta_1 + \theta_2)].$$

This establishes the first part of the following rule. The second part is left to you (see Exercise 120).

Product and Quotient of Two Complex Numbers

Let $z_1 = r_1(\cos\theta_1 + i\sin\theta_1)$ and $z_2 = r_2(\cos\theta_2 + i\sin\theta_2)$ be complex numbers.

$$z_1 z_2 = r_1 r_2[\cos(\theta_1 + \theta_2) + i\sin(\theta_1 + \theta_2)] \qquad \text{Product}$$

$$\frac{z_1}{z_2} = \frac{r_1}{r_2}[\cos(\theta_1 - \theta_2) + i\sin(\theta_1 - \theta_2)], \qquad z_2 \neq 0 \qquad \text{Quotient}$$

Note that this rule says that to *multiply* two complex numbers you multiply moduli and add arguments, whereas to *divide* two complex numbers you divide moduli and subtract arguments.

Example 4   Multiplying Complex Numbers in Trigonometric Form

Find the product $z_1 z_2$ of the complex numbers.

$$z_1 = 2\left(\cos \frac{2\pi}{3} + i \sin \frac{2\pi}{3}\right) \qquad z_2 = 8\left(\cos \frac{11\pi}{6} + i \sin \frac{11\pi}{6}\right)$$

Solution

$$z_1 z_2 = 2\left(\cos \frac{2\pi}{3} + i \sin \frac{2\pi}{3}\right) \cdot 8\left(\cos \frac{11\pi}{6} + i \sin \frac{11\pi}{6}\right)$$

$$= 16\left[\cos\left(\frac{2\pi}{3} + \frac{11\pi}{6}\right) + i \sin\left(\frac{2\pi}{3} + \frac{11\pi}{6}\right)\right]$$

$$= 16\left(\cos \frac{5\pi}{2} + i \sin \frac{5\pi}{2}\right)$$

$$= 16\left(\cos \frac{\pi}{2} + i \sin \frac{\pi}{2}\right)$$

$$= 16[0 + i(1)] = 16i$$

You can check this result by first converting to the standard forms $z_1 = -1 + \sqrt{3}i$ and $z_2 = 4\sqrt{3} - 4i$ and then multiplying algebraically, as in Section 2.3.

$$z_1 z_2 = \left(-1 + \sqrt{3}i\right)\left(4\sqrt{3} - 4i\right)$$

$$= -4\sqrt{3} + 4i + 12i + 4\sqrt{3} = 16i$$

✓ *Checkpoint* Now try Exercise 51.

> **TECHNOLOGY TIP**
>
> Some graphing utilities can multiply and divide complex numbers in trigonometric form. If you have access to such a graphing utility, use it to find $z_1 z_2$ and z_1/z_2 in Examples 4 and 5.

Example 5   Dividing Complex Numbers in Trigonometric Form

Find the quotient z_1/z_2 of the complex numbers.

$$z_1 = 24(\cos 300° + i \sin 300°) \qquad z_2 = 8(\cos 75° + i \sin 75°)$$

Solution

$$\frac{z_1}{z_2} = \frac{24(\cos 300° + i \sin 300°)}{8(\cos 75° + i \sin 75°)}$$

$$= \frac{24}{8}[\cos(300° - 75°) + i \sin(300° - 75°)]$$

$$= 3(\cos 225° + i \sin 225°)$$

$$= 3\left[\left(-\frac{\sqrt{2}}{2}\right) + i\left(-\frac{\sqrt{2}}{2}\right)\right] = -\frac{3\sqrt{2}}{2} - \frac{3\sqrt{2}}{2}i$$

✓ *Checkpoint* Now try Exercise 57.

Powers of Complex Numbers

The trigonometric form of a complex number is used to raise a complex number to a power. To accomplish this, consider repeated use of the multiplication rule.

$z = r(\cos\theta + i\sin\theta)$

$z^2 = r(\cos\theta + i\sin\theta)r(\cos\theta + i\sin\theta) = r^2(\cos 2\theta + i\sin 2\theta)$

$z^3 = r^2(\cos 2\theta + i\sin 2\theta)r(\cos\theta + i\sin\theta) = r^3(\cos 3\theta + i\sin 3\theta)$

$z^4 = r^4(\cos 4\theta + i\sin 4\theta)$

$z^5 = r^5(\cos 5\theta + i\sin 5\theta)$

$\vdots$

This pattern leads to **DeMoivre's Theorem,** which is named after the French mathematician Abraham DeMoivre (1667–1754).

DeMoivre's Theorem

If $z = r(\cos\theta + i\sin\theta)$ is a complex number and n is a positive integer, then

$$z^n = [r(\cos\theta + i\sin\theta)]^n$$

$$= r^n(\cos n\theta + i\sin n\theta).$$

Exploration

Plot the numbers i, i^2, i^3, i^4, and i^5 in the complex plane. Write each number in trigonometric form and describe what happens to the angle θ as you form higher powers of i^n.

Example 6 Finding Powers of a Complex Number

Use DeMoivre's Theorem to find $\left(-1 + \sqrt{3}i\right)^{12}$.

Solution

First convert the complex number to trigonometric form using

$$r = \sqrt{(-1)^2 + \left(\sqrt{3}\right)^2} = 2 \quad \text{and} \quad \theta = \arctan\frac{\sqrt{3}}{-1} = \frac{2\pi}{3}.$$

So, the trigonometric form is

$$-1 + \sqrt{3}i = 2\left(\cos\frac{2\pi}{3} + i\sin\frac{2\pi}{3}\right).$$

Then, by DeMoivre's Theorem, you have

$$\left(-1 + \sqrt{3}i\right)^{12} = \left[2\left(\cos\frac{2\pi}{3} + i\sin\frac{2\pi}{3}\right)\right]^{12}$$

$$= 2^{12}\left[\cos\left(12 \cdot \frac{2\pi}{3}\right) + i\sin\left(12 \cdot \frac{2\pi}{3}\right)\right]$$

$$= 4096(\cos 8\pi + i\sin 8\pi)$$

$$= 4096(1 + 0) = 4096.$$

✓ *Checkpoint* Now try Exercise 73.

Roots of Complex Numbers

Recall that a consequence of the Fundamental Theorem of Algebra is that a polynomial equation of degree n has n solutions in the complex number system. So, an equation such as $x^6 = 1$ has six solutions, and in this particular case you can find the six solutions by factoring and using the Quadratic Formula.

$$x^6 - 1 = (x^3 - 1)(x^3 + 1)$$
$$= (x - 1)(x^2 + x + 1)(x + 1)(x^2 - x + 1)$$
$$= 0$$

Consequently, the solutions are

$$x = \pm 1, \qquad x = \frac{-1 \pm \sqrt{3}i}{2}, \qquad \text{and} \qquad x = \frac{1 \pm \sqrt{3}i}{2}.$$

Each of these numbers is a sixth root of 1. In general, the **nth root of a complex number** is defined as follows.

Definition of nth Root of a Complex Number

The complex number $u = a + bi$ is an **nth root** of the complex number z if

$$z = u^n = (a + bi)^n.$$

To find a formula for an nth root of a complex number, let u be an nth root of z, where

$$u = s(\cos \beta + i \sin \beta) \qquad \text{and} \qquad z = r(\cos \theta + i \sin \theta).$$

By DeMoivre's Theorem and the fact that $u^n = z$, you have

$$s^n (\cos n\beta + i \sin n\beta) = r(\cos \theta + i \sin \theta).$$

Taking the absolute value of each side of this equation, it follows that $s^n = r$. Substituting back into the previous equation and dividing by r, you get

$$\cos n\beta + i \sin n\beta = \cos \theta + i \sin \theta.$$

So, it follows that

$$\cos n\beta = \cos \theta \qquad \text{and} \qquad \sin n\beta = \sin \theta.$$

Because both sine and cosine have a period of 2π, these last two equations have solutions if and only if the angles differ by a multiple of 2π. Consequently, there must exist an integer k such that

$$n\beta = \theta + 2\pi k$$
$$\beta = \frac{\theta + 2\pi k}{n}.$$

By substituting this value of β into the trigonometric form of u, you get the result stated in the theorem on the following page.

Exploration

The nth roots of a complex number are useful for solving some polynomial equations. For instance, explain how you can use DeMoivre's Theorem to solve the polynomial equation

$$x^4 + 16 = 0.$$

[*Hint:* Write -16 as

$$16(\cos \pi + i \sin \pi).]$$

---

nth Roots of a Complex Number

For a positive integer n, the complex number $z = r(\cos\theta + i\sin\theta)$ has exactly n distinct nth roots given by

$$\sqrt[n]{r}\left(\cos\frac{\theta + 2\pi k}{n} + i\sin\frac{\theta + 2\pi k}{n}\right)$$

where $k = 0, 1, 2, \ldots, n - 1$.

When $k > n - 1$ the roots begin to repeat. For instance, if $k = n$, the angle

$$\frac{\theta + 2\pi n}{n} = \frac{\theta}{n} + 2\pi$$

is coterminal with θ/n, which is also obtained when $k = 0$.

The formula for the nth roots of a complex number z has a nice geometrical interpretation, as shown in Figure 7.48. Note that because the nth roots of z all have the same magnitude $\sqrt[n]{r}$, they all lie on a circle of radius $\sqrt[n]{r}$ with center at the origin. Furthermore, because successive nth roots have arguments that differ by $2\pi/n$, the n roots are equally spaced around the circle.

You have already found the sixth roots of 1 by factoring and by using the Quadratic Formula. Example 7 shows how you can solve the same problem with the formula for nth roots.

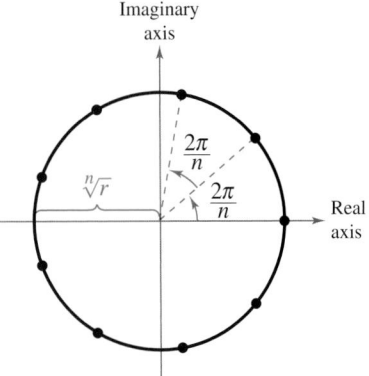

Figure 7.48

Example 7 Finding the nth Roots of a Real Number

Find all the sixth roots of 1.

Solution

First write 1 in the trigonometric form $1 = 1(\cos 0 + i\sin 0)$. Then, by the nth root formula with $n = 6$ and $r = 1$, the roots have the form

$$\sqrt[6]{1}\left(\cos\frac{0 + 2\pi k}{6} + i\sin\frac{0 + 2\pi k}{6}\right) = \cos\frac{\pi k}{3} + i\sin\frac{\pi k}{3}.$$

So, for $k = 0, 1, 2, 3, 4$, and 5, the sixth roots are as follows. (See Figure 7.49.)

$$\cos 0 + i\sin 0 = 1$$

$$\cos\frac{\pi}{3} + i\sin\frac{\pi}{3} = \frac{1}{2} + \frac{\sqrt{3}}{2}i \qquad \text{Incremented by } \frac{2\pi}{n} = \frac{2\pi}{6} = \frac{\pi}{3}$$

$$\cos\frac{2\pi}{3} + i\sin\frac{2\pi}{3} = -\frac{1}{2} + \frac{\sqrt{3}}{2}i$$

$$\cos\pi + i\sin\pi = -1$$

$$\cos\frac{4\pi}{3} + i\sin\frac{4\pi}{3} = -\frac{1}{2} - \frac{\sqrt{3}}{2}i$$

$$\cos\frac{5\pi}{3} + i\sin\frac{5\pi}{3} = \frac{1}{2} - \frac{\sqrt{3}}{2}i$$

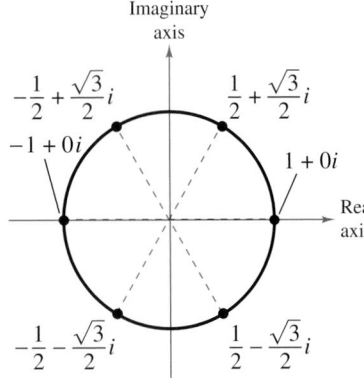

Figure 7.49

✓ *Checkpoint* Now try Exercise 103.

In Figure 7.49, notice that the roots obtained in Example 7 all have a magnitude of 1 and are equally spaced around the unit circle. Also notice that the complex roots occur in conjugate pairs, as discussed in Section 3.4. The n distinct nth roots of 1 are called the **nth roots of unity.**

Example 8   Finding the nth Roots of a Complex Number

Find the three cube roots of $z = -2 + 2i$.

Solution

The absolute value of z is

$$r = |-2 + 2i| = \sqrt{(-2)^2 + 2^2} = \sqrt{8}$$

and the angle θ is given by

$$\tan \theta = \frac{b}{a} = \frac{2}{-2} = -1.$$

Because z lies in Quadrant II, the trigonometric form of z is

$$z = -2 + 2i$$
$$= \sqrt{8}(\cos 135° + i \sin 135°).$$

By the formula for nth roots, the cube roots have the form

$$\sqrt[6]{8}\left(\cos \frac{135° + 360°k}{3} + i \sin \frac{135° + 360°k}{3}\right).$$

Finally, for $k = 0$, 1, and 2, you obtain the roots

$$\sqrt[6]{8}\left(\cos \frac{135° + 360°(0)}{3} + i \sin \frac{135° + 360°(0)}{3}\right)$$
$$= \sqrt{2}(\cos 45° + i \sin 45°)$$
$$= 1 + i$$

$$\sqrt[6]{8}\left(\cos \frac{135° + 360°(1)}{3} + i \sin \frac{135° + 360°(1)}{3}\right)$$
$$= \sqrt{2}(\cos 165° + i \sin 165°)$$
$$\approx -1.3660 + 0.3660i$$

$$\sqrt[6]{8}\left(\cos \frac{135° + 360°(2)}{3} + i \sin \frac{135° + 360°(2)}{3}\right)$$
$$= \sqrt{2}(\cos 285° + i \sin 285°)$$
$$\approx 0.3660 - 1.3660i.$$

See Figure 7.50.

✓ *Checkpoint* Now try Exercise 93.

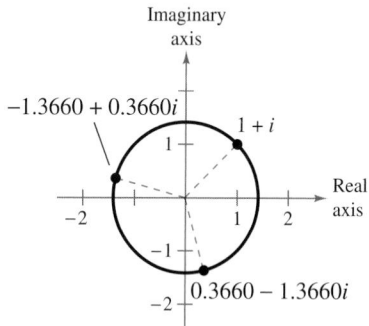

Figure 7.50

7.5   Exercises

Vocabulary Check

Fill in the blanks.

1. The _____ of a complex number $a + bi$ is the distance between the origin $(0, 0)$ and the point (a, b).

2. The _____ of a complex number $z = a + bi$ is given by $z = r(\cos \theta + i \sin \theta)$, where r is the _____ of z and θ is the _____ of z.

3. _____ Theorem states that if $z = r(\cos \theta + i \sin \theta)$ is a complex number and n is a positive integer, then $z^n = r^n(\cos n\theta + i \sin n\theta)$.

4. The complex number $u = a + bi$ is an _____ of the complex number z if $z = u^n = (a + bi)^n$.

In Exercises 1–8, plot the complex number and find its absolute value.

1. $6i$
2. $-2i$
3. -4
4. 7
5. $-4 + 4i$
6. $-5 - 12i$
7. $3 + 6i$
8. $10 - 3i$

In Exercises 9–12, write the complex number in trigonometric form.

9.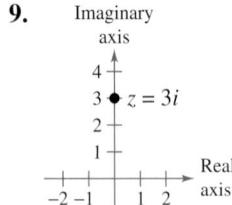

10.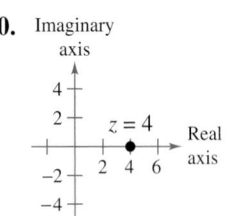

11.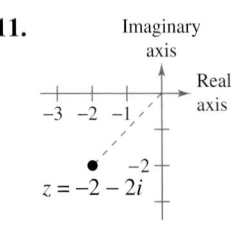

12.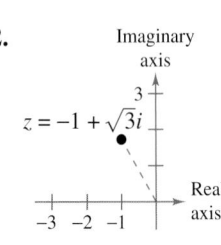

In Exercises 13–32, represent the complex number graphically, and find the trigonometric form of the number.

13. $5 - 5i$
14. $2 + 2i$
15. $\sqrt{3} + i$
16. $-1 - \sqrt{3}i$
17. $-2(1 + \sqrt{3}i)$
18. $\frac{5}{2}(\sqrt{3} - i)$
19. $-8i$
20. $4i$
21. $-7 + 4i$
22. $5 - i$

23. 3
24. 6
25. $3 + \sqrt{3}i$
26. $2\sqrt{2} - i$
27. $-1 - 2i$
28. $1 + 3i$
29. $5 + 2i$
30. $-3 + i$
31. $3\sqrt{2} - 7i$
32. $-8 - 5\sqrt{3}i$

In Exercises 33–44, represent the complex number graphically, and find the standard form of the number.

33. $2(\cos 120° + i \sin 120°)$
34. $5(\cos 135° + i \sin 135°)$
35. $\frac{3}{2}(\cos 330° + i \sin 330°)$
36. $\frac{3}{4}(\cos 315° + i \sin 315°)$
37. $3.75\left(\cos \dfrac{3\pi}{4} + i \sin \dfrac{3\pi}{4}\right)$
38. $1.5\left(\cos \dfrac{\pi}{2} + i \sin \dfrac{\pi}{2}\right)$
39. $6\left(\cos \dfrac{\pi}{3} + i \sin \dfrac{\pi}{3}\right)$
40. $8\left(\cos \dfrac{5\pi}{6} + i \sin \dfrac{5\pi}{6}\right)$
41. $4\left(\cos \dfrac{3\pi}{2} + i \sin \dfrac{3\pi}{2}\right)$
42. $9(\cos 0 + i \sin 0)$
43. $3[\cos(18° \, 45') + i \sin(18° \, 45')]$
44. $6[\cos(230° \, 30') + i \sin(230° \, 30')]$

In Exercises 45–48, use a graphing utility to represent the complex number in standard form.

45. $5\left(\cos \dfrac{\pi}{9} + i \sin \dfrac{\pi}{9}\right)$

46. $12\left(\cos\dfrac{3\pi}{5} + i\sin\dfrac{3\pi}{5}\right)$

47. $9(\cos 58° + i\sin 58°)$

48. $4(\cos 216.5° + i\sin 216.5°)$

In Exercises 49 and 50, represent the powers $z, z^2, z^3,$ **and** z^4 **graphically. Describe the pattern.**

49. $z = \dfrac{\sqrt{2}}{2}(1 + i)$

50. $z = \dfrac{1}{2}\left(1 + \sqrt{3}i\right)$

In Exercises 51–62, perform the operation and leave the result in trigonometric form.

51. $\left[3\left(\cos\dfrac{\pi}{3} + i\sin\dfrac{\pi}{3}\right)\right]\left[4\left(\cos\dfrac{\pi}{6} + i\sin\dfrac{\pi}{6}\right)\right]$

52. $\left[\dfrac{3}{2}\left(\cos\dfrac{\pi}{6} + i\sin\dfrac{\pi}{6}\right)\right]\left[6\left(\cos\dfrac{\pi}{4} + i\sin\dfrac{\pi}{4}\right)\right]$

53. $\left[\dfrac{5}{3}(\cos 140° + i\sin 140°)\right]\left[\dfrac{2}{3}(\cos 60° + i\sin 60°)\right]$

54. $\left[\dfrac{1}{2}(\cos 115° + i\sin 115°)\right]\left[\dfrac{4}{5}(\cos 300° + i\sin 300°)\right]$

55. $\left[\dfrac{11}{20}(\cos 290° + i\sin 290°)\right]\left[\dfrac{2}{5}(\cos 200° + i\sin 200°)\right]$

56. $(\cos 5° + i\sin 5°)(\cos 20° + i\sin 20°)$

57. $\dfrac{\cos 50° + i\sin 50°}{\cos 20° + i\sin 20°}$

58. $\dfrac{5(\cos 4.3 + i\sin 4.3)}{4(\cos 2.1 + i\sin 2.1)}$

59. $\dfrac{2(\cos 120° + i\sin 120°)}{4(\cos 40° + i\sin 40°)}$

60. $\dfrac{\cos\left(\dfrac{7\pi}{4}\right) + i\sin\left(\dfrac{7\pi}{4}\right)}{\cos \pi + i\sin \pi}$

61. $\dfrac{18(\cos 54° + i\sin 54°)}{3(\cos 102° + i\sin 102°)}$

62. $\dfrac{9(\cos 20° + i\sin 20°)}{5(\cos 75° + i\sin 75°)}$

In Exercises 63–68, (a) write the trigonometric forms of the complex numbers, (b) perform the indicated operation using the trigonometric forms, and (c) perform the indicated operation using the standard forms and check your result with that of part (b).

63. $(2 + 2i)(1 - i)$

64. $\left(\sqrt{3} + i\right)(1 + i)$

65. $-2i(1 + i)$

66. $\dfrac{3 + 4i}{1 - \sqrt{3}i}$

67. $\dfrac{5}{2 + 3i}$

68. $\dfrac{4i}{-4 + 2i}$

In Exercises 69–72, sketch the graph of all complex numbers z **satisfying the given condition.**

69. $|z| = 2$

70. $|z| = 5$

71. $\theta = \dfrac{\pi}{6}$

72. $\theta = \dfrac{\pi}{4}$

In Exercises 73–88, use DeMoivre's Theorem to find the indicated power of the complex number. Write the result in standard form.

73. $(1 + i)^3$

74. $(2 + 2i)^6$

75. $(-1 + i)^{10}$

76. $(1 - i)^8$

77. $2(\sqrt{3} + i)^5$

78. $4(1 - \sqrt{3}i)^3$

79. $[5(\cos 20° + i\sin 20°)]^3$

80. $[3(\cos 150° + i\sin 150°)]^4$

81. $\left(\cos\dfrac{5\pi}{4} + i\sin\dfrac{5\pi}{4}\right)^{10}$

82. $\left[2\left(\cos\dfrac{\pi}{2} + i\sin\dfrac{\pi}{2}\right)\right]^{12}$

83. $[4(\cos 2.8 + i\sin 2.8)]^5$

84. $(\cos 0 + i\sin 0)^{20}$

85. $(3 - 2i)^5$

86. $(\sqrt{5} - 4i)^4$

87. $[3(\cos 15° + i\sin 15°)]^4$

88. $\left[2\left(\cos\dfrac{\pi}{10} + i\sin\dfrac{\pi}{10}\right)\right]^5$

89. Show that $-\dfrac{1}{2}\left(1 + \sqrt{3}i\right)$ is a sixth root of 1.

90. Show that $2^{-1/4}(1 - i)$ is a fourth root of -2.

Graphical Reasoning   **In Exercises 91 and 92, use the graph of the roots of a complex number. (a) Write each of the roots in trigonometric form. (b) Identify the complex number whose roots are given. (c) Use a graphing utility to verify the results of part (b).**

91.

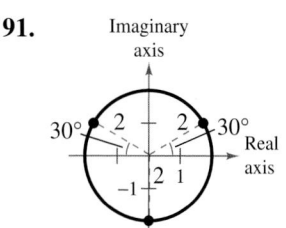

92.

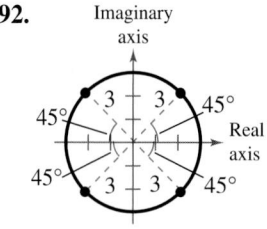

In Exercises 93–108, (a) use the theorem on page 578 to find the indicated roots of the complex number, (b) represent each of the roots graphically, and (c) write each of the roots in standard form.

93. Square roots of $5(\cos 120° + i \sin 120°)$

94. Square roots of $16(\cos 60° + i \sin 60°)$

95. Fourth roots of $16\left(\cos \dfrac{4\pi}{3} + i \sin \dfrac{4\pi}{3}\right)$

96. Fifth roots of $32\left(\cos \dfrac{5\pi}{6} + i \sin \dfrac{5\pi}{6}\right)$

97. Cube roots of $-27i$

98. Fourth roots of $625i$

99. Cube roots of $-\dfrac{125}{2}\left(1 + \sqrt{3}i\right)$

100. Cube roots of $-4\sqrt{2}(1 - i)$

101. Cube roots of $64i$

102. Fourth roots of i

103. Fifth roots of 1

104. Cube roots of 1000

105. Cube roots of -125

106. Fourth roots of -4

107. Fifth roots of $128(-1 + i)$

108. Sixth roots of $729i$

In Exercises 109–116, use the theorem on page 578 to find all the solutions of the equation, and represent the solutions graphically.

109. $x^4 - i = 0$

110. $x^3 + 27 = 0$

111. $x^5 + 243 = 0$

112. $x^4 - 81 = 0$

113. $x^4 + 16i = 0$

114. $x^6 - 64i = 0$

115. $x^3 - (1 - i) = 0$

116. $x^4 + (1 + i) = 0$

Synthesis

True or False? In Exercises 117–119, determine whether the statement is true or false. Justify your answer.

117. $\frac{1}{2}\left(1 - \sqrt{3}i\right)$ is a ninth root of -1.

118. $\sqrt{3} + i$ is a solution of the equation $x^2 - 8i = 0$.

119. Geometrically, the nth roots of any complex number z are all equally spaced around the unit circle centered at the origin.

120. Given two complex numbers $z_1 = r_1(\cos \theta_1 + i \sin \theta_1)$ and $z_2 = r_2(\cos \theta_2 + i \sin \theta_2)$, $z_2 \neq 0$, show that

$$\frac{z_1}{z_2} = \frac{r_1}{r_2}\left[\cos(\theta_1 - \theta_2) + i \sin(\theta_1 - \theta_2)\right].$$

121. Show that $\bar{z} = r[\cos(-\theta) + i \sin(-\theta)]$ is the complex conjugate of $z = r(\cos \theta + i \sin \theta)$.

122. Use the trigonometric forms of z and $\bar{z}$ in Exercise 121 to find (a) $z\bar{z}$ and (b) $z/\bar{z}$, $\bar{z} \neq 0$.

123. Show that the negative of $z = r(\cos \theta + i \sin \theta)$ is $-z = r[\cos(\theta + \pi) + i \sin(\theta + \pi)]$.

124. *Writing*　The famous formula

$$e^{a + bi} = e^a(\cos b + i \sin b)$$

is called Euler's Formula, after the Swiss mathematician Leonhard Euler (1707–1783). This formula gives rise to the equation

$$e^{\pi i} + 1 = 0.$$

This equation relates the five most famous numbers in mathematics—0, 1, π, e, and i—in a single equation. Show how Euler's Formula can be used to derive this equation. Write a short paragraph summarizing your work.

Review

Harmonic Motion　In Exercises 125–128, for the simple harmonic motion described by the trigonometric function, find the maximum displacement from equilibrium and the lowest possible positive value of t for which $d = 0$.

125. $d = 16 \cos \dfrac{\pi}{4}t$

126. $d = \dfrac{1}{16} \sin \dfrac{5\pi}{4}t$

127. $d = \frac{1}{8} \cos 12\pi t$

128. $d = \frac{1}{12} \sin 60\pi t$

In Exercises 129–132, find all solutions of the equation in the interval $[0, 2\pi)$. Use a graphing utility to verify your answers.

129. $2 \cos(x + \pi) + 2 \cos(x - \pi) = 0$

130. $\sin\left(x + \dfrac{3\pi}{2}\right) - \sin\left(x - \dfrac{3\pi}{2}\right) = 0$

131. $\sin\left(x - \dfrac{\pi}{3}\right) - \sin\left(x + \dfrac{\pi}{3}\right) = \dfrac{3}{2}$

132. $\tan(x + \pi) - \cos\left(x + \dfrac{5\pi}{2}\right) = 0$

7 Chapter Summary

What did you learn?

Section 7.1   Review Exercises
☐ Use the Law of Sines to solve oblique triangles (AAS, ASA, or SSA).   1–10
☐ Find areas of oblique triangles.   11–14
☐ Use the Law of Sines to model and solve real-life problems.   15–18

Section 7.2
☐ Use the Law of Cosines to solve oblique triangles (SSS or SAS).   19–28
☐ Use the Law of Cosines to model and solve real-life problems.   29–32
☐ Use Heron's Area Formula to find areas of triangles.   33–36

Section 7.3
☐ Represent vectors as directed line segments.   37, 38
☐ Write the component form of vectors.   39–44
☐ Perform basic vector operations and represent vectors graphically.   45–56
☐ Write vectors as linear combinations of unit vectors.   57–62
☐ Find the direction angles of vectors.   63–66
☐ Use vectors to model and solve real-life problems.   67–72

Section 7.4
☐ Find the dot product of two vectors and use properties of the dot product.   73–80
☐ Find angles between vectors and determine whether two vectors are orthogonal.   81–92
☐ Write vectors as sums of two vector components.   93–96
☐ Use vectors to find the work done by a force.   97, 98

Section 7.5
☐ Find absolute values of complex numbers.   99–102
☐ Write trigonometric forms of complex numbers.   103–108
☐ Multiply and divide complex numbers written in trigonometric form.   109–112
☐ Use DeMoivre's Theorem to find powers of complex numbers.   113–116
☐ Find nth roots of complex numbers.   117–124

7 Review Exercises

7.1 In Exercises 1–10, use the Law of Sines to solve the triangle. If two solutions exist, find both.

1. $A = 21°$, $B = 42°$, $a = 6$
2. $B = 110°$, $C = 30°$, $c = 11$
3. $A = 75°$, $a = 2.5$, $b = 16.5$
4. $A = 130°$, $a = 60$, $b = 48$
5. $B = 115°$, $a = 9$, $b = 14.5$
6. $C = 50°$, $a = 25$, $c = 22$
7. $A = 15°$, $a = 5$, $b = 10$
8. $B = 150°$, $a = 64$, $b = 10$
9. $B = 25°$, $a = 6.2$, $b = 4$
10. $A = 74°$, $b = 12.8$, $a = 12.5$

In Exercises 11–14, find the area of the triangle having the indicated angle and sides.

11. $A = 27°$, $b = 5$, $c = 8$
12. $B = 80°$, $a = 4$, $c = 8$
13. $C = 122°$, $b = 18$, $a = 29$
14. $C = 100°$, $a = 120$, $b = 74$

15. **Height** From a distance of 50 meters, the angle of elevation to the top of a building is 17°. Approximate the height of the building.

16. **Distance** A family is traveling due west on a road that passes a famous landmark. At a given time the bearing to the landmark is N 62° W, and after the family travels 5 miles farther, the bearing is N 38° W. What is the closest the family will come to the landmark while on the road?

17. **Height** A tree stands on a hillside of slope 28° from the horizontal. From a point 75 feet down the hill, the angle of elevation to the top of the tree is 45° (see figure). Find the height of the tree.

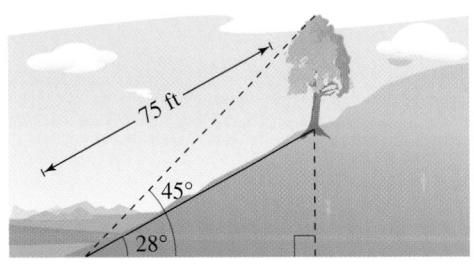

18. **Width** A surveyor finds that a tree on the opposite bank of a river has a bearing of N 22° 30′ E from a certain point and a bearing of N 15° W from a point 400 feet downstream. Find the width of the river.

7.2 In Exercises 19–28, use the Law of Cosines to solve the triangle.

19. $a = 9$, $b = 12$, $c = 20$
20. $a = 7$, $b = 15$, $c = 19$
21. $C = 45°$, $a = 6$, $b = 9$
22. $B = 90°$, $a = 5$, $c = 12$
23. $B = 110°$, $a = 4$, $c = 4$
24. $B = 12°$, $a = 32$, $c = 36$
25. $B = 150°$, $a = 10$, $c = 20$
26. $a = 42$, $b = 25$, $c = 58$
27. $a = 8.9$, $b = 6.1$, $c = 10.5$
28. $a = 7.5$, $b = 9.8$, $c = 4.5$

29. **Geometry** The lengths of the diagonals of a parallelogram are 10 feet and 16 feet. Find the lengths of the sides of the parallelogram if the diagonals intersect at an angle of 28°.

30. **Geometry** The lengths of the diagonals of a parallelogram are 30 meters and 40 meters. Find the lengths of the sides of the parallelogram if the diagonals intersect at an angle of 34°.

31. **Navigation** Two planes leave Washington, D.C.'s Dulles International Airport at approximately the same time. One is flying at 425 miles per hour at a bearing of 355°, and the other is flying at 530 miles per hour at a bearing of 67° (see figure). Determine the distance between the planes after they have flown for 2 hours.

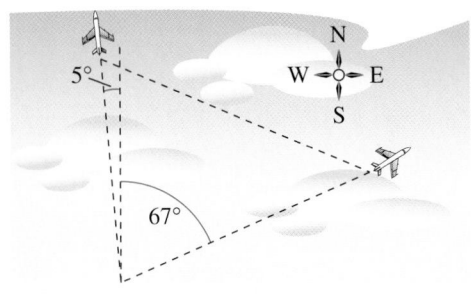

32. *Surveying*   To approximate the length of a marsh, a surveyor walks 425 meters from point A to point B. The surveyor then turns $65°$ and walks 300 meters to point C. Approximate the length AC of the marsh.

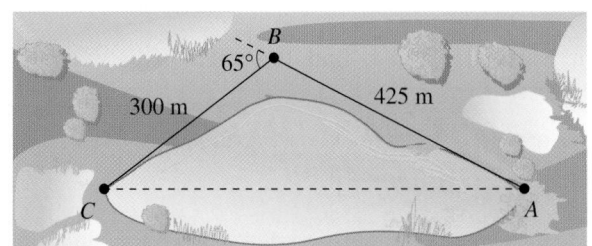

In Exercises 33–36, use Heron's Area Formula to find the area of the triangle with the given side lengths.

33. $a = 4$, $b = 5$, $c = 7$

34. $a = 15$, $b = 8$, $c = 10$

35. $a = 64.8$, $b = 49.2$, $c = 24.1$

36. $a = 8.55$, $b = 5.14$, $c = 12.73$

7.3 In Exercises 37 and 38, show that u = v.

37.

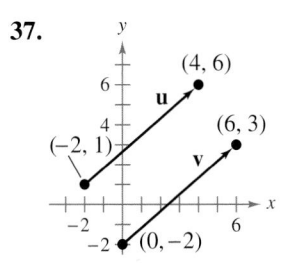

38.

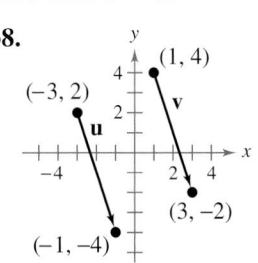

In Exercises 39–44, find the component form of the vector v satisfying the given conditions.

39.

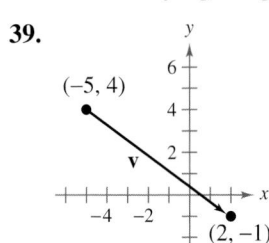

40.

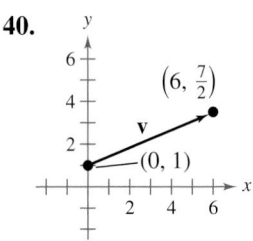

41. Initial point: $(0, 10)$; terminal point: $(7, 3)$

42. Initial point: $(1, 5)$; terminal point: $(15, 9)$

43. $\|\mathbf{v}\| = 8$, $\theta = 120°$ **44.** $\|\mathbf{v}\| = \frac{1}{2}$, $\theta = 225°$

In Exercises 45–52, find (a) u + v, (b) u − v, (c) 3u, and (d) 2v + 5u.

45. $\mathbf{u} = \langle -1, -3 \rangle$, $\mathbf{v} = \langle -3, 6 \rangle$

46. $\mathbf{u} = \langle 4, 5 \rangle$, $\mathbf{v} = \langle 0, -1 \rangle$

47. $\mathbf{u} = \langle -5, 2 \rangle$, $\mathbf{v} = \langle 4, 4 \rangle$

48. $\mathbf{u} = \langle 1, -8 \rangle$, $\mathbf{v} = \langle 3, -2 \rangle$

49. $\mathbf{u} = 2\mathbf{i} - \mathbf{j}$, $\mathbf{v} = 5\mathbf{i} + 3\mathbf{j}$

50. $\mathbf{u} = -6\mathbf{j}$, $\mathbf{v} = \mathbf{i} + \mathbf{j}$

51. $\mathbf{u} = 4\mathbf{i}$, $\mathbf{v} = -\mathbf{i} + 6\mathbf{j}$

52. $\mathbf{u} = -7\mathbf{i} - 3\mathbf{j}$, $\mathbf{v} = 4\mathbf{i} - \mathbf{j}$

In Exercises 53–56, find the component form of w and sketch the specified vector operations geometrically, where u = 6i − 5j and v = 10i + 3j.

53. $\mathbf{w} = 3\mathbf{v}$ **54.** $\mathbf{w} = \frac{1}{2}\mathbf{v}$

55. $\mathbf{w} = 4\mathbf{u} + 5\mathbf{v}$ **56.** $\mathbf{w} = 3\mathbf{v} - 2\mathbf{u}$

In Exercises 57–60, find a unit vector in the direction of the given vector.

57. $\mathbf{u} = \langle 0, -6 \rangle$ **58.** $\mathbf{v} = \langle -12, -5 \rangle$

59. $\mathbf{v} = 5\mathbf{i} - 2\mathbf{j}$ **60.** $\mathbf{w} = -7\mathbf{i}$

In Exercises 61 and 62, write a linear combination of the standard unit vectors i and j for the given initial and terminal points.

61. Initial point: $(-8, 3)$
Terminal point: $(1, -5)$

62. Initial point: $(2, -3.2)$
Terminal point: $(-6.4, 10.8)$

In Exercises 63 and 64, write the vector v in the form $\|\mathbf{v}\|[(\cos \theta)\mathbf{i} + (\sin \theta)\mathbf{j}]$.

63. $\mathbf{v} = -10\mathbf{i} + 10\mathbf{j}$ **64.** $\mathbf{v} = 4\mathbf{i} - \mathbf{j}$

In Exercises 65 and 66, graph the vectors and the resultant of the vectors. Find the magnitude and direction of the resultant.

65.

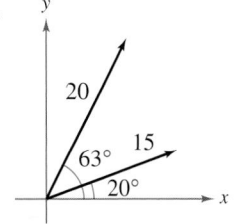

66.

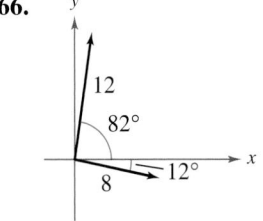

67. Resultant Force Three forces with magnitudes of 250 pounds, 100 pounds, and 200 pounds act on an object at angles of 60°, 150°, and −90°, respectively, with the positive x-axis. Find the direction and magnitude of the resultant of these forces.

68. Resultant Force Forces with magnitudes of 85 pounds and 50 pounds act on a single point. The angle between the forces is 15°. Describe the resultant force.

69. Tension A 180-pound weight is supported by two ropes, as shown in the figure. Find the tension in each rope.

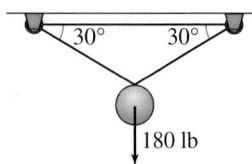

70. Cable Tension In a manufacturing process, an electric hoist lifts 200-pound ingots. Find the tension in the supporting cables (see figure).

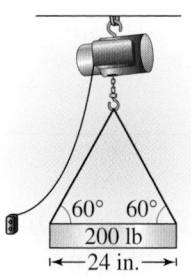

71. Navigation An airplane has an airspeed of 430 miles per hour at a bearing of 135°. The wind velocity is 35 miles per hour in the direction N 30° E. Find the resultant speed and direction of the plane.

72. Navigation An airplane has an airspeed of 724 kilometers per hour at a bearing of 30°. The wind velocity is from the west at 32 kilometers per hour. Find the resultant speed and direction of the plane.

7.4 In Exercises 73–76, find the dot product of u and v.

73. $\mathbf{u} = \langle 0, -2 \rangle$
$\mathbf{v} = \langle 1, 10 \rangle$

74. $\mathbf{u} = \langle -4, 5 \rangle$
$\mathbf{v} = \langle 3, -1 \rangle$

75. $\mathbf{u} = 6\mathbf{i} - \mathbf{j}$
$\mathbf{v} = 2\mathbf{i} + 5\mathbf{j}$

76. $\mathbf{u} = 8\mathbf{i} - 7\mathbf{j}$
$\mathbf{v} = 3\mathbf{i} - 4\mathbf{j}$

In Exercises 77–80, use the vectors $\mathbf{u} = \langle -3, -4 \rangle$ and $\mathbf{v} = \langle 2, 1 \rangle$ to find the indicated quantity.

77. $\mathbf{u} \cdot \mathbf{u}$

78. $\|\mathbf{v}\| - 3$

79. $4\mathbf{u} \cdot \mathbf{v}$

80. $(\mathbf{u} \cdot \mathbf{v})\mathbf{u}$

In Exercises 81–84, find the angle θ between the vectors.

81. $\mathbf{u} = \langle 2\sqrt{2}, -4 \rangle$, $\mathbf{v} = \langle -\sqrt{2}, 1 \rangle$

82. $\mathbf{u} = \langle 3, 1 \rangle$, $\mathbf{v} = \langle 4, 5 \rangle$

83. $\mathbf{u} = \cos\dfrac{7\pi}{4}\mathbf{i} + \sin\dfrac{7\pi}{4}\mathbf{j}$, $\mathbf{v} = \cos\dfrac{5\pi}{6}\mathbf{i} + \sin\dfrac{5\pi}{6}\mathbf{j}$

84. $\mathbf{u} = \cos 45°\mathbf{i} + \sin 45°\mathbf{j}$
$\mathbf{v} = \cos 300°\mathbf{i} + \sin 300°\mathbf{j}$

In Exercises 85–88, graph the vectors and find the degree measure of the angle between the vectors.

85. $\mathbf{u} = 4\mathbf{i} + \mathbf{j}$
$\mathbf{v} = \mathbf{i} - 4\mathbf{j}$

86. $\mathbf{u} = 6\mathbf{i} + 2\mathbf{j}$
$\mathbf{v} = -3\mathbf{i} - \mathbf{j}$

87. $\mathbf{u} = 7\mathbf{i} - 5\mathbf{j}$
$\mathbf{v} = 10\mathbf{i} + 3\mathbf{j}$

88. $\mathbf{u} = -5.3\mathbf{i} + 2.8\mathbf{j}$
$\mathbf{v} = -8.1\mathbf{i} - 4\mathbf{j}$

In Exercises 89–92, determine whether u and v are orthogonal, parallel, or neither.

89. $\mathbf{u} = \langle 39, -12 \rangle$
$\mathbf{v} = \langle -26, 8 \rangle$

90. $\mathbf{u} = \langle 8, -4 \rangle$
$\mathbf{v} = \langle 5, 10 \rangle$

91. $\mathbf{u} = \langle 8, 5 \rangle$
$\mathbf{v} = \langle -2, 4 \rangle$

92. $\mathbf{u} = \langle -15, 51 \rangle$
$\mathbf{v} = \langle 20, -68 \rangle$

In Exercises 93–96, find the projection of u onto v. Then write u as the sum of two orthogonal vectors, one of which is $\text{proj}_\mathbf{v}\,\mathbf{u}$.

93. $\mathbf{u} = \langle -4, 3 \rangle$, $\mathbf{v} = \langle -8, -2 \rangle$

94. $\mathbf{u} = \langle 5, 6 \rangle$, $\mathbf{v} = \langle 10, 0 \rangle$

95. $\mathbf{u} = \langle 2, 7 \rangle$, $\mathbf{v} = \langle 1, -1 \rangle$

96. $\mathbf{u} = \langle -3, 5 \rangle$, $\mathbf{v} = \langle -5, 2 \rangle$

97. Work Determine the work done by a crane lifting an 18,000-pound truck 48 inches.

98. Braking Force A 500-pound motorcycle is headed up a hill inclined at 12°. What force is required to keep the motorcycle from rolling back down the hill when stopped at a red light?

7.5 In Exercises 99–102, plot the complex number and find its absolute value.

99. $-i$

100. $5i$

101. $7 - 5i$

102. $-3 + 9i$

In Exercises 103–108, write the complex number in trigonometric form.

103.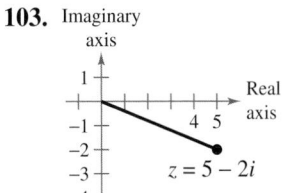

104.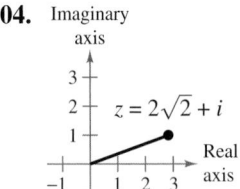

105. $5 - 5i$

106. $-3\sqrt{3} + 3i$

107. $5 + 12i$

108. $-7 + 3i$

In Exercises 109–112, perform the operation and leave the result in trigonometric form.

109. $\left[\dfrac{5}{2}\left(\cos\dfrac{\pi}{2} + i\sin\dfrac{\pi}{2}\right)\right]\left[4\left(\cos\dfrac{\pi}{4} + i\sin\dfrac{\pi}{4}\right)\right]$

110. $\left[2\left(\cos\dfrac{2\pi}{3} + i\sin\dfrac{2\pi}{3}\right)\right]\left[3\left(\cos\dfrac{\pi}{6} + i\sin\dfrac{\pi}{6}\right)\right]$

111. $\dfrac{20(\cos 320° + i\sin 320°)}{5(\cos 80° + i\sin 80°)}$

112. $\dfrac{3(\cos 230° + i\sin 230°)}{9(\cos 95° + i\sin 95°)}$

In Exercises 113–116, use DeMoivre's Theorem to find the indicated power of the complex number. Write the result in standard form.

113. $\left[5\left(\cos\dfrac{\pi}{12} + i\sin\dfrac{\pi}{12}\right)\right]^4$

114. $\left[2\left(\cos\dfrac{4\pi}{15} + i\sin\dfrac{4\pi}{15}\right)\right]^5$

115. $(2 + 3i)^6$

116. $(1 - i)^8$

In Exercises 117–120, (a) use the theorem on page 578 to find the indicated roots of the complex number, (b) represent each of the roots graphically, and (c) write each of the roots in standard form.

117. Sixth roots of $-729i$

118. Fourth roots of $256i$

119. Cube roots of 8

120. Fifth roots of -1024

In Exercises 121–124, use the theorem on page 578 to find all solutions of the equation, and represent the solutions graphically.

121. $x^4 + 256 = 0$

122. $x^5 - 32i = 0$

123. $x^3 + 8i = 0$

124. $x^4 + 81 = 0$

Synthesis

In Exercises 125 and 126, determine whether the statement is true or false. Justify your answer.

125. The Law of Sines is true if one of the angles in the triangle is a right angle.

126. When the Law of Sines is used, the solution is always unique.

127. What characterizes a vector in the plane?

128. Which vectors in the figure appear to be equivalent?

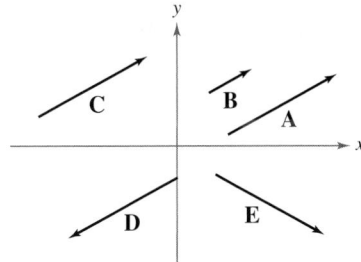

129. The figure shows z_1 and z_2. Describe $z_1 z_2$ and z_1/z_2.

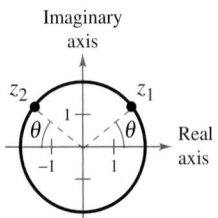

130. One of the fourth roots of a complex number z is shown in the graph.

(a) How many roots are not shown?

(b) Describe the other roots.

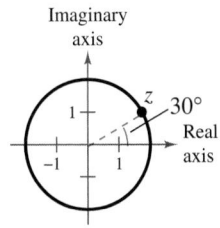

7 | Chapter Test

Take this test as you would take a test in class. After you are finished, check
your work against the answers given in the back of the book.

In Exercises 1–6, use the given information to solve the triangle. If two
solutions exist, find both.

1. $A = 36°$, $B = 98°$, $c = 18$ 2. $a = 4$, $b = 7$, $c = 9$

3. $A = 35°$, $b = 8$, $c = 11$ 4. $A = 25°$, $b = 28$, $a = 15$

5. $B = 130°$, $c = 10.1$, $b = 5.2$ 6. $A = 150°$, $b = 4.8$, $a = 9.4$

7. Find the length of the pond shown at the right.

8. A triangular parcel of land has borders of lengths 55 meters, 85 meters, and
   100 meters. Find the area of the parcel of land.

9. Find the component form and magnitude of the vector **w** that has initial point
   $(-8, -12)$ and terminal point $(4, 1)$.

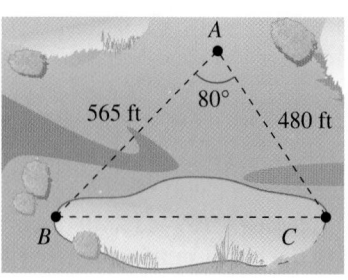

Figure for 7

In Exercises 10–13, find (a) $2\mathbf{v} + \mathbf{u}$, (b) $\mathbf{u} - 3\mathbf{v}$, and (c) $5\mathbf{u} - \mathbf{v}$.

10. $\mathbf{u} = \langle 0, -4 \rangle$, $\mathbf{v} = \langle -2, 4 \rangle$

11. $\mathbf{u} = \langle -2, -3 \rangle$, $\mathbf{v} = \langle 1, 5 \rangle$

12. $\mathbf{u} = \mathbf{i} - \mathbf{j}$, $\mathbf{v} = 6\mathbf{i} + 9\mathbf{j}$

13. $\mathbf{u} = 2\mathbf{i} + 3\mathbf{j}$, $\mathbf{v} = -\mathbf{i} - 2\mathbf{j}$

14. Find a unit vector in the direction of $\mathbf{v} = 7\mathbf{i} + 4\mathbf{j}$.

15. Find the component form of the vector **v** with $\|\mathbf{v}\| = 12$, in the same direction
    as $\mathbf{u} = \langle 3, -5 \rangle$.

16. Forces with magnitudes of 250 pounds and 130 pounds act on an object
    at angles of $45°$ and $-60°$, respectively, with the positive x-axis. Find the
    direction and magnitude of the resultant of these forces.

17. Find the dot product of $\mathbf{u} = \langle -9, 4 \rangle$ and $\mathbf{v} = \langle 1, 3 \rangle$.

18. Find the angle between the vectors $\mathbf{u} = 7\mathbf{i} + 2\mathbf{j}$ and $\mathbf{v} = -4\mathbf{j}$.

19. Are the vectors $\mathbf{u} = \langle 6, -4 \rangle$ and $\mathbf{v} = \langle 2, -3 \rangle$ orthogonal? Explain.

20. Find the projection of $\mathbf{u} = \langle 6, 7 \rangle$ onto $\mathbf{v} = \langle -5, -1 \rangle$. Then write **u** as the
    sum of two orthogonal vectors.

21. Write the complex number $z = -2 + 2i$ in trigonometric form.

22. Write the complex number $100(\cos 240° + i \sin 240°)$ in standard form.

In Exercises 23 and 24, use DeMoivre's Theorem to find the indicated power
of the complex number. Write the result in standard form.

23. $\left[3\left(\cos \dfrac{5\pi}{6} + i \sin \dfrac{5\pi}{6} \right) \right]^8$ 24. $(3 - 3i)^6$

25. Find the fourth roots of $128\left(1 + \sqrt{3}\,i\right)$.

26. Find all solutions of the equation $x^4 - 625i = 0$ and represent the solutions
    graphically.

5–7 Cumulative Test

Take this test to review the material from earlier chapters. After you are finished, check your work against the answers given in the back of the book.

1. Consider the angle $\theta = -120°$.

   (a) Sketch the angle in standard position.

   (b) Determine a coterminal angle in the interval $[0°, 360°)$.

   (c) Convert the angle to radian measure.

   (d) Find the reference angle θ'.

   (e) Find the exact values of the six trigonometric functions of θ.

2. Convert the angle $\theta = 2.35$ radians to degrees. Round your answer to one decimal place.

3. Find $\cos\theta$ if $\tan\theta = -\frac{4}{3}$ and $\sin\theta > 0$.

In Exercises 4–6, sketch the graph of the function by hand. (Include two full periods.) Use a graphing utility to verify your graph.

4. $f(x) = 3 - 2\sin\pi x$ 5. $f(x) = \tan 3x$ 6. $f(x) = \frac{1}{2}\sec(x + \pi)$

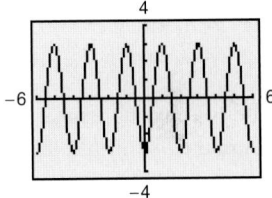

7. Find a, b, and c such that the graph of the function $h(x) = a\cos(bx + c)$ matches the graph in the figure at the right.

Figure for 7

In Exercises 8 and 9, find the exact value of the expression without using a calculator.

8. $\tan(\arctan 6.7)$ 9. $\tan\left(\arcsin\frac{3}{5}\right)$

10. Write an algebraic expression equivalent to $\sin(\arccos 2x)$.

11. Subtract and simplify: $\dfrac{\sin\theta - 1}{\cos\theta} - \dfrac{\cos\theta}{\sin\theta - 1}$.

In Exercises 12–14, verify the identity.

12. $\cot^2\alpha(\sec^2\alpha - 1) = 1$ 13. $\sin(x + y)\sin(x - y) = \sin^2 x - \sin^2 y$

14. $\sin^2 x\cos^2 x = \frac{1}{8}(1 - \cos 4x)$

In Exercises 15 and 16, solve the equation.

15. $\sin^2 x + 2\sin x + 1 = 0$ 16. $3\tan\theta - \cot\theta = 0$

17. Approximate the solutions to the equation $\cos^2 x - 5\cos x - 1 = 0$ in the interval $[0, 2\pi)$.

In Exercises 18 and 19, use a graphing utility to graph the function and approximate its zeros in the interval $[0, 2\pi)$. If possible, find the exact values of the zeros algebraically.

18. $y = \dfrac{1 + \sin x}{\cos x} + \dfrac{\cos x}{1 + \sin x} - 4$

19. $y = \tan^3 x - \tan^2 x + 3\tan x - 3$

20. Given that $\sin u = \frac{12}{13}$, $\cos v = \frac{3}{5}$, and angles u and v are both in Quadrant I, find $\tan(u - v)$.

21. If $\tan \theta = \frac{1}{2}$, find the exact value of $\tan 2\theta$, $0 < \theta < \frac{\pi}{2}$.

22. If $\tan \theta = \frac{4}{3}$, find the exact value of $\sin \frac{\theta}{2}$, $\pi < \theta < \frac{3\pi}{2}$.

23. Write $\cos 8x + \cos 4x$ as a product.

In Exercises 24–27, verify the identity.

24. $\tan x(1 - \sin^2 x) = \frac{1}{2} \sin 2x$

25. $\sin 3\theta \sin \theta = \frac{1}{2}(\cos 2\theta - \cos 4\theta)$

26. $\sin 3x \cos 2x = \frac{1}{2}(\sin 5x + \sin x)$

27. $\dfrac{2 \cos 3x}{\sin 4x - \sin 2x} = \csc x$

In Exercises 28–31, use the information to solve the triangle shown at the right.

28. $A = 46°$, $a = 14$, $b = 5$

29. $A = 30°$, $b = 8$, $c = 10$

30. $A = 24°$, $C = 101°$, $a = 10$

31. $a = 24$, $b = 30$, $c = 47$

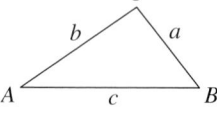

Figure for 28–31

32. Two sides of a triangle have lengths 14 inches and 19 inches. Their included angle measures 82°. Find the area of the triangle.

33. Find the area of a triangle with sides of lengths 11 inches, 16 inches, and 17 inches.

34. Write the vector $\mathbf{u} = \langle 3, 5 \rangle$ as a linear combination of the standard unit vectors $\mathbf{i}$ and $\mathbf{j}$.

35. Find a unit vector in the direction of $\mathbf{v} = \mathbf{i} + \mathbf{j}$.

36. Find $\mathbf{u} \cdot \mathbf{v}$ for $\mathbf{u} = 3\mathbf{i} + 4\mathbf{j}$ and $\mathbf{v} = \mathbf{i} - 2\mathbf{j}$.

37. Find the projection of $\mathbf{u} = \langle 8, -2 \rangle$ onto $\mathbf{v} = \langle 1, 5 \rangle$. Then write $\mathbf{u}$ as the sum of two orthogonal vectors.

38. Find the trigonometric form of the complex number shown at the right.

39. Write the complex number $8\left(\cos \dfrac{5\pi}{6} + i \sin \dfrac{5\pi}{6}\right)$ in standard form.

40. Find the product $[4(\cos 30° + i \sin 30°)][6(\cos 120° + i \sin 120°)]$. Write the answer in standard form.

41. Find the three cube roots of 1.

42. Write all the solutions of the equation $x^5 + 243 = 0$.

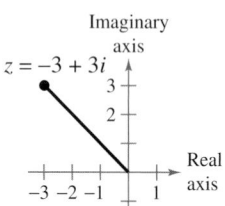

Figure for 38

43. From a point 200 feet from a flagpole, the angles of elevation to the bottom and top of the flag are $16° \, 45'$ and $18°$, respectively. Approximate the height of the flag to the nearest foot.

44. Write a model for a particle in simple harmonic motion with a displacement of 4 inches and a period of 8 seconds.

45. An airplane's velocity with respect to the air is 500 kilometers per hour, with a bearing of 30°. The wind at the altitude of the plane has a velocity of 50 kilometers per hour with a bearing of N 60° E. What is the true direction of the plane, and what is its speed relative to the ground?

46. Forces of 60 pounds and 100 pounds have a resultant force of 125 pounds. Find the angle between the two forces.

Systems of equations can be used to model the change in sales of consumer products. The growth in sales of DVD players is closely tied to the decline in sales of VCR players.

Bonn Sequenz/Imapress/The Image Works

8 Linear Systems and Matrices

8.1 Solving Systems of Equations

8.2 Systems of Linear Equations in Two Variables

8.3 Multivariable Linear Systems

8.4 Matrices and Systems of Equations

8.5 Operations with Matrices

8.6 The Inverse of a Square Matrix

8.7 The Determinant of a Square Matrix

8.8 Applications of Matrices and Determinants

What You Should Learn

In this chapter, you will learn how to:

- Solve systems of equations by substitution, by elimination, by Gaussian elimination, by Gauss-Jordan elimination, by using inverse matrices, by Cramer's Rule, and graphically.

- Recognize a linear system in row-echelon form and use back-substitution to solve the system.

- Solve nonsquare systems of equations.

- Use systems of equations to model and solve real-life problems.

- Write matrices, identify their order, and perform elementary row operations.

- Perform operations with matrices.

- Find inverses of matrices.

- Find the determinants of square matrices.

591

8.1 Solving Systems of Equations

The Method of Substitution

Up to this point in the text, most problems have involved either a function of one variable or a single equation in two variables. However, many problems in science, business, and engineering involve two or more equations in two or more variables. To solve such problems, you need to find solutions of **systems of equations.** Here is an example of a system of two equations in two unknowns, x and y.

$$\begin{cases} 2x + y = 5 & \text{Equation 1} \\ 3x - 2y = 4 & \text{Equation 2} \end{cases}$$

A **solution** of this system is an ordered pair that satisfies each equation in the system. Finding the set of all such solutions is called **solving the system of equations.** For instance, the ordered pair $(2, 1)$ is a solution of this system. To check this, you can substitute 2 for x and 1 for y in *each* equation.

In this chapter you will study six ways to solve systems of equations, beginning with the **method of substitution.**

	Method	*Section*	*Type of System*
1.	Substitution	8.1	Linear or nonlinear, two variables
2.	Graphical	8.1	Linear or nonlinear, two variables
3.	Elimination	8.2	Linear, two variables
4.	Gaussian Elimination	8.3	Linear, three or more variables
5.	Matrices	8.4	Linear, two or more variables
6.	Cramer's Rule	8.8	Linear, two or more variables

> **The Method of Substitution**
>
> **1.** Solve one of the equations for one variable in terms of the other.
>
> **2.** Substitute the expression found in Step 1 into the other equation to obtain an equation in one variable.
>
> **3.** Solve the equation obtained in Step 2.
>
> **4.** Back-substitute the value obtained in Step 3 into the expression obtained in Step 1 to find the value of the other variable.
>
> **5.** Check that the solution satisfies *each* of the original equations.

In the algebraic solution of Example 1, you use the method of substitution to solve the system of equations. In the graphical solution, note that the solution of the system corresponds to the **point of intersection** of the graphs.

What you should learn

- Use the method of substitution and the graphical method to solve systems of equations in two variables.
- Use systems of equations to model and solve real-life problems.

Why you should learn it

You can use systems of equations in situations in which the variables must satisfy two or more conditions. For instance, Exercise 72 on page 601 shows how to use a system of equations to compare two models for estimating the number of board feet in a 16-foot log.

Bruce Hands/Getty Images

Example 1   Solving a System of Equations

Solve the system of equations.

$$\begin{cases} x + y = 4 & \text{Equation 1} \\ x - y = 2 & \text{Equation 2} \end{cases}$$

Algebraic Solution

Begin by solving for y in Equation 1.

$y = 4 - x$ Solve for y in Equation 1.

Next, substitute this expression for y into Equation 2 and solve the resulting single-variable equation for x.

$x - y = 2$	Write Equation 2.
$x - (4 - x) = 2$	Substitute $4 - x$ for y.
$x - 4 + x = 2$	Distributive Property
$2x = 6$	Combine like terms.
$x = 3$	Divide each side by 2.

Finally, you can solve for y by *back-substituting* $x = 3$ into the equation $y = 4 - x$ to obtain

$y = 4 - x$	Write revised Equation 1.
$y = 4 - 3$	Substitute 3 for x.
$y = 1.$	Solve for y.

The solution is the ordered pair $(3, 1)$. Check this as follows.

Check $(3, 1)$ in Equation 1:

$x + y = 4$	Write Equation 1.
$3 + 1 \overset{?}{=} 4$	Substitute for x and y.
$4 = 4$	Solution checks in Equation 1. ✓

Check $(3, 1)$ in Equation 2:

$x - y = 2$	Write Equation 2.
$3 - 1 \overset{?}{=} 2$	Substitute for x and y.
$2 = 2$	Solution checks in Equation 2. ✓

✓ *Checkpoint* Now try Exercise 5.

Graphical Solution

Begin by solving both equations for y. Then use a graphing utility to graph the equations $y_1 = 4 - x$ and $y_2 = x - 2$ in the same viewing window. Use the *intersect* feature (see Figure 8.1) or the *zoom* and *trace* features of the graphing utility to approximate the point of intersection of the graphs.

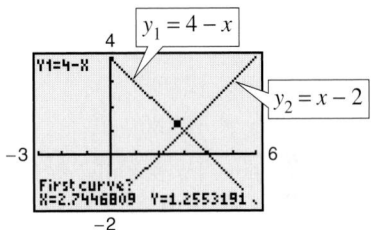

Figure 8.1

The point of intersection is $(3, 1)$, as shown in Figure 8.2.

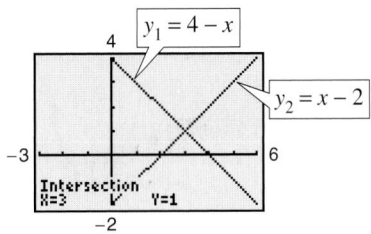

Figure 8.2

Check that $(3, 1)$ is the exact solution as follows.

Check $(3, 1)$ in Equation 1:

$3 + 1 \overset{?}{=} 4$	Substitute for x and y in Equation 1.
$4 = 4$	Solution checks in Equation 1. ✓

Check $(3, 1)$ in Equation 2:

$3 - 1 \overset{?}{=} 2$	Substitute for x and y in Equation 2.
$2 = 2$	Solution checks in Equation 2. ✓

In the algebraic solution of Example 1, note that the term *back-substitution* implies that you work *backwards*. First you solve for one of the variables, and then you substitute that value *back* into one of the equations in the system to find the value of the other variable.

Example 2   Solving a System by Substitution

A total of $12,000 is invested in two funds paying 9% and 11% simple interest. The yearly interest is $1180. How much is invested at each rate?

Solution

Verbal Model: $\boxed{\dfrac{9\%}{\text{fund}}} + \boxed{\dfrac{11\%}{\text{fund}}} = \boxed{\dfrac{\text{Total}}{\text{investment}}}$

$\boxed{\dfrac{9\%}{\text{interest}}} + \boxed{\dfrac{11\%}{\text{interest}}} = \boxed{\dfrac{\text{Total}}{\text{interest}}}$

Labels: Amount in 9% fund = x Amount in 11% fund = y (dollars)

Interest for 9% fund = $0.09x$ Interest for 11% fund = $0.11y$ (dollars)

Total investment = $12,000   Total interest = $1180   (dollars)

System: $\begin{cases} x + \quad y = 12{,}000 & \text{Equation 1} \\ 0.09x + 0.11y = \quad 1{,}180 & \text{Equation 2} \end{cases}$

To begin, it is convenient to multiply each side of Equation 2 by 100. This eliminates the need to work with decimals.

$9x + 11y = 118{,}000$ Revised Equation 2

To solve this system, you can solve for x in Equation 1.

$x = 12{,}000 - y$ Revised Equation 1

Next, substitute this expression for x into revised Equation 2 and solve the resulting equation for y.

$$9x + 11y = 118{,}000 \qquad \text{Write revised Equation 2.}$$
$$9(12{,}000 - y) + 11y = 118{,}000 \qquad \text{Substitute } 12{,}000 - y \text{ for } x.$$
$$108{,}000 - 9y + 11y = 118{,}000 \qquad \text{Distributive Property}$$
$$2y = 10{,}000 \qquad \text{Combine like terms.}$$
$$y = 5000 \qquad \text{Divide each side by 2.}$$

Finally, back-substitute the value $y = 5000$ to solve for x.

$$x = 12{,}000 - y \qquad \text{Write revised Equation 1.}$$
$$x = 12{,}000 - 5000 \qquad \text{Substitute 5000 for } y.$$
$$x = 7000 \qquad \text{Simplify.}$$

The solution is (7000, 5000). So, $7000 is invested at 9% and $5000 is invested at 11% to yield yearly interest of $1180. Check this in the original system.

 *Checkpoint* Now try Exercise 71.

The equations in Examples 1 and 2 are linear. Substitution can also be used to solve systems in which one or both of the equations are nonlinear.

TECHNOLOGY TIP

Remember that a good way to check the answers you obtain in this section is to use a graphing utility. For instance, enter the two equations in Example 2

$$y_1 = 12{,}000 - x$$
$$y_2 = \frac{1180 - 0.09x}{0.11}$$

and find an appropriate viewing window that shows where the lines intersect. Then use the *intersect* feature or the *zoom* and *trace* features to find the point of intersection.

STUDY TIP

When using the method of substitution, it does not matter which variable you choose to solve for first. Whether you solve for y first or x first, you will obtain the same solution. When making your choice, you should choose the variable and equation that are easier to work with. For instance, in Example 2, solving for x in the first equation was easier than solving for x in the second equation.

Example 3   Substitution: No-Solution Case

Solve the system of equations.

$$\begin{cases} -x + y = 4 & \text{Equation 1} \\ x^2 + y = 3 & \text{Equation 2} \end{cases}$$

Solution

Begin by solving for y in Equation 1 to obtain $y = x + 4$. Next, substitute this expression for y into Equation 2 and solve for x.

$$x^2 + y = 3 \qquad \text{Write Equation 2.}$$

$$x^2 + (x + 4) = 3 \qquad \text{Substitute } x + 4 \text{ for } y.$$

$$x^2 + x + 1 = 0 \qquad \text{Simplify.}$$

$$x = \frac{-1 \pm \sqrt{3}i}{2} \qquad \text{Quadratic Formula}$$

Because this yields two complex values, the equation $x^2 + x + 1 = 0$ has no *real* solution. So, the original system of equations has no *real* solution.

 Checkpoint Now try Exercise 23.

> ### STUDY TIP
>
> When using substitution, solve for the variable that is not raised to a power in either equation. For instance, in Example 3 it would not be practical to solve for x in Equation 2. Can you see why?

> ### Exploration
>
> Graph the system of equations in Example 3. Do the graphs of the equations intersect? Why or why not?

Example 4   Substitution: Two-Solution Case

Solve the system of equations: $\begin{cases} x^2 + 4x - y = 7 & \text{Equation 1} \\ 2x - y = -1 & \text{Equation 2} \end{cases}$.

Algebraic Solution

Begin by solving for y in Equation 2 to obtain $y = 2x + 1$. Next, substitute this expression for y into Equation 1 and solve for x.

$$x^2 + 4x - y = 7 \qquad \text{Write Equation 1.}$$

$$x^2 + 4x - (2x + 1) = 7 \qquad \text{Substitute } 2x + 1 \text{ for } y.$$

$$x^2 + 4x - 2x - 1 = 7 \qquad \text{Distributive Property}$$

$$x^2 + 2x - 8 = 0 \qquad \text{Write in general form.}$$

$$(x + 4)(x - 2) = 0 \qquad \text{Factor.}$$

$$x + 4 = 0 \implies x = -4 \qquad \text{Set 1st factor equal to 0.}$$

$$x - 2 = 0 \implies x = 2 \qquad \text{Set 2nd factor equal to 0.}$$

Back-substituting these values of x into Equation 2 produces

$$y = 2(-4) + 1 = -7 \quad \text{and} \quad y = 2(2) + 1 = 5.$$

So, the solutions are $(-4, -7)$ and $(2, 5)$. Check these in the original system.

 Checkpoint Now try Exercise 27.

Graphical Solution

To graph each equation, first solve both equations for y. Then use a graphing utility to graph the equations in the same viewing window. Use the *intersect* feature or the *zoom* and *trace* features to approximate the points of intersection of the graphs. The points of intersection are $(-4, -7)$ and $(2, 5)$, as shown in Figure 8.3. Check that $(-4, -7)$ and $(2, 5)$ are the exact solutions by substituting *both* ordered pairs into *both* equations.

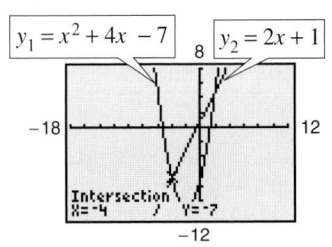

Figure 8.3

From Examples 2, 3, and 4, you can see that a system of two equations in two unknowns can have exactly one solution, more than one solution, or no solution. For instance, in Figure 8.4, the two equations graph as two lines with a *single point* of intersection. The two equations in Example 4 graph as a parabola and a line with *two points* of intersection, as shown in Figure 8.5. The two equations in Example 3 graph as a line and a parabola that have *no points* of intersection, as shown in Figure 8.6.

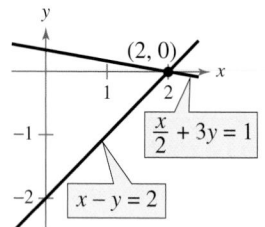

One Intersection Point
Figure 8.4

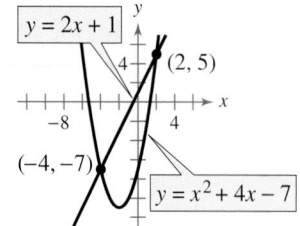

Two Intersection Points
Figure 8.5

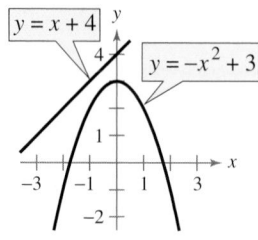

No Intersection Points
Figure 8.6

Example 5 shows the value of a graphical approach to solving systems of equations in two variables. Notice what would happen if you tried only the substitution method in Example 5. You would obtain the equation $x + \ln x = 1$. It would be difficult to solve this equation for x using standard algebraic techniques. In such cases, a graphical approach to solving a system of equations is more convenient.

Example 5 Solving a System of Equations Graphically

Solve the system of equations.

$$\begin{cases} y = \ln x & \text{Equation 1} \\ x + y = 1 & \text{Equation 2} \end{cases}$$

Solution

From the graphs of these equations, it is clear that there is only one point of intersection. Use the *intersect* feature or the *zoom* and *trace* features of a graphing utility to approximate the solution point as $(1, 0)$, as shown in Figure 8.7. You can confirm this by substituting $(1, 0)$ into *both* equations.

Check $(1, 0)$ in Equation 1:

$y = \ln x$	Write Equation 1.
$0 = \ln 1$	Equation 1 checks. ✓

Check $(1, 0)$ in Equation 2:

$x + y = 1$	Write Equation 2.
$1 + 0 = 1$	Equation 2 checks. ✓

✓ *Checkpoint* Now try Exercise 45.

TECHNOLOGY SUPPORT

For instructions on how to use the *intersect* feature and the *zoom* and *trace* features, see Appendix A; for specific keystrokes, go to the text website at *college.hmco.com*.

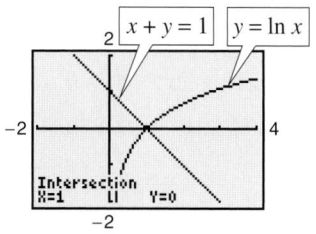

Figure 8.7

Points of Intersection and Applications

The total cost C of producing x units of a product typically has two components: the initial cost and the cost per unit. When enough units have been sold that the total revenue R equals the total cost C, the sales are said to have reached the **break-even point.** You will find that the break-even point corresponds to the point of intersection of the cost and revenue curves.

Example 6   Break–Even Analysis

A small business invests \$10,000 in equipment to produce a new soft drink. Each bottle of the soft drink costs \$0.65 to produce and is sold for \$1.20. How many items must be sold before the business breaks even?

Solution

The total cost of producing x bottles is

| Total cost | = | Cost per bottle | · | Number of bottles | + | Initial cost |

$$C = 0.65x + 10,000. \qquad \text{Equation 1}$$

The revenue obtained by selling x bottles is

| Total revenue | = | Price per bottle | · | Number of bottles |

$$R = 1.20x. \qquad \text{Equation 2}$$

Because the break-even point occurs when $R = C$, you have $C = 1.20x$, and the system of equations to solve is

$$\begin{cases} C = 0.65x + 10,000 \\ C = 1.20x \end{cases}.$$

Now you can solve by substitution.

$$1.20x = 0.65x + 10,000 \qquad \text{Substitute } 1.20x \text{ for } C \text{ in Equation 1.}$$

$$0.55x = 10,000 \qquad \text{Subtract } 0.65x \text{ from each side.}$$

$$x = \frac{10,000}{0.55} \approx 18,182 \text{ bottles.} \qquad \text{Divide each side by 0.55.}$$

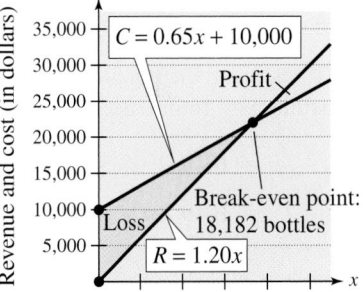

Break-Even Analysis

Figure 8.8

Note in Figure 8.8 that revenue less than the break-even point corresponds to an overall loss, whereas revenue greater than the break-even point corresponds to a profit. Verify the break-even point using the *intersect* feature or the *zoom* and *trace* features of a graphing utility.

 Checkpoint Now try Exercise 67.

Another way to view the solution in Example 6 is to consider the profit function $P = R - C$. The break-even point occurs when the profit is 0, which is the same as saying that $R = C$.

Example 7   State Populations

From 1991 to 2001, the population of Idaho was increasing at a faster rate than the population of New Hampshire. Two models that approximate the populations P (in thousands) are

$$\begin{cases} P = 1019 + 28.5t & \text{Idaho} \\ P = 1080 + 15.7t & \text{New Hampshire} \end{cases}$$

where t represents the year, with $t = 1$ corresponding to 1991.   (Source: U.S. Census Bureau)

a. According to these two models, when would you expect the population of Idaho to have exceeded the population of New Hampshire?

b. Use the two models to estimate the population of both states in 2006.

TECHNOLOGY SUPPORT

For instructions on how to use the *value* feature, see Appendix A; for specific keystrokes, go to the text website at *college.hmco.com.*

Algebraic Solution

a. Because the first equation has already been solved for P in terms of t, you can substitute this value into the second equation and solve for t, as follows.

$$1019 + 28.5t = 1080 + 15.7t$$

$$28.5t - 15.7t = 1080 - 1019$$

$$12.8t = 61$$

$$t \approx 4.8$$

So, from the given models, you would expect that the population of Idaho exceeded the population of New Hampshire after $t \approx 4.8$ years, which was sometime during 1994.

b. To estimate the population of both states in 2006, substitute $t = 16$ into each model and evaluate, as follows.

$$P = 1019 + 28.5t \quad \text{Model for Idaho}$$

$$= 1019 + 28.5(16) \quad \text{Substitute 16 for } t.$$

$$= 1475 \quad \text{Simplify.}$$

$$P = 1080 + 15.7t \quad \text{Model for New Hampshire}$$

$$= 1080 + 15.7(16) \quad \text{Substitute 16 for } t.$$

$$= 1331.2 \quad \text{Simplify.}$$

So, according to the models, Idaho's population in 2006 will be 1475 thousand and New Hampshire's population in 2006 will be 1331.2 thousand.

Graphical Solution

a. Use a graphing utility to graph $y_1 = 1019 + 28.5x$ and $y_2 = 1080 + 15.7x$ in the same viewing window. Use the *intersect* feature or the *zoom* and *trace* features of the graphing utility to approximate the point of intersection of the graphs. The point of intersection occurs at $x \approx 4.8$, as shown in Figure 8.9. So, it appears that the population of Idaho exceeded the population of New Hampshire sometime during 1994.

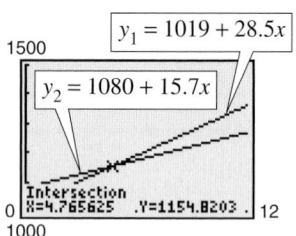

Figure 8.9

b. To estimate the population of both states in 2006, use the *value* feature or *zoom* and *trace* features of the graphing utility to find the value of y when $x = 16$. (Be sure to adjust your viewing window.) So, from Figure 8.10, you can see that Idaho's population in 2006 will be 1475 thousand and New Hampshire's population in 2006 will be 1331.2 thousand.

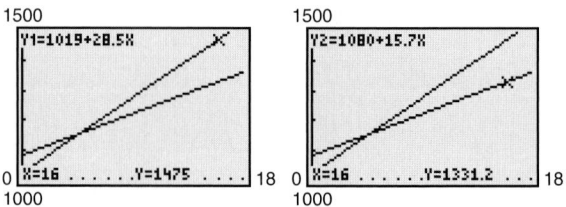

Figure 8.10

✓ *Checkpoint* Now try Exercise 73.

8.1 Exercises

Vocabulary Check

Fill in the blanks.

1. A set of two or more equations in two or more unknowns is called a _____ of _____ .

2. A _____ of a system of equations is an ordered pair that satisfies each equation in the system.

3. The first step in solving a system of equations by the _____ of _____ is to solve one of the equations for one variable in terms of the other variable.

4. Graphically, the solution to a system of equations is called the _____ of _____ .

5. In business applications, the _____ occurs when revenue equals cost.

In Exercises 1–4, determine whether each ordered pair is a solution of the system of equations.

1. $\begin{cases} 4x - y = 1 \\ 6x + y = -6 \end{cases}$
   (a) $(0, -3)$ (b) $(-1, -5)$
   (c) $\left(-\frac{3}{2}, 3\right)$ (d) $\left(-\frac{1}{2}, -3\right)$

2. $\begin{cases} 4x^2 + y = 3 \\ -x - y = 11 \end{cases}$
   (a) $(2, -13)$ (b) $(-2, -9)$
   (c) $\left(-\frac{3}{2}, 6\right)$ (d) $\left(-\frac{7}{4}, -\frac{37}{4}\right)$

3. $\begin{cases} y = -2e^x \\ 3x - y = 2 \end{cases}$
   (a) $(-2, 0)$ (b) $(0, -2)$
   (c) $(0, -3)$ (d) $(-1, -5)$

4. $\begin{cases} -\log_{10} x + 3 = y \\ \frac{1}{9}x + y = \frac{28}{9} \end{cases}$
   (a) $(100, 1)$ (b) $(10, 2)$
   (c) $(1, 3)$ (d) $(1, 1)$

In Exercises 5–14, solve the system by the method of substitution. Check your solution graphically.

5. $\begin{cases} 2x + y = 6 \\ -x + y = 0 \end{cases}$
6. $\begin{cases} x - y = -4 \\ x + 2y = 5 \end{cases}$

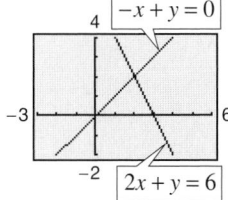

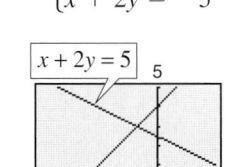

7. $\begin{cases} x - y = -4 \\ x^2 - y = -2 \end{cases}$
8. $\begin{cases} -2x + y = -5 \\ x^2 + y^2 = 25 \end{cases}$

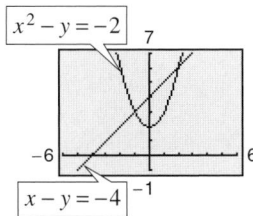

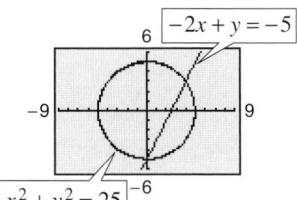

9. $\begin{cases} 3x + y = 2 \\ x^3 - 2 + y = 0 \end{cases}$
10. $\begin{cases} x + y = 0 \\ x^3 - 5x - y = 0 \end{cases}$

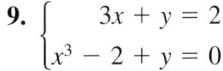

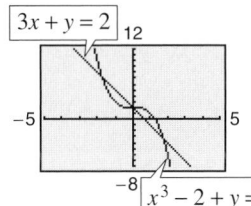

11. $\begin{cases} x^2 + y = 0 \\ x^2 - 4x - y = 0 \end{cases}$
12. $\begin{cases} y = -2x^2 + 2 \\ y = 2(x^4 - 2x^2 + 1) \end{cases}$

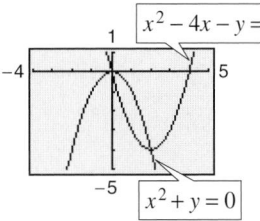

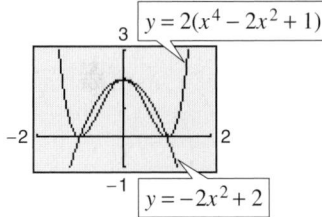

13. $\begin{cases} -\frac{7}{2}x - y = -18 \\ 8x^2 - 2y^3 = 0 \end{cases}$
14. $\begin{cases} y = x^3 - 3x^2 + 4 \\ y = -2x + 4 \end{cases}$

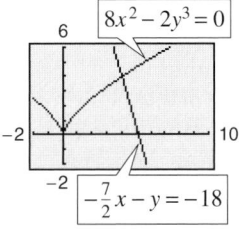

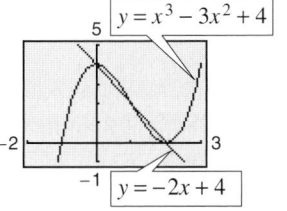

In Exercises 15–28, solve the system by the method of substitution. Use a graphing utility to verify your results.

15. $\begin{cases} x - y = 0 \\ 5x - 3y = 10 \end{cases}$

16. $\begin{cases} x + 2y = 1 \\ 5x - 4y = -23 \end{cases}$

17. $\begin{cases} 2x - y + 2 = 0 \\ 4x + y - 5 = 0 \end{cases}$

18. $\begin{cases} 6x - 3y - 4 = 0 \\ x + 2y - 4 = 0 \end{cases}$

19. $\begin{cases} 1.5x + 0.8y = 2.3 \\ 0.3x - 0.2y = 0.1 \end{cases}$

20. $\begin{cases} 0.5x + 3.2y = 9.0 \\ 0.2x - 1.6y = -3.6 \end{cases}$

21. $\begin{cases} \frac{1}{5}x + \frac{1}{2}y = 8 \\ x + y = 20 \end{cases}$

22. $\begin{cases} \frac{1}{2}x + \frac{3}{4}y = 10 \\ \frac{3}{4}x - y = 4 \end{cases}$

23. $\begin{cases} 6x + 5y = -3 \\ -x - \frac{5}{6}y = -7 \end{cases}$

24. $\begin{cases} 2x - y = 4 \\ -4x + 2y = -12 \end{cases}$

25. $\begin{cases} -\frac{5}{3}x + y = 5 \\ -5x + 3y = 6 \end{cases}$

26. $\begin{cases} -\frac{2}{3}x + y = 2 \\ 2x - 3y = 6 \end{cases}$

27. $\begin{cases} x^3 - y = 0 \\ x - y = 0 \end{cases}$

28. $\begin{cases} y = -x \\ y = x^3 + 3x^2 + 2x \end{cases}$

In Exercises 29–36, solve the system graphically. Verify your solutions algebraically.

29. $\begin{cases} -x + 2y = 2 \\ 3x + y = 15 \end{cases}$

30. $\begin{cases} x + y = 0 \\ 3x - 2y = 10 \end{cases}$

31. $\begin{cases} x - 3y = -2 \\ 5x + 3y = 17 \end{cases}$

32. $\begin{cases} -x + 2y = 1 \\ x - y = 2 \end{cases}$

33. $\begin{cases} x + y = 4 \\ x^2 + y^2 - 4x = 0 \end{cases}$

34. $\begin{cases} -x + y = 3 \\ x^2 + y^2 - 6x - 27 = 0 \end{cases}$

35. $\begin{cases} x - y + 3 = 0 \\ x^2 - 4x + 7 = y \end{cases}$

36. $\begin{cases} y^2 - 4x + 11 = 0 \\ -\frac{1}{2}x + y = -\frac{1}{2} \end{cases}$

In Exercises 37–50, use a graphing utility to approximate all points of intersection of the graph of the system of equations. Verify your solutions by checking them in the original system.

37. $\begin{cases} 7x + 8y = 24 \\ x - 8y = 8 \end{cases}$

38. $\begin{cases} x - y = 0 \\ 5x - 2y = 6 \end{cases}$

39. $\begin{cases} 2x - y + 3 = 0 \\ x^2 + y^2 - 4x = 0 \end{cases}$

40. $\begin{cases} 3x - 2y = 0 \\ x^2 + y^2 = 4 \end{cases}$

41. $\begin{cases} x^2 + y^2 = 8 \\ y = x^2 \end{cases}$

42. $\begin{cases} x^2 + y^2 = 25 \\ (x - 8)^2 + y^2 = 41 \end{cases}$

43. $\begin{cases} y = e^x \\ x - y + 1 = 0 \end{cases}$

44. $\begin{cases} y = -4e^{-x} \\ y + 3x + 8 = 0 \end{cases}$

45. $\begin{cases} x + 2y = 8 \\ y = 2 + \ln x \end{cases}$

46. $\begin{cases} y = -2 + \ln(x - 1) \\ 3y + 2x = 9 \end{cases}$

47. $\begin{cases} y = \sqrt{x} + 4 \\ y = 2x + 1 \end{cases}$

48. $\begin{cases} x - y = 3 \\ \sqrt{x} - y = 1 \end{cases}$

49. $\begin{cases} x^2 + y^2 = 169 \\ x^2 - 8y = 104 \end{cases}$

50. $\begin{cases} x^2 + y^2 = 4 \\ 2x^2 - y = 2 \end{cases}$

In Exercises 51–62, solve the system graphically or algebraically. Explain your choice of method.

51. $\begin{cases} 2x - y = 0 \\ x^2 - y = -1 \end{cases}$

52. $\begin{cases} x + y = 4 \\ x^2 + y = 2 \end{cases}$

53. $\begin{cases} 3x - 7y = -6 \\ x^2 - y^2 = 4 \end{cases}$

54. $\begin{cases} x^2 + y^2 = 25 \\ 2x + y = 10 \end{cases}$

55. $\begin{cases} y = 2x + 1 \\ y = \sqrt{x + 2} \end{cases}$

56. $\begin{cases} y = 2x - 1 \\ y = \sqrt{x + 1} \end{cases}$

57. $\begin{cases} y - e^{-x} = 1 \\ y - \ln x = 3 \end{cases}$

58. $\begin{cases} 2 \ln x + y = 4 \\ e^x - y = 0 \end{cases}$

59. $\begin{cases} y = x^3 - 2x^2 + 1 \\ y = 1 - x^2 \end{cases}$

60. $\begin{cases} y = x^3 - 2x^2 + x - 1 \\ y = -x^2 + 3x - 1 \end{cases}$

61. $\begin{cases} xy - 1 = 0 \\ 2x - 4y + 7 = 0 \end{cases}$

62. $\begin{cases} xy - 2 = 0 \\ 3x - 2y + 4 = 0 \end{cases}$

Break-Even Analysis **In Exercises 63–66, use a graphing utility to graph the cost and revenue functions in the same viewing window. Find the sales x necessary to break even $(R = C)$ and the corresponding revenue R obtained by selling x units. (Round to the nearest whole unit.)**

Cost	Revenue
63. $C = 8650x + 250{,}000$	$R = 9950x$
64. $C = 2.65x + 350{,}000$	$R = 4.15x$
65. $C = 5.5\sqrt{x} + 10{,}000$	$R = 3.29x$
66. $C = 7.8\sqrt{x} + 18{,}500$	$R = 12.84x$

67. Break-Even Analysis A small software company invests $16,000 to produce a software package that will sell for $55.95. Each unit can be produced for $35.45.

(a) Write the cost and revenue functions for x units produced and sold.

(b) Use a graphing utility to graph the cost and revenue functions in the same viewing window. Use the graph to approximate the number of units that must be sold to break even.

(c) Verify the result of part (b) algebraically.

68. Break-Even Analysis A small fast-food restaurant invests $5000 to produce a new food item that will sell for $3.49. Each item can be produced for $2.16.

(a) Write the cost and revenue functions for x items produced and sold.

(b) Use a graphing utility to graph the cost and revenue functions in the same viewing window. Use the graph to approximate the number of items that must be sold to break even.

(c) Verify the result of part (b) algebraically.

69. Choice of Two Jobs You are offered two different jobs selling dental supplies. One company offers a straight commission of 6% of sales. The other company offers a salary of $350 per week plus 3% of sales. How much would you have to sell in a week in order to make the straight commission offer the better offer?

70. Choice of Two Jobs You are offered two jobs selling college textbooks. One company offers an annual salary of $25,000 plus a year-end bonus of 1% of your total sales. The other company offers an annual salary of $20,000 plus a year-end bonus of 2% of your total sales. How much would you have to sell in a year to make the second offer the better offer?

71. Investment A total of $20,000 is invested in two funds paying 6.5% and 8.5% simple interest. The 6.5% investment has a lower risk. The investor wants a yearly interest check of $1600 from the investments.

(a) Write a system of equations in which one equation represents the total amount invested and the other equation represents the $1600 required in interest. Let x and y represent the amounts invested at 6.5% and 8.5%, respectively.

(b) Use a graphing utility to graph the two equations in the same viewing window. As the amount invested at 6.5% increases, how does the amount invested at 8.5% change? How does the amount of interest change? Explain.

(c) What amount should be invested at 6.5% to meet the requirement of $1600 per year in interest?

72. Log Volume You are offered two different rules for estimating the number of board feet in a 16-foot log. (A board foot is a unit of measure for lumber equal to a board 1 foot square and 1 inch thick.) One rule is the *Doyle Log Rule* and is modeled by

$$V = (D - 4)^2, \quad 5 \le D \le 40$$

and the other rule is the *Scribner Log Rule* and is modeled by

$$V = 0.79D^2 - 2D - 4, \quad 5 \le D \le 40$$

where D is the diameter (in inches) of the log and V is its volume in board feet.

(a) Use a graphing utility to graph the two log rules in the same viewing window.

(b) For what diameter do the two rules agree?

(c) You are selling large logs by the board foot. Which rule would you use? Explain your reasoning.

73. Sales The table shows the factory sales F (in millions of dollars) of VCRs and DVD players from 1997 to 2001. (Source: Consumer Electronics Association)

Year	VCR sales, F	DVD player sales, F
1997	2618	171
1998	2409	421
1999	2333	1099
2000	1869	1717
2001	1099	2145

(a) Use the *regression* feature of a graphing utility to find quadratic models for the data. Let x represent the year, with $x = 7$ corresponding to 1997.

(b) Use a graphing utility to graph the models with the original data in the same viewing window.

(c) Use the graph in part (b) to determine the year in which DVD player sales exceeded VCR sales.

(d) Algebraically determine the year in which DVD player sales exceeded VCR sales.

(e) Compare your results from parts (c) and (d).

74. Sales   The table shows the sales S (in billions of dollars) for grocery stores and general merchandise stores from 1995 to 2001.   (Source: U.S. Census Bureau)

Year	Grocery store sales, S_1	General merchandise store sales, S_2
1995	356.9	300.6
1996	366.1	315.4
1997	373.1	331.5
1998	382.4	351.8
1999	401.8	381.4
2000	415.3	405.9
2001	425.4	430.5

(a) Use the *regression* feature of a graphing utility to find quadratic models for the data. Let x represent the year, with $x = 5$ corresponding to 1995.

(b) Use a graphing utility to graph the models with the original data in the same viewing window.

(c) Use the graph in part (b) to determine the year in which general merchandise store sales exceeded grocery store sales.

(d) Algebraically determine the year in which general merchandise store sales exceeded grocery store sales.

(e) Compare your results from parts (c) and (d).

Geometry   In Exercises 75 and 76, find the dimensions of the rectangle meeting the specified conditions.

75. The perimeter is 30 meters and the length is 3 meters greater than the width.

76. The perimeter is 280 centimeters and the width is 20 centimeters less than the length.

77. Geometry   What are the dimensions of a rectangular tract of land if its perimeter is 40 miles and its area is 96 square miles?

78. Geometry   What are the dimensions of an isosceles right triangle with a two-inch hypotenuse and an area of 1 square inch?

Synthesis

True or False?   **In Exercises 79 and 80, determine whether the statement is true or false. Justify your answer.**

79. In order to solve a system of equations by substitution, you must always solve for y in one of the two equations and then back-substitute.

80. If a system consists of a parabola and a circle, then it can have at most two solutions.

81. Think About It   When solving a system of equations by substitution, how do you recognize that the system has no solution?

82. Writing   Write a brief paragraph describing any advantages of substitution over the graphical method of solving a system of equations.

83. Exploration   Find an equation of a line whose graph intersects the graph of the parabola $y = x^2$ at (a) two points, (b) one point, and (c) no points. (There are many correct answers.)

84. Conjecture   Consider the system of equations

$$\begin{cases} y = b^x \\ y = x^b \end{cases}$$

(a) Use a graphing utility to graph the system of equations for $b = 2$ and $b = 4$.

(b) For a fixed value of $b > 1$, make a conjecture about the number of points of intersection of the graphs in part (a).

Review

In Exercises 85–90, find the general form of the equation of the line passing through the two points.

85. $(-2, 7), (5, 5)$ **86.** $(3.5, 4), (10, 6)$

87. $(6, 3), (10, 3)$ **88.** $(4, -2), (4, 5)$

89. $\left(\frac{3}{5}, 0\right), (4, 6)$ **90.** $\left(-\frac{7}{3}, 8\right), \left(\frac{5}{2}, \frac{1}{2}\right)$

In Exercises 91–94, find the domain of the function and identify any horizontal or vertical asymptotes.

91. $f(x) = \dfrac{5}{x - 6}$ **92.** $f(x) = \dfrac{2x - 7}{3x + 2}$

93. $f(x) = \dfrac{x^2 + 2}{x^2 - 16}$ **94.** $f(x) = 3 - \dfrac{2}{x^2}$

8.2 Systems of Linear Equations in Two Variables

The Method of Elimination

In Section 8.1, you studied two methods for solving a system of equations: substitution and graphing. Now you will study the **method of elimination.** The key step in this method is to obtain, for one of the variables, coefficients that differ only in sign so that *adding* the equations eliminates the variable.

$$
\begin{array}{ll}
3x + 5y = 7 & \text{Equation 1} \\
\underline{-3x - 2y = -1} & \text{Equation 2} \\
3y = 6 & \text{Add equations.}
\end{array}
$$

Note that by adding the two equations, you eliminate the x-terms and obtain a single equation in y. Solving this equation for y produces $y = 2$, which you can then back-substitute into one of the original equations to solve for x.

Example 1   Solving a System by Elimination

Solving the system of linear equations.

$$
\begin{cases}
3x + 2y = 4 & \text{Equation 1} \\
5x - 2y = 8 & \text{Equation 2}
\end{cases}
$$

Solution

You can eliminate the y-terms by adding the two equations.

$$
\begin{array}{ll}
3x + 2y = 4 & \text{Write Equation 1.} \\
\underline{5x - 2y = 8} & \text{Write Equation 2.} \\
8x = 12 & \text{Add equations.}
\end{array}
$$

So, $x = \frac{3}{2}$. By back-substituting into Equation 1, you can solve for y.

$$
\begin{array}{ll}
3x + 2y = 4 & \text{Write Equation 1.} \\
3\left(\frac{3}{2}\right) + 2y = 4 & \text{Substitute } \frac{3}{2} \text{ for } x. \\
y = -\frac{1}{4} & \text{Solve for } y.
\end{array}
$$

The solution is $\left(\frac{3}{2}, -\frac{1}{4}\right)$. You can check the solution *algebraically* by substituting into the original system, or graphically as shown in Section 8.1.

Check

$$
\begin{array}{ll}
3\left(\frac{3}{2}\right) + 2\left(-\frac{1}{4}\right) \overset{?}{=} 4 & \text{Substitute into Equation 1.} \\
\frac{9}{2} - \frac{1}{2} = 4 & \text{Equation 1 checks.} \checkmark \\
5\left(\frac{3}{2}\right) - 2\left(-\frac{1}{4}\right) \overset{?}{=} 8 & \text{Substitute into Equation 2.} \\
\frac{15}{2} + \frac{1}{2} = 8 & \text{Equation 2 checks.} \checkmark
\end{array}
$$

✓ *Checkpoint* Now try Exercise 7.

What you should learn

- Use the method of elimination to solve systems of linear equations in two variables.
- Graphically interpret the number of solutions of a system of linear equations in two variables.
- Use systems of linear equations in two variables to model and solve real-life problems.

Why you should learn it

You can use systems of linear equations to model many business applications. For instance, Exercise 68 on page 611 shows how to use a system of linear equations to recover information about types of shoes that were sold in a shoe store.

Frank Siteman/PhotoEdit

Exploration

Use the method of substitution to solve the system given in Example 1. Which method is easier?

The Method of Elimination

To use the **method of elimination** to solve a system of two linear equations in x and y, perform the following steps.

1. Obtain coefficients for x (or y) that differ only in sign by multiplying all terms of one or both equations by suitably chosen constants.

2. Add the equations to eliminate one variable; solve the resulting equation.

3. Back-substitute the value obtained in Step 2 into either of the original equations and solve for the other variable.

4. Check your solution in both of the original equations.

Example 2 Solving a System by Elimination

Solve the system of linear equations.

$$\begin{cases} 5x + 3y = 9 & \text{Equation 1} \\ 2x - 4y = 14 & \text{Equation 2} \end{cases}$$

Algebraic Solution

You can obtain coefficients that differ only in sign by multiplying Equation 1 by 4 and multiplying Equation 2 by 3.

$$5x + 3y = 9 \implies 20x + 12y = 36 \quad \text{Multiply Equation 1 by 4.}$$
$$\underline{2x - 4y = 14} \implies \underline{6x - 12y = 42} \quad \text{Multiply Equation 2 by 3.}$$
$$26x \quad\quad\; = 78 \quad \text{Add equations.}$$

From this equation, you can see that $x = 3$. By back-substituting this value of x into Equation 2, you can solve for y.

$$2x - 4y = 14 \quad\quad \text{Write Equation 2.}$$
$$2(3) - 4y = 14 \quad\quad \text{Substitute 3 for } x.$$
$$-4y = 8 \quad\quad \text{Combine like terms.}$$
$$y = -2 \quad\quad \text{Solve for } y.$$

The solution is $(3, -2)$. You can check the solution algebraically by substituting into the original system.

✓ *Checkpoint* Now try Exercise 11.

Graphical Solution

Solve each equation for y. Then use a graphing utility to graph $y_1 = 3 - \frac{5}{3}x$ and $y_2 = -\frac{7}{2} + \frac{1}{2}x$ in the same viewing window. Use the *intersect* feature or the *zoom* and *trace* features to approximate the point of intersection of the graphs. The point of intersection is $(3, -2)$, as shown in Figure 8.11. You can determine that this is the exact solution by checking $(3, -2)$ in both equations.

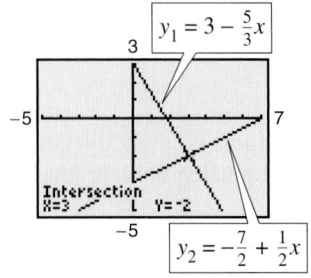

Figure 8.11

In Example 2, the original system and the system obtained by multiplying by constants are called **equivalent systems** because they have precisely the same solution set. The operations that can be performed on a system of linear equations to produce an equivalent system are (1) interchanging any two equations, (2) multiplying an equation by a nonzero constant, and (3) adding a multiple of one equation to any other equation in the system.

Graphical Interpretation of Two-Variable Systems

It is possible for a *general* system of equations to have exactly one solution, two or more solutions, or no solution. If a system of *linear* equations has two different solutions, it must have an *infinite* number of solutions. To see why this is true, consider the following graphical interpretations of a system of two linear equations in two variables.

Graphical Interpretation of Solutions

For a system of two linear equations in two variables, the number of solutions is one of the following.

Number of Solutions	*Graphical Interpretation*
1. Exactly one solution	The two lines intersect at one point.
2. Infinitely many solutions	The two lines are coincident (identical).
3. No solution	The two lines are parallel.

> **Exploration**
>
> Rewrite each system of equations in slope-intercept form and use a graphing utility to graph each system. What is the relationship between the slopes of the two lines and the number of points of intersection?
>
> **a.** $\begin{cases} y = 5x + 1 \\ y - x = -5 \end{cases}$
>
> **b.** $\begin{cases} 3y = 4x - 1 \\ -8x + 2 = -6y \end{cases}$
>
> **c.** $\begin{cases} 2y = -x + 3 \\ -4 = y + \frac{1}{2}x \end{cases}$

A system of linear equations is **consistent** if it has at least one solution. It is **inconsistent** if it has no solution.

Example 3 Recognizing Graphs of Linear Systems

Match each system of linear equations (a, b, c) with its graph (i, ii, iii) in Figure 8.12. Describe the number of solutions. Then state whether the system is consistent or inconsistent.

a. $\begin{cases} 2x - 3y = 3 \\ -4x + 6y = 6 \end{cases}$ **b.** $\begin{cases} 2x - 3y = 3 \\ x + 2y = 5 \end{cases}$ **c.** $\begin{cases} 2x - 3y = 3 \\ -4x + 6y = -6 \end{cases}$

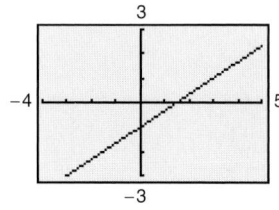
i.

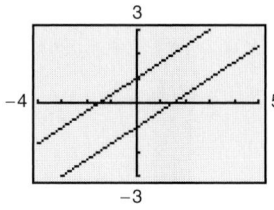
ii.

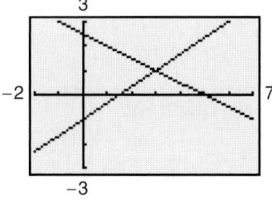
iii.

Figure 8.12

Solution

a. The graph is a pair of parallel lines (ii). The lines have no point of intersection, so the system has no solution. The system is inconsistent.

b. The graph is a pair of intersecting lines (iii). The lines have one point of intersection, so the system has exactly one solution. The system is consistent.

c. The graph is a pair of lines that coincide (i). The lines have infinitely many points of intersection, so the system has infinitely many solutions. The system is consistent.

✓ *Checkpoint* Now try Exercises 17–20.

In Examples 4 and 5, note how you can use the method of elimination to determine that a system of linear equations has no solution or infinitely many solutions.

Example 4 The Method of Elimination: No Solution Case

Solve the system of linear equations.

$$\begin{cases} x - 2y = 3 & \text{Equation 1} \\ -2x + 4y = 1 & \text{Equation 2} \end{cases}$$

Algebraic Solution

To obtain coefficients that differ only in sign, multiply Equation 1 by 2.

$$\begin{array}{ccc} x - 2y = 3 & \Longrightarrow & 2x - 4y = 6 \\ -2x + 4y = 1 & \Longrightarrow & -2x + 4y = 1 \\ \hline & & 0 = 7 \end{array}$$

By adding the equations, you obtain $0 = 7$. Because there are no values of x and y for which $0 = 7$, this is a false statement. So, you can conclude that the system is inconsistent and has no solution.

✓ *Checkpoint* Now try Exercise 23.

Graphical Solution

Solving each equation for y yields $y_1 = -\frac{3}{2} + \frac{1}{2}x$ and $y_2 = \frac{1}{4} + \frac{1}{2}x$. Notice that the lines have the same slope and different y-intercepts, so they are parallel. You can use a graphing utility to verify this by graphing both equations in the same viewing window, as shown in Figure 8.13. Then try using the *intersect* feature to find a point of intersection. Because the graphing utility cannot find a point of intersection, you will get an error message. Therefore, the system has no solution.

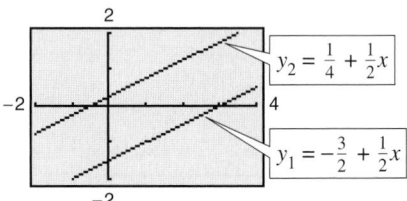

Figure 8.13

Example 5 The Method of Elimination: Infinitely Many Solutions Case

Solve the system of linear equations: $\begin{cases} 2x - y = 1 & \text{Equation 1} \\ 4x - 2y = 2 & \text{Equation 2} \end{cases}$.

Solution

To obtain coefficients that differ only in sign, multiply Equation 2 by $-\frac{1}{2}$.

$$\begin{array}{ccll} 2x - y = 1 & \Longrightarrow & 2x - y = 1 & \text{Write Equation 1.} \\ 4x - 2y = 2 & \Longrightarrow & -2x + y = -1 & \text{Multiply Equation 2 by } -\frac{1}{2}. \\ \hline & & 0 = 0 & \text{Add equations.} \end{array}$$

Because $0 = 0$ for all values of x and y, the two equations turn out to be equivalent (have the same solution set). You can conclude that the system has infinitely many solutions. The solution set consists of all points (x, y) lying on the line $2x - y = 1$, as shown in Figure 8.14.

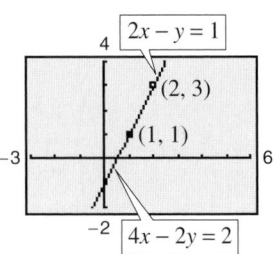

Figure 8.14

✓ *Checkpoint* Now try Exercise 25.

In Example 4, note that the occurrence of a false statement, such as $0 = 7$, indicates that the system has no solution. In Example 5, note that the occurrence of a statement that is true for all values of the variables—in this case, $0 = 0$—indicates that the system has infinitely many solutions.

Example 6 illustrates a strategy for solving a system of linear equations that has decimal coefficients.

Example 6   A Linear System Having Decimal Coefficients

Solve the system of linear equations.

$$\begin{cases} 0.02x - 0.05y = -0.38 & \text{Equation 1} \\ 0.03x + 0.04y = 1.04 & \text{Equation 2} \end{cases}$$

Solution

Because the coefficients in this system have two decimal places, you can begin by multiplying each equation by 100 to produce a system with integer coefficients.

$$\begin{cases} 2x - 5y = -38 & \text{Revised Equation 1} \\ 3x + 4y = 104 & \text{Revised Equation 2} \end{cases}$$

Now, to obtain coefficients that differ only in sign, multiply revised Equation 1 by 3 and multiply revised Equation 2 by -2.

$2x - 5y = -38$	$6x - 15y = -114$	Multiply revised Equation 1 by 3.
$\underline{3x + 4y = 104}$	$\underline{-6x - 8y = -208}$	Multiply revised Equation 2 by -2.
	$-23y = -322$	Add equations.

So, you can conclude that

$$y = \frac{-322}{-23}$$

$$= 14.$$

Back-substituting this value into revised Equation 2 produces the following.

$3x + 4y = 104$ Write revised Equation 2.

$3x + 4(14) = 104$ Substitute 14 for y.

$3x = 48$ Combine like terms.

$x = 16$ Solve for x.

The solution is $(16, 14)$. Check this in the original system.

✓ *Checkpoint* Now try Exercise 31.

STUDY TIP

The general solution of the linear system

$$\begin{cases} ax + by = c \\ dx + ey = f \end{cases}$$

is $x = (ce - bf)/(ae - bd)$ and $y = (af - cd)/(ae - bd)$. If $ae - bd = 0$, the system does not have a unique solution. A program (called Systems of Linear Equations) for solving such a system is available on our website, *college.hmco.com*. Try using this program to check the solution of the system in Example 6.

Application

At this point, you may be asking the question "How can I tell which application problems can be solved using a system of linear equations?" The answer comes from the following considerations.

1. Does the problem involve more than one unknown quantity?

2. Are there two (or more) equations or conditions to be satisfied?

If one or both of these conditions are met, the appropriate mathematical model for the problem may be a system of linear equations.

Example 7   An Application of a Linear System

An airplane flying into a headwind travels the 2000-mile flying distance between Fresno, California and Cleveland, Ohio in 4 hours and 24 minutes. On the return flight, the same distance is traveled in 4 hours. Find the airspeed of the plane and the speed of the wind, assuming that both remain constant.

Solution

The two unknown quantities are the speeds of the wind and the plane. If r_1 is the speed of the plane and r_2 is the speed of the wind, then

$$r_1 - r_2 = \text{speed of the plane } against \text{ the wind}$$

$$r_1 + r_2 = \text{speed of the plane } with \text{ the wind}$$

as shown in Figure 8.15. Using the formula distance $=$ (rate)(time) for these two speeds, you obtain the following equations.

$$2000 = (r_1 - r_2)\left(4 + \frac{24}{60}\right)$$

$$2000 = (r_1 + r_2)(4)$$

Original flight

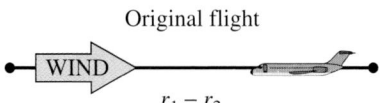

These two equations simplify as follows.

$$\begin{cases} 5000 = 11r_1 - 11r_2 & \text{Equation 1} \\ 500 = r_1 + r_2 & \text{Equation 2} \end{cases}$$

Return flight

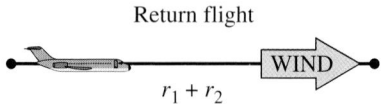

Figure 8.15

To solve this system by elimination, multiply Equation 2 by 11.

$5000 = 11r_1 - 11r_2$ ⟹ $5000 = 11r_1 - 11r_2$ Write Equation 1.

$500 = r_1 + r_2$ ⟹ $\underline{5500 = 11r_1 + 11r_2}$ Multiply Equation 2 by 11.

$10{,}500 = 22r_1$ Add equations.

So,

$$r_1 = \frac{10{,}500}{22} = \frac{5250}{11} \approx 477.27 \text{ miles per hour} \qquad \text{Speed of plane}$$

$$r_2 = 500 - \frac{5250}{11} = \frac{250}{11} \approx 22.73 \text{ miles per hour.} \qquad \text{Speed of wind}$$

Check this solution in the original statement of the problem.

 Checkpoint Now try Exercise 61.

8.2   Exercises

Vocabulary Check

Fill in the blanks.

1. The first step in solving a system of equations by the _____ of _____ is to obtain coefficients for x (or y) that differ only in sign.

2. Two systems of equations that have the same solution set are called _____ systems.

3. A system of linear equations that has at least one solution is called _____ , whereas a system of linear equations that has no solution is called _____ .

In Exercises 1–6, solve the system by the method of elimination. Label each line with its equation.

1. $\begin{cases} 2x + y = 5 \\ x - y = 1 \end{cases}$

2. $\begin{cases} x + 3y = 1 \\ -x + 2y = 4 \end{cases}$

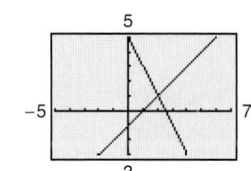   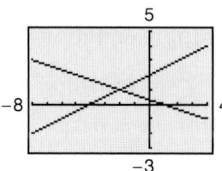

3. $\begin{cases} x + y = 0 \\ 3x + 2y = 1 \end{cases}$

4. $\begin{cases} 2x - y = 3 \\ 4x + 3y = 21 \end{cases}$

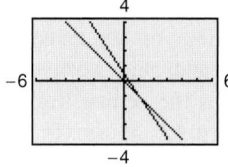   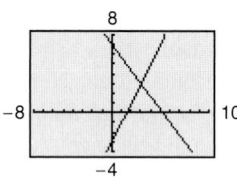

5. $\begin{cases} x - y = 2 \\ -2x + 2y = 5 \end{cases}$

6. $\begin{cases} 3x - 2y = 5 \\ -6x + 4y = -10 \end{cases}$

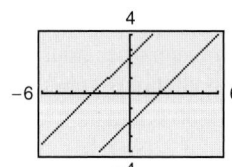   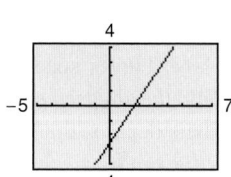

In Exercises 7–16, solve the system by the method of elimination and check any solutions algebraically.

7. $\begin{cases} x + 2y = 4 \\ x - 2y = 1 \end{cases}$

8. $\begin{cases} 3x - 2y = 5 \\ x + 2y = 7 \end{cases}$

9. $\begin{cases} 2x + 3y = 18 \\ 5x - y = 11 \end{cases}$

10. $\begin{cases} x + 7y = 12 \\ 3x - 5y = 10 \end{cases}$

11. $\begin{cases} 3r + 2s = 10 \\ 2r + 5s = 3 \end{cases}$

12. $\begin{cases} 2r + 4s = 5 \\ 16r + 50s = 55 \end{cases}$

13. $\begin{cases} 5u + 6v = 24 \\ 3u + 5v = 18 \end{cases}$

14. $\begin{cases} 3u + 11v = 4 \\ -2u - 5v = 9 \end{cases}$

15. $\begin{cases} 1.8x + 1.2y = 4 \\ 9x + 6y = 3 \end{cases}$

16. $\begin{cases} 3.1x - 2.9y = -10.2 \\ 31x - 12y = 34 \end{cases}$

In Exercises 17–20, match the system of linear equations with its graph. [The graphs are labeled (a), (b), (c), and (d).]

(a)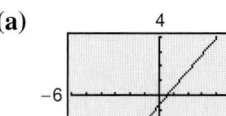

(b)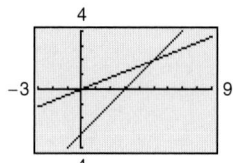

(c)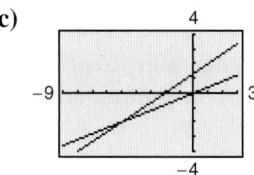

(d)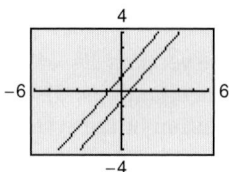

17. $\begin{cases} 2x - 5y = 0 \\ x - y = 3 \end{cases}$

18. $\begin{cases} -7x + 6y = -4 \\ 14x - 12y = 8 \end{cases}$

19. $\begin{cases} 2x - 5y = 0 \\ 2x - 3y = -4 \end{cases}$

20. $\begin{cases} 7x - 6y = -6 \\ -7x + 6y = -4 \end{cases}$

In Exercises 21–32, solve the system by the method of elimination and check any solutions using a graphing utility.

21. $\begin{cases} 4x + 3y = 3 \\ 3x + 11y = 13 \end{cases}$

22. $\begin{cases} 2x + 5y = 8 \\ 5x + 8y = 10 \end{cases}$

23. $\begin{cases} \dfrac{x}{4} + \dfrac{y}{6} = 1 \\ -3x - 2y = 0 \end{cases}$

24. $\begin{cases} \dfrac{2}{3}x + \dfrac{1}{6}y = \dfrac{2}{3} \\ 4x + y = 4 \end{cases}$

25. $\begin{cases} \dfrac{3}{4}x + y = \dfrac{1}{8} \\ \dfrac{9}{4}x + 3y = \dfrac{3}{8} \end{cases}$

26. $\begin{cases} \dfrac{2}{5}x - \dfrac{3}{2}y = 4 \\ \dfrac{1}{5}x - \dfrac{3}{4}y = -2 \end{cases}$

27. $\begin{cases} \dfrac{x+3}{4} + \dfrac{y-1}{3} = 1 \\ 2x - y = 12 \end{cases}$

28. $\begin{cases} \dfrac{x-1}{2} + \dfrac{y+2}{3} = 4 \\ x - 2y = 5 \end{cases}$

29. $\begin{cases} 2.5x - 3y = 1.5 \\ 2x - 2.4y = 1.2 \end{cases}$

30. $\begin{cases} 6.3x + 7.2y = 5.4 \\ 5.6x + 6.4y = 4.8 \end{cases}$

31. $\begin{cases} 0.2x - 0.5y = -27.8 \\ 0.3x + 0.4y = 68.7 \end{cases}$

32. $\begin{cases} 0.05x - 0.03y = 0.21 \\ 0.07x + 0.02y = 0.16 \end{cases}$

In Exercises 33–38, use a graphing utility to graph the lines in the system. Use the graphs to determine whether the system is consistent or inconsistent. If the system is consistent, determine the solution. Verify your results algebraically.

33. $\begin{cases} 2x - 5y = 0 \\ x - y = 3 \end{cases}$

34. $\begin{cases} 2x + y = 5 \\ x - 2y = -1 \end{cases}$

35. $\begin{cases} \dfrac{3}{5}x - y = 3 \\ -3x + 5y = 9 \end{cases}$

36. $\begin{cases} 4x - 6y = 9 \\ \dfrac{16}{3}x - 8y = 12 \end{cases}$

37. $\begin{cases} 8x - 14y = 5 \\ 2x - 3.5y = 1.25 \end{cases}$

38. $\begin{cases} -x + 7y = 3 \\ -\dfrac{1}{7}x + y = 5 \end{cases}$

In Exercises 39–44, use a graphing utility to graph the two equations. Use the graphs to approximate the solution of the system.

39. $\begin{cases} 6y = 42 \\ 6x - y = 16 \end{cases}$

40. $\begin{cases} 4y = -8 \\ 7x - 2y = 25 \end{cases}$

41. $\begin{cases} \dfrac{3}{2}x - \dfrac{1}{5}y = 8 \\ -2x + 3y = 3 \end{cases}$

42. $\begin{cases} \dfrac{3}{4}x - \dfrac{5}{2}y = -9 \\ -x + 6y = 28 \end{cases}$

43. $\begin{cases} 0.5x + 2.2y = 9 \\ 6x + 0.4y = -22 \end{cases}$

44. $\begin{cases} 2.4x + 3.8y = -17.6 \\ 4x - 0.2y = -3.2 \end{cases}$

In Exercises 45–52, use any method to solve the system.

45. $\begin{cases} 3x - 5y = 7 \\ 2x + y = 9 \end{cases}$

46. $\begin{cases} -x + 3y = 17 \\ 4x + 3y = 7 \end{cases}$

47. $\begin{cases} y = 4x + 3 \\ y = -5x - 12 \end{cases}$

48. $\begin{cases} 7x + 3y = 16 \\ y = x + 1 \end{cases}$

49. $\begin{cases} x - 5y = 21 \\ 6x + 5y = 21 \end{cases}$

50. $\begin{cases} y = -3x - 8 \\ y = 15 - 2x \end{cases}$

51. $\begin{cases} -2x + 8y = 19 \\ y = x - 3 \end{cases}$

52. $\begin{cases} 4x - 3y = 6 \\ -5x + 7y = -1 \end{cases}$

Exploration **In Exercises 53–56, find a system of linear equations that has the given solution. (There are many correct answers.)**

53. $(0, 8)$

54. $(3, -4)$

55. $\left(3, \dfrac{5}{2}\right)$

56. $\left(-\dfrac{2}{3}, -10\right)$

Supply and Demand **In Exercises 57–60, find the point of equilibrium of the demand and supply equations. The point of equilibrium is the price *p* and the number of units *x* that satisfy both the demand and supply equations.**

	Demand	Supply
57.	$p = 50 - 0.5x$	$p = 0.125x$
58.	$p = 100 - 0.05x$	$p = 25 + 0.1x$
59.	$p = 140 - 0.00002x$	$p = 80 + 0.00001x$
60.	$p = 400 - 0.0002x$	$p = 225 + 0.0005x$

61. *Airplane Speed* An airplane flying into a headwind travels the 1800-mile flying distance between Albuquerque, New Mexico and New York City in 3 hours and 36 minutes. On the return flight, the same distance is traveled in 3 hours. Find the airspeed of the plane and the speed of the wind, assuming that both remain constant.

62. *Airplane Speed* Two planes start from Boston's Logan International Airport and fly in opposite directions. The second plane starts $\frac{1}{2}$ hour after the first plane, but its speed is 80 kilometers per hour faster. Find the airspeed of each plane if 2 hours after the first plane departs, the planes are 3200 kilometers apart.

63. *Acid Mixture* Twenty liters of a 50% acid solution is obtained by mixing a 40% and a 65% solution.

(a) Write a system of equations in which one equation represents the amount of final mixture required and the other represents the amount of acid in the final mixture. Let *x* and *y* represent the amounts of 40% and 65% solutions, respectively.

(b) Use a graphing utility to graph the two equations in part (a) in the same viewing window. As the amount of the 40% solution increases, how does the amount of the 65% solution change?

(c) How much of each solution is required to obtain the specified concentration of the final mixture?

64. Fuel Mixture Five hundred gallons of 89 octane gasoline is obtained by mixing 87 octane gasoline with 92 octane gasoline.

(a) Write a system of equations in which one equation represents the amount of final mixture required and the other represents the amounts of 87 octane and 92 octane gasoline in the final mixture. Let x and y represent the gallons of 87 octane and 92 octane gasoline, respectively.

(b) Use a graphing utility to graph the two equations in part (a) in the same viewing window. As the amount of 87 octane gasoline increases, how does the amount of 92 octane gasoline change?

(c) How much of each type of gasoline is required to obtain the 500 gallons of 89 octane gasoline?

65. Investment Portfolio A total of $15,000 is invested in two corporate bonds that pay 7.5% and 6% simple interest. The investor wants an annual interest income of $990 from the investments. What is the most that can be invested in the 6% bond?

66. Investment Portfolio A total of $39,000 is invested in two municipal bonds that pay 5.75% and 6.25% simple interest. The investor wants an annual interest income of $2400 from the investments. What is the most that can be invested in the 5.75% bond?

67. Ticket Sales Five hundred tickets were sold for one performance of a play. The tickets for adults and children sold for $7.50 and $4.00, respectively, and the receipts for the performance totaled $3312.50. How many of each type of ticket were sold?

68. Sales On Saturday night, the manager of a shoe store evaluates the receipts of the previous week's sales. Two hundred and fifty pairs of two different styles of running shoes were sold. One style sold for $75.50 and the other sold for $89.95. The receipts totaled $20,031. The cash register that was supposed to record the number of each type of shoe sold malfunctioned. Can you recover the information? If so, how many shoes of each type were sold?

Fitting a Line to Data **In Exercises 69 and 70, find the least squares regression line $y = ax + b$ for the points $(x_1, y_1), (x_2, y_2), \ldots, (x_n, y_n)$ by solving the system for a and b. Then use the *regression* feature of a graphing utility to confirm your result. (For an explanation of how the coefficients of a and b in the system are obtained, see Appendix C.)**

69. $\begin{cases} 5b + 10a = 20.2 \\ 10b + 30a = 50.1 \end{cases}$ 70. $\begin{cases} 5b + 10a = 11.7 \\ 10b + 30a = 25.6 \end{cases}$

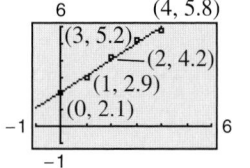

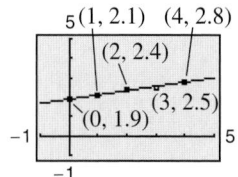

71. Data Analysis A farmer used four test plots to determine the relationship between wheat yield (in bushels per acre) and the amount of fertilizer applied (in hundreds of pounds per acre). The results are shown in the table.

Fertilizer, x	Yield, y
1.0	32
1.5	41
2.0	48
2.5	53

(a) Find the least squares regression line $y = ax + b$ for the data by solving the system for a and b.

$\begin{cases} 4b + 7.0a = 174 \\ 7b + 13.5a = 322 \end{cases}$

(b) Use the *regression* feature of a graphing utility to confirm the result in part (a).

(c) Use a graphing utility to plot the data and graph the linear model in the same viewing window.

(d) Use the linear model to predict the yield for a fertilizer application of 160 pounds per acre.

72. *Data Analysis* A candy store manager wants to know the demand for a candy bar as a function of the price. The daily sales for different prices of the product are shown in the table.

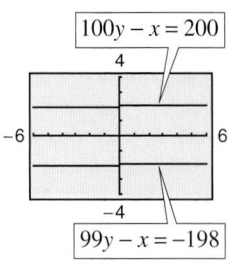

Price, x	Demand, y
$1.00	45
$1.20	37
$1.50	23

(a) Find the least squares regression line $y = ax + b$ for the data by solving the system for a and b.

$$\begin{cases} 3.00b + 3.70a = 105.00 \\ 3.70b + 4.69a = 123.90 \end{cases}$$

(b) Use the *regression* feature of a graphing utility to confirm the result in part (a).

(c) Use a graphing utility to plot the data and graph the linear model in part (a) in the same viewing window.

(d) Use the linear model in part (a) to predict the demand when the price is $1.75.

Synthesis

True or False? In Exercises 73 and 74, determine whether the statement is true or false. Justify your answer.

73. If a system of linear equations has two distinct solutions, then it has an infinite number of solutions.

74. If a system of linear equations has no solution, then the lines must be parallel.

Think About It In Exercises 75 and 76, the graphs of the two equations appear to be parallel. Yet, when the system is solved algebraically, it is found that the system does have a solution. Find the solution and explain why it does not appear on the portion of the graph that is shown.

75. $\begin{cases} 100y - x = 200 \\ 99y - x = -198 \end{cases}$

$100y - x = 200$

$99y - x = -198$

76. $\begin{cases} 21x - 20y = 0 \\ 13x - 12y = 120 \end{cases}$

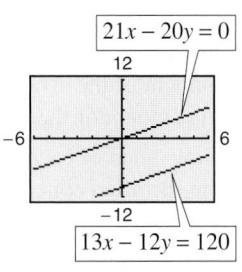

$21x - 20y = 0$

$13x - 12y = 120$

77. *Writing* Briefly explain whether or not it is possible for a consistent system of linear equations to have exactly two solutions.

78. *Think About It* Give examples of (a) a system of linear equations that has no solution and (b) a system that has an infinite number of solutions.

In Exercises 79 and 80, find the value of k such that the system of equations is inconsistent.

79. $\begin{cases} 4x - 8y = -3 \\ 2x + ky = 16 \end{cases}$ **80.** $\begin{cases} 15x + 3y = 6 \\ -10x + ky = 9 \end{cases}$

Advanced Applications In Exercises 81 and 82, solve the system of equations for u and v. While solving for these variables, consider the transcendental functions as constants. (Systems of this type are found in a course in differential equations.)

81. $\begin{cases} u \sin x + v \cos x = 0 \\ u \cos x - v \sin x = \sec x \end{cases}$

82. $\begin{cases} u \cos 2x + v \sin 2x = 0 \\ u(-2 \sin 2x) + v(2 \cos 2x) = \csc 2x \end{cases}$

Review

In Exercises 83–88, solve the inequality and graph the solution on a real number line.

83. $-11 - 6x \geq 33$ **84.** $-6 \leq 3x - 10 < 6$

85. $|x - 8| < 10$ **86.** $|x + 10| \geq -3$

87. $2x^2 + 3x - 35 < 0$ **88.** $3x^2 + 12x > 0$

In Exercises 89–92, write the expression as the logarithm of a single quantity.

89. $\ln x + \ln 6$ **90.** $\ln x - 5 \ln(x + 3)$

91. $\log_9 12 - \log_9 x$ **92.** $\frac{1}{4} \log_6 3 + \frac{1}{4} \log_6 x$

8.3 Multivariable Linear Systems

Row-Echelon Form and Back-Substitution

The method of elimination can be applied to a system of linear equations in more than two variables. When elimination is used to solve a system of linear equations, the goal is to rewrite the system in a form to which back-substitution can be applied. To see how this works, consider the following two systems of linear equations.

System of Three Linear Equations in Three Variables (See Example 2):

$$\begin{cases} x - 2y + 3z = 9 \\ -x + 3y = -4 \\ 2x - 5y + 5z = 17 \end{cases}$$

Equivalent System in Row-Echelon Form (See Example 1):

$$\begin{cases} x - 2y + 3z = 9 \\ y + 3z = 5 \\ z = 2 \end{cases}$$

The second system is said to be in **row-echelon form,** which means that it has a "stair-step" pattern with leading coefficients of 1. After comparing the two systems, it should be clear that it is easier to solve the system in row-echelon form, using back-substitution.

Example 1   Using Back-Substitution in Row-Echelon Form

Solve the system of linear equations.

$$\begin{cases} x - 2y + 3z = 9 & \text{Equation 1} \\ y + 3z = 5 & \text{Equation 2} \\ z = 2 & \text{Equation 3} \end{cases}$$

Solution

From Equation 3, you know the value of z. To solve for y, substitute $z = 2$ into Equation 2 to obtain

$$y + 3(2) = 5 \qquad \text{Substitute 2 for } z.$$
$$y = -1. \qquad \text{Solve for } y.$$

Finally, substitute $y = -1$ and $z = 2$ into Equation 1 to obtain

$$x - 2(-1) + 3(2) = 9 \qquad \text{Substitute } -1 \text{ for } y \text{ and 2 for } z.$$
$$x = 1. \qquad \text{Solve for } x.$$

The solution is $x = 1$, $y = -1$, and $z = 2$, which can be written as the **ordered triple** $(1, -1, 2)$. Check this in the original system of equations.

☑ *Checkpoint* Now try Exercise 5.

Andy Sacks/Getty Images

Gaussian Elimination

Two systems of equations are *equivalent* if they have the same solution set. To solve a system that is not in row-echelon form, first convert it to an *equivalent* system that *is* in row-echelon form by using one or more of the elementary row operations shown below. This process is called **Gaussian elimination,** after the German mathematician Carl Friedrich Gauss (1777–1855).

Elementary Row Operations

1. Interchange two equations.

2. Multiply one of the equations by a nonzero constant.

3. Add a multiple of one equation to another equation.

Example 2   Using Gaussian Elimination to Solve a System

Solve the system of linear equations.

$$\begin{cases} x - 2y + 3z = 9 & \text{Equation 1} \\ -x + 3y = -4 & \text{Equation 2} \\ 2x - 5y + 5z = 17 & \text{Equation 3} \end{cases}$$

Solution

Because the leading coefficient of the first equation is 1, you can begin by saving the x at the upper left and eliminating the other x-terms from the first column.

$$\begin{cases} x - 2y + 3z = 9 \\ y + 3z = 5 \\ 2x - 5y + 5z = 17 \end{cases}$$

> Adding the first equation to the second equation produces a new second equation.

$$\begin{cases} x - 2y + 3z = 9 \\ y + 3z = 5 \\ -y - z = -1 \end{cases}$$

> Adding -2 times the first equation to the third equation produces a new third equation.

Now that all but the first x have been eliminated from the first column, go to work on the second column. (You need to eliminate y from the third equation.)

$$\begin{cases} x - 2y + 3z = 9 \\ y + 3z = 5 \\ 2z = 4 \end{cases}$$

> Adding the second equation to the third equation produces a new third equation.

Finally, you need a coefficient of 1 for z in the third equation.

$$\begin{cases} x - 2y + 3z = 9 \\ y + 3z = 5 \\ z = 2 \end{cases}$$

> Multiplying the third equation by $\frac{1}{2}$ produces a new third equation.

This is the same system that was solved in Example 1. As in that example, you can conclude that the solution is $x = 1$, $y = -1$, and $z = 2$, written as $(1, -1, 2)$.

✓ *Checkpoint* Now try Exercise 13.

The goal of Gaussian elimination is to use elementary row operations on a system in order to isolate one variable. You can then solve for the value of the variable and use back-substitution to find the values of the remaining variables.

The next example involves an inconsistent system—one that has no solution. The key to recognizing an inconsistent system is that at some stage in the elimination process, you obtain a false statement such as $0 = -2$.

Example 3   An Inconsistent System

Solve the system of linear equations.

$$\begin{cases} x - 3y + z = 1 & \text{Equation 1} \\ 2x - y - 2z = 2 & \text{Equation 2} \\ x + 2y - 3z = -1 & \text{Equation 3} \end{cases}$$

Solution

$$\begin{cases} x - 3y + z = 1 \\ 5y - 4z = 0 \\ x + 2y - 3z = -1 \end{cases}$$

> Adding -2 times the first equation to the second equation produces a new second equation.

$$\begin{cases} x - 3y + z = 1 \\ 5y - 4z = 0 \\ 5y - 4z = -2 \end{cases}$$

> Adding -1 times the first equation to the third equation produces a new third equation.

$$\begin{cases} x - 3y + z = 1 \\ 5y - 4z = 0 \\ 0 = -2 \end{cases}$$

> Adding -1 times the second equation to the third equation produces a new third equation.

Because $0 = -2$ is a false statement, you can conclude that this system is inconsistent and so has no solution. Moreover, because this system is equivalent to the original system, you can conclude that the original system also has no solution.

✓ *Checkpoint* Now try Exercise 19.

As with a system of linear equations in two variables, the number of solutions of a system of linear equations in more than two variables must fall into one of three categories.

The Number of Solutions of a Linear System

For a system of linear equations, exactly one of the following is true.

1. There is exactly one solution.

2. There are infinitely many solutions.

3. There is no solution.

A system of linear equations is called *consistent* if it has at least one solution. A consistent system with exactly one solution is **independent.** A consistent system with infinitely many solutions is **dependent.** A system of linear equations is called *inconsistent* if it has no solution.

Example 4 A System with Infinitely Many Solutions

Solve the system of linear equations.

$$\begin{cases} x + y - 3z = -1 & \text{Equation 1} \\ y - z = 0 & \text{Equation 2} \\ -x + 2y = 1 & \text{Equation 3} \end{cases}$$

Solution

$$\begin{cases} x + y - 3z = -1 \\ y - z = 0 \\ 3y - 3z = 0 \end{cases}$$

Adding the first equation to the third equation produces a new third equation.

$$\begin{cases} x + y - 3z = -1 \\ y - z = 0 \\ 0 = 0 \end{cases}$$

Adding -3 times the second equation to the third equation produces a new third equation.

This result means that Equation 3 depends on Equations 1 and 2 in the sense that it gives us no additional information about the variables. So, the original system is equivalent to the system

$$\begin{cases} x + y - 3z = -1 \\ y - z = 0 \end{cases}.$$

In the last equation, solve for y in terms of z to obtain $y = z$. Back-substituting for y into the previous equation produces $x = 2z - 1$. Finally, letting $z = a$, where a is a real number, the solutions to the original system are all of the form

$$x = 2a - 1, \qquad y = a, \qquad \text{and} \qquad z = a.$$

So, every ordered triple of the form

$$(2a - 1, a, a), \qquad a \text{ is a real number}$$

is a solution of the system.

✓ *Checkpoint* Now try Exercise 23.

STUDY TIP

There are an infinite number of solutions to Example 4, but they are all of a specific form. By selecting, for example, a-values of 0, 1, and 3, you can verify that $(-1, 0, 0)$, $(1, 1, 1)$, and $(5, 3, 3)$ are specific solutions. It is incorrect to say simply that the solution to Example 4 is "infinite." You must also specify the form of the solutions.

In Example 4, there are other ways to write the same infinite set of solutions. For instance, the solutions could have been written as

$$\left(b, \tfrac{1}{2}(b + 1), \tfrac{1}{2}(b + 1)\right), \qquad b \text{ is a real number}.$$

This description produces the same set of solutions, as shown below.

Substitution	*Solution*	
$a = 0$	$(2(0) - 1, 0, 0) = (-1, 0, 0)$	Same solution
$b = -1$	$\left(-1, \tfrac{1}{2}(-1 + 1), \tfrac{1}{2}(-1 + 1)\right) = (-1, 0, 0)$	
$a = 1$	$(2(1) - 1, 1, 1) = (1, 1, 1)$	Same solution
$b = 1$	$\left(1, \tfrac{1}{2}(1 + 1), \tfrac{1}{2}(1 + 1)\right) = (1, 1, 1)$	
$a = 2$	$(2(2) - 1, 2, 2) = (3, 2, 2)$	Same solution
$b = 3$	$\left(3, \tfrac{1}{2}(3 + 1), \tfrac{1}{2}(3 + 1)\right) = (3, 2, 2)$	

Nonsquare Systems

So far, each system of linear equations you have looked at has been *square*, which means that the number of equations is equal to the number of variables. In a **nonsquare system of equations,** the number of equations differs from the number of variables. A system of linear equations cannot have a unique solution unless there are at least as many equations as there are variables in the system.

Example 5   A System with Fewer Equations Than Variables

Solve the system of linear equations.

$$\begin{cases} x - 2y + z = 2 & \text{Equation 1} \\ 2x - y - z = 1 & \text{Equation 2} \end{cases}$$

Solution

Begin by rewriting the system in row-echelon form.

$$\begin{cases} x - 2y + z = 2 \\ 3y - 3z = -3 \end{cases}$$

> Adding -2 times the first equation to the second equation produces a new second equation.

$$\begin{cases} x - 2y + z = 2 \\ y - z = -1 \end{cases}$$

> Multiplying the second equation by $\frac{1}{3}$ produces a new second equation.

Solve for y in terms of z to obtain $y = z - 1$. By back-substituting into Equation 1, you can solve for x as follows.

$$x - 2(z - 1) + z = 2 \qquad \text{Substitute for } y \text{ in Equation 1.}$$

$$x - 2z + 2 + z = 2 \qquad \text{Distributive Property}$$

$$x = z \qquad \text{Solve for } x.$$

Finally, by letting $z = a$ where a is a real number, you have the solution $x = a$, $y = a - 1$, and $z = a$. So, every ordered triple of the form

$$(a, a - 1, a), \qquad a \text{ is a real number}$$

is a solution of the system.

✓ *Checkpoint* Now try Exercise 31.

In Example 5, try choosing some values of a to obtain different solutions of the system, such as $(1, 0, 1)$, $(2, 1, 2)$, and $(3, 2, 3)$. Then check each of the solutions in the original system as follows.

Check: $(1, 0, 1)$	*Check:* $(2, 1, 2)$	*Check:* $(3, 2, 3)$
$1 - 2(0) + 1 \overset{?}{=} 2$	$2 - 2(1) + 2 \overset{?}{=} 2$	$3 - 2(2) + 3 \overset{?}{=} 2$
$2 = 2$ ✓	$2 = 2$ ✓	$2 = 2$ ✓
$2(1) - 0 - 1 \overset{?}{=} 1$	$2(2) - 1 - 2 \overset{?}{=} 1$	$2(3) - 2 - 3 \overset{?}{=} 1$
$1 = 1$ ✓	$1 = 1$ ✓	$1 = 1$ ✓

Graphical Interpretation of Three-Variable Systems

Solutions of equations in three variables can be pictured using a **three-dimensional coordinate system.** To construct such a system, begin with the xy-coordinate plane in a horizontal position. Then draw the z-axis as a vertical line through the origin.

Every ordered triple (x, y, z) corresponds to a point on the three-dimensional coordinate system. For instance, the points corresponding to

$$(-2, 5, 4), \qquad (2, -5, 3), \qquad \text{and} \qquad (3, 3, -2)$$

are shown in Figure 8.16.

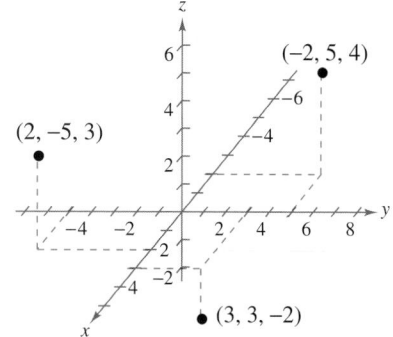

Figure 8.16

The **graph of an equation in three variables** consists of all points (x, y, z) that are solutions of the equation. The graph of a linear equation in three variables is a *plane*. Sketching graphs on a three-dimensional coordinate system is difficult because the sketch itself is only two-dimensional.

One technique for sketching a plane is to find the three points at which the plane intersects the axes. For instance, the plane

$$3x + 2y + 4z = 12$$

intersects the x-axis at the point $(4, 0, 0)$, the y-axis at the point $(0, 6, 0)$, and the z-axis at the point $(0, 0, 3)$. By plotting these three points, connecting them with line segments, and shading the resulting triangular region, you can sketch a portion of the graph, as shown in Figure 8.17.

The graph of a system of three linear equations in three variables consists of *three* planes. When these planes intersect in a single point, the system has exactly one solution (see Figure 8.18). When the three planes have no point in common, the system has no solution (see Figures 8.19 and 8.20). When the three planes intersect in a line or a plane, the system has infinitely many solutions (see Figures 8.21 and 8.22).

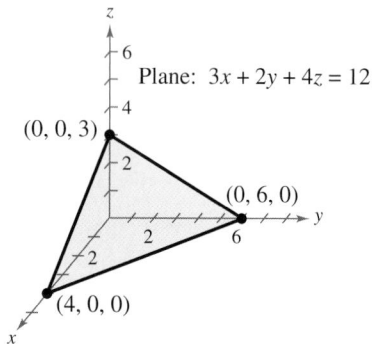

Figure 8.17

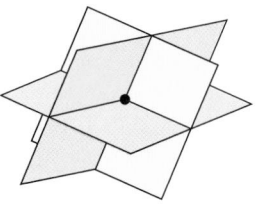

Solution: One point
Figure 8.18

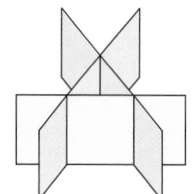

Solution: None
Figure 8.19

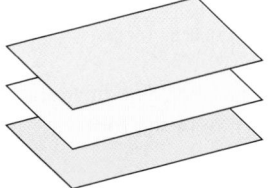

Solution: None
Figure 8.20

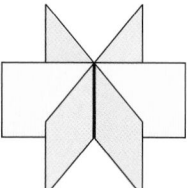

Solution: One line
Figure 8.21

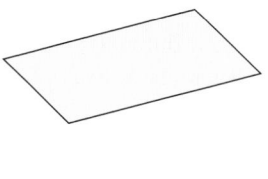

Solution: One plane
Figure 8.22

TECHNOLOGY TIP

Three-dimensional graphing utilities and computer algebra systems, such as *Derive* and *Mathematica*, are very efficient in producing three-dimensional graphs. They are good tools to use while studying calculus. If you have access to such a utility, try reproducing the plane shown in Figure 8.17.

Partial Fraction Decomposition and Other Applications

A rational expression can often be written as the sum of two or more simpler rational expressions. For example, the rational expression

$$\frac{x + 7}{x^2 - x - 6}$$

can be written as the sum of two fractions with linear denominators. That is,

$$\frac{x + 7}{x^2 - x - 6} = \underbrace{\frac{2}{x - 3}}_{\substack{\text{Partial} \\ \text{fraction}}} + \underbrace{\frac{-1}{x + 2}}_{\substack{\text{Partial} \\ \text{fraction}}}.$$

Each fraction on the right side of the equation is a **partial fraction,** and together they make up the **partial fraction decomposition** of the left side.

Decomposition of $N(x)/D(x)$ into Partial Fractions

1. *Divide if improper:* If $N(x)/D(x)$ is an improper fraction [degree of $N(x) \geq$ degree of $D(x)$], divide the denominator into the numerator to obtain

$$\frac{N(x)}{D(x)} = (\text{polynomial}) + \frac{N_1(x)}{D(x)}$$

   and apply Steps 2, 3, and 4 (below) to the proper rational expression $N_1(x)/D(x)$.

2. *Factor denominator:* Completely factor the denominator into factors of the form

$$(px + q)^m \quad \text{and} \quad (ax^2 + bx + c)^n$$

   where $(ax^2 + bx + c)$ is irreducible.

3. *Linear factors:* For *each* factor of the form $(px + q)^m$, the partial fraction decomposition must include the following sum of m fractions.

$$\frac{A_1}{(px + q)} + \frac{A_2}{(px + q)^2} + \cdots + \frac{A_m}{(px + q)^m}$$

4. *Quadratic factors:* For *each* factor of the form $(ax^2 + bx + c)^n$, the partial fraction decomposition must include the following sum of n fractions.

$$\frac{B_1x + C_1}{ax^2 + bx + c} + \frac{B_2x + C_2}{(ax^2 + bx + c)^2} + \cdots + \frac{B_nx + C_n}{(ax^2 + bx + c)^n}$$

One of the most important applications of partial fractions is in calculus. If you go on to take a course in calculus, you will learn how partial fractions can be used in a calculus operation called antidifferentiation.

Example 6   Partial Fraction Decomposition: Distinct Linear Factors

Write the partial fraction decomposition of

$$\frac{x+7}{x^2-x-6}.$$

Solution

Because $x^2 - x - 6 = (x - 3)(x + 2)$, you should include one partial fraction with a constant numerator for each linear factor of the denominator and write

$$\frac{x+7}{x^2-x-6} = \frac{A}{x-3} + \frac{B}{x+2}.$$

Multiplying each side of this equation by the least common denominator, $(x - 3)(x + 2)$, leads to the **basic equation**

$x + 7 = A(x + 2) + B(x - 3)$	Basic equation
$= Ax + 2A + Bx - 3B$	Distributive Property
$= (A + B)x + 2A - 3B.$	Write in polynomial form.

By equating coefficients of like terms on opposite sides of the equation, you obtain the following system of linear equations.

$$\begin{cases} A + B = 1 & \text{Equation 1} \\ 2A - 3B = 7 & \text{Equation 2} \end{cases}$$

You can solve the system of linear equations as follows.

$A + B = 1$	⟹	$3A + 3B = 3$	Multiply Equation 1 by 3.
$2A - 3B = 7$	⟹	$2A - 3B = 7$	Write Equation 2.
		$5A \quad\quad = 10$	Add equations.

From this equation, you can see that $A = 2$. By back-substituting this value of A into Equation 1, you can determine that $B = -1$. So, the partial fraction decomposition is

$$\frac{x+7}{x^2-x-6} = \frac{2}{x-3} - \frac{1}{x+2}.$$

Check this result by combining the two partial fractions on the right side of the equation.

✓ *Checkpoint*   Now try Exercise 59.

TECHNOLOGY TIP   You can graphically check the decomposition found in Example 6. To do this, use a graphing utility to graph

$$y_1 = \frac{x+7}{x^2-x-6} \quad \text{and} \quad y_2 = \frac{2}{x-3} - \frac{1}{x+2}$$

in the same viewing window. The graphs should be identical, as shown in Figure 8.23.

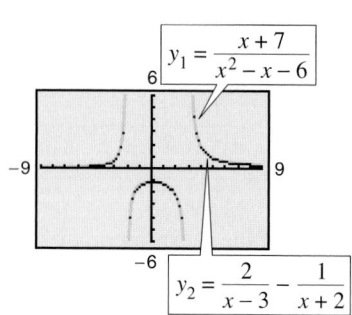

Figure 8.23

The next example shows how to find the partial fraction decomposition for a rational function whose denominator has a repeated linear factor.

Example 7   Partial Fraction Decomposition: Repeated Linear Factors

Write the partial fraction decomposition of $\dfrac{5x^2 + 20x + 6}{x^3 + 2x^2 + x}$.

Solution

Because the denominator factors as

$$x^3 + 2x^2 + x = x(x^2 + 2x + 1)$$

$$= x(x + 1)^2$$

you should include one partial fraction with a constant numerator for each power of x and $(x + 1)$ and write

$$\frac{5x^2 + 20x + 6}{x^3 + 2x^2 + x} = \frac{A}{x} + \frac{B}{x + 1} + \frac{C}{(x + 1)^2}.$$

Multiplying by the LCD, $x(x + 1)^2$, leads to the basic equation

$$5x^2 + 20x + 6 = A(x + 1)^2 + Bx(x + 1) + Cx \qquad \text{Basic equation}$$

$$= Ax^2 + 2Ax + A + Bx^2 + Bx + Cx \qquad \text{Expand.}$$

$$= (A + B)x^2 + (2A + B + C)x + A. \qquad \text{Polynomial form}$$

By equating coefficients of like terms on opposite sides of the equation, you obtain the following system of linear equations.

$$\begin{cases} A + B & = 5 \\ 2A + B + C & = 20 \\ A & = 6 \end{cases}$$

Substituting 6 for A in the first equation produces

$$6 + B = 5$$

$$B = -1.$$

Substituting 6 for A and -1 for B in the second equation produces

$$2(6) + (-1) + C = 20$$

$$C = 9.$$

So, the partial fraction decomposition is

$$\frac{5x^2 + 20x + 6}{x^3 + 2x^2 + x} = \frac{6}{x} - \frac{1}{x + 1} + \frac{9}{(x + 1)^2}.$$

Check this result by combining the three partial fractions on the right side of the equation.

✓ *Checkpoint* Now try Exercise 63.

Exploration

Partial fraction decomposition is practical only for rational functions whose denominators factor "nicely." For example, the factorization of the expression $x^2 - x - 5$ is

$$\left(x - \frac{1 - \sqrt{21}}{2}\right)\left(x - \frac{1 + \sqrt{21}}{2}\right).$$

Write the basic equation and try to complete the decomposition for

$$\frac{x + 7}{x^2 - x - 5}.$$

What problems do you encounter?

Example 8   Vertical Motion

The height at time t of an object that is moving in a (vertical) line with constant acceleration a is given by the *position equation* $s = \frac{1}{2}at^2 + v_0t + s_0$. The height s is measured in feet, t is measured in seconds, v_0 is the initial velocity (in feet per second) at $t = 0$, and s_0 is the initial height. Find the values of a, v_0, and s_0 if $s = 52$ at $t = 1$, $s = 52$ at $t = 2$, and $s = 20$ at $t = 3$, as shown in Figure 8.24.

Solution

You can obtain three linear equations in a, v_0, and s_0 as follows.

When $t = 1$: $\frac{1}{2}a(1)^2 + v_0(1) + s_0 = 52$ ⟹ $a + 2v_0 + 2s_0 = 104$

When $t = 2$: $\frac{1}{2}a(2)^2 + v_0(2) + s_0 = 52$ ⟹ $2a + 2v_0 + s_0 = 52$

When $t = 3$: $\frac{1}{2}a(3)^2 + v_0(3) + s_0 = 20$ ⟹ $9a + 6v_0 + 2s_0 = 40$

Solving this system yields $a = -32$, $v_0 = 48$, and $s_0 = 20$.

 Checkpoint   Now try Exercise 73.

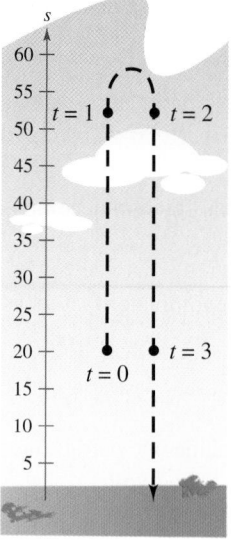

Figure 8.24

Example 9   Data Analysis: Curve-Fitting

Find a quadratic equation $y = ax^2 + bx + c$ whose graph passes through the points $(-1, 3)$, $(1, 1)$, and $(2, 6)$.

Solution

Because the graph of $y = ax^2 + bx + c$ passes through the points $(-1, 3)$, $(1, 1)$, and $(2, 6)$, you can write the following.

When $x = -1$, $y = 3$: $a(-1)^2 + b(-1) + c = 3$

When $x = 1$, $y = 1$: $a(1)^2 + b(1) + c = 1$

When $x = 2$, $y = 6$: $a(2)^2 + b(2) + c = 6$

This produces the following system of linear equations.

$$\begin{cases} a - b + c = 3 & \text{Equation 1} \\ a + b + c = 1 & \text{Equation 2} \\ 4a + 2b + c = 6 & \text{Equation 3} \end{cases}$$

The solution of this system is $a = 2$, $b = -1$, and $c = 0$. So, the equation of the parabola is $y = 2x^2 - x$, and its graph is shown in Figure 8.25.

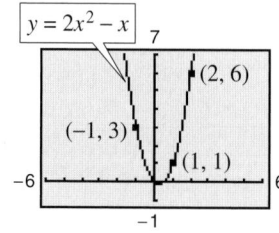

Figure 8.25

 Checkpoint Now try Exercise 77.

STUDY TIP

When you use a system of linear equations to solve an application problem, it is wise to interpret your solution in the context of the problem to see if it makes sense. For instance, in Example 8 the solution results in the position equation

$$s = -16t^2 + 48t + 20$$

which implies that the object was thrown upward at a velocity of 48 feet per second from a height of 20 feet. The object undergoes a constant downward acceleration of 32 feet per second squared. (In physics, this is the value of the acceleration due to gravity.)

8.3   Exercises

Vocabulary Check

Fill in the blanks.

1. A system of equations that is in _____ form has a "stair-step" pattern with leading coefficients of 1.

2. A solution to a system of three linear equations in three unknowns can be written as an _____ , which has the form (x, y, z).

3. The process used to write a system of equations in row-echelon form is called _____ elimination.

4. A system of linear equations that has exactly one solution is called _____ , whereas a system of linear equations that has infinitely many solutions is called _____ .

5. A system of equations is called _____ if the number of equations differs from the number of variables in the system.

6. Solutions of equations in three variables can be pictured using a _____ coordinate system.

7. The process of writing a rational expression as the sum of two or more simpler rational expressions is called _____ .

In Exercises 1–4, determine whether each ordered triple is a solution of the system of equations.

1. $\begin{cases} 3x - y + z = 1 \\ 2x - 3z = -14 \\ 5y + 2z = 8 \end{cases}$

   (a) $(2, 5, 0)$ (b) $(-2, 0, 4)$
   (c) $(0, -1, 3)$ (d) $(-1, 0, 4)$

2. $\begin{cases} 3x + 4y - z = 17 \\ 5x - y + 2z = -2 \\ 2x - 3y + 7z = -21 \end{cases}$

   (a) $(3, 2, 0)$ (b) $(1, 3, -2)$
   (c) $(4, 1, -3)$ (d) $(1, 5, -1)$

3. $\begin{cases} 4x + y - z = 0 \\ -8x - 6y + z = -\frac{7}{4} \\ 3x - y = -\frac{9}{4} \end{cases}$

   (a) $(0, 1, 1)$ (b) $\left(-\frac{3}{2}, \frac{5}{4}, -\frac{5}{4}\right)$
   (c) $\left(-\frac{1}{2}, \frac{3}{4}, -\frac{5}{4}\right)$ (d) $\left(-\frac{1}{2}, 2, 0\right)$

4. $\begin{cases} -4x - y - 8z = -6 \\ y + z = 0 \\ 4x - 7y = 6 \end{cases}$

   (a) $(-2, -2, 2)$ (b) $\left(-\frac{33}{2}, -10, 10\right)$
   (c) $\left(\frac{1}{8}, -\frac{1}{2}, \frac{1}{2}\right)$ (d) $\left(-\frac{11}{2}, -4, 4\right)$

In Exercises 5–10, use back-substitution to solve the system of linear equations.

5. $\begin{cases} 2x - y + 5z = 24 \\ y + 2z = 4 \\ z = 6 \end{cases}$

6. $\begin{cases} 4x - 3y - 2z = 21 \\ 6y - 5z = -8 \\ z = -2 \end{cases}$

7. $\begin{cases} 2x + y - 3z = 10 \\ y + z = 12 \\ z = 2 \end{cases}$

8. $\begin{cases} x - y + 2z = 22 \\ 3y - 8z = -9 \\ z = -3 \end{cases}$

9. $\begin{cases} 4x - 2y + z = 8 \\ -y + z = 4 \\ z = 2 \end{cases}$

10. $\begin{cases} 5x - 8z = 22 \\ 3y - 5z = 10 \\ z = -4 \end{cases}$

In Exercises 11 and 12, perform the row operation and write the equivalent system.

11. Add Equation 1 to Equation 2.

   $\begin{cases} x - 2y + 3z = 5 & \text{Equation 1} \\ -x + 3y - 5z = 4 & \text{Equation 2} \\ 2x - 3z = 0 & \text{Equation 3} \end{cases}$

   What did this operation accomplish?

12. Add -2 times Equation 1 to Equation 3.

   $\begin{cases} x - 2y + 3z = 5 & \text{Equation 1} \\ -x + 3y - 5z = 4 & \text{Equation 2} \\ 2x - 3z = 0 & \text{Equation 3} \end{cases}$

   What did this operation accomplish?

In Exercises 13–38, solve the system of linear equations and check any solution algebraically.

13. $\begin{cases} x + y + z = 6 \\ 2x - y + z = 3 \\ 3x \quad\;\; - z = 0 \end{cases}$
  14. $\begin{cases} x + y + z = 2 \\ -x + 3y + 2z = 8 \\ 4x + y \quad\quad = 4 \end{cases}$

15. $\begin{cases} 2x \quad\quad + 2z = 2 \\ 5x + 3y \quad\quad = 4 \\ \quad\; 3y - 4z = 4 \end{cases}$
  16. $\begin{cases} 4x + y - 3z = 11 \\ 2x - 3y + 2z = 9 \\ x + y + z = -3 \end{cases}$

17. $\begin{cases} \quad\quad 6y + 4z = -18 \\ 3x + 3y \quad\quad = 9 \\ 2x \quad\quad - 3z = 12 \end{cases}$

18. $\begin{cases} 2x + 4y + z = -4 \\ 2x - 4y + 6z = 13 \\ 4x - 2y + z = 6 \end{cases}$

19. $\begin{cases} 3x - 2y + 4z = 1 \\ x + y - 2z = 3 \\ 2x - 3y + 6z = 8 \end{cases}$
  20. $\begin{cases} 5x - 3y + 2z = 3 \\ 2x + 4y - z = 7 \\ x - 11y + 4z = 3 \end{cases}$

21. $\begin{cases} 3x + 3y + 5z = 1 \\ 3x + 5y + 9z = 0 \\ 5x + 9y + 17z = 0 \end{cases}$
  22. $\begin{cases} 2x + y + 3z = 1 \\ 2x + 6y + 8z = 3 \\ 6x + 8y + 18z = 5 \end{cases}$

23. $\begin{cases} x + 2y - 7z = -4 \\ 2x + y + z = 13 \\ 3x + 9y - 36z = -33 \end{cases}$

24. $\begin{cases} 2x + y - 3z = 4 \\ 4x \quad\quad + 2z = 10 \\ -2x + 3y - 13z = -8 \end{cases}$

25. $\begin{cases} 3x - 3y + 6z = 6 \\ x + 2y - z = 5 \\ 5x - 8y + 13z = 7 \end{cases}$

26. $\begin{cases} x \quad\quad + 4z = 13 \\ 4x - 2y + z = 7 \\ 2x - 2y - 7z = -19 \end{cases}$

27. $\begin{cases} x - 2y + 3z = 4 \\ 3x - y + 2z = 0 \\ x + 3y - 4z = -2 \end{cases}$

28. $\begin{cases} -x + 3y + z = 4 \\ 4x - 2y - 5z = -7 \\ 2x + 4y - 3z = 12 \end{cases}$

29. $\begin{cases} x \quad\quad + 4z = 1 \\ x + y + 10z = 10 \\ 2x - y + 2z = -5 \end{cases}$

30. $\begin{cases} 3x - 2y - 6z = -4 \\ -3x + 2y + 6z = 1 \\ x - y - 5z = -3 \end{cases}$

31. $\begin{cases} x - 2y + 5z = 2 \\ 4x \quad\quad - z = 0 \end{cases}$
  32. $\begin{cases} 12x + 5y + z = 0 \\ 23x + 4y - z = 0 \end{cases}$

33. $\begin{cases} 2x - 3y + z = -2 \\ -4x + 9y = 7 \end{cases}$
  34. $\begin{cases} 10x - 3y + 2z = 0 \\ 19x - 5y - z = 0 \end{cases}$

35. $\begin{cases} x - 3y + 2z = 18 \\ 5x - 13y + 12z = 80 \end{cases}$

36. $\begin{cases} 2x + 3y + 3z = 7 \\ 4x + 18y + 15z = 44 \end{cases}$

37. $\begin{cases} x \quad\quad + 3w = 4 \\ 2y - z - w = 0 \\ 3y \quad\quad - 2w = 1 \\ 2x - y + 4z \quad\quad = 5 \end{cases}$

38. $\begin{cases} x + y + z + w = 6 \\ 2x + 3y \quad\quad - w = 0 \\ -3x + 4y + z + 2w = 4 \\ x + 2y - z + w = 0 \end{cases}$

Exploration **In Exercises 39–42, find a system of linear equations that has the given solution. (There are many correct answers.)**

39. $(4, -1, 2)$
  40. $(-5, -2, 1)$

41. $\left(3, -\frac{1}{2}, \frac{7}{4}\right)$
  42. $\left(-\frac{3}{2}, 4, -7\right)$

Three-Dimensional Graphics **In Exercises 43–46, sketch the plane represented by the linear equation. Then list four points that lie in the plane.**

43. $2x + 3y + 4z = 12$
  44. $x + y + z = 6$

45. $2x + y + z = 4$
  46. $x + 2y + 2z = 6$

In Exercises 47–52, write the form of the partial fraction decomposition of the rational expression. Do not solve for the constants.

47. $\dfrac{7}{x^2 - 14x}$
  48. $\dfrac{x - 2}{x^2 + 4x + 3}$

49. $\dfrac{12}{x^3 - 10x^2}$
  50. $\dfrac{x^2 - 3x + 2}{4x^3 + 11x^2}$

51. $\dfrac{4x^2 + 3}{(x - 5)^3}$
  52. $\dfrac{6x + 5}{(x + 2)^4}$

In Exercises 53–70, (a) write the partial fraction decomposition for the rational expression, (b) check your result algebraically by combining the fractions, and (c) check your result graphically by using a graphing utility to graph the rational expression and the partial fractions in the same viewing window.

53. $\dfrac{1}{x^2 - 1}$

54. $\dfrac{1}{4x^2 - 9}$

55. $\dfrac{1}{x^2 + x}$

56. $\dfrac{3}{x^2 - 3x}$

57. $\dfrac{1}{2x^2 + x}$

58. $\dfrac{5}{x^2 + x - 6}$

59. $\dfrac{5 - x}{2x^2 + x - 1}$

60. $\dfrac{x - 2}{x^2 + 4x + 3}$

61. $\dfrac{x^2 + 12x + 12}{x^3 - 4x}$

62. $\dfrac{x^2 + 12x - 9}{x^3 - 9x}$

63. $\dfrac{4x^2 + 2x - 1}{x^2(x + 1)}$

64. $\dfrac{2x - 3}{(x - 1)^2}$

65. $\dfrac{27 - 7x}{x(x - 3)^2}$

66. $\dfrac{x^2 - x + 2}{x(x - 1)^2}$

67. $\dfrac{2x^3 - x^2 + x + 5}{x^2 + 3x + 2}$

68. $\dfrac{x^3 + 2x^2 - x + 1}{x^2 + 3x - 4}$

69. $\dfrac{x^4}{(x - 1)^3}$

70. $\dfrac{4x^4}{(2x - 1)^3}$

Graphical Analysis   In Exercises 71 and 72, write the partial fraction decomposition for the rational function. Identify the graph of the rational function and the graphs of each term of its decomposition. State any relationship between the vertical asymptotes of the rational function and the vertical asymptotes of the terms of the decomposition.

71. $y = \dfrac{x - 12}{x(x - 4)}$

72. $y = \dfrac{2(4x - 3)}{x^2 - 9}$

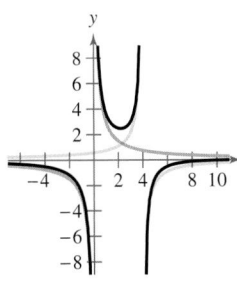

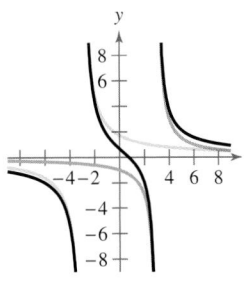

Vertical Motion   In Exercises 73–76, an object moving vertically is at the given heights at the specified times. Find the position equation $s = \frac{1}{2}at^2 + v_0 t + s_0$ for the object.

73. At $t = 1$ second, $s = 128$ feet.
At $t = 2$ seconds, $s = 80$ feet.
At $t = 3$ seconds, $s = 0$ feet.

74. At $t = 1$ second, $s = 48$ feet.
At $t = 2$ seconds, $s = 64$ feet.
At $t = 3$ seconds, $s = 48$ feet.

75. At $t = 1$ second, $s = 452$ feet.
At $t = 2$ seconds, $s = 372$ feet.
At $t = 3$ seconds, $s = 260$ feet.

76. At $t = 1$ second, $s = 132$ feet.
At $t = 2$ seconds, $s = 100$ feet.
At $t = 3$ seconds, $s = 36$ feet.

In Exercises 77–80, find the equation of the parabola

$$y = ax^2 + bx + c$$

that passes through the points. To verify your result, use a graphing utility to plot the points and graph the parabola.

77. $(0, 0), (2, -2), (4, 0)$ **78.** $(0, 3), (1, 4), (2, 3)$

79. $(2, 0), (3, -1), (4, 0)$ **80.** $(1, 3), (2, 2), (3, -3)$

In Exercises 81–84, find the equation of the circle

$$x^2 + y^2 + Dx + Ey + F = 0$$

that passes through the points. To verify your result, use a graphing utility to plot the points and graph the circle.

81. $(0, 0), (2, 2), (4, 0)$ **82.** $(0, 0), (0, 6), (3, 3)$

83. $(-3, -1), (2, 4), (-6, 8)$

84. $(-6, -1), (-4, 3), (2, -5)$

85. *Borrowing*   A small corporation borrowed $775,000 to expand its software line. Some of the money was borrowed at 8%, some at 9%, and some at 10%. How much was borrowed at each rate if the annual interest was $67,000 and the amount borrowed at 8% was four times the amount borrowed at 10%?

86. Borrowing A small corporation borrowed $1,000,000 to expand its line of toys. Some of the money was borrowed at 8%, some at 10%, and some at 12%. How much was borrowed at each rate if the annual interest was $97,200 and the amount borrowed at 8% was two times the amount borrowed at 10%?

Investment Portfolio **In Exercises 87 and 88, consider an investor with a portfolio totaling $500,000 that is invested in certificates of deposit, municipal bonds, blue-chip stocks, and growth or speculative stocks. How much is invested in each type of investment?**

87. The certificates of deposit pay 8% annually, and the municipal bonds pay 9% annually. Over a five-year period, the investor expects the blue-chip stocks to return 12% annually and the growth stocks to return 15% annually. The investor wants a combined annual return of 10% and also wants to have only one-fourth of the portfolio invested in municipal bonds.

88. The certificates of deposit pay 9% annually, and the municipal bonds pay 5% annually. Over a five-year period, the investor expects the blue-chip stocks to return 12% annually and the growth stocks to return 14% annually. The investor wants a combined annual return of 10% and also wants to have only one-fourth of the portfolio invested in stocks.

89. Agriculture A mixture of 12 liters of chemical A, 16 liters of chemical B, and 26 liters of chemical C is required to kill a destructive crop insect. Commercial spray X contains 1, 2, and 2 parts, respectively, of these chemicals. Commercial spray Y contains only chemical C. Commercial spray Z contains only chemicals A and B in equal amounts. How much of each type of commercial spray is needed to obtain the desired mixture?

90. Acid Mixture A chemist needs 10 liters of a 25% acid solution. The solution is to be mixed from three solutions whose concentrations are 10%, 20%, and 50%. How many liters of each solution should the chemist use so that as little as possible of the 50% solution is used?

91. Truck Scheduling A small company that manufactures two models of exercise machines has an order for 15 units of the standard model and 16 units of the deluxe model. The company has trucks of three different sizes that can haul the products, as shown in the table. How many trucks of each size are needed to deliver the order? Give two possible solutions.

Truck	Standard	Deluxe
Large	6	3
Medium	4	4
Small	0	3

Table for 91

92. Sports The University of Georgia and Florida State University scored a total of 39 points during the 2003 Sugar Bowl. The points came from a total of 11 different scoring plays, which were a combination of touchdowns, extra-point kicks, and field goals, worth 6, 1, and 3 points, respectively. The same numbers of touchdowns and field goals were scored. How many touchdowns, extra-point kicks, and field goals were scored during the game?   (Source: espn.com)

93. Electrical Networks When Kirchhoff's Laws are applied to the electrical network in the figure, the currents I_1, I_2, and I_3 are the solution of the system

$$\begin{cases} I_1 - I_2 + I_3 = 0 \\ 3I_1 + 2I_2 \qquad = 7. \\ \qquad 2I_2 + 4I_3 = 8 \end{cases}$$

Find the currents.

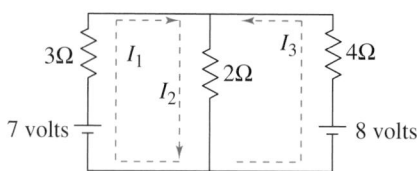

94. Pulley System A system of pulleys is loaded with 128-pound and 32-pound weights (see figure). The tensions t_1 and t_2 in the ropes and the acceleration a of the 32-pound weight are modeled by the system

$$\begin{cases} t_1 - 2t_2 \qquad = 0 \\ t_1 \qquad - 2a = 128 \\ \qquad t_2 + a = 32 \end{cases}$$

where t_1 and t_2 are measured in pounds and a is in feet per second squared. Solve the system.

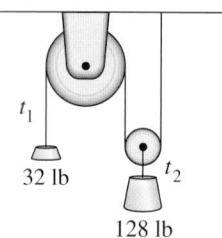

Fitting a Parabola   **In Exercises 95–98, find the least squares regression parabola $y = ax^2 + bx + c$ for the points $(x_1, y_1), (x_2, y_2), \ldots, (x_n, y_n)$ by solving the following system of linear equations for a, b, and c. Then use the *regression* feature of a graphing utility to confirm your result. (For an explanation of how the coefficients of a, b, and c in the system are obtained, see Appendix C.)**

95.
$$\begin{cases} 4c + 40a = 19 \\ 40b = -12 \\ 40c + 544a = 160 \end{cases}$$

96.
$$\begin{cases} 5c + 10a = 8 \\ 10b = 12 \\ 10c + 34a = 22 \end{cases}$$

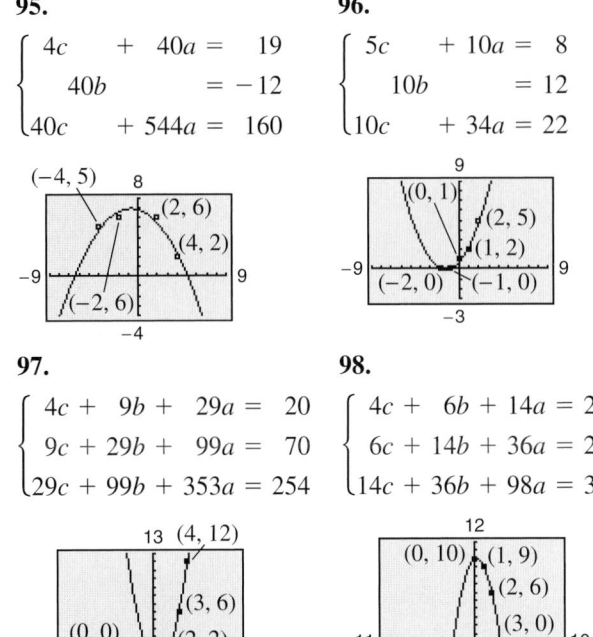

97.
$$\begin{cases} 4c + 9b + 29a = 20 \\ 9c + 29b + 99a = 70 \\ 29c + 99b + 353a = 254 \end{cases}$$

98.
$$\begin{cases} 4c + 6b + 14a = 25 \\ 6c + 14b + 36a = 21 \\ 14c + 36b + 98a = 33 \end{cases}$$

99. *Data Analysis*   During the testing of a new automobile braking system, the speeds x (in miles per hour) and the stopping distances y (in feet) were recorded in the table.

Speed, x	Stopping distance, y
30	55
40	105
50	188

(a) Use the data to create a system of linear equations. Then find the least squares regression parabola for the data by solving the system.

(b) Use a graphing utility to graph the parabola and the data in the same viewing window.

(c) Use the model to estimate the stopping distance for a speed of 70 miles per hour.

100. *Data Analysis*   A wildlife management team studied the reproduction rates of deer in three five-acre tracts of a wildlife preserve. In each tract, the number of females x and the percent of females y that had offspring the following year were recorded. The results are shown in the table.

Number, x	Percent, y
120	68
140	55
160	30

(a) Use the data to create a system of linear equations. Then find the least squares regression parabola for the data by solving the system.

(b) Use a graphing utility to graph the parabola and the data in the same viewing window.

(c) Use the model to predict the percent of females that had offspring when there were 170 females.

101. *Thermodynamics*   The magnitude of the range R of exhaust temperatures (in degrees Fahrenheit) in an experimental diesel engine is approximated by the model

$$R = \frac{2000(4 - 3x)}{(11 - 7x)(7 - 4x)}, \quad 0 \le x \le 1$$

where x is the relative load (in foot-pounds).

(a) Write the partial fraction decomposition for the rational function.

(b) The decomposition in part (a) is the difference of two fractions. The absolute values of the terms give the expected maximum and minimum temperatures of the exhaust gases. Use a graphing utility to graph each term.

102. *Environment*   The predicted cost C (in thousands of dollars) for a company to remove $p\%$ of a chemical from its waste water is given by the model

$$C = \frac{120p}{10,000 - p^2}, \quad 0 \le p < 100.$$

(a) Write the partial fraction decomposition for the rational function.

(b) Verify your result by using the *table* feature of a graphing utility to create a table comparing the original function to the partial fractions.

Synthesis

True or False?   **In Exercises 103–105, determine whether the statement is true or false. Justify your answer.**

103. The system $\begin{cases} x + 4y - 5z = 8 \\ \quad\quad 2y + \ z = 5 \\ \quad\quad\quad\quad z = 1 \end{cases}$ is in row-echelon form.

104. If a system of three linear equations is inconsistent, then its graph has no points common to all three equations.

105. For the rational expression

$$\frac{x}{(x + 10)(x - 10)^2}$$

the partial fraction decomposition is of the form

$$\frac{A}{x + 10} + \frac{B}{(x - 10)^2}.$$

106. *Error Analysis*   You are tutoring a student in algebra. In trying to find a partial fraction decomposition, your student writes the following.

$$\frac{x^2 + 1}{x(x - 1)} = \frac{A}{x} + \frac{B}{x - 1}$$

$$x^2 + 1 = A(x - 1) + Bx \quad \text{Basic equation}$$

$$x^2 + 1 = (A + B)x - A$$

Your student then forms the following system of linear equations.

$$\begin{cases} A + B = 0 \\ -A \quad\quad = 1 \end{cases}$$

Solve the system and check the partial fraction decomposition it yields. Has your student worked the problem correctly? If not, what went wrong?

In Exercises 107–110, write the partial fraction decomposition for the rational expression. Check your result algebraically. Then assign a value to the constant a and check the result graphically.

107. $\dfrac{1}{a^2 - x^2}$

108. $\dfrac{1}{(x + 1)(a - x)}$

109. $\dfrac{1}{y(a - y)}$

110. $\dfrac{1}{x(x + a)}$

111. *Think About It*   Are the two systems of equations equivalent? Give reasons for your answer.

$$\begin{cases} x + 3y - \ z = 6 \\ 2x - \ y + 2z = 1 \\ 3x + 2y - \ z = 2 \end{cases} \quad \begin{cases} x + 3y - \ z = \quad 6 \\ \quad -7y + 4z = \quad 1 \\ \quad -7y - 4z = -16 \end{cases}$$

112. *Writing*   When using Gaussian elimination to solve a system of linear equations, explain how you can recognize that the system has no solution. Give an example that illustrates your answer.

Advanced Applications   **In Exercises 113–116, find values of x, y, and λ that satisfy the system. These systems arise in certain optimization problems in calculus. (λ is called a *Lagrange multiplier*.)**

113. $\begin{cases} y + \lambda = 0 \\ x + \lambda = 0 \\ x + y - 10 = 0 \end{cases}$ **114.** $\begin{cases} 2x + \lambda = 0 \\ 2y + \lambda = 0 \\ x + y - 4 = 0 \end{cases}$

115. $\begin{cases} 2x - 2x\lambda = 0 \\ -2y + \lambda = 0 \\ y - x^2 = 0 \end{cases}$ **116.** $\begin{cases} 2 + 2x + 2\lambda = 0 \\ 2x + 1 + \lambda = 0 \\ 2x + y - 100 = 0 \end{cases}$

Review

In Exercises 117–122, sketch the graph of the function.

117. $f(x) = -3x + 7$ **118.** $f(x) = 6 - x$

119. $f(x) = -2x^2$ **120.** $f(x) = \frac{1}{4}x^2 + 1$

121. $f(x) = -x^2(x - 3)$ **122.** $f(x) = \frac{1}{2}x^3 - 1$

In Exercises 123–126, (a) determine the real zeros of f and (b) sketch the graph of f.

123. $f(x) = x^3 + x^2 - 12x$

124. $f(x) = -8x^4 + 32x^2$

125. $f(x) = 2x^3 + 5x^2 - 21x - 36$

126. $f(x) = 6x^3 - 29x^2 - 6x + 5$

In Exercises 127–130, use a graphing utility to create a table of values for the function. Then sketch the graph of the function by hand.

127. $y = 4^{-x-4} - 5$ **128.** $y = \left(\frac{5}{2}\right)^{x-1} - 4$

129. $y = 2.9^{0.8x} - 3$ **130.** $y = -3.5^{x+2} - 6$

8.4 Matrices and Systems of Equations

Matrices

In this section you will study a streamlined technique for solving systems of linear equations. This technique involves the use of a rectangular array of real numbers called a **matrix.** The plural of matrix is *matrices*.

> ### Definition of Matrix
>
> If m and n are positive integers, an $m \times n$ (read "m by n") matrix is a rectangular array
>
> $$
> \begin{array}{c}
> \quad\text{Column 1}\;\;\text{Column 2}\;\;\text{Column 3}\;\;\cdots\;\;\text{Column } n \\
> \begin{array}{l}
> \text{Row 1} \\
> \text{Row 2} \\
> \text{Row 3} \\
> \vdots \\
> \text{Row } m
> \end{array}
> \left[
> \begin{array}{ccccc}
> a_{11} & a_{12} & a_{13} & \cdots & a_{1n} \\
> a_{21} & a_{22} & a_{23} & \cdots & a_{2n} \\
> a_{31} & a_{32} & a_{33} & \cdots & a_{3n} \\
> \vdots & \vdots & \vdots & & \vdots \\
> a_{m1} & a_{m2} & a_{m3} & \cdots & a_{mn}
> \end{array}
> \right]
> \end{array}
> $$
>
> in which each **entry** a_{ij} of the matrix is a real number. An $m \times n$ matrix has m rows and n columns.

The entry in the ith row and jth column is denoted by the *double subscript* notation a_{ij}. For instance, the entry a_{23} is the entry in the second row and third column. A matrix having m rows and n columns is said to be of **order** $m \times n$. If $m = n$, the matrix is **square** of order n. For a square matrix, the entries $a_{11}, a_{22}, a_{33}, \ldots$ are the **main diagonal** entries.

Example 1   Order of Matrices

Determine the order of each matrix.

a. $\begin{bmatrix} 2 \end{bmatrix}$ **b.** $\begin{bmatrix} 1 & -3 & 0 & \frac{1}{2} \end{bmatrix}$ **c.** $\begin{bmatrix} 0 & 0 \\ 0 & 0 \end{bmatrix}$ **d.** $\begin{bmatrix} 5 & 0 \\ 2 & -2 \\ -7 & 4 \end{bmatrix}$

Solution

a. This matrix has *one* row and *one* column. The order of the matrix is 1×1.

b. This matrix has *one* row and *four* columns. The order of the matrix is 1×4.

c. This matrix has *two* rows and *two* columns. The order of the matrix is 2×2.

d. This matrix has *three* rows and *two* columns. The order of the matrix is 3×2.

✓ *Checkpoint* Now try Exercise 3.

A matrix that has only one row [such as the matrix in Example 1(b)] is called a **row matrix,** and a matrix that has only one column is called a **column matrix.**

What you should learn

- Write matrices and identify their orders.
- Perform elementary row operations on matrices.
- Use matrices and Gaussian elimination to solve systems of linear equations.
- Use matrices and Gauss-Jordan elimination to solve systems of linear equations.

Why you should learn it

Matrices can be used to solve systems of linear equations in two or more variables. For instance, Exercise 76 on page 642 shows how a matrix can be used to help find a model for the parabolic path of a baseball.

Michael Steele/Getty Images

A matrix derived from a system of linear equations (each written in standard form with the constant term on the right) is the **augmented matrix** of the system. Moreover, the matrix derived from the coefficients of the system (but not including the constant terms) is the **coefficient matrix** of the system.

System
$$\begin{cases} x - 4y + 3z = 5 \\ -x + 3y - z = -3 \\ 2x - 4z = 6 \end{cases}$$

Augmented Matrix
$$\begin{bmatrix} 1 & -4 & 3 & \vdots & 5 \\ -1 & 3 & -1 & \vdots & -3 \\ 2 & 0 & -4 & \vdots & 6 \end{bmatrix}$$

Coefficient Matrix
$$\begin{bmatrix} 1 & -4 & 3 \\ -1 & 3 & -1 \\ 2 & 0 & -4 \end{bmatrix}$$

Note the use of 0 for the missing coefficient of the y-variable in the third equation, and also note the fourth column (of constant terms) in the augmented matrix. The optional dotted line in the augmented matrix helps to separate the coefficients of the linear system from the constant terms.

When forming either the coefficient matrix or the augmented matrix of a system, you should begin by vertically aligning the variables in the equations and using 0's for any missing coefficients of variables.

Example 2   Writing an Augmented Matrix

Write the augmented matrix for the system of linear equations.

$$\begin{cases} x + 3y = 9 \\ -y + 4z = -2 \\ x - 5z = 0 \end{cases}$$

Solution

Begin by writing the linear system and aligning the variables.

$$\begin{cases} x + 3y = 9 \\ -y + 4z = -2 \\ x - 5z = 0 \end{cases}$$

Next, use the coefficients and constant terms as the matrix entries. Include zeros for each missing coefficient.

$$\begin{matrix} R_1 \\ R_2 \\ R_3 \end{matrix} \begin{bmatrix} 1 & 3 & 0 & \vdots & 9 \\ 0 & -1 & 4 & \vdots & -2 \\ 1 & 0 & -5 & \vdots & 0 \end{bmatrix}$$

The notation R_n is used to designate each row in the matrix. For example, Row 1 is represented by R_1.

✓ *Checkpoint* Now try Exercise 7.

Elementary Row Operations

In Section 8.3, you studied three operations that can be used on a system of linear equations to produce an equivalent system. These operations are: interchange two equations, multiply an equation by a nonzero constant, and add a multiple of an equation to another equation. In matrix terminology these three operations correspond to **elementary row operations.** An elementary row operation on an augmented matrix of a given system of linear equations produces a new augmented matrix corresponding to a new (but equivalent) system of linear equations. Two matrices are **row-equivalent** if one can be obtained from the other by a sequence of elementary row operations.

Elementary Row Operations

1. Interchange two rows.

2. Multiply a row by a nonzero constant.

3. Add a multiple of a row to another row.

Although elementary row operations are simple to perform, they involve a lot of arithmetic. Because it is easy to make a mistake, you should get in the habit of noting the elementary row operations performed in each step so that you can go back and check your work.

Example 3 demonstrates the elementary row operations described above.

Example 3   Elementary Row Operations

a. Interchange the first and second rows of the original matrix.

Original Matrix

$$\begin{bmatrix} 0 & 1 & 3 & 4 \\ -1 & 2 & 0 & 3 \\ 2 & -3 & 4 & 1 \end{bmatrix}$$

New Row-Equivalent Matrix

$$\begin{matrix} R_2 \\ R_1 \end{matrix} \begin{bmatrix} -1 & 2 & 0 & 3 \\ 0 & 1 & 3 & 4 \\ 2 & -3 & 4 & 1 \end{bmatrix}$$

b. Multiply the first row of the original matrix by $\frac{1}{2}$.

Original Matrix

$$\begin{bmatrix} 2 & -4 & 6 & -2 \\ 1 & 3 & -3 & 0 \\ 5 & -2 & 1 & 2 \end{bmatrix}$$

New Row-Equivalent Matrix

$$\frac{1}{2}R_1 \rightarrow \begin{bmatrix} 1 & -2 & 3 & -1 \\ 1 & 3 & -3 & 0 \\ 5 & -2 & 1 & 2 \end{bmatrix}$$

c. Add -2 times the first row of the original matrix to the third row.

Original Matrix

$$\begin{bmatrix} 1 & 2 & -4 & 3 \\ 0 & 3 & -2 & -1 \\ 2 & 1 & 5 & -2 \end{bmatrix}$$

New Row-Equivalent Matrix

$$-2R_1 + R_3 \rightarrow \begin{bmatrix} 1 & 2 & -4 & 3 \\ 0 & 3 & -2 & -1 \\ 0 & -3 & 13 & -8 \end{bmatrix}$$

Note that the elementary row operation is written beside the row that is *changed.*

✓ *Checkpoint* Now try Exercise 21.

TECHNOLOGY TIP

Most graphing utilities can perform elementary row operations on matrices. The top screen below shows how one graphing utility displays the original matrix in Example 3(a). The bottom screen below shows the new row-equivalent matrix in Example 3(a). The new row-equivalent matrix is obtained by using the *row swap* feature of the graphing utility. For instructions on how to use the *matrix* feature and the *row swap* feature (and other elementary row operations features) of a graphing utlity, see Appendix A; for specific keystrokes, go to the text website at *college.hmco.com.*

```
[A]
   [[0   1   3  4]
    [-1  2   0  3]
    [2  -3   4  1]]
```

```
rowSwap([A],1,2)
   [[-1  2   0  3]
    [0   1   3  4]
    [2  -3   4  1]]
```

Gaussian Elimination with Back Substitution

In Example 2 of Section 8.3, you used Gaussian elimination with back-substitution to solve a system of linear equations. The next example demonstrates the matrix version of Gaussian elimination. The two methods are essentially the same. The basic difference is that with matrices you do not need to keep writing the variables.

Example 4   Comparing Linear Systems and Matrix Operations

Linear System

$$\begin{cases} x - 2y + 3z = 9 \\ -x + 3y = -4 \\ 2x - 5y + 5z = 17 \end{cases}$$

Associated Augmented Matrix

$$\left[\begin{array}{ccc:c} 1 & -2 & 3 & 9 \\ -1 & 3 & 0 & -4 \\ 2 & -5 & 5 & 17 \end{array} \right]$$

Add the first equation to the second equation.

$$\begin{cases} x - 2y + 3z = 9 \\ y + 3z = 5 \\ 2x - 5y + 5z = 17 \end{cases}$$

Add the first row to the second row $(R_1 + R_2)$.

$$R_1 + R_2 \rightarrow \left[\begin{array}{ccc:c} 1 & -2 & 3 & 9 \\ 0 & 1 & 3 & 5 \\ 2 & -5 & 5 & 17 \end{array} \right]$$

Add -2 times the first equation to the third equation.

$$\begin{cases} x - 2y + 3z = 9 \\ y + 3z = 5 \\ -y - z = -1 \end{cases}$$

Add -2 times the first row to the third row $(-2R_1 + R_3)$.

$$-2R_1 + R_3 \rightarrow \left[\begin{array}{ccc:c} 1 & -2 & 3 & 9 \\ 0 & 1 & 3 & 5 \\ 0 & -1 & -1 & -1 \end{array} \right]$$

Add the second equation to the third equation.

$$\begin{cases} x - 2y + 3z = 9 \\ y + 3z = 5 \\ 2z = 4 \end{cases}$$

Add the second row to the third row $(R_2 + R_3)$.

$$R_2 + R_3 \rightarrow \left[\begin{array}{ccc:c} 1 & -2 & 3 & 9 \\ 0 & 1 & 3 & 5 \\ 0 & 0 & 2 & 4 \end{array} \right]$$

Multiply the third equation by $\frac{1}{2}$.

$$\begin{cases} x - 2y + 3z = 9 \\ y + 3z = 5 \\ z = 2 \end{cases}$$

Multiply the third row by $\frac{1}{2}$.

$$\tfrac{1}{2}R_3 \rightarrow \left[\begin{array}{ccc:c} 1 & -2 & 3 & 9 \\ 0 & 1 & 3 & 5 \\ 0 & 0 & 1 & 2 \end{array} \right]$$

At this point, you can use back-substitution to find that the solution is $x = 1$, $y = -1$, and $z = 2$, as was done in Example 2 of Section 8.3.

Remember that you should check a solution by substituting the values of x, y, and z into each equation in the original system.

The last matrix in Example 4 is in **row-echelon form.** The term *echelon* refers to the stair-step pattern formed by the nonzero elements of the matrix. To be in this form, a matrix must have the properties listed on the next page.

> **Row-Echelon Form and Reduced Row-Echelon Form**
>
> A matrix in **row-echelon form** has the following properties.
>
> 1. Any rows consisting entirely of zeros occur at the bottom of the matrix.
>
> 2. For each row that does not consist entirely of zeros, the first nonzero entry is 1 (called a **leading 1**).
>
> 3. For two successive (nonzero) rows, the leading 1 in the higher row is farther to the left than the leading 1 in the lower row.
>
> A matrix in *row-echelon form* is in **reduced row-echelon form** if every column that has a leading 1 has zeros in every position above and below its leading 1.

It is worth mentioning that the row-echelon form of a matrix is not unique. That is, two different sequences of elementary row operations may yield different row-echelon forms.

Example 5   Row-Echelon Form

Determine whether each matrix is in row-echelon form. If it is, determine whether the matrix is in reduced row-echelon form.

a. $\begin{bmatrix} 1 & 2 & -1 & 4 \\ 0 & 1 & 0 & 3 \\ 0 & 0 & 1 & -2 \end{bmatrix}$ **b.** $\begin{bmatrix} 1 & 2 & -1 & 2 \\ 0 & 0 & 0 & 0 \\ 0 & 1 & 2 & -4 \end{bmatrix}$

c. $\begin{bmatrix} 1 & -5 & 2 & -1 & 3 \\ 0 & 0 & 1 & 3 & -2 \\ 0 & 0 & 0 & 1 & 4 \\ 0 & 0 & 0 & 0 & 1 \end{bmatrix}$ **d.** $\begin{bmatrix} 1 & 0 & 0 & -1 \\ 0 & 1 & 0 & 2 \\ 0 & 0 & 1 & 3 \\ 0 & 0 & 0 & 0 \end{bmatrix}$

e. $\begin{bmatrix} 1 & 2 & -3 & 4 \\ 0 & 2 & 1 & -1 \\ 0 & 0 & 1 & -3 \end{bmatrix}$ **f.** $\begin{bmatrix} 0 & 1 & 0 & 5 \\ 0 & 0 & 1 & 3 \\ 0 & 0 & 0 & 0 \end{bmatrix}$

Solution

The matrices in (a), (c), (d), and (f) are in row-echelon form. The matrices in (d) and (f) are in *reduced* row-echelon form because every column that has a leading 1 has zeros in every position above and below its leading 1. The matrix in (b) is not in row-echelon form because a row of all zeros does not occur at the bottom of the matrix. The matrix in (e) is not in row-echelon form because the first nonzero entry in row 2 is not a leading 1.

 *Checkpoint* Now try Exercise 23.

Every matrix is row-equivalent to a matrix in row-echelon form. For instance, in Example 5, you can change the matrix in part (e) to row-echelon form by multiplying its second row by $\frac{1}{2}$. What elementary row operation could you perform on the matrix in part (b) so that it would be in row-echelon form?

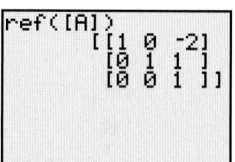

Gaussian elimination with back-substitution works well for solving systems of linear equations by hand or with a computer. For this algorithm, the order in which the elementary row operations are performed is important. You should operate *from left to right by columns*, using elementary row operations to obtain zeros in all entries directly below the leading 1's.

Example 6 Gaussian Elimination with Back-Substitution

Solve the system $\begin{cases} y + z - 2w = -3 \\ x + 2y - z = 2 \\ 2x + 4y + z - 3w = -2 \\ x - 4y - 7z - w = -19 \end{cases}$.

Solution

$$\begin{bmatrix} 0 & 1 & 1 & -2 & \vdots & -3 \\ 1 & 2 & -1 & 0 & \vdots & 2 \\ 2 & 4 & 1 & -3 & \vdots & -2 \\ 1 & -4 & -7 & -1 & \vdots & -19 \end{bmatrix}$$ Write augmented matrix.

$$\begin{matrix} R_2 \\ R_1 \end{matrix}\begin{bmatrix} 1 & 2 & -1 & 0 & \vdots & 2 \\ 0 & 1 & 1 & -2 & \vdots & -3 \\ 2 & 4 & 1 & -3 & \vdots & -2 \\ 1 & -4 & -7 & -1 & \vdots & -19 \end{bmatrix}$$ Interchange R_1 and R_2 so first column has leading 1 in upper left corner.

$$\begin{matrix} \\ \\ -2R_1 + R_3 \rightarrow \\ -R_1 + R_4 \rightarrow \end{matrix}\begin{bmatrix} 1 & 2 & -1 & 0 & \vdots & 2 \\ 0 & 1 & 1 & -2 & \vdots & -3 \\ 0 & 0 & 3 & -3 & \vdots & -6 \\ 0 & -6 & -6 & -1 & \vdots & -21 \end{bmatrix}$$ Perform operations on R_3 and R_4 so first column has zeros below its leading 1.

$$\begin{matrix} \\ \\ \\ 6R_2 + R_4 \rightarrow \end{matrix}\begin{bmatrix} 1 & 2 & -1 & 0 & \vdots & 2 \\ 0 & 1 & 1 & -2 & \vdots & -3 \\ 0 & 0 & 3 & -3 & \vdots & -6 \\ 0 & 0 & 0 & -13 & \vdots & -39 \end{bmatrix}$$ Perform operations on R_4 so second column has zeros below its leading 1.

$$\begin{matrix} \\ \\ \frac{1}{3}R_3 \rightarrow \\ -\frac{1}{13}R_4 \rightarrow \end{matrix}\begin{bmatrix} 1 & 2 & -1 & 0 & \vdots & 2 \\ 0 & 1 & 1 & -2 & \vdots & -3 \\ 0 & 0 & 1 & -1 & \vdots & -2 \\ 0 & 0 & 0 & 1 & \vdots & 3 \end{bmatrix}$$ Perform operations on R_3 and R_4 so third and fourth columns have leading 1's.

The matrix is now in row-echelon form, and the corresponding system is

$$\begin{cases} x + 2y - z = 2 \\ y + z - 2w = -3 \\ z - w = -2 \\ w = 3 \end{cases}.$$

Using back-substitution, you can determine that the solution is $x = -1$, $y = 2$, $z = 1$, and $w = 3$. Check this in the original system of equations.

✓ *Checkpoint* Now try Exercise 47.

The following steps summarize the procedure used in Example 6.

Gaussian Elimination with Back–Substitution

1. Write the augmented matrix of the system of linear equations.

2. Use elementary row operations to rewrite the augmented matrix in row-echelon form.

3. Write the system of linear equations corresponding to the matrix in row-echelon form and use back-substitution to find the solution.

Remember that it is possible for a system to have no solution. If, in the elimination process, you obtain a row with zeros except for the last entry, you can conclude that the system is inconsistent.

Example 7   A System with No Solution

Solve the system $\begin{cases} x - y + 2z = 4 \\ x \qquad + z = 6 \\ 2x - 3y + 5z = 4 \\ 3x + 2y - z = 1 \end{cases}$.

Solution

$$\begin{bmatrix} 1 & -1 & 2 & \vdots & 4 \\ 1 & 0 & 1 & \vdots & 6 \\ 2 & -3 & 5 & \vdots & 4 \\ 3 & 2 & -1 & \vdots & 1 \end{bmatrix}$$ Write augmented matrix.

$$\begin{array}{c} \\ -R_1 + R_2 \to \\ -2R_1 + R_3 \to \\ -3R_1 + R_4 \to \end{array} \begin{bmatrix} 1 & -1 & 2 & \vdots & 4 \\ 0 & 1 & -1 & \vdots & 2 \\ 0 & -1 & 1 & \vdots & -4 \\ 0 & 5 & -7 & \vdots & -11 \end{bmatrix}$$ Perform row operations.

$$\begin{array}{c} \\ \\ R_2 + R_3 \to \\ \\ \end{array} \begin{bmatrix} 1 & -1 & 2 & \vdots & 4 \\ 0 & 1 & -1 & \vdots & 2 \\ 0 & 0 & 0 & \vdots & -2 \\ 0 & 5 & -7 & \vdots & -11 \end{bmatrix}$$ Perform row operations.

Note that the third row of this matrix consists of zeros except for the last entry. This means that the original system of linear equations is *inconsistent*. You can see why this is true by converting back to a system of linear equations. Because the third equation is not possible, the system has no solution.

$$\begin{cases} x - y + 2z = 4 \\ y - z = 2 \\ 0 = -2 \\ 5y - 7z = -11 \end{cases}$$

✓ *Checkpoint* Now try Exercise 49.

Gauss–Jordan Elimination

With Gaussian elimination, elementary row operations are applied to a matrix to obtain a (row-equivalent) row-echelon form of the matrix. A second method of elimination, called **Gauss-Jordan elimination** after Carl Friedrich Gauss (1777–1855) and Wilhelm Jordan (1842–1899), continues the reduction process until a *reduced* row-echelon form is obtained. This procedure is demonstrated in Example 8.

Example 8   Gauss–Jordan Elimination

Use Gauss-Jordan elimination to solve the system.

$$\begin{cases} x - 2y + 3z = 9 \\ -x + 3y = -4 \\ 2x - 5y + 5z = 17 \end{cases}$$

Solution

In Example 4, Gaussian elimination was used to obtain the row-echelon form

$$\begin{bmatrix} 1 & -2 & 3 & \vdots & 9 \\ 0 & 1 & 3 & \vdots & 5 \\ 0 & 0 & 1 & \vdots & 2 \end{bmatrix}.$$

Now, rather than using back-substitution, apply additional elementary row operations until you obtain a matrix in *reduced* row-echelon form. To do this, you must produce zeros above each of the leading 1's, as follows.

$$\begin{array}{c} 2R_2 + R_1 \rightarrow \\ \\ \\ \end{array} \begin{bmatrix} 1 & 0 & 9 & \vdots & 19 \\ 0 & 1 & 3 & \vdots & 5 \\ 0 & 0 & 1 & \vdots & 2 \end{bmatrix}$$

Perform operations on R_1 so second column has a zero above its leading 1.

$$\begin{array}{c} -9R_3 + R_1 \rightarrow \\ -3R_3 + R_2 \rightarrow \\ \\ \end{array} \begin{bmatrix} 1 & 0 & 0 & \vdots & 1 \\ 0 & 1 & 0 & \vdots & -1 \\ 0 & 0 & 1 & \vdots & 2 \end{bmatrix}$$

Perform operations on R_1 and R_2 so third column has zeros above its leading 1.

The matrix is now in reduced row-echelon form. Converting back to a system of linear equations, you have

$$\begin{cases} x = 1 \\ y = -1 \\ z = 2 \end{cases}$$

which is the same solution that was obtained using Gaussian elimination.

✓ *Checkpoint* Now try Exercise 55.

The beauty of Gauss-Jordan elimination is that, from the reduced row-echelon form, you can simply read the solution. Which technique do you prefer: Gaussian elimination or Gauss-Jordan elimination?

TECHNOLOGY TIP

For a demonstration of a graphical approach to Gauss-Jordan elimination on a 2×3 matrix, see the Visualizing Row Operations Program, available for several models of graphing calculators at our website *college.hmco.com.*

The elimination procedures described in this section employ an algorithmic approach that is easily adapted to computer programs. However, the procedure makes no effort to avoid fractional coefficients. For instance, in the elimination procedure for the system

$$\begin{cases} 2x - 5y + 5z = 17 \\ 3x - 2y + 3z = 11 \\ -3x + 3y \quad\quad = -6 \end{cases}$$

you may be inclined to multiply the first row by $\frac{1}{2}$ to produce a leading 1, which will result in working with fractional coefficients. For hand computations, you can sometimes avoid fractions by judiciously choosing the order in which you apply elementary row operations.

Example 9   A System with an Infinite Number of Solutions

Solve the system $\begin{cases} 2x + 4y - 2z = 0 \\ 3x + 5y \quad\quad = 1 \end{cases}$.

Solution

$$\begin{bmatrix} 2 & 4 & -2 & \vdots & 0 \\ 3 & 5 & 0 & \vdots & 1 \end{bmatrix} \quad \frac{1}{2}R_1 \rightarrow \begin{bmatrix} 1 & 2 & -1 & \vdots & 0 \\ 3 & 5 & 0 & \vdots & 1 \end{bmatrix}$$

$$-3R_1 + R_2 \rightarrow \begin{bmatrix} 1 & 2 & -1 & \vdots & 0 \\ 0 & -1 & 3 & \vdots & 1 \end{bmatrix}$$

$$-R_2 \rightarrow \begin{bmatrix} 1 & 2 & -1 & \vdots & 0 \\ 0 & 1 & -3 & \vdots & -1 \end{bmatrix}$$

$$-2R_2 + R_1 \rightarrow \begin{bmatrix} 1 & 0 & 5 & \vdots & 2 \\ 0 & 1 & -3 & \vdots & -1 \end{bmatrix}$$

The corresponding system of equations is

$$\begin{cases} x + 5z = 2 \\ y - 3z = -1 \end{cases}.$$

Solving for x and y in terms of z, you have $x = -5z + 2$ and $y = 3z - 1$. To write a solution of the system that does not use any of the three variables of the system, let a represent any real number and let $z = a$. Now substitute a for z in the equations for x and y.

$$x = -5z + 2 = -5a + 2$$

$$y = 3z - 1 = 3a - 1$$

So, the solution set has the form

$$(-5a + 2, 3a - 1, a).$$

Recall from Section 8.3 that a solution set of this form represents an infinite number of solutions. Try substituting values for a to obtain a few solutions. Then check each solution in the original system of equations.

 Checkpoint Now try Exercise 57.

Example 10 Analysis of a Network

Set up a system of linear equations representing the network shown in Figure 8.26. In a network, it is assumed that the total flow into a junction (blue circle) is equal to the total flow out of the junction.

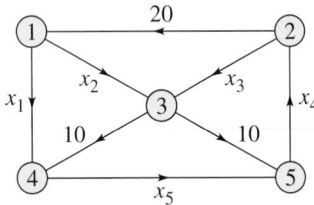

Figure 8.26

Solution

Because Junction 1 in Figure 8.26 has 20 units flowing into it, there must be 20 units flowing out of it. This is represented by the linear equation $x_1 + x_2 = 20$. Because Junction 2 has 20 units flowing out of it, there must be 20 units flowing into it. This is represented by $x_4 - x_3 = 20$ or $-x_3 + x_4 = 20$. A linear equation can be written for each of the network's five junctions, so the network is modeled by the following system.

$$
\begin{cases}
x_1 + x_2 & = 20 & \text{Junction 1} \\
-x_3 + x_4 & = 20 & \text{Junction 2} \\
x_2 + x_3 & = 20 & \text{Junction 3} \\
-x_1 \qquad\qquad + x_5 & = 10 & \text{Junction 4} \\
x_4 - x_5 & = 10 & \text{Junction 5}
\end{cases}
$$

Using Gauss-Jordan elimination on the augmented matrix produces the matrix in reduced row-echelon form.

Augmented Matrix

$$
\begin{bmatrix}
1 & 1 & 0 & 0 & 0 & \vdots & 20 \\
0 & 0 & -1 & 1 & 0 & \vdots & 20 \\
0 & 1 & 1 & 0 & 0 & \vdots & 20 \\
-1 & 0 & 0 & 0 & 1 & \vdots & 10 \\
0 & 0 & 0 & 1 & -1 & \vdots & 10
\end{bmatrix}
$$

Matrix in Reduced Row-Echelon Form

$$
\begin{bmatrix}
1 & 0 & 0 & 0 & -1 & \vdots & -10 \\
0 & 1 & 0 & 0 & 1 & \vdots & 30 \\
0 & 0 & 1 & 0 & -1 & \vdots & -10 \\
0 & 0 & 0 & 1 & -1 & \vdots & 10 \\
0 & 0 & 0 & 0 & 0 & \vdots & 0
\end{bmatrix}
$$

Letting $x_5 = t$, where t is a real number, you have $x_1 = t - 10$, $x_2 = -t + 30$, $x_3 = t - 10$, and $x_4 = t + 10$. So, this system has an infinite number of solutions.

✓ *Checkpoint* Now try Exercise 79.

8.4 Exercises

Vocabulary Check

Fill in the blanks.

1. A rectangular array of real numbers that can be used to solve a system of linear equations is called a _____ .

2. A matrix is _____ if the number of rows equals the number of columns.

3. A matrix with only one row is called a _____ and a matrix with only one column is called a _____ .

4. The matrix derived from a system of linear equations is called the _____ of the system.

5. The matrix derived from the coefficients of a system of linear equations is called the _____ of the system.

6. Two matrices are called _____ if one of the matrices can be obtained from the other by a sequence of elementary row operations.

7. A matrix in row-echelon form is in _____ if every column that has a leading 1 has zeros in every position above and below its leading one.

8. The process of using row operations to write a matrix in reduced row-echelon form is called _____ .

In Exercises 1–6, determine the order of the matrix.

1. $\begin{bmatrix} 7 & 0 \end{bmatrix}$

2. $\begin{bmatrix} 6 & -3 & 10 & 8 \end{bmatrix}$

3. $\begin{bmatrix} 4 \\ 32 \\ 3 \end{bmatrix}$

4. $\begin{bmatrix} -3 & 7 & 15 & 0 \\ 0 & 0 & 3 & 3 \\ 1 & 1 & 6 & 7 \end{bmatrix}$

5. $\begin{bmatrix} 33 & 45 \\ -9 & 20 \end{bmatrix}$

6. $\begin{bmatrix} 3 & -1 & 4 \\ 6 & 0 & -5 \end{bmatrix}$

In Exercises 7–10, write the augmented matrix for the system of linear equations.

7. $\begin{cases} 4x - 5y = 33 \\ -x + 5y = -27 \end{cases}$

8. $\begin{cases} 7x + 4y = 22 \\ 5x - 9y = 15 \end{cases}$

9. $\begin{cases} x + 10y - 2z = 2 \\ 5x - 3y + 4z = 0 \\ 2x + y = 6 \end{cases}$

10. $\begin{cases} x - 3y + z = 1 \\ 4y = 0 \\ 7z = -5 \end{cases}$

In Exercises 11–14, write the system of linear equations represented by the augmented matrix. (Use the variables x, y, z, and w if applicable.)

11. $\left[\begin{array}{cc:c} 1 & 2 & 7 \\ 2 & -3 & 4 \end{array}\right]$

12. $\left[\begin{array}{cc:c} 7 & -5 & 0 \\ 8 & 3 & -2 \end{array}\right]$

13. $\left[\begin{array}{ccc:c} 9 & 12 & 3 & 0 \\ -2 & 18 & 5 & 10 \\ 1 & 7 & -8 & -4 \end{array}\right]$

14. $\left[\begin{array}{cccc:c} 6 & 2 & -1 & -5 & -25 \\ -1 & 0 & 7 & 3 & 7 \\ 4 & -1 & -10 & 6 & 23 \\ 0 & 8 & 1 & -11 & -21 \end{array}\right]$

In Exercises 15–18, fill in the blanks using elementary row operations to form a row-equivalent matrix.

15. $\begin{bmatrix} 1 & 4 & 3 \\ 2 & 10 & 5 \end{bmatrix}$

   $\begin{bmatrix} 1 & 4 & 3 \\ 0 & & -1 \end{bmatrix}$

16. $\begin{bmatrix} 3 & 6 & 8 \\ 4 & -3 & 6 \end{bmatrix}$

   $\begin{bmatrix} 1 & & \frac{8}{3} \\ 4 & -3 & 6 \end{bmatrix}$

17. $\begin{bmatrix} 1 & 1 & 4 & -1 \\ 3 & 8 & 10 & 3 \\ -2 & 1 & 12 & 6 \end{bmatrix}$

   $\begin{bmatrix} 1 & 1 & 4 & -1 \\ 0 & 5 & & \\ 0 & 3 & & \end{bmatrix}$

   $\begin{bmatrix} 1 & 1 & 4 & -1 \\ 0 & 1 & -\frac{2}{5} & \frac{6}{5} \\ 0 & 3 & & \end{bmatrix}$

18. $\begin{bmatrix} 2 & 4 & 8 & 3 \\ 1 & -1 & -3 & 2 \\ 2 & 6 & 4 & 9 \end{bmatrix}$

   $\begin{bmatrix} 1 & & & \\ 1 & -1 & -3 & 2 \\ 2 & 6 & 4 & 9 \end{bmatrix}$

   $\begin{bmatrix} 1 & 2 & 4 & \frac{3}{2} \\ 0 & & -7 & \frac{1}{2} \\ 0 & 2 & & \end{bmatrix}$

In Exercises 19–22, identify the elementary row operation performed to obtain the new row-equivalent matrix.

Original Matrix   *New Row-Equivalent Matrix*

19. $\begin{bmatrix} -2 & 5 & 1 \\ 3 & -1 & -8 \end{bmatrix}$ $\begin{bmatrix} 13 & 0 & -39 \\ 3 & -1 & -8 \end{bmatrix}$

Original Matrix   *New Row-Equivalent Matrix*

20. $\begin{bmatrix} 3 & -1 & -4 \\ -4 & 3 & 7 \end{bmatrix}$ $\begin{bmatrix} 3 & -1 & -4 \\ 5 & 0 & -5 \end{bmatrix}$

Original Matrix   *New Row-Equivalent Matrix*

21. $\begin{bmatrix} 0 & -1 & -5 & 5 \\ -1 & 3 & -7 & 6 \\ 4 & -5 & 1 & 3 \end{bmatrix}$ $\begin{bmatrix} -1 & 3 & -7 & 6 \\ 0 & -1 & -5 & 5 \\ 4 & -5 & 1 & 3 \end{bmatrix}$

Original Matrix   *New Row-Equivalent Matrix*

22. $\begin{bmatrix} -1 & -2 & 3 & -2 \\ 2 & -5 & 1 & -7 \\ 5 & 4 & -7 & 6 \end{bmatrix}$ $\begin{bmatrix} -1 & -2 & 3 & -2 \\ 2 & -5 & 1 & -7 \\ 0 & -6 & 8 & -4 \end{bmatrix}$

In Exercises 23–26, determine whether the matrix is in row-echelon form. If it is, determine if it is also in reduced row-echelon form.

23. $\begin{bmatrix} 1 & 0 & 0 & 0 \\ 0 & 1 & 1 & 5 \\ 0 & 0 & 0 & 0 \end{bmatrix}$ **24.** $\begin{bmatrix} 1 & 3 & 0 & 0 \\ 0 & 0 & 1 & 8 \\ 0 & 0 & 0 & 0 \end{bmatrix}$

25. $\begin{bmatrix} 2 & 0 & 4 & 0 \\ 0 & -1 & 3 & 6 \\ 0 & 0 & 1 & 5 \end{bmatrix}$ **26.** $\begin{bmatrix} 1 & 0 & 2 & 1 \\ 0 & 1 & -3 & 10 \\ 0 & 0 & 1 & 0 \end{bmatrix}$

27. Perform the sequence of row operations on the matrix. What did the operations accomplish?

$$\begin{bmatrix} 1 & 2 & 3 \\ 2 & -1 & -4 \\ 3 & 1 & -1 \end{bmatrix}$$

(a) Add -2 times R_1 to R_2.

(b) Add -3 times R_1 to R_3.

(c) Add -1 times R_2 to R_3.

(d) Multiply R_2 by $-\frac{1}{5}$.

(e) Add -2 times R_2 to R_1.

28. Perform the sequence of row operations on the matrix. What did the operations accomplish?

$$\begin{bmatrix} 7 & 1 \\ 0 & 2 \\ -3 & 4 \\ 4 & 1 \end{bmatrix}$$

(a) Add R_3 to R_4.

(b) Interchange R_1 and R_4.

(c) Add 3 times R_1 to R_3.

(d) Add -7 times R_1 to R_4.

(e) Multiply R_2 by $\frac{1}{2}$.

(f) Add the appropriate multiples of R_2 to R_1, R_3, and R_4.

29. Repeat steps (a) through (e) in Exercise 27 using a graphing utility.

30. Repeat steps (a) through (f) in Exercise 28 using a graphing utility.

In Exercises 31–34, write the matrix in row-echelon form. Remember that the row-echelon form of a matrix is not unique.

31. $\begin{bmatrix} 1 & 1 & 0 & 5 \\ -2 & -1 & 2 & -10 \\ 3 & 6 & 7 & 14 \end{bmatrix}$

32. $\begin{bmatrix} 1 & 2 & -1 & 3 \\ 3 & 7 & -5 & 14 \\ -2 & -1 & -3 & 8 \end{bmatrix}$

33. $\begin{bmatrix} 1 & -1 & -1 & 1 \\ 5 & -4 & 1 & 8 \\ -6 & 8 & 18 & 0 \end{bmatrix}$

34. $\begin{bmatrix} 1 & -3 & 0 & -7 \\ -3 & 10 & 1 & 23 \\ 4 & -10 & 2 & -24 \end{bmatrix}$

In Exercises 35–38, use the matrix capabilities of a graphing utility to write the matrix in reduced row-echelon form.

35. $\begin{bmatrix} 3 & 3 & 3 \\ -1 & 0 & -4 \\ 2 & 4 & -2 \end{bmatrix}$ **36.** $\begin{bmatrix} 1 & 3 & 2 \\ 5 & 15 & 9 \\ 2 & 6 & 10 \end{bmatrix}$

37. $\begin{bmatrix} -3 & 5 & 1 & 12 \\ 1 & -1 & 1 & 4 \end{bmatrix}$

38. $\begin{bmatrix} 5 & 1 & 2 & 4 \\ -1 & 5 & 10 & -32 \end{bmatrix}$

In Exercises 39–42, write the system of linear equations represented by the augmented matrix. Then use back-substitution to find the solution. (Use the variables x, y, and z, if applicable.)

39. $\begin{bmatrix} 1 & -2 & \vdots & 4 \\ 0 & 1 & \vdots & -3 \end{bmatrix}$ **40.** $\begin{bmatrix} 1 & 5 & \vdots & 0 \\ 0 & 1 & \vdots & -1 \end{bmatrix}$

41. $\begin{bmatrix} 1 & -1 & 2 & \vdots & 4 \\ 0 & 1 & -1 & \vdots & 2 \\ 0 & 0 & 1 & \vdots & -2 \end{bmatrix}$

42. $\begin{bmatrix} 1 & 2 & -2 & \vdots & -1 \\ 0 & 1 & 1 & \vdots & 9 \\ 0 & 0 & 1 & \vdots & -3 \end{bmatrix}$

In Exercises 43–46, an augmented matrix that represents a system of linear equations (in the variables x and y or x, y, and z) has been reduced using Gauss-Jordan elimination. Write the solution represented by the augmented matrix.

43. $\begin{bmatrix} 1 & 0 & \vdots & 7 \\ 0 & 1 & \vdots & -5 \end{bmatrix}$ **44.** $\begin{bmatrix} 1 & 0 & \vdots & -2 \\ 0 & 1 & \vdots & 4 \end{bmatrix}$

45. $\begin{bmatrix} 1 & 0 & 0 & \vdots & -4 \\ 0 & 1 & 0 & \vdots & -8 \\ 0 & 0 & 1 & \vdots & 2 \end{bmatrix}$

46. $\begin{bmatrix} 1 & 0 & 0 & \vdots & 3 \\ 0 & 1 & 0 & \vdots & -1 \\ 0 & 0 & 1 & \vdots & 0 \end{bmatrix}$

In Exercises 47–60, use matrices to solve the system of equations if possible. Use Gaussian elimination with back-substitution or Gauss-Jordan elimination.

47. $\begin{cases} x + 2y = 7 \\ 2x + y = 8 \end{cases}$ **48.** $\begin{cases} 2x + 6y = 16 \\ 2x + 3y = 7 \end{cases}$

49. $\begin{cases} -x + y = -22 \\ 3x + 4y = 4 \\ 4x - 8y = 32 \end{cases}$ **50.** $\begin{cases} x + 2y = 0 \\ x + y = 6 \\ 3x - 2y = 8 \end{cases}$

51. $\begin{cases} 8x - 4y = 13 \\ 5x + 2y = 7 \end{cases}$ **52.** $\begin{cases} x - 3y = 5 \\ -2x + 6y = -10 \end{cases}$

53. $\begin{cases} -x + 2y = 1.5 \\ 2x - 4y = 3 \end{cases}$ **54.** $\begin{cases} 2x - y = -0.1 \\ 3x + 2y = 1.6 \end{cases}$

55. $\begin{cases} x - 3z = -2 \\ 3x + y - 2z = 5 \\ 2x + 2y + z = 4 \end{cases}$ **56.** $\begin{cases} 2x - y + 3z = 24 \\ 2y - z = 14 \\ 7x - 5y = 6 \end{cases}$

57. $\begin{cases} x + y - 5z = 3 \\ x - 2z = 1 \\ 2x - y - z = 0 \end{cases}$ **58.** $\begin{cases} 2x + 3z = 3 \\ 4x - 3y + 7z = 5 \\ 8x - 9y + 15z = 9 \end{cases}$

59. $\begin{cases} -x + y - z = -14 \\ 2x - y + z = 21 \\ 3x + 2y + z = 19 \end{cases}$ **60.** $\begin{cases} 2x + 2y - z = 2 \\ x - 3y + z = 28 \\ -x + y = 14 \end{cases}$

In Exercises 61–66, use the matrix capabilities of a graphing utility to reduce the augmented matrix corresponding to the system of equations, and solve the system.

61. $\begin{cases} 3x + 3y + 12z = 6 \\ x + y + 4z = 2 \\ 2x + 5y + 20z = 10 \\ -x + 2y + 8z = 4 \end{cases}$

62. $\begin{cases} 2x + 10y + 2z = 6 \\ x + 5y + 2z = 6 \\ x + 5y + z = 3 \\ -3x - 15y - 3z = -9 \end{cases}$

63. $\begin{cases} 2x + y - z + 2w = -6 \\ 3x + 4y + w = 1 \\ x + 5y + 2z + 6w = -3 \\ 5x + 2y - z - w = 3 \end{cases}$

64. $\begin{cases} x + 2y + 2z + 4w = 11 \\ 3x + 6y + 5z + 12w = 30 \end{cases}$

65. $\begin{cases} x + y + z = 0 \\ 2x + 3y + z = 0 \\ 3x + 5y + z = 0 \end{cases}$ **66.** $\begin{cases} x + 2y + z + 3w = 0 \\ x - y + w = 0 \\ y - z + 2w = 0 \end{cases}$

In Exercises 67–70, determine whether the two systems of linear equations yield the same solution. If so, find the solution.

67. (a) $\begin{cases} x - 2y + z = -6 \\ y - 5z = 16 \\ z = -3 \end{cases}$ (b) $\begin{cases} x + y - 2z = 6 \\ y + 3z = -8 \\ z = -3 \end{cases}$

68. (a) $\begin{cases} x - 3y + 4z = -11 \\ y - z = -4 \\ z = 2 \end{cases}$ (b) $\begin{cases} x + 4y = -11 \\ y + 3z = 4 \\ z = 2 \end{cases}$

69. (a) $\begin{cases} x - 4y + 5z = 27 \\ y - 7z = -54 \\ z = 8 \end{cases}$ (b) $\begin{cases} x - 6y + z = 15 \\ y + 5z = 42 \\ z = 8 \end{cases}$

70. (a) $\begin{cases} x + 3y - z = 19 \\ y + 6z = -18 \\ z = -4 \end{cases}$ (b) $\begin{cases} x - y + 3z = -15 \\ y - 2z = 14 \\ z = -4 \end{cases}$

In Exercises 71 and 72, use a system of equations to find the equation of the parabola $y = ax^2 + bx + c$ **that passes through the points. Solve the system using matrices. Use a graphing utility to verify your result.**

71.

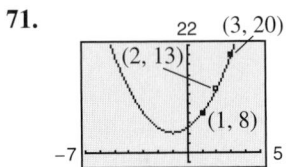

72.

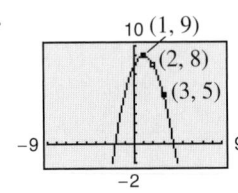

73. Borrowing Money A small corporation borrowed $1,500,000 to expand its line of shoes. Some of the money was borrowed at 7%, some at 8%, and some at 10%. Use a system of equations to determine how much was borrowed at each rate if the annual interest was $130,500 and the amount borrowed at 10% was four times the amount borrowed at 7%. Solve the system using matrices.

74. Borrowing Money A small corporation borrowed $500,000 to build a new office building. Some of the money was borrowed at 9%, some at 10%, and some at 12%. Use a system of equations to determine how much was borrowed at each rate if the annual interest was $52,000 and the amount borrowed at 10% was $2\frac{1}{2}$ times the amount borrowed at 9%. Solve the system using matrices.

75. Electrical Network The currents in an electrical network are given by the solution of the system

$$\begin{cases} I_1 - I_2 + I_3 = 0 \\ 2I_1 + 2I_2 \quad\;\; = 7 \\ \quad\;\; 2I_2 + 4I_3 = 8 \end{cases}$$

where I_1, I_2, and I_3 are measured in amperes. Solve the system of equations using matrices.

76. Mathematical Modeling A videotape of the path of a ball thrown by a baseball player was analyzed with a grid covering the TV screen. The tape was paused three times, and the position of the ball was measured each time. The coordinates obtained are shown in the table (x and y are measured in feet).

Horizontal distance, x	Height, y
0	5.0
15	9.6
30	12.4

(a) Use a system of equations to find the equation of the parabola $y = ax^2 + bx + c$ that passes through the points. Solve the system using matrices.

(b) Use a graphing utility to graph the parabola.

(c) Graphically approximate the maximum height of the ball and the point at which the ball strikes the ground.

(d) Algebraically approximate the maximum height of the ball and the point at which the ball strikes the ground.

77. Data Analysis The table shows the average price y (in dollars) of shares traded on the New York Stock Exchange from 1999 to 2001. (Source: New York Stock Exchange)

Year	Average price, y
1999	43.90
2000	42.10
2001	34.10

(a) Use a system of equations to find the equation of the parabola $y = at^2 + bt + c$ that passes through the points. Let $t = 9$ represent 1999. Solve the system using matrices.

(b) Use a graphing utility to graph the parabola.

(c) Use the equation in part (a) to estimate the average price of shares traded in 2002.

(d) Use the equation in part (a) to estimate the average price of shares traded in 2005. Is the estimate reasonable? Explain.

78. Data Analysis The table shows the average monthly bill y (in dollars) for cellular telephone subscribers from 1999 to 2001. (Source: Cellular Telecommunications & Internet Association)

Year	Average monthly bill, y
1999	41.24
2000	45.27
2001	47.37

(a) Use a system of equations to find the equation of the parabola $y = at^2 + bt + c$ that passes through the points. Let $t = 9$ represent 1999. Solve the system using matrices.

(b) Use a graphing utility to graph the parabola.

(c) Use the equation in part (a) to estimate the average monthly bill in 2002.

(d) Use the equation in part (a) to estimate the average monthly bill in 2005. Is the estimate reasonable? Explain.

Network Analysis   **In Exercises 79 and 80, answer the questions about the specified network.**

79. Water flowing through a network of pipes (in thousands of cubic meters per hour) is shown below.

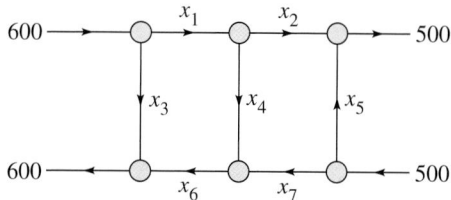

(a) Use matrices to solve this system for the water flow represented by x_i, $i = 1, 2, 3, 4, 5, 6,$ and 7.

(b) Find the network flow pattern when $x_6 = 0$ and $x_7 = 0$.

(c) Find the network flow pattern when $x_5 = 1000$ and $x_6 = 0$.

80. The flow of traffic (in vehicles per hour) through a network of streets is shown below.

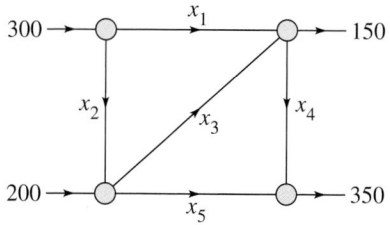

(a) Use matrices to solve this system for the traffic flow represented by x_i, $i = 1, 2, 3, 4,$ and 5.

(b) Find the traffic flow when $x_2 = 200$ and $x_3 = 50$.

(c) Find the traffic flow when $x_2 = 150$ and $x_3 = 0$.

Synthesis

True or False?   **In Exercises 81 and 82, determine whether the statement is true or false. Justify your answer.**

81. $\begin{bmatrix} 6 & 0 & -3 & 10 \\ -2 & 5 & -6 & 2 \end{bmatrix}$ is a 4 × 2 matrix.

82. Gaussian elimination reduces a matrix until a reduced row-echelon form is obtained.

83. *Think About It* The augmented matrix represents a system of linear equations (in the variables x, y, and z) that has been reduced using Gauss-Jordan elimination. Write a system of equations with *nonzero* coefficients that is represented by the reduced matrix. (There are many correct answers.)

$$\begin{bmatrix} 1 & 0 & 3 & \vdots & -2 \\ 0 & 1 & 4 & \vdots & 1 \\ 0 & 0 & 0 & \vdots & 0 \end{bmatrix}$$

84. *Think About It*

(a) Describe the row-echelon form of an augmented matrix that corresponds to a system of linear equations that is inconsistent.

(b) Describe the row-echelon form of an augmented matrix that corresponds to a system of linear equations that has an infinite number of solutions.

85. *Error Analysis* One of your classmates has submitted the following steps for the solution of a system by Gauss-Jordan elimination. Find the error(s) in the solution. Write a short paragraph explaining the error(s) to your classmate.

$$\begin{bmatrix} 1 & 1 & \vdots & 4 \\ 2 & 3 & \vdots & 5 \end{bmatrix}$$

$$-2R_1 + R_2 \rightarrow \begin{bmatrix} 1 & 1 & \vdots & 4 \\ 0 & 1 & \vdots & 5 \end{bmatrix}$$

$$-R_2 + R_1 \rightarrow \begin{bmatrix} 1 & 0 & \vdots & 4 \\ 0 & 1 & \vdots & 5 \end{bmatrix}$$

86. *Writing* In your own words, describe the difference between a matrix in row-echelon form and a matrix in reduced row-echelon form.

Review

In Exercises 87–92, sketch the graph of the function. Identify any asymptotes.

87. $f(x) = \dfrac{7}{-x - 1}$

88. $f(x) = \dfrac{4x}{5x^2 + 2}$

89. $f(x) = \dfrac{x^2 - 2x - 3}{x - 4}$

90. $f(x) = \dfrac{x^2 - 36}{x + 1}$

91. $f(x) = \dfrac{2x^2 - 4x}{3x - x^2}$

92. $f(x) = \dfrac{x^2 - 2x + 1}{x^2 - 1}$

8.5 Operations with Matrices

Equality of Matrices

In Section 8.4, you used matrices to solve systems of linear equations. There is a rich mathematical theory of matrices, and its applications are numerous. This section and the next two introduce some fundamentals of matrix theory. It is standard mathematical convention to represent matrices in any of the following three ways.

> **Representation of Matrices**
>
> **1.** A matrix can be denoted by an uppercase letter such as A, B, or C.
>
> **2.** A matrix can be denoted by a representative element enclosed in brackets, such as $[a_{ij}]$, $[b_{ij}]$, or $[c_{ij}]$.
>
> **3.** A matrix can be denoted by a rectangular array of numbers such as
>
> $$A = [a_{ij}] = \begin{bmatrix} a_{11} & a_{12} & a_{13} & \cdots & a_{1n} \\ a_{21} & a_{22} & a_{23} & \cdots & a_{2n} \\ a_{31} & a_{32} & a_{33} & \cdots & a_{3n} \\ \vdots & \vdots & \vdots & & \vdots \\ a_{m1} & a_{m2} & a_{m3} & \cdots & a_{mn} \end{bmatrix}.$$

Two matrices $A = [a_{ij}]$ and $B = [b_{ij}]$ are **equal** if they have the same order $(m \times n)$ and all of their corresponding entries are equal. For instance, using the matrix equation

$$\begin{bmatrix} a_{11} & a_{12} \\ a_{21} & a_{22} \end{bmatrix} = \begin{bmatrix} 2 & -1 \\ -3 & 0 \end{bmatrix}$$

you can conclude that $a_{11} = 2$, $a_{12} = -1$, and $a_{22} = 0$.

Matrix Addition and Scalar Multiplication

You can add two matrices (of the same order) by adding their corresponding entries.

> **Definition of Matrix Addition**
>
> If $A = [a_{ij}]$ and $B = [b_{ij}]$ are matrices of order $m \times n$, their sum is the $m \times n$ matrix given by
>
> $$A + B = [a_{ij} + b_{ij}].$$
>
> The sum of two matrices of different orders is undefined.

What you should learn

- Decide whether two matrices are equal.
- Add and subtract matrices and multiply matrices by a scalar.
- Multiply two matrices.
- Use matrix operations to model and solve real-life problems.

Why you should learn it

Matrix algebra provides a systematic way of performing mathematical operations on large arrays of numbers. In Exercise 70 on page 657, you will use matrix multiplication to help analyze the labor and wage requirements for a boat manufacturer.

Michael St. Maur Sheil/Corbis

Example 1   Addition of Matrices

a. $\begin{bmatrix} -1 & 2 \\ 0 & 1 \end{bmatrix} + \begin{bmatrix} 1 & 3 \\ -1 & 2 \end{bmatrix} = \begin{bmatrix} -1+1 & 2+3 \\ 0-1 & 1+2 \end{bmatrix} = \begin{bmatrix} 0 & 5 \\ -1 & 3 \end{bmatrix}$

b. $\begin{bmatrix} 1 \\ -3 \\ -2 \end{bmatrix} + \begin{bmatrix} -1 \\ 3 \\ 2 \end{bmatrix} = \begin{bmatrix} 0 \\ 0 \\ 0 \end{bmatrix}$

c. The sum of

$$A = \begin{bmatrix} 2 & 1 & 0 \\ 4 & 0 & -1 \end{bmatrix} \quad \text{and} \quad B = \begin{bmatrix} 0 & 1 \\ -1 & 3 \end{bmatrix}$$

is undefined because A is of order 2×3 and B is of order 2×2.

✓ *Checkpoint* Now try Exercise 7(a).

TECHNOLOGY TIP   Most graphing utilities can perform matrix operations. Example 2 shows how a graphing utility can be used to add two matrices.

Example 2   Addition of Matrices

Use a graphing utility to find the sum of

$$A = \begin{bmatrix} 0 & 1 & -2 \\ 1 & 2 & 3 \end{bmatrix} \quad \text{and} \quad B = \begin{bmatrix} 0 & 0 & 0 \\ 0 & 0 & 0 \end{bmatrix}.$$

Solution

Use the *matrix editor* to enter A and B in the graphing utility (see Figure 8.27). Then, find the sum as shown in Figure 8.28.

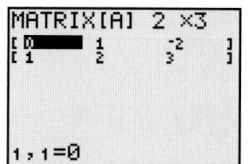
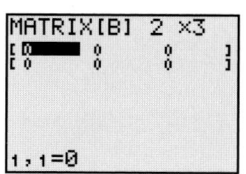
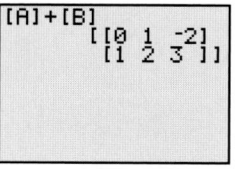

Matrix A Matrix B

Figure 8.27   **Figure 8.28**

✓ *Checkpoint* Now try Exercise 17.

In operations with matrices, numbers are usually referred to as **scalars**. In this text, scalars will always be real numbers. You can multiply a matrix A by a scalar c by multiplying each entry in A by c.

Definition of Scalar Multiplication

If $A = [a_{ij}]$ is an $m \times n$ matrix and c is a scalar, the **scalar multiple** of A by c is the $m \times n$ matrix given by

$$cA = [ca_{ij}].$$

TECHNOLOGY TIP

Try using a graphing utility to find the sum of the two matrices in part (c) of Example 1. Your graphing utility should display an error message similar to the one shown below.

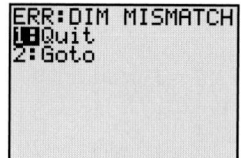

TECHNOLOGY SUPPORT

For instructions on how to use the *matrix editor*, see Appendix A; for specific keystrokes, go to the text website at *college.hmco.com*.

The symbol $-A$ represents the negation of A, which is the scalar product $(-1)A$. Moreover, if A and B are of the same order, then $A - B$ represents the sum of A and $(-1)B$. That is,

$$A - B = A + (-1)B.$$ Subtraction of matrices

Example 3 Scalar Multiplication and Matrix Subtraction

For the following matrices, find (a) $3A$, (b) $-B$, and (c) $3A - B$.

$$A = \begin{bmatrix} 2 & 2 & 4 \\ -3 & 0 & -1 \\ 2 & 1 & 2 \end{bmatrix} \quad \text{and} \quad B = \begin{bmatrix} 2 & 0 & 0 \\ 1 & -4 & 3 \\ -1 & 3 & 2 \end{bmatrix}$$

Solution

a. $3A = 3\begin{bmatrix} 2 & 2 & 4 \\ -3 & 0 & -1 \\ 2 & 1 & 2 \end{bmatrix}$ Scalar multiplication

$$= \begin{bmatrix} 3(2) & 3(2) & 3(4) \\ 3(-3) & 3(0) & 3(-1) \\ 3(2) & 3(1) & 3(2) \end{bmatrix}$$ Multiply each entry by 3.

$$= \begin{bmatrix} 6 & 6 & 12 \\ -9 & 0 & -3 \\ 6 & 3 & 6 \end{bmatrix}$$ Simplify.

b. $-B = (-1)\begin{bmatrix} 2 & 0 & 0 \\ 1 & -4 & 3 \\ -1 & 3 & 2 \end{bmatrix}$ Definition of negation

$$= \begin{bmatrix} -2 & 0 & 0 \\ -1 & 4 & -3 \\ 1 & -3 & -2 \end{bmatrix}$$ Multiply each entry by -1.

c. $3A - B = \begin{bmatrix} 6 & 6 & 12 \\ -9 & 0 & -3 \\ 6 & 3 & 6 \end{bmatrix} - \begin{bmatrix} 2 & 0 & 0 \\ 1 & -4 & 3 \\ -1 & 3 & 2 \end{bmatrix}$ Matrix subtraction

$$= \begin{bmatrix} 4 & 6 & 12 \\ -10 & 4 & -6 \\ 7 & 0 & 4 \end{bmatrix}$$ Subtract corresponding entries.

✓ *Checkpoint* Now try Exercises 7(b), (c), and (d).

It is often convenient to rewrite the scalar multiple cA by factoring c out of every entry in the matrix. For instance, in the following example, the scalar $\frac{1}{2}$ has been factored out of the matrix.

$$\begin{bmatrix} \frac{1}{2} & -\frac{3}{2} \\ \frac{5}{2} & \frac{1}{2} \end{bmatrix} = \begin{bmatrix} \frac{1}{2}(1) & \frac{1}{2}(-3) \\ \frac{1}{2}(5) & \frac{1}{2}(1) \end{bmatrix} = \frac{1}{2}\begin{bmatrix} 1 & -3 \\ 5 & 1 \end{bmatrix}$$

STUDY TIP

The order of operations for matrix expressions is similar to that for real numbers. In particular, you perform scalar multiplication before matrix addition and subtraction, as shown in Example 3(c).

Exploration

What do you observe about the relationship between the corresponding entries of A and B below? Use a graphing utility to find $A + B$. What conclusion can you make about the entries of A and B and the sum of $A + B$?

$$A = \begin{bmatrix} -1 & 5 \\ 2 & -6 \end{bmatrix}$$

$$B = \begin{bmatrix} 1 & -5 \\ -2 & 6 \end{bmatrix}$$

Example 4   Scalar Multiplication and Matrix Subtraction

For the following matrices, use a graphing utility to find $2A - 4B$.

$$A = \begin{bmatrix} -1 & 8 \\ 6 & 2 \end{bmatrix} \quad \text{and} \quad B = \begin{bmatrix} 0 & 4 \\ 5 & -3 \end{bmatrix}$$

Solution

Use the matrix editor to enter A and B into the graphing utility. Then, find $2A - 4B$ as shown in Figure 8.29

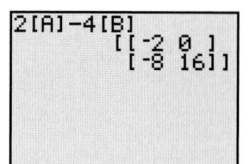

Figure 8.29

✓ *Checkpoint* Now try Exercise 19.

The properties of matrix addition and scalar multiplication are similar to those of addition and multiplication of real numbers.

Properties of Matrix Addition and Scalar Multiplication

Let A, B, and C be $m \times n$ matrices and let c and d be scalars.

1. $A + B = B + A$ Commutative Property of Matrix Addition

2. $A + (B + C) = (A + B) + C$ Associative Property of Matrix Addition

3. $(cd)A = c(dA)$ Associative Property of Scalar Multiplication

4. $1A = A$ Scalar Identity

5. $c(A + B) = cA + cB$ Distributive Property

6. $(c + d)A = cA + dA$ Distributive Property

STUDY TIP

Note that the Associative Property of Matrix Addition allows you to write expressions such as $A + B + C$ without ambiguity because the same sum occurs no matter how the matrices are grouped. This same reasoning applies to sums of four or more matrices.

Example 5   Addition of More Than Two Matrices

By adding corresponding entries, you obtain the following sum of four matrices.

$$\begin{bmatrix} 1 \\ 2 \\ -3 \end{bmatrix} + \begin{bmatrix} -1 \\ -1 \\ 2 \end{bmatrix} + \begin{bmatrix} 0 \\ 1 \\ 4 \end{bmatrix} + \begin{bmatrix} 2 \\ -3 \\ -2 \end{bmatrix} = \begin{bmatrix} 2 \\ -1 \\ 1 \end{bmatrix}$$

✓ *Checkpoint* Now try Exercise 13.

Example 6   Using the Distributive Property

$$3\left(\begin{bmatrix} -2 & 0 \\ 4 & 1 \end{bmatrix} + \begin{bmatrix} 4 & -2 \\ 3 & 7 \end{bmatrix} \right) = 3 \begin{bmatrix} -2 & 0 \\ 4 & 1 \end{bmatrix} + 3 \begin{bmatrix} 4 & -2 \\ 3 & 7 \end{bmatrix}$$

$$= \begin{bmatrix} -6 & 0 \\ 12 & 3 \end{bmatrix} + \begin{bmatrix} 12 & -6 \\ 9 & 21 \end{bmatrix} = \begin{bmatrix} 6 & -6 \\ 21 & 24 \end{bmatrix}$$

STUDY TIP

In Example 6, you could add the two matrices first and then multiply the resulting matrix by 3. The result would be the same.

✓ *Checkpoint* Now try Exercise 15.

One important property of addition of real numbers is that the number 0 is the additive identity. That is, $c + 0 = c$ for any real number c. For matrices, a similar property holds. That is, if A is an $m \times n$ matrix and O is the $m \times n$ **zero matrix** consisting entirely of zeros, then $A + O = A$.

In other words, O is the **additive identity** for the set of all $m \times n$ matrices. For example, the following matrices are the additive identities for the sets of all 2×3 and 2×2 matrices.

$$O = \begin{bmatrix} 0 & 0 & 0 \\ 0 & 0 & 0 \end{bmatrix} \quad \text{and} \quad O = \begin{bmatrix} 0 & 0 \\ 0 & 0 \end{bmatrix}.$$

$\underbrace{}$ 2×3 zero matrix $\underbrace{}$ 2×2 zero matrix

The algebra of real numbers and the algebra of matrices have many similarities. For example, compare the following solutions.

Real Numbers	*m × n Matrices*
(Solve for x.)	*(Solve for X.)*
$x + a = b$	$X + A = B$
$x + a + (-a) = b + (-a)$	$X + A + (-A) = B + (-A)$
$x + 0 = b - a$	$X + O = B - A$
$x = b - a$	$X = B - A$

The algebra of real numbers and the algebra of matrices also have important differences, which will be discussed later.

Example 7 Solving a Matrix Equation

Solve for X in the equation $3X + A = B$, where

$$A = \begin{bmatrix} 1 & -2 \\ 0 & 3 \end{bmatrix} \quad \text{and} \quad B = \begin{bmatrix} -3 & 4 \\ 2 & 1 \end{bmatrix}.$$

Solution

Begin by solving the equation for X to obtain

$$3X = B - A$$

$$X = \frac{1}{3}(B - A).$$

Now, using the matrices A and B, you have

$$X = \frac{1}{3}\left(\begin{bmatrix} -3 & 4 \\ 2 & 1 \end{bmatrix} - \begin{bmatrix} 1 & -2 \\ 0 & 3 \end{bmatrix} \right) \qquad \text{Substitute the matrices.}$$

$$= \frac{1}{3}\begin{bmatrix} -4 & 6 \\ 2 & -2 \end{bmatrix} \qquad \text{Subtract matrix } A \text{ from matrix } B.$$

$$= \begin{bmatrix} -\frac{4}{3} & 2 \\ \frac{2}{3} & -\frac{2}{3} \end{bmatrix}. \qquad \text{Multiply the resulting matrix by } \frac{1}{3}.$$

✓ *Checkpoint* Now try Exercise 25.

Matrix Multiplication

The third basic matrix operation is **matrix multiplication.** At first glance, the following definition may seem unusual. You will see later, however, that this definition of the product of two matrices has many practical applications.

Definition of Matrix Multiplication

If $A = [a_{ij}]$ is an $m \times n$ matrix and $B = [b_{ij}]$ is an $n \times p$ matrix, the product AB is an $m \times p$ matrix given by

$$AB = [c_{ij}]$$

where $c_{ij} = a_{i1}b_{1j} + a_{i2}b_{2j} + a_{i3}b_{3j} + \cdots + a_{in}b_{nj}.$

The definition of matrix multiplication indicates a *row-by-column* multiplication, where the entry in the ith row and jth column of the product AB is obtained by multiplying the entries in the ith row of A by the corresponding entries in the jth column of B and then adding the results. The general pattern for matrix multiplication is as follows.

$$
\begin{bmatrix}
a_{11} & a_{12} & a_{13} & \cdots & a_{1n} \\
a_{21} & a_{22} & a_{23} & \cdots & a_{2n} \\
a_{31} & a_{32} & a_{33} & \cdots & a_{3n} \\
\vdots & \vdots & \vdots & & \vdots \\
a_{i1} & a_{i2} & a_{i3} & \cdots & a_{in} \\
\vdots & \vdots & \vdots & & \vdots \\
a_{m1} & a_{m2} & a_{m3} & \cdots & a_{mn}
\end{bmatrix}
\begin{bmatrix}
b_{11} & b_{12} & \cdots & b_{1j} & \cdots & b_{1p} \\
b_{21} & b_{22} & \cdots & b_{2j} & \cdots & b_{2p} \\
b_{31} & b_{32} & \cdots & b_{3j} & \cdots & b_{3p} \\
\vdots & \vdots & & \vdots & & \vdots \\
b_{n1} & b_{n2} & \cdots & b_{nj} & \cdots & b_{np}
\end{bmatrix}
=
\begin{bmatrix}
c_{11} & c_{12} & \cdots & c_{1j} & \cdots & c_{1p} \\
c_{21} & c_{22} & \cdots & c_{2j} & \cdots & c_{2p} \\
\vdots & \vdots & & \vdots & & \vdots \\
c_{i1} & c_{i2} & \cdots & c_{ij} & \cdots & c_{ip} \\
\vdots & \vdots & & \vdots & & \vdots \\
c_{m1} & c_{m2} & \cdots & c_{mj} & \cdots & c_{mp}
\end{bmatrix}
$$

$$a_{i1}b_{1j} + a_{i2}b_{2j} + a_{i3}b_{3j} + \cdots + a_{in}b_{nj} = c_{ij}$$

Example 8   Finding the Product of Two Matrices

Find the product AB using $A = \begin{bmatrix} -1 & 3 \\ 4 & -2 \\ 5 & 0 \end{bmatrix}$ and $B = \begin{bmatrix} -3 & 2 \\ -4 & 1 \end{bmatrix}.$

Solution

First, note that the product AB is defined because the number of columns of A is equal to the number of rows of B. Moreover, the product AB has order 3×2. To find the entries of the product, multiply each row of A by each column of B.

$$AB = \begin{bmatrix} -1 & 3 \\ 4 & -2 \\ 5 & 0 \end{bmatrix}\begin{bmatrix} -3 & 2 \\ -4 & 1 \end{bmatrix}$$

$$= \begin{bmatrix} (-1)(-3) + (3)(-4) & (-1)(2) + (3)(1) \\ (4)(-3) + (-2)(-4) & (4)(2) + (-2)(1) \\ (5)(-3) + (0)(-4) & (5)(2) + (0)(1) \end{bmatrix} = \begin{bmatrix} -9 & 1 \\ -4 & 6 \\ -15 & 10 \end{bmatrix}$$

✓ *Checkpoint* Now try Exercise 29.

Be sure you understand that for the product of two matrices to be defined, the number of *columns* of the first matrix must equal the number of *rows* of the second matrix. That is, the middle two indices must be the same. The outside two indices give the order of the product, as shown in the following diagram.

$$A \quad \times \quad B \quad = \quad AB$$
$$m \times n \qquad n \times p \qquad m \times p$$

Equal
Order of AB

Example 9   Matrix Multiplication

a. $\begin{bmatrix} 1 & 0 & 3 \\ 2 & -1 & -2 \end{bmatrix} \begin{bmatrix} -2 & 4 & 2 \\ 1 & 0 & 0 \\ -1 & 1 & -1 \end{bmatrix} = \begin{bmatrix} -5 & 7 & -1 \\ -3 & 6 & 6 \end{bmatrix}$

$\qquad 2 \times 3 \qquad\qquad 3 \times 3 \qquad\qquad 2 \times 3$

b. $\begin{bmatrix} 3 & 4 \\ -2 & 5 \end{bmatrix} \begin{bmatrix} 1 & 0 \\ 0 & 1 \end{bmatrix} = \begin{bmatrix} 3 & 4 \\ -2 & 5 \end{bmatrix}$

$\qquad 2 \times 2 \qquad 2 \times 2 \qquad 2 \times 2$

c. $\begin{bmatrix} 1 & 2 \\ 1 & 1 \end{bmatrix} \begin{bmatrix} -1 & 2 \\ 1 & -1 \end{bmatrix} = \begin{bmatrix} 1 & 0 \\ 0 & 1 \end{bmatrix}$

$\qquad 2 \times 2 \qquad 2 \times 2 \qquad 2 \times 2$

d. $[1 \quad -2 \quad -3] \begin{bmatrix} 2 \\ -1 \\ 1 \end{bmatrix} = [1]$

$\qquad 1 \times 3 \qquad 3 \times 1 \quad 1 \times 1$

e. $\begin{bmatrix} 2 \\ -1 \\ 1 \end{bmatrix} [1 \quad -2 \quad -3] = \begin{bmatrix} 2 & -4 & -6 \\ -1 & 2 & 3 \\ 1 & -2 & -3 \end{bmatrix}$

$\quad 3 \times 1 \qquad 1 \times 3 \qquad\qquad 3 \times 3$

f. The product AB for the following matrices is not defined.

$$A = \begin{bmatrix} -2 & 1 \\ 1 & -3 \\ 1 & 4 \end{bmatrix} \text{ and } B = \begin{bmatrix} -2 & 3 & 1 & 4 \\ 0 & 1 & -1 & 2 \\ 2 & -1 & 0 & 1 \end{bmatrix}$$

$\qquad\qquad 3 \times 2 \qquad\qquad\qquad 3 \times 4$

✓ *Checkpoint* Now try Exercise 31.

In parts (d) and (e) of Example 9, note that the two products are different. Matrix multiplication is not, in general, commutative. That is, for most matrices, $AB \neq BA$. This is one way in which the algebra of real numbers and the algebra of matrices differ.

Exploration

Use the following matrices to find AB, BA, $(AB)C$, and $A(BC)$. What do your results tell you about matrix multiplication and commutativity and associativity?

$$A = \begin{bmatrix} 1 & 2 \\ 3 & 4 \end{bmatrix},$$

$$B = \begin{bmatrix} 0 & 1 \\ 2 & 3 \end{bmatrix},$$

$$C = \begin{bmatrix} 3 & 0 \\ 0 & 1 \end{bmatrix}$$

Example 10 Matrix Multiplication

Use a graphing utility to find the product AB using

$$A = \begin{bmatrix} 1 & 2 & 3 \\ 2 & -5 & 1 \end{bmatrix} \quad \text{and} \quad B = \begin{bmatrix} -3 & 2 & 1 \\ 4 & -2 & 0 \\ 1 & 2 & 3 \end{bmatrix}.$$

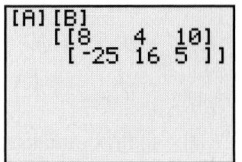

Solution

Note that the order of A is 2×3 and the order of B is 3×3. So, the product will have order 2×3. Use the matrix editor to enter A and B into the graphing utility. Then, find the product as shown in Figure 8.30.

Figure 8.30

✓ *Checkpoint* Now try Exercise 41.

Properties of Matrix Multiplication

Let A, B, and C be matrices and let c be a scalar.

1. $A(BC) = (AB)C$ Associative Property of Matrix Multiplication

2. $A(B + C) = AB + AC$ Left Distributive Property

3. $(A + B)C = AC + BC$ Right Distributive Property

4. $c(AB) = (cA)B = A(cB)$ Associative Property of Scalar Multiplication

---

Definition of Identity Matrix

The $n \times n$ matrix that consists of 1's on its main diagonal and 0's elsewhere is called the **identity matrix of order n** and is denoted by

$$I_n = \begin{bmatrix} 1 & 0 & 0 & \cdots & 0 \\ 0 & 1 & 0 & \cdots & 0 \\ 0 & 0 & 1 & \cdots & 0 \\ \vdots & \vdots & \vdots & & \vdots \\ 0 & 0 & 0 & \cdots & 1 \end{bmatrix}. \quad \text{Identity matrix}$$

Note that an identity matrix must be *square*. When the order is understood to be n, you can denote I_n simply by I.

If A is an $n \times n$ matrix, the identity matrix has the property that $AI_n = A$ and $I_n A = A$. For example,

$$\begin{bmatrix} 3 & -2 & 5 \\ 1 & 0 & 4 \\ -1 & 2 & -3 \end{bmatrix} \begin{bmatrix} 1 & 0 & 0 \\ 0 & 1 & 0 \\ 0 & 0 & 1 \end{bmatrix} = \begin{bmatrix} 3 & -2 & 5 \\ 1 & 0 & 4 \\ -1 & 2 & -3 \end{bmatrix} \quad AI = A$$

and

$$\begin{bmatrix} 1 & 0 & 0 \\ 0 & 1 & 0 \\ 0 & 0 & 1 \end{bmatrix} \begin{bmatrix} 3 & -2 & 5 \\ 1 & 0 & 4 \\ -1 & 2 & -3 \end{bmatrix} = \begin{bmatrix} 3 & -2 & 5 \\ 1 & 0 & 4 \\ -1 & 2 & -3 \end{bmatrix}. \quad IA = A$$

Applications

Matrix multiplication can be used to represent a system of linear equations. Note how the system

$$\begin{cases} a_{11}x_1 + a_{12}x_2 + a_{13}x_3 = b_1 \\ a_{21}x_1 + a_{22}x_2 + a_{23}x_3 = b_2 \\ a_{31}x_1 + a_{32}x_2 + a_{33}x_3 = b_3 \end{cases}$$

can be written as the matrix equation $AX = B$, where A is the *coefficient matrix* of the system and X and B are column matrices.

$$\underset{A}{\begin{bmatrix} a_{11} & a_{12} & a_{13} \\ a_{21} & a_{22} & a_{23} \\ a_{31} & a_{32} & a_{33} \end{bmatrix}} \times \underset{X}{\begin{bmatrix} x_1 \\ x_2 \\ x_3 \end{bmatrix}} = \underset{B}{\begin{bmatrix} b_1 \\ b_2 \\ b_3 \end{bmatrix}}$$

> **STUDY TIP**
>
> The column matrix B is also called a *constant* matrix. Its entries are the constant terms in the system of equations.

Example 11 Solving a System of Linear Equations

Consider the system of linear equations $\begin{cases} x_1 - 2x_2 + x_3 = -4 \\ x_2 + 2x_3 = 4. \\ 2x_1 + 3x_2 - 2x_3 = 2 \end{cases}$

a. Write this system as a matrix equation $AX = B$.

b. Use Gauss-Jordan elimination on $[A \vdots B]$ to solve for the matrix X.

Solution

a. In matrix form $AX = B$, the system can be written as follows.

$$\begin{bmatrix} 1 & -2 & 1 \\ 0 & 1 & 2 \\ 2 & 3 & -2 \end{bmatrix} \begin{bmatrix} x_1 \\ x_2 \\ x_3 \end{bmatrix} = \begin{bmatrix} -4 \\ 4 \\ 2 \end{bmatrix}$$

b. The augmented matrix is

$$[A \vdots B] = \begin{bmatrix} 1 & -2 & 1 & \vdots & -4 \\ 0 & 1 & 2 & \vdots & 4 \\ 2 & 3 & -2 & \vdots & 2 \end{bmatrix}.$$

Using Gauss-Jordan elimination, you can rewrite this equation as

$$[I \vdots X] = \begin{bmatrix} 1 & 0 & 0 & \vdots & -1 \\ 0 & 1 & 0 & \vdots & 2 \\ 0 & 0 & 1 & \vdots & 1 \end{bmatrix}.$$

So, the solution of the system of linear equations is $x_1 = -1$, $x_2 = 2$, and $x_3 = 1$. The solution of the matrix equation is

$$X = \begin{bmatrix} x_1 \\ x_2 \\ x_3 \end{bmatrix} = \begin{bmatrix} -1 \\ 2 \\ 1 \end{bmatrix}.$$

> **TECHNOLOGY TIP**
>
> Most graphing utilities can be used to obtain the reduced row-echelon form of a matrix. The screen below shows how one graphing utility displays the reduced row-echelon form of the augmented matrix in Example 11.
>
> ```
> rref([C])
>       [[1 0 0 -1]
>        [0 1 0 2 ]
>        [0 0 1 1 ]]
> ```

✓ *Checkpoint* Now try Exercise 59.

Example 12   Health Care

A company offers three types of health care plans with two levels of coverage to its employees. The current annual costs for these plans are represented by the matrix A. If the annual costs are expected to increase by 4% next year, what will be the annual costs for each plan next year?

$$A = \begin{matrix} & \overbrace{\text{Premium} \quad \text{HMO} \quad \text{HMO Plus}}^{\text{Plan}} & \\ \begin{bmatrix} 694 & 451 & 489 \\ 1725 & 1187 & 1248 \end{bmatrix} & \begin{matrix} \text{Single} \\ \text{Family} \end{matrix} \left.\begin{matrix} \\ \\ \end{matrix}\right\} \begin{matrix}\text{Coverage}\\\text{level}\end{matrix} \end{matrix}$$

Solution

Because an increase of 4% corresponds to 100% + 4%, multiply A by 104% or 1.04. So, the annual costs for each health care plan next year are as follows.

$$1.04A = 1.04\begin{bmatrix} 694 & 451 & 489 \\ 1725 & 1187 & 1248 \end{bmatrix} = \overset{\overbrace{\quad\text{Premium}\quad\text{HMO}\quad\text{HMO Plus}\quad}^{\text{Plan}}}{\begin{bmatrix} 722 & 469 & 509 \\ 1794 & 1234 & 1298 \end{bmatrix}} \begin{matrix} \text{Single} \\ \text{Family} \end{matrix} \left.\begin{matrix} \\ \\ \end{matrix}\right\} \begin{matrix}\text{Coverage}\\\text{level}\end{matrix}$$

 Checkpoint Now try Exercise 65.

Example 13   Softball Team Expenses

Two softball teams submit equipment lists to their sponsors, as shown in the table at the right. Each bat costs $80, each ball costs $6, and each glove costs $60. Use matrices to find the total cost of equipment for each team.

Equipment	Women's Team	Men's Team
Bats	12	15
Balls	45	38
Gloves	15	17

Solution

The equipment lists E and the costs per item C can be written in matrix form as

$$E = \begin{bmatrix} 12 & 15 \\ 45 & 38 \\ 15 & 17 \end{bmatrix} \quad \text{and} \quad C = \begin{bmatrix} 80 & 6 & 60 \end{bmatrix}.$$

You can find the total cost of the equipment for each team using the product CE because the number of columns of C (3 columns) equals the number of rows of E (3 rows). Therefore, the total cost of equipment for each team is given by

$$CE = \begin{bmatrix} 80 & 6 & 60 \end{bmatrix}\begin{bmatrix} 12 & 15 \\ 45 & 38 \\ 15 & 17 \end{bmatrix}$$

$$= \begin{bmatrix} 80(12) + 6(45) + 60(15) & 80(15) + 6(38) + 60(17) \end{bmatrix}$$

$$= \begin{bmatrix} 2130 & 2448 \end{bmatrix}.$$

So, the total cost of equipment for the women's team is $2130, and the total cost of equipment for the men's team is $2448.

 Checkpoint Now try Exercise 67.

STUDY TIP

Notice in Example 13 that you cannot find the total cost using the product EC because EC is not defined. That is, the number of columns of E (2 columns) does not equal the number of rows of C (1 row).

8.5   Exercises

Vocabulary Check

In Exercises 1–4, fill in the blanks.

1. Two matrices are _____ if all of their corresponding entries are equal.
2. When working with matrices, real numbers are often referred to as _____ .
3. A matrix consisting entirely of zeros is called a _____ matrix and is denoted by _____ .
4. The $n \times n$ matrix consisting of 1's on its main diagonal and 0's elsewhere is called the _____ matrix of order n.

In Exercises 5 and 6, match the matrix property with the correct form. A, B, and C are matrices, and c and d are scalars.

5. (a) $(cd)A = c(dA)$ (i) Commutative Property of Matrix Addition
   (b) $A + B = B + A$ (ii) Associative Property of Matrix Addition
   (c) $1A = A$ (iii) Associative Property of Scalar Multiplication
   (d) $c(A + B) = cA + cB$ (iv) Scalar Identity
   (e) $A + (B + C) = (A + B) + C$ (v) Distributive Property

6. (a) $A(B + C) = AB + AC$ (i) Associative Property of Matrix Multiplication
   (b) $c(AB) = (cA)B = A(cB)$ (ii) Left Distributive Property
   (c) $A(BC) = (AB)C$ (iii) Right Distributive Property
   (d) $(A + B)C = AC + BC$ (iv) Associative Property of Scalar Multiplication

---

In Exercises 1–4, find x, y, and z.

1. $\begin{bmatrix} x & -2 \\ 7 & y \end{bmatrix} = \begin{bmatrix} -4 & -2 \\ 7 & 22 \end{bmatrix}$

2. $\begin{bmatrix} -5 & x \\ y & 8 \end{bmatrix} = \begin{bmatrix} -5 & 13 \\ 12 & 8 \end{bmatrix}$

3. $\begin{bmatrix} 16 & 4 & 5 & 4 \\ -3 & 13 & 15 & 12 \\ 0 & 2 & 4 & 0 \end{bmatrix} = \begin{bmatrix} 16 & 4 & 2x + 7 & 4 \\ -3 & 13 & & 15 \ 3y \\ 0 & 2 & 3z - 14 & 0 \end{bmatrix}$

4. $\begin{bmatrix} x + 4 & 8 & -3 \\ 1 & 22 & 2y \\ 7 & -2 & z + 2 \end{bmatrix} = \begin{bmatrix} 2x + 9 & 8 & -3 \\ 1 & 22 & -8 \\ 7 & -2 & 11 \end{bmatrix}$

In Exercises 5–12, find, if possible, (a) $A + B$, (b) $A - B$, (c) $3A$, and (d) $3A - 2B$. Use the matrix capabilities of a graphing utility to verify your results.

5. $A = \begin{bmatrix} 1 & -1 \\ 2 & -1 \end{bmatrix}$, $B = \begin{bmatrix} 2 & -1 \\ -1 & 8 \end{bmatrix}$

6. $A = \begin{bmatrix} 1 & 2 \\ 2 & 1 \end{bmatrix}$, $B = \begin{bmatrix} -3 & -2 \\ 4 & 2 \end{bmatrix}$

7. $A = \begin{bmatrix} 8 & -1 \\ 2 & 3 \\ -4 & 5 \end{bmatrix}$, $B = \begin{bmatrix} 1 & 6 \\ -1 & -5 \\ 1 & 10 \end{bmatrix}$

8. $A = \begin{bmatrix} 2 & 3 & 1 \\ 0 & -1 & 4 \end{bmatrix}$, $B = \begin{bmatrix} 5 & 0 & 7 \\ -4 & 1 & -2 \end{bmatrix}$

9. $A = \begin{bmatrix} 4 & 5 & -1 & 3 & 4 \\ 1 & 2 & -2 & -1 & 0 \end{bmatrix}$,
   $B = \begin{bmatrix} 1 & 0 & -1 & 1 & 0 \\ -6 & 8 & 2 & -3 & -7 \end{bmatrix}$

10. $A = \begin{bmatrix} -1 & 4 & 0 \\ 3 & -2 & 2 \\ 5 & 4 & -1 \\ 0 & 8 & -6 \\ -4 & -1 & 0 \end{bmatrix}$, $B = \begin{bmatrix} -3 & 5 & 1 \\ 2 & -4 & -7 \\ 10 & -9 & -1 \\ 3 & 2 & -4 \\ 0 & 1 & -2 \end{bmatrix}$

11. $A = \begin{bmatrix} 6 & 0 & 3 \\ -1 & -4 & 0 \end{bmatrix}$, $B = \begin{bmatrix} 8 & -1 \\ 4 & -3 \end{bmatrix}$

12. $A = \begin{bmatrix} 3 \\ 2 \\ -1 \end{bmatrix}$, $B = \begin{bmatrix} -4 & 6 & 2 \end{bmatrix}$

In Exercises 13–16, evaluate the expression.

13. $\begin{bmatrix} -5 & 0 \\ 3 & -6 \end{bmatrix} + \begin{bmatrix} 7 & 1 \\ -2 & -1 \end{bmatrix} + \begin{bmatrix} -10 & -8 \\ 14 & 6 \end{bmatrix}$

14. $\begin{bmatrix} 6 & 9 \\ -1 & 0 \\ 7 & 1 \end{bmatrix} + \begin{bmatrix} 0 & 5 \\ -2 & -1 \\ 3 & -6 \end{bmatrix} + \begin{bmatrix} -13 & -7 \\ 4 & -1 \\ -6 & 0 \end{bmatrix}$

15. $4\left(\begin{bmatrix} -4 & 0 & 1 \\ 0 & 2 & 3 \end{bmatrix} - \begin{bmatrix} 2 & 1 & -2 \\ 3 & -6 & 0 \end{bmatrix} \right)$

16. $\frac{1}{2}([5 \quad -2 \quad 4 \quad 0] + [14 \quad 6 \quad -18 \quad 9])$

In Exercises 17–22, use the matrix capabilities of a graphing utility to evaluate the expression. Round your results to three decimal places, if necessary.

17. $\begin{bmatrix} 2 & 5 \\ -1 & -4 \end{bmatrix} + \begin{bmatrix} -3 & 0 \\ 2 & 2 \end{bmatrix}$

18. $\begin{bmatrix} 14 & -11 \\ -22 & 19 \end{bmatrix} + \begin{bmatrix} -22 & 20 \\ 13 & 6 \end{bmatrix}$

19. $-\frac{1}{2}\begin{bmatrix} 3.211 & 6.829 \\ -1.004 & 4.914 \\ 0.055 & -3.889 \end{bmatrix} - 8\begin{bmatrix} 1.630 & -3.090 \\ 5.256 & 8.335 \\ -9.768 & 4.251 \end{bmatrix}$

20. $-12\left(\begin{bmatrix} 6 & 20 \\ 1 & -9 \\ -2 & 5 \end{bmatrix} + \begin{bmatrix} 14 & -15 \\ -8 & -6 \\ 7 & 0 \end{bmatrix} + \begin{bmatrix} -31 & -19 \\ 16 & 10 \\ 24 & 10 \end{bmatrix} \right)$

21. $-3\left(\begin{bmatrix} 0 & -3 \\ 7 & 2 \end{bmatrix} + \begin{bmatrix} -6 & 3 \\ 8 & 1 \end{bmatrix} \right) - \begin{bmatrix} 4 & -4 \\ 7 & -9 \end{bmatrix}$

22. $-1\begin{bmatrix} 4 & 11 \\ -2 & -1 \\ 9 & 3 \end{bmatrix} + \frac{1}{6}\left(\begin{bmatrix} -5 & -1 \\ 3 & 4 \\ 0 & 13 \end{bmatrix} + \begin{bmatrix} 7 & 5 \\ -9 & -1 \\ 6 & -1 \end{bmatrix} \right)$

In Exercises 23–26, solve for X when

$A = \begin{bmatrix} -2 & -1 \\ 1 & 0 \\ 3 & -4 \end{bmatrix}$ and $B = \begin{bmatrix} 0 & 3 \\ 2 & 0 \\ -4 & -1 \end{bmatrix}$.

23. $X = 3A - 2B$

24. $2X = 2A - B$

25. $2X + 3A = B$

26. $2A + 4B = -2X$

In Exercises 27–34, find AB, if possible.

27. $A = \begin{bmatrix} 2 & 1 \\ -3 & 4 \\ -1 & 6 \end{bmatrix}$, $B = \begin{bmatrix} 0 & -3 & 0 \\ 4 & 0 & 2 \\ 8 & -2 & 7 \end{bmatrix}$

28. $A = \begin{bmatrix} 0 & -1 & 2 \\ 6 & 0 & 3 \\ 7 & -1 & 8 \end{bmatrix}$, $B = \begin{bmatrix} 2 & -1 \\ 4 & -5 \\ 1 & 6 \end{bmatrix}$

29. $A = \begin{bmatrix} -1 & 6 \\ -4 & 5 \\ 0 & 3 \end{bmatrix}$, $B = \begin{bmatrix} 2 & 3 \\ 0 & 9 \end{bmatrix}$

30. $A = \begin{bmatrix} 1 & 0 & 0 \\ 0 & 4 & 0 \\ 0 & 0 & -2 \end{bmatrix}$, $B = \begin{bmatrix} 3 & 0 & 0 \\ 0 & -1 & 0 \\ 0 & 0 & 5 \end{bmatrix}$

31. $A = \begin{bmatrix} 5 & 0 & 0 \\ 0 & -8 & 0 \\ 0 & 0 & 7 \end{bmatrix}$, $B = \begin{bmatrix} \frac{1}{5} & 0 & 0 \\ 0 & -\frac{1}{8} & 0 \\ 0 & 0 & \frac{1}{2} \end{bmatrix}$

32. $A = \begin{bmatrix} 0 & 0 & 5 \\ 0 & 0 & -3 \\ 0 & 0 & 4 \end{bmatrix}$, $B = \begin{bmatrix} 6 & -11 & 4 \\ 8 & 16 & 4 \\ 0 & 0 & 0 \end{bmatrix}$

33. $A = \begin{bmatrix} 5 \\ 6 \end{bmatrix}$, $B = [-3 \quad -1 \quad -5 \quad -9]$

34. $A = \begin{bmatrix} 1 & 0 & 3 & -2 \\ 6 & 13 & 8 & -17 \end{bmatrix}$, $B = \begin{bmatrix} 1 & 6 \\ 4 & 2 \end{bmatrix}$

In Exercises 35–40, find, if possible, (a) AB, (b) BA, and (c) A^2. (Note: $A^2 = AA$.) Use the matrix capabilities of a graphing utility to verify your results.

35. $A = \begin{bmatrix} 1 & 2 \\ 5 & 2 \end{bmatrix}$, $B = \begin{bmatrix} 2 & -1 \\ -1 & 8 \end{bmatrix}$

36. $A = \begin{bmatrix} 6 & 3 \\ -2 & -4 \end{bmatrix}$, $B = \begin{bmatrix} -2 & 0 \\ 2 & 4 \end{bmatrix}$

37. $A = \begin{bmatrix} 3 & -1 \\ 1 & 3 \end{bmatrix}$, $B = \begin{bmatrix} 1 & -3 \\ 3 & 1 \end{bmatrix}$

38. $A = \begin{bmatrix} 1 & -1 \\ 1 & 1 \end{bmatrix}$, $B = \begin{bmatrix} 1 & 3 \\ -3 & 1 \end{bmatrix}$

39. $A = \begin{bmatrix} 7 \\ 8 \\ -1 \end{bmatrix}$, $B = [1 \quad 1 \quad 2]$

40. $A = [3 \quad 2 \quad 1]$, $B = \begin{bmatrix} 2 \\ 3 \\ 0 \end{bmatrix}$

In Exercises 41–46, use the matrix capabilities of a graphing utility to find AB, if possible.

41. $A = \begin{bmatrix} 7 & 5 & -4 \\ -2 & 5 & 1 \\ 10 & -4 & -7 \end{bmatrix}$, $B = \begin{bmatrix} 2 & -2 & 3 \\ 8 & 1 & 4 \\ -4 & 2 & -8 \end{bmatrix}$

42. $A = \begin{bmatrix} 1 & -12 & 4 \\ 14 & 10 & 12 \\ 6 & -15 & 3 \end{bmatrix}$, $B = \begin{bmatrix} 12 & 10 \\ -6 & 12 \\ 10 & 16 \end{bmatrix}$

43. $A = \begin{bmatrix} -3 & 8 & -6 & 8 \\ -12 & 15 & 9 & 6 \\ 5 & -1 & 1 & 5 \end{bmatrix}$, $B = \begin{bmatrix} 3 & 1 & 6 \\ 24 & 15 & 14 \\ 16 & 10 & 21 \\ 8 & -4 & 10 \end{bmatrix}$

44. $A = \begin{bmatrix} -2 & 6 & 12 \\ 21 & -5 & 6 \\ 13 & -2 & 9 \end{bmatrix}$, $B = \begin{bmatrix} 3 & 0 \\ -7 & 18 \\ 34 & 14 \\ 0.5 & 1.4 \end{bmatrix}$

45. $A = \begin{bmatrix} 9 & 10 & -38 & 18 \\ 100 & -50 & 250 & 75 \end{bmatrix}$,

$B = \begin{bmatrix} 52 & -85 & 27 & 45 \\ 40 & -35 & 60 & 82 \end{bmatrix}$

46. $A = \begin{bmatrix} 16 & -18 \\ -4 & 13 \\ -9 & 21 \end{bmatrix}$, $B = \begin{bmatrix} -7 & 20 & -1 \\ 7 & 15 & 26 \end{bmatrix}$

In Exercises 47–50, use the matrix capabilities of a graphing utility to evaluate the expression.

47. $\begin{bmatrix} 3 & 1 \\ 0 & -2 \end{bmatrix}\begin{bmatrix} 1 & 0 \\ -2 & 2 \end{bmatrix}\begin{bmatrix} 1 & 0 \\ 2 & 4 \end{bmatrix}$

48. $-3\left(\begin{bmatrix} 6 & 5 & -1 \\ 1 & -2 & 0 \end{bmatrix}\begin{bmatrix} 0 & 3 \\ -1 & -3 \\ 4 & 1 \end{bmatrix} \right)$

49. $\begin{bmatrix} 0 & 2 & -2 \\ 4 & 1 & 2 \end{bmatrix}\left(\begin{bmatrix} 4 & 0 \\ 0 & -1 \\ -1 & 2 \end{bmatrix} + \begin{bmatrix} -2 & 3 \\ -3 & 5 \\ 0 & -3 \end{bmatrix} \right)$

50. $\begin{bmatrix} 3 \\ -1 \\ 5 \\ 7 \end{bmatrix}\left(\begin{bmatrix} 5 & -6 \end{bmatrix} + \begin{bmatrix} 7 & -1 \end{bmatrix} + \begin{bmatrix} -8 & 9 \end{bmatrix} \right)$

In Exercises 51–54, use matrix multiplication to determine whether each matrix is a solution of the system of equations. Use a graphing utility to verify your results.

51. $\begin{cases} x + 2y = 4 \\ 3x + 2y = 0 \end{cases}$

(a) $\begin{bmatrix} 2 \\ 1 \end{bmatrix}$ (b) $\begin{bmatrix} -2 \\ 3 \end{bmatrix}$

(c) $\begin{bmatrix} -4 \\ 4 \end{bmatrix}$ (d) $\begin{bmatrix} 2 \\ -3 \end{bmatrix}$

52. $\begin{cases} 6x + 2y = 0 \\ -x + 5y = 16 \end{cases}$

(a) $\begin{bmatrix} -1 \\ 3 \end{bmatrix}$ (b) $\begin{bmatrix} 2 \\ -6 \end{bmatrix}$

(c) $\begin{bmatrix} 3 \\ -9 \end{bmatrix}$ (d) $\begin{bmatrix} -3 \\ 9 \end{bmatrix}$

53. $\begin{cases} -2x - 3y = -6 \\ 4x + 2y = 20 \end{cases}$

(a) $\begin{bmatrix} 3 \\ 0 \end{bmatrix}$ (b) $\begin{bmatrix} 6 \\ -2 \end{bmatrix}$

(c) $\begin{bmatrix} -6 \\ 6 \end{bmatrix}$ (d) $\begin{bmatrix} 4 \\ 2 \end{bmatrix}$

54. $\begin{cases} 5x - 7y = -15 \\ 3x + y = 17 \end{cases}$

(a) $\begin{bmatrix} 4 \\ 5 \end{bmatrix}$ (b) $\begin{bmatrix} 5 \\ 2 \end{bmatrix}$

(c) $\begin{bmatrix} -4 \\ -5 \end{bmatrix}$ (d) $\begin{bmatrix} 2 \\ 11 \end{bmatrix}$

In Exercises 55–62, (a) write each system of equations as a matrix equation $AX = B$ and (b) use Gauss-Jordan elimination on the augmented matrix $[A \vdots B]$ to solve for the matrix X. Use a graphing utility to check your solution.

55. $\begin{cases} -x_1 + x_2 = 4 \\ -2x_1 + x_2 = 0 \end{cases}$

56. $\begin{cases} 2x_1 + 3x_2 = 5 \\ x_1 + 4x_2 = 10 \end{cases}$

57. $\begin{cases} -2x_1 - 3x_2 = -4 \\ 6x_1 + x_2 = -36 \end{cases}$

58. $\begin{cases} -4x_1 + 9x_2 = -13 \\ x_1 - 3x_2 = 12 \end{cases}$

59. $\begin{cases} x_1 - 2x_2 + 3x_3 = 9 \\ -x_1 + 3x_2 - x_3 = -6 \\ 2x_1 - 5x_2 + 5x_3 = 17 \end{cases}$

60. $\begin{cases} x_1 + x_2 - 3x_3 = -1 \\ -x_1 + 2x_2 = 1 \\ x_1 - x_2 + x_3 = 2 \end{cases}$

61. $\begin{cases} x_1 - 5x_2 + 2x_3 = -20 \\ -3x_1 + x_2 - x_3 = 8 \\ -2x_2 + 5x_3 = -16 \end{cases}$

62. $\begin{cases} x_1 - x_2 + 4x_3 = 17 \\ x_1 + 3x_2 = -11 \\ -6x_2 + 5x_3 = 40 \end{cases}$

In Exercises 63 and 64, use the matrix capabilities of a graphing utility to find $f(A) = a_0 I_n + a_1 A + a_2 A^2$.

63. $f(x) = x^2 - 5x + 2$, $A = \begin{bmatrix} 2 & 0 \\ 4 & 5 \end{bmatrix}$

64. $f(x) = x^2 - 7x + 6$, $A = \begin{bmatrix} 5 & 4 \\ 1 & 2 \end{bmatrix}$

65. *Manufacturing*   A corporation has three factories, each of which manufactures acoustic guitars and electric guitars. The number of units of guitars produced at factory j in one day is represented by a_{ij} in the matrix

$$A = \begin{bmatrix} 70 & 50 & 25 \\ 35 & 100 & 70 \end{bmatrix}.$$

Find the production levels if production is increased by 20%.

66. *Manufacturing*   A corporation has four factories, each of which manufactures sport utility vehicles and pickup trucks. The number of units of vehicle i produced at factory j in one day is represented by a_{ij} in the matrix

$$A = \begin{bmatrix} 100 & 90 & 70 & 30 \\ 40 & 20 & 60 & 60 \end{bmatrix}.$$

Find the production levels if production is increased by 10%.

67. *Agriculture*   A fruit grower raises two crops, apples and peaches. Each of these crops is shipped to three different outlets. The number of units of crop i that are shipped to outlet j is represented by a_{ij} in the matrix

$$A = \begin{bmatrix} 125 & 100 & 75 \\ 100 & 175 & 125 \end{bmatrix}.$$

The profit per unit is represented by the matrix

$$B = \begin{bmatrix} \$3.50 & \$6.00 \end{bmatrix}.$$

Find the product BA and state what each entry of the product represents.

68. *Revenue*   A manufacturer produces three models of portable CD players, which are shipped to two warehouses. The number of units of model i that are shipped to warehouse j is represented by a_{ij} in the matrix

$$A = \begin{bmatrix} 5{,}000 & 4{,}000 \\ 6{,}000 & 10{,}000 \\ 8{,}000 & 5{,}000 \end{bmatrix}.$$

The price per unit is represented by the matrix

$$B = \begin{bmatrix} \$39.50 & \$44.50 & \$56.50 \end{bmatrix}.$$

Compute BA and state what each entry of the product represents.

69. *Inventory*   A company sells five models of computers through three retail outlets. The inventories are given by S. The wholesale and retail prices are given by T. Compute ST and interpret the result.

Model

$$S = \begin{array}{c} \\ \\ \text{Outlet} \\ \\ \end{array} \begin{bmatrix} A & B & C & D & E \\ 3 & 2 & 2 & 3 & 0 \\ 0 & 2 & 3 & 4 & 3 \\ 4 & 2 & 1 & 3 & 2 \end{bmatrix} \begin{array}{c} 1 \\ 2 \\ 3 \end{array}$$

Price

$$T = \begin{bmatrix} \text{Wholesale} & \text{Retail} \\ \$840 & \$1100 \\ \$1200 & \$1350 \\ \$1450 & \$1650 \\ \$2650 & \$3000 \\ \$3050 & \$3200 \end{bmatrix} \begin{array}{c} A \\ B \\ C \\ D \\ E \end{array} \text{Model}$$

70. *Labor/Wage Requirements*   A company that manufactures boats has the following labor-hour and wage requirements. Compute ST and interpret the result.

Labor per Boat

Department

$$S = \begin{bmatrix} \text{Cutting} & \text{Assembly} & \text{Packaging} \\ 1.0 \text{ hr} & 0.5 \text{ hr} & 0.2 \text{ hr} \\ 1.6 \text{ hr} & 1.0 \text{ hr} & 0.2 \text{ hr} \\ 2.5 \text{ hr} & 2.0 \text{ hr} & 0.4 \text{ hr} \end{bmatrix} \begin{array}{c} \text{Small} \\ \text{Medium} \\ \text{Large} \end{array} \begin{array}{c} \text{Boat} \\ \text{Size} \end{array}$$

Wages per Hour

Plant

$$T = \begin{bmatrix} A & B \\ \$12 & \$10 \\ \$9 & \$8 \\ \$6 & \$5 \end{bmatrix} \begin{array}{c} \text{Cutting} \\ \text{Assembly} \\ \text{Packaging} \end{array} \text{Department}$$

71. *Voting Preference*   The matrix

From

$$P = \begin{bmatrix} R & D & I \\ 0.6 & 0.1 & 0.1 \\ 0.2 & 0.7 & 0.1 \\ 0.2 & 0.2 & 0.8 \end{bmatrix} \begin{array}{c} R \\ D \\ I \end{array} \text{To}$$

is called a *stochastic matrix*. Each entry $p_{ij}\,(i \neq j)$ represents the proportion of the voting population that changes from party i to party j, and p_{ii} represents the proportion that remains loyal to the party from one election to the next. Compute and interpret P^2.

72. *Voting Preference* Use a graphing utility to find P^3, P^4, P^5, P^6, P^7, and P^8 for the matrix given in Exercise 71. Can you detect a pattern as P is raised to higher powers?

Synthesis

True or False? **In Exercises 73 and 74, determine whether the statement is true or false. Justify your answer.**

73. Two matrices can be added only if they have the same order.

74. Matrix multiplication is commutative.

Think About It **In Exercises 75–82, let matrices A, B, C, and D be of orders 2×3, 2×3, 3×2, and 2×2, respectively. Determine whether the matrices are of proper order to perform the operation(s). If so, give the order of the answer.**

75. $A + 2C$

76. $B - 3C$

77. AB

78. BC

79. $BC - D$

80. $CB - D$

81. $D(A - 3B)$

82. $(BC - D)A$

83. *Think About It* If a, b, and c are real numbers such that $c \neq 0$ and $ac = bc$, then $a = b$. However, if A, B, and C are nonzero matrices such that $AC = BC$, then A is *not necessarily* equal to B. Illustrate this using the following matrices.

$$A = \begin{bmatrix} 0 & 1 \\ 0 & 1 \end{bmatrix}, \quad B = \begin{bmatrix} 1 & 0 \\ 1 & 0 \end{bmatrix}, \quad C = \begin{bmatrix} 2 & 3 \\ 2 & 3 \end{bmatrix}$$

84. *Think About It* If a and b are real numbers such that $ab = 0$, then $a = 0$ or $b = 0$. However, if A and B are matrices such that $AB = O$, it is *not necessarily* true that $A = O$ or $B = O$. Illustrate this using the following matrices.

$$A = \begin{bmatrix} 3 & 3 \\ 4 & 4 \end{bmatrix}, \quad B = \begin{bmatrix} 1 & -1 \\ -1 & 1 \end{bmatrix}$$

85. *Exploration* Let $i = \sqrt{-1}$ and let

$$A = \begin{bmatrix} i & 0 \\ 0 & i \end{bmatrix} \quad \text{and} \quad B = \begin{bmatrix} 0 & -i \\ i & 0 \end{bmatrix}.$$

(a) Find A^2, A^3, and A^4. Identify any similarities with i^2, i^3, and i^4.

(b) Find and identify B^2.

86. *Conjecture* Let A and B be unequal diagonal matrices of the same order. (A *diagonal matrix* is a square matrix in which each entry not on the main diagonal is zero.) Determine the products AB for several pairs of such matrices. Make a conjecture about a quick rule for such products.

87. *Exploration* Consider matrices of the form

$$A = \begin{bmatrix} 0 & a_{12} & a_{13} & a_{14} & \cdots & a_{1n} \\ 0 & 0 & a_{23} & a_{24} & \cdots & a_{2n} \\ 0 & 0 & 0 & a_{34} & \cdots & a_{3n} \\ \vdots & \vdots & \vdots & \vdots & \cdots & \vdots \\ 0 & 0 & 0 & 0 & \cdots & a_{(n-1)n} \\ 0 & 0 & 0 & 0 & \cdots & 0 \end{bmatrix}.$$

(a) Write a 2×2 matrix and a 3×3 matrix in the form of A.

(b) Use a graphing utility to raise each of the matrices to higher powers. Describe the result.

(c) Use the result of part (b) to make a conjecture about powers of A if A is a 4×4 matrix. Use a graphing utility to test your conjecture.

(d) Use the results of parts (b) and (c) to make a conjecture about powers of an $n \times n$ matrix A.

88. *Writing* Two competing companies offer cable television to a city with 100,000 households. Gold Cable Company has 25,000 subscribers and Galaxy Cable Company has 30,000 subscribers. (The other 45,000 households do not subscribe.) The percent changes in cable subscriptions each year are shown below. Write a short paragraph explaining how matrix multiplication can be used to find the number of subscribers each company will have in 1 year.

		Percent Changes	
	From Gold	From Galaxy	From Nonsubscriber
Percent Changes ⎧ To Gold	0.70	0.15	0.15
⎨ To Galaxy	0.20	0.80	0.15
⎩ To Nonsubscriber	0.10	0.05	0.70

Review

In Exercises 89–92, condense the expression to the logarithm of a single quantity.

89. $3 \ln 4 - \frac{1}{3} \ln(x^2 + 3)$

90. $\ln x - 3[\ln(x + 6) + \ln(x - 6)]$

91. $\frac{1}{2}[2 \ln(x + 5) + \ln x - \ln(x - 8)]$

92. $\frac{3}{2} \ln 7t^4 - \frac{3}{5} \ln t^5$

8.6   The Inverse of a Square Matrix

The Inverse of a Matrix

This section further develops the algebra of matrices. To begin, consider the real number equation $ax = b$. To solve this equation for x, multiply each side of the equation by a^{-1} (provided that $a \neq 0$).

$$ax = b$$
$$(a^{-1}a)x = a^{-1}b$$
$$(1)x = a^{-1}b$$
$$x = a^{-1}b$$

The number a^{-1} is called the *multiplicative inverse of a* because $a^{-1}a = 1$. The definition of the multiplicative **inverse of a matrix** is similar.

Definition of the Inverse of a Square Matrix

Let A be an $n \times n$ matrix and let I_n be the $n \times n$ identity matrix. If there exists a matrix A^{-1} such that

$$AA^{-1} = I_n = A^{-1}A$$

then A^{-1} is called the **inverse** of A. The symbol A^{-1} is read "A inverse."

Example 1   The Inverse of a Matrix

Show that B is the inverse of A, where $A = \begin{bmatrix} -1 & 2 \\ -1 & 1 \end{bmatrix}$ and $B = \begin{bmatrix} 1 & -2 \\ 1 & -1 \end{bmatrix}$.

Solution

To show that B is the inverse of A, show that $AB = I = BA$, as follows.

$$AB = \begin{bmatrix} -1 & 2 \\ -1 & 1 \end{bmatrix}\begin{bmatrix} 1 & -2 \\ 1 & -1 \end{bmatrix} = \begin{bmatrix} -1+2 & 2-2 \\ -1+1 & 2-1 \end{bmatrix} = \begin{bmatrix} 1 & 0 \\ 0 & 1 \end{bmatrix}$$

$$BA = \begin{bmatrix} 1 & -2 \\ 1 & -1 \end{bmatrix}\begin{bmatrix} -1 & 2 \\ -1 & 1 \end{bmatrix} = \begin{bmatrix} -1+2 & 2-2 \\ -1+1 & 2-1 \end{bmatrix} = \begin{bmatrix} 1 & 0 \\ 0 & 1 \end{bmatrix}$$

As you can see, $AB = I = BA$. This is an example of a square matrix that has an inverse. Note that not all square matrices have an inverse.

☑ *Checkpoint* Now try Exercise 3.

Recall that it is not always true that $AB = BA$, even if both products are defined. However, if A and B are both square matrices and $AB = I_n$, it can be shown that $BA = I_n$. So, in Example 1, you need only check that $AB = I_2$.

What you should learn

- Verify that two matrices are inverses of each other.
- Use Gauss-Jordan elimination to find inverses of matrices.
- Use a formula to find inverses of 2×2 matrices.
- Use inverse matrices to solve systems of linear equations.

Why you should learn it

A system of equations can be solved using the inverse of the coefficient matrix. This method is particularly useful when the coefficients are the same for several systems, but the constants are different. Exercise 61 on page 667 shows how to use an inverse matrix to find unknown currents in electrical circuits.

Firefly Productions/Corbis

If a matrix A has an inverse, A is called **invertible** (or **nonsingular**); otherwise, A is called **singular.** A nonsquare matrix cannot have an inverse. To see this, note that if A is of order $m \times n$ and B is of order $n \times m$ (where $m \neq n$), the products AB and BA are of different orders and so cannot be equal to each other. Not all square matrices have inverses, as you will see at the bottom of page 662. If, however, a matrix does have an inverse, that inverse is unique. Example 2 shows how to use systems of equations to find the inverse of a matrix.

Example 2 Finding the Inverse of a Matrix

Find the inverse of

$$A = \begin{bmatrix} 1 & 4 \\ -1 & -3 \end{bmatrix}.$$

Solution

To find the inverse of A, try to solve the matrix equation $AX = I$ for X.

$$\underset{A}{\begin{bmatrix} 1 & 4 \\ -1 & -3 \end{bmatrix}} \underset{X}{\begin{bmatrix} x_{11} & x_{12} \\ x_{21} & x_{22} \end{bmatrix}} = \underset{I}{\begin{bmatrix} 1 & 0 \\ 0 & 1 \end{bmatrix}}$$

$$\begin{bmatrix} x_{11} + 4x_{21} & x_{12} + 4x_{22} \\ -x_{11} - 3x_{21} & -x_{12} - 3x_{22} \end{bmatrix} = \begin{bmatrix} 1 & 0 \\ 0 & 1 \end{bmatrix}$$

Equating corresponding entries, you obtain the following two systems of linear equations.

$$\begin{cases} x_{11} + 4x_{21} = 1 \\ -x_{11} - 3x_{21} = 0 \end{cases} \qquad \begin{cases} x_{12} + 4x_{22} = 0 \\ -x_{12} - 3x_{22} = 1 \end{cases}$$

Solve the first system using elementary row operations to determine that $x_{11} = -3$ and $x_{21} = 1$. From the second system you can determine that $x_{12} = -4$ and $x_{22} = 1$. Therefore, the inverse of A is

$$X = A^{-1}$$

$$= \begin{bmatrix} -3 & -4 \\ 1 & 1 \end{bmatrix}.$$

You can use matrix multiplication to check this result.

Check

$$AA^{-1} = \begin{bmatrix} 1 & 4 \\ -1 & -3 \end{bmatrix} \begin{bmatrix} -3 & -4 \\ 1 & 1 \end{bmatrix} = \begin{bmatrix} 1 & 0 \\ 0 & 1 \end{bmatrix} \checkmark$$

$$A^{-1}A = \begin{bmatrix} -3 & -4 \\ 1 & 1 \end{bmatrix} \begin{bmatrix} 1 & 4 \\ -1 & -3 \end{bmatrix} = \begin{bmatrix} 1 & 0 \\ 0 & 1 \end{bmatrix} \checkmark$$

✓ *Checkpoint* Now try Exercise 13.

Exploration

Most graphing utilities are capable of finding the inverse of a square matrix. Try using a graphing utility to find the inverse of the matrix

$$A = \begin{bmatrix} 2 & -3 & 1 \\ -1 & 2 & -1 \\ -2 & 0 & 1 \end{bmatrix}.$$

After you find A^{-1}, store it as $[B]$ and use the graphing utility to find $[A] \times [B]$ and $[B] \times [A]$. What can you conclude?

Finding Inverse Matrices

In Example 2, note that the two systems of linear equations have the *same coefficient matrix A*. Rather than solve the two systems represented by

$$\begin{bmatrix} 1 & 4 & \vdots & 1 \\ -1 & -3 & \vdots & 0 \end{bmatrix}$$

and

$$\begin{bmatrix} 1 & 4 & \vdots & 0 \\ -1 & -3 & \vdots & 1 \end{bmatrix}$$

separately, you can solve them *simultaneously* by *adjoining* the identity matrix to the coefficient matrix to obtain

$$\overset{A}{} \qquad \overset{I}{}$$
$$\begin{bmatrix} 1 & 4 & \vdots & 1 & 0 \\ -1 & -3 & \vdots & 0 & 1 \end{bmatrix}.$$

This "doubly augmented" matrix can be represented as $[A \;\vdots\; I]$. By applying Gauss-Jordan elimination to this matrix, you can solve *both* systems with a single elimination process.

$$\begin{bmatrix} 1 & 4 & \vdots & 1 & 0 \\ -1 & -3 & \vdots & 0 & 1 \end{bmatrix}$$

$$R_1 + R_2 \to \begin{bmatrix} 1 & 4 & \vdots & 1 & 0 \\ 0 & 1 & \vdots & 1 & 1 \end{bmatrix}$$

$$-4R_2 + R_1 \to \begin{bmatrix} 1 & 0 & \vdots & -3 & -4 \\ 0 & 1 & \vdots & 1 & 1 \end{bmatrix}$$

So, from the "doubly augmented" matrix $[A \;\vdots\; I]$, you obtained the matrix $[I \;\vdots\; A^{-1}]$.

$$\overset{A}{} \qquad \overset{I}{} \qquad\qquad \overset{I}{} \qquad \overset{A^{-1}}{}$$
$$\begin{bmatrix} 1 & 4 & \vdots & 1 & 0 \\ -1 & -3 & \vdots & 0 & 1 \end{bmatrix} \implies \begin{bmatrix} 1 & 0 & \vdots & -3 & -4 \\ 0 & 1 & \vdots & 1 & 1 \end{bmatrix}$$

This procedure (or algorithm) works for any square matrix that has an inverse.

Exploration

Select two 2×2 matrices A and B that have inverses. Enter them into your graphing utility and calculate $(AB)^{-1}$. Then calculate $B^{-1}A^{-1}$ and $A^{-1}B^{-1}$. Make a conjecture about the inverse of the product of two invertible matrices.

Finding an Inverse Matrix

Let A be a square matrix of order n.

1. Write the $n \times 2n$ matrix that consists of the given matrix A on the left and the $n \times n$ identity matrix I on the right to obtain $[A \;\vdots\; I]$.

2. If possible, row reduce A to I using elementary row operations on the *entire* matrix $[A \;\vdots\; I]$. The result will be the matrix $[I \;\vdots\; A^{-1}]$. If this is not possible, A is not invertible.

3. Check your work by multiplying to see that $AA^{-1} = I = A^{-1}A$.

Example 3 Finding the Inverse of a Matrix

Find the inverse of $A = \begin{bmatrix} 1 & -1 & 0 \\ 1 & 0 & -1 \\ 6 & -2 & -3 \end{bmatrix}$.

Solution

Begin by adjoining the identity matrix to A to form the matrix

$$[A \vdots I] = \begin{bmatrix} 1 & -1 & 0 & \vdots & 1 & 0 & 0 \\ 1 & 0 & -1 & \vdots & 0 & 1 & 0 \\ 6 & -2 & -3 & \vdots & 0 & 0 & 1 \end{bmatrix}.$$

Use elementary row operations to obtain the form $[I \vdots A^{-1}]$, as follows.

$$\begin{bmatrix} 1 & 0 & 0 & \vdots & -2 & -3 & 1 \\ 0 & 1 & 0 & \vdots & -3 & -3 & 1 \\ 0 & 0 & 1 & \vdots & -2 & -4 & 1 \end{bmatrix}$$

Therefore, the matrix A is invertible and its inverse is

$$A^{-1} = \begin{bmatrix} -2 & -3 & 1 \\ -3 & -3 & 1 \\ -2 & -4 & 1 \end{bmatrix}.$$

Try using a graphing utility to confirm this result by multiplying A by A^{-1} to obtain I.

✓ *Checkpoint* Now try Exercise 21.

TECHNOLOGY TIP

Most graphing utilities can find the inverse of a matrix. A graphing utility can be used to check matrix operations. This saves valuable time otherwise spent doing minor arithmetic calculations.

The algorithm shown in Example 3 applies to any $n \times n$ matrix A. When using this algorithm, if the matrix A does not reduce to the identity matrix, then A does not have an inverse. For instance, the following matrix has no inverse.

$$A = \begin{bmatrix} 1 & 2 & 0 \\ 3 & -1 & 2 \\ -2 & 3 & -2 \end{bmatrix}$$

To confirm that matrix A above has no inverse, begin by adjoining the identity matrix to A to form

$$[A \vdots I] = \begin{bmatrix} 1 & 2 & 0 & \vdots & 1 & 0 & 0 \\ 3 & -1 & 2 & \vdots & 0 & 1 & 0 \\ -2 & 3 & -2 & \vdots & 0 & 0 & 1 \end{bmatrix}.$$

Then use elementary row operations to obtain

$$\begin{bmatrix} 1 & 2 & 0 & \vdots & 1 & 0 & 0 \\ 0 & -7 & 2 & \vdots & -3 & 1 & 0 \\ 0 & 0 & 0 & \vdots & -1 & 1 & 1 \end{bmatrix}.$$

At this point in the elimination process you can see that it is impossible to obtain the identity matrix I on the left. Therefore, A is not invertible.

Example 4   Finding the Inverse of a Matrix

Use a graphing utility to find the inverse of $A = \begin{bmatrix} 1 & 2 & -2 \\ 1 & -1 & 0 \\ 0 & -1 & 4 \end{bmatrix}$.

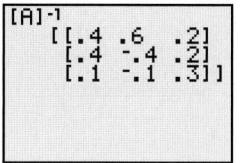

Solution

Use the *matrix editor* to enter A into the graphing utility. Use the inverse key $\boxed{x^{-1}}$ to find the inverse of the matrix, as shown in Figure 8.31. Check this result algebraically by multiplying A by A^{-1} to obtain I.

Figure 8.31

✓ *Checkpoint* Now try Exercise 27.

The Inverse of a 2 × 2 Matrix

Using Gauss-Jordan elimination to find the inverse of a matrix works well (even as a computer technique) for matrices of order 3×3 or greater. For 2×2 matrices, however, many people prefer to use a formula for the inverse rather than Gauss-Jordan elimination. This simple formula, which works *only* for 2×2 matrices, is explained as follows. If A is the 2×2 matrix given by

$$A = \begin{bmatrix} a & b \\ c & d \end{bmatrix}$$

then A is invertible if and only if $ad - bc \neq 0$. If $ad - bc \neq 0$, the inverse is given by

$$A^{-1} = \frac{1}{ad - bc} \begin{bmatrix} d & -b \\ -c & a \end{bmatrix}. \qquad \text{Formula for inverse of matrix } A$$

The denominator $ad - bc$ is called the *determinant* of the 2×2 matrix A. You will study determinants in the next section.

Example 5   Finding the Inverse of a 2 × 2 Matrix

If possible, find the inverse of $A = \begin{bmatrix} 3 & -1 \\ -2 & 2 \end{bmatrix}$.

Solution

Apply the formula for the inverse of a 2×2 matrix to obtain

$$ad - bc = (3)(2) - (-1)(-2) = 4.$$

Because this quantity is not zero, the inverse is formed by interchanging the entries on the main diagonal, changing the signs of the other two entries, and multiplying by the scalar $\frac{1}{4}$, as follows.

$$A^{-1} = \frac{1}{4} \begin{bmatrix} 2 & 1 \\ 2 & 3 \end{bmatrix} = \begin{bmatrix} \frac{1}{2} & \frac{1}{4} \\ \frac{1}{2} & \frac{3}{4} \end{bmatrix}$$

✓ *Checkpoint* Now try Exercise 33.

> **Exploration**
>
> Use a graphing utility to find the inverse of the matrix
>
> $$A = \begin{bmatrix} 1 & -3 \\ -2 & 6 \end{bmatrix}.$$
>
> What message appears on the screen? Why does the graphing utility display this message?

Systems of Linear Equations

You know that a system of linear equations can have exactly one solution, infinitely many solutions, or no solution. If the coefficient matrix A of a *square* system (a system that has the same number of equations as variables) is invertible, the system has a unique solution, which is defined as follows.

> **A System of Equations with a Unique Solution**
>
> If A is an invertible matrix, the system of linear equations represented by $AX = B$ has a unique solution given by
>
> $$X = A^{-1}B.$$

The formula $X = A^{-1}B$ is used on most graphing utilities to solve linear systems that have invertible coefficient matrices. That is, you enter the $n \times n$ coefficient matrix $[A]$ and the $n \times 1$ column matrix $[B]$. The solution X is given by $[A]^{-1}[B]$.

Example 6 Solving a System of Equations Using an Inverse

Use an inverse matrix to solve the system.

$$\begin{cases} 2x + 3y + z = -1 \\ 3x + 3y + z = 1 \\ 2x + 4y + z = -2 \end{cases}$$

Solution

Begin by writing the system as $AX = B$.

$$\begin{bmatrix} 2 & 3 & 1 \\ 3 & 3 & 1 \\ 2 & 4 & 1 \end{bmatrix} \begin{bmatrix} x \\ y \\ z \end{bmatrix} = \begin{bmatrix} -1 \\ 1 \\ -2 \end{bmatrix}$$

Then, use Gauss-Jordan elimination to find A^{-1}.

$$A^{-1} = \begin{bmatrix} -1 & 1 & 0 \\ -1 & 0 & 1 \\ 6 & -2 & -3 \end{bmatrix}$$

Finally, multiply B by A^{-1} on the left to obtain the solution.

$$X = A^{-1}B$$

$$= \begin{bmatrix} -1 & 1 & 0 \\ -1 & 0 & 1 \\ 6 & -2 & -3 \end{bmatrix} \begin{bmatrix} -1 \\ 1 \\ -2 \end{bmatrix} = \begin{bmatrix} 2 \\ -1 \\ -2 \end{bmatrix}$$

So, the solution is $x = 2$, $y = -1$, and $z = -2$. Use a graphing utility to verify A^{-1} for the system of equations.

✓ *Checkpoint* Now try Exercise 51.

STUDY TIP

Remember that matrix multiplication is not commutative. So, you must multiply matrices in the correct order. For instance, in Example 6, you must multiply B by A^{-1} on the left.

8.6   Exercises

Vocabulary Check

Fill in the blanks.

1. In a _____ matrix, the number of rows equals the number of columns.
2. If there exists an $n \times n$ matrix A^{-1} such that $AA^{-1} = I_n = A^{-1}A$, then A^{-1} is called the _____ of A.
3. If a matrix A has an inverse, it is called invertible or _____ ; if it does not have an inverse, it is called _____ .

In Exercises 1–8, show that B is the inverse of A.

1. $A = \begin{bmatrix} 2 & 1 \\ 5 & 3 \end{bmatrix}$, $B = \begin{bmatrix} 3 & -1 \\ -5 & 2 \end{bmatrix}$

2. $A = \begin{bmatrix} 1 & -1 \\ -1 & 2 \end{bmatrix}$, $B = \begin{bmatrix} 2 & 1 \\ 1 & 1 \end{bmatrix}$

3. $A = \begin{bmatrix} 1 & 2 \\ 3 & 4 \end{bmatrix}$, $B = \begin{bmatrix} -2 & 1 \\ \frac{3}{2} & -\frac{1}{2} \end{bmatrix}$

4. $A = \begin{bmatrix} 1 & -1 \\ 2 & 3 \end{bmatrix}$, $B = \begin{bmatrix} \frac{3}{5} & \frac{1}{5} \\ -\frac{2}{5} & \frac{1}{5} \end{bmatrix}$

5. $A = \begin{bmatrix} 2 & -17 & 11 \\ -1 & 11 & -7 \\ 0 & 3 & -2 \end{bmatrix}$, $B = \begin{bmatrix} 1 & 1 & 2 \\ 2 & 4 & -3 \\ 3 & 6 & -5 \end{bmatrix}$

6. $A = \begin{bmatrix} -4 & 1 & 5 \\ -1 & 2 & 4 \\ 0 & -1 & -1 \end{bmatrix}$, $B = \begin{bmatrix} -\frac{1}{2} & 1 & \frac{3}{2} \\ \frac{1}{4} & -1 & -\frac{11}{4} \\ -\frac{1}{4} & 1 & \frac{7}{4} \end{bmatrix}$

7. $A = \begin{bmatrix} -2 & 2 & 3 \\ 1 & -1 & 0 \\ 0 & 1 & 4 \end{bmatrix}$, $B = \frac{1}{3}\begin{bmatrix} -4 & -5 & 3 \\ -4 & -8 & 3 \\ 1 & 2 & 0 \end{bmatrix}$

8. $A = \begin{bmatrix} 1 & 0 & -1 \\ -1 & 1 & 0 \\ 1 & 2 & 0 \end{bmatrix}$, $B = \frac{1}{3}\begin{bmatrix} 0 & -2 & 1 \\ 0 & 1 & 1 \\ -3 & -2 & 1 \end{bmatrix}$

In Exercises 9–12, use the matrix capabilities of a graphing utility to show that B is the inverse of A.

9. $A = \begin{bmatrix} -1 & -4 \\ 1 & 2 \end{bmatrix}$, $B = \begin{bmatrix} 1 & 2 \\ -\frac{1}{2} & -\frac{1}{2} \end{bmatrix}$

10. $A = \begin{bmatrix} 11 & -12 \\ 2 & -2 \end{bmatrix}$, $B = \begin{bmatrix} -1 & 6 \\ -1 & \frac{11}{2} \end{bmatrix}$

11. $A = \begin{bmatrix} 1.6 & 2 \\ -3.5 & -4.5 \end{bmatrix}$, $B = \begin{bmatrix} 22.5 & 10 \\ -17.5 & -8 \end{bmatrix}$

12. $A = \begin{bmatrix} 4 & 0 & -2 \\ 1 & 2 & -4 \\ 0 & 3 & 1 \end{bmatrix}$, $B = \begin{bmatrix} 0.28 & -0.12 & 0.08 \\ -0.02 & 0.08 & 0.28 \\ 0.06 & -0.24 & 0.16 \end{bmatrix}$

In Exercises 13–24, find the inverse of the matrix (if it exists).

13. $\begin{bmatrix} 2 & 0 \\ 0 & 3 \end{bmatrix}$

14. $\begin{bmatrix} 1 & 2 \\ 3 & 7 \end{bmatrix}$

15. $\begin{bmatrix} 1 & -2 \\ 2 & -3 \end{bmatrix}$

16. $\begin{bmatrix} -7 & 33 \\ 4 & -19 \end{bmatrix}$

17. $\begin{bmatrix} -1 & 1 \\ -2 & 1 \end{bmatrix}$

18. $\begin{bmatrix} 2 & -4 \\ 4 & 8 \end{bmatrix}$

19. $\begin{bmatrix} 2 & 7 & 1 \\ -3 & -9 & 2 \end{bmatrix}$

20. $\begin{bmatrix} -2 & 5 \\ 6 & -15 \\ 0 & 1 \end{bmatrix}$

21. $\begin{bmatrix} 1 & 1 & 1 \\ 3 & 5 & 4 \\ 3 & 6 & 5 \end{bmatrix}$

22. $\begin{bmatrix} 1 & 2 & 2 \\ 3 & 7 & 9 \\ -1 & -4 & -7 \end{bmatrix}$

23. $\begin{bmatrix} -5 & 0 & 0 \\ 2 & 0 & 0 \\ -1 & 5 & 7 \end{bmatrix}$

24. $\begin{bmatrix} 1 & 0 & 0 \\ 3 & 5 & 0 \\ 2 & 5 & 0 \end{bmatrix}$

In Exercises 25–32, use the matrix capabilities of a graphing utility to find the inverse of the matrix (if it exists).

25. $\begin{bmatrix} 1 & 0 & -2 \\ 4 & 0 & 0 \\ -2 & 0 & 3 \end{bmatrix}$

26. $\begin{bmatrix} 1 & 2 & -1 \\ 3 & 7 & -10 \\ -5 & -7 & -15 \end{bmatrix}$

27. $\begin{bmatrix} -\frac{1}{2} & \frac{3}{4} & \frac{1}{4} \\ 1 & 0 & -\frac{3}{2} \\ 0 & -1 & \frac{1}{2} \end{bmatrix}$

28. $\begin{bmatrix} -\frac{5}{6} & \frac{1}{3} & \frac{11}{6} \\ 0 & \frac{2}{3} & 2 \\ 1 & -\frac{1}{2} & -\frac{5}{2} \end{bmatrix}$

29. $\begin{bmatrix} 0.1 & 0.2 & 0.3 \\ -0.3 & 0.2 & 0.2 \\ 0.5 & 0.4 & 0.4 \end{bmatrix}$

30. $\begin{bmatrix} 0.6 & 0 & -0.3 \\ 0.7 & -1 & 0.2 \\ 1 & 0 & -0.9 \end{bmatrix}$

31. $\begin{bmatrix} -1 & 0 & 1 & 0 \\ 0 & 2 & 0 & -1 \\ 2 & 0 & -1 & 0 \\ 0 & -1 & 0 & 1 \end{bmatrix}$

32. $\begin{bmatrix} 1 & -2 & -1 & -2 \\ 3 & -5 & -2 & -3 \\ 2 & -5 & -2 & -5 \\ -1 & 4 & 4 & 11 \end{bmatrix}$

In Exercises 33–36, use the formula on page 663 to find the inverse of the 2 × 2 matrix.

33. $\begin{bmatrix} 5 & 1 \\ -2 & -2 \end{bmatrix}$

34. $\begin{bmatrix} -8 & 0 \\ 11 & -10 \end{bmatrix}$

35. $\begin{bmatrix} \frac{7}{2} & -\frac{3}{4} \\ \frac{1}{5} & \frac{4}{5} \end{bmatrix}$

36. $\begin{bmatrix} -\frac{1}{4} & -\frac{2}{3} \\ \frac{1}{3} & \frac{8}{9} \end{bmatrix}$

In Exercises 37–40, use the inverse matrix found in Exercise 15 to solve the system of linear equations.

37. $\begin{cases} x - 2y = 5 \\ 2x - 3y = 10 \end{cases}$

38. $\begin{cases} x - 2y = 0 \\ 2x - 3y = 3 \end{cases}$

39. $\begin{cases} x - 2y = 4 \\ 2x - 3y = 2 \end{cases}$

40. $\begin{cases} x - 2y = 1 \\ 2x - 3y = -2 \end{cases}$

In Exercises 41 and 42, use the inverse matrix found in Exercise 21 to solve the system of linear equations.

41. $\begin{cases} x + y + z = 0 \\ 3x + 5y + 4z = 5 \\ 3x + 6y + 5z = 2 \end{cases}$

42. $\begin{cases} x + y + z = -1 \\ 3x + 5y + 4z = 2 \\ 3x + 6y + 5z = 0 \end{cases}$

In Exercises 43 and 44, use the inverse matrix found in Exercise 32 and the matrix capabilities of a graphing utility to solve the system of linear equations.

43. $\begin{cases} x_1 - 2x_2 - x_3 - 2x_4 = 0 \\ 3x_1 - 5x_2 - 2x_3 - 3x_4 = 1 \\ 2x_1 - 5x_2 - 2x_3 - 5x_4 = -1 \\ -x_1 + 4x_2 + 4x_3 + 11x_4 = 2 \end{cases}$

44. $\begin{cases} x_1 - 2x_2 - x_3 - 2x_4 = 1 \\ 3x_1 - 5x_2 - 2x_3 - 3x_4 = -2 \\ 2x_1 - 5x_2 - 2x_3 - 5x_4 = 0 \\ -x_1 + 4x_2 + 4x_3 + 11x_4 = -3 \end{cases}$

In Exercises 45–52, use an inverse matrix to solve (if possible) the system of linear equations.

45. $\begin{cases} 3x + 4y = -2 \\ 5x + 3y = 4 \end{cases}$

46. $\begin{cases} 18x + 12y = 13 \\ 30x + 24y = 23 \end{cases}$

47. $\begin{cases} -0.4x + 0.8y = 1.6 \\ 2x - 4y = 5 \end{cases}$

48. $\begin{cases} 0.2x - 0.6y = 2.4 \\ -x + 1.4y = -8.8 \end{cases}$

49. $\begin{cases} -\frac{1}{4}x + \frac{3}{8}y = -2 \\ \frac{3}{2}x + \frac{3}{4}y = -12 \end{cases}$

50. $\begin{cases} \frac{5}{6}x - y = -20 \\ \frac{4}{3}x - \frac{7}{2}y = -51 \end{cases}$

51. $\begin{cases} 4x - y + z = -5 \\ 2x + 2y + 3z = 10 \\ 5x - 2y + 6z = 1 \end{cases}$

52. $\begin{cases} 4x - 2y + 3z = -2 \\ 2x + 2y + 5z = 16 \\ 8x - 5y - 2z = 4 \end{cases}$

In Exercises 53–56, use the matrix capabilities of a graphing utility to solve (if possible) the system of linear equations.

53. $\begin{cases} 5x - 3y + 2z = 2 \\ 2x + 2y - 3z = 3 \\ -x + 7y - 8z = 4 \end{cases}$

54. $\begin{cases} 2x + 3y + 5z = 4 \\ 3x + 5y - 9z = 7 \\ 5x + 9y + 17z = 13 \end{cases}$

55. $\begin{cases} 7x - 3y + 2w = 41 \\ -2x + y - w = -13 \\ 4x + z - 2w = 12 \\ -x + y - w = -8 \end{cases}$

56. $\begin{cases} 2x + 5y + w = 11 \\ x + 4y + 2z - 2w = -7 \\ 2x - 2y + 5z + w = 3 \\ x - 3w = -1 \end{cases}$

Investment Portfolio **In Exercises 57–60, consider a person who invests in AAA-rated bonds, A-rated bonds, and B-rated bonds. The average yields are 6.5% on AAA bonds, 7% on A bonds, and 9% on B bonds. The person invests twice as much in B bonds as in A bonds. Let x, y, and z represent the amounts invested in AAA, A, and B bonds, respectively.**

$$\begin{cases} x + y + z = \text{(total investment)} \\ 0.065x + 0.07y + 0.09z = \text{(annual return)} \\ 2y - z = 0 \end{cases}$$

Use the inverse of the coefficient matrix of this system to find the amount invested in each type of bond.

	Total Investment	Annual Return
57.	$25,000	$1900
58.	$10,000	$760

Total Investment	Annual Return
59. $65,000	$5050
60. $500,000	$38,000

61. *Circuit Analysis*   Consider the circuit in the figure. The currents I_1, I_2, and I_3, in amperes, are given by the solution of the system of linear equations

$$\begin{cases} 2I_1 \qquad + 4I_3 = E_1 \\ \quad\;\; I_2 + 4I_3 = E_2 \\ \;\; I_1 + I_2 - \;\; I_3 = 0 \end{cases}$$

where E_1 and E_2 are voltages. Use the inverse of the coefficient matrix of this system to find the unknown currents for the voltages.

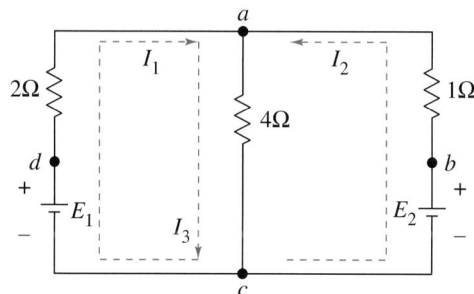

(a) $E_1 = 14$ volts, $E_2 = 28$ volts

(b) $E_1 = 10$ volts, $E_2 = 10$ volts

62. *Data Analysis*   The table shows the numbers y (in millions) of motor vehicle registrations in the United States from 1999 to 2001.   (Source: U.S. Federal Highway Administration)

Year	Registrations, y
1999	216.3
2000	221.5
2001	230.4

(a) This data can be approximated by a parabola. Create a system of linear equations for the data. Let t represent the year, with $t = 9$ corresponding to 1999.

(b) Use the matrix capabilities of a graphing utility to find an inverse matrix to solve the system in part (a) and find the least squares regression parabola $y = at^2 + bt + c$.

(c) Use the result of part (b) to determine the year in which the number of vehicle registrations will reach 300 million.

Synthesis

True or False?   **In Exercises 63 and 64, determine whether the statement is true or false. Justify your answer.**

63. Multiplication of an invertible matrix and its inverse is commutative.

64. No nonsquare matrices have inverses.

65. If A is a 2×2 matrix given by $A = \begin{bmatrix} a & b \\ c & d \end{bmatrix}$, then A is invertible if and only if $ad - bc \neq 0$. If $ad - bc \neq 0$, verify that the inverse is

$$A^{-1} = \frac{1}{ad - bc} \begin{bmatrix} d & -b \\ -c & a \end{bmatrix}.$$

66. *Exploration*   Consider the matrices of the form

$$A = \begin{bmatrix} a_{11} & 0 & 0 & 0 & \cdots & 0 \\ 0 & a_{22} & 0 & 0 & \cdots & 0 \\ 0 & 0 & a_{33} & 0 & \cdots & 0 \\ \vdots & \vdots & \vdots & \vdots & \cdots & \vdots \\ 0 & 0 & 0 & 0 & \cdots & a_{nn} \end{bmatrix}.$$

(a) Write a 2×2 matrix and a 3×3 matrix in the form of A. Find the inverse of each.

(b) Use the result of part (a) to make a conjecture about the inverse of a matrix in the form of A.

Review

In Exercises 67–70, simplify the complex fraction.

67. $\dfrac{\left(\dfrac{9}{x}\right)}{\left(\dfrac{6}{x} + 2\right)}$

68. $\dfrac{\left(1 + \dfrac{2}{x}\right)}{\left(1 - \dfrac{4}{x}\right)}$

69. $\dfrac{\left(\dfrac{4}{x^2 - 9} + \dfrac{2}{x - 2}\right)}{\left(\dfrac{1}{x + 3} + \dfrac{1}{x - 3}\right)}$

70. $\dfrac{\left(\dfrac{1}{x + 1} + \dfrac{1}{2}\right)}{\left(\dfrac{3}{2x^2 + 4x + 2}\right)}$

In Exercises 71–74, solve the equation algebraically. Round your result to three decimal places.

71. $e^{2x} + 2e^x - 15 = 0$

72. $e^{2x} - 10e^x + 24 = 0$

73. $7 \ln 3x = 12$

74. $\ln(x + 9) = 2$

8.7 The Determinant of a Square Matrix

The Determinant of a 2 × 2 Matrix

Every *square* matrix can be associated with a real number called its **determinant.** Determinants have many uses, and several will be discussed in this and the next section. Historically, the use of determinants arose from special number patterns that occur when systems of linear equations are solved. For instance, the system

$$\begin{cases} a_1x + b_1y = c_1 \\ a_2x + b_2y = c_2 \end{cases}$$

has a solution

$$x = \frac{c_1b_2 - c_2b_1}{a_1b_2 - a_2b_1}$$

and

$$y = \frac{a_1c_2 - a_2c_1}{a_1b_2 - a_2b_1}$$

provided that $a_1b_2 - a_2b_1 \neq 0$. Note that the denominator of each fraction is the same. This denominator is called the *determinant* of the coefficient matrix of the system.

Coefficient Matrix   *Determinant*

$$A = \begin{bmatrix} a_1 & b_1 \\ a_2 & b_2 \end{bmatrix} \qquad \det(A) = a_1b_2 - a_2b_1$$

The determinant of the matrix A can also be denoted by vertical bars on both sides of the matrix, as indicated in the following definition.

Definition of the Determinant of a 2 × 2 Matrix

The **determinant** of the matrix

$$A = \begin{bmatrix} a_1 & b_1 \\ a_2 & b_2 \end{bmatrix}$$

is given by

$$\det(A) = |A| = \begin{vmatrix} a_1 & b_1 \\ a_2 & b_2 \end{vmatrix}$$

$$= a_1b_2 - a_2b_1.$$

In this text, $\det(A)$ and $|A|$ are used interchangeably to represent the determinant of A. Although vertical bars are also used to denote the absolute value of a real number, the context will show which use is intended.

What you should learn

● Find the determinants of 2 × 2 matrices.
● Find minors and cofactors of square matrices.
● Find the determinants of square matrices.
● Find the determinants of triangular matrices.

Why you should learn it

Determinants are often used in other branches of mathematics. For instance, Exercises 53–58 on page 675 show some types of determinants that are useful in calculus.

A convenient method for remembering the formula for the determinant of a 2×2 matrix is shown in the following diagram.

$$\det(A) = \begin{vmatrix} a_1 & b_1 \\ a_2 & b_2 \end{vmatrix} = a_1 b_2 - a_2 b_1$$

Note that the determinant is the difference of the products of the two diagonals of the matrix.

Example 1   The Determinant of a 2 × 2 Matrix

Find the determinant of each matrix.

a. $A = \begin{bmatrix} 2 & -3 \\ 1 & 2 \end{bmatrix}$ **b.** $B = \begin{bmatrix} 2 & 1 \\ 4 & 2 \end{bmatrix}$ **c.** $C = \begin{bmatrix} 0 & \frac{3}{2} \\ 2 & 4 \end{bmatrix}$

Solution

a. $\det(A) = \begin{vmatrix} 2 & -3 \\ 1 & 2 \end{vmatrix} = 2(2) - 1(-3)$

$$= 4 + 3 = 7$$

b. $\det(B) = \begin{vmatrix} 2 & 1 \\ 4 & 2 \end{vmatrix} = 2(2) - 4(1)$

$$= 4 - 4 = 0$$

c. $\det(C) = \begin{vmatrix} 0 & \frac{3}{2} \\ 2 & 4 \end{vmatrix} = 0(4) - 2(\frac{3}{2})$

$$= 0 - 3 = -3$$

✓ *Checkpoint*   Now try Exercise 5.

Notice in Example 1 that the determinant of a matrix can be positive, zero, or negative.

The determinant of a matrix of order 1×1 is defined simply as the entry of the matrix. For instance, if $A = [-2]$, then $\det(A) = -2$.

TECHNOLOGY TIP   Most graphing utilities can evaluate the determinant of a matrix. For instance, you can evaluate the determinant of the matrix A in Example 1(a) by entering the matrix as [A] (see Figure 8.32) and then choosing the *determinant* feature. The result should be 7, as in Example 1(a) (see Figure 8.33).

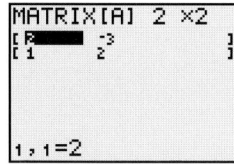

Figure 8.32

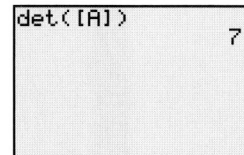

Figure 8.33

Exploration

Try using a graphing utility to find the determinant of

$$A = \begin{bmatrix} 3 & -1 & 1 \\ 0 & 2 & 1 \end{bmatrix}.$$

What message appears on the screen? Why does the graphing utility display this message?

Minors and Cofactors

To define the determinant of a square matrix of order 3×3 or higher, it is helpful to introduce the concepts of **minors** and **cofactors.**

Minors and Cofactors of a Square Matrix

If A is a square matrix, the **minor** M_{ij} of the entry a_{ij} is the determinant of the matrix obtained by deleting the ith row and jth column of A. The **cofactor** C_{ij} of the entry a_{ij} is given by

$$C_{ij} = (-1)^{i+j}M_{ij}.$$

Sign Pattern for Cofactors

$$\begin{bmatrix} + & - & + \\ - & + & - \\ + & - & + \end{bmatrix}$$

3×3 matrix

$$\begin{bmatrix} + & - & + & - \\ - & + & - & + \\ + & - & + & - \\ - & + & - & + \end{bmatrix}$$

4×4 matrix

$$\begin{bmatrix} + & - & + & - & + & \cdots \\ - & + & - & + & - & \cdots \\ + & - & + & - & + & \cdots \\ - & + & - & + & - & \cdots \\ + & - & + & - & + & \cdots \\ \vdots & \vdots & \vdots & \vdots & \vdots & \end{bmatrix}$$

$n \times n$ matrix

Example 2 Finding the Minors and Cofactors of a Matrix

Find all the minors and cofactors of

$$A = \begin{bmatrix} 0 & 2 & 1 \\ 3 & -1 & 2 \\ 4 & 0 & 1 \end{bmatrix}.$$

Solution

To find the minor M_{11}, delete the first row and first column of A and evaluate the determinant of the resulting matrix.

$$\begin{bmatrix} 0 & 2 & 1 \\ 3 & -1 & 2 \\ 4 & 0 & 1 \end{bmatrix}, \ M_{11} = \begin{vmatrix} -1 & 2 \\ 0 & 1 \end{vmatrix} = -1(1) - 0(2) = -1$$

Similarly, to find M_{12}, delete the first row and second column.

$$\begin{bmatrix} 0 & 2 & 1 \\ 3 & -1 & 2 \\ 4 & 0 & 1 \end{bmatrix}, \ M_{12} = \begin{vmatrix} 3 & 2 \\ 4 & 1 \end{vmatrix} = 3(1) - 4(2) = -5$$

Continuing this pattern, you obtain the minors.

$$M_{11} = -1 \qquad M_{12} = -5 \qquad M_{13} = \ \ 4$$

$$M_{21} = \ \ 2 \qquad M_{22} = -4 \qquad M_{23} = -8$$

$$M_{31} = \ \ 5 \qquad M_{32} = -3 \qquad M_{33} = -6$$

Now, to find the cofactors, combine these minors with the checkerboard pattern of signs for a 3×3 matrix shown at the upper right.

$$C_{11} = -1 \qquad C_{12} = \ \ 5 \qquad C_{13} = \ \ 4$$

$$C_{21} = -2 \qquad C_{22} = -4 \qquad C_{23} = \ \ 8$$

$$C_{31} = \ \ 5 \qquad C_{32} = \ \ 3 \qquad C_{33} = -6$$

✓ *Checkpoint* Now try Exercise 17.

STUDY TIP

In the sign pattern for cofactors above, notice that *odd* positions (where $i + j$ is odd) have negative signs and *even* positions (where $i + j$ is even) have positive signs.

The Determinant of a Square Matrix

The following definition is called *inductive* because it uses determinants of matrices of order $n - 1$ to define determinants of matrices of order n.

Determinant of a Square Matrix

If A is a square matrix (of order 2×2 or greater), the determinant of A is the sum of the entries in any row (or column) of A multiplied by their respective cofactors. For instance, expanding along the first row yields

$$|A| = a_{11}C_{11} + a_{12}C_{12} + \cdots + a_{1n}C_{1n}.$$

Applying this definition to find a determinant is called **expanding by cofactors.**

Try checking that for a 2×2 matrix

$$A = \begin{bmatrix} a_1 & b_1 \\ a_2 & b_2 \end{bmatrix}$$

the definition of the determinant above yields

$$|A| = a_1 b_2 - a_2 b_1$$

as previously defined.

Example 3   The Determinant of a Matrix of Order 3×3

Find the determinant of $A = \begin{bmatrix} 0 & 2 & 1 \\ 3 & -1 & 2 \\ 4 & 0 & 1 \end{bmatrix}$.

Solution

Note that this is the same matrix that was in Example 2. There you found the cofactors of the entries in the first row to be

$$C_{11} = -1, \qquad C_{12} = 5, \qquad \text{and} \qquad C_{13} = 4.$$

So, by the definition of the determinant of a square matrix, you have

$$
\begin{aligned}
|A| &= a_{11}C_{11} + a_{12}C_{12} + a_{13}C_{13} \qquad &&\text{First-row expansion} \\
&= 0(-1) + 2(5) + 1(4) \\
&= 14.
\end{aligned}
$$

✓ *Checkpoint* Now try Exercise 23.

In Example 3, the determinant was found by expanding by the cofactors in the first row. You could have used any row or column. For instance, you could have expanded along the second row to obtain

$$
\begin{aligned}
|A| &= a_{21}C_{21} + a_{22}C_{22} + a_{23}C_{23} \qquad &&\text{Second-row expansion} \\
&= 3(-2) + (-1)(-4) + 2(8) \\
&= 14.
\end{aligned}
$$

When expanding by cofactors, you do not need to find cofactors of zero entries, because zero times its cofactor is zero.

$$a_{ij}C_{ij} = (0)C_{ij} = 0$$

So, the row (or column) containing the most zeros is usually the best choice for expansion by cofactors.

Triangular Matrices

Evaluating determinants of matrices of order 4 or higher can be tedious. There is, however, an important exception: the determinant of a **triangular** matrix. A triangular matrix is a square matrix with all zero entries either below or above its main diagonal. A square matrix is **upper triangular** if it has all zero entries below its main diagonal and **lower triangular** if it has all zero entries above its main diagonal. A matrix that is both upper and lower triangular is called **diagonal.** That is, a diagonal matrix is a square matrix in which all entries above and below the main diagonal are zero.

Exploration

The formula for the determinant of a triangular matrix (discussed at the left) is only one of many properties of matrices. You can use a computer or calculator to discover other properties. For instance, how is $|cA|$ related to $|A|$? How are $|A|$ and $|B|$ related to $|AB|$?

Upper Triangular Matrix

$$\begin{bmatrix} a_{11} & a_{12} & a_{13} & \cdots & a_{1n} \\ 0 & a_{22} & a_{23} & \cdots & a_{2n} \\ 0 & 0 & a_{33} & \cdots & a_{3n} \\ \vdots & \vdots & \vdots & & \vdots \\ 0 & 0 & 0 & \cdots & a_{nn} \end{bmatrix}$$

Lower Triangular Matrix

$$\begin{bmatrix} a_{11} & 0 & 0 & \cdots & 0 \\ a_{21} & a_{22} & 0 & \cdots & 0 \\ a_{31} & a_{32} & a_{33} & \cdots & 0 \\ \vdots & \vdots & \vdots & & \vdots \\ a_{n1} & a_{n2} & a_{n3} & \cdots & a_{nn} \end{bmatrix}$$

Diagonal Matrix

$$\begin{bmatrix} a_{11} & 0 & 0 & \cdots & 0 \\ 0 & a_{22} & 0 & \cdots & 0 \\ 0 & 0 & a_{33} & \cdots & 0 \\ \vdots & \vdots & \vdots & & \vdots \\ 0 & 0 & 0 & \cdots & a_{nn} \end{bmatrix}$$

To find the determinant of a triangular matrix of any order, simply form the product of the entries on the main diagonal.

Example 4 The Determinant of a Triangular Matrix

a.
$$\begin{vmatrix} 2 & 0 & 0 & 0 \\ 4 & -2 & 0 & 0 \\ -5 & 6 & 1 & 0 \\ 1 & 5 & 3 & 3 \end{vmatrix} = (2)(-2)(1)(3) = -12$$

b.
$$\begin{vmatrix} -1 & 0 & 0 & 0 & 0 \\ 0 & 3 & 0 & 0 & 0 \\ 0 & 0 & 2 & 0 & 0 \\ 0 & 0 & 0 & 4 & 0 \\ 0 & 0 & 0 & 0 & -2 \end{vmatrix} = (-1)(3)(2)(4)(-2) = 48$$

✓ *Checkpoint* Now try Exercise 31.

8.7   Exercises

Vocabulary Check

Fill in the blanks.

1. Both $\det(A)$ and $|A|$ represent the _____ of the matrix A.

2. The _____ M_{ij} of the entry a_{ij} is the determinant of the matrix obtained by deleting the ith row and jth column of the square matrix A.

3. The _____ C_{ij} of the entry a_{ij} is given by $(-1)^{i+j}M_{ij}$.

4. One way of finding the determinant of a matrix of order 2×2 or greater is _____ .

5. A square matrix with all zero entries either above or below its main diagonal is called a _____ matrix.

6. A matrix that is both upper and lower triangular is called a _____ matrix.

In Exercises 1–12, find the determinant of the matrix.

1. $[4]$

2. $[-10]$

3. $\begin{bmatrix} 8 & 4 \\ 2 & 3 \end{bmatrix}$

4. $\begin{bmatrix} -9 & 0 \\ 6 & 2 \end{bmatrix}$

5. $\begin{bmatrix} 6 & 2 \\ -5 & 3 \end{bmatrix}$

6. $\begin{bmatrix} 3 & -3 \\ 4 & -8 \end{bmatrix}$

7. $\begin{bmatrix} -7 & 6 \\ \frac{1}{2} & 3 \end{bmatrix}$

8. $\begin{bmatrix} 4 & -3 \\ 0 & 0 \end{bmatrix}$

9. $\begin{bmatrix} 2 & -1 & 0 \\ 4 & 2 & 1 \\ 4 & 2 & 1 \end{bmatrix}$

10. $\begin{bmatrix} -2 & 2 & 3 \\ 1 & -1 & 0 \\ 0 & 1 & 4 \end{bmatrix}$

11. $\begin{bmatrix} -1 & 2 & -5 \\ 0 & 3 & 4 \\ 0 & 0 & 3 \end{bmatrix}$

12. $\begin{bmatrix} 1 & 0 & 0 \\ -4 & -1 & 0 \\ 5 & 1 & 5 \end{bmatrix}$

In Exercises 13 and 14, use the matrix capabilities of a graphing utility to find the determinant of the matrix.

13. $\begin{bmatrix} 0.3 & 0.2 & 0.2 \\ 0.2 & 0.2 & 0.2 \\ -0.4 & 0.4 & 0.3 \end{bmatrix}$

14. $\begin{bmatrix} 0.1 & 0.2 & 0.3 \\ -0.3 & 0.2 & 0.2 \\ 0.5 & 0.4 & 0.4 \end{bmatrix}$

In Exercises 15–18, find all (a) minors and (b) cofactors of the matrix.

15. $\begin{bmatrix} 3 & 4 \\ 2 & -5 \end{bmatrix}$

16. $\begin{bmatrix} 11 & 0 \\ -3 & 2 \end{bmatrix}$

17. $\begin{bmatrix} 3 & -2 & 8 \\ 3 & 2 & -6 \\ -1 & 3 & 6 \end{bmatrix}$

18. $\begin{bmatrix} -2 & 9 & 4 \\ 7 & -6 & 0 \\ 6 & 7 & -6 \end{bmatrix}$

In Exercises 19–22, find the determinant of the matrix by the method of expansion by cofactors. Expand using the indicated row or column.

19. $\begin{bmatrix} -3 & 2 & 1 \\ 4 & 5 & 6 \\ 2 & -3 & 1 \end{bmatrix}$

   (a) Row 1

   (b) Column 2

20. $\begin{bmatrix} -3 & 4 & 2 \\ 6 & 3 & 1 \\ 4 & -7 & -8 \end{bmatrix}$

   (a) Row 2

   (b) Column 3

21. $\begin{bmatrix} 6 & 0 & -3 & 5 \\ 4 & 13 & 6 & -8 \\ -1 & 0 & 7 & 4 \\ 8 & 6 & 0 & 2 \end{bmatrix}$

   (a) Row 2

   (b) Column 2

22. $\begin{bmatrix} 10 & 8 & 3 & -7 \\ 4 & 0 & 5 & -6 \\ 0 & 3 & 2 & 7 \\ 1 & 0 & -3 & 2 \end{bmatrix}$

   (a) Row 3

   (b) Column 1

In Exercises 23–30, find the determinant of the matrix. Expand by cofactors on the row or column that appears to make the computations easiest.

23. $\begin{bmatrix} 1 & 4 & -2 \\ 3 & 2 & 0 \\ -1 & 4 & 3 \end{bmatrix}$

24. $\begin{bmatrix} 2 & -1 & 3 \\ 1 & 4 & 4 \\ 1 & 0 & 2 \end{bmatrix}$

25. $\begin{bmatrix} 2 & 4 & 6 \\ 0 & 3 & 1 \\ 0 & 0 & -5 \end{bmatrix}$

26. $\begin{bmatrix} -3 & 0 & 0 \\ 7 & 11 & 0 \\ 1 & 2 & 2 \end{bmatrix}$

27. $\begin{bmatrix} 2 & 6 & 6 & 2 \\ 2 & 7 & 3 & 6 \\ 1 & 5 & 0 & 1 \\ 3 & 7 & 0 & 7 \end{bmatrix}$

28. $\begin{bmatrix} 3 & 6 & -5 & 4 \\ -2 & 0 & 6 & 0 \\ 1 & 1 & 2 & 2 \\ 0 & 3 & -1 & -1 \end{bmatrix}$

29. $\begin{bmatrix} 3 & 2 & 4 & -1 & 5 \\ -2 & 0 & 1 & 3 & 2 \\ 1 & 0 & 0 & 4 & 0 \\ 6 & 0 & 2 & -1 & 0 \\ 3 & 0 & 5 & 1 & 0 \end{bmatrix}$

30. $\begin{bmatrix} 5 & 2 & 0 & 0 & -2 \\ 0 & 1 & 4 & 3 & 2 \\ 0 & 0 & 2 & 6 & 3 \\ 0 & 0 & 3 & 4 & 1 \\ 0 & 0 & 0 & 0 & 2 \end{bmatrix}$

In Exercises 31–34, evaluate the determinant. Do not use a graphing utility.

31. $\begin{vmatrix} 4 & 0 & 0 & 0 \\ 6 & -5 & 0 & 0 \\ 1 & 3 & 1 & 0 \\ 1 & -2 & 7 & 3 \end{vmatrix}$

32. $\begin{vmatrix} 5 & -10 & 1 & 1 \\ 0 & 6 & 3 & 4 \\ 0 & 0 & -2 & -1 \\ 0 & 0 & 0 & -1 \end{vmatrix}$

33. $\begin{vmatrix} -6 & 7 & 2 & 0 & 5 \\ 0 & -1 & 3 & 4 & -3 \\ 0 & 0 & -7 & 0 & 4 \\ 0 & 0 & 0 & -2 & 1 \\ 0 & 0 & 0 & 0 & -2 \end{vmatrix}$

34. $\begin{vmatrix} -2 & 0 & 0 & 0 & 0 \\ -1 & 4 & 0 & 0 & 0 \\ 3 & 5 & 1 & 0 & 0 \\ 6 & -11 & 8 & 10 & 0 \\ 0 & 13 & -9 & 0 & -3 \end{vmatrix}$

In Exercises 35–38, use the matrix capabilities of a graphing utility to evaluate the determinant.

35. $\begin{vmatrix} 1 & -1 & 8 & 4 \\ 2 & 6 & 0 & -4 \\ 2 & 0 & 2 & 6 \\ 0 & 2 & 8 & 0 \end{vmatrix}$

36. $\begin{vmatrix} 0 & -3 & 8 & 2 \\ 8 & 1 & -1 & 6 \\ -4 & 6 & 0 & 9 \\ -7 & 0 & 0 & 14 \end{vmatrix}$

37. $\begin{vmatrix} 3 & -2 & 4 & 3 & 1 \\ -1 & 0 & 2 & 1 & 0 \\ 5 & -1 & 0 & 3 & 2 \\ 4 & 7 & -8 & 0 & 0 \\ 1 & 2 & 3 & 0 & 2 \end{vmatrix}$

38. $\begin{vmatrix} -2 & 0 & 0 & 0 & 0 \\ 0 & 3 & 0 & 0 & 0 \\ 0 & 0 & -1 & 0 & 0 \\ 0 & 0 & 0 & 2 & 0 \\ 0 & 0 & 0 & 0 & -4 \end{vmatrix}$

In Exercises 39–42, find (a) $|A|$, (b) $|B|$, (c) AB, and (d) $|AB|$.

39. $A = \begin{bmatrix} -1 & 0 \\ 0 & 3 \end{bmatrix}, \quad B = \begin{bmatrix} 2 & 0 \\ 0 & -1 \end{bmatrix}$

40. $A = \begin{bmatrix} 4 & 0 \\ 3 & -2 \end{bmatrix}, \quad B = \begin{bmatrix} -1 & 1 \\ -2 & 2 \end{bmatrix}$

41. $A = \begin{bmatrix} -1 & 2 & 1 \\ 1 & 0 & 1 \\ 0 & 1 & 0 \end{bmatrix}, \quad B = \begin{bmatrix} -1 & 0 & 0 \\ 0 & 2 & 0 \\ 0 & 0 & 3 \end{bmatrix}$

42. $A = \begin{bmatrix} 2 & 0 & 1 \\ 1 & -1 & 2 \\ 3 & 1 & 0 \end{bmatrix}, \quad B = \begin{bmatrix} 2 & -1 & 4 \\ 0 & 1 & 3 \\ 3 & -2 & 1 \end{bmatrix}$

In Exercises 43 and 44, use the matrix capabilities of a graphing utility to find (a) $|A|$, (b) $|B|$, (c) AB, and (d) $|AB|$.

43. $A = \begin{bmatrix} 6 & 4 & 0 & 1 \\ 2 & -3 & -2 & -4 \\ 0 & 1 & 5 & 0 \\ -1 & 0 & -1 & 1 \end{bmatrix},$

$B = \begin{bmatrix} 0 & -5 & 0 & -2 \\ -2 & 4 & -1 & -4 \\ 3 & 0 & 1 & 0 \\ 1 & -2 & 3 & 0 \end{bmatrix}$

44. $A = \begin{bmatrix} -1 & 5 & 2 & 0 \\ 0 & 0 & 1 & 1 \\ 3 & -3 & -1 & 0 \\ 4 & 2 & 4 & -1 \end{bmatrix},$

$B = \begin{bmatrix} 1 & 5 & 0 & 0 \\ 10 & -1 & 2 & 4 \\ 2 & 0 & 0 & 1 \\ -3 & 2 & 5 & 0 \end{bmatrix}$

In Exercises 45–50, evaluate the determinants to verify the equation.

45. $\begin{vmatrix} w & x \\ y & z \end{vmatrix} = -\begin{vmatrix} y & z \\ w & x \end{vmatrix}$

46. $\begin{vmatrix} w & cx \\ y & cz \end{vmatrix} = c\begin{vmatrix} w & x \\ y & z \end{vmatrix}$

47. $\begin{vmatrix} w & x \\ y & z \end{vmatrix} = \begin{vmatrix} w & x + cw \\ y & z + cy \end{vmatrix}$

48. $\begin{vmatrix} w & x \\ cw & cx \end{vmatrix} = 0$

49. $\begin{vmatrix} 1 & x & x^2 \\ 1 & y & y^2 \\ 1 & z & z^2 \end{vmatrix} = (y - x)(z - x)(z - y)$

50. $\begin{vmatrix} a + b & a & a \\ a & a + b & a \\ a & a & a + b \end{vmatrix} = b^2(3a + b)$

In Exercises 51 and 52, solve for x.

51. $\begin{vmatrix} x + 3 & 2 \\ 1 & x + 2 \end{vmatrix} = 0$ **52.** $\begin{vmatrix} x - 2 & -1 \\ -3 & x \end{vmatrix} = 0$

In Exercises 53–58, evaluate the determinant, in which the entries are functions. Determinants of this type occur when changes of variables are made in calculus.

53. $\begin{vmatrix} 4u & -1 \\ -1 & 2v \end{vmatrix}$

54. $\begin{vmatrix} 3x^2 & -3y^2 \\ 1 & 1 \end{vmatrix}$

55. $\begin{vmatrix} e^{2x} & e^{3x} \\ 2e^{2x} & 3e^{3x} \end{vmatrix}$

56. $\begin{vmatrix} e^{-x} & xe^{-x} \\ -e^{-x} & (1 - x)e^{-x} \end{vmatrix}$

57. $\begin{vmatrix} x & \ln x \\ 1 & 1/x \end{vmatrix}$

58. $\begin{vmatrix} x & x \ln x \\ 1 & 1 + \ln x \end{vmatrix}$

Synthesis

True or False? **In Exercises 59 and 60, determine whether the statement is true or false. Justify your answer.**

59. If a square matrix has an entire row of zeros, the determinant will always be zero.

60. If two columns of a square matrix are the same, the determinant of the matrix will be zero.

61. *Exploration*   Find square matrices A and B to demonstrate that $|A + B| \neq |A| + |B|$.

62. *Conjecture*   Consider square matrices in which the entries are consecutive integers. An example of such a matrix is

$$\begin{bmatrix} 4 & 5 & 6 \\ 7 & 8 & 9 \\ 10 & 11 & 12 \end{bmatrix}.$$

Use a graphing utility to evaluate four determinants of this type. Make a conjecture based on the results. Then verify your conjecture.

In Exercises 63–65, a property of determinants is given (A and B are square matrices). State how the property has been applied to the given determinants and use a graphing utility to verify the results.

63. If B is obtained from A by interchanging two rows of A or by interchanging two columns of A, then $|B| = -|A|$.

(a) $\begin{vmatrix} 1 & 3 & 4 \\ -7 & 2 & -5 \\ 6 & 1 & 2 \end{vmatrix} = -\begin{vmatrix} 1 & 4 & 3 \\ -7 & -5 & 2 \\ 6 & 2 & 1 \end{vmatrix}$

(b) $\begin{vmatrix} 1 & 3 & 4 \\ -2 & 2 & 0 \\ 1 & 6 & 2 \end{vmatrix} = -\begin{vmatrix} 1 & 6 & 2 \\ -2 & 2 & 0 \\ 1 & 3 & 4 \end{vmatrix}$

64. If B is obtained from A by adding a multiple of a row of A to another row of A or by adding a multiple of a column of A to another column of A, then $|B| = |A|$.

(a) $\begin{vmatrix} 1 & -3 \\ 5 & 2 \end{vmatrix} = \begin{vmatrix} 1 & -3 \\ 0 & 17 \end{vmatrix}$

(b) $\begin{vmatrix} 5 & 4 & 2 \\ 2 & -3 & 4 \\ 7 & 6 & 3 \end{vmatrix} = \begin{vmatrix} 1 & 10 & -6 \\ 2 & -3 & 4 \\ 7 & 6 & 3 \end{vmatrix}$

65. If B is obtained from A by multiplying a row of A by a nonzero constant c or by multiplying a column of A by a nonzero constant c, then $|B| = c|A|$.

(a) $\begin{vmatrix} 5 & 10 \\ 2 & -3 \end{vmatrix} = 5\begin{vmatrix} 1 & 2 \\ 2 & -3 \end{vmatrix}$

(b) $\begin{vmatrix} 1 & 8 & -3 \\ 3 & -12 & 6 \\ 7 & 4 & 9 \end{vmatrix} = 12\begin{vmatrix} 1 & 2 & -1 \\ 3 & -3 & 2 \\ 7 & 1 & 3 \end{vmatrix}$

66. *Writing*   Write an argument that explains why the determinant of a 3×3 triangular matrix is the product of its main diagonal entries.

Review

In Exercises 67–70, factor the expression.

67. $x^2 - 3x + 2$ **68.** $x^2 + 5x + 6$

69. $4y^2 - 12y + 9$ **70.** $4y^2 - 28y + 49$

In Exercises 71 and 72, solve the system of equations using the method of substitution or the method of elimination.

71. $\begin{cases} 3x - 10y = 46 \\ x + y = -2 \end{cases}$ **72.** $\begin{cases} 5x + 7y = 23 \\ -4x - 2y = -4 \end{cases}$

8.8 Applications of Matrices and Determinants

Area of a Triangle

In this section, you will study some additional applications of matrices and determinants. The first involves a formula for finding the area of a triangle whose vertices are given by three points on a rectangular coordinate system.

> **Area of a Triangle**
>
> The area of a triangle with vertices (x_1, y_1), (x_2, y_2), and (x_3, y_3) is
>
> $$\text{Area} = \pm\frac{1}{2}\begin{vmatrix} x_1 & y_1 & 1 \\ x_2 & y_2 & 1 \\ x_3 & y_3 & 1 \end{vmatrix}$$
>
> where the symbol ($\pm$) indicates that the appropriate sign should be chosen to yield a positive area.

Example 1   Finding the Area of a Triangle

Find the area of the triangle whose vertices are $(1, 0)$, $(2, 2)$, and $(4, 3)$, as shown in Figure 8.34.

Solution

Let $(x_1, y_1) = (1, 0)$, $(x_2, y_2) = (2, 2)$, and $(x_3, y_3) = (4, 3)$. Then, to find the area of the triangle, evaluate the determinant

$$\begin{vmatrix} x_1 & y_1 & 1 \\ x_2 & y_2 & 1 \\ x_3 & y_3 & 1 \end{vmatrix} = \begin{vmatrix} 1 & 0 & 1 \\ 2 & 2 & 1 \\ 4 & 3 & 1 \end{vmatrix}$$

$$= 1(-1)^2\begin{vmatrix} 2 & 1 \\ 3 & 1 \end{vmatrix} + 0(-1)^3\begin{vmatrix} 2 & 1 \\ 4 & 1 \end{vmatrix} + 1(-1)^4\begin{vmatrix} 2 & 2 \\ 4 & 3 \end{vmatrix}$$

$$= 1(-1) + 0 + 1(-2)$$

$$= -3.$$

Using this value, you can conclude that the area of the triangle is

$$\text{Area} = -\frac{1}{2}\begin{vmatrix} 1 & 0 & 1 \\ 2 & 2 & 1 \\ 4 & 3 & 1 \end{vmatrix}$$

$$= -\frac{1}{2}(-3)$$

$$= \frac{3}{2} \text{ square units.}$$

✓ *Checkpoint* Now try Exercise 1.

What you should learn

- Use determinants to find areas of triangles.
- Use determinants to decide whether points are collinear.
- Use Cramer's Rule to solve systems of linear equations.
- Use matrices to encode and decode messages.

Why you should learn it

A determinant can be used to find the area of a region of forest infected with gypsy moths, as shown in Exercise 25 on page 684.

Layne Kennedy/Corbis

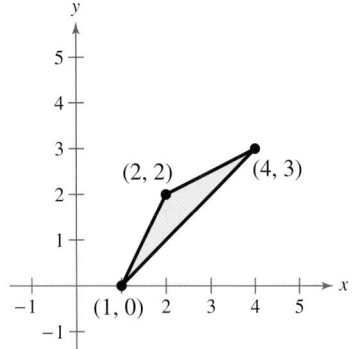

Figure 8.34

Collinear Points

What if the three points in Example 1 had been on the same line? What would have happened had the area formula been applied to three such points? The answer is that the determinant would have been zero. Consider, for instance, the three collinear points $(0, 1)$, $(2, 2)$, and $(4, 3)$, as shown in Figure 8.35. The area of the "triangle" that has these three points as vertices is

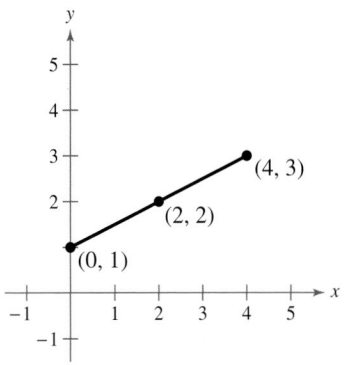

$$\frac{1}{2}\begin{vmatrix} 0 & 1 & 1 \\ 2 & 2 & 1 \\ 4 & 3 & 1 \end{vmatrix} = \frac{1}{2}\left[0(-1)^2\begin{vmatrix} 2 & 1 \\ 3 & 1 \end{vmatrix} + 1(-1)^3\begin{vmatrix} 2 & 1 \\ 4 & 1 \end{vmatrix} + 1(-1)^4\begin{vmatrix} 2 & 2 \\ 4 & 3 \end{vmatrix} \right]$$

$$= \frac{1}{2}[0 - 1(-2) + 1(-2)]$$

$$= 0$$

Figure 8.35

This result is generalized as follows.

Test for Collinear Points

Three points (x_1, y_1), (x_2, y_2), and (x_3, y_3) are **collinear** (lie on the same line) if and only if

$$\begin{vmatrix} x_1 & y_1 & 1 \\ x_2 & y_2 & 1 \\ x_3 & y_3 & 1 \end{vmatrix} = 0.$$

Example 2   Testing for Collinear Points

Determine whether the points $(-2, -2)$, $(1, 1)$, and $(7, 5)$ lie on the same line. (See Figure 8.36.)

Solution

Letting $(x_1, y_1) = (-2, -2)$, $(x_2, y_2) = (1, 1)$, and $(x_3, y_3) = (7, 5)$, you have

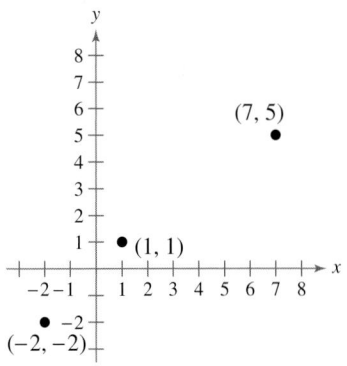

$$\begin{vmatrix} x_1 & y_1 & 1 \\ x_2 & y_2 & 1 \\ x_3 & y_3 & 1 \end{vmatrix} = \begin{vmatrix} -2 & -2 & 1 \\ 1 & 1 & 1 \\ 7 & 5 & 1 \end{vmatrix}$$

$$= -2(-1)^2\begin{vmatrix} 1 & 1 \\ 5 & 1 \end{vmatrix} + (-2)(-1)^3\begin{vmatrix} 1 & 1 \\ 7 & 1 \end{vmatrix} + 1(-1)^4\begin{vmatrix} 1 & 1 \\ 7 & 5 \end{vmatrix}$$

$$= -2(-4) + 2(-6) + 1(-2)$$

$$= -6.$$

Figure 8.36

Because the value of this determinant is *not* zero, you can conclude that the three points do not lie on the same line.

✓ *Checkpoint* Now try Exercise 9.

Cramer's Rule

So far, you have studied three methods for solving a system of linear equations: substitution, elimination with equations, and elimination with matrices. You will now study one more method, **Cramer's Rule,** named after Gabriel Cramer (1704–1752). This rule uses determinants to write the solution of a system of linear equations. To see how Cramer's Rule works, take another look at the solution described at the beginning of Section 8.7. There, it was pointed out that the system

$$\begin{cases} a_1 x + b_1 y = c_1 \\ a_2 x + b_2 y = c_2 \end{cases}$$

has a solution

$$x = \frac{c_1 b_2 - c_2 b_1}{a_1 b_2 - a_2 b_1} \quad \text{and} \quad y = \frac{a_1 c_2 - a_2 c_1}{a_1 b_2 - a_2 b_1}$$

provided that $a_1 b_2 - a_2 b_1 \neq 0$. Each numerator and denominator in this solution can be expressed as a determinant, as follows.

$$x = \frac{c_1 b_2 - c_2 b_1}{a_1 b_2 - a_2 b_1} = \frac{\begin{vmatrix} c_1 & b_1 \\ c_2 & b_2 \end{vmatrix}}{\begin{vmatrix} a_1 & b_1 \\ a_2 & b_2 \end{vmatrix}}$$

$$y = \frac{a_1 c_2 - a_2 c_1}{a_1 b_2 - a_2 b_1} = \frac{\begin{vmatrix} a_1 & c_1 \\ a_2 & c_2 \end{vmatrix}}{\begin{vmatrix} a_1 & b_1 \\ a_2 & b_2 \end{vmatrix}}$$

Relative to the original system, the denominators of x and y are simply the determinant of the *coefficient* matrix of the system. This determinant is denoted by D. The numerators of x and y are denoted by D_x and D_y, respectively. They are formed by using the column of constants as replacements for the coefficients of x and y, as follows.

Coefficient Matrix	D	D_x	D_y
$\begin{bmatrix} a_1 & b_1 \\ a_2 & b_2 \end{bmatrix}$	$\begin{vmatrix} a_1 & b_1 \\ a_2 & b_2 \end{vmatrix}$	$\begin{vmatrix} c_1 & b_1 \\ c_2 & b_2 \end{vmatrix}$	$\begin{vmatrix} a_1 & c_1 \\ a_2 & c_2 \end{vmatrix}$

For example, given the system

$$\begin{cases} 2x - 5y = 3 \\ -4x + 3y = 8 \end{cases}$$

the coefficient matrix, D, D_x, and D_y are as follows.

Coefficient Matrix	D	D_x	D_y
$\begin{bmatrix} 2 & -5 \\ -4 & 3 \end{bmatrix}$	$\begin{vmatrix} 2 & -5 \\ -4 & 3 \end{vmatrix}$	$\begin{vmatrix} 3 & -5 \\ 8 & 3 \end{vmatrix}$	$\begin{vmatrix} 2 & 3 \\ -4 & 8 \end{vmatrix}$

Cramer's Rule generalizes easily to systems of n equations in n variables. The value of each variable is given as the quotient of two determinants. The denominator is the determinant of the coefficient matrix, and the numerator is the determinant of the matrix formed by replacing the column corresponding to the variable being solved for with the column representing the constants. For instance, the solution for x_3 in the following system is shown.

$$\begin{cases} a_{11}x_1 + a_{12}x_2 + a_{13}x_3 = b_1 \\ a_{21}x_1 + a_{22}x_2 + a_{23}x_3 = b_2 \\ a_{31}x_1 + a_{32}x_2 + a_{33}x_3 = b_3 \end{cases} \qquad x_3 = \frac{|A_3|}{|A|} = \frac{\begin{vmatrix} a_{11} & a_{12} & b_1 \\ a_{21} & a_{22} & b_2 \\ a_{31} & a_{32} & b_3 \end{vmatrix}}{\begin{vmatrix} a_{11} & a_{12} & a_{13} \\ a_{21} & a_{22} & a_{23} \\ a_{31} & a_{32} & a_{33} \end{vmatrix}}$$

Cramer's Rule

If a system of n linear equations in n variables has a coefficient matrix A with a *nonzero* determinant $|A|$, the solution of the system is

$$x_1 = \frac{|A_1|}{|A|}, \quad x_2 = \frac{|A_2|}{|A|}, \quad \ldots, \quad x_n = \frac{|A_n|}{|A|}$$

where the ith column of A_i is the column of constants in the system of equations. If the determinant of the coefficient matrix is zero, the system has either no solution or infinitely many solutions.

STUDY TIP

Cramer's Rule does not apply when the determinant of the coefficient matrix is zero. This would create division by zero, which is undefined.

Example 3   Using Cramer's Rule for a 2 × 2 System

Use Cramer's Rule to solve the system $\begin{cases} 4x - 2y = 10 \\ 3x - 5y = 11 \end{cases}$.

Solution

To begin, find the determinant of the coefficient matrix.

$$D = \begin{vmatrix} 4 & -2 \\ 3 & -5 \end{vmatrix} = -20 - (-6) = -14$$

Because this determinant is not zero, apply Cramer's Rule.

$$x = \frac{D_x}{D} = \frac{\begin{vmatrix} 10 & -2 \\ 11 & -5 \end{vmatrix}}{-14} = \frac{(-50) - (-22)}{-14} = \frac{-28}{-14} = 2$$

$$y = \frac{D_y}{D} = \frac{\begin{vmatrix} 4 & 10 \\ 3 & 11 \end{vmatrix}}{-14} = \frac{44 - 30}{-14} = \frac{14}{-14} = -1$$

So, the solution is $x = 2$ and $y = -1$. Check this in the original system.

✓ *Checkpoint* Now try Exercise 15.

Example 4   Using Cramer's Rule for a 3×3 System

Use Cramer's Rule and a graphing utility, if possible, to solve the system of linear equations.

$$\begin{cases} -x \quad\;\;\; + \;\; z = \;\;\; 4 \\ 2x - y + \;\; z = -3 \\ \qquad\;\; y - 3z = \;\;\; 1 \end{cases}$$

Solution

Using a graphing utility to evaluate the determinant of the coefficient matrix A, you find that Cramer's Rule cannot be applied because $|A| = 0$.

✓ *Checkpoint* Now try Exercise 17.

TECHNOLOGY TIP

Try using a graphing utility to evaluate D_x/D from Example 4. You should obtain the error message shown below.

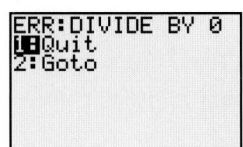

Example 5   Using Cramer's Rule for a 3×3 System

Use Cramer's Rule, if possible, to solve the system of linear equations.

$$\begin{cases} -x + 2y - 3z = 1 \\ 2x \qquad\;\; + \;\; z = 0 \\ 3x - 4y + 4z = 2 \end{cases}$$

Coefficient Matrix

$$\begin{bmatrix} -1 & 2 & -3 \\ 2 & 0 & 1 \\ 3 & -4 & 4 \end{bmatrix}$$

Solution

The coefficient matrix above can be expanded along the second row, as follows.

$$D = 2(-1)^3 \begin{vmatrix} 2 & -3 \\ -4 & 4 \end{vmatrix} + 0(-1)^4 \begin{vmatrix} -1 & -3 \\ 3 & 4 \end{vmatrix} + 1(-1)^5 \begin{vmatrix} -1 & 2 \\ 3 & -4 \end{vmatrix}$$

$$= -2(-4) + 0 - 1(-2) = 10$$

Because this determinant is not zero, you can apply Cramer's Rule.

$$x = \frac{D_x}{D} = \frac{\begin{vmatrix} 1 & 2 & -3 \\ 0 & 0 & 1 \\ 2 & -4 & 4 \end{vmatrix}}{10} = \frac{8}{10} = \frac{4}{5}$$

$$y = \frac{D_y}{D} = \frac{\begin{vmatrix} -1 & 1 & -3 \\ 2 & 0 & 1 \\ 3 & 2 & 4 \end{vmatrix}}{10} = \frac{-15}{10} = -\frac{3}{2}$$

$$z = \frac{D_z}{D} = \frac{\begin{vmatrix} -1 & 2 & 1 \\ 2 & 0 & 0 \\ 3 & -4 & 2 \end{vmatrix}}{10} = \frac{-16}{10} = -\frac{8}{5}$$

The solution is $\left(\frac{4}{5}, -\frac{3}{2}, -\frac{8}{5}\right)$. Check this in the original system.

✓ *Checkpoint* Now try Exercise 21.

Cryptography

A **cryptogram** is a message written according to a secret code. (The Greek word *kryptos* means "hidden.") Matrix multiplication can be used to encode and decode messages. To begin, you need to assign a number to each letter in the alphabet (with 0 assigned to a blank space), as follows.

0 = _	9 = I	18 = R
1 = A	10 = J	19 = S
2 = B	11 = K	20 = T
3 = C	12 = L	21 = U
4 = D	13 = M	22 = V
5 = E	14 = N	23 = W
6 = F	15 = O	24 = X
7 = G	16 = P	25 = Y
8 = H	17 = Q	26 = Z

Then the message is converted to numbers and partitioned into **uncoded row matrices,** each having n entries, as demonstrated in Example 6.

Example 6   Forming Uncoded Row Matrices

Write the uncoded row matrices of order 1×3 for the message

MEET ME MONDAY.

Solution

Partitioning the message (including blank spaces, but ignoring punctuation) into groups of three produces the following uncoded row matrices.

$$[13 \quad 5 \quad 5] \quad [20 \quad 0 \quad 13] \quad [5 \quad 0 \quad 13] \quad [15 \quad 14 \quad 4] \quad [1 \quad 25 \quad 0]$$
$$\text{M} \quad \text{E} \quad \text{E} \qquad \text{T} \qquad \text{M} \quad \text{E} \qquad \text{M} \qquad \text{O} \quad \text{N} \quad \text{D} \qquad \text{A} \quad \text{Y}$$

Note that a blank space is used to fill out the last uncoded row matrix.

✓ *Checkpoint* Now try Exercise 27.

To encode a message, choose an $n \times n$ invertible matrix A by using the techniques demonstrated in Section 8.6 and multiply the uncoded row matrices by A (on the right) to obtain **coded row matrices.** Here is an example.

Uncoded Matrix   Encoding Matrix A   Coded Matrix

$$[13 \quad 5 \quad 5] \begin{bmatrix} 1 & -2 & 2 \\ -1 & 1 & 3 \\ 1 & -1 & -4 \end{bmatrix} = [13 \quad -26 \quad 21]$$

This technique is further illustrated in Example 7.

Example 7   Encoding a Message

Use the following matrix to encode the message MEET ME MONDAY.

$$A = \begin{bmatrix} 1 & -2 & 2 \\ -1 & 1 & 3 \\ 1 & -1 & -4 \end{bmatrix}$$

Solution

The coded row matrices are obtained by multiplying each of the uncoded row matrices found in Example 6 by the matrix A, as follows.

Uncoded Matrix   Encoding Matrix A   Coded Matrix

$$[13 \quad 5 \quad 5] \begin{bmatrix} 1 & -2 & 2 \\ -1 & 1 & 3 \\ 1 & -1 & -4 \end{bmatrix} = [13 \; -26 \quad 21]$$

$$[20 \quad 0 \quad 13] \begin{bmatrix} 1 & -2 & 2 \\ -1 & 1 & 3 \\ 1 & -1 & -4 \end{bmatrix} = [33 \; -53 \; -12]$$

$$[5 \quad 0 \quad 13] \begin{bmatrix} 1 & -2 & 2 \\ -1 & 1 & 3 \\ 1 & -1 & -4 \end{bmatrix} = [18 \; -23 \; -42]$$

$$[15 \quad 14 \quad 4] \begin{bmatrix} 1 & -2 & 2 \\ -1 & 1 & 3 \\ 1 & -1 & -4 \end{bmatrix} = [5 \; -20 \quad 56]$$

$$[1 \quad 25 \quad 0] \begin{bmatrix} 1 & -2 & 2 \\ -1 & 1 & 3 \\ 1 & -1 & -4 \end{bmatrix} = [-24 \quad 23 \quad 77]$$

So, the sequence of coded row matrices is

$$[13 \; -26 \; 21][33 \; -53 \; -12][18 \; -23 \; -42][5 \; -20 \; 56][-24 \; 23 \; 77].$$

Finally, removing the matrix notation produces the following cryptogram.

$$13 \; -26 \; 21 \; 33 \; -53 \; -12 \; 18 \; -23 \; -42 \; 5 \; -20 \; 56 \; -24 \; 23 \; 77$$

✓ *Checkpoint* Now try Exercise 29.

For those who do not know the encoding matrix A, decoding the cryptogram found in Example 7 is difficult. But for an authorized receiver who knows the encoding matrix A, decoding is simple. The receiver need only multiply the coded row matrices by A^{-1} (on the right) to retrieve the uncoded row matrices. Here is an example.

$$\underbrace{[13 \; -26 \quad 21]}_{\text{Coded}} \underbrace{\begin{bmatrix} -1 & -10 & -8 \\ -1 & -6 & -5 \\ 0 & -1 & -1 \end{bmatrix}}_{A^{-1}} = \underbrace{[13 \quad 5 \quad 5]}_{\text{Uncoded}}$$

TECHNOLOGY TIP

An efficient method for encoding the message at the left with your graphing utility is to enter A as a 3×3 matrix. Let B be the 5×3 matrix whose rows are the uncoded row matrices

$$B = \begin{bmatrix} 13 & 5 & 5 \\ 20 & 0 & 13 \\ 5 & 0 & 13 \\ 15 & 14 & 4 \\ 1 & 25 & 0 \end{bmatrix}.$$

The product BA gives the coded row matrices.

Example 8   Decoding a Message

Use the inverse of the matrix

$$A = \begin{bmatrix} 1 & -2 & 2 \\ -1 & 1 & 3 \\ 1 & -1 & -4 \end{bmatrix}$$

to decode the cryptogram

13 −26 21 33 −53 −12 18 −23 −42 5 −20 56 −24 23 77

Solution

First find A^{-1} by using the techniques demonstrated in Section 8.6. A^{-1} is the decoding matrix. Next partition the message into groups of three to form the coded row matrices. Then multiply each coded row matrix by A^{-1} (on the right).

Coded Matrix   *Decoding Matrix A^{-1}*   *Decoded Matrix*

$$\begin{bmatrix} 13 & -26 & 21 \end{bmatrix} \begin{bmatrix} -1 & -10 & -8 \\ -1 & -6 & -5 \\ 0 & -1 & -1 \end{bmatrix} = \begin{bmatrix} 13 & 5 & 5 \end{bmatrix}$$

$$\begin{bmatrix} 33 & -53 & -12 \end{bmatrix} \begin{bmatrix} -1 & -10 & -8 \\ -1 & -6 & -5 \\ 0 & -1 & -1 \end{bmatrix} = \begin{bmatrix} 20 & 0 & 13 \end{bmatrix}$$

$$\begin{bmatrix} 18 & -23 & -42 \end{bmatrix} \begin{bmatrix} -1 & -10 & -8 \\ -1 & -6 & -5 \\ 0 & -1 & -1 \end{bmatrix} = \begin{bmatrix} 5 & 0 & 13 \end{bmatrix}$$

$$\begin{bmatrix} 5 & -20 & 56 \end{bmatrix} \begin{bmatrix} -1 & -10 & -8 \\ -1 & -6 & -5 \\ 0 & -1 & -1 \end{bmatrix} = \begin{bmatrix} 15 & 14 & 4 \end{bmatrix}$$

$$\begin{bmatrix} -24 & 23 & 77 \end{bmatrix} \begin{bmatrix} -1 & -10 & -8 \\ -1 & -6 & -5 \\ 0 & -1 & -1 \end{bmatrix} = \begin{bmatrix} 1 & 25 & 0 \end{bmatrix}$$

So, the message is as follows.

$$\begin{bmatrix} 13 & 5 & 5 \end{bmatrix} \quad \begin{bmatrix} 20 & 0 & 13 \end{bmatrix} \quad \begin{bmatrix} 5 & 0 & 13 \end{bmatrix} \quad \begin{bmatrix} 15 & 14 & 4 \end{bmatrix} \quad \begin{bmatrix} 1 & 25 & 0 \end{bmatrix}$$

M E E   T   M E   M   O N D   A Y

✓ *Checkpoint* Now try Exercise 33.

TECHNOLOGY TIP   An efficient method for decoding the cryptogram in Example 8 with your graphing utility is to enter A as a 3×3 matrix and then find A^{-1}. Let B be the 5×3 matrix whose rows are the coded row matrices, as shown at the right. The product BA^{-1} gives the decoded row matrices.

$$B = \begin{bmatrix} 13 & -26 & 21 \\ 33 & -53 & -12 \\ 18 & -23 & -42 \\ 5 & -20 & 56 \\ -24 & 23 & 77 \end{bmatrix}$$

8.8 Exercises

Vocabulary Check

Fill in the blanks.

1. Three points are _____ if they lie on the same line.
2. The method of using determinants to solve a system of linear equations is called _____ .
3. A message written according to a secret code is called a _____ .
4. To encode a message, choose an invertible matrix A and multiply the _____ row matrices by A (on the right) to obtain _____ row matrices.

In Exercises 1–6, use a determinant to find the area of the triangle with the given vertices.

1.
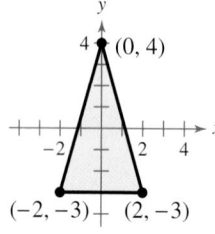

2.
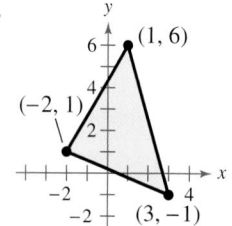

3. $(-2, 4), (2, 3), (-1, 5)$ 4. $(-3, 5), (2, 6), (3, -5)$
5. $\left(0, \frac{1}{2}\right), \left(\frac{5}{2}, 0\right), (4, 3)$ 6. $\left(\frac{9}{2}, 0\right), (2, 6), \left(0, -\frac{3}{2}\right)$

In Exercises 7 and 8, find x such that the triangle has an area of 4 square units.

7. $(-5, 1), (0, 2), (-2, x)$
8. $(-4, 2), (-3, 5), (-1, x)$

In Exercises 9–12, use a determinant to determine whether the points are collinear.

9. $(3, -1), (0, -3), (12, 5)$
10. $(3, -5), (6, 1), (4, 2)$
11. $\left(2, -\frac{1}{2}\right), (-4, 4), (6, -3)$
12. $\left(0, \frac{1}{2}\right), (2, -1), \left(-4, \frac{7}{2}\right)$

In Exercises 13 and 14, find x such that the points are collinear.

13. $(2, -5), (4, x), (5, -2)$
14. $(-6, 2), (-5, x), (-3, 5)$

In Exercises 15–22, use Cramer's Rule to solve (if possible) the system of equations.

15. $\begin{cases} -7x + 11y = -1 \\ 3x - 9y = 9 \end{cases}$ 16. $\begin{cases} 4x - 3y = -10 \\ 6x + 9y = 12 \end{cases}$

17. $\begin{cases} 3x + 2y = -2 \\ 6x + 4y = 4 \end{cases}$ 18. $\begin{cases} 6x - 5y = 17 \\ -13x + 3y = -76 \end{cases}$

19. $\begin{cases} -0.4x + 0.8y = 1.6 \\ 0.2x + 0.3y = 2.2 \end{cases}$ 20. $\begin{cases} 2.4x - 0.8y = 10.8 \\ 4.6x + 1.2y = 24.8 \end{cases}$

21. $\begin{cases} 4x - y + z = -5 \\ 2x + 2y + 3z = 10 \\ 5x - 2y + 6z = 1 \end{cases}$ 22. $\begin{cases} 4x - 2y + 3z = -2 \\ 2x + 2y + 5z = 16 \\ 8x - 5y - 2z = 4 \end{cases}$

In Exercises 23 and 24, use a graphing utility and Cramer's Rule to solve (if possible) the system of equations.

23. $\begin{cases} 3x + 3y + 5z = 1 \\ 3x + 5y + 9z = 2 \\ 5x + 9y + 17z = 4 \end{cases}$ 24. $\begin{cases} 2x + 3y + 5z = 4 \\ 3x + 5y + 9z = 7 \\ 5x + 9y + 17z = 13 \end{cases}$

25. **Area of a Region**   A large region of forest has been infected with gypsy moths. The region is roughly triangular, as shown in the figure. From the northernmost vertex A of the region, the distances to the other vertices are 25 miles south and 10 miles east (for vertex B), and 20 miles south and 28 miles east (for vertex C). Use a graphing utility to approximate the number of square miles in this region.

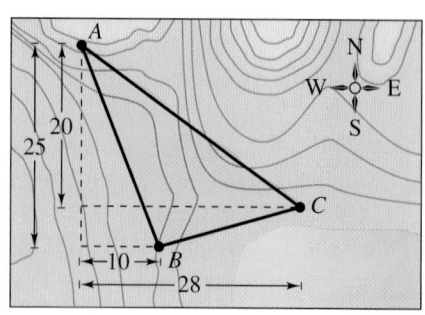

26. ***Data Analysis***   The table shows the numbers y (in millions) of families in the United States from 1998 to 2000.   (Source: U.S. Census Bureau)

Year	Families, y
1998	70.9
1999	71.5
2000	72.0

(a) This data can be approximated by a parabola. Create a system of linear equations for the data. Let t represent the years with $t = 8$ corresponding to 1998.

(b) Use Cramer's Rule to solve the system in part (a) and find the least squares regression parabola $y = at^2 + bt + c$.

(c) Use the result of part (b) to estimate the number of families in the United States in 2006. Is the estimate reasonable? Explain.

In Exercises 27 and 28, find the uncoded 1×3 row matrices for the message. Then encode the message using the encoding matrix.

Message   *Encoding Matrix*

27. CALL ME TOMORROW $\begin{bmatrix} 1 & -1 & 0 \\ 1 & 0 & -1 \\ -6 & 2 & 3 \end{bmatrix}$

28. PLEASE SEND MONEY $\begin{bmatrix} 4 & 2 & 1 \\ -3 & -3 & -1 \\ 3 & 2 & 1 \end{bmatrix}$

In Exercises 29 and 30, write a cryptogram for the message using the matrix A.

$$A = \begin{bmatrix} 1 & 2 & 2 \\ 3 & 7 & 9 \\ -1 & -4 & -7 \end{bmatrix}$$

29. GONE FISHING   **30.** HAPPY BIRTHDAY

In Exercises 31 and 32, use A^{-1} to decode the cryptogram.

31. $A = \begin{bmatrix} 1 & 2 \\ 3 & 5 \end{bmatrix}$ 11 21 64 112 25 50 29 53
23 46 40 75 55 92

32. $A = \begin{bmatrix} 2 & 3 \\ 3 & 4 \end{bmatrix}$ 85 120 6 8 10 15 84 117
42 56 90 125 60 80 30
45 19 26

33. Decode the cryptogram by using the inverse of the matrix A.

$$A = \begin{bmatrix} 1 & 2 & 2 \\ 3 & 7 & 9 \\ -1 & -4 & -7 \end{bmatrix}$$

16 −1 −48 5 −20 −65 8 4 −14
41 83 89 76 177 227

34. The following cryptogram was encoded with a 2×2 matrix.

8 21 −15 −10 −13 −13 5 10 5 25 5 19
−1 6 20 40 −18 −18 1 16

The last word of the message is _RON. What is the message?

Synthesis

True or False?   **In Exercises 35 and 36, determine whether the statement is true or false. Justify your answer.**

35. Cramer's Rule cannot be used to solve a system of linear equations if the determinant of the coefficient matrix is zero.

36. In a system of linear equations, if the determinant of the coefficient matrix is zero, the system has no solution.

37. ***Writing***   At this point in the book, you have learned several methods for solving a system of linear equations. Briefly describe which method(s) you find easiest to use and which method(s) you find most difficult to use.

38. ***Writing***   Use your school's library, the Internet, or some other reference source to research a few current real-life uses of cryptography. Write a short summary of these uses. Include a description of how messages are encoded and decoded in each case.

Review

In Exercises 39–42, find the general form of the equation of the line that passes through the two points.

39. $(-1, 5), (7, 3)$ **40.** $(0, -6), (-2, 10)$

41. $(3, -3), (10, -1)$ **42.** $(-4, 12), (4, 2)$

In Exercises 43 and 44, sketch the graph of the rational function. Identify any asymptotes.

43. $f(x) = \dfrac{2x^2}{x^2 + 4}$ **44.** $f(x) = \dfrac{2x}{x^2 + 3x - 18}$

8 Chapter Summary

What did you learn?

	Review Exercises
Section 8.1	
☐ Use the method of substitution and the graphical method to solve systems of equations in two variables.	1–12
☐ Use systems of equations to model and solve real-life problems.	13–16
Section 8.2	
☐ Use the method of elimination to solve systems of linear equations in two variables.	17–24
☐ Graphically interpret the number of solutions of a system of linear equations in two variables.	25–30
☐ Use systems of linear equations in two variables to model and solve real-life problems.	31–34
Section 8.3	
☐ Use back-substitution to solve linear systems in row-echelon form.	35, 36
☐ Use Gaussian elimination to solve systems of linear equations.	37–40
☐ Solve nonsquare systems of linear equations.	41, 42
☐ Graphically interpret three-variable linear systems.	43, 44
☐ Use systems of linear equations to write partial fraction decompositions of rational expressions.	45–48
☐ Use systems of linear equations in three or more variables to model and solve real-life problems.	49–52
Section 8.4	
☐ Write matrices and identify their orders.	53–62
☐ Perform elementary row operations on matrices.	63–68
☐ Use matrices and Gaussian elimination to solve systems of linear equations.	69–76
☐ Use matrices and Gauss-Jordan elimination to solve systems of linear equations.	77–84
Section 8.5	
☐ Decide whether two matrices are equal.	85–88
☐ Add and subtract matrices and multiply matrices by a scalar.	89–102
☐ Multiply two matrices.	103–110
☐ Use matrix operations to model and solve real-life problems.	111, 112
Section 8.6	
☐ Verify that two matrices are inverses of each other.	113, 114
☐ Use Gauss-Jordan elimination to find inverses of matrices.	115–122
☐ Use a formula to find inverses of 2×2 matrices.	123–126
☐ Use inverse matrices to solve systems of linear equations.	127–136

Section 8.7

☐ Find the determinants of 2 × 2 matrices.

☐ Find minors and cofactors of square matrices.

☐ Find the determinants of square matrices.

☐ Find the determinants of triangular matrices.

Review Exercises

137–140

141–144

145–150

151, 152

Section 8.8

☐ Use determinants to find areas of triangles.

☐ Use determinants to decide whether points are collinear.

☐ Use Cramer's Rule to solve systems of linear equations.

☐ Use matrices to encode and decode messages.

153–156

157, 158

159–166

167–170

8 Review Exercises

8.1 **In Exercises 1–6, solve the system by the method of substitution.**

1. $\begin{cases} x + y = 2 \\ x - y = 0 \end{cases}$ 2. $\begin{cases} 2x - 3y = 3 \\ x - y = 0 \end{cases}$

3. $\begin{cases} x^2 - y^2 = 9 \\ x - y = 1 \end{cases}$ 4. $\begin{cases} x^2 + y^2 = 169 \\ 3x + 2y = 39 \end{cases}$

5. $\begin{cases} y = 2x^2 \\ y = x^4 - 2x^2 \end{cases}$ 6. $\begin{cases} x = y + 3 \\ x = y^2 + 1 \end{cases}$

In Exercises 7–12, use a graphing utility to approximate all points of intersection of the graph of the system of equations. Verify your solutions by checking them in the original system.

7. $\begin{cases} 5x + 6y = 7 \\ -x - 4y = 0 \end{cases}$ 8. $\begin{cases} 8x - 3y = -3 \\ 2x + 5y = 28 \end{cases}$

9. $\begin{cases} y^2 - 2y + x = 0 \\ x + y = 0 \end{cases}$ 10. $\begin{cases} y = 2x^2 - 4x + 1 \\ y = x^2 - 4x + 3 \end{cases}$

11. $\begin{cases} y = 2(6 - x) \\ y = 2^{x-2} \end{cases}$ 12. $\begin{cases} y = \ln(x - 1) - 3 \\ y = 4 - \frac{1}{2}x \end{cases}$

13. **Break-Even Analysis**   You set up a business and make an initial investment of $10,000. The unit cost of the product is $2.85 and the selling price is $4.95. How many units must you sell to break even?

14. **Choice of Two Jobs**   You are offered two sales jobs. One company offers an annual salary of $22,500 plus a year-end bonus of 1.5% of your total sales. The other company offers a salary of $20,000 plus a year-end bonus of 2% of your total sales. How much would you have to sell in a year to make the second offer the better offer?

15. **Geometry**   The perimeter of a rectangle is 480 meters and its length is 1.5 times its width. Find the dimensions of the rectangle.

16. **Geometry**   The perimeter of a rectangle is 68 feet and its width is $\frac{8}{9}$ times its length. Find the dimensions of the rectangle.

8.2 **In Exercises 17–24, solve the system by the method of elimination.**

17. $\begin{cases} 2x - y = 2 \\ 6x + 8y = 39 \end{cases}$ 18. $\begin{cases} 40x + 30y = 24 \\ 20x - 50y = -14 \end{cases}$

19. $\begin{cases} \frac{1}{5}x + \frac{3}{10}y = \frac{7}{50} \\ \frac{2}{5}x + \frac{1}{2}y = \frac{1}{5} \end{cases}$ 20. $\begin{cases} \frac{5}{12}x - \frac{3}{4}y = \frac{25}{4} \\ -x + \frac{7}{8}y = -\frac{38}{5} \end{cases}$

21. $\begin{cases} 3x - 2y = 0 \\ 3x + 2(y + 5) = 10 \end{cases}$ 22. $\begin{cases} 7x + 12y = 63 \\ 2x + 3y = 15 \end{cases}$

23. $\begin{cases} 1.25x - 2y = 3.5 \\ 5x - 8y = 14 \end{cases}$ 24. $\begin{cases} 1.5x + 2.5y = 8.5 \\ 6x + 10y = 24 \end{cases}$

In Exercises 25–30, use a graphing utility to graph the lines in the system. Use the graphs to determine whether the system is consistent or inconsistent. If the system is consistent, determine the solution. Verify your results algebraically.

25. $\begin{cases} 3x + 2y = 0 \\ x - y = 4 \end{cases}$ 26. $\begin{cases} x + y = 6 \\ -2x - 2y = -12 \end{cases}$

27. $\begin{cases} \frac{1}{4}x - \frac{1}{5}y = 2 \\ -5x + 4y = 8 \end{cases}$ 28. $\begin{cases} \frac{7}{2}x - 7y = -1 \\ -x + 2y = 4 \end{cases}$

29. $\begin{cases} 2x - 2y = 8 \\ 4x - 1.5y = -5.5 \end{cases}$ 30. $\begin{cases} -x + 3.2y = 10.4 \\ -2x - 9.6y = 6.4 \end{cases}$

Supply and Demand   In Exercises 31 and 32, find the point of equilibrium of the demand and supply equations.

Demand Function	Supply Function
31. $p = 37 - 0.0002x$	$p = 22 + 0.00001x$
32. $p = 120 - 0.0001x$	$p = 45 + 0.0002x$

33. **Airplane Speed**   Two planes leave Pittsburgh and Philadelphia at the same time, each going to the other city. One plane flies 25 miles per hour faster than the other. Find the airspeed of each plane if the cities are 275 miles apart and the planes pass each other after 40 minutes of flying time.

34. **Investment Portfolio**   A total of $46,000 is invested in two corporate bonds that pay 6.75% and 7.25% simple interest. The investor wants an annual interest income of $3245 from the investments. What is the most that can be invested in the 6.75% bond?

8.3 In Exercises 35 and 36, use back-substitution to solve the system of linear equations.

35. $\begin{cases} x - 4y + 3z = 3 \\ -y + z = -1 \\ z = -5 \end{cases}$ 36. $\begin{cases} x - 7y + 8z = 85 \\ y - 9z = -35 \\ z = 3 \end{cases}$

In Exercises 37–42, solve the system of linear equations and check any solution algebraically.

37. $\begin{cases} x + 3y - z = 13 \\ 2x - 5z = 23 \\ 4x - y - 2z = 14 \end{cases}$ 38. $\begin{cases} x + 2y + 6z = 4 \\ 3x - 2y + z = 4 \\ 4x + 2z = 0 \end{cases}$

39. $\begin{cases} x - 2y + z = -6 \\ 2x - 3y = -7 \\ -x + 3y - 3z = 11 \end{cases}$

40. $\begin{cases} 2x + 6z = -9 \\ 3x - 2y + 11z = -16 \\ 3x - y + 7z = -11 \end{cases}$

41. $\begin{cases} 5x - 12y + 7z = 16 \\ 3x - 7y + 4z = 9 \end{cases}$

42. $\begin{cases} 2x + 5y - 19z = 34 \\ 3x + 8y - 31z = 54 \end{cases}$

In Exercises 43 and 44, sketch the plane represented by the linear equation. Then list four points that lie in the plane.

43. $2x - 4y + z = 8$ 44. $3x + 3y - z = 9$

In Exercises 45–48, (a) write the partial fraction decomposition for the rational expression, (b) check your result algebraically by combining the fractions, and (c) check your result graphically by using a graphing utility to graph the rational expression and the partial fractions in the same viewing window.

45. $\dfrac{4 - x}{x^2 + 6x + 8}$ 46. $\dfrac{-x}{x^2 + 3x + 2}$

47. $\dfrac{x^2 + 2x}{x^3 - x^2 + x - 1}$ 48. $\dfrac{3x^3 + 4x}{(x^2 + 1)^2}$

In Exercises 49 and 50, find the equation of the parabola $y = ax^2 + bx + c$ that passes through the points. To verify your result, use a graphing utility to plot the points and graph the parabola.

49. $(0, -5), (1, -2), (2, 5)$ 50. $(-5, 6), (1, 0), (2, 20)$

51. *Agriculture*   A mixture of 6 gallons of chemical A, 8 gallons of chemical B, and 13 gallons of chemical C is required to kill a destructive crop insect. Commercial spray X contains 1, 2, and 2 parts, respectively, of these chemicals. Commercial spray Y contains only chemical C. Commercial spray Z contains chemicals A, B, and C in equal amounts. How much of each type of commercial spray is needed to obtain the desired mixture?

52. *Investment Portfolio*   An inheritance of $20,000 is divided among three investments yielding $1780 in interest per year. The interest rates for the three investments are 7%, 9%, and 11%. Find the amount of each investment if the second and third were $3000 and $1000 less than the first, respectively.

8.4 In Exercises 53–56, determine the order of the matrix.

53. $\begin{bmatrix} -3 \\ 1 \\ 10 \end{bmatrix}$ 54. $\begin{bmatrix} 3 & -1 & 0 & 6 \\ -2 & 7 & 1 & 4 \end{bmatrix}$

55. $\begin{bmatrix} 14 \end{bmatrix}$ 56. $\begin{bmatrix} 6 & 7 & -5 & 0 & -8 \end{bmatrix}$

In Exercises 57–60, write the augmented matrix for the system of linear equations.

57. $\begin{cases} 3x - 10y = 15 \\ 5x + 4y = 22 \end{cases}$ 58. $\begin{cases} -x + y = 12 \\ 10x - 4y = -90 \end{cases}$

59. $\begin{cases} 8x - 7y + 4z = 12 \\ 3x - 5y + 2z = 20 \\ 5x + 3y - 3z = 26 \end{cases}$

60. $\begin{cases} 3x - 5y + z = 25 \\ -4x - 2z = -14 \\ 6x + y = 15 \end{cases}$

In Exercises 61 and 62, write the system of linear equations represented by the augmented matrix. (Use the variables x, y, z, and w, if applicable.)

61. $\left[\begin{array}{ccc:c} 5 & 1 & 7 & -9 \\ 4 & 2 & 0 & 10 \\ 9 & 4 & 2 & 3 \end{array}\right]$

62. $\left[\begin{array}{cccc:c} 13 & 16 & 7 & 3 & 2 \\ 1 & 21 & 8 & 5 & 12 \\ 4 & 10 & -4 & 3 & -1 \end{array}\right]$

In Exercises 63 and 64, write the matrix in row-echelon form. Remember that the row-echelon form of a matrix is not unique.

63. $\begin{bmatrix} 0 & 1 & 1 \\ 1 & 2 & 3 \\ 2 & 2 & 2 \end{bmatrix}$
64. $\begin{bmatrix} 3 & 5 & 2 \\ 1 & -2 & 4 \\ -2 & 0 & 5 \end{bmatrix}$

In Exercises 65–68, use the matrix capabilities of a graphing utility to write the matrix in reduced row-echelon form.

65. $\begin{bmatrix} 3 & -2 & 1 & 0 \\ 4 & -3 & 0 & 1 \end{bmatrix}$

66. $\begin{bmatrix} 1 & 1 & 2 & 1 & 0 & 0 \\ -1 & 0 & 3 & 0 & 1 & 0 \\ 1 & 2 & 8 & 0 & 0 & 1 \end{bmatrix}$

67. $\begin{bmatrix} 1 & 3 & 4 \\ 0 & 1 & 1 \\ 2 & 4 & 6 \end{bmatrix}$
68. $\begin{bmatrix} 4 & 8 & 16 \\ 3 & -1 & 2 \\ -2 & 10 & 12 \end{bmatrix}$

In Exercises 69–76, use matrices to solve the system of equations if possible. Use Gaussian elimination with back-substitution.

69. $\begin{cases} 5x + 4y = 2 \\ -x + y = -22 \end{cases}$
70. $\begin{cases} 2x - 5y = 2 \\ 3x - 7y = 1 \end{cases}$

71. $\begin{cases} 2x + y = 0.3 \\ 3x - y = -1.3 \end{cases}$
72. $\begin{cases} 0.2x - 0.1y = 0.07 \\ 0.4x - 0.5y = -0.01 \end{cases}$

73. $\begin{cases} 2x + 3y + 3z = 3 \\ 6x + 6y + 12z = 13 \\ 12x + 9y - z = 2 \end{cases}$

74. $\begin{cases} x + 2y + 6z = 1 \\ 2x + 5y + 15z = 4 \\ 3x + y + 3z = -6 \end{cases}$

75. $\begin{cases} 3x + 21y - 29z = -1 \\ 2x + 15y - 21z = 0 \end{cases}$

76. $\begin{cases} x + 2y + w = 3 \\ -3y + 3z = 0 \\ 4x + 4y + z + 2w = 0 \\ 2x - y + z = 3 \end{cases}$

In Exercises 77–80, use matrices to solve the system of equations if possible. Use Gauss-Jordan elimination.

77. $\begin{cases} -x + y + 2z = 1 \\ 2x + 3y + z = -2 \\ 5x + 4y + 2z = 4 \end{cases}$

78. $\begin{cases} 4x + 4y + 4z = 5 \\ 4x - 2y - 8z = 1 \\ 5x + 3y + 8z = 6 \end{cases}$

79. $\begin{cases} 2x - y + 9z = -8 \\ -x - 3y + 4z = -15 \\ 5x + 2y - z = 17 \end{cases}$

80. $\begin{cases} -3x + y + 7z = -20 \\ 5x - 2y - z = 34 \\ -x + y + 4z = -8 \end{cases}$

In Exercises 81–84, use the matrix capabilities of a graphing utility to reduce the augmented matrix corresponding to the system of equations and solve the system.

81. $\begin{cases} x + 2y - z = 7 \\ -y - z = 4 \\ 4x - z = 16 \end{cases}$
82. $\begin{cases} 3x + 6z = 0 \\ -2x + y = 5 \\ y + 2z = 3 \end{cases}$

83. $\begin{cases} 3x - y + 5z - 2w = -44 \\ x + 6y + 4z - w = 1 \\ 5x - y + z + 3w = -15 \\ 4y - z - 8w = 58 \end{cases}$

84. $\begin{cases} 4x + 12y + 2z = 20 \\ x + 6y + 4z = 12 \\ x + 6y + z = 8 \\ -2x - 10y - 2z = -10 \end{cases}$

8.5 In Exercises 85–88, find x and y.

85. $\begin{bmatrix} -1 & x \\ y & 9 \end{bmatrix} = \begin{bmatrix} -1 & 12 \\ -7 & 9 \end{bmatrix}$

86. $\begin{bmatrix} -1 & 0 \\ x & 5 \\ -4 & y \end{bmatrix} = \begin{bmatrix} -1 & 0 \\ 8 & 5 \\ -4 & 0 \end{bmatrix}$

87. $\begin{bmatrix} x+3 & 4 & -4y \\ 0 & -3 & 2 \\ -2 & y+5 & 6x \end{bmatrix} = \begin{bmatrix} 5x-1 & 4 & -44 \\ 0 & -3 & 2 \\ -2 & 16 & 6 \end{bmatrix}$

88. $\begin{bmatrix} -9 & 4 & 2 & -5 \\ 0 & -3 & 7 & -4 \\ 6 & -1 & 1 & 0 \end{bmatrix} = \begin{bmatrix} -9 & 4 & x-10 & -5 \\ 0 & -3 & 7 & 2y \\ \frac{1}{2}x & -1 & 1 & 0 \end{bmatrix}$

In Exercises 89–92, find, if possible, (a) $A + B$, (b) $A - B$, (c) $4A$, and (d) $A + 3B$.

89. $A = \begin{bmatrix} 7 & 3 \\ -1 & 5 \end{bmatrix}$, $B = \begin{bmatrix} 10 & -20 \\ 14 & -3 \end{bmatrix}$

90. $A = \begin{bmatrix} -11 & 16 & 19 \\ -7 & -2 & 1 \end{bmatrix}$, $B = \begin{bmatrix} 6 & 0 \\ 8 & -4 \\ -2 & 10 \end{bmatrix}$

91. $A = \begin{bmatrix} 6 & 0 & 7 \\ 5 & -1 & 2 \\ 3 & 2 & 3 \end{bmatrix}$, $B = \begin{bmatrix} 0 & 5 & 1 \\ -4 & 8 & 6 \\ 2 & -1 & 1 \end{bmatrix}$

92. $A = \begin{bmatrix} 2 & -3 & 6 \\ 0 & 4 & 1 \end{bmatrix}$, $B = \begin{bmatrix} -3 & 5 & 5 \\ 1 & 1 & 1 \end{bmatrix}$

In Exercises 93–96, evaluate the expression. If it is not possible, explain why.

93. $\begin{bmatrix} 2 & 1 & 0 \\ 0 & 5 & -4 \end{bmatrix} - 3\begin{bmatrix} 5 & 3 & -6 \\ 0 & -2 & 5 \end{bmatrix}$

94. $-2\begin{bmatrix} 1 & 2 \\ 5 & -4 \\ 6 & 0 \end{bmatrix} + 8\begin{bmatrix} 7 & 1 \\ 1 & 2 \\ 1 & 4 \end{bmatrix}$

95. $-\begin{bmatrix} 8 & -1 & 8 \\ -2 & 4 & 12 \\ 0 & -6 & 0 \end{bmatrix} - 5\begin{bmatrix} -2 & 0 & -4 \\ 3 & -1 & 1 \\ 6 & 12 & -8 \end{bmatrix}$

96. $6\begin{bmatrix} -4 & -1 & -3 & 4 \\ 2 & -5 & 7 & -10 \end{bmatrix} + 2\begin{bmatrix} -1 & 1 & 13 & -7 \\ 14 & -3 & 8 & -1 \end{bmatrix}$

In Exercises 97 and 98, use the matrix capabilities of a graphing utility to evaluate the expression.

97. $3\begin{bmatrix} 8 & -2 & 5 \\ 1 & 3 & -1 \end{bmatrix} + 6\begin{bmatrix} 4 & -2 & -3 \\ 2 & 7 & 6 \end{bmatrix}$

98. $-5\begin{bmatrix} 2 & 0 \\ 7 & -2 \\ 8 & 2 \end{bmatrix} + 4\begin{bmatrix} 4 & -2 \\ 6 & 11 \\ -1 & 3 \end{bmatrix}$

In Exercises 99–102, solve for X when

$$A = \begin{bmatrix} -4 & 0 \\ 1 & -5 \\ -3 & 2 \end{bmatrix} \quad \text{and} \quad B = \begin{bmatrix} 1 & 2 \\ -2 & 1 \\ 4 & 4 \end{bmatrix}.$$

99. $X = 3A - 2B$ **100.** $6X = 4A + 3B$

101. $3X + 2A = B$ **102.** $2A - 5B = 3X$

In Exercises 103–106, find AB if possible.

103. $A = \begin{bmatrix} 1 & 2 \\ 5 & -4 \\ 6 & 0 \end{bmatrix}$, $B = \begin{bmatrix} 6 & -2 & 8 \\ 4 & 0 & 0 \end{bmatrix}$

104. $A = \begin{bmatrix} 1 & 5 & 6 \\ 2 & -4 & 0 \end{bmatrix}$, $B = \begin{bmatrix} 7 & 5 & 2 \\ 0 & 1 & 0 \end{bmatrix}$

105. $A = \begin{bmatrix} 3 & -2 & 0 \\ 1 & 4 & 9 \end{bmatrix}$, $B = \begin{bmatrix} 7 & 0 \\ 5 & 3 \\ -1 & 3 \end{bmatrix}$

106. $A = \begin{bmatrix} 1 & 3 & 2 \\ 0 & 2 & -4 \\ 1 & -1 & 3 \end{bmatrix}$, $B = \begin{bmatrix} 4 & -3 & 2 \\ 0 & 3 & -1 \\ 0 & 6 & 2 \end{bmatrix}$

In Exercises 107–110, use the matrix capabilities of a graphing utility to evaluate the expression.

107. $\begin{bmatrix} 4 & 1 \\ 11 & -7 \\ 12 & 3 \end{bmatrix}\begin{bmatrix} 3 & -5 & 6 \\ 2 & -2 & -2 \end{bmatrix}$

108. $\begin{bmatrix} -2 & 3 & 10 \\ 4 & -2 & 2 \end{bmatrix}\begin{bmatrix} 1 & 1 \\ -5 & 2 \\ 3 & 2 \end{bmatrix}$

109. $\begin{bmatrix} 2 & 1 \\ 6 & 0 \end{bmatrix}\left(\begin{bmatrix} 4 & 2 \\ -3 & 1 \end{bmatrix} + \begin{bmatrix} -2 & 4 \\ 0 & 4 \end{bmatrix}\right)$

110. $\begin{bmatrix} 1 & -1 \\ 4 & 2 \end{bmatrix}\left(\begin{bmatrix} 0 & 3 \\ 1 & 2 \end{bmatrix}\begin{bmatrix} 1 & 0 \\ 5 & -3 \end{bmatrix}\right)$

111. *Manufacturing*   A corporation has four factories, each of which manufactures three types of cordless power tools. The number of units of cordless power tools produced at factory j in one day is represented by a_{ij} in the matrix

$$A = \begin{bmatrix} 80 & 70 & 90 & 40 \\ 50 & 30 & 80 & 20 \\ 90 & 60 & 100 & 50 \end{bmatrix}.$$

Find the production levels if production is increased by 20%.

112. *Manufacturing*   A manufacturing company produces three kinds of computer games that are shipped to two warehouses. The number of units of game i that are shipped to warehouse j is represented by a_{ij} in the matrix

$$A = \begin{bmatrix} 8200 & 7400 \\ 6500 & 9800 \\ 5400 & 4800 \end{bmatrix}.$$

The price per unit is represented by the matrix

$$B = [\$10.25 \quad \$14.50 \quad \$17.75].$$

Compute BA and state what each entry of the product represents.

8.6 In Exercises 113 and 114, show that B is the inverse of A.

113. $A = \begin{bmatrix} -4 & -1 \\ 7 & 2 \end{bmatrix}$, $B = \begin{bmatrix} -2 & -1 \\ 7 & 4 \end{bmatrix}$

114. $A = \begin{bmatrix} 1 & 1 & 0 \\ 1 & 0 & 1 \\ 6 & 2 & 3 \end{bmatrix}$, $B = \begin{bmatrix} -2 & -3 & 1 \\ 3 & 3 & -1 \\ 2 & 4 & -1 \end{bmatrix}$

In Exercises 115–118, find the inverse of the matrix (if it exists).

115. $\begin{bmatrix} -6 & 5 \\ -5 & 4 \end{bmatrix}$ 116. $\begin{bmatrix} -3 & -5 \\ 2 & 3 \end{bmatrix}$

117. $\begin{bmatrix} -1 & -2 & -2 \\ 3 & 7 & 9 \\ 1 & 4 & 7 \end{bmatrix}$ 118. $\begin{bmatrix} 0 & -2 & 1 \\ -5 & -2 & -3 \\ 7 & 3 & 4 \end{bmatrix}$

In Exercises 119–122, use the matrix capabilities of a graphing utility to find the inverse of the matrix (if it exists).

119. $\begin{bmatrix} 2 & 6 \\ 3 & -6 \end{bmatrix}$ 120. $\begin{bmatrix} 3 & -10 \\ 4 & 2 \end{bmatrix}$

121. $\begin{bmatrix} 2 & 0 & 3 \\ -1 & 1 & 1 \\ 2 & -2 & 1 \end{bmatrix}$ 122. $\begin{bmatrix} 1 & 4 & 6 \\ 2 & -3 & 1 \\ -1 & 18 & 16 \end{bmatrix}$

In Exercises 123–126, use the formula on page 663 to find the inverse of the 2×2 matrix.

123. $\begin{bmatrix} -7 & 2 \\ -8 & 2 \end{bmatrix}$ 124. $\begin{bmatrix} 10 & 4 \\ 7 & 3 \end{bmatrix}$

125. $\begin{bmatrix} -1 & 20 \\ \frac{3}{10} & -6 \end{bmatrix}$ 126. $\begin{bmatrix} -6 & -5 \\ 3 & 3 \end{bmatrix}$

In Exercises 127–132, use an inverse matrix to solve (if possible) the system of linear equations.

127. $\begin{cases} -x + 4y = 8 \\ 2x - 7y = -5 \end{cases}$ 128. $\begin{cases} 5x - y = 13 \\ -9x + 2y = -24 \end{cases}$

129. $\begin{cases} 3x + 2y - z = 6 \\ x - y + 2z = -1 \\ 5x + y + z = 7 \end{cases}$

130. $\begin{cases} -x + 4y - 2z = 12 \\ 2x - 9y + 5z = -25 \\ -x + 5y - 4z = 10 \end{cases}$

131. $\begin{cases} -2x + y + 2z = -13 \\ -x - 4y + z = -11 \\ -y - z = 0 \end{cases}$

132. $\begin{cases} 3x - y + 5z = -14 \\ -x + y + 6z = 8 \\ -8x + 4y - z = 44 \end{cases}$

In Exercises 133–136, use the matrix capabilities of a graphing utility to solve (if possible) the system of linear equations.

133. $\begin{cases} x + 2y = -1 \\ 3x + 4y = -5 \end{cases}$ 134. $\begin{cases} x + 3y = 23 \\ -6x + 2y = -18 \end{cases}$

135. $\begin{cases} -3x - 3y - 4z = 2 \\ y + z = -1 \\ 4x + 3y + 4z = -1 \end{cases}$

136. $\begin{cases} 2x + 3y - 4z = 1 \\ x - y + 2z = -4 \\ 3x + 7y - 10z = 0 \end{cases}$

8.7 In Exercises 137–140, find the determinant of the matrix.

137. $\begin{bmatrix} 8 & 5 \\ 2 & -4 \end{bmatrix}$ 138. $\begin{bmatrix} -9 & 11 \\ 7 & -4 \end{bmatrix}$

139. $\begin{bmatrix} 50 & -30 \\ 10 & 5 \end{bmatrix}$ 140. $\begin{bmatrix} 14 & -24 \\ 12 & -15 \end{bmatrix}$

In Exercises 141–144, find all (a) minors and (b) cofactors of the matrix.

141. $\begin{bmatrix} 2 & -1 \\ 7 & 4 \end{bmatrix}$ 142. $\begin{bmatrix} 3 & 6 \\ 5 & -4 \end{bmatrix}$

143. $\begin{bmatrix} 3 & 2 & -1 \\ -2 & 5 & 0 \\ 1 & 8 & 6 \end{bmatrix}$ 144. $\begin{bmatrix} 8 & 3 & 4 \\ 6 & 5 & -9 \\ -4 & 1 & 2 \end{bmatrix}$

In Exercises 145–150, find the determinant of the matrix. Expand by cofactors on the row or column that appears to make the computations easiest.

145. $\begin{bmatrix} -2 & 4 & 1 \\ -6 & 0 & 2 \\ 5 & 3 & 4 \end{bmatrix}$ 146. $\begin{bmatrix} 4 & 7 & -1 \\ 2 & -3 & 4 \\ -5 & 1 & -1 \end{bmatrix}$

147. $\begin{bmatrix} 1 & 0 & -2 \\ 0 & 1 & 0 \\ -2 & 0 & 1 \end{bmatrix}$ 148. $\begin{bmatrix} 0 & 3 & 1 \\ 5 & -2 & 1 \\ 1 & 6 & 1 \end{bmatrix}$

149. $\begin{bmatrix} 3 & 0 & -4 & 0 \\ 0 & 8 & 1 & 2 \\ 6 & 1 & 8 & 2 \\ 0 & 3 & -4 & 1 \end{bmatrix}$

150. $\begin{bmatrix} -5 & 6 & 0 & 0 \\ 0 & 1 & -1 & 2 \\ -3 & 4 & -5 & 1 \\ 1 & 6 & 0 & 3 \end{bmatrix}$

In Exercises 151 and 152, evaluate the determinant. Do not use a graphing utility.

151. $\begin{vmatrix} 8 & 6 & 0 & 2 \\ 0 & -1 & 1 & -4 \\ 0 & 0 & 4 & 5 \\ 0 & 0 & 0 & 3 \end{vmatrix}$

152. $\begin{vmatrix} -5 & 0 & 0 & 0 \\ 7 & -2 & 0 & 0 \\ 11 & 21 & 2 & 0 \\ -6 & 9 & 12 & 14 \end{vmatrix}$

8.8 In Exercises 153–156, use a determinant to find the area of the triangle with the given vertices.

153. $(1, 0), (5, 0), (5, 8)$

154. $(-4, 0), (4, 0), (0, 6)$

155. $\left(\frac{1}{2}, 1\right), \left(2, -\frac{5}{2}\right), \left(\frac{3}{2}, 1\right)$

156. $\left(\frac{3}{2}, 1\right), \left(4, -\frac{1}{2}\right), (4, 2)$

In Exercises 157 and 158, use a determinant to determine whether the points are collinear.

157. $(-1, 7), (2, 5), (4, 1)$

158. $(0, -5), (2, 1), (4, 7)$

In Exercises 159–164, use Cramer's Rule to solve (if possible) the system of equations.

159. $\begin{cases} x + 2y = 5 \\ -x + y = 1 \end{cases}$

160. $\begin{cases} 2x - y = -10 \\ 3x + 2y = -1 \end{cases}$

161. $\begin{cases} 5x - 2y = 6 \\ -11x + 3y = -23 \end{cases}$

162. $\begin{cases} 3x + 8y = -7 \\ 9x - 5y = 37 \end{cases}$

163. $\begin{cases} -2x + 3y - 5z = -11 \\ 4x - y + z = -3 \\ -x - 4y + 6z = 15 \end{cases}$

164. $\begin{cases} 5x - 2y + z = 15 \\ 3x - 3y - z = -7 \\ 2x - y - 7z = -3 \end{cases}$

In Exercises 165 and 166, use a graphing utility and Cramer's Rule to solve (if possible) the system of equations.

165. $\begin{cases} x - 3y + 2z = 2 \\ 2x + 2y - 3z = 3 \\ x - 7y + 8z = -4 \end{cases}$

166. $\begin{cases} 14x - 21y - 7z = 10 \\ -4x + 2y - 2z = 4 \\ 56x - 21y + 7z = 5 \end{cases}$

In Exercises 167 and 168, find the uncoded 1×3 row matrices for the message. Then encode the message using the encoding matrix.

| *Message* | *Encoding Matrix* |

167. LOOK OUT BELOW $\begin{bmatrix} 2 & -2 & 0 \\ 3 & 0 & -3 \\ -6 & 2 & 3 \end{bmatrix}$

168. CONGRATULATIONS $\begin{bmatrix} 2 & 1 & 0 \\ -6 & -6 & -2 \\ 3 & 2 & 1 \end{bmatrix}$

In Exercises 169 and 170, decode the cryptogram by using the inverse of the matrix

$$A = \begin{bmatrix} -5 & 4 & -3 \\ 10 & -7 & 6 \\ 8 & -6 & 5 \end{bmatrix}.$$

169. -5 11 -2 370 -265 225 -57 48 -33 32 -15 20 245 -171 147

170. 67 -43 43 84 -62 53 -17 14 -10 -30 26 -17 17 -9 12 -60 48 -36

Synthesis

True or False? **In Exercises 171 and 172, determine whether the statement is true or false. Justify your answer.**

171. Solving a system of equations graphically will always give an exact solution.

172. $\begin{vmatrix} a_{11} & a_{12} & a_{13} \\ a_{21} & a_{22} & a_{23} \\ a_{31} + c_1 & a_{32} + c_2 & a_{33} + c_3 \end{vmatrix} =$

$\begin{vmatrix} a_{11} & a_{12} & a_{13} \\ a_{21} & a_{22} & a_{23} \\ a_{31} & a_{32} & a_{33} \end{vmatrix} + \begin{vmatrix} a_{11} & a_{12} & a_{13} \\ a_{21} & a_{22} & a_{23} \\ c_1 & c_2 & c_3 \end{vmatrix}$

173. What is the relationship between the three elementary row operations performed on an augmented matrix and the operations that lead to equivalent systems of equations?

174. Under what conditions does a matrix have an inverse?

8 Chapter Test

Take this test as you would take a test in class. After you are finished, check your work against the answers given in the back of the book.

In Exercises 1–3, solve the system by the method of substitution. Check your solution graphically.

1. $\begin{cases} x - y = 6 \\ 3x + 5y = 2 \end{cases}$ **2.** $\begin{cases} y = x - 1 \\ y = (x - 1)^3 \end{cases}$ **3.** $\begin{cases} 4x - y^2 = 7 \\ x - y = 3 \end{cases}$

In Exercises 4–6, solve the system by the method of elimination.

4. $\begin{cases} 2x + 5y = -11 \\ 5x - y = 19 \end{cases}$ **5.** $\begin{cases} x - 2y + 3z = -5 \\ 2x - z = -4 \\ 3y + z = 17 \end{cases}$ **6.** $\begin{cases} 5x + 5y - z = 0 \\ 10x + 5y + 2z = 0 \\ 5x + 15y - 9z = 0 \end{cases}$

7. Find the equation of the parabola $y = ax^2 + bx + c$ that passes through the points $(0, 6)$, $(-2, 2)$, and $\left(3, \frac{9}{2}\right)$.

8. Write the partial fraction decomposition for the rational expression $\dfrac{5x - 2}{(x - 1)^2}$.

In Exercises 9 and 10, use matrices to solve the system of equations if possible.

9. $\begin{cases} 2x + y + 2z = 4 \\ 2x + 2y = 5 \\ 2x - y + 6z = 2 \end{cases}$ **10.** $\begin{cases} 2x + 3y + z = 10 \\ 2x - 3y - 3z = 22 \\ 4x - 2y + 3z = -2 \end{cases}$

11. If possible, find (a) $A - B$, (b) $3A$, (c) $3A - 2B$, and (d) AB.

$$A = \begin{bmatrix} 5 & 4 & 4 \\ -4 & -4 & 0 \\ 1 & 2 & 0 \end{bmatrix}, \quad B = \begin{bmatrix} 4 & 4 & 0 \\ 3 & 2 & 1 \\ 1 & -2 & 0 \end{bmatrix}$$

12. Find A^{-1} for $A = \begin{bmatrix} -6 & 4 \\ 10 & -5 \end{bmatrix}$ and use A^{-1} to solve the system at the right.

In Exercises 13 and 14, find the determinant of the matrix.

13. $\begin{bmatrix} -25 & 18 \\ 6 & -7 \end{bmatrix}$ **14.** $\begin{bmatrix} 4 & 0 & 3 \\ 1 & -8 & 2 \\ 3 & 2 & 2 \end{bmatrix}$

15. Use a determinant to find the area of the triangle shown at the right.

16. Use Cramer's Rule to solve (if possible) $\begin{cases} 20x + 8y = 11 \\ 12x - 24y = 21 \end{cases}$.

17. The flow of traffic (in vehicles per hour) through a network of streets is shown at the right. Solve the system for the traffic flow represented by x_i, $i = 1, 2, 3, 4,$ and 5.

$\begin{cases} -6x + 4y = 10 \\ 10x - 5y = 20 \end{cases}$

System for 12

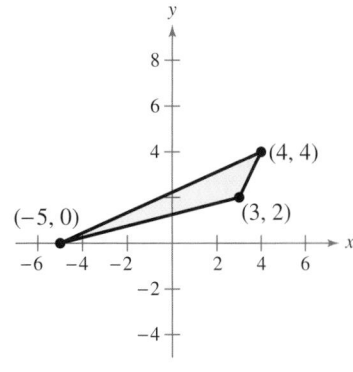

Figure for 15

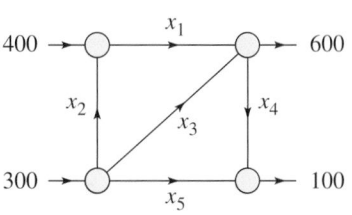

Figure for 17

Many states have established lotteries to increase revenues. You can use the probability theory developed in this chapter to calculate the odds of winning a state lottery.

Michael Simpson/Getty Images

9 Sequences, Series, and Probability

9.1 Sequences and Series

9.2 Arithmetic Sequences and Partial Sums

9.3 Geometric Sequences and Series

9.4 Mathematical Induction

9.5 The Binomial Theorem

9.6 Counting Principles

9.7 Probability

What You Should Learn

In this chapter, you will learn how to:

■ Use sequence, factorial, and summation notation to write the terms and sums of sequences.

■ Recognize, write, and use arithmetic sequences and geometric sequences.

■ Use mathematical induction to prove statements involving a positive integer n.

■ Use the Binomial Theorem and Pascal's Triangle to calculate binomial coefficients and write binomial expansions.

■ Solve counting problems using the Fundamental Counting Principle, permutations, and combinations.

■ Find the probabilities of events and their complements.

9.1 Sequences and Series

Sequences

In mathematics, the word *sequence* is used in much the same way as in ordinary English. Saying that a collection is listed *in sequence* means that it is ordered so that it has a first member, a second member, a third member, and so on.

Mathematically, you can think of a sequence as a *function* whose domain is the set of positive integers. Instead of using function notation, sequences are usually written using subscript notation, as shown in the following definition.

Definition of Sequence

An **infinite sequence** is a function whose domain is the set of positive integers. The function values

$$a_1, a_2, a_3, a_4, \ldots, a_n, \ldots$$

are the **terms** of the sequence. If the domain of a function consists of the first *n* positive integers only, the sequence is a **finite sequence.**

On occasion, it is convenient to begin subscripting a sequence with 0 instead of 1 so that the terms of the sequence become $a_0, a_1, a_2, a_3, \ldots$.

Example 1 Writing the Terms of a Sequence

Write the first four terms of the sequences given by

a. $a_n = 3n - 2$ **b.** $a_n = 3 + (-1)^n$.

Solution

a. The first four terms of the sequence given by $a_n = 3n - 2$ are

$$a_1 = 3(1) - 2 = 1 \qquad \text{1st term}$$
$$a_2 = 3(2) - 2 = 4 \qquad \text{2nd term}$$
$$a_3 = 3(3) - 2 = 7 \qquad \text{3rd term}$$
$$a_4 = 3(4) - 2 = 10. \qquad \text{4th term}$$

b. The first four terms of the sequence given by $a_n = 3 + (-1)^n$ are

$$a_1 = 3 + (-1)^1 = 3 - 1 = 2 \qquad \text{1st term}$$
$$a_2 = 3 + (-1)^2 = 3 + 1 = 4 \qquad \text{2nd term}$$
$$a_3 = 3 + (-1)^3 = 3 - 1 = 2 \qquad \text{3rd term}$$
$$a_4 = 3 + (-1)^4 = 3 + 1 = 4. \qquad \text{4th term}$$

✓ *Checkpoint* Now try Exercise 1.

What you should learn

- Use sequence notation to write the terms of sequences.
- Use factorial notation.
- Use summation notation to write sums.
- Find sums of infinite series.
- Use sequences and series to model and solve real-life problems.

Why you should learn it

Sequences and series are useful in modeling sets of values in order to identify a pattern. For instance, Exercise 111 on page 705 shows how a sequence can be used to model the number of children enrolled in Head Start programs from 1993 to 2001.

Cathy Melloan Resources/PhotoEdit

TECHNOLOGY TIP

To graph a sequence using a graphing utility, set the mode to *dot* and *sequence* and enter the sequence. Try graphing the sequences in Example 1 and using the *value* or *trace* feature to identify the terms. For instructions on how to use the *dot* mode, *sequence* mode, *value* feature, and *trace* feature, see Appendix A; for specific keystrokes, go to the text website at *college.hmco.com.*

Example 2   Writing the Terms of a Sequence

Write the first five terms of the sequence given by $a_n = \dfrac{(-1)^n}{2n-1}$.

Algebraic Solution

The first five terms of the sequence are as follows.

$$a_1 = \frac{(-1)^1}{2(1)-1} = \frac{-1}{2-1} = -1 \qquad \text{1st term}$$

$$a_2 = \frac{(-1)^2}{2(2)-1} = \frac{1}{4-1} = \frac{1}{3} \qquad \text{2nd term}$$

$$a_3 = \frac{(-1)^3}{2(3)-1} = \frac{-1}{6-1} = -\frac{1}{5} \qquad \text{3rd term}$$

$$a_4 = \frac{(-1)^4}{2(4)-1} = \frac{1}{8-1} = \frac{1}{7} \qquad \text{4th term}$$

$$a_5 = \frac{(-1)^5}{2(5)-1} = \frac{-1}{10-1} = -\frac{1}{9} \qquad \text{5th term}$$

✓ *Checkpoint* Now try Exercise 11.

Numerical Solution

Set your graphing utility to *sequence* mode. Enter the sequence into your graphing utility as shown in Figure 9.1. Use the *table* feature (in *ask* mode) to create a table showing the terms of the sequence u_n for $n = 1, 2, 3, 4,$ and 5. From Figure 9.2, you can estimate the first five terms of the sequence as follows.

$$u_1 = -1, \qquad u_2 = 0.33333 \approx \tfrac{1}{3}, \qquad u_3 = -0.2 = -\tfrac{1}{5},$$

$$u_4 = 0.14286 \approx \tfrac{1}{7}, \qquad \text{and} \qquad u_5 = -0.1111 \approx -\tfrac{1}{9}$$

```
Plot1 Plot2 Plot3
nMin=1
\u(n)⊟(-1)^n/(2n
-1)
u(nMin)⊟
\v(n)=
v(nMin)=
\w(n)=
```

Figure 9.1

n	$u(n)$
1	-1
2	.33333
3	-.2
4	.14286
5	-.1111

$n=1$

Figure 9.2

Simply listing the first few terms is not sufficient to define a unique sequence—the nth term *must be given*. To see this, consider the following sequences, both of which have the same first three terms.

$$\frac{1}{2}, \frac{1}{4}, \frac{1}{8}, \frac{1}{16}, \ldots, \frac{1}{2^n}, \ldots$$

$$\frac{1}{2}, \frac{1}{4}, \frac{1}{8}, \frac{1}{15}, \ldots, \frac{6}{(n+1)(n^2-n+6)}, \ldots$$

TECHNOLOGY SUPPORT

For instructions on how to use the *table* feature, see Appendix A; for specific keystrokes, go to the text website at *college.hmco.com*.

Example 3   Finding the nth Term of a Sequence

Write an expression for the apparent nth term (a_n) of each sequence.

a. $1, 3, 5, 7, \ldots$ **b.** $2, 5, 10, 17, \ldots$

Solution

a.   *n:* 1 2 3 4 . . . n

   Terms: 1 3 5 7 . . . a_n

   Apparent Pattern: Each term is 1 less than twice n. So, the apparent nth term is $a_n = 2n - 1$.

b.   *n:* 1 2 3 4 . . . n

   Terms: 2 5 10 17 . . . a_n

   Apparent Pattern: Each term is 1 more than the square of n. So, the apparent nth term is $a_n = n^2 + 1$.

✓ *Checkpoint* Now try Exercise 39.

Some sequences are defined **recursively.** To define a sequence recursively, you need to be given one or more of the first few terms. All other terms of the sequence are then defined using previous terms. A well-known example is the Fibonacci sequence, shown in Example 4.

Example 4 The Fibonacci Sequence: A Recursive Sequence

The Fibonacci sequence is defined recursively as follows.

$$a_0 = 1, \ a_1 = 1, \ a_k = a_{k-2} + a_{k-1}, \qquad \text{where } k \geq 2$$

Write the first six terms of this sequence.

Solution

$a_0 = 1$	0th term is given.
$a_1 = 1$	1st term is given.
$a_2 = a_{2-2} + a_{2-1} = a_0 + a_1 = 1 + 1 = 2$	Use recursion formula.
$a_3 = a_{3-2} + a_{3-1} = a_1 + a_2 = 1 + 2 = 3$	Use recursion formula.
$a_4 = a_{4-2} + a_{4-1} = a_2 + a_3 = 2 + 3 = 5$	Use recursion formula.
$a_5 = a_{5-2} + a_{5-1} = a_3 + a_4 = 3 + 5 = 8$	Use recursion formula.

✓ *Checkpoint* Now try Exercise 53.

Factorial Notation

Some very important sequences in mathematics involve terms that are defined with special types of products called **factorials.**

Definition of Factorial

If n is a positive integer, n **factorial** is defined as

$$n! = 1 \cdot 2 \cdot 3 \cdot 4 \ \cdots \ (n-1) \cdot n.$$

As a special case, zero factorial is defined as $0! = 1$.

Here are some values of $n!$ for the first few nonnegative integers. Notice that $0! = 1$ by definition.

$0! = 1$

$1! = 1$

$2! = 1 \cdot 2 = 2$

$3! = 1 \cdot 2 \cdot 3 = 6$

$4! = 1 \cdot 2 \cdot 3 \cdot 4 = 24$

$5! = 1 \cdot 2 \cdot 3 \cdot 4 \cdot 5 = 120$

The value of n does not have to be very large before the value of $n!$ becomes huge. For instance, $10! = 3{,}628{,}800$.

Exploration

Most graphing utilities have the capability to compute $n!$. Use your graphing utility to compare $3 \cdot 5!$ and $(3 \cdot 5)!$. How do they differ? How large a value of $n!$ will your graphing utility allow you to compute?

Factorials follow the same conventions for order of operations as do exponents. For instance,

$$2n! = 2(n!) = 2(1 \cdot 2 \cdot 3 \cdot 4 \cdots n)$$

whereas $(2n)! = 1 \cdot 2 \cdot 3 \cdot 4 \cdots 2n$.

Example 5   Writing the Terms of a Sequence Involving Factorials

Write the first five terms of the sequence given by $a_n = \dfrac{2^n}{n!}$. Begin with $n = 0$.

Algebraic Solution

$$a_0 = \frac{2^0}{0!} = \frac{1}{1} = 1 \qquad \text{0th term}$$

$$a_1 = \frac{2^1}{1!} = \frac{2}{1} = 2 \qquad \text{1st term}$$

$$a_2 = \frac{2^2}{2!} = \frac{4}{2} = 2 \qquad \text{2nd term}$$

$$a_3 = \frac{2^3}{3!} = \frac{8}{6} = \frac{4}{3} \qquad \text{3rd term}$$

$$a_4 = \frac{2^4}{4!} = \frac{16}{24} = \frac{2}{3} \qquad \text{4th term}$$

✓ *Checkpoint* Now try Exercise 61.

Graphical Solution

Using a graphing utility set to *dot* and *sequence* modes, enter the sequence $u_n = 2^n/n!$, as shown in Figure 9.3. Set the viewing window to $0 \le n \le 4$, $0 \le x \le 6$, and $0 \le y \le 4$. Then graph the sequence as shown in Figure 9.4. Use the *value* or *trace* feature to approximate the first five terms as follows.

$$u_0 = 1, \quad u_1 = 2, \quad u_2 = 2, \quad u_3 \approx 1.333 \approx \tfrac{4}{3}, \quad u_4 \approx 0.666 \approx \tfrac{2}{3}$$

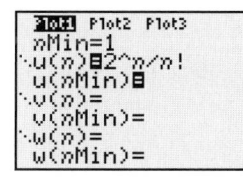

Figure 9.3

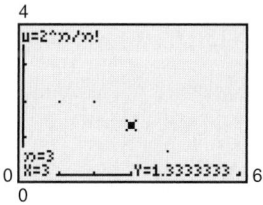

Figure 9.4

When working with fractions involving factorials, you will often find that the fractions can be reduced to simplify the computations.

Example 6   Evaluating Factorial Expressions

Evaluate each factorial expression.

a. $\dfrac{8!}{2! \cdot 6!}$ **b.** $\dfrac{2! \cdot 6!}{3! \cdot 5!}$ **c.** $\dfrac{n!}{(n-1)!}$

Solution

a. $\dfrac{8!}{2! \cdot 6!} = \dfrac{1 \cdot 2 \cdot 3 \cdot 4 \cdot 5 \cdot 6 \cdot 7 \cdot 8}{1 \cdot 2 \cdot 1 \cdot 2 \cdot 3 \cdot 4 \cdot 5 \cdot 6} = \dfrac{7 \cdot 8}{2} = 28$

b. $\dfrac{2! \cdot 6!}{3! \cdot 5!} = \dfrac{1 \cdot 2 \cdot 1 \cdot 2 \cdot 3 \cdot 4 \cdot 5 \cdot 6}{1 \cdot 2 \cdot 3 \cdot 1 \cdot 2 \cdot 3 \cdot 4 \cdot 5} = \dfrac{6}{3} = 2$

c. $\dfrac{n!}{(n-1)!} = \dfrac{1 \cdot 2 \cdot 3 \cdots (n-1) \cdot n}{1 \cdot 2 \cdot 3 \cdots (n-1)} = n$

✓ *Checkpoint* Now try Exercise 71.

Summation Notation

There is a convenient notation for the sum of the terms of a finite sequence. It is called **summation notation** or **sigma notation** because it involves the use of the uppercase Greek letter sigma, written as Σ.

> **Definition of Summation Notation**
>
> The sum of the first n terms of a sequence is represented by
>
> $$\sum_{i=1}^{n} a_i = a_1 + a_2 + a_3 + a_4 + \cdots + a_n$$
>
> where i is called the **index of summation,** n is the **upper limit of summation,** and 1 is the **lower limit of summation.**

STUDY TIP

Summation notation is an instruction to add the terms of a sequence. From the definition at the left, the upper limit of summation tells you where to end the sum. Summation notation helps you generate the appropriate terms of the sequence prior to finding the actual sum, which may be unclear.

Example 7   Sigma Notation for Sums

a. $\displaystyle\sum_{i=1}^{5} 3i = 3(1) + 3(2) + 3(3) + 3(4) + 3(5)$

$= 3(1 + 2 + 3 + 4 + 5)$

$= 3(15)$

$= 45$

b. $\displaystyle\sum_{k=3}^{6} (1 + k^2) = (1 + 3^2) + (1 + 4^2) + (1 + 5^2) + (1 + 6^2)$

$= 10 + 17 + 26 + 37 = 90$

c. $\displaystyle\sum_{n=0}^{8} \frac{1}{n!} = \frac{1}{0!} + \frac{1}{1!} + \frac{1}{2!} + \frac{1}{3!} + \frac{1}{4!} + \frac{1}{5!} + \frac{1}{6!} + \frac{1}{7!} + \frac{1}{8!}$

$= 1 + 1 + \frac{1}{2} + \frac{1}{6} + \frac{1}{24} + \frac{1}{120} + \frac{1}{720} + \frac{1}{5040} + \frac{1}{40,320}$

≈ 2.71828

For the summation in part (c), note that the sum is very close to the irrational number $e \approx 2.718281828$. It can be shown that as more terms of the sequence whose nth term is $1/n!$ are added, the sum becomes closer and closer to e.

✓ *Checkpoint* Now try Exercise 75.

In Example 7, note that the lower limit of a summation does not have to be 1. Also note that the index of summation does not have to be the letter i. For instance, in part (b), the letter k is the index of summation.

TECHNOLOGY TIP Most graphing utilities are able to sum the first n terms of a sequence. Figure 9.5 shows an example of how one graphing utility displays the sum of the terms of the sequence below using the *sum sequence* feature.

$$a_n = \frac{1}{n!} \quad \text{from} \quad n = 0 \quad \text{to} \quad n = 8$$

TECHNOLOGY SUPPORT

For instructions on how to use the *sum sequence* feature, see Appendix A; for specific keystrokes, go to the text website at *college.hmco.com*.

```
sum(seq(1/n!,n,0
,8))
        2.71827877
```

Figure 9.5

Properties of Sums

1. $\displaystyle\sum_{i=1}^{n} c = cn,$ c is a constant.   **2.** $\displaystyle\sum_{i=1}^{n} ca_i = c\sum_{i=1}^{n} a_i,$ c is a constant.

3. $\displaystyle\sum_{i=1}^{n} (a_i + b_i) = \sum_{i=1}^{n} a_i + \sum_{i=1}^{n} b_i$ **4.** $\displaystyle\sum_{i=1}^{n} (a_i - b_i) = \sum_{i=1}^{n} a_i - \sum_{i=1}^{n} b_i$

See Appendix B for a proof of Property 2.

Series

Many applications involve the sum of the terms of a finite or an infinite sequence. Such a sum is called a **series.**

Definition of a Series

Consider the infinite sequence $a_1, a_2, a_3, \ldots, a_i, \ldots$

1. The sum of the first n terms of the sequence is called a **finite series** or the **partial sum** of the sequence and is denoted by

$$a_1 + a_2 + a_3 + \cdots + a_n = \sum_{i=1}^{n} a_i.$$

2. The sum of all the terms of the infinite sequence is called an **infinite series** and is denoted by

$$a_1 + a_2 + a_3 + \cdots + a_i + \cdots = \sum_{i=1}^{\infty} a_i.$$

Example 8   Finding the Sum of a Series

For the series $\displaystyle\sum_{i=1}^{\infty} \frac{3}{10^i}$, find (a) the third partial sum and (b) the sum.

Solution

a. The third partial sum is

$$\sum_{i=1}^{3} \frac{3}{10^i} = \frac{3}{10^1} + \frac{3}{10^2} + \frac{3}{10^3} = 0.3 + 0.03 + 0.003 = 0.333.$$

b. The sum of the series is

$$\sum_{i=1}^{\infty} \frac{3}{10^i} = \frac{3}{10^1} + \frac{3}{10^2} + \frac{3}{10^3} + \frac{3}{10^4} + \frac{3}{10^5} + \cdots$$

$$= 0.3 + 0.03 + 0.003 + 0.0003 + 0.00003 + \cdots$$

$$= 0.33333\ldots = \frac{1}{3}.$$

✓ *Checkpoint* Now try Exercise 101.

Notice in Example 8(b) that the sum of an infinite series can be a finite number.

STUDY TIP

Variations in the upper and lower limits of summation can produce quite different-looking summation notations for *the same sum.* For example, the following two sums have identical terms.

$$\sum_{i=1}^{3} 3(2^i) = 3(2^1 + 2^2 + 2^3)$$

$$\sum_{i=0}^{2} 3(2^{i+1}) = 3(2^1 + 2^2 + 2^3)$$

Application

Sequences have many applications in situations that involve a recognizable pattern. One such model is illustrated in Example 9.

Example 9 Population of the United States

From 1970 to 2001, the resident population of the United States can be approximated by the model

$$a_n = 205.7 + 1.78n + 0.025n^2, \qquad n = 0, 1, \dots, 31$$

where a_n is the population in millions and n represents the year, with $n = 0$ corresponding to 1970. Find the last five terms of this finite sequence.   (Source: U.S. Census Bureau)

Algebraic Solution

The last five terms of this finite sequence are as follows.

$a_{27} = 205.7 + 1.78(27) + 0.025(27)^2$

≈ 272.0 1997 population

$a_{28} = 205.7 + 1.78(28) + 0.025(28)^2$

≈ 275.1 1998 population

$a_{29} = 205.7 + 1.78(29) + 0.025(29)^2$

≈ 278.3 1999 population

$a_{30} = 205.7 + 1.78(30) + 0.025(30)^2$

$= 281.6$ 2000 population

$a_{31} = 205.7 + 1.78(31) + 0.025(31)^2$

≈ 284.9 2001 population

✓ *Checkpoint* Now try Exercise 111.

Graphical Solution

Using a graphing utility set to *dot* and *sequence* modes, enter the sequence

$$u_n = 205.7 + 1.78n + 0.025n^2.$$

Set the viewing window to $0 \leq n \leq 32, 0 \leq x \leq 32,$ and $200 \leq y \leq 300$. Then graph the sequence. Use the *value* or *trace* feature to approximate the last five terms, as shown in Figure 9.6.

$a_{27} \approx 272.0,$

$a_{28} \approx 275.1,$

$a_{29} \approx 278.3,$

$a_{30} \approx 281.6,$

$a_{31} \approx 284.9$

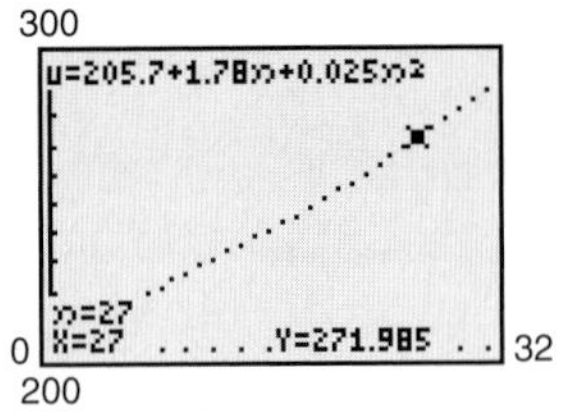

Figure 9.6

Exploration

A $3 \times 3 \times 3$ cube is created using 27 unit cubes (a unit cube has a length, width, and height of 1 unit) and only the faces of each cube that are visible are painted blue (see Figure 9.7). Complete the table below to determine how many unit cubes of the $3 \times 3 \times 3$ cube have 0 blue faces, 1 blue face, 2 blue faces, and 3 blue faces. Do the same for a $4 \times 4 \times 4$ cube, a $5 \times 5 \times 5$ cube, and a $6 \times 6 \times 6$ cube and add your results to the table below. What type of pattern do you observe in the table? Write a formula you could use to determine the column values for an $n \times n \times n$ cube.

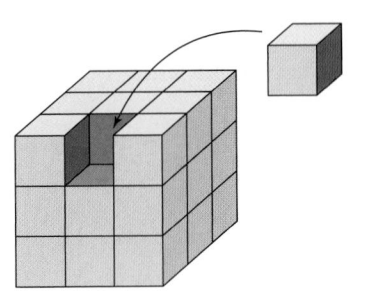

Figure 9.7

Cube \ Number of blue faces	0	1	2	3
$3 \times 3 \times 3$				

9.1   Exercises

Vocabulary Check

Fill in the blanks.

1. An _____ is a function whose domain is the set of positive integers.

2. The function values $a_1, a_2, a_3, a_4, \ldots, a_n, \ldots$ are called the _____ of a sequence.

3. A sequence is a _____ sequence if the domain of the function consists of the first n positive integers.

4. If you are given one or more of the first few terms of a sequence, and all other terms of the sequence are defined using previous terms, then the sequence is defined _____ .

5. If n is a positive integer, n _____ is defined as $n! = 1 \cdot 2 \cdot 3 \cdot 4 \cdots (n - 1) \cdot n$.

6. The notation used to represent the sum of the terms of a finite sequence is _____ or sigma notation.

7. For the sum $\sum_{i=1}^{n} a_i$, i is called the _____ of summation, n is the _____ of summation, and 1 is the _____ of summation.

8. The sum of the terms of a finite or an infinite sequence is called a _____

9. The _____ of a sequence is the sum of the first n terms of the sequence.

In Exercises 1–20, write the first five terms of the sequence. (Assume n begins with 1.) Use the *table* feature of a graphing utility to verify your results.

1. $a_n = 2n + 5$ 2. $a_n = 4n - 7$

3. $a_n = 2^n$ 4. $a_n = \left(\frac{1}{2}\right)^n$

5. $a_n = \left(-\frac{1}{2}\right)^n$ 6. $a_n = (-2)^n$

7. $a_n = \dfrac{n + 1}{n}$ 8. $a_n = \dfrac{n}{n + 1}$

9. $a_n = \dfrac{n}{n^2 + 1}$ 10. $a_n = \dfrac{2n}{n + 1}$

11. $a_n = \dfrac{1 + (-1)^n}{n}$ 12. $a_n = \dfrac{1 + (-1)^n}{2n}$

13. $a_n = 1 - \dfrac{1}{2^n}$ 14. $a_n = \dfrac{3^n}{4^n}$

15. $a_n = \dfrac{1}{n^{3/2}}$ 16. $a_n = \dfrac{1}{\sqrt{n}}$

17. $a_n = \dfrac{(-1)^n}{n^2}$ 18. $a_n = (-1)^n \left(\dfrac{n}{n + 1}\right)$

19. $a_n = (2n - 1)(2n + 1)$ 20. $a_n = n(n - 1)(n - 2)$

In Exercises 21–24, find the indicated term of the sequence.

21. $a_n = (-1)^n(3n - 2)$

  $a_{25} =$

22. $a_n = (-1)^{n-1}[n(n - 1)]$

  $a_{16} =$

23. $a_n = \dfrac{n^2}{n^2 + 1}$ 24. $a_n = \dfrac{n^2}{2n + 1}$

  $a_{10} =$ $a_5 =$

In Exercises 25–30, use a graphing utility to graph the first 10 terms of the sequence. (Assume n begins with 1.)

25. $a_n = \dfrac{2}{3}n$ 26. $a_n = 2 - \dfrac{4}{n}$

27. $a_n = 16(-0.5)^{n-1}$ 28. $a_n = 8(0.75)^{n-1}$

29. $a_n = \dfrac{2n}{n + 1}$ 30. $a_n = \dfrac{3n^2}{n^2 + 1}$

In Exercises 31–34, use the *table* feature of a graphing utility to find the first 10 terms of the sequence. (Assume n begins with 1.)

31. $a_n = 2(3n - 1) + 5$

32. $a_n = 2n(n + 1)(n + 2)$

33. $a_n = 1 + \dfrac{n + 1}{n}$ 34. $a_n = \dfrac{4n^2}{n + 2}$

In Exercises 35–38, match the sequence with its graph. [The graphs are labeled (a), (b), (c), and (d).]

(a)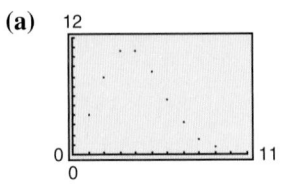

(b)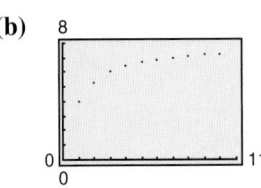

(c)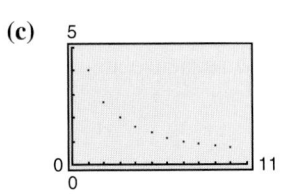

(d)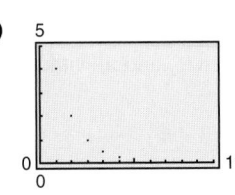

35. $a_n = \dfrac{8}{n+1}$

36. $a_n = \dfrac{8n}{n+1}$

37. $a_n = 4(0.5)^{n-1}$

38. $a_n = \dfrac{4^n}{n!}$

In Exercises 39–52, write an expression for the *apparent n*th term of the sequence. (Assume *n* begins with 1.)

39. $1, 4, 7, 10, 13, \ldots$

40. $3, 7, 11, 15, 19, \ldots$

41. $0, 3, 8, 15, 24, \ldots$

42. $1, \frac{1}{4}, \frac{1}{9}, \frac{1}{16}, \frac{1}{25}, \ldots$

43. $\frac{2}{3}, \frac{3}{4}, \frac{4}{5}, \frac{5}{6}, \frac{6}{7}, \ldots$

44. $\frac{2}{1}, \frac{3}{3}, \frac{4}{5}, \frac{5}{7}, \frac{6}{9}, \ldots$

45. $\frac{1}{2}, \frac{-1}{4}, \frac{1}{8}, \frac{-1}{16}, \ldots$

46. $\frac{1}{3}, -\frac{2}{9}, \frac{4}{27}, -\frac{8}{81}, \ldots$

47. $1 + \frac{1}{1}, 1 + \frac{1}{2}, 1 + \frac{1}{3}, 1 + \frac{1}{4}, 1 + \frac{1}{5}, \ldots$

48. $1 + \frac{1}{2}, 1 + \frac{3}{4}, 1 + \frac{7}{8}, 1 + \frac{15}{16}, 1 + \frac{31}{32}, \ldots$

49. $1, \frac{1}{2}, \frac{1}{6}, \frac{1}{24}, \frac{1}{120}, \ldots$

50. $1, 2, \dfrac{2^2}{2}, \dfrac{2^3}{6}, \dfrac{2^4}{24}, \dfrac{2^5}{120}, \ldots$

51. $1, 3, 1, 3, 1, \ldots$

52. $1, -1, 1, -1, 1, \ldots$

In Exercises 53–56, write the first five terms of the sequence defined recursively.

53. $a_1 = 28, \quad a_{k+1} = a_k - 4$

54. $a_1 = 15, \quad a_{k+1} = a_k + 3$

55. $a_1 = 3, \quad a_{k+1} = 2(a_k - 1)$

56. $a_1 = 32, \quad a_{k+1} = \frac{1}{2}a_k$

In Exercises 57–60, write the first five terms of the sequence defined recursively. Use the pattern to write the *n*th term of the sequence as a function of *n*. (Assume *n* begins with 1.)

57. $a_1 = 6, \quad a_{k+1} = a_k + 2$

58. $a_1 = 25, \quad a_{k+1} = a_k - 5$

59. $a_1 = 81, \quad a_{k+1} = \frac{1}{3}a_k$

60. $a_1 = 14, \quad a_{k+1} = -2a_k$

In Exercises 61–66, write the first five terms of the sequence. (Assume *n* begins with 0.) Use the *table* feature of a graphing utility to verify your results.

61. $a_n = \dfrac{1}{n!}$

62. $a_n = \dfrac{1}{(n+1)!}$

63. $a_n = \dfrac{n!}{2n+1}$

64. $a_n = \dfrac{n^2}{(n+1)!}$

65. $a_n = \dfrac{(-1)^{2n}}{(2n)!}$

66. $a_n = \dfrac{(-1)^{2n+1}}{(2n+1)!}$

In Exercises 67–74, simplify the factorial expression.

67. $\dfrac{2!}{4!}$

68. $\dfrac{5!}{7!}$

69. $\dfrac{12!}{4! \cdot 8!}$

70. $\dfrac{10! \cdot 3!}{4! \cdot 6!}$

71. $\dfrac{(n+1)!}{n!}$

72. $\dfrac{(n+2)!}{n!}$

73. $\dfrac{(2n-1)!}{(2n+1)!}$

74. $\dfrac{(2n+2)!}{(2n)!}$

In Exercises 75–86, find the sum.

75. $\displaystyle\sum_{i=1}^{5}(2i+1)$

76. $\displaystyle\sum_{i=1}^{6}(3i-1)$

77. $\displaystyle\sum_{k=1}^{4}10$

78. $\displaystyle\sum_{k=1}^{5}6$

79. $\displaystyle\sum_{i=0}^{4}i^2$

80. $\displaystyle\sum_{i=0}^{5}3i^2$

81. $\displaystyle\sum_{k=0}^{3}\dfrac{1}{k^2+1}$

82. $\displaystyle\sum_{j=3}^{5}\dfrac{1}{j}$

83. $\displaystyle\sum_{i=1}^{4}[(i-1)^2 + (i+1)^3]$

84. $\displaystyle\sum_{k=2}^{5}(k+1)(k-3)$

85. $\displaystyle\sum_{i=1}^{4} 2^i$

86. $\displaystyle\sum_{j=0}^{4} (-2)^j$

In Exercises 87–90, use a graphing utility to find the sum.

87. $\displaystyle\sum_{j=1}^{6} (24 - 3j)$

88. $\displaystyle\sum_{j=1}^{10} \frac{3}{j + 1}$

89. $\displaystyle\sum_{k=0}^{4} \frac{(-1)^k}{k + 1}$

90. $\displaystyle\sum_{k=0}^{4} \frac{(-1)^k}{k!}$

In Exercises 91–100, use sigma notation to write the sum. Then use a graphing utility to find the sum.

91. $\dfrac{1}{3(1)} + \dfrac{1}{3(2)} + \dfrac{1}{3(3)} + \cdots + \dfrac{1}{3(9)}$

92. $\dfrac{5}{1 + 1} + \dfrac{5}{1 + 2} + \dfrac{5}{1 + 3} + \cdots + \dfrac{5}{1 + 15}$

93. $\left[2\left(\tfrac{1}{8}\right) + 3\right] + \left[2\left(\tfrac{2}{8}\right) + 3\right] + \cdots + \left[2\left(\tfrac{8}{8}\right) + 3\right]$

94. $\left[1 - \left(\tfrac{1}{6}\right)^2\right] + \left[1 - \left(\tfrac{2}{6}\right)^2\right] + \cdots + \left[1 - \left(\tfrac{6}{6}\right)^2\right]$

95. $3 - 9 + 27 - 81 + 243 - 729$

96. $1 - \tfrac{1}{2} + \tfrac{1}{4} - \tfrac{1}{8} + \cdots - \tfrac{1}{128}$

97. $\dfrac{1}{1^2} - \dfrac{1}{2^2} + \dfrac{1}{3^2} - \dfrac{1}{4^2} + \cdots - \dfrac{1}{20^2}$

98. $\dfrac{1}{1 \cdot 3} + \dfrac{1}{2 \cdot 4} + \dfrac{1}{3 \cdot 5} + \cdots + \dfrac{1}{10 \cdot 12}$

99. $\tfrac{1}{4} + \tfrac{3}{8} + \tfrac{7}{16} + \tfrac{15}{32} + \tfrac{31}{64}$

100. $\tfrac{1}{2} + \tfrac{2}{4} + \tfrac{6}{8} + \tfrac{24}{16} + \tfrac{120}{32} + \tfrac{720}{64}$

In Exercises 101–104, find the indicated partial sum of the series.

101. $\displaystyle\sum_{i=1}^{\infty} 5\left(\tfrac{1}{2}\right)^i$

Fourth partial sum

102. $\displaystyle\sum_{i=1}^{\infty} 2\left(\tfrac{1}{3}\right)^i$

Fifth partial sum

103. $\displaystyle\sum_{n=1}^{\infty} 4\left(-\tfrac{1}{2}\right)^n$

Third partial sum

104. $\displaystyle\sum_{n=1}^{\infty} 8\left(-\tfrac{1}{4}\right)^n$

Fourth partial sum

In Exercises 105–108, find the sum of the infinite series.

105. $\displaystyle\sum_{i=1}^{\infty} 6\left(\tfrac{1}{10}\right)^i$

106. $\displaystyle\sum_{k=1}^{\infty} 4\left(\tfrac{1}{10}\right)^k$

107. $\displaystyle\sum_{k=1}^{\infty} \left(\tfrac{1}{10}\right)^k$

108. $\displaystyle\sum_{i=1}^{\infty} 2\left(\tfrac{1}{10}\right)^i$

109. *Compound Interest*   A deposit of \$5000 is made in an account that earns 3% interest compounded quarterly. The balance in the account after n quarters is given by

$$A_n = 5000\left(1 + \frac{0.03}{4}\right)^n, \quad n = 1, 2, 3, \ldots$$

(a) Compute the first eight terms of this sequence.

(b) Find the balance in this account after 10 years by computing the 40th term of the sequence.

110. *Compound Interest*   A deposit of \$100 is made *each month* in an account that earns 12% interest compounded monthly. The balance in the account after n months is given by

$$A_n = 100(101)\left[(1.01)^n - 1\right], \quad n = 1, 2, 3, \ldots$$

(a) Compute the first six terms of this sequence.

(b) Find the balance in this account after 5 years by computing the 60th term of the sequence.

(c) Find the balance in this account after 20 years by computing the 240th term of the sequence.

111. *Education*   The number a_n (in thousands) of children enrolled in Head Start programs from 1993 to 2001 can be approximated by the model

$$a_n = 1.37n^2 + 3.1n + 698, \quad n = 3, 4, \ldots, 11$$

where n is the year, with $n = 3$ corresponding to 1993.   (Source: U.S. Administration for Children and Families)

(a) Find the terms of this finite sequence and use a graphing utility to graph the sequence.

(b) What does the graph in part (a) say about the future enrollment in Head Start programs?

112. *Federal Debt*   From 1990 to 2002, the federal debt rose from just over \$3 trillion to over \$6 trillion. The federal debt a_n (in trillions of dollars) from 1990 to 2002 is approximated by the model

$$a_n = -0.0140n^2 + 0.394n + 3.25,$$
$$n = 0, 1, \ldots, 12$$

where n is the year, with $n = 0$ corresponding to 1990.   (Source: Office of Management and Budget)

(a) Find the terms of this finite sequence and construct a bar graph that represents the sequence.

(b) What does the pattern in the bar graph in part (a) say about the future of the federal debt?

113. Net Profit The net profits a_n (in millions of dollars) of Avon Products, Inc. for the years 1994 through 2002 are shown in the bar graph. These profits can be approximated by the model

$$a_n = 2.151n^2 + 235.9, \qquad n = 4, 5, \ldots, 12$$

where n is the year, with $n = 4$ corresponding to 1994. Use this model to approximate the total net profits from 1994 through 2002. Compare this sum with the result of adding the profits shown in the bar graph.   (Source: Avon Products, Inc.)

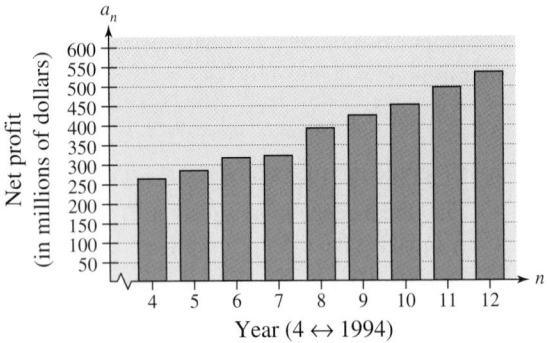

Year (4 ↔ 1994)

114. Sales The sales a_n (in millions of dollars) of Abercrombie & Fitch Company for the years 1996 through 2002 are shown in the bar graph. These sales can be approximated by the model

$$a_n = -2985.8 + 1829.9 \ln n, \qquad n = 6, 7, \ldots, 12$$

where $n = 6$ represents 1996. Use this model to approximate the total sales from 1996 through 2002. Compare this sum with the result of adding the sales shown in the bar graph.   (Source: Abercrombie & Fitch Company)

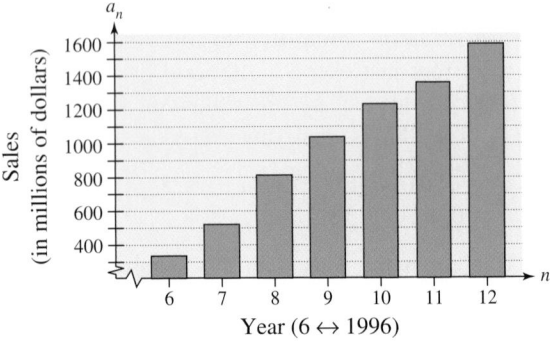

Year (6 ↔ 1996)

Synthesis

True or False? In Exercises 115 and 116, determine whether the statement is true or false. Justify your answer.

115. $\displaystyle\sum_{i=1}^{4} (i^2 + 2i) = \sum_{i=1}^{4} i^2 + 2\sum_{i=1}^{4} i$

116. $\displaystyle\sum_{j=1}^{4} 2^j = \sum_{j=3}^{6} 2^{j-2}$

Fibonacci Sequence In Exercises 117 and 118, use the Fibonacci sequence. (See Example 4.)

117. Write the first 12 terms of the Fibonacci sequence a_n and the first 10 terms of the sequence given by

$$b_n = \frac{a_{n+1}}{a_n}, \qquad n > 0.$$

118. Using the definition of b_n given in Exercise 117, show that b_n can be defined recursively by

$$b_n = 1 + \frac{1}{b_{n-1}}.$$

In Exercises 119–122, write the first five terms of the sequence.

119. $a_n = \dfrac{x^n}{n!}$ **120.** $a_n = \dfrac{(-1)^n x^{2n+1}}{2n+1}$

121. $a_n = \dfrac{(-1)^n x^{2n}}{(2n)!}$ **122.** $a_n = \dfrac{(-1)^n x^{2n+1}}{(2n+1)!}$

Review

In Exercises 123–126, find, if possible, (a) $A - B$, (b) $2B - 3A$, (c) AB, and (d) BA.

123. $A = \begin{bmatrix} 6 & 5 \\ 3 & 4 \end{bmatrix}$, $B = \begin{bmatrix} -2 & 4 \\ 6 & -3 \end{bmatrix}$

124. $A = \begin{bmatrix} 10 & 7 \\ -4 & 6 \end{bmatrix}$, $B = \begin{bmatrix} 0 & -12 \\ 8 & 11 \end{bmatrix}$

125. $A = \begin{bmatrix} -2 & -3 & 6 \\ 4 & 5 & 7 \\ 1 & 7 & 4 \end{bmatrix}$, $B = \begin{bmatrix} 1 & 4 & 2 \\ 0 & 1 & 6 \\ 0 & 3 & 1 \end{bmatrix}$

126. $A = \begin{bmatrix} -1 & 4 & 0 \\ 5 & 1 & 2 \\ 0 & -1 & 3 \end{bmatrix}$, $B = \begin{bmatrix} 0 & 4 & 0 \\ 3 & 1 & -2 \\ -1 & 0 & 2 \end{bmatrix}$

9.2   Arithmetic Sequences and Partial Sums

Arithmetic Sequences

A sequence whose consecutive terms have a common difference is called an **arithmetic sequence.**

Definition of Arithmetic Sequence

A sequence is **arithmetic** if the differences between consecutive terms are the same. So, the sequence

$$a_1, a_2, a_3, a_4, \ldots, a_n, \ldots$$

is arithmetic if there is a number d such that

$$a_2 - a_1 = a_3 - a_2 = a_4 - a_3 = \cdots = d.$$

The number d is the **common difference** of the arithmetic sequence.

What you should learn

- Recognize, write, and find the nth terms of arithmetic sequences.
- Find nth partial sums of arithmetic sequences.
- Use arithmetic sequences to model and solve real-life problems.

Why you should learn it

Arithmetic sequences can reduce the amount of time it takes to find the sum of a sequence of numbers with a common difference. In Exercise 77 on page 714, you will use an arithmetic sequence to find the number of bricks needed to lay a brick patio.

Index Stock

Example 1   Examples of Arithmetic Sequences

a. The sequence whose nth term is $4n + 3$ is arithmetic. For this sequence, the common difference between consecutive terms is 4.

$$7, 11, 15, 19, \ldots, 4n + 3, \ldots \qquad \text{Begin with } n = 1.$$

$$11 - 7 = 4$$

b. The sequence whose nth term is $7 - 5n$ is arithmetic. For this sequence, the common difference between consecutive terms is -5.

$$2, -3, -8, -13, \ldots, 7 - 5n, \ldots \qquad \text{Begin with } n = 1.$$

$$-3 - 2 = -5$$

c. The sequence whose nth term is $\frac{1}{4}(n + 3)$ is arithmetic. For this sequence, the common difference between consecutive terms is $\frac{1}{4}$.

$$1, \frac{5}{4}, \frac{3}{2}, \frac{7}{4}, \ldots, \frac{n + 3}{4}, \ldots \qquad \text{Begin with } n = 1.$$

$$\frac{5}{4} - 1 = \frac{1}{4}$$

✔ *Checkpoint* Now try Exercise 9.

The sequence 1, 4, 9, 16, . . . , whose nth term is n^2, is *not* arithmetic. The difference between the first two terms is

$$a_2 - a_1 = 4 - 1 = 3$$

but the difference between the second and third terms is

$$a_3 - a_2 = 9 - 4 = 5.$$

In Example 1, notice that each of the arithmetic sequences has an nth term that is of the form $dn + c$, where the common difference of the sequence is d.

> **The nth Term of an Arithmetic Sequence**
>
> The nth term of an arithmetic sequence has the form
>
> $$a_n = dn + c$$
>
> where d is the common difference between consecutive terms of the sequence and $c = a_1 - d$.

An arithmetic sequence $a_n = dn + c$ can be thought of as "counting by d's" after a shift of c units from d. For instance, the sequence

$$2, 6, 10, 14, 18, \ldots$$

has a common difference of 4, so you are counting by 4's after a shift of two units below 4 (beginning with $a_1 = 2$). So, the nth term is $4n - 2$. Similarly, the nth term of the sequence

$$6, 11, 16, 21, \ldots$$

is $5n + 1$ because you are counting by 5's after a shift of one unit above 5 (beginning with $a_1 = 6$).

Example 2   Finding the nth Term of an Arithmetic Sequence

Find a formula for the nth term of the arithmetic sequence whose common difference is 3 and whose first term is 2.

Solution

Because the sequence is arithmetic, you know that the formula for the nth term is of the form $a_n = dn + c$. Moreover, because the common difference is $d = 3$, the formula must have the form $a_n = 3n + c$. Because $a_1 = 2$, it follows that

$$c = a_1 - d = 2 - 3 = -1.$$

So, the formula for the nth term is $a_n = 3n - 1$. The sequence therefore has the following form.

$$2, 5, 8, 11, 14, \ldots, 3n - 1, \ldots$$

A graph of the first 15 terms of the sequence is shown in Figure 9.8. Notice that the points lie on a line. This makes sense because a_n is a linear function of n. In other words, the terms "arithmetic" and "linear" are closely connected.

✓ *Checkpoint* Now try Exercise 17.

Another way to find a formula for the nth term of the sequence in Example 2 is to begin by writing the terms of the sequence.

a_1	a_2	a_3	a_4	a_5	a_6	a_7	
2	$2+3$	$5+3$	$8+3$	$11+3$	$14+3$	$17+3$	$\ldots$
2	5	8	11	14	17	20	$\ldots$

From these terms, you can reason that the nth term is of the form

$$a_n = dn + c = 3n - 1.$$

Exploration

Consider the following sequences.

$$1, 4, 7, 10, 13, \ldots,$$
$$3n - 2, \ldots$$

$$-5, 1, 7, 13, 19, \ldots,$$
$$6n - 11, \ldots$$

$$\tfrac{5}{2}, \tfrac{3}{2}, \tfrac{1}{2}, -\tfrac{1}{2}, \ldots, \tfrac{7}{2} - n, \ldots$$

What relationship do you observe between successive terms of these sequences?

TECHNOLOGY TIP

You can use a graphing utility to generate the arithmetic sequence in Example 2 by using the following steps.

    2 [ENTER]

    3 [+] [ANS]

Now press the enter key repeatedly to generate the terms of the sequence.

Most graphing utilities have a built-in function that will display the terms of an arithmetic sequence. For instructions on how to use the *sequence* feature, see Appendix A; for specific keystrokes, go to the text website at *college.hmco.com*.

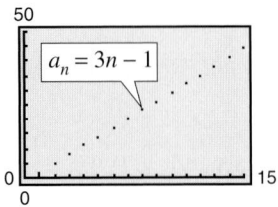

Figure 9.8

Example 3   Writing the Terms of an Arithmetic Sequence

The fourth term of an arithmetic sequence is 20, and the 13th term is 65. Write the first several terms of this sequence.

Solution

The fourth and 13th terms of the sequence are related by

$$a_{13} = a_4 + 9d.$$

Using $a_4 = 20$ and $a_{13} = 65$, you have $65 = 20 + 9d$. So, you can conclude that $d = 5$, which implies that the sequence is as follows.

a_1	a_2	a_3	a_4	a_5	a_6	a_7	a_8	a_9	a_{10}	a_{11}	a_{12}	a_{13}	
5,	10,	15,	20,	25,	30,	35,	40,	45,	50,	55,	60,	65,	. . .

✓ *Checkpoint* Now try Exercise 31.

If you know the nth term of an arithmetic sequence *and* you know the common difference of the sequence, you can find the $(n + 1)$th term by using the *recursion formula*

$$a_{n+1} = a_n + d. \qquad \text{Recursion formula}$$

With this formula, you can find any term of an arithmetic sequence, *provided* that you know the preceding term. For instance, if you know the first term, you can find the second term. Then, knowing the second term, you can find the third term, and so on.

If you substitute $a_1 - d$ for c in the formula $a_n = dn + c$, the nth term of an arithmetic sequence has the alternative recursion formula

$$a_n = a_1 + (n - 1)d. \qquad \text{Alternative recursion formula}$$

Use this formula to solve Example 4. You should obtain the same answer.

Example 4   Using a Recursion Formula

Find the seventh term of the arithmetic sequence whose first two terms are 2 and 9.

Solution

For this sequence, the common difference is $d = 9 - 2 = 7$. Next find a formula for the nth term. Because the first term is 2, it follows that

$$c = a_1 - d = 2 - 7 = -5.$$

Therefore, a formula for the nth term is

$$a_n = dn + c = 7n - 5.$$

which implies that the seventh term is

$$a_7 = 7(7) - 5 = 44.$$

✓ *Checkpoint* Now try Exercise 39.

STUDY TIP

Another way to find the seventh term in Example 4 is to determine the common difference, $d = 7$, and then simply write out the first seven terms (by repeatedly adding 7).

2, 9, 16, 23, 30, 37, 44

As you can see, the seventh term is 44.

The Sum of a Finite Arithmetic Sequence

There is a simple formula for the *sum* of a finite arithmetic sequence. See Appendix B for a proof of this formula.

> ### The Sum of a Finite Arithmetic Sequence
>
> The sum of a finite arithmetic sequence with n terms is given by
>
> $$S_n = \frac{n}{2}(a_1 + a_n).$$

Be sure you see that this formula works only for *arithmetic* sequences. Using this formula reduces the amount of time it takes to find the sum of an arithmetic sequence, as you will see in the following example.

Example 5   Finding the Sum of a Finite Arithmetic Sequence

Find each sum.

a. $1 + 3 + 5 + 7 + 9 + 11 + 13 + 15 + 17 + 19$

b. Sum of the integers from 1 to 100

Solution

a. To begin, notice that the sequence is arithmetic (with a common difference of 2). Moreover, the sequence has 10 terms. So, the sum of the sequence is

$$S_n = 1 + 3 + 5 + 7 + 9 + 11 + 13 + 15 + 17 + 19$$

$$= \frac{n}{2}(a_1 + a_n) \qquad \text{Formula for sum of an arithmetic sequence}$$

$$= \frac{10}{2}(1 + 19) \qquad \text{Substitute 10 for } n, \text{ 1 for } a_1, \text{ and 19 for } a_{10}.$$

$$= 5(20) = 100. \qquad \text{Simplify.}$$

b. The integers from 1 to 100 form an arithmetic sequence that has 100 terms. So, you can use the formula for the sum of an arithmetic sequence, as follows.

$$S_n = 1 + 2 + 3 + 4 + 5 + 6 + \cdots + 99 + 100$$

$$= \frac{n}{2}(a_1 + a_n) \qquad \text{Formula for sum of an arithmetic sequence}$$

$$= \frac{100}{2}(1 + 100) \qquad \text{Substitute 100 for } n, \text{ 1 for } a_1, \text{ and 100 for } a_{100}.$$

$$= 50(101) = 5050 \qquad \text{Simplify.}$$

✓ *Checkpoint* Now Try Exercise 53.

The sum of the first n terms of an infinite sequence is called the ***n*th partial sum.** The nth partial sum can be found by using the formula for the sum of a finite arithmetic sequence.

Example 6   Finding a Partial Sum of an Arithmetic Sequence

Find the 150th partial sum of the arithmetic sequence $5, 16, 27, 38, 49, \ldots$.

Solution

For this arithmetic sequence, you have $a_1 = 5$ and $d = 16 - 5 = 11$. So,

$$c = a_1 - d = 5 - 11 = -6$$

and the nth term is $a_n = 11n - 6$. Therefore, $a_{150} = 11(150) - 6 = 1644$, and the sum of the first 150 terms is

$$S_{150} = \frac{n}{2}(a_1 + a_{150}) \qquad \text{\small nth partial sum formula}$$

$$= \frac{150}{2}(5 + 1644) \qquad \text{\small Substitute 150 for n, 5 for a_1, and 1644 for a_{150}.}$$

$$= 75(1649) = 123{,}675. \qquad \text{\small Simplify.}$$

 Checkpoint Now try Exercise 63.

Applications

Example 7   Seating Capacity

An auditorium has 20 rows of seats. There are 20 seats in the first row, 21 seats in the second row, 22 seats in the third row, and so on (see Figure 9.9). How many seats are there in all 20 rows?

Solution

The numbers of seats in the 20 rows form an arithmetic sequence for which the common difference is $d = 1$. Because

$$c = a_1 - d = 20 - 1 = 19$$

you can determine that the formula for the nth term of the sequence is $a_n = n + 19$. So, the 20th term of the sequence is $a_{20} = 20 + 19 = 39$, and the total number of seats is

$$S_{20} = 20 + 21 + 22 + \cdots + 39$$

$$= \frac{20}{2}(20 + 39) \qquad \text{\small Substitute 20 for n, 20 for a_1, and 39 for a_{20}.}$$

$$= 10(59) = 590. \qquad \text{\small Simplify.}$$

 Checkpoint Now try Exercise 79.

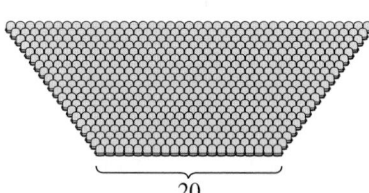

Figure 9.9

Example 8   Total Sales

A small business sells $10,000 worth of sports memorabilia during its first year. The owner of the business has set a goal of increasing annual sales by $7500 each year for 19 years. Assuming that this goal is met, find the total sales during the first 20 years this business is in operation.

Algebraic Solution

The annual sales form an arithmetic sequence in which $a_1 = 10{,}000$ and $d = 7500$. So,

$$c = a_1 - d$$
$$= 10{,}000 - 7500$$
$$= 2500$$

and the nth term of the sequence is

$$a_n = 7500n + 2500.$$

This implies that the 20th term of the sequence is

$$a_{20} = 7500(20) + 2500$$
$$= 152{,}500.$$

The sum of the first 20 terms of the sequence is

$$S_{20} = \frac{n}{2}(a_1 + a_{20}) \qquad \text{nth partial sum formula}$$

$$= \frac{20}{2}(10{,}000 + 152{,}500) \qquad \begin{array}{l}\text{Substitute 20 for } n, 10{,}000 \\ \text{for } a_1, \text{ and } 152{,}500 \text{ for } a_{20}.\end{array}$$

$$= 10(162{,}500) \qquad \text{Simplify.}$$

$$= 1{,}625{,}000. \qquad \text{Simplify.}$$

So, the total sales for the first 20 years are $1,625,000.

Numerical Solution

The annual sales form an arithmetic sequence in which $a_1 = 10{,}000$ and $d = 7500$. So,

$$c = a_1 - d$$
$$= 10{,}000 - 7500$$
$$= 2500.$$

So, the nth term of the sequence is given by

$$u_n = 7500n + 2500.$$

You can use the *list editor* of a graphing utility to create a table that shows the sales for each of the 20 years. First, enter the numbers 1 through 20 in L_1. Then enter $7500*L_1 + 2500$ for L_2. You should obtain a table like the one shown in Figure 9.10. Finally, use the *sum* feature of the graphing utility to find the sum of the data in L_2, as shown in Figure 9.11. So, the total sales for the first 20 years are $1,625,000.

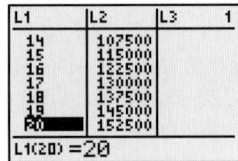

Figure 9.10

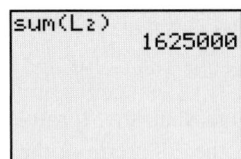

Figure 9.11

✓ *Checkpoint* Now try Exercise 81.

If you go on to take a course in calculus, you will study sequences and series in detail. You will learn that sequences and series play a major role in the study of calculus.

TECHNOLOGY SUPPORT

For instructions on how to use the *list editor* and *sum* features, see Appendix A; for specific keystrokes, go to the text website at *college.hmco.com*.

9.2 | Exercises

Vocabulary Check

Fill in the blanks.

1. A sequence is called an _____ sequence if the differences between consecutive terms are the same. This difference is called the _____ difference.

2. The nth term of an arithmetic sequence has the form _____ .

3. The formula $S_n = \dfrac{n}{2}(a_1 + a_n)$ can be used to find the sum of the first n terms of an arithmetic sequence, called the

_____ .

In Exercises 1–8, determine whether or not the sequence is arithmetic. If it is, find the common difference.

1. $10, 8, 6, 4, 2, \ldots$

2. $4, 9, 14, 19, 24, \ldots$

3. $3, \frac{5}{2}, 2, \frac{3}{2}, 1, \ldots$

4. $\frac{1}{3}, \frac{2}{3}, \frac{4}{3}, \frac{8}{3}, \frac{16}{3}, \ldots$

5. $-24, -16, -8, 0, 8, \ldots$

6. $\ln 1, \ln 2, \ln 3, \ln 4, \ln 5, \ldots$

7. $3.7, 4.3, 4.9, 5.5, 6.1, \ldots$

8. $1^2, 2^2, 3^2, 4^2, 5^2, \ldots$

In Exercises 9–16, write the first five terms of the sequence. Determine whether or not the sequence is arithmetic. If it is, find the common difference. (Assume n begins with 1.)

9. $a_n = 8 + 13n$

10. $a_n = (2^n)n$

11. $a_n = \dfrac{1}{n+1}$

12. $a_n = 1 + (n-1)4$

13. $a_n = 150 - 7n$

14. $a_n = 2^{n-1}$

15. $a_n = 3 + \dfrac{(-1)^n 2}{n}$

16. $a_n = 3 - 4(n+6)$

In Exercises 17–26, find a formula for a_n for the arithmetic sequence.

17. $a_1 = 1, d = 3$

18. $a_1 = 15, d = 4$

19. $a_1 = 100, d = -8$

20. $a_1 = 0, d = -\frac{2}{3}$

21. $4, \frac{3}{2}, -1, -\frac{7}{2}, \ldots$

22. $10, 5, 0, -5, -10, \ldots$

23. $a_1 = 5, a_4 = 15$

24. $a_1 = -4, a_5 = 16$

25. $a_3 = 94, a_6 = 85$

26. $a_5 = 190, a_{10} = 115$

In Exercises 27–34, write the first five terms of the arithmetic sequence. Use the *table* feature of a graphing utility to verify your results.

27. $a_1 = 5, d = 6$

28. $a_1 = 5, d = -\frac{3}{4}$

29. $a_1 = -10, d = -12$

30. $a_4 = 16, a_{10} = 46$

31. $a_8 = 26, a_{12} = 42$

32. $a_6 = -38, a_{11} = -73$

33. $a_3 = 19, a_{15} = -1.7$

34. $a_5 = 16, a_{14} = 38.5$

In Exercises 35–38, write the first five terms of the arithmetic sequence. Find the common difference and write the nth term of the sequence as a function of n.

35. $a_1 = 15, \quad a_{k+1} = a_k + 4$

36. $a_1 = 200, \quad a_{k+1} = a_k - 10$

37. $a_1 = \frac{7}{2}, \quad a_{k+1} = a_k - \frac{1}{4}$

38. $a_1 = 0.375, \quad a_{k+1} = a_k + 0.25$

In Exercises 39–42, the first two terms of the arithmetic sequence are given. Find the missing term. Use the *table* feature of a graphing utility to verify your results.

39. $a_1 = 5, \quad a_2 = 11, \quad a_{10} = $ ▢

40. $a_1 = 3, \quad a_2 = 13, \quad a_9 = $ ▢

41. $a_1 = 4.2, \quad a_2 = 6.6, \quad a_7 = $ ▢

42. $a_1 = -0.7, \quad a_2 = -13.8, \quad a_8 = $ ▢

In Exercises 43–46, use a graphing utility to graph the first 10 terms of the sequence. (Assume n begins with 1.)

43. $a_n = 15 - \frac{3}{2}n$

44. $a_n = -5 + 2n$

45. $a_n = 0.5n + 4$

46. $a_n = -0.9n + 2$

In Exercises 47–52, use the *table* feature of a graphing utility to find the first 10 terms of the sequence. (Assume *n* begins with 1.)

47. $a_n = 4n - 5$

48. $a_n = 17 + 3n$

49. $a_n = 20 - \frac{3}{4}n$

50. $a_n = \frac{4}{5}n + 12$

51. $a_n = 1.5 + 0.005n$

52. $a_n = -12.4n + 9$

In Exercises 53–58, find the indicated *n*th partial sum of the arithmetic sequence.

53. $8, 20, 32, 44, \ldots, \quad n = 10$

54. $-6, -2, 2, 6, \ldots, \quad n = 50$

55. $0.5, 1.3, 2.1, 2.9, \ldots, \quad n = 10$

56. $4.2, 3.7, 3.2, 2.7, \ldots, \quad n = 12$

57. $a_1 = 100, \ a_{25} = 220, \quad n = 25$

58. $a_1 = 15, \ a_{100} = 307, \quad n = 100$

59. Find the sum of the first 100 positive odd integers.

60. Find the sum of the integers from -10 to 50.

In Exercises 61–68, find the partial sum without using a graphing utility.

61. $\displaystyle\sum_{n=1}^{50} n$

62. $\displaystyle\sum_{n=1}^{100} 2n$

63. $\displaystyle\sum_{n=1}^{100} 5n$

64. $\displaystyle\sum_{n=51}^{100} 7n$

65. $\displaystyle\sum_{n=11}^{30} n - \sum_{n=1}^{10} n$

66. $\displaystyle\sum_{n=51}^{100} n - \sum_{n=1}^{50} n$

67. $\displaystyle\sum_{n=1}^{500} (n + 8)$

68. $\displaystyle\sum_{n=1}^{250} (1000 - n)$

In Exercises 69–74, use a graphing utility to find the partial sum.

69. $\displaystyle\sum_{n=1}^{20} (2n + 5)$

70. $\displaystyle\sum_{n=0}^{50} (100 - 5n)$

71. $\displaystyle\sum_{n=1}^{100} \frac{n + 4}{2}$

72. $\displaystyle\sum_{n=0}^{100} \frac{8 - 3n}{16}$

73. $\displaystyle\sum_{i=1}^{60} \left(250 - \frac{8}{3}i\right)$

74. $\displaystyle\sum_{j=1}^{200} (4.5 + 0.025j)$

Job Offer **In Exercises 75 and 76, consider a job offer with the given starting salary and guaranteed salary increase for the first 5 years of employment.**

(a) Determine the salary during the sixth year of employment.

(b) Determine the total compensation from the company through 6 full years of employment.

(c) Verify your results in parts (a) and (b) numerically.

	Starting Salary	Annual Raise
75.	$32,500	$1500
76.	$36,800	$1750

77. ***Brick Pattern*** A brick patio has the approximate shape of a trapezoid, as shown in the figure. The patio has 18 rows of bricks. The first row has 14 bricks and the 18th row has 31 bricks. How many bricks are in the patio?

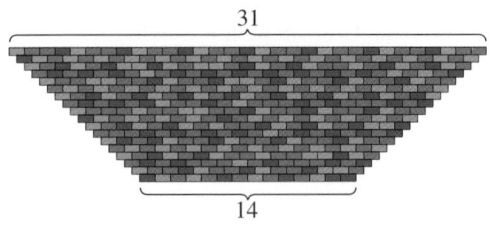

78. ***Number of Logs*** Logs are stacked in a pile, as shown in the figure. The top row has 15 logs and the bottom row has 24 logs. How many logs are in the stack?

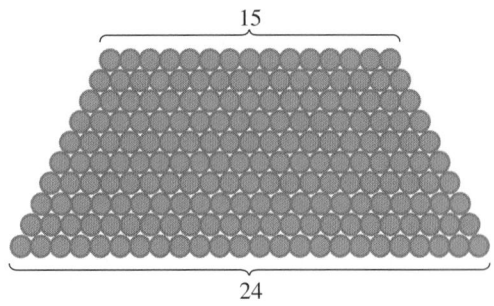

79. ***Seating Capacity*** Each row in a small auditorium has two more seats than the preceding row, as shown in the figure. Find the seating capacity of the auditorium if the front row seats 25 people and there are 15 rows of seats.

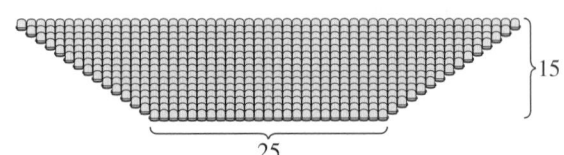

80. **Baling Hay**   In the first two trips around a field baling hay, a farmer makes 93 bales and 89 bales, respectively, as shown in the figure. Because each trip is shorter than the preceding trip, the farmer estimates that the same pattern will continue. Estimate the total number of bales made if there are another six trips around the field.

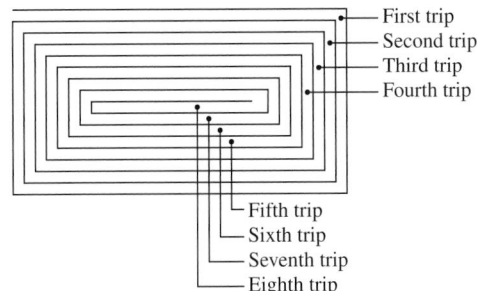

81. **Sales**   A small hardware store makes a profit of $20,000 during its first year. The store owner sets a goal of increasing profits by $5000 each year for 4 years. Assuming that this goal is met, find the total profit during the first 5 years of business.

82. **Falling Object**   An object with negligible air resistance is dropped from an airplane. During the first second of fall, the object falls 4.9 meters; during the second second, it falls 14.7 meters; and during the third second, it falls 24.5 meters; and during the fourth second, it falls 34.3 meters. If this arithmetic pattern continues, how many meters will the object fall in 10 seconds?

Synthesis

True or False?   In Exercises 83 and 84, determine whether the statement is true or false. Justify your answer.

83. Given an arithmetic sequence for which only the first and second terms are known, it is possible to find the nth term.

84. If the only known information about a finite arithmetic sequence is its first term and its last term, then it is possible to find the sum of the sequence.

In Exercises 85 and 86, find the first 10 terms of the sequence.

85. $a_1 = x, d = 2x$ **86.** $a_1 = -y, d = 5y$

87. **Think About It**   The sum of the first 20 terms of an arithmetic sequence with a common difference of 3 is 650. Find the first term.

88. **Think About It**   The sum of the first n terms of an arithmetic sequence with first term a_1 and common difference d is S_n. Determine the sum if each term is increased by 5. Explain.

89. **Pattern Recognition**
(a) Compute the following sums of positive odd integers.

$$1 + 3 = $$
$$1 + 3 + 5 = $$
$$1 + 3 + 5 + 7 = $$
$$1 + 3 + 5 + 7 + 9 = $$
$$1 + 3 + 5 + 7 + 9 + 11 = $$

(b) Use the sums in part (a) to make a conjecture about the sums of positive odd integers. Check your conjecture for the sum

$$1 + 3 + 5 + 7 + 9 + 11 + 13 = .$$

(c) Verify your conjecture algebraically.

90. **Think About It**   Decide whether it is possible to fill in the blanks in each of the sequences such that the resulting sequence is arithmetic. If so, find a recursion formula for the sequence. Write a short paragraph explaining how you made your decisions.

(a) $-7,$ ___, ___, ___, ___, ___, 11

(b) $17,$ ___, ___, ___, ___, ___, ___, 59

(c) $2, 6,$ ___, ___, 162

(d) $4, 7.5,$ ___, ___, ___, ___, ___, 28.5

(e) $8, 12,$ ___, ___, ___, 60.75

Review

In Exercises 91 and 92, use Gauss-Jordan elimination to solve the system of equations.

91. $\begin{cases} 2x - y + 7z = -10 \\ 3x + 2y - 4z = 17 \\ 6x - 5y + z = -20 \end{cases}$

92. $\begin{cases} -x + 4y + 10z = 4 \\ 5x - 3y + z = 31 \\ 8x + 2y - 3z = -5 \end{cases}$

In Exercises 93 and 94, use a determinant to find the area of the triangle with the given vertices.

93. $(0, 0), (4, -3), (2, 6)$ **94.** $(-1, 2), (5, 1), (3, 8)$

9.3 Geometric Sequences and Series

Geometric Sequences

In Section 9.2, you learned that a sequence whose consecutive terms have a common *difference* is an arithmetic sequence. In this section, you will study another important type of sequence called a **geometric sequence.** Consecutive terms of a geometric sequence have a common *ratio.*

Definition of Geometric Sequence

A sequence is **geometric** if the ratios of consecutive terms are the same. So, the sequence $a_1, a_2, a_3, a_4, \ldots, a_n, \ldots$ is geometric if there is a number r such that

$$\frac{a_2}{a_1} = \frac{a_3}{a_2} = \frac{a_4}{a_3} = \cdots = r, \qquad r \neq 0.$$

The number r is the **common ratio** of the sequence.

Example 1 Examples of Geometric Sequences

a. The sequence whose nth term is 2^n is geometric. For this sequence, the common ratio between consecutive terms is 2.

$$2, 4, 8, 16, \ldots, 2^n, \ldots \qquad \text{Begin with } n = 1.$$

$$\underbrace{\quad}\;\; \tfrac{4}{2} = 2$$

b. The sequence whose nth term is $4(3^n)$ is geometric. For this sequence, the common ratio between consecutive terms is 3.

$$12, 36, 108, 324, \ldots, 4(3^n), \ldots \qquad \text{Begin with } n = 1.$$

$$\underbrace{\quad}\;\; \tfrac{36}{12} = 3$$

c. The sequence whose nth term is $\left(-\tfrac{1}{3}\right)^n$ is geometric. For this sequence, the common ratio between consecutive terms is $-\tfrac{1}{3}$.

$$-\frac{1}{3}, \frac{1}{9}, -\frac{1}{27}, \frac{1}{81}, \ldots, \left(-\frac{1}{3}\right)^n, \ldots \qquad \text{Begin with } n = 1.$$

$$\underbrace{\quad}\;\; \frac{1/9}{-1/3} = -\tfrac{1}{3}$$

✓ *Checkpoint* Now try Exercise 1.

The sequence $1, 4, 9, 16, \ldots$, whose nth term is n^2, is *not* geometric. The ratio of the second term to first term is

$$\frac{a_2}{a_1} = \frac{4}{1} = 4$$

but the ratio of the third term to the second term is $\dfrac{a_3}{a_2} = \dfrac{9}{4}.$

What you should learn

- Recognize, write, and find the nth terms of geometric sequences.
- Find nth partial sums of geometric sequences.
- Find sums of infinite geometric series.
- Use geometric sequences to model and solve real-life problems.

Why you should learn it

Geometric sequences can reduce the amount of time it takes to find the sum of a sequence of numbers with a common ratio. For instance, Exercise 89 on page 724 shows how to use a geometric sequence to estimate the population growth of New Zealand.

Michael S. Yamashita/Corbis

STUDY TIP

In Example 1, notice that each of the geometric sequences has an nth term of the form ar^n, where r is the common ratio of the sequence.

The nth Term of a Geometric Sequence

The nth term of a geometric sequence has the form

$$a_n = a_1 r^{n-1}$$

where r is the common ratio of consecutive terms of the sequence. So, every geometric sequence can be written in the following form.

$$a_1, \quad a_2, \quad a_3, \quad a_4, \quad a_5, \quad \ldots, \quad a_n, \quad \ldots$$

$$a_1, a_1 r, a_1 r^2, a_1 r^3, a_1 r^4, \ldots, a_1 r^{n-1}, \ldots$$

If you know the nth term of a geometric sequence, you can find the $(n+1)$th term by multiplying by r. That is, $a_{n+1} = ra_n$.

Example 2   Finding the Terms of a Geometric Sequence

Write the first five terms of the geometric sequence whose first term is $a_1 = 3$ and whose common ratio is $r = 2$.

Solution

Starting with 3, repeatedly multiply by 2 to obtain the following.

$a_1 = 3$	1st term	$a_4 = 3(2^3) = 24$	4th term
$a_2 = 3(2^1) = 6$	2nd term	$a_5 = 3(2^4) = 48$	5th term
$a_3 = 3(2^2) = 12$	3rd term		

✓ *Checkpoint* Now try Exercise 11.

TECHNOLOGY TIP

You can use a graphing utility to generate the geometric sequence in Example 2 by using the following steps.

3 [ENTER]

2 [×] [ANS]

Now press the enter key repeatedly to generate the terms of the sequence.

Most graphing utilities have a built-in function that will display the terms of a geometric sequence.

Example 3   Finding a Term of a Geometric Sequence

Find the 15th term of the geometric sequence whose first term is 20 and whose common ratio is 1.05.

Algebraic Solution

$$a_n = a_1 r^{n-1} \qquad \text{Formula for a geometric sequence}$$

$$a_{15} = 20(1.05)^{15-1} \qquad \text{Substitute 20 for } a_1, 1.05 \text{ for } r, \text{ and 15 for } n.$$

$$\approx 39.599 \qquad \text{Use a calculator.}$$

Numerical Solution

For this sequence, $r = 1.05$ and $a_1 = 20$. So, $a_n = 20(1.05)^{n-1}$. Use the *table* feature of a graphing utility to create a table that shows the values of $u_n = 20(1.05)^{n-1}$ for $n = 1$ through $n = 15$. From Figure 9.12, the number in the 15th row is approximately 39.599, so the 15th term of the geometric sequence is about 39.599.

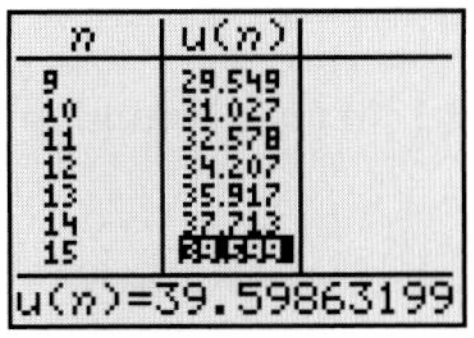

n	$u(n)$
9	28.549
10	31.027
11	32.578
12	34.207
13	35.917
14	37.713
15	39.599

$u(n)=39.59863199$

Figure 9.12

✓ *Checkpoint* Now try Exercise 25.

Example 4   Finding a Term of a Geometric Sequence

Find a formula for the nth term of the following geometric sequence. What is the ninth term of the sequence?

$$5, 15, 45, \ldots$$

Solution

The common ratio of this sequence is

$$r = \frac{15}{5} = 3.$$

Because the first term is $a_1 = 5$, the formula must have the form

$$a_n = a_1 r^{n-1} = 5(3)^{n-1}.$$

You can determine the ninth term ($n = 9$) to be

$$a_9 = 5(3)^{9-1} \qquad \text{Substitute 9 for } n.$$

$$= 5(6561) = 32,805. \qquad \text{Use a calculator.}$$

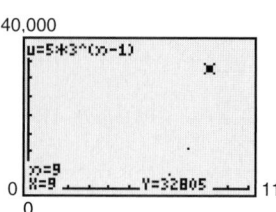

40,000

u=5*3^(x-1)

x=9
x=9   Y=32805   11

0

0

Figure 9.13

A graph of the first nine terms of the sequence is shown in Figure 9.13. Notice that the points lie on an exponential curve. This makes sense because a_n is an exponential function of n.

✓ *Checkpoint* Now try Exercise 33.

If you know *any* two terms of a geometric sequence, you can use that information to find a formula for the nth term of the sequence.

Example 5   Finding a Term of a Geometric Sequence

The 4th term of a geometric sequence is 125, and the 10th term is 125/64. Find the 14th term. (Assume that the terms of the sequence are positive.)

Solution

The 10th term is related to the fourth term by the equation

$$a_{10} = a_4 r^6. \qquad \text{Multiply 4th term by } r^{10-4}.$$

Because $a_{10} = 125/64$ and $a_4 = 125$, you can solve for r as follows.

$$\frac{125}{64} = 125 r^6$$

$$\frac{1}{64} = r^6 \implies \frac{1}{2} = r$$

You can obtain the 14th term by multiplying the 10th term by r^4.

$$a_{14} = a_{10} r^4 = \frac{125}{64}\left(\frac{1}{2}\right)^4 = \frac{125}{1024}$$

✓ *Checkpoint* Now try Exercise 31.

The Sum of a Finite Geometric Sequence

The formula for the sum of a *finite* geometric sequence is as follows. See Appendix B for a proof of this formula.

The Sum of a Finite Geometric Sequence

The sum of the finite geometric sequence

$$a_1, \ a_1r, \ a_1r^2, \ a_1r^3, \ a_1r^4, \ \ldots, \ a_1r^{n-1}$$

with common ratio $r \neq 1$ is given by

$$S_n = \sum_{i=1}^{n} a_1 r^{i-1} = a_1\left(\frac{1-r^n}{1-r}\right).$$

Example 6   Finding the Sum of a Finite Geometric Sequence

Find the sum $\displaystyle\sum_{n=1}^{12} 4(0.3)^n$.

Solution

By writing out a few terms, you have

$$\sum_{n=1}^{12} 4(0.3)^n = 4(0.3)^1 + 4(0.3)^2 + 4(0.3)^3 + \cdots + 4(0.3)^{12}.$$

Now, because $a_1 = 4(0.3)$, $r = 0.3$, and $n = 12$, you can apply the formula for the sum of a finite geometric sequence to obtain

$$\sum_{n=1}^{12} 4(0.3)^n = a_1\left(\frac{1-r^n}{1-r}\right) \qquad \text{Formula for sum of a finite geometric sequence}$$

$$= 4(0.3)\left[\frac{1-(0.3)^{12}}{1-0.3}\right] \qquad \text{Substitute } 4(0.3) \text{ for } a_1, \ 0.3 \text{ for } r, \text{ and } 12 \text{ for } n.$$

$$\approx 1.714. \qquad \text{Use a calculator.}$$

✓ *Checkpoint* Now try Exercise 49.

TECHNOLOGY TIP

Using the *sum sequence* feature of a graphing utility, you can calculate the sum of the sequence in Example 6 to be 1.7142848, as shown below.

Calculate the sum beginning at $n = 0$. You should obtain a sum of 1.7142848.

When using the formula for the sum of a geometric sequence, be careful to check that the index begins at $i = 1$. If the index begins at $i = 0$, you must adjust the formula for the nth partial sum. For instance, if the index in Example 6 had begun with $n = 0$, the sum would have been

$$\sum_{n=0}^{12} 4(0.3)^n = 4(0.3)^0 + \sum_{n=1}^{12} 4(0.3)^n$$

$$= 4 + \sum_{n=1}^{12} 4(0.3)^n$$

$$\approx 4 + 1.714$$

$$= 5.714.$$

Geometric Series

The sum of the terms of an infinite geometric sequence is called an **infinite geometric series** or simply a **geometric series.**

The formula for the sum of a *finite geometric sequence* can, depending on the value of r, be extended to produce a formula for the sum of an *infinite geometric series*. Specifically, if the common ratio r has the property that $|r| < 1$, it can be shown that r^n becomes arbitrarily close to zero as n increases without bound. Consequently,

$$a_1\left(\frac{1 - r^n}{1 - r}\right) \longrightarrow a_1\left(\frac{1 - 0}{1 - r}\right) \quad \text{as} \quad n \longrightarrow \infty.$$

This result is summarized as follows.

The Sum of an Infinite Geometric Series

If $|r| < 1$, then the infinite geometric series

$$a_1 + a_1 r + a_1 r^2 + a_1 r^3 + \cdots + a_1 r^{n-1} + \cdots$$

has the sum

$$S = \sum_{i=0}^{\infty} a_1 r^i = \frac{a_1}{1 - r}.$$

Note that if $|r| \geq 1$, the series does not have a sum.

Example 7   Finding the Sum of an Infinite Geometric Series

Use a graphing utility to find the first six partial sums of the series. Then find the sum of the series.

$$\sum_{n=1}^{\infty} 4(0.6)^{n-1}$$

Solution

You can use the *cumulative sum* feature to find the first six partial sums of the series, as shown in Figure 9.14. By scrolling to the right, you can determine that the first six partial sums are as follows.

    4, 6.4, 7.84, 8.704, 9.2224, 9.53344

Use the formula for the sum of an infinite geometric series to find the sum.

$$\sum_{n=1}^{\infty} 4(0.6)^{n-1} = 4(1) + 4(0.6) + 4(0.6)^2 + 4(0.6)^3 + \cdots + 4(0.6)^{n-1} + \cdots$$

$$= \frac{4}{1 - (0.6)} = 10 \qquad \frac{a_1}{1 - r}$$

✓ *Checkpoint* Now try Exercise 67.

Exploration

Notice that the formula for the sum of an infinite geometric series requires that $|r| < 1$. What happens if $r = 1$ or $r = -1$? Give examples of infinite geometric series for which $|r| > 1$ and convince yourself that they do not have finite sums.

TECHNOLOGY SUPPORT

For instructions on how to use the *cumulative sum* feature, see Appendix A; for specific keystrokes, go to the text website at *college.hmco.com*.

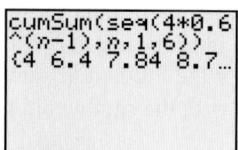

Figure 9.14

Example 8   Finding the Sum of an Infinite Geometric Series

Find the sum $3 + 0.3 + 0.03 + 0.003 + \cdots$.

Solution

$$3 + 0.3 + 0.03 + 0.003 + \cdots = 3 + 3(0.1) + 3(0.1)^2 + 3(0.1)^3 + \cdots$$

$$= \frac{3}{1 - (0.1)} \qquad \frac{a_1}{1 - r}$$

$$= \frac{10}{3}$$

$$\approx 3.33$$

✓ *Checkpoint* Now try Exercise 69.

Exploration

Notice in Example 7 that when using a graphing utility to find the sum of a series, you cannot enter ∞ as the upper limit of summation. Can you still find the sum using a graphing utility? If so, which partial sum will result in 10, the exact sum of the series?

Application

Example 9   Increasing Annuity

A deposit of $50 is made on the first day of each month in a savings account that pays 6% compounded monthly. What is the balance at the end of 2 years? (This type of savings plan is called an **increasing annuity.**)

Solution

The first deposit will gain interest for 24 months, and its balance will be

$$A_{24} = 50\left(1 + \frac{0.06}{12}\right)^{24} = 50(1.005)^{24}.$$

The second deposit will gain interest for 23 months, and its balance will be

$$A_{23} = 50\left(1 + \frac{0.06}{12}\right)^{23} = 50(1.005)^{23}.$$

The last deposit will gain interest for only 1 month, and its balance will be

$$A_1 = 50\left(1 + \frac{0.06}{12}\right)^1 = 50(1.005).$$

The total balance in the annuity will be the sum of the balances of the 24 deposits. Using the formula for the sum of a finite geometric sequence, with $A_1 = 50(1.005)$ and $r = 1.005$, you have

$$S_n = a_1\left(\frac{1 - r^n}{1 - r}\right) \qquad \text{Formula for sum of a finite geometric sequence}$$

$$S_{24} = 50(1.005)\left[\frac{1 - (1.005)^{24}}{1 - 1.005}\right] \qquad \text{Substitute } 50(1.005) \text{ for } a_1, \\ 1.005 \text{ for } r, \text{ and } 24 \text{ for } n.$$

$$\approx \$1277.96. \qquad \text{Simplify.}$$

✓ *Checkpoint* Now try Exercise 85.

STUDY TIP

Recall from Section 4.1 that the compound interest formula is

$$A = P\left(1 + \frac{r}{n}\right)^{nt}.$$

So, in Example 9, $50 is the principal, 0.06 is the interest rate, 12 is the number of compoundings per year, and 2 is the time in years. If you substitute these values, you obtain

$$A = 50\left(1 + \frac{0.06}{12}\right)^{12(2)}$$

$$= 50\left(1 + \frac{0.06}{12}\right)^{24}$$

9.3 Exercises

Vocabulary Check

Fill in the blanks.

1. A sequence is called a _____ sequence if the ratios between consecutive terms are the same. This ratio is called the _____ ratio.
2. The nth term of a geometric sequence has the form _____ .
3. The formula for the sum of a finite geometric sequence is given by _____ .
4. The sum of the terms of an infinite geometric sequence is called a _____ .
5. The formula for the sum of an infinite geometric series is given by _____ .

In Exercises 1–10, determine whether or not the sequence is geometric. If it is, find the common ratio.

1. $5, 15, 45, 135, \ldots$
2. $3, 12, 48, 192, \ldots$
3. $6, 18, 30, 42, \ldots$
4. $1, -2, 4, -8, \ldots$
5. $1, -\frac{1}{2}, \frac{1}{4}, -\frac{1}{8}, \ldots$
6. $5, 1, 0.2, 0.04, \ldots$
7. $\frac{1}{8}, \frac{1}{4}, \frac{1}{2}, 1, \ldots$
8. $9, -6, 4, -\frac{8}{3}, \ldots$
9. $1, \frac{1}{2}, \frac{1}{3}, \frac{1}{4}, \ldots$
10. $\frac{1}{5}, \frac{2}{7}, \frac{3}{9}, \frac{4}{11}, \ldots$

In Exercises 11–18, write the first five terms of the geometric sequence.

11. $a_1 = 6, \quad r = 3$
12. $a_1 = 4, \quad r = 2$
13. $a_1 = 1, \quad r = \frac{1}{2}$
14. $a_1 = 2, \quad r = \frac{1}{3}$
15. $a_1 = 5, \quad r = -\frac{1}{10}$
16. $a_1 = 6, \quad r = -\frac{1}{4}$
17. $a_1 = 1, \quad r = e$
18. $a_1 = 4, \quad r = \sqrt{3}$

In Exercises 19–24, write the first five terms of the geometric sequence. Find the common ratio and write the nth term of the sequence as a function of n.

19. $a_1 = 64, \quad a_{k+1} = \frac{1}{2}a_k$
20. $a_1 = 81, \quad a_{k+1} = \frac{1}{3}a_k$
21. $a_1 = 9, \quad a_{k+1} = 2a_k$
22. $a_1 = 5, \quad a_{k+1} = -3a_k$
23. $a_1 = 6, \quad a_{k+1} = -\frac{3}{2}a_k$
24. $a_1 = 30, \quad a_{k+1} = -\frac{2}{3}a_k$

In Exercises 25–32, find the nth term of the geometric sequence. Use the *table* feature of a graphing utility to verify your answer numerically.

25. $a_1 = 4, \quad r = \frac{1}{2}, \quad n = 10$
26. $a_1 = 5, \quad r = \frac{3}{2}, \quad n = 8$

27. $a_1 = 6, \quad r = -\frac{1}{3}, \quad n = 12$
28. $a_1 = 8, \quad r = -\frac{3}{4}, \quad n = 9$
29. $a_1 = 500, \quad r = 1.02, \quad n = 14$
30. $a_1 = 1000, \quad r = 1.005, \quad n = 11$
31. $a_2 = -18, \quad a_5 = \frac{2}{3}, \quad n = 6$
32. $a_3 = \frac{16}{3}, \quad a_5 = \frac{64}{27}, \quad n = 7$

In Exercises 33–36, find the indicated nth term of the geometric sequence.

33. 9th term: $7, 21, 63, \ldots$
34. 7th term: $3, 36, 432, \ldots$
35. 10th term: $5, 30, 180, \ldots$
36. 22nd term: $4, 8, 16, \ldots$

In Exercises 37–40, use a graphing utility to graph the first 10 terms of the sequence.

37. $a_n = 12(-0.75)^{n-1}$
38. $a_n = 20(1.25)^{n-1}$
39. $a_n = 2(1.3)^{n-1}$
40. $a_n = 10(-1.2)^{n-1}$

In Exercises 41 and 42, find the first four terms of the sequence of partial sums of the geometric series. In a sequence of partial sums, the term S_n is the sum of the first n terms of the sequence. For instance, S_2 is the sum of the first two terms.

41. $8, -4, 2, -1, \frac{1}{2}, \ldots$
42. $8, 12, 18, 27, \frac{81}{2}, \ldots$

In Exercises 43 and 44, use a graphing utility to create a table showing the sequence of partial sums for the first 10 terms of the series.

43. $\displaystyle\sum_{n=1}^{\infty} 16\left(\frac{1}{2}\right)^{n-1}$
44. $\displaystyle\sum_{n=1}^{\infty} 4(0.2)^{n-1}$

In Exercises 45–54, find the sum. Use a graphing utility to verify your result.

45. $\displaystyle\sum_{n=1}^{9} 2^{n-1}$

46. $\displaystyle\sum_{n=1}^{9} (-2)^{n-1}$

47. $\displaystyle\sum_{i=1}^{7} 64\left(-\tfrac{1}{2}\right)^{i-1}$

48. $\displaystyle\sum_{i=1}^{6} 32\left(\tfrac{1}{4}\right)^{i-1}$

49. $\displaystyle\sum_{n=0}^{20} 3\left(\tfrac{3}{2}\right)^{n}$

50. $\displaystyle\sum_{n=0}^{15} 2\left(\tfrac{4}{3}\right)^{n}$

51. $\displaystyle\sum_{i=1}^{10} 8\left(-\tfrac{1}{4}\right)^{i-1}$

52. $\displaystyle\sum_{i=1}^{10} 5\left(-\tfrac{1}{3}\right)^{i-1}$

53. $\displaystyle\sum_{n=0}^{5} 300(1.06)^{n}$

54. $\displaystyle\sum_{n=0}^{6} 500(1.04)^{n}$

In Exercises 55–58, use summation notation to write the sum.

55. $5 + 15 + 45 + \cdots + 3645$

56. $7 + 14 + 28 + \cdots + 896$

57. $2 - \tfrac{1}{2} + \tfrac{1}{8} - \cdots + \tfrac{1}{2048}$

58. $15 - 3 + \tfrac{3}{5} - \cdots - \tfrac{3}{625}$

In Exercises 59–72, find the sum of the infinite geometric series, if possible. If not possible, explain why.

59. $\displaystyle\sum_{n=0}^{\infty} \left(\tfrac{1}{2}\right)^{n}$

60. $\displaystyle\sum_{n=0}^{\infty} 2\left(\tfrac{2}{3}\right)^{n}$

61. $\displaystyle\sum_{n=0}^{\infty} \left(-\tfrac{1}{2}\right)^{n}$

62. $\displaystyle\sum_{n=0}^{\infty} 2\left(-\tfrac{2}{3}\right)^{n}$

63. $\displaystyle\sum_{n=1}^{\infty} 2\left(\tfrac{7}{3}\right)^{n-1}$

64. $\displaystyle\sum_{n=1}^{\infty} \tfrac{1}{2}(4)^{n}$

65. $\displaystyle\sum_{n=0}^{\infty} (0.4)^{n}$

66. $\displaystyle\sum_{n=0}^{\infty} 4(0.5)^{n}$

67. $\displaystyle\sum_{n=0}^{\infty} -3(0.9)^{n}$

68. $\displaystyle\sum_{n=0}^{\infty} -10(0.2)^{n}$

69. $8 + 6 + \tfrac{9}{2} + \tfrac{27}{8} + \cdots$

70. $9 + 6 + 4 + \tfrac{8}{3} + \cdots$

71. $3 - 1 + \tfrac{1}{3} - \tfrac{1}{9} + \cdots$

72. $-6 + 5 - \tfrac{25}{6} + \tfrac{125}{36} - \cdots$

In Exercises 73–76, find the rational number representation of the repeating decimal.

73. $0.\overline{36}$

74. $0.\overline{297}$

75. $0.3\overline{18}$

76. $1.3\overline{8}$

77. *Compound Interest* A principal of $1000 is invested at 3% interest. Find the amount after 10 years if the interest is compounded (a) annually, (b) semiannually, (c) quarterly, (d) monthly, and (e) daily.

78. *Compound Interest* A principal of $2500 is invested at 4% interest. Find the amount after 20 years if the interest is compounded (a) annually, (b) semi-annually, (c) quarterly, (d) monthly, and (e) daily.

79. *Annuity* A deposit of $100 is made at the beginning of each month in an account that pays 6% interest, compounded monthly. The balance A in the account at the end of 5 years is given by

$$A = 100\left(1 + \frac{0.06}{12}\right)^{1} + \cdots + 100\left(1 + \frac{0.06}{12}\right)^{60}.$$

Find A.

80. *Annuity* A deposit of $50 is made at the beginning of each month in an account that pays 8% interest, compounded monthly. The balance A in the account at the end of 5 years is given by

$$A = 50\left(1 + \frac{0.08}{12}\right)^{1} + \cdots + 50\left(1 + \frac{0.08}{12}\right)^{60}.$$

Find A.

81. *Annuity* A deposit of P dollars is made at the beginning of each month in an account earning an annual interest rate r, compounded monthly. The balance A after t years is given by

$$A = P\left(1 + \frac{r}{12}\right) + P\left(1 + \frac{r}{12}\right)^{2} + \cdots$$

$$+ P\left(1 + \frac{r}{12}\right)^{12t}.$$

Show that the balance is given by

$$A = P\left[\left(1 + \frac{r}{12}\right)^{12t} - 1\right]\left(1 + \frac{12}{r}\right).$$

82. *Annuity* A deposit of P dollars is made at the beginning of each month in an account earning an annual interest rate r, compounded continuously. The balance A after t years is given by

$$A = Pe^{r/12} + Pe^{2r/12} + \cdots + Pe^{12tr/12}.$$

Show that the balance is given by

$$A = \frac{Pe^{r/12}(e^{rt} - 1)}{e^{r/12} - 1}.$$

Annuities **In Exercises 83–86, consider making monthly deposits of P dollars in a savings account earning an annual interest rate r. Use the results of Exercises 81 and 82 to find the balance A after t years if the interest is compounded (a) monthly and (b) continuously.**

83. $P = \$50$, $r = 7\%$, $t = 20$ years

84. $P = \$75$, $r = 4\%$, $t = 25$ years

85. $P = \$100$, $r = 5\%$, $t = 40$ years

86. $P = \$20$, $r = 6\%$, $t = 50$ years

87. *Geometry* The sides of a square are 16 inches in length. A new square is formed by connecting the midpoints of the sides of the original square, and two of the resulting triangles are shaded (see figure). If this process is repeated five more times, determine the total area of the shaded region.

 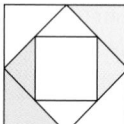 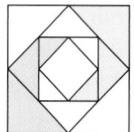 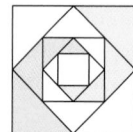

88. *Geometry* The sides of a square are 27 inches in length. New squares are formed by dividing the original square into nine squares. The center square is then shaded (see figure). If this process is repeated three more times, determine the total area of the shaded region.

 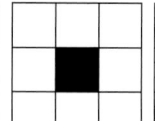 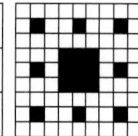 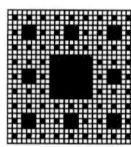

89. *Data Analysis* The table shows the population a_n (in thousands) of New Zealand from 1995 to 2001. (Source: U.S. Census Bureau)

Year	Population, a_n
1995	3566
1996	3621
1997	3676
1998	3726
1999	3774
2000	3820
2001	3864

(a) The data in the table can be approximated by the sequence

$a_n = 3343(1.013)^n$, $n = 5, 6, \ldots, 11$

where n represents the year, with $n = 5$ corresponding to 1995. Using this sequence, describe the rate at which the population of New Zealand is growing.

(b) Use the sequence in part (a) to predict the population of New Zealand in 2010.

(c) Use the sequence in part (a) to determine in what year the population of New Zealand will reach 4.1 million.

90. *Data Analysis* The table shows the revenue a_n (in billions of dollars) of AT&T Wireless Services from 1997 to 2002. (Source: AT&T Wireless Services)

Year	Revenue, a_n
1997	4.7
1998	5.4
1999	7.6
2000	10.4
2001	13.6
2002	15.6

(a) The data in the table can be approximated by the sequence

$a_n = 0.737(1.296)^n$, $n = 7, 8, \ldots, 12$

where n represents the year, with $n = 7$ corresponding to 1997. Using this sequence, describe the rate at which the revenues of AT&T Wireless Service are growing.

(b) Use the sequence in part (a) and the formula for the sum of a finite geometric sequence to approximate the total revenues earned during this six-year period.

91. *Salary* You go to work for a company that pays $\$0.01$ the first day, $\$0.02$ the second day, $\$0.04$ the third day, and so on. If the daily wage keeps doubling, what will your total income be after working (a) 29 days? (b) 30 days? (c) 31 days?

92. *Distance*   A ball is dropped from a height of 16 feet. Each time it drops h feet, it rebounds $0.81h$ feet.

(a) Find the total vertical distance traveled by the ball.

(b) The ball takes the following times (in seconds) for each fall.

$$s_1 = -16t^2 + 16, \qquad s_1 = 0 \text{ if } t = 1$$
$$s_2 = -16t^2 + 16(0.81), \qquad s_2 = 0 \text{ if } t = 0.9$$
$$s_3 = -16t^2 + 16(0.81)^2, \qquad s_3 = 0 \text{ if } t = (0.9)^2$$
$$s_4 = -16t^2 + 16(0.81)^3, \qquad s_4 = 0 \text{ if } t = (0.9)^3$$
$$\vdots \qquad\qquad\qquad \vdots$$
$$s_n = -16t^2 + 16(0.81)^{n-1}, \quad s_n = 0 \text{ if } t = (0.9)^{n-1}$$

Beginning with s_2, the ball takes the same amount of time to bounce up as it does to fall, and so the total time elapsed before it comes to rest is

$$t = 1 + 2\sum_{n=1}^{\infty}(0.9)^n.$$

Find this total time.

Synthesis

True or False?   **In Exercises 93 and 94, determine whether the statement is true or false. Justify your answer.**

93. A sequence is geometric if the ratios of consecutive differences of consecutive terms are the same.

94. You can find the nth term of a geometric sequence by multiplying its common ratio by the first term of the sequence raised to the $(n - 1)$th power.

In Exercises 95 and 96, write the first five terms of the geometric sequence.

95. $a_1 = 3, r = \dfrac{x}{2}$

96. $a_1 = \dfrac{1}{2}, r = 7x$

In Exercises 97 and 98, find the nth term of the geometric sequence.

97. $a_1 = 100, r = e^x, n = 9$

98. $a_1 = 4, r = \dfrac{4x}{3}, n = 6$

99. *Graphical Reasoning*   Use a graphing utility to graph each function. Identify the horizontal asymptote of the graph and determine its relationship to the sum.

(a) $f(x) = 6\left[\dfrac{1 - (0.5)^x}{1 - (0.5)}\right], \quad \displaystyle\sum_{n=0}^{\infty}6\left(\dfrac{1}{2}\right)^n$

(b) $f(x) = 2\left[\dfrac{1 - (0.8)^x}{1 - (0.8)}\right], \quad \displaystyle\sum_{n=0}^{\infty}2\left(\dfrac{4}{5}\right)^n$

100. *Writing*   Write a brief paragraph explaining why the terms of a geometric sequence decrease in magnitude when $-1 < r < 1$.

101. *Writing*   Write a brief paragraph explaining how to use the first two terms of a geometric sequence to find the nth term.

102. *Exploration*   You will need a piece of string or yarn, a pair of scissors, and a tape measure. Measure out any length of string at least 5 feet long. Double over the string and cut it in half. Take one of the resulting halves, double it over, and cut it in half. Continue this process until you are no longer able to cut a length of string in half. How many cuts were you able to make? Construct a sequence of the resulting string lengths after each cut, starting with the original length of the string. Find a formula for the nth term of this sequence. How many cuts could you theoretically make? Write a short paragraph discussing why you were not able to make that many cuts.

Review

103. *Average Speed*   A truck traveled at an average speed of 50 miles per hour on a 200-mile trip. On the return trip, the average speed was 42 miles per hour. Find the average speed for the round trip.

104. *Work Rate*   Your friend can mow a lawn in 4 hours and you can mow it in 6 hours. How long will it take both of you to mow the lawn working together?

In Exercises 105–108, find the determinant of the matrix.

105. $\begin{bmatrix} 4 & -1 \\ 6 & 2 \end{bmatrix}$

106. $\begin{bmatrix} 1 & 3 \\ -2 & 5 \end{bmatrix}$

107. $\begin{bmatrix} -1 & 3 & 4 \\ -2 & 8 & 0 \\ 2 & 5 & -1 \end{bmatrix}$

108. $\begin{bmatrix} -1 & 0 & 4 \\ -4 & 3 & 5 \\ 0 & 2 & -3 \end{bmatrix}$

9.4 Mathematical Induction

Introduction

In this section you will study a form of mathematical proof called **mathematical induction.** It is important that you clearly see the logical need for it, so let's take a closer look at a problem discussed in Example 5(a) on page 710.

$$S_1 = 1 = 1^2$$

$$S_2 = 1 + 3 = 2^2$$

$$S_3 = 1 + 3 + 5 = 3^2$$

$$S_4 = 1 + 3 + 5 + 7 = 4^2$$

$$S_5 = 1 + 3 + 5 + 7 + 9 = 5^2$$

Judging from the pattern formed by these first five sums, it appears that the sum of the first n odd integers is

$$S_n = 1 + 3 + 5 + 7 + 9 + \cdots + (2n - 1) = n^2.$$

Although this particular formula is valid, it is important for you to see that recognizing a pattern and then simply *jumping to the conclusion* that the pattern must be true for all values of n is *not* a logically valid method of proof. There are many examples in which a pattern appears to be developing for small values of n but then fails at some point. One of the most famous cases of this is the conjecture by the French mathematician Pierre de Fermat (1601–1665), who speculated that all numbers of the form

$$F_n = 2^{2^n} + 1, \quad n = 0, 1, 2, \ldots$$

are prime. For $n = 0, 1, 2, 3,$ and 4, the conjecture is true.

$$F_0 = 3$$

$$F_1 = 5$$

$$F_2 = 17$$

$$F_3 = 257$$

$$F_4 = 65,537$$

The size of the next *Fermat number* ($F_5 = 4,294,967,297$) is so great that it was difficult for Fermat to determine whether or not it was prime. However, another well-known mathematician, Leonhard Euler (1707–1783), later found a factorization

$$F_5 = 4,294,967,297$$

$$= 641(6,700,417)$$

which proved that F_5 is not prime and therefore Fermat's conjecture was false.

Just because a rule, pattern, or formula seems to work for several values of n, you cannot simply decide that it is valid for *all* values of n without going through a *legitimate proof.* Mathematical induction is one method of proof.

What you should learn

- Use mathematical induction to prove statements involving a positive integer n.
- Find the sums of powers of integers.
- Find finite differences of sequences.

Why you should learn it

Finite differences can be used to determine what type of model can be used to represent a sequence. For instance, in Exercise 49 on page 733, you will use finite differences to find a model that represents the average sales price of a new mobile home in the southern region of the United States.

Photodisc/Getty Images

The Principle of Mathematical Induction

Let P_n be a statement involving the positive integer n. If

   1. P_1 is true, and

   2. the truth of P_k implies the truth of P_{k+1} for every positive k

then P_n must be true for all positive integers n.

STUDY TIP

It is important to recognize that *both* parts of the Principle of Mathematical Induction are necessary.

To apply the Principle of Mathematical Induction, you need to be able to determine the statement P_{k+1} for a given statement P_k. To detemine P_{k+1}, substitute $k + 1$ for k in the statement P_k.

Example 1   A Preliminary Example

Find P_{k+1} for each P_k.

a. $P_k : S_k = \dfrac{k^2(k + 1)^2}{4}$

b. $P_k : S_k = 1 + 5 + 9 + \cdots + [4(k - 1) - 3] + (4k - 3)$

c. $P_k : k + 3 < 5k^2$

d. $P_k : 3^k \geq 2k + 1$

Solution

a. $P_{k+1} : S_{k+1} = \dfrac{(k + 1)^2(k + 1 + 1)^2}{4}$ Replace k by $k + 1$.

$\phantom{P_{k+1} : S_{k+1}} = \dfrac{(k + 1)^2(k + 2)^2}{4}$ Simplify.

b. $P_{k+1} : S_{k+1} = 1 + 5 + 9 + \cdots + \{4[(k + 1) - 1] - 3\} + [4(k + 1) - 3]$

$\phantom{P_{k+1} : S_{k+1}} = 1 + 5 + 9 + \cdots + (4k - 3) + (4k + 1)$

c. $P_{k+1} : (k + 1) + 3 < 5(k + 1)^2$

$\phantom{P_{k+1} :} k + 4 < 5(k^2 + 2k + 1)$

d. $P_{k+1} : 3^{k+1} \geq 2(k + 1) + 1$

$\phantom{P_{k+1} :} 3^{k+1} \geq 2k + 3$

✓ *Checkpoint* Now try Exercise 3.

A well-known illustration used to explain why the Principle of Mathematical Induction works is the unending line of dominoes represented by Figure 9.15. If the line actually contains infinitely many dominoes, it is clear that you could not knock down the entire line by knocking down only *one domino* at a time. However, suppose it were true that each domino would knock down the next one as it fell. Then you could knock them all down simply by pushing the first one and starting a chain reaction. Mathematical induction works in the same way. If the truth of P_k implies the truth of P_{k+1} and if P_1 is true, the chain reaction proceeds as follows: P_1 implies P_2, P_2 implies P_3, P_3 implies P_4, and so on.

Figure 9.15

When using mathematical induction to prove a *summation* formula (such as the one in Example 2), it is helpful to think of S_{k+1} as

$$S_{k+1} = S_k + a_{k+1}$$

where a_{k+1} is the $(k + 1)$th term of the original sum.

Example 2   Using Mathematical Induction

Use mathematical induction to prove the following formula.

$$S_n = 1 + 3 + 5 + 7 + \cdots + (2n - 1) = n^2$$

Solution

Mathematical induction consists of two distinct parts. First, you must show that the formula is true when $n = 1$.

1. When $n = 1$, the formula is valid because

$$S_1 = 1 = 1^2.$$

The second part of mathematical induction has two steps. The first step is to assume that the formula is valid for *some* integer k. The second step is to use this assumption to prove that the formula is valid for the next integer, $k + 1$.

2. Assuming that the formula

$$S_k = 1 + 3 + 5 + 7 + \cdots + (2k - 1) = k^2$$

is true, you must show that the formula $S_{k+1} = (k + 1)^2$ is true.

$$
\begin{aligned}
S_{k+1} &= 1 + 3 + 5 + 7 + \cdots + (2k - 1) + [2(k + 1) - 1] \\
&= [1 + 3 + 5 + 7 + \cdots + (2k - 1)] + (2k + 2 - 1) \\
&= S_k + (2k + 1) \qquad \text{Group terms to form } S_k. \\
&= k^2 + 2k + 1 \qquad \text{Replace } S_k \text{ by } k^2. \\
&= (k + 1)^2
\end{aligned}
$$

Combining the results of parts (1) and (2), you can conclude by mathematical induction that the formula is valid for all positive integer values of n.

✓ *Checkpoint* Now try Exercise 7.

It occasionally happens that a statement involving natural numbers is *not* true for the first $k - 1$ positive integers but *is* true for all values of $n \geq k$. In these instances, you use a slight variation of the Principle of Mathematical Induction in which you verify P_k rather than P_1. This variation is called the *extended principle of mathematical induction*. To see the validity of this principle, note from Figure 9.15 that all but the first $k - 1$ dominoes can be knocked down by knocking over the kth domino. This suggests that you can prove a statement P_n to be true for $n \geq k$ by showing that P_k is true and that P_k implies P_{k+1}. In Exercises 23–28 in this section, you are asked to apply this extension of mathematical induction.

Example 3   Using Mathematical Induction

Use mathematical induction to prove the formula

$$S_n = 1^2 + 2^2 + 3^2 + 4^2 + \cdots + n^2 = \frac{n(n+1)(2n+1)}{6}$$

for all integers $n \geq 1$.

Solution

1. When $n = 1$, the formula is valid because

$$S_1 = 1^2 = \frac{1(1+1)(2 \cdot 1 + 1)}{6} = \frac{1(2)(3)}{6}.$$

2. Assuming that

$$S_k = 1^2 + 2^2 + 3^2 + 4^2 + \cdots + k^2 = \frac{k(k+1)(2k+1)}{6}$$

you must show that

$$S_{k+1} = \frac{(k+1)(k+1+1)[2(k+1)+1]}{6} = \frac{(k+1)(k+2)(2k+3)}{6}.$$

To do this, write the following.

$$
\begin{aligned}
S_{k+1} &= S_k + a_{k+1} \\
&= (1^2 + 2^2 + 3^2 + 4^2 + \cdots + k^2) + (k+1)^2 \\
&= \frac{k(k+1)(2k+1)}{6} + (k+1)^2 \qquad \text{By assumption} \\
&= \frac{k(k+1)(2k+1) + 6(k+1)^2}{6} \\
&= \frac{(k+1)[k(2k+1) + 6(k+1)]}{6} \\
&= \frac{(k+1)(2k^2 + 7k + 6)}{6} \\
&= \frac{(k+1)(k+2)(2k+3)}{6}
\end{aligned}
$$

> **STUDY TIP**
>
> Remember that when adding rational expressions, you must first find the least common denominator (LCD). In Example 3, the LCD is 6.

Combining the results of parts (1) and (2), you can conclude by mathematical induction that the formula is valid for *all* integers $n \geq 1$.

✓ *Checkpoint* Now try Exercise 13.

When proving a formula by mathematical induction, the only statement that you *need* to verify is P_1. As a check, it is a good idea to try verifying some of the other statements. For instance, in Example 3, try verifying P_2 and P_3.

Sums of Powers of Integers

The formula in Example 3 is one of a collection of useful summation formulas. This and other formulas dealing with the sums of various powers of the first n positive integers are summarized below.

Sums of Powers of Integers

1. $\displaystyle\sum_{i=1}^{n} i = 1 + 2 + 3 + 4 + \cdots + n = \frac{n(n+1)}{2}$

2. $\displaystyle\sum_{i=1}^{n} i^2 = 1^2 + 2^2 + 3^2 + 4^2 + \cdots + n^2 = \frac{n(n+1)(2n+1)}{6}$

3. $\displaystyle\sum_{i=1}^{n} i^3 = 1^3 + 2^3 + 3^3 + 4^3 + \cdots + n^3 = \frac{n^2(n+1)^2}{4}$

4. $\displaystyle\sum_{i=1}^{n} i^4 = 1^4 + 2^4 + 3^4 + 4^4 + \cdots + n^4 = \frac{n(n+1)(2n+1)(3n^2+3n-1)}{30}$

5. $\displaystyle\sum_{i=1}^{n} i^5 = 1^5 + 2^5 + 3^5 + 4^5 + \cdots + n^5 = \frac{n^2(n+1)^2(2n^2+2n-1)}{12}$

Each of these formulas for sums can be proven by mathematical induction. (See Exercises 13–16 in this section.)

Example 4   Proving an Inequality by Mathematical Induction

Prove that $n < 2^n$ for all positive integers n.

Solution

1. For $n = 1$ and $n = 2$, the formula is true because

$$1 < 2^1 \text{ and } 2 < 2^2.$$

2. Assuming that

$$k < 2^k$$

you need to show that $k + 1 < 2^{k+1}$. Note first that

$$2^{k+1} = 2(2^k) > 2(k) = 2k. \qquad \text{By assumption}$$

Because $2k = k + k > k + 1$ for all $k > 1$, it follows that

$$2^{k+1} > 2k > k + 1$$

or

$$k + 1 < 2^{k+1}.$$

Combining the results of parts (1) and (2), you can conclude by mathematical induction that $n < 2^n$ for all integers $n \geq 1$.

✓ *Checkpoint* Now try Exercise 23.

Finite Differences

The **first differences** of a sequence are found by subtracting consecutive terms. The **second differences** are found by subtracting consecutive first differences. The first and second differences of the sequence $3, 5, 8, 12, 17, 23, \ldots$ are as follows.

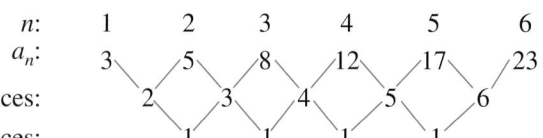

For this sequence, the second differences are all the same. When this happens, and the second differences are nonzero, the sequence has a perfect *quadratic* model. If the first differences are all the same nonzero number, the sequence has a *linear* model—that is, it is arithmetic.

Example 5   Finding a Quadratic Model

Find the quadratic model for the sequence $3, 5, 8, 12, 17, 23, \ldots$.

Solution

You know from the second differences shown above that the model is quadratic and has the form

$$a_n = an^2 + bn + c.$$

By substituting 1, 2, and 3 for n, you can obtain a system of three linear equations in three variables.

$a_1 = a(1)^2 + b(1) + c = 3$ Substitute 1 for n.
$a_2 = a(2)^2 + b(2) + c = 5$ Substitute 2 for n.
$a_3 = a(3)^2 + b(3) + c = 8$ Substitute 3 for n.

You now have a system of three equations in a, b, and c.

$$\begin{cases} a + b + c = 3 & \text{Equation 1} \\ 4a + 2b + c = 5 & \text{Equation 2} \\ 9a + 3b + c = 8 & \text{Equation 3} \end{cases}$$

Solving this system of equations using techniques discussed in Chapter 8, you can find the solution to be $a = \frac{1}{2}$, $b = \frac{1}{2}$, and $c = 2$. So, the quadratic model is

$$a_n = \tfrac{1}{2}n^2 + \tfrac{1}{2}n + 2.$$

Check the values of a_1, a_2, and a_3 as follows.

Check

$a_1 = \frac{1}{2}(1)^2 + \frac{1}{2}(1) + 2 = 3$ Solution checks. ✓
$a_2 = \frac{1}{2}(2)^2 + \frac{1}{2}(2) + 2 = 5$ Solution checks. ✓
$a_3 = \frac{1}{2}(3)^2 + \frac{1}{2}(3) + 2 = 8$ Solution checks. ✓

 *Checkpoint* Now try Exercise 45.

STUDY TIP

For a linear model, the *first* differences are the same nonzero number. For a quadratic model, the *second* differences are the same nonzero number.

9.4 Exercises

Vocabulary Check

Fill in the blanks.

1. The first step in proving a formula by _____ is to show that the formula is true when $n = 1$.
2. The _____ differences of a sequence are found by subtracting consecutive terms.
3. A sequence is an _____ sequence if the first differences are all the same nonzero number.
4. If the _____ differences of a sequence are all the same nonzero number, then the sequence has a perfect quadratic model.

In Exercises 1–6, find P_{k+1} for the given P_k.

1. $P_k = \dfrac{5}{k(k+1)}$ 2. $P_k = \dfrac{4}{(k+2)(k+3)}$

3. $P_k = \dfrac{3(2k+1)}{k-1}$ 4. $P_k = \dfrac{k}{2}(5k-3)$

5. $P_k = 1 + 6 + 11 + \cdots + [5(k-1)-4] + (5k-4)$
6. $P_k = 7 + 13 + 19 + \cdots + [6(k-1)+1] + (6k+1)$

In Exercises 7–18, use mathematical induction to prove the formula for every positive integer n.

7. $2 + 4 + 6 + 8 + \cdots + 2n = n(n+1)$
8. $3 + 11 + 19 + 27 + \cdots + (8n-5) = n(4n-1)$
9. $3 + 8 + 13 + 18 + \cdots + (5n-2) = \dfrac{n}{2}(5n+1)$
10. $1 + 4 + 7 + 10 + \cdots + (3n-2) = \dfrac{n}{2}(3n-1)$
11. $1 + 2 + 2^2 + 2^3 + \cdots + 2^{n-1} = 2^n - 1$
12. $2(1 + 3 + 3^2 + 3^3 + \cdots + 3^{n-1}) = 3^n - 1$
13. $1 + 2 + 3 + 4 + \cdots + n = \dfrac{n(n+1)}{2}$
14. $1^3 + 2^3 + 3^3 + 4^3 + \cdots + n^3 = \dfrac{n^2(n+1)^2}{4}$
15. $\displaystyle\sum_{i=1}^{n} i^4 = \dfrac{n(n+1)(2n+1)(3n^2+3n-1)}{30}$
16. $\displaystyle\sum_{i=1}^{n} i^5 = \dfrac{n^2(n+1)^2(2n^2+2n-1)}{12}$
17. $\displaystyle\sum_{i=1}^{n} i(i+1) = \dfrac{n(n+1)(n+2)}{3}$
18. $\displaystyle\sum_{i=1}^{n} \dfrac{1}{(2i-1)(2i+1)} = \dfrac{n}{2n+1}$

In Exercises 19–22, find the sum using the formulas for the sums of powers of integers.

19. $\displaystyle\sum_{n=1}^{10} n^3$ 20. $\displaystyle\sum_{n=1}^{5} n^4$

21. $\displaystyle\sum_{n=1}^{6} (n^2 - n)$ 22. $\displaystyle\sum_{n=1}^{20} (n^3 - n)$

In Exercises 23–28, prove the inequality for the indicated integer values of n.

23. $n! > 2^n, \quad n \geq 4$ 24. $\left(\dfrac{4}{3}\right)^n > n, \quad n \geq 7$

25. $\dfrac{1}{\sqrt{1}} + \dfrac{1}{\sqrt{2}} + \dfrac{1}{\sqrt{3}} + \cdots + \dfrac{1}{\sqrt{n}} > \sqrt{n}, \quad n \geq 2$

26. $\left(\dfrac{x}{y}\right)^{n+1} < \left(\dfrac{x}{y}\right)^n, \quad n \geq 1$ and $0 < x < y$

27. $(1 + a)^n \geq na, \quad n \geq 1$ and $a > 1$
28. $3^n > n \, 2^n, \quad n \geq 1$

In Exercises 29–36, use mathematical induction to prove the property for all positive integers n.

29. $(ab)^n = a^n b^n$ 30. $\left(\dfrac{a}{b}\right)^n = \dfrac{a^n}{b^n}$

31. If $x_1 \neq 0, \; x_2 \neq 0, \ldots, x_n \neq 0$, then
$(x_1 x_2 x_3 \cdots x_n)^{-1} = x_1^{-1} x_2^{-1} x_3^{-1} \cdots x_n^{-1}$.

32. If $x_1 > 0, \; x_2 > 0, \ldots, x_n > 0$, then
$\ln(x_1 x_2 \cdots x_n) = \ln x_1 + \ln x_2 + \cdots + \ln x_n$.

33. Generalized Distributive Law:
$x(y_1 + y_2 + \cdots + y_n) = xy_1 + xy_2 + \cdots + xy_n$

34. $(a + bi)^n$ and $(a - bi)^n$ are complex conjugates for all $n \geq 1$.

35. A factor of $(n^3 + 3n^2 + 2n)$ is 3.

36. A factor of $(n^3 + 5n + 6)$ is 3.

In Exercises 37–44, write the first five terms of the sequence beginning with the given term. Then calculate the first and second differences of the sequence. Does the sequence have a linear model, a quadratic model, or neither?

37. $a_1 = 0$

$a_n = a_{n-1} + 3$

38. $a_1 = 2$

$a_n = n - a_{n-1}$

39. $a_1 = 3$

$a_n = a_{n-1} - n$

40. $a_2 = -3$

$a_n = -2a_{n-1}$

41. $a_0 = 0$

$a_n = a_{n-1} + n$

42. $a_0 = 2$

$a_n = (a_{n-1})^2$

43. $a_1 = 2$

$a_n = a_{n-1} + 2$

44. $a_1 = 0$

$a_n = a_{n-1} + 2n$

In Exercises 45–48, find a quadratic model for the sequence with the indicated terms.

45. $a_0 = 3$, $a_1 = 3$, $a_4 = 15$

46. $a_0 = 7$, $a_1 = 6$, $a_3 = 10$

47. $a_0 = -3$, $a_2 = 1$, $a_4 = 9$

48. $a_0 = 3$, $a_2 = 0$, $a_6 = 36$

49. Data Analysis The table shows the average sales price a_n (in thousands of dollars) of a new mobile home in the southern region of the United States from 1995 to 2001. (Source: U.S. Census Bureau)

Year	Average sales price, a_n
1995	33.3
1996	35.5
1997	38.0
1998	40.1
1999	41.9
2000	44.2
2001	46.1

(a) Find the first differences of the data shown in the table.

(b) Use your results from part (a) to determine whether a linear model can be used to approximate the data. If so, use the *regression* feature of a graphing utility to find the model. Let n represent the year, with $n = 5$ corresponding to 1995.

(c) Use the model in part (b) and the *table* feature of a graphing utility to create a table of values for the model from 1995 to 2001. How closely does the model represent the original data?

(d) Use the model in part (b) to estimate the average sales price in 2006.

Synthesis

50. Writing In your own words, explain what is meant by a proof by mathematical induction.

True or False? **In Exercises 51–53, determine whether the statement is true or false. Justify your answer.**

51. If the statement P_k is true and P_k implies P_{k+1}, then P_1 is also true.

52. If a sequence is arithmetic, then the first differences of the sequence are all zero.

53. A sequence with n terms has $n - 1$ second differences.

54. Think About It What conclusion can be drawn from the given information about the sequence of statements P_n?

(a) P_3 is true and P_k implies P_{k+1}.

(b) $P_1, P_2, P_3, \ldots, P_{50}$ are all true.

(c) P_1, P_2, and P_3 are all true, but the truth of P_k does not imply that P_{k+1} is true.

(d) P_2 is true and P_{2k} implies P_{2k+2}.

Review

In Exercises 55–58, find the product.

55. $(2x^2 - 1)^2$

56. $(2x - y)^2$

57. $(5 - 4x)^3$

58. $(2x - 4y)^3$

In Exercises 59–62, use synthetic division to divide.

59. $(x^3 + x^2 - 10x + 8) \div (x + 4)$

60. $(x^3 - 4x^2 - 29x - 24) \div (x - 8)$

61. $(4x^3 + 11x^2 - 43x + 10) \div (x + 5)$

62. $(6x^3 - 35x^2 - 8x + 12) \div (x - 6)$

In Exercises 63–66, simplify the expression.

63. $3\sqrt{-27} - \sqrt{-12}$

64. $\sqrt[3]{125} + 4\sqrt[3]{-8} - 2\sqrt[3]{-54}$

65. $10(\sqrt[3]{64} - 2\sqrt[3]{-16})$

66. $(-5 + \sqrt{-9})^2$

9.5 The Binomial Theorem

Binomial Coefficients

Recall that a *binomial* is a polynomial that has two terms. In this section, you will study a formula that provides a quick method of raising a binomial to a power. To begin, look at the expansion of

$$(x + y)^n$$

for several values of n.

$$(x + y)^0 = 1$$

$$(x + y)^1 = x + y$$

$$(x + y)^2 = x^2 + 2xy + y^2$$

$$(x + y)^3 = x^3 + 3x^2y + 3xy^2 + y^3$$

$$(x + y)^4 = x^4 + 4x^3y + 6x^2y^2 + 4xy^3 + y^4$$

$$(x + y)^5 = x^5 + 5x^4y + 10x^3y^2 + 10x^2y^3 + 5xy^4 + y^5$$

There are several observations you can make about these expansions.

1. In each expansion, there are $n + 1$ terms.

2. In each expansion, x and y have symmetric roles. The powers of x decrease by 1 in successive terms, whereas the powers of y increase by 1.

3. The sum of the powers of each term is n. For instance, in the expansion of $(x + y)^5$, the sum of the powers of each term is 5.

$$4 + 1 = 5 \quad 3 + 2 = 5$$

$$(x + y)^5 = x^5 + 5x^4y^1 + 10x^3y^2 + 10x^2y^3 + 5x^1y^4 + y^5$$

4. The coefficients increase and then decrease in a symmetric pattern.

The coefficients of a binomial expansion are called **binomial coefficients.** To find them, you can use the **Binomial Theorem.** See Appendix B for a proof of this theorem.

What you should learn

- Use the Binomial Theorem to calculate binomial coefficients.
- Use Pascal's Triangle to calculate binomial coefficients.
- Use binomial coefficients to write binomial expansions.

Why you should learn it

You can use binomial coefficients to predict future behavior. For instance, in Exercise 86 on page 740, you are asked to use binomial coefficients to find the probability that a baseball player gets three hits during the next 10 times at bat.

Jonathan Daniel/Getty Images

The Binomial Theorem

In the expansion of $(x + y)^n$

$$(x + y)^n = x^n + nx^{n-1}y + \cdots +\ _nC_r\ x^{n-r}y^r + \cdots + nxy^{n-1} + y^n$$

the coefficient of $x^{n-r}y^r$ is

$$_nC_r = \frac{n!}{(n-r)!r!}.$$

The symbol $\binom{n}{r}$ is often used in place of $_nC_r$ to denote binomial coefficients.

Example 1   Finding Binomial Coefficients

Find each binomial coefficient.

a. $_8C_2$ **b.** $\binom{10}{3}$ **c.** $_7C_0$ **d.** $\binom{8}{8}$

Solution

a. $_8C_2 = \dfrac{8!}{6! \cdot 2!} = \dfrac{(8 \cdot 7) \cdot 6!}{6! \cdot 2!} = \dfrac{8 \cdot 7}{2 \cdot 1} = 28$

b. $\binom{10}{3} = \dfrac{10!}{7! \cdot 3!} = \dfrac{(10 \cdot 9 \cdot 8) \cdot 7!}{7! \cdot 3!} = \dfrac{10 \cdot 9 \cdot 8}{3 \cdot 2 \cdot 1} = 120$

c. $_7C_0 = \dfrac{7!}{7! \cdot 0!} = 1$

d. $\binom{8}{8} = \dfrac{8!}{0! \cdot 8!} = 1$

✓ *Checkpoint* Now try Exercise 5.

TECHNOLOGY TIP

Most graphing utilities are programmed to evaluate $_nC_r$. The figure below shows how one graphing utility evaluates the binomial coefficient in Example 1(a). For instructions on how to use the $_nC_r$ feature, see Appendix A; for specific keystrokes, go to the text website at *college.hmco.com*.

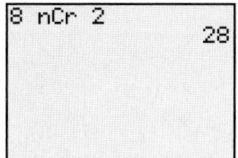

```
8 nCr 2
                    28
```

When $r \neq 0$ and $r \neq n$, as in parts (a) and (b) of Example 1, there is a simple pattern for evaluating binomial coefficients that works because there will always be factorial terms that divide out from the expression.

$$_8C_2 = \underbrace{\dfrac{\overbrace{8 \cdot 7}^{2 \text{ factors}}}{\underbrace{2 \cdot 1}_{2 \text{ factorial}}}} \quad \text{and} \quad \binom{10}{3} = \dfrac{\overbrace{10 \cdot 9 \cdot 8}^{3 \text{ factors}}}{\underbrace{3 \cdot 2 \cdot 1}_{3 \text{ factorial}}}$$

Example 2   Finding Binomial Coefficients

Find each binomial coefficient using the pattern shown above.

a. $_7C_3$ **b.** $_7C_4$ **c.** $_{12}C_1$ **d.** $_{12}C_{11}$

Solution

a. $_7C_3 = \dfrac{7 \cdot 6 \cdot 5}{3 \cdot 2 \cdot 1} = 35$ **b.** $_7C_4 = \dfrac{7 \cdot 6 \cdot 5 \cdot 4}{4 \cdot 3 \cdot 2 \cdot 1} = 35$

c. $_{12}C_1 = \dfrac{12}{1} = 12$

d. $_{12}C_{11} = \dfrac{12!}{1! \cdot 11!} = \dfrac{(12) \cdot 11!}{1! \cdot 11!} = \dfrac{12}{1} = 12$

✓ *Checkpoint* Now try Exercise 7.

It is not a coincidence that the results in parts (a) and (b) of Example 2 are the same and that the results in parts (c) and (d) are the same. In general, it is true that

$$_nC_r = {_nC_{n-r}}.$$

Exploration

Find each pair of binomial coefficients.

a. $_7C_0, {_7C_7}$ **d.** $_7C_1, {_7C_6}$

b. $_8C_0, {_8C_8}$ **e.** $_8C_1, {_8C_7}$

c. $_{10}C_0, {_{10}C_{10}}$ **f.** $_{10}C_1, {_{10}C_9}$

What do you observe about the pairs in (a), (b), and (c)? What do you observe about the pairs in (d), (e), and (f)? Write two conjectures from your observations. Develop a convincing argument for your two conjectures.

Pascal's Triangle

There is a convenient way to remember the pattern for binomial coefficients. By arranging the coefficients in a triangular pattern, you obtain the following array, which is called **Pascal's Triangle.** This triangle is named after the famous French mathematician Blaise Pascal (1623–1662).

$$4 + 6 = 10$$

$$15 + 6 = 21$$

The first and last number in each row of Pascal's Triangle is 1. Every other number in each row is formed by adding the two numbers immediately above the number. Pascal noticed that the numbers in this triangle are precisely the same numbers as the coefficients of binomial expansions, as follows.

$$(x + y)^0 = 1 \qquad \text{0th row}$$
$$(x + y)^1 = 1x + 1y \qquad \text{1st row}$$
$$(x + y)^2 = 1x^2 + 2xy + 1y^2 \qquad \text{2nd row}$$
$$(x + y)^3 = 1x^3 + 3x^2y + 3xy^2 + 1y^3 \qquad \text{3rd row}$$
$$(x + y)^4 = 1x^4 + 4x^3y + 6x^2y^2 + 4xy^3 + 1y^4 \qquad \vdots$$
$$(x + y)^5 = 1x^5 + 5x^4y + 10x^3y^2 + 10x^2y^3 + 5xy^4 + 1y^5$$
$$(x + y)^6 = 1x^6 + 6x^5y + 15x^4y^2 + 20x^3y^3 + 15x^2y^4 + 6xy^5 + 1y^6$$
$$(x + y)^7 = 1x^7 + 7x^6y + 21x^5y^2 + 35x^4y^3 + 35x^3y^4 + 21x^2y^5 + 7xy^6 + 1y^7$$

The top row of Pascal's Triangle is called the *zeroth row* because it corresponds to the binomial expansion $(x + y)^0 = 1$. Similarly, the next row is called the *first row* because it corresponds to the binomial expansion $(x + y)^1 = 1(x) + 1(y)$. In general, the *nth row* of Pascal's Triangle gives the coefficients of $(x + y)^n$.

Example 3 Using Pascal's Triangle

Use the seventh row of Pascal's Triangle to find the binomial coefficients.

$$_8C_0, \ _8C_1, \ _8C_2, \ _8C_3, \ _8C_4, \ _8C_5, \ _8C_6, \ _8C_7, \ _8C_8$$

Solution

✓ *Checkpoint* Now try Exercise 17.

Exploration

Complete the table and describe the result.

n	r	$_nC_r$	$_nC_{n-r}$
9	5		
7	1		
12	4		
6	0		
10	7		

What characteristics of Pascal's Triangle are illustrated by the table?

Binomial Expansions

As mentioned at the beginning of this section, when you write out the coefficients for a binomial that is raised to a power, you are **expanding a binomial.** The formulas for binomial coefficients give you an easy way to expand binomials, as demonstrated in the next four examples.

Example 4   Expanding a Binomial

Write the expansion for the expression $(x + 1)^3$.

Solution

The binomial coefficients from the third row of Pascal's Triangle are

$1, 3, 3, 1.$

Therefore, the expansion is as follows.

$$(x + 1)^3 = (1)x^3 + (3)x^2(1) + (3)x(1^2) + (1)(1^3)$$

$$= x^3 + 3x^2 + 3x + 1$$

✓ *Checkpoint* Now try Exercise 21.

To expand binomials representing *differences*, rather than sums, you alternate signs. Here are two examples.

$$(x - 1)^3 = x^3 - 3x^2 + 3x - 1$$

$$(x - 1)^4 = x^4 - 4x^3 + 6x^2 - 4x + 1$$

Example 5   Expanding Binomial Expressions

Write the expansion for each expression.

a. $(2x - 3)^4$

b. $(x - 2y)^4$

Solution

The binomial coefficients from the fourth row of Pascal's Triangle are

$1, 4, 6, 4, 1.$

Therefore, the expansions are as follows.

a. $(2x - 3)^4 = (1)(2x)^4 - (4)(2x)^3(3) + (6)(2x)^2(3^2) - (4)(2x)(3^3) + (1)(3^4)$

$$= 16x^4 - 96x^3 + 216x^2 - 216x + 81$$

b. $(x - 2y)^4 = (1)x^4 - (4)x^3(2y) + (6)x^2(2y)^2 - (4)x(2y)^3 + (1)(2y)^4$

$$= x^4 - 8x^3y + 24x^2y^2 - 32xy^3 + 16y^4$$

✓ *Checkpoint* Now try Exercise 29.

TECHNOLOGY TIP

You can use a graphing utility to check the expansion in Example 5(a) by graphing the original binomial expression and the expansion in the same viewing window. The graphs should coincide, as shown below.

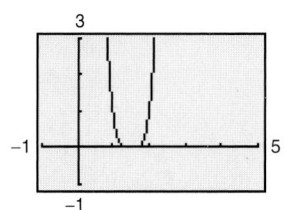

Example 6   Expanding a Binomial

Write the expansion for the expression $(x^2 + 4)^3$.

Solution

Use the third row of Pascal's Triangle, as follows.

$$(x^2 + 4)^3 = (1)(x^2)^3 + (3)(x^2)^2(4) + (3)x^2(4^2) + (1)(4^3)$$

$$= x^6 + 12x^4 + 48x^2 + 64$$

☑ *Checkpoint* Now try Exercise 35.

Sometimes you will need to find a specific term in a binomial expansion. Instead of writing out the entire expansion, you can use the fact that, from the Binomial Theorem, the $(r + 1)$st term is

$$_nC_r x^{n-r}y^r.$$

For example, if you wanted to find the third term of the expression in Example 6, you could use the above formula with $n = 3$ and $r = 2$ to obtain

$$_3C_2(x^2)^{3-2} \cdot 4^2 = 3(x^2) \cdot 16$$

$$= 48x^2.$$

Example 7   Finding a Term or Coefficient
in a Binomial Expansion

a. Find the sixth term of $(a + 2b)^8$.

b. Find the coefficient of the term a^6b^5 in the expansion of $(2a - 5b)^{11}$.

Solution

a. To find the sixth term in this binomial expansion, use $n = 8$ and $r = 5$ [the formula is for the $(r + 1)$st term, so r is one less than the number of the term that you are looking for] to get

$$_8C_5 a^{8-5}(2b)^5 = 56 \cdot a^3 \cdot (2b)^5$$

$$= 56(2^5)a^3b^5$$

$$= 1792a^3b^5.$$

b. In this case, $n = 11, r = 5, x = 2a$, and $y = -5b$. Substitute these values to obtain

$$_nC_r x^{n-r} y^r = {}_{11}C_5(2a)^6(-5b)^5$$

$$= (462)(64a^6)(-3125b^5)$$

$$= -92,400,000.$$

So, the coefficient is $-92,400,000$.

☑ *Checkpoint* Now try Exercise 47.

9.5   Exercises

Vocabulary Check

Fill in the blanks.

1. The coefficients of a binomial expansion are called _____ .
2. To find binomial coefficients you can use the _____ or _____ .
3. The notation used to denote a binomial coefficient is _____ or _____ .
4. When you write out the coefficients for a binomial that is raised to a power, you are _____ a _____ .

In Exercises 1–10, find the binomial coefficient.

1. $_7C_5$
2. $_9C_6$
3. $\binom{12}{0}$
4. $\binom{20}{20}$
5. $_{20}C_{15}$
6. $_{12}C_3$
7. $_{14}C_1$
8. $_{18}C_{17}$
9. $\binom{100}{98}$
10. $\binom{10}{7}$

In Exercises 11–16, use a graphing utility to find $_nC_r$.

11. $_{32}C_{28}$
12. $_{17}C_4$
13. $_{22}C_9$
14. $_{52}C_{47}$
15. $_{41}C_{36}$
16. $_{34}C_4$

In Exercises 17–20, use Pascal's Triangle to find the binomial coefficient.

17. $_7C_4$
18. $_6C_3$
19. $_8C_5$
20. $_5C_2$

In Exercises 21–42, use the Binomial Theorem to expand and simplify the expression.

21. $(x + 2)^4$
22. $(x + 1)^6$
23. $(a + 3)^3$
24. $(a + 2)^4$
25. $(y - 2)^4$
26. $(y - 2)^5$
27. $(x + y)^5$
28. $(x + y)^6$
29. $(3r + 2s)^6$
30. $(4x + 3y)^4$
31. $(x - y)^5$
32. $(2x - y)^5$
33. $(1 - 4x)^3$
34. $(5 - 2y)^3$
35. $(x^2 + y^2)^4$
36. $(x^2 + y^2)^6$
37. $\left(\dfrac{1}{x} + y\right)^5$
38. $\left(\dfrac{1}{x} + 2y\right)^6$

39. $2(x - 3)^4 + 5(x - 3)^2$
40. $3(x + 1)^5 + 4(x + 1)^3$
41. $-3(x - 2)^3 - 4(x + 1)^6$
42. $5(x + 2)^5 - 2(x - 1)^2$

In Exercises 43–46, expand the binomial by using Pascal's Triangle to determine the coefficients.

43. $(3t - s)^5$
44. $(3 - 2z)^4$
45. $(x + 2y)^5$
46. $(3y + 2)^5$

In Exercises 47–54, find the specified nth term in the expansion of the binomial.

47. $(x + 8)^{10},\ n = 4$
48. $(x - 5)^6,\ n = 7$
49. $(x - 6y)^5,\ n = 3$
50. $(x - 10z)^7,\ n = 4$
51. $(4x + 3y)^9,\ n = 8$
52. $(5a + 6b)^5,\ n = 5$
53. $(10x - 3y)^{12},\ n = 9$
54. $(7x + 2y)^{15},\ n = 8$

In Exercises 55–62, find the coefficient a of the term in the expansion of the binomial.

Binomial	Term
55. $(x + 3)^{12}$	ax^4
56. $(x + 4)^{12}$	ax^5
57. $(x - 2y)^{10}$	ax^8y^2
58. $(4x - y)^{10}$	ax^2y^8
59. $(3x - 2y)^9$	ax^6y^3
60. $(2x - 3y)^8$	ax^4y^4
61. $(x^2 + y)^{10}$	ax^8y^6
62. $(z^2 - 1)^{12}$	az^6

In Exercises 63–66, use the Binomial Theorem to expand and simplify the expression.

63. $\left(\sqrt{x} + 5\right)^4$
64. $\left(4\sqrt{t} - 1\right)^3$

65. $(x^{2/3} - y^{1/3})^3$ **66.** $(u^{3/5} + v^{1/5})^5$

∫ In Exercises 67–70, expand the expression in the difference quotient and simplify.

$$\frac{f(x+h) - f(x)}{h}$$

67. $f(x) = x^3$ **68.** $f(x) = x^4$

69. $f(x) = \sqrt{x}$ **70.** $f(x) = \dfrac{1}{x}$

In Exercises 71–76, use the Binomial Theorem to expand the complex number. Simplify your result.

71. $(1 + i)^4$ **72.** $(4 - i)^5$

73. $(2 - 3i)^6$ **74.** $\left(5 + \sqrt{-9}\right)^3$

75. $\left(-\dfrac{1}{2} + \dfrac{\sqrt{3}}{2}i\right)^3$ **76.** $\left(5 - \sqrt{3}i\right)^4$

Approximation In Exercises 77–80, use the Binomial Theorem to approximate the quantity accurate to three decimal places. For example, in Exercise 77, use the expansion

$$(1.02)^8 = (1 + 0.02)^8 = 1 + 8(0.02) + 28(0.02)^2 + \cdots.$$

77. $(1.02)^8$ **78.** $(2.005)^{10}$

79. $(2.99)^{12}$ **80.** $(1.98)^9$

Graphical Reasoning In Exercises 81 and 82, use a graphing utility to graph f and g in the same viewing window. What is the relationship between the two graphs? Use the Binomial Theorem to write the polynomial function g in standard form.

81. $f(x) = x^3 - 4x$, $g(x) = f(x + 3)$

82. $f(x) = -x^4 + 4x^2 - 1$, $g(x) = f(x - 5)$

Graphical Reasoning In Exercises 83 and 84, use a graphing utility to graph the functions in the given order and in the same viewing window. Compare the graphs. Which two functions have identical graphs and why?

83. (a) $f(x) = (1 - x)^3$

     (b) $g(x) = 1 - 3x$

     (c) $h(x) = 1 - 3x + 3x^2$

     (d) $p(x) = 1 - 3x + 3x^2 - x^3$

84. (a) $f(x) = \left(1 - \frac{1}{2}x\right)^4$

     (b) $g(x) = 1 - 2x + \frac{3}{2}x^2$

     (c) $h(x) = 1 - 2x + \frac{3}{2}x^2 - \frac{1}{2}x^3$

     (d) $p(x) = 1 - 2x + \frac{3}{2}x^2 - \frac{1}{2}x^3 + \frac{1}{16}x^4$

Probability In Exercises 85–88, consider n independent trials of an experiment in which each trial has two possible outcomes, success or failure. The probability of a success on each trial is p and the probability of a failure is $q = 1 - p$. In this context, the term $_nC_k \, p^k q^{n-k}$ in the expansion of $(p + q)^n$ gives the probability of k successes in the n trials of the experiment.

85. A fair coin is tossed seven times. To find the probability of obtaining four heads, evaluate the term

$$_7C_4\left(\tfrac{1}{2}\right)^4\left(\tfrac{1}{2}\right)^3$$

in the expansion of $\left(\frac{1}{2} + \frac{1}{2}\right)^7$.

86. The probability of a baseball player getting a hit during any given time at bat is $\frac{1}{4}$. To find the probability that the player gets three hits during the next 10 times at bat, evaluate the term

$$_{10}C_3\left(\tfrac{1}{4}\right)^3\left(\tfrac{3}{4}\right)^7$$

in the expansion of $\left(\frac{1}{4} + \frac{3}{4}\right)^{10}$.

87. The probability of a sales representative making a sale with any one customer is $\frac{1}{3}$. The sales representative makes eight contacts a day. To find the probability of making four sales, evaluate the term

$$_8C_4\left(\tfrac{1}{3}\right)^4\left(\tfrac{2}{3}\right)^4$$

in the expansion of $\left(\frac{1}{3} + \frac{2}{3}\right)^8$.

88. To find the probability that the sales representative in Exercise 87 makes four sales if the probability of a sale with any one customer is $\frac{1}{2}$, evaluate the term

$$_8C_4\left(\tfrac{1}{2}\right)^4\left(\tfrac{1}{2}\right)^4$$

in the expansion of $\left(\frac{1}{2} + \frac{1}{2}\right)^8$.

89. *Life Insurance* The average amount of life insurance per household f (in thousands of dollars) from 1985 through 2000 can be approximated by

$$f(t) = 0.018t^2 + 5.15t + 41.6, \ 5 \le t \le 20$$

where t represents the year, with $t = 5$ corresponding to 1985 (see figure). (Source: American Council of Life Insurance)

(a) You want to adjust the model so that $t = 5$ corresponds to 1995 rather than 1985. To do this, you shift the graph of f 10 units *to the left* and obtain $g(t) = f(t + 10)$. Write $g(t)$ in standard form.

(b) Use a graphing utility to graph f and g in the same viewing window.

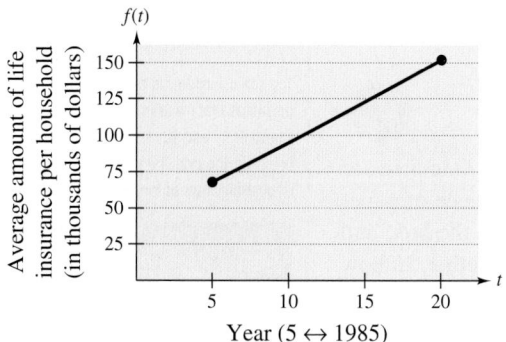

Figure for 89

90. ***Education***   The average tuition, room, and board costs f (in dollars) for undergraduates from 1980 through 2001 can be approximated by the model

$$f(t) = 3.65t^2 + 308.7t + 2846, \quad 0 \le t \le 21$$

where t represents the year, with $t = 0$ corresponding to 1980 (see figure).   (Source: U.S. Department of Education)

(a) You want to adjust the model so that $t = 0$ corresponds to 1990 rather than 1980. To do this, you shift the graph of f 10 units to the left and obtain $g(t) = f(t + 10)$. Write $g(t)$ in standard form.

(b) Use a graphing utility to graph f and g in the same viewing window.

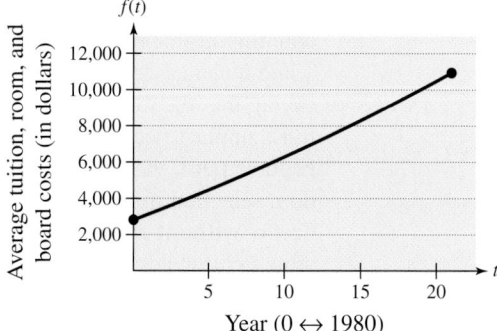

Synthesis

True or False?   **In Exercises 91 and 92, determine whether the statement is true or false. Justify your answer.**

91. One of the terms in the expansion of $(x - 2y)^{12}$ is $7920x^4y^8$.

92. The x^{10}-term and the x^{14}-term in the expansion of $(x^2 + 3)^{12}$ have identical coefficients.

93. ***Writing***   In your own words, explain how to form the rows of Pascal's Triangle.

94. Form rows 8–10 of Pascal's Triangle.

95. ***Think About It***   How do the expansions of $(x + y)^n$ and $(x - y)^n$ differ?

96. ***Error Analysis***   You are a math instructor and receive the following solutions from one of your students on a quiz. Find the error(s) in each solution and write a short paragraph discussing ways that your student could avoid the error(s) in the future.

(a) Find the second term in the expansion of $(2x - 3y)^5$.

$$5(2x)^4(3y)^2 = 720x^4y^2$$

(b) Find the fourth term in the expansion of $\left(\frac{1}{2}x + 7y\right)^6$.

$$_6C_4\left(\tfrac{1}{2}x\right)^2(7y)^4 = 9003.75x^2y^4$$

Proof   **In Exercises 97–100, prove the property for all integers r and n, where $0 \le r \le n$.**

97. $_nC_r = {_nC_{n-r}}$

98. $_nC_0 - {_nC_1} + {_nC_2} - \cdots \pm {_nC_n} = 0$

99. $_{n+1}C_r = {_nC_r} + {_nC_{r-1}}$

100. The sum of the numbers in the nth row of Pascal's Triangle is 2^n.

Review

In Exercises 101–104, describe the relationship between the graphs of f and g.

101. $g(x) = f(x) + 8$ 102. $g(x) = f(x - 3)$

103. $g(x) = f(-x)$ 104. $g(x) = -f(x)$

In Exercises 105 and 106, find the inverse of the matrix.

105. $\begin{bmatrix} -6 & 5 \\ -5 & 4 \end{bmatrix}$ 106. $\begin{bmatrix} 1.2 & -2.3 \\ -2 & 4 \end{bmatrix}$

9.6 Counting Principles

Simple Counting Problems

The last two sections of this chapter present a brief introduction to some of the basic counting principles and their application to probability. In the next section, you will see that much of probability has to do with counting the number of ways an event can occur.

Example 1   Selecting Pairs of Numbers at Random

Eight pieces of paper are numbered from 1 to 8 and placed in a box. One piece of paper is drawn from the box, its number is written down, and the piece of paper is *returned to the box*. Then, a second piece of paper is drawn from the box, and its number is written down. Finally, the two numbers are added together. In how many different ways can a sum of 12 be obtained?

Solution

To solve this problem, count the number of different ways that a sum of 12 can be obtained using two numbers from 1 to 8.

First number	4	5	6	7	8
Second number	8	7	6	5	4

From this list, you can see that a sum of 12 can occur in five different ways.

 Checkpoint Now try Exercise 7.

Example 2   Selecting Pairs of Numbers at Random

Eight pieces of paper are numbered from 1 to 8 and placed in a box. Two pieces of paper are drawn from the box *at the same time*, and the numbers on the pieces of paper are written down and totaled. In how many different ways can a sum of 12 be obtained?

Solution

To solve this problem, count the number of different ways that a sum of 12 can be obtained using two *different* numbers from 1 to 8.

First number	4	5	7	8
Second number	8	7	5	4

So, a sum of 12 can be obtained in four different ways.

 Checkpoint Now try Exercise 8.

What you should learn

- Solve simple counting problems.
- Use the Fundamental Counting Principle to solve more complicated counting problems.
- Use permutations to solve counting problems.
- Use combinations to solve counting problems.

Why you should learn it

You can use counting principles to solve counting problems that occur in real life. For instance, in Exercises 17 and 18 on page 749, you are asked to use counting principles to determine the number of possible ways of forming license plate numbers.

Tony Freeman/PhotoEdit

STUDY TIP

The difference between the counting problems in Examples 1 and 2 can be described by saying that the random selection in Example 1 occurs **with replacement,** whereas the random selection in Example 2 occurs **without replacement,** which eliminates the possibility of choosing two 6's.

The Fundamental Counting Principle

Examples 1 and 2 describe simple counting problems in which you can *list* each possible way that an event can occur. When it is possible, this is always the best way to solve a counting problem. However, some events can occur in so many different ways that it is not feasible to write out the entire list. In such cases, you must rely on formulas and counting principles. The most important of these is the **Fundamental Counting Principle.**

> **Fundamental Counting Principle**
>
> Let E_1 and E_2 be two events. The first event E_1 can occur in m_1 different ways. After E_1 has occurred, E_2 can occur in m_2 different ways. The number of ways that the two events can occur is $m_1 \cdot m_2$.

Example 3   Using the Fundamental Counting Principle

How many different pairs of letters from the English alphabet are possible?

Solution

There are two events in this situation. The first event is the choice of the first letter, and the second event is the choice of the second letter. Because the English alphabet contains 26 letters, it follows that the number of two-letter pairs is

$$26 \cdot 26 = 676.$$

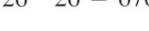 *Checkpoint* Now try Exercise 9.

Example 4   Using the Fundamental Counting Principle

Telephone numbers in the United States currently have 10 digits. The first three are the *area code* and the next seven are the *local telephone number*. How many different telephone numbers are possible within each area code? (Note that at this time, a local telephone number cannot begin with 0 or 1.)

Solution

Because the first digit cannot be 0 or 1, there are only eight choices for the first digit. For each of the other six digits, there are 10 choices.

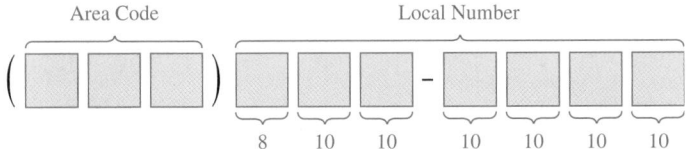

So, the number of local telephone numbers that are possible within each area code is $8 \cdot 10 \cdot 10 \cdot 10 \cdot 10 \cdot 10 \cdot 10 = 8{,}000{,}000$.

 Checkpoint Now try Exercise 21.

Permutations

One important application of the Fundamental Counting Principle is in determining the number of ways that n elements can be arranged (in order). An ordering of n elements is called a **permutation** of the elements.

Definition of Permutation

A **permutation** of n different elements is an ordering of the elements such that one element is first, one is second, one is third, and so on.

Example 5   Finding the Number of Permutations of n Elements

How many permutations are possible of the letters A, B, C, D, E, and F?

Solution

Consider the following reasoning.

First position:	Any of the *six* letters
Second position:	Any of the remaining *five* letters
Third position:	Any of the remaining *four* letters
Fourth position:	Any of the remaining *three* letters
Fifth position:	Any of the remaining *two* letters
Sixth position:	The *one* remaining letter

So, the number of choices for the six positions are as follows.

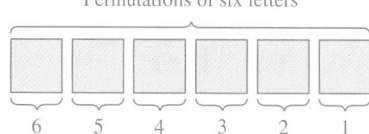

Permutations of six letters

The total number of permutations of the six letters is

$6! = 6 \cdot 5 \cdot 4 \cdot 3 \cdot 2 \cdot 1 = 720.$

✓ *Checkpoint* Now try Exercise 39.

Number of Permutations of n Elements

The number of permutations of n elements is given by

$$n \cdot (n - 1) \cdots 4 \cdot 3 \cdot 2 \cdot 1 = n!.$$

In other words, there are $n!$ different ways that n elements can be ordered.

It is useful, on occasion, to order a *subset* of a collection of elements rather than the entire collection. For example, you might want to choose and order r elements out of a collection of n elements. Such an ordering is called a **permutation of n elements taken r at a time.**

Example 6   *Counting Horse Race Finishes*

Eight horses are running in a race. In how many different ways can these horses come in first, second, and third? (Assume that there are no ties.)

Solution

Here are the different possibilities.

Win (first position):	*Eight* choices
Place (second position):	*Seven* choices
Show (third position):	*Six* choices

The numbers of choices for the three positions are as follows.

Different orders of horses

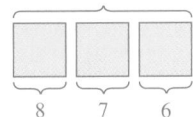

So, using the Fundamental Counting Principle, you can determine that there are

$$8 \cdot 7 \cdot 6 = 336$$

different ways in which the eight horses can come in first, second, and third.

✓ *Checkpoint* Now try Exercise 41.

Permutations of *n* Elements Taken *r* at a Time

The number of **permutations of *n* elements taken *r* at a time** is given by

$$_nP_r = \frac{n!}{(n-r)!}$$

$$= n(n-1)(n-2) \cdots (n-r+1).$$

Using this formula, you can rework Example 6 to find that the number of permutations of eight horses taken three at a time is

$$_8P_3 = \frac{8!}{5!}$$

$$= \frac{8 \cdot 7 \cdot 6 \cdot 5!}{5!}$$

$$= 336$$

which is the same answer obtained in the example.

TECHNOLOGY TIP Most graphing utilities are programmed to evaluate $_nP_r$. Figure 9.16 shows how one graphing utility evaluates the permutation $_8P_3$. For instructions on how to use the $_nP_r$ feature, see Appendix A; for specific keystrokes, go to the text website at *college.hmco.com*.

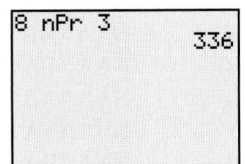

Figure 9.16

Remember that for permutations, order is important. So, if you are looking at the possible permutations of the letters A, B, C, and D taken three at a time, the permutations (A, B, D) and (B, A, D) would be counted as different because the *order* of the elements is different.

Suppose, however, that you are asked to find the possible permutations of the letters A, A, B, and C. The total number of permutations of the four letters would be $_4P_4 = 4!$. However, not all of these arrangements would be *distinguishable* because there are two A's in the list. To find the number of distinguishable permutations, you can use the following formula.

Distinguishable Permutations

Suppose a set of n objects has n_1 of one kind of object, n_2 of a second kind, n_3 of a third kind, and so on, with

$$n = n_1 + n_2 + n_3 + \cdots + n_k.$$

The number of **distinguishable permutations** of the n objects is given by

$$\frac{n!}{n_1! \cdot n_2! \cdot n_3! \cdots n_k!}.$$

Example 7   Distinguishable Permutations

In how many distinguishable ways can the letters in BANANA be written?

Solution

This word has six letters, of which three are A's, two are N's, and one is a B. So, the number of distinguishable ways in which the letters can be written is

$$\frac{6!}{3! \cdot 2! \cdot 1!} = \frac{6 \cdot 5 \cdot 4 \cdot 3!}{3! \cdot 2!} = 60.$$

The 60 different arrangements are as follows.

AAABNN	AAANBN	AAANNB	AABANN
AABNAN	AABNNA	AANABN	AANANB
AANBAN	AANBNA	AANNAB	AANNBA
ABAANN	ABANAN	ABANNA	ABNAAN
ABNANA	ABNNAA	ANAABN	ANAANB
ANABAN	ANABNA	ANANAB	ANANBA
ANBAAN	ANBANA	ANBNAA	ANNAAB
ANNABA	ANNBAA	BAAANN	BAANAN
BAANNA	BANAAN	BANANA	BANNAA
BNAAAN	BNAANA	BNANAA	BNNAAA
NAAABN	NAAANB	NAABAN	NAABNA
NAANAB	NAANBA	NABAAN	NABANA
NABNAA	NANAAB	NANABA	NANBAA
NBAAAN	NBAANA	NBANAA	NBNAAA
NNAAAB	NNAABA	NNABAA	NNBAAA

✓ *Checkpoint* Now try Exercise 45.

Combinations

When you count the number of possible permutations of a set of elements, order is important. As a final topic in this section, you will look at a method for selecting subsets of a larger set in which order *is not* important. Such subsets are called **combinations of *n* elements taken *r* at a time.** For instance, the combinations

$$\{A, B, C\} \quad \text{and} \quad \{B, A, C\}$$

are equivalent because both sets contain the same three elements, and the order in which the elements are listed is not important. So, you would count only one of the two sets. A common example of a combination is a card game in which the player is free to reorder the cards after they have been dealt.

Example 8   Combinations of *n* Elements Taken *r* at a Time

In how many different ways can three letters be chosen from the letters A, B, C, D, and E? (The order of the three letters is not important.)

Solution
The following subsets represent the different combinations of three letters that can be chosen from five letters.

$\{A, B, C\}$	$\{A, B, D\}$
$\{A, B, E\}$	$\{A, C, D\}$
$\{A, C, E\}$	$\{A, D, E\}$
$\{B, C, D\}$	$\{B, C, E\}$
$\{B, D, E\}$	$\{C, D, E\}$

From this list, you can conclude that there are 10 different ways in which three letters can be chosen from five letters.

 Checkpoint Now try Exercise 49.

Combination of *n* Elements Taken *r* at a Time

The number of **combinations of *n* elements taken *r* at a time** is given by

$$_nC_r = \frac{n!}{(n-r)!\,r!}.$$

Note that the formula for $_nC_r$ is the same one given for binomial coefficients. To see how this formula is used, solve the counting problem in Example 8. In that problem, you are asked to find the number of combinations of five elements taken three at a time. So, $n = 5$, $r = 3$, and the number of combinations is

$$_5C_3 = \frac{5!}{2!3!} = \frac{5 \cdot \overset{2}{\cancel{4}} \cdot 3!}{\cancel{2} \cdot 1 \cdot 3!} = 10$$

which is the same answer obtained in Example 8.

Example 9   Counting Card Hands

A standard poker hand consists of five cards dealt from a deck of 52. How many different poker hands are possible? (After the cards are dealt, the player may reorder them, so order is not important.)

Solution

You can find the number of different poker hands by using the formula for the number of combinations of 52 elements taken five at a time, as follows.

$$_{52}C_5 = \frac{52!}{47!5!}$$

$$= \frac{52 \cdot 51 \cdot 50 \cdot 49 \cdot 48 \cdot 47!}{5 \cdot 4 \cdot 3 \cdot 2 \cdot 1 \cdot 47!}$$

$$= 2{,}598{,}960$$

 *Checkpoint*   Now try Exercise 55.

Example 10   Forming a Team

You are forming a 12-member swim team from 10 girls and 15 boys. The team must consist of five girls and seven boys. How many different 12-member teams are possible?

Solution

There are $_{10}C_5$ ways of choosing five girls. There are $_{15}C_7$ ways of choosing seven boys. By the Fundamental Counting Principle, there are $_{10}C_5 \cdot {}_{15}C_7$ ways of choosing five girls and seven boys.

$$_{10}C_5 \cdot {}_{15}C_7 = \frac{10!}{5! \cdot 5!} \cdot \frac{15!}{8! \cdot 7!}$$

$$= 252 \cdot 6435$$

$$= 1{,}621{,}620$$

So, there are 1,621,620 12-member swim teams possible. You can verify this by using the $_nC_r$ feature of a graphing utility, as shown in Figure 9.17.

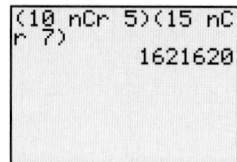

Figure 9.17

 Checkpoint   Now try Exercise 59.

9.6   Exercises

Vocabulary Check

Fill in the blanks.

1. The _____ states that if there are m_1 ways for one event to occur and m_2 ways for a second event to occur, then there are $m_1 \cdot m_2$ ways for both events to occur.

2. An ordering of n elements is called a _____ of the elements.

3. The number of permutations of n elements taken r at a time is given by the formula _____ .

4. The number of _____ of n objects is given by $\dfrac{n!}{n_1! \cdot n_2! \cdot n_3! \cdot \cdots \cdot n_k!}$.

5. When selecting subsets of a larger set in which order is not important, you are finding the number of _____ of n elements taken r at a time.

Random Selection   **In Exercises 1–8, determine the number of ways in which a computer can randomly generate one or more such integers from 1 through 12.**

1. An odd integer

2. An even integer

3. A prime integer

4. An integer that is greater than 6

5. An integer that is divisible by 4

6. An integer that is divisible by 3

7. Two integers whose sum is 8

8. Two distinct integers whose sum is 8

9. *Consumer Awareness*   A customer can choose one of four amplifiers, one of six compact disc players, and one of five speaker models for an entertainment system. Determine the number of possible system configurations.

10. *Consumer Awareness*   A customer in a computer store can choose one of four monitors, one of two keyboards, and one of three computers. If all the choices are compatible, determine the number of possible system configurations.

11. *Job Applicants*   A college needs two additional faculty members: a chemist and a statistician. In how many ways can these positions be filled if there are three applicants for the chemistry position and eight applicants for the statistics position?

12. *Course Schedule*   A college student is preparing a course schedule for the next semester. The student must select one of two mathematics courses, one of three science courses, and one of five courses from the social sciences and humanities. How many schedules are possible?

13. *True-False Exam*   In how many ways can a 10-question true-false exam be answered? (Assume that no questions are omitted.)

14. *True-False Exam*   In how many ways can a six-question true-false exam be answered? (Assume that no questions are omitted.)

15. *Recreation*   Four people are lining up for a ride on a toboggan, but only two of the four are willing to take the first position. With that constraint, in how many ways can the four people be seated on the toboggan?

16. *Travel*   Four people are taking a long trip in a four-seat car. Three of the people agree to share the driving. In how many different arrangements can the four people sit?

17. *License Plate*   In the state of Colorado the automobile license plates consist of a three-digit number followed by three letters. How many distinct license plates can be formed?

18. *License Plate*   In the state of Ohio the automobile license plates consist of two letters followed by a two-digit number, followed by two letters. How many distinct license plates can be formed?

19. *Three-Digit Numbers*   How many three-digit numbers can be formed under each condition?

    (a) The leading digit cannot be zero.

    (b) The leading digit cannot be zero and no repetition of digits is allowed.

(c) The leading digit cannot be zero and the number must be a multiple of 5.

(d) The number is at least 400.

20. Four-Digit Numbers How many four-digit numbers can be formed under each condition?

(a) The leading digit cannot be zero.

(b) The leading digit cannot be zero and no repetition of digits is allowed.

(c) The leading digit cannot be zero and the number must be less than 5000.

(d) The leading digit cannot be zero and the number must be even.

21. Telephone Numbers In 2003, the state of Nevada had two area codes. Using the information about telephone numbers given in Example 4, how many telephone numbers could Nevada's phone system have accommodated?

22. Telephone Numbers In 2003, the state of Kansas had four area codes. Using the information about telephone numbers given in Example 4, how many telephone numbers could Kansas's phone system have accommodated?

23. Entertainment Three couples have reserved seats in a row for a concert. In how many different ways can they be seated if

(a) there are no seating restrictions?

(b) the two members of each couple wish to sit together?

24. Single File In how many orders can five girls and three boys walk through a doorway single file if

(a) there are no restrictions?

(b) the girls walk through before the boys?

In Exercises 25–30, evaluate $_nP_r$ using the formula from this section.

25. $_4P_4$ **26.** $_5P_5$

27. $_8P_3$ **28.** $_{20}P_2$

29. $_5P_4$ **30.** $_7P_4$

In Exercises 31 and 32, solve for n.

31. $14 \cdot {}_nP_3 = {}_{n+2}P_4$ **32.** $_nP_5 = 18 \cdot {}_{n-2}P_4$

In Exercises 33–38, evaluate using a graphing utility.

33. $_{20}P_6$ **34.** $_{100}P_5$

35. $_{120}P_4$ **36.** $_{10}P_8$

37. $_{20}C_4$ **38.** $_{10}C_7$

39. Posing for a Photograph In how many ways can five children line up in a row?

40. Riding in a Car In how many ways can four people sit in a four-passenger car?

41. Choosing Officers From a pool of 12 candidates, the offices of president, vice-president, secretary, and treasurer will be filled. In how many ways can the offices be filled?

42. Manufacturing Four processes are involved in assembling a product, and they can be performed in any order. The management wants to test each order to determine which is the least time consuming. How many different orders will have to be tested?

In Exercises 43–46, find the number of distinguishable permutations of the group of letters.

43. A, A, G, E, E, E, M

44. B, B, B, T, T, T, T, T

45. A, L, G, E, B, R, A

46. M, I, S, S, I, S, S, I, P, P, I

47. Use the letters A, B, C, and D.

(a) Write all permutations of the letters.

(b) Write all permutations of the letters if the letters B and C must remain between the letters A and D.

48. Use the letters A, B, C, D, E, and F.

(a) Write all possible selections of two letters that can be formed from the letters. (The order of the two letters is not important.)

(b) Write all possible selections of three letters that can be formed from the letters. (The order of the three letters is not important.)

49. Forming an Experimental Group In order to conduct an experiment, four students are randomly selected from a class of 20. How many different groups of four students are possible?

50. Exam Questions You can answer any 12 questions from a total of 14 questions on an exam. In how many different ways can you select the questions?

51. Lottery In Maryland's Lotto game a player chooses six distinct numbers from 1 to 49. In how many ways can a player select the six numbers?

52. Lottery In Connecticut's Cash 5 game a player chooses five distinct numbers from 1 to 35. In how many ways can a player select the five numbers?

53. **Geometry**   Three points that are not collinear determine three lines. How many lines are determined by nine points, no three of which are collinear?

54. **Defective Units**   A shipment of 25 television sets contains three defective units. In how many ways can a vending company purchase four of these units and receive (a) all good units, (b) two good units, and (c) at least two good units?

55. **Poker Hand**   You are dealt five cards from an ordinary deck of 52 playing cards. In how many ways can you get a full house? (A full house consists of three of one kind and two of another. For example, 8-8-8-5-5 and K-K-K-10-10 are full houses.)

56. **Card Hand**   Five cards are chosen from a standard deck of 52 cards. How many five-card combinations contain two jacks and three aces?

57. **Job Applicants**   A clothing manufacturer interviews 12 people for four openings in the human resources department of the company. Five of the 12 people are women. If all 12 are qualified, in how many ways can the employer fill the four positions if (a) the selection is random and (b) exactly two women are selected?

58. **Job Applicants**   A law office interviews paralegals for 10 openings. There are 13 paralegals with two years of experience and 20 paralegals with one year of experience. How many combinations of seven paralegals with two years of experience and three paralegals with one year of experience are possible?

59. **Forming a Committee**   A six-member research committee is to be formed having one administrator, three faculty members, and two students. There are seven administrators, 12 faculty members, and 20 students in contention for the committee. How many six-member committees are possible?

60. **Interpersonal Relationships**   The number of possible interpersonal relationships increases dramatically as the size of a group increases. Determine the number of different two-person relationships that are possible in a group of people of size (a) 3, (b) 8, (c) 12, and (d) 20.

Geometry   In Exercises 61–64, find the number of diagonals of the polygon. (A line segment connecting any two nonadjacent vertices is called a *diagonal* of a polygon.)

61. Pentagon

62. Hexagon

63. Octagon

64. Decagon

Synthesis

True or False?   **In Exercises 65 and 66, determine whether the statement is true or false. Justify your answer.**

65. The number of pairs of letters that can be formed from any of the first 13 letters in the alphabet (A–M), where repetitions are allowed, is an example of a permutation.

66. The number of permutations of n elements can be derived by using the Fundamental Counting Principle.

67. **Think About It**   Can your calculator evaluate $_{100}P_{80}$? If not, explain why.

68. **Writing**   Explain in your own words the meaning of $_nP_r$.

69. What is the relationship between $_nC_r$ and $_nC_{n-r}$?

70. Without calculating the numbers, determine which of the following is greater. Explain.

    (a) The number of combinations of 10 elements taken six at a time

    (b) The number of permutations of 10 elements taken six at a time

Proof   **In Exercises 71–74, prove the identity.**

71. $_nP_{n-1} = {_nP_n}$

72. $_nC_n = {_nC_0}$

73. $_nC_{n-1} = {_nC_1}$

74. $_nC_r = \dfrac{_nP_r}{r!}$

Review

In Exercises 75–78, solve the equation. Round your answer to three decimal places, if necessary.

75. $\sqrt{x-3} = x - 6$

76. $\dfrac{4}{t} + \dfrac{3}{2t} = 1$

77. $\log_2(x-3) = 5$

78. $e^{x/3} = 16$

In Exercises 79–82, use Cramer's Rule to solve the system of equations.

79. $\begin{cases} -5x + 3y = -14 \\ 7x - 2y = 2 \end{cases}$

80. $\begin{cases} 8x + y = 35 \\ 6x + 2y = 10 \end{cases}$

81. $\begin{cases} -3x - 4y = -1 \\ 9x + 5y = -4 \end{cases}$

82. $\begin{cases} 10x - 11y = -74 \\ -8x - 4y = 8 \end{cases}$

9.7 Probability

The Probability of an Event

Any happening whose result is uncertain is called an **experiment.** The possible results of the experiment are **outcomes,** the set of all possible outcomes of the experiment is the **sample space** of the experiment, and any subcollection of a sample space is an **event.**

For instance, when a six-sided die is tossed, the sample space can be represented by the numbers 1 through 6. For this experiment, each of the outcomes is *equally likely.*

To describe a sample space in such a way that each outcome is equally likely, you must sometimes distinguish between or among various outcomes in ways that appear artificial. Example 1 illustrates such a situation.

Example 1   Finding the Sample Space

Find the sample space for each of the following.

a. One coin is tossed.

b. Two coins are tossed.

c. Three coins are tossed.

Solution

a. Because the coin will land either heads up (denoted by H) or tails up (denoted by T), the sample space is

$$S = \{H, T\}.$$

b. Because either coin can land heads up or tails up, the possible outcomes are as follows.

   HH = heads up on both coins

   HT = heads up on first coin and tails up on second coin

   TH = tails up on first coin and heads up on second coin

   TT = tails up on both coins

So, the sample space is

$$S = \{HH, HT, TH, TT\}.$$

Note that this list distinguishes between the two cases HT and TH, even though these two outcomes appear to be similar.

c. Following the notation of part (b), the sample space is

$$S = \{HHH, HHT, HTH, HTT, THH, THT, TTH, TTT\}.$$

Note that this list distinguishes between the cases HHT, HTH, and THH, and between the cases HTT, THT, and TTH.

✓ *Checkpoint* Now try Exercise 1.

What you should learn

● Find probabilities of events.

● Find probabilities of mutually exclusive events.

● Find probabilities of independent events.

● Find probabilities of complements of events.

Why you should learn it

You can use probability to solve a variety of problems that occur in real life. For instance, in Exercise 31 on page 761, you are asked to use probability to help analyze the age distribution of unemployed workers.

Tony Freeman/PhotoEdit

To calculate the probability of an event, count the number of outcomes in the event and in the sample space. The *number of outcomes* in event E is denoted by $n(E)$, and the number of outcomes in the sample space S is denoted by $n(S)$. The probability that event E will occur is given by $n(E)/n(S)$.

The Probability of an Event

If an event E has $n(E)$ equally likely outcomes and its sample space S has $n(S)$ equally likely outcomes, the **probability** of event E is given by

$$P(E) = \frac{n(E)}{n(S)}.$$

Because the number of outcomes in an event must be less than or equal to the number of outcomes in the sample space, the probability of an event must be a number from 0 to 1, inclusive. That is,

$$0 \le P(E) \le 1,$$

as indicated in Figure 9.18. If $P(E) = 0$, event E *cannot occur*, and E is called an **impossible event**. If $P(E) = 1$, event E *must occur*, and E is called a **certain event**.

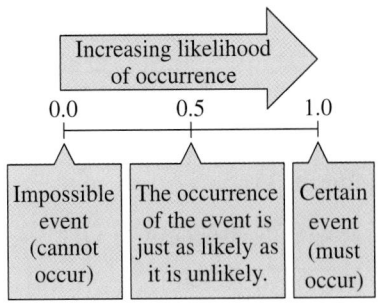

Figure 9.18

Example 2   Finding the Probability of an Event

a. Two coins are tossed. What is the probability that both land heads up?

b. A card is drawn from a standard deck of playing cards. What is the probability that it is an ace?

Solution

a. Following the procedure in Example 1(b), let

$$E = \{HH\}$$

and

$$S = \{HH, HT, TH, TT\}.$$

The probability of getting two heads is

$$P(E) = \frac{n(E)}{n(S)} = \frac{1}{4}.$$

b. Because there are 52 cards in a standard deck of playing cards and there are four aces (one of each suit), the probability of drawing an ace is

$$P(E) = \frac{n(E)}{n(S)}$$

$$= \frac{4}{52} = \frac{1}{13}.$$

✓ *Checkpoint* Now try Exercise 7.

Example 3   Finding the Probability of an Event

Two six-sided dice are tossed. What is the probability that a total of 7 is rolled? (See Figure 9.19.)

Solution

Because there are six possible outcomes on each die, you can use the Fundamental Counting Principle to conclude that there are $6 \cdot 6 = 36$ different outcomes when two dice are tossed. To find the probability of rolling a total of 7, you must first count the number of ways this can occur.

Figure 9.19

First die	1	2	3	4	5	6
Second die	6	5	4	3	2	1

So, a total of 7 can be rolled in six ways, which means that the probability of rolling a 7 is

$$P(E) = \frac{n(E)}{n(S)} = \frac{6}{36} = \frac{1}{6}.$$

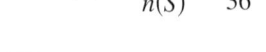 *Checkpoint*   Now try Exercise 15.

You could have written out each sample space in Examples 2 and 3 and simply counted the outcomes in the desired events. For larger sample spaces, however, using the counting principles discussed in Section 9.6 should save you time.

Example 4   Finding the Probability of an Event

Twelve-sided dice, as shown in Figure 9.20, can be constructed (in the shape of regular dodecahedrons) such that each of the numbers from 1 to 6 appears twice on each die. Prove that these dice can be used in any game requiring ordinary six-sided dice without changing the probabilities of different outcomes.

Solution

For an ordinary six-sided die, each of the numbers 1, 2, 3, 4, 5, and 6 occurs only once, so the probability of any particular number coming up is

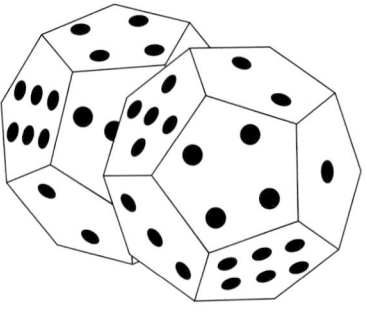

Figure 9.20

$$P(E) = \frac{n(E)}{n(S)} = \frac{1}{6}.$$

For a 12-sided die, each number occurs twice, so the probability of any particular number coming up is

$$P(E) = \frac{n(E)}{n(S)} = \frac{2}{12} = \frac{1}{6}.$$

 Checkpoint   Now try Exercise 17.

Example 5   The Probability of Winning a Lottery

In Delaware's Lotto game, a player chooses six different numbers from 1 to 38. If these six numbers match the six numbers drawn (in any order) by the lottery commission, the player wins (or shares) the top prize. What is the probability of winning the top prize if the player buys one ticket?

Solution

To find the number of elements in the sample space, use the formula for the number of combinations of 38 elements taken six at a time.

$$n(S) = {}_{38}C_6$$

$$= \frac{38 \cdot 37 \cdot 36 \cdot 35 \cdot 34 \cdot 33}{6 \cdot 5 \cdot 4 \cdot 3 \cdot 2 \cdot 1} = 2{,}760{,}681$$

If a person buys only one ticket, the probability of winning is

$$P(E) = \frac{n(E)}{n(S)} = \frac{1}{2{,}760{,}681}.$$

✓ *Checkpoint* Now try Exercise 19.

Example 6   Random Selection

The numbers of colleges and universities in various regions of the United States in 2001 are shown in Figure 9.21. One institution is selected at random. What is the probability that the institution is in one of the three southern regions?   (Source: U.S. National Center for Education Statistics)

Solution

From the figure, the total number of colleges and universities is 4178. Because there are $383 + 274 + 687 = 1344$ colleges and universities in the three southern regions, the probability that the institution is in one of these regions is

$$P(E) = \frac{n(E)}{n(S)} = \frac{1344}{4178} \approx 0.322.$$

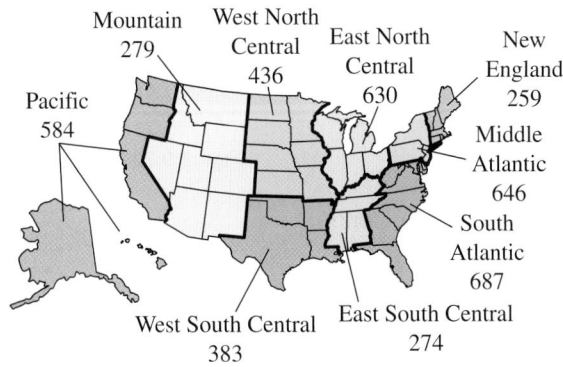

Figure 9.21

✓ *Checkpoint* Now try Exercise 31.

Mutually Exclusive Events

Two events A and B (from the same sample space) are **mutually exclusive** if A and B have no outcomes in common. In the terminology of sets, the intersection of A and B is the empty set, which is expressed as

$$P(A \cap B) = 0.$$

For instance, if two dice are tossed, the event A of rolling a total of 6 and the event B of rolling a total of 9 are mutually exclusive. To find the probability that one or the other of two mutually exclusive events will occur, you can *add* their individual probabilities.

Probability of the Union of Two Events

If A and B are events in the same sample space, the probability of A *or* B occurring is given by

$$P(A \cup B) = P(A) + P(B) - P(A \cap B).$$

If A and B are mutually exclusive, then

$$P(A \cup B) = P(A) + P(B).$$

Example 7   The Probability of a Union

One card is selected from a standard deck of 52 playing cards. What is the probability that the card is either a heart or a face card?

Solution

Because the deck has 13 hearts, the probability of selecting a heart (event A) is

$$P(A) = \frac{13}{52}.$$

Similarly, because the deck has 12 face cards, the probability of selecting a face card (event B) is

$$P(B) = \frac{12}{52}.$$

Because three of the cards are hearts and face cards (see Figure 9.22), it follows that

$$P(A \cap B) = \frac{3}{52}.$$

Finally, applying the formula for the probability of the union of two events, you can conclude that the probability of selecting a heart or a face card is

$$P(A \cup B) = P(A) + P(B) - P(A \cap B)$$

$$= \frac{13}{52} + \frac{12}{52} - \frac{3}{52} = \frac{22}{52} \approx 0.423.$$

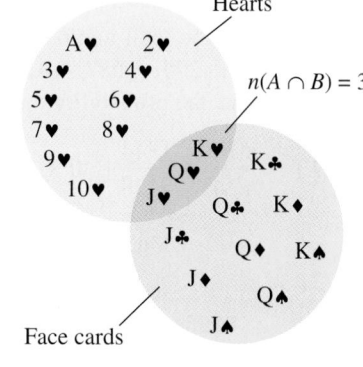

Figure 9.22

✅ *Checkpoint* Now try Exercise 43.

Example 8   Probability of Mutually Exclusive Events

The personnel department of a company has compiled data on the number of employees who have been with the company for various periods of time. The results are shown in the table.

Years of service	Number of employees
0–4	157
5–9	89
10–14	74
15–19	63
20–24	42
25–29	38
30–34	37
35–39	21
40–44	8

If an employee is chosen at random, what is the probability that the employee has (a) 4 or fewer years of service and (b) 9 or fewer years of service?

Solution

a. To begin, add the number of employees and find that the total is 529. Next, let event A represent choosing an employee with 0 to 4 years of service. Then the probability of choosing an employee who has 4 or fewer years of service is

$$P(A) = \frac{157}{529} \approx 0.297.$$

b. Let event B represent choosing an employee with 5 to 9 years of service. Then

$$P(B) = \frac{89}{529}.$$

Because event A from part (a) and event B have no outcomes in common, you can conclude that these two events are mutually exclusive and that

$$P(A \cup B) = P(A) + P(B)$$

$$= \frac{157}{529} + \frac{89}{529}$$

$$= \frac{246}{529}$$

$$\approx 0.465.$$

So, the probability of choosing an employee who has 9 or fewer years of service is about 0.465.

✓ *Checkpoint* Now try Exercise 45.

Independent Events

Two events are **independent** if the occurrence of one has no effect on the occurrence of the other. For instance, rolling a total of 12 with two six-sided dice has no effect on the outcome of future rolls of the dice. To find the probability that two independent events will occur, *multiply* the probabilities of each.

Probability of Independent Events

If A and B are **independent events,** the probability that both A and B will occur is given by

$$P(A \text{ and } B) = P(A) \cdot P(B).$$

Example 9   Probability of Independent Events

A random number generator on a computer selects three integers from 1 to 20. What is the probability that all three numbers are less than or equal to 5?

Solution

The probability of selecting a number from 1 to 5 is

$$P(A) = \frac{5}{20} = \frac{1}{4}.$$

So, the probability that all three numbers are less than or equal to 5 is

$$P(A) \cdot P(A) \cdot P(A) = \left(\frac{1}{4}\right)\left(\frac{1}{4}\right)\left(\frac{1}{4}\right) = \frac{1}{64}.$$

 *Checkpoint* Now try Exercise 46.

Example 10   Probability of Independent Events

In 2001, approximately 65% of the population of the United States was 25 years old or older. In a survey, 10 people were chosen at random from the population. What is the probability that all 10 were 25 years old or older? (Source: U.S. Census Bureau)

Solution

Let A represent choosing a person who was 25 years old or older. The probability of choosing a person who was 25 years old or older is 0.65, the probability of choosing a second person who was 25 years old or older is 0.65, and so on. Because these events are independent, you can conclude that the probability that all 10 people were 25 years old or older is

$$[P(A)]^{10} = (0.65)^{10} \approx 0.0135.$$

 Checkpoint Now try Exercise 47.

The Complement of an Event

The **complement of an event** A is the collection of all outcomes in the sample space that are *not* in A. The complement of event A is denoted by A'. Because $P(A \text{ or } A') = 1$ and because A and A' are mutually exclusive, it follows that $P(A) + P(A') = 1$. So, the probability of A' is given by

$$P(A') = 1 - P(A).$$

For instance, if the probability of *winning* a game is

$$P(A) = \frac{1}{4}$$

then the probability of *losing* the game is

$$P(A') = 1 - \frac{1}{4}$$

$$= \frac{3}{4}.$$

> **Exploration**
>
> You are in a class with 22 other people. What is the probability that at least two out of the 23 people will have a birthday on the same day of the year? What if you know the probability of everyone having the same birthday? Do you think this information would help you to find the answer?

Probability of a Complement

Let A be an event and let A' be its complement. If the probability of A is $P(A)$, then the probability of the complement is given by

$$P(A') = 1 - P(A).$$

Example 11   Finding the Probability of a Complement

A manufacturer has determined that a machine averages one faulty unit for every 1000 it produces. What is the probability that an order of 200 units will have one or more faulty units?

Solution

To solve this problem as stated, you would need to find the probabilities of having exactly one faulty unit, exactly two faulty units, exactly three faulty units, and so on. However, using complements, you can simply find the probability that all units are perfect and then subtract this value from 1. Because the probability that any given unit is perfect is 999/1000, the probability that all 200 units are perfect is

$$P(A) = \left(\frac{999}{1000}\right)^{200}$$

$$\approx 0.8186.$$

So, the probability that at least one unit is faulty is

$$P(A') = 1 - P(A)$$

$$\approx 0.1814.$$

 Checkpoint Now try Exercise 49.

9.7   Exercises

Vocabulary Check

In Exercises 1–7, fill in the blanks.

1. An _____ is an event whose result is uncertain, and the possible results of the event are called _____ .

2. The set of all possible outcomes of an experiment is called the _____ .

3. To determine the _____ of an event, you can use the formula $P(E) = \dfrac{n(E)}{n(S)}$, where $n(E)$ is the number of outcomes in the event and $n(S)$ is the number of outcomes in the sample space.

4. If $P(E) = 0$, then E is an _____ event, and if $P(E) = 1$, then E is a _____ event.

5. If two events from the same sample space have no outcomes in common, then the two events are _____ .

6. If the occurrence of one event has no effect on the occurrence of a second event, then the events are _____ .

7. The _____ of an event A is the collection of all outcomes in the sample space that are not in A.

8. Match the probability formula with the correct probability name.

   (a) Probability of the union of two events   (i) $P(A \cup B) = P(A) + P(B)$

   (b) Probability of mutually exclusive events   (ii) $P(A') = 1 - P(A)$

   (c) Probability of independent events   (iii) $P(A \cup B) = P(A) + P(B) - P(A \cap B)$

   (d) Probability of a complement   (iv) $P(A \text{ and } B) = P(A) \cdot P(B)$

In Exercises 1–6, determine the sample space for the experiment.

1. A coin and a six-sided die are tossed.

2. A six-sided die is tossed twice and the sum of the results is recorded.

3. A taste tester has to rank three varieties of orange juice, A, B, and C, according to preference.

4. Two marbles are selected (without replacement) from a sack containing two red marbles, two blue marbles, and one yellow marble. The color of each marble is recorded.

5. Two county supervisors are selected from five supervisors, A, B, C, D, and E, to study a recycling plan.

6. A sales representative makes presentations about a product in three homes per day. In each home there may be a sale (denote by S) or there may be no sale (denote by F).

Tossing a Coin   **In Exercises 7–10, find the probability for the experiment of tossing a coin three times. Use the sample space** $S = \{HHH, HHT, HTH, HTT, THH, THT, TTH, TTT\}$.

7. The probability of getting exactly two tails

8. The probability of getting a head on the first toss

9. The probability of getting at least one head

10. The probability of getting at least two heads

Drawing a Card   **In Exercises 11–14, find the probability for the experiment of selecting one card from a standard deck of 52 playing cards.**

11. The card is a face card.

12. The card is not a face card.

13. The card is a red face card.

14. The card is an 8 or lower. (Aces are low.)

Tossing a Die   **In Exercises 15–18, find the probability for the experiment of tossing a six-sided die twice.**

15. The sum is 5.

16. The sum is at least 8.

17. The sum is less than 11.

18. The sum is odd or prime.

Drawing Marbles   In Exercises 19–22, find the probability for the experiment of drawing two marbles (without replacement) from a bag containing one green, two yellow, and three red marbles.

19. Both marbles are red.

20. Both marbles are yellow.

21. Neither marble is yellow.

22. The marbles are of different colors.

In Exercises 23–26, you are given the probability that an event *will* happen. Find the probability that the event *will not* happen.

23. $P(E) = 0.8$ **24.** $P(E) = 0.29$

25. $P(E) = \frac{1}{3}$ **26.** $P(E) = \frac{5}{6}$

In Exercises 27–30, you are given the probability that an event *will not* happen. Find the probability that the event *will* happen.

27. $P(E') = 0.12$ **28.** $P(E') = 0.84$

29. $P(E') = \frac{13}{20}$ **30.** $P(E') = \frac{61}{100}$

31. *Graphical Reasoning*   In 2001 there were approximately 6.7 million unemployed workers in the United States. The circle graph shows the age profile of these unemployed workers. (Source: U.S. Bureau of Labor Statistics)

(a) Estimate the number of unemployed workers in the age group 16–19.

(b) What is the probability that a person selected at random from the population of unemployed workers is in the 25–44 age group?

(c) What is the probability that a person selected at random from the population of unemployed workers is in the 45–64 age group?

(d) What is the probability that a person selected at random from the population of unemployed workers is 45 or over?

Ages of Unemployed Workers

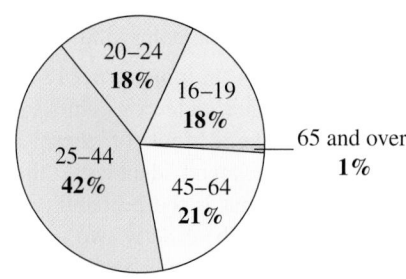

32. *Graphical Reasoning*   The circle graph shows the number of children of the 42 U.S. presidents. (Source: Time Almanac 2003)

(a) Determine the number of presidents who had no children.

(b) Determine the number of presidents who had four children.

(c) What is the probability that a president selected at random had five or more children?

(d) What is the probability that a president selected at random had three children?

Children of U.S. Presidents

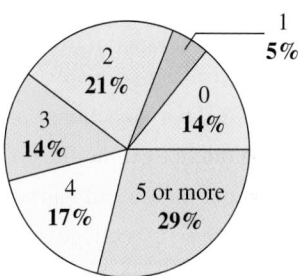

33. *Data Analysis*   One hundred college students were interviewed to determine their political-party affiliations and whether they favored a balanced-budget amendment to the Constitution. The results of the study are listed in the table, where D represents Democrat and R represents Republican.

	D	R	Total
Favor	23	32	55
Oppose	25	9	34
Unsure	7	4	11
Total	55	45	100

A person is selected at random from the sample. Find the probability that the described person is selected.

(a) A person who doesn't favor the amendment

(b) A Republican

(c) A Democrat who favors the amendment

34. *Data Analysis* A study of the effectiveness of a flu vaccine was conducted with a sample of 500 people. Some participants in the study were given no vaccine, some were given one injection, and some were given two injections. The results of the study are given in the table.

	Flu	No flu	Total
No vaccine	7	149	156
One injection	2	52	54
Two injections	13	277	290
Total	22	478	500

A person is selected at random from the sample. Find each probability.

(a) The person had two injections.

(b) The person did not get the flu.

(c) The person got the flu and had one injection.

35. *Alumni Association* A college sends a survey to selected members of the class of 2004. Of the 1254 people who graduated that year, 672 are women, of whom 124 went on to graduate school. Of the 582 male graduates, 198 went on to graduate school. An alumni member is selected at random. What is the probability that the person is (a) female, (b) male, and (c) female and did not attend graduate school?

36. *Education* In a high school graduating class of 128 students, 52 are on the honor roll. Of these, 48 are going on to college; of the other 76 students, 56 are going on to college. A student is selected at random from the class. What is the probability that the person chosen is (a) going to college, (b) not going to college, and (c) not going to college and on the honor roll?

37. *Election* Taylor, Moore, and Perez are candidates for public office. It is estimated that Moore and Perez have about the same probability of winning, and Taylor is believed to be twice as likely to win as either of the others. Find the probability of each candidate's winning the election.

38. *Payroll Error* The employees of a company work in six departments: 31 are in sales, 54 are in research, 42 are in marketing, 20 are in engineering, 47 are in finance, and 58 are in production. One employee's paycheck is lost. What is the probability that the employee works in the research department?

In Exercises 39–46, the sample spaces are large and you should use the counting principles discussed in Section 9.6.

39. *Preparing for a Test* A class is given a list of 20 study problems from which 10 will be chosen as part of an upcoming exam. A given student knows how to solve 15 of the problems. Find the probability that the student will be able to answer (a) all 10 questions on the exam, (b) exactly 8 questions on the exam, and (c) at least 9 questions on the exam.

40. *Payroll Mix-Up* Five paychecks and envelopes are addressed to five different people. The paychecks are randomly inserted into the envelopes. What is the probability that (a) exactly one paycheck is inserted in the correct envelope and (b) at least one paycheck is inserted in the correct envelope?

41. *Game Show* On a game show you are given five digits to arrange in the proper order to form the price of a car. If you are correct, you win the car. What is the probability of winning, given the following conditions?

(a) You guess the position of each digit.

(b) You know the first digit and guess the others.

42. *Card Game* The deck of a card game is made up of 108 cards. Twenty-five each are red, yellow, blue, and green, and eight are wild cards. Each player is randomly dealt a seven-card hand.

(a) What is the probability that a hand will contain exactly two wild cards?

(b) What is the probability that a hand will contain two wild cards, two red cards, and three blue cards?

43. *Drawing a Card* One card is selected at random from a standard deck of 52 playing cards. Find the probability that (a) the card is an even-numbered card, (b) the card is a heart or a diamond, and (c) the card is a nine or a face card.

44. *Poker Hand* Five cards are drawn from an ordinary deck of 52 playing cards. What is the probability of getting a full house? (A full house consists of three of one kind and two of another kind.)

45. *Defective Units* A shipment of 12 microwave ovens contains three defective units. A vending company has ordered four of these units, and because all are packaged identically, the selection will be random. What is the probability that (a) all four units are good, (b) exactly two units are good, and (c) at least two units are good?

46. *Random Number Generator*   Two integers from 1 through 40 are chosen by a random number generator. What is the probability that (a) the numbers are both even, (b) one number is even and one is odd, (c) both numbers are less than 30, and (d) the same number is chosen twice?

47. *Consumerism*   Suppose that the methods used by shoppers to pay for merchandise are as shown in the circle graph. Two shoppers are chosen at random. What is the probability that both shoppers paid for their purchases only in cash?

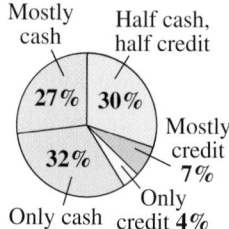

How Shoppers Pay
for Merchandise

48. *Flexible Work Hours*   In a survey, people were asked if they would prefer to work flexible hours—even if it meant slower career advancement—so they could spend more time with their families. The results of the survey are shown in the circle graph. Three people from the survey are chosen at random. What is the probability that all three people would prefer flexible work hours?

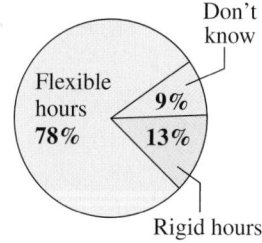

Flexible Work Hours

49. *Backup System*   A space vehicle has an independent backup system for one of its communication networks. The probability that either system will function satisfactorily for the duration of a flight is 0.985. What is the probability that during a given flight (a) both systems function satisfactorily, (b) at least one system functions satisfactorily, and (c) both systems fail?

50. *Backup Vehicle*   A fire company keeps two rescue vehicles to serve the community. Because of the demand on the vehicles and the chance of mechanical failure, the probability that a specific vehicle is available when needed is 90%. The availability of one vehicle is *independent* of the other. Find the probability that (a) both vehicles are available at a given time, (b) neither vehicle is available at a given time, and (c) at least one vehicle is available at a given time.

51. *Making a Sale*   A sales representative makes sales on approximately one-fifth of all calls. On a given day, the representative contacts six potential clients. What is the probability that a sale will be made with (a) all six contacts, (b) none of the contacts, and (c) at least one contact?

52. *A Boy or a Girl?*   Assume that the probability of the birth of a child of a particular sex is 50%. In a family with four children, what is the probability that (a) all the children are boys, (b) all the children are the same sex, and (c) there is at least one boy?

53. *Geometry*   You and a friend agree to meet at your favorite fast-food restaurant between 5:00 and 6:00 P.M. The one who arrives first will wait 15 minutes for the other, after which the first person will leave (see figure). What is the probability that the two of you will actually meet, assuming that your arrival times are random within the hour?

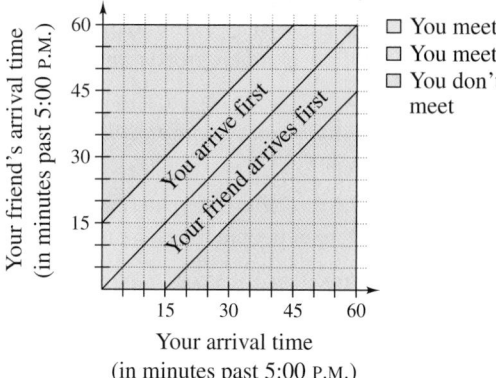

54. **Estimating π** A coin of diameter d is dropped onto a paper that contains a grid of squares d units on a side (see figure).

(a) Find the probability that the coin covers a vertex of one of the squares on the grid.

(b) Perform the experiment 100 times and use the results to approximate π.

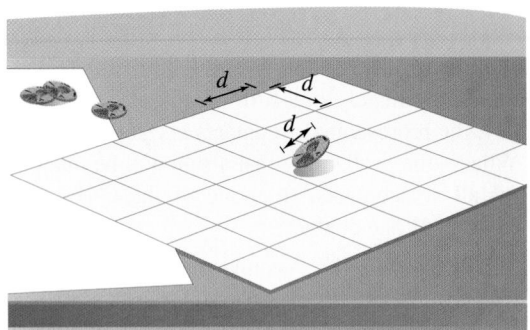

Synthesis

True or False? In Exercises 55 and 56, determine whether the statement is true or false. Justify your answer.

55. If the probability of an outcome in a sample space is 1, then the probability of the other outcomes in the sample space is 0.

56. Rolling a number less than 3 on a normal six-sided die has a probability of $\frac{1}{3}$. The complement of this event is to roll a number greater than 3, and its probability is $\frac{1}{2}$.

57. **Pattern Recognition and Exploration** Consider a group of n people.

(a) Explain why the following pattern gives the probability that the n people have distinct birthdays.

$$n = 2: \quad \frac{365}{365} \cdot \frac{364}{365} = \frac{365 \cdot 364}{365^2}$$

$$n = 3: \quad \frac{365}{365} \cdot \frac{364}{365} \cdot \frac{363}{365} = \frac{365 \cdot 364 \cdot 363}{365^3}$$

(b) Use the pattern in part (a) to write an expression for the probability that four people ($n = 4$) have distinct birthdays.

(c) Let P_n be the probability that the n people have distinct birthdays. Verify that this probability can be obtained recursively by

$$P_1 = 1 \quad \text{and} \quad P_n = \frac{365 - (n - 1)}{365} P_{n-1}.$$

(d) Explain why $Q_n = 1 - P_n$ gives the probability that at least two people in a group of n people have the same birthday.

(e) Use the results of parts (c) and (d) to complete the table.

n	10	15	20	23	30	40	50
P_n							
Q_n							

(f) How many people must be in a group so that the probability of at least two of them having the same birthday is greater than $\frac{1}{2}$? Explain.

58. **Think About It** The weather forecast indicates that the probability of rain is 40%. Explain what this means.

Review

In Exercises 59–62, solve the rational equation.

59. $\dfrac{2}{x - 5} = 4$

60. $\dfrac{3}{2x + 3} - 4 = \dfrac{-1}{2x + 3}$

61. $\dfrac{3}{x - 2} + \dfrac{x}{x + 2} = 1$

62. $\dfrac{2}{x} - \dfrac{5}{x - 2} = \dfrac{-13}{x^2 - 2x}$

In Exercises 63–66, solve the equation algebraically. Round your result to three decimal places.

63. $e^x + 7 = 35$

64. $200e^{-x} = 75$

65. $4 \ln 6x = 16$

66. $5 \ln 2x - 4 = 11$

In Exercises 67–70, evaluate $_nP_r$. Verify your result using a graphing utility.

67. $_5P_3$

68. $_{10}P_4$

69. $_{11}P_8$

70. $_9P_2$

In Exercises 71–74, evaluate $_nC_r$. Verify your result using a graphing utility.

71. $_6C_2$

72. $_9C_5$

73. $_{11}C_8$

74. $_{16}C_{13}$

9 Chapter Summary

What did you learn?

Section 9.1	Review Exercises
☐ Use sequence notation to write the terms of sequences.	1–8
☐ Use factorial notation.	9–12
☐ Use summation notation to write sums.	13–24
☐ Find sums of infinite series.	25–28
☐ Use sequences and series to model and solve real-life problems.	29, 30

Section 9.2	
☐ Recognize, write, and find the nth terms of arithmetic sequences.	31–44
☐ Find nth partial sums of arithmetic sequences.	45–50
☐ Use arithmetic sequences to model and solve real-life problems.	51, 52

Section 9.3	
☐ Recognize, write, and find the nth terms of geometric sequences.	53–68
☐ Find nth partial sums of geometric sequences.	69–76
☐ Find sums of infinite geometric series.	77–80
☐ Use geometric sequences to model and solve real-life problems.	81, 82

Section 9.4	
☐ Use mathematical induction to prove statements involving a positive integer n.	83–86
☐ Find the sums of powers of integers.	87–90
☐ Find finite differences of sequences.	91–94

Section 9.5	
☐ Use the Binomial Theorem to calculate binomial coefficients.	95–98
☐ Use Pascal's Triangle to calculate binomial coefficients.	99–102
☐ Use binomial coefficients to write binomial expansions.	103–108

Section 9.6	
☐ Solve simple counting problems.	109, 110
☐ Use the Fundamental Counting Principle to solve more complicated counting problems.	111, 112
☐ Use permutations to solve counting problems.	113–115
☐ Use combinations to solve counting problems.	116–118

Section 9.7	
☐ Find probabilities of events.	119, 120
☐ Find probabilities of mutually exclusive events.	121
☐ Find probabilities of independent events.	122, 123
☐ Find probabilities of complements of events.	124

9 Review Exercises

9.1 In Exercises 1–4, write the first five terms of the sequence. (Assume n begins with 1.)

1. $a_n = 2 + \dfrac{6}{n}$

2. $a_n = \dfrac{(-1)^n}{2n - 1}$

3. $a_n = \dfrac{72}{n!}$

4. $a_n = n(n - 1)$

In Exercises 5–8, use a graphing utility to graph the first 10 terms of the sequence (Assume n begins with 1.)

5. $a_n = \frac{3}{2}n$

6. $a_n = \dfrac{3n}{n + 2}$

7. $a_n = 4(0.4)^{n-1}$

8. $a_n = -8(0.5)^{n-1}$

In Exercises 9–12, simplify the factorial expression.

9. $\dfrac{18!}{20!}$

10. $\dfrac{10!}{8!}$

11. $\dfrac{2! \cdot 5!}{6!}$

12. $\dfrac{9! \cdot 6!}{6! \cdot 8!}$

In Exercises 13–20, find the sum.

13. $\displaystyle\sum_{i=1}^{6} 5$

14. $\displaystyle\sum_{k=2}^{5} 4k$

15. $\displaystyle\sum_{j=1}^{4} \dfrac{6}{j^2}$

16. $\displaystyle\sum_{i=1}^{8} \dfrac{i}{i + 1}$

17. $\displaystyle\sum_{k=1}^{10} 2k^3$

18. $\displaystyle\sum_{j=0}^{4} (j^2 + 1)$

19. $\displaystyle\sum_{n=0}^{10} (n^2 + 3)$

20. $\displaystyle\sum_{n=1}^{100} \left(\dfrac{1}{n} - \dfrac{1}{n + 1}\right)$

In Exercises 21–24, use sigma notation to write the sum. Then use a graphing utility to find the sum.

21. $\dfrac{1}{2(1)} + \dfrac{1}{2(2)} + \dfrac{1}{2(3)} + \cdots + \dfrac{1}{2(20)}$

22. $2(1^2) + 2(2^2) + 2(3^2) + \cdots + 2(9^2)$

23. $\dfrac{1}{2} + \dfrac{2}{3} + \dfrac{3}{4} + \cdots + \dfrac{9}{10}$

24. $1 - \dfrac{1}{3} + \dfrac{1}{9} - \dfrac{1}{27} + \cdots$

In Exercises 25–28, find (a) the fourth partial sum and (b) the sum of the infinite series.

25. $\displaystyle\sum_{k=1}^{\infty} \dfrac{5}{10^k}$

26. $\displaystyle\sum_{k=1}^{\infty} 8\left(\tfrac{1}{10}\right)^k$

27. $\displaystyle\sum_{k=1}^{\infty} 2\left(\tfrac{1}{100}\right)^k$

28. $\displaystyle\sum_{k=1}^{\infty} 7\left(\tfrac{1}{10}\right)^k$

29. *Compound Interest*   A deposit of \$2500 is made in an account that earns 8% interest compounded quarterly. The balance in the account after n quarters is given by

$$a_n = 2500\left(1 + \frac{0.08}{4}\right)^n, \qquad n = 1, 2, 3, \ldots$$

(a) Compute the first eight terms of this sequence.

(b) Find the balance in this account after 10 years by computing the 40th term of the sequence.

30. *Revenue*   The revenue a_n (in billions of dollars) for United Parcel Service, Inc. from 1997 to 2002 can be approximated by the model

$$a_n = -0.251n^2 + 6.58n - 11.5,$$

$$n = 7, 8, \ldots, 12$$

where n is the year, with $n = 7$ corresponding to 1997. Find the terms of this finite sequence and use a graphing utility to construct a bar graph that represents the sequence.   (Source: United Parcel Service, Inc.)

9.2 In Exercises 31–34, determine whether or not the sequence is arithmetic. If it is, find the common difference.

31. $5, 3, 1, -1, -3, \ldots$

32. $0, 1, 3, 6, 10, \ldots$

33. $\frac{1}{2}, 1, \frac{3}{2}, 2, \frac{5}{2}, \ldots$

34. $\frac{9}{9}, \frac{8}{9}, \frac{7}{9}, \frac{6}{9}, \frac{5}{9}, \ldots$

In Exercises 35–38, write the first five terms of the arithmetic sequence.

35. $a_1 = 3, \ d = 4$

36. $a_1 = 8, \ d = -2$

37. $a_4 = 10, \ a_{10} = 28$

38. $a_2 = 14, \ a_6 = 22$

In Exercises 39–42, write the first five terms of the arithmetic sequence. Find the common difference and write the nth term of the sequence as a function of n.

39. $a_1 = 35, \ a_{k+1} = a_k - 3$

40. $a_1 = 15, \quad a_{k+1} = a_k + \frac{5}{2}$

41. $a_1 = 9, \quad a_{k+1} = a_k + 7$

42. $a_1 = 100, \quad a_{k+1} = a_k - 5$

In Exercises 43 and 44, find a formula for a_n for the arithmetic sequence and find the sum of the first 20 terms of the sequence.

43. $a_1 = 100, \quad d = -3$ **44.** $a_1 = 10, \quad a_3 = 28$

In Exercises 45–48, find the partial sum. Use a graphing utility to verify your result.

45. $\sum_{j=1}^{10} (2j - 3)$

46. $\sum_{j=1}^{8} (20 - 3j)$

47. $\sum_{k=1}^{11} \left(\frac{2}{3}k + 4\right)$

48. $\sum_{k=1}^{25} \left(\frac{3k+1}{4}\right)$

49. Find the sum of the first 100 positive multiples of 5.

50. Find the sum of the integers from 20 to 80 (inclusive).

51. *Job Offer* The starting salary for an accountant is $34,000 with a guaranteed salary increase of $2250 per year for the first 4 years of employment. Determine (a) the salary during the fifth year and (b) the total compensation through 5 full years of employment.

52. *Baling Hay* In his first trip baling hay around a field, a farmer makes 123 bales. In his second trip he makes 11 fewer bales. Because each trip is shorter than the preceding trip, the farmer estimates that the same pattern will continue. Estimate the total number of bales made if there are another six trips around the field.

9.3 In Exercises 53–56, determine whether or not the sequence is geometric. If it is, find the common ratio.

53. $5, 10, 20, 40, \ldots$ **54.** $54, -18, 6, -2, \ldots$

55. $\frac{1}{2}, \frac{2}{3}, \frac{3}{4}, \frac{4}{5}, \ldots$ **56.** $\frac{1}{3}, -\frac{2}{3}, \frac{4}{3}, -\frac{8}{3}, \ldots$

In Exercises 57–60, write the first five terms of the geometric sequence.

57. $a_1 = 4, \ r = -\frac{1}{4}$ **58.** $a_1 = 2, \ r = 2$

59. $a_1 = 9, \ a_3 = 4$ **60.** $a_1 = 2, \ a_3 = 12$

In Exercises 61–64, write the first five terms of the geometric sequence. Find the common ratio and write the nth term of the sequence as a function of n.

61. $a_1 = 120, \quad a_{k+1} = \frac{1}{3}a_k$

62. $a_1 = 200, \quad a_{k+1} = 0.1a_k$

63. $a_1 = 25, \quad a_{k+1} = -\frac{3}{5}a_k$

64. $a_1 = 18, \quad a_{k+1} = \frac{5}{3}a_k$

In Exercises 65–68, write an expression for the nth term of the geometric sequence and find the sum of the first 20 terms of the sequence.

65. $a_1 = 16, \quad a_2 = -8$ **66.** $a_3 = 6, \quad a_4 = 1$

67. $a_1 = 100, \quad r = 1.05$ **68.** $a_1 = 5, \quad r = 0.2$

In Exercises 69–76, find the sum. Use a graphing utility to verify your result.

69. $\sum_{i=1}^{7} 2^{i-1}$

70. $\sum_{i=1}^{5} 3^{i-1}$

71. $\sum_{n=1}^{7} (-4)^{n-1}$

72. $\sum_{n=1}^{4} 12\left(-\frac{1}{2}\right)^{n-1}$

73. $\sum_{n=0}^{4} 250(1.02)^n$

74. $\sum_{n=0}^{5} 400(1.08)^n$

75. $\sum_{i=1}^{10} 10\left(\frac{3}{5}\right)^{i-1}$

76. $\sum_{i=1}^{15} 20(0.2)^{i-1}$

In Exercises 77–80, find the sum of the infinite geometric series.

77. $\sum_{i=1}^{\infty} \left(\frac{7}{8}\right)^{i-1}$

78. $\sum_{i=1}^{\infty} \left(\frac{1}{3}\right)^{i-1}$

79. $\sum_{k=1}^{\infty} 4\left(\frac{2}{3}\right)^{k-1}$

80. $\sum_{k=1}^{\infty} 1.3\left(\frac{1}{10}\right)^{k-1}$

81. *Depreciation* A company buys a fleet of six vans for $120,000. During the next 5 years, the fleet will depreciate at a rate of 30% per year. (That is, at the end of each year, the depreciated value is 70% of the value at the beginning of the year.)

(a) Find the formula for the nth term of a geometric sequence that gives the value of the fleet t full years after it was purchased.

(b) Find the depreciated value of the fleet at the end of 5 full years.

82. *Annuity* A deposit of $75 is made at the beginning of each month in an account that pays 4% interest, compounded monthly. The balance A in the account at the end of 4 years is given by

$$A = 75\left(1 + \frac{0.04}{12}\right)^1 + \cdots + 75\left(1 + \frac{0.04}{12}\right)^{48}.$$

Find A.

9.4 In Exercises 83–86, use mathematical induction to prove the formula for every positive integer n.

83. $2 + 7 + \cdots + (5n - 3) = \dfrac{n}{2}(5n - 1)$

84. $1 + \dfrac{3}{2} + 2 + \dfrac{5}{2} + \cdots + \dfrac{1}{2}(n + 1) = \dfrac{n}{4}(n + 3)$

85. $\displaystyle\sum_{i=0}^{n-1} ar^i = \dfrac{a(1 - r^n)}{1 - r}$

86. $\displaystyle\sum_{k=0}^{n-1} (a + kd) = \dfrac{n}{2}[2a + (n - 1)d]$

In Exercises 87–90, find the sum using the formulas for the sums of powers of integers.

87. $\displaystyle\sum_{n=1}^{30} n$

88. $\displaystyle\sum_{n=1}^{10} n^2$

89. $\displaystyle\sum_{n=1}^{7} (n^4 - n)$

90. $\displaystyle\sum_{n=1}^{6} (n^5 - n^2)$

In Exercises 91–94, write the first five terms of the sequence beginning with a_1. Then calculate the first and second differences of the sequence. Does the sequence have a linear model, a quadratic model, or neither?

91. $a_1 = 5$
$a_n = a_{n-1} + 5$

92. $a_1 = -3$
$a_n = a_{n-1} - 2n$

93. $a_1 = 16$
$a_n = a_{n-1} - 1$

94. $a_1 = 1$
$a_n = n - a_{n-1}$

9.5 In Exercises 95–98, find the binomial coefficient. Use a graphing utility to verify your result.

95. $_{10}C_8$

96. $_{12}C_5$

97. $\dbinom{9}{4}$

98. $\dbinom{14}{12}$

In Exercises 99–102, use Pascal's Triangle to find the binomial coefficient.

99. $_6C_3$

100. $_9C_7$

101. $\dbinom{8}{4}$

102. $\dbinom{10}{5}$

In Exercises 103–108, use the Binomial Theorem to expand and simplify the expression. Simplify your answer. $\left(\text{Remember that } i = \sqrt{-1}.\right)$

103. $(x + 5)^4$

104. $(y - 3)^3$

105. $(a - 4b)^5$

106. $(3x + y)^7$

107. $(7 + 2i)^4$

108. $(4 - 5i)^3$

9.6

109. *Numbers in a Hat*   Slips of paper numbered 1 through 14 are placed in a hat. In how many ways can two numbers be drawn so that the sum of the numbers is 12? Assume the random selection is without replacement.

110. *Aircraft Boarding*   Eight people are boarding an aircraft. Two have tickets for first class and board before those in economy class. In how many ways can the eight people board the aircraft?

111. *Course Schedule*   A college student is preparing a course schedule for the next semester. The student must select one of four mathematics courses, one of six biology courses, and one of two art courses. How many schedules are possible?

112. *Telephone Numbers*   The same three-digit prefix is used for all of the telephone numbers in a small town. How many different telephone numbers are possible by changing only the last four digits?

In Exercises 113 and 114, find the number of distinguishable permutations of the group of letters.

113. C, A, L, C, U, L, U, S

114. I, N, V, E, R, T, E, B, R, A, T, E

115. *Sports*   There are 10 bicyclists entered in a race. In how many different orders could the ten bicyclists finish?

116. *Sports*   From a pool of 7 juniors and 11 seniors, four co-captains will be chosen for the football team. How many different combinations are possible if two juniors and two seniors are to be chosen?

117. *Exam Questions*   A student can answer any 15 questions from a total of 20 questions on an exam. In how many different ways can the student select the questions?

118. *Lottery*   In the Lotto Texas game, a player chooses six distinct numbers from 1 to 54. In how many ways can a player select the six numbers?

9.7

119. *Apparel*   A man has five pairs of socks (no two pairs are the same color). He randomly selects two socks from a drawer. What is the probability that he gets a matched pair?

120. Bookshelf Order A child returns a five-volume set of books to a bookshelf. The child is not able to read, and so cannot distinguish one volume from another. What is the probability that the books are shelved in the correct order?

121. Data Analysis A sample of college students, faculty members, and administrators were asked whether they favored a proposed increase in the annual activity fee to enhance student life on campus. The results of the study are shown in the table.

	Favor	Oppose	Total
Students	237	163	400
Faculty	37	38	75
Admin.	18	7	25
Total	292	208	500

A person is selected at random from the sample. Find each probability.

(a) The person is not in favor of the proposal.

(b) The person is a student.

(c) The person is a faculty member and is in favor of the proposal.

122. Tossing a Die A six-sided die is rolled six times. What is the probability that each side appears exactly once?

123. Poker Hand Five cards are drawn from an ordinary deck of 52 playing cards. Find the probability of getting two pairs. (For example, the hand could be A-A-5-5-Q or 4-4-7-7-K.)

124. Drawing a Card You randomly select a card from a 52-card deck. What is the probability that the card is *not* a club?

Synthesis

True or False? **In Exercises 125 and 126, determine whether the statement is true or false. Justify your answer.**

125. $\dfrac{(n+2)!}{n!} = (n+2)(n+1)$

126. $\displaystyle\sum_{k=1}^{8} 3k = 3\sum_{k=1}^{8} k$

127. Writing In your own words, explain what makes a sequence (a) arithmetic and (b) geometric.

128. Think About It How do the two sequences differ?

(a) $a_n = \dfrac{(-1)^n}{n}$ (b) $a_n = \dfrac{(-1)^{n+1}}{n}$

129. Graphical Reasoning The graphs of two sequences are shown below. Identify each sequence as arithmetic or geometric. Explain your reasoning.

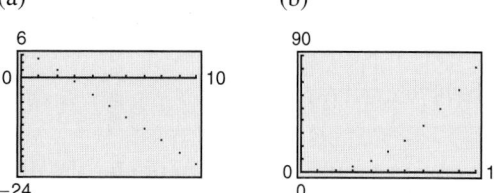

(a)   (b)

130. Population Growth Consider an idealized population with the characteristic that each member of the population produces one offspring at the end of every time period. If each member has a life span of three time periods and the population begins with 10 newborn members, then the following table shows the population during the first five time periods.

Age Bracket	Time Period				
	1	2	3	4	5
0–1	10	10	20	40	70
1–2		10	10	20	40
2–3			10	10	20
Total	10	20	40	70	130

The sequence for the total population has the property that

$$S_n = S_{n-1} + S_{n-2} + S_{n-3}, \quad n > 3.$$

Find the total population during the next five time periods.

131. Writing Explain what a recursive formula is.

132. Writing Explain why the terms of a geometric sequence of positive terms decrease when $0 < r < 1$.

133. Think About It How do the expansions of $(x-y)^n$ and $(-x+y)^n$ differ?

134. The probability of an event must be a real number in what interval? Is the interval open or closed?

9 | Chapter Test

Take this test as you would take a test in class. After you are finished, check your work against the answers given in the back of the book.

In Exercises 1 and 2, write the first five terms of the sequence.

1. $a_n = \left(-\frac{2}{3}\right)^{n-1}$ (Begin with $n = 1$.)

2. $a_1 = 12$ and $a_{k+1} = a_k + 4$

3. Simplify $\dfrac{11! \cdot 4!}{4! \cdot 7!}$.

In Exercises 4 and 5, find a formula for the nth term of the sequence.

4. Arithmetic: $a_1 = 5000, \quad d = -100$

5. Geometric: $a_1 = 4, \quad a_{k+1} = \frac{1}{2}a_k$

6. Use sigma notation to write $\dfrac{2}{3(1) + 1} + \dfrac{2}{3(2) + 1} + \cdots + \dfrac{2}{3(12) + 1}$.

In Exercises 7–9, find the sum.

7. $\displaystyle\sum_{n=1}^{7} (8n - 5)$ 8. $\displaystyle\sum_{n=1}^{8} 24\left(\frac{1}{6}\right)^{n-1}$ 9. $\displaystyle\sum_{n=1}^{\infty} 5\left(\frac{1}{10}\right)^{n-1}$

10. Use mathematical induction to prove the formula

$$3 + 6 + 9 + \cdots + 3n = \frac{3n(n+1)}{2}.$$

11. Use the Binomial Theorem to expand and simplify $(2a - 5b)^4$.

12. Find the coefficient of the term $x^3 y^5$ in the expansion of $(3x + 2y)^8$.

In Exercises 13–16, evaluate the expression.

13. $_9C_3$ 14. $_{20}C_3$ 15. $_9P_2$ 16. $_{70}P_3$

17. How many distinct license plates can be issued consisting of one letter followed by a three-digit number?

18. Four students are randomly selected from a class of 25 to answer questions from a reading assignment. In how many ways can the four be selected?

19. A card is drawn from a standard deck of 52 playing cards. Find the probability that it is a red face card.

20. Two spark plugs require replacement in a four-cylinder engine. The mechanic randomly removes two plugs. Find the probability that they are the two defective plugs.

21. Two integers from 1 to 60 are chosen by a random number generator. What is the probability that (a) both numbers are odd, (b) both numbers are less than 12, and (c) the same number is chosen twice?

22. A weather forecast indicates that the probability of snow is 75%. What is the probability that it will not snow?

The cables for suspension bridges are parabolic in shape. You can use the techniques illustrated in this chapter to determine the height of the cables above the roadway of the Golden Gate Bridge.

David W. Hamilton/Getty Images

10
Topics in Analytic Geometry

What You Should Learn

10.1 Conics
10.2 Translations of Conics
10.3 Parametric Equations
10.4 Polar Coordinates
10.5 Graphs of Polar Equations
10.6 Polar Equations of Conics

In this chapter, you will learn how to:

■ Recognize, graph, and write equations of conics with vertex or center at the origin.

■ Recognize, graph, and write equations of conics that have been shifted vertically and/or horizontally in the plane.

■ Evaluate sets of parametric equations for given values of the parameter and graph curves that are represented by sets of parametric equations.

■ Rewrite sets of parametric equations as single rectangular equations and find sets of parametric equations for graphs.

■ Plot points in the polar coordinate system and convert equations from rectangular to polar form and vice versa.

■ Graph polar equations.

■ Write conics in terms of eccentricity and write equations of conics in polar form.

771

10.1 Conics

Introduction

Conic sections were discovered during the classical Greek period, 600 to 300 B.C. The early Greek studies were largely concerned with the geometric properties of conics. It was not until the early 17th century that the broad applicability of conics became apparent and played a prominent role in the early development of calculus.

A **conic section** (or simply **conic**) is the intersection of a plane and a double-napped cone. Notice in Figure 10.1 that in the formation of the four basic conics, the intersecting plane does not pass through the vertex of the cone. When the plane does pass through the vertex, the resulting figure is a **degenerate conic,** as shown in Figure 10.2.

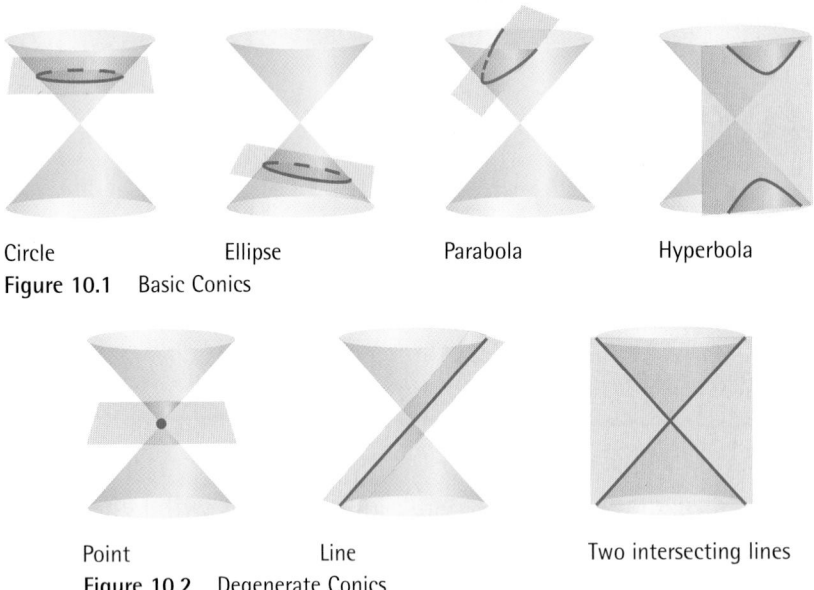

Circle   Ellipse   Parabola   Hyperbola

Figure 10.1   Basic Conics

Point   Line   Two intersecting lines

Figure 10.2   Degenerate Conics

There are several ways to approach the study of conics. You could begin by defining conics in terms of the intersections of planes and cones, as the Greeks did, or you could define them algebraically, in terms of the general second-degree equation

$$Ax^2 + Bxy + Cy^2 + Dx + Ey + F = 0.$$

However, you will study a third approach, in which each of the conics is defined as a *locus* (collection) of points satisfying a certain geometric property. For example, in Section P.5, you saw how the definition of a circle as *the collection of all points (x, y) that are equidistant from a fixed point (h, k)* led easily to the standard form of the equation of a circle

$$(x - h)^2 + (y - k)^2 = r^2. \qquad \text{Equation of circle}$$

From the equation above, the center of the circle is (h, k) and the radius is r. To review circles and their graphs, see Sections P.5 and 1.1.

Parabolas

In Section 3.1, you learned that the graph of the quadratic function

$$f(x) = ax^2 + bx + c$$

is a parabola that opens upward or downward. The following definition of a parabola is more general in the sense that it is independent of the orientation of the parabola.

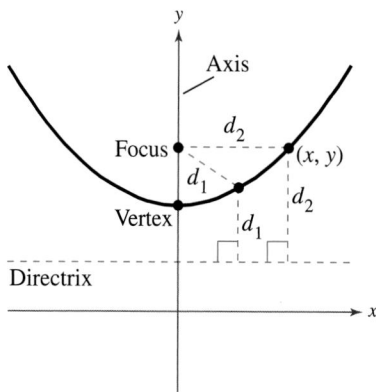

Figure 10.3

Definition of a Parabola

A **parabola** is the set of all points (x, y) in a plane that are equidistant from a fixed line, the **directrix,** and a fixed point, the **focus,** not on the line. (See Figure 10.3.) The midpoint between the focus and the directrix is the **vertex,** and the line passing through the focus and the vertex is the **axis** of the parabola.

Standard Equation of a Parabola (Vertex at Origin)

The **standard form of the equation of a parabola** with vertex at $(0, 0)$ and directrix $y = -p$ is given by

$$x^2 = 4py, \qquad p \neq 0. \qquad \text{Vertical axis}$$

For directrix $x = -p$, the equation is given by

$$y^2 = 4px, \qquad p \neq 0. \qquad \text{Horizontal axis}$$

The focus is on the axis p units (directed distance) from the vertex.

See Appendix B for a proof of the standard form of the equation of a parabola.

Notice that a parabola can have a vertical or a horizontal axis and that a parabola is symmetric with respect to its axis. Examples of each are shown in Figure 10.4. If you know the equation of the axis, it is easy to sketch the graph of a parabola by hand.

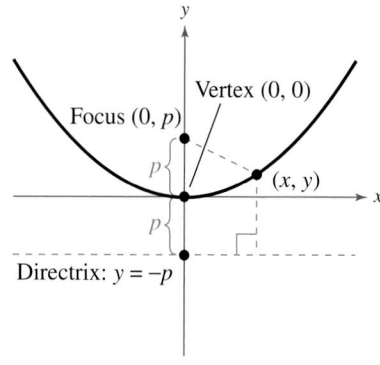

(a) Parabola with vertical axis: $x^2 = 4py$

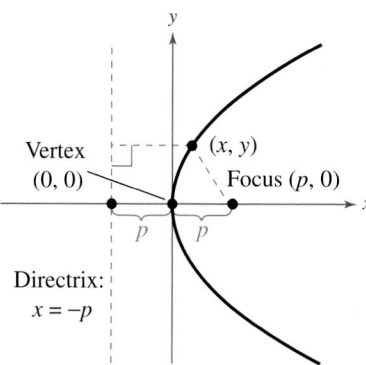

(b) Parabola with horizontal axis: $y^2 = 4px$

Figure 10.4

Example 1   Finding the Focus of a Parabola

Find the focus of the parabola whose equation is $y = -2x^2$.

Solution

Because the squared term in the equation involves x, you know that the axis is vertical, and the equation is of the form $x^2 = 4py$. You can write the original equation in this form as follows.

$$x^2 = -\tfrac{1}{2}y \quad \Longrightarrow \quad x^2 = 4\left(-\tfrac{1}{8}\right)y \qquad \text{Write in standard form.}$$

So, $p = -\tfrac{1}{8}$. Because p is negative, the parabola opens downward (see Figure 10.5), and the focus of the parabola is

$$(0, p) = \left(0, -\tfrac{1}{8}\right). \qquad \text{Focus}$$

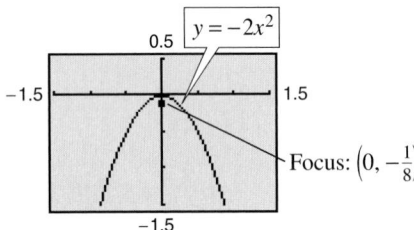

Figure 10.5

✓ *Checkpoint* Now try Exercise 5.

Example 2   A Parabola with a Horizontal Axis

Find the standard form of the equation of the parabola with vertex at the origin and focus at $(2, 0)$.

Solution

The axis of the parabola is horizontal, passing through $(0, 0)$ and $(2, 0)$, as shown in Figure 10.6. So, the standard form is $y^2 = 4px$. Because the focus is $p = 2$ units from the vertex, the equation is

$$y^2 = 4(2)x \quad \Longrightarrow \quad y^2 = 8x.$$

The equation $y^2 = 8x$ does not define y as a function of x. So, to use a graphing utility to graph $y^2 = 8x$, you need to break the graph into two equations, $y_1 = 2\sqrt{2x}$ and $y_2 = -2\sqrt{2x}$, each of which is a function of x.

✓ *Checkpoint* Now try Exercise 11.

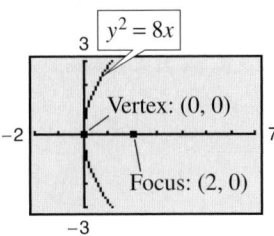

Figure 10.6

Parabolas occur in a wide variety of applications. For instance, a parabolic reflector can be formed by revolving a parabola about its axis. The resulting surface has the property that all incoming rays parallel to the axis are reflected through the focus of the parabola. This is the principle behind the construction of the parabolic mirrors used in reflecting telescopes. Conversely, the light rays emanating from the focus of a parabolic reflector used in a flashlight are all parallel to one another, as shown in Figure 10.7.

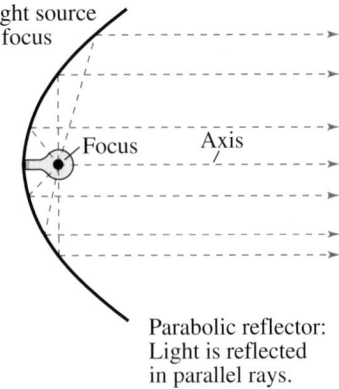

Parabolic reflector:
Light is reflected
in parallel rays.

Figure 10.7

Ellipses

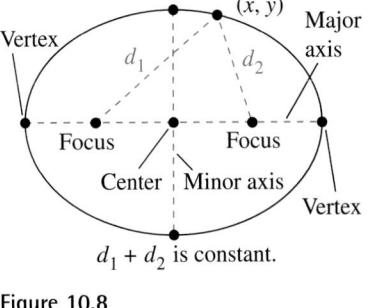

Figure 10.8

Definition of an Ellipse

An **ellipse** is the set of all points (x, y) in a plane, the sum of whose distances from two distinct fixed points (**foci**) is constant. (See Figure 10.8).

The line through the foci intersects the ellipse at two points called **vertices.** The chord joining the vertices is the **major axis**, and its midpoint is the **center** of the ellipse. The chord perpendicular to the major axis at the center is the **minor axis**. (See Figure 10.8).

You can visualize the definition of an ellipse by imagining two thumbtacks placed at the foci, as shown in Figure 10.9. If the ends of a fixed length of string are fastened to the thumbtacks and the string is drawn taut with a pencil, the path traced by the pencil will be an ellipse.

The standard form of the equation of an ellipse takes one of two forms, depending on whether the major axis is horizontal or vertical.

Standard Equation of an Ellipse (Center at Origin)

The **standard form of the equation of an ellipse** with center at the origin and major and minor axes of lengths $2a$ and $2b$, respectively (where $0 < b < a$), is given by

$$\frac{x^2}{a^2} + \frac{y^2}{b^2} = 1 \qquad \text{or} \qquad \frac{x^2}{b^2} + \frac{y^2}{a^2} = 1.$$

The vertices and foci lie on the major axis, a and c units, respectively, from the center, as shown in Figure 10.10. Moreover, a, b, and c are related by the equation $c^2 = a^2 - b^2$.

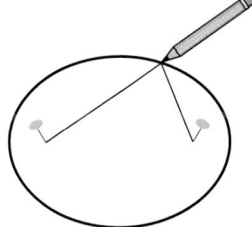

Figure 10.9

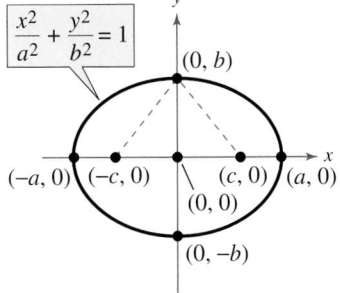

(a) Major axis is horizontal;
minor axis is vertical.

Figure 10.10

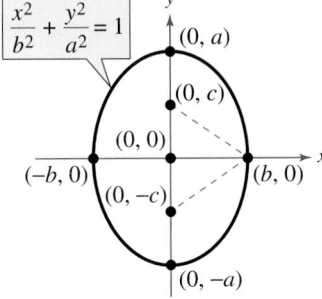

(b) Major axis is vertical;
minor axis is horizontal.

In Figure 10.10, note that because the sum of the distances from a point on the ellipse to each focus is constant, $c^2 = a^2 - b^2$ as follows.

$$2\sqrt{b^2 + c^2} = (a + c) + (a - c)$$
$$\sqrt{b^2 + c^2} = a$$
$$c^2 = a^2 - b^2$$

Exploration

An ellipse can be drawn using two thumbtacks placed at the foci of the ellipse, a string of fixed length (greater than the distance between the tacks), and a pencil, as shown in Figure 10.9. Try doing this. Vary the length of the string and the distance between the thumbtacks. Explain how to obtain ellipses that are almost circular. Explain how to obtain ellipses that are long and narrow.

Example 3 Finding the Standard Equation of an Ellipse

Find the standard form of the equation of the ellipse shown in Figure 10.11.

Solution

From Figure 10.11, the foci occur at $(-2, 0)$ and $(2, 0)$. So, the center of the ellipse is $(0, 0)$, the major axis is horizontal, and the ellipse has an equation of the form

$$\frac{x^2}{a^2} + \frac{y^2}{b^2} = 1. \qquad \text{Standard form}$$

Also from Figure 10.11, the length of the major axis is $2a = 6$. So, $a = 3$. Moreover, the distance from the center to either focus is $c = 2$. Finally,

$$b^2 = a^2 - c^2 = 3^2 - 2^2 = 9 - 4 = 5.$$

Substituting $a^2 = 3^2$ and $b^2 = \left(\sqrt{5}\right)^2$ yields the equation in standard form.

$$\frac{x^2}{3^2} + \frac{y^2}{\left(\sqrt{5}\right)^2} = 1$$

☑ *Checkpoint* Now try Exercise 45.

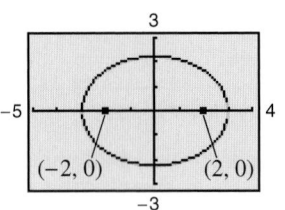

Figure 10.11

TECHNOLOGY SUPPORT

For instructions on how to use the *zoom* and *trace* features, see Appendix A; for specific keystrokes, go to the text website at *college.hmco.com*.

Example 4 Sketching an Ellipse

Sketch the ellipse given by $4x^2 + y^2 = 36$, and identify the vertices.

Algebraic Solution

$$\frac{4x^2}{36} + \frac{y^2}{36} = \frac{36}{36} \qquad \begin{array}{l}\text{Divide each side of}\\\text{original equation by 36.}\end{array}$$

$$\frac{x^2}{3^2} + \frac{y^2}{6^2} = 1 \qquad \text{Write in standard form.}$$

Because the denominator of the y^2-term is larger than the denominator of the x^2-term, you can conclude that the major axis is vertical. Moreover, because $a = 6$, the vertices are $(0, -6)$ and $(0, 6)$. Finally, because $b = 3$, the endpoints of the minor axis are $(-3, 0)$ and $(3, 0)$, as shown in Figure 10.12.

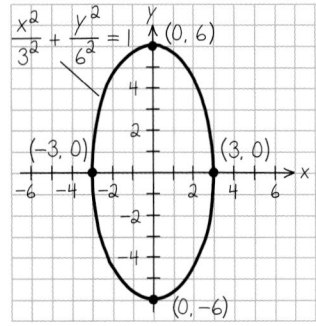

Figure 10.12

☑ *Checkpoint* Now try Exercise 33.

Graphical Solution

Solve the equation of the ellipse for y as follows.

$$4x^2 + y^2 = 36$$

$$y^2 = 36 - 4x^2$$

$$y = \pm\sqrt{36 - 4x^2}$$

Then use a graphing utility to graph $y_1 = \sqrt{36 - 4x^2}$ and $y_2 = -\sqrt{36 - 4x^2}$ in the same viewing window. Be sure to use a square setting. From the graph in Figure 10.13, you can see that the major axis is vertical. You can use the *zoom* and *trace* features to approximate the vertices to be $(0, 6)$ and $(0, -6)$.

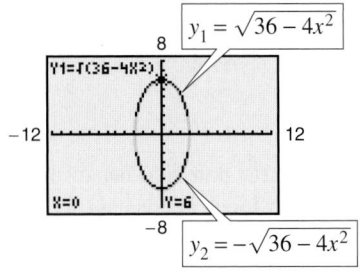

Figure 10.13

TECHNOLOGY TIP Note that in the graphical solution of Example 4, the ellipse was graphed using two separate equations. When a graphing utility is used to graph conics, it may not connect the two equations. This is because some graphing utilities are limited in their resolution. So, in this text, a blue curve is placed behind the graphing utility's display to indicate where the graph should appear.

Hyperbolas

The definition of a **hyperbola** is similar to that of an ellipse. The difference is that for an ellipse, the *sum* of the distances between the foci and a point on the ellipse is constant, whereas for a hyperbola the *difference* of the distances between the foci and a point on the hyperbola is constant.

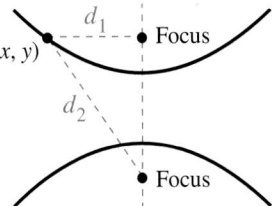

$d_2 - d_1$ is a positive constant.

(a)

> **Definition of a Hyperbola**
>
> A **hyperbola** is the set of all points (x, y) in a plane, the difference of whose distances from two distinct fixed points **(foci)** is a positive constant. [See Figure 10.14(a).]

The graph of a hyperbola has two disconnected parts **(branches)**. The line through the two foci intersects the hyperbola at two points **(vertices)**. The line segment connecting the vertices is the **transverse axis,** and the midpoint of the transverse axis is the **center** of the hyperbola. [See Figure 10.14(b).]

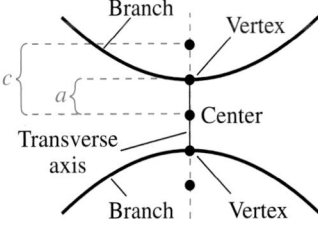

(b)

Figure 10.14

> **Standard Equation of a Hyperbola (Center at Origin)**
>
> The **standard form of the equation of a hyperbola** with center at the origin (where $a \neq 0$ and $b \neq 0$) is given by
>
> $$\frac{x^2}{a^2} - \frac{y^2}{b^2} = 1 \quad \text{or} \quad \frac{y^2}{a^2} - \frac{x^2}{b^2} = 1.$$
>
> The vertices and foci are a and c units from the center, respectively. Moreover, a, b, and c are related by the equation $b^2 = c^2 - a^2$. (See Figure 10.15.)

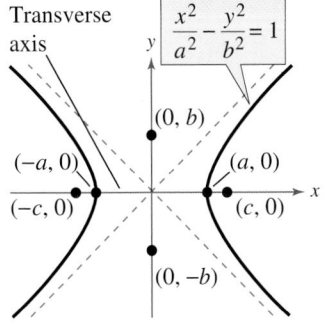

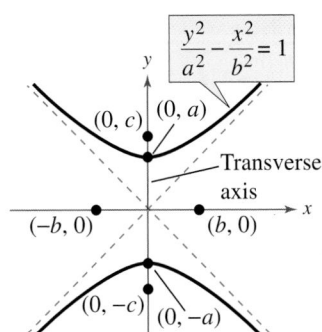

Figure 10.15

Example 5 Finding the Standard Equation of a Hyperbola

Find the standard form of the equation of the hyperbola with foci at $(-3, 0)$ and $(3, 0)$ and vertices at $(-2, 0)$ and $(2, 0)$, as shown in Figure 10.16.

Solution

From the graph, you can determine that $c = 3$ because the foci are three units from the center. Moreover, $a = 2$ because the vertices are two units from the center. So, it follows that

$$b^2 = c^2 - a^2$$

$$= 3^2 - 2^2$$

$$= 9 - 4$$

$$= 5.$$

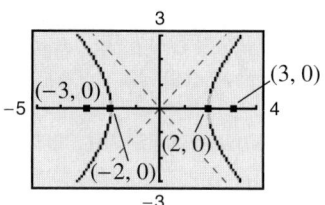

Figure 10.16

Because the transverse axis is horizontal, the standard form of the equation is

$$\frac{x^2}{a^2} - \frac{y^2}{b^2} = 1.$$

Finally, substitute $a^2 = 2^2$ and $b^2 = \left(\sqrt{5}\right)^2$ to obtain

$$\frac{x^2}{2^2} - \frac{y^2}{\left(\sqrt{5}\right)^2} = 1. \quad \text{Write in standard form.}$$

☑ *Checkpoint* Now try Exercise 61.

An important aid in sketching the graph of a hyperbola is the determination of its *asymptotes*, as shown in Figure 10.17. Each hyperbola has two asymptotes that intersect at the center of the hyperbola. Furthermore, the asymptotes pass through the corners of a rectangle of dimensions $2a$ by $2b$. The line segment of length $2b$, joining $(0, b)$ and $(0, -b)$ [or $(-b, 0)$ and $(b, 0)$], is the **conjugate axis** of the hyperbola.

TECHNOLOGY TIP

To use a graphing utility to graph the hyperbola in Example 5, first solve for y^2 to obtain $y^2 = 5(x^2 - 4)/4$. Then enter the positive and negative square roots of the right-hand side of the equation as

$$y_1 = \sqrt{5(x^2 - 4)}/2$$

$$y_2 = -\sqrt{5(x^2 - 4)}/2.$$

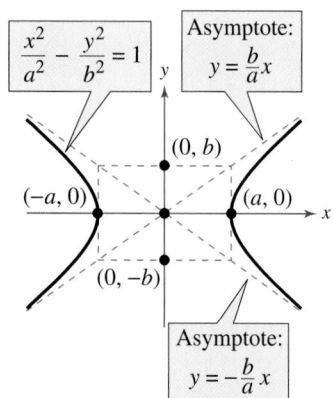

(a) Transverse axis is horizontal.
   Conjugate axis is vertical.

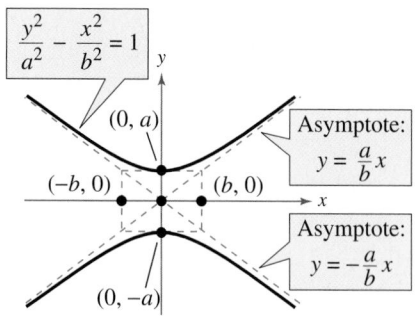

(b) Transverse axis is vertical.
   Conjugate axis is horizontal.

Figure 10.17

> **Asymptotes of a Hyperbola (Center at Origin)**
>
> The **asymptotes of a hyperbola** with center at $(0, 0)$ are given by
>
> $$y = \frac{b}{a}x \quad \text{and} \quad y = -\frac{b}{a}x \qquad \text{Transverse axis is horizontal.}$$
>
> or
>
> $$y = \frac{a}{b}x \quad \text{and} \quad y = -\frac{a}{b}x. \qquad \text{Transverse axis is vertical.}$$

Example 6   Sketching the Graph of a Hyperbola

Sketch the hyperbola whose equation is $4x^2 - y^2 = 16$.

Algebraic Solution

$$4x^2 - y^2 = 16 \qquad \text{Write original equation.}$$

$$\frac{4x^2}{16} - \frac{y^2}{16} = \frac{16}{16} \qquad \text{Divide each side by 16.}$$

$$\frac{x^2}{2^2} - \frac{y^2}{4^2} = 1 \qquad \text{Write in standard form.}$$

Because the x^2-term is positive, you can conclude that the transverse axis is horizontal and that the vertices occur at $(-2, 0)$ and $(2, 0)$. Moreover, the endpoints of the conjugate axis occur at $(0, -4)$ and $(0, 4)$, and you can sketch the rectangle shown in Figure 10.18. Finally, by drawing the asymptotes through the corners of this rectangle, you can complete the sketch shown in Figure 10.19. Note that the equations of the asymptotes are $y = 2x$ and $y = -2x$.

Graphical Solution

Solve the equation of the hyperbola for y as follows.

$$4x^2 - y^2 = 16$$

$$4x^2 - 16 = y^2$$

$$\pm\sqrt{4x^2 - 16} = y$$

Then use a graphing utility to graph $y_1 = \sqrt{4x^2 - 16}$ and $y_2 = -\sqrt{4x^2 - 16}$ in the same viewing window. Be sure to use a square setting. From the graph in Figure 10.20, you can see that the transverse axis is horizontal. You can use the *zoom* and *trace* features to approximate the vertices to be $(-2, 0)$ and $(2, 0)$.

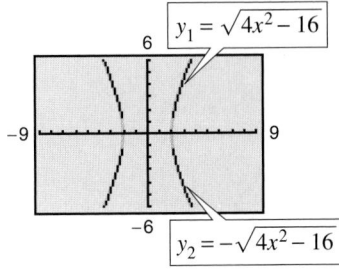

Figure 10.20

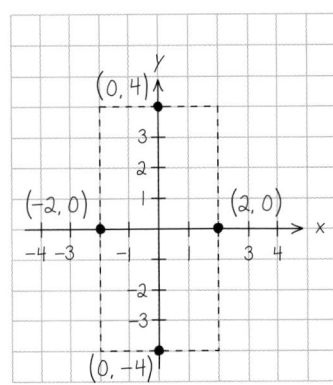

Figure 10.18

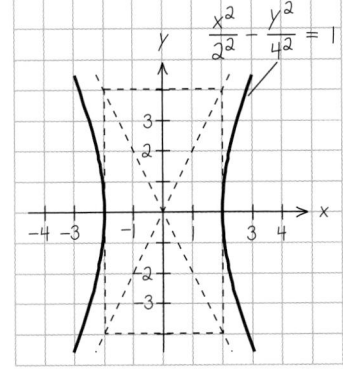

Figure 10.19

✓ *Checkpoint* Now try Exercise 55.

Example 7 Finding the Standard Equation of a Hyperbola

Find the standard form of the equation of the hyperbola that has vertices at $(0, -3)$ and $(0, 3)$ and asymptotes $y = -2x$ and $y = 2x$, as shown in Figure 10.21.

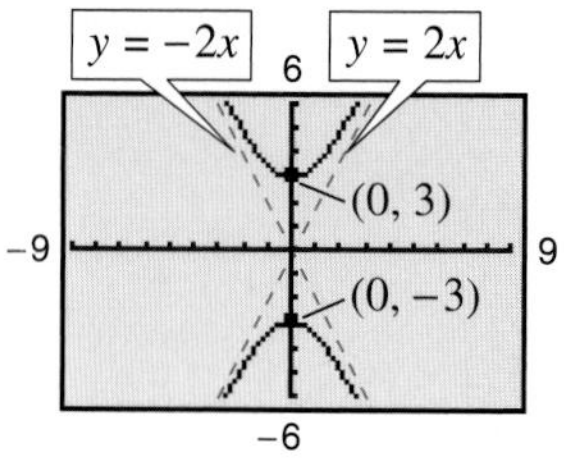

Solution

Because the transverse axis is vertical, the asymptotes are of the form

$$y = \frac{a}{b}x \quad \text{and} \quad y = -\frac{a}{b}x.$$

Using the fact that $y = 2x$ and $y = -2x$, you can determine that

$$\frac{a}{b} = 2.$$

Because $a = 3$, you can determine that $b = \frac{3}{2}$. Finally, you can conclude that the hyperbola has the following equation.

$$\frac{y^2}{3^2} - \frac{x^2}{(3/2)^2} = 1 \qquad \text{Write in standard form.}$$

Figure 10.21

✓ *Checkpoint* Now try Exercise 63.

Example 8 Identifying Conics

Identify each conic by writing its equation in standard form.

a. $6x^2 + y^2 - 36 = 0$ **b.** $4y^2 - 12x^2 - 48 = 0$

Solution

a. $6x^2 + y^2 - 36 = 0$ Write original equation.

$\qquad 6x^2 + y^2 = 36$ Add 36 to each side.

$\qquad \dfrac{x^2}{6} + \dfrac{y^2}{36} = 1$ Divide each side by 36.

$\qquad \dfrac{x^2}{\left(\sqrt{6}\right)^2} + \dfrac{y^2}{6^2} = 1$ Write in standard form.

From the standard form, you can see that the equation represents an ellipse.

b. $4y^2 - 12x^2 - 48 = 0$ Write original equation.

$\qquad 4y^2 - 12x^2 = 48$ Add 48 to each side.

$\qquad \dfrac{y^2}{12} - \dfrac{x^2}{4} = 1$ Divide each side by 48.

$\qquad \dfrac{y^2}{\left(\sqrt{12}\right)^2} - \dfrac{x^2}{2^2} = 1$ Write in standard form.

From the standard form, you can see that the equation represents a hyperbola.

✓ *Checkpoint* Now try Exercise 77.

10.1 Exercises

Vocabulary Check

Fill in the blanks.

1. A _____ is the intersection of a plane and a double-napped cone.

2. A _____ is the set of all points (x, y) in a plane that are equidistant from a fixed lined, called the _____ , and a fixed point, called the _____ , not on the line.

3. The _____ of a parabola is the midpoint between the focus and the directrix.

4. The line that passes through the focus and vertex of a parabola is called the _____ of the parabola.

5. An _____ is the set of all points (x, y) in a plane, the sum of whose distances from two distinct fixed points is constant.

6. The chord joining the vertices of an ellipse is called the _____ , and its midpoint is the _____ of the ellipse.

7. The chord perpendicular to the major axis at the center of an ellipse is called the _____ of the ellipse.

8. A _____ is the set of all points (x, y) in a plane, the difference of whose distances from two distinct fixed points is a positive constant.

9. The graph of a hyperbola has two disconnected parts called _____ .

10. The line segment connecting the vertices of a hyperbola is called the _____ , and the midpoint of the line segment is the _____ of the hyperbola.

In Exercises 1–4, find the standard form of the equation of the circle with the center at the origin and satisfying the given conditions.

1. Radius: 6
2. Radius: 1
3. Diameter: $\frac{10}{7}$
4. Diameter: $2\sqrt{7}$

In Exercises 5–10, find the vertex and focus of the parabola and sketch its graph. Use a graphing utility to verify your graph.

5. $y = \frac{1}{2}x^2$
6. $y = -4x^2$
7. $y^2 = -6x$
8. $y^2 = 3x$
9. $x^2 + 8y = 0$
10. $x + y^2 = 0$

In Exercises 11–20, find the standard form of the equation of the parabola with vertex at the origin.

11. Focus: $\left(0, -\frac{3}{2}\right)$
12. Focus: $\left(\frac{5}{2}, 0\right)$
13. Focus: $(-2, 0)$
14. Focus: $(0, -2)$
15. Directrix: $y = -1$
16. Directrix: $y = 2$

17. Directrix: $x = 3$
18. Directrix: $x = -2$
19. Horizontal axis and passes through the point $(4, 6)$
20. Vertical axis and passes through the point $(-2, -2)$

In Exercises 21–24, find the standard form of the equation of the parabola and determine the coordinates of the focus.

21.
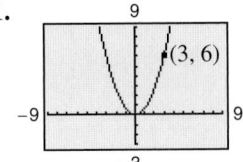

22.
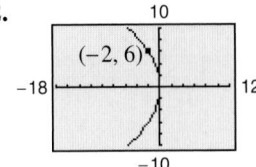

23.
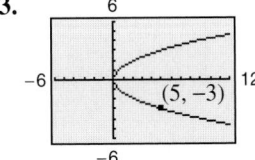

24.
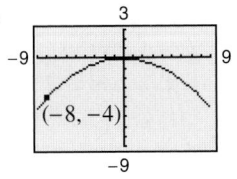

ƒ **In Exercises 25 and 26, use a graphing utility to graph the parabola and the line (called one of its *tangent lines*). Identify the point of intersection (called the *point of tangency*).**

	Parabola	*Tangent Line*
25.	$y^2 - 8x = 0$	$x - y + 2 = 0$
26.	$x^2 + 12y = 0$	$x + y - 3 = 0$

In Exercises 27–34, find the center and vertices of the ellipse and sketch its graph. Use a graphing utility to verify your graph.

27. $\dfrac{x^2}{25} + \dfrac{y^2}{16} = 1$ 　　 **28.** $\dfrac{x^2}{144} + \dfrac{y^2}{169} = 1$

29. $\dfrac{x^2}{\frac{25}{9}} + \dfrac{y^2}{\frac{16}{9}} = 1$ 　　 **30.** $\dfrac{x^2}{4} + \dfrac{y^2}{\frac{1}{4}} = 1$

31. $\dfrac{x^2}{9} + \dfrac{y^2}{5} = 1$ 　　 **32.** $\dfrac{x^2}{28} + \dfrac{y^2}{64} = 1$

33. $4x^2 + y^2 = 1$ 　　 **34.** $4x^2 + 9y^2 = 36$

In Exercises 35–38, use a graphing utility to graph the ellipse. (*Hint:* Use two equations.)

35. $5x^2 + 3y^2 = 15$ 　　 **36.** $x^2 + 16y^2 = 16$

37. $6x^2 + y^2 = 36$ 　　 **38.** $4x^2 + 25y^2 = 100$

In Exercises 39–48, find the standard form of the equation of the ellipse with center at the origin.

39.

(0, 2), (1, 0), (−1, 0), (0, −2)

40.

(0, 6), (5, 0), (−5, 0), (0, −6)

41.

$\left(0, \tfrac{3}{2}\right)$, (2, 0), (−2, 0), $\left(0, -\tfrac{3}{2}\right)$

42.

$\left(0, \tfrac{7}{2}\right)$, (7, 0), (−7, 0), $\left(0, -\tfrac{7}{2}\right)$

43. Vertices: $(\pm 5, 0)$; foci: $(\pm 2, 0)$

44. Vertices: $(0, \pm 8)$; foci: $(0, \pm 4)$

45. Foci: $(\pm 5, 0)$; major axis of length 12

46. Foci: $(\pm 2, 0)$; major axis of length 8

47. Vertices: $(0, \pm 5)$; passes through the point (4, 2)

48. Major axis vertical; passes through the points (0, 4) and (2, 0)

In Exercises 49–56, find the center, vertices, and foci of the hyperbola and sketch its graph, using asymptotes as sketching aids. Use a graphing utility to verify your graph.

49. $x^2 - y^2 = 1$ 　　 **50.** $\dfrac{x^2}{9} - \dfrac{y^2}{16} = 1$

51. $\dfrac{y^2}{1} - \dfrac{x^2}{9} = 1$ 　　 **52.** $\dfrac{y^2}{4} - \dfrac{x^2}{1} = 1$

53. $\dfrac{y^2}{25} - \dfrac{x^2}{144} = 1$ 　　 **54.** $\dfrac{x^2}{36} - \dfrac{y^2}{4} = 1$

55. $4y^2 - x^2 = 1$ 　　 **56.** $4y^2 - 9x^2 = 36$

In Exercises 57–60, use a graphing utility to graph the hyperbola and its asymptotes.

57. $2x^2 - 3y^2 = 6$ 　　 **58.** $3y^2 - 5x^2 = 15$

59. $4y^2 - 6x^2 = 12$ 　　 **60.** $8x^2 - 3y^2 = 24$

In Exercises 61–68, find the standard form of the equation of the hyperbola with center at the origin.

61. Vertices: $(0, \pm 2)$; foci: $(0, \pm 4)$

62. Vertices: $(\pm 3, 0)$; foci: $(\pm 5, 0)$

63. Vertices: $(\pm 1, 0)$; asymptotes: $y = \pm 3x$

64. Vertices: $(0, \pm 3)$; asymptotes: $y = \pm 3x$

65. Foci: $(0, \pm 8)$; asymptotes: $y = \pm 4x$

66. Foci: $(\pm 10, 0)$; asymptotes: $y = \pm \tfrac{3}{4}x$

67.

(−2, 5), (0, 3), (−2, −5)... (0, 3), (0, −3)

68.

(−2, 0), $(3, \sqrt{3})$, (2, 0)

In Exercises 69–76, match the equation with its graph. [The graphs are labeled (a), (b), (c), (d), (e), (f), (g), and (h).]

(a)

(b)

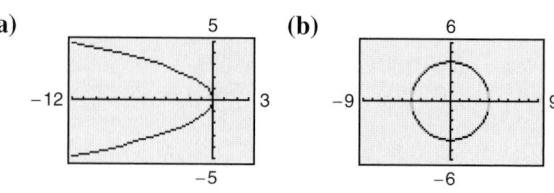

(c)
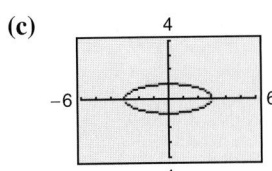

(d)
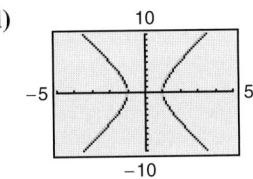

(e)
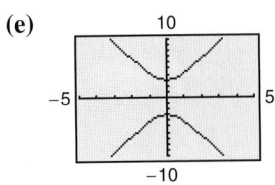

(f)
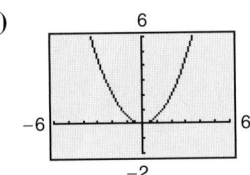

(g)
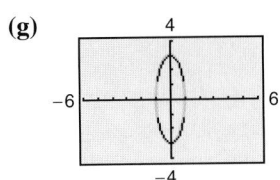

(h)
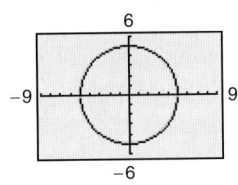

69. $x^2 = 2y$

70. $y^2 = -2x$

71. $9x^2 + y^2 = 9$

72. $x^2 + 9y^2 = 9$

73. $9x^2 - y^2 = 9$

74. $y^2 - 9x^2 = 9$

75. $x^2 + y^2 = 16$

76. $x^2 + y^2 = 25$

In Exercises 77–82, identify the conic by writing the equation in standard form.

77. $4x^2 + 4y^2 - 16 = 0$

78. $4y^2 - 5x^2 + 20 = 0$

79. $3y^2 - 6x = 0$

80. $2x^2 + 4y^2 - 12 = 0$

81. $4x^2 + y^2 - 16 = 0$

82. $2x^2 - 12y = 0$

83. *Satellite Antenna*   Write an equation for a cross section of the parabolic television dish antenna shown in the figure.

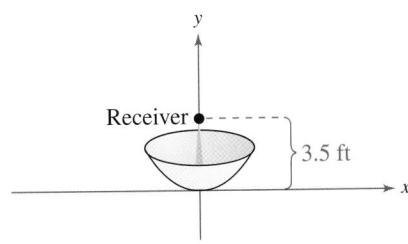

84. *Suspension Bridge*   Each cable of the Golden Gate Bridge is suspended (in the shape of a parabola) between two towers that are 1280 meters apart. The top of each tower is 152 meters above the roadway. The cables touch the roadway midway between the towers.

(a) Draw a sketch of the bridge. Locate the origin of a rectangular coordinate system at the center of the roadway. Label the coordinates of the known points.

(b) Write an equation that models the cables.

(c) Complete the table by finding the height y of the suspension cables over the roadway at a distance of x meters from the center of the bridge.

x	0	200	400	500	600
y					

Table for 84

85. *Beam Deflection*   A simply supported beam is 64 feet long and has a load at the center (see figure). The deflection (bending) of the beam at its center is 1 inch. The shape of the deflected beam is parabolic.

(a) Find an equation of the parabola. (Assume that the origin is at the center of the beam.)

(b) How far from the center of the beam is the deflection equal to $\frac{1}{2}$ inch?

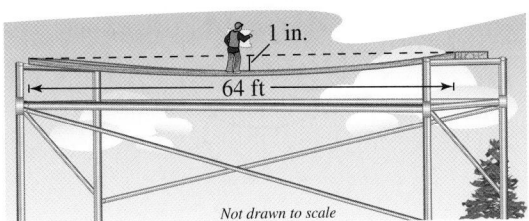

Not drawn to scale

86. *Architecture*   A fireplace arch is to be constructed in the shape of a semiellipse. The opening is to have a height of 2 feet at the center and a width of 6 feet along the base (see figure). The contractor draws the outline of the ellipse on the wall by the method discussed on page 775. Give the required positions of the tacks and the length of the string.

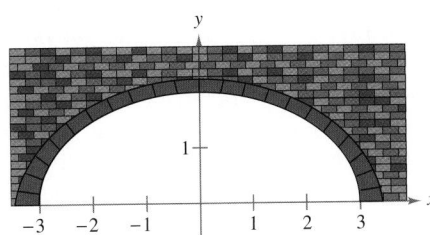

87. Architecture A semielliptical arch over a tunnel for a road through a mountain has a major axis of 110 feet and a height at the center of 40 feet.

(a) Draw a rectangular coordinate system on a sketch of the tunnel with the center of the road entering the tunnel at the origin. Identify the coordinates of the known points.

(b) Find an equation of the semielliptical arch over the tunnel.

(c) Determine the height of the arch 5 feet from the edge of the tunnel.

88. Geometry A line segment through a focus of an ellipse with endpoints on the ellipse and perpendicular to the major axis is called a **latus rectum** of the ellipse. Therefore, an ellipse has two latera recta. Knowing the length of the latera recta is helpful in sketching an ellipse because this information yields other points on the curve (see figure). Show that the length of each latus rectum is $2b^2/a$.

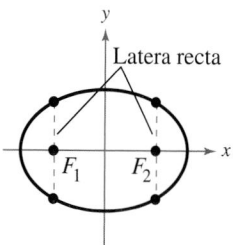

In Exercises 89–92, sketch the graph of the ellipse using the latera recta (see Exercise 88).

89. $\dfrac{x^2}{4} + \dfrac{y^2}{1} = 1$ **90.** $\dfrac{x^2}{9} + \dfrac{y^2}{16} = 1$

91. $9x^2 + 4y^2 = 36$ **92.** $5x^2 + 3y^2 = 15$

93. Navigation Long distance radio navigation for aircraft and ships uses synchronized pulses transmitted by widely separated transmitting stations. These pulses travel at the speed of light (186,000 miles per second). The difference in the times of arrival of these pulses at an aircraft or ship is constant on a hyperbola having the transmitting stations as foci. Assume that two stations 300 miles apart are positioned on a rectangular coordinate system at coordinates $(-150, 0)$ and $(150, 0)$ and that a ship is traveling on a path with coordinates $(x, 75)$, as shown in the figure. Find the x-coordinate of the position of

the ship when the time difference between the pulses from the transmitting stations is 1000 microseconds (0.001 second).

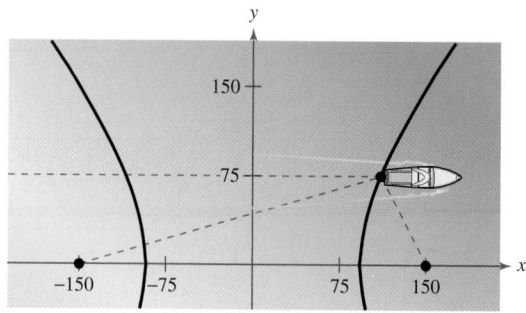

Figure for 93

94. Optics A hyperbolic mirror (used in some telescopes) has the property that a light ray directed at the focus will be reflected to the other focus. The focus of a hyperbolic mirror (see figure) has coordinates $(24, 0)$. Find the vertex of the mirror if its mount at the top edge of the mirror has coordinates $(24, 24)$.

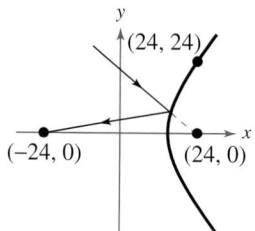

Synthesis

True or False? In Exercises 95–97, determine whether the statement is true or false. Justify your answer.

95. The equation $9x^2 - 16y^2 = 144$ represents an ellipse.

96. The major axis of the ellipse given by $y^2 + 16x^2 = 64$ is vertical.

97. It is possible for a parabola to intersect its directrix.

98. Exploration Consider the parabola $x^2 = 4py$.

(a) Use a graphing utility to graph the parabola for $p = 1$, $p = 2$, $p = 3$, and $p = 4$. Describe the effect on the graph as p increases.

(b) Locate the focus of each parabola in part (a).

(c) For each parabola in part (a), find the length of the chord passing through the focus parallel to the directrix. How can the length of this chord be determined directly from $x^2 = 4py$?

(d) Explain how the result of part (c) can be used as a sketching aid when graphing parabolas.

99. *Exploration* Let (x_1, y_1) be the coordinates of a point on the parabola $x^2 = 4py$. The equation of the line that just touches the parabola at the point (x_1, y_1), called a *tangent line*, is given by

$$y - y_1 = \frac{x_1}{2p}(x - x_1).$$

(a) What is the slope of the tangent line?

(b) For each parabola in Exercise 98, find the equations of the tangent lines at the endpoints of the chord. Use a graphing utility to graph the parabola and tangent lines.

100. *Exploration* Consider the ellipse

$$\frac{x^2}{a^2} + \frac{y^2}{b^2} = 1, \quad a + b = 20.$$

(a) The area of the ellipse is given by $A = \pi ab$. Write the area of the ellipse as a function of a.

(b) Find the equation of an ellipse with an area of 264 square centimeters.

(c) Complete the table using your equation from part (a) and make a conjecture about the shape of the ellipse with maximum area.

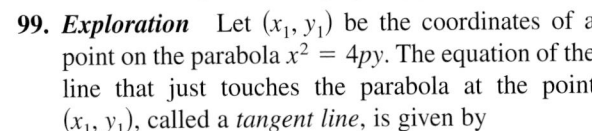

a	8	9	10	11	12	13
A						

(d) Use a graphing utility to graph the area function to support your conjecture in part (c).

Think About It **In Exercises 101 and 102, which part of the graph of the ellipse $4x^2 + 9y^2 = 36$ is represented by the equation? (Do not graph.)**

101. $x = -\frac{3}{2}\sqrt{4 - y^2}$ **102.** $y = \frac{2}{3}\sqrt{9 - x^2}$

Think About It **In Exercises 103 and 104, which part of the graph of the hyperbola $4x^2 - 9y^2 = 36$ is represented by the equation? (Do not graph.)**

103. $y = -\frac{2}{3}\sqrt{x^2 - 9}$ **104.** $x = \frac{3}{2}\sqrt{y^2 + 4}$

105. *Think About It* Is the graph of $x^2 + 4y^4 = 4$ an ellipse? Explain.

106. *Think About It* The graph of $x^2 - y^2 = 0$ is a degenerate conic. Sketch this graph and identify the degenerate conic.

107. *Writing* Write a paragraph discussing the change in the shape and orientation of the graph of the ellipse

$$\frac{x^2}{a^2} + \frac{y^2}{16} = 1$$

as a increases from 1 to 8.

108. *Writing* At the beginning of this section, you learned that each type of conic section can be formed by the intersection of a plane and a double-napped cone. Write a short paragraph describing examples of physical situations in which hyperbolas are formed.

109. Use the definition of an ellipse to derive the standard form of the equation of an ellipse.

110. Use the definition of a hyperbola to derive the standard form of the equation of a hyperbola.

Review

In Exercises 111–114, factor the expression completely.

111. $12x^2 + 7x - 10$ **112.** $25x^3 - 60x^2 + 36x$

113. $12z^4 + 17z^3 + 5z^2$ **114.** $x^3 + 3x^2 - 4x - 12$

In Exercises 115–118, find a polynomial with real coefficients that has the given zeros.

115. $0, 3, 4$ **116.** $-6, 1$

117. $-3, 1 + \sqrt{2}, 1 - \sqrt{2}$

118. $3, 2 + i, 2 - i$

119. Find all the zeros of $f(x) = 2x^3 - 3x^2 + 50x - 75$ if one of the zeros is $x = \frac{3}{2}$.

120. List the possible rational zeros of the function

$$g(x) = 6x^4 + 7x^3 - 29x^2 - 28x + 20.$$

121. *Aircraft Boarding* In how many different ways can 11 people board an airplane?

122. *Exam Questions* A student can answer any 15 questions from a total of 18 questions on an exam. In how many different ways can the student select the questions?

10.2 Translations of Conics

Vertical and Horizontal Shifts of Conics

In Section 10.1 you looked at conic sections whose graphs were in *standard position* (centered at the origin). In this section you will study the equations of conic sections that have been shifted vertically or horizontally in the plane.

Standard Forms of Equations of Conics

Circle: Center $= (h, k)$; radius $= r$

$$(x - h)^2 + (y - k)^2 = r^2$$

Ellipse: Center $= (h, k)$

  Major axis length $= 2a$; minor axis length $= 2b$

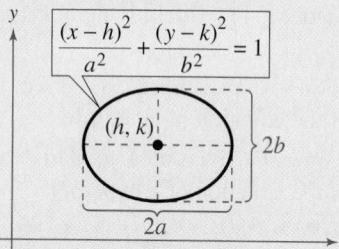

$$\frac{(x-h)^2}{a^2} + \frac{(y-k)^2}{b^2} = 1$$

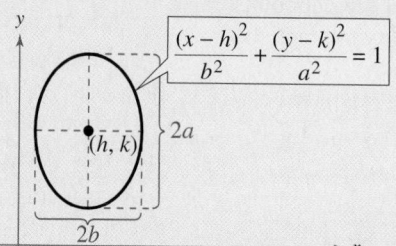

$$\frac{(x-h)^2}{b^2} + \frac{(y-k)^2}{a^2} = 1$$

Hyperbola: Center $= (h, k)$

  Transverse axis length $= 2a$; conjugate axis length $= 2b$

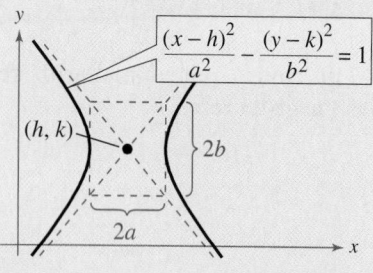

$$\frac{(x-h)^2}{a^2} - \frac{(y-k)^2}{b^2} = 1$$

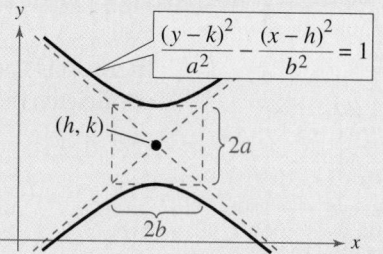

$$\frac{(y-k)^2}{a^2} - \frac{(x-h)^2}{b^2} = 1$$

Parabola: Vertex $= (h, k)$

  Directed distance from vertex to focus $= p$

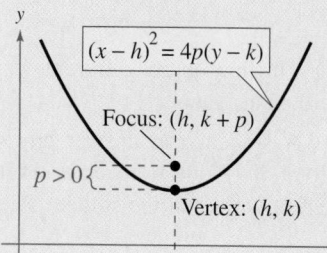

$$(x - h)^2 = 4p(y - k)$$

Focus: $(h, k + p)$
$p > 0$
Vertex: (h, k)

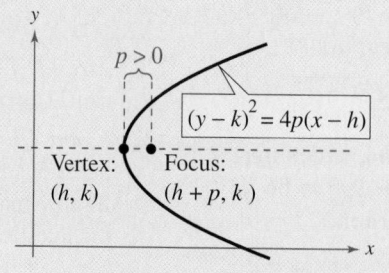

$$(y - k)^2 = 4p(x - h)$$

$p > 0$
Vertex: (h, k)
Focus: $(h + p, k)$

What you should learn

- Recognize equations of conics that have been shifted vertically and/or horizontally in the plane.
- Write and graph equations of conics that have been shifted vertically and/or horizontally in the plane.

Why you should learn it

In some real-life applications, it is convenient to use a conic whose center or vertex is not the origin. For instance, Exercise 77 on page 793 shows how an ellipse can be used to model the equation of a satellite's orbit around Earth. In this application, it is convenient to have one of the ellipse's foci at the origin.

eStock Photo

Example 1   Translations of Conic Sections

Describe the translation of the graph of each conic.

a. $(x - 1)^2 + (y + 2)^2 = 3^2$ **b.** $\dfrac{(x - 2)^2}{3^2} + \dfrac{(y - 1)^2}{2^2} = 1$

c. $\dfrac{(x - 3)^2}{1^2} - \dfrac{(y - 2)^2}{3^2} = 1$ **d.** $(x + 2)^2 = 4(-1)(y - 3)$

Solution

a. The graph of $(x - 1)^2 + (y + 2)^2 = 3^2$ is a circle whose center is the point $(1, -2)$ and whose radius is 3, as shown in Figure 10.22. Note that the graph of the circle has been shifted one unit to the right and two units downward from standard position.

b. The graph of

$$\frac{(x - 2)^2}{3^2} + \frac{(y - 1)^2}{2^2} = 1$$

is an ellipse whose center is the point $(2, 1)$. The major axis of the ellipse is horizontal and of length $2(3) = 6$, and the minor axis of the ellipse is vertical and of length $2(2) = 4$, as shown in Figure 10.23. Note that the graph of the ellipse has been shifted two units to the right and one unit upward from standard position.

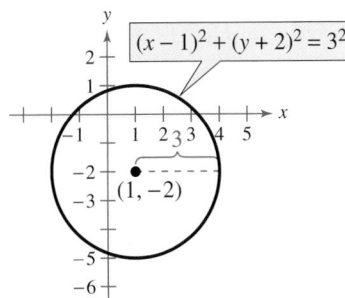
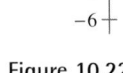

Figure 10.22

Figure 10.23

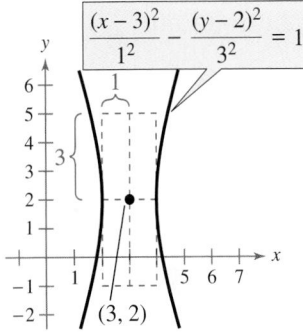

Figure 10.24

c. The graph of

$$\frac{(x - 3)^2}{1^2} - \frac{(y - 2)^2}{3^2} = 1$$

is a hyperbola whose center is the point $(3, 2)$. The transverse axis is horizontal and of length $2(1) = 2$, and the conjugate axis is vertical and of length $2(3) = 6$, as shown in Figure 10.24. Note that the graph of the hyperbola has been shifted three units to the right and two units upward from standard position.

d. The graph of $(x + 2)^2 = 4(-1)(y - 3)$ is a parabola whose vertex is the point $(-2, 3)$. The axis of the parabola is vertical. The focus is one unit above or below the vertex and, because $p = -1$, it follows that the focus lies *below* the vertex and the parabola opens downward, as shown in Figure 10.25. Note that the graph of the parabola has been shifted two units to the left and three units upward from standard position.

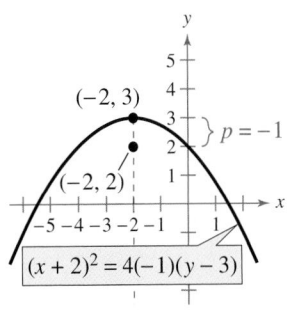

Figure 10.25

✓ *Checkpoint* Now try Exercise 3.

Equations of Conics in Standard Form

Example 2 Finding the Standard Form of a Parabola

Find the vertex and focus of the parabola $x^2 - 2x + 4y - 3 = 0$.

Solution

$$x^2 - 2x + 4y - 3 = 0 \qquad \text{Write original equation.}$$
$$x^2 - 2x + 1 = -4y + 3 + 1 \qquad \text{Group terms and add 1 to each side.}$$
$$(x - 1)^2 = -4y + 4 \qquad \text{Write in completed square form.}$$
$$(x - 1)^2 = 4(-1)(y - 1) \qquad \text{Write in standard form.}$$

From this standard form, it follows that $h = 1$, $k = 1$, and $p = -1$. Because the axis is vertical and p is negative, the parabola opens downward. The vertex is $(h, k) = (1, 1)$, and the focus is $(h, k + p) = (1, 0)$. See Figure 10.26.

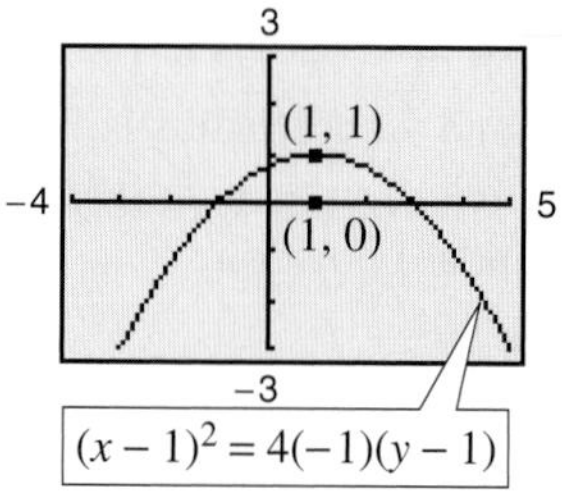

✓ *Checkpoint* Now try Exercise 23.

STUDY TIP

For a review of completing the square, refer to Section 2.4.

$(x - 1)^2 = 4(-1)(y - 1)$

Figure 10.26

Example 3 Sketching an Ellipse

Sketch the graph of the ellipse $x^2 + 4y^2 + 6x - 8y + 9 = 0$.

Algebraic Solution

$$x^2 + 4y^2 + 6x - 8y + 9 = 0 \qquad \text{Write original equation.}$$
$$(x^2 + 6x + \quad) + 4(y^2 - 2y + \quad) = -9 \qquad \text{Group terms and factor 4 out of } y\text{-terms.}$$
$$(x^2 + 6x + 9) + 4(y^2 - 2y + 1) = 4 \qquad \text{Add 9 and } 4(1) = 4 \text{ to each side.}$$
$$(x + 3)^2 + 4(y - 1)^2 = 4 \qquad \text{Write in completed square form.}$$
$$\frac{(x + 3)^2}{2^2} + \frac{(y - 1)^2}{1^2} = 1 \qquad \text{Write in standard form.}$$

From this standard form, it follows that the center is $(h, k) = (-3, 1)$. Because $a^2 = 2^2$ and $b^2 = 1^2$, the endpoints of the major axis lie two units to the right and left of the center and the endpoints of the minor axis lie one unit up and down from the center. The ellipse is shown in Figure 10.27.

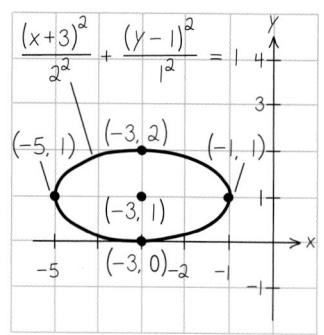

Figure 10.27

✓ *Checkpoint* Now try Exercise 37.

Graphical Solution

Write the completed square form of the ellipse as shown in the *Algebraic Solution*. Then solve the equation for y.

$$(y - 1)^2 = 1 - \frac{(x + 3)^2}{4}$$

$$y_1 = 1 + \sqrt{1 - \frac{(x + 3)^2}{4}}$$

$$y_2 = 1 - \sqrt{1 - \frac{(x + 3)^2}{4}}$$

Then use a graphing utility to graph y_1 and y_2 in the same viewing window, as shown in Figure 10.28. Use the *zoom* and *trace* features to approximate the endpoints of the major and minor axes.

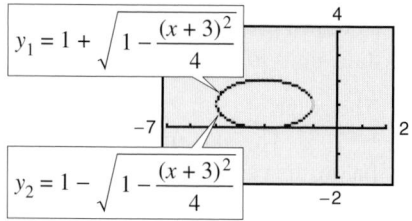

Figure 10.28

Example 4   Sketching a Hyperbola

Sketch the graph of the hyperbola given by the equation

$$y^2 - 4x^2 + 4y + 24x - 41 = 0.$$

Solution

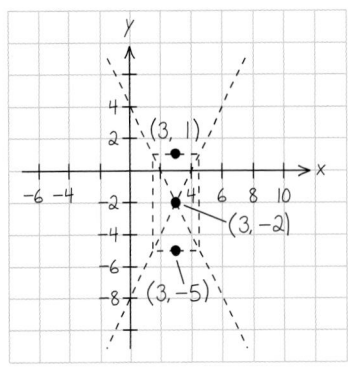

Figure 10.29

$y^2 - 4x^2 + 4y + 24x - 41 = 0$	Write original equation.
$(y^2 + 4y + \quad) - (4x^2 - 24x + \quad) = 41$	Group terms.
$(y^2 + 4y + \quad) - 4(x^2 - 6x + \quad) = 41$	Factor 4 out of x-terms.
$(y^2 + 4y + 4) - 4(x^2 - 6x + 9) = 41 + 4 - 4(9)$	Add 4 to and subtract $4(9) = 36$ from each side.
$(y + 2)^2 - 4(x - 3)^2 = 9$	Write in completed square form.
$\dfrac{(y + 2)^2}{9} - \dfrac{4(x - 3)^2}{9} = 1$	Divide each side by 9.
$\dfrac{(y + 2)^2}{9} - \dfrac{(x - 3)^2}{\dfrac{9}{4}} = 1$	Rewrite 4 as $\dfrac{1}{\frac{1}{4}}$.
$\dfrac{(y + 2)^2}{3^2} - \dfrac{(x - 3)^2}{\left(\dfrac{3}{2}\right)^2} = 1$	Write in standard form.

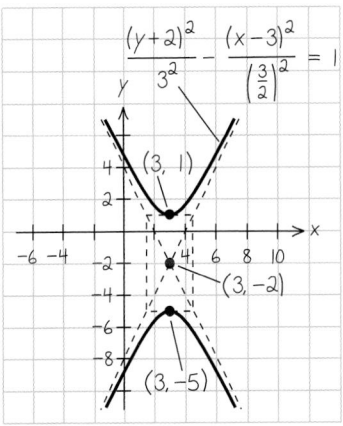

Figure 10.30

From this standard form, it follows that the transverse axis is vertical and the center lies at $(h, k) = (3, -2)$. Because the denominator of the y-term is $a^2 = 3^2$, you know that the vertices occur three units above and below the center.

$$(3, 1) \quad \text{and} \quad (3, -5) \qquad \text{Vertices}$$

To sketch the hyperbola, draw a rectangle whose top and bottom pass through the vertices. Because the denominator of the x-term is $b^2 = \left(\frac{3}{2}\right)^2$, locate the sides of the rectangle $\frac{3}{2}$ units to the right and left of the center. Sketch the asymptotes by drawing lines through the opposite corners of the rectangle, as shown in Figure 10.29. Using these asymptotes, you can complete the graph of the hyperbola, as shown in Figure 10.30.

 Checkpoint Now try Exercise 55.

To find the foci in Example 4, first find c.

$$c^2 = a^2 + b^2 = 9 + \frac{9}{4} = \frac{45}{4} \quad \Longrightarrow \quad c = \frac{3\sqrt{5}}{2}$$

Because the transverse axis is vertical, the foci lie c units above and below the center.

$$\left(3, -2 + \tfrac{3}{2}\sqrt{5}\right) \quad \text{and} \quad \left(3, -2 - \tfrac{3}{2}\sqrt{5}\right) \qquad \text{Foci}$$

Example 5 Finding the Standard Equation of an Ellipse

Find the standard form of the equation of the ellipse whose vertices are $(2, -2)$ and $(2, 4)$. The length of the minor axis of the ellipse is 4, as shown in Figure 10.31.

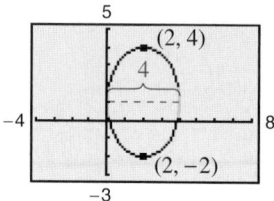

Figure 10.31

Solution

The center of the ellipse lies at the midpoint of its vertices. So, the center is

$$(h, k) = (2, 1). \qquad \text{Center}$$

Because the vertices lie on a vertical line and are six units apart, it follows that the major axis is vertical and has a length of $2a = 6$. So, $a = 3$. Moreover, because the minor axis has a length of 4, it follows that $2b = 4$, which implies that $b = 2$. Therefore, the standard form of the ellipse is as follows.

$$\frac{(x - h)^2}{b^2} + \frac{(y - k)^2}{a^2} = 1 \qquad \text{Major axis is vertical.}$$

$$\frac{(x - 2)^2}{2^2} + \frac{(y - 1)^2}{3^2} = 1 \qquad \text{Write in standard form.}$$

✓ *Checkpoint* Now try Exercise 43.

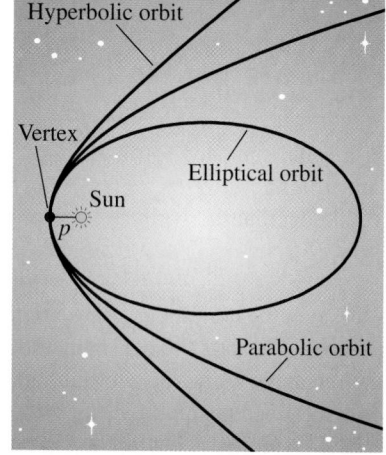

Figure 10.32

An interesting application of conics involves the orbits of comets in our solar system. Of the 610 comets identified prior to 1970, 245 have elliptical orbits, 295 have parabolic orbits, and 70 have hyperbolic orbits. For example, Halley's comet has an elliptical orbit, and the reappearance of this comet can be predicted to occur every 76 years. The center of the sun is a focus of each of these orbits, and each orbit has a vertex at the point where the comet is closest to the sun, as shown in Figure 10.32.

If p is the distance between the vertex and the focus in meters, and v is the speed of the comet at the vertex in meters per second, then the type of orbit is determined as follows.

1. Ellipse: $v < \sqrt{\dfrac{2GM}{p}}$

2. Parabola: $v = \sqrt{\dfrac{2GM}{p}}$

3. Hyperbola: $v > \sqrt{\dfrac{2GM}{p}}$

In each of these equations, $M = 1.989 \times 10^{30}$ kilograms (the mass of the sun) and $G \approx 6.67 \times 10^{-11}$ cubic meters per kilogram-second squared (the universal gravitational constant).

10.2 Exercises

Vocabulary Check

In Exercises 1–7, match the description of the conic with its standard equation. [The equations are labeled (a), (b), (c), (d), (e), (f), and (g).]

(a) $\dfrac{(x-h)^2}{a^2} - \dfrac{(y-k)^2}{b^2} = 1$

(b) $(x-h)^2 = 4p(y-k)$

(c) $\dfrac{(x-h)^2}{a^2} + \dfrac{(y-k)^2}{b^2} = 1$

(d) $\dfrac{(x-h)^2}{b^2} + \dfrac{(y-k)^2}{a^2} = 1$

(e) $(x-h)^2 + (y-k)^2 = r^2$

(f) $(y-k)^2 = 4p(x-h)$

(g) $\dfrac{(y-k)^2}{a^2} - \dfrac{(x-h)^2}{b^2} = 1$

1. Circle

2. Ellipse with vertical major axis

3. Parabola with vertical axis

4. Hyperbola with horizontal transverse axis

5. Ellipse with horizontal major axis

6. Parabola with horizontal axis

7. Hyperbola with vertical transverse axis

In Exercises 1–6, describe the translation of the graph of the conic.

1.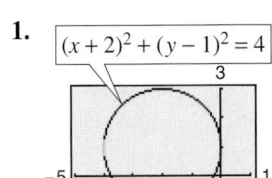
$(x+2)^2 + (y-1)^2 = 4$

2.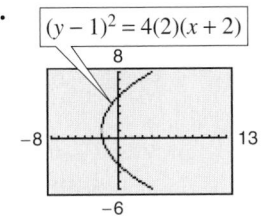
$(y-1)^2 = 4(2)(x+2)$

3.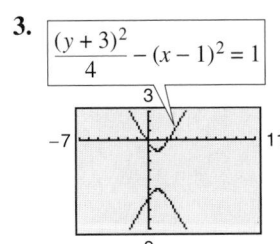
$\dfrac{(y+3)^2}{4} - (x-1)^2 = 1$

4.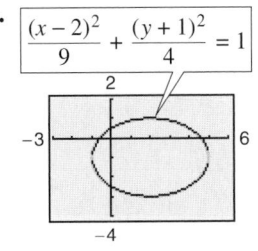
$\dfrac{(x-2)^2}{9} + \dfrac{(y+1)^2}{4} = 1$

5.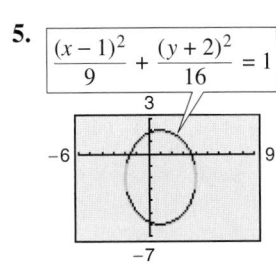
$\dfrac{(x-1)^2}{9} + \dfrac{(y+2)^2}{16} = 1$

6.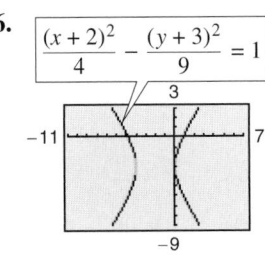
$\dfrac{(x+2)^2}{4} - \dfrac{(y+3)^2}{9} = 1$

In Exercises 7–12, identify the center and radius of the circle.

7. $x^2 + y^2 = 49$

8. $x^2 + y^2 = 1$

9. $(x+2)^2 + (y-7)^2 = 16$

10. $(x+9)^2 + (y+1)^2 = 36$

11. $(x-1)^2 + y^2 = 15$

12. $x^2 + (y+12)^2 = 24$

In Exercises 13–16, write the equation of the circle in standard form. Then identify its center and radius.

13. $x^2 + y^2 - 2x + 6y + 9 = 0$

14. $x^2 + y^2 - 10x - 6y + 25 = 0$

15. $4x^2 + 4y^2 + 12x - 24y + 41 = 0$

16. $9x^2 + 9y^2 + 54x - 36y + 17 = 0$

In Exercises 17–24, find the vertex, focus, and directrix of the parabola, and sketch its graph. Use a graphing utility to verify your graph.

17. $(x+1)^2 + 8(y+2) = 0$

18. $(x+3) + (y-2)^2 = 0$

19. $\left(y - \tfrac{1}{2}\right)^2 = 2(x-5)$ 20. $\left(x - \tfrac{1}{2}\right)^2 = 4(y+3)$

21. $y = \tfrac{1}{4}(x^2 - 2x + 5)$

22. $4x - y^2 - 2y - 33 = 0$

23. $y^2 + 6y + 8x + 25 = 0$

24. $y^2 - 4y - 4x = 0$

In Exercises 25–32, find the standard form of the equation of the parabola.

25.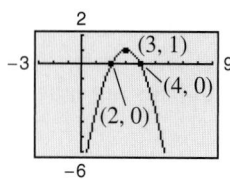

26.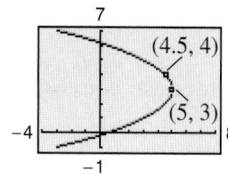

27. Vertex: $(3, 2)$; focus: $(1, 2)$
28. Vertex: $(-1, 2)$; focus: $(-1, 0)$
29. Vertex: $(0, 4)$; directrix: $y = 2$
30. Vertex: $(-2, 1)$; directrix: $x = 1$
31. Focus: $(2, 2)$; directrix: $x = -2$
32. Focus: $(0, 0)$; directrix: $y = 4$

In Exercises 33–40, find the center, foci, and vertices of the ellipse, and sketch its graph. Use a graphing utility to verify your answer.

33. $\dfrac{(x - 1)^2}{9} + \dfrac{(y - 3)^2}{25} = 1$

34. $\dfrac{(x - 6)^2}{4} + \dfrac{(y + 7)^2}{16} = 1$

35. $(x + 2)^2 + \dfrac{(y - 4)^2}{\frac{1}{4}} = 1$

36. $\dfrac{(x - 3)^2}{\frac{25}{9}} + (y - 8)^2 = 1$

37. $9x^2 + 4y^2 + 36x - 24y + 36 = 0$
38. $9x^2 + 4y^2 - 36x + 8y + 31 = 0$
39. $16x^2 + 25y^2 - 32x + 50y + 16 = 0$
40. $9x^2 + 25y^2 - 36x - 50y + 61 = 0$

In Exercises 41–50, find the standard form of the equation of the ellipse.

41.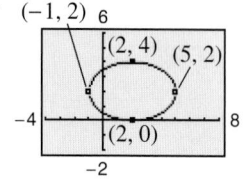

42.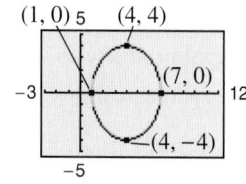

43. Vertices: $(0, 2)$, $(4, 2)$; minor axis of length 2
44. Foci: $(0, 0)$, $(4, 0)$; major axis of length 8
45. Foci: $(0, 0)$, $(0, 8)$; major axis of length 16

46. Center: $(2, -1)$; vertex: $\left(2, \frac{1}{2}\right)$; minor axis of length 2
47. Vertices: $(3, 1)$, $(3, 9)$; minor axis of length 6
48. Center: $(3, 2)$; $a = 3c$; foci: $(1, 2)$, $(5, 2)$
49. Center: $(0, 4)$; $a = 2c$; vertices: $(-4, 4)$, $(4, 4)$
50. Vertices: $(5, 0)$, $(5, 12)$; endpoints of minor axis: $(0, 6)$, $(10, 6)$

In Exercises 51–60, find the center, vertices, and foci of the hyperbola, and sketch its graph, using asymptotes as sketching aids. Use a graphing utility to verify your graph.

51. $\dfrac{(x + 1)^2}{4} - \dfrac{(y - 2)^2}{1} = 1$

52. $\dfrac{(x - 1)^2}{144} - \dfrac{(y + 4)^2}{25} = 1$

53. $(y + 6)^2 - (x - 2)^2 = 1$

54. $\dfrac{(y + 1)^2}{\frac{1}{4}} - \dfrac{(x + 3)^2}{\frac{1}{9}} = 1$

55. $9x^2 - y^2 - 36x - 6y + 18 = 0$
56. $x^2 - 9y^2 + 36y - 72 = 0$
57. $x^2 - 9y^2 + 2x - 54y - 80 = 0$
58. $16y^2 - x^2 + 2x + 64y + 63 = 0$
59. $9y^2 - 4x^2 + 8x + 18y + 41 = 0$
60. $11y^2 - 3x^2 + 12x + 44y + 48 = 0$

In Exercises 61–68, find the standard form of the equation of the hyperbola.

61.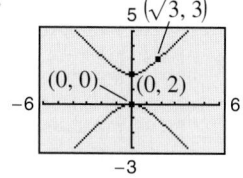

62.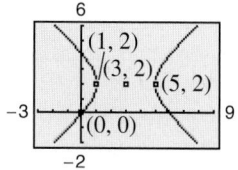

63. Vertices: $(2, 0)$, $(6, 0)$; foci: $(0, 0)$, $(8, 0)$
64. Vertices: $(2, 3)$, $(2, -3)$; foci: $(2, 5)$, $(2, -5)$
65. Vertices: $(4, 1)$, $(4, 9)$; foci: $(4, 0)$, $(4, 10)$
66. Vertices: $(-2, 1)$, $(2, 1)$; foci: $(-3, 1)$, $(3, 1)$
67. Vertices: $(2, 3)$, $(2, -3)$; passes through the point $(0, 5)$
68. Vertices: $(3, 0)$, $(3, 4)$; asymptotes: $y = \frac{2}{3}x$, $y = 4 - \frac{2}{3}x$

In Exercises 69–76, identify the conic by writing the equation in standard form. Then sketch its graph.

69. $x^2 + y^2 - 6x + 4y + 9 = 0$

70. $x^2 + 4y^2 - 6x + 16y + 21 = 0$

71. $4x^2 - y^2 - 4x - 3 = 0$

72. $y^2 - 4y - 4x = 0$

73. $4x^2 + 3y^2 + 8x - 24y + 51 = 0$

74. $4y^2 - 2x^2 - 4y - 8x - 15 = 0$

75. $25x^2 - 10x - 200y - 119 = 0$

76. $4x^2 + 4y^2 - 16y + 15 = 0$

77. *Satellite Orbit*   A satellite in a 100-mile-high circular orbit around Earth has a velocity of approximately 17,500 miles per hour. If this velocity is multiplied by $\sqrt{2}$, the satellite will have the minimum velocity necessary to escape Earth's gravity, and it will follow a parabolic path with the center of Earth as the focus.

(a) Find the escape velocity of the satellite.

(b) Find an equation of its path (assume the radius of Earth is 4000 miles).

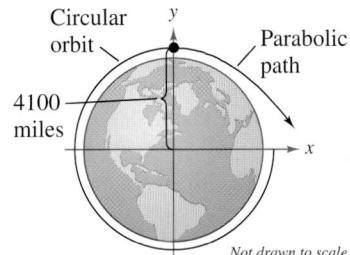

Not drawn to scale

78. *Projectile Motion*   A cargo plane is flying at an altitude of 30,000 feet and a speed of 540 miles per hour (792 feet per second). How many feet will a supply crate dropped from the plane travel horizontally before it hits the ground if the path of the crate is modeled by

$$x^2 = -39{,}204(y - 30{,}000)?$$

79. *Path of a Projectile*   The path of a softball is modeled by

$$-12.5(y - 7.125) = (x - 6.25)^2.$$

The coordinates x and y are measured in feet, with $x = 0$ corresponding to the position from which the ball was thrown.

(a) Use a graphing utility to graph the trajectory of the softball.

(b) Use the *trace* feature of the graphing utility to approximate the highest point the ball reaches and the distance the ball travels.

80. *Revenue*   The revenue R generated by the sale of x 32-inch televisions is modeled by

$$R = 375x - \tfrac{3}{2}x^2.$$

(a) Use a graphing utility to graph the function.

(b) Use the *trace* feature of the graphing utility to approximate *graphically* the sales that will maximize the revenue.

(c) Use the *table* feature of the graphing utility to approximate *numerically* the sales that will maximize the revenue.

(d) Find the coordinates of the vertex to find *algebraically* the sales that will maximize the revenue.

(e) Compare the results of parts (b), (c), and (d). What did you learn as a result of using all three approaches?

In Exercises 81–84, e is called the *eccentricity* of an ellipse and is defined by $e = c/a$. It measures the flatness of the ellipse.

81. Find an equation of the ellipse with vertices $(\pm 5, 0)$ and eccentricity $e = \tfrac{3}{5}$.

82. Find an equation of the ellipse with vertices $(0, \pm 8)$ and eccentricity $e = \tfrac{1}{2}$.

83. *Planetary Motion*   The planet Pluto moves in an elliptical orbit with the sun at one of the foci. The length of half of the major axis is 3.67×10^9 miles and the eccentricity is 0.249. Find the smallest distance (*perihelion*) and the greatest distance (*aphelion*) of Pluto from the center of the sun.

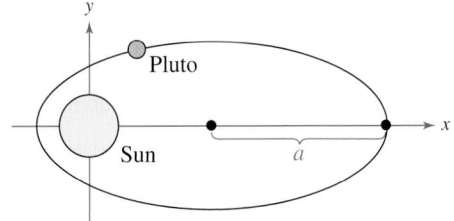

84. *Satellite Orbit* The first artificial satellite to orbit Earth was Sputnik I (launched by the former Soviet Union in 1957). Its highest point above Earth's surface was 947 kilometers, and its lowest point was 228 kilometers. The center of Earth is the focus of the elliptical orbit, and the radius of Earth is 6378 kilometers. Find the eccentricity of the orbit.

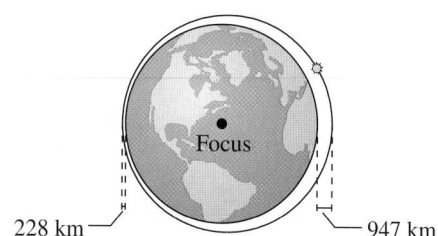

85. *Sports* In Australia, football by *Australian Rules* (or rugby) is played on elliptical fields. The fields can be a maximum of 170 yards wide and a maximum of 200 yards long. Let the center of a field of maximum size be represented by the point $(0, 85)$. Find the standard form of the equation of the ellipse that represents this field.   (Source: Australian Football League)

86. *Astronomy* Halley's comet has an elliptical orbit with the sun at one focus. The eccentricity of the orbit is approximately 0.97. The length of the major axis of the orbit is approximately 35.88 astronomical units. (An astronomical unit is about 93 million miles.) Find the standard form of the equation of the orbit. Place the center of the orbit at the origin and place the major axis on the x-axis.

Synthesis

True or False? **In Exercises 87 and 88, determine whether the statement is true or false. Justify your answer.**

87. The conic represented by the equation $3x^2 + 2y^2 - 18x - 16y + 58 = 0$ is an ellipse.

88. The graphs of $x^2 + 10y - 10x + 5 = 0$ and $x^2 + 16y^2 + 10x - 32y - 23 = 0$ do not intersect.

Think About It **In Exercises 89 and 90, change the equation so that its graph matches the description.**

89. $(y - 3)^2 = 6(x + 1)$; upper half of parabola

90. $(y + 1)^2 = 2(x - 2)$; lower half of parabola

Think About It **In Exercises 91 and 92, change the equation so that its graph matches the description.**

91. $\dfrac{(x - 3)^2}{9} + \dfrac{y^2}{4} = 1$; right half of ellipse

92. $\dfrac{(x + 1)^2}{16} + \dfrac{(y - 2)^2}{25} = 1$; bottom half of ellipse

93. *Exploration* Consider the ellipse $\dfrac{x^2}{a^2} + \dfrac{y^2}{b^2} = 1$.

(a) Show that the equation of the ellipse can be written as

$$\frac{(x - h)^2}{a^2} + \frac{(y - k)^2}{a^2(1 - e^2)} = 1$$

where e is the eccentricity.

(b) Use a graphing utility to graph the ellipse

$$\frac{(x - 2)^2}{4} + \frac{(y - 3)^2}{4(1 - e^2)} = 1$$

for $e = 0.95, 0.75, 0.5, 0.25,$ and 0.

(c) Make a conjecture about the change in the shape of the ellipse as e approaches 0.

94. *Writing* Use your school's library, the Internet, or some other reference source to research information about the orbits of comets in our solar system. What can you find about the orbits of comets that have been identified since 1970? Write a summary of your results. Identify your source(s).

Review

In Exercises 95–98, use sigma notation to write the sum. Then use a graphing utility to find the sum.

95. $\dfrac{1}{6(1)} + \dfrac{1}{6(2)} + \dfrac{1}{6(3)} + \cdots + \dfrac{1}{6(9)}$

96. $\dfrac{7}{2 + 1} + \dfrac{7}{2 + 2} + \dfrac{7}{2 + 3} + \cdots + \dfrac{7}{2 + 12}$

97. $1 - \dfrac{1}{4} + \dfrac{1}{16} - \cdots + \dfrac{1}{65536}$

98. $\dfrac{1}{9} + \dfrac{4}{27} + \dfrac{7}{81} + \dfrac{10}{243}$

In Exercises 99–102, use the Binomial Theorem to expand and simplify the expression.

99. $(x - 4)^4$ **100.** $(x - 3)^6$

101. $(3x + 1)^5$ **102.** $(x^2 - 2)^5$

10.3 Parametric Equations

Plane Curves

Up to this point, you have been representing a graph by a single equation involving *two* variables such as x and y. In this section, you will study situations in which it is useful to introduce a *third* variable to represent a curve in the plane.

To see the usefulness of this procedure, consider the path of an object that is propelled into the air at an angle of $45°$. If the initial velocity of the object is 48 feet per second, it can be shown that the object follows the parabolic path

$$y = -\frac{x^2}{72} + x \qquad \text{Rectangular equation}$$

as shown in Figure 10.33. However, this equation does not tell the whole story. Although it does tell you *where* the object has been, it doesn't tell you *when* the object was at a given point (x, y) on the path. To determine this time, you can introduce a third variable t, called a **parameter.** It is possible to write both x and y as functions of t to obtain the **parametric equations**

$$x = 24\sqrt{2}\,t \qquad \text{Parametric equation for } x$$

$$y = -16t^2 + 24\sqrt{2}\,t. \qquad \text{Parametric equation for } y$$

From this set of equations you can determine that at time $t = 0$, the object is at the point $(0, 0)$. Similarly, at time $t = 1$, the object is at the point $\left(24\sqrt{2},\ 24\sqrt{2} - 16\right)$, and so on.

What you should learn

- Evaluate sets of parametric equations for given values of the parameter.
- Graph curves that are represented by sets of parametric equations.
- Rewrite sets of parametric equations as single rectangular equations by eliminating the parameter.
- Find sets of parametric equations for graphs.

Why you should learn it

Parametric equations are useful for modeling the path of an object. For instance, in Exercise 59 on page 802, a set of parametric equations is used to model the path of a baseball.

SuperStock

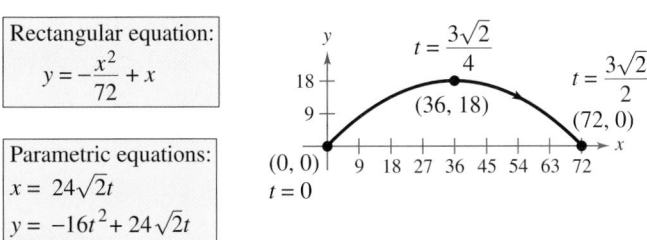

Rectangular equation:
$$y = -\frac{x^2}{72} + x$$

Parametric equations:
$$x = 24\sqrt{2}\,t$$
$$y = -16t^2 + 24\sqrt{2}\,t$$

Curvilinear motion: two variables for position, one variable for time
Figure 10.33

For this particular motion problem, x and y are continuous functions of t, and the resulting path is a **plane curve.** (Recall that a *continuous function* is one whose graph can be traced without lifting the pencil from the paper.)

Definition of a Plane Curve

If f and g are continuous functions of t on an interval I, the set of ordered pairs $(f(t), g(t))$ is a **plane curve** C. The equations given by

$$x = f(t) \qquad \text{and} \qquad y = g(t)$$

are **parametric equations** for C, and t is the **parameter.**

STUDY TIP

It is not necessary for the parameter in a set of parametric equations to represent time. The parameter is often used to represent an *angle*, as shown in Example 4.

Sketching a Plane Curve

One way to sketch a curve represented by a pair of parametric equations is to plot points in the *xy*-plane. Each set of coordinates (x, y) is determined from a value chosen for the parameter *t*. By plotting the resulting points in the order of *increasing* values of *t*, you trace the curve in a specific direction. This is called the **orientation** of the curve.

Example 1   Sketching a Plane Curve

Sketch the curve given by the parametric equations

$$x = t^2 - 4 \quad \text{and} \quad y = \frac{t}{2}, \quad -2 \le t \le 3.$$

Describe the orientation of the curve.

Solution

Using values of *t* in the interval, the parametric equations yield the points (x, y) shown in the table.

t	−2	−1	0	1	2	3
x	0	−3	−4	−3	0	5
y	−1	$-\frac{1}{2}$	0	$\frac{1}{2}$	1	$\frac{3}{2}$

By plotting these points in the order of increasing *t*, you obtain the curve shown in Figure 10.34. The arrows on the curve indicate its orientation as *t* increases from −2 to 3. So, if a particle were moving on this curve, it would start at $(0, -1)$ and then move along the curve to the point $\left(5, \frac{3}{2}\right)$.

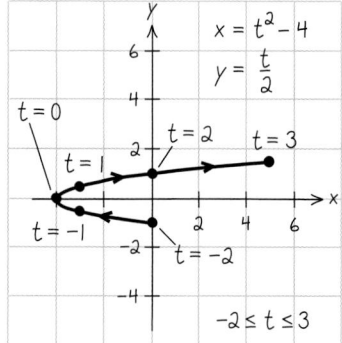

Figure 10.34

 Checkpoint Now try Exercises 7(a) and (b).

Note that the graph shown in Figure 10.34 does not define *y* as a function of *x*. This points out one benefit of parametric equations—they can be used to represent graphs that are more general than graphs of functions.

Two different sets of parametric equations can have the same graph. For example, the set of parametric equations

$$x = 4t^2 - 4 \quad \text{and} \quad y = t, \quad -1 \le t \le \tfrac{3}{2}$$

has the same graph as the set given in Example 1. However, by comparing the values of *t* in Figures 10.34 and 10.35, you can see that this second graph is traced out more *rapidly* (considering *t* as time) than the first graph. So, in applications, different parametric representations can be used to represent various *speeds* at which objects travel along a given path.

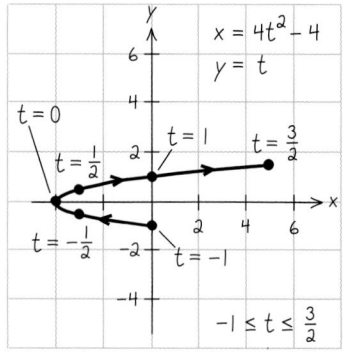

Figure 10.35

TECHNOLOGY TIP   Most graphing utilities have a *parametric* mode. So, another way to display a curve represented by a pair of parametric equations is to use a graphing utility, as shown in Example 2. For instructions on how to use the *parametric* mode, see Appendix A; for specifice keystrokes, go to the text website at *college.hmco.com*.

Example 2 Using a Graphing Utility in Parametric Mode

Use a graphing utility to graph the curves represented by the parametric equations. Using the graph and the Vertical Line Test, for which curve is y a function of x?

a. $x = t^2, y = t^3$ **b.** $x = t, y = t^3$ **c.** $x = t^2, y = t$

Solution

Begin by setting the graphing utility to *parametric* mode. When choosing a viewing window, you must set not only minimum and maximum values of x and y, but also minimum and maximum values of t.

a. Enter the parametric equations for x and y, as shown in Figure 10.36. Use the viewing window shown in Figure 10.37. The curve is shown in Figure 10.38. From the graph, you can see that y *is not* a function of x.

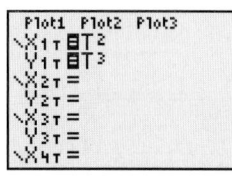
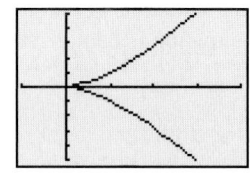

Figure 10.36   Figure 10.37   Figure 10.38

b. Enter the parametric equations for x and y, as shown in Figure 10.39. Use the viewing window shown in Figure 10.40. The curve is shown in Figure 10.41. From the graph, you can see that y *is* a function of x.

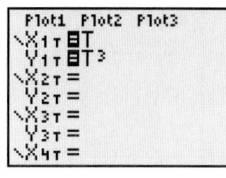
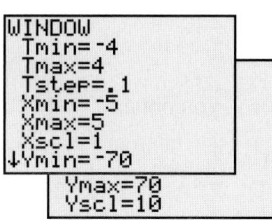
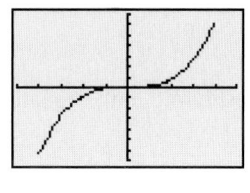

Figure 10.39   Figure 10.40   Figure 10.41

c. Enter the parametric equations for x and y, as shown in Figure 10.42. Use the viewing window shown in Figure 10.43. The curve is shown in Figure 10.44. From the graph, you can see that y *is not* a function of x.

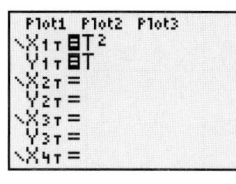
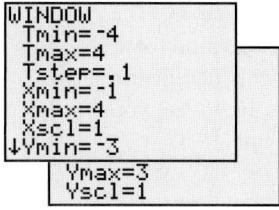
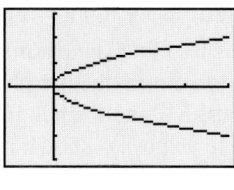

Figure 10.42   Figure 10.43   Figure 10.44

✓ *Checkpoint* Now try Exercise 7(c).

Exploration

Use a graphing utility set in *parametric* mode to graph the curve

$$X_{1T} = T \quad \text{and}$$
$$Y_{1T} = 1 - T^2.$$

Set the viewing window so that $-4 \le x \le 4$ and $-12 \le y \le 2$. Now, graph the curve with various settings for t. Use the following.

a. $0 \le t \le 3$

b. $-3 \le t \le 0$

c. $-3 \le t \le 3$

Compare the curves given by the different t settings. Repeat this experiment using $X_{1T} = -T$. How does this change the results?

TECHNOLOGY TIP

Notice in Example 2 that in order to set the viewing windows of parametric graphs, you have to scroll down to enter the Ymax and Yscl values.

Eliminating the Parameter

Many curves that are represented by sets of parametric equations have graphs that can also be represented by rectangular equations (in x and y). The process of finding the rectangular equation is called **eliminating the parameter.**

Parametric equations	⇒	Solve for t in one equation.	⇒	Substitute in second equation.	⇒	Rectangular equation

$x = t^2 - 4$ $\qquad$ $t = 2y$ $\qquad$ $x = (2y)^2 - 4$ $\qquad$ $x = 4y^2 - 4$

$y = \frac{1}{2}t$

Now you can recognize that the equation $x = 4y^2 - 4$ represents a parabola with a horizontal axis and vertex at $(-4, 0)$.

When converting equations from parametric to rectangular form, you may need to alter the domain of the rectangular equation so that its graph matches the graph of the parametric equations. This situation is demonstrated in Example 3.

Example 3   Eliminating the Parameter

Identify the curve represented by the equations

$$x = \frac{1}{\sqrt{t + 1}} \qquad \text{and} \qquad y = \frac{t}{t + 1}.$$

Solution

Solving for t in the equation for x produces

$$x^2 = \frac{1}{t + 1} \qquad \text{or} \qquad \frac{1}{x^2} = t + 1$$

which implies that $t = (1/x^2) - 1$. Substituting in the equation for y, you obtain

$$y = \frac{t}{t + 1}$$

$$= \frac{\left(\dfrac{1}{x^2}\right) - 1}{\left(\dfrac{1}{x^2}\right) - 1 + 1} = \frac{\dfrac{1 - x^2}{x^2}}{\left(\dfrac{1}{x^2}\right)} \cdot \frac{x^2}{x^2} = 1 - x^2.$$

From the rectangular equation, you can recognize that the curve is a parabola that opens downward and has its vertex at $(0, 1)$, as shown in Figure 10.45. The rectangular equation is defined for all values of x. The parametric equation for x, however, is defined only when $t > -1$. From the graph of the parametric equations, you can see that x is always positive, as shown in Figure 10.46. So, you should restrict the domain of x to positive values, as shown in Figure 10.47.

✓ *Checkpoint* Now try Exercise 7(d).

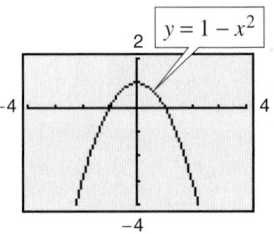

Figure 10.45

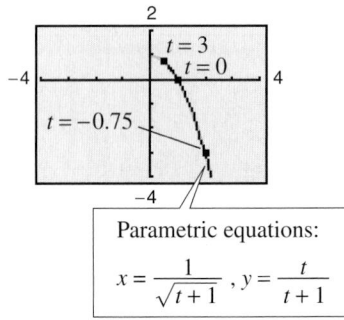

Figure 10.46

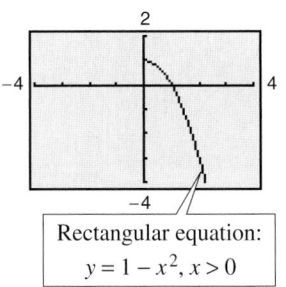

Figure 10.47

Example 4   Eliminating the Parameter

Sketch the curve represented by $x = 3 \cos \theta$ and $y = 4 \sin \theta$, $0 \le \theta \le 2\pi$, by eliminating the parameter.

Solution

Begin by solving for $\cos \theta$ and $\sin \theta$ in the equations.

$$\cos \theta = \frac{x}{3} \quad \text{and} \quad \sin \theta = \frac{y}{4} \qquad \text{Solve for } \cos \theta \text{ and } \sin \theta.$$

Use the identity $\sin^2 \theta + \cos^2 \theta = 1$ to form an equation involving only x and y.

$$\cos^2 \theta + \sin^2 \theta = 1 \qquad \text{Pythagorean identity}$$

$$\left(\frac{x}{3}\right)^2 + \left(\frac{y}{4}\right)^2 = 1 \qquad \text{Substitute } \tfrac{x}{3} \text{ for } \cos \theta \text{ and } \tfrac{y}{4} \text{ for } \sin \theta.$$

$$\frac{x^2}{9} + \frac{y^2}{16} = 1 \qquad \text{Rectangular equation}$$

From this rectangular equation, you can see that the graph is an ellipse centered at $(0, 0)$, with vertices $(0, 4)$ and $(0, -4)$, and minor axis of length $2b = 6$, as shown in Figure 10.48. Note that the elliptic curve is traced out *counterclockwise*.

 Checkpoint   Now try Exercise 19.

Exploration

In Example 4 you made use of the trigonometric identity $\sin^2 \theta + \cos^2 \theta = 1$ to sketch an ellipse. Which trigonometric identity would you use to obtain the graph of a hyperbola? Sketch the curve represented by $x = 3 \sec \theta$ and $y = 4 \tan \theta$, $0 \le \theta \le 2\pi$, by eliminating the parameter.

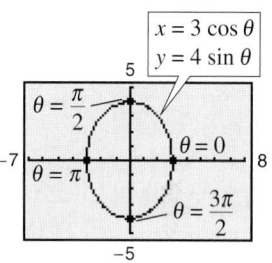

Figure 10.48

Finding Parametric Equations for a Graph

How can you determine a set of parametric equations for a given graph or a given physical description? From the discussion following Example 1, you know that such a representation is not unique. This is further demonstrated in Example 5.

Example 5   Finding Parametric Equations for a Given Graph

Find a set of parametric equations to represent the graph of $y = 1 - x^2$ using the parameters (a) $t = x$ and (b) $t = 1 - x$.

Solution

a. Letting $t = x$, you obtain the following parametric equations.

$$x = t \qquad \text{Parametric equation for } x$$

$$y = 1 - t^2 \qquad \text{Parametric equation for } y$$

The graph of these equations is shown in Figure 10.49.

b. Letting $t = 1 - x$, you obtain the following parametric equations.

$$x = 1 - t \qquad \text{Parametric equation for } x$$

$$y = 1 - (1 - t)^2 = 2t - t^2 \qquad \text{Parametric equation for } y$$

The graph of these equations is shown in Figure 10.50. Note that the graphs in Figures 10.49 and 10.50 have opposite orientations.

 Checkpoint   Now try Exercise 43.

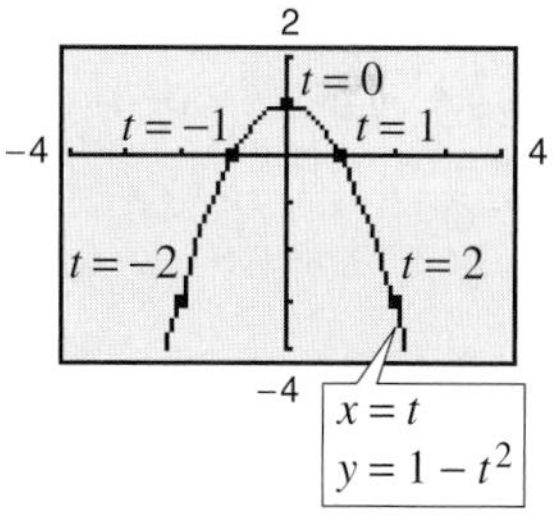

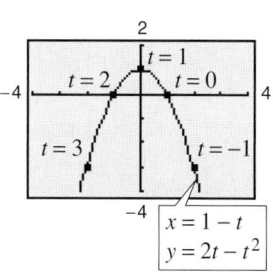

Figure 10.49

Figure 10.50

10.3 Exercises

Vocabulary Check

Fill in the blanks.

1. If f and g are continuous functions of t on an interval I, the set of ordered pairs $(f(t), g(t))$ is a _____ C. The equations given by $x = f(t)$ and $y = g(t)$ are _____ for C, and t is the _____.

2. The _____ of a curve is the direction in which the curve is traced out for increasing values of the parameter.

3. The process of converting a set of parametric equations to rectangular form is called _____ the _____.

In Exercises 1–6, match the set of parametric equations with its graph. [The graphs are labeled (a), (b), (c), (d), (e), and (f).]

(a)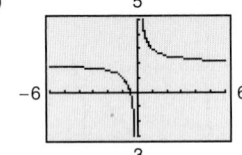

(b)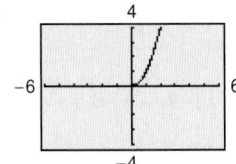

(c)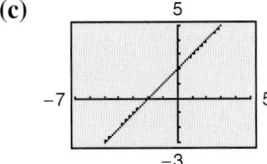

(d)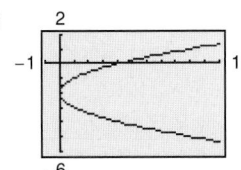

(e)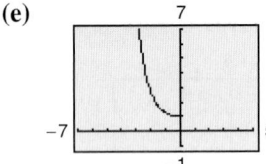

(f)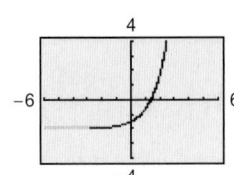

1. $x = t$
   $y = t + 2$

2. $x = t^2$
   $y = t - 2$

3. $x = \sqrt{t}$
   $y = t$

4. $x = \dfrac{1}{t}$
   $y = t + 2$

5. $x = \ln t$
   $y = \frac{1}{2}t - 2$

6. $x = -2\sqrt{t}$
   $y = e^t$

7. Consider the parametric equations $x = \sqrt{t}$ and $y = 2 - t$.

   (a) Create a table of x- and y-values using $t = 0, 1, 2, 3,$ and 4.

   (b) Plot the points (x, y) generated in part (a) and sketch a graph of the parametric equations.

   (c) Use a graphing utility to graph the curve represented by the parametric equations.

   (d) Find the rectangular equation by eliminating the parameter. Sketch its graph. How does the graph differ from those in parts (b) and (c)?

8. Consider the parametric equations $x = 4 \cos^2 \theta$ and $y = 2 \sin \theta$.

   (a) Create a table of x- and y-values using $\theta = -\pi/2, -\pi/4, 0, \pi/4,$ and $\pi/2$.

   (b) Plot the points (x, y) generated in part (a) and sketch a graph of the parametric equations.

   (c) Use a graphing utility to graph the curve represented by the parametric equations.

   (d) Find the rectangular equation by eliminating the parameter. Sketch its graph. How does the graph differ from those in parts (b) and (c)?

In Exercises 9–24, sketch the curve represented by the parametric equations (indicate the orientation of the curve). Use a graphing utility to confirm your result. Then eliminate the parameter and write the corresponding rectangular equation whose graph represents the curve. Adjust the domain of the resulting rectangular equation, if necessary.

9. $x = t$
   $y = -4t$

10. $x = t$
    $y = \frac{1}{2}t$

11. $x = 3t - 3$
    $y = 2t + 1$

12. $x = 3 - 2t$
    $y = 2 + 3t$

13. $x = \frac{1}{4}t$
    $y = t^2$

14. $x = t$
    $y = t^3$

15. $x = t + 2$
   $y = t^2$

16. $x = \sqrt{t}$
   $y = 1 - t$

17. $x = 2t$
   $y = |t - 2|$

18. $x = |t - 1|$
   $y = t + 2$

19. $x = 3 \cos \theta$
   $y = 3 \sin \theta$

20. $x = \cos \theta$
   $y = 3 \sin \theta$

21. $x = e^{-t}$
   $y = e^{3t}$

22. $x = e^{2t}$
   $y = e^t$

23. $x = t^3$
   $y = 3 \ln t$

24. $x = \ln 2t$
   $y = 2t^2$

In Exercises 25–30, use a graphing utility to graph the curve represented by the parametric equations.

25. $x = 4 + 2 \cos \theta$
   $y = -1 + \sin \theta$

26. $x = 4 + 2 \cos \theta$
   $y = -1 + 2 \sin \theta$

27. $x = 4 \sec \theta$
   $y = 3 \tan \theta$

28. $x = \sec \theta$
   $y = \tan \theta$

29. $x = t/2$
   $y = \ln(t^2 + 1)$

30. $x = 10 - 0.01e^t$
   $y = 0.4t^2$

In Exercises 31 and 32, determine how the plane curves differ from each other.

31. (a) $x = t$
      $y = 2t + 1$

   (b) $x = \cos \theta$
      $y = 2 \cos \theta + 1$

   (c) $x = e^{-t}$
      $y = 2e^{-t} + 1$

   (d) $x = e^t$
      $y = 2e^t + 1$

32. (a) $x = 2\sqrt{t}$
      $y = 4 - \sqrt{t}$

   (b) $x = 2\sqrt[3]{t}$
      $y = 4 - \sqrt[3]{t}$

   (c) $x = 2(t + 1)$
      $y = 3 - t$

   (d) $x = -2t^2$
      $y = 4 + t^2$

In Exercises 33–36, eliminate the parameter and obtain the standard form of the rectangular equation.

33. Line through (x_1, y_1) and (x_2, y_2):
   $x = x_1 + t(x_2 - x_1)$
   $y = y_1 + t(y_2 - y_1)$

34. Circle: $x = h + r \cos \theta$
      $y = k + r \sin \theta$

35. Ellipse: $x = h + a \cos \theta$
      $y = k + b \sin \theta$

36. Hyperbola: $x = h + a \sec \theta$
      $y = k + b \tan \theta$

In Exercises 37–42, use the results of Exercises 33–36 to find a set of parametric equations for the line or conic.

37. Line: Passes through $(0, 0)$ and $(5, -2)$

38. Line: Passes through $(1, 4)$ and $(5, -2)$

39. Circle: Center: $(2, 1)$; Radius: 4

40. Circle: Center: $(-3, 1)$; Radius: 3

41. Ellipse: Vertices: $(\pm 5, 0)$; Foci: $(\pm 4, 0)$

42. Hyperbola: Vertices: $(0, \pm 1)$; Foci: $(0, \pm 2)$

In Exercises 43–50, find two different sets of parametric equations for the given rectangular equation.

43. $y = 4x - 3$

44. $y = 5 - 7x$

45. $y = \dfrac{1}{x}$

46. $y = \dfrac{1}{2x}$

47. $y = x^2 + 4$

48. $y = 6x^2 - 5$

49. $y = x^3 + 2x$

50. $y = 1 - 8x^3$

In Exercises 51–54, use a graphing utility to graph the curve represented by the parametric equations.

51. Cycloid: $x = 2(\theta - \sin \theta), y = 2(1 - \cos \theta)$

52. Prolate cycloid: $x = 2\theta - 4 \sin \theta, y = 2 - 4 \cos \theta$

53. Witch of Agnesi: $x = 2 \cot \theta, y = 2 \sin^2 \theta$

54. Folium of Descartes: $x = \dfrac{3t}{1 + t^3}, y = \dfrac{3t^2}{1 + t^3}$

In Exercises 55–58, match the parametric equations with the correct graph. [The graphs are labeled (a), (b), (c), and (d).]

(a)
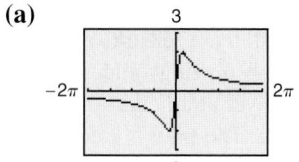

(b)
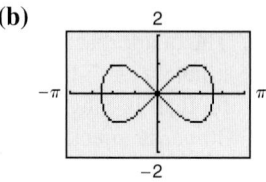

(c)
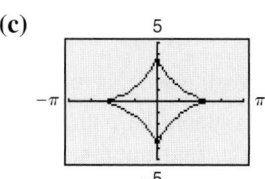

(d)
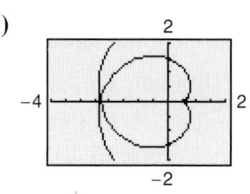

55. Lissajous curve: $x = 2 \cos \theta, y = \sin 2\theta$

56. Evolute of ellipse: $x = 2 \cos^3 \theta, y = 4 \sin^3 \theta$

57. Involute of circle: $x = \frac{1}{2}(\cos\theta + \theta\sin\theta)$

$\qquad\qquad\qquad\quad y = \frac{1}{2}(\sin\theta - \theta\cos\theta)$

58. Serpentine curve: $x = \frac{1}{2}\cot\theta$, $y = 4\sin\theta\cos\theta$

Projectile Motion **In Exercises 59 and 60, consider a projectile launched at a height of h feet above the ground at an angle of θ with the horizontal. The initial velocity is v_0 feet per second and the path of the projectile is modeled by the parametric equations**

$$x = (v_0\cos\theta)t \quad \text{and} \quad y = h + (v_0\sin\theta)t - 16t^2.$$

59. The center-field fence in a ballpark is 10 feet high and 400 feet from home plate. A baseball is hit 3 feet above the ground. It leaves the bat at an angle of θ degrees with the horizontal at a speed of 100 miles per hour (see figure).

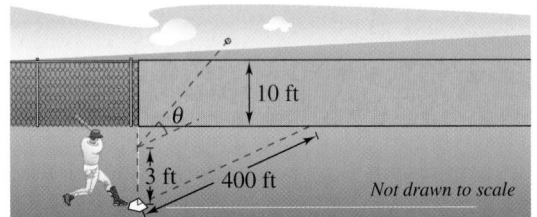

Not drawn to scale

(a) Write a set of parametric equations for the path of the baseball.

(b) Use a graphing utility to graph the path of the baseball for $\theta = 15°$. Is the hit a home run?

(c) Use a graphing utility to graph the path of the baseball for $\theta = 23°$. Is the hit a home run?

(d) Find the minimum angle required for the hit to be a home run.

60. The quarterback of a football team releases a pass at a height of 7 feet above the playing field, and the football is caught by a receiver at a height of 4 feet, 30 yards directly downfield. The pass is released at an angle of 35° with the horizontal.

(a) Write a set of parametric equations for the path of the football.

(b) Find the speed of the football when it is released.

(c) Use a graphing utility to graph the path of the football and approximate its maximum height.

(d) Find the time the receiver has to position himself after the quarterback releases the football.

Synthesis

True or False? **In Exercises 61 and 62, determine whether the statement is true or false. Justify your answer.**

61. The two sets of parametric equations $x = t$, $y = t^2 + 1$ and $x = 3t$, $y = 9t^2 + 1$ correspond to the same rectangular equation.

62. The graph of the parametric equations $x = t^2$ and $y = t^2$ is the line $y = x$.

63. As θ increases, the ellipse given by the parametric equations $x = \cos\theta$ and $y = 2\sin\theta$ is traced out *counterclockwise*. Find a parametric representation for which the same ellipse is traced out *clockwise*.

64. ***Think About It*** The graph of the parametric equations $x = t^3$ and $y = t - 1$ is shown below. Would the graph change for the equations $x = (-t)^3$ and $y = -t - 1$? If so, how would it change?

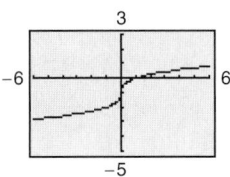

65. ***Writing*** Write a short paragraph explaining why parametric equations are useful.

66. ***Writing*** Explain the process of sketching a plane curve given by parametric equations. What is meant by the orientation of the curve?

Review

In Exercises 67–70, find all solutions of the equation.

67. $5x^2 + 8 = 0$

68. $x^2 - 6x + 4 = 0$

69. $4x^2 + 4x - 11 = 0$

70. $x^4 - 18x^2 + 18 = 0$

In Exercises 71–74, find the sum. Use a graphing utility to verify your result.

71. $\displaystyle\sum_{n=1}^{50} 8n$

72. $\displaystyle\sum_{n=1}^{200}(n - 8)$

73. $\displaystyle\sum_{n=1}^{40}\left(300 - \frac{1}{2}n\right)$

74. $\displaystyle\sum_{n=1}^{70}\frac{7 - 5n}{12}$

10.4 Polar Coordinates

Introduction

So far, you have been representing graphs of equations as collections of points (x, y) on the rectangular coordinate system, where x and y represent the directed distances from the coordinate axes to the point (x, y). In this section, you will study a second coordinate system called the **polar coordinate system.**

To form the polar coordinate system in the plane, fix a point O, called the **pole** (or **origin**), and construct from O an initial ray called the **polar axis,** as shown in Figure 10.51. Then each point P in the plane can be assigned **polar coordinates** (r, θ) as follows.

1. $r = \textit{directed distance}$ from O to P

2. $\theta = \textit{directed angle}$, counterclockwise from the polar axis to segment $\overline{OP}$

What you should learn
- Plot points and find multiple representations of points in the polar coordinate system.
- Convert points from rectangular to polar form and vice versa.
- Convert equations from rectangular to polar form and vice versa.

Why you should learn it
Polar coordinates offer a different mathematical perspective on graphing. For instance, in Exercises 5–12 on page 807, you see that a polar coordinate can be written in more than one way.

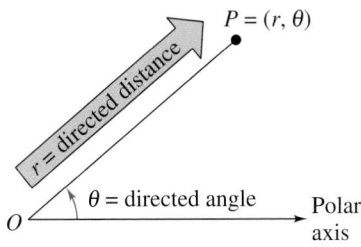

Figure 10.51

Example 1   Plotting Points in the Polar Coordinate System

a. The point $(r, \theta) = (2, \pi/3)$ lies two units from the pole on the terminal side of the angle $\theta = \pi/3$, as shown in Figure 10.52.

b. The point $(r, \theta) = (3, -\pi/6)$ lies three units from the pole on the terminal side of the angle $\theta = -\pi/6$, as shown in Figure 10.53.

c. The point $(r, \theta) = (3, 11\pi/6)$ coincides with the point $(3, -\pi/6)$, as shown in Figure 10.54.

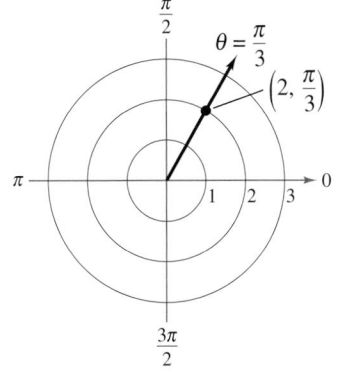

Figure 10.52

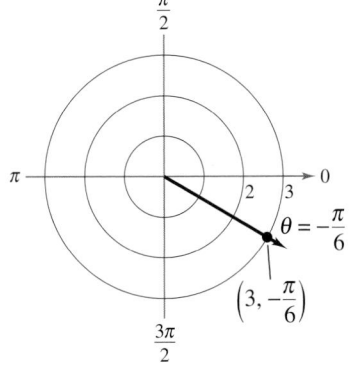

Figure 10.53

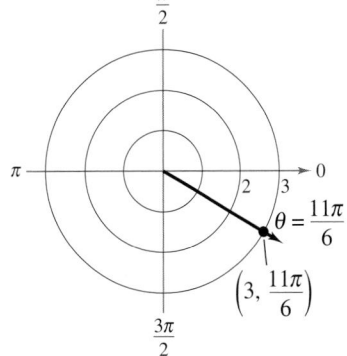

Figure 10.54

 Checkpoint Now try Exercise 5.

In rectangular coordinates, each point (x, y) has a unique representation. This is not true for polar coordinates. For instance, the coordinates (r, θ) and $(r, \theta + 2\pi)$ represent the same point, as illustrated in Example 1. Another way to obtain multiple representations of a point is to use negative values for r. Because r is a *directed distance*, the coordinates (r, θ) and $(-r, \theta + \pi)$ represent the same point. In general, the point (r, θ) can be represented as

$$(r, \theta) = (r, \theta \pm 2n\pi) \qquad \text{or} \qquad (r, \theta) = (-r, \theta \pm (2n + 1)\pi)$$

where n is any integer. Moreover, the pole is represented by $(0, \theta)$, where θ is any angle.

Example 2   Multiple Representations of Points

Plot the point $(3, -3\pi/4)$ and find three additional polar representations of this point, using $-2\pi < \theta < 2\pi$.

Solution

The point is shown in Figure 10.55. Three other representations are as follows.

$$\left(3, -\frac{3\pi}{4} + 2\pi\right) = \left(3, \frac{5\pi}{4}\right) \qquad \text{Add } 2\pi \text{ to } \theta.$$

$$\left(-3, -\frac{3\pi}{4} - \pi\right) = \left(-3, -\frac{7\pi}{4}\right) \qquad \text{Replace } r \text{ by } -r; \text{ subtract } \pi \text{ from } \theta.$$

$$\left(-3, -\frac{3\pi}{4} + \pi\right) = \left(-3, \frac{\pi}{4}\right) \qquad \text{Replace } r \text{ by } -r; \text{ add } \pi \text{ to } \theta.$$

✓ *Checkpoint* Now try Exercise 7.

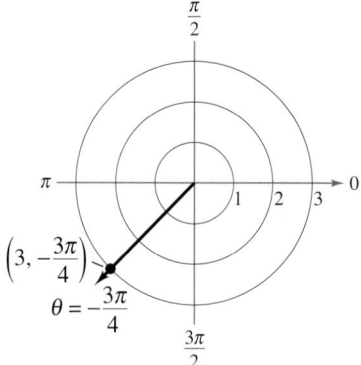

$$\left(3, -\tfrac{3\pi}{4}\right) = \left(3, \tfrac{5\pi}{4}\right) = \left(-3, -\tfrac{7\pi}{4}\right) = \left(-3, \tfrac{\pi}{4}\right) = \cdots$$

Figure 10.55

Coordinate Conversion

To establish the relationship between polar and rectangular coordinates, let the polar axis coincide with the positive x-axis and the pole with the origin, as shown in Figure 10.56. Because (x, y) lies on a circle of radius r, it follows that $r^2 = x^2 + y^2$. Moreover, for $r > 0$, the definitions of the trigonometric functions imply that

$$\tan \theta = \frac{y}{x}, \qquad \cos \theta = \frac{x}{r}, \qquad \text{and} \qquad \sin \theta = \frac{y}{r}.$$

You can show that the same relationships hold for $r < 0$.

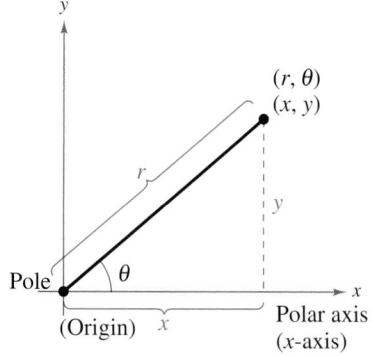

Figure 10.56

> **Coordinate Conversion**
>
> The polar coordinates (r, θ) are related to the rectangular coordinates (x, y) as follows.
>
> $$x = r \cos \theta \qquad \text{and} \qquad \tan \theta = \frac{y}{x}$$
>
> $$y = r \sin \theta \qquad \qquad r^2 = x^2 + y^2$$

Example 3   Polar-to-Rectangular Conversion

Convert each point to rectangular coordinates.

a. $(2, \pi)$ **b.** $\left(\sqrt{3}, \dfrac{\pi}{6}\right)$

Solution

a. For the point $(r, \theta) = (2, \pi)$, you have the following.

$$x = r \cos \theta = 2 \cos \pi = -2$$

$$y = r \sin \theta = 2 \sin \pi = 0$$

The rectangular coordinates are $(x, y) = (-2, 0)$. (See Figure 10.57.)

b. For the point $(r, \theta) = \left(\sqrt{3}, \pi/6\right)$, you have the following.

$$x = \sqrt{3} \cos \frac{\pi}{6} = \sqrt{3}\left(\frac{\sqrt{3}}{2}\right) = \frac{3}{2}$$

$$y = \sqrt{3} \sin \frac{\pi}{6} = \sqrt{3}\left(\frac{1}{2}\right) = \frac{\sqrt{3}}{2}$$

The rectangular coordinates are $(x, y) = \left(3/2, \sqrt{3}/2\right)$. (See Figure 10.57.)

✓ *Checkpoint* Now try Exercise 13.

Example 4   Rectangular-to-Polar Conversion

Convert each point to polar coordinates.

a. $(-1, 1)$ **b.** $(0, 2)$

Solution

a. For the second-quadrant point $(x, y) = (-1, 1)$, you have

$$\tan \theta = \frac{y}{x} = \frac{1}{-1} = -1$$

$$\theta = \frac{3\pi}{4}.$$

Because θ lies in the same quadrant as (x, y), use positive r.

$$r = \sqrt{x^2 + y^2} = \sqrt{(-1)^2 + (1)^2} = \sqrt{2}$$

So, *one* set of polar coordinates is $(r, \theta) = \left(\sqrt{2}, 3\pi/4\right)$, as shown in Figure 10.58.

b. Because the point $(x, y) = (0, 2)$ lies on the positive y-axis, choose

$$\theta = \pi/2 \quad \text{and} \quad r = 2.$$

This implies that one set of polar coordinates is $(r, \theta) = (2, \pi/2)$, as shown in Figure 10.59.

✓ *Checkpoint* Now try Exercise 27.

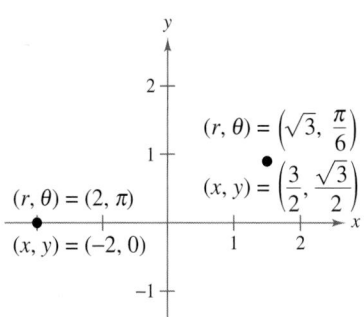

Figure 10.57

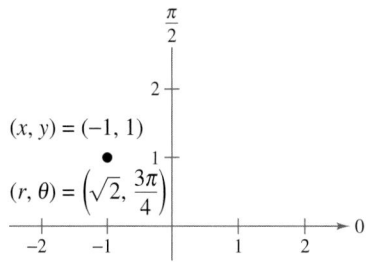

Figure 10.58

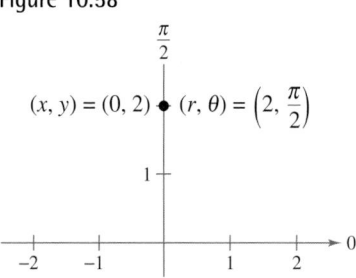

Figure 10.59

Equation Conversion

By comparing Examples 3 and 4, you see that point conversion from the polar to the rectangular system is straightforward, whereas point conversion from the rectangular to the polar system is more involved. For equations, the opposite is true. To convert a rectangular equation to polar form, you simply replace x by $r\cos\theta$ and y by $r\sin\theta$. For instance, the rectangular equation $y = x^2$ can be written in polar form as follows.

$y = x^2$ Rectangular equation

$r\sin\theta = (r\cos\theta)^2$ Polar equation

$r = \sec\theta\tan\theta$ Simplest form

On the other hand, converting a polar equation to rectangular form requires considerable ingenuity.

Example 5 demonstrates several polar-to-rectangular conversions that enable you to sketch the graphs of some polar equations.

Example 5   Converting Polar Equations to Rectangular Form

Describe the graph of each polar equation and find the corresponding rectangular equation.

a. $r = 2$ **b.** $\theta = \dfrac{\pi}{3}$ **c.** $r = \sec\theta$

Solution

a. The graph of the polar equation $r = 2$ consists of all points that are two units from the pole. In other words, this graph is a circle centered at the origin with a radius of 2, as shown in Figure 10.60. You can confirm this by converting to rectangular form, using the relationship $r^2 = x^2 + y^2$.

$\underbrace{r = 2}_{\text{Polar equation}}$ ⟹ $r^2 = 2^2$ ⟹ $\underbrace{x^2 + y^2 = 2^2}_{\text{Rectangular equation}}$

b. The graph of the polar equation $\theta = \pi/3$ consists of all points on the line that make an angle of $\pi/3$ with the positive x-axis, as shown in Figure 10.61. To convert to rectangular form, you make use of the relationship $\tan\theta = y/x$.

$\underbrace{\theta = \dfrac{\pi}{3}}_{\text{Polar equation}}$ ⟹ $\tan\theta = \sqrt{3}$ ⟹ $\underbrace{y = \sqrt{3}x}_{\text{Rectangular equation}}$

c. The graph of the polar equation $r = \sec\theta$ is not evident by simple inspection, so you convert to rectangular form by using the relationship $r\cos\theta = x$.

$\underbrace{r = \sec\theta}_{\text{Polar equation}}$ ⟹ $r\cos\theta = 1$ ⟹ $\underbrace{x = 1}_{\text{Rectangular equation}}$

Now you see that the graph is a vertical line, as shown in Figure 10.62.

✓ *Checkpoint* Now try Exercise 75.

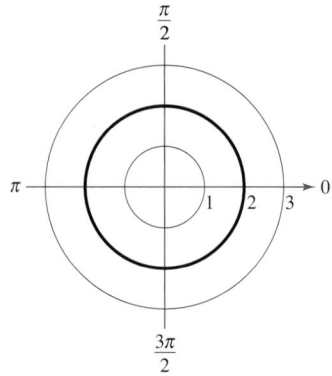

Figure 10.60

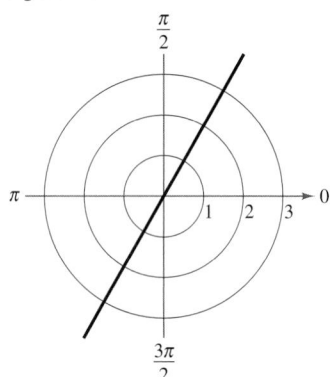

Figure 10.61

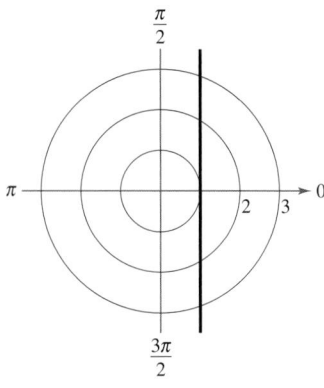

Figure 10.62

10.4 Exercises

Vocabulary Check

Fill in the blanks.

1. The origin of the polar coordinate system is called the _____ .
2. For the point (r, θ), r is the _____ from O to P and θ is the _____ counterclockwise from the polar axis to segment $\overline{OP}$.
3. To graph the point (r, θ), you use the _____ coordinate system.

In Exercises 1–4, a point in polar coordinates is given. Find the corresponding rectangular coordinates for the point.

1. $\left(4, \dfrac{\pi}{2}\right)$

2. $\left(4, \dfrac{3\pi}{2}\right)$

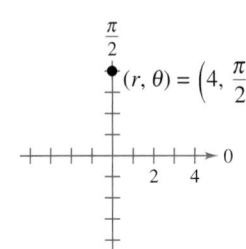

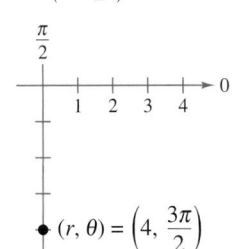

3. $\left(-1, \dfrac{5\pi}{4}\right)$

4. $\left(2, -\dfrac{\pi}{4}\right)$

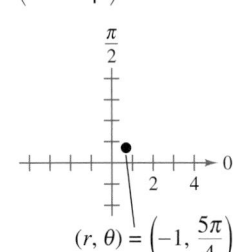

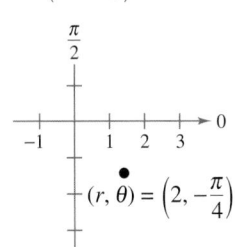

In Exercises 5–12, plot the point given in polar coordinates and find three additional polar representations of the point, using $-2\pi < \theta < 2\pi$.

5. $\left(3, \dfrac{5\pi}{6}\right)$

6. $\left(2, \dfrac{3\pi}{4}\right)$

7. $\left(-1, -\dfrac{\pi}{3}\right)$

8. $\left(-3, -\dfrac{7\pi}{6}\right)$

9. $\left(\sqrt{3}, \dfrac{5\pi}{6}\right)$

10. $\left(5\sqrt{2}, -\dfrac{11\pi}{6}\right)$

11. $\left(\dfrac{3}{2}, -\dfrac{3\pi}{2}\right)$

12. $\left(0, -\dfrac{\pi}{4}\right)$

In Exercises 13–20, plot the point given in polar coordinates and find the corresponding rectangular coordinates for the point.

13. $\left(4, -\dfrac{\pi}{3}\right)$

14. $\left(2, \dfrac{7\pi}{6}\right)$

15. $\left(-1, -\dfrac{3\pi}{4}\right)$

16. $\left(-3, -\dfrac{2\pi}{3}\right)$

17. $\left(0, -\dfrac{7\pi}{6}\right)$

18. $\left(0, \dfrac{5\pi}{4}\right)$

19. $\left(\sqrt{2}, 2.36\right)$

20. $(-3, -1.57)$

In Exercises 21–24, use a graphing utility to find the rectangular coordinates for the point given in polar coordinates.

21. $\left(2, \dfrac{3\pi}{4}\right)$

22. $\left(-2, \dfrac{7\pi}{6}\right)$

23. $(-4.5, 1.3)$

24. $(8.25, 3.5)$

In Exercises 25–32, plot the point given in rectangular coordinates and find *two* sets of polar coordinates for the point for $0 \le \theta < 2\pi$.

25. $(-7, 0)$

26. $(0, -5)$

27. $(1, 1)$

28. $(-3, -3)$

29. $\left(-\sqrt{3}, -\sqrt{3}\right)$

30. $\left(\sqrt{3}, -1\right)$

31. $(6, 9)$

32. $(5, 12)$

In Exercises 33–38, use a graphing utility to find one set of polar coordinates for the point given in rectangular coordinates.

33. $(3, -2)$

34. $(-4, 1)$

35. $\left(\sqrt{3}, 2\right)$

36. $\left(3\sqrt{2}, 3\sqrt{2}\right)$

37. $\left(\dfrac{5}{2}, \dfrac{4}{3}\right)$

38. $\left(\dfrac{11}{4}, -\dfrac{5}{8}\right)$

In Exercises 39–56, convert the rectangular equation to polar form. Assume $a > 0$.

39. $x^2 + y^2 = 81$

40. $x^2 + y^2 = 16$

41. $y = 4$

42. $y = x$

43. $x = 8$

44. $x = a$

45. $3x - 6y + 2 = 0$

46. $4x + 7y - 2 = 0$

47. $xy = 4$

48. $2xy = 1$

49. $(x^2 + y^2)^2 = 9(x^2 - y^2)$

50. $y^2 - 8x - 16 = 0$

51. $x^2 + y^2 - 6x = 0$

52. $x^2 + y^2 - 8y = 0$

53. $x^2 + y^2 - 2ax = 0$

54. $x^2 + y^2 - 2ay = 0$

55. $y^2 = x^3$

56. $x^2 = y^3$

In Exercises 57–72, convert the polar equation to rectangular form.

57. $r = 6 \sin \theta$

58. $r = 2 \cos \theta$

59. $\theta = \dfrac{4\pi}{3}$

60. $\theta = \dfrac{5\pi}{3}$

61. $r = 4$

62. $r = 10$

63. $r = -3 \csc \theta$

64. $r = 2 \sec \theta$

65. $r^2 = \cos \theta$

66. $r^2 = \sin 2\theta$

67. $r = 2 \sin 3\theta$

68. $r = 3 \cos 2\theta$

69. $r = \dfrac{1}{1 - \cos \theta}$

70. $r = \dfrac{2}{1 + \sin \theta}$

71. $r = \dfrac{6}{2 - 3 \sin \theta}$

72. $r = \dfrac{6}{2 \cos \theta - 3 \sin \theta}$

In Exercises 73–78, describe the graph of the polar equation and find the corresponding rectangular equation. Sketch its graph.

73. $r = 7$

74. $r = 8$

75. $\theta = \dfrac{\pi}{4}$

76. $\theta = \dfrac{7\pi}{6}$

77. $r = 3 \sec \theta$

78. $r = 2 \csc \theta$

Synthesis

True or False? **In Exercises 79 and 80, determine whether the statement is true or false. Justify your answer.**

79. If (r_1, θ_1) and (r_2, θ_2) represent the same point in the polar coordinate system, then $|r_1| = |r_2|$.

80. If (r, θ_1) and (r, θ_2) represent the same point in the polar coordinate system, then $\theta_1 = \theta_2 + 2\pi n$ for some integer n.

81. *Think About It*

(a) Show that the distance between the points (r_1, θ_1) and (r_2, θ_2) is

$$\sqrt{r_1^2 + r_2^2 - 2r_1 r_2 \cos(\theta_1 - \theta_2)}.$$

(b) Describe the positions of the points relative to each other for $\theta_1 = \theta_2$. Simplify the Distance Formula for this case. Is the simplification what you expected? Explain.

(c) Simplify the Distance Formula for $\theta_1 - \theta_2 = 90°$. Is the simplification what you expected? Explain.

(d) Choose two points on the polar coordinate system and find the distance between them. Then choose different polar representations of the same two points and apply the Distance Formula again. Discuss the result.

82. *Writing* Write a short paragraph explaining the differences between the rectangular coordinate system and the polar coordinate system.

Review

In Exercises 83–88, use the Law of Sines or the Law of Cosines to solve the triangle.

83. $a = 13, b = 19, c = 25$

84. $A = 24°, a = 10, b = 6$

85. $A = 56°, C = 38°, c = 12$

86. $B = 71°, a = 21, c = 29$

87. $C = 35°, a = 8, b = 4$

88. $B = 64°, b = 52, c = 44$

In Exercises 89–92, use any method to solve the system of equations.

89. $\begin{cases} 5x - 7y = -11 \\ -3x + y = -3 \end{cases}$

90. $\begin{cases} 3x + 5y = 10 \\ 4x - 2y = -5 \end{cases}$

91. $\begin{cases} 3a - 2b + c = 0 \\ 2a + b - 3c = 0 \\ a - 3b + 9c = 0 \end{cases}$

92. $\begin{cases} 5u + 7v + 9w = 15 \\ u - 2v - 3w = 7 \\ 8u - 2v + w = 0 \end{cases}$

10.5 Graphs of Polar Equations

Introduction

In previous chapters you sketched graphs on rectangular coordinate systems. You began with the basic point-plotting method. Then you used sketching aids such as a graphing utility, symmetry, intercepts, asymptotes, periods, and shifts to further investigate the nature of the graph. This section approaches curve sketching on the polar coordinate system similarly.

Example 1   Graphing a Polar Equation by Point Plotting

Sketch the graph of the polar equation $r = 4 \sin \theta$ by hand.

Solution

The sine function is periodic, so you can get a full range of r-values by considering values of θ in the interval $0 \le \theta \le 2\pi$, as shown in the table.

θ	0	$\dfrac{\pi}{6}$	$\dfrac{\pi}{3}$	$\dfrac{\pi}{2}$	$\dfrac{2\pi}{3}$	$\dfrac{5\pi}{6}$	π	$\dfrac{7\pi}{6}$	$\dfrac{3\pi}{2}$	$\dfrac{11\pi}{6}$	2π
r	0	2	$2\sqrt{3}$	4	$2\sqrt{3}$	2	0	-2	-4	-2	0

By plotting these points as shown in Figure 10.63, it appears that the graph is a circle of radius 2 whose center is the point $(x, y) = (0, 2)$.

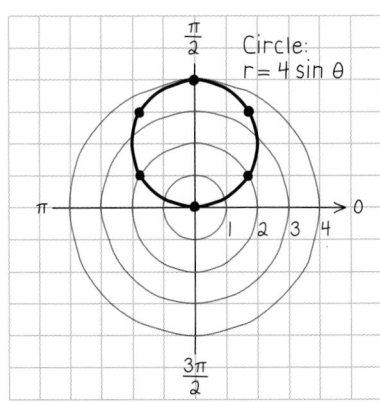

Figure 10.63

✓ *Checkpoint* Now try Exercise 23.

You can confirm the graph found in Example 1 in three ways.

1. *Convert to Rectangular Form*   Multiply each side of the polar equation by r and convert the result to rectangular form.

2. *Use a Polar Coordinate Mode*   Set your graphing utility to *polar* mode and graph the polar equation. (Use $0 \le \theta \le \pi$, $-6 \le x \le 6$, and $-4 \le y \le 4$.)

3. *Use a Parametric Mode*   Set your graphing utility to *parametric* mode and graph $x = (4 \sin t) \cos t$ and $y = (4 \sin t) \sin t$.

What you should learn

- Graph polar equations by point plotting.
- Use symmetry as a sketching aid.
- Use zeros and maximum r-values as sketching aids.
- Recognize special polar graphs.

Why you should learn it

Several common figures, such as the circle in Exercise 3 on page 816, are easier to graph in the polar coordinate system than in the rectangular coordinate system.

Most graphing utilities have a *polar* graphing mode. If yours doesn't, you can rewrite the polar equation $r = f(\theta)$ in parametric form, using t as a parameter, as follows.

$$x = f(t) \cos t \qquad \text{and} \qquad y = f(t) \sin t$$

Symmetry

In Figure 10.63, note that as θ increases from 0 to 2π the graph is traced out twice. Moreover, note that the graph is *symmetric with respect to the line* $\theta = \pi/2$. Had you known about this symmetry and retracing ahead of time, you could have used fewer points. The three important types of symmetry to consider in polar curve sketching are shown in Figure 10.64.

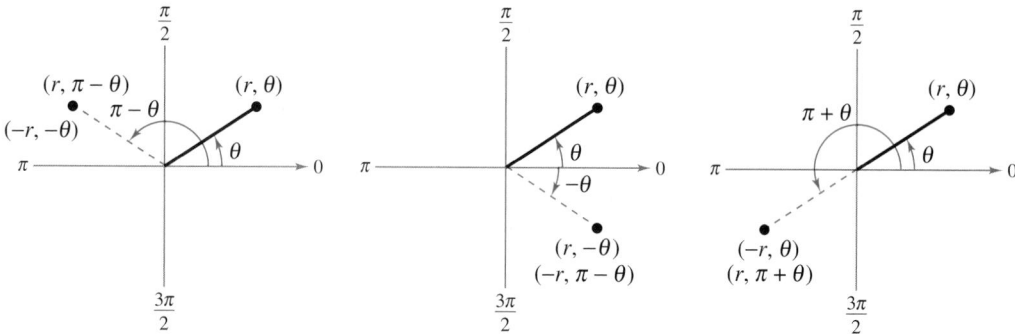

Symmetry with Respect
to the Line $\theta = \dfrac{\pi}{2}$

Symmetry with Respect
to the Polar Axis

Symmetry with Respect
to the Pole

Figure 10.64

Testing for Symmetry in Polar Coordinates

The graph of a polar equation is symmetric with respect to the following if the given substitution yields an equivalent equation.

1. The line $\theta = \dfrac{\pi}{2}$:   Replace (r, θ) by $(r, \pi - \theta)$ or $(-r, -\theta)$.

2. The polar axis: Replace (r, θ) by $(r, -\theta)$ or $(-r, \pi - \theta)$.

3. The pole: Replace (r, θ) by $(r, \pi + \theta)$ or $(-r, \theta)$.

You can determine the symmetry of the graph of $r = 2 \sin \theta$ as follows.

1. Replace (r, θ) by $(-r, -\theta)$:

$$-r = 2 \sin(-\theta) \quad \Longrightarrow \quad r = -2 \sin(-\theta) = 2 \sin \theta$$

2. Replace (r, θ) by $(r, -\theta)$: $r = 2 \sin(-\theta) = -2 \sin \theta$

3. Replace (r, θ) by $(-r, \theta)$: $-r = 2 \sin \theta \quad \Longrightarrow \quad r = -2 \sin \theta$

So, the graph of $r = 2 \sin \theta$ is symmetric with respect to the line $\theta = \pi/2$.

STUDY TIP

Recall from Section 5.3 that the sine function is odd. That is, $\sin(-\theta) = -\sin \theta$.

Example 2   Using Symmetry to Sketch a Polar Graph

Use symmetry to sketch the graph of $r = 3 + 2 \cos \theta$ by hand.

Solution

Replacing (r, θ) by $(r, -\theta)$ produces

$$r = 3 + 2 \cos(-\theta) = 3 + 2 \cos \theta. \qquad \cos(-u) = \cos u$$

So, by using the even trigonometric identity, you can conclude that the curve is symmetric with respect to the polar axis. Plotting the points in the table and using polar axis symmetry, you obtain the graph shown in Figure 10.65. This graph is called a **limaçon.**

θ	0	$\dfrac{\pi}{6}$	$\dfrac{\pi}{3}$	$\dfrac{\pi}{2}$	$\dfrac{2\pi}{3}$	$\dfrac{5\pi}{6}$	π
r	5	$3 + \sqrt{3}$	4	3	2	$3 - \sqrt{3}$	1

Use a graphing utility to confirm this graph.

 Checkpoint Now try Exercise 27.

The three tests for symmetry in polar coordinates on page 810 are sufficient to guarantee symmetry, but they are not necessary. For instance, Figure 10.66 shows the graph of

$$r = \theta + 2\pi. \qquad \text{Spiral of Archimedes}$$

From the figure, you can see that the graph is symmetric with respect to the line $\theta = \pi/2$. Yet the tests on page 810 fail to indicate symmetry because neither of the following replacements yields an equivalent equation.

Original Equation	*Replacement*	*New Equation*
$r = \theta + 2\pi$	(r, θ) by $(-r, -\theta)$	$-r = -\theta + 2\pi$
$r = \theta + 2\pi$	(r, θ) by $(r, \pi - \theta)$	$r = -\theta + 3\pi$

The equations discussed in Examples 1 and 2 are of the form

$$r = 4 \sin \theta = f(\sin \theta)$$

and

$$r = 3 + 2 \cos \theta = g(\cos \theta).$$

The graph of the first equation is symmetric with respect to the line $\theta = \pi/2$, and the graph of the second equation is symmetric with respect to the polar axis. This observation can be generalized to yield the following *quick tests for symmetry.*

1. The graph of $r = f(\sin \theta)$ is symmetric with respect to the line $\theta = \dfrac{\pi}{2}$.

2. The graph of $r = g(\cos \theta)$ is symmetric with respect to the polar axis.

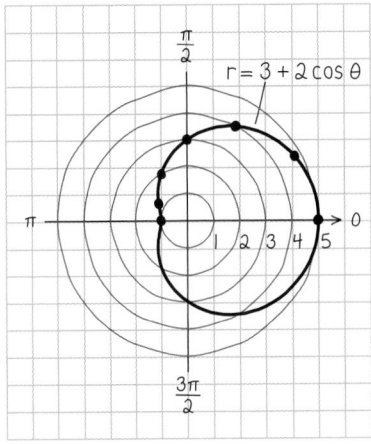

Figure 10.65

TECHNOLOGY TIP

The *table* feature of a graphing utility is very useful in constructing tables of values for polar equations. Set your graphing utility to *polar* mode and enter the polar equation in Example 2. You can verify the table of values in Example 2 by starting the table at $\theta = 0$ and incrementing the value of θ by $\pi/6$. For instructions on how to use the *table* feature and *polar* mode, see Appendix A; for specific keystrokes, go to the text website at *college.hmco.com.*

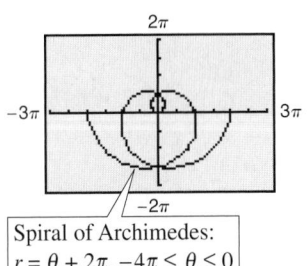

Spiral of Archimedes:
$r = \theta + 2\pi, -4\pi \le \theta \le 0$

Figure 10.66

Zeros and Maximum *r*-Values

Two additional aids to sketching graphs of polar equations involve knowing the θ-values for which $|r|$ is maximum and knowing the θ-values for which $r = 0$. In Example 1, the maximum value of $|r|$ for $r = 4 \sin \theta$ is $|r| = 4$, and this occurs when $\theta = \pi/2$ (see Figure 10.63). Moreover, $r = 0$ when $\theta = 0$.

Example 3   Finding Maximum *r*-Values of a Polar Graph

Find the maximum value of r for the graph of $r = 1 - 2 \cos \theta$.

Graphical Solution

Because the polar equation is of the form

$$r = 1 - 2 \cos \theta = g(\cos \theta)$$

you know the graph is symmetric with respect to the polar axis. You can confirm this by graphing the polar equation. Set your graphing utility to *polar* mode and enter the equation, as shown in Figure 10.67. (In the graph, θ varies from 0 to 2π.) To find the maximum *r*-value for the graph, use your graphing utility's *trace* feature and you should find that the graph has a maximum *r*-value of 3, as shown in Figure 10.68. This value of r occurs when $\theta = \pi$. In the graph, note that the point $(3, \pi)$ is farthest from the pole.

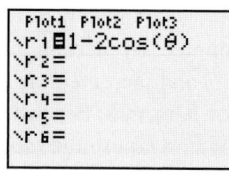

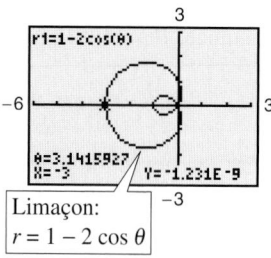

Limaçon:
$r = 1 - 2 \cos \theta$

Figure 10.67   Figure 10.68

Note how the negative *r*-values determine the *inner loop* of the graph in Figure 10.68. This type of graph is a limaçon.

 Checkpoint Now try Exercise 15.

Numerical Solution

To approximate the maximum value of r for the graph of $r = 1 - 2 \cos \theta$, use the *table* feature of a graphing utility to create a table that begins at $\theta = 0$ and increments by $\pi/12$, as shown in Figure 10.69. From the table, the maximum value of r appears to be 3 when $\theta = 3.1416 \approx \pi$. By creating a second table that begins at $\theta = \pi/2$ and increments by $\pi/24$, as shown in Figure 10.70, the maximum value of r still appears to be 3 when $\theta = 3.1416 \approx \pi$.

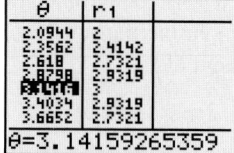

Figure 10.69

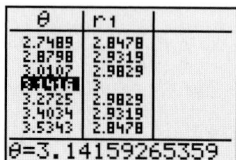

Figure 10.70

Exploration

The graph of the polar equation $r = e^{\cos \theta} - 2 \cos 4\theta + \sin^5(\theta/12)$ is called *the butterfly curve*, as shown in Figure 10.71.

a. The graph at the right was produced using $0 \le \theta \le 2\pi$. Does this show the entire graph? Explain your reasoning.

b. Use the *trace* feature of your graphing utility to approximate the maximum *r*-value of the graph. Does this value change if you use $0 \le \theta \le 4\pi$ instead of $0 \le \theta \le 2\pi$? Explain.

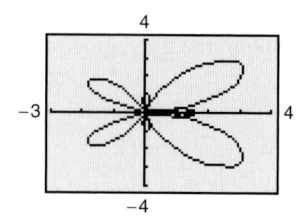

Figure 10.71

Some curves reach their zeros and maximum r-values at more than one point, as shown in Example 4.

Example 4   Analyzing a Polar Graph

Analyze the graph of $r = 2 \cos 3\theta$.

Solution

Symmetry: With respect to the polar axis

Maximum value of $|r|$: $|r| = 2$ when $3\theta = 0, \pi, 2\pi, 3\pi$

or $\theta = 0, \pi/3, 2\pi/3, \pi$

Zeros of r: $r = 0$ when $3\theta = \pi/2, 3\pi/2, 5\pi/2$

or $\theta = \pi/6, \pi/2, 5\pi/6$

θ	0	$\dfrac{\pi}{12}$	$\dfrac{\pi}{6}$	$\dfrac{\pi}{4}$	$\dfrac{\pi}{3}$	$\dfrac{5\pi}{12}$	$\dfrac{\pi}{2}$
r	2	$\sqrt{2}$	0	$-\sqrt{2}$	-2	$-\sqrt{2}$	0

By plotting these points and using the specified symmetry, zeros, and maximum values, you can obtain the graph shown in Figure 10.72. This graph is called a **rose curve,** and each loop on the graph is called a *petal*. Note how the entire curve is generated as θ increases from 0 to π.

$0 \le \theta \le \dfrac{\pi}{6}$

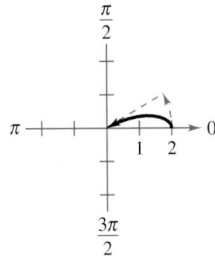

$0 \le \theta \le \dfrac{\pi}{3}$

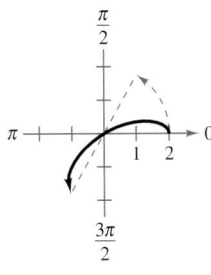

$0 \le \theta \le \dfrac{\pi}{2}$

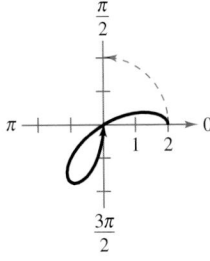

$0 \le \theta \le \dfrac{2\pi}{3}$

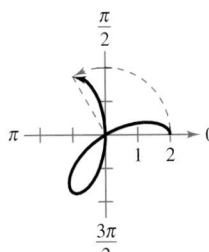

$0 \le \theta \le \dfrac{5\pi}{6}$

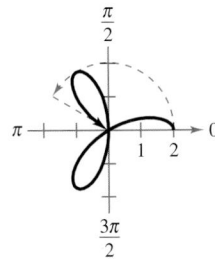

$0 \le \theta \le \pi$

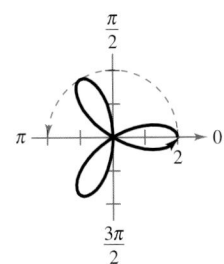

Figure 10.72

✓ *Checkpoint* Now try Exercise 31.

Exploration

Notice that the rose curve in Example 4 has three petals. How many petals do the rose curves $r = 2 \cos 4\theta$ and $r = 2 \sin 3\theta$ have? Determine the numbers of petals for the curves $r = 2 \cos n\theta$ and $r = 2 \sin n\theta$, where n is a positive integer.

Special Polar Graphs

Several important types of graphs have equations that are simpler in polar form than in rectangular form. For example, the circle

$$r = 4 \sin \theta$$

in Example 1 has the more complicated rectangular equation

$$x^2 + (y - 2)^2 = 4.$$

Several other types of graphs that have simple polar equations are shown below.

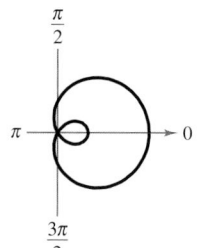

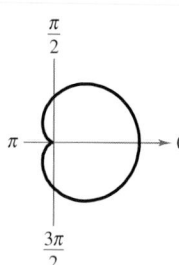

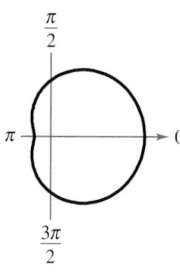

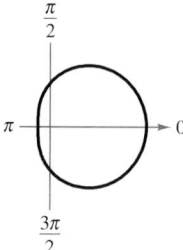

Limaçons

$r = a \pm b \cos \theta$

$r = a \pm b \sin \theta$

$(a > 0, b > 0)$

$\dfrac{a}{b} < 1$

Limaçon with inner loop

$\dfrac{a}{b} = 1$

Cardioid (heart-shaped)

$1 < \dfrac{a}{b} < 2$

Dimpled limaçon

$\dfrac{a}{b} \geq 2$

Convex limaçon

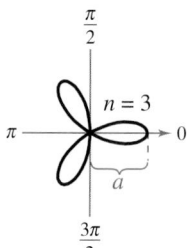

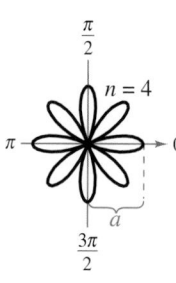

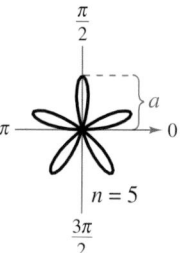

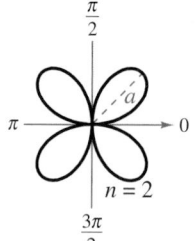

Rose Curves

n petals if n is odd

$2n$ petals if n is even

$(n \geq 2)$

$r = a \cos n\theta$
Rose curve

$r = a \cos n\theta$
Rose curve

$r = a \sin n\theta$
Rose curve

$r = a \sin n\theta$
Rose curve

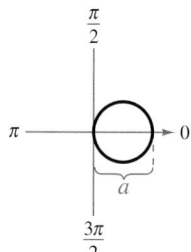

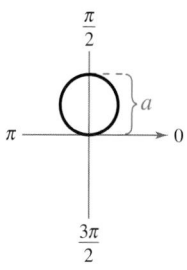

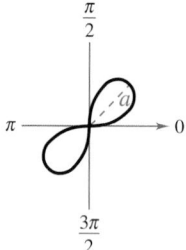

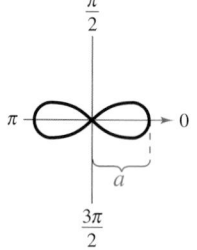

Circles and Lemniscates

$r = a \cos \theta$
Circle

$r = a \sin \theta$
Circle

$r^2 = a^2 \sin 2\theta$
Lemniscate

$r^2 = a^2 \cos 2\theta$
Lemniscate

Example 5   Analyzing a Rose Curve

Analyze the graph of $r = 3 \cos 2\theta$.

Solution

Type of curve: Rose curve with $2n = 4$ petals

Symmetry: With respect to the polar axis, the line $\theta = \pi/2$, and
                       the pole

Maximum value of $|r|$: $|r| = 3$ when $\theta = 0, \pi/2, \pi, 3\pi/2$

Zeros of r: $r = 0$ when $\theta = \pi/4, 3\pi/4$

Using a graphing utility, enter the equation as shown in Figure 10.73 (with
$0 \le \theta \le 2\pi$). You should obtain the graph shown in Figure 10.74.

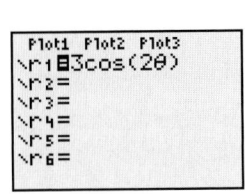

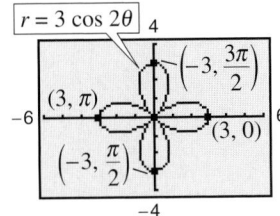

Figure 10.73   **Figure 10.74**

 Checkpoint Now try Exercise 35.

Example 6   Analyzing a Lemniscate

Analyze the graph of $r^2 = 9 \sin 2\theta$.

Solution

Type of curve: Lemniscate

Symmetry: With respect to the pole

Maximum value of $|r|$: $|r| = 3$ when $\theta = \pi/4$

Zeros of r: $r = 0$ when $\theta = 0, \pi/2$

Using a graphing utility, enter the equation as shown in Figure 10.75 (with
$0 \le \theta \le 2\pi$). You should obtain the graph shown in Figure 10.76.

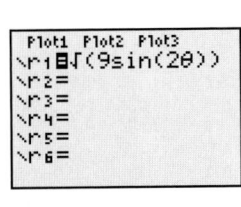

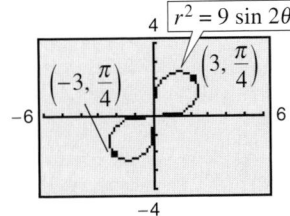

Figure 10.75   **Figure 10.76**

 Checkpoint Now try Exercise 43.

10.5   Exercises

Vocabulary Check

Fill in the blanks.

1. The graph of $r = f(\sin \theta)$ is symmetric with respect to the line _____ .
2. The graph of $r = g(\cos \theta)$ is symmetric with respect to the _____ .
3. The equation $r = 2 + \cos \theta$ represents a _____ .
4. The equation $r = 2 \cos \theta$ represents a _____ .
5. The equation $r^2 = 4 \sin 2\theta$ represents a _____ .
6. The equation $r = 1 + \sin \theta$ represents a _____ .

In Exercises 1–6, identify the type of polar graph.

1.

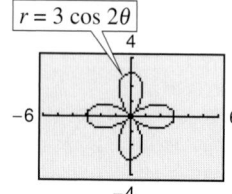

$r = 3 \cos 2\theta$

2.

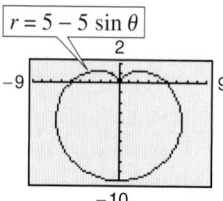

$r = 5 - 5 \sin \theta$

3.

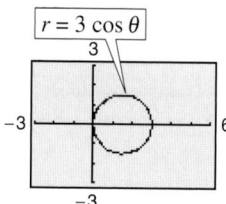

$r = 3 \cos \theta$

4.

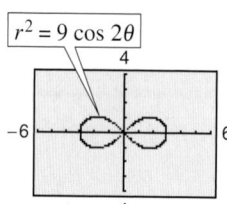

$r^2 = 9 \cos 2\theta$

5.

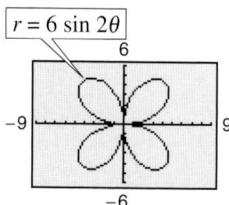

$r = 6 \sin 2\theta$

6.

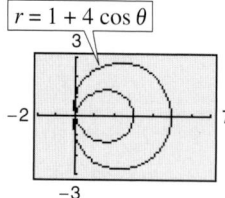

$r = 1 + 4 \cos \theta$

In Exercises 7–14, test for symmetry with respect to $\theta = \pi/2$, the polar axis, and the pole.

7. $r = 10 + 4 \cos \theta$ **8.** $r = 16 \cos 3\theta$

9. $r = \dfrac{4}{1 + \sin \theta}$ **10.** $r = \dfrac{2}{1 - \cos \theta}$

11. $r = 6 \sin \theta$ **12.** $r = 2 \csc \theta \cos \theta$

13. $r^2 = 25 \sin 2\theta$ **14.** $r^2 = 36 \cos 4\theta$

In Exercises 15–18, find the maximum value of $|r|$ and any zeros of r. Verify your answers numerically.

15. $r = 10 - 10 \sin \theta$ **16.** $r = 6 + 12 \cos \theta$

17. $r = 4 \cos 3\theta$ **18.** $r = \sin 2\theta$

In Exercises 19–34, sketch the graph of the polar equation. Use a graphing utility to verify your graph.

19. $r = 4$ **20.** $r = 2$

21. $\theta = \dfrac{\pi}{4}$ **22.** $\theta = -\dfrac{5\pi}{3}$

23. $r = 3 \sin \theta$ **24.** $r = 2 \cos \theta$

25. $r = 3(1 - \cos \theta)$ **26.** $r = 4(1 + \sin \theta)$

27. $r = 3 - 4 \cos \theta$ **28.** $r = 1 - 2 \sin \theta$

29. $r = 3 + 6 \sin \theta$ **30.** $r = 4 + 5 \cos \theta$

31. $r = 5 \cos 3\theta$ **32.** $r = -\sin 5\theta$

33. $r = 7 \sin 2\theta$ **34.** $r = 3 \cos 5\theta$

In Exercises 35–48, use a graphing utility to graph the polar equation. Describe your viewing window.

35. $r = 6 \cos 2\theta$ **36.** $r = \cos 2\theta$

37. $r = 2(3 - \sin \theta)$ **38.** $r = 6 - 4 \sin \theta$

39. $r = 3 - 6 \cos \theta$ **40.** $r = 3 - 2 \sin \theta$

41. $r = \dfrac{3}{\sin \theta - 2 \cos \theta}$ **42.** $r = \dfrac{6}{2 \sin \theta - 3 \cos \theta}$

43. $r^2 = 4 \cos 2\theta$ **44.** $r^2 = 9 \sin \theta$

45. $r = 4 \sin \theta \cos^2 \theta$ **46.** $r = 2 \cos(3\theta - 2)$

47. $r = 2 \csc \theta + 5$ **48.** $r = 4 - \sec \theta$

In Exercises 49–54, use a graphing utility to graph the polar equation. Find an interval for θ for which the graph is traced *only once*.

49. $r = 3 - 2 \cos \theta$

50. $r = 2(1 - 2 \sin \theta)$

51. $r = 2 \cos\left(\dfrac{3\theta}{2}\right)$

52. $r = 3 \sin\left(\dfrac{5\theta}{2}\right)$

53. $r^2 = \sin 2\theta$

54. $r^2 = \dfrac{1}{\theta}$

In Exercises 55–58, use a graphing utility to graph the polar equation and show that the indicated line is an asymptote of the graph.

	Name of Graph	*Polar Equation*	*Asymptote*
55.	Conchoid	$r = 2 - \sec \theta$	$x = -1$
56.	Conchoid	$r = 2 + \csc \theta$	$y = 1$
57.	Hyperbolic spiral	$r = \dfrac{2}{\theta}$	$y = 2$
58.	Strophoid	$r = 2 \cos 2\theta \sec \theta$	$x = -2$

Synthesis

True or False?   **In Exercises 59 and 60, determine whether the statement is true or false. Justify your answer.**

59. The graph of $r = 10 \sin 5\theta$ is a rose curve with 5 petals.

60. A rose curve will always have symmetry with respect to the line $\theta = \pi/2$.

61. ***Writing***   Use a graphing utility to graph the polar equation

$$r = \cos 5\theta + n \cos \theta, \quad 0 \le \theta < \pi$$

for the integers $n = -5$ to $n = 5$. As you graph these equations, you should see the graph change shape from a heart to a bell. Write a short paragraph explaining what values of n produce the heart portion of the curve and what values of n produce the bell.

62. The graph of $r = f(\theta)$ is rotated about the pole through an angle ϕ. Show that the equation of the rotated graph is $r = f(\theta - \phi)$.

63. Consider the graph of $r = f(\sin \theta)$.

(a) Show that if the graph is rotated counterclockwise $\pi/2$ radians about the pole, the equation of the rotated graph is $r = f(-\cos \theta)$.

(b) Show that if the graph is rotated counterclockwise π radians about the pole, the equation of the rotated graph is $r = f(-\sin \theta)$.

(c) Show that if the graph is rotated counterclockwise $3\pi/2$ radians about the pole, the equation of the rotated graph is $r = f(\cos \theta)$.

In Exercises 64–66, use the results of Exercises 62 and 63.

64. Write an equation for the limaçon $r = 2 - \sin \theta$ after it has been rotated through the given angle.

(a) $\dfrac{\pi}{4}$ (b) $\dfrac{\pi}{2}$ (c) π (d) $\dfrac{3\pi}{2}$

65. Write an equation for the rose curve $r = 2 \sin 2\theta$ after it has been rotated through the given angle.

(a) $\dfrac{\pi}{6}$ (b) $\dfrac{\pi}{2}$ (c) $\dfrac{2\pi}{3}$ (d) π

66. Sketch the graph of each equation.

(a) $r = 1 - \sin \theta$ (b) $r = 1 - \sin\left(\theta - \dfrac{\pi}{4}\right)$

67. ***Exploration***   Use a graphing utility to graph the polar equation $r = 2 + k \cos \theta$ for $k = 0$, $k = 1$, $k = 2$, and $k = 3$. Identify each graph.

68. ***Exploration***   Consider the polar equation $r = 3 \sin k\theta$.

(a) Use a graphing utility to graph the equation for $k = 1.5$. Find the interval for θ for which the graph is traced only once.

(b) Use a graphing utility to graph the equation for $k = 2.5$. Find the interval for θ for which the graph is traced only once.

(c) Is it possible to find an interval for θ for which the graph is traced only once for any rational number k? Explain.

Review

In Exercises 69–74, sketch the graph of the function. (Include two full periods.)

69. $f(x) = \frac{1}{2} \sin 2x$

70. $f(x) = \cos\left(x - \dfrac{3\pi}{4}\right)$

71. $g(x) = \tan\dfrac{x}{3}$

72. $g(x) = 1 + \csc x$

73. $h(x) = \sec\left(x + \dfrac{\pi}{4}\right)$

74. $h(x) = 2 \cot x$

10.6 Polar Equations of Conics

Alternative Definition of Conics

In Section 10.1, you learned that the rectangular equations of ellipses and hyperbolas take simple forms when the origin lies at the *center*. As it happens, there are many important applications of conics in which it is more convenient to use one of the *foci* as the origin. In this section you will learn that polar equations of conics take simple forms if one of the foci lies at the pole.

To begin, consider the following alternative definition of a conic that uses the concept of eccentricity (a measure of the flatness of the conic).

> ### Alternative Definition of a Conic
>
> The locus of a point in the plane which moves so that its distance from a fixed point (focus) is in a constant ratio to its distance from a fixed line (directrix) is a **conic**. The constant ratio is the **eccentricity** of the conic and is denoted by e. Moreover, the conic is an **ellipse** if $e < 1$, a **parabola** if $e = 1$, and a **hyperbola** if $e > 1$. (See Figure 10.77.)

In Figure 10.77, note that for each type of conic, the focus is at the pole.

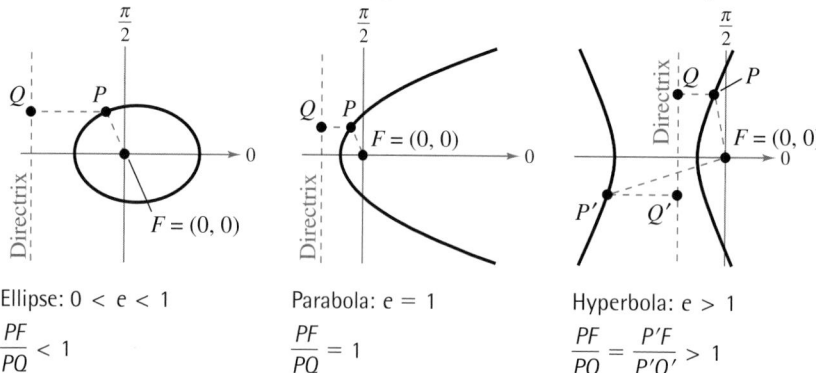

Ellipse: $0 < e < 1$
$\dfrac{PF}{PQ} < 1$

Parabola: $e = 1$
$\dfrac{PF}{PQ} = 1$

Hyperbola: $e > 1$
$\dfrac{PF}{PQ} = \dfrac{P'F}{P'Q'} > 1$

Figure 10.77

Polar Equations of Conics

The benefit of locating a focus of a conic at the pole is that the equation of the conic becomes simpler. See Appendix B for a proof of the polar equations of conics.

> ### Polar Equations of Conics
>
> The graph of a polar equation of the form
>
> $$\textbf{1. } r = \frac{ep}{1 \pm e \cos \theta} \quad \text{or} \quad \textbf{2. } r = \frac{ep}{1 \pm e \sin \theta}$$
>
> is a conic, where $e > 0$ is the eccentricity and $|p|$ is the distance between the focus (pole) and the directrix.

Equations of the form

$$r = \frac{ep}{1 \pm e \cos \theta} \qquad \text{Vertical directrix}$$

correspond to conics with vertical directrices and equations of the form

$$r = \frac{ep}{1 \pm e \sin \theta} \qquad \text{Horizontal directrix}$$

correspond to conics with horizontal directrices. Moreover, the converse is also true—that is, any conic with a focus at the pole and having a horizontal or vertical directrix can be represented by one of the given equations.

Example 1   Identifying a Conic from Its Equation

Identify the type of conic represented by the equation $r = \dfrac{15}{3 - 2 \cos \theta}$.

Algebraic Solution

To identify the type of conic, rewrite the equation in the form $r = ep/(1 \pm e \cos \theta)$.

$$r = \frac{15}{3 - 2 \cos \theta}$$

$$= \frac{5}{1 - (2/3) \cos \theta} \qquad \begin{array}{l}\text{Divide numerator}\\ \text{and denominator by 3.}\end{array}$$

Because $e = \frac{2}{3} < 1$, you can conclude that the graph is an ellipse.

✓ **Checkpoint** Now try Exercise 9.

Graphical Solution

Use a graphing utility in *polar* mode to graph $r = \dfrac{15}{3 - 2 \cos \theta}$.

Be sure to use a square setting. From the graph in Figure 10.78, you can see that the conic appears to be an ellipse.

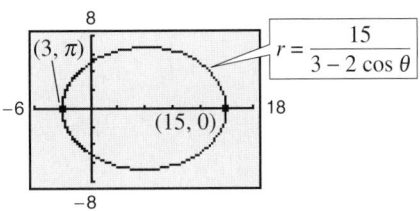

Figure 10.78

For the ellipse in Figure 10.78, the major axis is horizontal and the vertices lie at $(r, \theta) = (15, 0)$ and $(r, \theta) = (3, \pi)$. So, the length of the *major* axis is $2a = 18$. To find the length of the *minor* axis, you can use the equations $e = c/a$ and $b^2 = a^2 - c^2$ to conclude that

$$b^2 = a^2 - c^2$$

$$= a^2 - (ea)^2$$

$$= a^2(1 - e^2). \qquad \text{Ellipse}$$

Because $e = \frac{2}{3}$, you have $b^2 = 9^2 \left[1 - \left(\frac{2}{3}\right)^2\right] = 45$, which implies that $b = \sqrt{45} = 3\sqrt{5}$. So, the length of the minor axis is $2b = 6\sqrt{5}$. A similar analysis for hyperbolas yields

$$b^2 = c^2 - a^2$$

$$= (ea)^2 - a^2$$

$$= a^2(e^2 - 1). \qquad \text{Hyperbola}$$

STUDY TIP

Because

$$r = \frac{ep}{1 \pm e \cos \theta}$$

is of the form $r = g(\cos \theta)$, you know that the graph of r is symmetric with respect to the polar axis. Similarly,

$$r = \frac{ep}{1 \pm e \sin \theta}$$

is of the form $r = f(\sin \theta)$, so the graph of r is symmetric with respect to the line $\theta = \pi/2$.

Example 2   Analyzing the Graph of a Polar Equation

Analyze the graph of the polar equation

$$r = \frac{32}{3 + 5 \sin \theta}.$$

Solution

Dividing the numerator and denominator by 3 produces

$$r = \frac{32/3}{1 + (5/3) \sin \theta}.$$

Because $e = \frac{5}{3} > 1$, the graph is a hyperbola. The transverse axis of the hyperbola lies on the line $\theta = \pi/2$ and the vertices occur at $(r, \theta) = (4, \pi/2)$ and $(r, \theta) = (-16, 3\pi/2)$. Because the length of the transverse axis is 12, you can see that $a = 6$. To find b, write

$$b^2 = a^2(e^2 - 1) = 6^2 \left[\left(\frac{5}{3} \right)^2 - 1 \right] = 64.$$

So, $b = 8$. The asymptotes are $y = 10 \pm \frac{3}{4}x$, as shown in Figure 10.79.

✓ *Checkpoint* Now try Exercise 21.

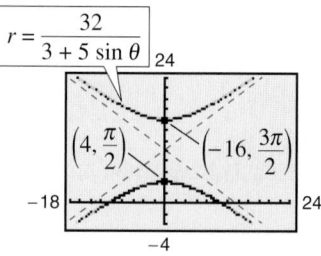

Figure 10.79

In the next example, you are asked to find a polar equation for a specified conic. To do this, let p be the distance between the pole and the directrix.

1. Horizontal directrix above the pole: $r = \dfrac{ep}{1 + e \sin \theta}$

2. Horizontal directrix below the pole: $r = \dfrac{ep}{1 - e \sin \theta}$

3. Vertical directrix to the right of the pole: $r = \dfrac{ep}{1 + e \cos \theta}$

4. Vertical directrix to the left of the pole: $r = \dfrac{ep}{1 - e \cos \theta}$

Example 3   Finding the Polar Equation of a Conic

Find the polar equation of the parabola whose focus is the pole and whose directrix is the line $y = 3$.

Solution

From Figure 10.80, you can see that the directrix is horizontal and above the pole. Moreover, because the eccentricity of a parabola is $e = 1$ and the distance between the pole and the directrix is $p = 3$, you have the equation

$$r = \frac{ep}{1 + e \sin \theta} = \frac{3}{1 + \sin \theta}.$$

✓ *Checkpoint* Now try Exercise 27.

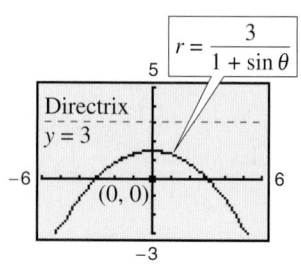

Figure 10.80

Application

Kepler's Laws (listed below), named after the German astronomer Johannes Kepler (1571–1630), can be used to describe the orbits of the planets about the sun.

1. Each planet moves in an elliptical orbit with the sun as a focus.

2. A ray from the sun to the planet sweeps out equal areas of the ellipse in equal times.

3. The square of the period (the time it takes for a planet to orbit the sun) is proportional to the cube of the mean distance between the planet and the sun.

Although Kepler simply stated these laws on the basis of observation, they were later validated by Isaac Newton (1642–1727). In fact, Newton was able to show that each law can be deduced from a set of universal laws of motion and gravitation that govern the movement of all heavenly bodies, including comets and satellites. This is illustrated in the next example, which involves the comet named after the English mathematician and physicist Edmund Halley (1656–1742).

If you use Earth as a reference with a period of 1 year and a distance of 1 astronomical unit (an *astronomical unit* is defined as the mean distance between Earth and the sun, or about 93 million miles), the proportionality constant in Kepler's third law is 1. For example, because Mars has a mean distance to the sun of $d \approx 1.524$ astronomical units, its period P is given by $d^3 = P^2$. So, the period of Mars is $P \approx 1.88$ years.

Example 4   Halley's Comet

Halley's comet has an elliptical orbit with an eccentricity of $e \approx 0.967$. The length of the major axis of the orbit is approximately 35.88 astronomical units. Find a polar equation for the orbit. How close does Halley's comet come to the sun?

Solution

Using a vertical axis, as shown in Figure 10.81, choose an equation of the form $r = ep/(1 + e \sin \theta)$. Because the vertices of the ellipse occur at $\theta = \pi/2$ and $\theta = 3\pi/2$, you can determine the length of the major axis to be the sum of the r-values of the vertices. That is,

$$2a = \frac{0.967p}{1 + 0.967} + \frac{0.967p}{1 - 0.967} \approx 29.79p \approx 35.88.$$

So, $p \approx 1.204$ and $ep \approx (0.967)(1.204) \approx 1.164$. Using this value of ep in the equation, you have

$$r = \frac{1.164}{1 + 0.967 \sin \theta}$$

where r is measured in astronomical units. To find the closest point to the sun (the focus), substitute $\theta = \pi/2$ into this equation to obtain

$$r = \frac{1.164}{1 + 0.967 \sin(\pi/2)} \approx 0.59 \text{ astronomical units} \approx 55{,}000{,}000 \text{ miles.}$$

✓ *Checkpoint* Now try Exercise 41.

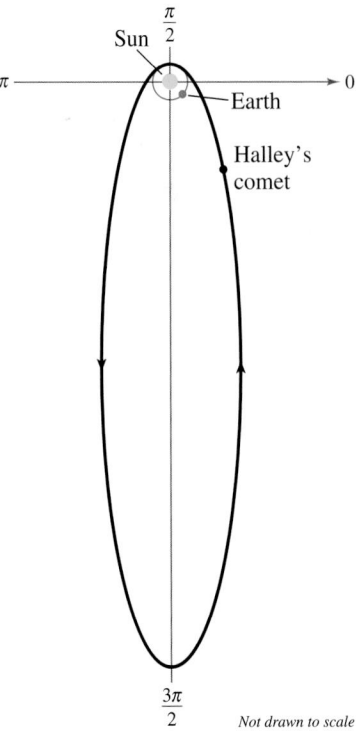

Figure 10.81

Not drawn to scale

10.6 Exercises

Vocabulary Check

In Exercises 1 and 2, fill in the blanks.

1. The locus of a point in the plane which moves so that its distance from a fixed point (focus) is in a constant ratio to its distance from a fixed line (directrix) is a _____ .

2. The constant ratio is the _____ of the conic and is denoted by _____ .

3. Match the conic with its eccentricity.

(a) $e < 1$ (i) ellipse

(b) $e = 1$ (ii) hyperbola

(c) $e > 1$ (iii) parabola

Graphical Reasoning **In Exercises 1–4, use a graphing utility to graph the polar equation when (a) $e = 1$, (b) $e = 0.5$, and (c) $e = 1.5$. Identify the conic for each equation.**

1. $r = \dfrac{2e}{1 + e \cos \theta}$ **2.** $r = \dfrac{2e}{1 - e \cos \theta}$

3. $r = \dfrac{2e}{1 - e \sin \theta}$ **4.** $r = \dfrac{2e}{1 + e \sin \theta}$

In Exercises 5–8, match the polar equation with its graph. [The graphs are labeled (a), (b), (c), and (d).]

(a)

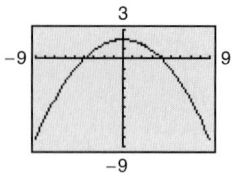

(b)

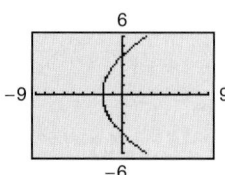

(c)

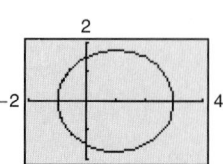

(d)

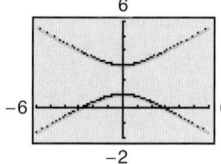

5. $r = \dfrac{4}{1 - \cos \theta}$ **6.** $r = \dfrac{3}{2 - \cos \theta}$

7. $r = \dfrac{3}{1 + 2 \sin \theta}$ **8.** $r = \dfrac{4}{1 + \sin \theta}$

In Exercises 9–18, identify the conic represented by the equation algebraically. Use a graphing utility to confirm your result.

9. $r = \dfrac{3}{1 - \cos \theta}$ **10.** $r = \dfrac{2}{1 + \sin \theta}$

11. $r = \dfrac{4}{4 - \cos \theta}$ **12.** $r = \dfrac{7}{7 + \sin \theta}$

13. $r = \dfrac{8}{4 + 3 \sin \theta}$ **14.** $r = \dfrac{6}{3 - 2 \cos \theta}$

15. $r = \dfrac{6}{2 + \sin \theta}$ **16.** $r = \dfrac{5}{-1 + 2 \cos \theta}$

17. $r = \dfrac{3}{4 - 8 \cos \theta}$ **18.** $r = \dfrac{10}{3 + 9 \sin \theta}$

In Exercises 19–22, use a graphing utility to graph the polar equation. Identify the graph.

19. $r = \dfrac{-5}{1 - \sin \theta}$ **20.** $r = \dfrac{-1}{2 + 4 \sin \theta}$

21. $r = \dfrac{14}{14 + 17 \sin \theta}$ **22.** $r = \dfrac{12}{2 - \cos \theta}$

In Exercises 23–26, use a graphing utility to graph the rotated conic.

23. $r = \dfrac{3}{1 - \cos(\theta - \pi/4)}$ (See Exercise 9.)

24. $r = \dfrac{7}{7 + \sin(\theta - \pi/3)}$ (See Exercise 12.)

25. $r = \dfrac{8}{4 + 3 \sin(\theta + \pi/6)}$ (See Exercise 13.)

26. $r = \dfrac{5}{-1 + 2 \cos(\theta + 2\pi/3)}$ (See Exercise 16.)

In Exercises 27–38, find a polar equation of the conic with its focus at the pole.

	Conic	Eccentricity	Directrix
27.	Parabola	$e = 1$	$x = -1$
28.	Parabola	$e = 1$	$y = -4$
29.	Ellipse	$e = \frac{1}{2}$	$y = 1$
30.	Ellipse	$e = \frac{3}{4}$	$y = -4$
31.	Hyperbola	$e = 2$	$x = 1$
32.	Hyperbola	$e = \frac{3}{2}$	$x = -1$

	Conic	Vertex or Vertices
33.	Parabola	$\left(1, -\dfrac{\pi}{2}\right)$
34.	Parabola	$(8, 0)$
35.	Ellipse	$(2, 0), (10, \pi)$
36.	Ellipse	$\left(2, \dfrac{\pi}{2}\right), \left(4, \dfrac{3\pi}{2}\right)$
37.	Hyperbola	$\left(1, \dfrac{3\pi}{2}\right), \left(9, \dfrac{3\pi}{2}\right)$
38.	Hyperbola	$\left(4, \dfrac{\pi}{2}\right), \left(-1, \dfrac{3\pi}{2}\right)$

39. *Planetary Motion*   The planets travel in elliptical orbits with the sun at one focus. Assume that the focus is at the pole, the major axis lies on the polar axis, and the length of the major axis is $2a$ (see figure). Show that the polar equation of the orbit of a planet is

$$r = \dfrac{(1 - e^2)a}{1 - e \cos \theta}$$

where e is the eccentricity.

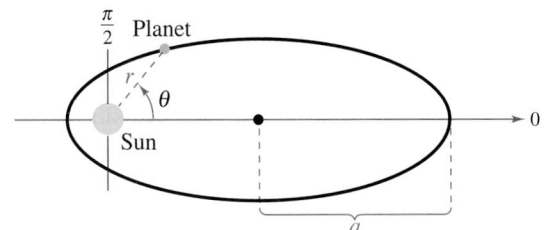

40. *Planetary Motion*   Use the result of Exercise 39 to show that the minimum distance (*perihelion*) from the sun to a planet is

$$r = a(1 - e)$$

and that the maximum distance (*aphelion*) is

$$r = a(1 + e).$$

Planetary Motion   **In Exercises 41–44, use the results of Exercises 39 and 40 to find the polar equation of the orbit of the planet and the perihelion and aphelion distances.**

41. Earth $a = 92.956 \times 10^6$ miles

$e = 0.0167$

42. Mercury $a = 35.983 \times 10^6$ miles

$e = 0.2056$

43. Jupiter $a = 77.841 \times 10^7$ kilometers

$e = 0.0484$

44. Saturn $a = 142.673 \times 10^7$ kilometers

$e = 0.0542$

45. *Planetary Motion*   Use the results of Exercises 39 and 40, where for the planet Neptune, $a = 4.498 \times 10^9$ kilometers and $e = 0.0086$ and for the planet Pluto, $a = 5.906 \times 10^9$ kilometers and $e = 0.2488$.

(a) Find the polar equation of the orbit of each planet.

(b) Find the perihelion and aphelion distances for each planet.

(c) Use a graphing utility to graph both Neptune's and Pluto's equation of orbit in the same viewing window.

(d) Do the orbits of the two planets intersect? Will the two planets ever collide? Why or why not?

(e) Is Pluto ever closer to the sun than Neptune? Why is Pluto called the ninth planet and Neptune the eighth planet?

46. *Explorer 18* On November 27, 1963, the United States launched *Explorer 18*. Its low and high points above the surface of Earth were 119 miles and 122,800 miles, respectively (see figure). The center of Earth is at one focus of the orbit.

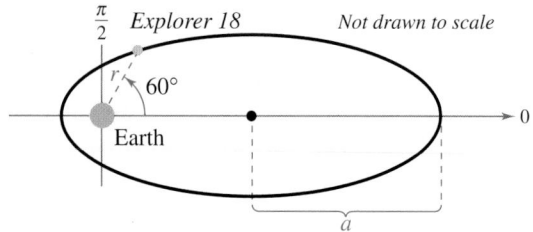

(a) Find the polar equation for the orbit (assume the radius of Earth is 4000 miles).

(b) Find the distance between the surface of Earth and the satellite when $\theta = 60°$.

(c) Find the distance between the surface of Earth and the satellite when $\theta = 30°$.

Synthesis

True or False? **In Exercises 47 and 48, determine whether the statement is true or false. Justify your answer.**

47. The graph of $r = 4/(-3 - 3 \sin \theta)$ has a horizontal directrix above the pole.

48. The conic represented by the following equation is an ellipse.

$$r^2 = \frac{16}{9 - 4 \cos\left(\theta + \frac{\pi}{4}\right)}$$

49. Show that the polar equation for the ellipse

$$\frac{x^2}{a^2} + \frac{y^2}{b^2} = 1 \quad \text{is} \quad r^2 = \frac{b^2}{1 - e^2 \cos^2 \theta}.$$

50. Show that the polar equation for the hyperbola

$$\frac{x^2}{a^2} - \frac{y^2}{b^2} = 1 \quad \text{is} \quad r^2 = \frac{-b^2}{1 - e^2 \cos^2 \theta}.$$

In Exercises 51 and 52, use the results of Exercises 49 and 50 to write the polar form of the equation of the conic.

51. $\dfrac{x^2}{169} + \dfrac{y^2}{144} = 1$ **52.** $\dfrac{x^2}{9} - \dfrac{y^2}{16} = 1$

53. *Exploration* Consider the polar equation

$$r = \frac{4}{1 - 0.4 \cos \theta}.$$

(a) Identify the conic without graphing the equation.

(b) Without graphing the following polar equations, describe how each differs from the given polar equation.

$$r = \frac{4}{1 + 0.4 \cos \theta}, \quad r = \frac{4}{1 - 0.4 \sin \theta}$$

(c) Use a graphing utility to verify your results in part (b).

54. *Exploration* The equation

$$r = \frac{ep}{1 \pm e \sin \theta}$$

is the equation of an ellipse with $e < 1$. What happens to the lengths of both the major axis and the minor axis when the value of e remains fixed and the value of p changes? Use an example to explain your reasoning.

55. *Writing* In your own words, define the term *eccentricity* and explain how it can be used to classify conics.

56. What conic does the polar equation given by $r = a \sin \theta + b \cos \theta$ represent?

Review

In Exercises 57–60, solve the equation.

57. $4\sqrt{3} \tan \theta - 3 = 1$

58. $6 \cos x - 2 = 1$

59. $12 \sin^2 \theta = 9$

60. $9 \csc^2 x - 10 = 2$

In Exercises 61–64, find the value of the trigonometric function given that u and v are in Quadrant IV and $\sin u = -\frac{3}{5}$ and $\cos v = 1/\sqrt{2}$.

61. $\cos(u + v)$ **62.** $\sin(u + v)$

63. $\sin(u - v)$ **64.** $\cos(u - v)$

In Exercises 65–68, evaluate the expression. Do not use a calculator.

65. $_{12}C_9$ **66.** $_{18}C_{16}$

67. $_{10}P_3$ **68.** $_{29}P_2$

10 Chapter Summary

What did you learn?

Section 10.1	Review Exercises
☐ Recognize the four basic conics: circles, parabolas, ellipses, and hyperbolas.	1–6
☐ Recognize, graph, and write equations of parabolas (vertex at origin).	7–16
☐ Recognize, graph, and write equations of ellipses (center at origin).	17–26
☐ Recognize, graph, and write equations of hyperbolas (center at origin).	27–34

Section 10.2

☐ Recognize equations of conics that have been shifted vertically and/or horizontally in the plane. — 35–42

☐ Write and graph equations of conics that have been shifted vertically and/or horizontally in the plane. — 43–56

Section 10.3

☐ Evaluate sets of parametric equations for given values of the parameter. — 57, 58

☐ Graph curves that are represented by sets of parametric equations. — 59–70

☐ Rewrite sets of parametric equations as single rectangular equations by eliminating the parameter. — 59–64

☐ Find sets of parametric equations for graphs. — 71–74

Section 10.4

☐ Plot points and find multiple representations of points in the polar coordinate system. — 75–78

☐ Convert points from rectangular to polar form and vice versa. — 79–86

☐ Convert equations from rectangular to polar form and vice versa. — 87–98

Section 10.5

☐ Graph polar equations by point plotting. — 99–104

☐ Use symmetry as a sketching aid. — 105–112

☐ Use zeros and maximum r-values as sketching aids. — 105–112

☐ Recognize special polar graphs. — 105–112

Section 10.6

☐ Define conics in terms of eccentricities. — 113–118

☐ Write and graph equations of conics in polar form. — 119–122

☐ Use equations of conics in polar form to model real-life problems. — 123, 124

10 Review Exercises

10.1 In Exercises 1–6, match the equation with its graph. [The graphs are labeled (a), (b), (c), (d), (e), and (f).]

(a)

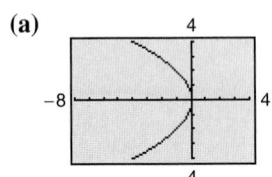

(b)

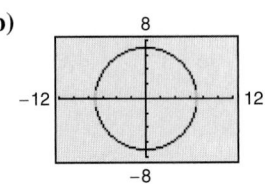

(c)

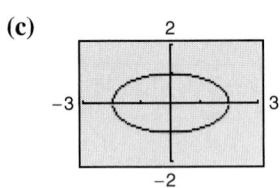

(d)

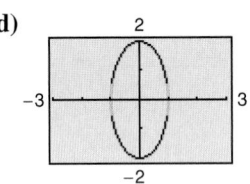

(e)

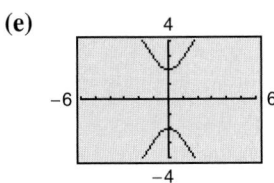

(f)

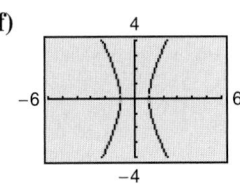

1. $4x^2 + y^2 = 4$ **2.** $y^2 = -4x$

3. $x^2 + 4y^2 = 4$ **4.** $x^2 + y^2 = 49$

5. $4x^2 - y^2 = 4$ **6.** $y^2 - 4x^2 = 4$

In Exercises 7–10, find the standard form of the equation of the parabola.

7. Vertex: $(0, 0)$; passes through: $(1, 2)$; vertical axis

8. Vertex: $(0, 0)$; passes through: $(4, -2)$; vertical axis

9. Vertex: $(0, 0)$; focus: $(-6, 0)$

10. Vertex: $(0, 0)$; focus: $(0, 3)$

In Exercises 11–14, find the vertex and focus of the parabola and sketch its graph. Use a graphing utility to verify your graph.

11. $4x - y^2 = 0$ **12.** $y = -\frac{1}{8}x^2$

13. $\frac{1}{2}y^2 + 18x = 0$ **14.** $\frac{1}{4}y - 8x^2 = 0$

15. *Satellite Antenna*   A cross section of a large parabolic antenna (see figure) is modeled by

$$y = \frac{x^2}{200}, \quad -100 \le x \le 100.$$

The receiving and transmitting equipment is positioned at the focus. Find the coordinates of the focus.

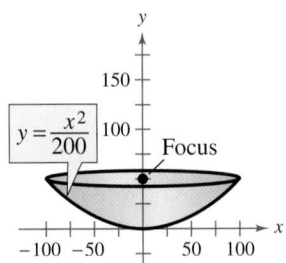

16. *Suspension Bridge*   Each cable of a suspension bridge is suspended (in the shape of a parabola) between two towers (see figure). An equation that models the cables is given by $y = \frac{1}{180}x^2$, where x and y are measured in meters. Find the coordinates of the focus.

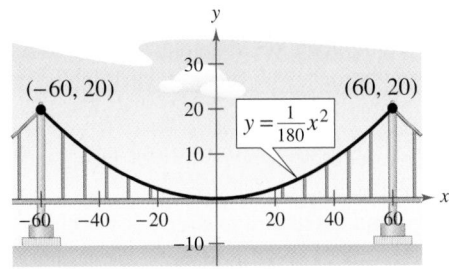

In Exercises 17–20, find the standard form of the equation of the ellipse with center at the origin.

17. Vertices: $(\pm 5, 0)$;   foci: $(\pm 4, 0)$

18. Vertices: $(0, \pm 10)$;   foci: $(0, \pm 8)$

19. Vertices: $(0, \pm 6)$;   passes through $(2, 2)$

20. Vertices: $(\pm 7, 0)$;   passes through $(0, \pm 6)$

In Exercises 21–24, find the center and vertices of the ellipse and sketch its graph. Use a graphing utility to verify your graph.

21. $\frac{x^2}{4} + \frac{y^2}{16} = 1$ **22.** $\frac{x^2}{9} + \frac{y^2}{8} = 1$

23. $6x^2 + 4y^2 = 36$ **24.** $3x^2 + 8y^2 = 48$

25. *Architecture*   A semielliptical archway is to be formed over the entrance to an estate. The arch is to be set on pillars that are 10 feet apart and is to have a height (atop the pillars) of 4 feet. Where should the foci be in order to sketch the arch?

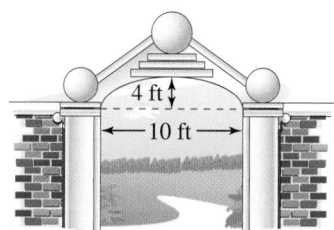

26. *Wading Pool*   You are building a wading pool that is in the shape of an ellipse. Your plans give an equation for the elliptical shape of the pool measured in feet as

$$\frac{x^2}{324} + \frac{y^2}{196} = 1.$$

Find the longest distance across the pool, the shortest distance, and the distance between the foci.

In Exercises 27–30, find the standard form of the equation of the hyperbola with center at the origin.

27. Vertices: $(\pm 1, 0)$;   asymptotes: $y = \pm 2x$

28. Vertices: $(0, \pm 2)$;   asymptotes: $y = \pm \dfrac{2}{\sqrt{5}}x$

29. Vertices: $(0, \pm 1)$;   foci: $(0, \pm 3)$

30. Vertices: $(\pm 4, 0)$;   foci: $(\pm 6, 0)$

In Exercises 31–34, find the center, vertices, and foci of the hyperbola and sketch its graph. Use a graphing utility to verify your graph.

31. $\dfrac{y^2}{9} - \dfrac{x^2}{64} = 1$ **32.** $\dfrac{x^2}{49} - \dfrac{y^2}{36} = 1$

33. $5y^2 - 4x^2 = 20$ **34.** $x^2 - y^2 = \dfrac{9}{4}$

10.2 **In Exercises 35–42, identify the conic by writing its equation in standard form. Then sketch its graph and describe the translation.**

35. $x^2 - 6x + 2y + 9 = 0$

36. $y^2 - 12y - 8x + 20 = 0$

37. $x^2 + 9y^2 + 10x - 18y + 25 = 0$

38. $16x^2 + 16y^2 - 16x + 24y - 3 = 0$

39. $4x^2 - 4y^2 - 4x + 8y - 11 = 0$

40. $x^2 - 9y^2 + 10x + 18y + 7 = 0$

41. $4x^2 + y^2 - 16x + 15 = 0$

42. $9x^2 - y^2 - 72x + 8y + 119 = 0$

In Exercises 43–46, find the standard form of the equation of the parabola.

43. Vertex: $(4, 2)$;   focus: $(4, 0)$

44. Vertex: $(2, 0)$;   focus: $(0, 0)$

45. Vertex: $(0, 2)$;   directrix: $x = -3$

46. Vertex: $(2, 2)$;   directrix: $y = 0$

In Exercises 47–50, find the standard form of the equation of the ellipse.

47. Vertices: $(-3, 0), (7, 0)$;   foci: $(0, 0), (4, 0)$

48. Vertices: $(2, 0), (2, 4)$;   foci: $(2, 1), (2, 3)$

49. Vertices: $(0, 1), (4, 1)$;

endpoints of the minor axis: $(2, 0), (2, 2)$

50. Vertices: $(-4, -1), (-4, 11)$;

endpoints of the minor axis: $(-6, 5), (-2, 5)$

In Exercises 51–54, find the standard form of the equation of the hyperbola.

51. Vertices: $(-10, 3), (6, 3)$;   foci: $(-12, 3), (8, 3)$

52. Vertices: $(2, 2), (-2, 2)$;   foci: $(4, 2), (-4, 2)$

53. Foci: $(0, 0), (8, 0)$;   asymptotes: $y = \pm 2(x - 4)$

54. Foci: $(3, \pm 2)$;   asymptotes: $y = \pm 2(x - 3)$

55. *Architecture*   A church window (see figure) is bounded on top by a parabola and below by the arc of a circle.

(a) Find equations for the parabola and circle.

(b) Use a graphing utility to complete the table showing the vertical distance d between the circle and the parabola for the given values of x.

x	0	1	2	3	4
d					

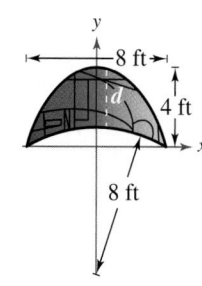

56. *Astronomy*   The comet Encke has an elliptical orbit with the sun at one focus. Encke's orbit ranges from 0.34 to 4.08 astronomical units from the sun. Find the standard equation of the orbit. Place the center of the orbit at the origin and place the major axis on the x-axis.

10.3 **In Exercises 57 and 58, complete the table for each set of parametric equations. Plot the points (x, y) and sketch a graph of the parametric equations.**

57. $x = 3t - 2$ and $y = 7 - 4t$

t	-2	-1	0	1	2	3
x						
y						

58. $x = \dfrac{1}{5}t$ and $y = \dfrac{4}{t - 1}$

t	-1	0	2	3	4	5
x						
y						

In Exercises 59–64, sketch the curve represented by the parametric equations (indicate the orientation of the curve). Then eliminate the parameter and write the corresponding rectangular equation whose graph represents the curve. Adjust the domain of the resulting rectangular equation, if necessary.

59. $x = 5t - 1$
$y = 2t + 5$

60. $x = 4t + 1$
$y = 8 - 3t$

61. $x = t^2 + 2$
$y = 4t^2 - 3$

62. $x = \dfrac{4}{t}$
$y = t^2 - 1$

63. $x = \dfrac{1}{t}$
$y = t$

64. $x = t$
$y = \dfrac{1}{t}$

In Exercises 65–70, use a graphing utility to graph the curve represented by the parametric equations.

65. $x = \sqrt[3]{t}$
$y = t$

66. $x = t$
$y = \sqrt[3]{t}$

67. $x = t^2$
$y = \sqrt{t}$

68. $x = t + 4$
$y = t^2$

69. $x = 6 \cos \theta$
$y = 6 \sin \theta$

70. $x = 3 + 3 \cos \theta$
$y = 2 + 5 \sin \theta$

In Exercises 71–74, find two different sets of parametric equations for the given rectangular equation.

71. $y = 6x + 2$

72. $y = 10 - x$

73. $y = x^2 + 2$

74. $y = 2x^3 + 5x$

10.4 **In Exercises 75–78, plot the point given in polar coordinates and find three additional polar representations of the point, using $-2\pi < \theta < 2\pi$.**

75. $\left(1, \dfrac{\pi}{4}\right)$

76. $\left(-5, -\dfrac{\pi}{3}\right)$

77. $\left(\sqrt{5}, -\dfrac{4\pi}{3}\right)$

78. $\left(\sqrt{10}, \dfrac{3\pi}{4}\right)$

In Exercises 79–82, plot the point given in polar coordinates and find the corresponding rectangular coordinates for the point.

79. $\left(5, -\dfrac{7\pi}{6}\right)$

80. $\left(-4, \dfrac{2\pi}{3}\right)$

81. $\left(3, \dfrac{3\pi}{4}\right)$

82. $\left(0, \dfrac{\pi}{2}\right)$

In Exercises 83–86, plot the point given in rectangular coordinates and find two sets of polar coordinates for the point for $0 \le \theta < 2\pi$.

83. $(0, -9)$

84. $(-3, 4)$

85. $(5, -5)$

86. $\left(-3, -\sqrt{3}\right)$

In Exercises 87–92, convert the rectangular equation to polar form.

87. $x^2 + y^2 = 9$

88. $x^2 + y^2 = 20$

89. $x^2 + y^2 - 4x = 0$

90. $x^2 + y^2 - 6y = 0$

91. $xy = 5$

92. $xy = -2$

In Exercises 93–98, convert the polar equation to rectangular form.

93. $r = 5$

94. $r = 12$

95. $r = 3 \cos \theta$

96. $r = 8 \sin \theta$

97. $r^2 = \cos 2\theta$

98. $r^2 = \sin \theta$

10.5 In Exercises 99–104, sketch the graph of the polar equation.

99. $r = 5$

100. $r = 3$

101. $\theta = \dfrac{\pi}{2}$

102. $\theta = -\dfrac{5\pi}{6}$

103. $r = 5 \cos \theta$

104. $r = 2 \sin \theta$

In Exercises 105–112, identify and then sketch the graph of the polar equation. Identify any symmetry, maximum *r*-values, and zeros of *r*. Use a graphing utility to verify your graph.

105. $r = 5 + 4 \cos \theta$

106. $r = 1 + 4 \sin \theta$

107. $r = 3 - 5 \sin \theta$

108. $r = 2 - 6 \cos \theta$

109. $r = -3 \cos 2\theta$

110. $r = \cos 5\theta$

111. $r^2 = 5 \sin 2\theta$

112. $r^2 = \cos 2\theta$

10.6 In Exercises 113–118, identify the conic represented by the equation algebraically. Then use a graphing utility to graph the polar equation.

113. $r = \dfrac{2}{1 - \sin \theta}$

114. $r = \dfrac{1}{1 + 2 \sin \theta}$

115. $r = \dfrac{4}{5 - 3 \cos \theta}$

116. $r = \dfrac{6}{-1 + 4 \cos \theta}$

117. $r = \dfrac{5}{6 + 2 \sin \theta}$

118. $r = \dfrac{3}{4 - 4 \cos \theta}$

In Exercises 119–122, find a polar equation of the conic with its focus at the pole.

Conic	Vertex or Vertices
119. Parabola	Vertex: $(2, \pi)$
120. Parabola	Vertex: $(2, \pi/2)$
121. Ellipse	Vertices: $(5, 0), (1, \pi)$
122. Hyperbola	Vertices: $(1, 0), (7, 0)$

123. *Planetary Motion* The planet Mars has an elliptical orbit with an eccentricity of $e \approx 0.093$. The length of the major axis of the orbit is approximately 3.05 astronomical units. Find a polar equation for the orbit and its perihelion and aphelion distances.

124. *Astronomy* An asteroid takes a parabolic path with Earth as its focus. It is about 6,000,000 miles from Earth at its closest approach. Write the polar equation of the path of the asteroid with its vertex at $\theta = -\pi/2$. Find the distance between the asteroid and Earth when $\theta = -\pi/3$.

Synthesis

True or False? In Exercises 125 and 126, determine whether the statement is true or false. Justify your answer.

125. The graph of $\frac{1}{4}x^2 - y^4 = 1$ represents the equation of a hyperbola.

126. There is only one set of parametric equations that represents the line $y = 3 - 2x$.

Writing In Exercises 127 and 128, an equation and four variations are given. In your own words, describe how the graph of each of the variations differs from the graph of the original equation.

127. $y^2 = 8x$

(a) $(y - 2)^2 = 8x$

(b) $y^2 = 8(x + 1)$

(c) $y^2 = -8x$

(d) $y^2 = 4x$

128. $\dfrac{x^2}{4} + \dfrac{y^2}{9} = 1$

(a) $\dfrac{x^2}{9} + \dfrac{y^2}{4} = 1$

(b) $\dfrac{x^2}{4} + \dfrac{y^2}{4} = 1$

(c) $\dfrac{x^2}{4} + \dfrac{y^2}{25} = 1$

(d) $\dfrac{(x - 3)^2}{4} + \dfrac{y^2}{9} = 1$

129. Consider an ellipse whose major axis is horizontal and 10 units in length. The number *b* in the standard form of the equation of the ellipse must be less than what real number? Describe the change in the shape of the ellipse as *b* approaches this number.

130. The graph of the parametric equations $x = 2 \sec t$ and $y = 3 \tan t$ is shown in the figure. Would the graph change for the equations $x = 2 \sec(-t)$ and $y = 3 \tan(-t)$? If so, how would it change?

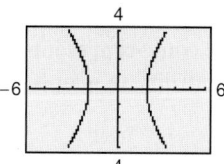

Figure for 130

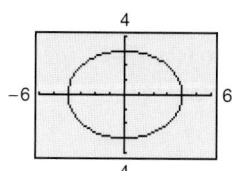

Figure for 131

131. The path of a moving object is modeled by the parametric equations $x = 4 \cos t$ and $y = 3 \sin t$, where *t* is time (see figure). How would the path change for each of the following?

(a) $x = 4 \cos 2t$, $y = 3 \sin 2t$

(b) $x = 5 \cos t$, $y = 3 \sin t$

10 Chapter Test

Take this test as you would take a test in class. After you are finished, check your work against the answers given in the back of the book.

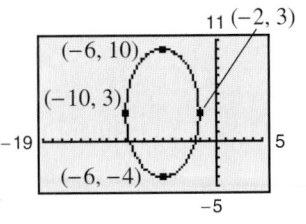

Figure for 5

In Exercises 1–3, graph the conic and identify any vertices and foci.

1. $y^2 - 8x = 0$ 2. $y^2 - 4x + 4 = 0$ 3. $x^2 - 4y^2 - 4x = 0$

4. Find the standard form of the equation of the parabola with focus $(8, -2)$ and directrix $x = 4$, and sketch the parabola.

5. Find the standard form of the equation of the ellipse shown at the right.

6. Find the standard form of the equation of the hyperbola with vertices $(0, \pm 3)$ and asymptotes $y = \pm \frac{3}{2}x$.

7. Use a graphing utility to graph the conic $x^2 - \dfrac{y^2}{4} = 1$. Describe your viewing window.

In Exercises 8–10, sketch the curve represented by the parametric equations. Then eliminate the parameter and write the corresponding rectangular equation whose graph represents the curve.

8. $x = t^2 - 6$ 9. $x = \sqrt{t^2 + 2}$ 10. $x = 2 + 3\cos\theta$

   $y = \dfrac{1}{2}t - 1$ $y = \dfrac{t}{4}$ $y = 2\sin\theta$

In Exercises 11–13, find two different sets of parametric equations for the given rectangular equation.

11. $y = 7x + 6$ 12. $y = x^2 + 10$ 13. $y = \frac{1}{4}x - 5$

14. Convert the polar coordinate $\left(-14, \dfrac{5\pi}{3}\right)$ to rectangular form.

15. Convert the rectangular coordinate $(2, -2)$ to polar form and find two additional representations of this point.

16. Convert the rectangular equation $x^2 + y^2 - 12y = 0$ to polar form.

In Exercises 17–20, identify the conic represented by the polar equation algebraically. Then use a graphing utility to graph the polar equation.

17. $r = 2 + 3\sin\theta$ 18. $r = 8\cos 3\theta$

19. $r = \dfrac{4}{2 + \cos\theta}$ 20. $r = \dfrac{8}{4 + 6\sin\theta}$

21. Find a polar equation of an ellipse with its focus at the pole, an eccentricity of $e = \frac{1}{4}$, and directrix at $y = 4$.

22. Find a polar equation of a hyperbola with its focus at the pole, an eccentricity of $e = \frac{5}{4}$, and directrix $y = 2$.

8–10 Cumulative Test

Take this test to review the material from earlier chapters. After you are finished, check your work against the answers given in the back of the book.

In Exercises 1–4, use any method to solve the system of equations.

1. $\begin{cases} -x - 3y = 5 \\ 4x + 2y = 10 \end{cases}$

2. $\begin{cases} 2x - y^2 = 0 \\ x - y = 4 \end{cases}$

3. $\begin{cases} 2x - 3y + z = 13 \\ -4x + y - 2z = -6 \\ x - 3y + 3z = 12 \end{cases}$

4. $\begin{cases} x - 4y + 3z = 5 \\ 5x + 2y - z = 1 \\ -2x - 8y = 30 \end{cases}$

In Exercises 5–8, perform the matrix operations given

$$A = \begin{bmatrix} -3 & 0 & -4 \\ 2 & 4 & 5 \\ -4 & 8 & 1 \end{bmatrix} \quad \text{and} \quad B = \begin{bmatrix} -1 & 5 & 2 \\ 6 & -3 & 3 \\ 0 & 4 & -2 \end{bmatrix}.$$

5. $3A - 2B$ **6.** $5A + 3B$ **7.** AB **8.** BA

9. Find (a) the inverse of A (if it exists), and (b) the determinant of A.

$$A = \begin{bmatrix} 1 & 2 & -1 \\ 3 & 7 & -10 \\ -5 & -7 & -15 \end{bmatrix}$$

10. Use a determinant to find the area of the triangle with vertices $(0, 0)$, $(6, 2)$, and $(8, 10)$.

11. Write the first five terms of each sequence a_n. (Assume n begins with 1.)

(a) $a_n = \dfrac{(-1)^{n+1}}{2n + 3}$ (b) $a_n = 3(2)^{n-1}$

In Exercises 12–15, find the sum. Use a graphing utility to verify your result.

12. $\displaystyle\sum_{k=1}^{6}(7k - 2)$ **13.** $\displaystyle\sum_{k=1}^{4}\frac{2}{k^2 + 4}$ **14.** $\displaystyle\sum_{n=0}^{10}9\left(\frac{3}{4}\right)^n$ **15.** $\displaystyle\sum_{n=1}^{\infty}8(0.9)^{n-1}$

16. Use mathematical induction to prove the formula

$$3 + 7 + 11 + 15 + \cdots + (4n - 1) = n(2n + 1).$$

In Exercises 17–20, use the Binomial Theorem to expand and simplify the expression.

17. $(x + 3)^4$ **18.** $(2x + y^2)^5$ **19.** $(x - 2y)^6$ **20.** $(3a - 4b)^8$

In Exercises 21 and 22, find the number of distinguishable permutations of the group of letters.

21. B, A, S, K, E, T, B, A, L, L   **22.** A, N, T, A, R, C, T, I, C, A

In Exercises 23–26, identify the conic and sketch its graph.

23. $\dfrac{(y + 3)^2}{36} - \dfrac{(x - 5)^2}{121} = 1$ **24.** $\dfrac{(x - 2)^2}{4} + \dfrac{(y + 1)^2}{9} = 1$

25. $y^2 - x^2 = 16$ **26.** $x^2 + y^2 - 2x - 4y + 1 = 0$

In Exercises 27–29, find the standard form of the equation of the conic.

27.   **28.**   **29.**

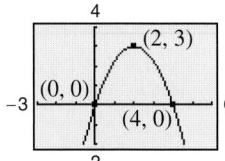 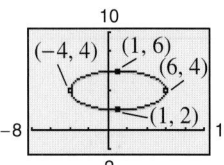 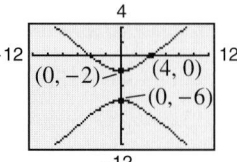

In Exercises 30–32, (a) sketch the curve represented by the parametric equations, (b) use a graphing utility to verify your graph, and (c) eliminate the parameter and write the corresponding rectangular equation whose graph represents the curve. Adjust the domain of the resulting rectangular equation, if necessary.

30. $x = 2t + 1$ **31.** $x = \cos \theta$ **32.** $x = 4 \ln t$

      $y = t^2$ $y = 2 \sin^2 \theta$ $y = \frac{1}{2}t^2$

In Exercises 33–36, plot the point given in polar coordinates and find three additional polar representations for $-2\pi < \theta < 2\pi$.

33. $\left(8, \dfrac{5\pi}{6}\right)$ **34.** $\left(5, -\dfrac{3\pi}{4}\right)$ **35.** $\left(-2, \dfrac{5\pi}{4}\right)$ **36.** $\left(-3, -\dfrac{11\pi}{6}\right)$

37. Convert the rectangular equation $-8x - 3y + 5 = 0$ to polar form.

38. Convert the polar equation $r = \dfrac{2}{4 - 5 \cos \theta}$ to rectangular form.

In Exercises 39–41, identify the graph represented by the polar equation algebraically. Then use a graphing utility to graph the polar equation.

39. $r = -\dfrac{\pi}{6}$ **40.** $r = 3 - 2 \sin \theta$ **41.** $r = 2 + 5 \cos \theta$

42. The salary for the first year of a job is $28,000. During the next 14 years, the salary increases by 5% each year. Determine the total compensation over the 15-year period.

43. On a game show, the digits 3, 4, and 5 must be arranged in the proper order to form the price of an appliance. If they are arranged correctly, the contestant wins the appliance. What is the probability of winning if the contestant knows that the price is at least $400?

44. A parabolic archway is 16 meters high at the vertex. At a height of 14 meters, the width of the archway is 12 meters, as shown in the figure at the right. How wide is the archway at ground level?

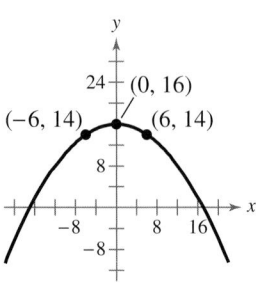

Figure for 44

Appendix A Technology Support

Introduction

Graphing utilities such as graphing calculators and computers with graphing software are very valuable tools for visualizing mathematical principles, verifying solutions to equations, exploring mathematical ideas, and developing mathematical models. Although graphing utilities are extremely helpful in learning mathematics, their use does not mean that learning algebra is any less important. In fact, the combination of knowledge of mathematics and the use of graphing utilities enables you to explore mathematics more easily and to a greater depth. If you are using a graphing utility in this course, it is up to you to learn its capabilities and to practice using this tool to enhance your mathematical learning.

In this text, there are many opportunities to use a graphing utility, some of which are described below.

Uses of a Graphing Utility

1. Check or validate answers to problems obtained using algebraic methods.

2. Discover and explore algebraic properties, rules, and concepts.

3. Graph functions, and approximate solutions to equations involving functions.

4. Efficiently perform complicated mathematical procedures such as those found in many real-life applications.

5. Find mathematical models for sets of data.

In this appendix, the features of graphing utilities are discussed from a generic perspective and are listed in alphabetical order. To learn how to use the features of a specific graphing utility, consult your user's manual or the website for this text found at *college.hmco.com*. Additional keystroke guides are available for most graphing utilities, and your college library may have a videotape on how to use your graphing utility.

Many graphing utilities are designed to act as "function graphers." In this course, functions and their graphs are studied in detail. You may recall from previous courses that a function can be thought of as a rule that describes the relationship between two variables. These rules are frequently written in terms of x and y. For example, the equation

$$y = 3x + 5$$

represents y as a function of x.

Many graphing utilities have an *equation editor* that requires that an equation be written in "$y =$" form in order to be entered, as shown in Figure A.1. (You should note that your *equation editor* screen may not look like the screen shown in Figure A.1.)

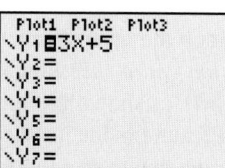

Figure A.1

Cumulative Sum Feature

The *cumulative sum* feature finds partial sums of a series. For example, to find the first four partial sums of the series

$$\sum_{k=1}^{4} 2(0.1)^k$$

choose the *cumulative sum* feature, which is found in the *operations* menu of the *list* feature (see Figure A.2). To use this feature, you will also have to use the *sequence* feature (see Figure A.2 and page A15). You must enter an expression for the sequence, a variable, the lower limit of summation, and the upper limit of summation, as shown in Figure A.3. After pressing ENTER, you can see that the first four partial sums are 0.2, 0.22, 0.222, and 0.2222. You may have to scroll to the right in order to see all the partial sums.

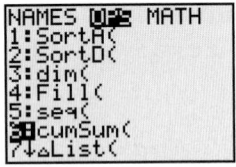

Figure A.2   Figure A.3

Determinant Feature

The *determinant* feature evaluates the determinant of a square matrix. For example, to evaluate the determinant of the matrix shown at the right, enter the 3×3 matrix into the graphing utility using the *matrix editor*, as shown in Figure A.4. Then choose the *determinant* feature from the *math* menu of the *matrix* feature, as shown in Figure A.5. Once you choose the matrix name, A, press ENTER and you should obtain a determinant of -50, as shown in Figure A.6.

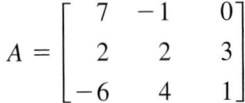

$$A = \begin{bmatrix} 7 & -1 & 0 \\ 2 & 2 & 3 \\ -6 & 4 & 1 \end{bmatrix}$$

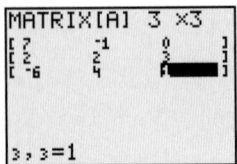
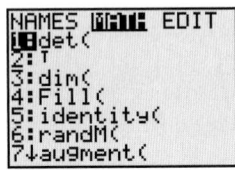
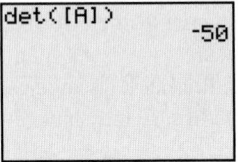

Figure A.4   Figure A.5   Figure A.6

Draw Inverse Feature

The *draw inverse* feature graphs the inverse function of a one-to-one function. For instance, to graph the inverse function of $f(x) = x^3 + 4$, first enter the function into the *equation editor* (see Figure A.7) and graph the function (using a square viewing window), as shown in Figure A.8. Then choose the *draw inverse* feature from the *draw* feature menu, as shown in Figure A.9. You must enter the function you want to graph the inverse function of, as shown in Figure A.10. Finally, press ENTER to obtain the inverse function of $f(x) = x^3 + 4$, as shown in Figure A.11. This feature can only be used when the graphing utility is in *function* mode.

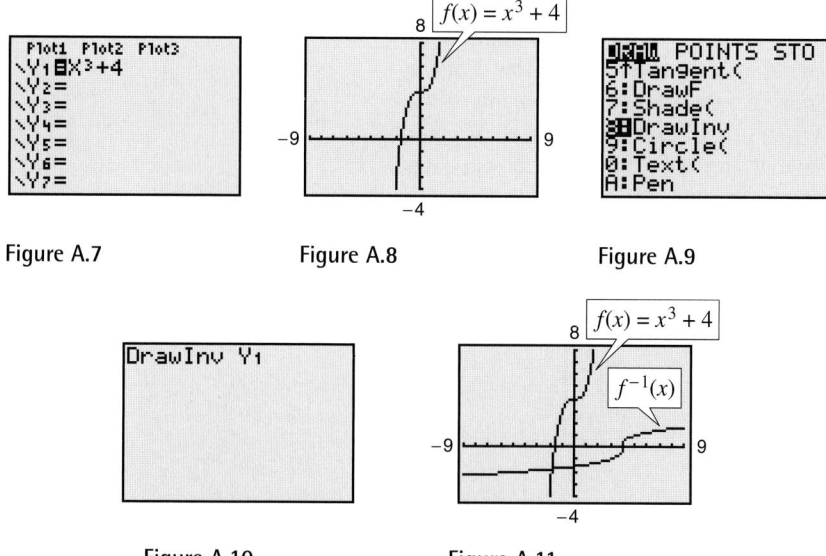

Figure A.7   Figure A.8   Figure A.9

Figure A.10   Figure A.11

Elementary Row Operations Features

Most graphing utilities can perform elementary row operations on matrices.

Row Swap Feature

The *row swap* feature interchanges two rows of a matrix. To interchange rows 1 and 3 of the matrix shown at the right, first enter the matrix into the graphing utility using the *matrix editor*, as shown in Figure A.12. Then choose the *row swap* feature from the *math* menu of the *matrix* feature, as shown in Figure A.13. When using this feature, you must enter the name of the matrix and the two rows that are to be interchanged. After pressing ENTER, you should obtain the matrix shown in Figure A.14. Because the resulting matrix will be used to demonstrate the other elementary row operation features, use the *store* feature to copy the resulting matrix to [A], as shown in Figure A.15.

$$A = \begin{bmatrix} -1 & -2 & 1 & 2 \\ 2 & -4 & 6 & -2 \\ 1 & 3 & -3 & 0 \end{bmatrix}$$

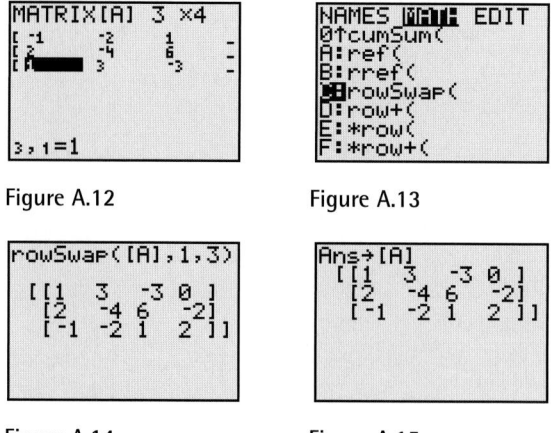

Figure A.12   Figure A.13

Figure A.14   Figure A.15

TECHNOLOGY TIP

The *store* feature of a graphing utility is used to store a value in a variable or to copy one matrix to another matrix. For instance, as shown at the left, after performing a row operation on a matrix, you can copy the answer to another matrix (see Figure A.15). You can then perform another row operation on the copied matrix. If you want to continue performing row operations to obtain a matrix in row-echelon form or reduced row-echelon form, you must copy the resulting matrix to a new matrix before each operation.

Row Addition and Row Multiplication and Addition Features

The *row addition* and *row multiplication and addition* features add a multiple of a row of a matrix to another row of the same matrix. To add row 1 to row 3 of the matrix stored in [A], choose the *row addition* feature from the *math* menu of the *matrix* feature, as shown in Figure A.16. When using this feature, you must enter the name of the matrix and the two rows that are to be added. After pressing ENTER, you should obtain the matrix shown in Figure A.17. Copy the resulting matrix to [A].

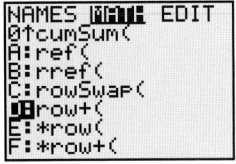

Figure A.16   Figure A.17

To add -2 times row 1 to row 2 of the matrix stored in [A], choose the *row multiplication and addition* feature from the *math* menu of the *matrix* feature, as shown in Figure A.18. When using this feature, you must enter the constant, the name of the matrix, the row the constant is multiplied by, and the row to be added to. After pressing ENTER, you should obtain the matrix shown in Figure A.19. Copy the resulting matrix to [A].

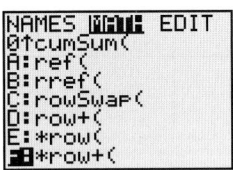

Figure A.18   Figure A.19

Row Multiplication Feature

The *row multiplication* feature multiplies a row of a matrix by a nonzero constant. To multiply row 2 of the matrix stored in [A] by $-\frac{1}{10}$, choose the *row multiplication* feature from the *math* menu of the *matrix* feature, as shown in Figure A.20. When using this feature, you must enter the constant, the name of the matrix, and the row to be multiplied. After pressing ENTER, you should obtain the matrix shown in Figure A.21.

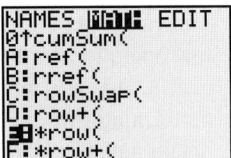

Figure A.20   Figure A.21

Intersect Feature

The *intersect* feature finds the point(s) of intersection of two graphs. The *intersect* feature is found in the *calculate* menu (see Figure A.22). To find the point(s) of intersection of the graphs of $y_1 = -x + 2$ and $y_2 = x + 4$, first enter the equations in the *equation editor*, as shown in Figure A.23. Then graph the equations, as shown in Figure A.24. Next, use the *intersect* feature to find the point of intersection. Trace the cursor along the graph of y_1 near the intersection and press ENTER (see Figure A.25). Then trace the cursor along the graph of y_2 near the intersection and press ENTER (see Figure A.26). Marks are then placed on the graph at these points (see Figure A.27). Finally, move the cursor near the point of intersection and press ENTER. From Figure A.28, you can see that the coordinates of the point of intersection are displayed in the bottom of the window. So, the point of intersection is $(-1, 3)$.

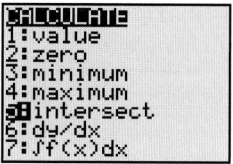

Figure A.22

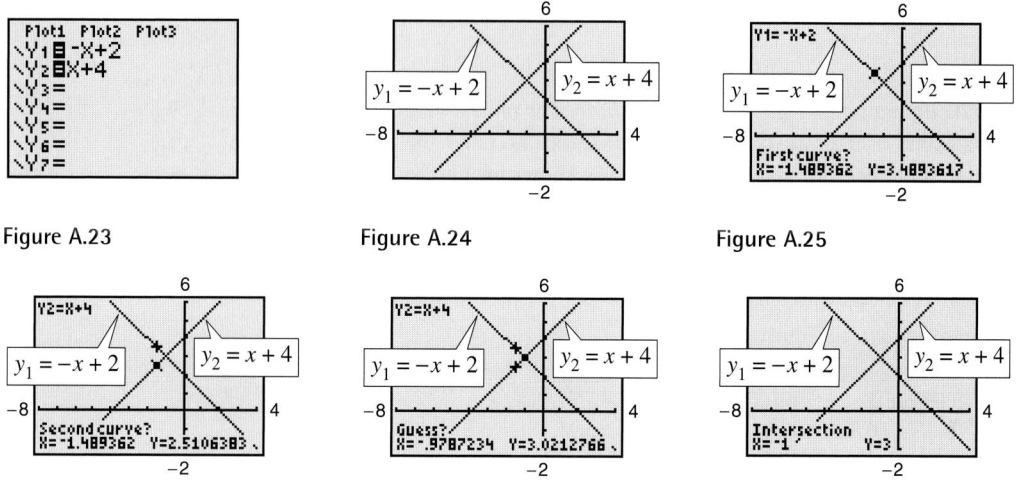

Figure A.23   Figure A.24   Figure A.25

Figure A.26   Figure A.27   Figure A.28

List Editor

Most graphing utilities can hold data in lists. The *list editor* can be used to create tables and to hold statistical data. The *list editor* can be found in the *edit* menu of the *statistics* feature, as shown in Figure A.29. To enter the numbers 1 through 10 into a list, first choose a list (L_1) and then begin entering the data into each row, as shown in Figure A.30.

Figure A.29

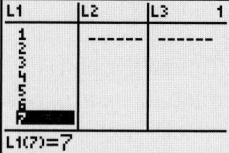

Figure A.30

You can also attach a formula to a list. For instance, you can multiply each of the data values in L_1 by 3. First, display the *list editor* and move the cursor to the top line. Then move the cursor onto the list to which you want to attach the formula (L_2). Finally, enter the formula $3* L_1$ (see Figure A.31) and then press ENTER. You should obtain the list shown in Figure A.32.

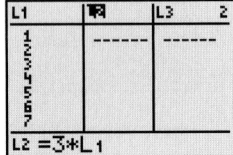   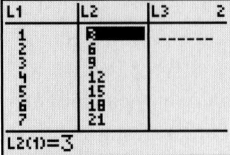

Figure A.31   Figure A.32

Matrix Feature

The *matrix* feature of a graphing utility has many uses, such as evaluating a determinant and performing row operations.

Matrix Editor

You can define, display, and edit matrices using the *matrix editor*. The *matrix editor* can be found in the *edit* menu of the *matrix* feature. For instance, to enter the matrix shown at the right, first choose the matrix name [A], as shown in Figure A.33. Then enter the dimension of the matrix (in this case, the dimension is 2×3) and enter the entries of the matrix, as shown in Figure A.34. To display the matrix on the home screen, choose the *name* menu of the *matrix* feature and select the matrix [A] (see Figure A.35), then press ENTER. The matrix A should now appear on the home screen, as shown in Figure A.36.

$$A = \begin{bmatrix} 6 & -3 & 4 \\ 9 & 0 & -1 \end{bmatrix}$$

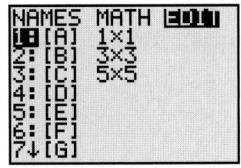   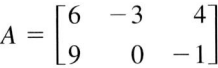

Figure A.33   Figure A.34

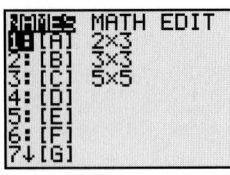   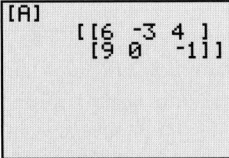

Figure A.35   Figure A.36

Matrix Operations

Most graphing utilities can perform matrix operations. To find the sum $A + B$ of the matrices shown at the right, first enter the matrices into the *matrix editor* as [A] and [B]. Then find the sum as shown in Figure A.37. Scalar multiplication can be performed in a similar manner. For example, you can evaluate $7A$, where A is the matrix at the right, as shown in Figure A.38. To find the product AB of the matrices A and B at the right, first be sure that the product is defined. Because the number of columns of A (2 columns) equals the number of rows of B (2 rows), you can find the product AB, as shown in Figure A.39.

$$A = \begin{bmatrix} -3 & 5 \\ 0 & 4 \end{bmatrix}$$

$$B = \begin{bmatrix} 7 & -2 \\ -1 & 2 \end{bmatrix}$$

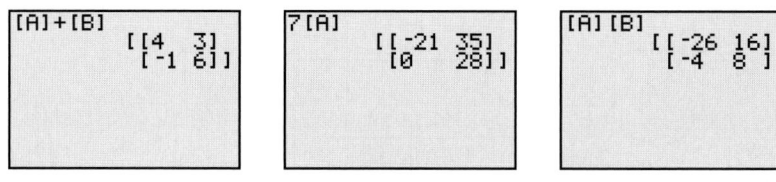

Figure A.37   Figure A.38   Figure A.39

Inverse Matrix

Some graphing utilities may not have an *inverse matrix* feature. However, you can find the inverse of a square matrix by using the inverse key $\boxed{x^{-1}}$. To find the inverse of the matrix shown at the right, enter the matrix in the *matrix editor* as [A]. Then find the inverse as shown in Figure A.40.

$$A = \begin{bmatrix} 1 & -2 & 1 \\ -1 & 3 & 0 \\ 2 & 4 & 5 \end{bmatrix}$$

Figure A.40

Maximum and Minimum Features

The *maximum* and *minimum* features find relative extrema of a function. For instance, the graph of $y = x^3 - 3x$ is shown in Figure A.41. From the figure, the graph appears to have a relative maximum at $x = -1$ and a relative minimum at $x = 1$. To find the exact values of the relative extrema, you can use the *maximum* and *minimum* features found in the *calculate* menu (see Figure A.42). First, to find the relative maximum, choose the *maximum* feature and trace the cursor along the graph to a point left of the maximum and press $\boxed{\text{ENTER}}$ (see Figure A.43). Then trace the cursor along the graph to a point right of the maximum and press $\boxed{\text{ENTER}}$ (see Figure A.44). Note the two arrows near the top of the display marking the left and right bounds, as shown in Figure A.45. Next, trace the cursor along the graph between the two bounds and as close to the maximum as you can (see Figure A.45) and press $\boxed{\text{ENTER}}$. From Figure A.46, you can see that the coordinates of the maximum point are displayed in the bottom of the window. So, the relative maximum is $(-1, 2)$.

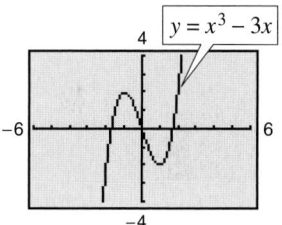

Figure A.41

   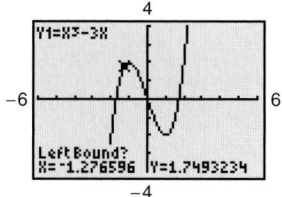   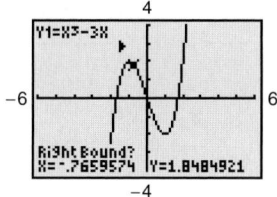

Figure A.42   Figure A.43   Figure A.44

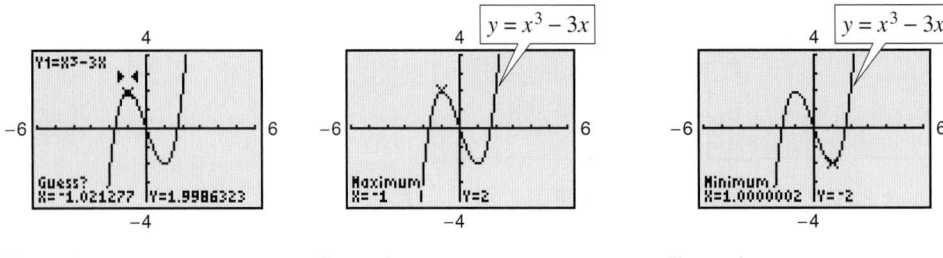

Figure A.45   Figure A.46   Figure A.47

You can find the relative minimum in a similar manner. From Figure A.47, you can see that the relative minimum is $(1, -2)$.

Mean and Median Features

In real-life applications, you often encounter large data sets and want to calculate statistical values. The *mean* and *median* features calculate the mean and median of a data set. For instance, in a survey, 100 people were asked how much money (in dollars) per week they withdraw from an automatic teller machine (ATM). The results are shown in the table below. The frequency represents the number of responses.

Amount	10	20	30	40	50	60	70	80	90	100
Frequency	3	8	10	19	24	13	13	7	2	1

To find the mean and median of the data set, first enter the data in the *list editor*, as shown in Figure A.48. Enter the amount in L_1 and the frequency in L_2. Then choose the *mean* feature from the *math* menu of the *list* feature, as shown in Figure A.49. When using this feature, you must enter a list and a frequency list (if applicable). In this case, the list is L_1 and the frequency list is L_2. After pressing [ENTER], you should obtain a mean of $49.80, as shown in Figure A.50. You can follow the same steps (except choose the *median* feature) to find the median of the data. You should obtain a median of $50, as shown in Figure A.51.

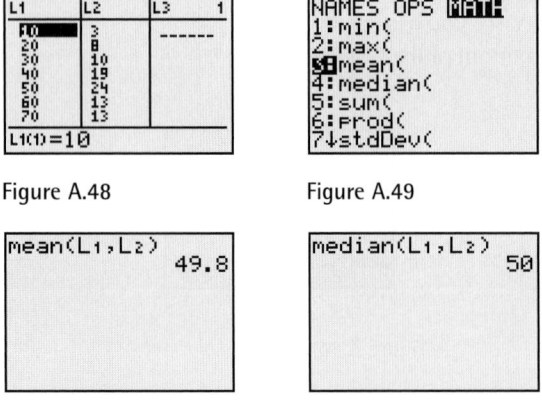

Figure A.48   Figure A.49

Figure A.50   Figure A.51

Mode Settings

Mode settings of a graphing utility control how the utility displays and interprets numbers and graphs. The default mode settings are shown in Figure A.52.

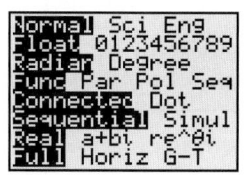

Figure A.52

Radian and Degree Modes

The trigonometric functions can be applied to angles measured in either radians or degrees. When your graphing utility is in *radian* mode, it interprets angle values as radians and displays answers in radians. When your graphing utility is in *degree* mode, it interprets angle values as degrees and displays answers in degrees. For instance, to calculate $\sin(\pi/6)$, make sure the calculator is in *radian* mode. You should obtain an answer of 0.5, as shown in Figure A.53. To calculate $\sin 45°$, make sure the calculator is in *degree* mode, as shown in Figure A.54. You should obtain an approximate answer of 0.7071, as shown in Figure A.55. If you did not change the mode of the calculator before evaluating $\sin 45°$, you would obtain an answer of approximately 0.8509, which is the sine of 45 radians.

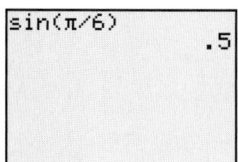

Figure A.53

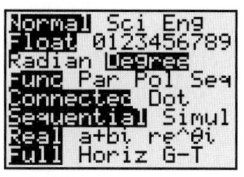

Figure A.54

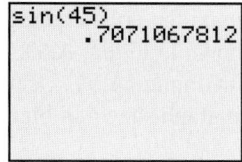

Figure A.55

Function, Parametric, Polar, and Sequence Modes

Most graphing utilities can graph using four different modes.

Function Mode   The *function* mode is used to graph standard algebraic and trigonometric functions. For instance, to graph $y = 2x^2$, use the *function* mode, as shown in Figure A.52. Then enter the equation in the *equation editor*, as shown in Figure A.56. Using a standard viewing window (see Figure A.57), you obtain the graph shown in Figure A.58.

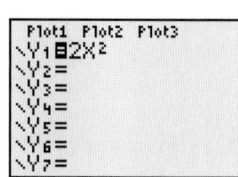

Figure A.56

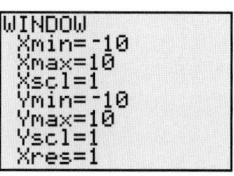

Figure A.57

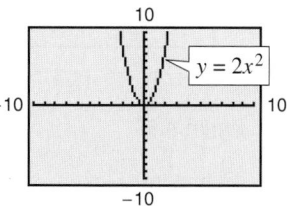

Figure A.58

Parametric Mode   To graph parametric equations such as $x = t + 1$ and $y = t^2$, use the *parametric* mode, as shown in Figure A.59. Then enter the equations in the *equation editor*, as shown in Figure A.60. Using the viewing window shown in Figure A.61, you obtain the graph shown in Figure A.62.

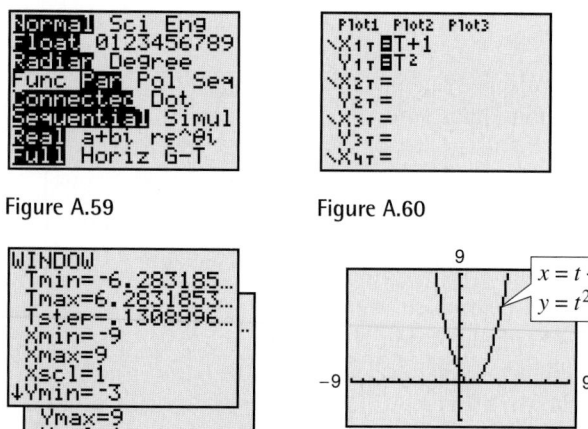

Figure A.59　　　　Figure A.60

Figure A.61　　　　Figure A.62

Polar Mode To graph polar equations of the form $r = f(\theta)$, you can use the *polar* mode of a graphing utility. For instance, to graph the polar equation $r = 2 \cos \theta$, use the *polar* mode (and *radian* mode), as shown in Figure A.63. Then enter the equation in the *equation editor*, as shown in Figure A.64. Using the viewing window shown in Figure A.65, you obtain the graph shown in Figure A.66.

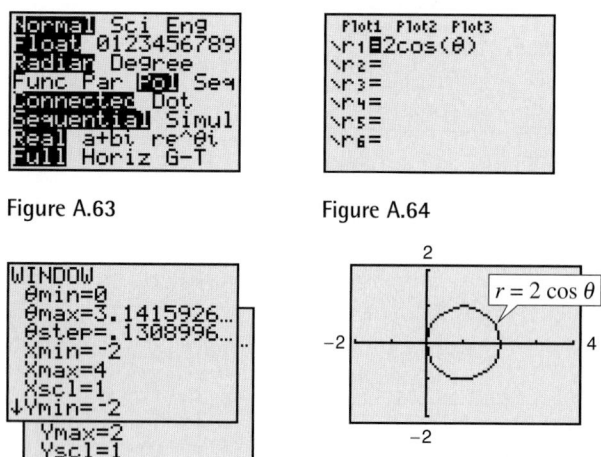

Figure A.63　　　　Figure A.64

Figure A.65　　　　Figure A.66

Sequence Mode To graph the first five terms of a sequence such as $a_n = 4n - 5$, use the *sequence* mode, as shown in Figure A.67. Then enter the sequence in the *equation editor*, as shown in Figure A.68 (assume that n begins with 1). Using the viewing window shown in Figure A.69, you obtain the graph shown in Figure A.70.

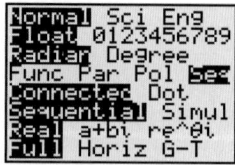

Figure A.67

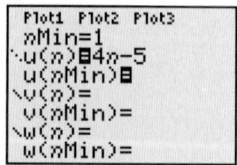

Figure A.68

TECHNOLOGY TIP

Note that when using the different graphing modes of a graphing utility, the utility uses different variables. When the utility is in *function* mode, it uses the variables x and y. In *parametric* mode, the utility uses the variables x, y, and t. In *polar* mode, the utility uses the variables r and θ. In *sequence* mode, the utility uses the variables u (instead of a) and n.

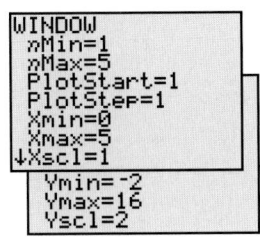

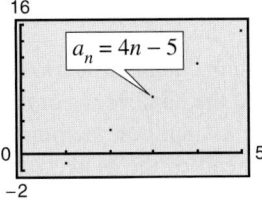

Figure A.69

Figure A.70

Connected and Dot Modes

Graphing utilities use the point-plotting method to graph functions. When a graphing utility is in *connected* mode, the utility connects the points that are plotted. When the utility is in *dot* mode, it does not connect the points that are plotted. For example, the graph of $y = x^3$ in *connected* mode is shown in Figure A.71. To graph this function using *dot* mode, first change the mode to *dot* mode (see Figure A.72) and then graph the equation, as shown in Figure A.73. As you can see from Figure A.73, the graph is a collection of dots.

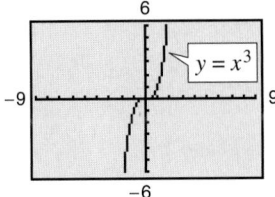

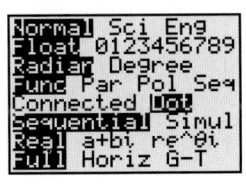

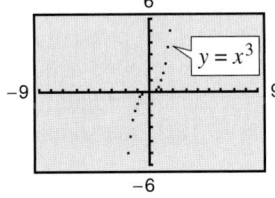

Figure A.71

Figure A.72

Figure A.73

A problem arises when using the *connected* mode of some graphing utilities. Graphs with vertical asymptotes, such as rational functions and tangent functions, appear to be connected. For instance, the graph of

$$y = \frac{1}{x + 3}$$

is shown in Figure A.74. Notice how the two portions of the graph appear to be connected with a vertical line at $x = -3$. From your study of rational functions, you know that the graph has a vertical asymptote at $x = -3$ and therefore is undefined when $x = -3$. When using a graphing utility to graph rational functions and other functions that have vertical asymptotes, you should use the *dot* mode to eliminate extraneous vertical lines. Because the *dot* mode of a graphing utility displays graphs as a collection of dots rather than as a smooth curve, in this text, a blue or light red curve is placed behind the graphing utility's display to indicate where the graph should appear, as shown in Figure A.75.

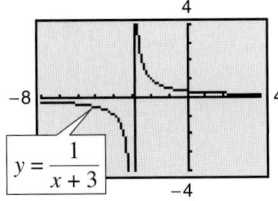

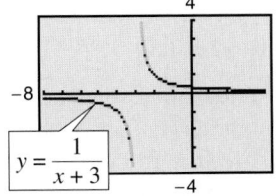

Figure A.74

Figure A.75

$_nC_r$ Feature

The $_nC_r$ feature calculates binomial coefficients and the number of combinations of n elements taken r at a time. For example, to find the number of combinations of eight elements taken five at a time, enter 8 (the n-value) on the home screen and choose the $_nC_r$ feature from the *probability* menu of the *math* feature (see Figure A.76). Next, enter 5 (the r-value) on the home screen and press ⎡ENTER⎤. You should obtain 56, as shown in Figure A.77.

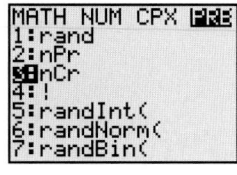

Figure A.76

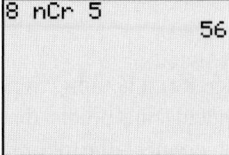

Figure A.77

$_nP_r$ Feature

The $_nP_r$ feature calculates the number of permutations of n elements taken r at a time. For example, to find the number of permutations of six elements taken four at a time, enter 6 (the n-value) on the home screen and choose the $_nP_r$ feature from the *probability* menu of the *math* feature (see Figure A.78). Next enter 4 (the r-value) on the home screen and press ⎡ENTER⎤. You should obtain 360, as shown in Figure A.79.

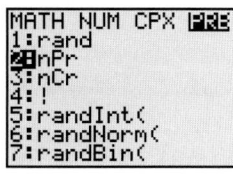

Figure A.78

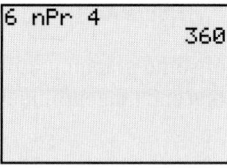

Figure A.79

One-Variable Statistics Feature

Graphing utilities are useful when calculating statistical values for a set of data. The *one-variable statistics* feature analyzes data with one measured variable. This feature outputs the mean of the data, the sum of the data, the sum of the data squared, the sample standard deviation of the data, the population standard deviation of the data, the number of data points, the minimum data value, the maximum data value, the first quartile of the data, the median of the data, and the third quartile of the data. Consider the following data, which shows the hourly earnings (in dollars) for 12 retail sales associates.

5.95, 8.15, 6.35, 7.05, 6.80, 6.10, 7.15, 8.20, 6.50, 7.50, 7.95, 9.25

You can use the *one-variable statistics* feature to determine the mean and standard deviation of the data. First, enter the data in the *list editor*, as shown in Figure A.80. Then choose the *one-variable statistics* feature from the *calculate* menu of the *statistics* feature, as shown in Figure A.81. When using this feature, you must enter a list. In this case, the list is L_1. From Figure A.82, you can see that the mean of the data is $\bar{x} \approx 7.25$ and the standard deviation of the data is $\sigma x \approx 0.95$.

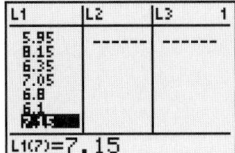

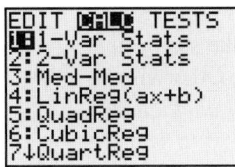

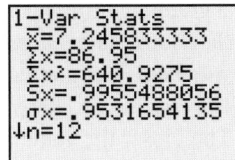

Figure A.80   Figure A.81   Figure A.82

Regression Feature

Throughout the text, you are asked to use the *regression* feature of a graphing utility to find models for sets of data. Most graphing utilities have built-in regression programs for the following.

Regression	*Form of Model*
Linear	$y = ax + b$ or $y = a + bx$
Quadratic	$y = ax^2 + bx + c$
Cubic	$y = ax^3 + bx^2 + cx + d$
Quartic	$y = ax^4 + bx^3 + cx^2 + dx + e$
Logarithmic	$y = a + b \ln(x)$
Exponential	$y = ab^x$
Power	$y = ax^b$
Logistic	$y = \dfrac{c}{1 + ae^{-bx}}$
Sine	$y = a \sin(bx + c) + d$

For example, you can find a linear model for the number y of television sets (in millions) in U.S. households for the years 1996 through 2003, shown in the table.   (Source: Nielsen Media Research)

Year	Number, y
1996	222.8
1997	228.7
1998	235.0
1999	240.3
2000	245.0
2001	248.2
2002	254.4
2003	260.2

First, let x represent the year, with $x = 6$ corresponding to 1996. Then enter the data in the *list editor*, as shown in Figure A.83. Note that L_1 contains the years and L_2 contains the numbers of television sets that correspond to the years. Now choose the *linear regression* feature from the *calculate* menu of the *statistics* feature, as shown in Figure A.84. From Figure A.85, you can see that a linear model for the data is given by $y = 5.17x + 192.7$.

When you use the *regression* feature of a graphing utility, you will notice that the program may also output an "*r*-value." (For some calculators, make sure you select the *diagnostics on* feature before you use the *regression* feature. Otherwise, the calculator will not output an *r*-value.) The *r*-value or *correlation coefficient* measures how well the model fits the data. The closer the value of $|r|$ is to 1, the better the fit. For the data above, $r \approx 0.998$, which implies that the model is a good fit for the data.

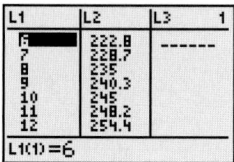

Figure A.83

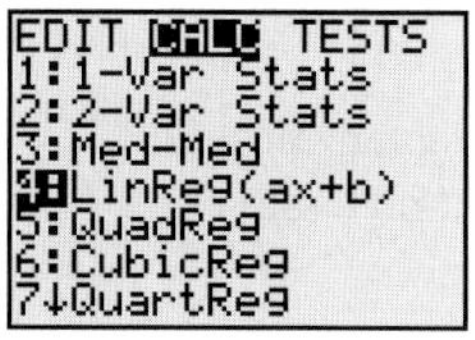

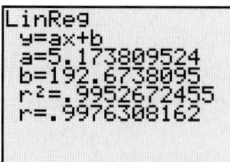

Figure A.84

Figure A.85

STUDY TIP

In this text, when regression models are found, the number of decimal places in the constant term of the model is the same as the number of decimal places in the data, and the number of decimal places increases by one for terms of increasing powers of the independent variable.

Row-Echelon and Reduced Row-Echelon Features

Some graphing utilities have features that can automatically transform a matrix to row-echelon form and reduced row-echelon form. These features can be used to check your solutions to systems of equations.

Row-Echelon Feature

Consider the system of equations and the corresponding augmented matrix shown below.

$$
\begin{array}{cc}
\textit{Linear System} & \textit{Augmented Matrix} \\
\begin{cases} 2x + 5y - 3z = 4 \\ 4x + y = 2 \\ -x + 3y - 2z = -1 \end{cases} &
\left[\begin{array}{ccc:c} 2 & 5 & -3 & 4 \\ 4 & 1 & 0 & 2 \\ -1 & 3 & -2 & -1 \end{array} \right]
\end{array}
$$

You can use the *row-echelon* feature of a graphing utility to write the augmented matrix in row-echelon form. First, enter the matrix into the graphing utility using the *matrix editor*, as shown in Figure A.86. Next, choose the *row-echelon* feature from the *math* menu of the *matrix* feature, as shown in Figure A.87. When using this feature, you must enter the name of the matrix. In this case, the matrix is [A]. You should obtain the matrix shown in Figure A.88. You may have to scroll to the right in order to see all the entries of the matrix.

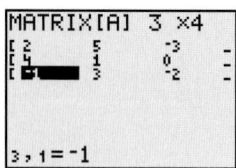

Figure A.86

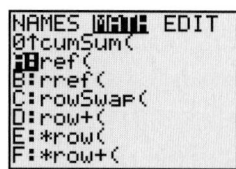

Figure A.87

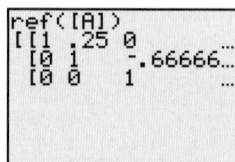

Figure A.88

Reduced Row-Echelon Feature

To write the augmented matrix in reduced row-echelon form, follow the same steps used to write a matrix in row-echelon form except choose the *reduced row-echelon form* feature, as shown in Figure A.89. You should obtain the matrix shown in Figure A.90. From Figure A.90, you can conclude that the solution to the system is $x = 3$, $y = -10$, and $z = -16$.

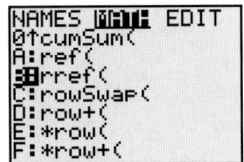

Figure A.89

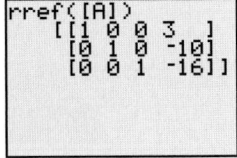

Figure A.90

Sequence Feature

The *sequence* feature is used to display the terms of sequences. For instance, to determine the first five terms of the arithmetic sequence

$a_n = 3n + 5$ Assume *n* begins with 1.

set the graphing utility to *sequence* mode. Then choose the *sequence* feature from the *operations* menu of the *list* feature, as shown in Figure A.91. When using this feature, you must enter the sequence, the variable (in this case n), the beginning value (in this case 1), and the end value (in this case 5). The first five terms of the sequence are 8, 11, 14, 17, and 20, as shown in Figure A.92. You may have to scroll to the right in order to see all the terms of the sequence.

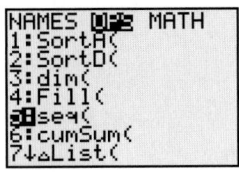

Figure A.91

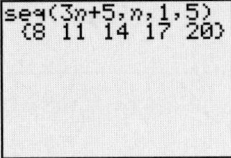

Figure A.92

Shade Feature

Most graphing utilities have a *shade* feature that can be used to graph inequalities. For instance, to graph the inequality $y \le 2x - 3$, first enter the equation $y = 2x - 3$ into the *equation editor*, as shown in Figure A.93. Next, using a standard viewing window (see Figure A.94), graph the equation, as shown in Figure A.95.

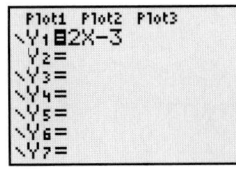

Figure A.93

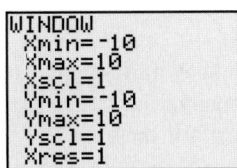

Figure A.94

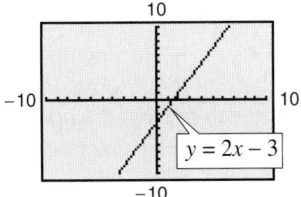

Figure A.95

Because the inequality sign is ≤, you want to shade the region below the line $y = 2x - 3$. Choose the *shade* feature from the *draw* feature menu, as shown in Figure A.96. You must enter a lower function and an upper function. In this case, the lower function is -10 (this is the least y-value in the viewing window) and the upper function is Y_1 $(y = 2x - 3)$, as shown in Figure A.97. Then press $\boxed{\text{ENTER}}$ to obtain the graph shown in Figure A.98.

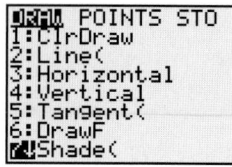

Figure A.96

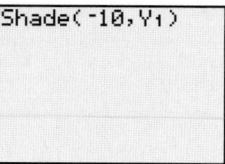

Figure A.97

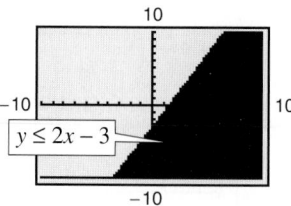

Figure A.98

If you wanted to graph the inequality $y \geq 2x - 3$ (using a standard viewing window), you would enter the lower function as Y_1 $(y = 2x - 3)$ and the upper function as 10 (the greatest y-value in the viewing window).

Sum Feature

The *sum* feature finds the sum of a list of data. For instance, the data below represents a student's quiz scores on 10 quizzes throughout an algebra course.

22, 23, 19, 24, 20, 15, 25, 21, 18, 24

To find the total quiz points the student earned, enter the data in the *list editor*, as shown in Figure A.99. To find the sum, choose the *sum* feature from the *math* menu of the *list* feature, as shown in Figure A.100. You must enter a list. In this case the list is L_1. You should obtain a sum of 211, as shown in Figure A.101.

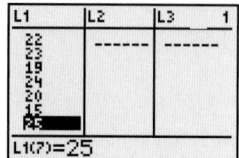

Figure A.99

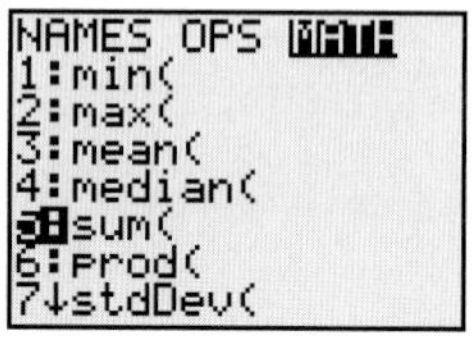

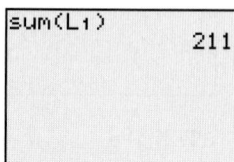

Figure A.100

Figure A.101

Sum Sequence Feature

The *sum* feature and the *sequence* feature can be combined to find the sum of sequences and series. For example, to find the sum

$$\sum_{k=0}^{10} 5^{k+1}$$

first choose the *sum* feature from the *math* menu of the *list* feature, as shown in Figure A.102. Then choose the *sequence* feature from the *operations* menu of the *list* feature, as shown in Figure A.103. You must enter an expression for the sequence, a variable, the lower limit of summation, and the upper limit of summation. After pressing $\boxed{\text{ENTER}}$, you should obtain the sum 61,035,155, as shown in Figure A.104.

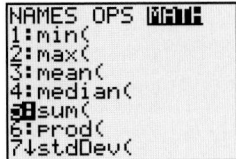

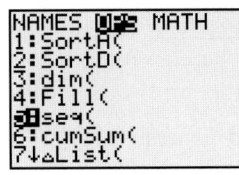

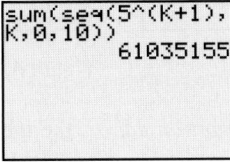

Figure A.102   Figure A.103   Figure A.104

Table Feature

Most graphing utilities are capable of displaying a table of values with x-values and one or more corresponding y-values. These tables can be used to check solutions of an equation and to generate ordered pairs to assist in graphing an equation by hand.

Figure A.105

To use the *table* feature, enter an equation into the *equation editor*. The table may have a setup screen, which allows you to select the starting x-value and the table step or x-increment. You may then have the option of automatically generating values for x and y or building your own table using the *ask* mode (see Figure A.105).

For example, enter the equation

$$y = \frac{3x}{x + 2}$$

into the *equation editor*, as shown in Figure A.106. In the table setup screen, set the table to start at $x = -4$ and set the table step to 1, as shown in Figure A.107. When you view the table, notice that the first x-value is -4 and that each value after it increases by 1. Also notice that the Y_1 column gives the resulting y-value for each x-value, as shown in Figure A.108. The table shows that the y-value when $x = -2$ is ERROR. This means that the equation is undefined when $x = -2$.

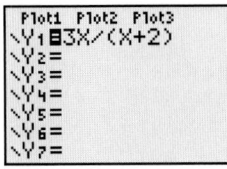

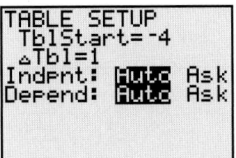

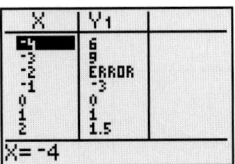

Figure A.106   Figure A.107   Figure A.108

With the same equation in the *equation editor*, set the independent variable in the table to *ask* mode, as shown in Figure A.109. In this mode, you do not need to set the starting x-value or the table step because you are entering any value you choose for x. You may enter any real value for x—integers, fractions, decimals, irrational numbers, and so forth. If you enter $x = 1 + \sqrt{3}$, the graphing utility may rewrite the number as a decimal approximation, as shown in Figure A.110. You can continue to build your own table by entering additional x-values in order to generate y-values, as shown in Figure A.111.

Figure A.109

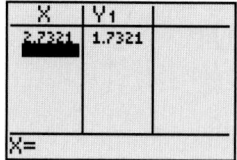

Figure A.110

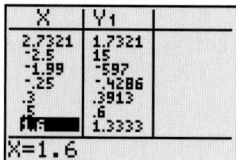

Figure A.111

If you have several equations in the *equation editor*, the table may generate *y*-values for each equation.

Tangent Feature

Some graphing utilities have the capability of drawing a tangent line to a graph at a given point. For instance, consider the equation

$$y = -x^3 + x + 2.$$

To draw the line tangent to the point $(1, 2)$, enter the equation into the *equation editor*, as shown in Figure A.112. Using the viewing window shown in Figure A.113, graph the equation, as shown in Figure A.114. Next, choose the *tangent* feature from the *draw* feature menu, as shown in Figure A.115. You can either move the cursor to select a point or you can enter the *x*-value at which you want the tangent line to be drawn. Because you want the tangent line to the point $(1, 2)$, enter 1 (see Figure A.116) and then press [ENTER]. The *x*-value you entered and the equation of the tangent line are displayed at the bottom of the window, as shown in Figure A.117.

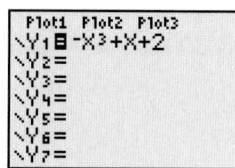

Figure A.112

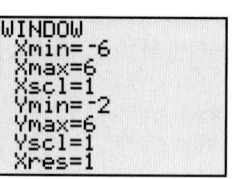

Figure A.113

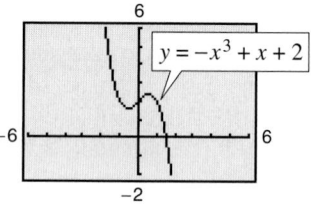

Figure A.114

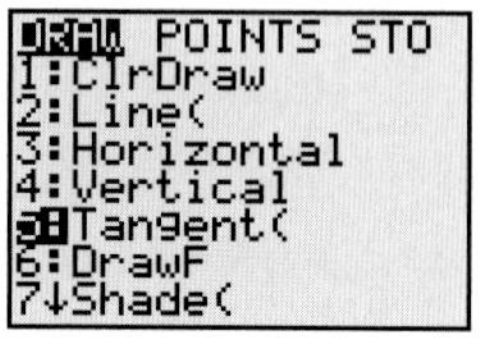

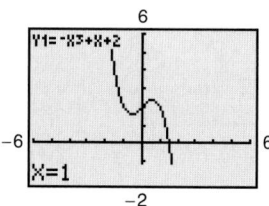

Figure A.115

Figure A.116

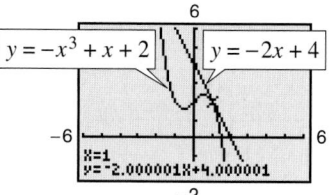

Figure A.117

Trace Feature

For instructions on how to use the *trace* feature, see the Zoom and Trace Features description on page A22.

Value Feature

The *value* feature finds the value of a function y for a given x-value. To find the value of a function such as $f(x) = 0.5x^2 - 1.5x$ at $x = 1.8$, first enter the function into the *equation editor* (see Figure A.118) and then graph the function (using a standard viewing window), as shown in Figure A.119. Next, choose the *value* feature from the *calculate* menu, as shown in Figure A.120. You will see "X= " displayed at the bottom of the window. Enter the x-value, in this case $x = 1.8$, as shown in Figure A.121. When entering an x-value, be sure it is between the Xmin and Xmax values you entered for the viewing window. Then press $\boxed{\text{ENTER}}$. From Figure A.122, you can see that when $x = 1.8$, $y = -1.08$.

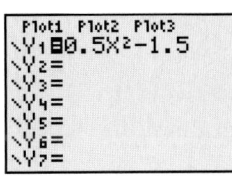

Figure A.118

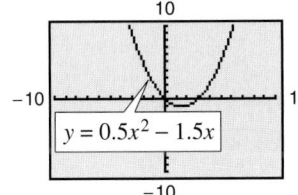

Figure A.119

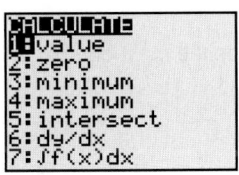

Figure A.120

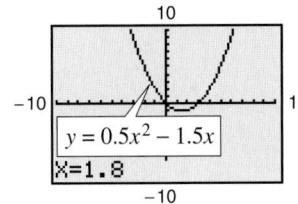

Figure A.121

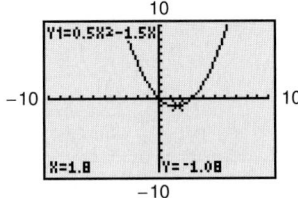

Figure A.122

Viewing Window

A viewing window for a graph is a rectangular portion of the coordinate plane. A viewing window is determined by the following six values (see Figure A.123).

Xmin = the smallest value of x

Xmax = the largest value of x

Xscl = the number of units per tick mark on the x-axis

Ymin = the smallest value of y

Ymax = the largest value of y

Yscl = the number of units per tick mark on the y-axis

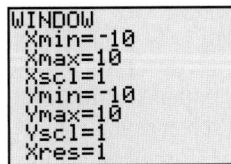

Figure A.123

When you enter these six values into a graphing utility, you are setting the viewing window. On some graphing utilities there is a seventh value on the viewing window labeled Xres. This sets the pixel resolution (1 through 8). For instance, when Xres = 1, functions are evaluated and graphed at each pixel on the *x*-axis. Some graphing utilities have a standard viewing window, as shown in Figure A.124. To initialize the standard viewing window quickly, choose the *standard viewing window* feature from the *zoom* feature menu (see page A22), as shown in Figure A.125.

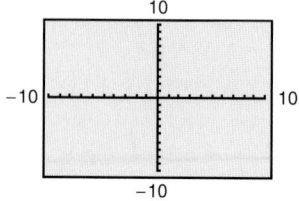

Figure A.124   Figure A.125

By choosing different viewing windows for a graph, it is possible to obtain different impressions of the graph's shape. For instance, Figure A.126 shows four different viewing windows for the graph of

$$y = 0.1x^4 - x^3 + 2x^2.$$

Of these, the view shown in part (a) is the most complete.

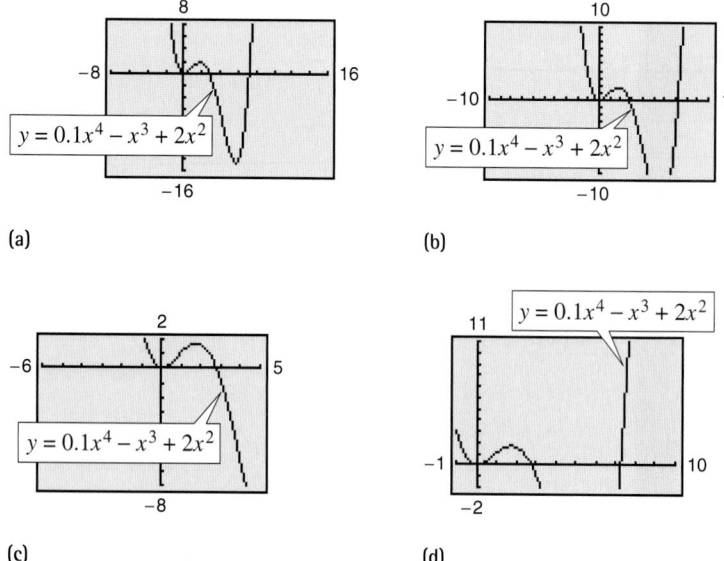

(a)   (b)

(c)   (d)
Figure A.126

On most graphing utilities, the display screen is two-thirds as high as it is wide. On such screens, you can obtain a graph with a true geometric perspective by using a square setting—one in which

$$\frac{\text{Ymax} - \text{Ymin}}{\text{Xmax} - \text{Xmin}} = \frac{2}{3}.$$

One such setting is shown in Figure A.127. Notice that the *x* and *y* tick marks are equally spaced on a square setting, but not on a standard setting (see Figure A.124). To initialize the square viewing window quickly, choose the *square viewing window* feature from the *zoom* feature menu (see page A22), as shown in Figure A.128.

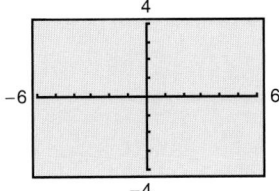

Figure A.127

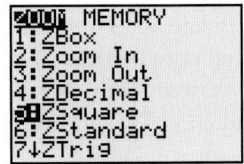

Figure A.128

To see how the viewing window affects the geometric perspective, graph the semicircles $y_1 = \sqrt{9 - x^2}$ and $y_2 = -\sqrt{9 - x^2}$ using a standard viewing window, as shown in Figure A.129. Notice how the circle appears elliptical rather than circular. Now graph y_1 and y_2 using a square viewing window, as shown in Figure A.130. Notice how the circle appears circular. (Note that when you graph the two semicircles, your graphing utility may not connect them. This is because some graphing utilities are limited in their resolution. So, in this text, a blue or light red curve is placed behind the graphing utility's display to indicate where the graph should appear.)

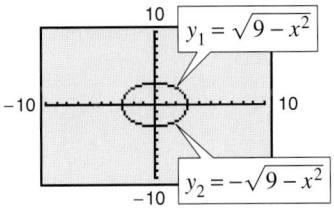

Figure A.129

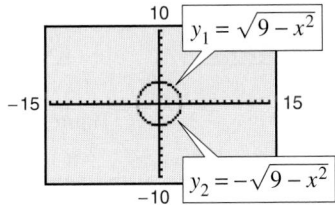

Figure A.130

Zero or Root Feature

The *zero* or *root* feature finds the real zeros of the various types of functions studied in this text. To find the zeros of a function such as

$$f(x) = 2x^3 - 4x$$

first enter the function into the *equation editor*, as shown in Figure A.131. Now graph the equation (using a standard viewing window), as shown in Figure A.132. From the graph you can see that the graph of the function crosses the x-axis three times, so the function has three zeros.

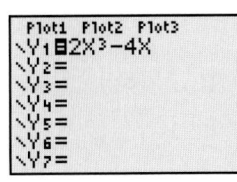

Figure A.131

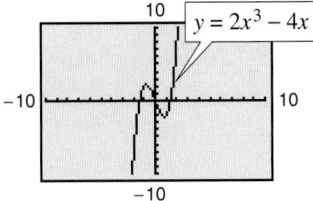

Figure A.132

To find these zeros, choose the *zero* feature found in the *calculate* menu (see Figure A.133). Next, trace the cursor along the graph to a point left of one of the zeros and press [ENTER] (see Figure A.134). Then trace the cursor along the graph to a point right of the zero and press [ENTER] (see Figure A.135). Note the two arrows near the top of the display marking the left and right bounds, as shown in Figure A.136. Now trace the cursor along the graph between the two bounds and as close to the zero as you can (see Figure A.137) and press [ENTER] . From Figure A.138, you can see that one zero of the function is $x \approx -1.414214$.

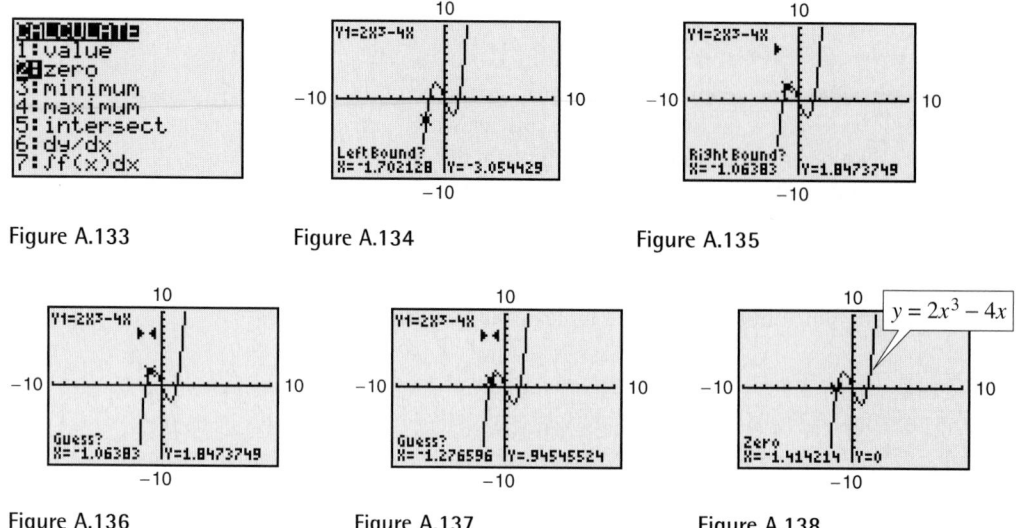

Figure A.133   Figure A.134   Figure A.135

Figure A.136   Figure A.137   Figure A.138

Repeat this process to determine that the other two zeros of the function are $x = 0$ (see Figure A.139) and $x \approx 1.414214$ (see Figure A.140).

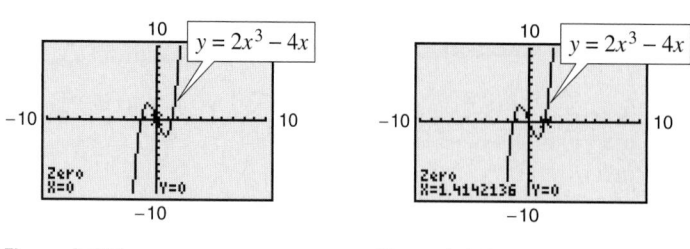

Figure A.139   Figure A.140

Zoom and Trace Features

The *zoom* feature enables you to quickly adjust the viewing window of a graph (see Figure A.141). For example, the *zoom box* feature allows you to create a new viewing window by drawing a box around any part of the graph.

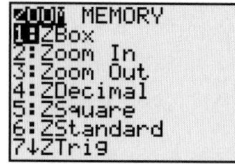

Figure A.141

The *trace* feature moves from point to point along a graph. For instance, enter the equation $y = 2x^3 - 3x + 2$ into the *equation editor* (see Figure A.142) and graph the equation, as shown in Figure A.143. To activate the *trace* feature, press TRACE; then use the arrow keys to move the cursor along the graph. As you trace the graph, the coordinates of each point are displayed, as shown in Figure A.144.

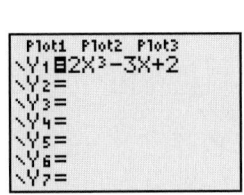

Figure A.142

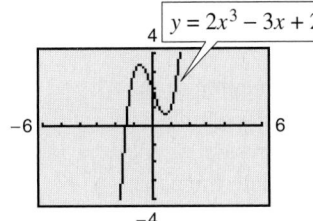

Figure A.143

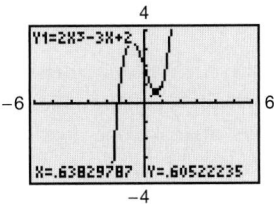

Figure A.144

The *trace* feature combined with the *zoom* feature enables you to obtain better and better approximations of desired points on a graph. For instance, you can use the *zoom* feature to approximate the *x*-intercept of the graph of $y = 2x^3 - 3x + 2$. From the viewing window shown in Figure A.143, the graph appears to have only one *x*-intercept. This intercept lies between -2 and -1. To zoom in on the *x*-intercept, choose the *zoom-in* feature from the *zoom* feature menu, as shown in Figure A.145. Next, trace the cursor to the point you want to zoom in on, in this case the *x*-intercept (see Figure A.146). Then press ENTER. You should obtain the graph shown in Figure A.147. Now, using the *trace* feature, you can approximate the *x*-intercept to be $x \approx -1.468085$, as shown in Figure A.148. Use the *zoom-in* feature again to obtain the graph shown in Figure A.149. Using the *trace* feature, you can approximate the *x*-intercept to be $x \approx -1.476064$, as shown in Figure A.150.

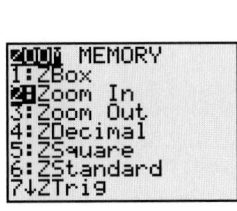

Figure A.145

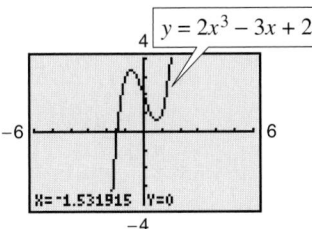

Figure A.146

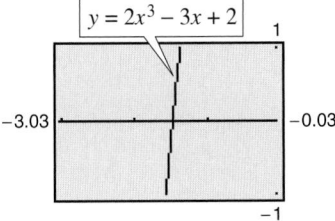

Figure A.147

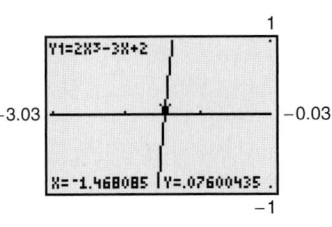

Figure A.148

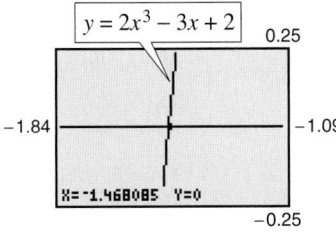

Figure A.149

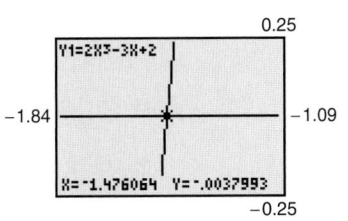

Figure A.150

Here are some suggestions for using the *zoom* feature.

1. With each successive zoom-in, adjust the scale so that the viewing window shows at least one tick mark on each side of the *x*-intercept.

2. The error in your approximation will be less than the distance between two scale marks.

3. The *trace* feature can usually be used to add one more decimal place of accuracy without changing the viewing window.

You can adjust the scale in Figure A.150 to obtain a better approximation of the *x*-intercept. Using the suggestions above, change the viewing window settings so that the viewing window shows at least one tick mark on each side of the *x*-intercept, as shown in Figure A.151. From Figure A.151, you can determine that the error in your approximation will be less than 0.001 (the Xscl value). Then, using the *trace* feature, you can improve the approximation, as shown in Figure A.152. To three decimal places, the *x*-intercept is $x \approx -1.476$.

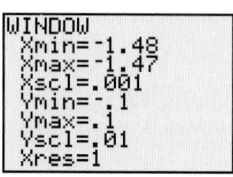

Figure A.151   Figure A.152

Appendix B Proofs of Selected Theorems

Section P.5, page 51

> **The Midpoint Formula**
>
> The midpoint of the line segment joining the points (x_1, y_1) and (x_2, y_2) is given by the Midpoint Formula
>
> $$\text{Midpoint} = \left(\frac{x_1 + x_2}{2}, \frac{y_1 + y_2}{2} \right).$$

Proof

Using the figure, you must show that

$$d_1 = d_2 \quad \text{and} \quad d_1 + d_2 = d_3.$$

By the Distance Formula, you obtain

$$d_1 = \sqrt{\left(\frac{x_1 + x_2}{2} - x_1 \right)^2 + \left(\frac{y_1 + y_2}{2} - y_1 \right)^2}.$$

Now, to simplify the expressions within the parentheses, you must find the least common denominator. The least common denominator is 2. Because both expressions have a denominator of 2^2, factor $\frac{1}{4}$ out of the expressions and then simplify the radical as follows.

$$d_1 = \tfrac{1}{2} \sqrt{(x_2 - x_1)^2 + (y_2 - y_1)^2}$$

To find d_2 and d_3, use the same procedure as above to obtain

$$d_2 = \sqrt{\left(x_2 - \frac{x_1 + x_2}{2} \right)^2 + \left(y_2 - \frac{y_1 + y_2}{2} \right)^2} = \frac{1}{2} \sqrt{(x_2 - x_1)^2 + (y_2 - y_1)^2}$$

$$d_3 = \sqrt{(x_2 - x_1)^2 + (y_2 - y_1)^2}.$$

So, it follows that $d_1 = d_2$ and $d_1 + d_2 = d_3$.

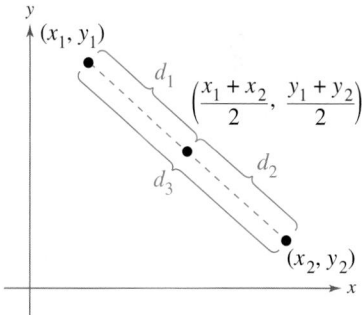

Midpoint Formula

Section 3.3, page 268

> **The Remainder Theorem**
>
> If a polynomial $f(x)$ is divided by $x - k$, the remainder is
>
> $$r = f(k).$$

Proof

From the Division Algorithm, you have

$$f(x) = (x - k)q(x) + r(x)$$

and because either $r(x) = 0$ or the degree of $r(x)$ is less than the degree of $x - k$, you know that $r(x)$ must be a constant. That is, $r(x) = r$. Now, by evaluating $f(x)$ at $x = k$, you have

$$f(k) = (k - k)q(k) + r = (0)q(k) + r = r.$$

Section 3.3, page 268

> **The Factor Theorem**
>
> A polynomial $f(x)$ has a factor $(x - k)$ if and only if $f(k) = 0$.

Proof

Using the Division Algorithm with the factor $(x - k)$, you have

$$f(x) = (x - k)q(x) + r(x).$$

By the Remainder Theorem, $r(x) = r = f(k)$, and you have

$$f(x) = (x - k)q(x) + f(k)$$

where $q(x)$ is a polynomial of lesser degree than $f(x)$. If $f(k) = 0$, then

$$f(x) = (x - k)q(x)$$

and you see that $(x - k)$ is a factor of $f(x)$. Conversely, if $(x - k)$ is a factor of $f(x)$, division of $f(x)$ by $(x - k)$ yields a remainder of 0. So, by the Remainder Theorem, you have $f(k) = 0$.

Section 3.4, page 279

> **Linear Factorization Theorem**
>
> If $f(x)$ is a polynomial of degree n, where $n > 0$, then f has precisely n linear factors
>
> $$f(x) = a_n(x - c_1)(x - c_2) \cdots (x - c_n)$$
>
> where $c_1, c_2, \ldots, c_n$ are complex numbers.

Proof

Using the Fundamental Theorem of Algebra, you know that f must have at least one zero, c_1. Consequently, $(x - c_1)$ is a factor of $f(x)$, and you have

$$f(x) = (x - c_1)f_1(x).$$

If the degree of $f_1(x)$ is greater than zero, you again apply the Fundamental Theorem to conclude that f_1 must have a zero c_2, which implies that

$$f(x) = (x - c_1)(x - c_2)f_2(x).$$

It is clear that the degree of $f_1(x)$ is $n - 1$, that the degree of $f_2(x)$ is $n - 2$, and that you can repeatedly apply the Fundamental Theorem n times until you obtain

$$f(x) = a_n(x - c_1)(x - c_2) \cdots (x - c_n)$$

where a_n is the leading coefficient of the polynomial $f(x)$.

Section 3.4, page 281

> **Factors of a Polynomial**
>
> Every polynomial of degree $n > 0$ with real coefficients can be written as the product of linear and quadratic factors with real coefficients, where the quadratic factors have no real zeros.

Proof

To begin, use the Linear Factorization Theorem to conclude that $f(x)$ can be completely factored in the form

$$f(x) = d(x - c_1)(x - c_2)(x - c_3) \cdots (x - c_n).$$

If each c_i is real, there is nothing more to prove. If any c_i is complex ($c_i = a + bi$, $b \neq 0$), then, because the coefficients of $f(x)$ are real, you know that the conjugate $c_j = a - bi$ is also a zero. By multiplying the corresponding factors, you obtain

$$(x - c_i)(x - c_j) = [x - (a + bi)][x - (a - bi)]$$
$$= x^2 - 2ax + (a^2 + b^2)$$

where each coefficient is real.

Section 4.3, page 344

> **Properties of Logarithms**
>
> Let a be a positive number such that $a \neq 1$, and let n be a real number. If u and v are positive real numbers, the following properties are true.
>
> | *Logarithm with Base a* | *Natural Logarithm* |
> |---|---|
> | **1.** $\log_a(uv) = \log_a u + \log_a v$ | **1.** $\ln(uv) = \ln u + \ln v$ |
> | **2.** $\log_a \dfrac{u}{v} = \log_a u - \log_a v$ | **2.** $\ln \dfrac{u}{v} = \ln u - \ln v$ |
> | **3.** $\log_a u^n = n \log_a u$ | **3.** $\ln u^n = n \ln u$ |

Proof

Each of the above three properties of logarithms can be proved by using properties of exponential functions. To prove Property 1, let

$$x = \log_a u \quad \text{and} \quad y = \log_a v.$$

The corresponding exponential forms of these two equations are

$$a^x = u \quad \text{and} \quad a^y = v.$$

Multiplying u and v produces $uv = a^x a^y = a^{x+y}$. The corresponding logarithmic form of $uv = a^{x+y}$ is $\log_a(uv) = x + y$. So, $\log_a(uv) = \log_a u + \log_a v$. The other two properties can be proved in a similar manner.

Section 6.4, page 508

Sum and Difference Formulas

$\sin(u + v) = \sin u \cos v + \cos u \sin v$ $\tan(u + v) = \dfrac{\tan u + \tan v}{1 - \tan u \tan v}$

$\sin(u - v) = \sin u \cos v - \cos u \sin v$

$\cos(u + v) = \cos u \cos v - \sin u \sin v$ $\tan(u - v) = \dfrac{\tan u - \tan v}{1 + \tan u \tan v}$

$\cos(u - v) = \cos u \cos v + \sin u \sin v$

Proof

You can use the figures at the right for the proofs of the formulas for $\cos(u \pm v)$. In the top figure, let A be the point $(1, 0)$ and then use u and v to locate the points $B = (x_1, y_1)$, $C = (x_2, y_2)$, and $D = (x_3, y_3)$ on the unit circle. So, $x_i^2 + y_i^2 = 1$ for $i = 1, 2,$ and 3. For convenience, assume that $0 < v < u < 2\pi$. In the bottom figure, note that arcs AC and BD have the same length. So, line segments AC and BD are also equal in length, which implies that

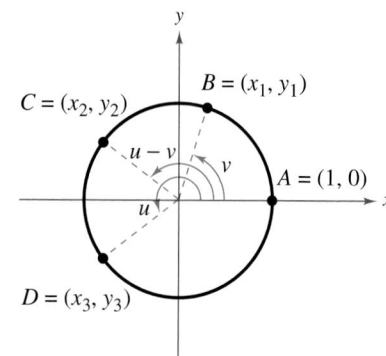

$$\sqrt{(x_2 - 1)^2 + (y_2 - 0)^2} = \sqrt{(x_3 - x_1)^2 + (y_3 - y_1)^2}$$

$$x_2^2 - 2x_2 + 1 + y_2^2 = x_3^2 - 2x_1x_3 + x_1^2 + y_3^2 - 2y_1y_3 + y_1^2$$

$$(x_2^2 + y_2^2) + 1 - 2x_2 = (x_3^2 + y_3^2) + (x_1^2 + y_1^2) - 2x_1x_3 - 2y_1y_3$$

$$1 + 1 - 2x_2 = 1 + 1 - 2x_1x_3 - 2y_1y_3$$

$$x_2 = x_3x_1 + y_3y_1.$$

Finally, by substituting the values $x_2 = \cos(u - v)$, $x_3 = \cos u$, $x_1 = \cos v$, $y_3 = \sin u$, and $y_1 = \sin v$, you obtain

$$\cos(u - v) = \cos u \cos v + \sin u \sin v.$$

The formula for $\cos(u + v)$ can be established by considering $u + v = u - (-v)$ and using the formula just derived to obtain

$$\cos(u + v) = \cos[u - (-v)]$$

$$= \cos u \cos(-v) + \sin u \sin(-v)$$

$$= \cos u \cos v - \sin u \sin v.$$

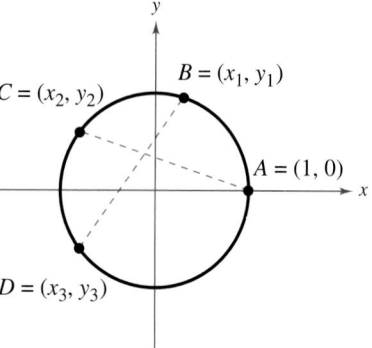

Section 6.5, page 515

Double-Angle Formulas

$\sin 2u = 2 \sin u \cos u$ $\cos 2u = \cos^2 u - \sin^2 u$

$\tan 2u = \dfrac{2 \tan u}{1 - \tan^2 u}$ $\qquad = 2 \cos^2 u - 1$

$\qquad\qquad\qquad\qquad\quad = 1 - 2 \sin^2 u$

Proof

To prove all three formulas, let $v = u$ in the corresponding sum formulas.

$$\sin 2u = \sin(u + u)$$
$$= \sin u \cos u + \cos u \sin u = 2 \sin u \cos u$$

$$\cos 2u = \cos(u + u)$$
$$= \cos u \cos u - \sin u \sin u = \cos^2 u - \sin^2 u$$

$$\tan 2u = \tan(u + u)$$
$$= \frac{\tan u + \tan u}{1 - \tan u \tan u} = \frac{2 \tan u}{1 - \tan^2 u}$$

Section 6.5, page 517

Power-Reducing Formulas

$$\sin^2 u = \frac{1 - \cos 2u}{2} \qquad \cos^2 u = \frac{1 + \cos 2u}{2} \qquad \tan^2 u = \frac{1 - \cos 2u}{1 + \cos 2u}$$

Proof

The first two formulas can be verified by solving for $\sin^2 u$ and $\cos^2 u$, respectively, in the double-angle formulas

$$\cos 2u = 1 - 2 \sin^2 u \qquad \text{and} \qquad \cos 2u = 2 \cos^2 u - 1.$$

The third formula can be verified using the fact that

$$\tan^2 u = \frac{\sin^2 u}{\cos^2 u}.$$

Section 6.5, page 520

Sum-to-Product Formulas

$$\sin u + \sin v = 2 \sin\left(\frac{u + v}{2}\right) \cos\left(\frac{u - v}{2}\right)$$

$$\sin u - \sin v = 2 \cos\left(\frac{u + v}{2}\right) \sin\left(\frac{u - v}{2}\right)$$

$$\cos u + \cos v = 2 \cos\left(\frac{u + v}{2}\right) \cos\left(\frac{u - v}{2}\right)$$

$$\cos u - \cos v = -2 \sin\left(\frac{u + v}{2}\right) \sin\left(\frac{u - v}{2}\right)$$

Proof

To prove the first formula, let $x = u + v$ and $y = u - v$. Then substitute $u = (x + y)/2$ and $v = (x - y)/2$ in the product-to-sum formula.

$$\sin u \cos v = \frac{1}{2}[\sin(u + v) + \sin(u - v)]$$

$$\sin\left(\frac{x + y}{2}\right) \cos\left(\frac{x - y}{2}\right) = \frac{1}{2}(\sin x + \sin y)$$

$$2 \sin\left(\frac{x + y}{2}\right) \cos\left(\frac{x - y}{2}\right) = \sin x + \sin y$$

Section 7.1, page 532

Law of Sines

If ABC is a triangle with sides a, b, and c, then

$$\frac{a}{\sin A} = \frac{b}{\sin B} = \frac{c}{\sin C}.$$

Oblique Triangles

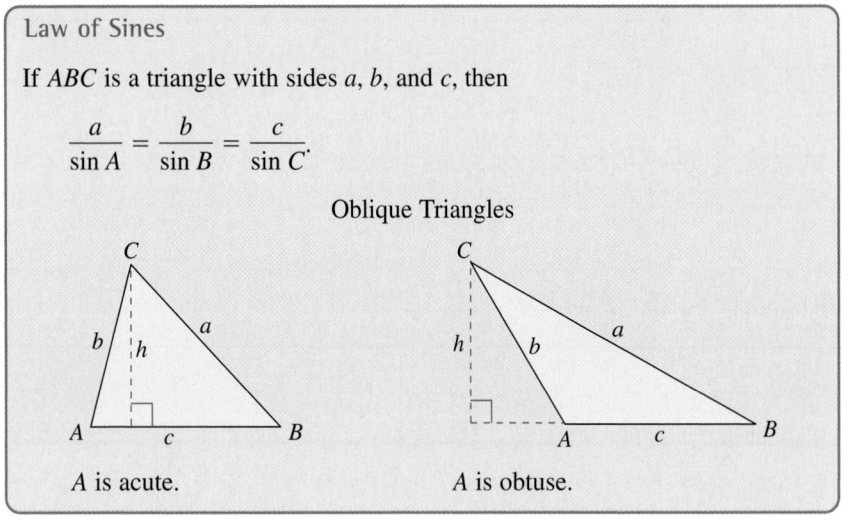

A is acute. A is obtuse.

Proof

Let h be the altitude of either triangle found in the figure above. Then you have

$$\sin A = \frac{h}{b} \quad \text{or} \quad h = b \sin A \quad \text{and} \quad \sin B = \frac{h}{a} \quad \text{or} \quad h = a \sin B.$$

Equating these two values of h, you have

$$a \sin B = b \sin A \quad \text{or} \quad \frac{a}{\sin A} = \frac{b}{\sin B}.$$

Note that $\sin A \neq 0$ and $\sin B \neq 0$ because no angle of a triangle can have a measure of $0°$ or $180°$. In a similar manner, by constructing an altitude from vertex B to side AC (extended in the obtuse triangle), as shown at the right, you have

$$\sin A = \frac{h}{c} \quad \text{or} \quad h = c \sin A \quad \text{and} \quad \sin C = \frac{h}{a} \quad \text{or}$$

$$h = a \sin C.$$

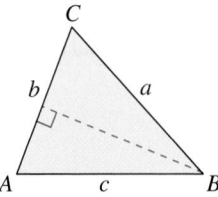

A is acute.

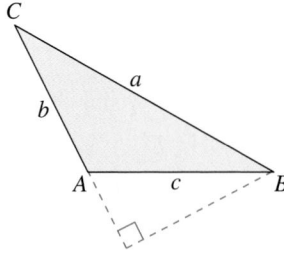

A is obtuse.

Equating these two values of h, you have

$$a \sin C = c \sin A \qquad \text{or} \qquad \frac{a}{\sin A} = \frac{c}{\sin C}.$$

By the Transitive Property of Equality you know that

$$\frac{a}{\sin A} = \frac{b}{\sin B} = \frac{c}{\sin C}.$$

So, the Law of Sines is established.

Section 7.2, page 541

Law of Cosines

Standard Form	*Alternative Form*
$a^2 = b^2 + c^2 - 2bc \cos A$	$\cos A = \dfrac{b^2 + c^2 - a^2}{2bc}$
$b^2 = a^2 + c^2 - 2ac \cos B$	$\cos B = \dfrac{a^2 + c^2 - b^2}{2ac}$
$c^2 = a^2 + b^2 - 2ab \cos C$	$\cos C = \dfrac{a^2 + b^2 - c^2}{2ab}$

Proof

Consider a triangle that has three acute angles, as shown in the figure. Note that vertex B has coordinates $(c, 0)$. Furthermore, C has coordinates (x, y), where $x = b \cos A$ and $y = b \sin A$. Because a is the distance from vertex C to vertex B, it follows that

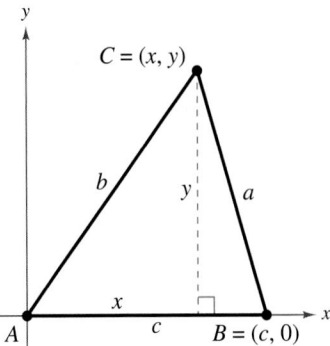

$$a = \sqrt{(x - c)^2 + (y - 0)^2} \qquad \text{Distance Formula}$$

$$a^2 = (b \cos A - c)^2 + (b \sin A)^2 \qquad \text{Square each side and substitute for } x \text{ and } y.$$

$$a^2 = b^2 \cos^2 A - 2bc \cos A + c^2 + b^2 \sin^2 A \qquad \text{Expand.}$$

$$a^2 = b^2(\sin^2 A + \cos^2 A) + c^2 - 2ab \cos A \qquad \text{Factor out } b^2.$$

$$a^2 = b^2 + c^2 - 2bc \cos A. \qquad \sin^2 A + \cos^2 A = 1$$

A similar argument can be used for a triangle having an obtuse angle.

Section 7.2, page 544

Heron's Area Formula

Given any triangle with sides of lengths a, b, and c, the area of the triangle is given by

$$\text{Area} = \sqrt{s(s - a)(s - b)(s - c)}$$

where $s = \dfrac{a + b + c}{2}$.

Proof

From Section 7.1, you know that

$$\text{Area} = \frac{1}{2}bc \sin A$$
Formula for the area of
an oblique triangle

$$= \sqrt{\frac{1}{4}b^2c^2 \sin^2 A}$$
Square the right side.
Then take the square
root of the right side.

$$= \sqrt{\frac{1}{4}b^2c^2(1 - \cos^2 A)}$$
Pythagorean Identity

$$= \sqrt{\left[\frac{1}{2}bc(1 + \cos A)\right]\left[\frac{1}{2}bc(1 - \cos A)\right]}.$$
Factor.

Using the Law of Cosines, you can show that

$$\frac{1}{2}bc(1 + \cos A) = \frac{a + b + c}{2} \cdot \frac{-a + b + c}{2}$$

and

$$\frac{1}{2}bc(1 - \cos A) = \frac{a - b + c}{2} \cdot \frac{a + b - c}{2}.$$

Letting $s = (a + b + c)/2$, these two equations can be rewritten as

$$\frac{1}{2}bc(1 + \cos A) = s(s - a)$$

and

$$\frac{1}{2}bc(1 - \cos A) = (s - b)(s - c).$$

So, by substituting into the last formula for area, you can conclude that

$$\text{Area} = \sqrt{s(s - a)(s - b)(s - c)}.$$

Section 7.4, page 562

Properties of the Dot Product

Let $\mathbf{u}$, $\mathbf{v}$, and $\mathbf{w}$ be vectors in the plane or in space and let c be a scalar.

1. $\mathbf{u} \cdot \mathbf{v} = \mathbf{v} \cdot \mathbf{u}$

2. $\mathbf{0} \cdot \mathbf{v} = 0$

3. $\mathbf{u} \cdot (\mathbf{v} + \mathbf{w}) = \mathbf{u} \cdot \mathbf{v} + \mathbf{u} \cdot \mathbf{w}$

4. $\mathbf{v} \cdot \mathbf{v} = \|\mathbf{v}\|^2$

5. $c(\mathbf{u} \cdot \mathbf{v}) = c\mathbf{u} \cdot \mathbf{v} = \mathbf{u} \cdot c\mathbf{v}$

Proof

Let $\mathbf{u} = \langle u_1, u_2 \rangle$, $\mathbf{v} = \langle v_1, v_2 \rangle$, $\mathbf{w} = \langle w_1, w_2 \rangle$, $\mathbf{0} = \langle 0, 0 \rangle$, and let c be a scalar.

1. $\mathbf{u} \cdot \mathbf{v} = u_1 v_1 + u_2 v_2 = v_1 u_1 + v_2 u_2 = \mathbf{v} \cdot \mathbf{u}$

2. $\mathbf{0} \cdot \mathbf{v} = 0 \cdot v_1 + 0 \cdot v_2 = 0$

3. $\mathbf{u} \cdot (\mathbf{v} + \mathbf{w}) = \mathbf{u} \cdot \langle v_1 + w_1, v_2 + w_2 \rangle$

$$= u_1(v_1 + w_1) + u_2(v_2 + w_2)$$
$$= u_1 v_1 + u_1 w_1 + u_2 v_2 + u_2 w_2$$
$$= (u_1 v_1 + u_2 v_2) + (u_1 w_1 + u_2 w_2)$$
$$= \mathbf{u} \cdot \mathbf{v} + \mathbf{u} \cdot \mathbf{w}$$

4. $\mathbf{v} \cdot \mathbf{v} = v_1^2 + v_2^2$

$$= \left(\sqrt{v_1^2 + v_2^2} \right)^2$$
$$= \|\mathbf{v}\|^2$$

5. $c(\mathbf{u} \cdot \mathbf{v}) = c(\langle u_1, u_2 \rangle \cdot \langle v_1, v_2 \rangle)$

$$= c(u_1 v_1 + u_2 v_2)$$
$$= (cu_1)v_1 + (cu_2)v_2$$
$$= \langle cu_1, cu_2 \rangle \cdot \langle v_1, v_2 \rangle = c\mathbf{u} \cdot \mathbf{v}$$
$$= u_1(cv_1) + u_2(cv_2)$$
$$= \langle u_1, u_2 \rangle \cdot \langle cv_1, cv_2 \rangle = \mathbf{u} \cdot c\mathbf{v}$$

Section 7.4, page 563

> **Angle Between Two Vectors**
>
> If θ is the angle between two nonzero vectors $\mathbf{u}$ and $\mathbf{v}$, then
>
> $$\cos \theta = \frac{\mathbf{u} \cdot \mathbf{v}}{\|\mathbf{u}\| \, \|\mathbf{v}\|}.$$

Proof

Consider the triangle determined by vectors $\mathbf{u}$, $\mathbf{v}$, and $\mathbf{v} - \mathbf{u}$, as shown in the figure. By the Law of Cosines, you can write

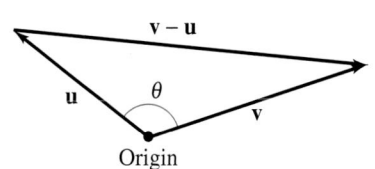

$$\|\mathbf{v} - \mathbf{u}\|^2 = \|\mathbf{u}\|^2 + \|\mathbf{v}\|^2 - 2\|\mathbf{u}\| \, \|\mathbf{v}\| \cos \theta$$
$$(\mathbf{v} - \mathbf{u}) \cdot (\mathbf{v} - \mathbf{u}) = \|\mathbf{u}\|^2 + \|\mathbf{v}\|^2 - 2\|\mathbf{u}\| \, \|\mathbf{v}\| \cos \theta$$
$$(\mathbf{v} - \mathbf{u}) \cdot \mathbf{v} - (\mathbf{v} - \mathbf{u}) \cdot \mathbf{u} = \|\mathbf{u}\|^2 + \|\mathbf{v}\|^2 - 2\|\mathbf{u}\| \, \|\mathbf{v}\| \cos \theta$$
$$\mathbf{v} \cdot \mathbf{v} - \mathbf{u} \cdot \mathbf{v} - \mathbf{v} \cdot \mathbf{u} + \mathbf{u} \cdot \mathbf{u} = \|\mathbf{u}\|^2 + \|\mathbf{v}\|^2 - 2\|\mathbf{u}\| \, \|\mathbf{v}\| \cos \theta$$
$$\|\mathbf{v}\|^2 - 2\mathbf{u} \cdot \mathbf{v} + \|\mathbf{u}\|^2 = \|\mathbf{u}\|^2 + \|\mathbf{v}\|^2 - 2\|\mathbf{u}\| \, \|\mathbf{v}\| \cos \theta$$
$$-2\mathbf{u} \cdot \mathbf{v} = -2\|\mathbf{u}\| \, \|\mathbf{v}\| \cos \theta$$
$$\cos \theta = \frac{\mathbf{u} \cdot \mathbf{v}}{\|\mathbf{u}\| \, \|\mathbf{v}\|}.$$

Section 9.1, page 701

> **Properties of Sums**
>
> **1.** $\displaystyle\sum_{i=1}^{n} c = cn,$ c is a constant.   **2.** $\displaystyle\sum_{i=1}^{n} ca_i = c\sum_{i=1}^{n} a_i,$ c is a constant.
>
> **3.** $\displaystyle\sum_{i=1}^{n} (a_i + b_i) = \sum_{i=1}^{n} a_i + \sum_{i=1}^{n} b_i$
>
> **4.** $\displaystyle\sum_{i=1}^{n} (a_i - b_i) = \sum_{i=1}^{n} a_i - \sum_{i=1}^{n} b_i$

Proof

Each of these properties follows directly from the properties of real numbers. For example, note the use of the Distributive Property in the proof of Property 2.

$$\sum_{i=1}^{n} ca_i = ca_1 + ca_2 + ca_3 + \cdots + ca_n$$

$$= c(a_1 + a_2 + a_3 + \cdots + a_n) = c\sum_{i=1}^{n} a_i$$

Section 9.2, page 710

> **The Sum of a Finite Arithmetic Sequence**
>
> The sum of a finite arithmetic sequence with n terms is given by
>
> $$S_n = \frac{n}{2}(a_1 + a_n).$$

Proof

Begin by generating the terms of the arithmetic sequence in two ways. In the first way, repeatedly add d to the first term to obtain

$$S_n = a_1 + a_2 + a_3 + \cdots + a_{n-2} + a_{n-1} + a_n$$
$$= a_1 + [a_1 + d] + [a_1 + 2d] + \cdots + [a_1 + (n-1)d].$$

In the second way, repeatedly subtract d from the nth term to obtain

$$S_n = a_n + a_{n-1} + a_{n-2} + \cdots + a_3 + a_2 + a_1$$
$$= a_n + [a_n - d] + [a_n - 2d] + \cdots + [a_n - (n-1)d].$$

If you add these two versions of S_n, the multiples of d subtract out and you obtain

$$2S_n = (a_1 + a_n) + (a_1 + a_n) + (a_1 + a_n) + \cdots + (a_1 + a_n) \quad \text{n terms}$$
$$2S_n = n(a_1 + a_n)$$

$$S_n = \frac{n}{2}(a_1 + a_n).$$

Section 9.3, page 719

The Sum of a Finite Geometric Sequence

The sum of the geometric sequence

$$a_1, \ a_1r, \ a_1r^2, \ a_1r^3, \ a_1r^4, \ldots, a_1r^{n-1}$$

with common ratio $r \neq 1$ is given by $S_n = \sum_{i=1}^{n} a_1r^{i-1} = a_1\left(\dfrac{1 - r^n}{1 - r}\right)$.

Proof

Begin by writing out the nth partial sum.

$$S_n = a_1 + a_1r + a_1r^2 + \cdots + a_1r^{n-2} + a_1r^{n-1}$$

Multiplication by r yields

$$rS_n = a_1r + a_1r^2 + a_1r^3 + \cdots + a_1r^{n-1} + a_1r^n.$$

Subtracting the second equation from the first yields

$$S_n - rS_n = a_1 - a_1r^n.$$

So, $S_n(1 - r) = a_1(1 - r^n)$, and, because $r \neq 1$, you have

$$S_n = a_1\left(\frac{1 - r^n}{1 - r}\right).$$

Section 9.5, page 734

The Binomial Theorem

In the expansion of $(x + y)^n$

$$(x + y)^n = x^n + nx^{n-1}y + \cdots + {}_nC_r\, x^{n-r}y^r + \cdots + nxy^{n-1} + y^n$$

the coefficient of $x^{n-r}y^r$ is ${}_nC_r = \dfrac{n!}{(n - r)!r!}$.

Proof

The Binomial Theorem can be proved quite nicely using mathematical induction. The steps are straightforward but look complicated, so only an outline of the proof is presented.

1. If $n = 1$, you have

$$(x + y)^1 = x^1 + y^1 = {}_1C_0x + {}_1C_1y$$

   and the formula is valid.

2. Assuming that the formula is true for $n = k$, the coefficient of $x^{k-r}y^r$ is

$$_kC_r = \frac{k!}{(k - r)!r!} = \frac{k(k - 1)(k - 2) \cdots (k - r + 1)}{r!}.$$

To show that the formula is true for $n = k + 1$, look at the coefficient of $x^{k+1-r}y^r$ in the expansion of

$$(x + y)^{k+1} = (x + y)^k(x + y).$$

From the right-hand side, you can determine that the term involving $x^{k+1-r}y^r$ is the sum of two products.

$$({}_kC_r x^{k-r}y^r)(x) + ({}_kC_{r-1}x^{k+1-r}y^{r-1})(y)$$

$$= \left[\frac{k!}{(k-r)!r!} + \frac{k!}{(k+1-r)!(r-1)!}\right]x^{k+1-r}y^r$$

$$= \left[\frac{(k+1-r)k!}{(k+1-r)!r!} + \frac{k!r}{(k+1-r)!r!}\right]x^{k+1-r}y^r$$

$$= \left[\frac{k!(k+1-r+r)}{(k+1-r)!r!}\right]x^{k+1-r}y^r$$

$$= \left[\frac{(k+1)!}{(k+1-r)!r!}\right]x^{k+1-r}y^r$$

$$= {}_{k+1}C_r x^{k+1-r}y^r$$

So, by mathematical induction, the Binomial Theorem is valid for all positive integers n.

Section 10.1, page 773

> **Standard Equation of a Parabola (Vertex at Origin)**
>
> The standard form of the equation of a parabola with vertex at $(0, 0)$ and directrix $y = -p$ is
>
> $$x^2 = 4py, \qquad p \neq 0. \qquad \text{Vertical axis}$$
>
> For directrix $x = -p$, the equation is
>
> $$y^2 = 4px, \qquad p \neq 0. \qquad \text{Horizontal axis}$$
>
> The focus is on the axis p units (directed distance) from the vertex.

Proof

Because the two cases are similar, a proof will be given for the first case only. Suppose the directrix $(y = -p)$ is parallel to the x-axis. In the figure, you assume that $p > 0$, and because p is the directed distance from the vertex to the focus, the focus must lie above the vertex. Because the point (x, y) is equidistant from $(0, p)$ and $y = -p$, you can apply the Distance Formula to obtain

$$\sqrt{(x - 0)^2 + (y - p)^2} = y + p$$

$$x^2 + (y - p)^2 = (y + p)^2$$

$$x^2 + y^2 - 2py + p^2 = y^2 + 2py + p^2$$

$$x^2 = 4py.$$

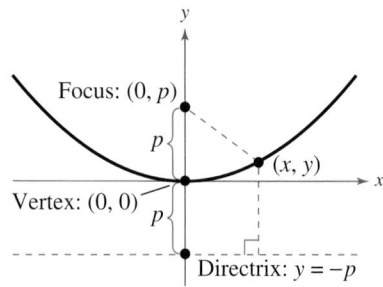

Section 10.6, page 818

Polar Equations of Conics

The graph of a polar equation of the form

$$\textbf{1. } r = \frac{ep}{1 \pm e \cos \theta} \quad \text{or} \quad \textbf{2. } r = \frac{ep}{1 \pm e \sin \theta}$$

is a conic, where $e > 0$ is the eccentricity and $|p|$ is the distance between the focus (pole) and the directrix.

Proof

A proof for $r = ep/(1 + e \cos \theta)$ with $p > 0$ is listed here. The proofs of the other cases are similar. In the figure, consider a vertical directrix, p units to the right of the focus $F = (0, 0)$. If $P = (r, \theta)$ is a point on the graph of

$$r = \frac{ep}{1 + e \cos \theta}$$

the distance between P and the directrix is

$$
\begin{aligned}
PQ &= |p - x| \\
&= |p - r \cos \theta| \\
&= \left| p - \left(\frac{ep}{1 + e \cos \theta} \right) \cos \theta \right| \\
&= \left| p \left(1 - \frac{e \cos \theta}{1 + e \cos \theta} \right) \right| \\
&= \left| p \left(\frac{1 + e \cos \theta - e \cos \theta}{1 + e \cos \theta} \right) \right| \\
&= \left| \frac{p}{1 + e \cos \theta} \right| \\
&= \left| \frac{r}{e} \right|.
\end{aligned}
$$

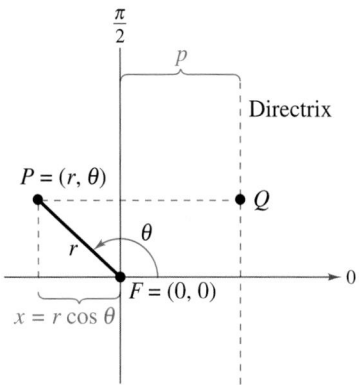

Moreover, because the distance between P and the pole is simply $PF = |r|$, the ratio of PF to PQ is

$$
\begin{aligned}
\frac{PF}{PQ} &= \frac{|r|}{|r/e|} \\
&= |e| \\
&= e
\end{aligned}
$$

and by definition, the graph of the equation must be a conic.

Appendix C Concepts in Statistics

C.1 Measures of Central Tendency and Dispersion

Mean, Median, and Mode

In many real-life situations, it is helpful to describe data by a single number that is most representative of the entire collection of numbers. Such a number is called a **measure of central tendency.** The most commonly used measures are as follows.

1. The **mean,** or **average,** of n numbers is the sum of the numbers divided by n.
2. The **median** of n numbers is the middle number when the numbers are written in numerical order. If n is even, the median is the average of the two middle numbers.
3. The **mode** of n numbers is the number that occurs most frequently. If two numbers tie for most frequent occurrence, the collection has two modes and is called **bimodal.**

What you should learn

- Find and interpret the mean, median, and mode of a set of data.
- Determine the measure of central tendency that best represents a set of data.
- Find the standard deviation of a set of data.
- Use box-and-whisker plots.

Why you should learn it

Measures of central tendency and dispersion provide a convenient way to describe and compare sets of data. For instance, in Exercise 32 on page A46, the mean and standard deviation are used to analyze the price of gold for the years 1982 through 2001.

Example 1 Comparing Measures of Central Tendency

On an interview for a job, the interviewer tells you that the average annual income of the company's 25 employees is $60,849. The actual annual incomes of the 25 employees are shown below. What are the mean, median, and mode of the incomes?

$17,305,	$478,320,	$45,678,	$18,980,	$17,408,
$25,676,	$28,906,	$12,500,	$24,540,	$33,450,
$12,500,	$33,855,	$37,450,	$20,432,	$28,956,
$34,983,	$36,540,	$250,921,	$36,853,	$16,430,
$32,654,	$98,213,	$48,980,	$94,024,	$35,671

Solution

The mean of the incomes is

$$\text{Mean} = \frac{17,305 + 478,320 + 45,678 + 18,980 + \cdots + 35,671}{25}$$

$$= \frac{1,521,225}{25} = \$60,849.$$

To find the median, order the incomes as follows.

$12,500,	$12,500,	$16,430,	$17,305,	$17,408,
$18,980,	$20,432,	$24,540,	$25,676,	$28,906,
$28,956,	$32,654,	$33,450,	$33,855,	$34,983,
$35,671,	$36,540,	$36,853,	$37,450,	$45,678,
$48,980,	$94,024,	$98,213,	$250,921,	$478,320

From this list, you can see that the median income is $33,450. You can also see that $12,500 is the only income that occurs more than once. So, the mode is $12,500.

 Checkpoint Now try Exercise 1.

In Example 1, was the interviewer telling you the truth about the annual incomes? Technically, the person was telling the truth because the average is (generally) defined to be the mean. However, of the three measures of central tendency—*mean:* $60,849, *median:* $33,450, *mode:* $12,500—it seems clear that the median is most representative. The mean is inflated by the two highest salaries.

Choosing a Measure of Central Tendency

Which of the three measures of central tendency is most representative of a particular data set? The answer is that it depends on the distribution of the data *and* the way in which you plan to use the data.

For instance, in Example 1, the mean salary of $60,849 does not seem very representative to a potential employee. To a city income tax collector who wants to estimate 1% of the total income of the 25 employees, however, the mean is precisely the right measure.

Example 2   Choosing a Measure of Central Tendency

Which measure of central tendency is most representative of the data given in each frequency distribution?

a.

Number	1	2	3	4	5	6	7	8	9
Frequency	7	20	15	11	8	3	2	0	15

b.

Number	1	2	3	4	5	6	7	8	9
Frequency	9	8	7	6	5	6	7	8	9

c.

Number	1	2	3	4	5	6	7	8	9
Frequency	6	1	2	3	5	5	4	3	0

Solution

a. For this data, the mean is 4.23, the median is 3, and the mode is 2. Of these, the median or mode is probably the most representative measure.

b. For this data, the mean and median are each 5 and the modes are 1 and 9 (the distribution is bimodal). Of these, the mean or median is the most representative measure.

c. For this data, the mean is 4.59, the median is 5, and the mode is 1. Of these, the mean or median is the most representative measure.

 *Checkpoint* Now try Exercise 13.

Variance and Standard Deviation

Very different sets of numbers can have the same mean. You will now study two **measures of dispersion,** which give you an idea of how much the numbers in a set differ from the mean of the set. These two measures are called the *variance* of the set and the *standard deviation* of the set.

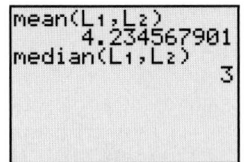

> **Definition of Variance and Standard Deviation**
>
> Consider a set of numbers $\{x_1, x_2, \ldots, x_n\}$ with a mean of $\bar{x}$. The **variance** of the set is
>
> $$v = \frac{(x_1 - \bar{x})^2 + (x_2 - \bar{x})^2 + \cdots + (x_n - \bar{x})^2}{n}$$
>
> and the **standard deviation** of the set is $\sigma = \sqrt{v}$ (σ is the lowercase Greek letter *sigma*).

The standard deviation of a set is a measure of how much a typical number in the set differs from the mean. The greater the standard deviation, the more the numbers in the set vary from the mean. For instance, each of the following sets has a mean of 5.

$$\{5, 5, 5, 5\}, \qquad \{4, 4, 6, 6\}, \qquad \text{and} \qquad \{3, 3, 7, 7\}$$

The standard deviations of the sets are 0, 1, and 2.

$$\sigma_1 = \sqrt{\frac{(5-5)^2 + (5-5)^2 + (5-5)^2 + (5-5)^2}{4}} = 0$$

$$\sigma_2 = \sqrt{\frac{(4-5)^2 + (4-5)^2 + (6-5)^2 + (6-5)^2}{4}} = 1$$

$$\sigma_3 = \sqrt{\frac{(3-5)^2 + (3-5)^2 + (7-5)^2 + (7-5)^2}{4}} = 2$$

Example 3   Estimations of Standard Deviation

Consider the three frequency distributions represented by the bar graphs in Figure C.1. Which set has the smallest standard deviation? Which has the largest?

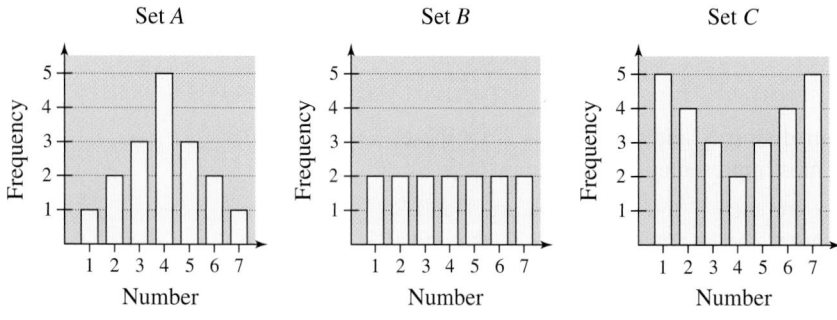

Figure C.1

Solution

Of the three sets, the numbers in set A are grouped most closely to the center and the numbers in set C are the most dispersed. So, set A has the smallest standard deviation and set C has the largest standard deviation.

✓ *Checkpoint* Now try Exercise 15.

Example 4   Find Standard Deviation

Find the standard deviation of each set shown in Example 3.

Solution

Because of the symmetry of each bar graph, you can conclude that each has a mean of $\bar{x} = 4$. The standard deviation of set A is

$$\sigma = \sqrt{\dfrac{(-3)^2 + 2(-2)^2 + 3(-1)^2 + 5(0)^2 + 3(1)^2 + 2(2)^2 + (3)^2}{17}}$$

$$\approx 1.53.$$

The standard deviation of set B is

$$\sigma = \sqrt{\dfrac{2(-3)^2 + 2(-2)^2 + 2(-1)^2 + 2(0)^2 + 2(1)^2 + 2(2)^2 + 2(3)^2}{14}}$$

$$= 2.$$

The standard deviation of set C is

$$\sigma = \sqrt{\dfrac{5(-3)^2 + 4(-2)^2 + 3(-1)^2 + 2(0)^2 + 3(1)^2 + 4(2)^2 + 5(3)^2}{26}}$$

$$\approx 2.22.$$

These values confirm the results of Example 3. That is, set A has the smallest standard deviation and set C has the largest.

✅ *Checkpoint* Now try Exercise 21.

The following alternative formula provides a more efficient way to compute the standard deviation.

Alternative Formula for Standard Deviation

The standard deviation of $\{x_1, x_2, \ldots, x_n\}$ is given by

$$\sigma = \sqrt{\dfrac{x_1^2 + x_2^2 + \cdots + x_n^2}{n} - \bar{x}^2}.$$

Because of lengthy computations, this formula is difficult to verify. Conceptually, however, the process is straightforward. It consists of showing that the expressions

$$\sqrt{\dfrac{(x_1 - \bar{x})^2 + (x_2 - \bar{x})^2 + \cdots + (x_n - \bar{x})^2}{n}}$$

and

$$\sqrt{\dfrac{x_1^2 + x_2^2 + \cdots + x_n^2}{n} - \bar{x}^2}$$

are equivalent. Try verifying this equivalence for the set $\{x_1, x_2, x_3\}$ with $\bar{x} = (x_1 + x_2 + x_3)/3$.

TECHNOLOGY TIP

Calculating the standard deviation of a large data set can become time consuming. Most graphing utilities have *statistical* features that can be used to find different statistical values of data sets. Enter the data from set A of Example 3 into the *list editor* of a graphing utility. Then use the *one-variable statistics* feature to verify the solution to Example 4 as shown below.

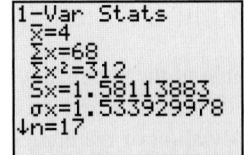

In the figure above, the standard deviation is represented as σx, which is about 1.53. For instructions on how to use the *one-variable statistics* feature, see Appendix A; for specific keystrokes, go to the text website at *college.hmco.com*.

Example 5 Using the Alternative Formula

Use the alternative formula for standard deviation to find the standard deviation of the following set of numbers.

5, 6, 6, 7, 7, 8, 8, 8, 9, 10

Solution

Begin by finding the mean of the set, which is 7.4. So, the standard deviation is

$$\sigma = \sqrt{\frac{5^2 + 2(6^2) + 2(7^2) + 3(8^2) + 9^2 + 10^2}{10} - (7.4)^2}$$

$$= \sqrt{\frac{568}{10} - 54.76} = \sqrt{2.04} \approx 1.43.$$

You can use the *one-variable statistics* feature of a graphing utility to check this result.

 Checkpoint Now try Exercise 27.

A well-known theorem in statistics, called *Chebychev's Theorem*, states that at least

$$1 - \frac{1}{k^2}$$

of the numbers in a distribution must lie within k standard deviations of the mean. So, at least 75% of the numbers in a collection must lie within two standard deviations of the mean, and at least 88.9% of the numbers must lie within three standard deviations of the mean. For most distributions, these percentages are low. For instance, in all three distributions shown in Example 3, 100% of the numbers lie within two standard deviations of the mean.

Example 6 Describing a Distribution

The table at the right shows the number of outpatient visits to hospitals (in millions) in each state and the District of Columbia in 2000. Find the mean and standard deviation of the numbers. What percent of the numbers lie within two standard deviations of the mean? (Source: Health Forum)

Solution

Begin by entering the numbers into a graphing utility. Then use the *one-variable statistics* feature to obtain $\bar{x} \approx 10.24$ and $\sigma = 10.52$. The interval that contains all numbers that lie within two standard deviations of the mean is

$$[10.24 - 2(10.52), 10.24 + 2(10.52)] \quad \text{or} \quad [-10.80, 31.28].$$

From the table you can see that all but three of the numbers (96%) lie in this interval—all but the numbers that correspond to the numbers of outpatient visits to hospitals in California, New York, and Pennsylvania.

 Checkpoint Now try Exercise 32.

AK	1	MT	3
AL	8	NC	12
AR	4	ND	2
AZ	5	NE	3
CA	45	NH	3
CO	7	NJ	16
CT	7	NM	3
DC	1	NV	2
DE	2	NY	46
FL	22	OH	27
GA	11	OK	5
HI	3	OR	7
IA	9	PA	32
ID	2	RI	2
IL	25	SC	8
IN	14	SD	2
KS	5	TN	10
KY	9	TX	29
LA	10	UT	5
MA	17	VA	10
MD	6	VT	1
ME	3	WA	10
MI	25	WI	11
MN	7	WV	5
MO	15	WY	1
MS	4		

Box-and-Whisker Plots

Standard deviation is the measure of dispersion that is associated with the mean. **Quartiles** measure dispersion associated with the median.

Definition of Quartiles

Consider an ordered set of numbers whose median is m. The **lower quartile** is the median of the numbers that occur on or before m. The **upper quartile** is the median of the numbers that occur on or after m.

Example 7   Finding Quartiles of a Set

Find the lower and upper quartiles of the following set.

34, 14, 24, 16, 12, 18, 20, 24, 16, 26, 13, 27

Solution

Begin by ordering the set.

12, 13, 14,	16, 16, 18,	20, 24, 24,	26, 27, 34
1st 25%	2nd 25%	3rd 25%	4th 25%

The median of the entire set is 19. The median of the six numbers that are less than 19 is 15. So, the lower quartile is 15. The median of the six numbers that are greater than 19 is 25. So, the upper quartile is 25.

✓ *Checkpoint* Now try Exercise 35(a).

Quartiles are represented graphically by a **box-and-whisker plot,** as shown in Figure C.2. In the plot, notice that five numbers are listed: the smallest number, the lower quartile, the median, the upper quartile, and the largest number. Also notice that the numbers are spaced proportionally, as though they were on a real number line.

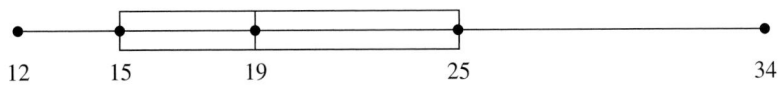

| 12 | 15 | 19 | 25 | 34 |

Figure C.2

TECHNOLOGY TIP   You can use a graphing utility to graph the box-and-whisker plot in Figure C.2. First enter the data into the graphing utility's *list editor*, as shown in Figure C.3. Then use the *statistical plotting* feature to set up the box-and-whisker plot, as shown in Figure C.4. Finally, display the box-and-whisker plot (using the *ZoomStat* feature), as shown in Figure C.5.

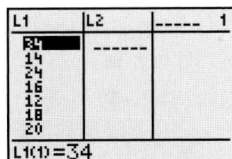

Figure C.3

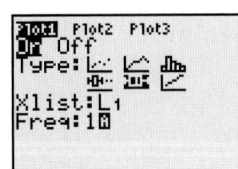

Figure C.4

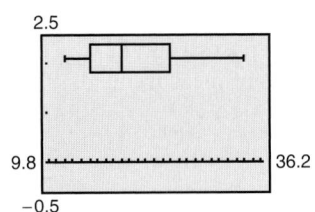

Figure C.5

The next example shows how to find quartiles when the number of elements in a set is not divisible by 4.

Example 8   Sketching Box-and-Whisker Plots

Sketch a box-and-whisker plot for each data set.

a. 82, 82, 83, 85, 87, 89, 90, 94, 95, 95, 96, 98, 99

b. 11, 13, 13, 15, 17, 17, 20, 24, 24, 27

Solution

a. This set has 13 numbers. The median is 90 (the seventh number). The lower quartile is 84 (the median of the first six numbers). The upper quartile is 95.5 (the median of the last six numbers). See Figure C.6.

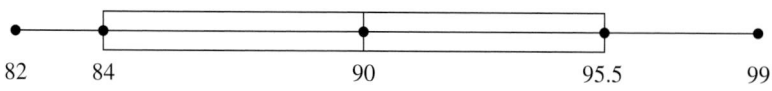

82   84   90   95.5   99

Figure C.6

b. This set has 10 numbers. The median is 17 (the average of the fifth and sixth numbers). The lower quartile is 13 (the median of the first five numbers). The upper quartile is 24 (the median of the last five numbers). See Figure C.7.

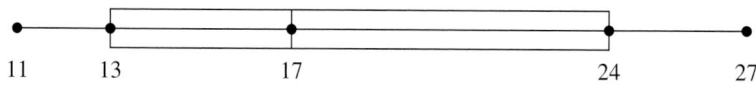

11   13   17   24   27

Figure C.7

✓ *Checkpoint* Now try Exercise 37(b).

C.1   Exercises

Vocabulary Check

Fill in the blanks.

1. A single number that is the most representative of a data set is called a _____ of _____ .

2. If two numbers are tied for the most frequent occurrence, the collection has two _____ and is called _____ .

3. Two measures of dispersion are called the _____ and the _____ of a data set.

4. _____ measure dispersion associated with the median.

In Exercises 1–6, find the mean, median, and mode of the set of measurements.

1. 5, 12, 7, 14, 8, 9, 7

2. 30, 37, 32, 39, 33, 34, 32

3. 5, 12, 7, 24, 8, 9, 7

4. 20, 37, 32, 39, 33, 34, 32

5. 5, 12, 7, 14, 9, 7

6. 30, 37, 32, 39, 34, 32

7. Reasoning

(a) Compare your answers in Exercises 1 and 3 with those in Exercises 2 and 4. Which of the measures of central tendency is sensitive to extreme measurements? Explain your reasoning.

(b) Add 6 to each measurement in Exercise 1 and calculate the mean, median, and mode of the revised measurements. How are the measures of central tendency changed?

(c) If a constant k is added to each measurement in a set of data, how will the measures of central tendency change?

8. Consumer Awareness   A person had the following monthly bills for electricity. What are the mean and median of the collection of bills?

January	$67.92	February	$59.84
March	$52.00	April	$52.50
May	$57.99	June	$65.35
July	$81.76	August	$74.98
September	$87.82	October	$83.18
November	$65.35	December	$57.00

9. Car Rental   A car rental company kept the following record of the numbers of miles a rental car was driven. What are the mean, median, and mode of this data?

Monday	410	Tuesday	260
Wednesday	320	Thursday	320
Friday	460	Saturday	150

10. Families   A study was done on families having six children. The table shows the numbers of families in the study with the indicated numbers of girls. Determine the mean, median, and mode of the data.

Number of girls	0	1	2	3	4	5	6
Frequency	1	24	45	54	50	19	7

11. Think About It   Construct a collection of numbers that has the following properties. If this is not possible, explain why.

Mean = 6, median = 4, mode = 4

12. Think About It   Construct a collection of numbers that has the following properties. If this is not possible, explain why.

mean = 6, median = 6, mode = 4

13. Test Scores   An English professor records the following scores for a 100-point exam.

99, 64, 80, 77, 59, 72, 87, 79, 92, 88, 90, 42, 20, 89, 42, 100, 98, 84, 78, 91

Which measure of central tendency best describes these test scores?

14. Shoe Sales   A salesman sold eight pairs of men's brown dress shoes. The sizes of the eight pairs were as follows: $10\frac{1}{2}$, 8, 12, $10\frac{1}{2}$, 10, $9\frac{1}{2}$, 11, and $10\frac{1}{2}$. Which measure (or measures) of central tendency best describes the typical shoe size for this data?

In Exercises 15 and 16, line plots of data sets are given. Determine the mean and standard deviation of each set.

15. (a)

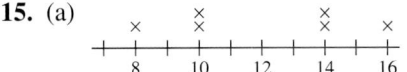

(b)

(c)

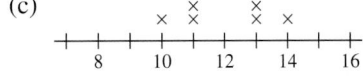

(d)

16. (a)

(b)

(c)

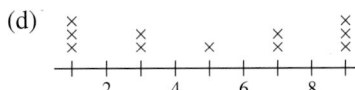

(d)

In Exercises 17–24, find the mean ($\bar{x}$), variance (v), and standard deviation (σ) of the set.

17. 4, 10, 8, 2
18. 3, 15, 6, 9, 2
19. 0, 1, 1, 2, 2, 2, 3, 3, 4
20. 2, 2, 2, 2, 2, 2
21. 1, 2, 3, 4, 5, 6, 7
22. 1, 1, 1, 5, 5, 5
23. 49, 62, 40, 29, 32, 70
24. 1.5, 0.4, 2.1, 0.7, 0.8

In Exercises 25–28, use the alternative formula to find the standard deviation of the set.

25. 2, 4, 6, 6, 13, 5
26. 246, 336, 473, 167, 219, 359
27. 8.1, 6.9, 3.7, 4.2, 6.1   **28.** 9.0, 7.5, 3.3, 7.4, 6.0

29. *Reasoning*   Without calculating the standard deviation, explain why the set {4, 4, 20, 20} has a standard deviation of 8.

30. *Reasoning*   If the standard deviation of a set of numbers is 0, what does this imply about the set?

31. *Test Scores*   An instructor adds five points to each student's exam score. Will this change the mean or standard deviation of the exam scores? Explain.

32. *Price of Gold*   The following data represents the average prices of gold (in dollars per fine ounce) for the years 1982 to 2001. Use a computer or graphing utility to find the mean, variance, and standard deviation of the data. What percent of the data lies within two standard deviations of the mean?   (Source: U.S. Bureau of Mines and U.S. Geological Survey)

376,	424,	361,	318,	368,
478,	438,	383,	385,	363,
345,	361,	385,	386,	389,
332,	295,	280,	280,	272

33. *Think About It*   The histograms represent the test scores of two classes of a college course in mathematics. Which histogram has the smaller standard deviation?

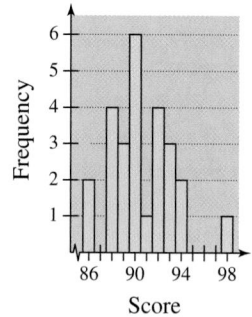
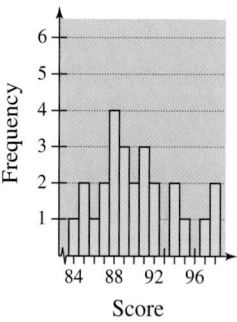

34. *Test Scores*   The scores on a mathematics exam given to 600 science and engineering students at a college had a mean and standard deviation of 235 and 28, respectively. Use Chebychev's Theorem to determine the intervals containing at least $\frac{3}{4}$ and at least $\frac{8}{9}$ of the scores. How would the intervals change if the standard deviation were 16?

In Exercises 35–38, (a) find the lower and upper quartiles of the data and (b) sketch a box-and-whisker plot for the data without using a graphing utility.

35. 23, 15, 14, 23, 13, 14, 13, 20, 12
36. 11, 10, 11, 14, 17, 16, 14, 11, 8, 14, 20
37. 46, 48, 48, 50, 52, 47, 51, 47, 49, 53
38. 25, 20, 22, 28, 24, 28, 25, 19, 27, 29, 28, 21

In Exercises 39–42, use a graphing utility to create a box-and-whisker plot for the data.

39. 19, 12, 14, 9, 14, 15, 17, 13, 19, 11, 10, 19
40. 9, 5, 5, 5, 6, 5, 4, 12, 7, 10, 7, 11, 8, 9, 9
41. 20.1, 43.4, 34.9, 23.9, 33.5, 24.1, 22.5, 42.4, 25.7, 17.4, 23.8, 33.3, 17.3, 36.4, 21.8
42. 78.4, 76.3, 107.5, 78.5, 93.2, 90.3, 77.8, 37.1, 97.1, 75.5, 58.8, 65.6

43. *Product Lifetime*   A company has redesigned a product in an attempt to increase the lifetime of the product. The two sets of data list the lifetimes (in months) of 20 units with the original design and 20 units with the new design. Create a box-and-whisker plot for each set of data, and then comment on the differences between the plots.

Original Design

15.1	78.3	56.3	68.9	30.6
27.2	12.5	42.7	72.7	20.2
53.0	13.5	11.0	18.4	85.2
10.8	38.3	85.1	10.0	12.6

New Design

55.8	71.5	25.6	19.0	23.1
37.2	60.0	35.3	18.9	80.5
46.7	31.1	67.9	23.5	99.5
54.0	23.2	45.5	24.8	87.8

C.2   Least Squares Regression

What you should learn

● Use the sum of squared differences to determine a least squares regression line.

● Find a least squares regression line for a set of data.

● Find a least squares regression parabola for a set of data.

Why you should learn it

The method of least squares provides a way of creating a mathematical model for a set of data, which can then be analyzed.

In many of the examples and exercises in this text, you have been asked to use the *regression* feature of a graphing utility to find mathematical models for sets of data. The *regression* feature of a graphing utility uses the **method of least squares** to find a mathematical model for a set of data. As a measure of how well a model fits a set of data points

$$\{(x_1, y_1), (x_2, y_2), (x_3, y_3), \ldots, (x_n, y_n)\}$$

you can add the squares of the differences between the actual y-values and the values given by the model to obtain the **sum of the squared differences.** For instance, the table shows the heights x (in feet) and the diameters y (in inches) of eight trees. The table also shows the values of a linear model $y^* = 0.54x - 29.5$ for each x-value. The sum of squared differences for the model is 51.7.

x	70	72	75	76	85	78	77	80
y	8.3	10.5	11.0	11.4	12.9	14.0	16.3	18.0
y^*	8.3	9.38	11.0	11.54	16.4	12.62	12.08	13.7
$(y - y^*)^2$	0	1.2544	0	0.0196	12.25	1.9044	17.8084	18.49

The model that has the *least* sum of squared differences is the **least squares regression** line for the data. The least squares regression line for the data in the table is $y \approx 0.43x - 20.3$. The sum of squared differences is 43.3.

To find the least squares regression line $y = ax + b$ for the points $\{(x_1, y_1), (x_2, y_2), (x_3, y_3), \ldots, (x_n, y_n)\}$ algebraically, you need to solve the following system for a and b.

$$\begin{cases} nb + \left(\displaystyle\sum_{i=1}^{n} x_i \right) a = \displaystyle\sum_{i=1}^{n} y_i \\ \left(\displaystyle\sum_{i=1}^{n} x_i \right) b + \left(\displaystyle\sum_{i=1}^{n} x_i^2 \right) a = \displaystyle\sum_{i=1}^{n} x_i y_i \end{cases}$$

In the system,

$$\sum_{i=1}^{n} x_i = x_1 + x_2 + \cdots + x_n$$

$$\sum_{i=1}^{n} y_i = y_1 + y_2 + \cdots + y_n$$

$$\sum_{i=1}^{n} x_i^2 = x_1^2 + x_2^2 + \cdots + x_n^2$$

$$\sum_{i=1}^{n} x_i y_i = x_1 y_1 + x_2 y_2 + \cdots + x_n y_n.$$

TECHNOLOGY SUPPORT

For instructions on how to use the *regression* feature, see Appendix A; for specific keystrokes, go to the text website at *college.hmco.com*.

TECHNOLOGY TIP   Recall from Section 2.6 that when you use the *regression* feature of a graphing utility, the program may output a correlation coefficient, r. When $|r|$ is close to 1, the model is a good fit for the data.

Example 1 Finding a Least Squares Regression Line

Find the least squares regression line for $(-3, 0)$, $(-1, 1)$, $(0, 2)$, and $(2, 3)$.

Solution

Begin by constructing a table, as shown below.

x	y	xy	x^2
-3	0	0	9
-1	1	-1	1
0	2	0	0
2	3	6	4
$\displaystyle\sum_{i=1}^{n} x_i = -2$	$\displaystyle\sum_{i=1}^{n} y_i = 6$	$\displaystyle\sum_{i=1}^{n} x_i y_i = 5$	$\displaystyle\sum_{i=1}^{n} x_i^2 = 14$

Applying the system for the least squares regression line with $n = 4$ produces

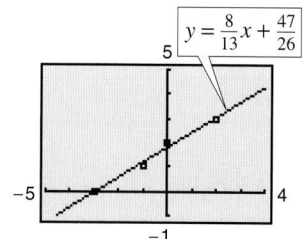

$$\begin{cases} nb + \left(\displaystyle\sum_{i=1}^{n} x_i\right) a = \displaystyle\sum_{i=1}^{n} y_i \\ \left(\displaystyle\sum_{i=1}^{n} x_i\right) b + \left(\displaystyle\sum_{i=1}^{n} x_i^2\right) a = \displaystyle\sum_{i=1}^{n} x_i y_i \end{cases} \implies \begin{cases} 4b - 2a = 6 \\ -2b + 14a = 5 \end{cases}.$$

Solving this system of equations produces $a = \frac{8}{13}$ and $b = \frac{47}{26}$. So, the least squares regression line is $y = \frac{8}{13}x + \frac{47}{26}$, as shown in Figure C.8.

Figure C.8

The least squares regression parabola $y = ax^2 + bx + c$ for the points

$$\{(x_1, y_1), (x_2, y_2), (x_3, y_3), \ldots, (x_n, y_n)\}$$

is obtained in a similar manner by solving the following system of three equations in three unknowns for a, b, and c.

$$\begin{cases} nc + \left(\displaystyle\sum_{i=1}^{n} x_i\right) b + \left(\displaystyle\sum_{i=1}^{n} x_i^2\right) a = \displaystyle\sum_{i=1}^{n} y_i \\ \left(\displaystyle\sum_{i=1}^{n} x_i\right) c + \left(\displaystyle\sum_{i=1}^{n} x_i^2\right) b + \left(\displaystyle\sum_{i=1}^{n} x_i^3\right) a = \displaystyle\sum_{i=1}^{n} x_i y_i \\ \left(\displaystyle\sum_{i=1}^{n} x_i^2\right) c + \left(\displaystyle\sum_{i=1}^{n} x_i^3\right) b + \left(\displaystyle\sum_{i=1}^{n} x_i^4\right) a = \displaystyle\sum_{i=1}^{n} x_i^2 y_i \end{cases}$$

C.2 Exercises

In Exercises 1–4, find the least squares regression line for the points. Verify your answer with a graphing utility.

1. $(-4, 1)$, $(-3, 3)$, $(-2, 4)$, $(-1, 6)$

2. $(0, -1)$, $(2, 0)$, $(4, 3)$, $(6, 5)$

3. $(-3, 1)$, $(-1, 2)$, $(1, 2)$, $(4, 3)$

4. $(0, -1)$, $(2, 1)$, $(3, 2)$, $(5, 3)$

Appendix D Solving Linear Equations and Inequalities

Linear Equations

A *linear equation* in one variable x is an equation that can be written in the standard form $ax + b = 0$, where a and b are real numbers with $a \neq 0$.

A linear equation has exactly one solution. To see this, consider the following steps. (Remember that $a \neq 0$.)

$$ax + b = 0 \qquad \text{Original equation}$$

$$ax = -b \qquad \text{Subtract } b \text{ from each side.}$$

$$x = -\frac{b}{a} \qquad \text{Divide each side by } a.$$

To solve a linear equation in x, isolate x on one side of the equation by creating a sequence of *equivalent* (and usually simpler) equations, each having the same solution(s) as the original equation. The operations that yield equivalent equations come from the Substitution Principle and the Properties of Equality studied in Chapter P.

Generating Equivalent Equations

An equation can be transformed into an *equivalent equation* by one or more of the following steps.

	Original Equation	*Equivalent Equation*
1. Remove symbols of grouping, combine like terms, or simplify fractions on one or both sides of the equation.	$2x - x = 4$	$x = 4$
2. Add (or subtract) the same quantity to (from) *each* side of the equation.	$x + 1 = 6$	$x = 5$
3. Multiply (or divide) *each* side of the equation by the same *nonzero* quantity.	$2x = 6$	$x = 3$
4. Interchange the two sides of the equation.	$2 = x$	$x = 2$

After solving an equation, you should check each solution in the original equation. For example, you can check the solution to the equation in step 2 above as follows.

$$x + 1 = 6 \qquad \text{Write original equation.}$$

$$5 + 1 \overset{?}{=} 6 \qquad \text{Substitute 5 for } x.$$

$$6 = 6 \qquad \text{Solution checks.} \quad \checkmark$$

Example 1   Solving Linear Equations

a.

$$3x - 6 = 0 \qquad \text{Original equation}$$

$$3x - 6 + 6 = 0 + 6 \qquad \text{Add 6 to each side.}$$

$$3x = 6 \qquad \text{Simplify.}$$

$$x = 2 \qquad \text{Divide each side by 3.}$$

b.

$$4(2x + 3) = 6 \qquad \text{Original equation}$$

$$8x + 12 = 6 \qquad \text{Distributive Property}$$

$$8x + 12 - 12 = 6 - 12 \qquad \text{Subtract 12 from each side.}$$

$$8x = -6 \qquad \text{Simplify.}$$

$$\frac{8x}{8} = \frac{-6}{8} \qquad \text{Divide each side by 8.}$$

$$x = -\frac{3}{4} \qquad \text{Simplify.}$$

✓ *Checkpoint* Now try Exercise 15.

Linear Inequalities

Solving a linear inequality in one variable is much like solving a linear equation in one variable. To solve the inequality, you isolate the variable on one side using transformations that produce *equivalent inequalities*, which have the same solution(s) as the original inequality.

Generating Equivalent Inequalities

An inequality can be transformed into an *equivalent inequality* by one or more of the following steps.

	Original Inequality	*Equivalent Inequality*
1. Remove symbols of grouping, combine like terms, or simplify fractions on one or both sides of the inequality.	$4x + x \geq 2$	$5x \geq 2$
2. Add (or subtract) the same number to (from) *each* side of the inequality.	$x - 3 < 5$	$x < 8$
3. Multiply (or divide) each side of the inequality by the same *positive* number.	$\frac{1}{2}x > 3$	$x > 6$
4. Multiply (or divide) each side of the inequality by the same *negative* number and *reverse* the inequality symbol.	$-2x \leq 6$	$x \geq -3$

Example 2 Solving Linear Inequalities

a.

$x + 5 \geq 3$	Original inequality
$x + 5 - 5 \geq 3 - 5$	Subtract 5 from each side.
$x \geq -2$	Simplify.

The solution is all real numbers greater than or equal to -2, which is denoted by $[-2, \infty)$. Check several numbers that are greater than or equal to -2 in the original inequality.

b.

$-4.2m > 6.3$	Original inequality
$\dfrac{-4.2m}{-4.2} < \dfrac{6.3}{-4.2}$	Divide each side by -4.2 and reverse inequality symbol.
$m < -1.5$	Simplify.

The solution is all real numbers less than -1.5, which is denoted by $(-\infty, -1.5)$. Check several numbers that are less than -1.5 in the original inequality.

> **STUDY TIP**
>
> Remember that when you multiply or divide by a negative number, you *must reverse* the inequality symbol, as shown in Example 2(b).

 Checkpoint Now try Exercise 29.

D Exercises

Vocabulary Check

Fill in the blanks.

1. A _____ equation in one variable x is an equation that can be written in the standard form $ax + b = 0$.

2. To solve a linear inequality, isolate the variable on one side using transformations that produce _____ .

In Exercises 1–22, solve the equation and check your solution.

1. $x + 11 = 15$
2. $x + 3 = 9$
3. $x - 2 = 5$
4. $x - 5 = 1$
5. $3x = 12$
6. $2x = 6$
7. $\dfrac{x}{5} = 4$
8. $\dfrac{x}{4} = 5$
9. $8x + 7 = 39$
10. $12x - 5 = 43$
11. $24 - 7x = 3$
12. $13 + 6x = 61$
13. $8x - 5 = 3x + 20$
14. $7x + 3 = 3x - 17$
15. $-2(x + 5) = 10$
16. $4(3 - x) = 9$
17. $2x + 3 = 2x - 2$
18. $8(x - 2) = 4(2x - 4)$
19. $\frac{3}{2}(x + 5) - \frac{1}{4}(x + 24) = 0$
20. $\frac{3}{2}x + \frac{1}{4}(x - 2) = 10$
21. $0.25x + 0.75(10 - x) = 3$
22. $0.60x + 0.40(100 - x) = 50$

In Exercises 23–44, solve the inequality and check your solution.

23. $x + 6 < 8$
24. $3 + x > -10$
25. $-x - 8 > -17$
26. $-3 + x < 19$
27. $6 + x \leq -8$
28. $x - 10 \geq -6$
29. $\frac{4}{5}x > 8$
30. $\frac{2}{3}x < -4$
31. $-\frac{3}{4}x > -3$
32. $-\frac{1}{6}x < -2$
33. $4x < 12$
34. $10x > -40$
35. $-11x \leq -22$
36. $-7x \geq 21$
37. $x - 3(x + 1) \geq 7$
38. $2(4x - 5) - 3x \leq -15$
39. $7x - 12 < 4x + 6$
40. $11 - 6x \leq 2x + 7$
41. $\frac{3}{4}x - 6 \leq x - 7$
42. $3 + \frac{2}{7}x > x - 2$
43. $3.6x + 11 \geq -3.4$
44. $15.6 - 1.3x < -5.2$

Appendix E   Systems of Inequalities

E.1   Solving Systems of Inequalities

The Graph of an Inequality

The statements $3x - 2y < 6$ and $2x^2 + 3y^2 \geq 6$ are inequalities in two variables. An ordered pair (a, b) is a **solution of an inequality** in x and y if the inequality is true when a and b are substituted for x and y, respectively. The **graph of an inequality** is the collection of all solutions of the inequality. To sketch the graph of an inequality, begin by sketching the graph of the *corresponding equation*. The graph of the equation will normally separate the plane into two or more regions. In each such region, one of the following must be true.

1. *All* points in the region are solutions of the inequality.

2. *No* point in the region is a solution of the inequality.

So, you can determine whether the points in an entire region satisfy the inequality by simply testing *one* point in the region.

> #### Sketching the Graph of an Inequality in Two Variables
>
> **1.** Replace the inequality sign with an equal sign and sketch the graph of the corresponding equation. Use a dashed line for $<$ or $>$ and a solid line for $\leq$ or $\geq$. (A dashed line means all points on the line or curve *are not* solutions of the inequality. A solid line means all points on the line or curve *are* solutions of the inequality.)
>
> **2.** Test one point in each of the regions formed by the graph in Step 1. If the point satisfies the inequality, shade the entire region to denote that every point in the region satisfies the inequality.

Example 1   Sketching the Graph of an Inequality

Sketch the graph of $y \geq x^2 - 1$ by hand.

Solution

Begin by graphing the corresponding *equation* $y = x^2 - 1$, which is a parabola, as shown in Figure E.1. By testing a point *above* the parabola $(0, 0)$ and a point *below* the parabola $(0, -2)$, you can see that $(0, 0)$ satisfies the inequality because $0 \geq 0^2 - 1$ and that $(0, -2)$ does not satisfy the inequality because $-2 \not\geq 0^2 - 1$. So, the points that satisfy the inequality are those lying above and those lying on the parabola.

 Checkpoint Now try Exercise 9.

The inequality in Example 1 is a nonlinear inequality in two variables. Most of the following examples involve **linear inequalities** such as $ax + by < c$ (a and b are not both zero). The graph of a linear inequality is a half-plane lying on one side of the line $ax + by = c$.

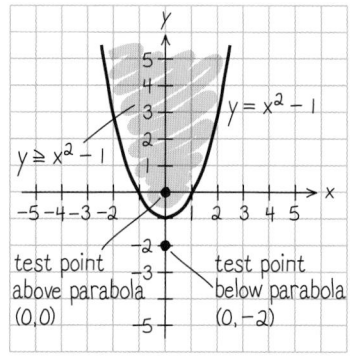

Figure E.1

Example 2   Sketching the Graphs of Linear Inequalities

Sketch the graph of each linear inequality.

a. $x > -2$ **b.** $y \le 3$

Solution

a. The graph of the corresponding equation $x = -2$ is a vertical line. The points that satisfy the inequality $x > -2$ are those lying to the right of (but not on) this line, as shown in Figure E.2.

b. The graph of the corresponding equation $y = 3$ is a horizontal line. The points that satisfy the inequality $y \le 3$ are those lying below (or on) this line, as shown in Figure E.3.

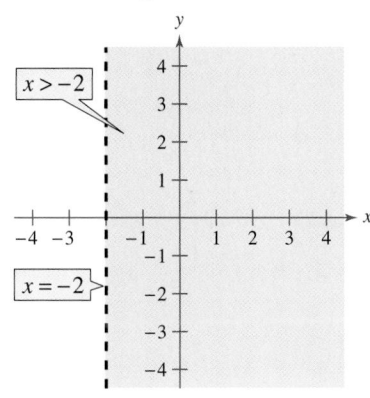

Figure E.2

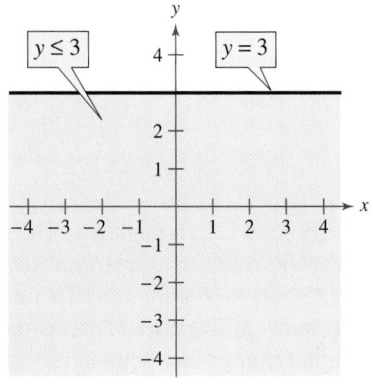

Figure E.3

 Checkpoint Now try Exercise 13.

Example 3   Sketching the Graph of a Linear Inequality

Sketch the graph of $x - y < 2$.

Solution

The graph of the corresponding equation $x - y = 2$ is a line, as shown in Figure E.4. Because the origin $(0, 0)$ satisfies the inequality, the graph consists of the half-plane lying above the line. (Try checking a point below the line. Regardless of which point below the line you choose, you will see that it does not satisfy the inequality.)

 Checkpoint Now try Exercise 15.

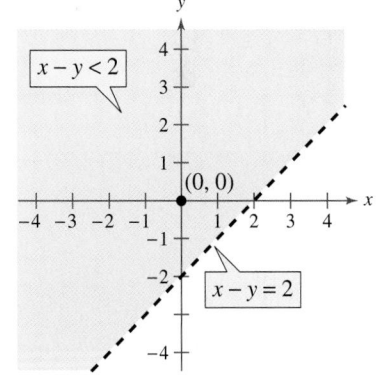

Figure E.4

To graph a linear inequality, it can help to write the inequality in slope-intercept form. For instance, by writing $x - y < 2$ in Example 3 in the form

$y > x - 2$

you can see that the solution points lie *above* the line $y = x - 2$ (or $x - y = 2$), as shown in Figure E.4.

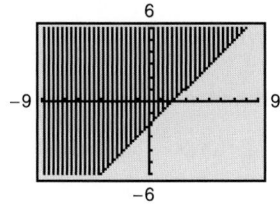

Systems of Inequalities

Many practical problems in business, science, and engineering involve systems of linear inequalities. A **solution of a system of inequalities** in x and y is a point (x, y) that satisfies each inequality in the system.

To sketch the graph of a system of inequalities in two variables, first sketch the graph of each individual inequality (on the same coordinate system) and then find the region that is *common* to every graph in the system. For systems of *linear* inequalities, it is helpful to find the vertices of the solution region.

Example 4   Solving a System of Inequalities

Sketch the graph (and label the vertices) of the solution set of the system.

$$\begin{cases} x - y < 2 & \text{Inequality 1} \\ x > -2 & \text{Inequality 2} \\ y \le 3 & \text{Inequality 3} \end{cases}$$

Solution

The graphs of these inequalities are shown in Figures E.2 through E.4. The triangular region common to all three graphs can be found by superimposing the graphs on the same coordinate system, as shown in Figure E.5. To find the vertices of the region, solve the three systems of corresponding equations obtained by taking pairs of equations representing the boundaries of the individual regions and solving these pairs of equations.

Vertex A: $(-2, -4)$ *Vertex B:* $(5, 3)$ *Vertex C:* $(-2, 3)$

$$\begin{cases} x - y = 2 \\ x = -2 \end{cases} \qquad \begin{cases} x - y = 2 \\ y = 3 \end{cases} \qquad \begin{cases} x = -2 \\ y = 3 \end{cases}$$

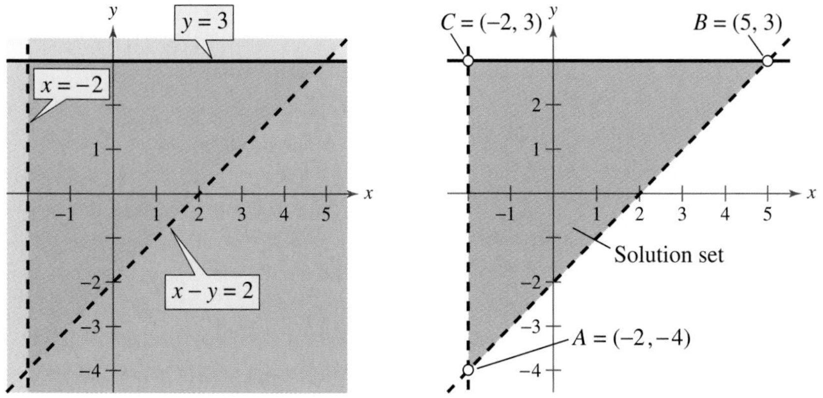

Figure E.5

> **STUDY TIP**
>
> Using different colored pencils to shade the solution of each inequality in a system makes identifying the solution of the system of inequalities easier. The region common to every graph in the system is where all shaded regions overlap. This region represents the solution set of the system.

Note in Figure E.5 that the vertices of the region are represented by open dots. This means that the vertices *are not* solutions of the system of inequalities.

✓ *Checkpoint* Now try Exercise 39.

For the triangular region shown in Figure E.5, each point of intersection of a pair of boundary lines corresponds to a vertex. With more complicated regions, two border lines can sometimes intersect at a point that is not a vertex of the region, as shown in Figure E.6. To keep track of which points of intersection are actually vertices of the region, you should sketch the region and refer to your sketch as you find each point of intersection.

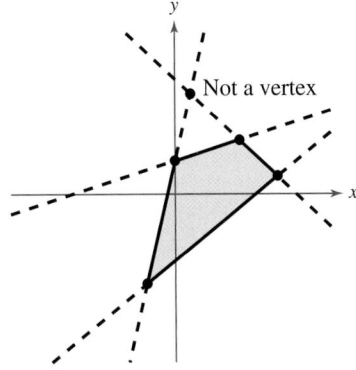

Figure E.6

Example 5   Solving a System of Inequalities

Sketch the region containing all points that satisfy the system of inequalities.

$$\begin{cases} x^2 - y \le 1 & \text{Inequality 1} \\ -x + y \le 1 & \text{Inequality 2} \end{cases}$$

Solution

As shown in Figure E.7, the points that satisfy the inequality $x^2 - y \le 1$ are the points lying above (or on) the parabola given by

$$y = x^2 - 1. \qquad \text{Parabola}$$

The points that satisfy the inequality $-x + y \le 1$ are the points lying below (or on) the line given by

$$y = x + 1. \qquad \text{Line}$$

To find the points of intersection of the parabola and the line, solve the system of corresponding equations.

$$\begin{cases} x^2 - y = 1 \\ -x + y = 1 \end{cases}$$

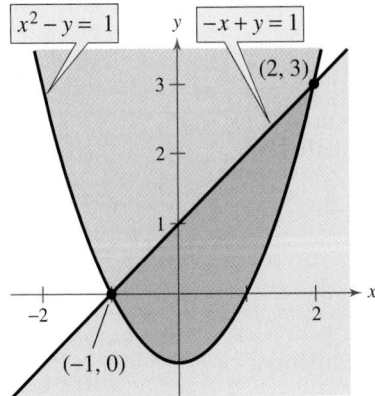

Figure E.7

Using the method of substitution, you can find the solutions to be $(-1, 0)$ and $(2, 3)$. So, the region containing all points that satisfy the system is indicated by the purple shaded region in Figure E.7.

✓ *Checkpoint* Now try Exercise 47.

When solving a system of inequalities, you should be aware that the system might have no solution, or it might be represented by an unbounded region in the plane. These two possibilities are shown in Examples 6 and 7.

Example 6   A System with No Solution

Sketch the solution set of the system of inequalities.

$$\begin{cases} x + y > 3 & \text{Inequality 1} \\ x + y < -1 & \text{Inequality 2} \end{cases}$$

Solution

From the way the system is written, it is clear that the system has no solution, because the quantity $(x + y)$ cannot be both less than -1 and greater than 3. Graphically, the inequality $x + y > 3$ is represented by the half-plane lying above the line $x + y = 3$, and the inequality $x + y < -1$ is represented by the half-plane lying below the line $x + y = -1$, as shown in Figure E.8. These two half-planes have no points in common. So the system of inequalities has no solution.

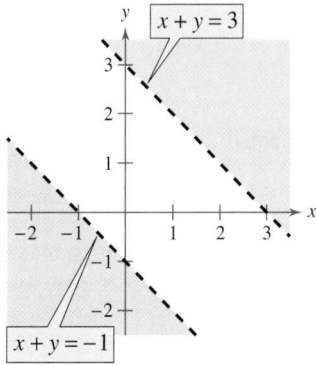

Figure E.8   No Solution

✓ *Checkpoint*   Now try Exercise 43.

Example 7   An Unbounded Solution Set

Sketch the solution set of the system of inequalities.

$$\begin{cases} x + y < 3 & \text{Inequality 1} \\ x + 2y > 3 & \text{Inequality 2} \end{cases}$$

Solution

The graph of the inequality $x + y < 3$ is the half-plane that lies below the line $x + y = 3$, as shown in Figure E.9. The graph of the inequality $x + 2y > 3$ is the half-plane that lies above the line $x + 2y = 3$. The intersection of these two half-planes is an *infinite wedge* that has a vertex at $(3, 0)$. This unbounded region represents the solution set.

✓ *Checkpoint*   Now try Exercise 45.

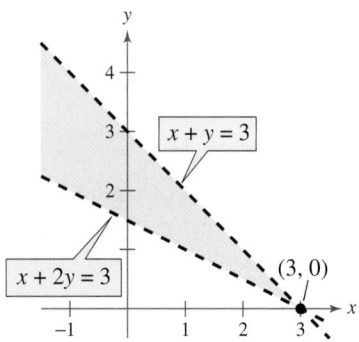

Figure E.9   Unbounded Region

Applications

The next example discusses two concepts that economists call *consumer surplus* and *producer surplus*. As shown in Figure E.10, the *point of equilibrium* is defined by the price p and the number of units x that satisfy both the demand and supply equations. Consumer surplus is defined as the area of the region that lies *below* the demand curve, *above* the horizontal line passing through the equilibrium point, and to the right of the p-axis. Similarly, the producer surplus is defined as the area of the region that lies *above* the supply curve, *below* the horizontal line passing through the equilibrium point, and to the right of the p-axis. The consumer surplus is a measure of the amount that consumers would have been willing to pay *above what they actually paid*, whereas the producer surplus is a measure of the amount that producers would have been willing to receive *below what they actually received*.

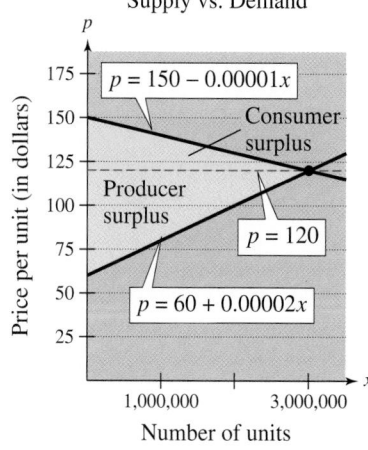

Figure E.10

Example 8   Consumer Surplus and Producer Surplus

The demand and supply functions for a new type of calculator are given by

$$\begin{cases} p = 150 - 0.00001x & \text{Demand equation} \\ p = 60 + 0.00002x & \text{Supply equation} \end{cases}$$

where p is the price (in dollars) and x represents the number of units. Find the consumer surplus and producer surplus for these two equations.

Solution

Begin by finding the point of equilibrium by setting the two equations equal to each other and solving for x.

$$60 + 0.00002x = 150 - 0.00001x \qquad \text{Set equations equal to each other.}$$

$$0.00003x = 90 \qquad \text{Combine like terms.}$$

$$x = 3{,}000{,}000 \qquad \text{Solve for } x.$$

So, the solution is $x = 3{,}000{,}000$, which corresponds to an equilibrium price of $p = \$120$. So, the consumer surplus and producer surplus are the areas of the following triangular regions.

Consumer Surplus

$$\begin{cases} p \le 150 - 0.00001x \\ p \ge 120 \\ x \ge 0 \end{cases}$$

Producer Surplus

$$\begin{cases} p \ge 60 + 0.00002x \\ p \le 120 \\ x \ge 0 \end{cases}$$

In Figure E.11, you can see that the consumer and producer surpluses are defined as the areas of the shaded triangles.

Consumer surplus $= \frac{1}{2}(\text{base})(\text{height}) = \frac{1}{2}(3{,}000{,}000)(30) = \$45{,}000{,}000$

Producer surplus $= \frac{1}{2}(\text{base})(\text{height}) = \frac{1}{2}(3{,}000{,}000)(60) = \$90{,}000{,}000$

✓ *Checkpoint* Now try Exercise 65.

Example 9 Nutrition

The minimum daily requirements from the liquid portion of a diet are 300 calories, 36 units of vitamin A, and 90 units of vitamin C. A cup of dietary drink X provides 60 calories, 12 units of vitamin A, and 10 units of vitamin C. A cup of dietary drink Y provides 60 calories, 6 units of vitamin A, and 30 units of vitamin C. Set up a system of linear inequalities that describes how many cups of each drink should be consumed each day to meet the minimum daily requirements for calories and vitamins.

Solution

Begin by letting x and y represent the following.

x = number of cups of dietary drink X

y = number of cups of dietary drink Y

To meet the minimum daily requirements, the following inequalities must be satisfied.

$$\begin{cases} 60x + 60y \geq 300 & \text{Calories} \\ 12x + 6y \geq 36 & \text{Vitamin A} \\ 10x + 30y \geq 90 & \text{Vitamin C} \\ x \geq 0 \\ y \geq 0 \end{cases}$$

The last two inequalities are included because x and y cannot be negative. The graph of this system of inequalities is shown in Figure E.12. (More is said about this application in Example 6 of Section E.2.)

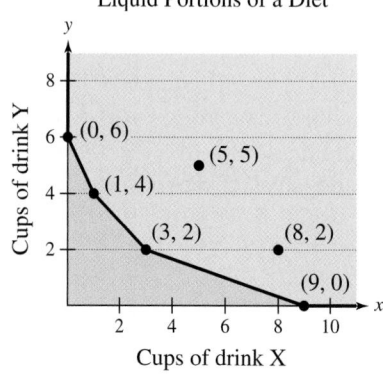

Liquid Portions of a Diet

Figure E.12

From the graph, you can see that two solutions (other than the vertices) that will meet the minimum daily requirements for calories and vitamins are $(5, 5)$ and $(8, 2)$. There are many other solutions.

✓ *Checkpoint* Now try Exercise 71.

E.1   Exercises

Vocabulary Check

Fill in the blanks.

1. An ordered pair (a, b) is a _____ of an inequality in x and y if the inequality is true when a and b are substituted for x and y, respectively.

2. The _____ of an inequality is the collection of all solutions of the inequality.

3. The graph of a _____ inequality is a half-plane lying on one side of the line $ax + by = c$.

4. The _____ of _____ is defined by the price p and the number of units x that satisfy both the demand and supply equations.

In Exercises 1–8, match the inequality with its graph. [The graphs are labeled (a), (b), (c), (d), (e), (f), (g), and (h).]

1. $x < 2$
2. $y \geq 3$
3. $2x + 3y \geq 6$
4. $2x - y \leq -2$
5. $x^2 + y^2 < 9$
6. $(x - 2)^2 + (y - 3)^2 > 9$
7. $xy > 1$
8. $y \leq 1 - x^2$

(a)
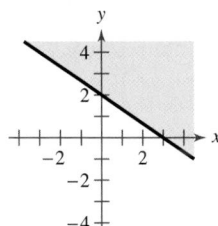

(b)
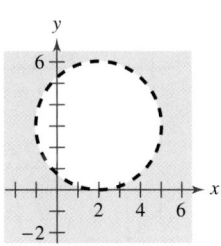

(c)
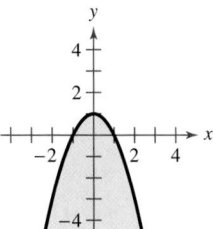

(d)
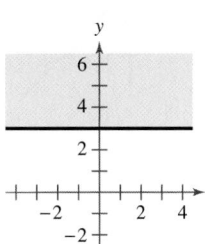

(e)
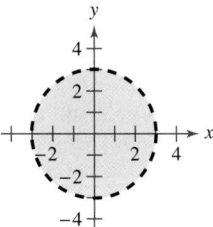

(f)
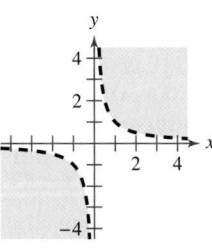

(g)
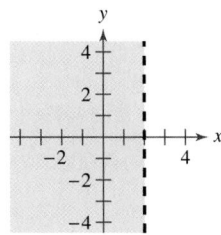

(h)
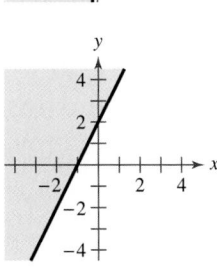

In Exercises 9–20, sketch the graph of the inequality.

9. $y < 2 - x^2$
10. $y^2 - x < 0$
11. $x \geq 4$
12. $x \leq -5$
13. $y \geq -1$
14. $y \leq 3$
15. $2y - x \geq 4$
16. $5x + 3y \geq -15$
17. $y > 3x^2 + 1$
18. $4x + y^2 > 1$
19. $(x + 1)^2 + y^2 < 9$
20. $(x - 1)^2 + (y - 4)^2 > 9$

In Exercises 21–32, use a graphing utility to graph the inequality. Use the *shade* feature to shade the region representing the solution.

21. $y \geq \frac{2}{3}x - 1$
22. $y \leq 6 - \frac{3}{2}x$
23. $y < -3.8x + 1.1$
24. $y \geq -20.74 + 2.66x$
25. $x^2 + 5y - 10 \leq 0$
26. $2x^2 - y - 3 > 0$
27. $y \leq \dfrac{1}{1 + x^2}$
28. $y > \dfrac{-10}{x^2 + x + 4}$
29. $y < \ln x$
30. $y \geq 4 - \ln(x + 5)$
31. $y > 3^{-x-4}$
32. $y \leq 2^{2x-1} - 3$

In Exercises 33–36, write an inequality for the shaded region shown in the graph.

33.

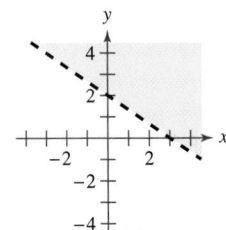

34.

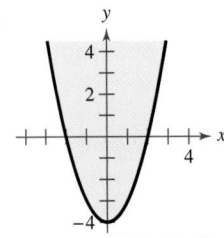

35.

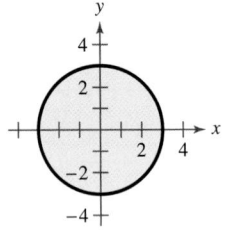

36.

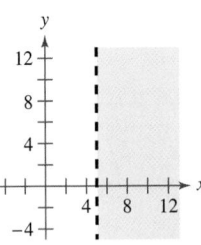

In Exercises 37 and 38, determine whether each ordered pair is a solution of the system of inequalities.

37. $\begin{cases} -2x + 5y \geq 3 \\ \qquad y < 4 \\ -4x + 2y < 7 \end{cases}$ (a) $(0, 2)$ (b) $(-6, 4)$
(c) $(-8, -2)$ (d) $(-3, 2)$

38. $\begin{cases} x^2 + y^2 \geq 36 \\ -3x + y \leq 10 \\ \frac{2}{3}x - y \geq 5 \end{cases}$ (a) $(-1, 7)$ (b) $(-5, 1)$
(c) $(6, 0)$ (d) $(4, -8)$

In Exercises 39–56, sketch the graph of the solution of the system of inequalities.

39. $\begin{cases} x + y \leq 1 \\ -x + y \leq 1 \\ \qquad y \geq 0 \end{cases}$ **40.** $\begin{cases} 3x + 2y < 6 \\ x \qquad > 0 \\ \qquad y > 0 \end{cases}$

41. $\begin{cases} -3x + 2y < 6 \\ x - 4y > -2 \\ 2x + y < 3 \end{cases}$ **42.** $\begin{cases} x - 7y > -36 \\ 5x + 2y > 5 \\ 6x - 5y > 6 \end{cases}$

43. $\begin{cases} 3x + y \leq y^2 \\ x - y > 0 \end{cases}$ **44.** $\begin{cases} y^2 - 3x \geq 9 \\ x + y \geq -3 \end{cases}$

45. $\begin{cases} 2x + y < 2 \\ x + 3y > 2 \end{cases}$ **46.** $\begin{cases} x - 2y < -6 \\ 2x - 4y > -9 \end{cases}$

47. $\begin{cases} x < y^2 \\ x > y + 2 \end{cases}$ **48.** $\begin{cases} x - y^2 > 0 \\ x - y < 2 \end{cases}$

49. $\begin{cases} x^2 + y^2 \leq 9 \\ x^2 + y^2 \geq 1 \end{cases}$ **50.** $\begin{cases} x^2 + y^2 \leq 25 \\ 4x - 3y \leq 0 \end{cases}$

51. $\begin{cases} y \leq \sqrt{3x} + 1 \\ y \geq x^2 + 1 \end{cases}$ **52.** $\begin{cases} y < -x^2 + 2x + 3 \\ y > x^2 - 4x + 3 \end{cases}$

53. $\begin{cases} y < x^3 - 2x + 1 \\ y > -2x \\ x \leq 1 \end{cases}$ **54.** $\begin{cases} y \geq x^4 - 2x^2 + 1 \\ y \leq 1 - x^2 \end{cases}$

55. $\begin{cases} x^2 y \geq 1 \\ 0 < x \leq 4 \\ y \leq 4 \end{cases}$ **56.** $\begin{cases} y \leq e^{-x^2/2} \\ y \geq 0 \\ -2 \leq x \leq 2 \end{cases}$

In Exercises 57–64, find a set of inequalities to describe the region.

57.

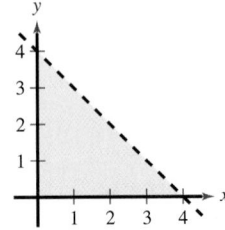

58.

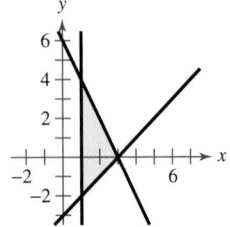

59.

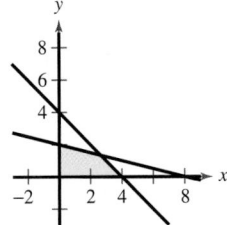

60.

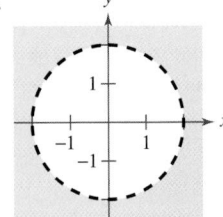

61. Rectangle: Vertices at $(2, 1)$, $(5, 1)$, $(5, 7)$, $(2, 7)$

62. Parallelogram: Vertices at $(0, 0)$, $(4, 0)$, $(1, 4)$, $(5, 4)$

63. Triangle: Vertices at $(0, 0)$, $(5, 0)$, $(2, 3)$

64. Triangle: Vertices at $(-1, 0)$, $(1, 0)$, $(0, 1)$

Supply and Demand In Exercises 65–68, graph the system representing the consumer surplus and producer surplus for the supply and demand equations. Be sure to shade the region representing the solution of the system. Find the consumer surplus and the producer surplus.

	Demand	Supply
65.	$p = 50 - 0.5x$	$p = 0.125x$
66.	$p = 100 - 0.05x$	$p = 25 + 0.1x$
67.	$p = 300 - 0.0002x$	$p = 225 + 0.0005x$
68.	$p = 140 - 0.00002x$	$p = 80 + 0.00001x$

In Exercises 69–72, (a) find a system of inequalities that models the problem and (b) graph the system, shading the region that represents the solution of the system.

69. *Investment Analysis*   A person plans to invest some or all of $30,000 in two different interest-bearing accounts. Each account is to contain at least $7500, and one account should have at least twice the amount that is in the other account.

70. *Ticket Sales*   For a summer concert event, one type of ticket costs $20 and another costs $35. The promoter of the concert must sell at least 20,000 tickets, including at least 10,000 of the $20 tickets and at least 5000 of the $35 tickets, and the gross receipts must total at least $300,000 in order for the concert to be held.

71. *Nutrition*   A dietitian is asked to design a special dietary supplement using two different foods. The minimum daily requirements of the new supplement are 280 units of calcium, 160 units of iron, and 180 units of vitamin B. Each ounce of food X contains 20 units of calcium, 15 units of iron, and 10 units of vitamin B. Each ounce of food Y contains 10 units of calcium, 10 units of iron, and 20 units of vitamin B.

72. *Inventory*   A store sells two models of computers. Because of the demand, the store stocks at least twice as many units of model A as units of model B. The costs to the store for models A and B are $800 and $1200, respectively. The management does not want more than $20,000 in computer inventory at any one time, and it wants at least four model A computers and two model B computers in inventory at all times.

73. *Construction*   You plan an exercise facility that has an indoor running track with an exercise floor inside the track (see figure). The track must be at least 125 meters long, and the exercise floor must have an area of at least 500 square meters.

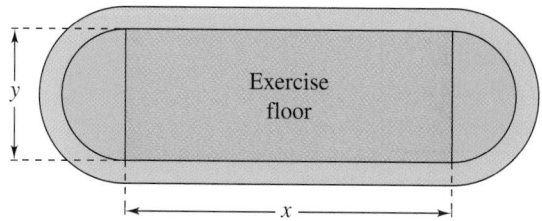

Exercise floor

(a) Find a system of inequalities describing the requirements of the facility.

(b) Sketch the graph of the system in part (a).

74. *Graphical Reasoning*   Two concentric circles have radii of x and y meters, where $y > x$ (see figure). The area between the boundaries of the circles must be at least 10 square meters.

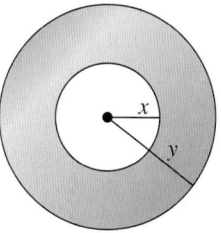

(a) Find an inequality describing the constraints on the circles.

(b) Graph the inequality in part (a).

(c) Identify the graph of the line $y = x$ in relation to the boundary of the inequality. Explain its meaning in the context of the problem.

Synthesis

True or False?   **In Exercises 75 and 76, determine whether the statement is true or false. Justify your answer.**

75. The area of the figure defined by the system below is 99 square units.
$$\begin{cases} x \geq -3 \\ x \leq 6 \\ y \leq 5 \\ y \geq -6 \end{cases}$$

76. The graph below shows the solution of the system
$$\begin{cases} y \leq 6 \\ -4x - 9y > 6. \\ 3x + y^2 \geq 2 \end{cases}$$

77. *Think About It*   After graphing the boundary of an inequality in x and y, how do you decide on which side of the boundary the solution set of the inequality lies?

78. *Writing*   Describe the difference between the solution set of a system of equations and the solution set of a system of inequalities.

E.2   Linear Programming

Linear Programming: A Graphical Approach

Many applications in business and economics involve a process called **optimization,** in which you are asked to find the minimum or maximum value of a quantity. In this section you will study an optimization strategy called **linear programming.**

A two-dimensional linear programming problem consists of a linear **objective function** and a system of linear inequalities called **constraints.** The objective function gives the quantity that is to be maximized (or minimized), and the constraints determine the set of **feasible solutions.** For example, suppose you are asked to maximize the value of

$$z = ax + by \qquad \text{Objective function}$$

subject to a set of constraints that determines the region in Figure E.13. Because every point in the shaded region satisfies each constraint, it is not clear how you should find the point that yields a maximum value of z. Fortunately, it can be shown that if there is an optimal solution, it must occur at one of the vertices. So, *you can find the maximum value of z by testing z at each of the vertices.*

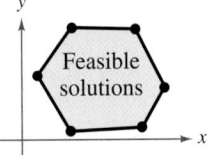

Figure E.13

Optimal Solution of a Linear Programming Problem

If a linear programming problem has a solution, it must occur at a vertex of the set of feasible solutions. If there is more than one solution, at least one of them must occur at such a vertex. In either case, the value of the objective function is unique.

Here are some guidelines for solving a linear programming problem in two variables in which an objective function is to be maximized *or* minimized.

Solving a Linear Programming Problem

   1. Sketch the region corresponding to the system of constraints. (The points inside or on the boundary of the region are *feasible solutions*.)

   2. Find the vertices of the region.

   3. Test the objective function at each of the vertices and select the values of the variables that optimize the objective function. For a bounded region, both a minimum and a maximum value will exist. (For an unbounded region, *if* an optimal solution exists, it will occur at a vertex.)

Example 1   Solving a Linear Programming Problem

Find the maximum value of

$z = 3x + 2y$ Objective function

subject to the following constraints.

$$\left.\begin{array}{r} x \geq 0 \\ y \geq 0 \\ x + 2y \leq 4 \\ x - y \leq 1 \end{array}\right\}$$ Constraints

Solution

The constraints form the region shown in Figure E.14. At the four vertices of this region, the objective function has the following values.

At $(0, 0)$: $z = 3(0) + 2(0) = 0$

At $(1, 0)$: $z = 3(1) + 2(0) = 3$

At $(2, 1)$: $z = 3(2) + 2(1) = 8$ Maximum value of z

At $(0, 2)$: $z = 3(0) + 2(2) = 4$

So, the maximum value of z is 8, and this value occurs when $x = 2$ and $y = 1$.

✓ *Checkpoint* Now try Exercise 13.

In Example 1, try testing some of the *interior* points in the region. You will see that the corresponding values of z are less than 8. Here are some examples.

At $(1, 1)$: $z = 3(1) + 2(1) = 5$

At $\left(1, \frac{1}{2}\right)$: $z = 3(1) + 2\left(\frac{1}{2}\right) = 4$

At $\left(\frac{1}{2}, \frac{3}{2}\right)$: $z = 3\left(\frac{1}{2}\right) + 2\left(\frac{3}{2}\right) = \frac{9}{2}$

To see why the maximum value of the objective function in Example 1 must occur at a vertex, consider writing the objective function in the form

$$y = -\frac{3}{2}x + \frac{z}{2}$$ Family of lines

where $z/2$ is the y-intercept of the objective function. This equation represents a family of lines, each of slope $-\frac{3}{2}$. Of these infinitely many lines, you want the one that has the largest z-value while still intersecting the region determined by the constraints. In other words, of all the lines with a slope of $-\frac{3}{2}$, you want the one that has the largest y-intercept *and* intersects the given region, as shown in Figure E.15. It should be clear that such a line will pass through one (or more) of the vertices of the region.

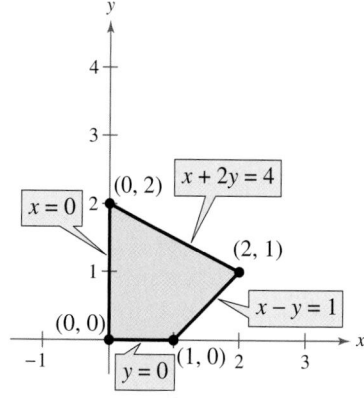

Figure E.14

STUDY TIP

Remember that a vertex of a region can be found using a system of linear equations. The system will consist of the equations of the lines passing through the vertex.

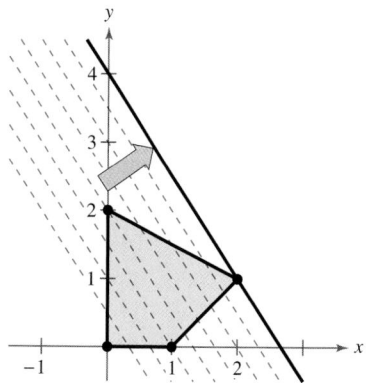

Figure E.15

The next example shows that the same basic procedure can be used to solve a problem in which the objective function is to be *minimized*.

Example 2   Solving a Linear Programming Problem

Find the minimum value of

$$z = 5x + 7y \qquad \text{Objective function}$$

where $x \geq 0$ and $y \geq 0$, subject to the following constraints.

$$\left. \begin{array}{r} 2x + 3y \geq 6 \\ 3x - y \leq 15 \\ -x + y \leq 4 \\ 2x + 5y \leq 27 \end{array} \right\} \qquad \text{Constraints}$$

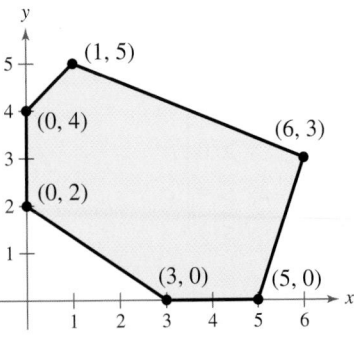

Figure E.16

Solution

The region bounded by the constraints is shown in Figure E.16. By testing the objective function at each vertex, you obtain the following.

At $(0, 2)$: $z = 5(0) + 7(2) = 14$ Minimum value of z

At $(0, 4)$: $z = 5(0) + 7(4) = 28$

At $(1, 5)$: $z = 5(1) + 7(5) = 40$

At $(6, 3)$: $z = 5(6) + 7(3) = 51$

At $(5, 0)$: $z = 5(5) + 7(0) = 25$

At $(3, 0)$: $z = 5(3) + 7(0) = 15$

So, the minimum value of z is 14, and this value occurs when $x = 0$ and $y = 2$.

✓ *Checkpoint* Now try Exercise 15.

Example 3   Solving a Linear Programming Problem

Find the maximum value of

$$z = 5x + 7y \qquad \text{Objective function}$$

where $x \geq 0$ and $y \geq 0$, subject to the following constraints.

$$\left. \begin{array}{r} 2x + 3y \geq 6 \\ 3x - y \leq 15 \\ -x + y \leq 4 \\ 2x + 5y \leq 27 \end{array} \right\} \qquad \text{Constraints}$$

Solution

This linear programming problem is identical to that given in Example 2 above, *except* that the objective function is *maximized* instead of minimized. Using the values of z at the vertices shown above, you can conclude that the maximum value of z is 51, and that this value occurs when $x = 6$ and $y = 3$.

✓ *Checkpoint* Now try Exercise 17.

It is possible for the maximum (or minimum) value in a linear programming problem to occur at *two* different vertices. For instance, at the vertices of the region shown in Figure E.17, the objective function

$$z = 2x + 2y \qquad \text{Objective function}$$

has the following values.

At $(0, 0)$: $z = 2(0) + 2(0) = 0$

At $(0, 4)$: $z = 2(0) + 2(4) = 8$

At $(2, 4)$: $z = 2(2) + 2(4) = 12$ Maximum value of z

At $(5, 1)$: $z = 2(5) + 2(1) = 12$ Maximum value of z

At $(5, 0)$: $z = 2(5) + 2(0) = 10$

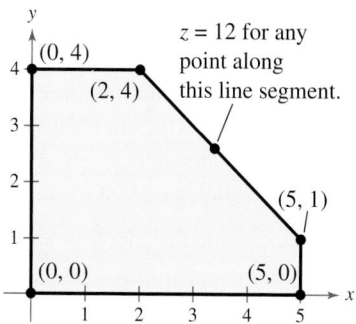

Figure E.17

In this case, you can conclude that the objective function has a maximum value (of 12) not only at the vertices $(2, 4)$ and $(5, 1)$, but also at *any point on the line segment connecting these two vertices*, as shown in Figure E.17. Note that by rewriting the objective function as

$$y = -x + \frac{1}{2}z$$

you can see that its graph has the same slope as the line through the vertices $(2, 4)$ and $(5, 1)$.

Some linear programming problems have no optimal solutions. This can occur if the region determined by the constraints is *unbounded*.

Example 4   An Unbounded Region

Find the maximum value of

$$z = 4x + 2y \qquad \text{Objective function}$$

where $x \geq 0$ and $y \geq 0$, subject to the following constraints.

$$\left. \begin{aligned} x + 2y &\geq 4 \\ 3x + y &\geq 7 \\ -x + 2y &\leq 7 \end{aligned} \right\} \qquad \text{Constraints}$$

Solution

The region determined by the constraints is shown in Figure E.18. For this unbounded region, there is no maximum value of z. To see this, note that the point $(x, 0)$ lies in the region for all values of $x \geq 4$. By choosing large values of x, you can obtain values of $z = 4(x) + 2(0) = 4x$ that are as large as you want. So, there is no maximum value of z. For the vertices of the region, the objective function has the following values. So, there *is* a minimum value of z, $z = 10$, which occurs at the vertex $(2, 1)$.

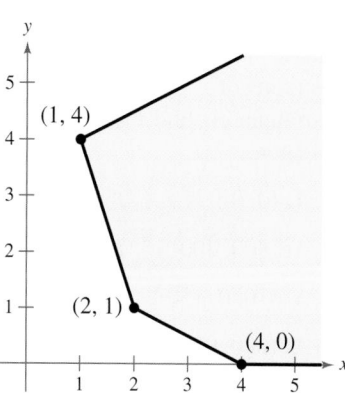

Figure E.18

At $(1, 4)$: $z = 4(1) + 2(4) = 12$

At $(2, 1)$: $z = 4(2) + 2(1) = 10$ Minimum value of z

At $(4, 0)$: $z = 4(4) + 2(0) = 16$

✓ *Checkpoint* Now try Exercise 27.

Applications

Example 5 shows how linear programming can be used to find the maximum profit in a business application.

Example 5   Optimizing Profit

A manufacturer wants to maximize the profit for selling two types of boxed chocolates. A box of chocolate covered creams yields a profit of $1.50 per box and a box of chocolate covered cherries yields a profit of $2.00 per box. Market tests and available resources have indicated the following constraints.

1. The combined production level should not exceed 1200 boxes per month.

2. The demand for a box of chocolate covered cherries is no more than half the demand for a box of chocolate covered creams.

3. The production level of a box of chocolate covered creams is less than or equal to 600 boxes plus three times the production level of a box of chocolate covered cherries.

Solution

Let x be the number of boxes of chocolate covered creams and y be the number of boxes of chocolate covered cherries. The objective function (for the combined profit) is given by

$$P = 1.5x + 2y. \qquad \text{Objective function}$$

The three constraints translate into the following linear inequalities.

1. $x + y \le 1200$ ⟹ $x + y \le 1200$

2. $ y \le \frac{1}{2}x$ ⟹ $-x + 2y \le 0$

3. $ x \le 3y + 600$ ⟹ $x - 3y \le 600$

Because neither x nor y can be negative, you also have the two additional constraints of $x \ge 0$ and $y \ge 0$. Figure E.19 shows the region determined by the constraints. To find the maximum profit, test the value of P at the vertices of the region.

At $(0, 0)$: $P = 1.5(0) + 2(0) = 0$

At $(800, 400)$: $P = 1.5(800) + 2(400) = 2000$ Maximum profit

At $(1050, 150)$: $P = 1.5(1050) + 2(150) = 1875$

At $(600, 0)$: $P = 1.5(600) + 2(0) = 900$

So, the maximum profit is $2000, and it occurs when the monthly production consists of 800 boxes of chocolate covered creams and 400 boxes of chocolate covered cherries.

✓ *Checkpoint* Now try Exercise 31.

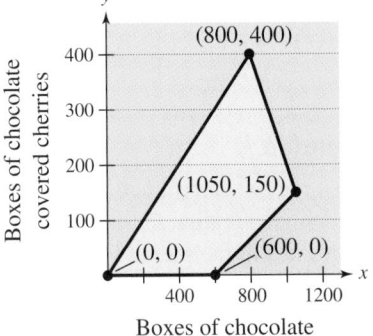

Figure E.19

In Example 5, suppose the manufacturer improves the production of chocolate covered creams so that a profit of $2.50 per box is obtained. The maximum profit can now be found using the objective function $P = 2.5x + 2y$. By testing the values of P at the vertices of the region, you find that the maximum profit is now $2925, which occurs when $x = 1050$ and $y = 150$.

Example 6   Optimizing Cost

The minimum daily requirements from the liquid portion of a diet are 300 calories, 36 units of vitamin A, and 90 units of vitamin C. A cup of dietary drink X costs $0.12 and provides 60 calories, 12 units of vitamin A, and 10 units of vitamin C. A cup of dietary drink Y costs $0.15 and provides 60 calories, 6 units of vitamin A, and 30 units of vitamin C. How many cups of each drink should be consumed each day to minimize the cost and still meet the daily requirements?

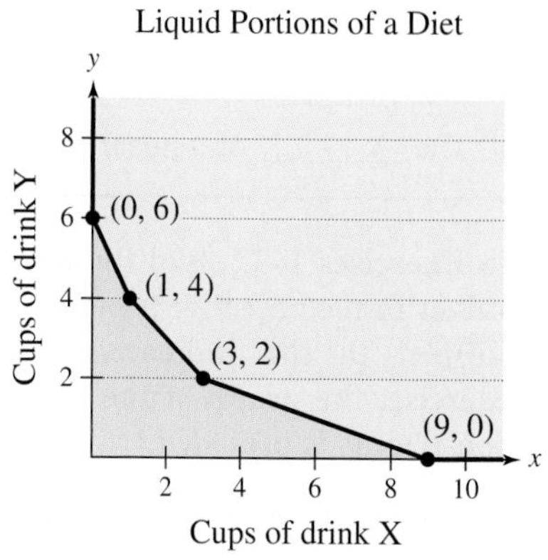

Liquid Portions of a Diet

Cups of drink Y (vertical axis)

Points plotted: $(0, 6)$, $(1, 4)$, $(3, 2)$, $(9, 0)$

Cups of drink X (horizontal axis)

Figure E.20

Solution

As in Example 9 on page A58, let x be the number of cups of dietary drink X and let y be the number of cups of dietary drink Y.

$$
\left.
\begin{array}{lrcr}
\text{For Calories:} & 60x + 60y & \geq & 300 \\
\text{For Vitamin A:} & 12x + 6y & \geq & 36 \\
\text{For Vitamin C:} & 10x + 30y & \geq & 90 \\
& x & \geq & 0 \\
& y & \geq & 0
\end{array}
\right\} \quad \text{Constraints}
$$

The cost C is given by

$$C = 0.12x + 0.15y. \qquad \text{Objective function}$$

The graph of the region determined by the constraints is shown in Figure E.20. To determine the minimum cost, test C at each vertex of the region.

At $(0, 6)$: $C = 0.12(0) + 0.15(6) = 0.90$

At $(1, 4)$: $C = 0.12(1) + 0.15(4) = 0.72$

At $(3, 2)$: $C = 0.12(3) + 0.15(2) = 0.66$ Minimum value of C

At $(9, 0)$: $C = 0.12(9) + 0.15(0) = 1.08$

So, the minimum cost is $0.66 per day, and this cost occurs when three cups of drink X and two cups of drink Y are consumed each day.

✓ *Checkpoint* Now try Exercise 33.

E.2 Exercises

Vocabulary Check

Fill in the blanks.

1. In the process called _____ , you are asked to find the minimum or maximum value of a quantity.
2. The _____ of a linear programming problem gives the quantity that is to be maximized or minimized.
3. The _____ of a linear programming problem determine the set of _____ .

In Exercises 1–12, find the minimum and maximum values of the objective function and where they occur, subject to the indicated constraints. (For each exercise, the graph of the region determined by the constraints is provided.)

1. Objective function:

$z = 3x + 5y$

Constraints:

$x \geq 0$

$y \geq 0$

$x + y \leq 6$

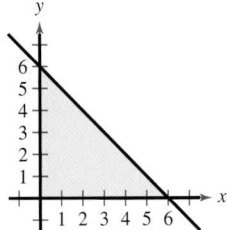

2. Objective function:

$z = 2x + 8y$

Constraints:

$x \geq 0$

$y \geq 0$

$2x + y \leq 4$

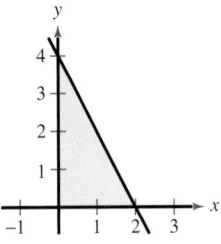

3. Objective function:

$z = 10x + 7y$

Constraints:
See Exercise 1.

4. Objective function:

$z = 7x + 3y$

Constraints:
See Exercise 2.

5. Objective function:

$z = 3x + 2y$

Constraints:

$x \geq 0$

$y \geq 0$

$x + 3y \leq 15$

$4x + y \leq 16$

6. Objective function:

$z = 4x + 3y$

Constraints:

$x \geq 0$

$2x + 3y \geq 6$

$3x - 2y \leq 9$

$x + 5y \leq 20$

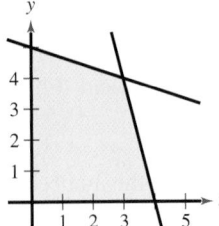

Figure for 5

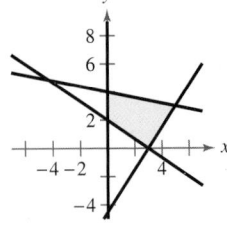

Figure for 6

7. Objective function:

$z = 5x + 0.5y$

Constraints:
See Exercise 5.

8. Objective function:

$z = x + 6y$

Constraints:
See Exercise 6.

9. Objective function:

$z = 10x + 7y$

Constraints:

$0 \leq x \leq 60$

$0 \leq y \leq 45$

$5x + 6y \leq 420$

10. Objective function:

$z = 50x + 35y$

Constraints:

$x \geq 0$

$y \geq 0$

$8x + 9y \leq 7200$

$8x + 9y \geq 5400$

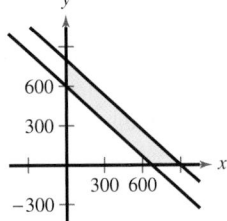

11. Objective function:

$z = 25x + 30y$

Constraints:
See Exercise 9.

12. Objective function:

$z = 15x + 20y$

Constraints:
See Exercise 10.

In Exercises 13–22, sketch the region determined by the constraints. Then find the minimum and maximum values of the objective function and where they occur, subject to the indicated constraints.

13. Objective function:

$z = 6x + 10y$

Constraints:

$$x \geq 0$$
$$y \geq 0$$
$$2x + 5y \leq 10$$

14. Objective function:

$z = 7x + 8y$

Constraints:

$$x \geq 0$$
$$y \geq 0$$
$$x + \tfrac{1}{2}y \leq 4$$

15. Objective function:

$z = 3x + 4y$

Constraints:

$$x \geq 0$$
$$y \geq 0$$
$$2x + 5y \leq 50$$
$$4x + y \leq 28$$

16. Objective function:

$z = 4x + 5y$

Constraints:

$$x \geq 0$$
$$y \geq 0$$
$$2x + 2y \leq 10$$
$$x + 2y \leq 6$$

17. Objective function:

$z = 4x + y$

Constraints:

$$x \geq 0$$
$$y \geq 0$$
$$x + 2y \leq 40$$
$$2x + 3y \geq 72$$

18. Objective function:

$z = x$

Constraints:

$$x \geq 0$$
$$y \geq 0$$
$$2x + 3y \leq 60$$
$$2x + y \leq 28$$
$$4x + y \leq 48$$

19. Objective function:

$z = x + 4y$

Constraints:
See Exercise 17.

20. Objective function:

$z = y$

Constraints:
See Exercise 18.

21. Objective function:

$z = 2x + 3y$

Constraints:
See Exercise 17.

22. Objective function:

$z = 3x + 2y$

Constraints:
See Exercise 18.

Exploration In Exercises 23–26, perform the following.

(a) Graph the region bounded by the following constraints.

$$3x + y \leq 15$$
$$4x + 3y \leq 30$$
$$x \geq 0$$
$$y \geq 0$$

(b) Graph the objective function for the given maximum value of z on the same set of coordinate axes as the graph of the constraints.

(c) Use the graph to determine the feasible point or points that yield the maximum. Explain how you arrived at your answer.

Objective Function	Maximum
23. $z = 2x + y$	$z = 12$
24. $z = 5x + y$	$z = 25$
25. $z = x + y$	$z = 10$
26. $z = 3x + y$	$z = 15$

In Exercises 27–30, the linear programming problem has an unusual characteristic. Sketch a graph of the solution region for the problem and describe the unusual characteristic. The objective function is to be maximized in each case.

27. Objective function:

$z = x + y$

Constraints:

$$x \geq 0$$
$$y \geq 0$$
$$-x + y \leq 1$$
$$-x + 2y \leq 4$$

28. Objective function:

$z = 2.5x + y$

Constraints:

$$x \geq 0$$
$$y \geq 0$$
$$3x + 5y \leq 15$$
$$5x + 2y \leq 10$$

29. Objective function:

$z = x + y$

Constraints:

$$x \geq 0$$
$$y \geq 0$$
$$-x + y \leq 0$$
$$-3x + y \geq 3$$

30. Objective function:

$z = -x + 2y$

Constraints:

$$x \geq 0$$
$$y \geq 0$$
$$x \leq 10$$
$$x + y \leq 7$$

31. *Optimizing Revenue*   An accounting firm has 800 hours of staff time and 96 hours of reviewing time available each week. The firm charges $2000 for an audit and $300 for a tax return. Each audit requires 100 hours of staff time and 8 hours of review time. Each tax return requires 12.5 hours of staff time and 2 hours of review time. What numbers of audits and tax returns will yield the maximum revenue? What is the maximum revenue?

32. *Optimizing Profit* A manufacturer produces two models of snowboards. The amounts of time (in hours) required for assembling, painting, and packaging the two models are as follows.

	Model A	Model B
Assembling	2.5	3
Painting	2	1
Packaging	0.75	1.25

The total amounts of time available for assembling, painting, and packaging are 4000 hours, 2500 hours, and 1500 hours, respectively. The profits per unit are $50 for model A and $52 for model B. How many of each model should be produced to maximize profit? What is the maximum profit?

33. *Optimizing Cost* A farming cooperative mixes two brands of cattle feed. Brand X costs $25 per bag and contains two units of nutritional element A, two units of element B, and two units of element C. Brand Y costs $20 per bag and contains one unit of nutritional element A, nine units of element B, and 3 units of element C. The minimum requirements for nutrients A, B, and C are 12 units, 36 units, and 24 units, respectively. Find the number of bags of each brand that should be mixed to produce a mixture having a minimum cost per bag. What is the minimum cost?

34. *Optimizing Cost* A pet supply company mixes two brands of dry dog food. Brand X costs $15 per bag and contains eight units of nutritional element A, one unit of nutritional element B, and two units of nutritional element C. Brand Y costs $30 per bag and contains two units of nutritional element A, one unit of nutritional element B, and seven units of nutritional element C. Each bag of mixed dog food must contain at least 16 units, 5 units, and 20 units of nutritional elements A, B, and C, respectively. Find the numbers of bags of brands X and Y that should be mixed to produce a mixture meeting the minimum nutritional requirements and having a minimum cost per bag. What is the minimum cost?

Synthesis

True or False? **In Exercises 35 and 36, determine whether the statement is true or false. Justify your answer.**

35. If an objective function has a maximum value at the adjacent vertices $(4, 7)$ and $(8, 3)$, you can conclude that it also has a maximum value at the points $(4.5, 6.5)$ and $(7.8, 3.2)$.

36. When solving a linear programming problem, if the objective function has a maximum value at two adjacent vertices, you can assume that there are an infinite number of points that will produce the maximum value.

Think About It **In Exercises 37–40, find an objective function that has a maximum or minimum value at the indicated vertex of the constraint region shown below. (There are many correct answers.)**

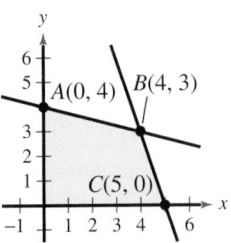

37. The maximum occurs at vertex A.

38. The maximum occurs at vertex B.

39. The maximum occurs at vertex C.

40. The minimum occurs at vertex C.

In Exercises 41 and 42, determine values of t such that the objective function has a maximum value at each indicated vertex.

41. Objective function:

$z = 3x + ty$

Constraints:

$$x \geq 0$$
$$y \geq 0$$
$$x + 3y \leq 15$$
$$4x + y \leq 16$$

(a) $(0, 5)$

(b) $(3, 4)$

42. Objective function:

$z = 3x + ty$

Constraints:

$$x \geq 0$$
$$y \geq 0$$
$$x + 2y \leq 4$$
$$x - y \leq 1$$

(a) $(2, 1)$

(b) $(0, 2)$

Answers to Odd-Numbered Exercises and Tests

Chapter P

Section P.1   (page 9)

Vocabulary Check   (page 9)

1. rational   2. Irrational   3. absolute value
4. composite   5. prime   6. variables, constants
7. terms   8. coefficient   9. Zero-Factor Property

1. (a) 5, 1   (b) 5, 0, 1   (c) $-9, 5, 0, 1, -4, -1$
   (d) $-9, -\frac{7}{2}, 5, \frac{2}{3}, 0, 1, -4, -1$ (e) $\sqrt{2}$

3. (a) 1, 20   (b) 1, 20   (c) $-13, 1, -10, 20$
   (d) $2.01, 0.666\ldots, -13, 1, -10, 20$
   (e) $0.010110111\ldots$

5. (a) $\frac{6}{3}, 3$ (b) $\frac{6}{3}, 3$ (c) $\frac{6}{3}, -2, 3, -3$
   (d) $-\frac{1}{3}, \frac{6}{3}, -7.5, -2, 3, -3$ (e) $-\pi, \frac{1}{2}\sqrt{2}$

7. 0.625   9. $0.\overline{123}$ 11. $-9.\overline{09}$ 13. $\frac{23}{5}$ 15. $\frac{13}{2}$

17. $-1 < 2.5$

19.
$-4 > -8$

21.
$\frac{3}{2} < 7$

23.
$\frac{5}{6} > \frac{2}{3}$

25. (a) $x \le 5$ is the set of all real numbers less than or equal to 5.
   (b)   (c) Unbounded

27. (a) $x < 0$ is the set of all negative real numbers.
   (b)   (c) Unbounded

29. (a) $-2 < x < 2$ is the set of all real numbers greater than -2 and less than 2.
   (b)   (c) Bounded

31. (a) $-1 \le x < 0$ is the set of all negative real numbers greater than or equal to -1.
   (b)   (c) Bounded

33. $x < 0; (-\infty, 0)$ 35. $y \ge 0; [0, \infty)$

37. $-1 \le p < 9; [-1, 9)$

39. The set of all real numbers greater than -6

41. The set of all real numbers less than or equal to 2

43. 10   45. -9

47. 1 for $x > -2$; undefined for $x = -2$; -1 for $x < -2$

49. $|-3| > -|3|$ 51. $-5 = -|5|$

53. $-|-2| = -|2|$ 55. 51   57. $\frac{5}{2}$ 59. $\frac{128}{75}$

61. $|x - 5| \le 3$ 63. $|y - 0| \ge 6$ 65. 179 miles

67. $|\$113{,}356 - \$112{,}700| = \$656 > \$500$

   $0.05(\$112{,}700) = \$5635$

   Because the actual expenses differ from the budget by more than \$500, there is failure to meet the "budget variance test."

69. $|\$37{,}335 - \$37{,}640| = \$305 < \$500$

   $0.05(\$37{,}640) = \$1882$

   Because the difference between the actual expenses and the budget is less than \$500 and less than 5% of the budgeted amount, there is compliance with the "budget variance test."

71. Receipts = \$92.5 billion,

   $|\text{Receipts} - \text{Expenditures}| = \$0.3$ billion

   There was a surplus of \$0.3 billion.

73. Receipts = \$517.1 billion,

   $|\text{Receipts} - \text{Expenditures}| = \$73.8$ billion

   There was a deficit of \$73.8 billion.

75. Receipts = \$2025.2 billion,

   $|\text{Receipts} - \text{Expenditures}| = \$236.4$ billion

   There was a surplus of \$236.4 billion.

77. Terms: $7x, 4$; coefficient: 7

79. Terms: $\sqrt{3}x^2, -8x, -11$; coefficients: $\sqrt{3}, -8$

81. Terms: $4x^3, \frac{x}{2}, -5$; coefficients: $4, \frac{1}{2}$

83. (a) -10 (b) -6 85. (a) -10 (b) 0

87. Commutative Property of Addition

89. Multiplicative Inverse Property

91. Distributive Property

93. Associative Property of Addition

95. $\dfrac{1}{2}$ **97.** $\dfrac{3}{8}$ **99.** $\dfrac{11x}{12}$ **101.** $\dfrac{96}{x}$ **103.** $-\dfrac{7}{5}$

105. -36 **107.** 1.56   **109.** 13.33

111. (a)

n	1	0.5	0.01	0.0001	0.000001
$5/n$	5	10	500	50,000	5,000,000

(b) $5/n$ approaches ∞ as n approaches 0.

113. False. A contradiction can be shown using the numbers $a = 2$ and $b = 1$. $2 > 1$, but $\frac{1}{2} \not> \frac{1}{1}$.

115. (a) $-A$ is negative.   (b) $B - A$ is negative.

117. (a) No. If u is negative while v is positive, or vice versa, the expressions will not be equal.

(b) $|u + v| \leq |u| + |v|$

119. Answers will vary. Sample answer: Natural numbers are the integers from 1 to infinity. Whole numbers are integers from 0 to infinity. A rational number can be expressed as the ratio of two integers; an irrational number cannot.

Section P.2   (page 21)

Vocabulary Check   (page 21)

1. exponent, base   **2.** scientific notation

3. square root   **4.** principal nth root

5. index, radicand   **6.** simplest form

7. conjugates   **8.** rationalizing   **9.** power, index

---

1. (a) 48   (b) 81   **3.** (a) 729   (b) -9

5. (a) 243   (b) $-\frac{3}{4}$ **7.** (a) $\frac{5}{6}$ (b) 4   **9.** $\frac{7}{4}$

11. -54 **13.** 1   **15.** (a) $-125z^3$ (b) $5x^6$

17. (a) $\dfrac{7}{x}$ (b) $\dfrac{4}{3}(x + y)^2$, $x + y \neq 0$

19. (a) $\dfrac{x^2}{y^2}$, $x \neq 0$ (b) $\dfrac{b^5}{a^5}$, $b \neq 0$

21. -1600 **23.** 2.125   **25.** 5.73×10^7

27. 8.99×10^{-5} **29.** 564,000,000

31. 0.0000000000000000016022   **33.** 5×10^4 or 50,000

35. (a) 4.907×10^{17} (b) 1.479

37. (a) 67,082.039   (b) 39.791   **39.** 11   **41.** 3

43. -125 **45.** $\frac{1}{8}$ **47.** -4 **49.** -7.225

51. 21.316   **53.** 14.499

55. (a) 3   (b) $2x\sqrt[5]{3}$

57. (a) $3y^2\sqrt{6x}$ (b) $2\sqrt[3]{4a^2/b^2}$

59. (a) $34\sqrt{2}$ (b) $22\sqrt{2}$

61. (a) $13\sqrt{x + 1}$ (b) $18\sqrt{5x}$

63. $\sqrt{5} + \sqrt{3} > \sqrt{5 + 3}$ **65.** $5 > \sqrt{3^2 + 2^2}$

67. $\dfrac{\sqrt{3}}{3}$ **69.** $\dfrac{\sqrt{14} + 2}{2}$ **71.** $\dfrac{2}{\sqrt{2}}$

73. $\dfrac{2}{3(\sqrt{5} - \sqrt{3})}$ **75.** $64^{1/3} = 4$ **77.** $\sqrt[5]{32} = 2$

79. $(-216)^{1/3} = -6$ **81.** $8^{3/4} = 27$ **83.** $\dfrac{2}{x}$

85. $\dfrac{1}{x^3}$, $x > 0$ **87.** (a) $\sqrt{3}$ (b) $\sqrt[3]{(x + 1)^2}$

89. (a) $2\sqrt[4]{2}$ (b) $\sqrt[8]{2x}$ **91.** $T = \dfrac{\pi}{2} \approx 1.57$ seconds

93. 0.026 inches   **95.** True. $x^{k+1}/x = x^k x/x = x^k$ $(x \neq 0)$.

97. $1 = \dfrac{a^n}{a^n} = a^{n-n} = a^0$

99. When any positive integer is squared, the units digit is 0, 1, 4, 5, 6, or 9. Therefore, $\sqrt{5233}$ is not an integer.

Section P.3   (page 32)

Vocabulary Check   (page 32)

1. n, a_n **2.** zero polynomial   **3.** monomial

4. First, Outer, Inner, Last   **5.** prime

6. perfect square trinomial

---

1. d   **2.** e   **3.** b   **4.** a   **5.** f   **6.** c

7. Answers will vary, but first term is $-2x^3$.

9. Answers will vary, but first term has form $-ax^4$, $a > 0$.

11. $4x^2 + 3x + 2$

Degree: 2; leading coefficient: 4

13. $x^7 + 1$

Degree: 7; leading coefficient: 1

15. $-2x^5 + 6x^4 - x + 1$

Degree: 5; leading coefficient: -2

17. Polynomial: $-2x^3 + 7x + 10$ **19.** Not a polynomial

21. $-2x - 10$ **23.** $3x^3 - 2x + 2$

25. $8.1x^3 + 29.7x^2 + 11$ **27.** $3x^3 - 6x^2 + 3x$

29. $-15z^2 + 5z$ **31.** $-4x^4 + 4x$ **33.** $-7.5x^3 - 15x$

35. $-\frac{1}{4}x^2 - 6x$ **37.** $x^2 + 7x + 12$ **39.** $6x^2 - 7x - 5$

41. $4x^2 - 20xy + 25y^2$ **43.** $x^2 - 100$ **45.** $x^2 - 4y^2$

47. $4r^4 - 25$ **49.** $x^3 + 3x^2 + 3x + 1$

51. $8x^3 - 12x^2y + 6xy^2 - y^3$ **53.** $\frac{1}{4}x^2 - 5x + 25$

55. $\frac{1}{16}x^2 - 9$ **57.** $5.76x^2 + 14.4x + 9$

59. $-3x^4 - x^3 - 12x^2 - 19x - 5$

61. $m^2 - 6m + 9 - n^2$

63. $x^2 + 2xy + y^2 - 6y - 6x + 9$ **65.** $2x^2 + 2x$

67. $u^4 - 16$ **69.** $2(x + 4)$ **71.** $2x(x^2 - 3)$

73. $(x - 5)(3x + 8)$ **75.** $(x + 8)(x - 8)$

77. $2(4y + 3)(4y - 3)$ **79.** $\left(2x - \frac{1}{3}\right)\left(2x + \frac{1}{3}\right)$

81. $[(x - 1) - 2][(x - 1) + 2] = (x - 3)(x + 1)$

83. $(x - 2)^2$ **85.** $\left(x + \frac{1}{2}\right)^2$ **87.** $(2t + 1)^2$

89. $\left(3t + \frac{1}{4}\right)^2$ **91.** $(x - 2)(x^2 + 2x + 4)$

93. $(y + 6)(y^2 - 6y + 36)$ **95.** $\left(x - \frac{2}{3}\right)\left(x^2 + \frac{2}{3}x + \frac{4}{9}\right)$

97. $(2x - 1)(4x^2 + 2x + 1)$ **99.** $\left(\frac{1}{2}x + 1\right)\left(\frac{1}{4}x^2 - \frac{1}{2}x + 1\right)$

101. $(x - 1)(x + 2)$ **103.** $(s - 2)(s - 3)$

105. $-(y - 4)(y + 5)$ **107.** $(3x - 2)(x - 1)$

109. $(2x + 1)(x - 1)$ **111.** $(5x + 1)(x + 5)$

113. $-(5u - 2)(u + 3)$ **115.** $(x - 1)(x^2 + 2)$

117. $(3x + 2)(2x - 1)$ **119.** $x(x + 4)(x - 4)$

121. $x^2(x - 1)$ **123.** $(x - 1)^2$ **125.** $(2x - 1)^2$

127. $-2x(x - 2)(x + 1)$ **129.** $(9x + 1)(x + 1)$

131. $\frac{1}{96}(3x + 2)(4x - 3)$ **133.** $(3x + 1)(x^2 + 5)$

135. $(u + 2)(3 - u^2)$ **137.** $-z(z + 10)$

139. $(x + 1)^2(x - 1)^2$ **141.** $2(t - 2)(t^2 + 2t + 4)$

143. $2(2x - 1)(4x - 1)$ **145.** $-(x + 1)(x - 3)(x + 9)$

147. $7(x^2 + 1)(3x^2 - 1)$ **149.** $-2x(x - 5)^3(x + 5)$

151. (a) $500r^2 + 1000r + 500$

(b)

r	$2\frac{1}{2}\%$	3%	4%
$500(1 + r)^2$	525.31	530.45	540.80

r	$4\frac{1}{2}\%$	5%
$500(1 + r)^2$	546.01	551.25

(c) Amount increases with increasing r.

153. $V = x(15 - 2x)\left(\dfrac{45 - 3x}{2}\right)$

$ = \dfrac{3}{2}x(x - 15)(2x - 15)$

x (cm)	3	5	7
V (cu cm)	486	375	84

155. (a) $T(x) = 0.0475x^2 + 1.099x + 0.23$

(b)

x (mi/hr)	30	40	55
T (ft)	75.95	120.19	204.36

(c) Stopping distance increases as speed increases.

157. b   **158.** c   **159.** a   **160.** d

161.

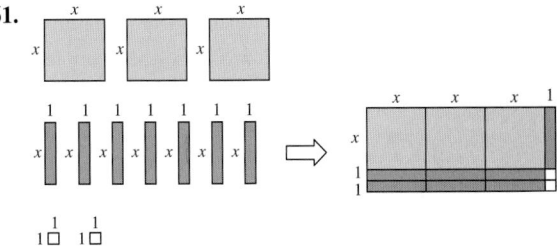

163.

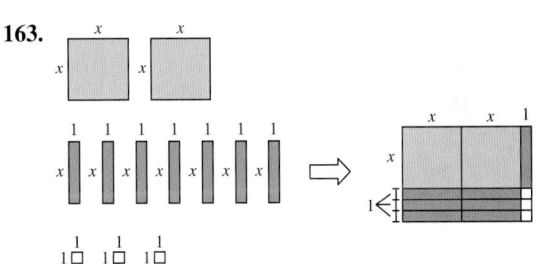

165. $4\pi(r + 1)$ **167.** $4(6 - x)(6 + x)$

169. $-14, 14, -2, 2$ **171.** $-51, 51, -15, 15, -27, 27$

173. $2, -3$ (Answers will vary.)

175. $3, -8$ (Answers will vary.)

177. (a) $V = \pi h(R - r)(R + r)$

(b) $V = 2\pi\left[\left(\dfrac{R + r}{2}\right)(R - r)\right]h$

179. False. $(x^2 - 1)(x^2 + 1)$ becomes a fourth-degree polynomial.

181. False. Counterexample:

$x^2 + 2^2 \neq (x + 2)^2$ if $x = 3$.

183. n

185. A polynomial is in factored form if it is written as a product, not as a sum.

187. $9x^2 - 9x - 54 = 9(x^2 - x - 6)$

$ = 9(x + 2)(x - 3)$

189. No. $(-3x^2 + 2x + 1) + (3x^2 - x - 2)$

$= x - 1$, which is a first-degree polynomial.

Section P.4 (page 44)

1. All real numbers **3.** All nonnegative real numbers

5. All real numbers such that $x \neq 3$

7. All real numbers such that $x \geq -7$

9. $3x$, $x \neq 0$ **11.** $\dfrac{3x}{2}$, $x \neq 0$ **13.** $\dfrac{3y}{y+1}$, $x \neq 0$

15. $-\dfrac{4y}{5}$, $y \neq \dfrac{1}{2}$ **17.** $-\dfrac{1}{2}$, $x \neq 5$

19. $y - 4$, $y \neq -4$ **21.** $\dfrac{x(x+3)}{x-2}$, $x \neq -2$

23. $\dfrac{y-4}{y+6}$, $y \neq 3$ **25.** $-(x^2+1)$, $x \neq 2$ **27.** $z - 2$

29.

x	0	1	2	3	4	5	6
$\dfrac{x^2-2x-3}{x-3}$	1	2	3	Undef.	5	6	7
$x + 1$	1	2	3	4	5	6	7

The expressions are equivalent except at $x = 3$.

31. Only common factors of the numerator and denominator can be canceled. In this case, factors of terms were incorrectly canceled.

33. $\dfrac{\pi}{4}$ **35.** $\dfrac{1}{5(x-2)}$, $x \neq 1$ **37.** $\dfrac{r+1}{r}$, $r \neq 1$

39. $\dfrac{t-3}{(t+3)(t-2)}$, $t \neq -2$ **41.** $\dfrac{3}{2}$, $x \neq -y$

43. $\dfrac{x+5}{x-1}$ **45.** $-\dfrac{2x^2-5x-18}{(2x+1)(x+3)}$ **47.** $-\dfrac{2}{x-2}$

49. $-\dfrac{x^2+3}{(x+1)(x-2)(x-3)}$ **51.** $-\dfrac{x^2-2x+2}{x(x^2+1)}$

53. $\dfrac{1}{2}$, $x \neq 2$ **55.** $x(x+1)$, $x \neq -1, 0$

57. $-\dfrac{2x+h}{x^2(x+h)^2}$, $h \neq 0$ **59.** $\dfrac{2x-1}{2x}$, $x > 0$

61. $x^{-2}(x^7-2) = \dfrac{x^7-2}{x^2}$ **63.** $-\dfrac{1}{(x^2+1)^5}$

65. $\dfrac{2x^3-2x^2-5}{(x-1)^{1/2}}$ **67.** $\dfrac{2x^2-1}{x^{5/2}}$ **69.** $\dfrac{1}{\sqrt{x+2}+\sqrt{x}}$

71. (a) $\dfrac{1}{16}$ minute (b) $\dfrac{x}{16}$ minute(s) (c) $\dfrac{60}{16} = \dfrac{15}{4}$ minutes

73. $\dfrac{x}{2(2x+1)}$

75. (a)

t	0	2	4	6	8	10
T	75	55.9	48.3	45	43.3	42.3

t	12	14	16	18	20	22
T	41.7	41.3	41.1	40.9	40.7	40.6

(b) 40

77. False. The domain of the left-hand side is $x^n \neq 1$.

79. Completely factor the numerator and denominator to determine if they have any common factors.

Section P.5 (page 54)

1. A: $(2, 6)$; B: $(-6, -2)$; C: $(4, -4)$; D: $(-3, 2)$

3.

5.

7. $(-5, 4)$ **9.** $(-6, -6)$ **11.** Quadrant IV

13. Quadrant II **15.** Quadrant III or IV

17. Quadrant III **19.** Quadrants I and III

21.

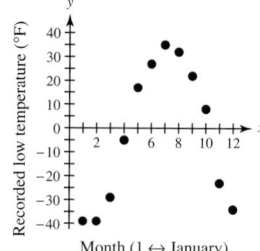

Month (1 ↔ January)

23. 8 **25.** 5 **27.** 13 **29.** $\dfrac{\sqrt{277}}{6}$

31. $\sqrt{71.78}$ **33.** (a) 4, 3, 5 (b) $4^2 + 3^2 = 5^2$

35. (a) 10, 3, $\sqrt{109}$ (b) $10^2 + 3^2 = \left(\sqrt{109}\right)^2$

37. $\left(\sqrt{5}\right)^2 + \left(\sqrt{45}\right)^2 = \left(\sqrt{50}\right)^2$

39. Opposite sides have equal lengths of $2\sqrt{5}$ and $\sqrt{85}$.

41. (a) 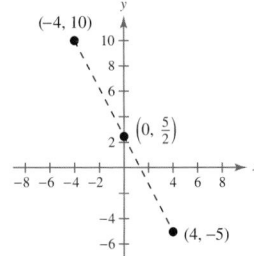 (b) 10

(c) $(5, 4)$

43. (a) 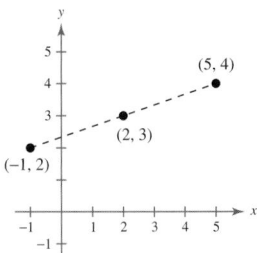 (b) 17

(c) $\left(0, \frac{5}{2}\right)$

45. (a) 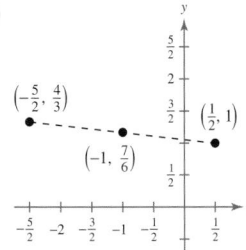 (b) $2\sqrt{10}$

(c) $(2, 3)$

47. (a) 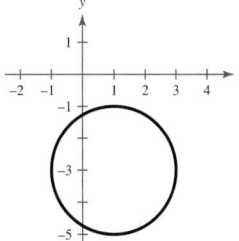 (b) $\dfrac{\sqrt{82}}{3}$

(c) $\left(-1, \dfrac{7}{6}\right)$

49. (a) 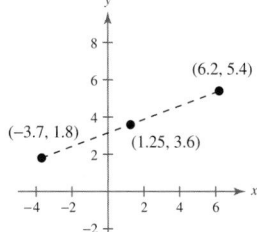 (b) $\sqrt{110.97}$

(c) $(1.25, 3.6)$

51. $1159.8 million

53. $(2x_m - x_1, 2y_m - y_1)$; (a) $(7, 0)$ (b) $(9, -3)$

55. $x^2 + y^2 = 9$ **57.** $(x - 2)^2 + (y + 1)^2 = 16$

59. $(x + 1)^2 + (y - 2)^2 = 5$

61. $(x - 3)^2 + (y - 4)^2 = 25$

63. 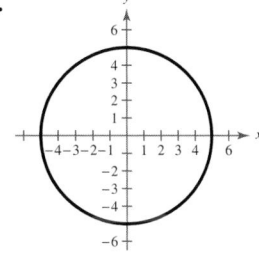 Center: $(0, 0)$

Radius $= 5$

65. Center: $(1, -3)$ **67.** Center: $\left(\frac{1}{2}, \frac{1}{2}\right)$

Radius $= 2$ Radius $= \frac{3}{2}$

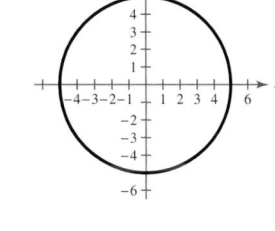

69. $(0, 1), (4, 2), (1, 4)$

71. $(-1, 5), (2, 8), (4, 5), (1, 2)$ **73.** 65

75. (a) Answers will vary. Sample answer: The number of artists elected each year seems to be nearly steady except for the first few years. Estimate: between 6 and 8 new members in 2005.

(b) The Rock and Roll Hall of Fame was opened in 1986.

77. $5\sqrt{74} \approx 43$ yards **79.** False; 15 times

81. False. It could be a rhombus.

83. No. The scales depend on the magnitudes of the quantities measured.

Section P.6 (page 63)

1. (a) $1.709 (b) 0.19

3. 15

5. *Interval* *Tally*

$[800, 1000)$	$\|\|$
$[1000, 1200)$	$\cancel{\|\|\|\|}$ $\cancel{\|\|\|\|}$ $\|\|\|\|$
$[1200, 1400)$	$\cancel{\|\|\|\|}$ $\cancel{\|\|\|\|}$ $\cancel{\|\|\|\|}$ $\|$
$[1400, 1600)$	$\cancel{\|\|\|\|}$ $\cancel{\|\|\|\|}$
$[1600, 1800)$	$\cancel{\|\|\|\|}$ $\|\|$
$[1800, 2000)$	$\|$
$[2000, 2200)$	$\|$

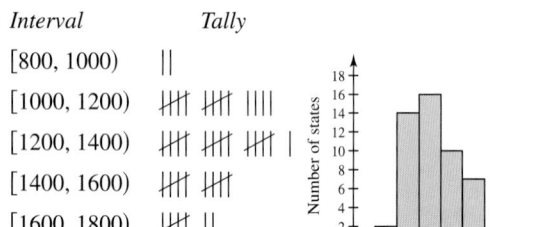

7. 25.2%; 6.5%

9.

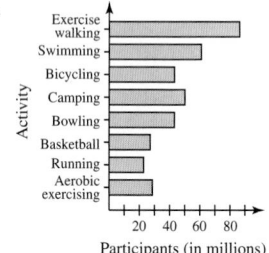

11. $2.14; 2000 **13.** $\approx 73\%$

15.

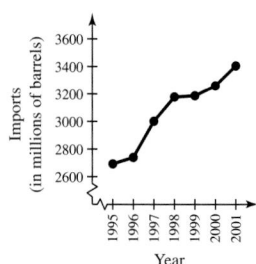

Answers will vary. Sample answer: The graph shows crude oil imports have risen from 1995 to 2001.

17.

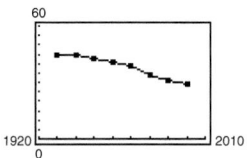

19.

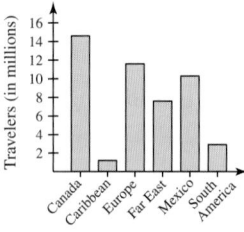

21. A bar graph is similar to a histogram, except that the bars can be either horizontal or vertical and the labels of the bars are not necessarily numbers. Another difference between a bar graph and a histogram is that the bars in a bar graph are usually separated by spaces.

23. Answers will vary.

Review Exercises (page 68)

1. (a) 11 (b) 11 (c) 11, -14

(d) 11, -14, $-\frac{8}{9}$, $\frac{5}{2}$, 0.4 (e) $\sqrt{6}$

3. (a) $0.8\overline{3}$ (b) 0.875

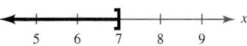

$\frac{5}{6} < \frac{7}{8}$

5. The set consists of all real numbers less than or equal to 7.

7. 122 **9.** $|x - 8| \geq 3$ **11.** $|y + 30| < 5$

13. (a) -13 (b) 27 **15.** (a) -18 (b) -12

17. Associative Property of Addition

19. Commutative Property of Multiplication **21.** $\frac{14}{9}$

23. $\frac{1}{24}$ **25.** $\frac{47x}{60}$ **27.** (a) $-8z^3$ (b) $3a^3b^2$

29. (a) $\frac{3u^5}{v^4}$ (b) m^{-2} **31.** 4.38×10^{10}

33. 483,600,000 **35.** 78 **37.** $2x^2$ **39.** $\frac{3}{4}$

41. $\frac{x}{3}\sqrt[3]{2}$ **43.** $2\sqrt{2}$ **45.** $3\sqrt{3x}$ **47.** $\sqrt{2x}(2x + 1)$

49. 288 square inches. Square, because the width and height are equal.

51. $2 + \sqrt{3}$ **53.** $\frac{5}{2\sqrt{5}}$ **55.** 729 **57.** $6x^{9/10}$

59. $-2x^5 - x^4 + 3x^3 + 15x^2 + 5$; degree: 5; leading coefficient: -2

61. $-3x^2 - 7x + 1$ **63.** $2x^3 - x^2 + 3x - 9$

65. $x^5 - 2x^4 + x^3 - x^2 + 2x - 1$ **67.** $y^6 + y^4 - y^3 - y$

69. $x^2 - 64$ **71.** $x^3 - 12x^2 + 48x - 64$

73. $m^2 - 8m - n^2 + 16$

75. $(x + 3)(x + 5) = 5(x + 3) + x(x + 3)$

Distributive Property

77. $7(x + 5)$ **79.** $x(x^2 - 1) = x(x - 1)(x + 1)$

81. $2x(x^2 + 9x - 2)$

83. (a)

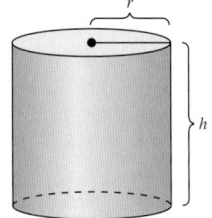

$2\pi r^2 =$ area of top and bottom

$2\pi rh =$ surface area of lateral face

(b) $S = 2\pi r(r + h)$

85. $(x - 13)(x + 13)$ **87.** $(x + 6)(x^2 - 6x + 36)$

89. $(x - 9)(x + 3)$ **91.** $(2x + 1)(x + 10)$

93. $(x - 4)(x^2 - 3)$ **95.** $(x - 3)(2x + 5)$

97. All real numbers   **99.** All real numbers $x \neq \frac{3}{2}$

101. $\dfrac{x}{x^2 + 7}$, $x \neq 0$ **103.** $\dfrac{x - 6}{x - 5}$, $x \neq -5$

105. $\dfrac{1}{x^2}$, $x \neq \pm 2$ **107.** $\dfrac{1}{5}x(5x - 6)$, $x \neq 0$, $-\dfrac{3}{2}$

109. $\dfrac{x^3 - x + 3}{(x - 1)(x + 2)}$ **111.** $\dfrac{x + 1}{x(x^2 + 1)}$

113. $-\dfrac{1}{xy(x + y)}$, $x \neq y$

115.   **117.**

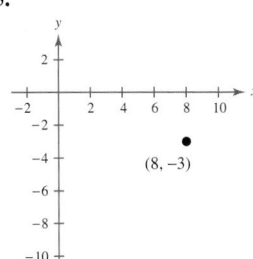   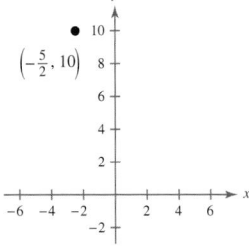

Quadrant IV   Quadrant II

119. Quadrant IV

121.

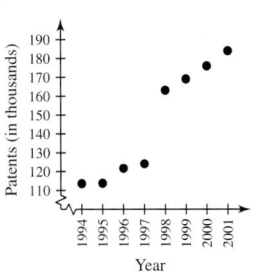

123.

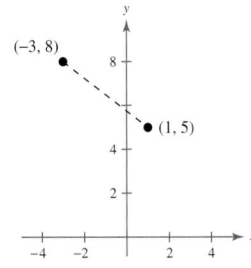

Distance $= 5$

125.

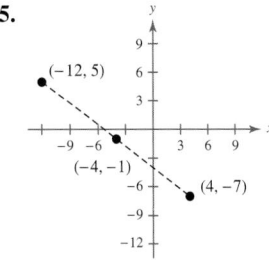

Midpoint: $(-4, -1)$

127. $(x - 3)^2 + (y + 1)^2 = 68$

129. $(2, 5), (4, 5), (2, 0), (4, 0)$

131.

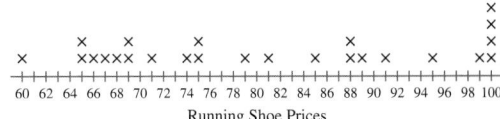

The price with the greatest frequency is \$100.

133.

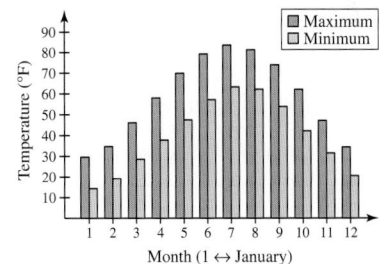

135. False. $\dfrac{x^3 - 1}{x - 1}$ is undefined at $x = 1$.

137. You must raise 2 to the fourth power as well.

$(2x)^4 = 2^4 x^4 = 16x^4$

139. Radicals cannot be combined unless the index and the radicand are the same.

Chapter Test   (page 72)

1. $-\frac{10}{3} > -|-4|$ **2.** 56

3. Additive Identity Property

4. (a) -18 (b) $\frac{4}{27}$ (c) $-\frac{8}{343}$ (d) $\frac{8}{729}$

5. (a) 25 (b) 6 (c) 1.8×10^5 (d) 2.7×10^{13}

6. (a) $12z^8$ (b) $\dfrac{1}{(u-2)^7}$ (c) $\dfrac{3x^2}{y^2}$

7. (a) $15z\sqrt{2z}$ (b) $-10\sqrt{y}$ (c) $\dfrac{2}{v}\sqrt[3]{\dfrac{2}{v^2}}$

8. $-2x^5 - x^4 + 3x^3 + 3$; degree: 5; leading coefficient: -2

9. $2x^2 - 3x - 5$ **10.** $x^2 - 5$ **11.** $8,\ x \neq 3$

12. $\dfrac{x-1}{2x},\ x \neq \pm 1$ **13.** $x^2(2x+1)(x-2)$

14. $(x-2)(x+2)^2$ **15.** $(2x-3)(4x^2+6x+9)$

16. (a) $4\sqrt[3]{4}$ (b) $-3(1+\sqrt{3})$

17. $\frac{5}{6}\sqrt{3}x^2$

18.

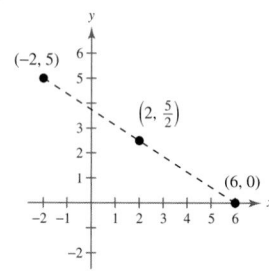

19.

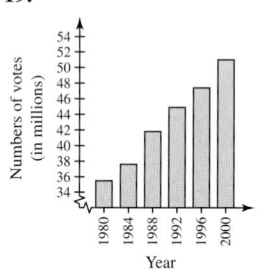

Midpoint: $\left(2, \frac{5}{2}\right)$; Distance: $\sqrt{89}$

Chapter 1

Section 1.1   (page 82)

Vocabulary Check   (page 82)

1. solution point   **2.** graph   **3.** intercepts

---

1. (a) Yes   (b) Yes   **3.** (a) No   (b) Yes

5. (a) No   (b) Yes

7.

x	-1	0	1	$\frac{3}{2}$	2
y	5	3	1	0	-1
Solution point	$(-1, 5)$	$(0, 3)$	$(1, 1)$	$\left(\frac{3}{2}, 0\right)$	$(2, -1)$

9.

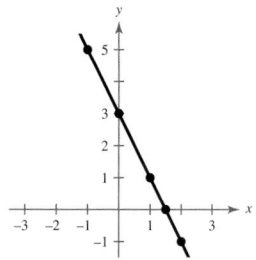

x	-1	0	1	2	3
y	3	0	-1	0	3
Solution point	$(-1, 3)$	$(0, 0)$	$(1, -1)$	$(2, 0)$	$(3, 3)$

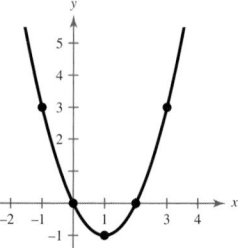

11. (a)

x	-2	-1	0	1	2
y	$-\frac{7}{2}$	$-\frac{13}{4}$	-3	$-\frac{11}{4}$	$-\frac{5}{2}$

(b)

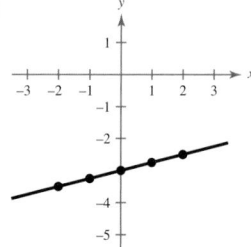

(c)

x	-2	-1	0	1	2
y	$-\frac{5}{2}$	$-\frac{11}{4}$	-3	$-\frac{13}{4}$	$-\frac{7}{2}$

The lines have opposite slopes but the same y-intercept.

13. d   **14.** c   **15.** f   **16.** e   **17.** a   **18.** b

19.
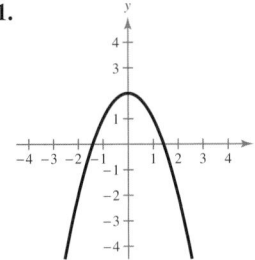

21.

23.
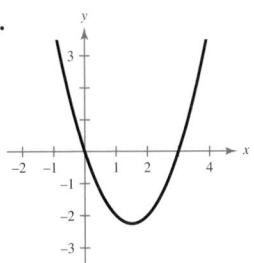

25.
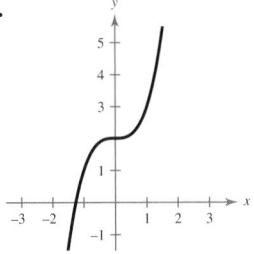

27.
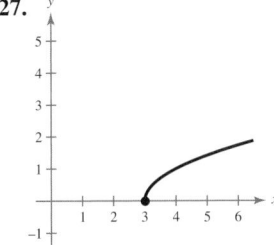

29.
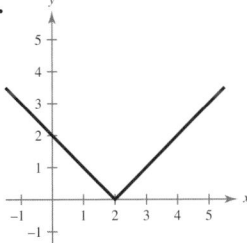

31.
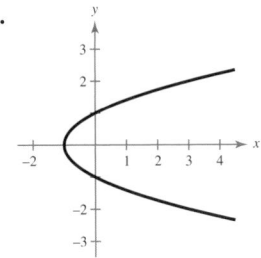

33.
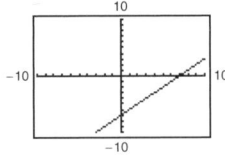

Intercepts: $(7, 0), (0, -7)$

35.
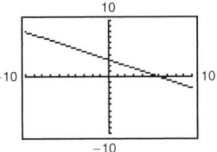

Intercepts: $(6, 0), (0, 3)$

37.
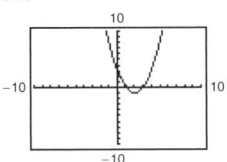
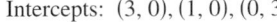

Intercepts: $(3, 0), (1, 0), (0, 3)$

39.
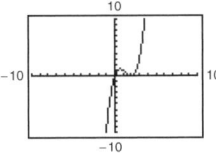

Intercepts: $(0, 0), (2, 0)$

41.
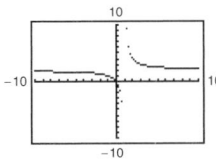

Intercept: $(0, 0)$

43.
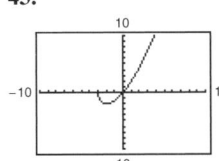

Intercepts: $(-3, 0), (0, 0)$

45.
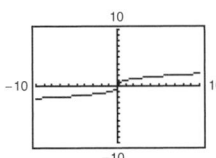

Intercept: $(0, 0)$

47.
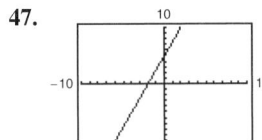

The standard setting gives a more complete graph.

49.
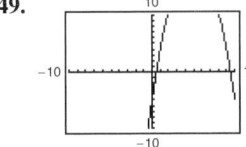

The specified setting gives a more complete graph.

51.

Xmin = -5
Xmax = 5
Xscl = 1
Ymin = -30
Ymax = 10
Yscl = 5

53.

Xmin = -30
Xmax = 30
Xscl = 5
Ymin = -10
Ymax = 50
Yscl = 5

55. $y_1 = \sqrt{64 - x^2}$

$y_2 = -\sqrt{64 - x^2}$

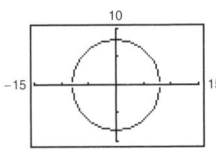

57. $y_1 = 2 + \sqrt{16 - (x - 1)^2}$

$y_2 = 2 - \sqrt{16 - (x - 1)^2}$

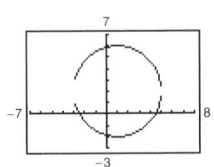

59. The graphs are identical. Distributive Property

61. The graphs are identical. Associative Property of Multiplication

63.

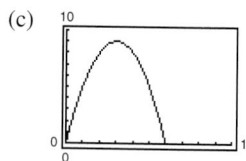

(a) $(2, 1.73)$

(b) $(-4, 3)$

65.

(a) $(-0.5, 2.47)$

(b) $(1, -4), (-1.65, -4)$

67. (a)

Xmin = 0
Xmax = 8
Xscl = 1
Ymin = 60000
Ymax = 230000
Yscl = 10000

(b)

(c) \$109,000   (d) \$178,000

69. (a)

(b) $2w + 2x = 12$

$w + x = 6$

$w = 6 - x$

$A = xw$

$A = x(6 - x)$

(c)

(d) $A \approx 5.4$

(e) $x = 3, w = 3$

71. (a) The life expectancy of a child born in 1930.

(b) 1983   (c) ≈ 65.8 years   (d) ≈ 76.9 years

73. False. A parabola can have no x-intercepts, one x-intercept, or two x-intercepts.

75. Answers will vary.   **77.** $27\sqrt{2}$

79. $7^7 = 823{,}543$ **81.** $2x^2 + 8x + 11$

Section 1.2   (page 94)

1. (a) L_2 (b) L_3 (c) L_1

3.

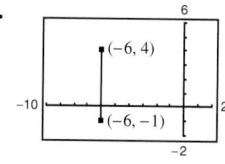

5. $\frac{3}{2}$

7.

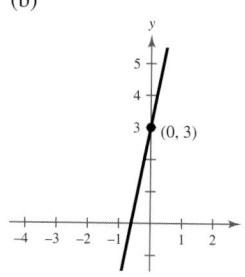

$m = -\frac{5}{2}$

9.

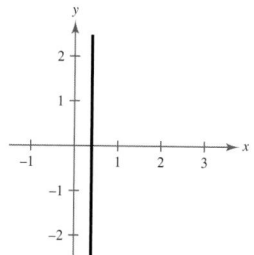

m is undefined.

11. $(0, 1), (3, 1), (-1, 1)$ **13.** $(1, 4), (1, 6), (1, 9)$

15. $(-1, -7), (-2, -5), (-5, 1)$

17. $(3, -4), (5, -3), (9, -1)$

19. (a) $m = 5$; intercept: $(0, 3)$

(b)

21. (a) m is undefined. There is no y-intercept.

(b)

23. (a) $m = 0$; intercept: $\left(0, -\frac{5}{3}\right)$

(b)

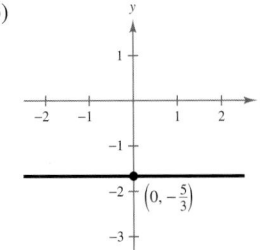

25. $3x - y - 2 = 0$

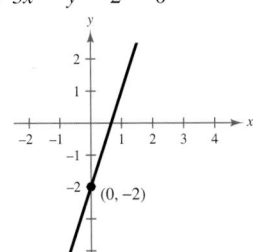

27. $4x - y = 0$

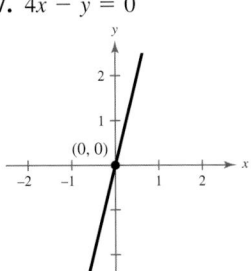

29. $x - 6 = 0$

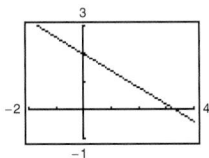

31. $y - \frac{3}{2} = 0$

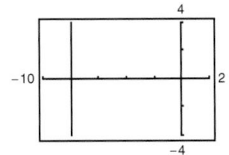

33. $y = -\frac{3}{5}x + 2$

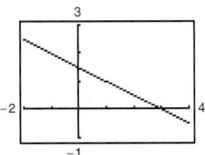

35. $x + 8 = 0$

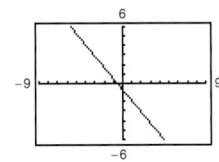

37. $y = -\frac{1}{2}x + \frac{3}{2}$

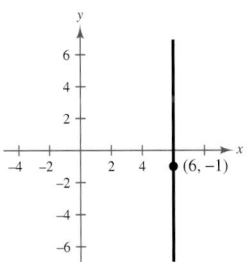

39. $y = -\frac{6}{5}x - \frac{18}{25}$

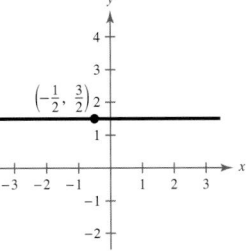

41. $y = \frac{2}{5}x + \frac{1}{5}$

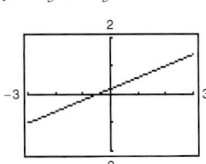

43. \$41,700

45. $\frac{1}{2}$; $(0, -2)$; a line that rises from the left to the right

47. Undefined; none; a vertical line at $x = -6$

49.

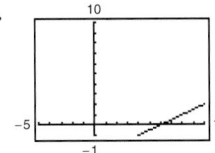 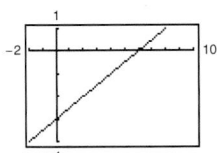

The second setting gives a more complete graph, with a better view of the intercepts.

51. Perpendicular   **53.** Parallel

55. (a) $y = 2x - 3$ (b) $y = -\frac{1}{2}x + 2$

57. (a) $y = -\frac{3}{4}x + \frac{3}{8}$ (b) $y = \frac{4}{3}x + \frac{127}{2}$

59. (a) $x = 3$ (b) $y = -2$

61.

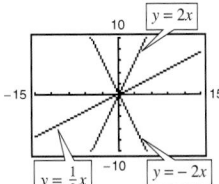

$y = \frac{1}{2}x$ and $y = -2x$ are perpendicular.

63.

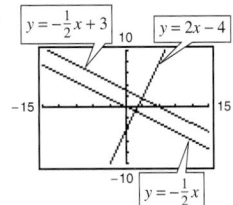

$y = -\frac{1}{2}x$ and $y = -\frac{1}{2}x + 3$ are parallel. Both are perpendicular to $y = 2x - 4$.

65. (a) Sales increase of \$135

(b) No sales increase

(c) Sales decrease of \$40

67. (a) Increase: 1998–1999; Decrease: 2001–2002

(b) $y = -0.05x + 0.68$

(c) There is a decrease of \$0.05 per year.

(d) Using the equation from part (b),
$y = -0.05(16) + 0.68 = -0.12$.

Answers will vary.

69. 12 feet   **71.** $V = 125t + 2040$

73. $V = -2000t + 28,400$

75. b; slope $= -10$; the amount owed decreases by \$10 per week.

76. c; slope $= 1.50$; the hourly wage increases by 1.50 per unit produced.

77. a; slope = 0.35; expenses increase by \$0.35 per mile.

78. d; slope = −100; the value depreciates \$100 per year.

79. $F = \frac{9}{5}C + 32$

81. (a) $V = -175t + 875$

(b)

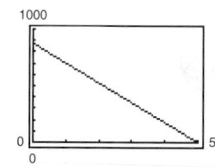

t	0	1	2	3	4	5
V	875	700	525	350	175	0

83. (a) $C = 16.75t + 36,500$ (b) $R = 27t$

(c) $P = 10.25t - 36,500$ (d) $t \approx 3561$ hours

85. (a) Increase of ≈ 639 students per year

(b) 71,531; 79,838; 81,755

(c) $y = 639t + 75,365$; $m = 639$; the slope determines the average increase in enrollment.

87. False. The slopes $\left(\frac{2}{7}\text{ and } -\frac{11}{7}\right)$ are not equal.

89.

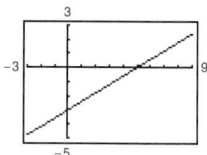

x- and y-intercepts

91. $3x + 2y - 6 = 0$ **93.** $12x + 3y + 2 = 0$

95. The line with slope -3 is steeper than the line with slope $\frac{5}{2}$.

97. Use the slope formula to show that $\overline{AB}$ is perpendicular to $\overline{AC}$.

99. Yes. $x + 20$ **101.** No **103.** No

105. $(x - 9)(x + 3)$ **107.** $(2x - 5)(x + 8)$

Section 1.3 (page 107)

1. Yes; each element of the domain is assigned to exactly one element of the range.

3. No; the National League, an element in the domain, is assigned to three items in the range, the Cubs, the Pirates, and the Dodgers; the American League, an element in the domain, is also assigned to three items in the range, the Orioles, the Yankees, and the Twins.

5. Yes. Each input value is matched with one output value.

7. No. The same input value is matched with two different output values.

9. (a) Function

(b) Not a function because the element 1 in A corresponds to two elements, -2 and 1, in B.

(c) Function (d) Not a function because the element 2 in A corresponds to no element in B.

11. Each is a function. To each year there corresponds one and only one circulation.

13. Not a function **15.** Function **17.** Function

19. Not a function **21.** Function **23.** Not a function

25. (a) $\frac{1}{5}$ (b) 1 (c) $\frac{1}{4t + 1}$ (d) $\frac{1}{x + c + 1}$

27. (a) -1 (b) -9 (c) $2x - 5$

29. (a) 0 (b) -0.75 (c) $x^2 + 2x$

31. (a) 1 (b) 2.5 (c) $3 - 2|x|$

33. (a) $-\frac{1}{9}$ (b) Undefined (c) $\frac{1}{y^2 + 6y}$

35. (a) 1 (b) -1 (c) $1, x \neq 0$

37. (a) -1 (b) 2 (c) 6

39.

t	-5	-4	-3	-2	-1
$h(t)$	1	$\frac{1}{2}$	0	$\frac{1}{2}$	1

41.

x	-2	-1	0	1	2
$f(x)$	5	$\frac{9}{2}$	4	1	0

43. 5 **45.** $\frac{4}{3}$ **47.** $2, -1$ **49.** All real numbers x

51. All real numbers t except $t = 0$ **53.** All real numbers x

55. All real numbers x except $x = 0, -2$

57. All real numbers y such that $y > 10$

59.

Domain: $[-2, 2]$; range: $[0, 2]$

61.

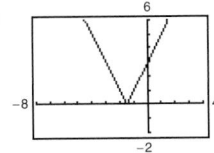

Domain: $(-\infty, \infty)$; range: $[0, \infty)$

63. $\{(-2, 4), (-1, 1), (0, 0), (1, 1), (2, 4)\}$

65. $\{(-2, 4), (-1, 3), (0, 2), (1, 3), (2, 4)\}$

67. $A = \dfrac{C^2}{4\pi}$

69. (a) \$3375

(b)

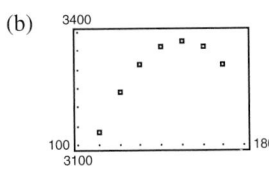

Yes, it is a function.

(c) $P(x) = \begin{cases} 30x, & x \le 100 \\ 45x - 0.15x^2, & x > 100 \end{cases}$

71. $A = \dfrac{x^2}{2(x - 2)}, \ x > 2$

73. (a) $V = x^2 y$ (b) $0 < x < 27$

$= x^2(108 - 4x)$

$= 108x^2 - 4x^3$

(c)

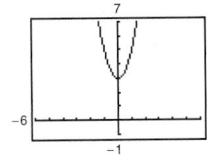

(d) $x = 18$ in., $y = 36$ in.

75. $7 \le x \le 12, 1 \le x \le 6$; Answers will vary.

77. 4.63; \$4630 in monthly revenue in November.

79.

t	0	1	2	3	4	5
$n(t)$	575	650.3	707.2	745.7	765.8	791

t	6	7	8	9	10
$n(t)$	817.8	844.6	871.4	898.2	925

81. (a)

y	5	10	20
$F(y)$	26,474	149,760	847,170

y	30	40
$F(y)$	2,334,527	4,792,320

Each time the depth is doubled, the force increases by more than 2 times.

(b)

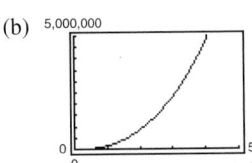

Xmin = 0
Xmax = 50
Xscl = 10
Ymin = 0
Ymax = 5,000,000
Yscl = 500,000

(c) Depth ≈ 21.37 feet

Use the *trace* and *zoom* features on a graphing utility.

83. $2, c \ne 0$ **85.** $3 + h, h \ne 0$ **87.** $-\dfrac{1}{t}, t \ne 1$

89. False. The range is $[-1, \infty)$. **91.** $r(x) = \dfrac{32}{x}; c = 32$

93. The domain is the set of input values of a function. The range is the set of output values.

95. $\dfrac{12x + 20}{x + 2}$ **97.** $\dfrac{(x + 6)(x + 10)}{5(x + 3)}, x \ne 0, \dfrac{1}{2}$

Section 1.4   (page 121)

Vocabulary Check   (page 121)

1. ordered pairs   **2.** Vertical Line Test

3. decreasing   **4.** minimum

5. greatest integer   **6.** even

1. Domain: $(-\infty, \infty)$; range: $(-\infty, 1]$; 1

3. Domain: $[-4, 4]$; range: $[0, 4]$; 4

5.

Domain: $(-\infty, \infty)$

Range: $[3, \infty)$

7. 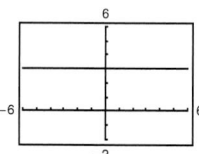 Domain: $[1, \infty)$
Range: $[0, \infty)$

9. Domain: $(-\infty, \infty)$
Range: $[0, \infty)$

11. Function. Graph the given function over the window shown in the figure.

13. Not a function. Solve for y and graph the two resulting functions.

15. Function. Solve for y and graph the resulting function.

17. Increasing on $(-\infty, \infty)$

19. Increasing on $(-\infty, 0)$, $(2, \infty)$
Decreasing on $(0, 2)$

21. (a)

(b) Constant: $(-\infty, \infty)$

23. (a)

(b) Decreasing on $(-\infty, 0)$
Increasing on $(0, \infty)$

25. (a)

(b) Increasing on $(-2, \infty)$
Decreasing on $(-3, -2)$

27. (a)

(b) Decreasing on $(-\infty, -1)$
Constant on $(-1, 1)$;
Increasing on $(1, \infty)$

29.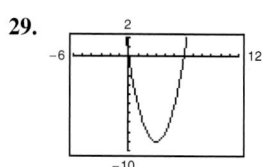

Relative minimum: $(3, -9)$

31. Relative minimum: $(1, -7)$
Relative maximum: $(-2, 20)$

33. Minimum: $(0.33, -0.38)$

35. (a) Answers will vary.
(b) Relative minimum at $(2, -9)$
(c) Answers will vary.

37. (a) Answers will vary.
(b) Relative minimum at $(1.63, -8.71)$
Relative maximum at $(-1.63, 8.71)$
(c) Answers will vary.

39. (a) Answers will vary.   (b) Relative minimum at $(4, 0)$
(c) Answers will vary.

41.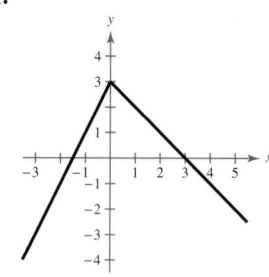

43.

45.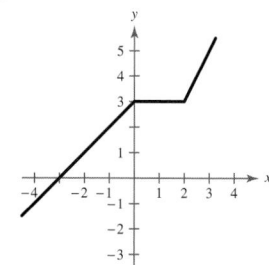

47.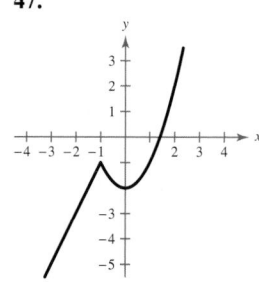

49. Neither even nor odd   **51.** Odd function

53. Odd function   **55.** Even function

57. (a) $\left(\frac{3}{2}, 4\right)$ (b) $\left(\frac{3}{2}, -4\right)$

59. (a) $(-4, 9)$ (b) $(-4, -9)$

61. (a) $(-x, -y)$ (b) $(-x, y)$

63. Even function

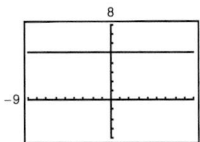

65. Neither even nor odd

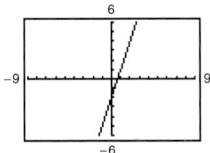

67. Even function

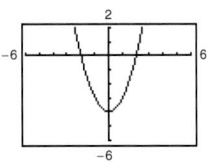

69. Neither even nor odd

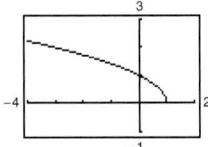

71. Neither even nor odd

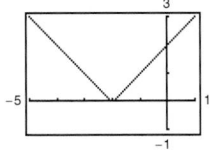

73. $(-\infty, 4]$ **75.** $(-\infty, -3], [3, \infty)$

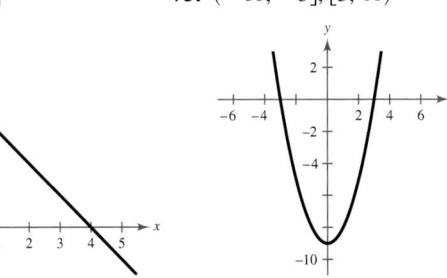

77.

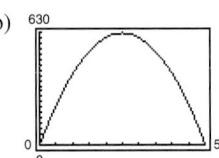

Domain: $(-\infty, \infty)$

Range: $[0, 2)$

Sawtooth pattern

79. (a) Answers will vary.

(b)

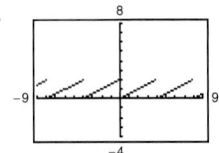

(c) 625 square meters; 25×25 meters

81. (a) C_2 is the appropriate model. The cost of the first minute is \$1.05 and the cost increases \$0.38 when the next minute begins, and so on.

(b)

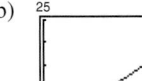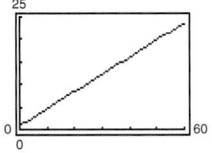

\$7.89

83. $h = -x^2 + 4x - 3,\ 1 \le x \le 3$

85. $L = \frac{1}{2}y^2,\ 0 \le y \le 4$

87. (a)

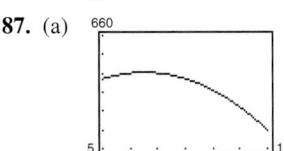

(b) Increasing from 1995 to 1996; decreasing from 1996 to 2001

(c) $\approx 650{,}200$

89. False. Counterexample: $f(x) = \sqrt{1 + x^2}$

91. If $y = a_{2n+1}x^{2n+1} + a_{2n-1}x^{2n-1} + \cdots + a_3x^3 + a_1x$, each exponent is odd. Then

$$f(-x) = -a_{2n+1}x^{2n+1} - a_{2n-1}x^{2n-1} - \cdots - a_3x^3 - a_1x,$$

which is equal to $-f(x)$. Therefore, by definition, the original function is odd.

93. (a) Even. g is a reflection in the x-axis.

(b) Even. g is a reflection in the y-axis.

(c) Even. g is a vertical shift downward.

(d) Neither even nor odd. g is shifted to the right and reflected in the x-axis.

95. No. x is not a function of y because horizontal lines can be drawn to intersect the graph twice. Therefore, each y-value corresponds to two distinct x-values when $-5 < y < 5$.

97. Terms: $-2x^2, 8x$; coefficients: $-2, 8$

99. Terms: $\dfrac{x}{3}, -5x^2, x^3$; coefficients: $\dfrac{1}{3}, -5, 1$

101. (a) $d = 4\sqrt{5}$ (b) Midpoint: $(2, 5)$

103. (a) $d = \sqrt{41}$ (b) Midpoint: $\left(\frac{1}{2}, \frac{3}{2}\right)$

105. (a) 29   (b) -6 (c) $5x - 16$

107. (a) 0   (b) 36   (c) $6\sqrt{3}$ **109.** $h + 4,\ h \ne 0$

Section 1.5   (page 131)

Vocabulary Check   (page 131)

1. quadratic function   **2.** absolute value function

3. rigid transformations   **4.** $-f(x), f(-x)$

5. $c > 1, 0 < c < 1$

6. (a) ii   (b) iv   (c) iii   (d) i

1.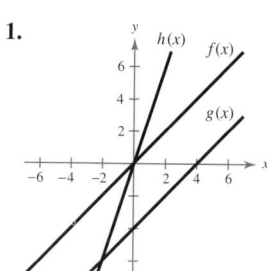

3.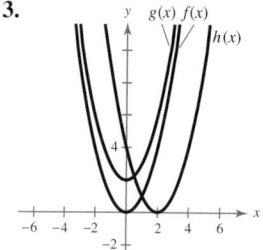

5.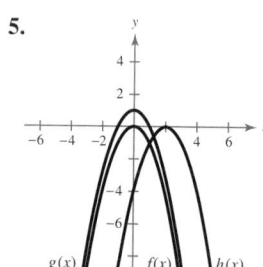

7.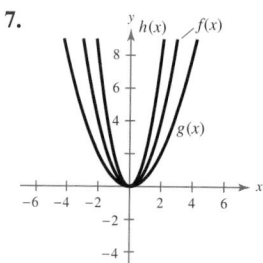

9.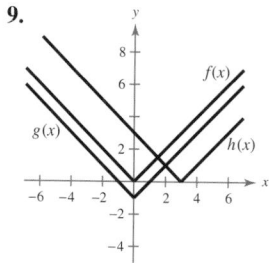

11.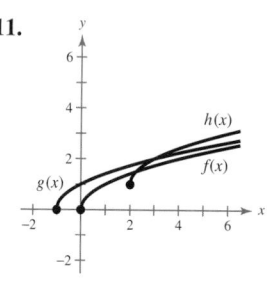

13. (a)   (b)

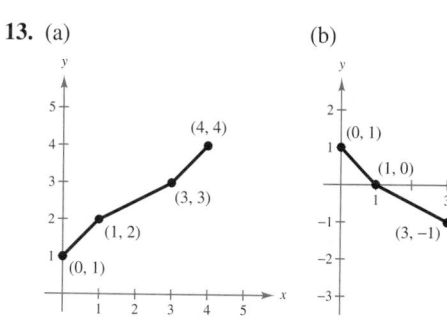

(c)   (d)

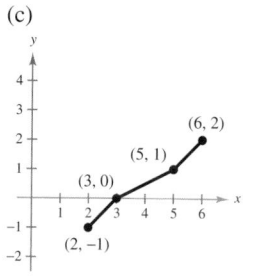
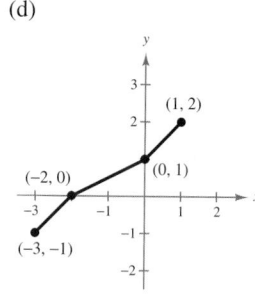

(e)   (f)

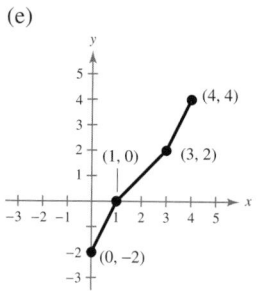
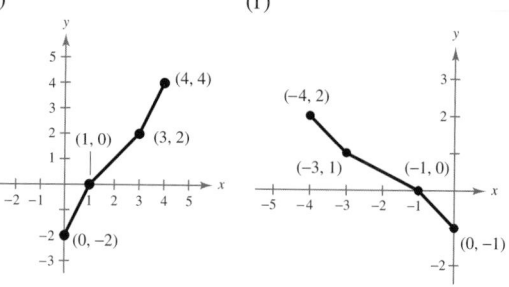

(g)

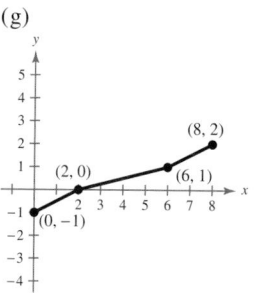

15. Vertical shrink of $y = x$

$y = \frac{1}{2}x$

17. Constant function

$y = 7$

19. Reflection in the x-axis and a vertical shift of $y = \sqrt{x}$

$y = 1 - \sqrt{x}$

21. Horizontal shift of $y = |x|$

$y = |x + 2|$

23. Vertical shift of $y = x^2$

$y = x^2 - 1$

25. Reflection in the x-axis of $y = x^3$, followed by a vertical shift

$y = 1 - x^3$

27. Reflection in the x-axis and vertical shift one unit downward

29. Horizontal shift two units to the right

31. Horizontal shrink

33. Horizontal shift five units to the left

35. Reflection in the x-axis   **37.** Vertical stretch

39. Reflection in the x-axis and vertical shift four units upward

41. Horizontal shift two units to the left and vertical shrink

43. Horizontal stretch and vertical shift two units upward

45.

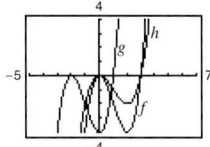

g is a horizontal shift and h is a vertical shrink.

47.

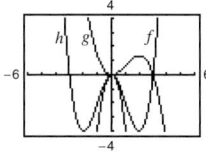

g is a vertical shrink and a reflection in the x-axis and h is a reflection in the y-axis.

49. $g(x) = -(x^3 - 3x^2) + 1$

51. (a) $f(x) = x^2$

(b) Horizontal shift five units to the left, reflection in the x-axis, and vertical shift two units upward

(c)

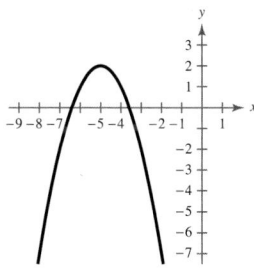

(d) $g(x) = 2 - f(x + 5)$

53. (a) $f(x) = x^2$

(b) Horizontal shift four units to the right, vertical stretch, and vertical shift three units upward

(c)

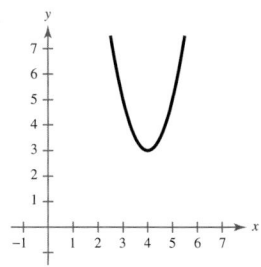

(d) $g(x) = 3 + 2f(x - 4)$

55. (a) $f(x) = x^3$

(b) Horizontal shift two units to the right and vertical stretch

(c)

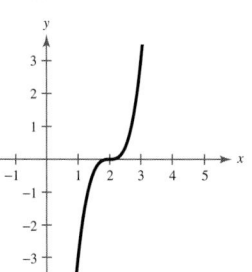

(d) $g(x) = 3f(x - 2)$

57. (a) $f(x) = x^3$

(b) Horizontal shift one unit to the right and vertical shift two units upward

(c)

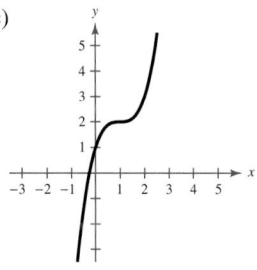

(d) $g(x) = f(x - 1) + 2$

59. (a) $f(x) = |x|$

(b) Horizontal shift four units to the left and vertical shift eight units upward

(c)

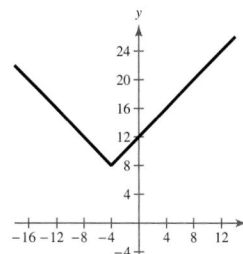

(d) $g(x) = f(x + 4) + 8$

61. (a) $f(x) = |x|$

(b) Horizontal shift one unit to the right, reflection in the x-axis, vertical stretch, and vertical shift four units downward

(c)

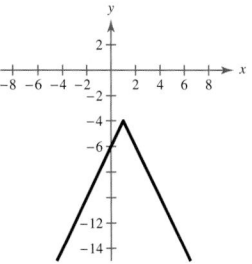

(d) $g(x) = -2f(x - 1) - 4$

63. (a) $f(x) = \sqrt{x}$

   (b) Horizontal shift three units to the left, reflection in the *x*-axis, vertical shrink, and vertical shift one unit downward

   (c)

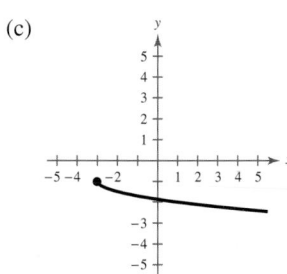

   (d) $g(x) = -\frac{1}{2}f(x + 3) - 1$

65. (a)

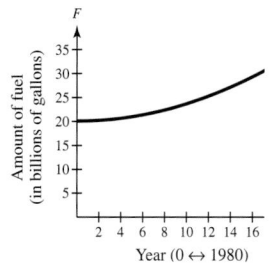

   (b) $P(x) = 55 + 20x - 0.5x^2$; vertical shift

   (c) $P(x) = 80 + \dfrac{1}{5}x - \dfrac{x^2}{20,000}$; horizontal stretch

67. (a) Vertical shrink and vertical shift

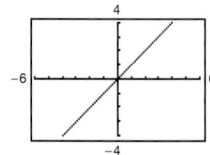

   (b) $G(t) = 0.036t^2 + 0.72t + 23.7$, $-10 \leq t \leq 10$

69. True. The absolute value function is an even function.

71. (a)   (b)

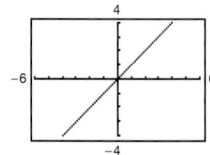

   (c)   (d)

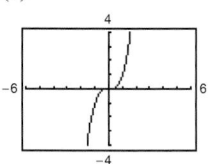
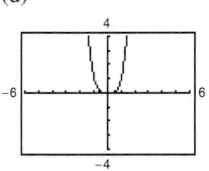

(e)   (f)

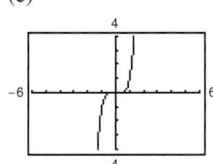
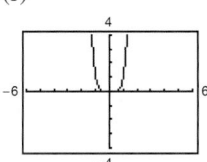

All the graphs pass through the origin. The graphs of the odd powers of *x* are symmetric with respect to the origin and the graphs of the even powers are symmetric with respect to the *y*-axis. As the powers increase, the graphs become flatter in the interval $-1 < x < 1$.

73. Neither   **75.** All real numbers *x* except $x = 9$

77. All real numbers *x* such that $-10 \leq x \leq 10$

Section 1.6   (page 141)

Vocabulary Check   (page 141)

1. addition, subtraction, multiplication, division

2. composition   **3.** $g(x)$ **4.** inner, outer

---

1.   **3.**

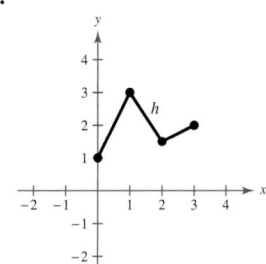
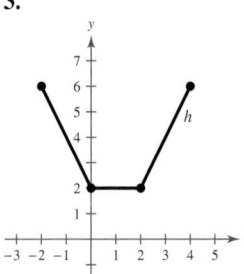

5. (a) $2x$ (b) 6   (c) $x^2 - 9$ (d) $\dfrac{x + 3}{x - 3}, x \neq 3$

7. (a) $x^2 - x + 1$ (b) $x^2 + x - 1$ (c) $x^2 - x^3$

   (d) $\dfrac{x^2}{1 - x}, x \neq 1$

9. (a) $x^2 + 5 + \sqrt{1 - x}$ (b) $x^2 + 5 - \sqrt{1 - x}$

   (c) $(x^2 + 5)\sqrt{1 - x}$ (d) $\dfrac{x^2 + 5}{\sqrt{1 - x}}, x < 1$

11. (a) $\dfrac{x + 1}{x^2}$ (b) $\dfrac{x - 1}{x^2}$ (c) $\dfrac{1}{x^3}$ (d) $x, x \neq 0$

13. 9   **15.** 5   **17.** 0   **19.** $-\frac{26}{9}$ **21.** $4t^2 - 2t + 5$

23. $-125t^3 - 100t^2 - 5t - 4$ **25.** $\dfrac{t^2 + 1}{-t - 4} = -\dfrac{t^2 + 1}{t + 4}$

27. 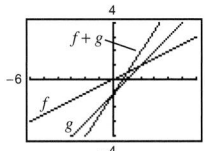 **29.**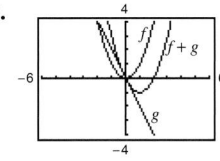

31. 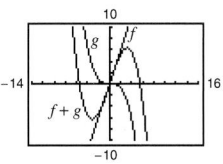 $f(x), 0 \leq x \leq 2;$

$g(x), x > 6$

33. 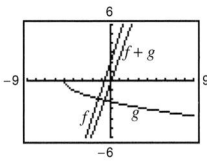 $f(x), 0 \leq x \leq 2;$

$f(x), x > 6$

35. (a) $(x - 1)^2$ (b) $x^2 - 1$ (c) 1

37. (a) $20 - 3x$ (b) $-3x$ (c) 20

39. (a) $(f \circ g)(x) = \sqrt{x^2 + 4}$

$(g \circ f)(x) = x + 4, \ x \geq -4;$

Domain: all real numbers

(b) 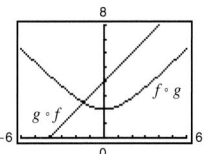   Not equal

41. (a) $(f \circ g)(x) = x - \frac{8}{3}; (g \circ f)(x) = x - 8;$

Domain: all real numbers

(b) 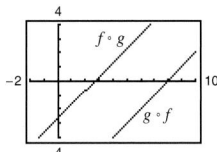   Not equal

43. (a) $(f \circ g)(x) = x^4; (g \circ f)(x) = x^4;$

Domain: all real numbers

(b) 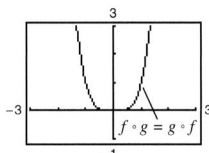   Equal

45. (a) $(f \circ g)(x) = 24 - 5x; (g \circ f)(x) = -5x$

(b) $24 - 5x \neq -5x$

(c)

x	0	1	2	3
$g(x)$	4	3	2	1
$(f \circ g)(x)$	24	19	14	9

x	0	1	2	3
$f(x)$	4	9	14	19
$(g \circ f)(x)$	0	-5	-10	-15

47. (a) $(f \circ g)(x) = \sqrt{x^2 + 1}; (g \circ f)(x) = x + 1, \ x \geq -6$

(b) $x + 1 \neq \sqrt{x^2 + 1}$

(c)

x	0	1	2	3
$g(x)$	-5	-4	-1	4
$(f \circ g)(x)$	1	$\sqrt{2}$	$\sqrt{5}$	$\sqrt{10}$

x	0	1	2	3
$f(x)$	$\sqrt{6}$	$\sqrt{7}$	$\sqrt{8}$	3
$(g \circ f)(x)$	1	2	3	4

49. (a) $(f \circ g)(x) = |2x + 2|; (g \circ f)(x) = 2|x + 3| - 1$

(b) $(f \circ g)(x) = \begin{cases} 2x + 2, & x \geq -1 \\ -2x - 2, & x < -1 \end{cases}$

$(g \circ f)(x) = \begin{cases} 2x + 5, & x \geq -3 \\ -2x - 7, & x < -3 \end{cases}$

$(f \circ g)(x) \neq (g \circ f)(x)$

(c)

x	0	-1	-3	-5
$g(x)$	-1	-3	-7	-11
$(f \circ g)(x)$	2	0	4	8

x	0	-1	-3	-5
$f(x)$	3	2	0	2
$(g \circ f)(x)$	5	3	-1	3

51. (a) 3   (b) 0   **53.** (a) 0   (b) 4

55. $f(x) = x^2, g(x) = 2x + 1$

57. $f(x) = \sqrt[3]{x}, \ g(x) = x^2 - 4$

59. $f(x) = \dfrac{1}{x}, \ g(x) = x + 2$

61. $f(x) = x^2 + 2x, \ g(x) = x + 4$

63. (a) All real numbers x such that $x \geq -4$

(b) All real numbers

(c) All real numbers

65. (a) All real numbers

(b) All real numbers x such that $x \geq 0$

(c) All real numbers x such that $x \geq 0$

67. (a) All real numbers x except $x = 0$

(b) All real numbers

(c) All real numbers x except $x = -3$

69. (a) All real numbers   (b) All real numbers

(c) All real numbers

71. (a) All real numbers

(b) All real numbers x except $x = \pm 2$

(c) All real numbers x except $x = \pm 2$

73. (a) $T = \frac{3}{4}x + \frac{1}{15}x^2$

(b)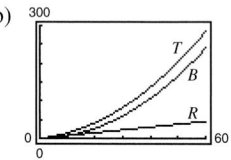

(c) B. For example, $B(60) = 240$, whereas $R(60)$ is only 45.

75.

Year	1994	1995	1996	1997
y_1	138.7	147.7	156.6	165.5
y_2	314.9	326.7	342.2	361.4
y_3	40.3	45.0	49.0	52.3

Year	1998	1999	2000
y_1	174.4	183.4	192.3
y_2	384.5	411.3	441.9
y_3	54.9	56.7	57.8

77. $(A \circ r)(t) = 0.36\pi t^2$

$(A \circ r)(t)$ represents the area of the circle at time t.

79. (a) $(C \circ x)(t) = 3000t + 750$

$(C \circ x)(t)$ represents the cost after t production hours.

(b) 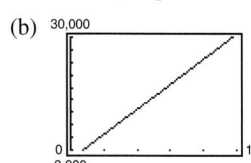   4.75 hours

81. $g(f(x))$ represents three percent of an amount over \$500,000.

83. False. $(f \circ g)(x) = 6x + 1 \neq 6x + 6 = (g \circ f)(x)$

85. To prove that the product of two odd functions f and g is an even function, show that $(fg)(-x) = (fg)(x)$.

$$(fg)(-x) = f(-x)g(-x)$$
$$= [-f(x)][-g(x)] = f(x)g(x) = (fg)(x)$$

To prove that the product of two even functions f and g is an even function, show that $(fg)(-x) = (fg)(x)$.

$$(fg)(-x) = f(-x)g(-x) = f(x)g(x) = (fg)(x)$$

87. Prove $g(-x) = g(x)$.

$g(-x) = \frac{1}{2}[f(-x) + f(x)] = \frac{1}{2}[f(x) + f(-x)] = g(x)$

Prove $h(-x) = -h(x)$.

$h(-x) = \frac{1}{2}[f(-x) - f(x)] = -\frac{1}{2}[f(x) - f(-x)]$
$$= -h(x)$$

89. $(0, -5), (1, -5), (2, -7)$ (Answers will vary.)

91. $\left(0, 2\sqrt{6}\right), \left(1, \sqrt{23}\right), \left(2, 2\sqrt{5}\right)$ (Answers will vary.)

93. $10x - y + 38 = 0$ **95.** $30x + 11y - 34 = 0$

97.   **99.**

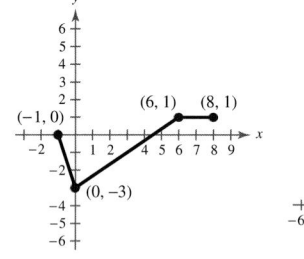   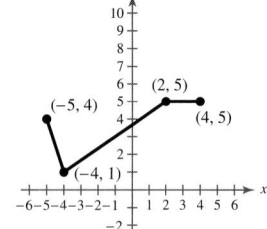

101.

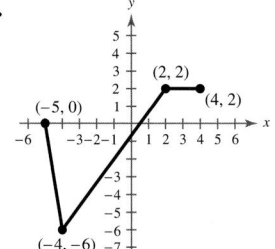

Section 1.7   (page 152)

Vocabulary Check   (page 152)

1. inverse, f^{-1} **2.** range, domain   **3.** $y = x$

4. one-to-one   **5.** Horizontal

---

1. $f^{-1}(x) = \dfrac{x}{6}$ **3.** $f^{-1}(x) = x - 7$

5. $f^{-1}(x) = \frac{1}{2}(x-1)$ **7.** $f^{-1}(x) = x^3$

9. (a) $f(g(x)) = f\left(-\dfrac{2x+6}{7}\right)$

$$= -\dfrac{7}{2}\left(-\dfrac{2x+6}{7}\right) - 3 = x$$

$$g(f(x)) = g\left(-\dfrac{7}{2}x - 3\right)$$

$$= -\dfrac{2\left(-\frac{7}{2}x - 3\right) + 6}{7} = x$$

(b)

x	0	2	-2	6
$f(x)$	-3	-10	4	-24

x	-3	-10	4	-24
$g(x)$	0	2	-2	6

11. (a) $f(g(x)) = f\left(\sqrt[3]{x-5}\right) = \left(\sqrt[3]{x-5}\right)^3 + 5 = x$

$g(f(x)) = g(x^3 + 5) = \sqrt[3]{(x^3 + 5) - 5} = x$

(b)

x	0	1	-1	-2	4
$f(x)$	5	6	4	-3	69

x	5	6	4	-3	69
$g(x)$	0	1	-1	-2	4

13. (a) $f(g(x)) = f(8 + x^2)$

$$= -\sqrt{(8 + x^2) - 8}$$

$$= -\sqrt{x^2} = -(-x) = x, \ x \le 0$$

$$g(f(x)) = g\left(-\sqrt{x-8}\right)$$

$$= 8 + \left(-\sqrt{x-8}\right)^2$$

$$= 8 + (x - 8) = x, \ x \ge 8$$

(b)

x	8	9	12	15
$f(x)$	0	-1	-2	$-\sqrt{7}$

x	0	-1	-2	$-\sqrt{7}$
$g(x)$	8	9	12	15

15. $f(g(x)) = f\left(\sqrt[3]{x}\right) = \left(\sqrt[3]{x}\right)^3 = x$

$g(f(x)) = g(x^3) = \sqrt[3]{x^3} = x$

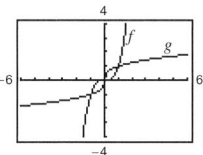

Reflections in the line $y = x$

17. $f(g(x)) = f(x^2 + 4), \ x \ge 0$

$$= \sqrt{(x^2 + 4) - 4} = x$$

$$g(f(x)) = g\left(\sqrt{x-4}\right)$$

$$= \left(\sqrt{x-4}\right)^2 + 4 = x$$

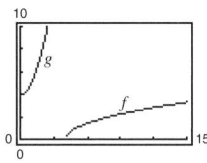

Reflections in the line $y = x$

19. $f(g(x)) = f\left(\sqrt[3]{1-x}\right) = 1 - \left(\sqrt[3]{1-x}\right)^3 = x$

$g(f(x)) = g(1 - x^3) = \sqrt[3]{1 - (1 - x^3)} = x$

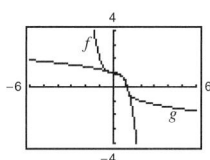

Reflections in the line $y = x$

21. c   **22.** b   **23.** a   **24.** d

25. (a)

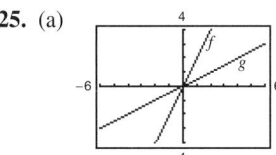

(b)

x	-4	-2	0	2	4
$f(x)$	-8	-4	0	4	8

x	-8	-4	0	4	8
$g(x)$	-4	-2	0	2	4

27. (a)

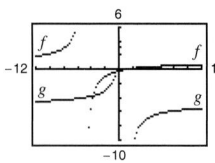

(b)

x	-3	-2	-1	0	2	3	4
$f(x)$	-2	-1	$-\frac{1}{2}$	$-\frac{1}{5}$	$\frac{1}{7}$	$\frac{1}{4}$	$\frac{1}{3}$

x	-2	-1	$-\frac{1}{2}$	$-\frac{1}{5}$	$\frac{1}{7}$	$\frac{1}{4}$	$\frac{1}{3}$
$g(x)$	-3	-2	-1	0	2	3	4

29.

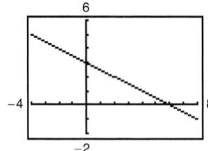

One-to-one

31.

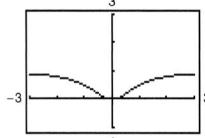

Not one-to-one

33.

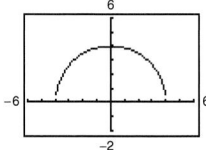

Not one-to-one

35.

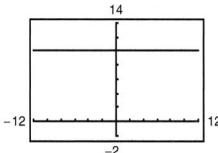

Not one-to-one

37.

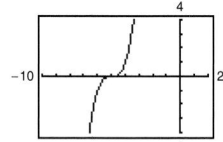

One-to-one

39.

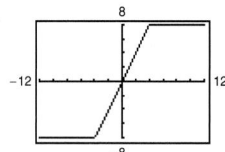

Not one-to-one

41. Not one-to-one   **43.** $f^{-1}(x) = \dfrac{5x - 4}{3}$

45. Not one-to-one   **47.** $f^{-1}(x) = \sqrt{x} - 3,\, x \geq 0$

49. $f^{-1}(x) = \dfrac{x^2 - 3}{2},\, x \geq 0$ **51.** $f^{-1}(x) = 2 - x,\, x \geq 0$

53. $f^{-1}(x) = \dfrac{x + 3}{2}$

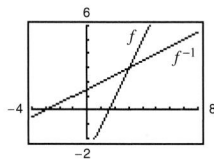

Reflections in the line $y = x$

55. $f^{-1}(x) = \sqrt[5]{x}$

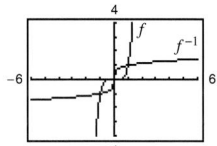

Reflections in the line $y = x$

57. $f^{-1}(x) = x^{5/3}$

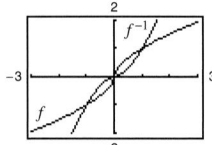

Reflections in the line $y = x$

59. $f^{-1}(x) = \sqrt{4 - x^2},\, 0 \leq x \leq 2$

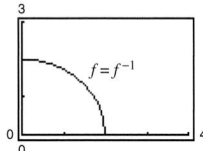

The graphs are the same.

61. $f^{-1}(x) = \dfrac{4}{x}$

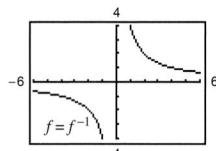

The graphs are the same.

63. $y = \sqrt{x} + 2,\, x \geq 0$ **65.** $y = x - 2,\, x \geq 0$

67.

x	-4	-2	2	3
$f^{-1}(x)$	-2	-1	1	3

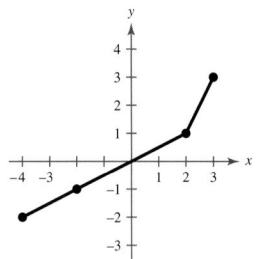

69. (a) and (b)

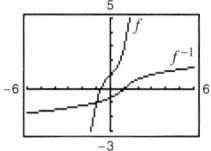

(c) Inverse function because it satisfies the Vertical Line Test

71. (a) and (b)

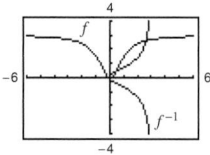

(c) Not an inverse function because the inverse relation does not satisfy the Vertical Line Test

73. 32   **75.** 600   **77.** $2\sqrt[3]{x+3}$

79. $\dfrac{x+1}{2}$ **81.** $\dfrac{x+1}{2}$

83. (a) Yes

(b) $f^{-1}(t)$ represents the year new car sales totaled $\$t$ billion.

(c) 10 or 2000

(d) No. The inverse is not a function because f is not one-to-one.

85. False. For example, $y = x^2$ is even, but does not have an inverse.

87. Answers will vary.   **89.** $9x$, $x \neq 0$

91. $-(x+6)$, $x \neq 6$ **93.** Function

95. Not a function   **97.** Function

Review Exercises   (page 156)

1.

x	-2	0	2	3	4
y	3	2	1	$\frac{1}{2}$	0
Solution point	$(-2, 3)$	$(0, 2)$	$(2, 1)$	$\left(3, \frac{1}{2}\right)$	$(4, 0)$

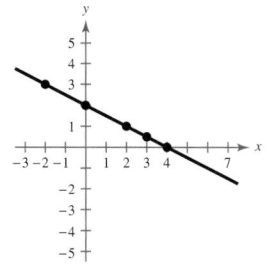

3.

x	-2	-1	0	1	2
y	0	3	4	3	0
Solution point	$(-2, 0)$	$(-1, 3)$	$(0, 4)$	$(1, 3)$	$(2, 0)$

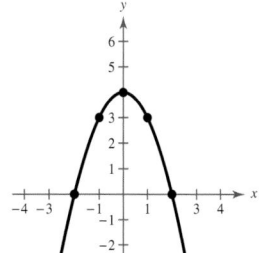

5.

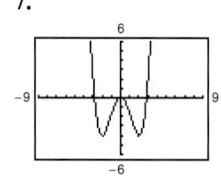

Intercepts: $(-1, 0), \left(0, \frac{1}{4}\right)$

7.

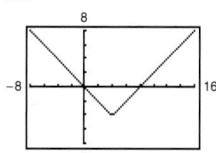

Intercepts: $(0, 0), \left(\pm 2\sqrt{2}, 0\right)$

9.

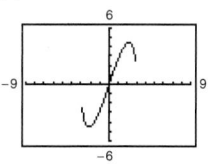

Intercepts: $(0, 0), (\pm 3, 0)$

11.

Intercepts: $(0, 0), (8, 0)$

13.

Xmin = -20
Xmax = 50
Xscl = 10
Ymin = -2
Ymax = 1
Yscl = 0.5

15. (a)

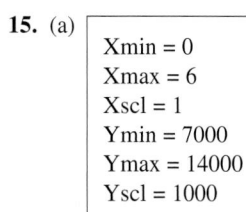

Xmin = 0
Xmax = 6
Xscl = 1
Ymin = 7000
Ymax = 14000
Yscl = 1000

(b)

(c) 4

17.

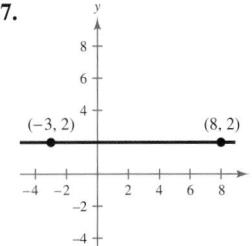

$m = 0$

19.

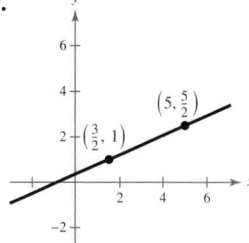

$m = \frac{3}{7}$

21.

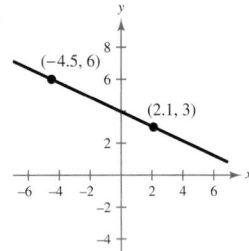

$m = -\frac{5}{11}$

23. $x - 4y - 6 = 0;\ (6, 0),\ (10, 1),\ (-2, -2)$

25. $3x - 2y - 10 = 0;\ (4, 1),\ (2, -2),\ (-2, 8)$

27. $5x + 5y + 24 = 0;\ \left(-5, \frac{1}{5}\right),\ \left(-4, -\frac{4}{5}\right),\ \left(-6, \frac{6}{5}\right)$

29. $y = 6;\ (0, 6),\ (1, 6),\ (-1, 6)$

31. $x = 10;\ (10, 1),\ (10, 3),\ (10, -2)$

33. $y = -1$

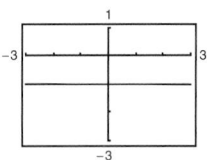

35. $y = \frac{2}{7}x + \frac{2}{7}$

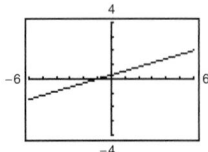

37. $V = 850t + 8250$　　**39.** \$210,000

41. (a) $5x - 4y - 23 = 0$　　**43.** (a) $x = -6$

　　(b) $4x + 5y - 2 = 0$　　　　　(b) $y = 2$

45. (a) Not a function because element 20 in A corresponds to two elements, 4 and 6, in B.

　　(b) Function

(c) Function

(d) Not a function because 30 in A corresponds to no element in B.

47. Not a function　　**49.** Function

51. (a) 5　(b) 17　(c) $t^4 + 1$　(d) $-x^2 - 1$

53. (a) -3　(b) -1　(c) 2　(d) 6

55. All real numbers　　**57.** $[-5, 5]$

59. All real numbers s except $s = 3$

61. (a) $C = 5.35x + 16,000$　(b) $P = 2.85x - 16,000$

63. $2h + 4x + 3,\ h \neq 0$

65.

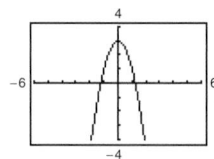

Domain: $(-\infty, \infty)$
Range: $(-\infty, 3]$

67.

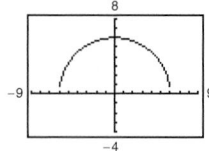

Domain: $[-6, 6]$
Range: $[0, 6]$

69. (a)

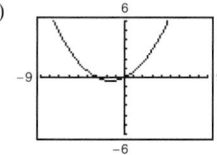

(b) Function

71. (a)

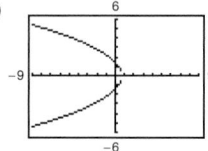

(b) Not a function

73. (a)

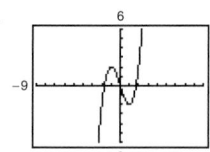

(b) Increasing on $(-\infty, -1),\ (1, \infty)$

　　Decreasing on $(-1, 1)$

75. (a)

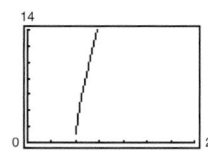

(b) Increasing on $(6, \infty)$

77. Relative maximum: $(0, 16)$

　　Relative minimums: $(-2, 0),\ (2, 0)$

79. Relative maximum: $(3, 27)$

81.

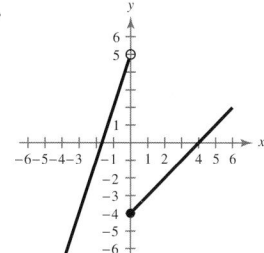

83. Even

85. Constant function $f(x) = C$; vertical shift 2 units downward; $g(x) = -2$

87. Cubic function $f(x) = x^3$; reflection in the x-axis and vertical shift two units downward; $g(x) = -x^3 - 2$

89. (a) Quadratic function

(b) Vertical shift six units downward

(c)

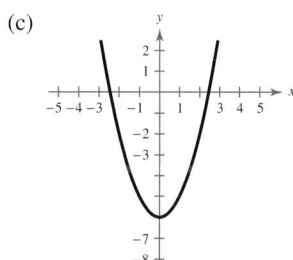

(d) $h(x) = f(x) - 6$

91. (a) Cubic function

(b) Horizontal shift one unit to the right, and vertical shift seven units upward

(c)

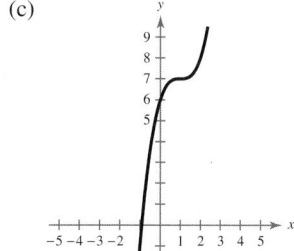

(d) $h(x) = f(x - 1) + 7$

93. (a) Square root function

(b) Vertical shift five units downward

(c)

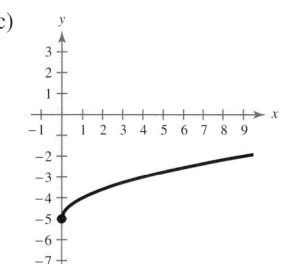

(d) $h(x) = f(x) - 5$

95. (a) Quadratic function

(b) Reflection in the x-axis and vertical shift three units downward

(c)

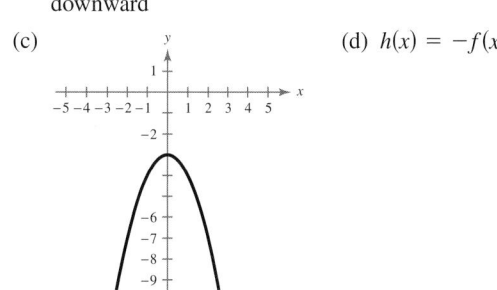

(d) $h(x) = -f(x) - 3$

97. (a) Quadratic function

(b) Vertical stretch, reflection in the x-axis, and vertical shift three units upward

(c)

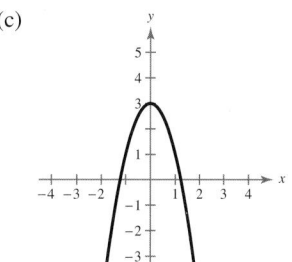

(d) $h(x) = -2f(x) + 3$

99. (a) Absolute value function

(b) Vertical shrink, reflection in the x-axis, and vertical shift nine units upward

(c)

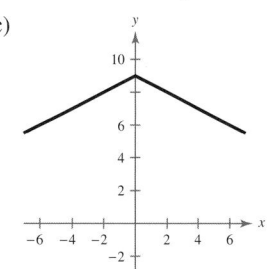

(d) $h(x) = -\frac{1}{2}f(x) + 9$

101. -7 **103.** -42 **105.** 5

107. 23 **109.** -97

111.

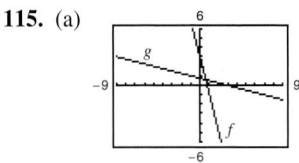

113. $f^{-1}(x) = \dfrac{x}{6}; f(f^{-1}(x)) = f\left(\dfrac{x}{6}\right) = 6\left(\dfrac{x}{6}\right) = x$

$f^{-1}(f(x)) = f^{-1}(6x) = \dfrac{6x}{6} = x$

115. (a)

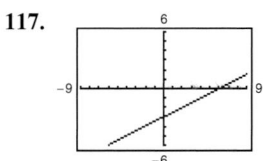

(b)

x	-2	-1	0	1	2
$f(x)$	11	7	3	-1	-5

x	11	7	3	-1	-5
$g(x)$	-2	-1	0	1	2

117.

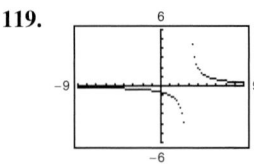

One-to-one

119.

One-to-one

121. $f^{-1}(x) = 12x$ **123.** $f^{-1}(x) = \sqrt[3]{\dfrac{x+3}{4}}$

125. $f^{-1}(x) = x^2 - 10,\ x \geq 0$

127. False. The point $(-1, 28)$ does not lie on the graph of the function $g(x) = -(x - 6)^2 - 3$.

129. False. For example, $f(x) = 4 - x = f^{-1}(x)$

Chapter Test   (page 160)

1.

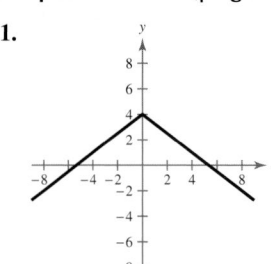

2.

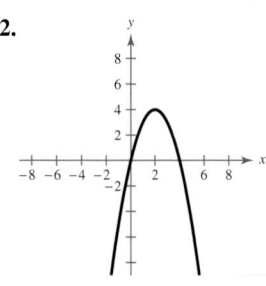

$(0, 4), \left(-\dfrac{16}{3}, 0\right), \left(\dfrac{16}{3}, 0\right)$ $(0, 0), (4, 0)$

3.

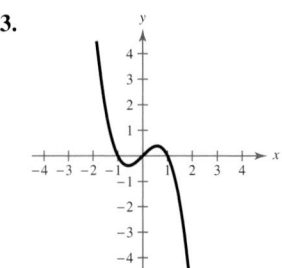

4.

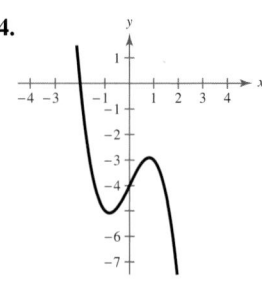

$(0, 0), (1, 0), (-1, 0)$ $(-2, 0), (0, -4)$

5.

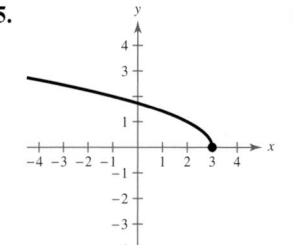

6.

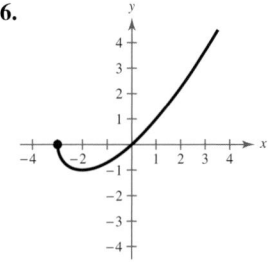

$\left(0, \sqrt{3}\right), (3, 0)$ $(-3, 0), (0, 0)$

7. $(1, -4), (5, 2), (7, 5)$

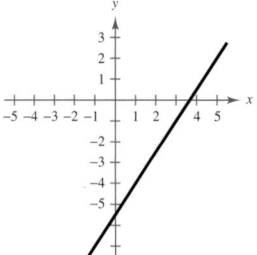

8. (a) $5x + 2y - 8 = 0$ (b) $2x - 5y + 20 = 0$

9. No. To some x there corresponds more than one value of y.

10. (a) -9 (b) 1 (c) $|t - 4| - 15$

11. $(-\infty, 3]$ **12.** $C = 5.60x + 24,000$

$P = 93.9x - 24,000$

13. Increasing: $(-2, 0), (2, \infty)$

Decreasing: $(-\infty, -2), (0, 2)$

14. Increasing: $(-2, 2)$

Constant: $(-\infty, -2), (2, \infty)$

15. 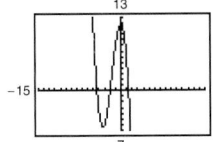   Relative maximum: $(0, 12)$

Relative minimum:

$(-3.33, -6.52)$

16.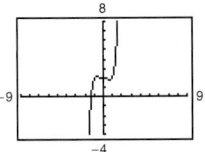

Relative minimum: $(0.77, 1.81)$

Relative maximum: $(-0.77, 2.19)$

17. (a) $f(x) = x^3$

(b) Horizontal shift five units to the right, reflection in the x-axis, vertical stretch, and vertical shift three units upward

(c)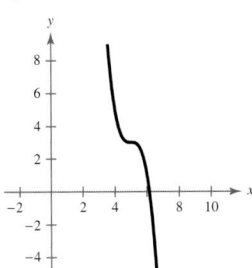

18. (a) $f(x) = \sqrt{x}$

(b) Reflection in the y-axis and a horizontal shift seven units to the left

(c)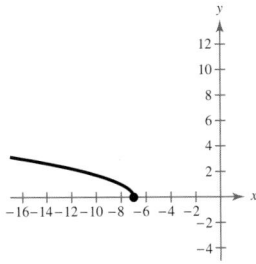

19. (a) $f(x) = |x|$

(b) Reflection in the y-axis (no effect), vertical stretch, and vertical shift seven units downward

(c)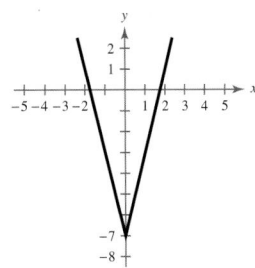

20. (a) $x^2 - \sqrt{2 - x}, (-\infty, 2]$ (b) $\dfrac{x^2}{\sqrt{2 - x}}, (-\infty, 2)$

(c) $2 - x, (-\infty, 2]$ (d) $\sqrt{2 - x^2}, \left[-\sqrt{2}, \sqrt{2}\right]$

21. $f^{-1}(x) = \sqrt[3]{x - 8}$ **22.** No inverse

23. $f^{-1}(x) = \left(\frac{8}{3}x\right)^{2/3}, x \geq 0$

Chapter 2

Section 2.1   (page 168)

1. (a) Yes   (b) No   (c) No   (d) No

3. (a) Yes   (b) No   (c) No   (d) No

5. (a) No   (b) No   (c) No   (d) Yes

7. Identity   **9.** Identity   **11.** Conditional   **13.** $-\frac{96}{23}$

15. -10 **17.** $-\frac{6}{5}$ **19.** 10   **21.** 4   **23.** 5

25. $\dfrac{11}{6}$ **27.** $\dfrac{5}{3}$ **29.** No solution   **31.** $h = \dfrac{2A}{b}$

33. $P = A\left(1 + \dfrac{r}{n}\right)^{-nt}$ **35.** $r = \dfrac{S - a}{S - L}$ **37.** $b = \dfrac{3V}{4\pi a^2}$

39. 61.2 inches

41. (a)   (b) $l = 1.5w; P = 5w$

(c) 5 meters $\times$ 7.5 meters

43. (a) Test average $= \dfrac{\text{test 1 + test 2 + test 3 + test 4}}{4}$

(b) 97

45. 3 hours **47.** ≈ 46.3 miles per hour

49. ≈ 8.33 minutes

51. (a) 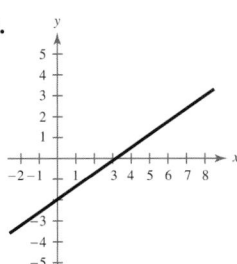 (b) 91.4 feet

h

4 ft

$\mid\!\!\leftarrow 80\text{ ft}\rightarrow\!\!\mid$ $3\frac{1}{2}$ ft

Not drawn to scale

53. $4000 **55.** 50 pounds of each kind

57. $h = 27$ feet **59.** $r = 22.50$ centimeters

61. $x = 6$ feet

63. False. It is quadratic; $x(3 - x) = 10 \Rightarrow 3x - x^2 = 10$.

65. Answers will vary. Sample answer: $9x + 27 = 0$

67. Equations with the same solution set

$4x + 16 = 0, 2x + 8 = 0$

69.

71.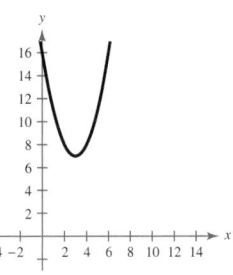

73. 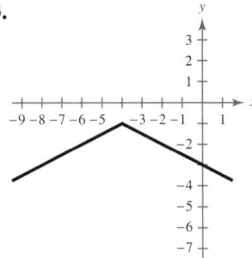 **75.** -28 **77.** -2580

79. -357

Section 2.2 (page 179)

1. $(5, 0), (0, -5)$ **3.** $(-2, 0), (1, 0), (0, -2)$

5. $(-2, 0), (0, 0)$ **7.** No intercepts

9. $(-2, 0), (6, 0), (0, -2)$ **11.** $(1, 0), \left(0, \frac{1}{2}\right)$

13. $f(4) = 5(4 - 4) = 0$

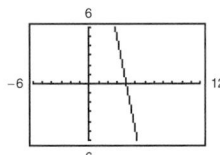

15. $f(0) = (0)^3 - 6(0)^2 + 5(0) = 0$

$f(5) = (5)^3 - 6(5)^2 + 5(5) = 0$

$f(1) = (1)^3 - 6(1)^2 + 5(1) = 0$

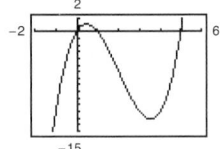

17. $f(1) = \dfrac{1 + 2}{3} - \dfrac{1 - 1}{5} - 1 = 0$

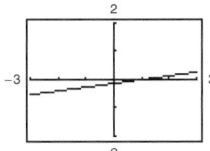

19. 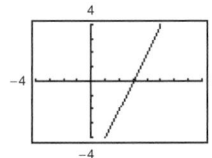 **21.**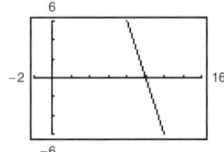

$(3, 0)$ $(10, 0)$

23. $\frac{12}{23}; f(x) = 2.3x - 1.2 = 0$

25. $\frac{89}{13}; f(x) = 13x - 89 = 0$

27. $6; f(x) = 7x - 42 = 0$

29. $-194; f(x) = 0.20x - 38.8 = 0$

31. $3, 12; f(x) = 2x^2 - 30x + 72 = 0$

33. $1, -1.2; f(x) = 5x^2 + x - 6 = 0$

35. $-\frac{3}{10}; f(x) = 10x + 3 = 0$ **37.** $2.172, 7.828$

39. -1.379 **41.** $0.5, -3, 3$ **43.** $-0.717, 2.107$

45. -1.333 **47.** $-1, 7$ **49.** 11

51. (a)

x	-1	0	1	2	3	4
$3.2x - 5.8$	-9	-5.8	-2.6	0.6	3.8	7

(b) $1 < x < 2$; Answers will vary.

(c)

x	1.5	1.6	1.7
$3.2x - 5.8$	-1	-0.68	-0.36

x	1.8	1.9	2
$3.2x - 5.8$	-0.04	0.28	0.6

(d) $1.8 < x < 1.9$

To improve accuracy, evaluate the expression in this interval and determine where the sign changes.

(e) $x = 1.8125$

53. $(1, 1)$ **55.** $(2, 2)$ **57.** $(-1, 3), (2, 6)$ **59.** $(4, 1)$

61. $(1.449, 1.899), (-3.449, -7.899)$

63. $(0, 0), (-2, 8), (2, 8)$

65. (a) 6.46

(b) $\frac{1.73}{0.27} \approx 6.41$. The second method decreases the accuracy.

67. (a) $t(x) = \dfrac{x}{63} + \dfrac{280 - x}{54}$

(b) 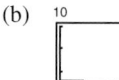 $0 \le x \le 280$

(c) 164.5 miles

69. (a) $A = 0.33(55 - x) + x$

(b) 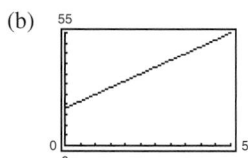 $0 \le x \le 55$

(c) 22.2 gallons

71. (a) $A(x) = 12x$

(b) 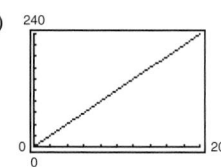   (c) 16.7 units

73. (a) 5200 cubic feet   (b) $y = \frac{1}{8}x$

(c) Answers will vary.

(d)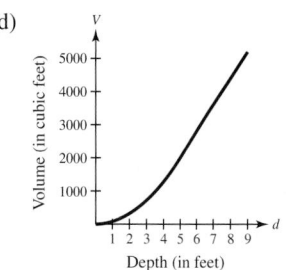

(e)

d	3	5	7	9
V	720	2000	3600	5200

(f) 8.5 feet   (g) 38,896 gallons

75. 1993; To answer the question algebraically, solve the equation $0.91t + 56.4 = 60$. To answer the question graphically, graph the model $y_1 = 0.91x + 56.4$ and the horizontal line $y_2 = 60$ in the same viewing window and determine where the lines intersect.

77. True   **79.** False. The lines could be identical.

81. $\dfrac{4\sqrt{3}}{5}$ **83.** $\dfrac{3(8 - \sqrt{11})}{53}$

85. $3x^2 + 13x - 30$ **87.** $4x^2 - 81$

Section 2.3   (page 189)

Vocabulary Check   (page 189)

1. (a) ii   (b) iii   (c) i   **2.** $\sqrt{-1}, -1$

3. complex, $a + bi$ **4.** real, imaginary

5. Mandelbrot Set

1. $a = -9, b = 4$ **3.** $a = 6, b = 5$ **5.** $4 + 5i$

7. 7   **9.** $-1 - 5i$ **11.** -75 **13.** $0.3i$

15. $11 - i$ **17.** $7 - 3\sqrt{2}i$ **19.** $-14 + 20i$

21. $\frac{19}{6} + \frac{37}{6}i$ **23.** $-4.2 + 7.5i$ **25.** $-2\sqrt{3}$

27. -10 **29.** $5 + i$ **31.** $-20 + 32i$ **33.** 24

35. $80i$ **37.** $4 - 3i$; 25   **39.** $-6 + \sqrt{5}i$; 41

41. $-\sqrt{20}i$; 20   **43.** $3 + \sqrt{-2}$; 11

45. $-6i$ **47.** $\frac{8}{41} + \frac{10}{41}i$ **49.** $\frac{3}{5} + \frac{4}{5}i$

51. $-\frac{40}{1681} - \frac{9}{1681}i$ **53.** $-\frac{1}{2} - \frac{5}{2}i$ **55.** $\frac{62}{949} + \frac{297}{949}i$

57. $-1 + 6i$ **59.** $-375\sqrt{3}i$ **61.** i

63. (a) 8   (b) 8   (c) 8; Answers will vary.

65. $4 + 3i$

67.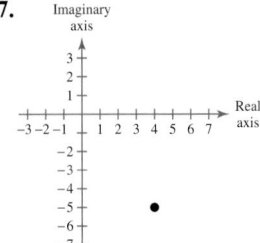

69.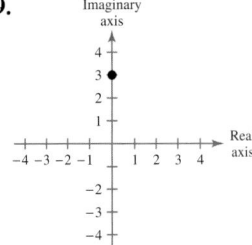

71.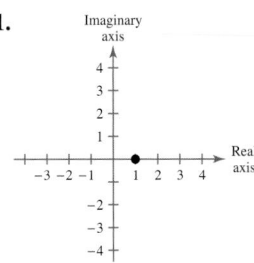

73. $0.5i, -0.25 + 0.5i, -0.1875 + 0.25i, -0.0273 + 0.4063i,$
$-0.1643 + 0.4778i, -0.2013 + 0.3430i$; Yes, bounded

75. 1, 2, 5, 26, 677, 458,330; No, unbounded

77. $3.12 - 0.97i$

79. False. Any real number is equal to its conjugate.

81. $16x^2 - 25$ **83.** $3x^2 + \frac{23}{2}x - 2$

Section 2.4   (page 205)

Vocabulary Check   (page 205)

1. quadratic equation

2. factoring, extracting square roots, completing the square, quadratic formula

3. discriminant

4. position, $-16t^2 + v_0 t + s_0$, initial velocity, initial height

---

1. $2x^2 + 5x - 3 = 0$ **3.** $3x^2 - 60x - 10 = 0$

5. $0, -\frac{1}{2}$ **7.** $4, -2$ **9.** $3, -\frac{1}{2}$ **11.** $2, -6$

13. $-a - b, -a + b$ **15.** ± 7

17. $16, 8$ **19.** $\frac{1}{2} \pm \sqrt{3}$; $2.23, -1.23$

21. 2 **23.** $-8, 4$ **25.** $-3 \pm \sqrt{7}$ **27.** $1 \pm \frac{\sqrt{6}}{3}$

29. $2 \pm 2\sqrt{3}$ **31.** $-\frac{5}{4} \pm \frac{\sqrt{89}}{4}$

33. (a)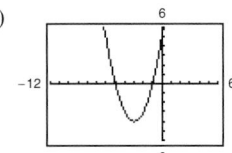

(b) and (c)

$(-1, 0), (-5, 0)$

(d) They are the same.

35. (a)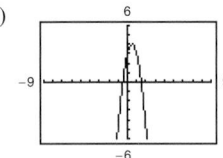

(b) and (c)

$\left(-\frac{1}{2}, 0\right), \left(\frac{3}{2}, 0\right)$

(d) They are the same.

37. (a)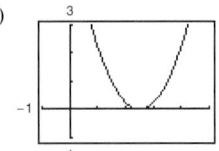

(b) and (c)

$\left(\frac{5}{2}, 0\right)$

(d) They are the same.

39. No real solutions   **41.** One real solution

43. No real solutions   **45.** $1 \pm \sqrt{3}$ **47.** $-4 \pm 2\sqrt{5}$

49. $\frac{2}{7}$ **51.** $-2 \pm \frac{1}{2}i$ **53.** $1 \pm \sqrt{2}$ **55.** $6, -12$

57. $\frac{1}{2} \pm \sqrt{3}$ **59.** $-\frac{1}{2}$ **61.** $0, \pm \frac{3\sqrt{2}}{2}$

63. $\pm 1, \pm \sqrt{3}$ **65.** $-3, 0$ **67.** $3, 1, -1$

69. $\pm \frac{1}{2}, \pm 4$ **71.** $-\frac{1}{5}, -\frac{1}{3}$ **73.** $2, -\frac{3}{5}$ **75.** $\frac{1}{4}$

77. $1, -\frac{125}{8}$

79. (a)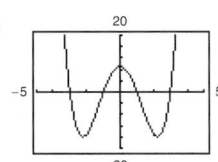

(b) and (c)

$x = 0, 3, -1$

(d) They are the same.

81. (a)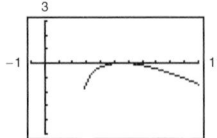

(b) and (c)

$x = \pm 3, \pm 1$

(d) They are the same.

83. 26   **85.** 0   **87.** -256.5 **89.** 9

91. $-59, 69$ **93.** 1

95. (a)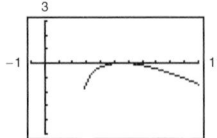

(b) and (c)

$x = 5, 6$

(d) They are the same.

97. (a)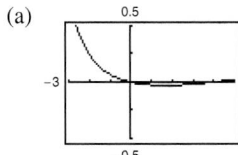

(b) and (c)

$x = 0, 4$

(d) They are the same.

99. $4, -5$ **101.** $\dfrac{-3 \pm \sqrt{21}}{6}$ **103.** $2, -\dfrac{3}{2}$

105. $3, -2$ **107.** $\sqrt{3}, -3$

109. (a)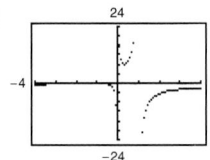

(b) and (c)

$x = -1$

(d) They are the same.

111. (a)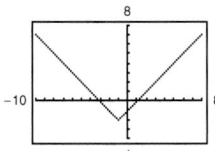

(b) and (c)

$x = 1, -3$

(d) They are the same.

113. $x^2 + x - 30 = 0$ **115.** $x^3 - 4x^2 - 2x + 8 = 0$

117. $x^4 - 3x^2 - 4 = 0$ **119.** $x = 6$ or -4

121. (a)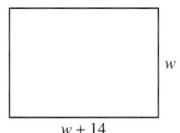

(b) $1632 = w^2 + 14w$

(c) Width: 34 feet; length: 48 feet

123. 14 centimeters $\times$ 14 centimeters

125. (a) $s = -16t^2 + 1815$

(b)

t	0	2	4	6
s	1815	1751	1559	1239

t	8	10	12
s	791	215	-489

(c) $[10, 12]$; 10 seconds; ≈ 10.65 seconds

127. (a) $s = -16t^2 + 45t + 5.5$ (b) 24 feet

(c) ≈ 2.8 seconds

129. (a)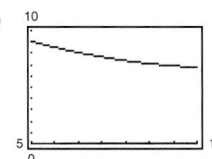

(b) Yes; 2010

131. (a)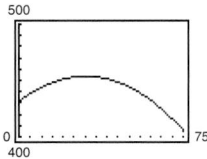

(b) 453 miles; 15 hours

(c) 439 miles; 54.9 miles per hour

133. (a)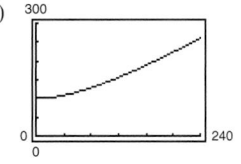

$h \approx 173.21$

(b)

h	160	165	170	175	180	185
d	188.7	192.9	197.2	201.6	205.9	210.3

(c) 173.2

(d) Solving graphically or numerically yields an approximate solution. An exact solution is obtained by solving algebraically.

135. Eastbound plane: ≈ 550 miles per hour

Northbound plane: ≈ 600 miles per hour

137. False. Both solutions are complex.

139. False. For example, $|x| = x^2 + x + 3$ has two extraneous solutions.

141. (a) $0, -\dfrac{b}{a}$ (b) $0, 1$ **143.** $x^2(x - 3)(x^2 + 3x + 9)$

145. $(x + 5)(x - \sqrt{2})(x + \sqrt{2})$ **147.** Function

149. Not a function   **151.** Function

Section 2.5   (page 219)

Vocabulary Check   (page 219)

1. negative   **2.** double   **3.** $-a \le x \le a$

4. $x \le -a, x \ge a$ **5.** zeros, undefined values

1. d   **2.** a   **3.** c   **4.** b

5. (a) Yes   (b) No   (c) Yes   (d) No

7. (a) No   (b) Yes   (c) Yes   (d) No

9. $x > -4$ **11.** $x < -\dfrac{1}{2}$

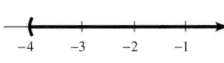   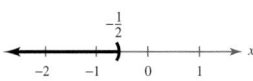

13. $x \geq 4$

15. $-2 < x \leq 5$

17. $-\frac{9}{2} < x < \frac{15}{2}$

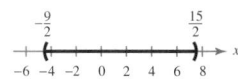

19.

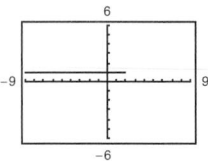

21.

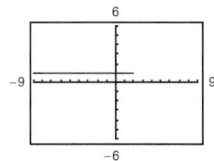

$x \leq 2$ $x < 2$

23.

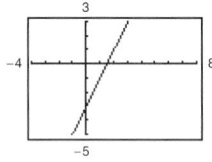

25.

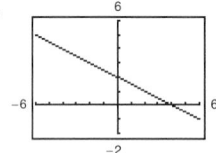

(a) $x \geq 2$ (a) $-2 \leq x \leq 4$
(b) $x \leq \frac{3}{2}$ (b) $x \leq 4$

27. $x < -2,\ x > 2$

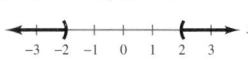

29. $1 < x < 13$

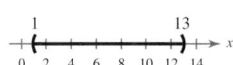

31. $x < -28,\ x > 0$

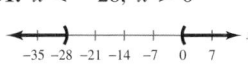

33. $\frac{1}{4} < x < \frac{3}{4}$

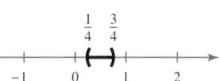

35.

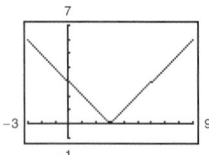

(a) $1 \leq x \leq 5$ (b) $x \leq -1, x \geq 7$

37. $|x| \leq 3$ **39.** $|x| > 3$ **41.** $|x - 7| \leq 10$

43. positive on: $(-\infty, -1) \cup (5, \infty)$
negative on: $(-1, 5)$

45. $(-7, 3)$

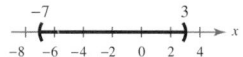

47. $(-\infty, -5], [1, \infty)$

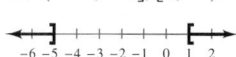

49. $[-2, 0], [2, \infty)$

51.

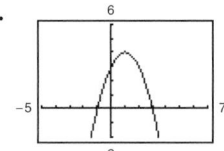

(a) $x \leq -1,\ x \geq 3$
(b) $0 \leq x \leq 2$

53. $(-\infty, -1), (0, 1)$

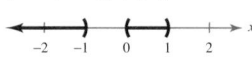

55. $(-\infty, -1), (4, \infty)$

57.

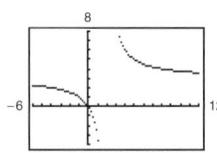

(a) $0 \leq x < 2$
(b) $2 < x \leq 4$

59. $[5, \infty)$ **61.** $(-\infty, \infty)$ **63.** $(-\infty, -2], [2, \infty)$

65. (a) and (b)

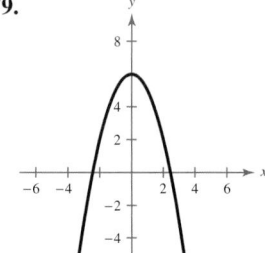

(c) 181.5 pounds
(d) Answers will vary.

67. $333\frac{1}{3}$ vibrations per second   **69.** $1.2 < t < 2.4$

71. False. $10 \geq -x$ **73.** a, b

75. $d = 5\sqrt{5} \approx 11.18$; midpoint: $(-1.5, 7)$

77. $d = 2\sqrt{65} \approx 16.12$; midpoint: $(-1, -1)$

79.

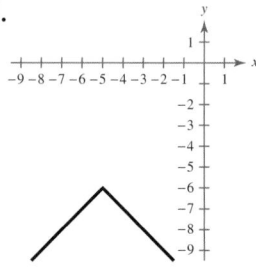

81.

83. $y^{-1} = \dfrac{x}{12}$ **85.** $y^{-1} = \sqrt[3]{x - 7}$

Section 2.6   (page 227)

Vocabulary Check   (page 227)

1. positive   **2.** negative   **3.** fitting a line to data

4. $-1, 1$

1. (a)
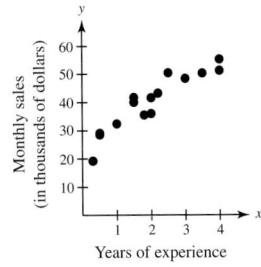

(b) Yes. The monthly sales increase as the experience of the sales representatives increases.

3. Negative correlation   **5.** No correlation

7. (a)
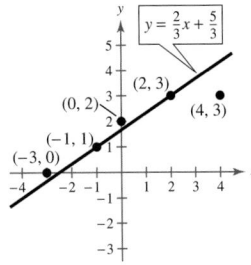

(b) $y = 0.46x + 1.6$

(c)
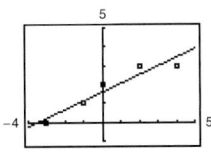

(d) The models appear valid.

9. (a)
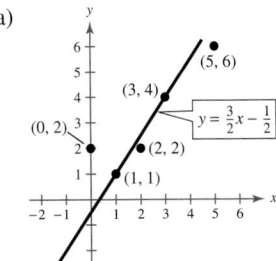

(b) $y = 0.95x + 0.92$

(c)
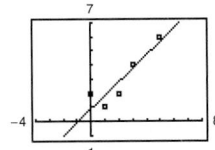

(d) The models appear valid.

11. (a)
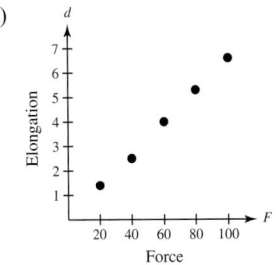

(b) $d = 0.07F - 0.3$

(c) $d = 0.066F$; This model fits the data better.

(d) 3.63 centimeters

13. (a) $S = 0.2t - 0.14$

(b)
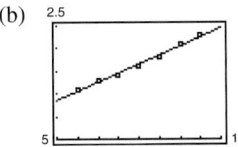

(c) The slope represents the average annual increase in salaries (in millions of dollars).

(d) $3.1 million

15. (a) $S = 0.183t + 7.013$

(b)
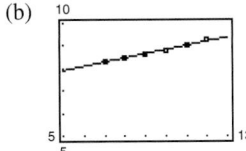

(c) The slope represents the average annual increase in spending.

(d) $10.31

(e)

Year	1997	1998	1999
Actual, S	8.30	8.50	8.65
Model, S	8.29	8.48	8.66

Year	2000	2001	2002
Actual, S	8.80	9.00	9.25
Model, S	8.84	9.03	9.21

The model fits well.

17. (a) $y = -0.024x + 5.06$

(b) The winning times decrease as time in years increases.

(c)

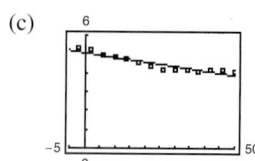

(d) The model is a reasonably close fit.

(e) Answers will vary.

19. True. To have positive correlation, the y-values tend to increase as x increases.

21. Answers will vary.   **23.** $P \le 2$ **25.** $-3 \le z \le 10$

27. $5x - 10, x \ne -2$ **29.** (a) 10   (b) $2w^2 + 5w + 7$

31. (a) 5   (b) 1   **33.** $-\frac{3}{5}$ **35.** $-\frac{1}{4}, \frac{3}{2}$

37. $\dfrac{7 \pm \sqrt{17}}{4}$

Review Exercises   (page 232)

1. (a) No   (b) No   (c) No   (d) Yes

3. $x = 9$ **5.** $x = \frac{1}{2}$ **7.** $x = \frac{7}{3}$

9. September: \$325,000; October: \$364,000

11. $2\frac{6}{7}$ liters

13. (a)

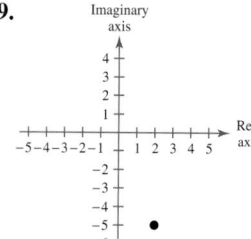

8 m

2 m   75 cm

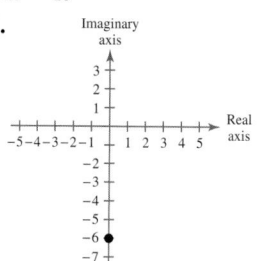

(b) $h = \frac{64}{3}$ meters

15. $-3.5°C$ **17.** $(-3, 0), (0, 3)$ **19.** $(1, 0), (8, 0), (0, 8)$

21. $(0, -7)$ **23.** $x = 2.2$ **25.** $x = -1.301$

27. $x = 0.338, 1.307$ **29.** $(1, -2)$

31. $(4.5, -3.125), (-3, 2.5)$ **33.** $6 + 5i$ **35.** $2 + 7i$

37. $3 + 7i$ **39.** $40 + 65i$ **41.** $-4 - 46i$

43. -80 **45.** $1 - 6i$ **47.** $\frac{17}{26} + \frac{7}{26}i$

49.

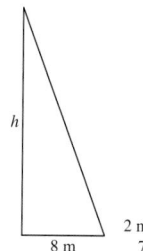

51.

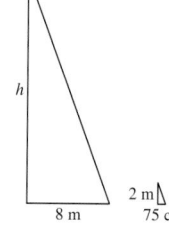

53.

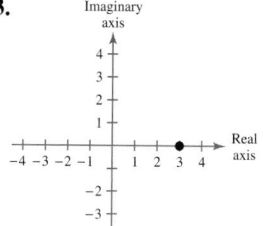

55. $0, 2$ **57.** $-4 \pm 3\sqrt{2}$

59. $6 \pm \sqrt{6}$ **61.** $\frac{1}{2}, -5$ **63.** $-2 \pm \sqrt{6}i$

65. $0, \frac{2}{3}, 8$ **67.** $0, \frac{12}{5}$ **69.** 5   **71.** $\frac{25}{4}$

73. No solution   **75.** $-124, 126$

77. $-2 \pm \dfrac{\sqrt{95}}{5}, -4$

79. $\frac{1}{5}$ **81.** $2, 6$ **83.** $-5, 15$ **85.** $1, 3$

87. (a) 1998

(b)

t	1995	1996	1997	1998
P	738.25	740.96	743.89	747.04

t	1999	2000	2001
P	750.41	754	757.81

(c)

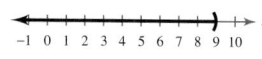

(d) 1995

89. $(-\infty, 9)$

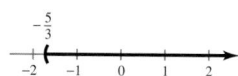

91. $\left(-\frac{5}{3}, \infty\right)$

93. $[-3, 9)$

95. $(1, 3)$

97. $(-\infty, 0], [3, \infty)$

99. $\left[-\frac{1}{2}, \frac{7}{2}\right]$

101. $(-\infty, 1], [3, \infty)$

103. $\left[-\frac{1}{4}, 6\right]$

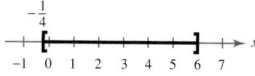

105. $[-4, 0], [4, \infty)$

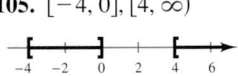

107. $(-\infty, 3), (5, \infty)$

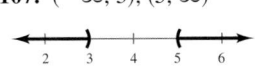

109. $(-\infty, 3), [20, \infty)$

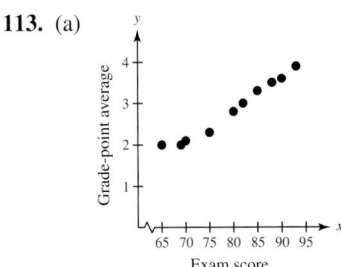

111. $[430.044, 435.244]$

113. (a)

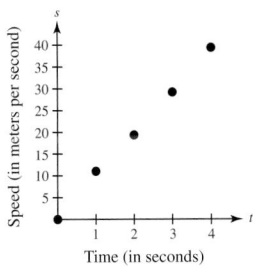

(b) Yes. Answers will vary.

115. (a)

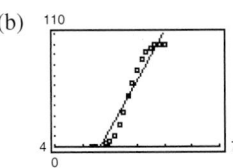

(b) Answers will vary. Sample answer: $S = 10t - 0.4$

(c) $s = 9.7t + 0.4$; This model better fits the data.

(d) 24.7 meters per second

117. (a) $y = 95.17x - 458.4$

(b)

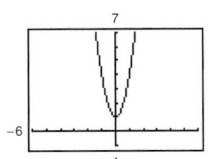

(c) The model fits only a few points.

(d) No.

119. False. If a graph has two y-intercepts, one input value ($x = 0$) is matched with two output values, so the graph is not the graph of a function.

121. False. For example, the slope of the regression line for $(1, 4)$, $(2, 3)$, $(3, 2)$, and $(4, 1)$ is -1.

123. The real zeros of a function are the values of x at which the graph of the function crosses the x-axis (the x-intercepts). They are also the values of x that satisfy the equation $f(x) = 0$.

125. $\sqrt{-6} \cdot \sqrt{-6} = 6i^2$ or -6, not 6.

127. (a) 1   (b) i (c) -1 (d) $-i$

Chapter Test   (page 236)

1. $x = 3$ **2.** $x = \frac{2}{15}$ **3.** $-9 - 18i$

4. $6 + (2\sqrt{5} + \sqrt{14})i$ **5.** $13 + 4i$ **6.** $-17 + 14i$

7. $\frac{43}{37} + \frac{38}{37}i$ **8.** $1 + 2i$

9.

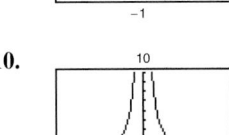

No x-intercepts

No real zeros

10.

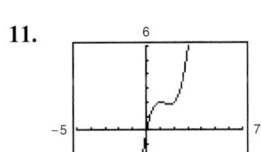

No x-intercepts

No real zeros

11.

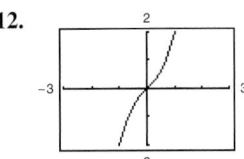

One x-intercept: $(0, 0)$

One real zero: 0

12.

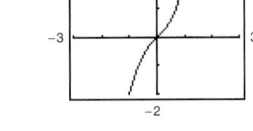

One x-intercept: $(0, 0)$

One real zero: 0

13. $1, 9$ **14.** $-6 \pm \sqrt{38}$ **15.** $\pm\frac{9}{2}$

16. $-3, \frac{1}{5}$ **17.** $\pm 2, \frac{4}{3}$ **18.** 2   **19.** $\pm\sqrt{58}$

20. $-\frac{5}{2}, \frac{11}{4}$

21. $\left(\frac{7}{6}, \frac{17}{8}\right)$ **22.** $(3, 13)$

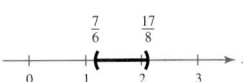

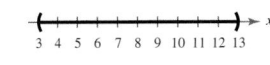

23. $\left(-7, -\frac{2}{3}\right)$

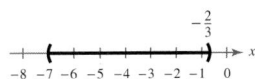

24. $L = 14.8t + 92$; 2004

Cumulative Test for Chapters P–2
(page 237)

1. $\dfrac{7x^3}{16y^5}, x \neq 0$ **2.** $9\sqrt{15}$ **3.** $2x^2y\sqrt{7y}$

4. $7x - 10$ **5.** $x^3 - x^2 - 5x + 6$ **6.** $\dfrac{x - 1}{(x + 1)(x + 3)}$

7. $(3 + x)(7 - x)$ **8.** $x(1 + x)(1 - 6x)$

9. $2(3 - 2x)(9 + 6x + 4x^2)$

10. Midpoint: $(1.5, -2)$; $d = 2\sqrt{61} \approx 15.62$

11. $\left(x + \frac{1}{2}\right)^2 + (y + 8)^2 = \frac{25}{16}$

12. 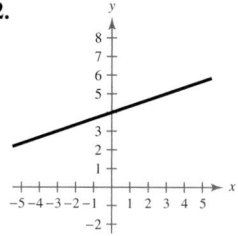   **13.**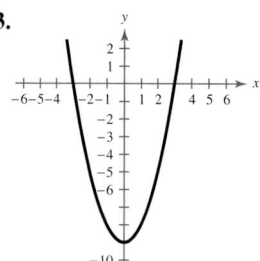

14.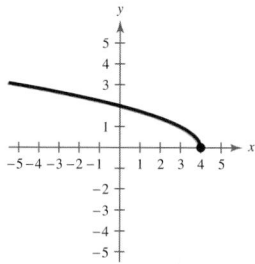

15. (a) $28x + 11y + 52 = 0$

(b) $\left(0, -\frac{52}{11}\right), \left(-\frac{52}{28}, 0\right), \left(-2, \frac{4}{11}\right)$

16. (a) $2x + y = 0$ (b) $(0, 0), (1, -2), (2, -4)$

17. (a) $x = -\frac{3}{7}$ (b) $\left(-\frac{3}{7}, 0\right), \left(-\frac{3}{7}, 1\right), \left(-\frac{3}{7}, -3\right)$

18. (a) $\dfrac{3}{2}$ (b) Undefined   (c) $\dfrac{s + 2}{s}$

19. (a) -13 (b) -14 (c) -8

20. No. It doesn't pass the Vertical Line Test.

21. 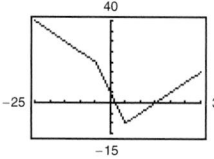   Decreasing on $(-\infty, 5)$
Increasing on $(5, \infty)$

22. (a) Vertical shrink   (b) Vertical shift
(c) Horizontal shift

23. -53 **24.** $\frac{197}{16}$ **25.** -79 **26.** 42

27. $h^{-1}(x) = \dfrac{x + 2}{5}$

28.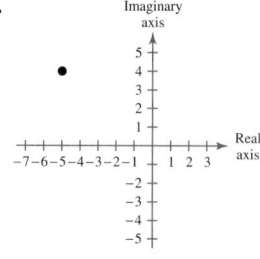

29. 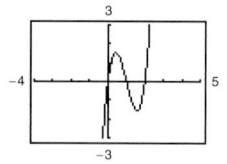   **30.**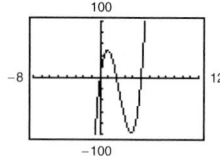

x-intercepts: $0, 1, 2$ x-intercepts: $0, 2, 5$

31. 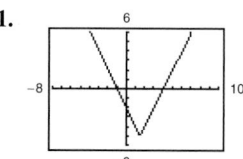   **32.**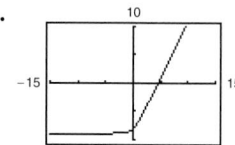

x-intercepts: $-1, 4$ x-intercept: $4.\overline{44}$

33. $X = \pm\sqrt{R^2 - Z^2}$ **34.** $p = \dfrac{k}{3\pi r^2 L}$

35. $\left(-\infty, \frac{120}{7}\right]$ **36.** $\left(-\infty, -3\right], \left[\frac{5}{2}, \infty\right)$

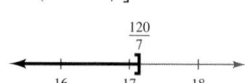   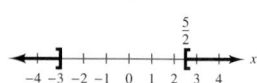

37. $\left(-\infty, -\frac{3}{2}\right), \left(-\frac{1}{4}, \infty\right)$ **38.** $(-1, 2]$

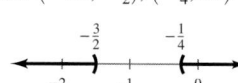   

39. ≈ 4.456 inches

40. (a) $A = x(273 - x)$

(b) $0 < x < 273$

(c) ≈ 76.2 feet $\times$ 196.8 feet

41. (a) $R = 129.25t - 389.3$

(b)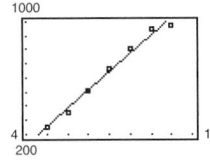

(c) As time increases, revenues increase.

(d) $1,808,000,000

(e)

Year	1995	1996	1997	1998
Actual, R	253.4	360.1	508.8	669.8
Model, R	257.0	386.2	515.5	644.7

Year	1999	2000	2001
Actual, R	805.3	944.7	971.2
Model, R	774.0	903.2	1032.5

The model is a good fit.

Chapter 3

Section 3.1   (page 247)

Vocabulary Check   (page 247)

1. nonnegative integer, real   **2.** quadratic, parabola

3. axis   **4.** positive, minimum

5. negative, maximum

1. g   **2.** c   **3.** b   **4.** h   **5.** f   **6.** a

7. e   **8.** d

9.

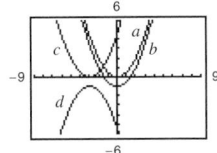

(a) Vertical shrink

(b) Vertical shrink and vertical shift one unit downward

(c) Vertical shrink and a horizontal shift three units to the left

(d) Vertical shrink, reflection in the x-axis, a horizontal shift three units to the left, and a vertical shift one unit downward

11.

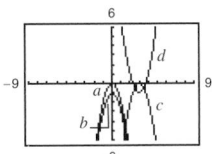

(a) Vertical stretch and a reflection in the x-axis

(b) Vertical stretch, a reflection in the x-axis, and vertical shift one unit down

(c) Vertical stretch, reflection in the x-axis, and horizontal shift three units to the right

(d) Vertical stretch, horizontal shift three units to the right, and vertical shift one unit downward

13. Vertex: $(0, 25)$

x-intercepts: $(\pm 5, 0)$

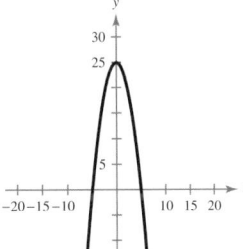

15. Vertex: $(0, -4)$

x-intercepts: $(\pm 2\sqrt{2}, 0)$

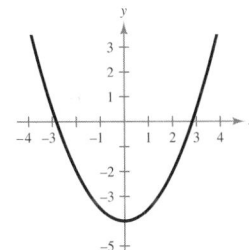

17. Vertex: $(-4, -3)$

x-intercepts:

$(\pm\sqrt{3} - 4, 0)$

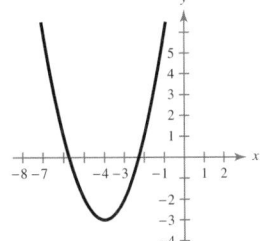

19. Vertex: $(4, 0)$

x-intercept: $(4, 0)$

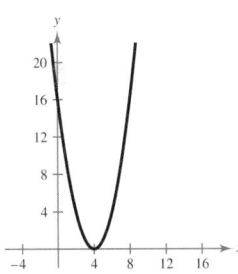

21. Vertex: $\left(\frac{1}{2}, 1\right)$

x-intercept: None

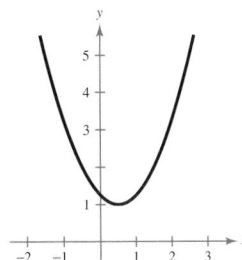

23. Vertex: $(1, 6)$

x-intercepts:

$(1 \pm \sqrt{6}, 0)$

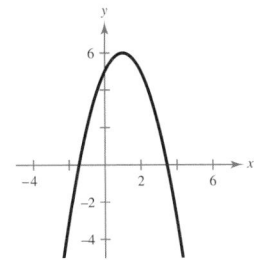

25. Vertex: $\left(\frac{1}{2}, 20\right)$

x-intercept: None

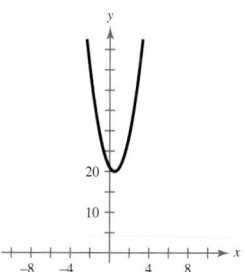

27. Vertex: $(-1, 4)$

x-intercepts:

$(1, 0), (-3, 0)$

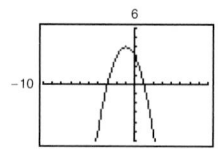

29. Vertex: $(-4, -5)$

x-intercepts:

$\left(-4 \pm \sqrt{5}, 0\right)$

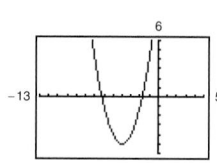

31. Vertex: $(4, 1)$

x-intercepts:

$\left(4 \pm \frac{1}{2}\sqrt{2}, 0\right)$

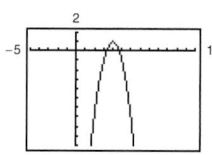

33. Vertex: $(-2, -3)$

x-intercepts:

$\left(-2 \pm \sqrt{6}, 0\right)$

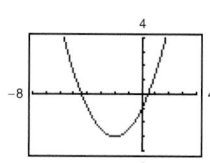

35. $y = (x - 1)^2$ **37.** $y = -(x + 1)^2 + 4$

39. $f(x) = (x + 2)^2 + 5$ **41.** $f(x) = \frac{19}{81}\left(x - \frac{5}{2}\right)^2 - \frac{3}{4}$

43. $(5, 0), (-1, 0)$; They are the same.

45. $(-4, 0)$; They are the same.

47.

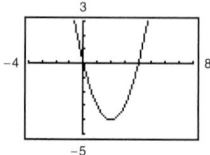

$(0, 0), (4, 0)$; They are the same.

49.

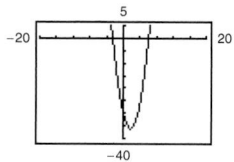

$\left(-\frac{5}{2}, 0\right), (6, 0)$; They are the same.

51.

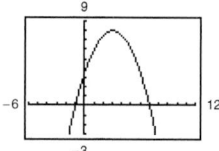

$(7, 0), (-1, 0)$; They are the same.

53. $f(x) = x^2 - 2x - 3$ **55.** $f(x) = 2x^2 + 7x + 3$

$g(x) = -x^2 + 2x + 3$ $g(x) = -2x^2 - 7x - 3$

57. 55, 55   **59.** 12, 6

61. (a)

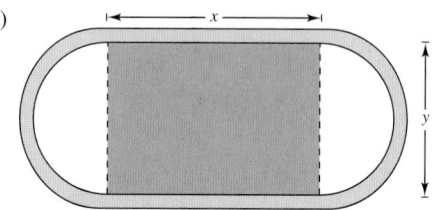

(b) $r = \frac{1}{2}y; \ d = y\pi$ (c) $y = \dfrac{200 - 2x}{\pi}$

(d) $A = x\left(\dfrac{200 - 2x}{\pi}\right)$

(e)

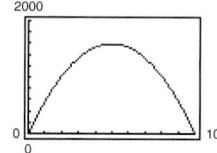

$x = 50$ meters, $y = \dfrac{100}{\pi}$ meters

63. (a)

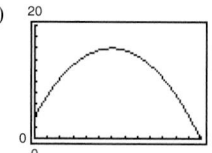

(b) 4 feet

(c) 16 feet

(d) 25.86 feet

65. Must produce 20 fixtures to yield a minimum cost.

67. (a)

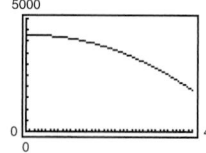

(b) 4276 cigarettes per person; Answers will vary.

(c) ≈ 8564 cigarettes per smoker per year;

    ≈ 23.5 cigarettes per smoker per day

69. True. The vertex is $(0, -1)$ and the parabola opens down.

71. Model (a). The profits are positive and rising.

73. $(1.2, 6.8)$ **75.** $(2, 5), (-3, 0)$ **77.** $-5 - 3i$

79. $19 - 25i$

Section 3.2   (page 260)

Vocabulary Check   (page 260)

1. continuous   **2.** Leading Coefficient Test

3. $n, n - 1$, relative extrema

4. solution, $(x - a)$, x-intercept   **5.** touches, crosses

6. Intermediate Value

---

1. f   **2.** h   **3.** c   **4.** a   **5.** e   **6.** d

7. g   **8.** b

9. (a)

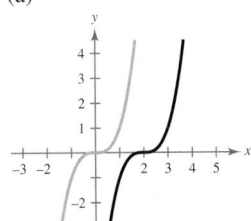

(b)

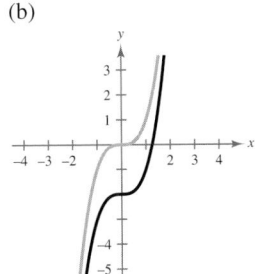

(c)

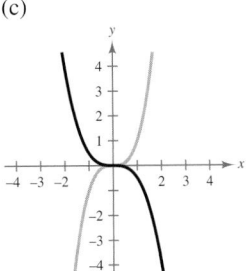

(d)

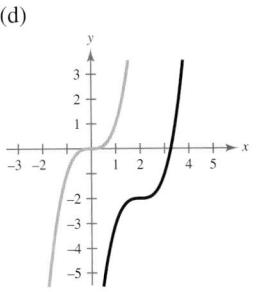

11. (a)

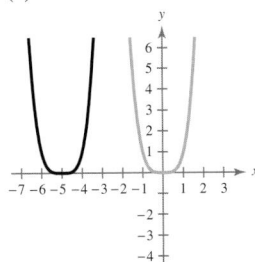

(b)

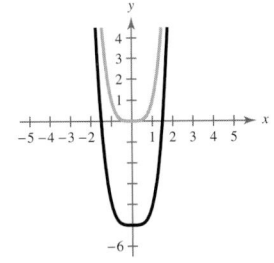

(c)

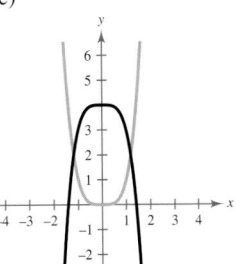

(d)

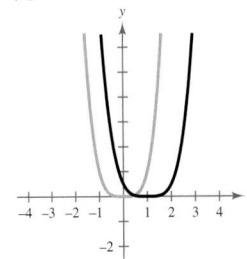

13.

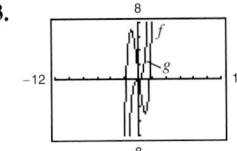

15.

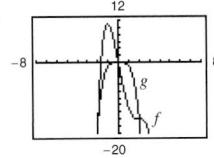

17. Rises to the left, rises to the right

19. Falls to the left, falls to the right

21. Rises to the left, falls to the right

23. Falls to the left, falls to the right

25. ± 5 **27.** 3 (multiplicity 2)   **29.** $1, -2$

31. 2 (multiplicity 2), 0   **33.** $\dfrac{-5 \pm \sqrt{37}}{2}$

35. (a)

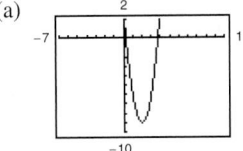

(b) $(0.268, 0), (3.732, 0)$

(c) $\left(2 - \sqrt{3}, 0\right), \left(2 + \sqrt{3}, 0\right)$

37. (a)

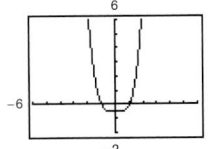

(b) $(-1, 0), (1, 0)$ (c) $(-1, 0), (1, 0)$

39. (a)

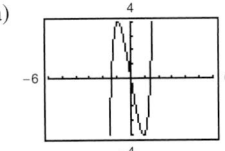

(b) $(-1.414, 0), (0, 0), (1.414, 0)$

(c) $(0, 0), \left(-\sqrt{2}, 0\right), \left(\sqrt{2}, 0\right)$

41. (a)

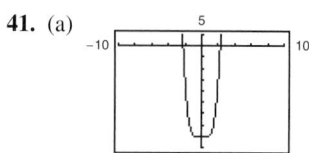

(b) $(-2.236, 0), (2.236, 0)$ (c) $\left(-\sqrt{5}, 0\right), \left(\sqrt{5}, 0\right)$

43. (a)

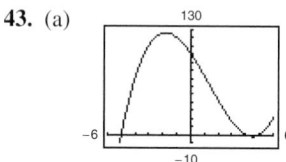

(b) $(-5, 0), (4, 0), (5, 0)$ (c) $(4, 0), (-5, 0), (5, 0)$

45. (a)

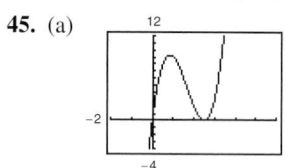

(b) $(0, 0), (2.5, 0)$ (c) $(0, 0), \left(\frac{5}{2}, 0\right)$

47.

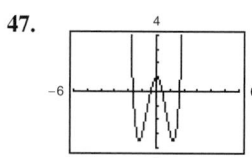

Zeros: $\pm 1.680, \pm 0.421$

Relative maximum: $(0, 1)$

Relative minima:

$(\pm 1.225, -3.500)$

49.

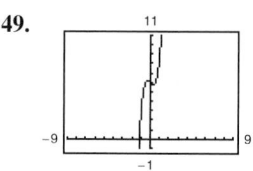

Zero: -1.178

Relative maximum:

$(-0.324, 6.218)$

Relative minimum:

$(0.324, 5.782)$

51. $f(x) = x^2 - 4x$ **53.** $f(x) = x^3 + 5x^2 + 6x$

55. $f(x) = x^4 - 4x^3 - 9x^2 + 36x$

57. $f(x) = x^2 - 2x - 2$

59. $f(x) = x^3 - 10x^2 + 27x - 22$

61. (a) Falls to the left, rises to the right

(b) $(0, 0), (3, 0), (-3, 0)$

(c)

x	-3.3	-2	-1	1	2	3.3
y	-6.2	10	8	-8	-10	6.2

63. (a) Rises to the left and right

(b) No zeros

(c)

t	-3	-2	-1	0	1	2	3
y	7.5	5.8	4.5	3.8	3.5	3.8	4.5

(d)

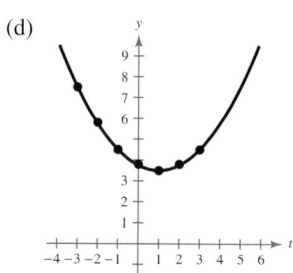

65. (a) Falls to the left, rises to the right

(b) $(0, 0), (3, 0)$

(c)

x	-2.5	-1	1	2	4
y	-34.4	-4	-2	-4	16

(d)

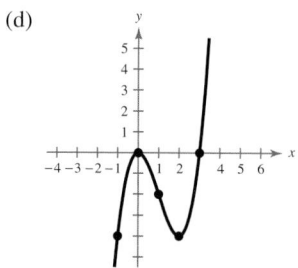

67. (a) Rises to the left, falls to the right

(b) $(0, 0), (-5, 0)$

(c)

x	-6	-4	-3	-2	1	2
y	36	-16	-18	-12	-6	-28

(d)

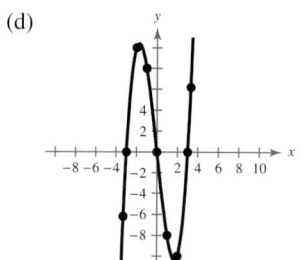

(d)

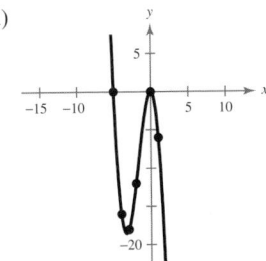

69. (a) Falls to the left, rises to the right

(b) $(0, 0), (4, 0)$

(c)

x	-2	-1	1	2	3	5
y	-24	-5	-3	-8	-9	25

(d)

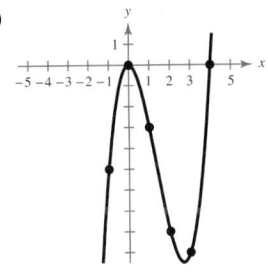

71. (a) Falls to the left and right

(b) $(-2, 0), (2, 0)$

(c)

t	-4	-3	-1	0	1	3
y	-36	-6.3	-2.3	-4	-2.3	-6.3

(d)

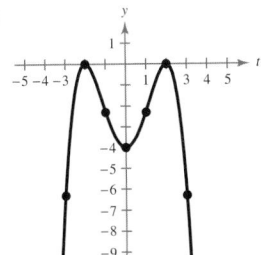

73. (a)

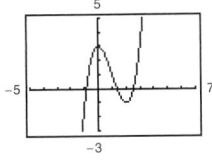

(b) $-0.879, 1.347, 2.532$

$(-1, 0), (1, 2), (2, 3)$

75. (a)

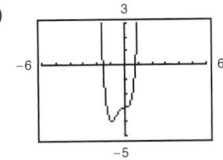

(b) $-1.585, 0.779$

$(-2, -1), (0, 1)$

77.

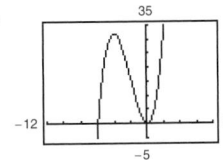

Two x-intercepts

79.

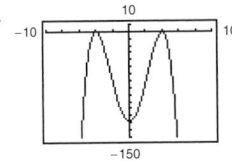

Symmetric to the y-axis
Two x-intercepts

81.

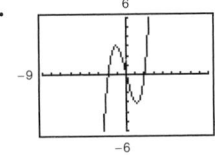

Symmetric to the origin
Three x-intercepts

83.

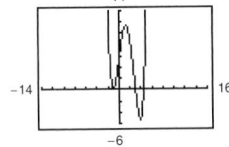

Three x-intercepts

85. (a) Answers will vary.

(b) Domain: $0 < x < 18$

(c)

Height, x	Volume, V
1	$1[36 - 2(1)]^2 = 1156$
2	$2[36 - 2(2)]^2 = 2048$
3	$3[36 - 2(3)]^2 = 2700$
4	$4[36 - 2(4)]^2 = 3136$
5	$5[36 - 2(5)]^2 = 3380$
6	$6[36 - 2(6)]^2 = 3456$
7	$7[36 - 2(7)]^2 = 3388$

$5 < x < 7$

(d)

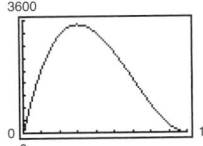

$x = 6$

87. $(200, 160)$

89.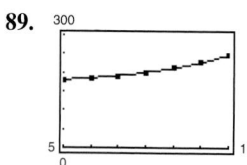

The model is a good fit.

91. Northeast: $505,920; South: $81,085; Answers will vary.

93. False. It can have at most five turning points.

95. b; Answers will vary; No; Answers will vary.

96. d; Answers will vary; No; Answers will vary.

97. a; Answers will vary; No; Answers will vary.

98. c; Answers will vary; No; Answers will vary.

99. 69   **101.** $-\frac{1408}{49} \approx -28.73$ **103.** 109

105. $x > -8$ **107.** $-26 \le x < 7$

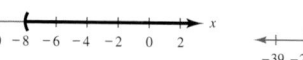

Section 3.3   (page 275)

1. $2x + 4$, $x \ne -3$ **3.** $x^2 - 3x + 1$, $x \ne -\frac{5}{4}$

5. $7 - \dfrac{11}{x + 2}$

7. $3x + 5 - \dfrac{2x - 3}{2x^2 + 1}$ **9.** $x - \dfrac{x + 9}{x^2 + 1}$

11. $2x - \dfrac{17x - 5}{x^2 - 2x + 1}$ **13.** $3x^2 - 2x + 5$, $x \ne 5$

15. $6x^2 + 25x + 74 + \dfrac{248}{x - 3}$ **17.** $9x^2 - 16$, $x \ne 2$

19. $x^2 - 8x + 64$, $x \ne -8$

21. $4x^2 + 14x - 30$, $x \ne -\frac{1}{2}$

23.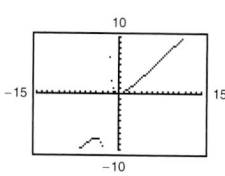

25. $f(x) = (x - 4)(x^2 + 3x - 2) + 3$, $f(4) = 3$

27. $f(x) = \left(x - \sqrt{2}\right)\left[x^2 + \left(3 + \sqrt{2}\right)x + 3\sqrt{2}\right] - 8$, $f\left(\sqrt{2}\right) = -8$

29. $f(x) = \left(x - 1 + \sqrt{3}\right)\left[4x^2 - \left(2 + 4\sqrt{3}\right)x - \left(2 + 2\sqrt{3}\right)\right]$, $f\left(1 - \sqrt{3}\right) = 0$

31. (a) 1   (b) 4   (c) 4   (d) 1954

33. (a) 97   (b) $-\frac{5}{3}$ (c) 17   (d) -199

35. $(x - 2)(x + 3)(x - 1)$ **37.** $(2x - 1)(x - 5)(x - 2)$
Zeros: $2, -3, 1$ Zeros: $\frac{1}{2}, 5, 2$

39. (a) Answers will vary.   (b) $(2x - 1)$
(c) $(x + 2)(x - 1)(2x - 1)$ (d) $-2, 1, \frac{1}{2}$

41. (a) Answers will vary.   (b) $(x - 1), (x - 2)$
(c) $(x - 5)(x + 4)(x - 1)(x - 2)$ (d) $-4, 1, 2, 5$

43. (a) Answers will vary.   (b) $(x + 7)$
(c) $(2x + 1)(3x - 2)(x + 7)$ (d) $-7, -\frac{1}{2}, \frac{2}{3}$

45. $\pm 1, \pm 3$

47. $\pm 1, \pm 3, \pm 5, \pm 9, \pm 15, \pm 45, \pm\frac{1}{2}, \pm\frac{3}{2}, \pm\frac{5}{2}, \pm\frac{9}{2}, \pm\frac{15}{2}, \pm\frac{45}{2}$

49. $-1, 2$ **51.** $-6, \frac{1}{2}, 1$

53. (a) $-2, 0.268, 3.732$ (b) -2
(c) $h(t) = (t + 2)\left(t - 2 + \sqrt{3}\right)\left(t - 2 - \sqrt{3}\right)$

55. (a) $0, 3, 4, -1.414, 1.414$ (b) $0, 3, 4$
(c) $h(x) = x(x - 3)(x - 4)\left(x + \sqrt{2}\right)\left(x - \sqrt{2}\right)$

57. 4, 2 or 0 positive real zeros, no negative real zeros

59. 2 or 0 positive real zeros, 1 negative real zero

61. (a) 1 positive real zero, 2 or 0 negative real zeros
(b) $\pm 1, \pm 2, \pm 4$
(c)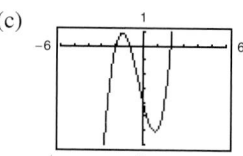

(d) $-2, -1, 2$

63. (a) 3 or 1 positive real zeros, 1 negative real zero
(b) $\pm 1, \pm 2, \pm 4, \pm 8, \pm\frac{1}{2}$
(c)

(d) $-\frac{1}{2}, 1, 2, 4$

65. (a) 2 or 0 positive real zeros, 1 negative real zero

(b) $\pm 1, \pm 3, \pm\frac{1}{2}, \pm\frac{3}{2}, \pm\frac{1}{4}, \pm\frac{3}{4}, \pm\frac{1}{8}, \pm\frac{3}{8}, \pm\frac{1}{16}, \pm\frac{3}{16}, \pm\frac{1}{32}, \pm\frac{3}{32}$

(c)

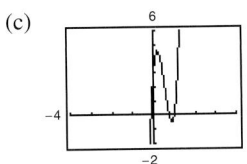

(d) $-\frac{1}{8}, \frac{3}{4}, 1$

67 and 69. Answers will vary.   **71.** $\pm 2, \pm\frac{3}{2}$ **73.** $\pm 1, \frac{1}{4}$

75. d   **76.** a   **77.** b   **78.** c

79. (a)

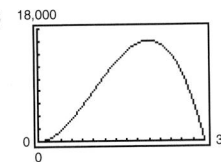

The model is a good fit.

(b)

Year	1995	1996	1997	1998
Actual, R	23.07	24.41	26.48	27.81
Model, R	22.92	24.81	26.30	27.60

Year	1999	2000	2001
Actual, R	28.92	30.37	32.87
Model, R	28.96	30.60	32.77

The model is a close fit.

(c) $R(18) = 82.10$. No; the model will turn sharply upward.

81. (a) Answers will vary.

(b) $20 \times 20 \times 40$

(c) $15, \dfrac{15 \pm 15\sqrt{5}}{2}$;

$\dfrac{15 - 15\sqrt{5}}{2}$ represents a negative volume.

83. False. If $(7x + 4)$ is a factor of f, then $-\frac{4}{7}$ is a zero of f.

85. $x^{2n} + 6x^n + 9$

87. (a) $x + 1, \quad x \neq 1$

(b) $x^2 + x + 1, \quad x \neq 1$

(c) $x^3 + x^2 + x + 1, \quad x \neq 1$

$\dfrac{x^n - 1}{x - 1} = x^{n-1} + x^{n-2} + \cdots + x^2 + x + 1, \quad x \neq 1$

89. $\pm\dfrac{5}{3}$ **91.** $\dfrac{-3 \pm \sqrt{3}}{2}$ **93.** $f(x) = x^2 + 12x$

95. $f(x) = x^4 - 6x^3 + 3x^2 + 10x$

Section 3.4   (page 284)

1. $-3, 0, 0$ **3.** $-9, -2i, 2i$

5. Zeros: $4, -i, i$. One real zero; they are the same.

7. Zeros: $\sqrt{2}i, \sqrt{2}i, -\sqrt{2}i, -\sqrt{2}i$. No real zeros; they are the same.

9. $2 \pm \sqrt{3}$

$(x - 2 - \sqrt{3})(x - 2 + \sqrt{3})$

11. $6 \pm \sqrt{10}$

$(x - 6 - \sqrt{10})(x - 6 + \sqrt{10})$

13. $\pm 5i$

$(x + 5i)(x - 5i)$

15. $\pm 3, \pm 3i$

$(x + 3)(x - 3)(x + 3i)(x - 3i)$

17. $\dfrac{1 \pm \sqrt{223}i}{2}$

$\left(z - \dfrac{1 - \sqrt{223}i}{2}\right)\left(z - \dfrac{1 + \sqrt{223}i}{2}\right)$

19. $-5, 4 \pm 3i$

$(t + 5)(t - 4 + 3i)(t - 4 - 3i)$

21. $1 \pm \sqrt{5}i, -\frac{1}{5}$

$(5x + 1)(x - 1 + \sqrt{5}i)(x - 1 - \sqrt{5}i)$

23. $\pm i, \pm 3i$

$(x + i)(x - i)(x + 3i)(x - 3i)$

25. $2, 2, \pm 2i$

$(x - 2)^2(x + 2i)(x - 2i)$

27. (a) $7 \pm \sqrt{3}$

(b) $(x - 7 - \sqrt{3})(x - 7 + \sqrt{3})$

(c) $(7 \pm \sqrt{3}, 0)$

29. (a) $-7 \pm \sqrt{5}$

(b) $(x + 7 - \sqrt{5})(x + 7 + \sqrt{5})$

(c) $(-7 \pm \sqrt{5}, 0)$

31. (a) $-6, 3 \pm 4i$

(b) $(x + 6)(x - 3 - 4i)(x - 3 + 4i)$

(c) $(-6, 0)$

33. (a) $\pm 4i, \pm 3i$

(b) $(x + 4i)(x - 4i)(x + 3i)(x - 3i)$

(c) None

35. $x^3 - 3x^2 + x - 3$ **37.** $x^3 + 6x^2 + x - 34$

39. $x^4 + 8x^3 + 9x^2 - 10x + 100$

41. (a) $(x^2 + 1)(x^2 - 7)$

(b) $(x^2 + 1)(x + \sqrt{7})(x - \sqrt{7})$

(c) $(x + i)(x - i)(x + \sqrt{7})(x - \sqrt{7})$

43. (a) $(x^2 - 6)(x^2 - 2x + 3)$

(b) $(x + \sqrt{6})(x - \sqrt{6})(x^2 - 2x + 3)$

(c) $(x + \sqrt{6})(x - \sqrt{6})(x - 1 - \sqrt{2}i)(x - 1 + \sqrt{2}i)$

45. $-\frac{3}{2}, \pm 5i$ **47.** $-3, 5 \pm 2i$

49. $-\frac{2}{3}, 1 \pm \sqrt{3}i$ **51.** $\frac{3}{4}, \frac{1}{2}(1 \pm \sqrt{5}i)$

53. (a) $1.000, 2.000$ (b) $-3 \pm \sqrt{2}i$

55. (a) 0.750 (b) $\frac{1}{2} \pm \frac{\sqrt{5}}{2}i$

57. No. Setting $h = 64$ and solving the resulting equation yields imaginary roots.

59. False. A polynomial can only have an even number of complex zeros, so one of the zeros of a third-degree polynomial must be real.

61. (a) $k = 4$ (b) $k < 0$

63.

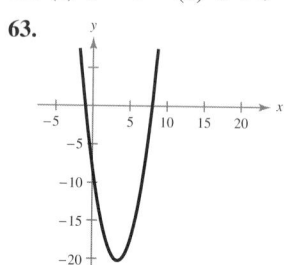

Vertex: $(3.5, -20.25)$

Intercepts:

$(-1, 0), (8, 0), (0, -8)$

65.

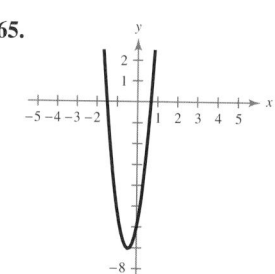

Vertex: $\left(-\frac{5}{12}, -7\frac{1}{24}\right)$

Intercepts:

$\left(-\frac{3}{2}, 0\right), \left(\frac{2}{3}, 0\right), (0, -6)$

Section 3.5   (page 292)

Vocabulary Check   (page 292)

1. rational functions   **2.** vertical asymptote

3. horizontal asymptote

1. (a)

x	$f(x)$	x	$f(x)$
0.5	-2	1.5	2
0.9	-10	1.1	10
0.99	-100	1.01	100
0.999	-1000	1.001	1000

x	$f(x)$	x	$f(x)$
5	0.25	-5	$-0.\overline{16}$
10	$0.\overline{1}$	-10	$-0.\overline{09}$
100	$0.\overline{01}$	-100	$-0.\overline{0099}$
1000	$0.\overline{001}$	-1000	$-0.\overline{000999}$

(b) Vertical asymptote: $x = 1$

Horizontal asymptote: $y = 0$

(c) Domain: all real numbers x except $x = 1$

3. (a)

x	$f(x)$	x	$f(x)$
0.5	3	1.5	9
0.9	27	1.1	33
0.99	297	1.01	303
0.999	2997	1.001	3003

x	$f(x)$	x	$f(x)$
5	3.75	-5	-2.5
10	$3.\overline{33}$	-10	-2.727
100	$3.\overline{03}$	-100	-2.97
1000	$3.\overline{003}$	-1000	-2.997

(b) Vertical asymptote: $x = 1$

Horizontal asymptotes: $y = \pm 3$

(c) Domain: all real numbers x except $x = 1$

5. (a)

x	$f(x)$	x	$f(x)$
0.5	-1	1.5	5.4
0.9	-12.79	1.1	17.29
0.99	-147.8	1.01	152.3
0.999	-1498	1.001	1502.3

x	$f(x)$	x	$f(x)$
5	3.125	-5	3.125
10	$3.\overline{03}$	-10	$3.\overline{03}$
100	$3.\overline{0003}$	-100	$3.\overline{0003}$
1000	3	-1000	3.000003

(b) Vertical asymptotes: $x = \pm 1$

Horizontal asymptote: $y = 3$

(c) Domain: all real numbers x except $x = \pm 1$

7. a   **8.** d   **9.** c   **10.** e

11. b   **12.** f

13. (a) Domain: all real numbers x except $x = 0$

(b) Vertical asymptote: $x = 0$

Horizontal asymptote: $y = 0$

15. (a) Domain: all real numbers x except $x = 2$

(b) Vertical asymptote: $x = 2$

Horizontal asymptote: $y = -1$

17. (a) Domain: all real numbers x except $x = 0, \frac{1}{2}$

(b) Vertical asymptote: $x = \frac{1}{2}$

Horizontal asymptote: $y = \frac{1}{2}$

19. (a) Domain: all real numbers

(b) Vertical asymptote: none

Horizontal asymptote: $y = 3$

21. (a) Domain: all real numbers x except $x = 0$

(b) Vertical asymptote: $x = 0$

Horizontal asymptotes: $y = \pm 1$

23. (a) Domain of f: all real numbers x except $x = -2$

Domain of g: all real numbers

(b) Vertical asymptote: None

(c)

x	-4	-3	-2.5	-2	-1.5	-1	0
$f(x)$	-6	-5	-4.5	Undef.	-3.5	-3	-2
$g(x)$	-6	-5	-4.5	-4	-3.5	-3	-2

(d) Values differ only where f is undefined.

25. (a) Domain of f: all real numbers x except $x = 0, 3$; domain of g: all real numbers x except $x = 0$

(b) Vertical asymptote: $x = 0$

(c)

x	-1	-0.5	0	0.5	2	3	4
$f(x)$	-1	-2	Undef.	2	$\frac{1}{2}$	Undef.	$\frac{1}{4}$
$g(x)$	-1	-2	Undef.	2	$\frac{1}{2}$	$\frac{1}{3}$	$\frac{1}{4}$

(d) Values differ only where f is undefined and g is defined.

27. 4; less than; greater than

29. 2; greater than; less than   **31.** ± 2 **33.** 7

35. (a) $28.33 million   (b) $170 million

(c) $765 million

(d)

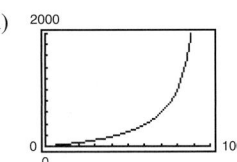

Answers will vary.

(e) No. The function is undefined at the 100% level.

37. (a) $y = \dfrac{1}{0.445 - 0.007x}$

(b)

Age, x	16	32	44	50	60
Near point, y	3.0	4.5	7.3	10.5	40

(c) No; the function is negative for $x = 70$.

39. (a)

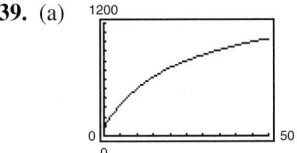

(b) 333 deer, 500 deer, 800 deer

(c) 1500. Because the degrees of the numerator and the denominator are equal, the limiting size is the ratio of the leading coefficients, $60/0.04 = 1500$.

41. False. The degree of the denominator gives the maximum possible number of vertical asymptotes, and the degree is finite.

43. $f(x) = \dfrac{1}{x^2 + x - 2}$ **45.** $f(x) = \dfrac{2x^2}{1 + x^2}$

47. $x - y - 1 = 0$ **49.** $3x - y + 1 = 0$

51. $x + 9 + \dfrac{42}{x - 4}$ **53.** $2x - 9 + \dfrac{34}{x + 5}$

Section 3.6   (page 301)

Vocabulary Check   (page 301)

1. slant, asymptote   **2.** vertical

1.
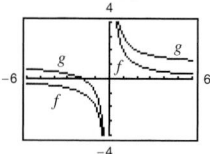
Vertical shift

3.
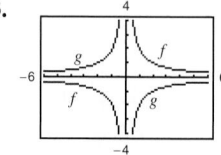
Reflection in the x-axis

5.
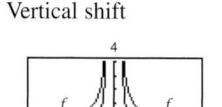
Vertical shift

7.
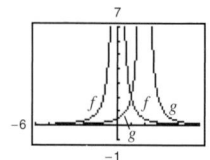
Horizontal shift

9.
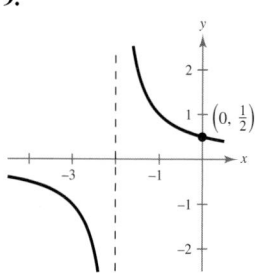

11.
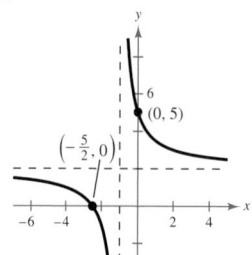

13.
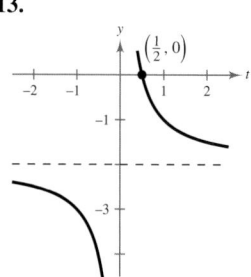

15.
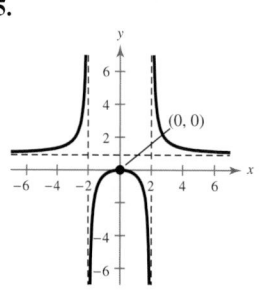

17.
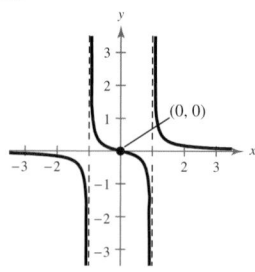

19.
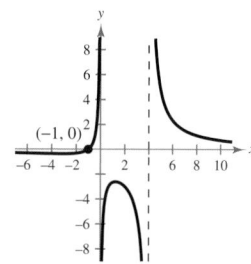

21.
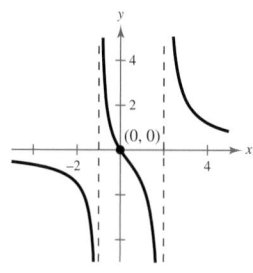

23.
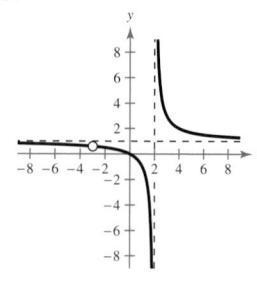

There is a hole at $x = -3$.

25.
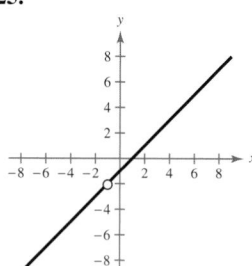

There is a hole at $x = -1$.

27.
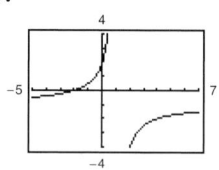

Domain: $(-\infty, 1), (1, \infty)$

Vertical asymptote: $x = 1$

Horizontal asymptote:
$y = -1$

29.
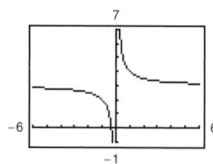

Domain: $(-\infty, 0), (0, \infty)$

Vertical asymptote: $t = 0$

Horizontal asymptote: $y = 3$

31.
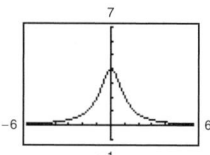

Domain: $(-\infty, \infty)$

Horizontal asymptote: $y = 0$

33.

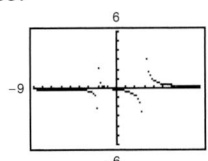

Domain: $(-\infty, -2)$,
    $(-2, 3), (3, \infty)$

Vertical asymptote:
    $x = -2, x = 3$

Horizontal asymptote: $y = 0$

35.

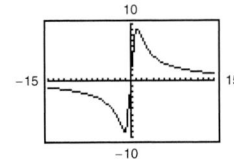

Domain: $(-\infty, 0), (0, \infty)$

Vertical asymptote: $x = 0$

Horizontal asymptote:
    $y = 0$

37.

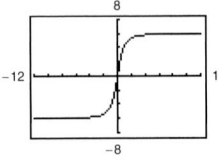

There are two horizontal asymptotes, $y = 6$ and $y = -6$.

39.

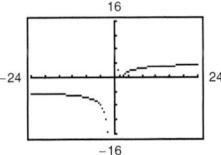

There are two horizontal asymptotes, $y = 4$ and $y = -4$, and one vertical asymptote, $x = -1$.

41.

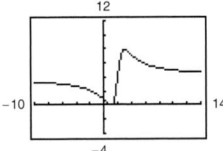

The graph crosses the horizontal asymptote, $y = 4$.

43.

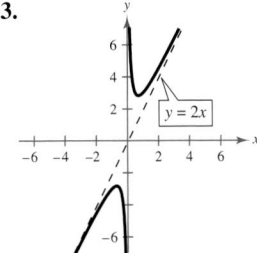

45.

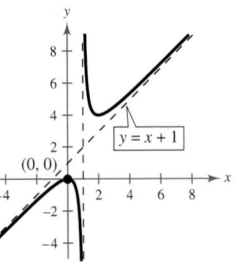

47.

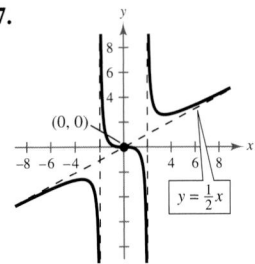

49.

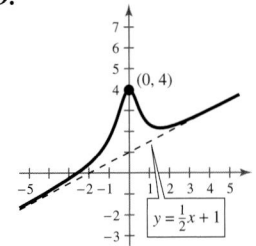

51. $(-1, 0)$ **53.** $(1, 0), (-1, 0)$

55.

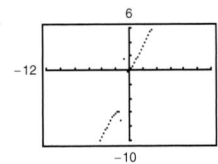

Domain: $(-\infty, -1), (-1, \infty)$

Vertical asymptote: $x = -1$

Slant asymptote: $y = 2x - 1$

57.

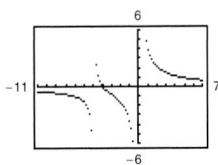

Domain: $(-\infty, 0), (0, \infty)$

Vertical asymptote: $x = 0$

Slant asymptote: $y = -x + 3$

59.

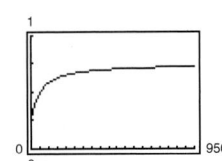

$(-4, 0)$

61.

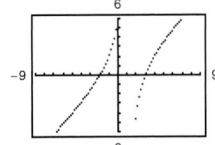

$(3, 0), (-2, 0)$

63. (a) Answers will vary.   (b) $[0, 950]$

(c)

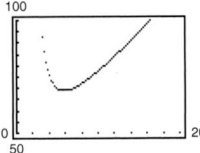

The concentration increases more slowly; the concentration reaches 72.5% when the tank is full.

65. (a) Answers will vary.   (b) $(2, \infty)$

(c)

5.9 inches $\times$ 11.8 inches

67.

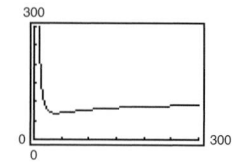

$x \approx 40$

69. (a) $C = 0$. The chemical will eventually dissipate.

(b)

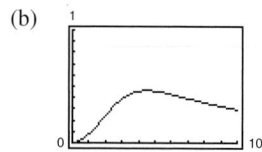

$t \approx 4.5$ hours

(c) Before ≈ 2.6 hours and after ≈ 8.3 hours

71. (a) $y = 0.44t + 1.8$ (b) $y = \dfrac{1}{-0.016t + 0.32}$

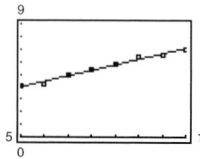 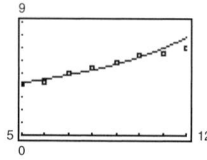

(c)

t	5	6	7	8	9
Linear model	4.0	4.4	4.9	5.3	5.8
Rational model	4.2	4.5	4.8	5.2	5.7

t	10	11	12
Linear model	6.2	6.6	7.1
Rational model	6.3	6.9	7.8

The linear model more closely represents the actual data.

73. False. A graph with a vertical asymptote is not continuous.

75.

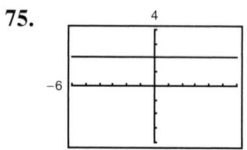

The denominator is a factor of the numerator.

77. $f(x) = \dfrac{x^2 - x - 6}{x - 2}$ **79.** $\dfrac{512}{x^3}$ **81.** $\dfrac{x^2}{5y^2}, x \neq 0$

83. 3

85.

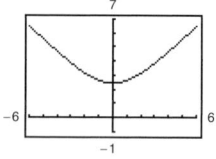

Domain: $(-\infty, \infty)$

Range: $\left[\sqrt{6}, \infty\right)$

87.

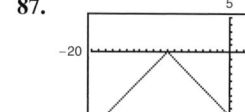

Domain: $(-\infty, \infty)$

Range: $(-\infty, 0]$

Section 3.7 (page 309)

1. Quadratic **3.** Linear **5.** Neither

7. (a) (b) Linear

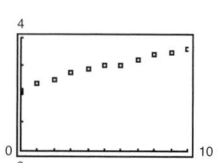

(c) $y = 0.14x + 2.2$

(d)

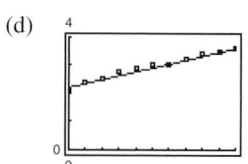

(e)

x	0	1	2	3	4	5
Actual, y	2.1	2.4	2.5	2.8	2.9	3.0
Model, y	2.2	2.3	2.5	2.6	2.8	2.9

x	6	7	8	9	10
Actual, y	3.0	3.2	3.4	3.5	3.6
Model, y	3.0	3.2	3.3	3.5	3.6

9. (a) (b) Quadratic

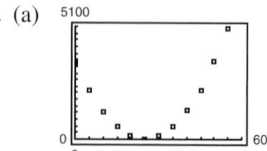

(c) $y = 5.55x^2 - 277.5x + 3478$

(d)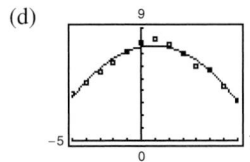

(e)

x	0	5	10	15	20
Actual, y	3480	2235	1250	565	150
Model, y	3478	2229	1258	564	148

x	25	30	35	40
Actual, y	12	145	575	1275
Model, y	9	148	564	1258

x	45	50	55
Actual, y	2225	3500	5010
Model, y	2229	3478	5004

11. (a) 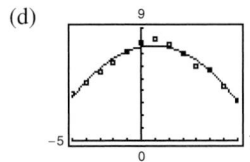   (b) Quadratic

(c) $y = -0.120x^2 + 0.21x + 7.5$

(d)

(e)

x	-5	-4	-3	-2	-1	0
Actual, y	3.8	4.7	5.5	6.2	7.1	7.9
Model, y	3.5	4.7	5.8	6.6	7.2	7.5

x	1	2	3	4	5	6	7
Actual, y	8.1	7.7	6.9	6.0	5.6	4.4	3.2
Model, y	7.6	7.4	7.1	6.4	5.6	4.4	3.1

13. (a)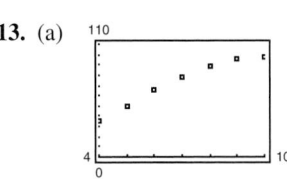

(b) $y = -1.30t^2 + 29.0t - 61$

(c) 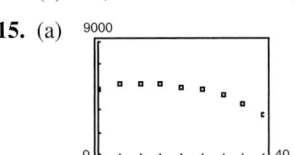   (d) 2000

The model is a good fit.

(e) No; the model turns sharply downward as time increases.

15. (a)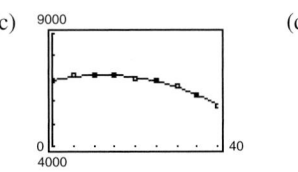

(b) $y = -1.68t^2 + 40.6t + 6903$

(c) 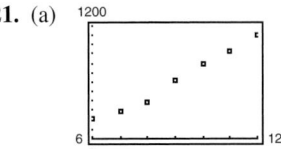   (d) 1972

The model is a good fit.

(e) No; the model continues to decrease as time increases.

17. (a) $y = 2.48x + 1.1$; $y = 0.071x^2 + 1.69x + 2.7$

(b) 0.990, 0.995

(c) Quadratic

19. (a) $y = -0.89x + 0.2$

$y = 0.001x^2 - 0.89x + 0.2$

(b) 0.9998, 0.9999

(c) Quadratic

21. (a)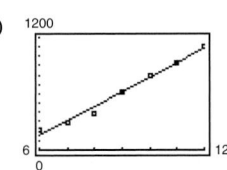

(b) $S = 155.01t - 774.2$

(c)

(d) $S = 6.660t^2 + 35.14t - 261.4$

(e)

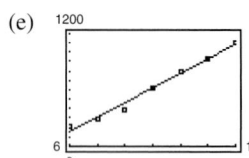

(f) Linear; $1861.1 million

23. True. The Leading Coefficient Test guarantees that a parabola with a negative leading coefficient will have a maximum as its vertex.

25. (a) $(f \circ g)(x) = 2x^2 + 5$

(b) $(g \circ f)(x) = 4(x^2 - x + 1)$

27. (a) $(f \circ g)(x) = x$

(b) $(g \circ f)(x) = x$

29. $f^{-1}(x) = \dfrac{x - 5}{2}$ **31.** $f^{-1}(x) = \sqrt{x - 5}$

33.

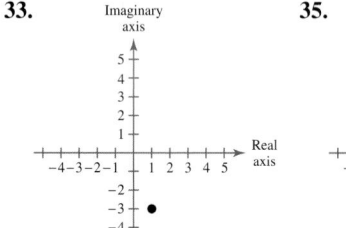

35.

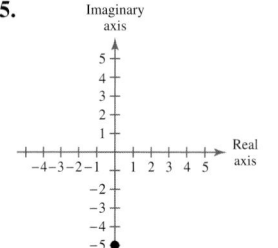

Review Exercises   (page 313)

1.

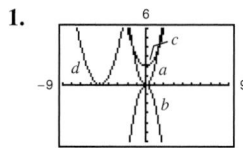

(a) Vertical stretch

(b) Vertical stretch and reflection in the x-axis

(c) Vertical shift

(d) Horizontal shift

3.

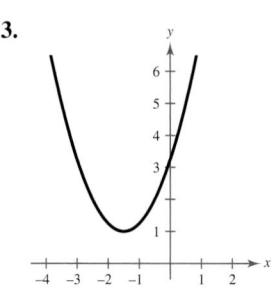

Vertex: $\left(-\frac{3}{2}, 1\right)$

Intercept: $\left(0, \frac{13}{4}\right)$

5.

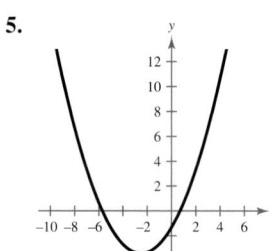

Vertex: $\left(-\dfrac{5}{2}, -\dfrac{41}{12}\right)$

Intercepts:

$\left(0, -\dfrac{4}{3}\right), \left(\dfrac{-5 \pm \sqrt{41}}{2}, 0\right)$

7. $f(x) = (x - 1)^2 - 4$ **9.** $y = 2(x + 2)^2 - 2$

11. (a) $A = x\left(\dfrac{8 - x}{2}\right), 0 < x < 8$

(b)

x	Area
1	$(1)\left[4 - \frac{1}{2}(1)\right] = \frac{7}{2}$
2	$(2)\left[4 - \frac{1}{2}(2)\right] = 6$
3	$(3)\left[4 - \frac{1}{2}(3)\right] = \frac{15}{2}$
4	$(4)\left[4 - \frac{1}{2}(4)\right] = 8$
5	$(5)\left[4 - \frac{1}{2}(5)\right] = \frac{15}{2}$
6	$(6)\left[4 - \frac{1}{2}(6)\right] = 6$

$x = 4, y = 2$

(c)

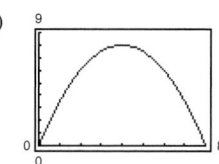

$x = 4, y = 2$

(d) $A = -\frac{1}{2}(x - 4)^2 + 8$

(e) Answers will vary.

13. (a)

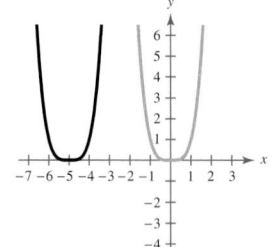

(b)

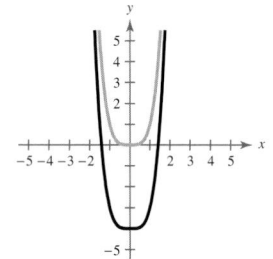

(c)

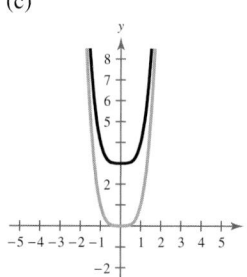

(d)

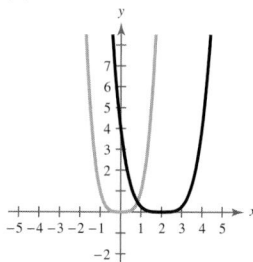

15. (a)

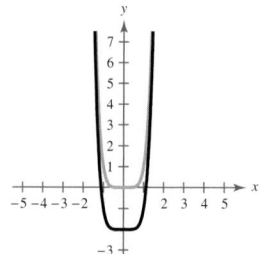

(b)

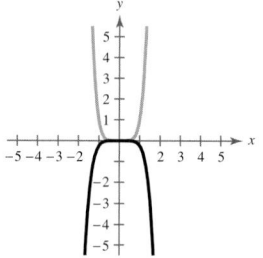

(c)

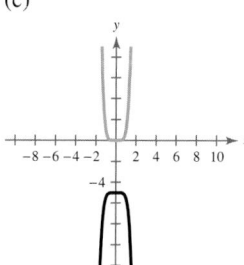

(d)

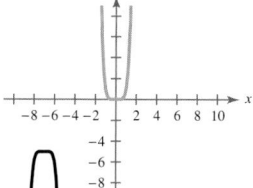

17.

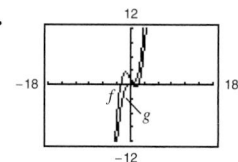

19. Falls to the left,
falls to the right

21. Rises to the left,
rises to the right

23. (a)

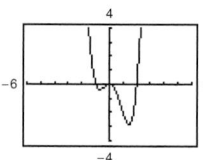

(b) and (c) $x = -1, 0, 2$

25. (a)

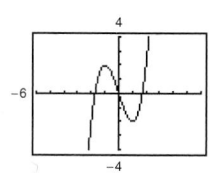

(b) and (c) $t = 0, \pm\sqrt{3}$

27. (a)

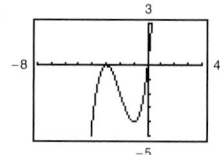

(b) and (c) $x = -3, 0$

29. (a) $(-3, -2), (-1, 0), (0, 1)$

(b) $(-2.247, 0), (-0.555, 0), (0.802, 0)$

31. (a) $(-3, -2), (2, 3)$ (b) $(-2.570, 0), (2.570, 0)$

33.

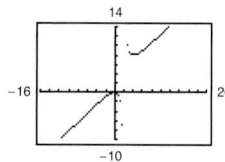

35. $8x + 5 + \dfrac{2}{3x - 2}$

37. $x^2 - 2, \ x \neq \pm 1$ **39.** $5x + 2, \ x \neq \dfrac{3 \pm \sqrt{5}}{2}$

41. $3x^2 + 5x + 8 + \dfrac{10}{2x^2 - 1}$

43. $\dfrac{1}{4}x^3 - \dfrac{9}{2}x^2 + 9x - 18 + \dfrac{36}{x + 2}$

45. $6x^3 - 27x, \ x \neq \dfrac{2}{3}$ **47.** $3x^2 + 2x + 20 + \dfrac{58}{x - 4}$

49. (a) -421 (b) -9

51. (a) Answers will vary.

(b) $(x + 1)(x + 7)$

(c) $f(x) = (x - 4)(x + 1)(x + 7)$

(d) $x = 4, -1, -7$

53. (a) Answers will vary.

(b) $(x + 1)(x - 4)$

(c) $f(x) = (x + 2)(x - 3)(x + 1)(x - 4)$

(d) $x = -2, 3, -1, 4$

55. $\pm 1, \pm 3, \pm\dfrac{3}{2}, \pm\dfrac{3}{4}, \pm\dfrac{1}{2}, \pm\dfrac{1}{4}$

57. $\dfrac{5}{6}, \pm 2i$ **59.** $-1, \dfrac{3}{2}, 3, \dfrac{2}{3}$

61. 2 or 0 positive real zeros

1 negative real zero

63. Answers will vary.

65. $x = 0, 2, 2$ **67.** $x = -4, 6, \pm 2i$

69. Zeros: $2, -\dfrac{3}{2}, 1 \pm i$;

$(x - 2)(2x + 3)[x - (1 - i)][x - (1 + i)]$

71. Zeros: $4, \dfrac{3 \pm \sqrt{15}i}{2}$;

$(x - 4)\left[x - \left(\dfrac{3 + \sqrt{15}i}{2}\right)\right]\left[x - \dfrac{3 - \sqrt{15}i}{2}\right]$

73. (a) $2, 1 \pm i$

(b) $(x - 2)(x - 1 - i)(x - 1 + i)$ (c) $(2, 0)$

75. (a) $-4, -1 \pm \sqrt{2}i$

(b) $(x + 4)\left(x + 1 + \sqrt{2}i\right)\left(x + 1 - \sqrt{2}i\right)$

(c) $(-4, 0)$

77. (a) $\pm 3i, \pm 5i$

(b) $(x - 3i)(x + 3i)(x - 5i)(x + 5i)$ (c) None

79. $f(x) = x^4 + 4x^3 + 29x^2 + 100x + 100$

81. $f(x) = x^4 + 9x^3 + 48x^2 + 78x - 136$

83. (a) $(x^2 + 4)(x^2 - 2)$

(b) $(x^2 + 4)\left(x - \sqrt{2}\right)\left(x + \sqrt{2}\right)$

(c) $(x + 2i)(x - 2i)\left(x - \sqrt{2}\right)\left(x + \sqrt{2}\right)$

85. (a) $(x^2 + 9)(x^2 - 2x - 1)$

(b) $(x^2 + 9)\left(x - 1 + \sqrt{2}\right)\left(x - 1 - \sqrt{2}\right)$

(c) $(x + 3i)(x - 3i)\left(x - 1 + \sqrt{2}\right)\left(x - 1 - \sqrt{2}\right)$

87. (a) Domain: all real numbers x except $x = 1$

(b) Vertical asymptote: $x = 1$

Horizontal asymptote: $y = -1$

89. (a) Domain: all real numbers x except $x = 6, -3$

(b) Vertical asymptotes: $x = 6, x = -3$

Horizontal asymptote: $y = 0$

91. (a) Domain: all real numbers x except $x = 7$

(b) Vertical asymptote: $x = 7$

Horizontal asymptote: $y = -1$

93. (a) Domain: all real numbers x except $x = \pm\dfrac{\sqrt{6}}{2}$

(b) Vertical asymptotes: $x = \pm\dfrac{\sqrt{6}}{2}$

Horizontal asymptote: $y = 2$

95. (a) Domain: all real numbers x except $x = 5, -3$

(b) Vertical asymptotes: $x = -3$

Horizontal asymptote: $y = 0$

97. (a) Domain: all real numbers

(b) Vertical asymptote: none

Horizontal asymptotes: $y = \pm 1$

99. (a) \$176 million; \$528 million; \$1584 million

(b)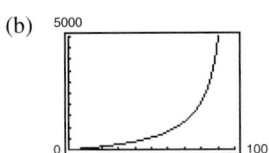

Answers will vary.

(c) No. As $p \to 100$, the cost approaches ∞.

101.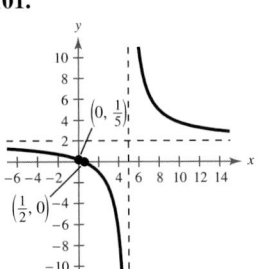

103.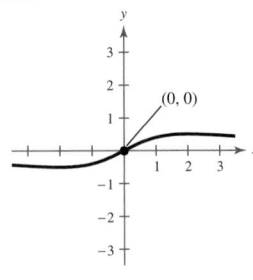

105.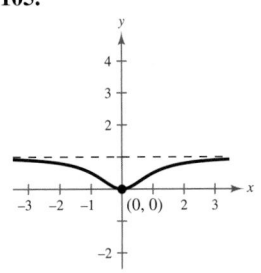

107.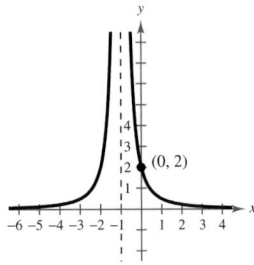

109.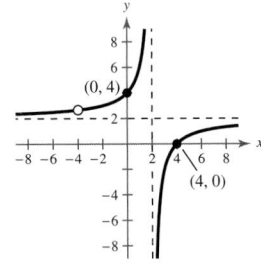

111.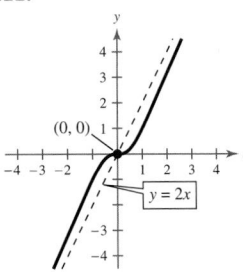

There is a hole at $x = -4$.

113.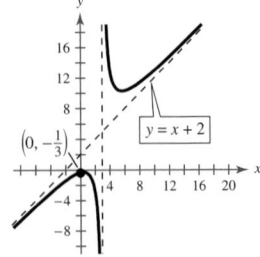

115. (a)
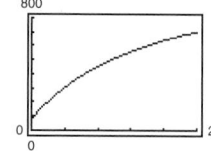

(b) 304,000; 453,333; 702,222

(c) 1,200,000, because N has a horizontal asymptote at $y = 1,200,000$.

117. Quadratic   **119.** Linear

121. (a)
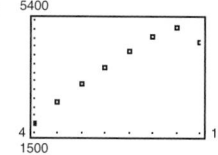

(b) $R = -68.707t^2 + 1485.31t - 3126.7$

(c)
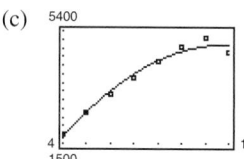

Answers will vary.

(d) 2000

(e) No; the model begins to decrease rapidly over time.

123. False. For the graph of a rational function to have a slant asymptote, the degree of its numerator must be exactly one more than the degree of its denominator.

125. The divisor is a factor of the dividend.

Chapter Test   (page 318)

1. (a) Reflection in the x-axis followed by a vertical shift six units up

(b) Horizontal shift of $\frac{3}{2}$ units to the right

2. Vertex: $(-2, -1)$

Intercepts: $(0, 3), (-3, 0), (-1, 0)$

3. $y = (x - 3)^2 - 6$

4. (a) 50 feet

(b) 5; Changing the constant term results in a vertical shift of the graph and therefore changes the maximum height.

5. $3x + \dfrac{x - 1}{x^2 + 1}$ **6.** $2x^3 + 4x^2 + 3x + 6 + \dfrac{9}{x - 2}$

7. $\pm 1, \pm 2, \pm 3, \pm 4, \pm 6, \pm 8, \pm 12, \pm 24, \pm \frac{1}{2}, \pm \frac{3}{2}$

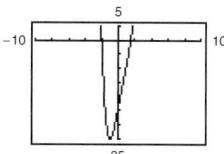

$-2, \frac{3}{2}$

8. $\pm 1, \pm 2, \pm \frac{1}{3}, \pm \frac{2}{3}$

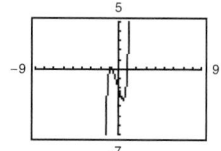

$\pm 1, -\frac{2}{3}$

9. $-0.819, 1.380$ **10.** $-1.414, -0.667, 1.414$

11. $f(x) = x^4 - 9x^3 + 28x^2 - 30x$

12. $f(x) = x^4 - 6x^3 + 16x^2 - 24x + 16$

13. $f(x) = x^4 + 3x^3 - 8x^2 + 10x$

14.
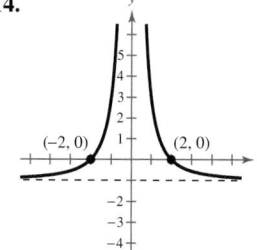

15.
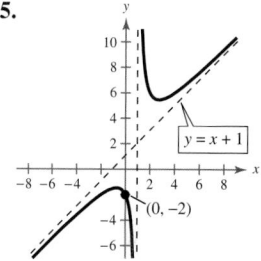

16.
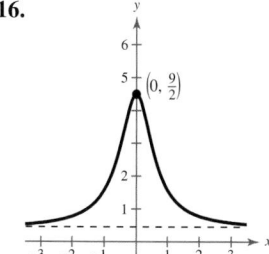

17. (a)
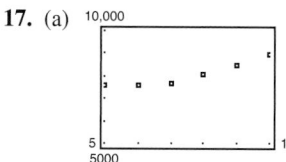

(b) $y = 62.55x^2 - 654.9x + 9269$

(c)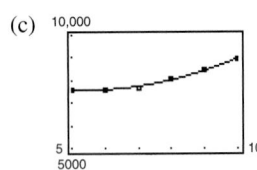

The model is a good fit.

(d) 2006

Chapter 4

Section 4.1   (page 329)

Vocabulary Check   (page 329)

1. algebraic   **2.** transcendental

3. natural exponential, natural

4. $A = P\left(1 + \dfrac{r}{n}\right)^{nt}$ **5.** $A = Pe^{rt}$

1. 4112.033   **3.** 0.006   **5.** 18,297.851

7.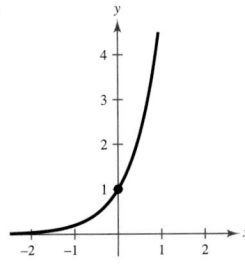

$y = 0, (0, 1)$, increasing

9.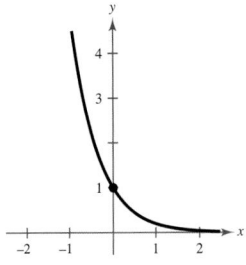

$y = 0, (0, 1)$, decreasing

11.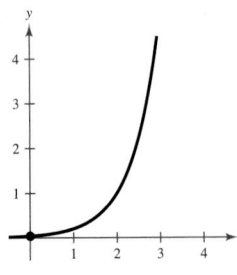

$y = 0, \left(0, \frac{1}{25}\right)$, increasing

13.

$y = -3, (0, -2)$,
$(-0.683, 0)$, decreasing

15. d   **16.** a   **17.** c   **18.** b

19. Right shift of five units

21. Left shift of four units and reflection in the x-axis

23. 9897.129   **25.** 54.164   **27.** 1.516

29.

x	-1	0	1	2	3
$f(x)$	0.4	1	2.5	6.3	15.6

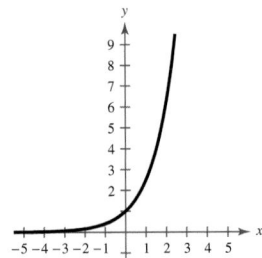

31.

x	-1	0	1	2
$f(x)$	0.2	1	6	36

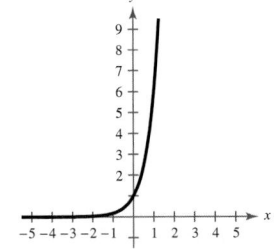

33.

x	-3	-2	0	1
$f(x)$	$\frac{1}{3}$	1	9	27

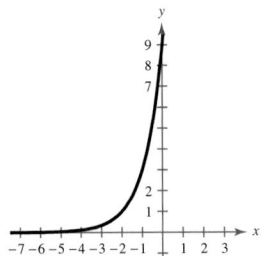

35.

x	-7	-6	-5	-4	-3
$f(x)$	0.1	0.4	1.1	3	8

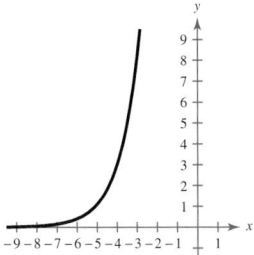

37.

x	2	3	4	5	6	7
$f(x)$	2.0	2.1	2.4	3	4.7	9.4

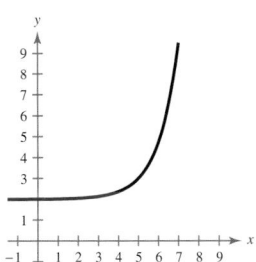

39.

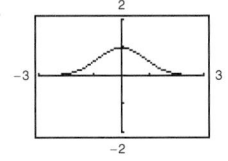

$y = 0$

41.

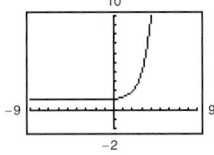

$y = 1$

43.

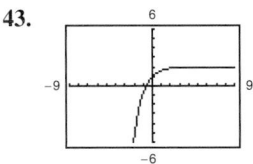

$y = 2$

45.

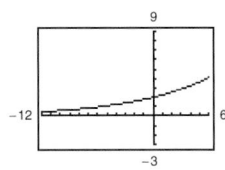

$y = 0$

47. (a)

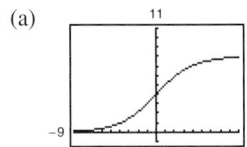

(b)

x	-30	-20	-10	0
$f(x)$	0.0000024	0.00036	0.054	4

x	10	20	30
$f(x)$	7.95	7.9996	7.999998

$y = 0, y = 8$

49. (a)

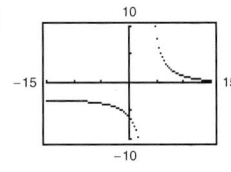

(b)

x	-20	-10	0	3	3.4	3.46
$f(x)$	-3.03	-3.22	-6	-34	-230	-2617

x	3.47	4	5	7	10	15	25
$f(x)$	3516	27	8	2.9	1.1	0.3	0.04

$y = -3, y = 0, x \approx 3.46$

51. (a)

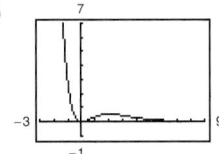

(b) Decreasing on $(-\infty, 0), (2, \infty)$
Increasing on $(0, 2)$

(c) Relative minimum at $(0, 0)$
Relative maximum at $(2, 0.541)$

53. (a)

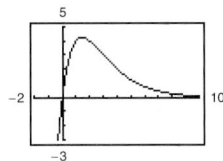

(b) Increasing on $(-\infty, 1.443)$
Decreasing on $(1.443, \infty)$

(c) Relative maximum at $(1.443, 4.246)$

55.

n	1	2	4	12
A	3200.21	3205.09	3207.57	3209.23

n	365	Continuous
A	3210.04	3210.06

57.

n	1	2	4	12
A	5477.81	5520.10	5541.79	5556.46

n	365	Continuous
A	5563.61	5563.85

59.

t	1	10	20
A	12,489.73	17,901.90	26,706.49

t	30	40	50
A	39,841.40	59,436.39	88,668.67

61.

t	1	10	20
A	12,427.44	17,028.81	24,165.03

t	30	40	50
A	34,291.81	48,662.40	69,055.23

63. (a)

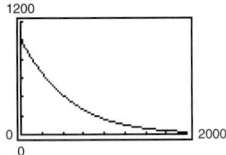

(b) $421.12

(c) $350.13

(d)

x	100	200	300	400
p	849.53	717.64	603.25	504.94

x	500	600	700
p	421.12	350.13	290.35

65. (a) 25 grams　　(b) 16.30 grams

(c)

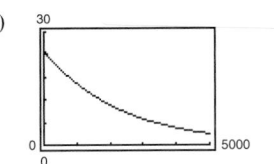

(d) Never. The graph has a horizontal asymptote at $Q = 0$.

67. (a)

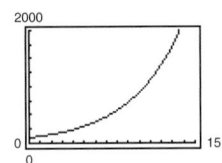

(b) and (c) $P(0) = 100$; $P(5) \approx 300$; $P(10) \approx 900$

69. (a)

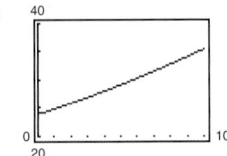

(b) and (c) $35.45

71. True. $f(x) = 1^x$ is not an exponential function because the definition of an exponential function is $f(x) = a^x$, $a > 0$, $a \neq 1$.

73.

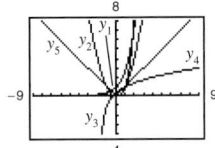

(a) $y_1 = e^x$

(b) The exponential function increases at a faster rate.

(c) It usually implies rapid growth.

75.

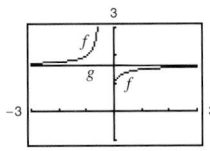

$f(x)$ approaches $g(x) = 1.6487$.

77. $f^{-1}(x) = \dfrac{x + 7}{5}$　　**79.** $f^{-1}(x) = x^3 - 8$

81.

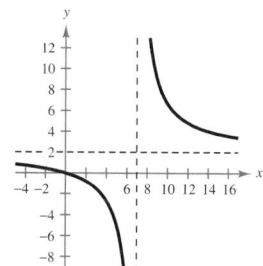

Section 4.2 (page 339)

Vocabulary Check (page 339)

1. logarithmic function   **2.** 10

3. natural logarithmic   **4.** $a^{\log_a x} = x$ **5.** $x = y$

1. $4^3 = 64$ **3.** $7^{-2} = \frac{1}{49}$ **5.** $32^{2/5} = 4$ **7.** $e^0 = 1$

9. $\log_5 125 = 3$ **11.** $\log_{81} 3 = \frac{1}{4}$ **13.** $\log_6 \frac{1}{36} = -2$

15. $\ln 20.0855 \ldots = 3$ **17.** 4   **19.** -2

21. 2.538   **23.** 7.022   **25.** 9   **27.** 2   **29.** $\frac{1}{10}$

31.

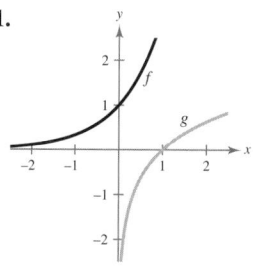

Reflections in the line $y = x$

$g = f^{-1}$

33.

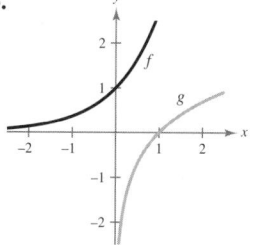

Reflections in the line $y = x$

$g = f^{-1}$

35. Domain: $(0, \infty)$

  Vertical asymptote: $x = 0$

  x-intercept: $(1, 0)$

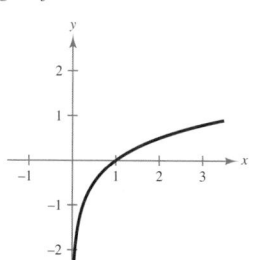

37. Domain: $(0, \infty)$

  Vertical asymptote: $x = 0$

  x-intercept: $(5, 0)$

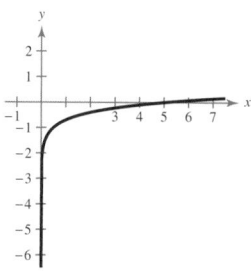

39. Domain: $(3, \infty)$

  Vertical asymptote: $x = 3$

  x-intercept: $(4, 0)$

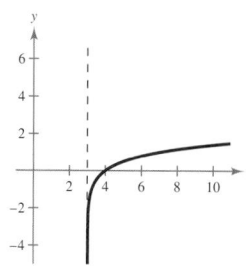

41. Domain: $(0, \infty)$

  Vertical asymptote: $x = 0$

  x-intercept: $(100, 0)$

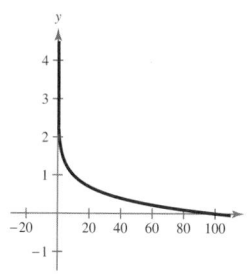

43. Domain: $(3, \infty)$

  Vertical asymptote: $x = 3$

  x-intercept:

  $(3 + 6^{-6}, 0) \approx (3, 0)$

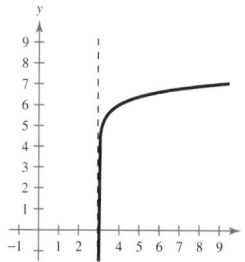

45. b   **46.** c   **47.** d   **48.** a

49. Because $g(x) = -f(x)$, the graph of g can be obtained by reflecting the graph of f in the x-axis.

51. Because $g(x) = 4 - f(x)$, the graph of g can be obtained by reflecting the graph of f in the x-axis and then shifting the graph of f 4 units upward.

53. 1.869   **55.** 0.693   **57.** 2   **59.** 1.8

61. Domain: $(1, \infty)$

  Vertical asymptote: $x = 1$

  x-intercept: $(2, 0)$

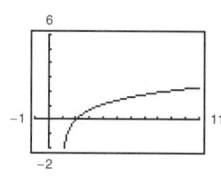

63. Domain: $(-\infty, 0)$

Vertical asymptote: $x = 0$

x-intercept: $(-1, 0)$

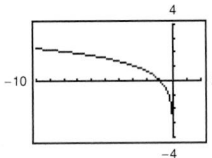

65. (a)

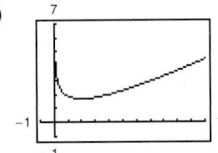

(b) Domain: $(0, \infty)$

(c) Decreasing on $(0, 2)$; increasing on $(2, \infty)$

(d) Relative minimum: $(2, 1.693)$

67. (a)

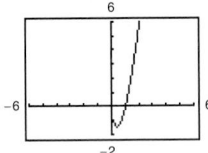

(b) Domain: $(0, \infty)$

(c) Decreasing on $(0, 0.37)$; increasing on $(0.37, \infty)$

(d) Relative minimum: $(0.37, -1.47)$

69. (a) 80   (b) 68.1   (c) 62.3

71. (a)

K	1	2	4	6	8	10	12
t	0	12.6	25.2	32.6	37.8	41.9	45.2

Answers will vary.

(b)

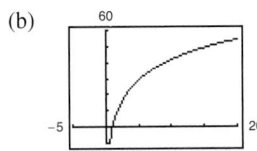

73. (a) 120 decibels   (b) 100 decibels

(c) No. Answers will vary.

75.

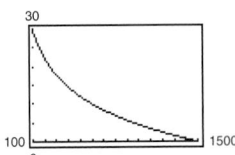

17.66 cubic feet per minute

77. False. Reflect $g(x)$ in the line $y = x$.

79. $\log_a x$ is the inverse of a^x only if $0 < a < 1$ and $a > 1$, so $\log_a x$ is defined only for $0 < a < 1$ and $a > 1$.

81. (a) False   (b) True   (c) True   (d) False

83. (a)

x	1	5	10	10^2
$f(x)$	0	0.322	0.230	0.046

x	10^4	10^6
$f(x)$	0.00092	0.0000138

(b) 0

(c)

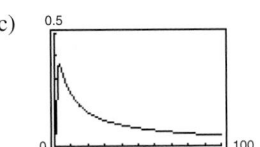

85. $(x + 3)(x - 1)$ **87.** $(4x + 3)(3x - 1)$

89. $(4x + 5)(4x - 5)$ **91.** $x(2x - 9)(x + 5)$

93. 15   **95.** 4300   **97.** $x = 2.75$ **99.** $x = 27.\overline{6}$

101. Vertical asymptote: $x = -8$

Horizontal asymptote: $y = 0$

103. Vertical asymptotes: $x = \frac{5}{2}, x = -3$

Horizontal asymptote: $y = 0$

105. Vertical asymptote: $x = 6$

Horizontal asymptote: $y = 1$

Section 4.3   (page 347)

Vocabulary Check   (page 347)

1. change-of-base   **2.** $\dfrac{\ln x}{\ln a}$ **3.** $\log_a u^n$

4. $\ln u + \ln v$

1. (a) $\dfrac{\log_{10} x}{\log_{10} 5}$ (b) $\dfrac{\ln x}{\ln 5}$ **3.** (a) $\dfrac{\log_{10} x}{\log_{10} \frac{1}{5}}$ (b) $\dfrac{\ln x}{\ln \frac{1}{5}}$

5. (a) $\dfrac{\log_{10} \frac{3}{10}}{\log_{10} a}$ (b) $\dfrac{\ln \frac{3}{10}}{\ln a}$

7. (a) $\dfrac{\log_{10} x}{\log_{10} 2.6}$ (b) $\dfrac{\ln x}{\ln 2.6}$

9. 1.771   **11.** -2 **13.** -0.102 **15.** 2.691

17. $\frac{3}{2}$ **19.** $6 + \ln 5$

21. $\log_5 \frac{1}{250} = \log_5 1 - \log_5 250$

$= 0 - \log_5 (125 \cdot 2)$

$= -(\log_5 125 + \log_5 2)$

$= -3 - \log_5 2$

23. $\log_{10} 5 + \log_{10} x$ **25.** $\log_{10} 5 - \log_{10} x$

27. $4 \log_8 x$ **29.** $\frac{1}{2} \ln z$ **31.** $\ln x + \ln y + \ln z$

33. $2 \ln a + \frac{1}{2} \ln(a - 1)$ **35.** $\frac{1}{3} \ln x - \frac{1}{3} \ln y$

37. $\ln(x + 1) + \ln(x - 1) - 3 \ln x, \ x > 1$

39. $4 \ln x + \frac{1}{2} \ln y - 5 \ln z$

41. $2 \log_b x - 2 \log_b y - 3 \log_b z$

43. (a)

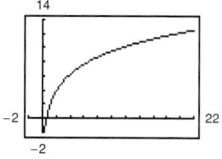

(b)

x	1	2	3	4	5	6
y_1	1.6094	3.8712	5.2417	6.2383	7.0255	7.6779
y_2	1.6094	3.8712	5.2417	6.2383	7.0255	7.6779

x	7	8	9	10	11
y_1	8.2356	8.7232	9.1566	9.5468	9.9017
y_2	8.2356	8.7232	9.1566	9.5468	9.9017

(c) $y_1 = y_2$ for positive values of x.

45. $\ln 4x$ **47.** $\log_4 \dfrac{z}{y}$ **49.** $\log_2(x + 3)^2$

51. $\log_3 \sqrt[3]{7x}$ **53.** $\ln \dfrac{x}{(x + 1)^3}$ **55.** $\ln \dfrac{x - 2}{x + 2}$

57. $\ln \dfrac{x}{(x^2 - 4)^2}$ **59.** $\ln \sqrt[3]{\dfrac{x(x + 3)^2}{x^2 - 1}}$

61. $\ln \dfrac{\sqrt[3]{y(y + 4)^2}}{y - 1}$

63. (a)

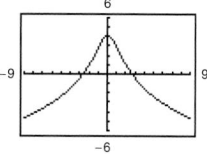

(b)

x	-5	-4	-3	-2	-1
y_1	-2.3573	-1.5075	-0.4463	0.9400	2.7726
y_2	-2.3573	-1.5075	-0.4463	0.9400	2.7726

x	0	1	2	3	4	5
y_1	4.1589	2.7726	0.9400	-0.4463	-1.5075	-2.3573
y_2	4.1589	2.7726	0.9400	-0.4463	-1.5075	-2.3573

(c) $y_1 = y_2$

65. (a)

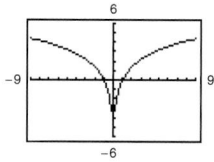

(b)

x	-5	-4	-3	-2	-1	0
y_1	3.2189	2.7726	2.1972	1.3863	0	Error
y_2	Error	Error	Error	Error	Error	Error

x	1	2	3	4	5
y_1	0	1.3863	2.1972	2.7726	3.2189
y_2	0	1.3863	2.1972	2.7726	3.2189

(c) No. The domains differ.

67. 2   **69.** 6.8   **71.** -4 is not in the domain of $\log_2 x$.

73. 2   **75.** -4 **77.** 8   **79.** $-\frac{1}{2}$

81. (a) $120 + 10 \log_{10} I$

(b) and (c)

I	10^{-4}	10^{-6}	10^{-8}	10^{-10}	10^{-12}	10^{-14}
β	80	60	40	20	0	-20

83. (a)

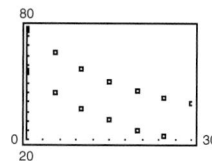

(b) $T = 54.438(0.964)^t + 21$

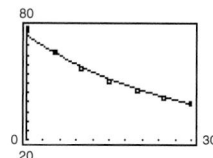

(c) $\ln(T - 21) = -0.037t + 3.997$

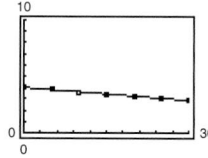

$$T = e^{(-0.037t + 3.997)} + 21$$

(d) $\dfrac{1}{T-21} = 0.0012t + 0.0162$

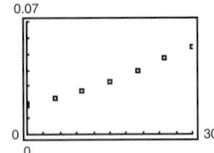

$$T = \dfrac{1}{0.0012t + 0.0162} + 21$$

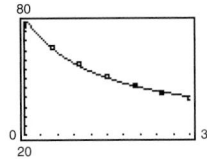

85. False. $\ln 1 = 0$ **87.** True

89. False. $f(\sqrt{x}) = \frac{1}{2}f(x)$ **91.** True

93. $\log_b u^n = \log_b(\underbrace{u \times u \times u \times \cdots \times u}_{n \ u\text{'s multiplied together}})$

$$= \underbrace{\log_b u + \log_b u + \cdots + \log_b u}_{n \ \text{terms}}$$

$$= n \log_b u$$

95. $f(x) = \dfrac{\log_{10} x}{\log_{10} 2}$ **97.** $f(x) = \dfrac{\log_{10} \sqrt{x}}{\log_{10} 3}$

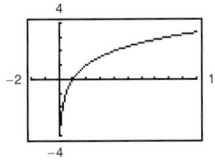   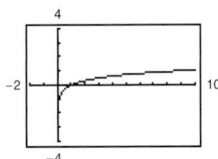

99. $f(x) = \dfrac{\log_{10}(x/3)}{\log_{10} 5}$

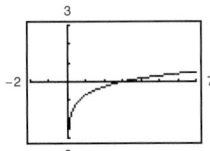

101. $f(x) = h(x)$

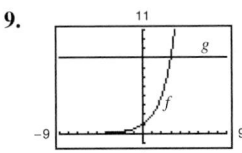

The graphs are identical because for each positive value of x, Property 2 of logarithms holds.

103. $\dfrac{3x^4}{2y^3}$ **105.** $1, x \neq 0, y \neq 0$ **107.** $3 \pm \sqrt{7}$

109. $\pm 4, \pm \sqrt{3}$ **111.** $\pm 2, 6$

Section 4.4   (page 357)

1. (a) Yes   (b) No

3. (a) No   (b) Yes   (c) Yes, approximate

5. (a) Yes, approximate   (b) No   (c) Yes

7. (a) Yes   (b) Yes, approximate   (c) No

9.   **11.**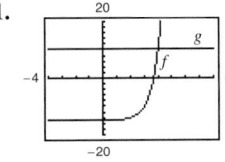

$(3, 8)$ $(4, 10)$

13.   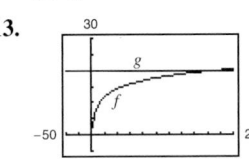   **15.**

$(243, 20)$ $(-4, -3)$

17. 2   **19.** -4 **21.** -2 **23.** -4

25. $\ln 4 \approx 1.386$ **27.** 5   **29.** $e^{-7} \approx 0.00091$

31. 5   **33.** 0.1   **35.** $\dfrac{e^5 + 1}{2} \approx 74.71$ **37.** x^2

39. $5x + 2$ **41.** x^2 **43.** 0.944   **45.** 0.439

47. 0.511   **49.** 0   **51.** 2   **53.** -6.142

55. $\ln 5 \approx 1.609$ **57.** 1.946   **59.** 6.960

61.

x	0.6	0.7	0.8	0.9	1.0
e^{3x}	6.05	8.17	11.02	14.88	20.09

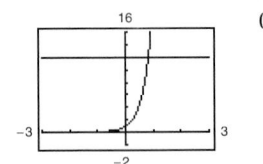   0.828

63.

x	5	6	7	8	9
$20(100 - e^{x/2})$	1756	1598	1338	908	200

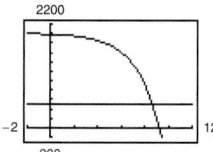

8.635

65. 21.330   **67.** 3.656

69. 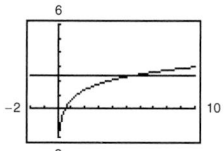   **71.**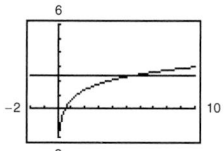

   -0.427 12.207

73. 0.050   **75.** 2.042   **77.** 4453.242   **79.** 103

81. 17.945   **83.** 5.389   **85.** 1.718, -3.718 **87.** 2

89. No real solution   **91.** 180.384

93.

x	2	3	4	5	6
$\ln 2x$	1.39	1.79	2.08	2.30	2.48

5.512

95.

x	12	13	14	15	16
$6 \log_3(0.5x)$	9.79	10.22	10.63	11.00	11.36

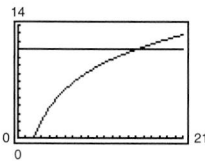

14.988

97. 1.469, 0.001   **99.** 3.791   **101.** 3.423

103. 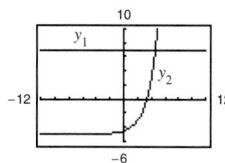   **105.**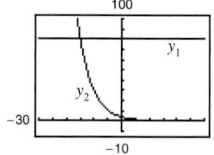

   (4.585, 7) $(-14.979, 80)$

107.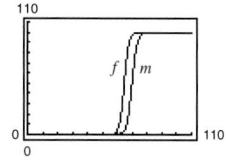

   (663.142, 3.25)

109. (a) 8.2 years   (b) 12.9 years

111. (a) 1426 units   (b) 1498 units   **113.** 12.76 inches

115. (a)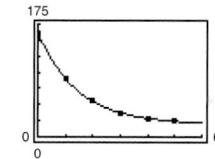

   (b) $y = 100$ and $y = 0$; answers will vary.

   (c) Males: 69.71 inches; females: 64.51 inches

117. (a)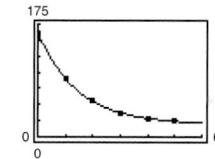

   (b) $y = 20$. Room temperature

   (c) 0.81 hour

119. True

121. (a) When solving exponential equations, rewrite the original equation in a form that allows you to use the One-to-One Properties of exponential functions. You can also rewrite the exponential equation in logarithmic form and apply the Inverse Property of logarithmic functions.

   (b) When solving logarithmic equations, rewrite the original equation in a form that allows you to use the One-to-One Properties of logarithmic functions. You can also rewrite the logarithmic equation in exponential form and apply the Inverse Property of exponential functions.

123. Yes. Doubling time: $t = \dfrac{\ln 2}{r}$

   Quadrupling time: $t = \dfrac{\ln 4}{r} = 2\left(\dfrac{\ln 2}{r}\right)$

125.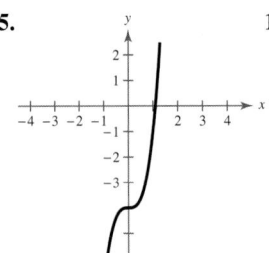

127.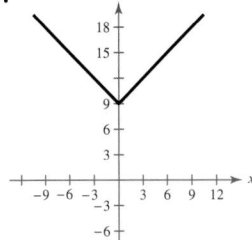

129.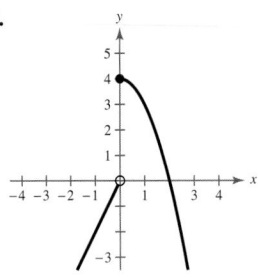

Section 4.5 (page 368)

Vocabulary Check (page 368)

1. $y = ae^{bx}, b > 0$

2. $y = a + b \ln x, \quad y = a + b \log_{10} x$

3. logistic growth **4.** bell-shaped curve

5. sigmoidal

---

1. c **2.** e **3.** b **4.** a **5.** d **6.** f

Initial Investment	Annual % Rate	Time to Double	Amount After 10 Years
7. $1000	3.5%	19.8 yr	$1419.07
9. $750	8.94%	7.75 yr	$1833.67
11. $500	9.5%	7.30 yr	$1292.85
13. $6376.28	4.5%	15.4 yr	$10,000.00

15.

r	2%	4%	6%	8%	10%	12%
t	54.93	27.47	18.31	13.73	10.99	9.16

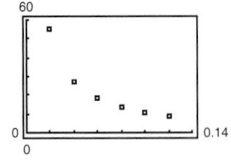

17.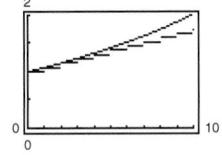

Continuous compounding

Isotope	Half-Life (years)	Initial Quantity	Amount After 1000 Years
19. ^{226}Ra	1600	10 g	6.48 g
21. ^{14}C	5730	3 g	2.66 g

23. $y = e^{0.768x}$ **25.** $y = 4e^{-0.2773x}$

27. (a) Australia: $y = 19.2e^{0.00848t}$; 24.8 million

Canada: $y = 31.3e^{0.00915t}$; 41.2 million

Philippines: $y = 81.2e^{0.0187t}$; 142.3 million

South Africa: $y = 43.4e^{-0.0054t}$; 36.9 million

Turkey: $y = 65.7e^{0.01095t}$; 91.2 million

(b) b; Population changes at a faster rate for a greater magnitude of b.

(c) b; b is positive when the population is increasing and negative when the population is decreasing.

29. 3.15 hours **31.** 95.8%

33. (a) $V = -7000t + 32,000$ (b) $V = 32,000e^{-0.2877t}$

(c)

Exponential

(d) 1 year: Linear: $25,000$; exponential: $24,000$
3 years: Linear: $11,000$; exponential: $13,499$

(e) Value decreases by $7000 each year

35. (a) $S(t) = 100(1 - e^{-0.1625t})$

(b)

(c) 55,625 units

37. (a)

(b) 100

39. (a)
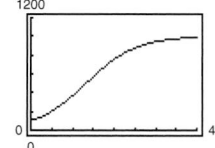

$y = 0$, $y = 1000$. The population size will approach 1000 as time increases.

(b) 203   (c) Between 13 and 14 months

41. (a) 3,162,300   (b) 79,433,000   (c) 158,500

43. (a) 20 decibels   (b) 70 decibels   (c) 120 decibels

45. 97%   **47.** 4.64   **49.** 10,000,000 times

51. (a)
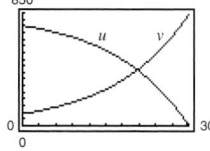

(b) Interest. $t \approx 20.7$ years

(c)
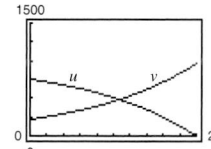   Interest. $t \approx 10.7$ years

53. 3:00 A.M.   **55.** False   **57.** True

59. a; $(0, -3)$, $\left(\frac{9}{4}, 0\right)$ **60.** b; $(0, 2)$, $(5, 0)$

61. d; $(0, 25)$, $\left(\frac{100}{9}, 0\right)$ **62.** c; $(0, 4)$, $(2, 0)$

63. The graph falls to the left and rises to the right.

65. The graph rises to the left and falls to the right.

67. $2x^2 + 3 + \dfrac{3}{x - 4}$

Section 4.6   (page 378)

Vocabulary Check   (page 378)

1. $y = ax + b$ **2.** quadratic

3. $y = ax^b$ **4.** sum, squared differences

5. $y = ab^x$, ae^{cx}

1. Logarithmic model   **3.** Quadratic model

5. Exponential model   **7.** Quadratic model

9.
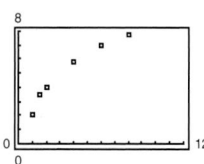
Logarithmic model

11.
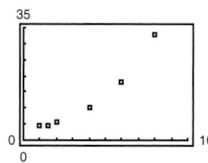
Exponential model

13.
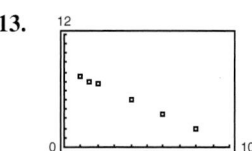
Linear model

15. $y = 3.807(1.3057)^x$
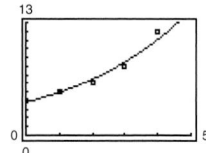

17. $y = 8.463(0.7775)^x$
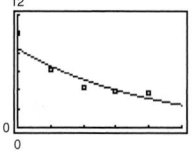

19. $y = 2.083 + 1.257 \ln x$
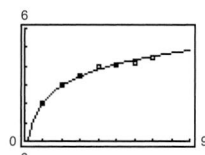

21. $y = 9.826 - 4.097 \ln x$
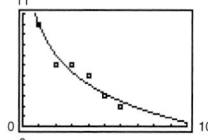

23. $y = 1.985x^{0.760}$
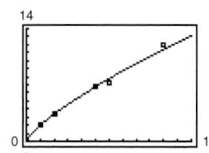

25. $y = 16.103x^{-3.174}$
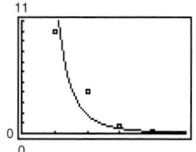

27. (a) Quadratic model: $R = 0.013x^2 + 1.64x + 94.9$
Exponential model: $R = 95.324(1.017)^x$
Power model: $R = 81.230x^{0.168}$

(b) Quadratic model:
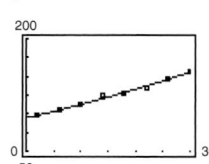

Exponential model:
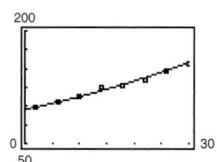

Power model:

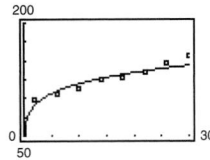

(c) Quadratic   (d) 165.7 million

29. (a) $y = 3.1x + 251$

(b) $y = (251.5)(1.01)^x$

(c) No. The linear model is a better fit than the exponential model because the r-value of the linear model has an absolute value closer to one.

(d) Linear model: 306.8 million

Exponential model: 300.8 million

31. (a) Linear model: $T = -1.24t + 73.0$;

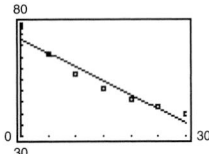

The data does not appear to be linear. Answers may vary.

(b) Quadratic model: $T = 0.034t^2 - 2.26t + 77.3$;

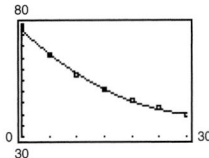

The data appears to be quadratic. When $t = 60$, the temperature of the water should decrease, not increase according to the model.

(c) Exponential model: $T = 54.438(0.964)^t + 21$

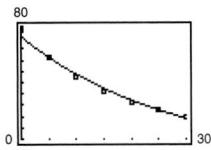

(d) Answers will vary.

33. (a) $S = 925.73(1.15)^x$

(b)
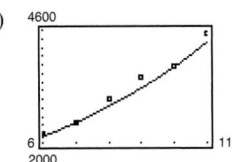

(c) The model represents the data well.

(d) \$9,962,000,000

35. (a) Linear model: $y = 15.79x + 47.9$

Logarithmic model: $y = -97.5 + 131.92 \ln x$

Quadratic model: $y = -1.968x^2 + 49.24x - 88.6$

Exponential model: $y = 83.94(1.09)^x$

Power model: $y = 36.51x^{0.7525}$

(b) Linear model: Logarithmic model:

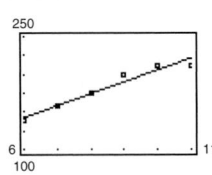   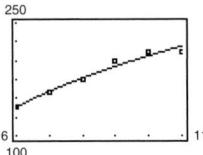

Quadratic model: Exponential model:

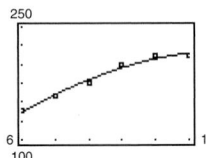   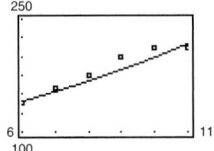

Power model:

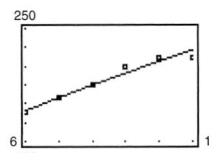

By comparing the graphs, the quadratic model best fits the data.

(c) Linear: 217.2

Logarithmic: 120.91

Quadratic: 72.7

Exponential: 523.2

Power: 189.0

By comparing the sums of the squared differences, the quadratic model best fits the data.

(d) Linear: 0.9526

Logarithmic: 0.9736

Quadratic: 0.9841

Exponential: 0.9402

Power: 0.9697

By comparing the r^2-values, the quadratic model best fits the data.

(e) The quadratic model best fits the data.

37. True

39. Slope: $-\frac{2}{5}$; y-intercept: $(0, 2)$

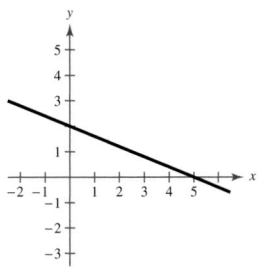

41. Slope: $-\frac{12}{35}$; y-intercept: $(0, 3)$

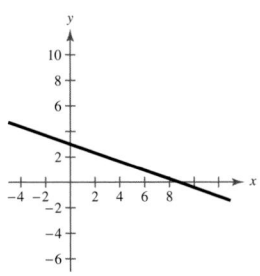

Review Exercises   (page 383)

1. 10.3254   **3.** 0.0001   **5.** c   **6.** d

7. b   **8.** a

9.

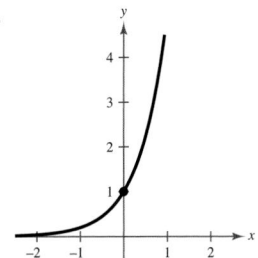

Horizontal asymptote: x-axis

y-intercept: $(0, 1)$

Increasing on $(-\infty, \infty)$

11.

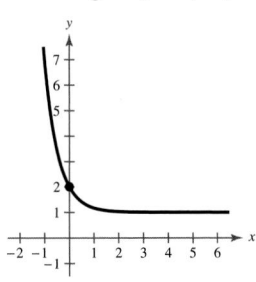

Horizontal asymptote: $y = 1$

y-intercept: $(0, 2)$

Decreasing on $(-\infty, \infty)$

13. 2980.958   **15.** 0.122

17.

x	$h(x)$
-5	0.0025
-4	0.0067
-3	0.0183
-2	0.0498
-1	0.1353
0	0.3679
1	1
2	2.7183
3	7.3891
4	20.0855

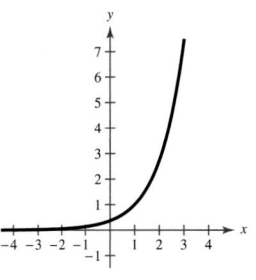

19.

x	$h(x)$
-5	-0.0067
-4	-0.0183
-3	-0.0498
-2	-0.1353
-1	-0.3679
0	-1
1	-2.7183
2	-7.3891
3	-20.0855
4	-54.5982

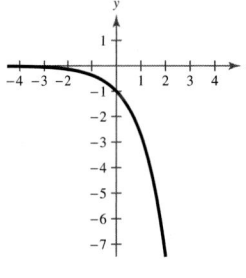

21.

x	$f(x)$
-5	48.7300
-4	29.5562
-3	17.9268
-2	10.8731
-1	6.5949
0	4
1	2.4261
2	1.4715
3	0.8925
4	0.5413
5	0.3283

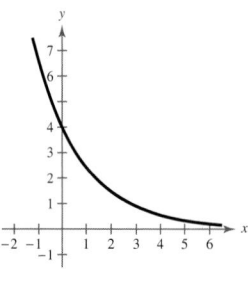

23.

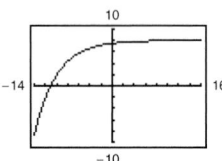

$y = 8$

25.

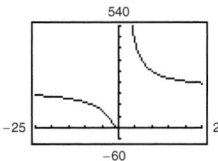

$y = 200, x = 0$

27.

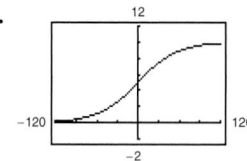

$y = 0, y = 10$

29.

t	1	10	20
A	\$10,832.87	\$22,255.41	\$49,530.32

t	30	40	50
A	\$110,231.76	\$245,325.30	\$545,981.50

31. (a)

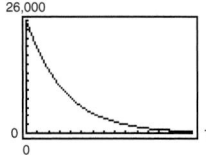

(b) \$14,625

(c) When it is first sold; Yes; Answers will vary.

33. $\log_4 64 = 3$ **35.** $\log_{25} 125 = \frac{3}{2}$ **37.** 3   **39.** -1

41.

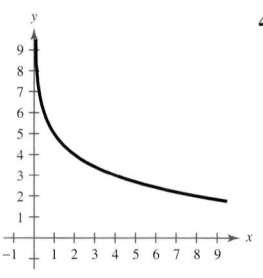

Domain: $(0, \infty)$

Vertical asymptote: $x = 0$

x-intercept:

   $(32, 0)$

43.

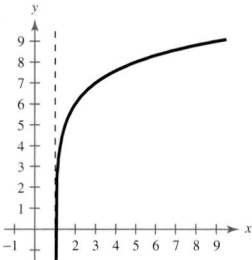

Domain: $(1, \infty)$

Vertical asymptote: $x = 1$

x-intercept:

   $(2^{-6} + 1, 0) \approx (1.016, 0)$

45. 3.068   **47.** 7   **49.** 0.896

51.

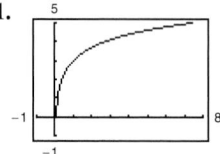

Domain: $(0, \infty)$

Vertical asymptote: $x = 0$

x-intercept:

$(e^{-3}, 0) \approx (0.05, 0)$

53.

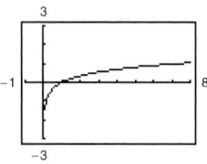

Domain: $(0, \infty)$

Vertical asymptote: $x = 0$

x-intercept:

   $(1, 0)$

55. (a) $0 \le h < 18,000$

(b)

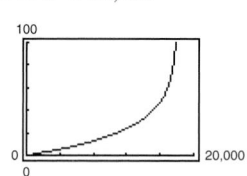

$h = 18,000$

(c) The time required to further increase its altitude increases.

(d) 5.46 minutes

57. 1.585   **59.** 2.132   **61.** $\ln 4 + \ln 5$

63. $-\log_5(3) - 1$ **65.** $1 + 2 \log_5 x$

67. $\log_{10} 5 + \frac{1}{2} \log_{10} y - 2 \log_{10} x$

69. $\ln(x + 3) - \ln x - \ln y$ **71.** $\log_2 5x$

73. $\ln \dfrac{\sqrt{2x - 1}}{(x + 1)^2}$ **75.** $\ln \dfrac{3\sqrt[3]{4 - x^2}}{x}$

77. (a)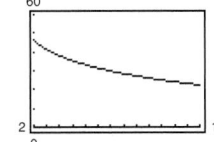

(b)

h	4	6	8	10	12	14
s	38	33	30	27	25	23

(c) The decrease in productivity starts to level off.

79. 3   **81.** -3 **83.** 2401   **85.** $e^4 \approx 54.598$

87. $\ln 12 \approx 2.485$ **89.** $-\dfrac{\ln 44}{5} \approx -0.757$

91. $\dfrac{\ln 22}{\ln 2} \approx 4.459$ **93.** $\log_5 17 \approx 1.760$

95. $\ln 5 \approx 1.609, \ln 2 \approx 0.693$

97. $\frac{1}{3}e^{8.2} \approx 1213.650$ **99.** $\frac{1}{4}e^{15/2} \approx 452.011$

101. $3e^2 \approx 22.167$ **103.** $e^4 - 1 \approx 53.598$

105. No solution   **107.** $\frac{9}{10}$ **109.** ≈ 15.2 years

111. e   **112.** b   **113.** f   **114.** d   **115.** a

116. c   **117.** $y = 2e^{0.1014x}$

119. $y = \frac{1}{2}e^{0.4605x}$ **121.** $k \approx 0.0259; 606,000$

123. (a) 5.78%   (b) \$10,595.03

125. (a) 7.7 weeks   (b) 13.3 weeks

127. Logistic model   **129.** Logarithmic model

131. (a) Quadratic model: $m = 0.03x^2 + 0.1x + 10$

Exponential model: $m = 8.73(1.05)^x$

Power model: $m = 3.466x^{0.647}$

(b) Quadratic model: Exponential model:

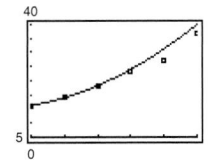   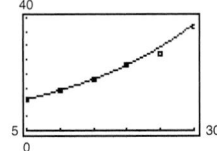

Power model:

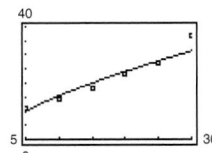

(c) Exponential model

(d) 53,000 screens

133. (a) $P = \dfrac{9999.887}{1 + 19.0e^{-0.2x}}$

(b)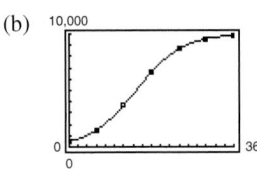

(c) The model fits the data well.

(d) 10,000 fish

135. True   **137.** False. $\ln(xy) = \ln x + \ln y$

139. False. $x > 0$

141. (a)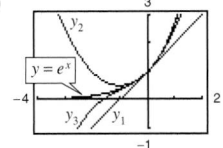

(b) $y_4 = 1 + \dfrac{x}{1!} + \dfrac{x^2}{2!} + \dfrac{x^3}{3!} + \dfrac{x^4}{4!}$

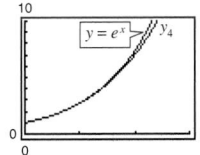

The graph of y_4 is close to the graph of $y = e^x$ near the point $(0, 1)$. As n becomes larger, the polynomials are better approximations of $y = e^x$.

Chapter Test   (page 388)

1. 1123.690   **2.** 687.291   **3.** 0.497   **4.** 22.198

5.

x	$f(x)$
-2	100
-1	10
0	1
1	0.1
2	0.01
3	0.001
4	0.0001

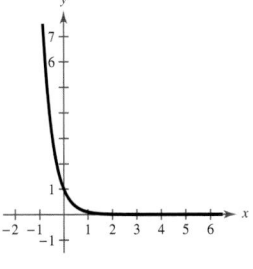

6.

x	$f(x)$
-2.0	-0.00077
-1.5	-0.00189
-1.0	-0.00463
-0.5	-0.01134
0	-0.02778
0.5	-0.06804
1.0	-0.16667
1.5	-0.40825
2	-1
2.5	-2.44949
3	-6
3.5	-14.69694
4	-36

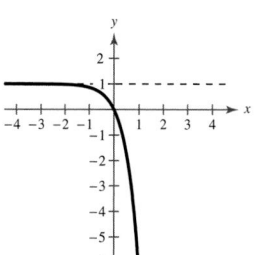

7.

x	$f(x)$
-4	0.9997
-3	0.9975
-2	0.9817
-1	0.8647
0	0
1	-6.3891
2	-53.5982
3	-402.4288

8. (a) -0.89 (b) 9.2

9.

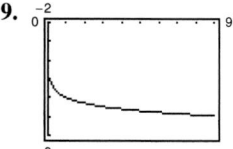

Domain: $(0, \infty)$

Vertical asymptote: $x = 0$

x-intercept: $(1 \times 10^{-6}, 0) \approx (0, 0)$

10.

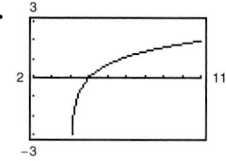

Domain: $(4, \infty)$

Vertical asymptote: $x = 4$

x-intercept: $(5, 0)$

11.

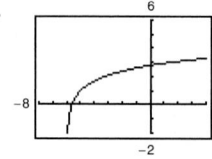

Domain: $(-6, \infty)$

Vertical asymptote: $x = -6$

x-intercept: $(e^{-1} - 6, 0) \approx (-5.632, 0)$

12. 1.945 **13.** 0.115 **14.** 1.328

15. $\log_2 3 + 4 \log_2 a$ **16.** $\ln 5 + \frac{1}{2} \ln x - \ln 6$

17. $\log_3 13y$ **18.** $\ln\left(\dfrac{x^4}{y^4}\right)$ **19.** 1.321

20. $\dfrac{800}{501} \approx 1.597$ **21.** 54.96%

22. (a) Quadratic model: $R = -0.031x^2 + 2.37x + 41.4$

Exponential model: $R = 44.863(1.0328)^x$

Power model: $R = 35.06298x^{0.2466}$

(b) Quadratic model:

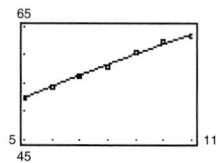

Exponential model:

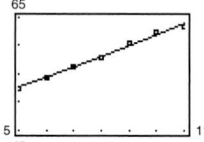

Power model:

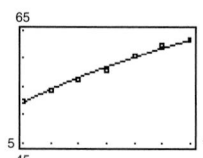

(c) Quadratic model (d) $\$72{,}700{,}000{,}000$

Cumulative Test for Chapters 3–4
(page 389)

1.

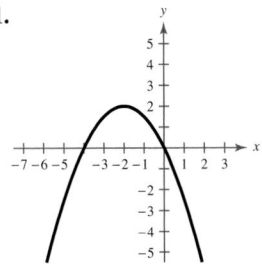

2.

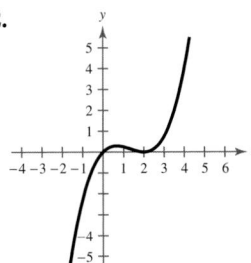

3.

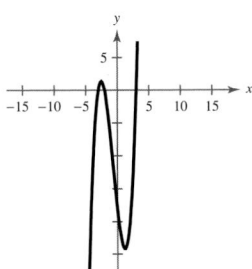

4. $-2, \pm 2i$

5. 1.424

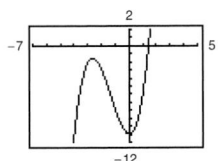

6. $4x + 2 - \dfrac{15}{x + 3}$

7. $2x^2 + 7x + 48 + \dfrac{268}{x - 6}$

8. $f(x) = x^4 + x^3 + 18x$

9.

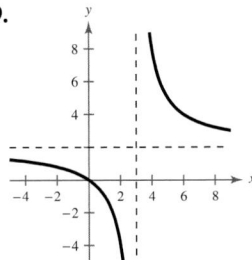

Asymptotes:
$x = 3, y = 2$

10.

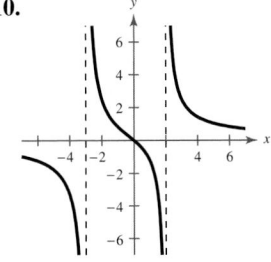

Asymptotes:
$x = -3, x = 2, y = 0$

11.

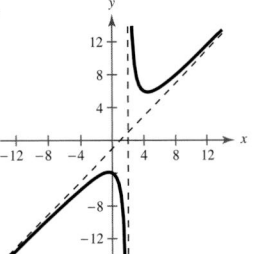

Asymptotes: $x = 2, y = x - 1$

12. $f(x) = \dfrac{4x^2}{x^2 + 1}$ **13.** 6   **14.** -4 **15.** 10

16. -3 **17.** 6.733   **18.** 8772.934   **19.** 0.162

20. 51.743

21.

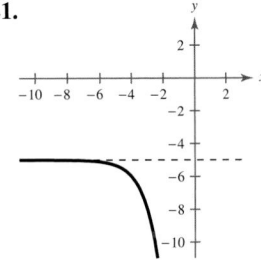

22.

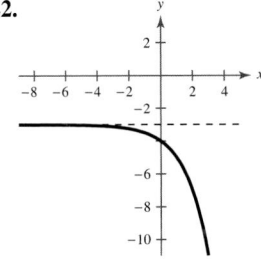

23.

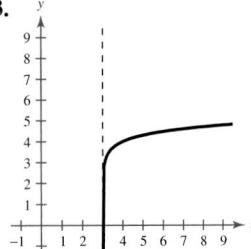

24.

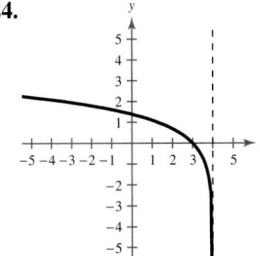

25. 1.892   **26.** 0.872   **27.** -7.484 **28.** -3.036

29. $\ln \dfrac{x^2}{\sqrt{x + 5}}, \quad x > 0$ **30.** $\ln x + \dfrac{1}{3}\ln(x - 5)$

31. $\frac{1}{2} \ln 12 \approx 1.242$ **32.** $\ln\left(\frac{9}{4}\right) + 3 \approx 3.811$

33. 1.099, 2.079   **34.** 5.021   **35.** 401.429

36. $\frac{64}{5} = 12.8$ **37.** \$2000

38. $\overline{C}(10,000) = 50$

$\overline{C}(100,000) = 9.5$

$\overline{C}(1,000,000) = 5.45$

\$5

39. \$16,302.05   **40.** \$108.63

41. $k \approx 0.01058,\ 253{,}445$

42. (a) 300   (b) 570.44   (c) ≈ 9 years

43. (a) Quadratic model: $y = 0.248x^2 - 0.28x + 50.3$

Exponential model: $y = 42.62(1.05)^x$

Power model: $y = 32.45x^{0.3329}$

(b) Quadratic model: Exponential model:

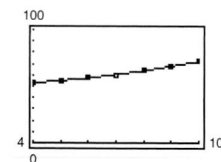   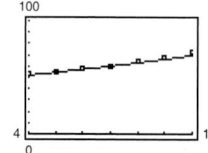

Power model:

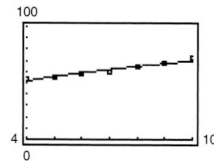

(c) Quadratic model

(d) 109,000

Chapter 5

Section 5.1   (page 399)

Vocabulary Check   (page 399)

1. Trigonometry   **2.** angle

3. standard position   **4.** coterminal   **5.** degree

6. complementary   **7.** supplementary

8. radian   **9.** linear   **10.** angular

---

1. $210°$ **3.** $-45°$

5. (a) Quadrant II   (b) Quadrant IV

7. (a) Quadrant III   (b) Quadrant I

9. (a)   (b)

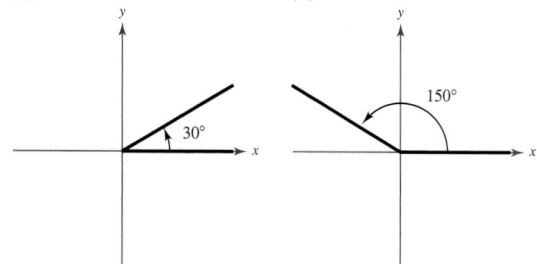

11. (a)   (b)

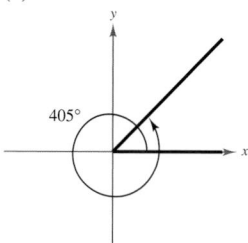   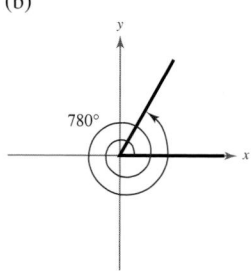

13. (a) $412°, -308°$ (b) $324°, -396°$

15. (a) $225°, -135°$ (b) $590°, -130°$

17. $64.75°$ **19.** $85.308°$ **21.** $-125.01°$

23. $280° 36'$ **25.** $-345° 7' 12''$ **27.** $-20° 20' 24''$

29. (a) Complement: $66°$; supplement: $156°$

(b) Complement: none; supplement: $54°$

31. 2 **33.** -3 **35.** (a) Quadrant I   (b) Quadrant III

37. (a) Quadrant IV   (b) Quadrant II

39. (a) Quadrant III   (b) Quadrant II

41. (a)   (b)

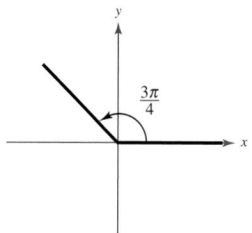   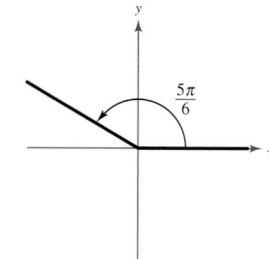

43. (a)   (b)

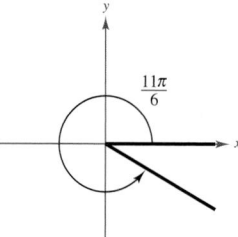   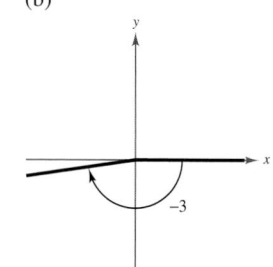

45. (a) $\dfrac{25\pi}{12}, -\dfrac{23\pi}{12}$ (b) $\dfrac{8\pi}{3}, -\dfrac{4\pi}{3}$

47. (a) $\dfrac{7\pi}{4}, -\dfrac{\pi}{4}$ (b) $\dfrac{28\pi}{15}, -\dfrac{32\pi}{15}$

49. (a) Complement: $\dfrac{\pi}{6}$; supplement: $\dfrac{2\pi}{3}$

(b) Complement: none; supplement: $\dfrac{\pi}{4}$

51. (a) $\dfrac{\pi}{6}$ (b) $\dfrac{5\pi}{6}$ **53.** (a) $-\dfrac{\pi}{9}$ (b) $-\dfrac{4\pi}{3}$

55. (a) $270°$ (b) $-210°$ **57.** (a) $420°$ (b) $-39°$

59. 2.199   **61.** -3.776 **63.** -0.014 **65.** $25.714°$

67. $292.5°$ **69.** $-114.592°$ **71.** $\dfrac{6}{5}$ rad   **73.** $4\dfrac{4}{7}$ rad

75. $\dfrac{8}{29}$ rad   **77.** $2\dfrac{12}{29}$ rad

79. 15π inches ≈ 47.12 inches

81. 2 meters   **83.** 1141.81 miles   **85.** $4°\,2'\,33.02''$

87. $\dfrac{5}{12}$ rad $\approx 23.87°$

89. (a) $540° \approx 9.42$ rad   (b) $900° \approx 15.71$ rad

(c) $1260° \approx 21.99$ rad

91. 20.16π inches per second

93. False. A radian is larger: 1 rad $\approx 57.3°$.

95. (a) An angle is in standard position when the origin is the vertex and the initial side coincides with the positive x-axis.

(b) A negative angle is generated by a clockwise rotation.

(c) Angles that have the same initial and terminal sides are called coterminal angles.

(d) An obtuse angle is between $90°$ and $180°$.

97. $\dfrac{50\pi}{3}$ square meters

99. (a) $A = 0.4r^2,\ r > 0;\ s = 0.8r,\ r > 0$

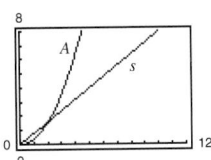

The area function changes more rapidly for $r > 1$ because it is quadratic, whereas the arc length function is linear.

(b) $A = 50\theta,\ 0 < \theta < 2\pi;\ s = 10\theta,\ 0 < \theta < 2\pi$

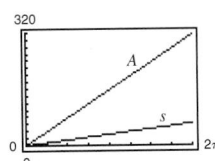

101. $y = 4.54x + 16.4$ **103.** $x = -7, -4$

105. $x = -5, 0, 2$

Section 5.2   (page 410)

1. $\sin\theta = \dfrac{3}{5}$

$\cos\theta = \dfrac{4}{5}$

$\tan\theta = \dfrac{3}{4}$

$\csc\theta = \dfrac{5}{3}$

$\sec\theta = \dfrac{5}{4}$

$\cot\theta = \dfrac{4}{3}$

3. $\sin\theta = \dfrac{8}{17}$

$\cos\theta = \dfrac{15}{17}$

$\tan\theta = \dfrac{8}{15}$

$\csc\theta = \dfrac{17}{8}$

$\sec\theta = \dfrac{17}{15}$

$\cot\theta = \dfrac{15}{8}$

5. $\sin\theta = \dfrac{1}{3}$

$\cos\theta = \dfrac{2\sqrt{2}}{3}$

$\tan\theta = \dfrac{\sqrt{2}}{4}$

$\csc\theta = 3$

$\sec\theta = \dfrac{3\sqrt{2}}{4}$

$\cot\theta = 2\sqrt{2}$

The triangles are similar and corresponding sides are proportional.

7. $\sin\theta = \dfrac{3}{5}$

$\cos\theta = \dfrac{4}{5}$

$\tan\theta = \dfrac{3}{4}$

$\csc\theta = \dfrac{5}{3}$

$\sec\theta = \dfrac{5}{4}$

$\cot\theta = \dfrac{4}{3}$

The triangles are similar and corresponding sides are proportional.

9. $\cos\theta = \dfrac{\sqrt{5}}{3}$

$\tan\theta = \dfrac{2\sqrt{5}}{5}$

$\csc\theta = \dfrac{3}{2}$

$\sec\theta = \dfrac{3\sqrt{5}}{5}$

$\cot\theta = \dfrac{\sqrt{5}}{2}$

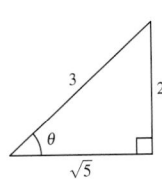

11. $\sin \theta = \dfrac{\sqrt{15}}{4}$

$\cos \theta = \dfrac{1}{4}$

$\tan \theta = \sqrt{15}$

$\csc \theta = \dfrac{4\sqrt{15}}{15}$

$\cot \theta = \dfrac{\sqrt{15}}{15}$

13. $\sin \theta = \dfrac{3\sqrt{10}}{10}$

$\cos \theta = \dfrac{\sqrt{10}}{10}$

$\csc \theta = \dfrac{\sqrt{10}}{3}$

$\sec \theta = \sqrt{10}$

$\cot \theta = \dfrac{1}{3}$

15. $\sin \theta = \dfrac{4\sqrt{97}}{97}$

$\cos \theta = \dfrac{9\sqrt{97}}{97}$

$\tan \theta = \dfrac{4}{9}$

$\csc \theta = \dfrac{\sqrt{97}}{4}$

$\sec \theta = \dfrac{\sqrt{97}}{9}$

17. $\dfrac{\pi}{6}, \dfrac{1}{2}$ **19.** $60°, \sqrt{3}$ **21.** $60°, \dfrac{\pi}{3}$ **23.** $30°, \dfrac{\sqrt{3}}{2}$

25. $45°, \dfrac{\pi}{4}$ **27.** (a) $\sqrt{3}$ (b) $\dfrac{1}{2}$ (c) $\dfrac{\sqrt{3}}{2}$ (d) $\dfrac{\sqrt{3}}{3}$

29. (a) $\dfrac{1}{3}$ (b) $\dfrac{2\sqrt{2}}{3}$ (c) $\dfrac{\sqrt{2}}{4}$ (d) 3

31. (a) 4 (b) $\pm\dfrac{\sqrt{15}}{4}$ (c) $\pm\dfrac{\sqrt{15}}{15}$ (d) $\dfrac{1}{4}$

33–39. Answers will vary.   **41.** (a) 0.2079   (b) 0.3090

43. (a) 1.3499   (b) 1.3432

45. (a) 5.0273   (b) 0.1989

47. (a) $30° = \dfrac{\pi}{6}$ (b) $30° = \dfrac{\pi}{6}$

49. (a) $60° = \dfrac{\pi}{3}$ (b) $45° = \dfrac{\pi}{4}$

51. (a) $60° = \dfrac{\pi}{3}$ (b) $45° = \dfrac{\pi}{4}$

53. $35\sqrt{3}$ **55.** $\dfrac{38\sqrt{3}}{3}$

57. (a) 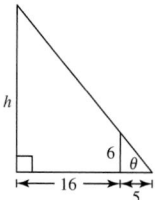   (b) $\tan \theta = \dfrac{6}{5}$

$\theta \approx 50.194°$

$\tan \theta = \dfrac{h}{21}$

(c) $h = 25.2$ feet

59. 160.03 feet

61. (a) 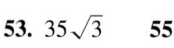   (b) $\sin \theta = \dfrac{3\frac{1}{3}}{20} = \dfrac{1}{6}$

(c) $\theta \approx 9.59°$

63. (a) 235.84 feet   (b) 124.97 feet

65. 6.57 centimeters   **67.** True. $\csc x = \dfrac{1}{\sin x}$

69. False. $\dfrac{\sqrt{2}}{2} + \dfrac{\sqrt{2}}{2} \neq 1$

71. (a)

θ	0°	20°	40°	60°	80°
$\sin \theta$	0	0.3420	0.6428	0.8660	0.9848
$\cos \theta$	1	0.9397	0.7660	0.5000	0.1736
$\tan \theta$	0	0.3640	0.8391	1.7321	5.6713

(b) Sine: increasing

Cosine: decreasing

Tangent: increasing

(c)

θ	0°	20°	40°	60°	80°
$\tan \theta = \dfrac{\sin \theta}{\cos \theta}$	0	0.3640	0.8391	1.7321	5.6713

73. 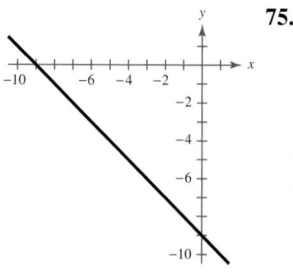   **75.**

x-intercept: $(-9, 0)$ *x*-intercept: $\left(-\dfrac{16}{3}, 0\right)$

y-intercept: $(0, -9)$ *y*-intercept: $(0, 2)$

77. 18.661   **79.** 17.420

Section 5.3   (page 423)

1. (a) $\sin\theta = \frac{3}{5}$ (b) $\sin\theta = -\frac{15}{17}$

$\cos\theta = \frac{4}{5}$ $\cos\theta = -\frac{8}{17}$

$\tan\theta = \frac{3}{4}$ $\tan\theta = \frac{15}{8}$

$\csc\theta = \frac{5}{3}$ $\csc\theta = -\frac{17}{15}$

$\sec\theta = \frac{5}{4}$ $\sec\theta = -\frac{17}{8}$

$\cot\theta = \frac{4}{3}$ $\cot\theta = \frac{8}{15}$

3. (a) $\sin\theta = -\frac{1}{2}$ (b) $\sin\theta = \frac{\sqrt{17}}{17}$

$\cos\theta = -\frac{\sqrt{3}}{2}$ $\cos\theta = -\frac{4\sqrt{17}}{17}$

$\tan\theta = \frac{\sqrt{3}}{3}$ $\tan\theta = -\frac{1}{4}$

$\csc\theta = -2$ $\csc\theta = \sqrt{17}$

$\sec\theta = -\frac{2\sqrt{3}}{3}$ $\sec\theta = -\frac{\sqrt{17}}{4}$

$\cot\theta = \sqrt{3}$ $\cot\theta = -4$

5. $\sin\theta = \frac{24}{25}$ **7.** $\sin\theta = -\frac{12}{13}$

$\cos\theta = \frac{7}{25}$ $\cos\theta = \frac{5}{13}$

$\tan\theta = \frac{24}{7}$ $\tan\theta = -\frac{12}{5}$

$\csc\theta = \frac{25}{24}$ $\csc\theta = -\frac{13}{12}$

$\sec\theta = \frac{25}{7}$ $\sec\theta = \frac{13}{5}$

$\cot\theta = \frac{7}{24}$ $\cot\theta = -\frac{5}{12}$

9. $\sin\theta = \frac{5\sqrt{29}}{29}$ **11.** $\sin\theta = \frac{9\sqrt{85}}{85}$

$\cos\theta = -\frac{2\sqrt{29}}{29}$ $\cos\theta = -\frac{2\sqrt{85}}{85}$

$\tan\theta = -\frac{5}{2}$ $\tan\theta = -\frac{9}{2}$

$\csc\theta = \frac{\sqrt{29}}{5}$ $\csc\theta = \frac{\sqrt{85}}{9}$

$\sec\theta = -\frac{\sqrt{29}}{2}$ $\sec\theta = -\frac{\sqrt{85}}{2}$

$\cot\theta = -\frac{2}{5}$ $\cot\theta = -\frac{2}{9}$

13. Quadrant III   **15.** Quadrant IV

17. $\sin\theta = \frac{3}{5}$ **19.** $\sin\theta = -\frac{15}{17}$

$\cos\theta = -\frac{4}{5}$ $\cos\theta = \frac{8}{17}$

$\tan\theta = -\frac{3}{4}$ $\tan\theta = -\frac{15}{8}$

$\csc\theta = \frac{5}{3}$ $\csc\theta = -\frac{17}{15}$

$\sec\theta = -\frac{5}{4}$ $\sec\theta = \frac{17}{8}$

$\cot\theta = -\frac{4}{3}$ $\cot\theta = -\frac{8}{15}$

21. $\sin\theta = \frac{\sqrt{3}}{2}$ **23.** $\sin\theta = 0$

$\cos\theta = -\frac{1}{2}$ $\cos\theta = -1$

$\tan\theta = -\sqrt{3}$ $\tan\theta = 0$

$\csc\theta = \frac{2\sqrt{3}}{3}$ $\csc\theta$ is undefined.

$\sec\theta = -2$ $\sec\theta = -1$

$\cot\theta = -\frac{\sqrt{3}}{3}$ $\cot\theta$ is undefined.

25. $\sin\theta = \frac{\sqrt{2}}{2}$ **27.** $\sin\theta = -\frac{2\sqrt{5}}{5}$

$\cos\theta = -\frac{\sqrt{2}}{2}$ $\cos\theta = -\frac{\sqrt{5}}{5}$

$\tan\theta = -1$ $\tan\theta = 2$

$\csc\theta = \sqrt{2}$ $\csc\theta = -\frac{\sqrt{5}}{2}$

$\sec\theta = -\sqrt{2}$ $\sec\theta = -\sqrt{5}$

$\cot\theta = -1$ $\cot\theta = \frac{1}{2}$

29. -1 **31.** 0   **33.** 1   **35.** Undefined

37. $\theta' = 60°$ **39.** $\theta' = 45°$

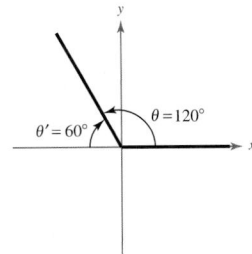   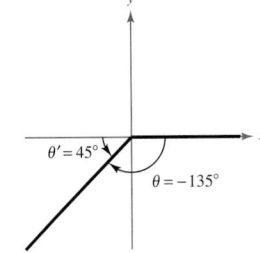

41. $\theta' = \frac{\pi}{3}$ **43.** $\theta' = \frac{\pi}{6}$

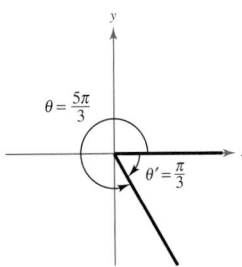   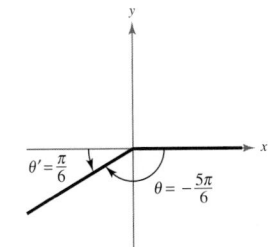

45. $\theta' = 28°$

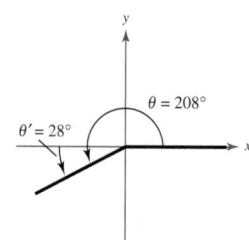

47. $\theta' = 68°$

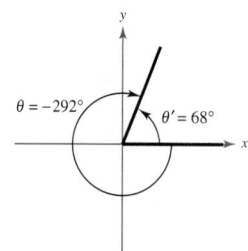

49. $\theta' = \dfrac{\pi}{5}$

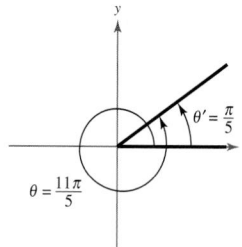

51. $\theta' = 3.5 - \pi \approx 0.358$

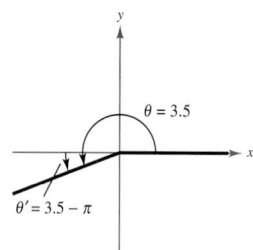

53. $\sin 225° = -\dfrac{\sqrt{2}}{2}$

$\cos 225° = -\dfrac{\sqrt{2}}{2}$

$\tan 225° = 1$

55. $\sin(-750°) = -\dfrac{1}{2}$

$\cos(-750°) = \dfrac{\sqrt{3}}{2}$

$\tan(-750°) = -\dfrac{\sqrt{3}}{3}$

57. $\sin(-240°) = \dfrac{\sqrt{3}}{2}$

$\cos(-240°) = -\dfrac{1}{2}$

$\tan(-240°) = -\sqrt{3}$

59. $\sin\dfrac{5\pi}{3} = -\dfrac{\sqrt{3}}{2}$

$\cos\dfrac{5\pi}{3} = \dfrac{1}{2}$

$\tan\dfrac{5\pi}{3} = -\sqrt{3}$

61. $\sin\left(-\dfrac{7\pi}{6}\right) = \dfrac{1}{2}$

$\cos\left(-\dfrac{7\pi}{6}\right) = -\dfrac{\sqrt{3}}{2}$

$\tan\left(-\dfrac{7\pi}{6}\right) = -\dfrac{\sqrt{3}}{3}$

63. $\sin\dfrac{11\pi}{4} = \dfrac{\sqrt{2}}{2}$

$\cos\dfrac{11\pi}{4} = -\dfrac{\sqrt{2}}{2}$

$\tan\dfrac{11\pi}{4} = -1$

65. $\sin\left(-\dfrac{17\pi}{6}\right) = -\dfrac{1}{2}$

$\cos\left(-\dfrac{17\pi}{6}\right) = -\dfrac{\sqrt{3}}{2}$

$\tan\left(-\dfrac{17\pi}{6}\right) = \dfrac{\sqrt{3}}{3}$

67. $\dfrac{4}{5}$ **69.** $-\dfrac{\sqrt{13}}{2}$

71. $\frac{8}{5}$ **73.** 0.1736 **75.** 2.1445 **77.** -0.3420

79. 5.7588 **81.** 0.6052 **83.** -0.2369

85. 0.8391 **87.** -2.9238

89. (a) $30° = \dfrac{\pi}{6}$, $150° = \dfrac{5\pi}{6}$ (b) $210° = \dfrac{7\pi}{6}$, $330° = \dfrac{11\pi}{6}$

91. (a) $60° = \dfrac{\pi}{3}$, $120° = \dfrac{2\pi}{3}$ (b) $135° = \dfrac{3\pi}{4}$, $315° = \dfrac{7\pi}{4}$

93. (a) $150° = \dfrac{5\pi}{6}$, $210° = \dfrac{7\pi}{6}$ (b) $60° = \dfrac{\pi}{3}$, $300° = \dfrac{5\pi}{3}$

95. $\left(\dfrac{\sqrt{2}}{2}, \dfrac{\sqrt{2}}{2}\right)$

$\sin\dfrac{\pi}{4} = \dfrac{\sqrt{2}}{2}$

$\cos\dfrac{\pi}{4} = \dfrac{\sqrt{2}}{2}$

$\tan\dfrac{\pi}{4} = 1$

97. $\left(-\dfrac{\sqrt{3}}{2}, \dfrac{1}{2}\right)$

$\sin\dfrac{5\pi}{6} = \dfrac{1}{2}$

$\cos\dfrac{5\pi}{6} = -\dfrac{\sqrt{3}}{2}$

$\tan\dfrac{5\pi}{6} = -\dfrac{\sqrt{3}}{3}$

99. $\left(-\dfrac{1}{2}, -\dfrac{\sqrt{3}}{2}\right)$

$\sin\dfrac{4\pi}{3} = -\dfrac{\sqrt{3}}{2}$

$\cos\dfrac{4\pi}{3} = -\dfrac{1}{2}$

$\tan\dfrac{4\pi}{3} = \sqrt{3}$

101. $(0, -1)$

$\sin\dfrac{3\pi}{2} = -1$

$\cos\dfrac{3\pi}{2} = 0$

$\tan\dfrac{3\pi}{2}$ is undefined.

103. (a) -1 (b) -0.4

105. (a) $0.25, 2.89$ (b) $1.82, 4.46$

107. (a) $29°\text{F}$ (b) $70°\text{F}$ (c) $31.75°\text{F}$

109. (a) 2 centimeters

(b)

t	0.50	1.02	1.54	2.07	2.59
y	-1.20	0.71	-0.42	0.25	-0.15

(c) Friction within the system damps the oscillations and is modeled by the factor e^{-t}.

(d) 0.26 second, 0.79 second

111. 0.79 amperes   **113.** True. $\theta' = 180° - \theta$

115. True

117. (a)

θ	0°	20°	40°	60°	80°
$\sin\theta$	0	0.3420	0.6428	0.8660	0.9848
$\sin(180° - \theta)$	0	0.3420	0.6428	0.8660	0.9848

(b) $\sin\theta = \sin(180° - \theta)$

119. (a)

Function	$\sin x$	$\cos x$	$\tan x$
Domain	$(-\infty, \infty)$	$(-\infty, \infty)$	All reals except $\frac{\pi}{2} + n\pi$
Range	$[-1, 1]$	$[-1, 1]$	$(-\infty, \infty)$
Even/Odd	Odd	Even	Odd
Period	2π	2π	π
Zeros	$n\pi$	$\frac{\pi}{2} + n\pi$	$n\pi$

Function	$\csc x$	$\sec x$	$\cot x$
Domain	All reals except $n\pi$	All reals except $\frac{\pi}{2} + n\pi$	All reals except $n\pi$
Range	$(-\infty, -1) \cup (1, \infty)$	$(-\infty, -1) \cup (1, \infty)$	$(-\infty, \infty)$
Even/Odd	Odd	Even	Odd
Period	2π	2π	π
Zeros	None	None	$\frac{\pi}{2} + n\pi$

Patterns and conclusions may vary.

121.

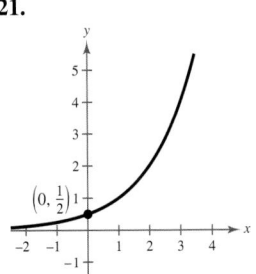

Asymptote at $y = 0$
y-intercept: $\left(0, \frac{1}{2}\right)$

123.

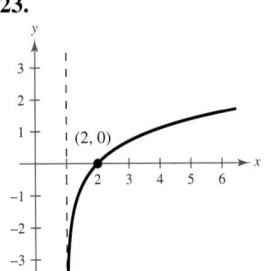

(2, 0)

Asymptote at $x = 1$
x-intercept: $(2, 0)$

125. $x = -1.752$ **127.** $x = 0.002$

Section 5.4   (page 434)

1. Period: π
Amplitude: 3

3. Period: 4π
Amplitude: $\frac{5}{2}$

5. Period: 2
Amplitude: $\frac{2}{3}$

7. Period: 2π
Amplitude: 2

9. Period: $\dfrac{\pi}{5}$
Amplitude: 3

11. Period: 3π
Amplitude: $\frac{1}{4}$

13. Period: $\frac{1}{2}$
Amplitude: $\frac{1}{3}$

15. g is a shift of f π units to the right.

17. g is a reflection of f in the x-axis.

19. g is a reflection of f in the x-axis and has five times the amplitude of f.

21. g is a shift of f five units upward.

23. g has twice the amplitude of f.

25. g is a horizontal shift of f π units to the right.

27.

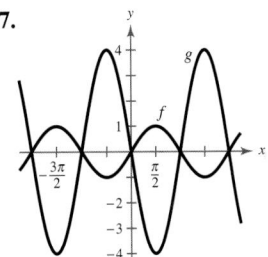

29.

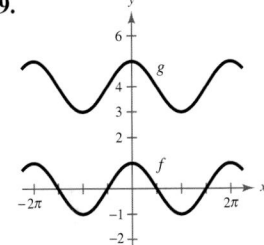

31.

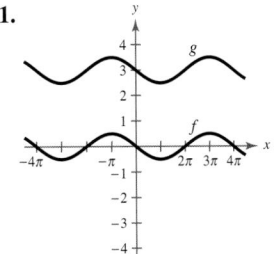

33.

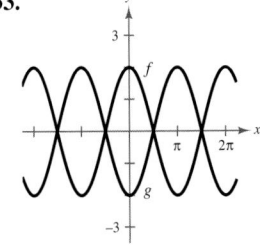

35.

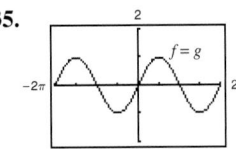

37.

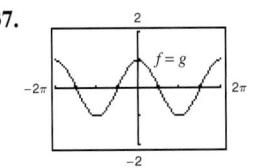

39.
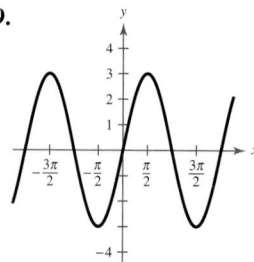

41.
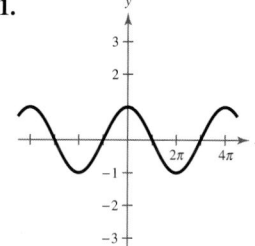

43.
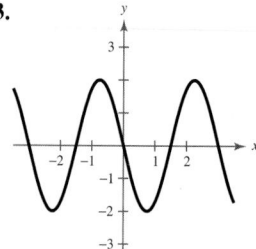

45.
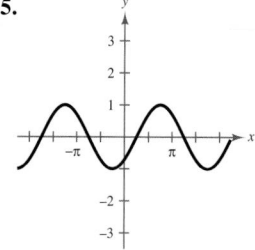

47.
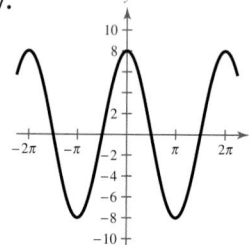

49.
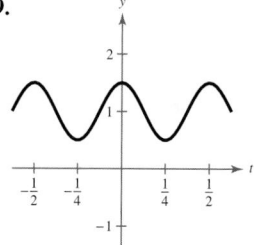

51.
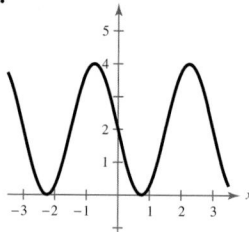

53.
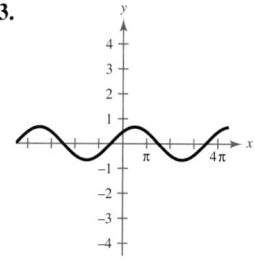

55.
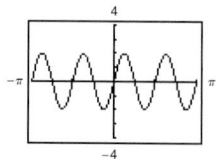

Amplitude: 2

Period: $\dfrac{\pi}{2}$

57.
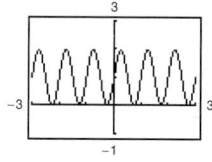

Amplitude: 1

Period: 1

59.
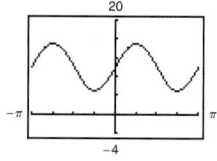

Amplitude: 5

Period: π

61.
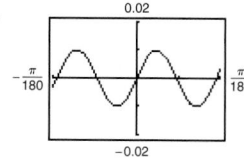

Amplitude: $\dfrac{1}{100}$

Period: $\dfrac{1}{60}$

63. $f(x) = 4 - 4\cos x$

65. $f(x) = 1 - 6\cos x$

67. $f(x) = -3\sin(2x)$

69. $f(x) = \sin\!\left(x - \dfrac{\pi}{4}\right)$

71.
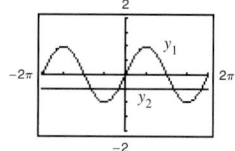

$$x = -\frac{\pi}{6}, -\frac{5\pi}{6}, \frac{7\pi}{6}, \frac{11\pi}{6}$$

73. (a)
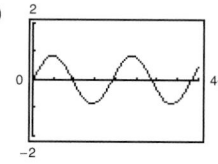

(b) 6 seconds

(c) 10 cycles per minute

(d) The period of the model would change because the time for a respiratory cycle would decrease.

75. (a)
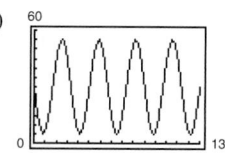

(b) Minimum height: 5 feet

Maximum height: 55 feet

77. (a) 365 days. The cycle is 1 year.

(b) 30.3 gallons per day; the average is the constant term of the model.

(c)
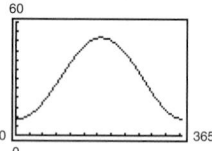

Consumption exceeds 40 gallons per day from the beginning of May through part of September.

79. (a)

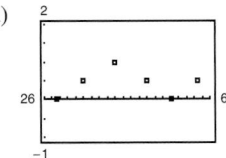

(b) $y = 0.508 \sin(0.216x - 1.616) + 0.539$

(c)

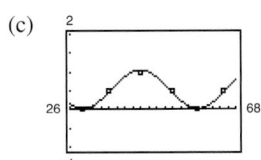

The model is a good fit.

(d) 29.09

(e) 100%

81. True. $2\pi \cdot \dfrac{10}{3} = \dfrac{20\pi}{3}$ **83.** True

85. (a)

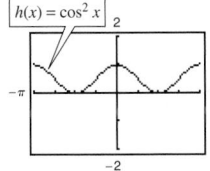

Even

(b)

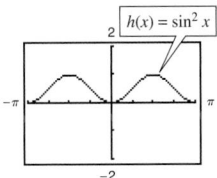

Even

(c)

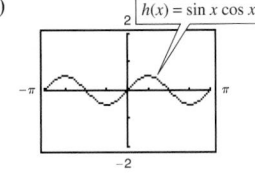

Odd

87.

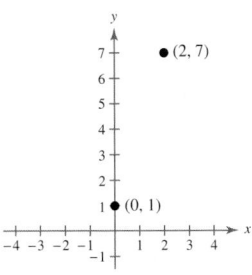

$m = 3$

89. 487.014°

Section 5.5   (page 445)

Vocabulary Check   (page 445)

1. vertical   **2.** reciprocal   **3.** damping

1. c   **2.** d   **3.** e   **4.** f   **5.** a   **6.** b

7.

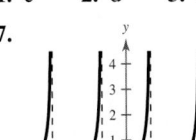
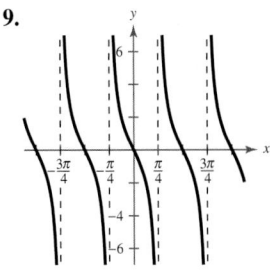

9.

11.

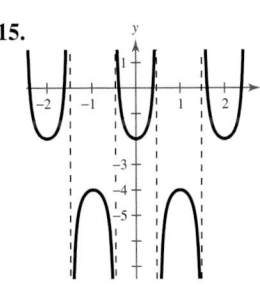

13.

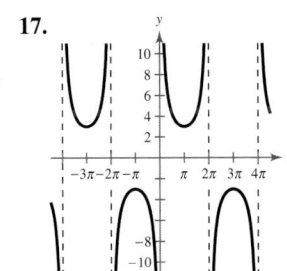

15.

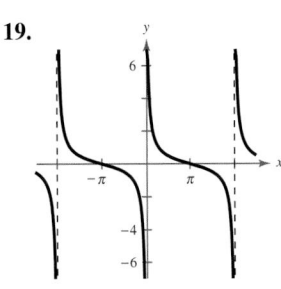

17.

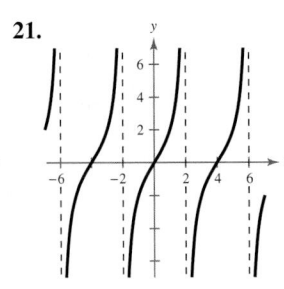

19.

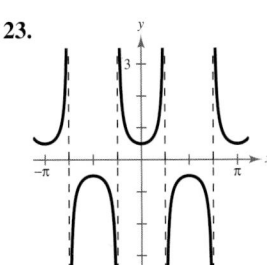

21.

23.

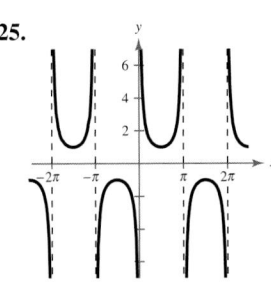

25.

27.

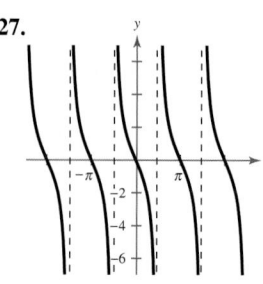

29.

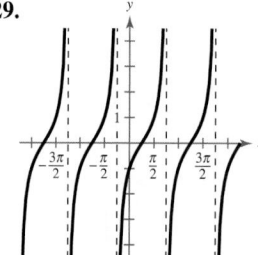

31.

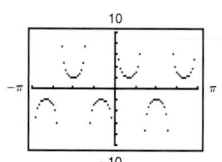

Answers will vary.

33.

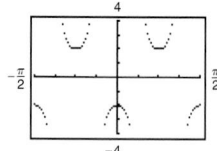

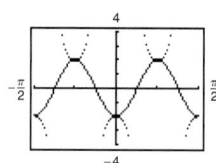

Answers will vary.

35.

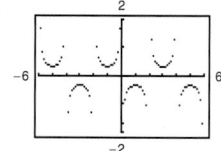

Answers will vary.

37. $-\dfrac{7\pi}{4}, -\dfrac{3\pi}{4}, \dfrac{\pi}{4}, \dfrac{5\pi}{4}$ **39.** $-\dfrac{4\pi}{3}, -\dfrac{2\pi}{3}, \dfrac{2\pi}{3}, \dfrac{4\pi}{3}$

41. Even   **43.** Odd

45.

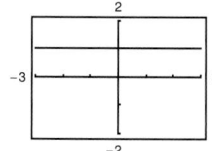

47.

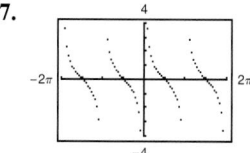

Not equivalent;   Equivalent
y_1 is undefined at $x = 0$.

49. d; as x approaches 0, $f(x)$ approaches 0.

50. a; as x approaches 0, $f(x)$ approaches 0.

51. b; as x approaches 0, $g(x)$ approaches 0.

52. c; as x approaches 0, $g(x)$ approaches 0.

53.

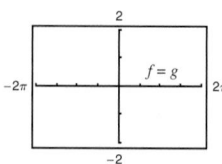

55.

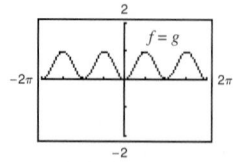

57.

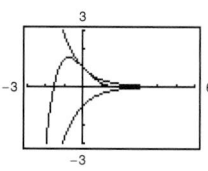

$f \to 0$ as $x \to \infty$.

59.

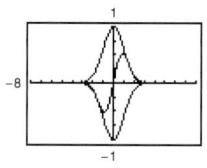

$g \to 0$ as $x \to \infty$.

61.

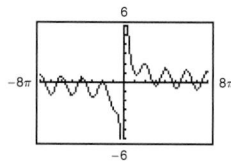

As $x \to 0$ from the left, $f \to -\infty$

As $x \to 0$ from the right, $f \to \infty$

63.

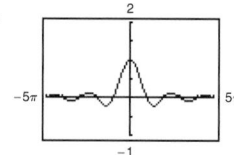

Approaches 1

65.

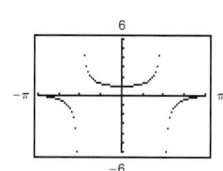

Approaches 1

67. $d = 5 \cot x$

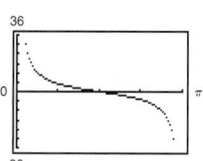

69. As the predator population increases, the number of prey decreases. When the number of prey is small, the number of predators decreases.

71. (a)

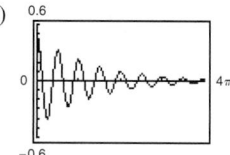

(b) Not periodic and damped; goes to 0 as t increases.

73. (a) Yes. To each t there corresponds one and only one value of y.

(b) 1.3 oscillations per second

(c) $y = 12(0.221)^t \cos(8.2t)$

(d) $y = 12e^{-1.5t} \cos(8.2t)$

(e)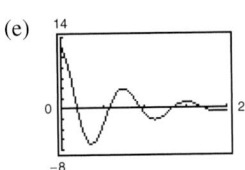

Answers will vary.

75. True

77. $f(x)$ approaches ∞ as x approaches $\pi/2$ from the left.
$f(x)$ approaches $-\infty$ as x approaches $\pi/2$ from the right.

79. (a)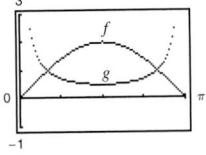

(b) $\dfrac{\pi}{6} < x < \dfrac{5\pi}{6}$

(c) Sine approaches 0 and cosecant approaches ∞ because the cosecant is the reciprocal of the sine.

81. Distributive Property   **83.** Additive Identity Property

85. Not one-to-one

87. One-to-one. $f^{-1}(x) = \dfrac{x^2 + 14}{3},\ x \geq 0$

Section 5.6   (page 456)

Vocabulary Check   (page 456)

1. $\sin^{-1} x,\ -1 \leq x \leq 1$

2. $y = \arccos x,\ 0 \leq y \leq \pi$

3. $y = \tan^{-1} x,\ -\infty < x < \infty,\ -\dfrac{\pi}{2} < y < \dfrac{\pi}{2}$

1. (a) $\dfrac{\pi}{6}$ (b) 0   **3.** (a) $\dfrac{\pi}{6}$ (b) $-\dfrac{\pi}{4}$

5. (a) $-\dfrac{\pi}{3}$ (b) $\dfrac{\pi}{3}$ **7.** (a) $\dfrac{\pi}{3}$ (b) $-\dfrac{\pi}{6}$

9. (a)

x	-1	-0.8	-0.6	-0.4	-0.2
y	3.1416	2.4981	2.2143	1.9823	1.7722

x	0	0.2	0.4	0.6	0.8	1
y	1.5708	1.3694	1.1593	0.9273	0.6435	0

(b)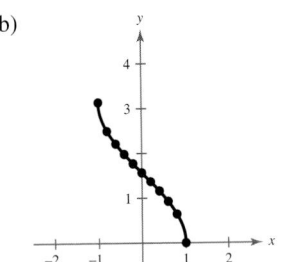

(c)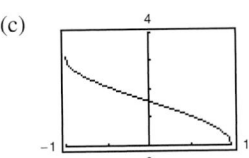

(d) Intercepts: $\left(0, \dfrac{\pi}{2}\right),\ (1, 0)$

11. $-\dfrac{\pi}{3},\ -\dfrac{\sqrt{3}}{3},\ 1$ **13.** 0.72   **15.** -0.85

17. -1.41 **19.** 0.19   **21.** 2.11   **23.** 0.92

25.   **27.** $\theta = \arctan \dfrac{x}{8}$

29. $\theta = \arcsin \dfrac{x + 2}{5}$ **31.** 0.7   **33.** -0.3

35. 0   **37.** $-\dfrac{\pi}{6}$ **39.** $\dfrac{4}{5}$ **41.** $\dfrac{7}{25}$

43. $\dfrac{\sqrt{34}}{5}$ **45.** $\dfrac{\sqrt{5}}{3}$ **47.** $\dfrac{1}{x}$ **49.** $\sqrt{-x^2 - 4x - 3}$

51. $\dfrac{\sqrt{25 - x^2}}{x}$ **53.** $\dfrac{\sqrt{x^2 + 7}}{x}$

55.

$y = \pm 1$

57. $\dfrac{14}{\sqrt{x^2 + 196}}$ **59.** $\dfrac{|x - 1|}{\sqrt{x^2 - 2x + 10}}$

61.

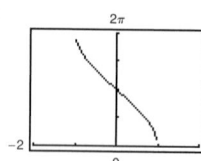

63.

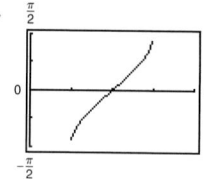

65.

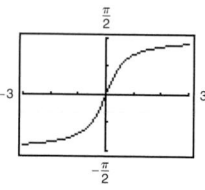

67.

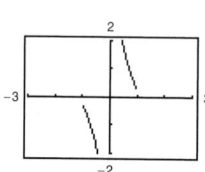

69. $3\sqrt{2}\sin\left(2t + \dfrac{\pi}{4}\right)$

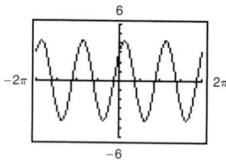

The two forms are equivalent.

71. (a) $\theta = \arcsin\dfrac{10}{s}$ (b) 0.19 rad, 0.39 rad

73. (a) $\theta = \arctan\dfrac{s}{750}$ (b) 0.49 rad, 1.13 rad

75. (a) $\theta = \arctan\dfrac{6}{x}$ (b) 0.54 rad, 1.11 rad

77. False. $5\pi/6$ is not in the range of the arcsine.

79.

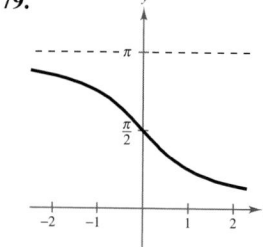

81.

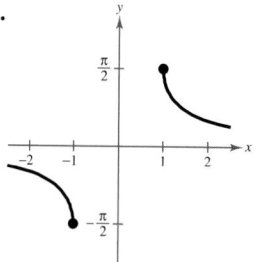

83–85. Answers will vary.   **87.** $\dfrac{\sqrt{2}}{2}$ **89.** $\dfrac{\sqrt{3}}{3}$

91. $\cos\theta = \dfrac{\sqrt{11}}{6}$

$\tan\theta = \dfrac{5\sqrt{11}}{11}$

$\csc\theta = \dfrac{6}{5}$

$\sec\theta = \dfrac{6\sqrt{11}}{11}$

$\cot\theta = \dfrac{\sqrt{11}}{5}$

93. $\cos\theta = \dfrac{\sqrt{7}}{4}$

$\tan\theta = \dfrac{3\sqrt{7}}{7}$

$\csc\theta = \dfrac{4}{3}$

$\sec\theta = \dfrac{4\sqrt{7}}{7}$

$\cot\theta = \dfrac{\sqrt{7}}{3}$

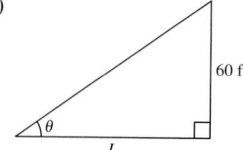

Section 5.7   (page 466)

Vocabulary Check   (page 466)

1. elevation, depression   **2.** bearing

3. harmonic motion

1. $B = 70°$ **3.** $a \approx 8.26$ **5.** $c \approx 17.09$

    $a \approx 3.64$ $c \approx 25.38$ $A \approx 20.6°$

    $c \approx 10.64$ $A = 19°$ $A \approx 69.4°$

7. $a \approx 45.25$ **9.** $a \approx 91.34$

    $A \approx 70.5°$ $b \approx 420.70$

    $B \approx 19.5°$ $B = 77°45'$

11. 2.56 inches   **13.** 6.30 feet

15. (a)   (b) $L = 60\cot\theta$

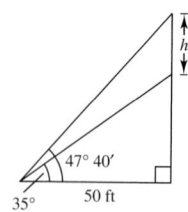

(c)

θ	$10°$	$20°$	$30°$	$40°$	$50°$
L	340	165	104	72	50

(d) No. Cotangent is not a linear function.

17. 19.7 feet

19. (a)

(b) $h = 50(\tan 47° 40' - \tan 35°)$ (c) 19.9 feet

21. ≈ 2090 feet   **23.** $\approx 38.3°$ **25.** 75.97°

27. ≈ 5099feet   **29.** ≈ 0.66 mile

31. About 105 nautical miles south and 58 nautical miles west

33. (a) N 58° E   (b) ≈ 68.82 meters   **35.** N 56.31° W

37. ≈ 1933.3 feet   **39.** 17,054 feet ≈ 3.23 miles

41. 78.69°   **43.** ≈ 35.3°   **45.** $y = \sqrt{3}\,r$

47. 29.4 inches   **49.** $a ≈ 12.2, b ≈ 7$

51. $y = 8 \sin \pi t$ **53.** $d = 3 \cos\left(\dfrac{4\pi}{3}t\right)$

55. (a) 4   (b) 4   (c) 4   (d) $\frac{1}{16}$

57. (a) $\frac{1}{16}$ (b) 70   (c) 0   (d) $\frac{1}{140}$ **59.** $\omega = 528\pi$

61. (a) 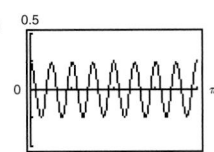   (b) $\dfrac{\pi}{8}$ second

(c) $\dfrac{\pi}{32}$ second

63. (a)

Base 1	Base 2	Altitude	Area
8	8 + 16 cos 10°	8 sin 10°	22.1
8	8 + 16 cos 20°	8 sin 20°	42.5
8	8 + 16 cos 30°	8 sin 30°	59.7
8	8 + 16 cos 40°	8 sin 40°	72.7
8	8 + 16 cos 50°	8 sin 50°	80.5
8	8 + 16 cos 60°	8 sin 60°	83.1
8	8 + 16 cos 70°	8 sin 70°	80.7

(b)

Base 1	Base 2	Altitude	Area
8	8 + 16 cos 56°	8 sin 56°	82.73
8	8 + 16 cos 58°	8 sin 58°	83.04
8	8 + 16 cos 59°	8 sin 59°	83.11
8	8 + 16 cos 60°	8 sin 60°	83.14
8	8 + 16 cos 61°	8 sin 61°	83.11
8	8 + 16 cos 62°	8 sin 62°	83.04

83.14 square feet

(c) $A = 64(1 + \cos \theta)(\sin \theta)$

(d)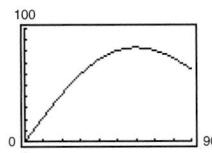

83.1 square feet

65. (a)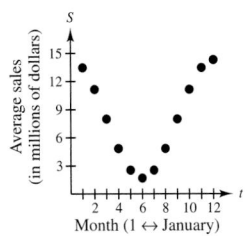

(b)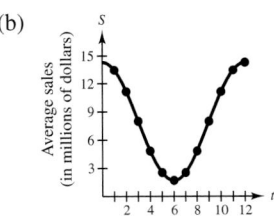

$$S = 8 + 6.3 \cos\left(\dfrac{\pi t}{6}\right)$$

The model is a good fit.

(c) 12 months. Yes; sales of outerwear is seasonal.

(d) Maximum displacement of 6.3 million dollars from the average sales of 8 million dollars

67. False. $a = \dfrac{22.56}{\tan(48.1°)}$ **69.** $4x - y + 6 = 0$

71. $4x + 5y - 22 = 0$ **73.** All real numbers

75. All real numbers

77. All real numbers x except $x = 0, x = 2$

79. All real numbers   **81.** $x = 1.994$

83. $x = ±4.851$

Review Exercises   (page 473)

1. $-320°$

3. (a) 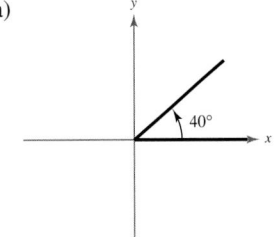   (b) Quadrant I

(c) $400°, -320°$

5. (a) 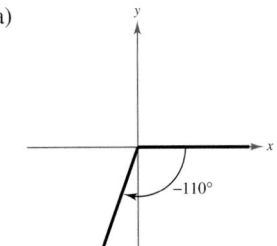   (b) Quadrant III

(c) $250°, -470°$

7. Complement: $85°$; supplement: $175°$

9. Complement: none; supplement: $9°$ **11.** $135.279°$

13. $5.381°$ **15.** $135°\,17'24''$ **17.** $-85°\,21'36''$

19. (a)   (b) Quadrant I

(c) $\dfrac{33\pi}{16},\ -\dfrac{31\pi}{16}$

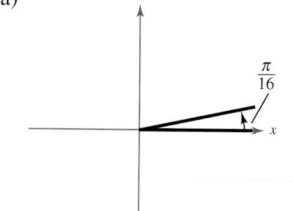

21. (a)   (b) Quadrant III

(c) $\dfrac{21\pi}{15},\ -\dfrac{39\pi}{15}$

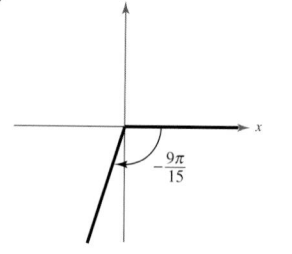

23. Complement: $\dfrac{3\pi}{8}$; supplement: $\dfrac{7\pi}{8}$

25. Complement: $\dfrac{\pi}{5}$; supplement: $\dfrac{7\pi}{10}$

27. 8.3776 rad   **29.** -0.5760 rad   **31.** $128.57°$

33. $-200.54°$ **35.** 2.083 rad   **37.** 48.171 meters

39. 100π centimeters per second

41. $\sin\theta = \dfrac{5\sqrt{61}}{61}$

$\cos\theta = \dfrac{6\sqrt{61}}{61}$

$\tan\theta = \dfrac{5}{6}$

$\csc\theta = \dfrac{\sqrt{61}}{5}$

$\sec\theta = \dfrac{\sqrt{61}}{6}$

$\cot\theta = \dfrac{6}{5}$

43. $\sin\theta = \dfrac{\sqrt{65}}{9}$

$\cos\theta = \dfrac{4}{9}$

$\tan\theta = \dfrac{\sqrt{65}}{4}$

$\csc\theta = \dfrac{9\sqrt{65}}{65}$

$\sec\theta = \dfrac{9}{4}$

$\cot\theta = \dfrac{4\sqrt{65}}{65}$

45. Answers will vary.   **47.** (a) 0.1045 (b) 0.1045

49. (a) 0.7071 (b) 1.4142 **51.** ≈ 235 feet

53. $\sin\theta = \dfrac{4}{5}$

$\cos\theta = \dfrac{3}{5}$

$\tan\theta = \dfrac{4}{3}$

$\csc\theta = \dfrac{5}{4}$

$\sec\theta = \dfrac{5}{3}$

$\cot\theta = \dfrac{3}{4}$

55. $\sin\theta = \dfrac{2\sqrt{53}}{53}$

$\cos\theta = -\dfrac{7\sqrt{53}}{53}$

$\tan\theta = -\dfrac{2}{7}$

$\csc\theta = \dfrac{\sqrt{53}}{2}$

$\sec\theta = -\dfrac{\sqrt{53}}{7}$

$\cot\theta = -\dfrac{7}{2}$

57. $\sin\theta = \dfrac{15\sqrt{241}}{241}$

$\cos\theta = \dfrac{4\sqrt{241}}{241}$

$\tan\theta = \dfrac{15}{4}$

$\csc\theta = \dfrac{\sqrt{241}}{15}$

$\sec\theta = \dfrac{\sqrt{241}}{4}$

$\cot\theta = \dfrac{4}{15}$

59. $\sin\theta = -\dfrac{\sqrt{11}}{6}$

$\cos\theta = \dfrac{5}{6}$

$\tan\theta = -\dfrac{\sqrt{11}}{5}$

$\csc\theta = -\dfrac{6\sqrt{11}}{11}$

$\cot\theta = -\dfrac{5\sqrt{11}}{11}$

61. $\cos\theta = -\dfrac{\sqrt{55}}{8}$

$\tan\theta = -\dfrac{3\sqrt{55}}{55}$

$\csc\theta = \dfrac{8}{3}$

$\sec\theta = -\dfrac{8\sqrt{55}}{55}$

$\cot\theta = -\dfrac{\sqrt{55}}{3}$

63. $\theta' = 84°$

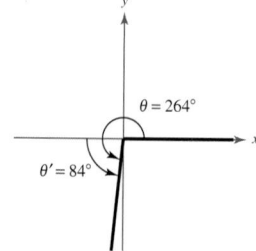

65. $\theta' = \dfrac{\pi}{5}$

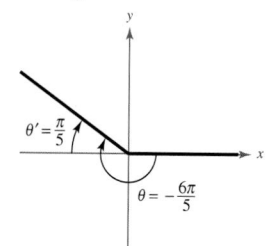

67. $\sin 240° = -\dfrac{\sqrt{3}}{2}$

$\cos 240° = -\dfrac{1}{2}$

$\tan 240° = \sqrt{3}$

69. $\sin(-210°) = \dfrac{1}{2}$

$\cos(-210°) = -\dfrac{\sqrt{3}}{2}$

$\tan(-210°) = -\dfrac{\sqrt{3}}{3}$

71. $\sin\left(-\dfrac{9\pi}{4}\right) = -\dfrac{\sqrt{2}}{2}$

$\cos\left(-\dfrac{9\pi}{4}\right) = \dfrac{\sqrt{2}}{2}$

$\tan\left(-\dfrac{9\pi}{4}\right) = -1$

73. $\sin\dfrac{\pi}{2} = 1$

$\cos\dfrac{\pi}{2} = 0$

$\tan\dfrac{\pi}{2}$ is undefined.

75. $\left(-\dfrac{1}{2}, \dfrac{\sqrt{3}}{2}\right)$

$\sin\dfrac{2\pi}{3} = \dfrac{\sqrt{3}}{2}$

$\cos\dfrac{2\pi}{3} = -\dfrac{1}{2}$

$\tan\dfrac{2\pi}{3} = -\sqrt{3}$

77. $\left(-\dfrac{\sqrt{3}}{2}, -\dfrac{1}{2}\right)$

$\sin\dfrac{7\pi}{6} = -\dfrac{1}{2}$

$\cos\dfrac{7\pi}{6} = -\dfrac{\sqrt{3}}{2}$

$\tan\dfrac{7\pi}{6} = \dfrac{\sqrt{3}}{3}$

79.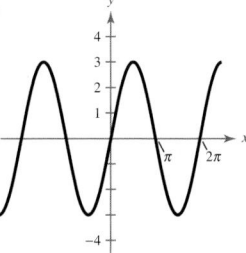

81.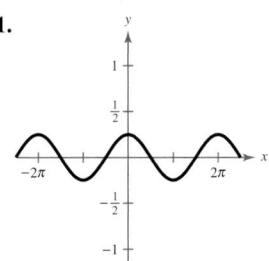

83. Period: 2; amplitude: 5

85. Period: π; amplitude: 3.4

87.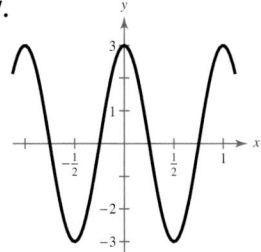

89.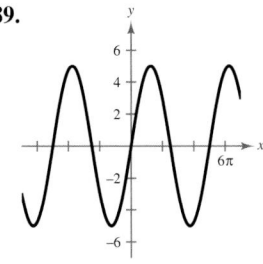

91.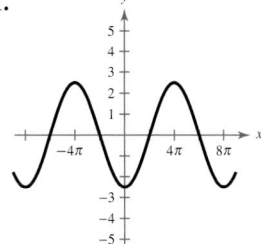

93.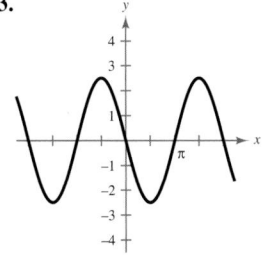

95.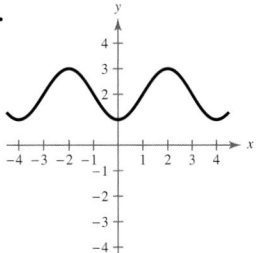

97.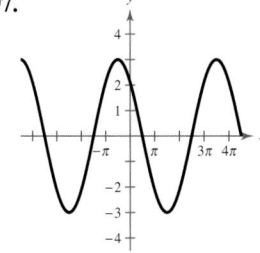

99. $f(x) = -2\cos\left(x - \dfrac{\pi}{4}\right)$

101. $f(x) = -4\cos\left(2x - \dfrac{\pi}{2}\right)$

103.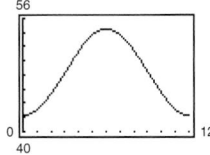

Maximum sales: June

Minimum sales: December

105.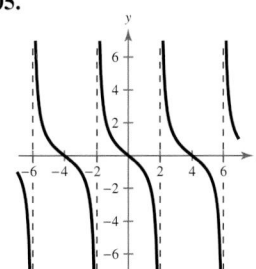

107.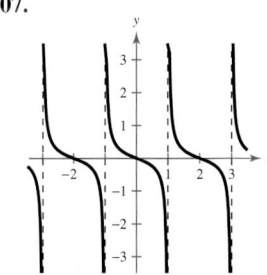

109.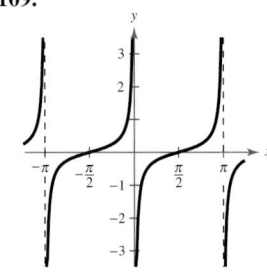

111.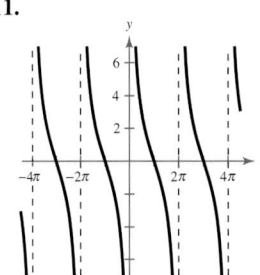

113.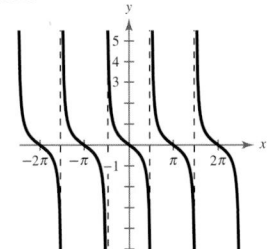

115.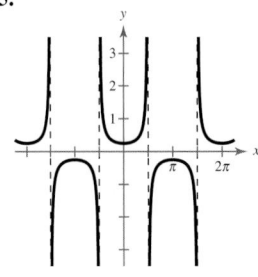

117.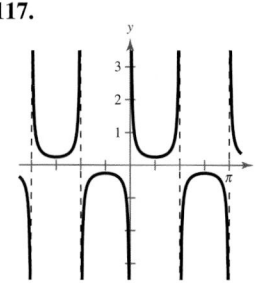

119.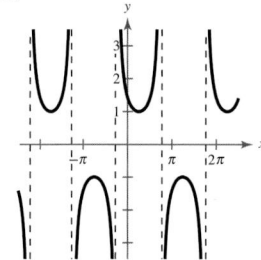

121.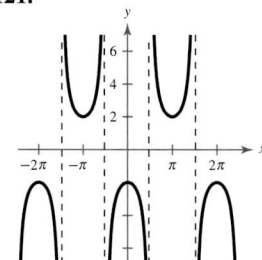

123.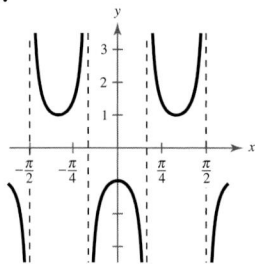

125.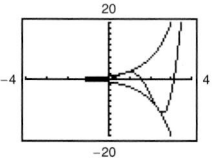

As $x \to \infty$, f cycles between $-\infty$ and ∞, but always increasing in absolute value.

127.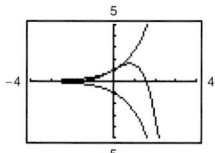

As $x \to \infty$, f cycles between $-\infty$ and ∞, but always increasing in absolute value.

129. (a) $\dfrac{\pi}{2}$ (b) Does not exist **131.** (a) $\dfrac{\pi}{4}$ (b) $\dfrac{5\pi}{6}$

133. 1.14 **135.** -1.22 **137.** -1.49

139. 0.68 **141.** $\theta = \arcsin\left(\dfrac{x+3}{16}\right)$

143. $\dfrac{\sqrt{-x^2+2x}}{-x^2+2x}$ **145.** $\dfrac{2\sqrt{4-2x^2}}{4-x^2}$ **147.** $\theta \approx 57.3°$

149. $6.8°$, 2516 feet **151.** $49{,}987$ feet ≈ 9.47 miles

153. $y = 3\cos\left(\dfrac{2\pi t}{15}\right)$

155. False. y is a function but is not one-to-one on $30° \le \theta \le 150°$.

157. As θ increases from $0°$ to $90°$, x will decrease from 12 to 0 centimeters and y will increase from 0 to 12 centimeters. Therefore,

$\sin\theta = \dfrac{y}{12}$ will increase from 0 to 1 and

$\cos\theta = \dfrac{x}{12}$ will decrease from 1 to 0. So,

$\tan\theta = \dfrac{y}{x}$ will increase without bound.

When $\theta = 90°$, the tangent will be undefined.

159. (a)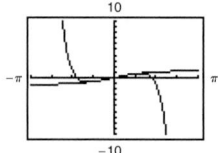

The graphs are close for $-\dfrac{\pi}{2} < x < \dfrac{\pi}{2}$.

(b) $\arctan x \approx x - \dfrac{x^3}{3} + \dfrac{x^5}{5} - \dfrac{x^7}{7} + \dfrac{x^9}{9}$

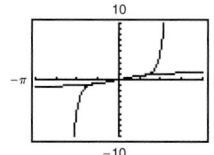

The accuracy of the approximation increases as additional terms are added.

Chapter Test (page 478)

1. (a)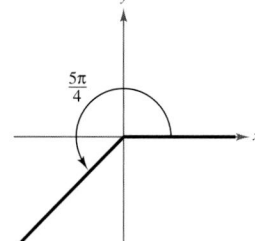

(b) $\dfrac{13\pi}{4}$, $-\dfrac{3\pi}{4}$

(c) $225°$

2. 3000 radians per minute

3. $\sin \theta = \dfrac{4\sqrt{17}}{17}$

$\cos \theta = -\dfrac{\sqrt{17}}{17}$

$\tan \theta = -4$

$\csc \theta = \dfrac{\sqrt{17}}{4}$

$\sec \theta = -\sqrt{17}$

$\cot \theta = -\dfrac{1}{4}$

4. $\sin \theta = \pm\dfrac{6\sqrt{61}}{61}$

$\cos \theta = \pm\dfrac{5\sqrt{61}}{61}$

$\csc \theta = \pm\dfrac{\sqrt{61}}{6}$

$\sec \theta = \pm\dfrac{\sqrt{61}}{5}$

$\cot \theta = \dfrac{5}{6}$

5. $\theta' = 75°$

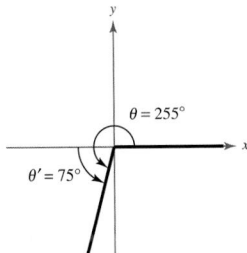

6. Quadrant III   **7.** $150°, 210°$ **8.** $1.33, 1.81$

9. $\sin \theta = \dfrac{4}{5}$

$\tan \theta = -\dfrac{4}{3}$

$\csc \theta = \dfrac{5}{4}$

$\sec \theta = -\dfrac{5}{3}$

$\cot \theta = -\dfrac{3}{4}$

10.

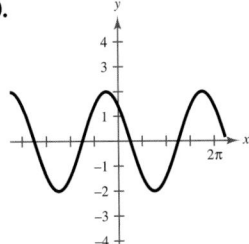

11.

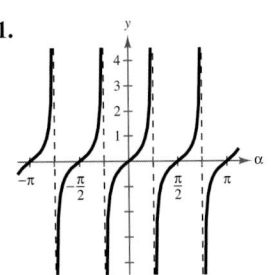

12.

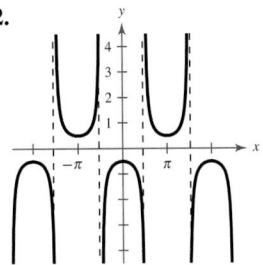

13.

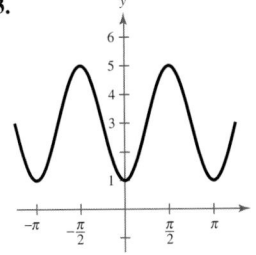

14.

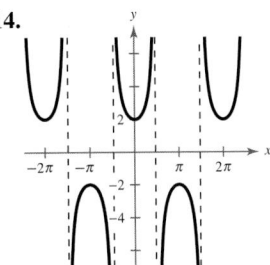

15.

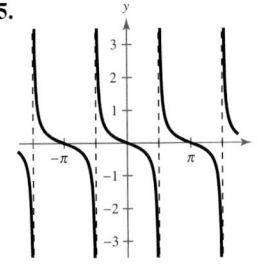

16.

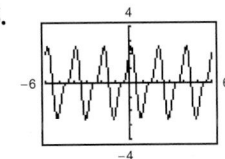

Period: 2

17.

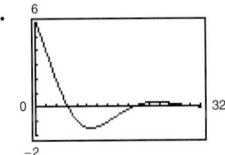

Not periodic

18. $y = -2 \sin\left(\dfrac{x}{2} - \dfrac{\pi}{4}\right)$

19. $\dfrac{\sqrt{5}}{2}$

20.

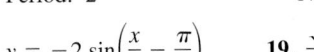

21.

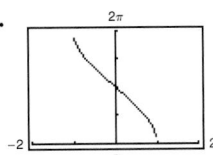

22.

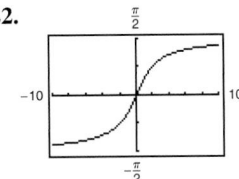

23. S 34.5° W

Chapter 6

Section 6.1   (page 485)

Vocabulary Check   (page 485)

1. sec u **2.** tan u **3.** cot u **4.** csc u

5. $\cot^2 u$ **6.** $\sec^2 u$ **7.** sin u **8.** csc u

9. $-\sin u$ **10.** cos u

---

1. $\tan x = \sqrt{3}$

$\csc x = \dfrac{2\sqrt{3}}{3}$

$\sec x = 2$

$\cot x = \dfrac{\sqrt{3}}{3}$

3. $\cos \theta = \dfrac{\sqrt{2}}{2}$

$\tan \theta = -1$

$\csc \theta = -\sqrt{2}$

$\cot \theta = -1$

5. $\sin x = -\dfrac{7}{25}$

$\cos x = -\dfrac{24}{25}$

$\csc x = -\dfrac{25}{7}$

$\cot x = \dfrac{24}{7}$

7. $\cos \phi = -\dfrac{12}{13}$

$\tan \phi = -\dfrac{5}{12}$

$\csc \phi = \dfrac{13}{5}$

$\cot \phi = -\dfrac{12}{5}$

9. $\sin x = \dfrac{2}{3}$

$\cos x = -\dfrac{\sqrt{5}}{3}$

$\csc x = \dfrac{3}{2}$

$\sec x = -\dfrac{3\sqrt{5}}{5}$

$\cot x = -\dfrac{\sqrt{5}}{2}$

11. $\sin \theta = -\dfrac{2\sqrt{5}}{5}$

$\cos \theta = -\dfrac{\sqrt{5}}{5}$

$\csc \theta = -\dfrac{\sqrt{5}}{2}$

$\sec \theta = -\sqrt{5}$

$\cot \theta = \dfrac{1}{2}$

13. $\sin \theta = 0$

$\cos \theta = -1$

$\tan \theta = 0$

$\sec \theta = -1$

$\cot \theta$ is undefined

15. d   **16.** a   **17.** b   **18.** f   **19.** e

20. c   **21.** b   **22.** c   **23.** f   **24.** a

25. e   **26.** d   **27.** $\cos x$ **29.** $\cos^2 \phi$

31. $\cos x$ **33.** 1   **35.** $\cot x$ **37.** $1 + \sin y$

39–49. Answers will vary.   **51.** $\cos^2 x$ **53.** $\cos x + 2$

55. $\sec^4 x$ **57.** $\sin^2 x - \cos^2 x$ **59.** $(\csc x - 1)\cot^2 x$

61. $1 + 2\sin x \cos x$ **63.** $\tan^2 x$ **65.** $2\csc^2 x$

67. $-\cot x$ **69.** $1 + \cos y$ **71.** $3(\sec x + \tan x)$

73.

x	0.2	0.4	0.6	0.8
y_1	0.1987	0.3894	0.5646	0.7174
y_2	0.1987	0.3894	0.5646	0.7174

x	1.0	1.2	1.4
y_1	0.8415	0.9320	0.9854
y_2	0.8415	0.9320	0.9854

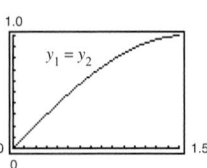

75.

x	0.2	0.4	0.6	0.8
y_1	1.2230	1.5085	1.8958	2.4650
y_2	1.2230	1.5085	1.8958	2.4650

x	1.0	1.2	1.4
y_1	3.4082	5.3319	11.6814
y_2	3.4082	5.3319	11.6814

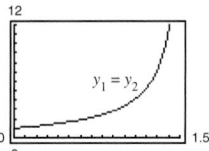

77. $\csc x$ **79.** $\tan x$ **81.** $5\cos \theta$ **83.** $3\tan \theta$

85. $0 \leq \theta \leq \pi$ **87.** $0 \leq \theta < \dfrac{\pi}{2}, \dfrac{3\pi}{2} < \theta < 2\pi$

89. $\ln|\cot \theta|$ **91.** $\ln|(\cos x)(1 + \sin x)|$

93. (a) $\csc^2(132°) - \cot^2(132°) \approx 1.8107 - 0.8107 = 1$

(b) $\csc^2\left(\dfrac{2\pi}{7}\right) - \cot^2\left(\dfrac{2\pi}{7}\right) \approx 1.63596 - 0.63596 = 1$

95. (a) $\cos(90° - 80°) = \cos(10°) \approx 0.9848$;

$\sin(80°) \approx 0.9848$

(b) $\cos\left(\dfrac{\pi}{2} - 0.8\right) \approx 0.7174$; $\sin(0.8) \approx 0.7174$

97. Answers will vary.   **99.** True, for all $\theta \neq n\pi$.

101. 1, 1   **103.** $\infty, 0$

105. $\cos \theta = \pm\sqrt{1 - \sin^2 \theta}$

$\tan \theta = \pm\dfrac{\sin \theta}{\sqrt{1 - \sin^2 \theta}}$

$\csc \theta = \dfrac{1}{\sin \theta}$

$\sec \theta = \pm\dfrac{1}{\sqrt{1 - \sin^2 \theta}}$

$\cot \theta = \pm\dfrac{\sqrt{1 - \sin^2 \theta}}{\sin \theta}$

The sign depends on the choice of θ.

107. Answers will vary. Sample answer:

$\sin \theta = \dfrac{o}{h}$

$\cos \theta = \dfrac{a}{h}$

$o^2 + a^2 = h^2$

$\dfrac{o^2}{h^2} + \dfrac{a^2}{h^2} = 1$

$\left(\dfrac{o}{h}\right)^2 + \left(\dfrac{a}{h}\right)^2 = 1$

$\sin^2 \theta + \cos^2 \theta = 1$

109.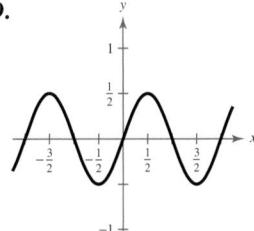

111.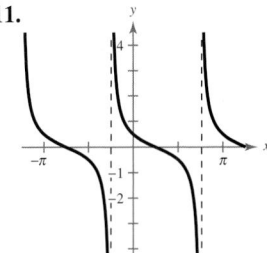

Section 6.2   (page 493)

Vocabulary Check   (page 493)

1. conditional   **2.** identity   **3.** $\cot u$ **4.** $\sin u$

5. $\tan u$ **6.** $\cos u$ **7.** $\cos^2 u$ **8.** $\cos u$

9. $-\tan u$ **10.** $\sec u$

1–9. Answers will vary.

11.

x	0.2	0.4	0.6	0.8
y_1	4.8348	2.1785	1.2064	0.6767
y_2	4.8348	2.1785	1.2064	0.6767

x	1.0	1.2	1.4
y_1	0.3469	0.1409	0.0293
y_2	0.3469	0.1409	0.0293

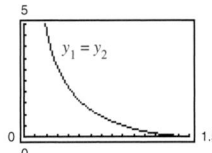

13.

x	0.2	0.4	0.6	0.8
y_1	4.8348	2.1785	1.2064	0.6767
y_2	4.8348	2.1785	1.2064	0.6767

x	1.0	1.2	1.4
y_1	0.3469	0.1409	0.0293
y_2	0.3469	0.1409	0.0293

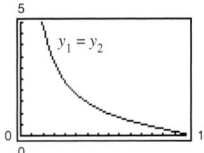

15.

x	0.2	0.4	0.6	0.8
y_1	5.0335	2.5679	1.7710	1.3940
y_2	5.0335	2.5679	1.7710	1.3940

x	1.0	1.2	1.4
y_1	1.1884	1.0729	1.0148
y_2	1.1884	1.0729	1.0148

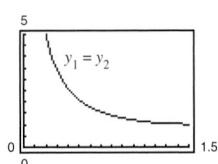

17.

x	0.2	0.4	0.6	0.8
y_1	5.1359	2.7880	2.1458	2.0009
y_2	5.1359	2.7880	2.1458	2.0009

x	1.0	1.2	1.4
y_1	2.1995	2.9609	5.9704
y_2	2.1995	2.9609	5.9704

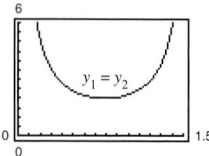

19. $\cot(-x) = -\cot(x)$, so
$(1 + \tan x)[1 + \cot(-x)] = \tan x - \cot x.$

21–49. Answers will vary.

51.

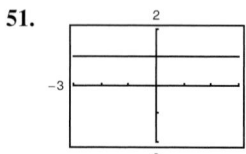

$y = 1$

53.

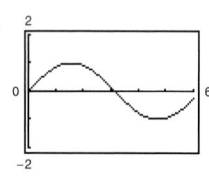

$y = \sin x$

55 and 57. Answers will vary. **59.** 1 **61.** 2

63 and 65. Answers will vary. **67.** $\mu = \tan \theta, W \neq 0$

69. True **71.** False. $\sin^2\left(\dfrac{\pi}{4}\right) + \cos^2\left(\dfrac{\pi}{4}\right) \neq 1 + \tan^2\left(\dfrac{\pi}{4}\right)$

73. $\sqrt{\tan^2 x} = |\tan x|; \dfrac{3\pi}{4}$ **75.** Answers will vary.

77. Answers will vary.

Sample answer: $y = x^3 - x^2 + 64x - 64$

79. Answers will vary.

Sample answer: $y = x^3 - 16x^2 + 85x - 148$

81.

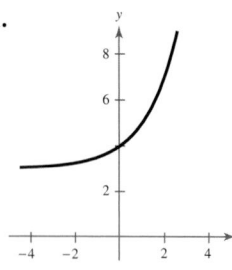

83.

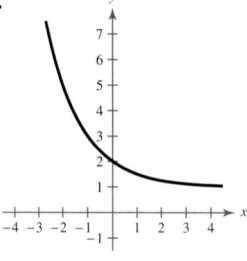

85. Quadrant II **87.** Quadrant IV

89. $A = 10°$ **91.** $A = 60.26°$
$\quad b \approx 90.74$ $\quad B \approx 29.74°$
$\quad c \approx 92.14$ $\quad c \approx 16.12$

Section 6.3 (page 504)

Vocabulary Check (page 504)

1. general **2.** quadratic **3.** extraneous

1–5. Answers will vary. **7.** $\dfrac{2\pi}{3} + 2n\pi, \dfrac{4\pi}{3} + 2n\pi$

9. $\dfrac{\pi}{6} + 2n\pi, \dfrac{11\pi}{6} + 2n\pi$

11. $\dfrac{\pi}{3} + n\pi, \dfrac{2\pi}{3} + n\pi$ **13.** $\dfrac{\pi}{3} + n\pi, \dfrac{2\pi}{3} + n\pi$

15. $\dfrac{\pi}{3} + n\pi, \dfrac{2\pi}{3} + n\pi$ **17.** $\dfrac{2\pi}{3}, \dfrac{5\pi}{3}$

19. $\dfrac{\pi}{4}, \dfrac{3\pi}{4}, \dfrac{5\pi}{4}, \dfrac{7\pi}{4}$ **21.** $0, \dfrac{\pi}{6}, \dfrac{5\pi}{6}, \pi, \dfrac{7\pi}{6}, \dfrac{11\pi}{6}$

23. $\dfrac{\pi}{3}, \pi, \dfrac{5\pi}{3}$ **25.** No solution **27.** $\dfrac{\pi}{3}, \dfrac{5\pi}{3}$

29. $2.0344, 5.1760, \dfrac{\pi}{4}, \dfrac{5\pi}{4}$ **31.** $3.6652, 4.7124, 5.7596$

33. $0.8614, 5.4218$ **35.** 1.5708 **37.** $0.5236, 2.6180$

39. $\dfrac{2\pi}{3} + n\pi, \dfrac{5\pi}{6} + n\pi$ **41.** $\dfrac{\pi}{8} + \dfrac{n\pi}{4}$

43. $\dfrac{n\pi}{3}, \dfrac{\pi}{4} + n\pi$ **45.** $\dfrac{\pi}{2} + 4n\pi, \dfrac{7\pi}{2} + 4n\pi$ **47.** $-1, 3$

49. ± 2 **51.** $1.1071, 4.2487$ **53.** $0.8603, 3.4256$

55. $0, 2.6779, 3.1416, 5.8195$

57. $0.3398, 0.8481, 2.2935, 2.8018$ **59.** $-1.154, 0.534$

61. 1.110

63. (a)

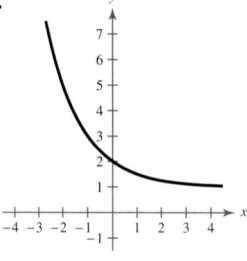

Maximum: $(0.785, 1.41)$
Minimum: $(3.93, -1.41)$

(b) $\dfrac{\pi}{4}, \dfrac{5\pi}{4}$

65. 1

67. (a) All real numbers x except $x = 0$

(b) y-axis symmetry; horizontal asymptote: $y = 1$

(c) Oscillates   (d) Infinite number of solutions

(e) Yes. 0.6366

69. 0.04 second, 0.43 second, 0.83 second

71. May, June, July   **73.** $37°, 53°$

75. (a)

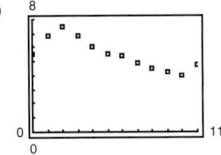

(b)

The model fits the data.

(c) The constant term; 5.51%

(d) Approximately 13 years

(e) 2007

77. False. Reasons will vary.

79. False. The domain of the sine function does not include 3.4.

81. 2.164 rad   **83.** -0.007 rad

85. 24.249   **87.** 2290.4 feet

Section 6.4   (page 512)

Vocabulary Check   (page 512)

1. $\sin u \cos v - \cos u \sin v$

2. $\cos u \cos v - \sin u \sin v$ **3.** $\dfrac{\tan u + \tan v}{1 - \tan u \tan v}$

4. $\sin u \cos v + \cos u \sin v$

5. $\cos u \cos v + \sin u \sin v$ **6.** $\dfrac{\tan u - \tan v}{1 + \tan u \tan v}$

---

1. (a) $-\dfrac{1}{2}$ (b) $-\dfrac{3}{2}$ **3.** (a) 0   (b) $\dfrac{1 + \sqrt{3}}{2}$

5. (a) $\dfrac{-\sqrt{2} - \sqrt{6}}{4}$ (b) $\dfrac{-\sqrt{2} - \sqrt{3}}{2}$

7. $\sin 105° = \dfrac{\sqrt{6} + \sqrt{2}}{4}$

$\cos 105° = \dfrac{\sqrt{2} - \sqrt{6}}{4}$

$\tan 105° = -2 - \sqrt{3}$

9. $\sin 195° = \dfrac{\sqrt{2} - \sqrt{6}}{4}$

$\cos 195° = \dfrac{-\sqrt{2} - \sqrt{6}}{4}$

$\tan 195° = 2 - \sqrt{3}$

11. $\sin \dfrac{11\pi}{12} = \dfrac{\sqrt{6} - \sqrt{2}}{4}$

$\cos \dfrac{11\pi}{12} = \dfrac{-\sqrt{6} - \sqrt{2}}{4}$

$\tan \dfrac{11\pi}{12} = -2 + \sqrt{3}$

13. $\sin\left(-\dfrac{\pi}{12}\right) = \dfrac{\sqrt{2} - \sqrt{6}}{4}$

$\cos\left(-\dfrac{\pi}{12}\right) = \dfrac{\sqrt{6} + \sqrt{2}}{4}$

$\tan\left(-\dfrac{\pi}{12}\right) = -2 + \sqrt{3}$

15. $\sin 75° = \dfrac{\sqrt{2} + \sqrt{6}}{4}$

$\cos 75° = \dfrac{\sqrt{6} - \sqrt{2}}{4}$

$\tan 75° = \sqrt{3} + 2$

17. $\sin(-225°) = \dfrac{\sqrt{2}}{2}$

$\cos(-225°) = -\dfrac{\sqrt{2}}{2}$

$\tan(-225°) = -1$

19. $\sin \dfrac{13\pi}{12} = \dfrac{-\sqrt{6} + \sqrt{2}}{4}$

$\cos \dfrac{13\pi}{12} = \dfrac{-\sqrt{6} - \sqrt{2}}{4}$

$\tan \dfrac{13\pi}{12} = 2 - \sqrt{3}$

21. $\sin\left(-\dfrac{7\pi}{12}\right) = -\dfrac{\sqrt{6} + \sqrt{2}}{4}$

$\cos\left(-\dfrac{7\pi}{12}\right) = \dfrac{\sqrt{2} - \sqrt{6}}{4}$

$\tan\left(-\dfrac{7\pi}{12}\right) = 2 + \sqrt{3}$

23. $\cos 70°$ **25.** $\tan 239°$

27. $\sin 2.3$ **29.** $\cos \dfrac{12\pi}{35}$

31.

x	0.2	0.4	0.6	0.8
y_1	0.6621	0.7978	0.9017	0.9696
y_2	0.6621	0.7978	0.9017	0.9696

x	1.0	1.2	1.4
y_1	0.9989	0.9883	0.9384
y_2	0.9989	0.9883	0.9384

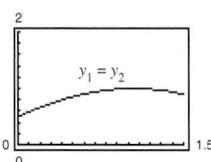

33.

x	0.2	0.4	0.6	0.8
y_1	0.9605	0.8484	0.6812	0.4854
y_2	0.9605	0.8484	0.6812	0.4854

x	1.0	1.2	1.4
y_1	0.2919	0.1313	0.0289
y_2	0.2919	0.1313	0.0289

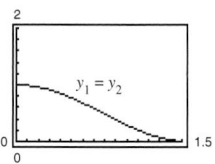

35. $-\frac{63}{65}$ **37.** $-\frac{63}{16}$ **39.** $\frac{3}{5}$ **41.** $\frac{44}{125}$ **43.** 1

45. $\dfrac{2x^2 - \sqrt{1 - x^2}}{\sqrt{4x^2 + 1}}$ **47–53.** Answers will vary.

55. $\dfrac{\pi}{2}$ **57.** $0, \dfrac{\pi}{3}, \pi, \dfrac{5\pi}{3}$ **59.** 0.7854, 5.4978

61. 0, 3.1416   **63.** Answers will vary.

65. False. $\cos(u \pm v) = \cos u \cos v \mp \sin u \sin v$

67 and 69. Answers will vary.

71. (a) $\sqrt{2}\sin\left(\theta + \dfrac{\pi}{4}\right)$ (b) $\sqrt{2}\cos\left(\theta - \dfrac{\pi}{4}\right)$

73. (a) $13\sin(3\theta + 0.3948)$ (b) $13\cos(3\theta - 1.1760)$

75. $2\cos\theta$ **77.** Answers will vary.

79. $u + v = w$. Answers will vary.   **81.** $(0, 19), (38, 0)$

83. $(0, 4), (2, 0), (7, 0)$ **85.** $\dfrac{\pi}{6}$ **87.** $\dfrac{\pi}{2}$

Section 6.5   (page 522)

Vocabulary Check   (page 522)

1. $2\sin u \cos u$ **2.** $\dfrac{1 + \cos 2u}{2}$ **3.** $\cos 2u$

4. $\tan\dfrac{u}{2}$ **5.** $\dfrac{2\tan u}{1 - \tan^2 u}$

6. $\frac{1}{2}[\cos(u - v) + \cos(u + v)]$ **7.** $\sin^2 u$

8. $\cos\dfrac{u}{2}$ **9.** $\dfrac{1}{2}[\sin(u + v) + \sin(u - v)]$

10. $2\sin\left(\dfrac{u + v}{2}\right)\cos\left(\dfrac{u - v}{2}\right)$

1. $\frac{3}{5}$ **3.** $\frac{7}{25}$ **5.** $\frac{24}{7}$ **7.** $\frac{25}{24}$

9. $0, 1.0472, 3.1416, 5.2360; 0, \dfrac{\pi}{3}, \pi, \dfrac{5\pi}{3}$

11. $0.2618, 1.3090, 3.4034, 4.4506; \dfrac{\pi}{12}, \dfrac{5\pi}{12}, \dfrac{13\pi}{12}, \dfrac{17\pi}{12}$

13. $0, 2.0944, 4.1888; 0, \dfrac{2\pi}{3}, \dfrac{4\pi}{3}$

15. $0, 1.5708, 3.1416, 4.7124; 0, \dfrac{\pi}{2}, \pi, \dfrac{3\pi}{2}$

17. $\sin 2u = \frac{24}{25}$ **19.** $\sin 2u = \frac{4}{5}$
$\cos 2u = \frac{7}{25}$ $\cos 2u = \frac{3}{5}$
$\tan 2u = \frac{24}{7}$ $\tan 2u = \frac{4}{3}$

21. $\sin 2u = -\dfrac{4\sqrt{21}}{25}$

$\cos 2u = -\dfrac{17}{25}$

$\tan 2u = \dfrac{4\sqrt{21}}{17}$

23. $4\sin 2x$ **25.** $6\cos 2x$

27. $\frac{1}{8}(3 + 4\cos 2x + \cos 4x)$ **29.** $\frac{1}{8}(1 - \cos 4x)$

31. $\frac{1}{32}(2 + \cos 2x - 2\cos 4x - \cos 6x)$

33. $\dfrac{4\sqrt{17}}{17}$ **35.** $\dfrac{1}{4}$ **37.** $\sqrt{17}$ **39.** $\dfrac{8}{17}$

41. $\sin 15° = \dfrac{\sqrt{2 - \sqrt{3}}}{2}$ **43.** $\sin 112° 30' = \dfrac{\sqrt{2 + \sqrt{2}}}{2}$

$\cos 15° = \dfrac{\sqrt{2 + \sqrt{3}}}{2}$ $\cos 112° 30' = -\dfrac{\sqrt{2 - \sqrt{2}}}{2}$

$\tan 15° = 2 - \sqrt{3}$ $\tan 112° 30' = -1 - \sqrt{2}$

45. $\sin\dfrac{\pi}{8} = \dfrac{\sqrt{2-\sqrt{2}}}{2}$ **47.** $\sin\dfrac{3\pi}{8} = \dfrac{\sqrt{2+\sqrt{2}}}{2}$

$\cos\dfrac{\pi}{8} = \dfrac{\sqrt{2+\sqrt{2}}}{2}$ $\cos\dfrac{3\pi}{8} = \dfrac{\sqrt{2-\sqrt{2}}}{2}$

$\tan\dfrac{\pi}{8} = \sqrt{2} - 1$ $\tan\dfrac{3\pi}{8} = \sqrt{2} + 1$

49. $\sin\dfrac{u}{2} = \dfrac{5\sqrt{26}}{26}$ **51.** $\sin\dfrac{u}{2} = \sqrt{\dfrac{89 - 5\sqrt{89}}{178}}$

$\cos\dfrac{u}{2} = \dfrac{\sqrt{26}}{26}$ $\cos\dfrac{u}{2} = -\sqrt{\dfrac{89 + 5\sqrt{89}}{178}}$

$\tan\dfrac{u}{2} = 5$ $\tan\dfrac{u}{2} = \dfrac{5 - \sqrt{89}}{8}$

53. $\sin\dfrac{u}{2} = \dfrac{3\sqrt{10}}{10}$

$\cos\dfrac{u}{2} = -\dfrac{\sqrt{10}}{10}$

$\tan\dfrac{u}{2} = -3$

55. $|\sin 3x|$ **57.** $-|\tan 4x|$ **59.** $\dfrac{\pi}{3}, \dfrac{5\pi}{3}$

61. $\dfrac{\pi}{3}, \pi, \dfrac{5\pi}{3}$ **63.** $3\sin\dfrac{2\pi}{3}$ **65.** $\dfrac{1}{2}(\sin 8\theta + \sin 2\theta)$

67. $\dfrac{5}{2}(\cos 8\beta + \cos 2\beta)$ **69.** $2\cos 3\theta \sin 2\theta$

71. $2\cos\alpha\sin\beta$ **73.** $-2\sin\theta\sin\dfrac{\pi}{2} = -2\sin\theta$

75. $\dfrac{\sqrt{2}}{2}$ **77.** $\dfrac{\sqrt{6}}{2}$ **79.** $0, \dfrac{\pi}{4}, \dfrac{\pi}{2}, \dfrac{3\pi}{4}, \pi, \dfrac{5\pi}{4}, \dfrac{3\pi}{2}, \dfrac{7\pi}{4}$

81. $\dfrac{\pi}{6}, \dfrac{5\pi}{6}$ **83.** $\dfrac{25}{169}$ **85.** $\dfrac{4}{13}$

87–97. Answers will vary.

99. 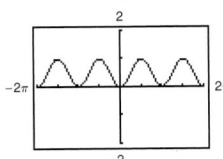   **101.**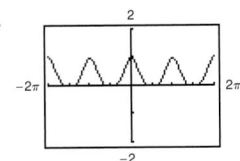

103. (a)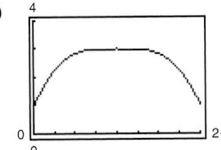

Maximum: $(3.1416, 3)$

(b) π

105. (a)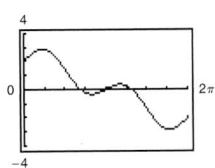

Minimum: $(5.5839, -2.8642)$

Maximum: $(0.6993, 2.8642)$

(b) $0.6993, 2.6078, 3.6754, 5.5839$

107. $2x\sqrt{1-x^2}$ **109.** $1 - 2x^2$ **111.** $\dfrac{1-x^2}{1+x^2}$

113. $r = \dfrac{1}{16}v_0^2 \sin\theta\cos\theta$

115. (a) $\theta = \pi$ (c) 760 mph; 3420 mph

(b) $\theta = 0.4482$ (d) $\cos\theta = 1 - \dfrac{2}{m^2}$

117. False. $\sin\dfrac{x}{2} = -\sqrt{\dfrac{1-\cos x}{2}}$ for $\pi \le \dfrac{x}{2} \le 2\pi$.

119. (a) 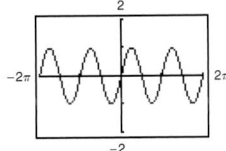   (b) $y = \sin 2x$

(c) Answers will vary.

121. Answers will vary.

123. (a) 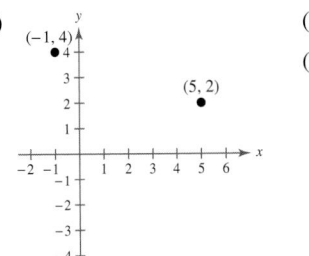   (b) $2\sqrt{10}$

(c) $(2, 3)$

125. (a) 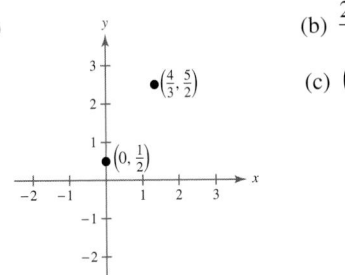   (b) $\dfrac{2\sqrt{13}}{3}$

(c) $\left(\dfrac{2}{3}, \dfrac{3}{2}\right)$

127. (a) Complement: $35°$; supplement: $125°$

(b) Complement: none; supplement: $18°$

129. (a) Complement: $\dfrac{4\pi}{9}$; supplement: $\dfrac{17\pi}{18}$

(b) Complement: $\dfrac{\pi}{20}$; supplement: $\dfrac{11\pi}{20}$

131. 0.467 rad

133.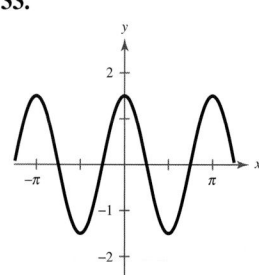

135.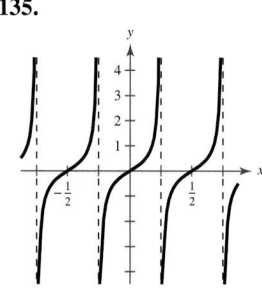

Review Exercises   (page 527)

1. $\sec x$ **3.** $\cos x$ **5.** $\pm \sin x$

7. $\sec x$ **9.** $\sec x$

11. $\tan x = \dfrac{4}{3}$

$\csc x = \dfrac{5}{4}$

$\sec x = \dfrac{5}{3}$

$\cot x = \dfrac{3}{4}$

13. $\cos x = \dfrac{\sqrt{2}}{2}$

$\tan x = -1$

$\csc x = -\sqrt{2}$

$\sec x = \sqrt{2}$

$\cot x = -1$

15. $\sin^2 x$ **17.** $1 + \cot \alpha$ **19.** 1 **21.** $\csc x$

23–35. Answers will vary.

37. $\dfrac{\pi}{6} + 2n\pi, \dfrac{5\pi}{6} + 2n\pi$ **39.** $\dfrac{\pi}{3} + 2n\pi, \dfrac{2\pi}{3} + 2n\pi$

41. $\dfrac{\pi}{6} + n\pi$ **43.** $\dfrac{\pi}{3} + n\pi, \dfrac{2\pi}{3} + n\pi$

45. $\dfrac{\pi}{6} + n\pi, \dfrac{5\pi}{6} + n\pi$ **47.** $n\pi$

49. $0, \dfrac{2\pi}{3}, \dfrac{4\pi}{3}$ **51.** $0, \dfrac{\pi}{2}, \pi$ **53.** $\dfrac{\pi}{8}, \dfrac{3\pi}{8}, \dfrac{9\pi}{8}, \dfrac{11\pi}{8}$

55. $0, \dfrac{\pi}{8}, \dfrac{3\pi}{8}, \dfrac{5\pi}{8}, \dfrac{7\pi}{8}, \dfrac{9\pi}{8}, \dfrac{11\pi}{8}, \dfrac{13\pi}{8}, \dfrac{15\pi}{8}$ **57.** $\dfrac{\pi}{2}, \dfrac{3\pi}{2}$

59. $0, \pi$ **61.** 1.2490, 1.8158, 4.3906, 4.9574

63. $\sin 285° = -\dfrac{\sqrt{6} + \sqrt{2}}{4}$

$\cos 285° = \dfrac{\sqrt{6} - \sqrt{2}}{4}$

$\tan 285° = -2 - \sqrt{3}$

65. $\sin \dfrac{25\pi}{12} = \dfrac{\sqrt{6} - \sqrt{2}}{4}$

$\cos \dfrac{25\pi}{12} = \dfrac{\sqrt{6} + \sqrt{2}}{4}$

$\tan \dfrac{25\pi}{12} = 2 - \sqrt{3}$

67. $\sin 190°$ **69.** $\tan 35°$ **71.** $\dfrac{-15 - 12\sqrt{7}}{52}$

73. $\dfrac{507\sqrt{7} - 960}{1121}$ **75.** $\dfrac{5\sqrt{7} - 36}{52}$

77–81. Answers will vary.   **83.** $\dfrac{\pi}{6}, \dfrac{11\pi}{6}$

85. $\sin 2u = \dfrac{20\sqrt{6}}{49}$

$\cos 2u = -\dfrac{1}{49}$

$\tan 2u = -20\sqrt{6}$

87. $\sin 2u = -\dfrac{36}{85}$

$\cos 2u = \dfrac{77}{85}$

$\tan 2u = -\dfrac{36}{77}$

89 and 91. Answers will vary.   **93.** $15°, 75°$

95. $\frac{1}{32}(10 - 15 \cos 2x + 6 \cos 4x - \cos 6x)$

97. $\frac{1}{8}(3 + 4 \cos 4x + \cos 8x)$

99. $\sin 105° = \dfrac{\sqrt{2 + \sqrt{3}}}{2}$

$\cos 105° = -\dfrac{\sqrt{2 - \sqrt{3}}}{2}$

$\tan 105° = -2 - \sqrt{3}$

101. $\sin \dfrac{7\pi}{8} = \dfrac{\sqrt{2 - \sqrt{2}}}{2}$

$\cos \dfrac{7\pi}{8} = -\dfrac{\sqrt{2 + \sqrt{2}}}{2}$

$\tan \dfrac{7\pi}{8} = 1 - \sqrt{2}$

103. $\sin \dfrac{u}{2} = \dfrac{\sqrt{10}}{10}$

$\cos \dfrac{u}{2} = \dfrac{3\sqrt{10}}{10}$

$\tan \dfrac{u}{2} = \dfrac{1}{3}$

105. $\sin \dfrac{u}{2} = \dfrac{3\sqrt{14}}{14}$

$\cos \dfrac{u}{2} = \dfrac{\sqrt{70}}{14}$

$\tan \dfrac{u}{2} = \dfrac{3\sqrt{5}}{5}$

107. $-|\cos 5x|$ **109.** $V = \sin \dfrac{\theta}{2} \cos \dfrac{\theta}{2}$ cubic meters

111. $3 \sin \dfrac{\pi}{2} = 3$ **113.** $\frac{1}{2}(\cos \alpha - \cos 5\alpha)$

115. $2 \cos \dfrac{5\theta}{2} \cos \dfrac{\theta}{2}$ **117.** $2 \cos x \sin \dfrac{\pi}{4} = \sqrt{2} \cos x$

119. $y = \frac{1}{2}\sqrt{10} \sin\left(8t - \arctan \frac{1}{3}\right)$ **121.** $\frac{1}{2}\sqrt{10}$

123. False. $\cos \dfrac{\theta}{2} > 0$ **125.** True

127. Answers will vary.   **129.** $y_3 = y_2 + 1$

Chapter Test   (page 530)

1. $\sin \theta = -\dfrac{6\sqrt{61}}{61}$ **2.** 1   **3.** 1

$\cos \theta = -\dfrac{5\sqrt{61}}{61}$

$\csc \theta = -\dfrac{\sqrt{61}}{6}$

$\sec \theta = -\dfrac{\sqrt{61}}{5}$

$\cot \theta = \dfrac{5}{6}$

4. $\csc \theta \sec \theta$ **5.** $\dfrac{\pi}{2} < \theta \le \pi, \dfrac{3\pi}{2} < \theta < 2\pi$

6.

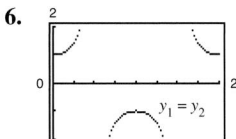

7–12. Answers will vary.   **13.** $-2 - \sqrt{3}$

14. $\dfrac{1}{16}\left[\dfrac{10 - 15\cos 2x + 6\cos 4x - \cos 6x}{1 + \cos 2x}\right]$

15. $\tan 2\theta$ **16.** $3(\cos 2\theta - \cos 10\theta)$

17. $2\cos 4\theta \cos \theta$ **18.** $0, \dfrac{3\pi}{4}, \pi, \dfrac{7\pi}{4}$

19. $\dfrac{\pi}{6}, \dfrac{\pi}{2}, \dfrac{5\pi}{6}, \dfrac{3\pi}{2}$ **20.** $\dfrac{\pi}{6}, \dfrac{5\pi}{6}, \dfrac{7\pi}{6}, \dfrac{11\pi}{6}$

21. $\dfrac{\pi}{6}, \dfrac{5\pi}{6}, \dfrac{3\pi}{2}$ **22.** 1.306

23. $\sin 2u = \dfrac{4}{5}$ **24.** $76.52°$

$\cos 2u = -\dfrac{3}{5}$

$\tan 2u = -\dfrac{4}{3}$

Chapter 7

Section 7.1   (page 538)

Vocabulary Check   (page 538)

1. oblique   **2.** $\dfrac{b}{\sin B}$

3. $\frac{1}{2}bc \sin A; \frac{1}{2}ab \sin C; \frac{1}{2}ac \sin B$

1. $C = 105°$, $b \approx 16.97$, $c \approx 23.18$

3. $C = 110°$, $b \approx 22.44$, $c \approx 24.35$

5. $B \approx 21.6°$, $C \approx 122.4°$, $c \approx 11.49$

7. $B = 60.9°$, $b \approx 19.32$, $c \approx 6.36$

9. $B = 42°4'$, $a \approx 22.05$, $b \approx 14.88$

11. $A \approx 10°11'$, $C \approx 154°19'$, $c \approx 11.03$

13. $B \approx 18°13'$, $C \approx 51°32'$, $c \approx 40.06$

15. $B \approx 48.74°$, $C \approx 21.26°$, $c \approx 48.23$

17. No solution

19. Two solutions

$B \approx 72.2°$, $C \approx 49.8°$, $c \approx 10.27$

$B \approx 107.8°$, $C \approx 14.2°$, $c \approx 3.3$

21. ≈ 28.2 square units   **23.** ≈ 1782.3 square units

25. 2878.4 square units

27. (a)

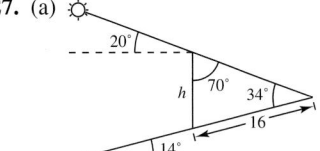

(b) $\dfrac{16}{\sin 70°} = \dfrac{h}{\sin 34°}$ (c) ≈ 9.5 meters

29. $240°$

31. (a)

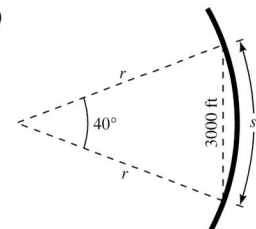

(b) 4385.71 feet

(c) 3061.80 feet

33. ≈ 15.53 kilometers; ≈ 42.43 kilometers   **35.** $\approx 16.1°$

37. (a) $\alpha \approx 5.36°$

(b) $\beta = \sin^{-1}\left(\dfrac{d \sin \theta}{58.36}\right)$

(c) $d = \sin(84.64 - \theta)\left[\dfrac{58.36}{\sin \theta}\right]$

(d)

θ	10°	20°	30°	40°	50°	60°
d	324.1	154.2	95.2	63.8	43.3	28.1

39. False. The triangle can't be solved if only three angles are known.

41. Yes, the Law of Sines can be used to solve a right triangle provided that at least one side is given.

43. $\tan \theta = -\frac{12}{5}$; $\csc \theta = -\frac{13}{12}$; $\sec \theta = \frac{13}{5}$; $\cot \theta = -\frac{5}{12}$

45. $\sin \theta = \frac{\sqrt{122}}{122}$; $\cos \theta = -\frac{11\sqrt{122}}{122}$; $\tan \theta = -\frac{1}{11}$;

$\csc \theta = \sqrt{122}$

47. $3(\sin 11\theta + \sin 5\theta)$ **49.** $\frac{3}{2}\left(\sin \frac{11\pi}{6} + \sin \frac{3\pi}{2}\right)$

Section 7.2 (page 545)

Vocabulary Check   (page 545)

1. $c^2 = a^2 + b^2 - 2ab \cos C$ **2.** Heron's Area

3. $\frac{1}{2}bh$, $\sqrt{s(s-a)(s-b)(s-c)}$

---

1. $A \approx 26.4°$, $B \approx 36.3°$, $C \approx 117.3°$

3. $B \approx 29.4°$, $C \approx 100.6°$, $a \approx 23.38$

5. $A \approx 36.9°$, $B \approx 53.1°$, $C = 90°$

7. $A \approx 103.5°$, $B \approx 38.2°$, $C \approx 38.2°$

9. $b \approx 8.58$, $A \approx 154°14'$, $C \approx 17°31'$

11. $b \approx 9.94$, $A \approx 37.1°$, $C \approx 67.6°$

	a	b	c	d	θ	ϕ
13.	4	8	11.64	4.96	30°	150°
15.	10	14	20	13.86	68.2°	111.8°
17.	15	16.96	25	20	77.2°	102.8°

19. ≈ 19.81 square units   **21.** ≈ 15.52 square units

23. ≈ 35.19 square units

25.

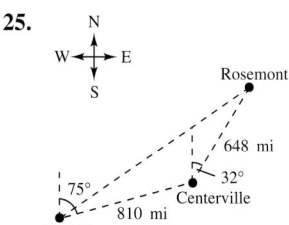

1357.8 miles, 236°

27. 483.4 meters   **29.** 43.3 miles

31. (a) N 58.4° W   (b) S 81.5° W

33. $PQ \approx 9.4$, $QS \approx 5.0$, $RS \approx 12.8$

35. $\approx 18,618$ square feet

37. (a) $49 = 2.25 + x^2 - 3x \cos \theta$

(b) $x = \frac{1}{2}\left(3 \cos \theta + \sqrt{9 \cos^2\theta + 187}\right)$

(c)

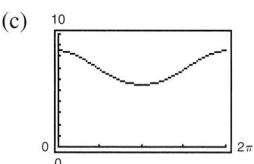

(d) 6 inches

39. False. A triangle cannot be formed with sides of lengths 10 feet, 16 feet, and 5 feet.

41. False. $s = \dfrac{a + b + c}{2}$ **43.** $-\dfrac{\pi}{2}$ **45.** $\dfrac{\pi}{3}$

47. $-2 \sin\left(\dfrac{7\pi}{12}\right)\sin\left(\dfrac{\pi}{4}\right)$

Section 7.3 (page 557)

Vocabulary Check   (page 557)

1. directed line segment   **2.** initial, terminal

3. magnitude or length   **4.** vector

5. standard position   **6.** unit vector

7. multiplication, addition   **8.** resultant

9. linear combination, horizontal, vertical

---

1. $\|\mathbf{u}\| = \|\mathbf{v}\| = \sqrt{17}$, $\text{slope}_{\mathbf{u}} = \text{slope}_{\mathbf{v}} = \frac{1}{4}$

$\mathbf{u}$ and $\mathbf{v}$ have the same magnitude and direction, so they are equal.

3. $\langle 4, 3 \rangle$, $\|\mathbf{v}\| = 5$ **5.** $\langle -3, 2 \rangle$, $\|\mathbf{v}\| = \sqrt{13} \approx 3.61$

7. $\langle 0, 5 \rangle$, $\|\mathbf{v}\| = 5$ **9.** $\left\langle -\dfrac{9}{2}, -\dfrac{5}{2} \right\rangle$, $\|\mathbf{v}\| = \dfrac{\sqrt{106}}{2} \approx 5.15$

11. $\langle 8, 6 \rangle$, $\|\mathbf{v}\| = 10$

13. 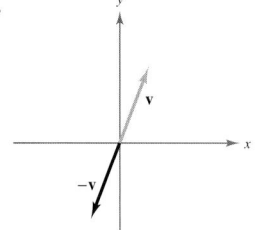   **15.**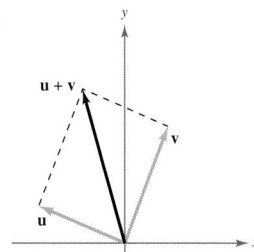

17.

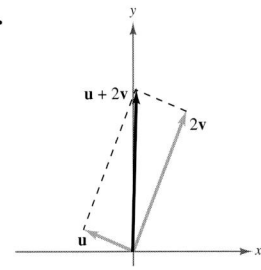

19. (a) $\langle 11, 3 \rangle$ (b) $\langle -3, 1 \rangle$ (c) $\langle -13, 1 \rangle$ (d) $\langle 23, 9 \rangle$

21. (a) $\langle -4, -4 \rangle$ (b) $\langle -8, -12 \rangle$ (c) $\langle -18, -28 \rangle$
     (d) $\langle -22, -28 \rangle$

23. (a) $3\mathbf{i} - 2\mathbf{j}$ (b) $-\mathbf{i} + 4\mathbf{j}$ (c) $-4\mathbf{i} + 11\mathbf{j}$
     (d) $6\mathbf{i} + \mathbf{j}$

25. $\langle 1, 0 \rangle$ **27.** $\left\langle -\frac{\sqrt{2}}{2}, \frac{\sqrt{2}}{2} \right\rangle$ **29.** $\left\langle -\frac{24}{25}, -\frac{7}{25} \right\rangle$

31. $\frac{4}{5}\mathbf{i} - \frac{3}{5}\mathbf{j}$ **33.** $\mathbf{j}$ **35.** $\frac{40\sqrt{61}}{61}\mathbf{i} + \frac{48\sqrt{61}}{61}\mathbf{j}$

37. $\frac{21}{5}\mathbf{i} + \frac{28}{5}\mathbf{j}$ **39.** $-8\mathbf{i}$ **41.** $7\mathbf{i} + 4\mathbf{j}$ **43.** $3\mathbf{i} + 8\mathbf{j}$

45. $\mathbf{v} = \left\langle 3, -\frac{3}{2} \right\rangle$ **47.** $\mathbf{v} = \langle 4, 3 \rangle$

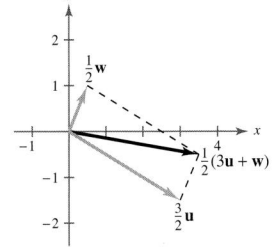

49. $\mathbf{v} = \left\langle \frac{7}{2}, -\frac{1}{2} \right\rangle$ **51.** $\|\mathbf{v}\| = 5$, $\theta = 30°$

53. $\|\mathbf{v}\| = 6\sqrt{2}$, $\theta = 315°$ **55.** $\|\mathbf{v}\| = \sqrt{29}$, $\theta = 111.8°$

57. $\mathbf{v} = \langle 3, 0 \rangle$ **59.** $\mathbf{v} = \left\langle -\frac{3\sqrt{6}}{2}, \frac{3\sqrt{2}}{2} \right\rangle$

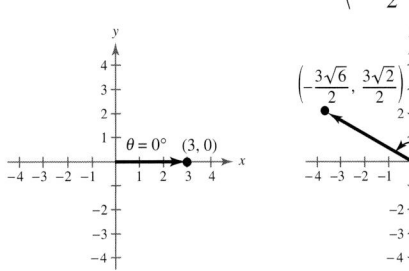

61. $\mathbf{v} = \left\langle \frac{\sqrt{10}}{5}, \frac{3\sqrt{10}}{5} \right\rangle$ **63.** $\left\langle \frac{5}{2}, \frac{5\sqrt{3} + 10}{2} \right\rangle$

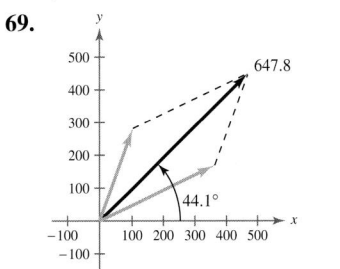

65. $\langle 10\sqrt{2} - 25\sqrt{3}, 10\sqrt{2} + 25 \rangle$ **67.** $90°$

69.

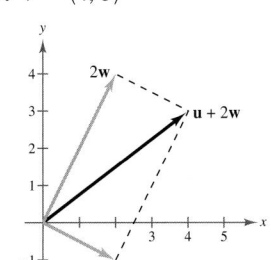

$\|\mathbf{v}\| = 647.8$, $\theta \approx 44.1°$

71. $62.7°$ **73.** $8.7°$, 2396.19 newtons

75. Horizontal component: $70 \cos 40° \approx 53.62$ feet per second
     Vertical component: $70 \sin 40° \approx 45.00$ feet per second

77. $T_{AC} \approx 3611.1$ pounds, $T_{BC} \approx 2169.5$ pounds

79. (a) $T = 3000 \sec \theta$; Domain: $0° \leq \theta < 90°$

(b)

θ	10°	20°	30°
T	3046.3	3192.5	3464.1

θ	40°	50°	60°
T	3916.2	4667.2	6000.0

(c)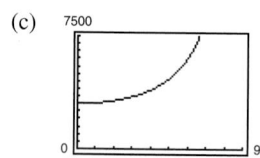

(d) The component in the direction of the motion of the barge decreases.

81. N 26.7° E, 130.35 kilometers per hour

83. (a) 12.1°, 357.85 newtons

(b) $M = 10\sqrt{660\cos\theta + 709}$,

$\alpha = \arctan\dfrac{15\sin\theta}{15\cos\theta + 22}$

(c)

θ	0°	30°	60°	90°
M	370.0	357.9	322.3	266.3
α	0°	12.1°	23.8°	34.3°

θ	120°	150°	180°
M	194.7	117.2	70.0
α	41.9°	39.8°	0°

(d)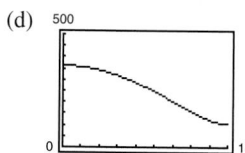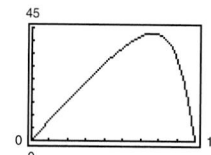

(e) For increasing θ, the two vectors tend to work against each other, resulting in a decrease in the magnitude of the resultant.

85. True   **87.** True. $a = b = 0$

89. (a) 0°   (b) 180°

(c) No. The magnitude is equal to the sum when the angle between the vectors is 0°.

91. Answers will vary.   **93.** $\langle 1, 3\rangle$ or $\langle -1, -3\rangle$

95. $12x^3y^7$, $x \neq 0$, $y \neq 0$ **97.** $48xy^2$, $x \neq 0$

99. 7.14×10^5 **101.** $7\cos\theta$ **103.** $10\csc\theta$

105. $\dfrac{\pi}{2} + n\pi$, $\pi + 2n\pi$ **107.** $\dfrac{\pi}{3} + 2n\pi$, $\dfrac{5\pi}{3} + 2n\pi$

Section 7.4   (page 569)

Vocabulary Check   (page 569)

1. dot product   **2.** $\dfrac{\mathbf{u}\cdot\mathbf{v}}{\|\mathbf{u}\|\,\|\mathbf{v}\|}$ **3.** orthogonal

4. $\left(\dfrac{\mathbf{u}\cdot\mathbf{v}}{\|\mathbf{v}\|^2}\right)\mathbf{v}$ **5.** $\|\text{proj}_{\overrightarrow{PQ}}\,\mathbf{F}\|\,\|\overrightarrow{PQ}\|$, $\mathbf{F}\cdot\overrightarrow{PQ}$

1. 0   **3.** 14   **5.** 8, scalar   **7.** $\langle 2, -8\rangle$, vector

9. 4, scalar   **11.** 13   **13.** $5\sqrt{41}$ **15.** 4

17. 90°   **19.** 70.56°   **21.** 90°   **23.** $\dfrac{5\pi}{12}$

25. 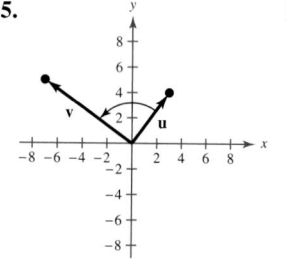   **27.**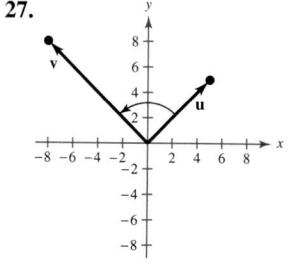

91.33°   90°

29. 26.6°, 63.4°, 90°   **31.** -20 **33.** Parallel

35. Neither   **37.** Orthogonal

39. $\dfrac{16}{17}\langle 4, 1\rangle$, $\mathbf{u} = \left\langle\dfrac{64}{17}, \dfrac{16}{17}\right\rangle + \left\langle -\dfrac{13}{17}, \dfrac{52}{17}\right\rangle$

41. $\dfrac{45}{229}\langle 2, 15\rangle$, $\mathbf{u} = \left\langle\dfrac{90}{229}, \dfrac{675}{229}\right\rangle + \left\langle -\dfrac{90}{229}, \dfrac{12}{229}\right\rangle$ **43.** $\mathbf{u}$

45. 0   **47.** $\langle 3, -1\rangle$, $\langle -3, 1\rangle$ **49.** $-\dfrac{3}{4}\mathbf{i} - \dfrac{1}{2}\mathbf{j}$, $\dfrac{3}{4}\mathbf{i} + \dfrac{1}{2}\mathbf{j}$

51. 32   **53.** \$37,289; total revenue

55. (a) Force $= 30{,}000\sin d°$

(b)

d	0°	1°	2°	3°	4°	5°
Force	0	523.6	1047.0	1570.1	2092.7	2614.7

d	6°	7°	8°	9°	10°
Force	3135.9	3656.1	4175.2	4693.0	5209.4

(c) 29,885.8 pounds

57. (a) $W = 15{,}691\dfrac{\sqrt{3}}{2}d$

(b)

d	0	200	400	800
Work	0	2,717,760.9	5,435,521.8	10,871,043.7

59. 725.0 foot-pounds

61. True. The zero vector is orthogonal to every vector.

63. Orthogonal. $\mathbf{u} \cdot \mathbf{v} = 0$

65. (a) $\mathbf{u}$ and $\mathbf{v}$ are parallel. (b) $\mathbf{u}$ and $\mathbf{v}$ are orthogonal.

67. Answers will vary.

69. g is a horizontal shift four units to the right.

71. g is a vertical shift six units upward.

73. $-1 + 2i$ **75.** $15 + 12i$ **77.** 10 **79.** $\frac{47}{26} - \frac{27}{26}i$

81.

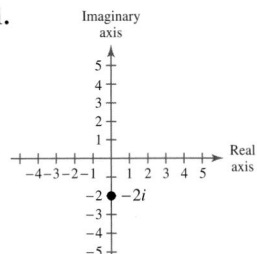

83.

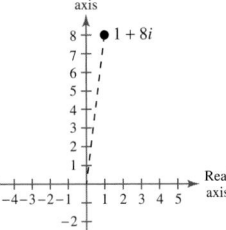

85. 8 people

Section 7.5   (page 580)

1.

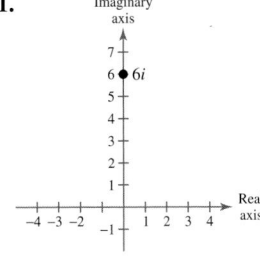

6

3.

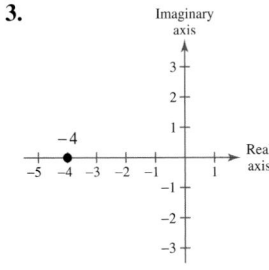

4

5.

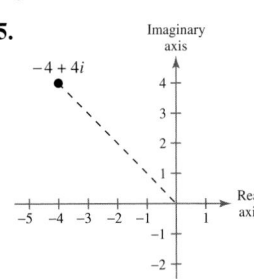

$4\sqrt{2}$

7.

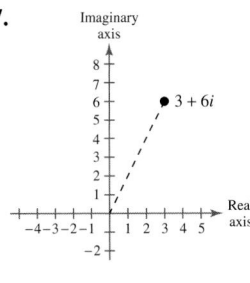

$3\sqrt{5}$

9. $3\left(\cos \dfrac{\pi}{2} + i \sin \dfrac{\pi}{2}\right)$

11. $2\sqrt{2}\left(\cos \dfrac{5\pi}{4} + i \sin \dfrac{5\pi}{4}\right)$

13.

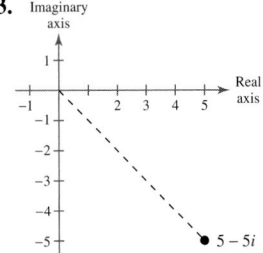

15.

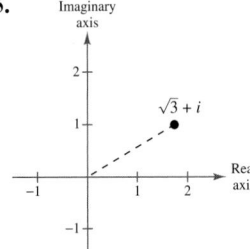

$5\sqrt{2}\left(\cos \dfrac{7\pi}{4} + i \sin \dfrac{7\pi}{4}\right)$

$2\left(\cos \dfrac{\pi}{6} + i \sin \dfrac{\pi}{6}\right)$

17.

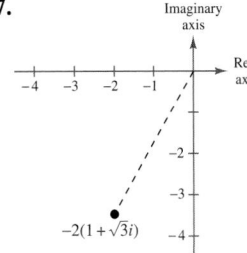

19.

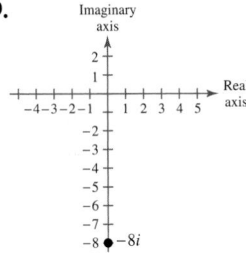

$4\left(\cos \dfrac{4\pi}{3} + i \sin \dfrac{4\pi}{3}\right)$

$8\left(\cos \dfrac{3\pi}{2} + i \sin \dfrac{3\pi}{2}\right)$

21.

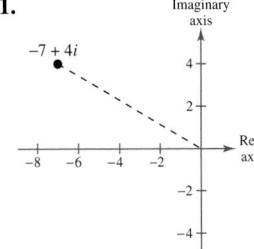

$\sqrt{65}(\cos 150.26° + i \sin 150.26°)$

23.

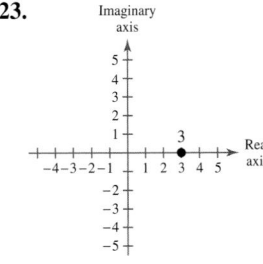

25.

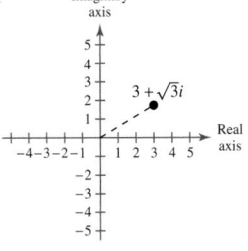

$3(\cos 0 + i \sin 0)$

$2\sqrt{3}\left(\cos \dfrac{\pi}{6} + i \sin \dfrac{\pi}{6}\right)$

27.

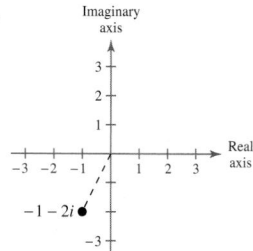

$\sqrt{5}(\cos 243.4° + i \sin 243.4°)$

29.

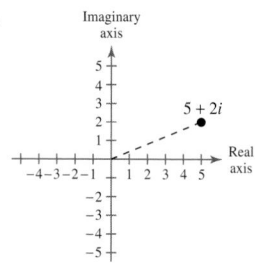

$\sqrt{29}(\cos 21.8° + i \sin 21.8°)$

31.

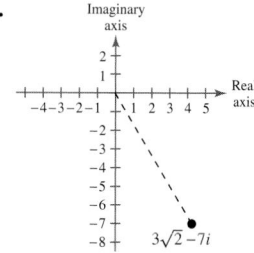

$\sqrt{67}(\cos 301.2° + i \sin 301.2°)$

33.

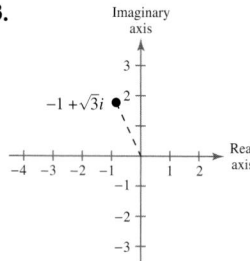

$-1 + \sqrt{3}i$

35.

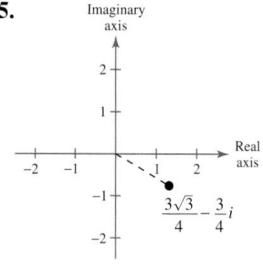

$\dfrac{3\sqrt{3}}{4} - \dfrac{3}{4}i$

37.

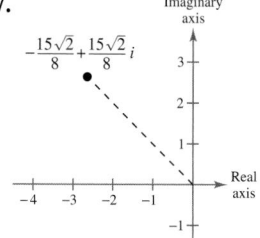

$\dfrac{-15\sqrt{2}}{8} + \dfrac{15\sqrt{2}}{8}i$

39.

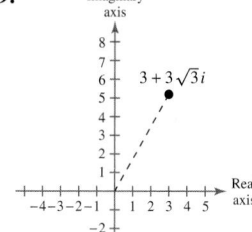

$3 + 3\sqrt{3}i$

41.

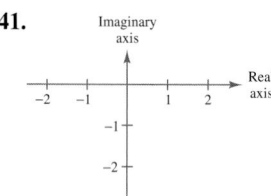

$-4i$

43.

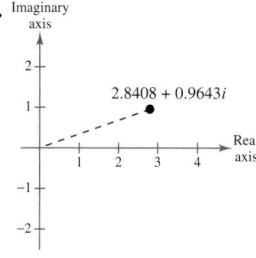

$2.8408 + 0.9643i$

45. $4.6985 + 1.7101i$ **47.** $4.7693 + 7.6324i$

49.

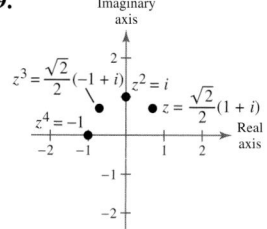

The absolute value of each is 1.

51. $12\left(\cos\dfrac{\pi}{2} + i \sin\dfrac{\pi}{2}\right)$ **53.** $\dfrac{10}{9}(\cos 200° + i \sin 200°)$

55. $\dfrac{11}{50}(\cos 130° + i \sin 130°)$ **57.** $\cos 30° + i \sin 30°$

59. $\dfrac{1}{2}(\cos 80° + i \sin 80°)$

61. $6[\cos(-48°) + i \sin(-48°)]$

63. (a) $2\sqrt{2}\left(\cos\dfrac{\pi}{4} + i \sin\dfrac{\pi}{4}\right)$

$\sqrt{2}\left[\cos\left(-\dfrac{\pi}{4}\right) + i \sin\left(-\dfrac{\pi}{4}\right)\right]$

(b) $4(\cos 0 + i \sin 0) = 4$

(c) 4

65. (a) $2\left[\cos\left(-\dfrac{\pi}{2}\right) + i\sin\left(-\dfrac{\pi}{2}\right)\right]$

$\sqrt{2}\left(\cos\dfrac{\pi}{4} + i\sin\dfrac{\pi}{4}\right)$

(b) $2\sqrt{2}\left[\cos\left(-\dfrac{\pi}{4}\right) + i\sin\left(-\dfrac{\pi}{4}\right)\right] = 2 - 2i$

(c) $2 - 2i$

67. (a) $5(\cos 0 + i\sin 0)$

$\sqrt{13}(\cos 56.31° + i\sin 56.31°)$

(b) $\dfrac{5\sqrt{13}}{13}[\cos(-56.31°) + i\sin(-56.31°)]$

$\approx 0.7692 - 1.1538i$

(c) $\dfrac{10}{13} - \dfrac{15}{13}i \approx 0.7692 - 1.1538i$

69.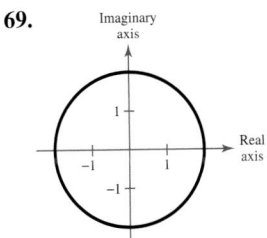

71.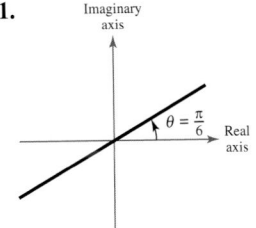

73. $-2 + 2i$ **75.** $-32i$ **77.** $-32\sqrt{3} + 32i$

79. $\dfrac{125}{2} + \dfrac{125\sqrt{3}}{2}i$ **81.** i

83. $140.0189 + 1014.3819i$ **85.** $-597.00 - 122.00i$

87. $\dfrac{81}{2} + \dfrac{81\sqrt{3}}{2}i$

89. $\sqrt[6]{1}\left[\cos\dfrac{0 + 2\pi(4)}{6} + i\sin\dfrac{0 + 2\pi(4)}{6}\right] = -\dfrac{1}{2}(1 + \sqrt{3}i)$

91. (a) $2(\cos 30° + i\sin 30°)$ (b) and (c) $8i$

$2(\cos 150° + i\sin 150°)$

$2(\cos 270° + i\sin 270°)$

93. (a) $\sqrt{5}(\cos 60° + i\sin 60°)$

$\sqrt{5}(\cos 240° + i\sin 240°)$

(b)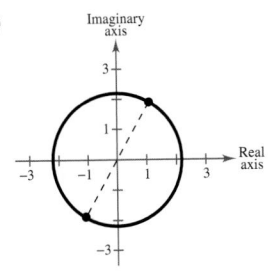

(c) $\dfrac{\sqrt{5}}{2} + \dfrac{\sqrt{15}}{2}i, \ -\dfrac{\sqrt{5}}{2} - \dfrac{\sqrt{15}}{2}i$

95. (a) $2\left(\cos\dfrac{\pi}{3} + i\sin\dfrac{\pi}{3}\right)$

$2\left(\cos\dfrac{5\pi}{6} + i\sin\dfrac{5\pi}{6}\right)$

$2\left(\cos\dfrac{4\pi}{3} + i\sin\dfrac{4\pi}{3}\right)$

$2\left(\cos\dfrac{11\pi}{6} + i\sin\dfrac{11\pi}{6}\right)$

(b)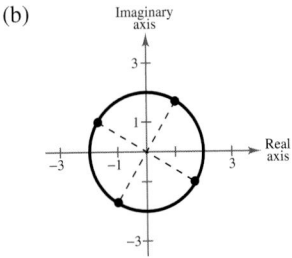

(c) $1 + \sqrt{3}i, \ -\sqrt{3} + i, \ -1 - \sqrt{3}i, \ \sqrt{3} - i$

97. (a) $3\left(\cos\dfrac{\pi}{2} + i\sin\dfrac{\pi}{2}\right)$

$3\left(\cos\dfrac{7\pi}{6} + i\sin\dfrac{7\pi}{6}\right)$

$3\left(\cos\dfrac{11\pi}{6} + i\sin\dfrac{11\pi}{6}\right)$

(b)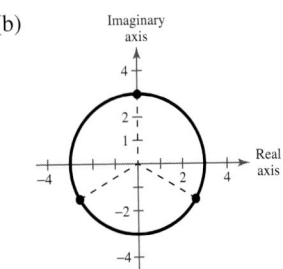

(c) $3i, \ -\dfrac{3\sqrt{3}}{2} - \dfrac{3}{2}i, \ \dfrac{3\sqrt{3}}{2} - \dfrac{3}{2}i$

99. (a) $5\left(\cos\dfrac{4\pi}{9} + i\sin\dfrac{4\pi}{9}\right)$

$5\left(\cos\dfrac{10\pi}{9} + i\sin\dfrac{10\pi}{9}\right)$

$5\left(\cos\dfrac{16\pi}{9} + i\sin\dfrac{16\pi}{9}\right)$

(b)

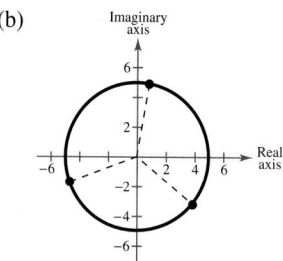

(c) $0.8682 + 4.9240i, -4.6985 - 1.7101i,$

$3.8302 - 3.2139i$

101. (a) $4\left(\cos\dfrac{\pi}{6} + i \sin\dfrac{\pi}{6}\right)$

$4\left(\cos\dfrac{5\pi}{6} + i \sin\dfrac{5\pi}{6}\right)$

$4\left(\cos\dfrac{3\pi}{2} + i \sin\dfrac{3\pi}{2}\right)$

(b)

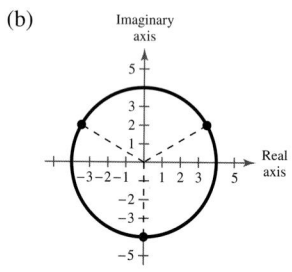

(c) $2\sqrt{3} + 2i, \ -2\sqrt{3} + 2i, \ -4i$

103. (a) $\cos 0 + i \sin 0$

$\cos\dfrac{2\pi}{5} + i \sin\dfrac{2\pi}{5}$

$\cos\dfrac{4\pi}{5} + i \sin\dfrac{4\pi}{5}$

$\cos\dfrac{6\pi}{5} + i \sin\dfrac{6\pi}{5}$

$\cos\dfrac{8\pi}{5} + i \sin\dfrac{8\pi}{5}$

(b)

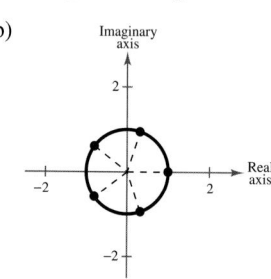

(c) $1, 0.3090 + 0.9511i, -0.8090 + 0.5878i,$

$-0.8090 - 0.5878i, 0.3090 - 0.9511i$

105. (a) $5\left(\cos\dfrac{\pi}{3} + i \sin\dfrac{\pi}{3}\right)$

$5(\cos\pi + i \sin\pi)$

$5\left(\cos\dfrac{5\pi}{3} + i \sin\dfrac{5\pi}{3}\right)$

(b)

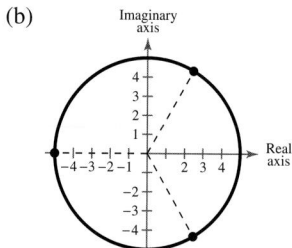

(c) $\dfrac{5}{2} + \dfrac{5\sqrt{3}}{2}i, -5, \dfrac{5}{2} - \dfrac{5\sqrt{3}}{2}i$

107. (a) $2\sqrt{2}\left(\cos\dfrac{3\pi}{20} + i \sin\dfrac{3\pi}{20}\right)$

$2\sqrt{2}\left(\cos\dfrac{11\pi}{20} + i \sin\dfrac{11\pi}{20}\right)$

$2\sqrt{2}\left(\cos\dfrac{19\pi}{20} + i \sin\dfrac{19\pi}{20}\right)$

$2\sqrt{2}\left(\cos\dfrac{27\pi}{20} + i \sin\dfrac{27\pi}{20}\right)$

$2\sqrt{2}\left(\cos\dfrac{7\pi}{4} + i \sin\dfrac{7\pi}{4}\right)$

(b)

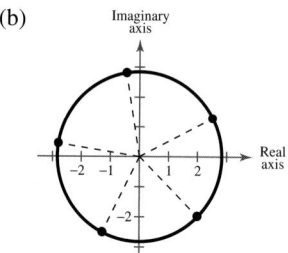

(c) $2.5201 + 1.2841i, -0.4425 + 2.7936i,$

$-2.7936 + 0.4425i, -1.2841 - 2.5201i,$

$2.0000 - 2.0000i$

109. $\cos\dfrac{\pi}{8} + i \sin\dfrac{\pi}{8}$

$\cos\dfrac{5\pi}{8} + i \sin\dfrac{5\pi}{8}$

$\cos\dfrac{9\pi}{8} + i \sin\dfrac{9\pi}{8}$

$\cos\dfrac{13\pi}{8} + i \sin\dfrac{13\pi}{8}$

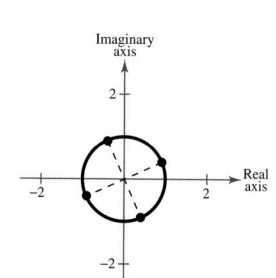

111. $3\left(\cos\dfrac{\pi}{5} + i\sin\dfrac{\pi}{5}\right)$

$3\left(\cos\dfrac{3\pi}{5} + i\sin\dfrac{3\pi}{5}\right)$

$3(\cos\pi + i\sin\pi)$

$3\left(\cos\dfrac{7\pi}{5} + i\sin\dfrac{7\pi}{5}\right)$

$3\left(\cos\dfrac{9\pi}{5} + i\sin\dfrac{9\pi}{5}\right)$

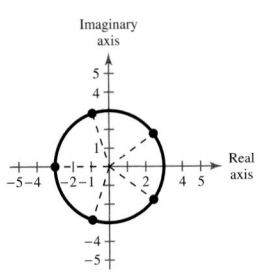

113. $2\left(\cos\dfrac{3\pi}{8} + i\sin\dfrac{3\pi}{8}\right)$

$2\left(\cos\dfrac{7\pi}{8} + i\sin\dfrac{7\pi}{8}\right)$

$2\left(\cos\dfrac{11\pi}{8} + i\sin\dfrac{11\pi}{8}\right)$

$2\left(\cos\dfrac{15\pi}{8} + i\sin\dfrac{15\pi}{8}\right)$

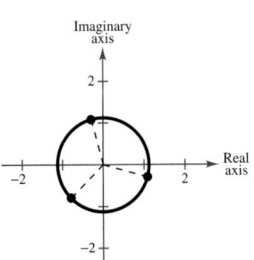

115. $\sqrt[6]{2}\left(\cos\dfrac{7\pi}{12} + i\sin\dfrac{7\pi}{12}\right)$

$\sqrt[6]{2}\left(\cos\dfrac{5\pi}{4} + i\sin\dfrac{5\pi}{4}\right)$

$\sqrt[6]{2}\left(\cos\dfrac{23\pi}{12} + i\sin\dfrac{23\pi}{12}\right)$

117. True   **119.** True

121 and 123. Answers will vary.

125. 16, 2   **127.** $\dfrac{1}{8}, \dfrac{1}{24}$ **129.** $\dfrac{\pi}{2}, \dfrac{3\pi}{2}$

131. $\dfrac{5\pi}{6}, \dfrac{7\pi}{6}$

Review Exercises   (page 584)

1. $C = 117°, b \approx 11.20, c \approx 14.92$ **3.** No solution

5. $A \approx 34.2°, C \approx 30.8°, c \approx 8.18$

7. Two solutions

$B \approx 31.2°, C \approx 133.8°, c \approx 13.94$

$B \approx 148.8°, C \approx 16.2°, c \approx 5.38$

9. Two solutions

$A \approx 40.9°, C \approx 114.1°, c \approx 8.64$

$A \approx 139.1°, C \approx 15.9°, c \approx 2.60$

11. ≈ 9.08 square units   **13.** ≈ 221.3 square units

15. ≈ 15.3 meters   **17.** ≈ 31.0 feet

19. $A \approx 15.3°, B \approx 20.6°, C \approx 144.1°$

21. $A \approx 41.7°, B \approx 93.3°, c \approx 6.37$

23. $A = 35°, C = 35°, b \approx 6.55$

25. $b \approx 29.09, A \approx 9.9°, C \approx 20.1°$

27. $A \approx 57.8°, B \approx 35.5°, C \approx 86.7°$

29. ≈ 4.3 feet, ≈ 12.6 feet   **31.** ≈ 1135.5 miles

33. ≈ 9.8 square units   **35.** ≈ 511.7 square units

37. $\|\mathbf{u}\| = \|\mathbf{v}\| = \sqrt{61}$, $\text{slope}_{\mathbf{u}} = \text{slope}_{\mathbf{v}} = \dfrac{5}{6}$

39. $\langle 7, -5\rangle$ **41.** $\langle 7, -7\rangle$ **43.** $\langle -4, 4\sqrt{3}\rangle$

45. (a) $\langle -4, 3\rangle$ (b) $\langle 2, -9\rangle$ (c) $\langle -3, -9\rangle$

(d) $\langle -11, -3\rangle$

47. (a) $\langle -1, 6\rangle$ (b) $\langle -9, -2\rangle$ (c) $\langle -15, 6\rangle$

(d) $\langle -17, 18\rangle$

49. (a) $7\mathbf{i} + 2\mathbf{j}$ (b) $-3\mathbf{i} - 4\mathbf{j}$ (c) $6\mathbf{i} - 3\mathbf{j}$

(d) $20\mathbf{i} + \mathbf{j}$

51. (a) $3\mathbf{i} + 6\mathbf{j}$ (b) $5\mathbf{i} - 6\mathbf{j}$ (c) $12\mathbf{i}$ (d) $18\mathbf{i} + 12\mathbf{j}$

53. $\langle 30, 9\rangle$ **55.** $\langle 74, -5\rangle$

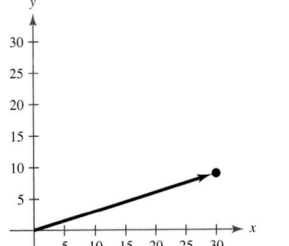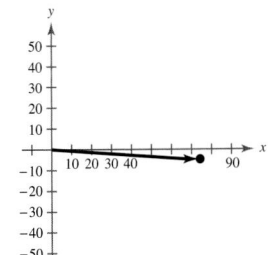

57. $\langle 0, -1\rangle$ **59.** $\dfrac{1}{\sqrt{29}}\langle 5, -2\rangle$ **61.** $9\mathbf{i} - 8\mathbf{j}$

63. $10\sqrt{2}[(\cos 135°)\mathbf{i} + (\sin 135°)\mathbf{j}]$

65.

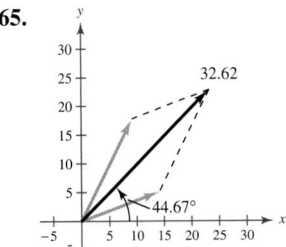

Magnitude: 32.62

Direction: 44.67°

67. 60°, 76.8 pounds   **69.** 180 pounds

71. 422.3 miles per hour, 130.4°   **73.** -20 **75.** 7

77. 25   **79.** -40 **81.** 160.5°   **83.** $\dfrac{11\pi}{12}$

85.

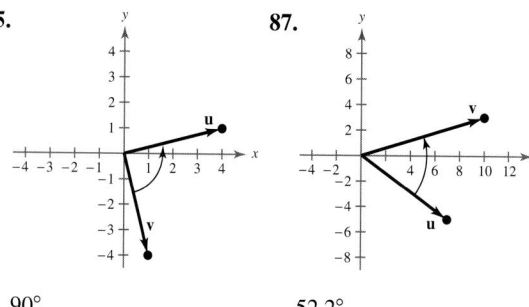

90°

87.

52.2°

89. Parallel   **91.** Neither

93. $\frac{13}{17}\langle -4, -1 \rangle$, $\left\langle -\frac{52}{17}, -\frac{13}{17} \right\rangle + \left\langle -\frac{16}{17}, \frac{64}{17} \right\rangle$

95. $-\frac{5}{2}\langle 1, -1 \rangle$, $\left\langle -\frac{5}{2}, \frac{5}{2} \right\rangle + \left\langle \frac{9}{2}, \frac{9}{2} \right\rangle$

97. 72,000 foot-pounds

99.

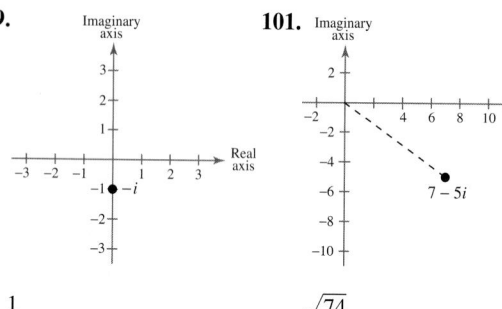

1

101.

$\sqrt{74}$

103. $\sqrt{29}(\cos 338.2° + i \sin 338.2°)$

105. $5\sqrt{2}(\cos 315° + i \sin 315°)$

107. $13(\cos 67.38° + i \sin 67.38°)$

109. $10\left(\cos \frac{3\pi}{4} + i \sin \frac{3\pi}{4}\right)$ **111.** $4(\cos 240° + i \sin 240°)$

113. $\frac{625}{2} + \frac{625\sqrt{3}}{2}i$ **115.** $2035 - 828i$

117. (a)

$3\left(\cos \frac{\pi}{4} + i \sin \frac{\pi}{4}\right)$

$3\left(\cos \frac{7\pi}{12} + i \sin \frac{7\pi}{12}\right)$

$3\left(\cos \frac{11\pi}{12} + i \sin \frac{11\pi}{12}\right)$

$3\left(\cos \frac{5\pi}{4} + i \sin \frac{5\pi}{4}\right)$

$3\left(\cos \frac{19\pi}{12} + i \sin \frac{19\pi}{12}\right)$

$3\left(\cos \frac{23\pi}{12} + i \sin \frac{23\pi}{12}\right)$

(b)

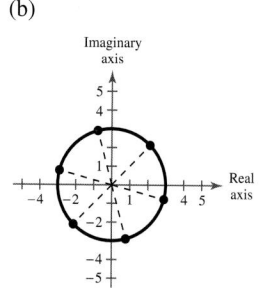

(c)

$\frac{3\sqrt{2}}{2} + \frac{3\sqrt{2}}{2}i, -0.7765 + 2.898i, -2.898 + 0.7765i,$

$-\frac{3\sqrt{2}}{2} - \frac{3\sqrt{2}}{2}i, 0.7765 - 2.898i, 2.898 - 0.7765i$

119. (a) $2(\cos 0 + i \sin 0)$

$2\left(\cos \frac{2\pi}{3} + i \sin \frac{2\pi}{3}\right)$

$2\left(\cos \frac{4\pi}{3} + i \sin \frac{4\pi}{3}\right)$

(b)

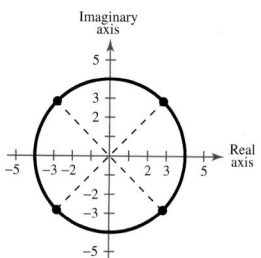

(c) $2, -1 + \sqrt{3}i, -1 - \sqrt{3}i$

121. $4\left(\cos \frac{\pi}{4} + i \sin \frac{\pi}{4}\right) = 2\sqrt{2} + 2\sqrt{2}i$

$4\left(\cos \frac{3\pi}{4} + i \sin \frac{3\pi}{4}\right) = -2\sqrt{2} + 2\sqrt{2}i$

$4\left(\cos \frac{5\pi}{4} + i \sin \frac{5\pi}{4}\right) = -2\sqrt{2} - 2\sqrt{2}i$

$4\left(\cos \frac{7\pi}{4} + i \sin \frac{7\pi}{4}\right) = 2\sqrt{2} - 2\sqrt{2}i$

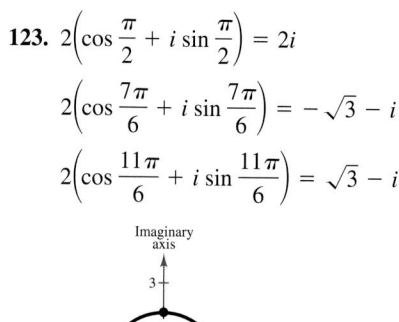

123. $2\left(\cos \frac{\pi}{2} + i \sin \frac{\pi}{2}\right) = 2i$

$2\left(\cos \frac{7\pi}{6} + i \sin \frac{7\pi}{6}\right) = -\sqrt{3} - i$

$2\left(\cos \frac{11\pi}{6} + i \sin \frac{11\pi}{6}\right) = \sqrt{3} - i$

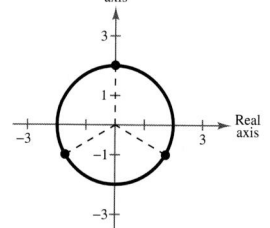

125. True   **127.** Direction and magnitude

129. $z_1 z_2 = -4, \dfrac{z_1}{z_2} = -\dfrac{1}{4}z_1^{\,2}$

Chapter Test   (page 588)

1. $C = 46°, a \approx 14.71, b \approx 24.78$

2. $A \approx 25.2°, B \approx 48.2°, C \approx 106.6°$

3. $B \approx 45.9°, C \approx 99.1°, a \approx 6.39$

4. Two solutions

$B \approx 52.1°, C \approx 102.9°, c \approx 34.59$

$B \approx 127.9°, C \approx 27.1°, c \approx 16.16$

5. No solution   **6.** $B \approx 14.8°, C \approx 15.2°, c \approx 4.93$

7. ≈ 675 feet   **8.** ≈ 2337 square meters

9. $\mathbf{w} = \langle 12, 13 \rangle, \|\mathbf{w}\| \approx 17.69$

10. (a) $\langle -4, 4 \rangle$ (b) $\langle 6, -16 \rangle$ (c) $\langle 2, -24 \rangle$

11. (a) $\langle 0, 7 \rangle$ (b) $\langle -5, -18 \rangle$ (c) $\langle -11, -20 \rangle$

12. (a) $\langle 13, 17 \rangle$ (b) $\langle -17, -28 \rangle$ (c) $\langle -1, -14 \rangle$

13. (a) $\langle 0, -1 \rangle$ (b) $\langle 5, 9 \rangle$ (c) $\langle 11, 17 \rangle$

14. $\dfrac{\sqrt{65}}{65}\langle 7, 4 \rangle$ **15.** $\left\langle \dfrac{18\sqrt{34}}{17}, -\dfrac{30\sqrt{34}}{17} \right\rangle$

16. $\theta \approx 14.9°, \approx 250.2$ pounds   **17.** 3

18. $\approx 105.9°$ **19.** No, because $\mathbf{u} \cdot \mathbf{v} = 24$, not 0.

20. $\left\langle \dfrac{185}{26}, \dfrac{37}{26} \right\rangle, \mathbf{u} = \left\langle \dfrac{185}{26}, \dfrac{37}{26} \right\rangle + \left\langle -\dfrac{29}{26}, \dfrac{145}{26} \right\rangle$

21. $z = 2\sqrt{2}\left(\cos\dfrac{3\pi}{4} + i \sin\dfrac{3\pi}{4} \right)$ **22.** $-50 - 50\sqrt{3}\,i$

23. $-\dfrac{6561}{2} + \dfrac{6561\sqrt{3}}{2}\,i$ **24.** $5832i$

25. $4\left(\cos\dfrac{\pi}{12} + i \sin\dfrac{\pi}{12} \right) \approx 3.8637 + 1.0353i$

$4\left(\cos\dfrac{7\pi}{12} + i \sin\dfrac{7\pi}{12} \right) \approx -1.0353 + 3.8637i$

$4\left(\cos\dfrac{13\pi}{12} + i \sin\dfrac{13\pi}{12} \right) \approx -3.8637 - 1.0353i$

$4\left(\cos\dfrac{19\pi}{12} + i \sin\dfrac{19\pi}{12} \right) \approx 1.0353 - 3.8637i$

26. $5\left(\cos\dfrac{\pi}{8} + i \sin\dfrac{\pi}{8} \right)$

$5\left(\cos\dfrac{5\pi}{8} + i \sin\dfrac{5\pi}{8} \right)$

$5\left(\cos\dfrac{9\pi}{8} + i \sin\dfrac{9\pi}{8} \right)$

$5\left(\cos\dfrac{13\pi}{8} + i \sin\dfrac{13\pi}{8} \right)$

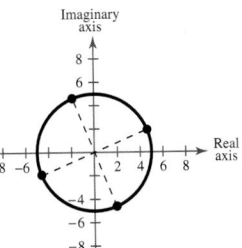

Cumulative Test for Chapters 5–7 (page 589)

1. (a)

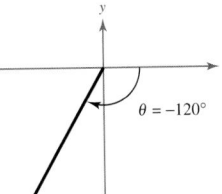

(b) $240°$

(c) $-\dfrac{2\pi}{3}$

(d) $60°$

(e) $\sin(-120°) = -\dfrac{\sqrt{3}}{2}$

$\cos(-120°) = -\dfrac{1}{2}$

$\tan(-120°) = \sqrt{3}$

$\csc(-120°) = -\dfrac{2\sqrt{3}}{3}$

$\sec(-120°) = -2$

$\cot(-120°) = \dfrac{\sqrt{3}}{3}$

2. $134.6°$ **3.** $-\dfrac{3}{5}$

4.

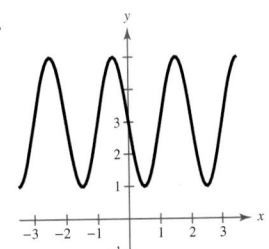

5.

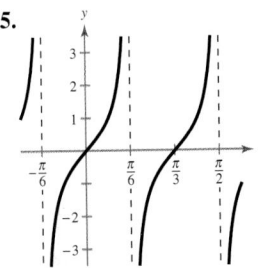

6.

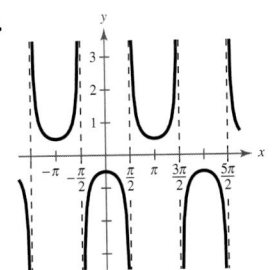

7. $a = -3, b = \pi, c = 0$

8. 6.7 **9.** $\dfrac{3}{4}$ **10.** $\sqrt{1 - 4x^2}$ **11.** $2\tan\theta$

12–14. Answers will vary.   **15.** $\dfrac{3\pi}{2} + 2n\pi$

16. $\dfrac{\pi}{6} + n\pi, \dfrac{5\pi}{6} + n\pi$ **17.** $1.7646, 4.5186$

18. 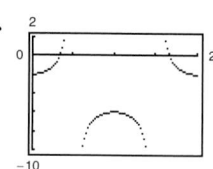   **19.**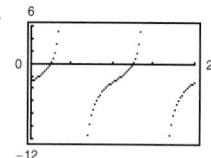

$\dfrac{\pi}{3}, \dfrac{5\pi}{3}$ $\dfrac{\pi}{4}, \dfrac{5\pi}{4}$

20. $\dfrac{16}{63}$ **21.** $\dfrac{4}{3}$ **22.** $\dfrac{2\sqrt{5}}{5}$

23. $2 \cos 6x \cos 2x$ **24–27.** Answers will vary.

28. $B \approx 14.9°$ **29.** $B \approx 52.5°$

  $C \approx 119.1°$ $C \approx 97.5°$

  $c \approx 17.00$ $a \approx 5.04$

30. $B = 55°$ **31.** $A \approx 26.1°$

  $b \approx 20.14$ $B \approx 33.3°$

  $c \approx 24.13$ $C \approx 120.6°$

32. 131.71 square inches   **33.** 85.21 square inches

34. $3\mathbf{i} + 5\mathbf{j}$ **35.** $\left\langle \dfrac{\sqrt{2}}{2}, \dfrac{\sqrt{2}}{2} \right\rangle$ **36.** -5

37. $\left\langle -\dfrac{1}{13}, -\dfrac{5}{13} \right\rangle;\ \mathbf{u} = \left\langle \dfrac{105}{13}, -\dfrac{21}{13} \right\rangle + \left\langle -\dfrac{1}{13}, -\dfrac{5}{13} \right\rangle$

38. $3\sqrt{2}\left(\cos \dfrac{3\pi}{4} + i \sin \dfrac{3\pi}{4} \right)$ **39.** $-4\sqrt{3} + 4i$

40. $-12\sqrt{3} + 12i$

41. $\cos 0 + i \sin 0 = 1$

$\cos \dfrac{2\pi}{3} + i \sin \dfrac{2\pi}{3} = -\dfrac{1}{2} + \dfrac{\sqrt{3}}{2}i$

$\cos \dfrac{4\pi}{3} + i \sin \dfrac{4\pi}{3} = -\dfrac{1}{2} - \dfrac{\sqrt{3}}{2}i$

42. $3\left(\cos \dfrac{\pi}{5} + i \sin \dfrac{\pi}{5} \right)$

$3\left(\cos \dfrac{3\pi}{5} + i \sin \dfrac{3\pi}{5} \right)$

$3(\cos \pi + i \sin \pi) = -3$

$3\left(\cos \dfrac{7\pi}{5} + i \sin \dfrac{7\pi}{5} \right)$

$3\left(\cos \dfrac{9\pi}{5} + i \sin \dfrac{9\pi}{5} \right)$

43. ≈ 4.79 feet   **44.** $d = 4 \sin \dfrac{\pi}{4}t$

45. 32.63°; 543.88 kilometers per hour   **46.** $\approx 80.28°$

Chapter 8

Section 8.1   (page 599)

1. (a) No   (b) No   (c) No   (d) Yes

3. (a) No   (b) Yes   (c) No   (d) No

5. $(2, 2)$ **7.** $(2, 6), (-1, 3)$

9. $(0, 2), \left(\sqrt{3}, 2 - 3\sqrt{3}\right), \left(-\sqrt{3}, 2 + 3\sqrt{3}\right)$

11. $(0, 0), (2, -4)$ **13.** $(4, 4)$ **15.** $(5, 5)$ **17.** $\left(\dfrac{1}{2}, 3\right)$

19. $(1, 1)$ **21.** $\left(\dfrac{20}{3}, \dfrac{40}{3}\right)$ **23.** No solution

25. No solution   **27.** $(0, 0), (1, 1), (-1, -1)$

29. $(4, 3)$ **31.** $\left(\dfrac{5}{2}, \dfrac{3}{2}\right)$ **33.** $(2, 2), (4, 0)$

35. $(1, 4), (4, 7)$

37. 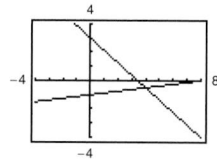   **39.**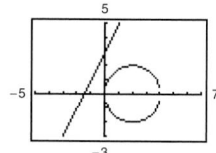

$(4, -0.5)$ No points of intersection

41. 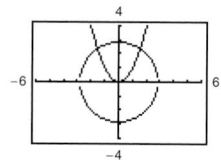   **43.**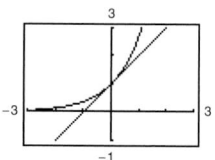

$(\pm 1.540, 2.372)$ $(0, 1)$

45. 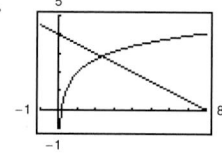   **47.**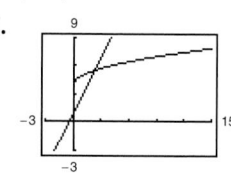

$(2.318, 2.841)$ $(2.25, 5.5)$

49. 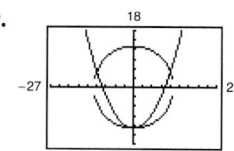   **51.** $(1, 2)$

$(0, -13), (\pm 12, 5)$

53. $(-2, 0), \left(\frac{29}{10}, \frac{21}{10}\right)$ **55.** $(0.25, 1.5)$ **57.** $(0.287, 1.751)$

59. $(0, 1), (1, 0)$ **61.** $\left(-4, -\frac{1}{4}\right), \left(\frac{1}{2}, 2\right)$

63. 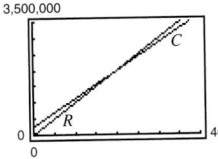   **65.**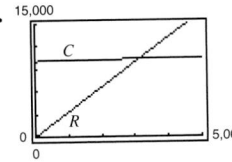

192 units; $1,910,400   3133 units; $10,308

67. (a) $C = 35.45x + 16,000$

$R = 55.95x$

(b)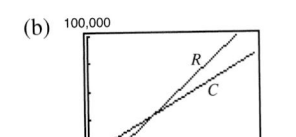

781 units

69. Sales greater than $11,667

71. (a) $\begin{cases} x + \quad y = 20,000 \\ 0.065x + 0.085y = \quad 1600 \end{cases}$

(b)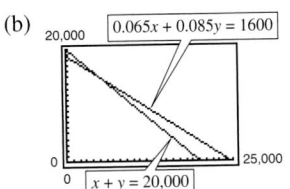

More invested at 6.5% means less invested at 8.5% and less interest.

(c) $5000

73. (a) $F_{\text{VCR}} = -107.86x^2 + 1583.6x - 3235$

$F_{\text{DVD}} = 21.14x^2 + 143.8x - 1939$

(b)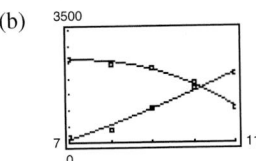

(c) and (d) 2000

(e) They are the same.

75. 6 meters $\times$ 9 meters   **77.** 8 miles $\times$ 12 miles

79. False. You could solve for either variable.

81. For a linear system the result will be a contradictory equation such as $0 = N$, where N is a nonzero real number. For a nonlinear system there may be an equation with imaginary roots.

83. (Answers are not unique.)

(a) $y = x + 1$ (b) $y = 0$ (c) $y = -2$

85. $2x + 7y - 45 = 0$ **87.** $y - 3 = 0$

89. $30x - 17y - 18 = 0$

91. Domain: All real numbers x except $x = 6$

Asymptotes: $y = 0, x = 6$

93. Domain: All real numbers x except $x = \pm 4$

Asymptotes: $y = 1, x = \pm 4$

Section 8.2   (page 609)

Vocabulary Check   (page 609)

1. method, elimination   **2.** equivalent

3. consistent, inconsistent

1. 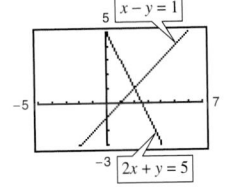   **3.**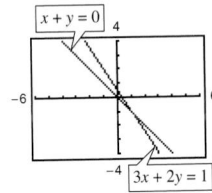

$(2, 1)$ $(1, -1)$

5.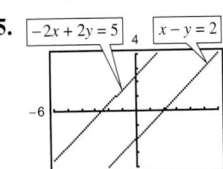

Inconsistent

7. $\left(\frac{5}{2}, \frac{3}{4}\right)$ **9.** $(3, 4)$ **11.** $(4, -1)$ **13.** $\left(\frac{12}{7}, \frac{18}{7}\right)$

15. Inconsistent   **17.** b   **18.** a   **19.** c   **20.** d

21. $\left(-\frac{6}{35}, \frac{43}{35}\right)$ **23.** Inconsistent

25. All points on the line $6x + 8y - 1 = 0$ **27.** $(5, -2)$

29. All points on the line $5x - 6y - 3 = 0$ **31.** $(101, 96)$

33. 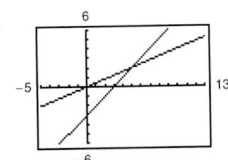   **35.**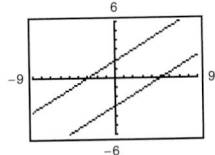

Consistent; $(5, 2)$ Inconsistent

37.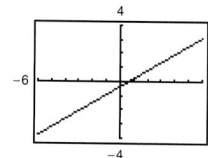

Consistent; all points
on the line $8x - 14y = 5$

39.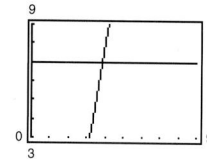

$\left(\frac{23}{6}, 7\right)$

41.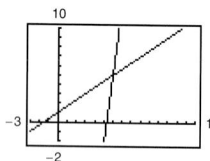

$(6, 5)$

43.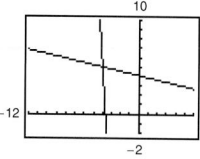

$(-4, 5)$

45. $(4, 1)$ **47.** $\left(-\frac{5}{3}, -\frac{11}{3}\right)$ **49.** $(6, -3)$ **51.** $\left(\frac{43}{6}, \frac{25}{6}\right)$

53. $\begin{cases} 3x + \frac{1}{2}y = 4 \\ x + 3y = 24 \end{cases}$ **55.** $\begin{cases} 2x + 2y = 11 \\ x - 4y = -7 \end{cases}$

Answer is not unique.   Answer is not unique.

57. $(80, 10)$ **59.** $(2{,}000{,}000, 100)$

61. Plane: 550 miles per hour; wind: 50 miles per hour

63. (a) $\begin{cases} x + y = 20 \\ 0.4x + 0.65y = 10 \end{cases}$

(b)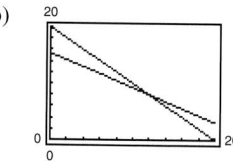

Decreases

(c) 40% solution: 12 liters; 65% solution: 8 liters

65. \$9000   **67.** 375 adults, 125 children

69. $y = 0.97x + 2.10$

71. (a) and (b) $y = 14x + 19$ **73.** True

(c)

60

0

3

(d) 41.4 bushels per acre

75. $(39{,}600, 398)$. It is necessary to change the scale on the
axes to see the point of intersection.

77. Not possible. Two lines will intersect only once or they will
coincide and the system will have infinitely many solutions.

79. $k = -4$ **81.** $u = 1, v = -\tan x$

83. $x \le -\frac{22}{3}$

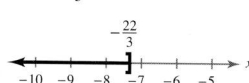

85. $-2 < x < 18$

87. $-5 < x < 3.5$

89. $\ln 6x$ **91.** $\log_9 \dfrac{12}{x}$

Section 8.3   (page 623)

Vocabulary Check   (page 623)

1. row-echelon   **2.** ordered triple   **3.** Gaussian

4. independent, dependent   **5.** nonsquare

6. three-dimensional

7. partial fraction decomposition

1. (a) No   (b) No   (c) No   (d) Yes

3. (a) No   (b) No   (c) Yes   (d) No

5. $(-7, -8, 6)$ **7.** $(3, 10, 2)$ **9.** $\left(\frac{1}{2}, -2, 2\right)$

11. $\begin{cases} x - 2y + 3z = 5 \\ y - 2z = 9 \\ 2x - 3z = 0 \end{cases}$

First step in putting the system in row-echelon form

13. $(1, 2, 3)$ **15.** $(-4, 8, 5)$ **17.** $(6, -3, 0)$

19. Inconsistent   **21.** $\left(1, -\frac{3}{2}, \frac{1}{2}\right)$

23. $(-3a + 10, 5a - 7, a)$ **25.** $(-a + 3, a + 1, a)$

27. Inconsistent   **29.** Inconsistent

31. $(2a, 21a - 1, 8a)$ **33.** $\left(-\frac{3}{2}a + \frac{1}{2}, -\frac{2}{3}a + 1, a\right)$

35. $(-5a + 3, -a - 5, a)$ **37.** $(1, 1, 1, 1)$

39. $\begin{cases} 3x + y - z = 9 \\ x + 2y - z = 0 \\ -x + y + 3z = 1 \end{cases}$

(Answer is not unique.)

41. $\begin{cases} x + 6y + 4z = 7 \\ 2x - 2y - 4z = 0 \\ -x + y + z = -\frac{7}{4} \end{cases}$

(Answer is not unique.)

43.

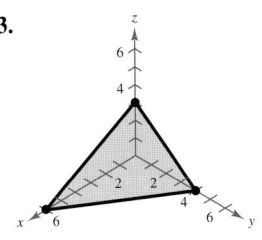

$(6, 0, 0), (0, 4, 0),$
$(0, 0, 3), (4, 0, 1)$

45.

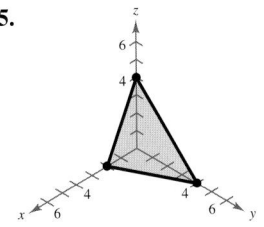

$(2, 0, 0), (0, 4, 0),$
$(0, 0, 4), (0, 2, 2)$

47. $\dfrac{A}{x} + \dfrac{B}{x - 14}$ **49.** $\dfrac{A}{x} + \dfrac{B}{x^2} + \dfrac{C}{x - 10}$

51. $\dfrac{A}{x - 5} + \dfrac{B}{(x - 5)^2} + \dfrac{C}{(x - 5)^3}$

53. (a) $\dfrac{1}{2}\left(\dfrac{1}{x - 1} - \dfrac{1}{x + 1}\right)$ **55.** (a) $\dfrac{1}{x} - \dfrac{1}{x + 1}$

57. (a) $\dfrac{1}{x} - \dfrac{2}{2x + 1}$ **59.** (a) $\dfrac{3}{2x - 1} - \dfrac{2}{x + 1}$

61. (a) $-\dfrac{3}{x} - \dfrac{1}{x + 2} + \dfrac{5}{x - 2}$ **63.** (a) $\dfrac{3}{x} - \dfrac{1}{x^2} + \dfrac{1}{x + 1}$

65. (a) $\dfrac{3}{x} - \dfrac{3}{x - 3} + \dfrac{2}{(x - 3)^2}$

67. (a) $2x - 7 + \dfrac{17}{x + 2} + \dfrac{1}{x + 1}$

69. (a) $x + 3 + \dfrac{6}{x - 1} + \dfrac{4}{(x - 1)^2} + \dfrac{1}{(x - 1)^3}$

71. $\dfrac{3}{x} - \dfrac{2}{x - 4}$

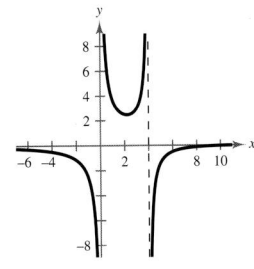
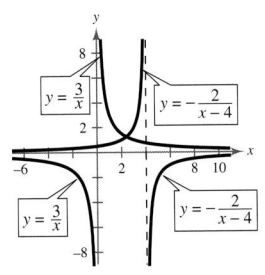

Vertical asymptotes are the same.

73. $s = -16t^2 + 144$ **75.** $s = -16t^2 - 32t + 500$

77. $y = \dfrac{1}{2}x^2 - 2x$ **79.** $y = x^2 - 6x + 8$

81. $x^2 + y^2 - 4x = 0$ **83.** $x^2 + y^2 + 6x - 8y = 0$

85. \$366,666.67 at 8%, \$316,666.67 at 9%, and
\$91,666.67 at 10%

87. \$156,250 + 0.75s in certificates of deposit

\$125,000 in municipal bonds

\$218,750 − 1.75s in blue-chip stocks

s in growth stocks

89. 20 liters of spray X, 18 liters of spray Y, and 16 liters of
spray Z

91. Use four medium trucks or two large trucks, one medium
truck, and two small trucks. (Other answers are possible.)

93. $I_1 = 1, I_2 = 2, I_3 = 1$ **95.** $y = -\dfrac{5}{24}x^2 - \dfrac{3}{10}x + \dfrac{41}{6}$

97. $y = x^2 - x$

99. (a) $y = 0.165x^2 - 6.55x + 103$

(b)

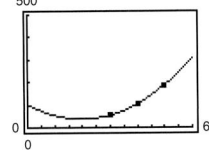

(c) 453 feet

101. (a) $\dfrac{2000}{7 - 4x} - \dfrac{2000}{11 - 7x}, \ 0 \le x \le 1$

(b)

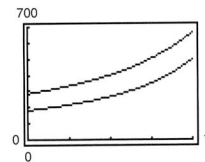

103. False. The leading coefficients are not all 1.

105. False. $\dfrac{A}{x + 10} + \dfrac{B}{x - 10} + \dfrac{C}{(x - 10)^2}$

107. $\dfrac{1}{2a}\left(\dfrac{1}{a + x} + \dfrac{1}{a - x}\right)$ **109.** $\dfrac{1}{a}\left(\dfrac{1}{y} + \dfrac{1}{a - y}\right)$

Answers will vary.   Answers will vary.

111. No. There are two arithmetic errors. They are the constant
in the second equation and the coefficient of z in the third
equation.

113. $x = 5, y = 5, \lambda = -5$

115. $x = \dfrac{\sqrt{2}}{2}, y = \dfrac{1}{2}, \lambda = 1$

$x = -\dfrac{\sqrt{2}}{2}, y = \dfrac{1}{2}, \lambda = 1$

$x = 0, y = 0, \lambda = 0$

117.

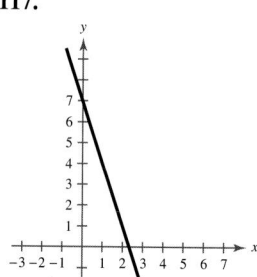

119.

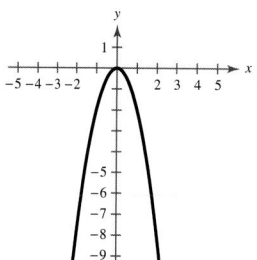

121.

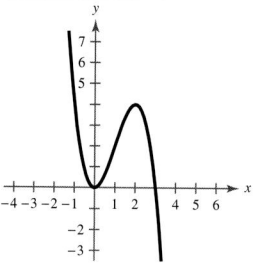

123. (a) $-4, 0, 3$

(b)

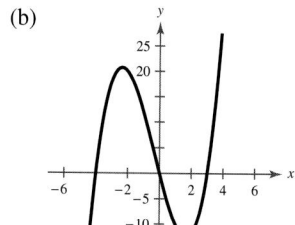

125. (a) $-4, -\frac{3}{2}, 3$

(b)

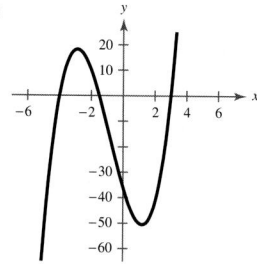

127.

x	-6	-5	-4	-3	0
y	11	-1	-4	-4.75	-4.996

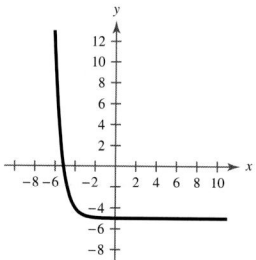

129.

x	-3	-1	0	1	2	3
y	-2.9	-2.6	-2	-0.7	2.5	9.9

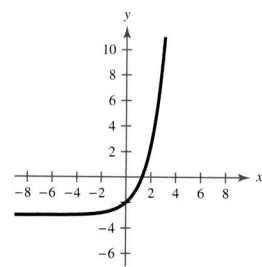

Section 8.4   (page 639)

Vocabulary Check   (page 639)

1. matrix   **2.** square

3. row matrix, column matrix   **4.** augmented matrix

5. coefficient matrix   **6.** row-equivalent

7. reduced row-echelon form

8. Gauss-Jordan elimination

1. 1×2 **3.** 3×1 **5.** 2×2

7. $\begin{bmatrix} 4 & -5 & \vdots & 33 \\ -1 & 5 & \vdots & -27 \end{bmatrix}$

9. $\begin{bmatrix} 1 & 10 & -2 & \vdots & 2 \\ 5 & -3 & 4 & \vdots & 0 \\ 2 & 1 & 0 & \vdots & 6 \end{bmatrix}$

11. $\begin{cases} x + 2y = 7 \\ 2x - 3y = 4 \end{cases}$ **13.** $\begin{cases} 9x + 12y + 3z = 0 \\ -2x + 18y + 5z = 10 \\ x + 7y - 8z = -4 \end{cases}$

15. $\begin{bmatrix} 1 & 4 & 3 \\ 0 & 2 & -1 \end{bmatrix}$

17. $\begin{bmatrix} 1 & 1 & 4 & -1 \\ 0 & 5 & -2 & 6 \\ 0 & 3 & 20 & 4 \end{bmatrix}, \begin{bmatrix} 1 & 1 & 4 & -1 \\ 0 & 1 & -\frac{2}{5} & \frac{6}{5} \\ 0 & 3 & 20 & 4 \end{bmatrix}$

19. Add 5 times R_2 to R_1.   **21.** Interchange R_1 and R_2.

23. Reduced row-echelon form

25. Not in row-echelon form

27. (a) $\begin{bmatrix} 1 & 2 & 3 \\ 0 & -5 & -10 \\ 3 & 1 & -1 \end{bmatrix}$ (b) $\begin{bmatrix} 1 & 2 & 3 \\ 0 & -5 & -10 \\ 0 & -5 & -10 \end{bmatrix}$

(c) $\begin{bmatrix} 1 & 2 & 3 \\ 0 & -5 & -10 \\ 0 & 0 & 0 \end{bmatrix}$ (d) $\begin{bmatrix} 1 & 2 & 3 \\ 0 & 1 & 2 \\ 0 & 0 & 0 \end{bmatrix}$

(e) $\begin{bmatrix} 1 & 0 & -1 \\ 0 & 1 & 2 \\ 0 & 0 & 0 \end{bmatrix}$

The matrix is in reduced row-echelon form.

29. (a) ```
*row+(-2,[A],1,2
)→[B]
  [[1 2 3]
   [0 -5 -10]
   [3 1 -1]]
```
(b) ```
*row+(-3,[B],1,3
)→[C]
  [[1 2  3  ]
   [0 -5 -10]
   [0 -5 -10]]
```

(c) ```
*row+(-1,[C],2,3
)→[D]
  [[1 2 3]
   [0 -5 -10]
   [0 0 0]]
```
(d) ```
*row(-1/5,[D],2)
→[E]
  [[1 2 3]
   [0 1 2]
   [0 0 0]]
```

(e) ```
*row+(-2,[E],2,1
)
  [[1 0 -1]
   [0 1 2]
   [0 0 0]]
```

The matrix is in reduced row-echelon form.

**31.** $\begin{bmatrix} 1 & 1 & 0 & 5 \\ 0 & 1 & 2 & 0 \\ 0 & 0 & 1 & -1 \end{bmatrix}$    **33.** $\begin{bmatrix} 1 & -1 & -1 & 1 \\ 0 & 1 & 6 & 3 \\ 0 & 0 & 0 & 0 \end{bmatrix}$

**35.** $\begin{bmatrix} 1 & 0 & 0 \\ 0 & 1 & 0 \\ 0 & 0 & 1 \end{bmatrix}$    **37.** $\begin{bmatrix} 1 & 0 & 3 & 16 \\ 0 & 1 & 2 & 12 \end{bmatrix}$

**39.** $\begin{cases} x - 2y = 4 \\ y = -3 \end{cases}$    **41.** $\begin{cases} x - y + 2z = 4 \\ y - z = 2 \\ z = -2 \end{cases}$

$(-2, -3)$          $(8, 0, -2)$

**43.** $(7, -5)$    **45.** $(-4, -8, 2)$    **47.** $(3, 2)$

**49.** Inconsistent    **51.** $\left(\frac{3}{2}, -\frac{1}{4}\right)$    **53.** Inconsistent

**55.** $(4, -3, 2)$    **57.** $(2a + 1, 3a + 2, a)$    **59.** $(7, -3, 4)$

**61.** $(0, 2 - 4a, a)$    **63.** $(1, 0, 4, -2)$    **65.** $(-2a, a, a)$

**67.** Yes; $(-1, 1, -3)$    **69.** No    **71.** $y = x^2 + 2x + 5$

**73.** \$150,000 at 7%, \$750,000 at 8%, and \$600,000 at 10%

**75.** $I_1 = \frac{13}{10}, I_2 = \frac{11}{5}, I_3 = \frac{9}{10}$

**77.** (a) $y = -3.1t^2 + 57.1t - 218.9$

(b)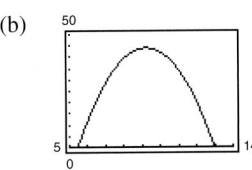

(c) \$19.90

(d) $-\$59.90$; No. The average price is negative.

**79.** (a) $x_1 = s, x_2 = t, x_3 = 600 - s,$

$x_4 = s - t, x_5 = 500 - t, x_6 = s, x_7 = t$

(b) $x_1 = 0, x_2 = 0, x_3 = 600, x_4 = 0, x_5 = 500,$

$x_6 = 0, x_7 = 0$

(c) $x_1 = 0, x_2 = -500, x_3 = 600, x_4 = 500,$

$x_5 = 1000, x_6 = 0, x_7 = -500$

**81.** False. It is a $2 \times 4$ matrix.

**83.** $\begin{cases} x + y + 7z = -1 \\ x + 2y + 11z = 0 \\ 2x + y + 10z = -3 \end{cases}$

(Answer is not unique.)

**85.** Gauss-Jordan elimination was not performed on the last column of the matrix. Answers will vary.

**87.**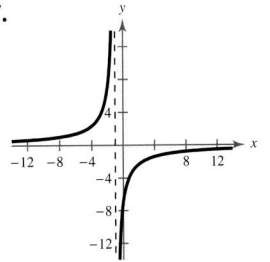

**89.**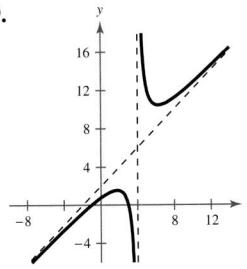

Asymptotes:          Asymptotes:

$x = -1, y = 0$          $x = 4, y = x + 2$
```

91.

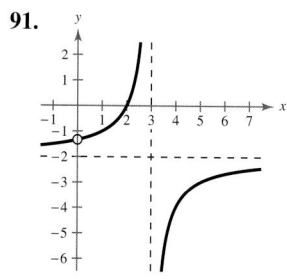

Asymptotes: $x = 3$, $y = -2$

There is a hole at $x = 0$.

Section 8.5   (page 654)

Vocabulary Check   (page 654)

1. equal   **2.** scalars   **3.** zero, O **4.** identity

5. (a) iii   (b) i   (c) iv   (d) v   (e) ii

6. (a) ii   (b) iv   (c) i   (d) iii

1. $x = -4$, $y = 22$ **3.** $x = -1$, $y = 4$, $z = 6$

5. (a) $\begin{bmatrix} 3 & -2 \\ 1 & 7 \end{bmatrix}$ (b) $\begin{bmatrix} -1 & 0 \\ 3 & -9 \end{bmatrix}$

(c) $\begin{bmatrix} 3 & -3 \\ 6 & -3 \end{bmatrix}$ (d) $\begin{bmatrix} -1 & -1 \\ 8 & -19 \end{bmatrix}$

7. (a) $\begin{bmatrix} 9 & 5 \\ 1 & -2 \\ -3 & 15 \end{bmatrix}$ (b) $\begin{bmatrix} 7 & -7 \\ 3 & 8 \\ -5 & -5 \end{bmatrix}$

(c) $\begin{bmatrix} 24 & -3 \\ 6 & 9 \\ -12 & 15 \end{bmatrix}$ (d) $\begin{bmatrix} 22 & -15 \\ 8 & 19 \\ -14 & -5 \end{bmatrix}$

9. (a) $\begin{bmatrix} 5 & 5 & -2 & 4 & 4 \\ -5 & 10 & 0 & -4 & -7 \end{bmatrix}$

(b) $\begin{bmatrix} 3 & 5 & 0 & 2 & 4 \\ 7 & -6 & -4 & 2 & 7 \end{bmatrix}$

(c) $\begin{bmatrix} 12 & 15 & -3 & 9 & 12 \\ 3 & 6 & -6 & -3 & 0 \end{bmatrix}$

(d) $\begin{bmatrix} 10 & 15 & -1 & 7 & 12 \\ 15 & -10 & -10 & 3 & 14 \end{bmatrix}$

11. (a) Not possible   (b) Not possible

(c) $\begin{bmatrix} 18 & 0 & 9 \\ -3 & -12 & 0 \end{bmatrix}$ (d) Not possible

13. $\begin{bmatrix} -8 & -7 \\ 15 & -1 \end{bmatrix}$ **15.** $\begin{bmatrix} -24 & -4 & 12 \\ -12 & 32 & 12 \end{bmatrix}$

17. $\begin{bmatrix} -1 & 5 \\ 1 & -2 \end{bmatrix}$ **19.** $\begin{bmatrix} -14.646 & 21.306 \\ -41.546 & -69.137 \\ 78.117 & -32.064 \end{bmatrix}$

21. $\begin{bmatrix} 14 & 4 \\ -52 & 0 \end{bmatrix}$ **23.** $\begin{bmatrix} -6 & -9 \\ -1 & 0 \\ 17 & -10 \end{bmatrix}$

25. $\begin{bmatrix} 3 & 3 \\ -0.5 & 0 \\ -6.5 & 5.5 \end{bmatrix}$ **27.** Not possible   **29.** $\begin{bmatrix} -2 & 51 \\ -8 & 33 \\ 0 & 27 \end{bmatrix}$

31. $\begin{bmatrix} 1 & 0 & 0 \\ 0 & 1 & 0 \\ 0 & 0 & \frac{7}{2} \end{bmatrix}$ **33.** $\begin{bmatrix} -15 & -5 & -25 & -45 \\ -18 & -6 & -30 & -54 \end{bmatrix}$

35. (a) $\begin{bmatrix} 0 & 15 \\ 8 & 11 \end{bmatrix}$ (b) $\begin{bmatrix} -3 & 2 \\ 39 & 14 \end{bmatrix}$ (c) $\begin{bmatrix} 11 & 6 \\ 15 & 14 \end{bmatrix}$

37. (a) $\begin{bmatrix} 0 & -10 \\ 10 & 0 \end{bmatrix}$ (b) $\begin{bmatrix} 0 & -10 \\ 10 & 0 \end{bmatrix}$ (c) $\begin{bmatrix} 8 & -6 \\ 6 & 8 \end{bmatrix}$

39. (a) $\begin{bmatrix} 7 & 7 & 14 \\ 8 & 8 & 16 \\ -1 & -1 & -2 \end{bmatrix}$ (b) $[13]$ (c) Not possible

41. $\begin{bmatrix} 70 & -17 & 73 \\ 32 & 11 & 6 \\ 16 & -38 & 70 \end{bmatrix}$ **43.** $\begin{bmatrix} 151 & 25 & 48 \\ 516 & 279 & 387 \\ 47 & -20 & 87 \end{bmatrix}$

45. Not possible   **47.** $\begin{bmatrix} 5 & 8 \\ -4 & -16 \end{bmatrix}$ **49.** $\begin{bmatrix} -4 & 10 \\ 3 & 14 \end{bmatrix}$

51. (a) No   (b) Yes   (c) No   (d) No

53. (a) No   (b) Yes   (c) No   (d) No

55. (a) $\begin{bmatrix} -1 & 1 \\ -2 & 1 \end{bmatrix}\begin{bmatrix} x_1 \\ x_2 \end{bmatrix} = \begin{bmatrix} 4 \\ 0 \end{bmatrix}$ (b) $\begin{bmatrix} 4 \\ 8 \end{bmatrix}$

57. (a) $\begin{bmatrix} -2 & -3 \\ 6 & 1 \end{bmatrix}\begin{bmatrix} x_1 \\ x_2 \end{bmatrix} = \begin{bmatrix} -4 \\ -36 \end{bmatrix}$ (b) $\begin{bmatrix} -7 \\ 6 \end{bmatrix}$

59. (a) $\begin{bmatrix} 1 & -2 & 3 \\ -1 & 3 & -1 \\ 2 & -5 & 5 \end{bmatrix}\begin{bmatrix} x_1 \\ x_2 \\ x_3 \end{bmatrix} = \begin{bmatrix} 9 \\ -6 \\ 17 \end{bmatrix}$ (b) $\begin{bmatrix} 1 \\ -1 \\ 2 \end{bmatrix}$

61. (a) $\begin{bmatrix} 1 & -5 & 2 \\ -3 & 1 & -1 \\ 0 & -2 & 5 \end{bmatrix}\begin{bmatrix} x_1 \\ x_2 \\ x_3 \end{bmatrix} = \begin{bmatrix} -20 \\ 8 \\ -16 \end{bmatrix}$ (b) $\begin{bmatrix} -1 \\ 3 \\ -2 \end{bmatrix}$

63. $\begin{bmatrix} -4 & 0 \\ 8 & 2 \end{bmatrix}$ **65.** $\begin{bmatrix} 84 & 60 & 30 \\ 42 & 120 & 84 \end{bmatrix}$

67. $[\$1037.50 \quad \$1400.00 \quad \$1012.50]$

The entries represent the total profit made at each outlet.

69. $\begin{bmatrix} \$15{,}770 & \$18{,}300 \\ \$26{,}500 & \$29{,}250 \\ \$21{,}260 & \$24{,}150 \end{bmatrix}$

The entries are the total wholesale and retail prices of the inventory at each outlet.

71. $\begin{bmatrix} 0.40 & 0.15 & 0.15 \\ 0.28 & 0.53 & 0.17 \\ 0.32 & 0.32 & 0.68 \end{bmatrix}$

P^2 represents the changes in party affiliations after two elections.

73. True. To add two matrices, you add corresponding entries.

75. Not possible   **77.** Not possible   **79.** 2×2

81. 2×3 **83.** $AC = BC = \begin{bmatrix} 2 & 3 \\ 2 & 3 \end{bmatrix}$

85. (a) $A^2 = \begin{bmatrix} -1 & 0 \\ 0 & -1 \end{bmatrix}, A^3 = \begin{bmatrix} -i & 0 \\ 0 & -i \end{bmatrix}, A^4 = \begin{bmatrix} 1 & 0 \\ 0 & 1 \end{bmatrix}$

The entries on the main diagonal are i^2 in A^2, i^3 in A^3, and i^4 in A^4.

(b) $B^2 = \begin{bmatrix} 1 & 0 \\ 0 & 1 \end{bmatrix}$

B^2 is the identity matrix.

87. (a) $A = \begin{bmatrix} 0 & 2 \\ 0 & 0 \end{bmatrix}, B = \begin{bmatrix} 0 & 2 & 3 \\ 0 & 0 & 4 \\ 0 & 0 & 0 \end{bmatrix}$

(Answers are not unique.)

(b) A^2 and B^3 are zero matrices.

(c) $A = \begin{bmatrix} 0 & 2 & 3 & 4 \\ 0 & 0 & 5 & 6 \\ 0 & 0 & 0 & 7 \\ 0 & 0 & 0 & 0 \end{bmatrix}$

A^4 is the zero matrix.

(d) A^n is the zero matrix.

89. $\ln\left(\dfrac{64}{\sqrt[3]{x^2+3}}\right)$ **91.** $\ln\left(\dfrac{\sqrt{x}(x+5)}{\sqrt{x-8}}\right)$

Section 8.6   (page 665)

1–11. Answers will vary.

13. $\begin{bmatrix} \frac{1}{2} & 0 \\ 0 & \frac{1}{3} \end{bmatrix}$ **15.** $\begin{bmatrix} -3 & 2 \\ -2 & 1 \end{bmatrix}$ **17.** $\begin{bmatrix} 1 & -1 \\ 2 & -1 \end{bmatrix}$

19. Does not exist   **21.** $\begin{bmatrix} 1 & 1 & -1 \\ -3 & 2 & -1 \\ 3 & -3 & 2 \end{bmatrix}$

23. Does not exist   **25.** Does not exist

27. $\begin{bmatrix} -12 & -5 & -9 \\ -4 & -2 & -4 \\ -8 & -4 & -6 \end{bmatrix}$ **29.** $\frac{5}{11}\begin{bmatrix} 0 & -4 & 2 \\ -22 & 11 & 11 \\ 22 & -6 & -8 \end{bmatrix}$

31. $\begin{bmatrix} 1 & 0 & 1 & 0 \\ 0 & 1 & 0 & 1 \\ 2 & 0 & 1 & 0 \\ 0 & 1 & 0 & 2 \end{bmatrix}$ **33.** $\begin{bmatrix} \frac{1}{4} & \frac{1}{8} \\ -\frac{1}{4} & -\frac{5}{8} \end{bmatrix}$

35. $\frac{1}{59}\begin{bmatrix} 16 & 15 \\ -4 & 70 \end{bmatrix}$ **37.** $(5, 0)$ **39.** $(-8, -6)$

41. $(3, 8, -11)$ **43.** $(2, 1, 0, 0)$ **45.** $(2, -2)$

47. Not possible because A is not invertible

49. $(-4, -8)$ **51.** $(-1, 3, 2)$

53. Not possible because A is not invertible

55. $(5, 0, -2, 3)$

57. \$10,000 in AAA-rated bonds, \$5000 in A-rated bonds, and \$10,000 in B-rated bonds

59. \$20,000 in AAA-rated bonds, \$15,000 in A-rated bonds, and \$30,000 in B-rated bonds

61. (a) $I_1 = -3$ amperes, $I_2 = 8$ amperes, $I_3 = 5$ amperes

(b) $I_1 = \frac{5}{7}$ ampere, $I_2 = \frac{10}{7}$ amperes, $I_3 = \frac{15}{7}$ amperes

63. True   **65.** Answers will vary.

67. $\dfrac{9}{2x+6}$, $x \neq 0$ **69.** $\dfrac{x^2 + 2x - 13}{x(x-2)}$, $x \neq \pm 3$

71. $\ln 3 \approx 1.099$ **73.** $\dfrac{e^{12/7}}{3} \approx 1.851$

Section 8.7   (page 673)

1. 4   **3.** 16   **5.** 28   **7.** -24 **9.** 0

11. -9 **13.** -0.002

15. (a) $M_{11} = -5, M_{12} = 2, M_{21} = 4, M_{22} = 3$

(b) $C_{11} = -5, C_{12} = -2, C_{21} = -4, C_{22} = 3$

17. (a) $M_{11} = 30, M_{12} = 12, M_{13} = 11, M_{21} = -36,$
$M_{22} = 26, M_{23} = 7, M_{31} = -4, M_{32} = -42,$
$M_{33} = 12$

(b) $C_{11} = 30, C_{12} = -12, C_{13} = 11, C_{21} = 36, C_{22} = 26,$
$C_{23} = -7, C_{31} = -4, C_{32} = 42, C_{33} = 12$

19. (a) -75 (b) -75 **21.** (a) 170   (b) 170

23. -58 **25.** -30 **27.** -168 **29.** 412

31. -60 **33.** -168 **35.** -336 **37.** 410

39. (a) -3 (b) -2 (c) $\begin{bmatrix} -2 & 0 \\ 0 & -3 \end{bmatrix}$ (d) 6

41. (a) 2   (b) -6 (c) $\begin{bmatrix} 1 & 4 & 3 \\ -1 & 0 & 3 \\ 0 & 2 & 0 \end{bmatrix}$ (d) -12

43. (a) -25 (b) -220

(c) $\begin{bmatrix} -7 & -16 & -1 & -28 \\ -4 & -14 & -11 & 8 \\ 13 & 4 & 4 & -4 \\ -2 & 3 & 2 & 2 \end{bmatrix}$ (d) 5500

45–49. Answers will vary.   **51.** $-4, -1$

53. $8uv - 1$ **55.** e^{5x} **57.** $1 - \ln x$ **59.** True

61. Answers will vary.

Sample answer: $A = \begin{bmatrix} 1 & 3 \\ -2 & 4 \end{bmatrix}$, $B = \begin{bmatrix} -4 & 0 \\ 3 & 5 \end{bmatrix}$

$|A + B| = -30$, $|A| + |B| = -10$

63. (a) Columns 2 and 3 are interchanged.

(b) Rows 1 and 3 are interchanged.

65. (a) 5 is factored from the first row.

(b) 4 and 3 are factored from the second and third columns, respectively.

67. $(x - 2)(x - 1)$ **69.** $(2y - 3)^2$ **71.** $(2, -4)$

Section 8.8   (page 684)

Vocabulary Check   (page 684)

1. collinear   **2.** Cramer's Rule   **3.** cryptogram

4. uncoded, coded

1. 14   **3.** $\frac{5}{2}$ **5.** $\frac{33}{8}$ **7.** $x = \frac{16}{5}, 0$

9. Collinear   **11.** Not collinear   **13.** $x = -3$

15. $(-3, -2)$ **17.** Not possible   **19.** $\left(\frac{32}{7}, \frac{30}{7}\right)$

21. $(-1, 3, 2)$ **23.** $\left(0, -\frac{1}{2}, \frac{1}{2}\right)$ **25.** 250 square miles

27. Uncoded: $\begin{bmatrix} 3 & 1 & 12 \end{bmatrix}, \begin{bmatrix} 12 & 0 & 13 \end{bmatrix}, \begin{bmatrix} 5 & 0 & 20 \end{bmatrix},$
$\begin{bmatrix} 15 & 13 & 15 \end{bmatrix}, \begin{bmatrix} 18 & 18 & 15 \end{bmatrix}, \begin{bmatrix} 23 & 0 & 0 \end{bmatrix}$

Encoded: -68 21 35 -66 14 39 -115 35 60
-62 15 32 -54 12 27 23 -23 0

29. 38 63 51 -1 -14 -32 58 119 133 44 88 95

31. HAPPY NEW YEAR   **33.** TEST ON FRIDAY

35. True   **37.** Answers will vary.

39. $x + 4y - 19 = 0$ **41.** $2x - 7y - 27 = 0$

43.

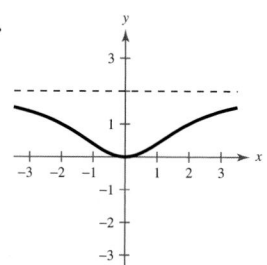

Asymptote: $y = 2$

Review Exercises   (page 688)

1. $(1, 1)$ **3.** $(5, 4)$ **5.** $(0, 0), (2, 8), (-2, 8)$

7. $\left(2, -\frac{1}{2}\right)$ **9.** $(0, 0), (-3, 3)$

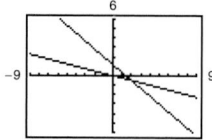 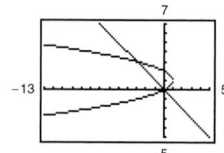

11. $(4, 4)$

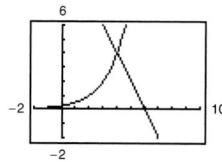

13. 4762 units   **15.** 96 meters $\times$ 144 meters   **17.** $\left(\frac{5}{2}, 3\right)$

19. $\left(-\frac{1}{2}, \frac{4}{5}\right)$ **21.** $(0, 0)$ **23.** $\left(\frac{14}{5} + \frac{8}{5}a, a\right)$

25.   **27.**

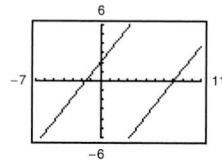

Consistent; $(1.6, -2.4)$ Inconsistent

29.

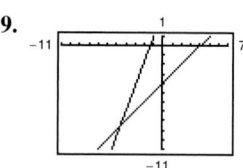

Consistent; $(-4.6, -8.6)$

31. $\left(\frac{500{,}000}{7}, \frac{159}{7}\right)$

33. 218.75 miles per hour; 193.75 miles per hour

35. $(2, -4, -5)$ **37.** $\left(\frac{38}{17}, \frac{40}{17}, -\frac{63}{17}\right)$

39. $(3a + 4, 2a + 5, a)$

41. $(a - 4, a - 3, a)$

43.

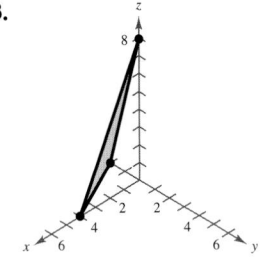

$(0, 0, 8), (0, -2, 0), (4, 0, 0), (1, -1, 2)$

45. (a) $\dfrac{3}{x + 2} - \dfrac{4}{x + 4}$ **47.** (a) $\dfrac{1}{2}\left(\dfrac{3}{x - 1} - \dfrac{x - 3}{x^2 + 1}\right)$

49. $y = 2x^2 + x - 5$

51. Spray X: 10 gallons; Spray Y: 5 gallons;
Spray Z: 12 gallons

53. 3×1 **55.** 1×1

57. $\begin{bmatrix} 3 & -10 & \vdots & 15 \\ 5 & 4 & \vdots & 22 \end{bmatrix}$ **59.** $\begin{bmatrix} 8 & -7 & 4 & \vdots & 12 \\ 3 & -5 & 2 & \vdots & 20 \\ 5 & 3 & -3 & \vdots & 26 \end{bmatrix}$

61. $\begin{cases} 5x + y + 7z = -9 \\ 4x + 2y \quad\quad = 10 \\ 9x + 4y + 2z = 3 \end{cases}$

63. $\begin{bmatrix} 1 & 0 & 0 \\ 0 & 1 & 0 \\ 0 & 0 & 1 \end{bmatrix}$ **65.** $\begin{bmatrix} 1 & 0 & 3 & -2 \\ 0 & 1 & 4 & -3 \end{bmatrix}$

67. $\begin{bmatrix} 1 & 0 & 1 \\ 0 & 1 & 1 \\ 0 & 0 & 0 \end{bmatrix}$ **69.** $(10, -12)$ **71.** $(-0.2, 0.7)$

73. $\left(\frac{1}{2}, -\frac{1}{3}, 1\right)$ **75.** $\left(-2a - 5, \frac{5}{3}a + \frac{2}{3}, a\right)$

77. $(2, -3, 3)$ **79.** $(2, 3, -1)$

81. $(3, 0, -4)$ **83.** $(2, 6, -10, -3)$

85. $x = 12, y = -7$ **87.** $x = 1, y = 11$

89. (a) $\begin{bmatrix} 17 & -17 \\ 13 & 2 \end{bmatrix}$ (b) $\begin{bmatrix} -3 & 23 \\ -15 & 8 \end{bmatrix}$

(c) $\begin{bmatrix} 28 & 12 \\ -4 & 20 \end{bmatrix}$ (d) $\begin{bmatrix} 37 & -57 \\ 41 & -4 \end{bmatrix}$

91. (a) $\begin{bmatrix} 6 & 5 & 8 \\ 1 & 7 & 8 \\ 5 & 1 & 4 \end{bmatrix}$ (b) $\begin{bmatrix} 6 & -5 & 6 \\ 9 & -9 & -4 \\ 1 & 3 & 2 \end{bmatrix}$

(c) $\begin{bmatrix} 24 & 0 & 28 \\ 20 & -4 & 8 \\ 12 & 8 & 12 \end{bmatrix}$ (d) $\begin{bmatrix} 6 & 15 & 10 \\ -7 & 23 & 20 \\ 9 & -1 & 6 \end{bmatrix}$

93. $\begin{bmatrix} -13 & -8 & 18 \\ 0 & 11 & -19 \end{bmatrix}$ **95.** $\begin{bmatrix} 2 & 1 & 12 \\ -13 & 1 & -17 \\ -30 & -54 & 40 \end{bmatrix}$

97. $\begin{bmatrix} 48 & -18 & -3 \\ 15 & 51 & 33 \end{bmatrix}$ **99.** $\begin{bmatrix} -14 & -4 \\ 7 & -17 \\ -17 & -2 \end{bmatrix}$

101. $\dfrac{1}{3}\begin{bmatrix} 9 & 2 \\ -4 & 11 \\ 10 & 0 \end{bmatrix}$ **103.** $\begin{bmatrix} 14 & -2 & 8 \\ 14 & -10 & 40 \\ 36 & -12 & 48 \end{bmatrix}$

105. $\begin{bmatrix} 11 & -6 \\ 18 & 39 \end{bmatrix}$ **107.** $\begin{bmatrix} 14 & -22 & 22 \\ 19 & -41 & 80 \\ 42 & -66 & 66 \end{bmatrix}$

109. $\begin{bmatrix} 1 & 17 \\ 12 & 36 \end{bmatrix}$ **111.** $\begin{bmatrix} 96 & 84 & 108 & 48 \\ 60 & 36 & 96 & 24 \\ 108 & 72 & 120 & 60 \end{bmatrix}$

113. Answers will vary.

115. $\begin{bmatrix} 4 & -5 \\ 5 & -6 \end{bmatrix}$ **117.** $\begin{bmatrix} 13 & 6 & -4 \\ -12 & -5 & 3 \\ 5 & 2 & -1 \end{bmatrix}$

119. $\begin{bmatrix} \frac{1}{5} & \frac{1}{5} \\ \frac{1}{10} & -\frac{1}{15} \end{bmatrix}$ **121.** $\begin{bmatrix} \frac{1}{2} & -1 & -\frac{1}{2} \\ \frac{1}{2} & -\frac{2}{3} & -\frac{5}{6} \\ 0 & \frac{2}{3} & \frac{1}{3} \end{bmatrix}$

123. $\begin{bmatrix} 1 & -1 \\ 4 & -\frac{7}{2} \end{bmatrix}$ **125.** Does not exist   **127.** $(36, 11)$

129. $(2, -1, -2)$ **131.** $(6, 1, -1)$ **133.** $(-3, 1)$

135. $(1, 1, -2)$ **137.** -42 **139.** 550

141. (a) $M_{11} = 4, M_{12} = 7, M_{21} = -1, M_{22} = 2$

(b) $C_{11} = 4, C_{12} = -7, C_{21} = 1, C_{22} = 2$

143. (a) $M_{11} = 30, M_{12} = -12, M_{13} = -21, M_{21} = 20,$
$M_{22} = 19, M_{23} = 22, M_{31} = 5, M_{32} = -2,$
$M_{33} = 19$

(b) $C_{11} = 30, C_{12} = 12, C_{13} = -21, C_{21} = -20,$
$C_{22} = 19, C_{23} = -22, C_{31} = 5, C_{32} = 2, C_{33} = 19$

145. 130   **147.** -3 **149.** 279   **151.** -96

153. 16   **155.** 1.75   **157.** Not collinear   **159.** $(1, 2)$

161. $(4, 7)$ **163.** $(-1, 4, 5)$ **165.** $(0, -2.4, -2.6)$

167. Uncoded: $[12 \ 15 \ 15], [11 \ 0 \ 15], [21 \ 20 \ 0],$
$[2 \ 5 \ 12], [15 \ 23 \ 0]$

Encoded: $-21 \ 6 \ 0 \ -68 \ 8 \ 45 \ 102 \ -42$
$-60 \ -53 \ 20 \ 21 \ 99 \ -30 \ -69$

169. SEE YOU FRIDAY

171. False, the solution may have irrational numbers.

173. Elementary row operations correspond to the operations performed on a system of equations.

Chapter Test   (page 694)

1. $(4, -2)$ **2.** $(0, -1), (1, 0), (2, 1)$

3. $(8, 5), (2, -1)$ **4.** $\left(\frac{28}{9}, -\frac{31}{9}\right)$ **5.** $(-1, 5, 2)$

6. $\left(-\frac{3}{5}a, \frac{4}{5}a, a\right)$ **7.** $y = -\frac{1}{2}x^2 + x + 6$

8. $\dfrac{5}{x-1} + \dfrac{3}{(x-1)^2}$ **9.** $(-2a + 1.5, 2a + 1, a)$

10. $(5, 2, -6)$

11. (a) $\begin{bmatrix} 1 & 0 & 4 \\ -7 & -6 & -1 \\ 0 & 4 & 0 \end{bmatrix}$

(b) $\begin{bmatrix} 15 & 12 & 12 \\ -12 & -12 & 0 \\ 3 & 6 & 0 \end{bmatrix}$

(c) $\begin{bmatrix} 7 & 4 & 12 \\ -18 & -16 & -2 \\ 1 & 10 & 0 \end{bmatrix}$

(d) $\begin{bmatrix} 36 & 20 & 4 \\ -28 & -24 & -4 \\ 10 & 8 & 2 \end{bmatrix}$

12. $A^{-1} = \begin{bmatrix} \frac{1}{2} & \frac{2}{5} \\ 1 & \frac{3}{5} \end{bmatrix}$; $(13, 22)$

13. 67   **14.** -2 **15.** 7   **16.** $\left(\frac{3}{4}, -\frac{1}{2}\right)$

17. $x_1 = 700 - s - t, x_2 = 300 - s - t,$
  $x_3 = s, x_4 = 100 - t, x_5 = t$

Chapter 9

Section 9.1   (page 703)

Vocabulary Check   (page 703)

1. infinite sequence   **2.** terms   **3.** finite

4. recursively   **5.** factorial

6. summation notation

7. index, upper limit, lower limit   **8.** series

9. nth partial sum

---

1. 7, 9, 11, 13, 15   **3.** 2, 4, 8, 16, 32

5. $-\frac{1}{2}, \frac{1}{4}, -\frac{1}{8}, \frac{1}{16}, -\frac{1}{32}$ **7.** $2, \frac{3}{2}, \frac{4}{3}, \frac{5}{4}, \frac{6}{5}$ **9.** $\frac{1}{2}, \frac{2}{5}, \frac{3}{10}, \frac{4}{17}, \frac{5}{26}$

11. $0, 1, 0, \frac{1}{2}, 0$ **13.** $\frac{1}{2}, \frac{3}{4}, \frac{7}{8}, \frac{15}{16}, \frac{31}{32}$

15. $1, \dfrac{1}{2^{3/2}}, \dfrac{1}{3^{3/2}}, \dfrac{1}{4^{3/2}} = \dfrac{1}{8}, \dfrac{1}{5^{3/2}}$ **17.** $-1, \dfrac{1}{4}, -\dfrac{1}{9}, \dfrac{1}{16}, -\dfrac{1}{25}$

19. 3, 15, 35, 63, 99   **21.** -73 **23.** $\frac{100}{101}$

25.

27.

29.

31. 9, 15, 21, 27, 33, 39, 45, 51, 57, 63

33. $3, \frac{5}{2}, \frac{7}{3}, \frac{9}{4}, \frac{11}{5}, \frac{13}{6}, \frac{15}{7}, \frac{17}{8}, \frac{19}{9}, \frac{21}{10}$ **35.** c   **36.** b

37. d   **38.** a   **39.** $a_n = 3n - 2$ **41.** $a_n = n^2 - 1$

43. $a_n = \dfrac{n+1}{n+2}$ **45.** $a_n = \dfrac{(-1)^{n+1}}{2^n}$

47. $a_n = 1 + \dfrac{1}{n}$ **49.** $a_n = \dfrac{1}{n!}$

51. $a_n = (-1)^n + 2(1)^n = (-1)^n + 2$

53. 28, 24, 20, 16, 12   **55.** 3, 4, 6, 10, 18

57. 6, 8, 10, 12, 14; $a_n = 2n + 4$

59. 81, 27, 9, 3, 1; $a_n = \dfrac{243}{3^n}$ **61.** $1, 1, \dfrac{1}{2}, \dfrac{1}{6}, \dfrac{1}{24}$

63. $1, \dfrac{1}{3}, \dfrac{2}{5}, \dfrac{6}{7}, \dfrac{8}{3}$ **65.** $1, \dfrac{1}{2}, \dfrac{1}{24}, \dfrac{1}{720}, \dfrac{1}{40{,}320}$ **67.** $\dfrac{1}{12}$

69. 495   **71.** $n + 1$ **73.** $\dfrac{1}{2n(2n+1)}$ **75.** 35

77. 40   **79.** 30   **81.** $\frac{9}{5}$ **83.** 238   **85.** 30

87. 81   **89.** $\dfrac{47}{60}$ **91.** $\displaystyle\sum_{i=1}^{9} \dfrac{1}{3i} \approx 0.94299$

93. $\displaystyle\sum_{i=1}^{8} \left[2\left(\dfrac{i}{8}\right) + 3 \right] = 33$ **95.** $\displaystyle\sum_{i=1}^{6} (-1)^{i+1}3i = -546$

97. $\displaystyle\sum_{i=1}^{20} \dfrac{(-1)^{i+1}}{i^2} \approx 0.821$ **99.** $\displaystyle\sum_{i=1}^{5} \dfrac{2^i - 1}{2^{i+1}} \approx 2.0156$

101. $\frac{75}{16}$ **103.** $-\frac{3}{2}$ **105.** $\frac{2}{3}$ **107.** $\frac{1}{9}$

109. (a) $A_1 = \$5037.50, A_2 = \$5075.28,$
  $A_3 = \$5113.35, A_4 = \$5151.70,$
  $A_5 = \$5190.33, A_6 = \$5229.26,$
  $A_7 = \$5268.48, A_8 = \$5307.99$

(b) $\$6741.74$

111. (a) $a_3 = 719{,}630, a_4 = 732{,}320,$
  $a_5 = 747{,}750, a_6 = 765{,}920,$
  $a_7 = 786{,}830, a_8 = 810{,}480,$
  $a_9 = 836{,}870, a_{10} = 866{,}000, a_{11} = 897{,}870$

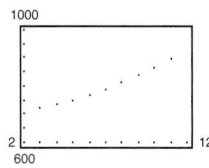

(b) Enrollment will increase.

113. $3,491,000,000$; The sums are approximately the same.

115. True

117. $1, 1, 2, 3, 5, 8, 13, 21, 34, 55, 89, 144$;

$1, 2, \frac{3}{2}, \frac{5}{3}, \frac{8}{5}, \frac{13}{8}, \frac{21}{13}, \frac{34}{21}, \frac{55}{34}, \frac{89}{55}$

119. $x, \dfrac{x^2}{2}, \dfrac{x^3}{6}, \dfrac{x^4}{24}, \dfrac{x^5}{120}$

121. $-\dfrac{x^2}{2}, \dfrac{x^4}{24}, -\dfrac{x^6}{720}, \dfrac{x^8}{40{,}320}, -\dfrac{x^{10}}{3{,}628{,}800}$

123. (a) $\begin{bmatrix} 8 & 1 \\ -3 & 7 \end{bmatrix}$ (b) $\begin{bmatrix} -22 & -7 \\ 3 & -18 \end{bmatrix}$

(c) $\begin{bmatrix} 18 & 9 \\ 18 & 0 \end{bmatrix}$ (d) $\begin{bmatrix} 0 & 6 \\ 27 & 18 \end{bmatrix}$

125. (a) $\begin{bmatrix} -3 & -7 & 4 \\ 4 & 4 & 1 \\ 1 & 4 & 3 \end{bmatrix}$ (b) $\begin{bmatrix} 8 & 17 & -14 \\ -12 & -13 & -9 \\ -3 & -15 & -10 \end{bmatrix}$

(c) $\begin{bmatrix} -2 & 7 & -16 \\ 4 & 42 & 45 \\ 1 & 23 & 48 \end{bmatrix}$ (d) $\begin{bmatrix} 16 & 31 & 42 \\ 10 & 47 & 31 \\ 13 & 22 & 25 \end{bmatrix}$

Section 9.2   (page 713)

1. Arithmetic sequence, $d = -2$

3. Arithmetic sequence, $d = -\frac{1}{2}$

5. Arithmetic sequence, $d = 8$

7. Arithmetic sequence, $d = 0.6$

9. $21, 34, 47, 60, 73$

Arithmetic sequence, $d = 13$

11. $\frac{1}{2}, \frac{1}{3}, \frac{1}{4}, \frac{1}{5}, \frac{1}{6}$

Not an arithmetic sequence

13. $143, 136, 129, 122, 115$

Arithmetic sequence, $d = -7$

15. $1, 4, \frac{7}{3}, \frac{7}{2}, \frac{13}{5}$

Not an arithmetic sequence

17. $a_n = -2 + 3n$ **19.** $a_n = 108 - 8n$

21. $a_n = \frac{13}{2} - \frac{5}{2}n$ **23.** $a_n = \frac{10}{3}n + \frac{5}{3}$

25. $a_n = 103 - 3n$ **27.** $5, 11, 17, 23, 29$

29. $-10, -22, -34, -46, -58$ **31.** $-2, 2, 6, 10, 14$

33. $22.45, 20.725, 19, 17.275, 15.55$

35. $15, 19, 23, 27, 31; d = 4; a_n = 11 + 4n$

37. $\frac{7}{2}, \frac{13}{4}, 3, \frac{11}{4}, \frac{5}{2}; d = -\frac{1}{4}; a_n = -\frac{1}{4}n + \frac{15}{4}$

39. 59 **41.** 18.6

43. 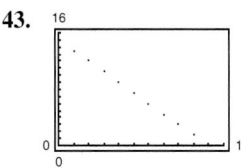   **45.**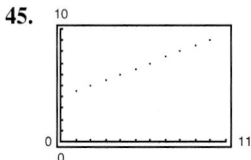

47. $-1, 3, 7, 11, 15, 19, 23, 27, 31, 35$

49. $19.25, 18.5, 17.75, 17, 16.25, 15.5, 14.75, 14, 13.25, 12.5$

51. $1.505, 1.51, 1.515, 1.52, 1.525, 1.53, 1.535, 1.54, 1.545, 1.55$

53. 620 **55.** 41 **57.** 4000 **59.** $10,000$

61. 1275 **63.** $25,250$ **65.** 355 **67.** $129,250$

69. 520 **71.** 2725 **73.** $10,120$

75. (a) $\$40,000$ (b) $\$217,500$

77. 405 bricks   **79.** 585 seats   **81.** $\$150,000$

83. True. Given a_1 and a_2, you know $d = a_2 - a_1$. Hence, $a_n = a_1 + (n - 1)d$.

85. $x, 3x, 5x, 7x, 9x, 11x, 13x, 15x, 17x, 19x$ **87.** 4

89. (a) $4, 9, 16, 25, 36$

(b) The sum of the first n positive odd integers is n^2; 49

(c) $\dfrac{n}{2}[1 + (2n - 1)] = n^2$

91. $(1, 5, -1)$ **93.** 15 square units

Section 9.3   (page 722)

1. Geometric sequence, $r = 3$

3. Not a geometric sequence

5. Geometric sequence, $r = -\frac{1}{2}$

7. Geometric sequence, $r = 2$

9. Not a geometric sequence   **11.** 6, 18, 54, 162, 486

13. $1, \frac{1}{2}, \frac{1}{4}, \frac{1}{8}, \frac{1}{16}$ **15.** $5, -\frac{1}{2}, \frac{1}{20}, -\frac{1}{200}, \frac{1}{2000}$

17. $1, e, e^2, e^3, e^4$

19. 64, 32, 16, 8, 4; $r = \frac{1}{2}$;   **21.** 9, 18, 36, 72, 144; $r = 2$;
$a_n = 128\left(\frac{1}{2}\right)^n$ $a_n = 9(2)^{n-1}$

23. $6, -9, \frac{27}{2}, -\frac{81}{4}, \frac{243}{8}; r = -\frac{3}{2}$;
$a_n = 6\left(-\frac{3}{2}\right)^{n-1}$

25. $\left(\frac{1}{2}\right)^7$ **27.** $-\dfrac{2}{3^{10}}$ **29.** $500(1.02)^{13}$ **31.** $-\frac{2}{9}$

33. 45,927   **35.** 50,388,480

37. 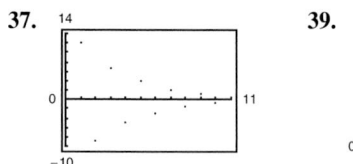   **39.**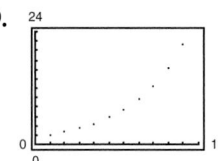

41. 8, 4, 6, 5

43.

n	S_n
1	16
2	24
3	28
4	30
5	31
6	31.5
7	31.75
8	31.875
9	31.9375
10	31.96875

45. 511   **47.** 43

49. 29,921.31   **51.** 6.4   **53.** 2092.60

55. $\displaystyle\sum_{n=1}^{7} 5(3)^{n-1}$ **57.** $\displaystyle\sum_{n=1}^{7} 2\left(-\frac{1}{4}\right)^{n-1}$ **59.** 2   **61.** $\frac{2}{3}$

63. Series does not have a finite sum.   **65.** $\frac{5}{3}$

67. -30 **69.** 32   **71.** $\frac{9}{4}$ **73.** $\frac{4}{11}$ **75.** $\frac{7}{22}$

77. (a) \$1343.92   (b) \$1346.86   (c) \$1348.35
(d) \$1349.35   (e) \$1349.84

79. \$7011.89   **81.** Answers will vary.

83. (a) \$26,198.27   (b) \$26,263.88

85. (a) \$153,237.86   (b) \$153,657.02

87. 126 square inches

89. (a) 1.3%   (b) 4,328,000 people   (c) 2005

91. (a) \$5,368,709.11   (b) \$10,737,418.23
(c) \$21,474,836.47

93. False. Any arithmetic sequence can be used as a counter-example.

95. $3, \dfrac{3x}{2}, \dfrac{3x^2}{4}, \dfrac{3x^3}{8}, \dfrac{3x^4}{16}$ **97.** $100e^{8x}$

99. (a)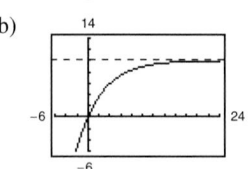

Horizontal asymptote: $y = 12$

Corresponds to the sum of the series

(b)

Horizontal asymptote: $y = 10$

Corresponds to the sum of the series

101. Divide the second term by the first to obtain the common ratio. The nth term is the first term times the common ratio raised to the $n - 1$ power.

103. 45.65 miles per hour   **105.** 14   **107.** -102

Section 9.4   (page 732)

Vocabulary Check   (page 732)

1. mathematical induction   **2.** first

3. arithmetic   **4.** second

---

1. $\dfrac{5}{(k+1)(k+2)}$ **3.** $\dfrac{3(2k+3)}{k}$

5. $1 + 6 + 11 + \cdots + (5k - 4) + (5k + 1)$

7–17. Answers will vary.   **19.** 3025   **21.** 70

23–35. Answers will vary.

37. 0, 3, 6, 9, 12

First differences: 3, 3, 3, 3

Second differences: 0, 0, 0

Linear

39. $3, 1, -2, -6, -11$

First differences: $-2, -3, -4, -5$

Second differences: $-1, -1, -1$

Quadratic

41. 0, 1, 3, 6, 10

First differences: 1, 2, 3, 4

Second differences: 1, 1, 1

Quadratic

43. 2, 4, 6, 8, 10

First differences: 2, 2, 2, 2

Second differences: 0, 0, 0

Linear

45. $a_n = n^2 - n + 3$ **47.** $a_n = \frac{1}{2}n^2 + n - 3$

49. (a) First differences: 2.2, 2.5, 2.1, 1.8, 2.3, 1.9

(b) Yes; $a_n = 2.13n + 22.8$

(c)

Year	Original data	Data using model
1995	33.3	33.5
1996	35.5	35.6
1997	38.0	37.7
1998	40.1	39.8
1999	41.9	42.0
2000	44.2	44.1
2001	46.1	46.2

The model represents the data well.

(d) \$56,900

51. False. Not necessarily

53. False. It has $n - 2$ second differences.

55. $4x^4 - 4x^2 + 1$ **57.** $-64x^3 + 240x^2 - 300x + 125$

59. $x^2 - 3x + 2$ **61.** $4x^2 - 9x + 2$

63. $7\sqrt{3}i$ **65.** $40(1 + \sqrt[3]{2})$

Section 9.5 (page 739)

1. 21 **3.** 1 **5.** 15,504 **7.** 14 **9.** 4950

11. 35,960 **13.** 497,420 **15.** 749,398 **17.** 35

19. 56 **21.** $x^4 + 8x^3 + 24x^2 + 32x + 16$

23. $a^3 + 9a^2 + 27a + 27$

25. $y^4 - 8y^3 + 24y^2 - 32y + 16$

27. $x^5 + 5x^4y + 10x^3y^2 + 10x^2y^3 + 5xy^4 + y^5$

29. $729r^6 + 2916r^5s + 4860r^4s^2 + 4320r^3s^3 + 2160r^2s^4$
$+ 576rs^5 + 64s^6$

31. $x^5 - 5x^4y + 10x^3y^2 - 10x^2y^3 + 5xy^4 - y^5$

33. $1 - 12x + 48x^2 - 64x^3$

35. $x^8 + 4x^6y^2 + 6x^4y^4 + 4x^2y^6 + y^8$

37. $\frac{1}{x^5} + \frac{5y}{x^4} + \frac{10y^2}{x^3} + \frac{10y^3}{x^2} + \frac{5y^4}{x} + y^5$

39. $2x^4 - 24x^3 + 113x^2 - 246x + 207$

41. $-4x^6 - 24x^5 - 60x^4 - 83x^3 - 42x^2 - 60x + 20$

43. $243t^5 - 405t^4s + 270t^3s^2 - 90t^2s^3 + 15ts^4 - s^5$

45. $x^5 + 10x^4y + 40x^3y^2 + 80x^2y^3 + 80xy^4 + 32y^5$

47. $61,440x^7$ **49.** $360x^3y^2$ **51.** $1,259,712x^2y^7$

53. $32,476,950,000x^4y^8$ **55.** 3,247,695 **57.** 180

59. $-489,888$ **61.** 210

63. $x^2 + 20x^{3/2} + 150x + 500x^{1/2} + 625$

65. $x^2 - 3x^{4/3}y^{1/3} + 3x^{2/3}y^{2/3} - y$

67. $3x^2 + 3xh + h^2, h \neq 0$

69. $\dfrac{\sqrt{x+h} - \sqrt{x}}{h} = \dfrac{1}{\sqrt{x+h} + \sqrt{x}}, h \neq 0$

71. -4 **73.** $2035 + 828i$ **75.** 1 **77.** 1.172

79. 510,568.785

81.

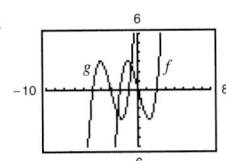

g is shifted three units to the left.

$g(x) = x^3 + 9x^2 + 23x + 15$

83. **85.** 0.273 **87.** 0.171

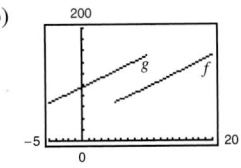

$p(x)$ is the expansion of $f(x)$.

89. (a) $g(t) = 0.018t^2 + 5.51t + 94.9, -5 \leq t \leq 10$

(b)

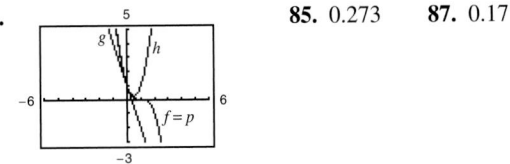

91. False. The correct term is $126{,}720x^4y^8$.

93. The first and last numbers in each row are 1. Every other number in each row is formed by adding the two numbers immediately above the number.

95. Alternating terms of $(x - y)^n$ are negative.

97 and 99. Answers will vary.

101. $g(x)$ is shifted eight units up from $f(x)$.

103. $g(x)$ is the reflection of $f(x)$ in the y-axis.

105. $\begin{bmatrix} 4 & -5 \\ 5 & -6 \end{bmatrix}$

Section 9.6   (page 749)

Vocabulary Check   (page 749)

1. Fundamental Counting Principle   **2.** permutation

3. $_nP_r = \dfrac{n!}{(n - r)!}$ **4.** distinguishable permutations

5. combinations

1. 6   **3.** 5   **5.** 3   **7.** 7   **9.** 120   **11.** 24

13. 1024   **15.** 12   **17.** 17,576,000

19. (a) 900   (b) 648   (c) 180   (d) 600

21. 16,000,000   **23.** (a) 720   (b) 48   **25.** 24

27. 336   **29.** 120   **31.** $n = 5$ or $n = 6$

33. 27,907,200   **35.** 197,149,680   **37.** 4845

39. 120   **41.** 11,880   **43.** 420   **45.** 2520

47. (a) ABCD, ABDC, ACBD, ACDB, ADBC, ADCB,
BACD, BADC, CABD, CADB, DABC, DACB,
BCAD, BDAC, CBAD, CDAB, DBAC, DCAB,
BCDA, BDCA, CBDA, CDBA, DBCA, DCBA

(b) ABCD, ACBD, DBCA, DCBA

49. 4845   **51.** 13,983,816   **53.** 36   **55.** 3744

57. (a) 495   (b) 210   **59.** 292,600   **61.** 5

63. 20   **65.** False. This is an example of a combination.

67. For some calculators the answer is too large.

69. They are equal.   **71 and 73.** Answers will vary.

75. 8.303   **77.** 35   **79.** $(-2, -8)$ **81.** $(-1, 1)$

Section 9.7   (page 760)

Vocabulary Check   (page 760)

1. experiment, outcomes   **2.** sample space

3. probability   **4.** impossible, certain

5. mutually exclusive   **6.** independent

7. complement   **8.** (a) iii   (b) i   (c) iv   (d) ii

1. $\{(H, 1), (H, 2), (H, 3), (H, 4), (H, 5), (H, 6),$
$(T, 1), (T, 2), (T, 3), (T, 4), (T, 5), (T, 6)\}$

3. $\{$ABC, ACB, BAC, BCA, CAB, CBA$\}$

5. $\{(A, B), (A, C), (A, D), (A, E), (B, C), (B, D),$
$(B, E), (C, D), (C, E), (D, E)\}$

7. $\frac{3}{8}$ **9.** $\frac{7}{8}$ **11.** $\frac{3}{13}$ **13.** $\frac{3}{26}$ **15.** $\frac{1}{9}$ **17.** $\frac{11}{12}$

19. $\frac{1}{5}$ **21.** $\frac{2}{5}$ **23.** 0.2   **25.** $\frac{2}{3}$ **27.** 0.88   **29.** $\frac{7}{20}$

31. (a) 1.2 million   (b) 0.42   (c) 0.21   (d) Over 0.22

33. (a) 0.34   (b) 0.45   (c) 0.23

35. (a) $\frac{672}{1254}$ (b) $\frac{582}{1254}$ (c) $\frac{548}{1254}$

37. $P(\{\text{Taylor wins}\}) = \frac{1}{2}$
$P(\{\text{Moore wins}\}) = P(\{\text{Perez wins}\}) = \frac{1}{4}$

39. (a) $\frac{21}{1292} \approx 0.016$ (b) $\frac{225}{646} \approx 0.348$ (c) $\frac{49}{323} \approx 0.152$

41. (a) $\frac{1}{120}$ (b) $\frac{1}{24}$ **43.** (a) $\frac{5}{13}$ (b) $\frac{1}{2}$ (c) $\frac{4}{13}$

45. (a) $\frac{14}{55}$ (b) $\frac{12}{55}$ (c) $\frac{54}{55}$ **47.** 0.1024

49. (a) 0.9702   (b) 0.9998   (c) 0.0002

51. (a) $\dfrac{1}{15{,}625}$ (b) $\dfrac{4096}{15{,}625}$ (c) $\dfrac{11{,}529}{15{,}625}$

53. $\frac{7}{16}$ **55.** True

57. (a) As you consider successive people with distinct birthdays, the probabilities must decrease to take into account the birth dates already used. Because the birth dates of people are independent events, multiply the respective probabilities of distinct birthdays.

(b) $\frac{365}{365} \cdot \frac{364}{365} \cdot \frac{363}{365} \cdot \frac{362}{365}$

(c) Answers will vary.

(d) Q_n is the probability that the birthdays are *not* distinct, which is equivalent to at least two people having the same birthday.

(e)

n	10	15	20	23	30	40	50
P_n	0.88	0.75	0.59	0.49	0.29	0.11	0.03
Q_n	0.12	0.25	0.41	0.51	0.71	0.89	0.97

(f) 23

59. $x = \frac{11}{2}$ **61.** $x = -10$ **63.** $\ln 28 \approx 3.332$

65. $x = \frac{1}{6}e^4 \approx 9.100$ **67.** 60   **69.** 6,652,800

71. 15   **73.** 165

Review Exercises   (page 766)

1. $8, 5, 4, \frac{7}{2}, \frac{16}{5}$ **3.** $72, 36, 12, 3, \frac{3}{5}$

5. 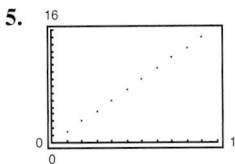   **7.**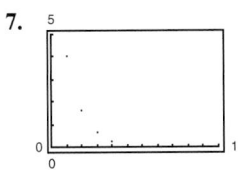

9. $\frac{1}{380}$ **11.** $\frac{1}{3}$ **13.** 30   **15.** $\frac{205}{24}$ **17.** 6050

19. 418   **21.** $\displaystyle\sum_{k=1}^{20} \frac{1}{2k}$; 1.799   **23.** $\displaystyle\sum_{k=1}^{9} \frac{k}{k+1}$; 7.071

25. (a) $\dfrac{1111}{2000}$ (b) $\dfrac{5}{9}$ **27.** (a) $\dfrac{2,020,202}{100,000,000}$ (b) $\dfrac{2}{99}$

29. (a) $a_1 = \$2550.00$, $a_2 = \$2601.00$, $a_3 = \$2653.02$,
$a_4 = \$2706.08$, $a_5 = \$2760.20$, $a_6 = \$2815.41$,
$a_7 = \$2871.71$, $a_8 = \$2929.15$
(b) \$5520.10

31. Arithmetic sequence, $d = -2$

33. Arithmetic sequence, $d = \frac{1}{2}$

35. 3, 7, 11, 15, 19   **37.** 1, 4, 7, 10, 13

39. 35, 32, 29, 26, 23; $d = -3$;
$a_n = 38 - 3n$

41. 9, 16, 23, 30, 37; $d = 7$;
$a_n = 2 + 7n$

43. $a_n = 103 - 3n$; 1430   **45.** 80   **47.** 88

49. 25,250   **51.** (a) \$43,000   (b) \$192,500

53. Geometric sequence, $r = 2$

55. Not a geometric sequence

57. $4, -1, \frac{1}{4}, -\frac{1}{16}, \frac{1}{64}$ **59.** $9, 6, 4, \frac{8}{3}, \frac{16}{9}$ or $9, -6, 4, -\frac{8}{3}, \frac{16}{9}$

61. $120, 40, \frac{40}{3}, \frac{40}{9}, \frac{40}{27}$; $r = \frac{1}{3}$;
$a_n = 120\left(\frac{1}{3}\right)^{n-1}$

63. $25, -15, 9, -\frac{27}{5}, \frac{81}{25}$; $r = -\frac{3}{5}$;
$a_n = 25\left(-\frac{3}{5}\right)^{n-1}$

65. $a_n = 16\left(-\frac{1}{2}\right)^{n-1}$; 10.67

67. $a_n = 100(1.05)^{n-1}$; 3306.60   **69.** 127   **71.** 3277

73. 1301.01   **75.** 24.85   **77.** 8   **79.** 12

81. (a) $a_t = 120,000(0.7)^t$ (b) \$20,168.40

83 and 85. Answers will vary.   **87.** 465   **89.** 4648

91. 5, 10, 15, 20, 25
First differences: 5, 5, 5, 5
Second differences: 0, 0, 0
Linear model

93. 16, 15, 14, 13, 12
First differences: $-1, -1, -1, -1$
Second differences: 0, 0, 0
Linear model

95. 45   **97.** 126   **99.** 20   **101.** 70

103. $x^4 + 20x^3 + 150x^2 + 500x + 625$

105. $a^5 - 20a^4b + 160a^3b^2 - 640a^2b^3 + 1280ab^4 - 1024b^5$

107. $1241 + 2520i$ **109.** 10   **111.** 48   **113.** 5040

115. 3,628,800   **117.** 15,504   **119.** $\frac{1}{9}$

121. (a) 0.416   (b) 0.8   (c) 0.074   **123.** 0.0475

125. True. $\dfrac{(n+2)!}{n!} = \dfrac{(n+2)(n+1)n!}{n!} = (n+2)(n+1)$

127. (a) Each term is obtained by adding the same constant (common difference) to the preceding term.
(b) Each term is obtained by multiplying the same constant (common ratio) by the preceding term.

129. (a) Arithmetic. There is a constant difference between consecutive terms.
(b) Geometric. Each term is a constant multiple of the preceding term. In this case the common ratio is greater than 1.

131. Each term of the sequence is defined using a previous term or terms.

133. If n is even, the expressions are the same. If n is odd, the expressions are negatives of each other.

Chapter Test   (page 770)

1. $1, -\frac{2}{3}, \frac{4}{9}, -\frac{8}{27}, \frac{16}{81}$ **2.** 12, 16, 20, 24, 28   **3.** 7920

4. $a_n = 5100 - 100n$ **5.** $a_n = 4\left(\frac{1}{2}\right)^{n-1}$

6. $\displaystyle\sum_{n=1}^{12} \frac{2}{3n+1}$ **7.** 189   **8.** 28.80   **9.** $\frac{50}{9}$

10. Answers will vary.

11. $16a^4 - 160a^3b + 600a^2b^2 - 1000ab^3 + 625b^4$

12. 48,384   **13.** 84   **14.** 1140   **15.** 72

16. 328,440   **17.** 26,000   **18.** 12,650   **19.** $\frac{3}{26}$

20. $\frac{1}{6}$ **21.** (a) $\frac{1}{4}$ (b) $\frac{121}{3600}$ (c) $\frac{1}{60}$ **22.** 0.25

Chapter 10

Section 10.1   (page 781)

1. $x^2 + y^2 = 36$ **3.** $x^2 + y^2 = \frac{25}{49}$

5. Vertex: $(0, 0)$ **7.** Vertex: $(0, 0)$

Focus: $\left(0, \frac{1}{2}\right)$ Focus: $\left(-\frac{3}{2}, 0\right)$

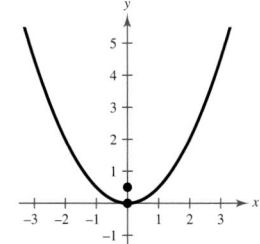 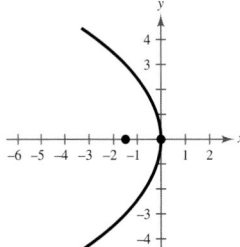

9. Vertex: $(0, 0)$

Focus: $(0, -2)$

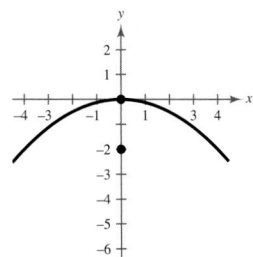

11. $x^2 = -6y$ **13.** $y^2 = -8x$ **15.** $x^2 = 4y$

17. $y^2 = -12x$ **19.** $y^2 = 9x$

21. $y = \frac{2}{3}x^2$; focus: $\left(0, \frac{3}{8}\right)$ **23.** $x = \frac{5}{9}y^2$; focus: $\left(\frac{9}{20}, 0\right)$

25.

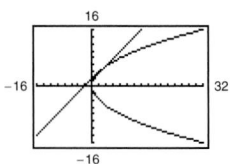

$(2, 4)$

27. Center: $(0, 0)$ **29.** Center: $(0, 0)$

Vertices: $(\pm 5, 0)$ Vertices: $\left(\pm\frac{5}{3}, 0\right)$

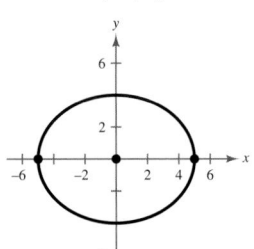 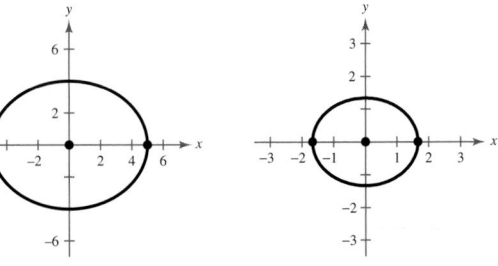

31. Center: $(0, 0)$ **33.** Center: $(0, 0)$

Vertices: $(\pm 3, 0)$ Vertices: $(0, \pm 1)$

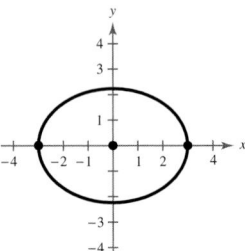 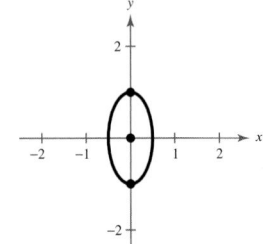

35.   **37.**

$$\begin{array}{cc} \text{[graph]} & \text{[graph]} \end{array}$$

39. $\dfrac{x^2}{1} + \dfrac{y^2}{4} = 1$ **41.** $\dfrac{x^2}{4} + \dfrac{y^2}{\frac{9}{4}} = 1$ **43.** $\dfrac{x^2}{25} + \dfrac{y^2}{21} = 1$

45. $\dfrac{x^2}{36} + \dfrac{y^2}{11} = 1$ **47.** $\dfrac{x^2}{\frac{400}{21}} + \dfrac{y^2}{25} = 1$

49. Center: $(0, 0)$

Vertices: $(\pm 1, 0)$

Foci: $\left(\pm\sqrt{2}, 0\right)$

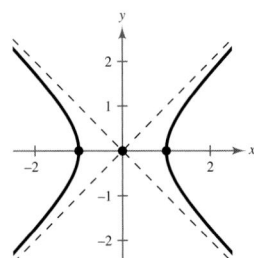

51. Center: $(0, 0)$
Vertices: $(0, \pm 1)$
Foci: $(0, \pm \sqrt{10})$

53. Center: $(0, 0)$
Vertices: $(0, \pm 5)$
Foci: $(0, \pm 13)$

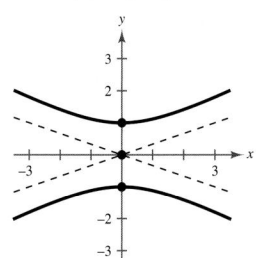
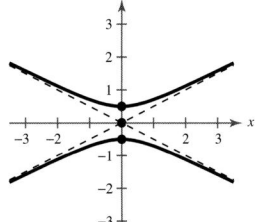

55. Center: $(0, 0)$
Vertices: $\left(0, \pm \frac{1}{2}\right)$
Foci: $\left(0, \pm \frac{\sqrt{5}}{2}\right)$

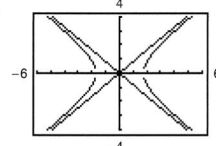

57. 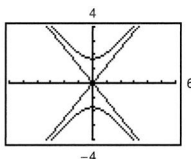 **59.**

61. $\dfrac{y^2}{4} - \dfrac{x^2}{12} = 1$ **63.** $\dfrac{x^2}{1} - \dfrac{y^2}{9} = 1$

65. $\dfrac{y^2}{\frac{1024}{17}} - \dfrac{x^2}{\frac{64}{17}} = 1$ **67.** $\dfrac{y^2}{9} - \dfrac{x^2}{\frac{9}{4}} = 1$

69. f **70.** a **71.** g **72.** c
73. d **74.** e **75.** b **76.** h
77. $x^2 + y^2 = 4$; circle **79.** $y^2 = 2x$; parabola
81. $\dfrac{x^2}{4} + \dfrac{y^2}{16} = 1$; ellipse **83.** $x^2 = 14y$
85. (a) $x^2 = 12{,}228y$ (in feet) (b) 22.6 feet
87. (a)

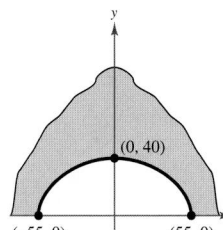

(b) $\dfrac{x^2}{3025} + \dfrac{y^2}{1600} = 1$
(c) 16.66 feet

89. 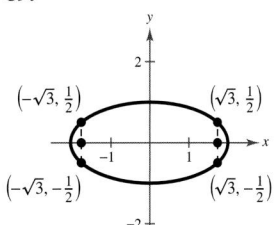 **91.**

93. $x \approx 110.3$ miles
95. False. The equation represents a hyperbola.
97. False. If the graph intersected the directrix, there would exist points nearer the directrix than the focus.
99. (a) $\dfrac{x_1}{2p}$
(b) $x - y - 1 = 0$ $x - y - 2 = 0$
$x + y + 1 = 0$ $x + y + 2 = 0$

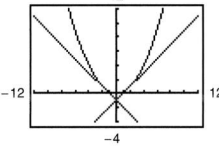
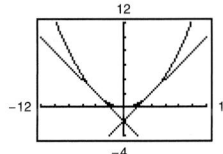

$x - y - 3 = 0$ $x - y - 4 = 0$
$x + y + 3 = 0$ $x + y + 4 = 0$

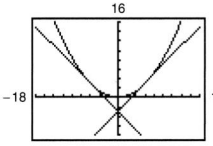
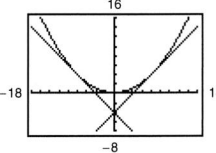

101. Left half **103.** Bottom half
105. No. Only second-degree equations can be ellipses.
107. The shape continuously changes from an ellipse with a vertical major axis of length 8 and a minor axis of length 2 to a circle with a diameter of 8 and then to an ellipse with a horizontal major axis of length 16 and a minor axis of length 8.
109. Answers will vary. **111.** $(3x - 2)(4x + 5)$
113. $z^2(12z + 5)(z + 1)$
115. Answers will vary. **117.** Answers will vary.
Sample answer: Sample answer:
$f(x) = x^3 - 7x^2 + 12x$ $f(x) = x^3 + x^2 - 7x - 3$
119. $\frac{3}{2}, \pm 5i$ **121.** 39,916,800

Section 10.2   (page 791)

1. The graph is a circle whose center is the point $(-2, 1)$ and whose radius is 2.

3. The graph is a hyperbola whose center is the point $(1, -3)$. The transverse axis is vertical and of length 4, and the conjugate axis is horizontal and of length 2.

5. The graph is an ellipse whose center is the point $(1, -2)$. The major axis of the ellipse is vertical and of length 8. The minor axis of the ellipse is horizontal and of length 6.

7. Center: $(0, 0)$
Radius: 7

9. Center: $(-2, 7)$
Radius: 4

11. Center: $(1, 0)$
Radius: $\sqrt{15}$

13. $(x - 1)^2 + (y + 3)^2 = 1$
Center: $(1, -3)$
Radius: 1

15. $\left(x + \frac{3}{2}\right)^2 + (y - 3)^2 = 1$
Center: $\left(-\frac{3}{2}, 3\right)$
Radius: 1

17. Vertex: $(-1, -2)$
Focus: $(-1, -4)$
Directrix: $y = 0$

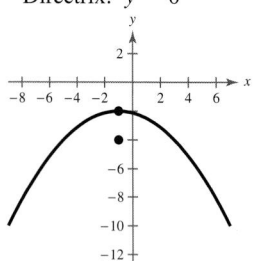

19. Vertex: $\left(5, \frac{1}{2}\right)$
Focus: $\left(\frac{11}{2}, \frac{1}{2}\right)$
Directrix: $x = \frac{9}{2}$

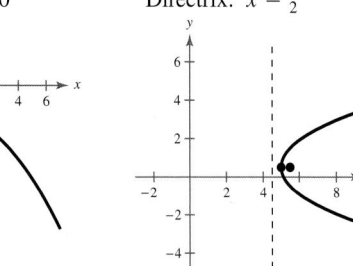

21. Vertex: $(1, 1)$
Focus: $(1, 2)$
Directrix: $y = 0$

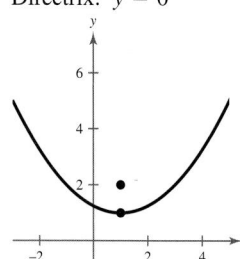

23. Vertex: $(-2, -3)$
Focus: $(-4, -3)$
Directrix: $x = 0$

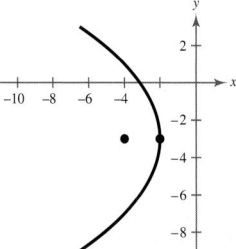

25. $(x - 3)^2 = -(y - 1)$ **27.** $(y - 2)^2 = -8(x - 3)$

29. $x^2 = 8(y - 4)$ **31.** $(y - 2)^2 = 8x$

33. Center: $(1, 3)$
Vertices: $(1, -2), (1, 8)$
Foci: $(1, -1), (1, 7)$

35. Center: $(-2, 4)$
Vertices: $(-1, 4), (-3, 4)$
Foci: $\left(-2 \pm \frac{\sqrt{3}}{2}, 4\right)$

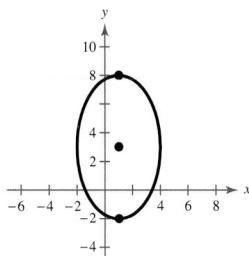

37. Center: $(-2, 3)$
Vertices: $(-2, 6),$
$(-2, 0)$
Foci: $\left(-2, 3 \pm \sqrt{5}\right)$

39. Center: $(1, -1)$
Vertices: $\left(\frac{9}{4}, -1\right),$
$\left(-\frac{1}{4}, -1\right)$
Foci: $\left(\frac{7}{4}, -1\right), \left(\frac{1}{4}, -1\right)$

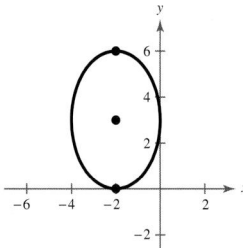

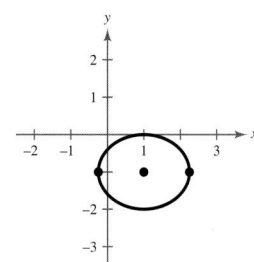

41. $\dfrac{(x - 2)^2}{9} + \dfrac{(y - 2)^2}{4} = 1$

43. $\dfrac{(x - 2)^2}{4} + \dfrac{(y - 2)^2}{1} = 1$

45. $\dfrac{x^2}{48} + \dfrac{(y - 4)^2}{64} = 1$

47. $\dfrac{(x - 3)^2}{9} + \dfrac{(y - 5)^2}{16} = 1$

49. $\dfrac{x^2}{16} + \dfrac{(y - 4)^2}{12} = 1$

51. Center: $(-1, 2)$
Vertices: $(-3, 2), (1, 2)$
Foci: $\left(-1 \pm \sqrt{5}, 2\right)$

53. Center: $(2, -6)$
Vertices: $(2, -5), (2, -7)$
Foci: $\left(2, -6 \pm \sqrt{2}\right)$

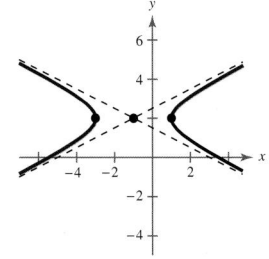

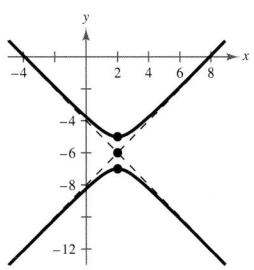

55. Center: $(2, -3)$
   Vertices: $(3, -3), (1, -3)$
   Foci: $\left(2 \pm \sqrt{10}, -3\right)$

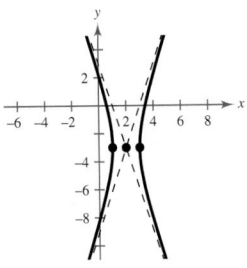

57. The graph of this equation is two lines intersecting at $(-1, -3)$.

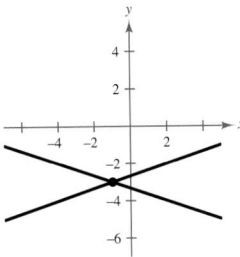

59. Center: $(1, -1)$
   Vertices: $(-2, -1),$
       $(4, -1)$
   Foci: $\left(1 \pm \sqrt{13}, -1\right)$

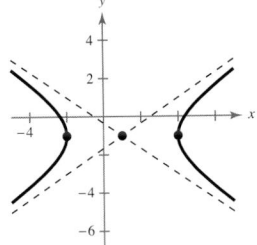

61. $(y - 1)^2 - x^2 = 1$ **63.** $\dfrac{(x - 4)^2}{4} - \dfrac{y^2}{12} = 1$

65. $\dfrac{(y - 5)^2}{16} - \dfrac{(x - 4)^2}{9} = 1$ **67.** $\dfrac{y^2}{9} - \dfrac{4(x - 2)^2}{9} = 1$

69. $(x - 3)^2 + (y + 2)^2 = 4$; circle

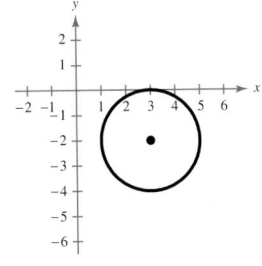

71. $\left(x - \dfrac{1}{2}\right)^2 - \dfrac{y^2}{4} = 1$; hyperbola

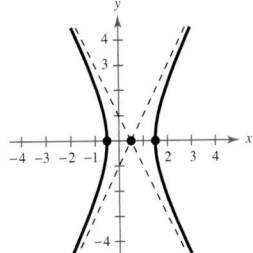

73. $\dfrac{(x + 1)^2}{1/4} + \dfrac{(y - 4)^2}{1/3} = 1$; ellipse

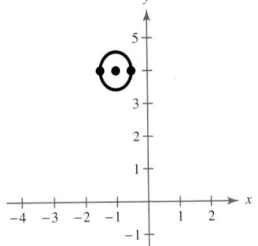

75. $\left(x - \frac{1}{5}\right)^2 = 8\left(y + \frac{3}{5}\right)$; parabola

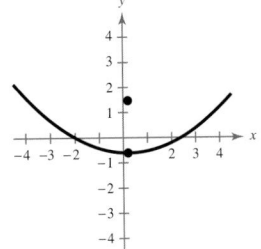

77. (a) $17,500\sqrt{2} \approx 24,749$ miles per hour
   (b) $x^2 = -16,400(y - 4100)$

79. (a)

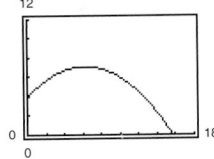

   (b) Highest point: $(6.25, 7.125)$
      Distance: 15.69 feet

81. $\dfrac{x^2}{25} + \dfrac{y^2}{16} = 1$

83. $2,756,170,000$ miles; $4,583,830,000$ miles

85. $\dfrac{x^2}{100^2} + \dfrac{(y - 85)^2}{85^2} = 1$ **87.** True

89. $y = \sqrt{6(x + 1)} + 3$ **91.** $x = \frac{3}{2}(2 + \sqrt{4 - y^2})$

93. (a) Answers will vary.

(b) $e = 0.95$ $e = 0.75$

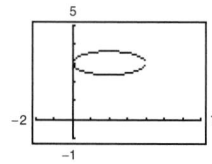   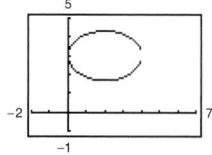

$e = 0.5$ $e = 0.25$

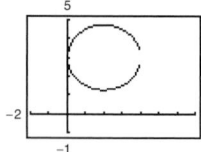   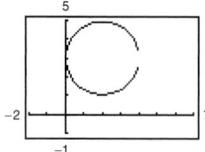

$e = 0$

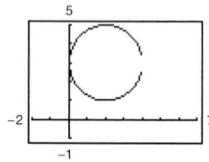

(c) The ellipse becomes more circular.

95. $\displaystyle\sum_{n=1}^{9} \frac{1}{6n} = 0.4715$ **97.** $\displaystyle\sum_{n=0}^{8} \left(-\frac{1}{4}\right)^n = 0.80$

99. $x^4 - 16x^3 + 96x^2 - 256x + 256$

101. $243x^5 + 405x^4 + 270x^3 + 90x^2 + 15x + 1$

Section 10.3   (page 800)

Vocabulary Check   (page 800)

1. plane curve, parametric equations, parameter

2. orientation   **3.** eliminating, parameter

1. c   **2.** d   **3.** b   **4.** a   **5.** f   **6.** e

7. (a)

t	0	1	2	3	4
x	0	1	1.414	1.732	2
y	2	1	0	-1	-2

(b) 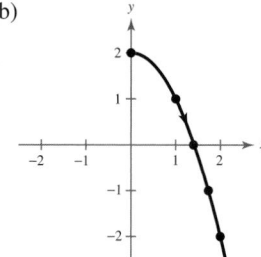   (c)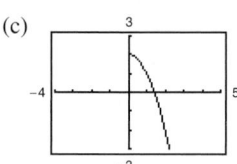

(d) $y = 2 - x^2$

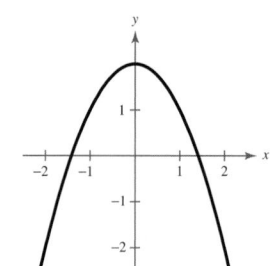

The graph is an entire parabola rather than just the right half.

9. 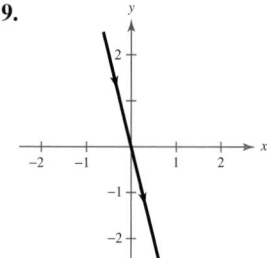   **11.**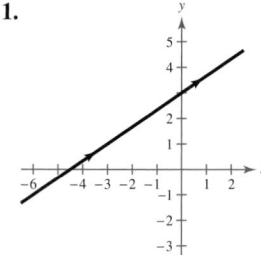

$y = -4x$ $y = \frac{2}{3}x + 3$

13. 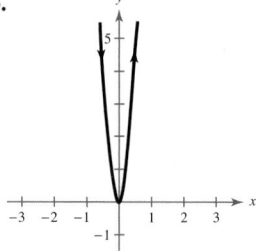   **15.**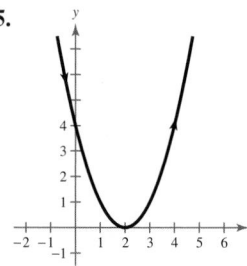

$y = 16x^2$ $y = (x - 2)^2$

17.

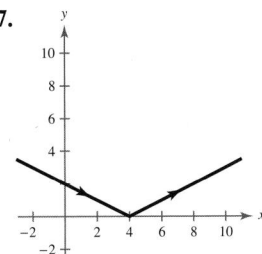

$y = \frac{1}{2}|x - 4|$

19.

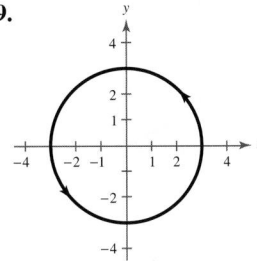

$x^2 + y^2 = 9$

21.

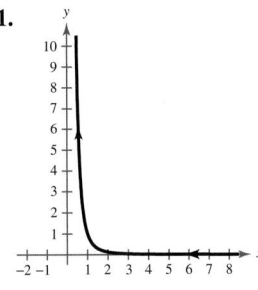

$y = e^{-3 \ln x} = x^{-3}, \; x > 0$

23.

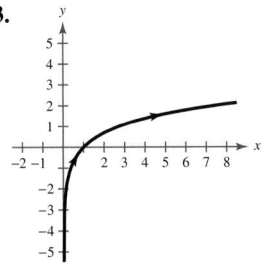

$y = \ln x$

25.

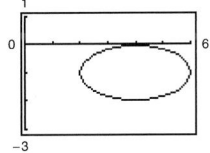

27.

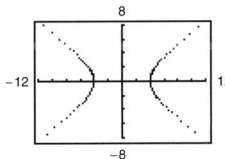

29.

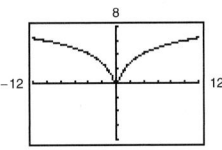

31. Each curve represents a portion of the line $y = 2x + 1$.

	Domain	Orientation
(a)	$(-\infty, \infty)$	Left to right
(b)	$[-1, 1]$	Depends on θ
(c)	$(0, \infty)$	Right to left
(d)	$(0, \infty)$	Left to right

33. $y - y_1 = \dfrac{y_2 - y_1}{x_2 - x_1}(x - x_1)$

35. $\dfrac{(x - h)^2}{a^2} + \dfrac{(y - k)^2}{b^2} = 1$

37. $x = 5t$ \qquad **39.** $x = 2 + 4 \cos \theta$ \qquad **41.** $x = 5 \cos \theta$
$\quad\;\; y = -2t$ \qquad\qquad $y = 1 + 4 \sin \theta$ \qquad\qquad $y = 3 \sin \theta$

43. Answers will vary. Sample answers:
$x = t, \; y = 4t - 3$
$x = \frac{1}{4}t + \frac{3}{4}, \; y = t$

45. Answers will vary. Sample answers:
$x = t, \; y = \dfrac{1}{t}$
$x = t^3, \; y = \dfrac{1}{t^3}$

47. Answers will vary. Sample answers:
$x = t, \; y = t^2 + 4$
$x = t^3, \; y = t^6 + 4$

49. Answers will vary. Sample answers:
$x = t, \; y = t^3 + 2t$
$x = \frac{1}{2}t, \; y = \frac{1}{8}t^3 + t$

51.

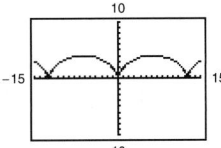

53.

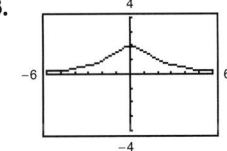

55. b \qquad **56.** c \qquad **57.** d \qquad **58.** a

59. (a) $x = (146.67 \cos \theta)t$
$\qquad y = 3 + (146.67 \sin \theta)t - 16t^2$

(b) $x = 141.7t$
$\quad\;\; y = 3 + 38.0t - 16t^2$

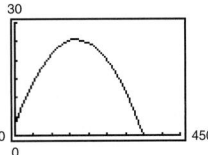

No

(c) $x = 135.0t$
$\quad\;\; y = 3 + 57.3t - 16t^2$

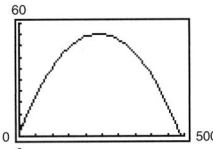

Yes

(d) About $19.4°$

61. True. Both sets of parametric equations correspond to $y = x^2 + 1$.

63. $x = \cos \theta$ or $x = -\cos \theta$

$y = -2 \sin \theta$ $y = 2 \sin \theta$

65. Answers will vary.   **67.** $x = \pm\dfrac{2\sqrt{10}}{5}i$

69. $x = -\dfrac{1}{2} \pm \sqrt{3}$ **71.** 10,200   **73.** 11,590

Section 10.4   (page 807)

Vocabulary Check   (page 807)

1. pole   **2.** directed distance, directed angle

3. polar

1. $(0, 4)$ **3.** $\left(\dfrac{\sqrt{2}}{2}, \dfrac{\sqrt{2}}{2}\right)$

5.

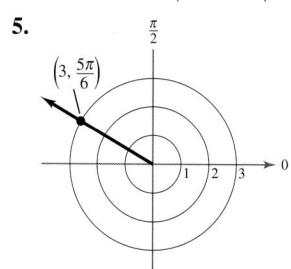

$\left(3, -\dfrac{7\pi}{6}\right), \left(-3, \dfrac{11\pi}{6}\right), \left(-3, -\dfrac{\pi}{6}\right)$

7.

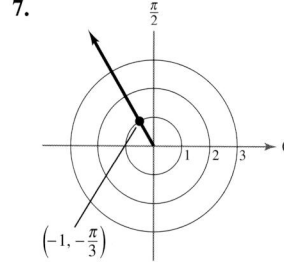

$\left(-1, \dfrac{5\pi}{3}\right), \left(1, \dfrac{2\pi}{3}\right), \left(1, -\dfrac{4\pi}{3}\right)$

9.

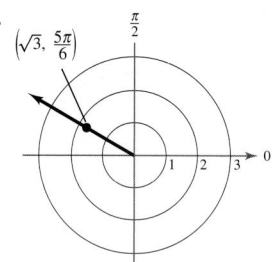

$\left(-\sqrt{3}, \dfrac{11\pi}{6}\right), \left(\sqrt{3}, -\dfrac{7\pi}{6}\right), \left(-\sqrt{3}, -\dfrac{\pi}{6}\right)$

11.

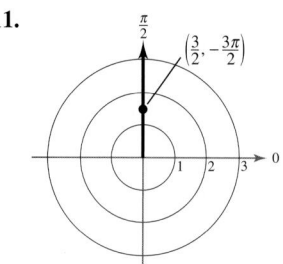

$\left(\dfrac{3}{2}, \dfrac{\pi}{2}\right), \left(-\dfrac{3}{2}, \dfrac{3\pi}{2}\right), \left(-\dfrac{3}{2}, -\dfrac{\pi}{2}\right)$

13.   **15.**

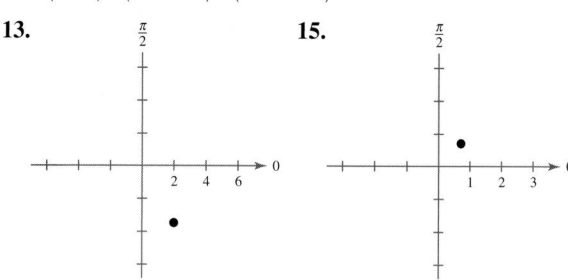

$\left(2, -2\sqrt{3}\right)$ $\left(\dfrac{\sqrt{2}}{2}, \dfrac{\sqrt{2}}{2}\right)$

17.   **19.**

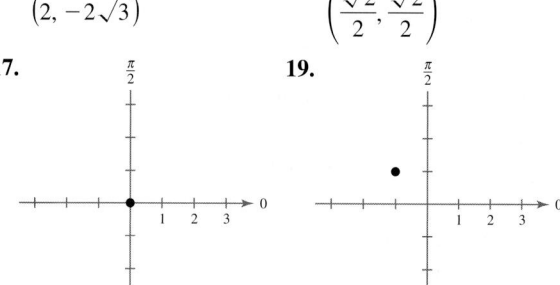

$(0, 0)$ $(-1.004, 0.996)$

21. $\left(-\sqrt{2}, \sqrt{2}\right)$ **23.** $(-1.204, -4.336)$

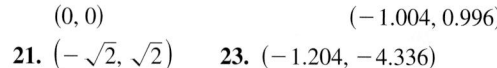

25.
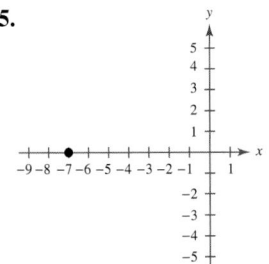

27.
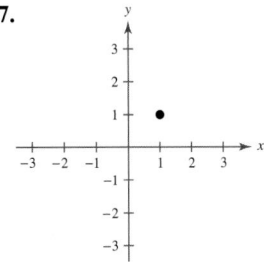

$(7, \pi), (-7, 0)$

$\left(\sqrt{2}, \dfrac{\pi}{4} \right), \left(-\sqrt{2}, \dfrac{5\pi}{4} \right)$

29.
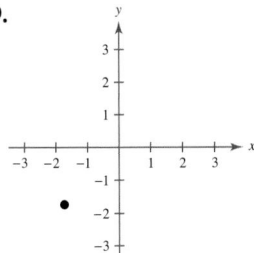

31.
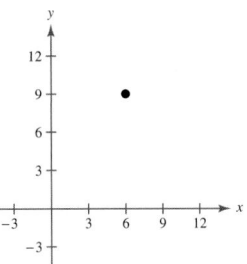

$\left(\sqrt{6}, \dfrac{5\pi}{4} \right), \left(-\sqrt{6}, \dfrac{\pi}{4} \right)$ $(10.8, 0.983), (-10.8, 4.124)$

33. $\left(\sqrt{13}, -0.588 \right)$ **35.** $\left(\sqrt{7}, 0.857 \right)$ **37.** $\left(\frac{17}{6}, 0.490 \right)$

39. $r = 9$ **41.** $r = 4 \csc \theta$ **43.** $r = 8 \sec \theta$

45. $r = -\dfrac{2}{3 \cos \theta - 6 \sin \theta}$

47. $r^2 = 4 \csc \theta \sec \theta = 8 \csc 2\theta$ **49.** $r^2 = 9 \cos 2\theta$

51. $r = 6 \cos \theta$ **53.** $r = 2a \cos \theta$

55. $r = \tan^2 \theta \sec \theta$ **57.** $x^2 + y^2 - 6y = 0$

59. $y = \sqrt{3}x$ **61.** $x^2 + y^2 = 16$ **63.** $y = -3$

65. $(x^2 + y^2)^3 = x^2$ **67.** $(x^2 + y^2)^2 = 6x^2y - 2y^3$

69. $y^2 = 2x + 1$ **71.** $4x^2 - 5y^2 - 36y - 36 = 0$

73. The graph is a circle centered at the origin with a radius of 7; $x^2 + y^2 = 49$.

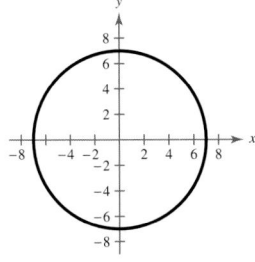

75. The graph consists of all points on the line that make an angle of $\pi/4$ with the positive x-axis; $x - y = 0$.

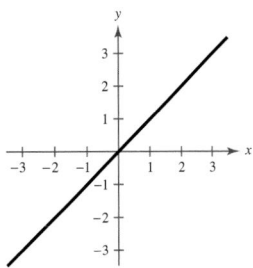

77. The graph is a vertical line through $(3, 0)$; $x - 3 = 0$.

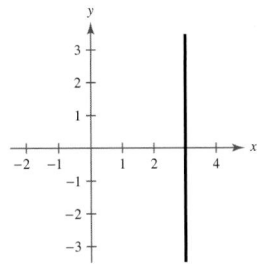

79. True. Because r is a directed distance, (r, θ) can be represented by $(-r, \theta \pm (2n + 1)\pi)$, so $|r| = |-r|$.

81. (a) Answers will vary.

(b) The points lie on a line.
$$d = \sqrt{r_1^2 + r_2^2 - 2r_1 r_2} = |r_1 - r_2|$$

(c) $d = \sqrt{r_1^2 + r_2^2}$ (Pythagorean Theorem)

Answers will vary.

(d) Answers will vary. The distance formulas should give the same results.

83. $A \approx 30.7°$ **85.** $a \approx 16.16$ **87.** $A \approx 119.1°$
$B \approx 48.2°$ $b \approx 19.44$ $B \approx 25.9°$
$C \approx 101.1°$ $B = 86°$ $c \approx 5.25$

89. $(2, 3)$ **91.** $(0, 0, 0)$

Section 10.5   (page 816)

Vocabulary Check   (page 816)

1. $\theta = \dfrac{\pi}{2}$ **2.** polar axis   **3.** convex limaçon

4. circle   **5.** lemniscate   **6.** cardioid

---

1. Rose curve   **3.** Circle   **5.** Rose curve

7. Polar axis   **9.** $\theta = \dfrac{\pi}{2}$ **11.** $\theta = \dfrac{\pi}{2}$ **13.** Pole

15. Maximum: $|r| = 20$ when $\theta = \dfrac{3\pi}{2}$

Zero: $r = 0$ when $\theta = \dfrac{\pi}{2}$

17. Maximum: $|r| = 4$ when $\theta = 0, \dfrac{\pi}{3}, \dfrac{2\pi}{3}, \pi$

Zeros: $r = 0$ when $\theta = \dfrac{\pi}{6}, \dfrac{\pi}{2}, \dfrac{5\pi}{6}$

19.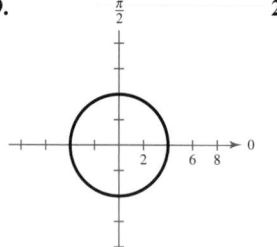

21.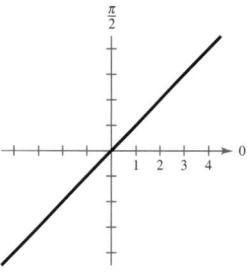

23.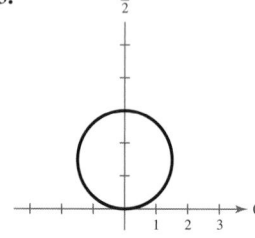

25.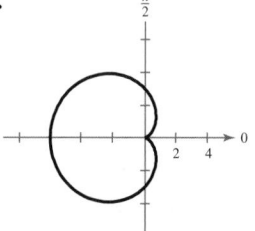

27.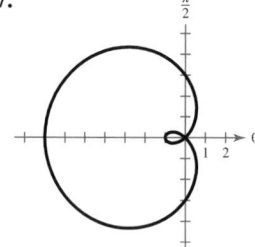

29.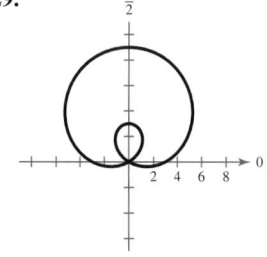

31.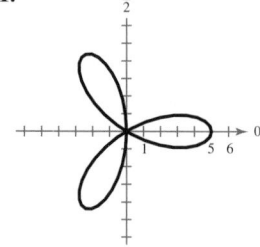

33.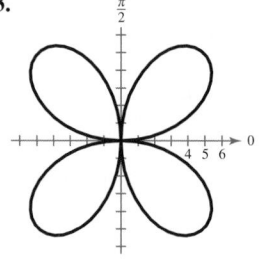

35.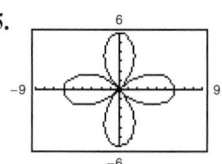

$0 \le \theta < 2\pi$

37.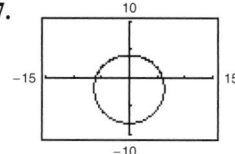

$0 \le \theta < 2\pi$

39.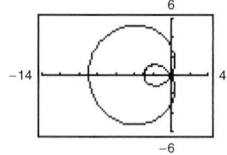

$0 \le \theta < 2\pi$

41.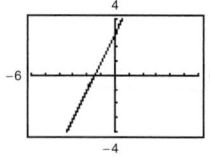

$0 \le \theta < \dfrac{\pi}{2}$

43.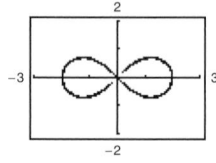

$-2\pi \le \theta < 2\pi$

45.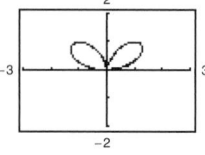

$0 \le \theta < \pi$

47.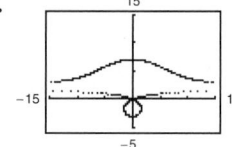

$0 \le \theta < 2\pi$

49.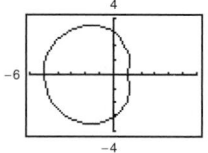

$0 \le \theta < 2\pi$

51.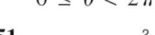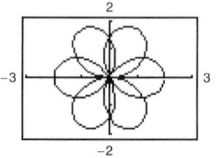

$0 \le \theta < 4\pi$

53.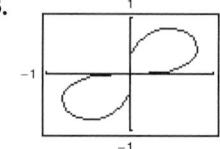

$0 \le \theta < \dfrac{\pi}{2}$

55.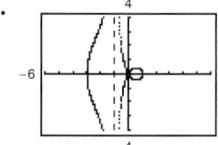

57.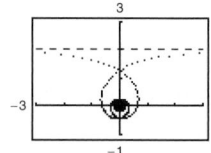

59. True

61. $n = -5$ $n = -4$

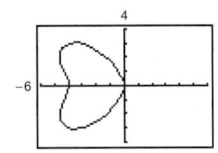 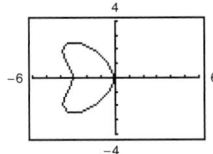

$n = -3$ $n = -2$

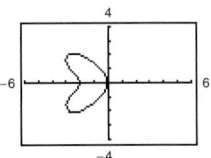 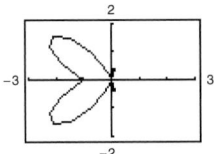

$n = -1$ $n = 0$

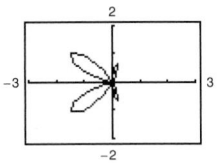 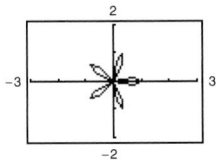

$n = 1$ $n = 2$

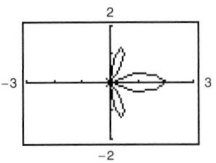 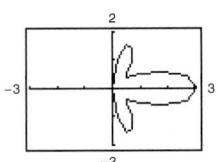

$n = 3$ $n = 4$

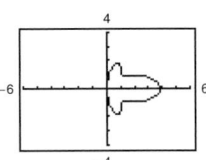 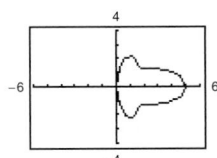

$n = 5$

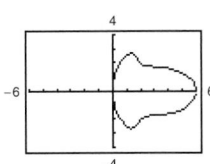

Negative values of n produce the heart portion, positive values of n produce the bell portion.

63. (a), (b), and (c) Answers will vary.

65. (a) $r = 4 \sin\left(\theta - \dfrac{\pi}{6}\right)\cos\left(\theta - \dfrac{\pi}{6}\right)$

(b) $r = -4 \sin\theta \cos\theta$

(c) $r = 4 \sin\left(\theta - \dfrac{2\pi}{3}\right)\cos\left(\theta - \dfrac{2\pi}{3}\right)$

(d) $r = 4 \sin\theta \cos\theta$

67.

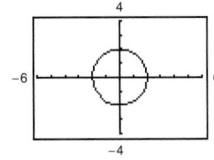 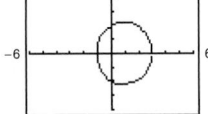

$k = 0$: circle $k = 1$: convex limaçon

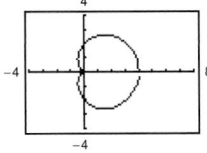 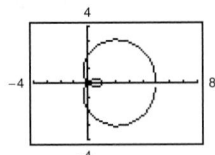

$k = 2$: cardioid $k = 3$: limaçon with inner loop

69.   **71.**

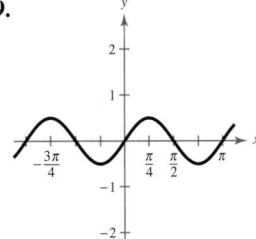 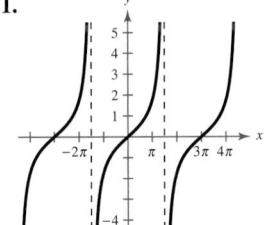

73.

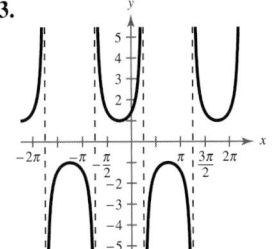

Section 10.6   (page 822)

Vocabulary Check   (page 822)

1. conic   **2.** eccentricity, e

3. (a) i   (b) iii   (c) ii

1. (a) parabola

(b) ellipse

(c) hyperbola

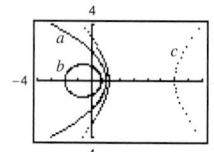

3. (a) parabola

(b) ellipse

(c) hyperbola

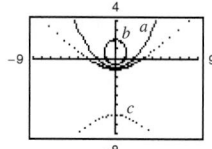

5. b   **6.** c   **7.** d   **8.** a

9. Parabola   **11.** Ellipse   **13.** Ellipse

15. Ellipse   **17.** Hyperbola

19.

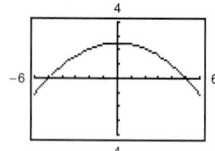

Parabola

21.

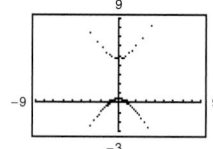

Hyperbola

23.

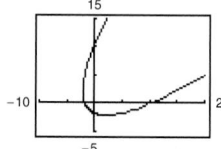

25.

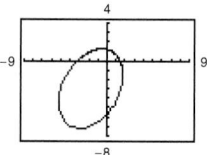

27. $r = \dfrac{1}{1 - \cos \theta}$ **29.** $r = \dfrac{1}{2 + \sin \theta}$

31. $r = \dfrac{2}{1 + 2 \cos \theta}$ **33.** $r = \dfrac{2}{1 - \sin \theta}$

35. $r = \dfrac{10}{3 + 2 \cos \theta}$ **37.** $r = \dfrac{9}{4 - 5 \sin \theta}$

39. Answers will vary.

41. $r = \dfrac{9.2930 \times 10^7}{1 - 0.0167 \cos \theta}$

Perihelion: 9.1404×10^7 miles

Aphelion: 9.4508×10^7 miles

43. $r = \dfrac{7.7659 \times 10^8}{1 - 0.0484 \cos \theta}$

Perihelion: 7.4073×10^8 kilometers

Aphelion: 8.1609×10^8 kilometers

45. (a) $r_{\text{Neptune}} = \dfrac{4.4977 \times 10^9}{1 - 0.0086 \cos \theta}$

$r_{\text{Pluto}} = \dfrac{5.5404 \times 10^9}{1 - 0.2488 \cos \theta}$

(b) Neptune: Perihelion = 4.4593×10^9 kilometers

Aphelion = 4.5367×10^9 kilometers

Pluto: Perihelion = 4.4366×10^9 kilometers

Aphelion = 7.3754×10^9 kilometers

(c)

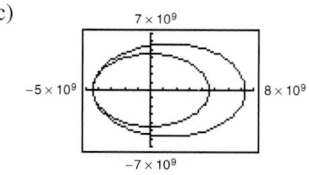

(d) No. Answers will vary.

(e) Answers will vary.

47. False. The equation can be rewritten as

$$r = \frac{-4/3}{1 + \sin \theta}.$$

Because ep is negative, you know that e is positive and p is negative and that p represents the distance between the pole and the directrix, so the directrix has to be below the pole.

49. Answers will vary.   **51.** $r^2 = \dfrac{24{,}336}{169 - 25 \cos^2 \theta}$

53. (a) Ellipse

(b) $r = \dfrac{4}{1 + 0.4 \cos \theta}$ is reflected about the line $\theta = \dfrac{\pi}{2}$.

$r = \dfrac{4}{1 - 0.4 \sin \theta}$ is rotated 90° counterclockwise.

55. Answers will vary.   **57.** $\dfrac{\pi}{6} + n\pi$

59. $\dfrac{\pi}{3} + n\pi, \dfrac{2\pi}{3} + n\pi$

61. $\dfrac{\sqrt{2}}{10}$ **63.** $\dfrac{\sqrt{2}}{10}$ **65.** 220   **67.** 720

Review Exercises   (page 826)

1. d   **2.** a   **3.** c   **4.** b   **5.** f   **6.** e

7. $x^2 = \frac{1}{2}y$ **9.** $y^2 = -24x$

11. Vertex: $(0, 0)$

Focus: $(1, 0)$

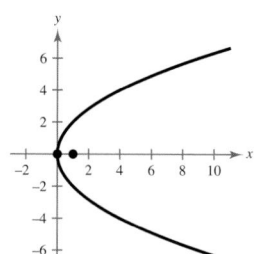

13. Vertex: $(0, 0)$

Focus: $(-9, 0)$

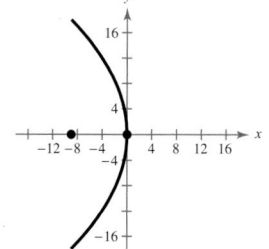

15. $(0, 50)$ **17.** $\dfrac{x^2}{25} + \dfrac{y^2}{9} = 1$ **19.** $\dfrac{2x^2}{9} + \dfrac{y^2}{36} = 1$

21. Center: $(0, 0)$

Vertices: $(0, \pm 4)$

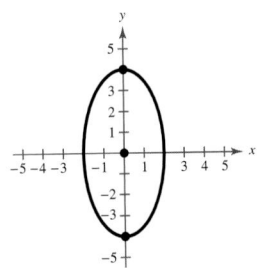

23. Center: $(0, 0)$

Vertices: $(0, \pm 3)$

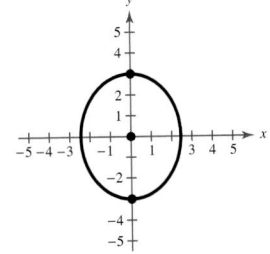

25. $(\pm 3, 0)$ **27.** $x^2 - \dfrac{y^2}{4} = 1$ **29.** $y^2 - \dfrac{x^2}{8} = 1$

31. Center: $(0, 0)$

Vertices: $(0, \pm 3)$

Foci: $\left(0, \pm \sqrt{73}\right)$

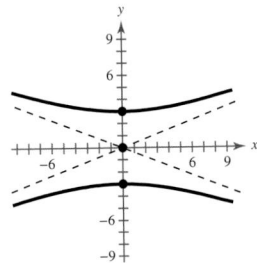

33. Center: $(0, 0)$

Vertices: $(0, \pm 2)$

Foci: $(0, \pm 3)$

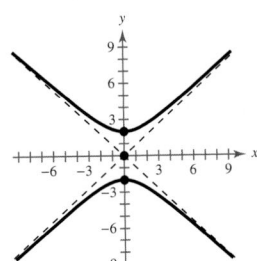

35. $(x - 3)^2 = -2y$; parabola

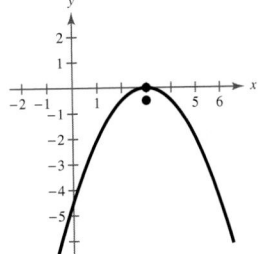

The parabola is shifted three units to the right.

37. $\dfrac{(x + 5)^2}{9} + \dfrac{(y - 1)^2}{1} = 1$; ellipse

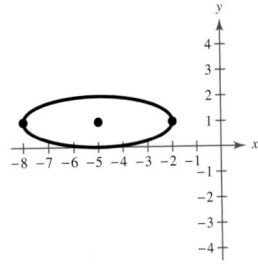

The ellipse is shifted five units to the left and one unit upward.

39. $\dfrac{\left(x - \frac{1}{2}\right)^2}{2} - \dfrac{(y - 1)^2}{2} = 1$; hyperbola

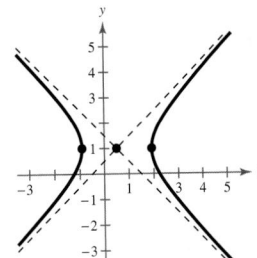

The hyperbola is shifted $\frac{1}{2}$ unit to the right and one unit upward.

41. $\dfrac{(x - 2)^2}{\frac{1}{4}} + y^2 = 1$; ellipse

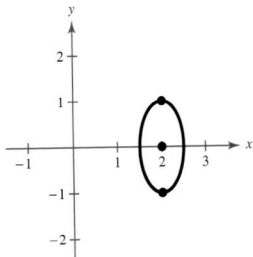

The ellipse is shifted two units to the right.

43. $(x - 4)^2 = -8(y - 2)$

45. $(y - 2)^2 = 12x$

47. $\dfrac{(x - 2)^2}{25} + \dfrac{y^2}{21} = 1$ **49.** $\dfrac{(x - 2)^2}{4} + (y - 1)^2 = 1$

51. $\dfrac{(x + 2)^2}{64} - \dfrac{(y - 3)^2}{36} = 1$ **53.** $\dfrac{5(x - 4)^2}{16} - \dfrac{5y^2}{64} = 1$

55. (a) $y = 4 - \frac{1}{4}x^2$

$x^2 + \left(y + 4\sqrt{3}\right)^2 = 64$

(b)

x	0	1	2	3	4
d	2.928	2.741	2.182	1.262	0

57.

t	-2	-1	0	1	2	3
x	-8	-5	-2	1	4	7
y	15	11	7	3	-1	-5

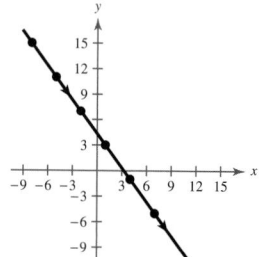

59.

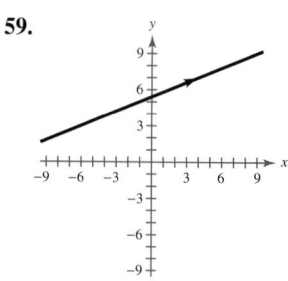

$y = \frac{27}{5} + \frac{2}{5}x$

61.

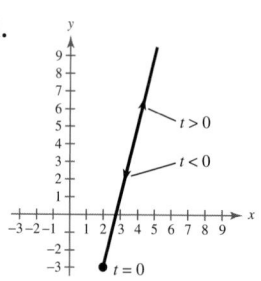

$y = 4x - 11, \quad x \geq 2$

63.

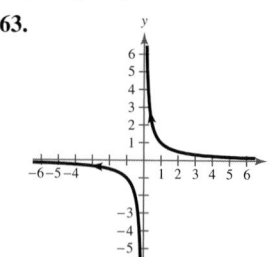

$y = \dfrac{1}{x}$

65.

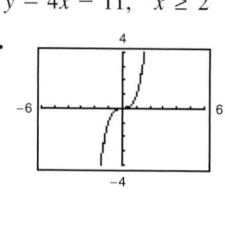

67.

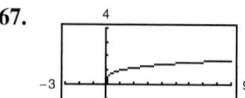

69.

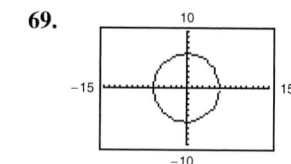

71. Answers will vary. Sample answers:

$x = t, \ y = 6t + 2; \ x = 3t, \ y = 18t + 2$

73. Answers will vary. Sample answers:

$x = t, \ y = t^2 + 2; \ x = -t, \ y = t^2 + 2$

75.

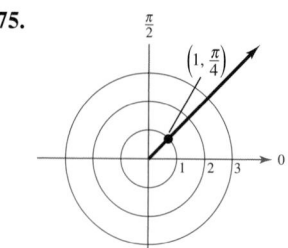

$\left(1, -\dfrac{7\pi}{4}\right), \left(-1, \dfrac{5\pi}{4}\right), \left(-1, -\dfrac{3\pi}{4}\right)$

77.

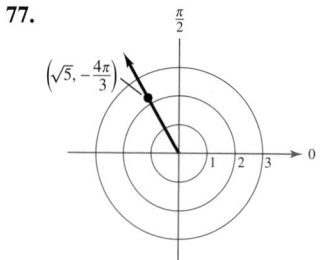

$\left(\sqrt{5}, \dfrac{2\pi}{3}\right), \left(-\sqrt{5}, -\dfrac{\pi}{3}\right), \left(-\sqrt{5}, \dfrac{5\pi}{3}\right)$

79. **81.**

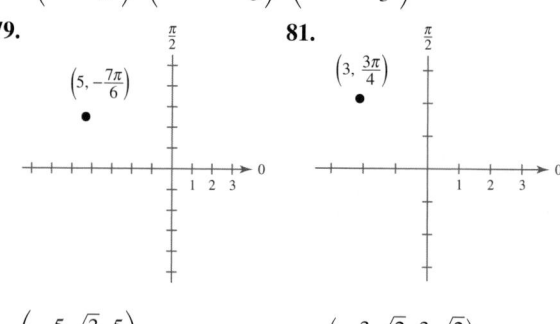

$\left(-\dfrac{5\sqrt{3}}{2}, \dfrac{5}{2}\right)$ $\left(-\dfrac{3\sqrt{2}}{2}, \dfrac{3\sqrt{2}}{2}\right)$

83.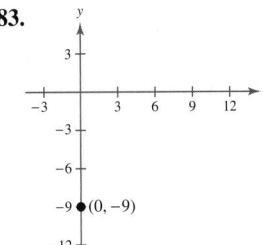

85.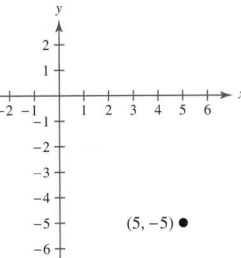

$\left(-9, \dfrac{\pi}{2}\right), \left(9, \dfrac{3\pi}{2}\right)$

$\left(-5\sqrt{2}, \dfrac{3\pi}{4}\right), \left(5\sqrt{2}, \dfrac{7\pi}{4}\right)$

87. $r = 3$ **89.** $r = 4\cos\theta$ **91.** $r^2 = 5\sec\theta\csc\theta$

93. $x^2 + y^2 = 25$ **95.** $x^2 + y^2 = 3x$

97. $(x^2 + y^2)^2 - x^2 + y^2 = 0$

99.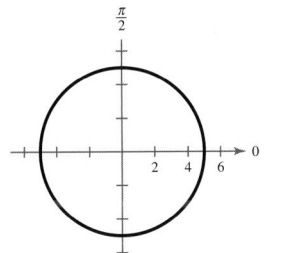

101.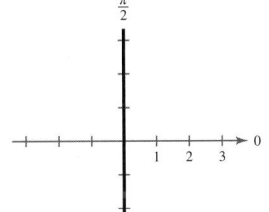

103.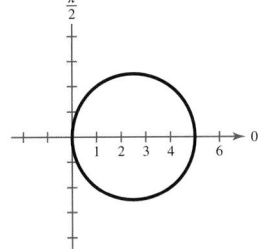

105. Dimpled limaçon

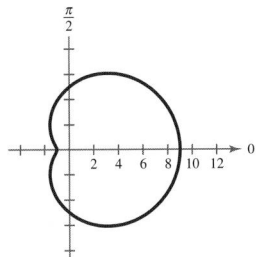

Symmetry: Polar axis

Maximum: $|r| = 9$ when $\theta = 0, 2\pi$

Zeros of r: None

107. Limaçon with a loop

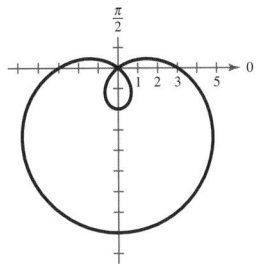

Symmetry: The line $\theta = \dfrac{\pi}{2}$

Maximum: $|r| = 8$ when $\theta = \dfrac{3\pi}{2}$

Zeros: $r = 0$ when $\theta = 0.644, 2.498$

109. Rose curve

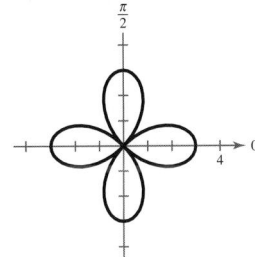

Symmetry: Pole, polar axis, and the line $\theta = \dfrac{\pi}{2}$

Maximum: $|r| = 3$ when $\theta = 0, \dfrac{\pi}{2}, \pi, \dfrac{3\pi}{2}, 2\pi$

Zeros of r: $r = 0$ when $\theta = \dfrac{\pi}{4}, \dfrac{3\pi}{4}, \dfrac{5\pi}{4}, \dfrac{7\pi}{4}$

111. Lemniscate

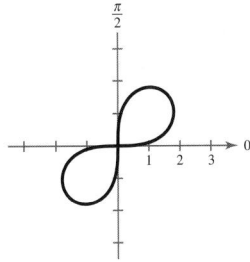

Symmetry: With respect to the pole

Maximum: $|r| = \sqrt{5}$ when $\theta = \dfrac{\pi}{4}, \dfrac{5\pi}{4}$

Zeros: $r = 0$ when $\theta = 0, \dfrac{\pi}{2}, \pi, \dfrac{3\pi}{2}$

113. Parabola

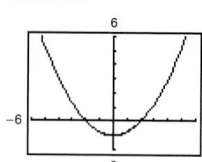

115. Ellipse

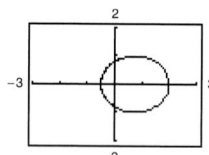

117. Ellipse

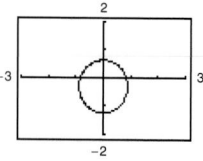

119. $r = \dfrac{4}{1 - \cos \theta}$

121. $r = \dfrac{5}{3 - 2\cos \theta}$

123. $r = \dfrac{1.512}{1 - 0.093\cos \theta}$

Perihelion: 1.3833 astronomical units

Aphelion: 1.6670 astronomical units

125. False. The equation of a hyperbola is a second-degree equation.

127. (a) Vertical translation

(b) Horizontal translation

(c) Reflection in the y-axis

(d) Parabola opens more slowly.

129. 5; The ellipse becomes more circular and approaches a circle of radius 5.

131. (a) The speed would double.

(b) The elliptical orbit would be flatter. The length of the major axis is greater.

Chapter Test   (page 830)

1.

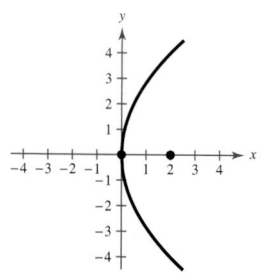

Vertex: $(0, 0)$

Focus: $(2, 0)$

2.

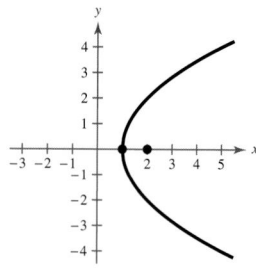

Vertex: $(1, 0)$

Focus: $(2, 0)$

3.

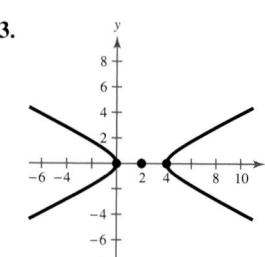

Vertices: $(0, 0), (4, 0)$

Foci: $\left(2 - \sqrt{5}, 0\right),$

$\left(2 + \sqrt{5}, 0\right)$

4. $(y + 2)^2 = 8(x - 6)$

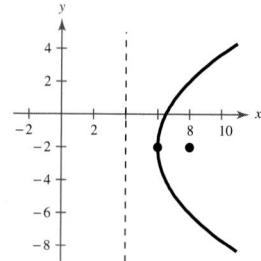

5. $\dfrac{(x + 6)^2}{16} + \dfrac{(y - 3)^2}{49} = 1$

6. $\dfrac{y^2}{9} - \dfrac{x^2}{4} = 1$

7.

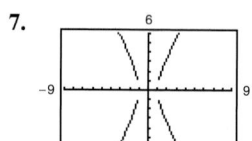

$-9 \le x \le 9$

$-6 \le y \le 6$

8.

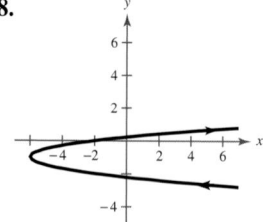

$(y + 1)^2 = \dfrac{1}{4}(x + 6)$

9.

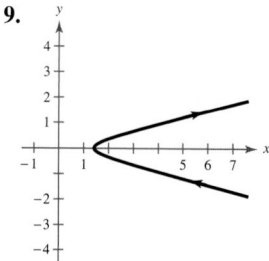

Right branch of the hyperbola

$\dfrac{x^2}{2} - \dfrac{y^2}{0.125} = 1$

10.

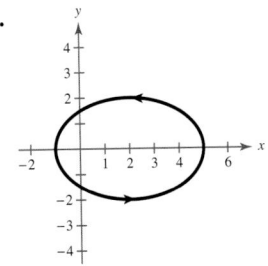

$$\frac{(x-2)^2}{9} + \frac{y^2}{4} = 1$$

11. Answers will vary. Sample answers:

$x = t, y = 7t + 6; x = 2t, y = 14t + 6$

12. Answers will vary. Sample answers:

$x = t, y = t^2 + 10; x = 2t, y = 4t^2 + 10$

13. Answers will vary. Sample answers:

$x = t, y = \frac{1}{4}t - 5; x = 2t, y = \frac{1}{2}t - 5$

14. $(x, y) = \left(-7, 7\sqrt{3}\right)$

15. $\left(2\sqrt{2}, \frac{7\pi}{4}\right), \left(2\sqrt{2}, -\frac{\pi}{4}\right), \left(-2\sqrt{2}, \frac{3\pi}{4}\right)$

16. $r = 12 \sin \theta$

17. Limaçon

18. Rose curve

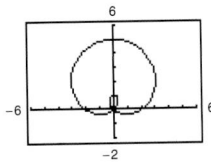

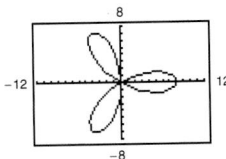

19. Ellipse

20. Hyperbola

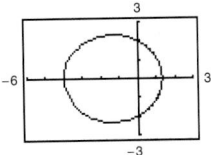

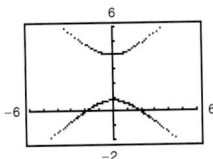

21. $r = \dfrac{4}{4 + \sin \theta}$ **22.** $r = \dfrac{10}{4 + 5 \sin \theta}$

Cumulative Test for Chapters 8–10 (page 831)

1. $(4, -3)$ **2.** $(8, 4), (2, -2)$ **3.** $(0.6, -4, -0.2)$

4. $(1, -4, -4)$

5. $\begin{bmatrix} -7 & -10 & -16 \\ -6 & 18 & 9 \\ -12 & 16 & 7 \end{bmatrix}$ **6.** $\begin{bmatrix} -18 & 15 & -14 \\ 28 & 11 & 34 \\ -20 & 52 & -1 \end{bmatrix}$

7. $\begin{bmatrix} 3 & -31 & 2 \\ 22 & 18 & 6 \\ 52 & -40 & 14 \end{bmatrix}$ **8.** $\begin{bmatrix} 5 & 36 & 31 \\ -36 & 12 & -36 \\ 16 & 0 & 18 \end{bmatrix}$

9. (a) $\begin{bmatrix} -175 & 37 & -13 \\ 95 & -20 & 7 \\ 14 & -3 & 1 \end{bmatrix}$

(b) 1

10. 22 square units

11. (a) $\frac{1}{5}, -\frac{1}{7}, \frac{1}{9}, -\frac{1}{11}, \frac{1}{13}$ (b) 3, 6, 12, 24, 48

12. 135   **13.** $\frac{47}{52} \approx 0.9038$ **14.** ≈ 34.4795 **15.** 80

16. Answers will vary.

17. $x^4 + 12x^3 + 54x^2 + 108x + 81$

18. $32x^5 + 80x^4y^2 + 80x^3y^4 + 40x^2y^6 + 10xy^8 + y^{10}$

19. $x^6 - 12x^5y + 60x^4y^2 - 160x^3y^3 + 240x^2y^4$
$- 192xy^5 + 64y^6$

20. $6561a^8 - 69,984a^7b + 326,592a^6b^2 - 870,912a^5b^3$
$+ 1,451,520a^4b^4 - 1,548,288a^3b^5 + 1,032,192a^2b^6$
$- 393,216ab^7 + 65,536b^8$

21. 453,600   **22.** 151,200

23. Hyperbola

24. Ellipse

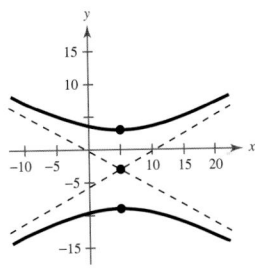

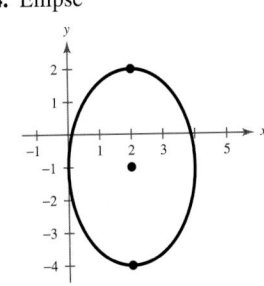

25. Hyperbola

26. Circle

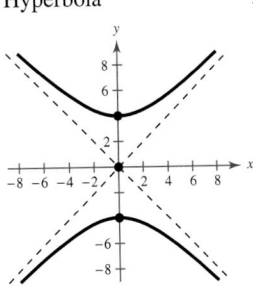

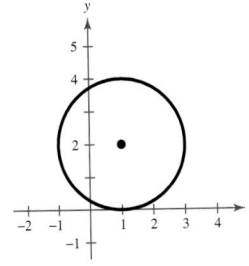

27. $(x - 2)^2 = -\frac{4}{3}(y - 3)$ **28.** $\dfrac{(x - 1)^2}{25} + \dfrac{(y - 4)^2}{4} = 1$

29. $\dfrac{(y + 4)^2}{4} - \dfrac{x^2}{16/3} = 1$

30. (a)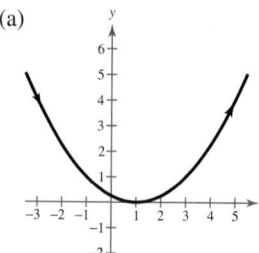

(b)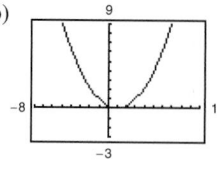

(c) $y = \dfrac{x^2 - 2x + 1}{4}$

31. (a)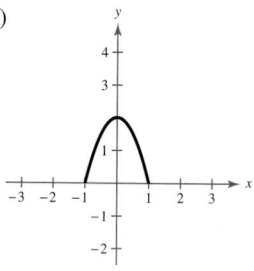

(b)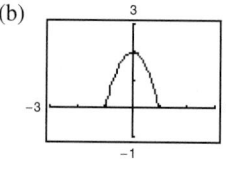

(c) $y = 2 - 2x^2,\ -1 \le x \le 1$

32. (a)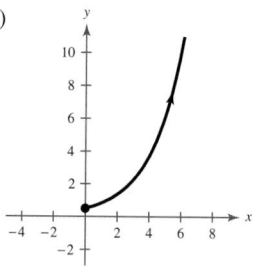

(b)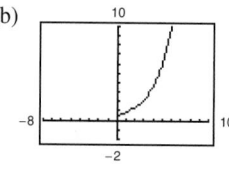

(c) $y = 0.5e^{0.5x},\ x \ge 0$

33.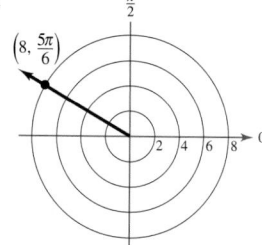

$\left(8, -\dfrac{7\pi}{6}\right), \left(-8, -\dfrac{\pi}{6}\right), \left(-8, \dfrac{11\pi}{6}\right)$

34.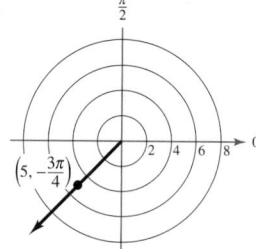

$\left(5, \dfrac{5\pi}{4}\right), \left(-5, -\dfrac{7\pi}{4}\right), \left(-5, \dfrac{\pi}{4}\right)$

35.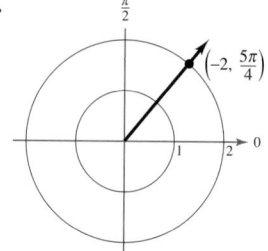

$\left(-2, -\dfrac{3\pi}{4}\right), \left(2, -\dfrac{7\pi}{4}\right), \left(2, \dfrac{\pi}{4}\right)$

36.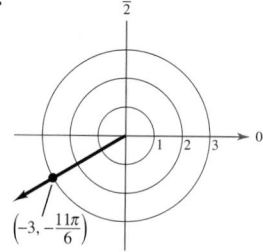

$\left(-3, \dfrac{\pi}{6}\right), \left(3, -\dfrac{5\pi}{6}\right), \left(3, \dfrac{7\pi}{6}\right)$

37. $r = \dfrac{5}{8\cos\theta + 3\sin\theta}$

38. $16y^2 - 9x^2 - 20x = 4$

39. Circle

40. Dimpled limaçon

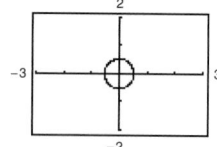

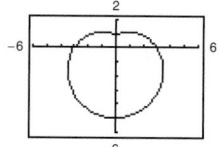

41. Limaçon

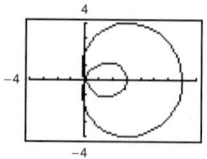

42. $604,199.78 ≈ $604,000   **43.** $\frac{1}{4}$

44. $24\sqrt{2}$ meters ≈ 33.9 meters

Appendices
Appendix C.1   (page A44)

> ### Vocabulary Check   (page A44)
>
> **1.** measure, central tendency   **2.** modes, bimodal
>
> **3.** variance, standard deviation   **4.** Quartiles

1. Mean: 8.86; median: 8; mode: 7

3. Mean: 10.29; median: 8; mode: 7

5. Mean: 9; median: 8; mode: 7

7. (a) The mean is sensitive to extreme values.

   (b) Mean: 14.86; median: 14; mode: 13

   Each is increased by 6.

   (c) Each will increase by k.

9. Mean: 320; median: 320; mode: 320

11. One possibility: {4, 4, 10}

13. The median gives the most representative description.

15. (a) $\bar{x} = 12$; $\sigma = 2.83$ (b) $\bar{x} = 20$; $\sigma = 2.83$

   (c) $\bar{x} = 12$; $\sigma = 1.41$ (d) $\bar{x} = 9$; $\sigma = 1.41$

17. $\bar{x} = 6$, $v = 10$, $\sigma = 3.16$

19. $\bar{x} = 2$, $v = \frac{4}{3}$, $\sigma = 1.15$ **21.** $\bar{x} = 4$, $v = 4$, $\sigma = 2$

23. $\bar{x} = 47$, $v = 226$, $\sigma = 15.03$ **25.** 3.42   **27.** 1.65

29. $\bar{x} = 12$ and $|x_i - 12| = 8$ for all x_i.

31. The mean will increase by 5, but the standard deviation will not change.

33. First histogram

35. (a) Upper quartile: 21.5

   Lower quartile: 13

   (b)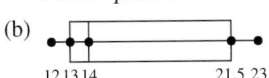
   12 13 14   21.5 23

37. (a) Upper quartile: 51

   Lower quartile: 47

   (b)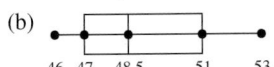
   46 47   48.5   51   53

39.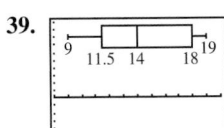
9   19
11.5 14   18

41.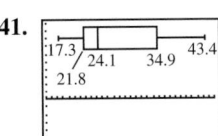
17.3   43.4
  24.1   34.9
21.8

43.

Original design   New design

13.05   24.15

10   28.9   62.6   85.2   18.9   41.35   63.95   99.5

From the plots, you can see that the lifetimes of the sample units made by the new design are greater than the lifetimes of the sample units made by the original design. (The median lifetime increased by more than 12 months.)

Appendix C.2   (page A48)

1. $y = 1.6x + 7.5$ **3.** $y = 0.262x + 1.93$

Appendix D   (page A51)

> ### Vocabulary Check   (page A51)
>
> **1.** linear   **2.** equivalent equations

1. 4   **3.** 7   **5.** 4   **7.** 20   **9.** 4   **11.** 3

13. 5   **15.** -10 **17.** No solution   **19.** $-\frac{6}{5}$

21. 9   **23.** $x < 2$ **25.** $x < 9$ **27.** $x \leq -14$

29. $x > 10$ **31.** $x < 4$ **33.** $x < 3$ **35.** $x \geq 2$

37. $x \leq -5$ **39.** $x < 6$ **41.** $x \geq 4$ **43.** $x \geq -4$

Appendix E.1   (page A59)

> ### Vocabulary Check   (page A59)
>
> **1.** solution   **2.** graph   **3.** linear
>
> **4.** point, equilibrium

1. g   **2.** d   **3.** a   **4.** h   **5.** e   **6.** b

7. f   **8.** c

9. 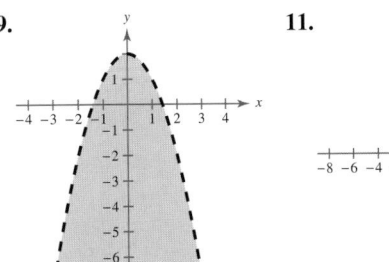   **11.**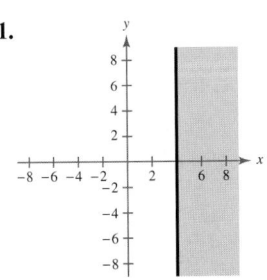

13.
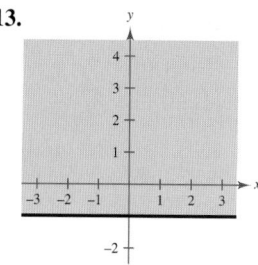

15.
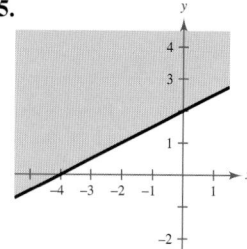

43.
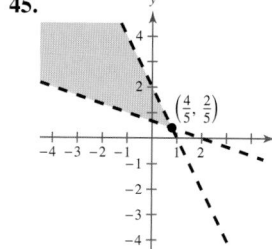

45.
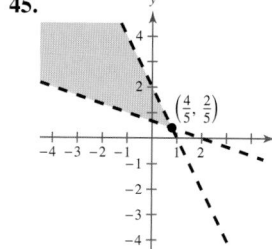

17.
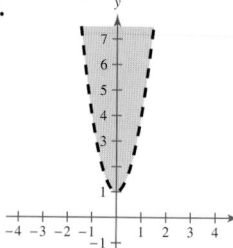

19.
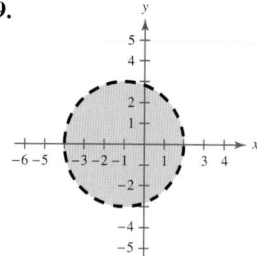

47.
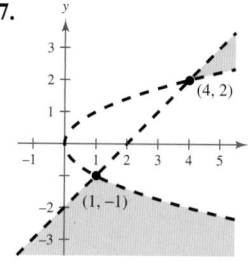

49.
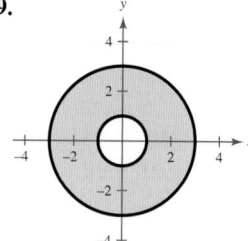

21.
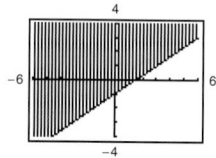

23.
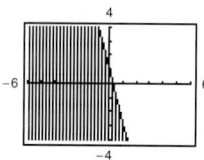

51.
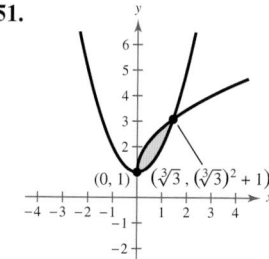

53.
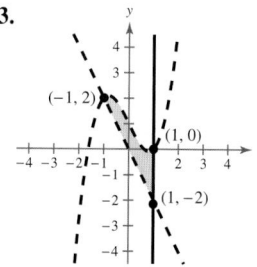

25.
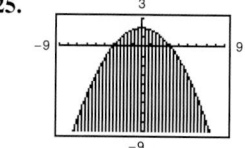

27.
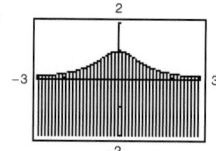

29.
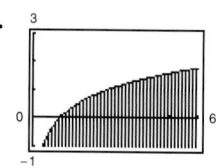

31.
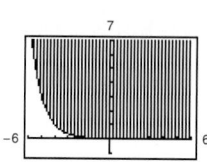

55.
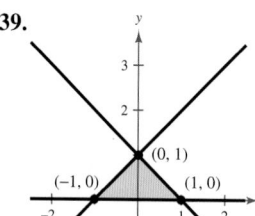

57. $\begin{cases} \frac{1}{4}x + \frac{1}{4}y < 1 \\ \quad\quad x \geq 0 \\ \quad\quad y \geq 0 \end{cases}$

33. $\dfrac{x}{3} + \dfrac{y}{2} > 1$ **35.** $x^2 + y^2 \leq 9$

37. (a) Yes   (b) No   (c) No   (d) No

39.
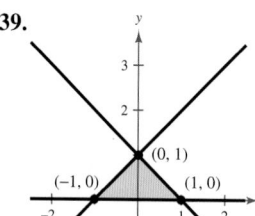

41.
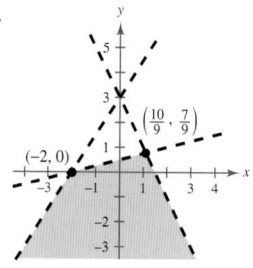

59. $\begin{cases} y \leq 4 - x \\ y \leq 2 - \frac{1}{4}x \\ x \geq 0 \\ y \geq 0 \end{cases}$ **61.** $\begin{cases} 2 \leq x \leq 5 \\ 1 \leq y \leq 7 \end{cases}$ **63.** $\begin{cases} y \leq \frac{3}{2}x \\ y \leq -x + 5 \\ y \geq 0 \end{cases}$

65.
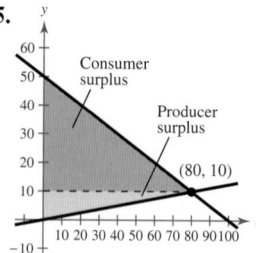

Consumer surplus: 1600

Producer surplus: 400

67.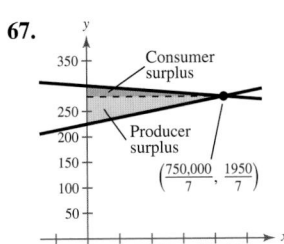

Consumer surplus: $\approx 1,147,959.18$

Producer surplus: $\approx 2,869,897.96$

69. (a) $\begin{cases} x + y \le 30,000 \\ \quad x \ge \quad 7500 \\ \quad y \ge \quad 7500 \\ \quad x \ge \quad 2y \end{cases}$ (b)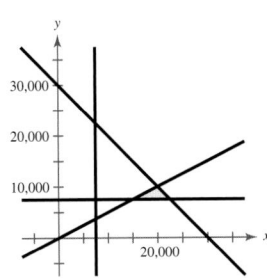

71. (a) $\begin{cases} 20x + 10y \ge 280 \\ 15x + 10y \ge 160 \\ 10x + 20y \ge 180 \\ \quad x \ge \quad 0 \\ \quad y \ge \quad 0 \end{cases}$ (b)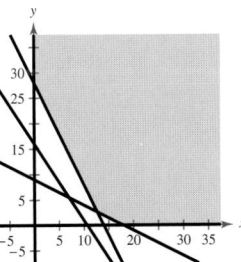

73. (a) $\begin{cases} \quad xy \ge 500 \\ 2x + \pi y \ge 125 \\ \quad x \ge \quad 0 \\ \quad y \ge \quad 0 \end{cases}$ (b)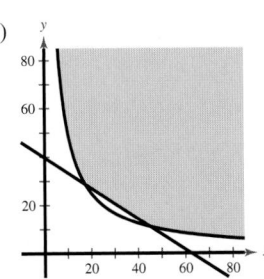

75. True   **77.** Test a point on either side.

Appendix E.2   (page A68)

Vocabulary Check   (page A68)

1. optimization   **2.** objective function

3. constraints, feasible solutions

1. Minimum at $(0, 0)$: 0

Maximum at $(0, 6)$: 30

3. Minimum at $(0, 0)$: 0

Maximum at $(6, 0)$: 60

5. Minimum at $(0, 0)$: 0

Maximum at $(3, 4)$: 17

7. Minimum at $(0, 0)$: 0

Maximum at $(4, 0)$: 20

9. Minimum at $(0, 0)$: 0

Maximum at $(60, 20)$: 740

11. Minimum at $(0, 0)$: 0

Maximum at any point on the line segment connecting $(60, 20)$ and $(30, 45)$: 2100

13.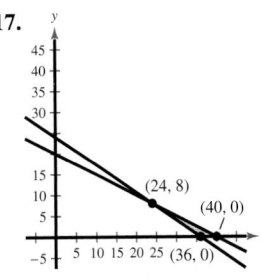

15.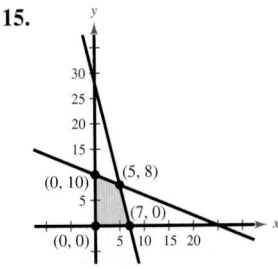

Minimum at $(0, 0)$: 0

Maximum at $(5, 0)$: 30

Minimum at $(0, 0)$: 0

Maximum at $(5, 8)$: 47

17.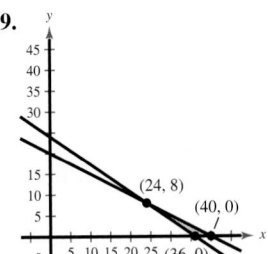

Minimum at $(24, 8)$: 104

Maximum at $(40, 0)$: 160

19.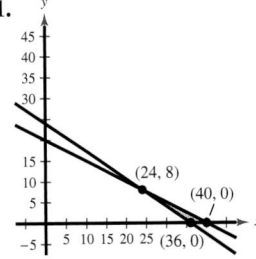

Minimum at $(36, 0)$: 36

Maximum at $(24, 8)$: 56

21.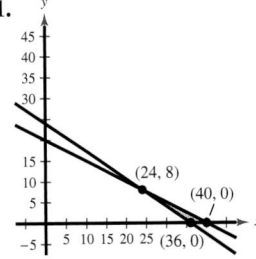

Minimum at any point on the line segment connecting $(24, 8)$ and $(36, 0)$: 72

Maximum at $(40, 0)$: 80

23. (a) and (b)   (c) $(3, 6)$

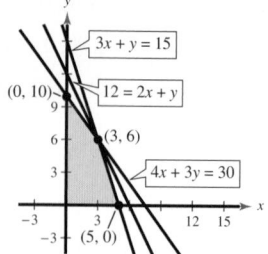

25. (a) and (b)   (c) $(0, 10)$

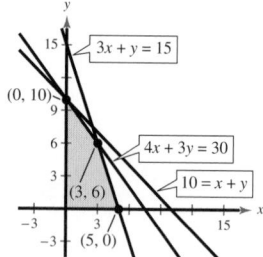

27.

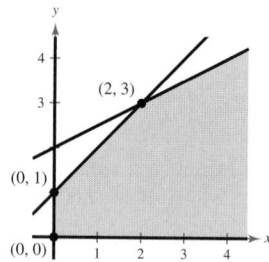

The constraints do not form a closed set of points. Therefore, $z = x + y$ is unbounded.

29.

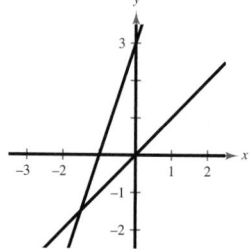

The feasible set is empty.

31. Four audits, 32 tax returns

Maximum revenue: $17,600

33. Three bags of Brand X, six bags of Brand Y

Minimum cost: $195

35. True   **37.** $z = x + 5y$ (Answer is not unique.)

39. $z = 4x + y$ (Answer is not unique.)

41. (a) $t > 9$ (b) $\frac{3}{4} < t < 9$

Index of Applications

Biology and Life Sciences

Anthropology, 169
Average heights of males and females, 359
Bacteria count, 140
Bacteria growth, 331, 369
Defoliation caused by gypsy moth, 377
Environment, 23
  cost of removing a chemical from waste water, 627
  growth of a red oak, 262
  pollution, 293
  recycling, 294
Erosion, 23
Forestry
  forest yield, 359
  trees per acre, 359
Health
  blood pressure, 436
  respiratory cycle, 436
Human memory model, 338, 340, 348, 359, 385
Metabolic rate, 208
Nutrition, A58, A61
Plants, 46
Population growth, 769
  of fruit flies, 328, 363
Population of a species, 390
Predator-prey model, 447
Wildlife
  food consumed by a moth, 316
  growth of a herd, 370
  population of deer, 295
  population of fish, 316, 387
  reproduction rates of deer, 627
  threatened and endangered species, 295
Yeast growth, 371

Business

Advertising, 65
Advertising and sales, 229
Average cost, 303, 390
Average price of shares traded, 642
Break-even analysis, 597, 600, 601, 688
Budget variance, 10
Car rental, A45
Cost, 143, 158, 246, 249, 303, 313
Cost-benefit model, 290
Cost, revenue, and profit, 97, 110, 123, 160
Cost sharing, 232
Defective units, 751, 759, 762, 770
Demand, 330, 359, 385, 612
Depreciation, 84, 97, 157, 331, 370, 383, 767

Earnings per share
  Circuit City Stores, Inc., 96
  Harley-Davidson, Inc., 96
Flexible work hours, 763
Inventory, 165, 657, A61
Job applicants, 749, 751
Making a sale, 763
Manufacturing, 547, 657, 691, 750
Net profit
  Avon Products, Inc., 706
Number of stores
  The Gap, Inc., 156
  Target Corp., 228
  Wal-Mart, 55
Oil imports, 65
Optimizing cost, A67, A70
Optimizing profit, A66, A70
Optimizing revenue, A69
Partnership costs, 571
Patents, 70
Product lifetime, A46
Production, 181
Profit, 109, 133, 232, 250, 285, 390
Rate of change
  of a product, 97, 157
Rental demand, 98
Revenue, 70, 96, 111, 262, 570, 657, 793
  AT&T Wireless Services, 724
  collected by IRS, 376
  OfficeMax, Inc., 317
  Papa John's International, 238
  Target Corporation, 68
  United Parcel Service, Inc., 766
  U.S. Postal Service, 388
Sales, 60, 96, 143, 157, 227, 370, 425, 436, 471, 475, 506, 611, 715
  Abercrombie & Fitch Company, 706
  Carnival Corporation, 380
  for grocery and general merchandise stores, 602
  Guitar Center, Inc., 311
  Home Depot, Inc., 380
  Nike, Inc., 89
  PETCO Animal Supplies, Inc., 56
  PetsMART, Inc., 56
  Timberland Co., 234
  of VCRs and DVD players, 601
  Wm. Wrigley Jr. Company, 51
Sales presentations, 760
Shares listed on the New York Stock Exchange, 225
Shoe sales, A45
Softball team expenses, 653
Supply and demand, 610, 688, A57, A60
Ticket sales, 611, A61

Total sales, 712
Truck scheduling, 626
Years of service for employees, 757

Chemistry and Physics

Acid mixture, 610, 626
Air traffic control, 144
Astronomy
  asteroid, 829
  comet Encke, 828
  Halley's comet, 821
  orbits of comets, 790, 794
Atmospheric pressure, 379
Automobile aerodynamics, 133, 250
Automobile braking system, 627
Automobile emissions, 278
Boiling temperature of water and pressure, 340
Braking force, 586
Braking load, 570
Cable tension, 586
Carbon dating, 364, 370
Charge of electron, 22
Chemical reaction, 375
Circuit analysis, 667
Concentration of a mixture, 302
Damped harmonic motion, 506
Distance between Sun and Jupiter, 68
Distinct vision, 294
Effectiveness of a flu vaccine, 762
Electric circuits, 426
Electric hoist, 401
Electrical network, 626, 642
Electronics, 85
Engine design, 547
Engineering, 34
Explorer 18, 824
Falling object, 715
Fluid flow, 124
Force, 567
Friction, 495
Fuel consumption, 436
Fuel efficiency, 208
Fuel mixture, 611
Gallons of water on Earth, 14
Geology, magnitude of earthquakes, 367, 371, 386
Harmonic motion, 425, 426, 436, 447, 448, 464, 465, 469, 506, 513, 529, 582, 590
Hooke's Law, 228
Impedance, 190
Index of refraction, 530
Instrumentation, 401
Interior temperature of sun, 22
Kepler's Laws, 821
Land area of Earth, 21

Light year, 21
Mach number, 524
Mean distance and period of planets, 346
Medicine, 303
   number of hospitals, 310
Meteorology, 97, 100
   average daily high temperatures for Nantucket, Massachusetts and Athens, Georgia, 437
   average daily January temperature in Juneau, Alaska, 232
   average daily temperature in San Diego, California, 167
   lowest temperature in Duluth, Minnesota, 55
   monthly normal precipitation for Houston, Texas, 60
   monthly normal precipitation for San Francisco, California, 310
   monthly normal temperature for Santa Fe, New Mexico, 425
   normal daily maximum and minimum temperatures in Chicago, 71
   normal monthly high temperatures for Erie, Pennsylvania, 447
   North Atlantic tropical storms and hurricanes, 107
   relative humidity, 234
   temperature, 10, 117
   temperature in Buffalo, New York, 171
Newton's Law of Cooling, 372
Optics, 784
Percent of moon's face illuminated, 436
pH levels, 371
Physics experiment, 294
Physics, force of water, 111
Planetary motion, 793, 823, 829
Projectile motion, 506, 524, 528, 793, 802
Pulley system, 626
Radio waves, 170
Radioactive decay, 328, 330, 331, 369, 370, 383, 386, 388
Rate of change of autocatalytic reaction, 36
Refrigeration, 46
Relative density of hydrogen, 22
Resultant force, 559, 560, 586, 590
Ripples, 143
Satellite orbit, 793, 794
Saturated steam, 208
Sound intensity, 341, 348, 371
Standing waves, 513
Statics, 171
Stopping distance, 34
Strength of a wooden beam, 69
Stress test, 234

Temperature
   of a cup of water, 348, 380
   of an object, 360
Tension, 559, 560, 586
Thermodynamics, 627
Tides, 433
Tuning fork, 469
Ultraviolet radiation, 291
Velocity, 555, 559
Ventilation rates, 341
Wave motion, 470, 477
Weight of boat and trailer, 555
Work, 568, 570, 571, 586

Construction

Architecture
   church window, 827
   fireplace arch, 783
   parabolic archway, 832
   semielliptical archway, 827
   tunnel arch, 784
Awning design, 546
Beam deflection, 783
Brick pattern, 714
Bridge design, 539
Circular saw blade, 402
Electric saw, 447
Exercise facility, A61
Hardware, 469
Jin Mao Building, 412
Landau Building, 547
Log volume, 601
Machine shop calculations, 413
Railroad track, 525
Railroad track design, 539
Streetlight design, 546
Surveying, 468, 545, 585
Suspension bridge, 783, 826
Truss, 469, 546
Wading pool, 827

Consumer

Annual salary
   jeweler, 95
   librarian, 95
Average annual income, A38
Average monthly cellular telephone bill, 642
Average room rate, 304
Average sales price for a new mobile home, 733
Basic cable rates, 277
Charity donations, 381
Choice of two jobs, 601, 688
Consumer awareness, 144, 749
   average price for a computer, 317
   electric bills, A45
   gasoline prices, 63
   prices of running shoes, 71
   retail price of ice cream, 379

Consumerism, 84, 156, 762
   retail sales for lawn care products and services, 158
   retail sales of prescription drugs, 112
Delivery charges, 123
Home mortgage, 341, 371, 372, 384
Hourly earnings, A12
Hourly wage, 154
Income tax, 182
Inflation rate, 390
Job offer, 714, 767
Labor/wage requirements, 657
Monthly wage, 81, 85
Personal savings, 66
Retail price of chicken breast, 64
Salary, 144, 724, 832
VCR usage, 250
Withdrawals from an automatic teller machine, A8

Geometry

Accuracy of a measurement, 234
Angle between diagonal of a cube and diagonal of its base, 469
Angle between diagonal of a cube and its edge, 469
Angle between path and river's edge, 408
Angle between two nonvertical lines, 469
Angle of depression, 461, 467
Angle of elevation, 412, 459, 467, 476, 539
Area of the base of a tank, 143
Area of a circle, 109
Area of a circular sector, 402
Area of a corral, 249
Area of corrals, 207
Area of an equilateral triangle, 109
Area of a figure, 36, 45
Area of a horse corral, 181
Area of an isosceles triangle, 524
Area of a lot, 537
Area model, 69
Area of a parcel of land, 588
Area of a parking lot, 547
Area of plot of land, 238
Area of a rectangle, 84, 110, 313, 506
Area of a region, 72, 181, 684
Area of a right triangle, 110
Area of a shaded region, 724
Area of a triangle, 538, 544, 545, 584, 585, 590, 676, 684, 693, 694
Concentric circles, A61
Cross section of an irrigation canal, 470
Diagonals of polygons, 751
Dimensions of an isosceles right triangle, 602
Dimensions of a package, 170
Dimensions of a picture frame, 169

Dimensions of a pool, 207
Dimensions of a rectangle, 602, 688
Dimensions of a rectangular tract of land, 602
Dimensions of a region, 302
Dimensions of a room, 164, 169
Equilateral triangle, 209
Estimating π, 764
Floor space, 207
Geometric modeling, 35
Geometric probability, 46
Granular angle of repose, 458
Height, of an attic, 96
Latus rectum, 784
Length of a grain elevator, 470
Length of a guy wire, 412
Length of a pond, 588
Length of a shadow, 466
Length of a sidewalk, 204
Length of a skateboard ramp, 409
Length of the sides of a parallelogram, 545, 584
Length of two guy wires, 546
Maximum volume, of an open box, 110
Meeting a friend, 763
Meters in one foot, 68
Minimum area, 300
One micron, 22
Packaging, 207
Page design, 302, 316
Perimeter of an indoor physical fitness room, 249
Perimeter of a rectangle, 123
Points not on a line, 751
Postal regulations, 110
Regular hexagon, 469
Regular pentagon, 469
Right triangle, 303
Road grade, 97
Shadow length, 495, 540
Surface area of a honeycomb, 503
Surface area of a right circular cylinder, 69
Volume of a basketball and a baseball, 232
Volume of a box, 34, 262
Volume of a cylindrical can, 167
Volume of cylindrical shell, 36
Volume of a globe, 170
Volume of a package, 278
Volume of a soccer ball, 238
Volume of a swimming pool, 181
Volume of a trough, 529
Width of a river, 412, 474, 584

Interest Rate

Annuity, 721, 723, 724, 767
Borrowing, 625, 626
Borrowing money, 642
Comparing investments, 369

Compound interest, 34, 69, 327, 330, 341, 359, 368, 383, 385, 386, 390, 705, 723, 766
Doubling an investment, 356
Finance, mortgage debt outstanding, 133
Inflation, 331
Investment, 170, 232, 601
Investment analysis, A61
Investment portfolio, 611, 626, 666, 688, 689
Monthly payment, 46
Simple interest, 594

Miscellaneous

Agriculture
    fruit crops, 657
    number of farms, 64
    number of sheep and lambs, 208
    pesticide, 626, 689
    production and exports, 64
    weights of cattle, 63
    wheat yield, 611
Aircraft boarding, 768, 785
Alumni association, 762
Apparel, 768
Average height of a male child, 100
Backup system, 763
Backup vehicle, 763
Baling hay, 715, 767
Birthday problem, 759, 764
Bookshelf order, 769
A boy or a girl?, 763
Cable television subscribers, 658
Card game, 762
Card hand, 751
Choosing officers, 750
Communications, 123, 229
Computer graphics, 53
Counting card hands, 748
Counting horse race finishes, 745
Course grade, 169, 170
Course schedule, 749, 768
Cryptography, 681, 682, 683, 685, 693
Docking a boat, 458
Drawing a card, 753, 756, 760, 762, 769, 770
Drawing marbles, 760, 761
Education, 762
    bachelor's degrees, 61
    children enrolled in Head Start programs, 705
    college degrees, 66
    entrance exam scores and grade-point averages, 234
    expenditures, 63
    increase in fee, 769
    math lab use, 370
    number of bachelor's degrees, 221
    number of colleges and universities, 755

Penn State enrollment, 98
public schools with access to the Internet, 309
SAT and ACT test takers, 159
tuition, room, and board costs, 741
Elected president, 100
Election, 762
Elections, 230
    registered voters, 379
Entertainment, 750
    hours spent playing video games, 309
    number of CDs sold, 64
    number of movie theater screens, 386
    television ownership, 65
Exam questions, 750, 768, 785
Families, A45
Floppy disk, 402
Forming a committee, 751
Forming an experimental group, 750
Forming a team, 748
Game show, 762, 832
Government, 760
Health care, 653
Interpersonal relationships, 751
IQ scores, 370
License plate numbers, 749, 770
Lottery, 750, 755, 768
Meteorology, 209
Military, 208
Mixture problem, 170, 181, 232
Music, 221, 473
Network analysis, 638, 643, 694
Number of logs, 714
Numbers in a hat, 768
Pairs of letters, 743
Payroll error, 762
Payroll mix-up, 762
Period of a pendulum, 23
Photography, 458
Poker hand, 751, 762, 769
Political party affiliation, 761
Posing for a photograph, 750
Position of the sun, 506
Preparing for a test, 762
Probability, 740
Quiz and exam scores, 63
Quiz scores, 227, A16
Radio, 228
Random number generator, 758, 763, 770
Random selection, 742, 749, 770
Rate of a photocopier, 45
Recreation, 436, 749
Riding in a car, 750
Rock and Roll Hall of Fame, 57
SAT scores, 365
Satellite antenna, 783, 826
Seating capacity, 711, 714
Security patrol, 459

Seizure of illegal drugs, 316
Shoe sizes and heights of men, 226
Single file, 750
Snow removal, 385
Sports, 208, 220, 546, 768
    attendance at women's college
        basketball games, 303
    Australian rules football, 794
    average salary for professional
        baseball players, 228
    figure skating, 402
    football pass, 57
    free-throw percentages, 71
    men's 1500-meter speed skating
        event, 235
    number of municipal golf facilities,
        387
    participants, 64
    points scored during the Sugar Bowl,
        626
    running a marathon, 80
    women's 400-meter freestyle
        swimming event, 229
Spread of a virus, 366
Study hours and television hours, 223
Taste testing, 760
Telephone numbers, 743, 750, 768
Television coverage, 446
Test and exam scores, 57
Test scores, 58, 386, A45, A46
Time for a funnel to empty, 23
Times of sunset, 471
Tossing a coin, 752, 753, 760
Tossing a die, 754, 760, 769
Transportation, 111, 208
    value of new car sales, 154
Travel, 66, 71, 749
True-false exam, 749
Typing speed, 386
Voting preference, 657, 658
Weather forecast, 770
Width of human hair, 22
Work rate, 725

Time and Distance
Airplane ascent, 467
Airplane speed, 608, 610, 688
Altitude, 468
Angular and linear speed, of a lawn
    roller, 398
Angular speed
    of a car's wheels, 402, 473
    of a truck's wheels, 478
Average speed, 170, 232, 303, 725
Climb rate, 384
CN Tower, 207
Current speed, 571
Depth of a submarine, 467
Difference in latitudes, 401
Distance, 507, 539, 584
    a ball drops, 725

between cities, 401
between pitcher's mound and first
    base, 543
between radar antenna and plane,
    446
between two cities, 477
between two ships, 468, 546
between two towns, 468, 477
from boat to shoreline, 539
from observer to plane, 426
of a race course, 537
Falling object, 234
Falling time, 202
Flight path, 538
Flying distance, 57, 209
Flying speed, 209
Glide path, 539
Height, 466
    of Aon Center Building, 165
    of a ball, 249, 318
    of a balloon, 412
    of a baseball, 285
    of a basketball, 307
    of a building, 584
    of a flag, 590
    of a flagpole, 170, 467, 538
    of a kite, 467
    of a mountain, 412, 468
    of a platform, 474
    of a pole, 533
    of a projectile, 218, 240
    of a sail, 170
    of a shuttle, 476
    of a silo, 170
    of a smokestack, 461
    of a steeple, 467
    of a streetlight, 412
    of a tree, 232, 408, 538, 584
    of a waterslide, 466
Linear speed
    of the second hand of a clock, 398
Locating a fire, 468, 539
Maximum height of a baseball, 245
Maximum safe rescue height, 461
Mountain descent, 467, 476
Navigation, 462, 468, 478, 543, 545,
    546, 556, 560, 584, 586, 590, 784
Path of a baseball, 105, 642
Path of a diver, 249
Path of a projectile, 793
Railroad grade, 477
Ski slope, 468
Speed and mileage, 306
Speed of light, 170
Springs, 470
Stopping distance, 142
Travel, 10
Travel time, 164, 170, 181
Vertical motion, 622, 625
Wind speed, 170

U.S. Demographics
Ages of unemployed workers, 761
Amount spent on archery equipment,
    48
Amount spent on books and maps, 308
Average salary for public school
    teachers, 356
Cellular phone subscribers, 105
Children of U.S. presidents, 761
Cigarette consumption, 250
Circulation of newspapers, 108
Coca-Cola products consumption, 22
Federal debt, 705
Federal deficit, 10
Fuel use, 133
Government
    U.S. representatives, 65
    votes cast, 72
Hairdressers and cosmetologists, 246
Health care expenditures, 143
Height of women, 235
Immigrants, 62
Internet use, 203
Labor force, 182, 222, 224
Life insurance, 233, 740
Local telephone access lines, 236
Lottery ticket sales, 277
Median price of a new home in the
    South and Northeast, 263
Median sales price of a new home, 84
Motor vehicle registrations, 667
Number of banks, 360
Number of families, 685
Number of morning and evening
    newspapers, 178
Number of pilots and copilots, 390
Number of television sets in U.S.
    households, A13
Outpatient visits to hospitals, A42
Population, 59, 341
    of Arizona and Minnesota, 182
    of Baton Rouge, Louisiana, 390
    of Bellevue, Washington, 369
    in the coastal regions, 64
    of Colorado Springs, Colorado, 386
    of Idaho and New Hampshire, 598
    of New Zealand, 724
    of North Dakota, 123
    of South Dakota, 233
    of the United States, 379, 702
        25 or older, 758
    of world countries, 369
Population growth, 331
    of the world, 362
Population statistics, life expectancy,
    85
Price of gold, A46
Supreme Court cases, 318
Unemployment rate, 507
Vital statistics, 381
Women in U.S. military, 62

Index

A

Absolute value
  of a complex number, 572
  function, 102
  inequality, solution of, 213
  properties of, 5
  of a real number, 5
Acute angle, 393
Addition
  of a complex number, 184
  of fractions
    with like denominators, 8
    with unlike denominators, 8
  matrix, 644
  vector, 550
    properties of, 552
    resultant of, 550
Additive identity
  for a complex number, 184
  for a matrix, 648
  for a real number, 7
Additive inverse, 6
  for a complex number, 184
  for a real number, 7
Adjacent side of a right triangle, 403
Adjoining matrices, 661
Air navigation, 462
Algebraic equation, 163
Algebraic expression, 6
  domain of, 37
  equivalent, 37
  evaluate, 6
  term of, 6
Algebraic function, 320
Alternative definition of conic, 818
Alternative form of Law of Cosines,
    541
Alternative formula for standard
    deviation, A41
Ambiguous Case (SSA), 534
Amplitude of sine and cosine curves,
    429
Angle, 392
  acute, 393
  between two vectors, 563, A33
  central, 395
  complementary, 394
  conversions between radians and
    degrees, 396
  coterminal, 392
  degree, 393
  of depression, 408, 460
  of elevation, 408, 460
  initial side, 392
  negative, 392
  obtuse, 393
  positive, 392
  radian, 395
  reference, 416
  of repose, 458
  standard position, 392
  supplementary, 394
  terminal side, 392
  vertex, 392
Angular speed, 397
Aphelion, 793, 823
Arc length, 396
Arccosine function, 451
Arcsine function, 449, 451
Arctangent function, 451
Area
  common formulas for, 166
  of an oblique triangle, 536
  of a triangle, 676
    formulas for, 544
Argument of a complex number, 573
Arithmetic combination, 134
Arithmetic sequence, 707
  common difference of, 707
  nth term of, 708
  sum of a finite, 710, A34
Associative Property of Addition
  for complex numbers, 185
  for matrices, 647
  for real numbers, 7
Associative Property of Multiplication
  for complex numbers, 185
  for matrices, 647
  for real numbers, 7
Associative property of scalar
    multiplication, for matrices, 647,
    651
Astronomical unit, 821
Asymptote(s)
  horizontal, 287
  of a hyperbola, 779
  oblique, 299
  of a rational function, 288
  slant, 299
  vertical, 287
Augmented matrix, 630
Average, A38
Axis
  imaginary, 187
  of a parabola, 240
  polar, 803
  real, 187
  of symmetry, 240

B

Back-substitution, 593
Bar graph, 60
Base, 12
  natural, 324

Basic equation, 620
Basic Rules of Algebra, 7
Bearings, 462
Bell-shaped curve, 365
Bimodal, A38
Binomial, 24, 734
  coefficient, 734
  cube of, 26
  expanding, 737
  square of, 26
Binomial Theorem, 734, A35
Bounded, 187
  intervals, 3
Box-and-whisker plot, A43
Branches of a hyperbola, 777
Break-even point, 597

C

Cardioid, 814
Cartesian plane, 47
Center
  of a circle, 52
  of an ellipse, 775
  of a hyperbola, 777
Central angle of a circle, 395
Certain event, 753
Change-of-base formula, 343
Characteristics of a function from
    set A to set B, 99
Chebychev's Theorem, A42
Circle, 52, 814
  center of, 52
  central angle of, 395
  radius of, 52
  of radius r, 51
  standard form of the equation of,
    52, 786
  unit, 420
Circumference, common formulas for,
    166
Closed interval, 3
Coded row matrices, 681
Coefficient
  binomial, 734
  correlation, 226
  leading, 24
  matrix, 630, 652
  of a polynomial, 24
  of a variable term, 6
Cofactor(s)
  expanding by, 671
  of a matrix, 670
Cofunction identities, 480
Collinear points, 677
  test for, 677
Column matrix, 629
Combination of n elements taken r at
    a time, 747

Common difference, 707
Common formulas, 166
  area, 166
  circumference, 166
  perimeter, 166
  volume, 166
Common logarithmic function, 333
Common ratio, 716
Commutative Property of Addition
  for complex numbers, 185
  for matrices, 647
  for real numbers, 7
Commutative Property of
    Multiplication
  for complex numbers, 185
  for real numbers, 7
Complement
  of an event, 759
  probability of, 759
Complementary angles, 394
Completely factored, 27
Completing the square, 191
Complex conjugates, 186
Complex fraction, 41
Complex number, 183
  absolute value of, 572
  addition of, 184
  additive identity, 184
  additive inverse, 184
  argument of, 573
  Associative Property of Addition,
    185
  Associative Property of
    Multiplication, 185
  Commutative Property of Addition,
    185
  Commutative Property of
    Multiplication, 185
  Distributive Property, 185
  equality of, 183
  imaginary part of, 183
  modulus of, 573
  nth root of, 577, 578
  nth roots of unity, 579
  polar form, 573
  product of two, 574
  quotient of two, 574
  real part of, 183
  standard form of, 183
  subtraction of, 184
  trigonometric form of, 573
Complex plane, 187
Complex zeros occur in conjugate
    pairs, 281
Component form of a vector $\mathbf{v}$, 549
Components, vector, 565, 566
Composite number, 8
Composition, 136
Compound interest
  continuous compounding, 326
  formulas for, 326
Conditional equation, 162, 488

Conics (or conic section), 772
  alternative definition, 818
  degenerate, 772
  eccentricity of, 818
  ellipse, 775
  hyperbola, 777
  parabola, 773
  polar equations of, 818, A37
  standard forms of equations of, 786
Conjugate, 18, 281
  of a complex number, 186
Conjugate axis of a hyperbola, 778
Connected mode, A11
Consistent system of linear equations,
    605, 615
  dependent, 615
  independent, 615
Constant, 6
  function, 115, 240
  matrix, 652
  term, 6, 24
Constraints, A62
Consumer surplus, A57
Continuous compounding, 326
Continuous function, 251, 795
Conversions between degrees and
    radians, 396
Convex limaçon, 814
Coordinate, 2, 47
  polar, 803
  x-coordinate, 47
  y-coordinate, 47
Coordinate axes, reflection in, 128
Coordinate conversion, 804
Coordinate system
  polar, 803
  rectangular, 47
  three-dimensional, 618
Correlation
  coefficient, 226
  negative, 223
  positive, 223
Correspondence, one-to-one, 2
Cosecant function, 403
  of any angle, 414
  graph of, 441, 444
Cosine curve, amplitude of, 429
Cosine function, 403
  of any angle, 414
  common angles, 417
  domain of, 421
  graph of, 431, 444
  inverse, 451
  period of, 430
  range of, 421
  special angles, 405
Cotangent function, 403
  of any angle, 414
  graph of, 440, 444
Coterminal angle, 392
Cramer's Rule, 678, 679
Critical numbers
  of a polynomial inequality, 214

  of a rational inequality, 217
Cryptogram, 681
Cube
  of a binomial, 26
  root, 15
Cubic function, 252
Cumulative sum feature, A2
Curve
  orientation, 796
  plane, 795
  rose, 813, 814

D

Damping factor, 443
Data-defined function, 100
Decomposition of $N(x)/D(x)$ into
    partial fractions, 619
Decreasing function, 115
Definitions of trigonometric functions
    of any angle, 414
Degenerate conic, 772
Degree
  of an angle, 393
  conversions to radians, 396
  of a polynomial, 24
Degree mode, A9
DeMoivre's Theorem, 576
Denominator, 6
  rationalizing, 18, 491
Dependent system of linear equations,
    615
Dependent variable, 101, 106
Descartes's Rule of Signs, 272
Determinant
  of a matrix, 668, 671
  of a 2×2 matrix, 663, 668
Determinant feature, A2
Diagonal
  of a matrix, 672
  of a polygon, 751
Diagonal matrix, 658, 672
Difference(s)
  common, 707
  first, 731
  of functions, 134
  quotient, 106
  second, 731
  of two cubes, 28
  of two squares, 28
  of vectors, 550
Differentiation, 455
Dimpled limaçon, 814
Directed line segment, 548
  initial point, 548
  length of, 548
  magnitude, 548
  terminal point, 548
Direction angle of a vector, 554
Directrix of a parabola, 773
Discriminant, 196
Distance between two points on the
    real number line, 5

Distance Formula, 49
Distinguishable permutations, 746
Distributive Property
    for complex numbers, 185
    for matrices, 647
    of real numbers, 7
Divide fractions, 8
Division
    long, 264
    synthetic, 267
Division Algorithm, 265
Divisors, 8
Domain
    of an algebraic expression, 37
    of cosine function, 421
    defined, 106
    of a function, 99, 106
    implied, 103, 106, 218
    of a rational function, 286
    of sine function, 421
    undefined, 106
Dot mode, A11
Dot product, 562
    properties of, 562, A32
Double inequality, 212
Double-angle formulas, 515, A28
Doyle Log Rule, 601
Draw inverse feature, A2

E
Eccentricity
    of a conic, 818
    of an ellipse, 793, 818
    of a hyperbola, 818
    of a parabola, 818
Elementary row operations, 631
Elementary row operations features, A3
Eliminating the parameter, 798
Elimination
    Gaussian, 614
        with back-substitution, 635
    Gauss-Jordan, 636
    method of, 603, 604
Ellipse, 775, 818
    aphelion, 793, 823
    center of, 775
    eccentricity of, 793, 818
    foci of, 775
    latus rectum of, 784
    major axis of, 775
    minor axis of, 775
    perihelion, 793, 823
    standard form of the equation of,
        775, 786
    vertices of, 775
Endpoints of an interval, 3
Entry of a matrix, 629
Equal matrices, 644
Equality
    of complex numbers, 183
    hidden, 163
    properties of, 7

of vectors, 549
Equation(s), 75, 162
    algebraic, 163
    basic, 620
    circle, standard form, 52, 786
    conditional, 162, 488
    conics, standard form, 786
    ellipse, standard form, 775, 786
    equivalent, A49
    exponential, 350
    graph of, 75
        in three variables, 618
        using a graphing utility, 77
    hyperbola, standard form, 777, 786
    identity, 162
    of a line
        general form, 91
        point-slope form, 88, 91
        slope-intercept form, 90, 91
        summary of, 91
        two-point form, 88
    linear, A49
        in one variable, 162
    logarithmic, 350
    parabola, standard form, 773, 786,
        A36
    parametric, 795
    position, 202, 218, 622
    quadratic, 191
    second-degree polynomial, 191
    solution of, 162
        graphical approximations, 174
    solution point, 75
    system of, 592
        nonsquare, 617
    in three variables, graph of, 618
Equivalent
    equations, A49
        generating, A49
    expressions, 37
    fractions, 8
        generate, 8
    inequalities, 210, A50
        generating, A50
    systems, 604
        in row-echelon form, 613
Evaluate an algebraic expression, 6
Evaluating trigonometric functions of
    any angle, 417
Even function, 119
    test for, 119
    trigonometric, 422
Even/odd identities, 480
Even and odd trigonometric functions,
    422
Event, 752
    certain, 753
    complement of, 759
        probability of, 759
    impossible, 753
    independent, 758

probability of, 758
    mutually exclusive, 756
        probability of, 753
        the union of two, 756
Existence of an inverse function, 149
Existence theorems, 279
Expanding
    a binomial, 737
    by cofactors, 671
Experiment, 752
    outcome of, 752
    sample space of, 752
Exponent, 12
    properties of, 12
    rational, 19
Exponential decay model, 361
Exponential equation, 350
    solving, 350
Exponential form, 12
Exponential function, 320, 322
    f with base a, 320
    natural, 324
Exponential growth model, 361
Exponentiating, 353
Expression
    algebraic, 6
    equivalent, 37
    fractional, 37
    rational, 37
Extended principle of mathematical
    induction, 728
Extracting square roots, 191
Extraneous solution, 163
Extrema, 254
    maxima, 254
    minima, 254

F
Factor Theorem, 268, A26
Factorial, 698
Factoring, 27, 191
    completely, 27
    by grouping, 31
    polynomials, guidelines for, 31
    special polynomial forms, 28
Factors
    of an integer, 8
    of a polynomial, 281, A27
Feasible solutions, A62
Finding an inverse function, 150
Finding an inverse matrix, 661
Finding test intervals for a polynomial,
    214
Finite sequence, 696
Finite series, 701
First differences, 731
Fitting a line to data, 223
Fixed point, 505
Focus (foci)
    of an ellipse, 775
    of a hyperbola, 777
    of a parabola, 773

FOIL Method, 25
Formula(s)
    for area of a triangle, 544
    change-of-base, 343
    common, 166
    for compound interest, 326
    double-angle, 515, A28
    half-angle, 518
    Heron's Area, 544, A31
    power-reducing, 517, A29
    product-to-sum, 519
    Quadratic, 191
    reduction, 510
    sum and difference, 508, A28
    sum-to-product, 520, A29
Fractal, 187
Fractal geometry, 187
Fraction(s)
    addition of
        with like denominators, 8
        with unlike denominators, 8
    complex, 41
    denominator of, 6
    divide, 8
    equivalent, 8
        generate, 8
    multiply, 8
    numerator of, 6
    operations of, 8
    partial, 619
        decomposition, 619
    properties of, 8
    subtraction of
        with like denominators, 8
        with unlike denominators, 8
Fractional expression, 37
Frequency, 58
    of simple harmonic motion, 463
Frequency distribution, 59
Function(s), 99, 106
    absolute value, 102
    algebraic, 320
    arithmetic combination of, 134
    characteristics of, 99
    common logarithmic, 333
    composition, 136
    constant, 115, 240
    continuous, 251, 795
    cosecant, 403
    cosine, 403
    cotangent, 403
    cubic, 252
    damping factor, 443
    data-defined, 100
    decreasing, 115
    difference of, 134
    domain of, 99, 106
    even, 119
        test for, 119
    exponential, 320, 322
    extrema, 254

    maxima, 254
    minima, 254
    fixed point of, 505
    graph of, 113
    greatest integer, 118
    of half-angles, 515
    implied domain of, 103, 106, 218
    increasing, 115
    input, 99
    inverse, 145, 146
        cosine, 451
        existence of, 149
        sine, 449, 451
        tangent, 451
    linear, 89, 240
    logarithmic, 332, 335
    of multiple angles, 515
    name of, 101, 106
    natural exponential, 324
    natural logarithmic, 336
    notation, 101, 106
    objective, A62
    odd, 119
        test for, 119
    one-to-one, 149
    output, 99
    period of, 421
    periodic, 421
    piecewise-defined, 102
    polynomial, 240, 252
    product of, 134
    quadratic, 240, 241
        maximum value of, 245
        minimum value of, 245
    quotient of, 134
    radical, 103
    range of, 99, 106
    rational, 286, 287
    reciprocal, 287
    secant, 403
    sine, 403
    square root, 103
    squaring, 241
    step, 118
    sum of, 134
    summary of terminology, 106
    tangent, 403
    transcendental, 320
    trigonometric, 403
    value of, 101, 106
    Vertical Line Test, 114
    zero of, 254
Function mode, A9
Fundamental Counting Principle, 743
Fundamental Theorem
    of Algebra, 279
    of Arithmetic, 8
Fundamental trigonometric identities,
    406, 480
    Pythagorean, 406, 480
    quotient, 406, 480

    reciprocal, 406, 480

G
Gaussian elimination, 614
    with back-substitution, 635
Gaussian model, 361
Gauss-Jordan elimination, 636
General form of the equation of a line,
    91
Generate equivalent fractions, 8
Generating equivalent
    equations, A49
    inequalities, A50
Geometric sequence, 716
    common ratio of, 716
    nth term of, 717
    sum of a finite, 719, A35
Geometric series, 720
    sum of an infinite, 720
Graph(s), 75
    bar, 60
    of cosecant function, 441, 444
    of cosine function, 431, 444
    of cotangent function, 440, 444
    of an equation, 75
        in three variables, 618
        using a graphing utility, 77
    of a function, 113
    of an inequality, 210, A52
        in two variables, A52
    intercepts of, 76
    of inverse cosine function, 451
    of inverse sine function, 451
    of inverse tangent function, 451
    line, 61
    point of intersection, 176
    point-plotting method, 75
    of a rational function, 296
    of secant function, 441, 444
    of sine function, 431, 444
    special polar, 814
    of tangent function, 438, 444
Graphical approximations of solutions
    of an equation, 174
Graphical interpretations of solutions,
    605
Graphing utility
    features
        cumulative sum, A2
        determinant, A2
        draw inverse, A2
        elementary row operations, A3
        intersect, A5
        matrix, A6
        maximum, A7
        mean, A8
        median, A8
        minimum, A7
        $_nC_r$, A12
        $_nP_r$, A12
        one-variable statistics, A12

reduced row-echelon, A15
regression, A13
row addition and row
    multiplication and addition, A4
row-echelon, A14
row multiplication, A4
row swap, A3
sequence, A15
shade, A15
sum, A16
sum sequence, A16
table, A17
tangent, A18
trace, A19, A22
value, A19
zero or root, A21
zoom, A22
inverse matrix, A7
list editor, A5
matrix editor, A6
matrix operations, A6
mode settings, A9
    connected, A11
    degree, A9
    dot, A11
    function, A9
    parametric, A9
    polar, A10
    radian, A9
    sequence, A10
uses of, A1
viewing window, A19
Greater than, 3
    or equal to, 3
Greatest integer function, 118
Guidelines
    for factoring polynomials, 31
    for graphing rational functions, 296
    for verifying trigonometric identities,
        488

H
Half-angle formulas, 518
Harmonic motion, simple, 463, 464
    frequency of, 463
Heron's Area Formula, 544, A31
Hidden equality, 163
Histogram, 59
Horizontal asymptote, 287
Horizontal components of v, 553
Horizontal line, 91
Horizontal Line Test, 149
Horizontal shift, 126
Horizontal shrink, 130
Horizontal stretch, 130
Human memory model, 338
Hyperbola, 777, 818
    asymptotes of, 779
    branches of, 777
    center of, 777
    conjugate axis of, 778

eccentricity of, 818
foci of, 777
standard form of the equation of,
    777, 786
transverse axis of, 777
vertices of, 777
Hypotenuse of a right triangle, 403

I
Identity (identities), 162, 488
    cofunction, 480
    even/odd, 480
    fundamental trigonometric, 480
    guidelines for verifying
        trigonometric, 488
    matrix of order n, 651
    Pythagorean, 480
    quotient, 480
    reciprocal, 480
Imaginary
    axis, 187
    number, pure, 183
    part of a complex number, 183
    unit i, 183
Implied domain, 103, 106, 218
Impossible event, 753
Improper rational expression, 265
Inclusive or, 8
Inconsistent system of linear equations,
    605, 615
Increasing annuity, 721
Increasing function, 115
Independent events, 758
    probability of, 758
Independent system of linear
    equations, 615
Independent variable, 101, 106
Index
    of a radical, 15
    of summation, 700
Inductive, 671
Inequality (inequalities), 3
    absolute value, solution of, 213
    double, 212
    equivalent, 210, A50
    graph of, 210, A52
    linear, 104, 211, A52
    properties of, 210, 211
    satisfy, 210
    solution of, 210, A52
    solution set, 210
    symbol, 3
Infinite geometric series, 720
    sum of, 720
Infinite sequence, 696
Infinite series, 701
Infinity
    negative, 4
    positive, 4
Initial point, 548

Initial side of an angle, 392
Input, 99
Integer(s), 2
    divisors of, 8
    factors of, 8
    irreducible over, 27
Integration, 455
Intercept(s), 76, 172
    x-intercept, 172
    y-intercept, 172
Intermediate Value Theorem, 259
Intersect feature, A5
Interval(s)
    bounded, 3
    closed, 3
    endpoints, 3
    open, 3
    on the real number line, 3
    unbounded, 4
Inverse
    additive, 6
    multiplicative, 6
Inverse function, 145, 146
    cosine, 451
    existence of, 149
    finding, 150
    Horizontal Line Test, 149
    sine, 449, 451
    tangent, 451
Inverse of a matrix, 659
    finding an, 661
Inverse matrix with a graphing utility,
    A7
Inverse properties
    of logarithms, 333, 350
    of natural logarithms, 336
    of trigonometric functions, 453
Inverse trigonometric functions, 451,
    455
Invertible matrix, 660
Irrational number, 2
Irreducible
    over the integers, 27
    over the rationals, 282
    over the reals, 282

K
Kepler's Laws, 821
Key points
    of the graph of a trigonometric
        function, 428
    intercepts, 428
    maximum points, 428
    minimum points, 428

L
Latus rectum of an ellipse, 784
Law of Cosines, 541, A31
    alternative form, 541

standard form, 541
Law of Sines, 532, A30
Law of Trichotomy, 4
Leading 1, 633
Leading coefficient of a polynomial, 24
Leading Coefficient Test, 253
Least squares regression, A47
Least squares regression line, 224
Lemniscate, 814
Length of a directed line segment, 548
Less than, 3
    or equal to, 3
Like
    radicals, 17
    terms of a polynomial, 25
Limaçon, 811, 814
    convex, 814
    dimpled, 814
    with inner loop, 814
Line graph, 61
Line(s) in the plane
    horizontal, 91
    least squares regression, 224
    parallel, 92
    perpendicular, 92
    slope of, 86, 87
    tangent, 782, 785
    vertical, 91
Line plot, 58
Linear combination of vectors, 553
Linear equation, A49
    general form, 91
    in one variable, 162
    point-slope form, 88, 91
    slope-intercept form, 90, 91
    summary of, 91
    two-point form, 88
Linear extrapolation, 89
Linear Factorization Theorem, 279,
    A26
Linear function, 89, 240
Linear inequality, 104, 211, A52
Linear interpolation, 89
Linear programming, A62
Linear speed, 397
List editor, A5
Logarithm(s)
    change-of-base formula, 343
    natural, properties of, 336, 344, A27
        inverse, 336
        one-to-one, 336
    properties of, 333, 344, A27
        inverse, 333, 350
        one-to-one, 333, 350
Logarithmic equation
    solving, 350
        exponentiating, 353
Logarithmic function, 332, 335
    with base a, 332
    common, 333
    natural, 336
Logarithmic model, 361

Logistic
    curve, 366
    growth model, 361
Long division, 264
Lower bound, 273
Lower limit of summation, 700
Lower quartile, A43
Lower triangular matrix, 672

M

Magnitude
    of a directed line segment, 548
    of a real number, 5
    of a vector, 549
Main diagonal of a square matrix, 629
Major axis of an ellipse, 775
Mandelbrot Set, 187
Mathematical induction, 726
    extended principle of, 728
    Principle of, 727
Mathematical model, 222
Mathematical modeling, 163
Matrix (matrices), 629
    addition, 644
        properties of, 647
    additive identity, 648
    adjoining, 661
    augmented, 630
    coded row, 681
    coefficient, 630, 652
    cofactor of, 670
    column, 629
    constant, 652
    determinant of, 663, 668, 671
    diagonal, 658, 672
    elementary row operations, 631
    entry of a, 629
    equal, 644
        identity, 651
    inverse of, 659
        finding, 661
    invertible, 660
    main diagonal, 649
    minor of, 670
    multiplication, 649
        properties of, 651
    nonsingular, 660
    order of a, 629
    in reduced row-echelon form, 633
    representation of, 644
    row, 629
    in row-echelon form, 632, 633
    row-equivalent, 631
    scalar identity, 647
    scalar multiplication, 645
        properties of, 647
    singular, 660
    square, 629
    stochastic, 657
    triangular, 672
        lower, 672
        upper, 672

uncoded row, 681
    zero, 648
Matrix editor, A6
Matrix feature, A6
Matrix operations with a graphing
    utility, A6
Maxima, 254
Maximum feature, A7
Maximum value of a quadratic
    function, 245
Mean, A38
Mean feature, A8
Measure of central tendency, A38
    average, A38
    mean, A38
    median, A38
    mode, A38
Measure of dispersion, A39
    standard deviation, A40
    variance, A40
Median, A38
Median feature, A8
Method
    of elimination, 603, 604
    of least squares, A47
    of substitution, 592
Midpoint Formula, 50, 51, A25
Midpoint of a line segment, 50
Minima, 254
Minimum feature, A7
Minimum value of a quadratic
    function, 245
Minor axis of an ellipse, 775
Minor of a matrix, 670
Minors and cofactors of a square
    matrix, 670
Mode, A38
Mode settings, A9
    connected, A11
    degree, A9
    dot, A11
    function, A9
    parametric, A9
    polar, A10
    radian, A9
    sequence, A10
Model
    mathematical, 163, 222
    verbal, 163
Modulus of a complex number, 573
Monomial, 24
Multiplication
    matrix, 649
    scalar, 645
Multiplicative identity of a real
    number, 7
Multiplicative inverse, 6
    for a matrix, 659
    of a real number, 7
Multiplicity, 256
Multiply fractions, 8
Mutually exclusive events, 756

N

n factorial, 698
Name of a function, 101, 106
Natural base, 324
Natural exponential function, 324
Natural logarithm, properties of, 336, 344, A27
Natural logarithmic function, 336
Natural number, 2
$_nC_r$ feature, A12
Negation, properties of, 7
Negative
  angle, 392
  correlation, 223
  infinity, 4
  of a vector, 550
Nonnegative number, 2
Nonrigid transformation, 130
Nonsingular matrix, 660
Nonsquare system of linear equations, 617
Normally distributed, 365
$_nP_r$ feature, A12
*n*th partial sum, 701, 711
*n*th root(s),
  of *a*, 15
  of a complex number, 577, 578
  principal, 15
  of unity, 579
*n*th term
  of an arithmetic sequence, 708
  of a geometric sequence, 717
Number
  complex, 183
  composite, 8
  critical, 214, 217
  irrational, 2
  natural, 2
  nonnegative, 2
  prime, 8
  rational, 2
  real, 2
  whole, 2
Number of combinations of *n* elements taken *r* at a time, 747
Number of permutations of *n* elements, 744
  taken *r* at a time, 744, 745
Number of solutions of a linear system, 615
Numerator, 6

O

Objective function, A62
Oblique
  asymptote, 299
  triangles, 532
    area of, 536
Obtuse angle, 393
Odd function, 119
  test for, 119
  trigonometric, 422

One cycle of a sine curve, 427
One-to-one
  correspondence, 2
  function, 149
  property of logarithms, 333, 344, A27
  property of natural logarithms, 336, 344, A27
One-variable statistics feature, A12
Open interval, 3
Operations of fractions, 8
Opposite side of a right triangle, 403
Optimal solution of a linear programming problem, A62
Optimization, A62
Order
  of a matrix, 629
  on the real number line, 3
Ordered pair, 47
Ordered triple, 613
Orientation of a curve, 796
Origin, 2, 47
  of polar coordinate system, 803
  symmetry, 119
Orthogonal vectors, 564
Outcome, 752
Output, 99

P

Parabola, 240, 773, 818
  axis of, 240
  directrix of, 773
  eccentricity of, 818
  focus of, 773
  standard form of the equation of, 773, 786, A36
  tangent line, 782, 785
  vertex of, 240, 773
Parallel lines, 92
Parallelogram law, 550
Parameter, 795
  eliminating the, 798
Parametric equations, 795
Parametric mode, A9
Partial fraction, 619
  basic equation, 620
  decomposition, 619
Pascal's Triangle, 736
Perfect
  cube, 16
  square, 16
  square trinomial, 28
Perihelion, 793, 823
Perimeter, common formulas for, 166
Period
  of a function, 421
  of sine and cosine functions, 430
Periodic function, 421
Permutation, 744
  distinguishable, 746
  of *n* elements, 744
    taken *r* at a time, 744, 745

Perpendicular lines, 92
Phase shift, 431
Piecewise-defined function, 102
Plane curve, 795
  orientation of, 796
Point
  of diminishing returns, 262
  of equilibrium, 610, A57
  of intersection, 176, 592
  of tangency, 782
Point-plotting method, 75
Point-slope form, 88, 91
Polar axis, 803
Polar coordinate system, 803
Polar coordinates, 803
  conversion, 804
  quick test for symmetry in, 811
  test for symmetry in, 810
Polar equations of conics, 818, A37
Polar form of a complex number, 573
Polar mode, A10
Pole, 803
Polynomial(s), 24
  coefficient of, 24
  completely factored, 27
  constant term, 24
  degree of, 24
  equation, second-degree, 191
  factors of, 281, A27
  finding test intervals for, 214
  function, 240, 252
    real zeros of, 255
    of *x* with degree *n*, 240
  guidelines for factoring, 31
  inequality
    critical numbers, 214
    test intervals, 214
  irreducible, 27
  leading coefficient of, 24
  like terms, 25
    long division of, 264
  prime, 27
  prime factor, 282
  standard form of, 24
  synthetic division, 267
  in *x*, 24
  zero, 24
Position equation, 202, 218, 622
Positive
  angle, 392
  correlation, 223
  infinity, 4
Power, 12
Power-reducing formulas, 517, A29
Prime
  factor of a polynomial, 282
  factorization, 8
  number, 8
  polynomial, 27
Principal *n*th root
  of *a*, 15
  of a number, 15

Principle of Mathematical Induction, 727
Probability
    of a complement, 759
    of an event, 753
    of independent events, 758
    of the union of two events, 756
Producer surplus, A57
Product
    of functions, 134
    of trigonometric functions, 515
    of two complex numbers, 574
Product-to-sum formulas, 519
Projection of a vector, 566
Proper rational expression, 265
Properties
    of absolute value, 5
    of the dot product, 562, A32
    of equality, 7
    of exponents, 12
    of fractions, 8
    of inequalities, 210, 211
    of inverse trigonometric functions, 453
    of logarithms, 333, 344, A27
        inverse, 333, 350
        one-to-one, 333, 350
    of matrix addition and scalar multiplication, 647
    of matrix multiplication, 651
    of natural logarithms, 336, 344, A27
        inverse, 336
        one-to-one, 336
    of negation, 7
    of radicals, 16
    of sums, 701, A34
    vector addition and scalar multiplication, 552
    of zero, 8
Pure imaginary number, 183
Pythagorean identities, 406, 480
Pythagorean Theorem, 204

Q
Quadrant, 47
Quadratic equation, 191
    solving
        by completing the square, 191
        by extracting square roots, 191
        by factoring, 191
        using Quadratic Formula, 191
Quadratic form, 198
Quadratic Formula, 191
    discriminant, 196
Quadratic function, 240, 241
    maximum value of, 245
    minimum value of, 245
    standard form, 243
Quartile, A43
    lower, A43
    upper, A43
Quick test for symmetry in polar coordinates, 811

Quotient
    difference, 106
    of functions, 134
    identities, 406, 480
    of two complex numbers, 574

R
Radian, 395
    conversion to degrees, 396
Radian mode, A9
Radical
    function, 103
    index of, 15
    like, 17
    properties of, 16
    simplest form, 17
    symbol, 15
Radicand, 15
Radius of a circle, 52
Random selection
    with replacement, 742
    without replacement, 742
Range, 58
    of a function, 99, 106
Rational exponent, 19
Rational expression(s), 37
    improper, 265
    proper, 265
    undefined values of, 217
    zero of, 217
Rational function, 286, 287
    asymptotes of, 288
    domain of, 286
    guidelines for graphing, 296
Rational number, 2
Rational Zero Test, 270
Rationalizing a denominator, 18, 491
Real axis, 187
Real number(s), 2
    absolute value of, 5
    coordinate, 2
    magnitude of, 5
    subset, 2
Real number line, 2
    bounded intervals on, 3
    distance between two points, 5
    interval on, 3
    order on, 3
    origin, 2
    unbounded intervals on, 4
Real part of a complex number, 183
Real zeros of polynomial functions, 255
Reciprocal
    function, 287
    identities, 406, 480
Rectangular coordinate system, 47
Recursion formula, 709
Recursive sequence, 698
Reduced row-echelon feature, A15
Reduced row-echelon form, 633
Reducible over the reals, 282

Reduction formulas, 510
Reference angle, 416
Reflection, 128
Regression feature, A13
Relation, 99
Relative maximum, 116
Relative minimum, 116
Remainder Theorem, 268, A25
Repeated zero, 256
    multiplicity, 256
Representation of matrices, 644
Resultant of vector addition, 550
Right triangle
    definitions of trigonometric functions, 403
    hypotenuse, 403
    opposite side, 403
    right side of, 403
    solving, 408
Rigid transformation, 130
Root(s)
    of a complex number, 577, 578
    cube, 15
    principal nth, 15
    square, 15
Rose curve, 813, 814
Row addition and row multiplication and addition features, A4
Row-echelon feature, A14
Row-echelon form, 613, 632, 633
    reduced, 633
Row-equivalent, 631
Row matrix, 629
Row multiplication feature, A4
Row operations, 614
    elementary, 614
Row swap feature, A3
Rule of signs, 8

S
Sample space, 752
Satisfy the inequality, 210
Scalar, 645
    identity, 647
    multiple, 645
        of a vector, 550
Scalar multiplication
    for a matrix, 645
    properties of, 647
    of a vector, 550
        properties of, 552
Scatter plot, 48, 222
Scientific notation, 14
Scribner Log Rule, 601
Secant function, 403
    of any angle, 414
    graph of, 441, 444
Second differences, 731
Second-degree polynomial equation, 191
Sequence, 696
    arithmetic, 707
    nth term, 708

bounded, 187
finite, 696
first differences of, 731
geometric, 716
    nth term, 717
infinite, 696
recursive, 698
second differences of, 731
term, 696
unbounded, 187
Sequence feature, A15
Sequence mode, A10
Series, 701
finite, 701
geometric, 720
infinite, 701
    geometric, 720
Shade feature, A15
Sigma notation, 700
Sigmoidal curve, 366
Simple harmonic motion, 463, 464
frequency of, 463
Simplest form, 17
Sine curve, 427
amplitude of, 429
one cycle of, 427
Sine function, 403
of any angle, 414
common angles, 417
curve, 427
domain of, 421
graph of, 431, 444
inverse, 449, 451
period of, 430
range of, 421
special angles, 405
Sines, cosines, and tangents of special
    angles, 405
Singular matrix, 659
Sketching the graph of an equation by
    point plotting, 75
Sketching the graph of an inequality
    in two variables, A52
Slant asymptote, 299
Slope of a line, 86, 87
Slope-intercept form, 90, 91
Solution
of an absolute value inequality, 213
of an equation, 162
    graphical approximations, 174
extraneous, 163
of an inequality, 210, A52
point, 75
set of an inequality, 210
of a system of equations, 592
    graphical interpretations, 605
of a system of inequalities, A54
Solving
an absolute value inequality, 213
an equation, 162
exponential and logarithmic
    equations, 350

an inequality, 210
a linear programming problem, A62
a quadratic equation, 191
    completing the square, 191
    extracting square roots, 191
    factoring, 191
    Quadratic Formula, 191
right triangles, 408
a system of equations, 592
    Gaussian elimination, 614
        with back-substitution, 635
    Gauss-Jordan elimination, 636
    method of elimination, 603, 604
    method of substitution, 592
Special polar graphs, 814
Special products, 26
Speed
angular, 397
linear, 397
Square of a binomial, 26
Square matrix, 629
determinant of, 668
main diagonal of, 629
minors and cofactors of, 670
Square root(s), 15
extracting, 191
function, 103
Square system of linear equations, 617
Square of trigonometric functions, 515
Squaring function, 241
Standard deviation, A40
alternative formula for, A41
Standard form
of a complex number, 183
of the equation of a circle, 52, 786
of the equation of an ellipse, 775,
    786
of the equation of a hyperbola, 777,
    786
of the equation of a parabola, 773,
    786, A36
of the equations of conics, 786
of Law of Cosines, 541
of a polynomial, 24
of a quadratic function, 243
Standard position
of an angle, 392
of a vector, 549
Standard unit vector, 553
Step function, 118
Stochastic matrix, 657
Strategies for solving exponential and
    logarithmic equations, 350
Subset, 2
Substitution
method of, 592
Principle, 6
Subtraction
of a complex number, 184
of fractions
    with like denominators, 8
    with unlike denominators, 8

Sum
of a finite arithmetic sequence, 710,
    A34
of a finite geometric sequence, 719,
    A35
of functions, 134
of an infinite geometric series, 720
nth partial, 701, 711
of powers of integers, 730
properties of, 701, A34
of the squared differences, 224, 374,
    A47
of vectors, 550
Sum and difference formulas, 508, A28
Sum and difference of same terms, 26
Sum or difference of two cubes, 28
Sum feature, A16
Sum-to-product formulas, 520, A29
Sum sequence feature, A16
Summary
of equations of lines, 91
of function terminology, 106
Summation
index of, 700
lower limit of, 700
notation, 700
upper limit of, 700
Supplementary angles, 394
Surplus
consumer, A57
producer, A57
Symmetry
axis of, 240
quick test for, in polar coordinates,
    811
with respect to the origin, 119
with respect to the x-axis, 119
with respect to the y-axis, 119
test for, in polar coordinates, 810
Synthetic division, 267
using the remainder, 269
System of equations, 592
equivalent, 604
solution of, 592
solving, 592
    Gaussian elimination, 614
        with back-substitution, 635
    Gauss-Jordan elimination, 636
    method of elimination, 603, 604
    method of substitution, 592
with a unique solution, 664
System of inequalities, solution of, A54
System of linear equations
consistent, 605, 615
dependent, 615
inconsistent, 605, 615
independent, 615
nonsquare, 617
number of solutions, 615
row operations, 614
square, 617
System of three linear equations in
    three variables, 613

T

Table feature, A17
Tangent feature, A18
Tangent function, 403
  of any angle, 414
  common angles, 417
  graph of, 438, 444
  inverse, 451
  special angles, 405
Tangent line, 782, 785
Term
  of an algebraic expression, 6
  constant, 6, 24
  of a sequence, 696
  variable, 6
Terminal point, 548
Terminal side of an angle, 392
Test
  for collinear points, 677
  for even and odd functions, 119
  for symmetry in polar coordinates,
    810
Test intervals, 214
  finding, 214
Three-dimensional coordinate system,
  618
Trace feature, A19, A23
Transcendental function, 320
Transformation
  nonrigid, 130
  rigid, 130
Transverse axis of a hyperbola, 777
Triangle
  area of, 676
  formulas for area, 544
  oblique, 532
    area of, 536
Triangular matrix, 672
  lower, 672
  upper, 672
Trigonometric form
  argument of, 573
  of a complex number, 573
  modulus of, 573
Trigonometric function, 422
  of any angle, 414
    evaluating, 417
  cosecant, 403
  cosine, 403
  cotangent, 403
  even and odd, 422
  inverse properties of, 453
  key points, 428
    intercepts, 428
    maximum points, 428
    minimum points, 428
  product of, 515
  right triangle definitions of, 403
  secant, 403
  sine, 403
  square of, 515

tangent, 403
Trigonometric identities, 480
  guidelines for verifying, 488
Trigonometric values of common
  angles, 417
Trigonometry, 392
Trinomial, 24
  perfect square, 28
Two-point form, 88

U

Unbounded, 187
  intervals, 4
Uncoded row matrices, 681
Undefined domain, 106
Undefined values of a rational
  expression, 217
Unit circle, 420
Unit vector, 549, 554
  in the direction of **v**, 552
  standard, 553
Upper bound, 273
Upper limit of summation, 700
Upper and Lower Bound Rules, 273
Upper quartile, A43
Upper triangular matrix, 672
Uses of a graphing utility, A1
Using a graphing utility to graph an
  equation, 77
Using the remainder in synthetic
  division, 269

V

Value feature, A19
Value of a function, 101, 106
Variable, 6
  dependent, 101, 106
  independent, 101, 106
  term, 6
Variance, A40
Variation in sign, 273
Vector(s)
  addition, 550
    properties of, 552
    resultant of, 550
  angle between two, 563, A33
  component form of, 549
  components, 565, 566
  difference of, 550
  directed line segment of, 548
  direction angle of, 554
  dot product of, 562
    properties of, 562, A32
  equality of, 549
  horizontal component of, 553
  linear combination of, 553
  magnitude of, 549
  negative of, 550
  orthogonal, 564
  parallelogram law, 550
  projection, 566

resultant, 550
  scalar multiple of, 550
  scalar multiplication of, 550
    properties of, 552
  standard position of, 549
  sum of, 550
  unit, 549, 554
    in the direction of **v**, 552
    standard, 553
  v in the plane, 548
  vertical component of, 553
  zero, 549
Verbal model, 163
Vertex (vertices)
  of an angle, 392
  of an ellipse, 775
  of a hyperbola, 777
  of a parabola, 240, 773
Vertical asymptote, 287
Vertical components of **v**, 553
Vertical line, 91
Vertical Line Test, 114
Vertical shift, 126
Vertical shrink, 130
Vertical stretch, 130
Viewing window, A19
Volume, common formulas for, 166

W

Whole number, 2
With replacement, 742
Without replacement, 742
Work, 568

X

x-axis, 47
  symmetry, 119
x-coordinate, 47
x-intercept, 172

Y

y-axis, 47
  symmetry, 119
y-coordinate, 47
y-intercept, 172

Z

Zero
  of a function, 173, 254
  matrix, 648
  polynomial, 24
  of a polynomial function, 255
    real, 255
  properties of, 8
  of a rational expression, 217
  repeated, 256
  vector, 549
Zero-Factor Property, 8
Zero or root feature, A21
Zoom feature, A22

COMMON FORMULAS

Temperature

$$F = \frac{9}{5}C + 32$$

F = degrees Fahrenheit

C = degrees Celsius

Distance

$$d = rt$$

d = distance traveled

t = time

r = rate

Simple Interest

$$I = Prt$$

I = interest

P = principal

r = annual interest rate

t = time in years

Compound Interest

$$A = P\left(1 + \frac{r}{n}\right)^{nt}$$

A = balance

P = principal

r = annual interest rate

n = compoundings per year

t = time in years

Coordinate Plane: Midpoint Formula

$$\left(\frac{x_1 + x_2}{2}, \frac{y_1 + y_2}{2}\right)$$

midpoint of line segment joining (x_1, y_1) and (x_2, y_2)

Coordinate Plane: Distance Formula

$$d = \sqrt{(x_2 - x_1)^2 + (y_2 - y_1)^2}$$

d = distance between points (x_1, y_1) and (x_2, y_2)

Quadratic Formula

If $p(x) = ax^2 + bx + c$, $a \neq 0$ and $b^2 - 4ac \geq 0$, then the real zeros of p are

$$x = \frac{-b \pm \sqrt{b^2 - 4ac}}{2a}.$$

CONVERSIONS

Length and Area

1 foot = 12 inches
1 mile = 5280 feet
1 kilometer = 1000 meters
1 kilometer ≈ 0.621 mile
1 meter ≈ 3.281 feet
1 foot ≈ 0.305 meter

1 yard = 3 feet
1 mile = 1760 yards
1 meter = 100 centimeters
1 mile ≈ 1.609 kilometers
1 meter ≈ 39.370 inches
1 foot ≈ 30.480 centimeters

1 meter = 1000 millimeters
1 centimeter ≈ 0.394 inch
1 inch ≈ 2.540 centimeters
1 acre = 4840 square yards
1 square mile = 640 acres

Volume

1 gallon = 4 quarts
1 gallon = 231 cubic inches
1 liter = 1000 milliliters
1 liter ≈ 1.057 quarts
1 gallon ≈ 3.785 liters

1 quart = 2 pints
1 gallon ≈ 0.134 cubic foot
1 liter = 100 centiliters
1 liter ≈ 0.264 gallon
1 quart ≈ 0.946 liter

1 pint = 16 fluid ounces
1 cubic foot ≈ 7.48 gallons

Weight and Mass on Earth

1 ton = 2000 pounds
1 kilogram ≈ 2.205 pounds

1 pound = 16 ounces
1 pound ≈ 0.454 kilogram

1 kilogram = 1000 grams
1 gram ≈ 0.035 ounce

FORMULAS FROM GEOMETRY

Triangle

$h = a \sin \theta$

$\text{Area} = \dfrac{1}{2}bh$

Laws of Cosines:

$c^2 = a^2 + b^2 - 2ab \cos \theta$

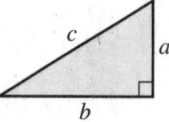

Right Triangle

Pythagorean Theorem:

$c^2 = a^2 + b^2$

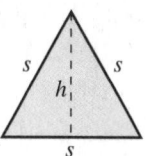

Equilateral Triangle

$h = \dfrac{\sqrt{3}s}{2}$

$\text{Area} = \dfrac{\sqrt{3}s^2}{4}$

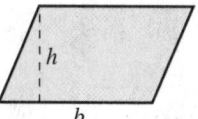

Parallelogram

$\text{Area} = bh$

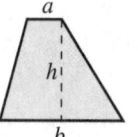

Trapezoid

$\text{Area} = \dfrac{h}{2}(a + b)$

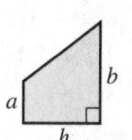

Circle

$\text{Area} = \pi r^2$

$\text{Circumference} = 2\pi r$

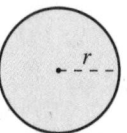

Sector of Circle

$\text{Area} = \dfrac{\theta r^2}{2}$

$s = r\theta$

(θ in radians)

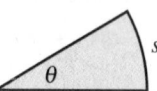

Circular Ring

$\text{Area} = \pi(R^2 - r^2)$

$\quad\quad = 2\pi p w$

(p = average radius,

w = width of ring)

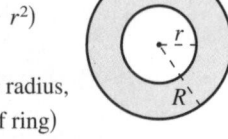
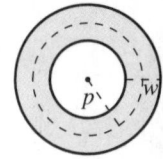

Ellipse

$\text{Area} = \pi a b$

$\text{Circumference} \approx 2\pi \sqrt{\dfrac{a^2 + b^2}{2}}$

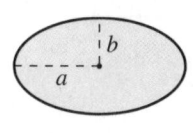

Cone

(A = area of base)

$\text{Volume} = \dfrac{Ah}{3}$

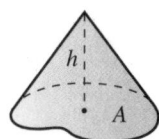

Right Circular Cone

$\text{Volume} = \dfrac{\pi r^2 h}{3}$

$\text{Lateral Surface Area} = \pi r \sqrt{r^2 + h^2}$

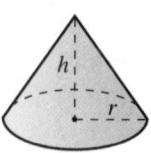

Frustum of Right Circular Cone

$\text{Volume} = \dfrac{\pi(r^2 + rR + R^2)h}{3}$

$\text{Lateral Surface Area} = \pi s(R + r)$

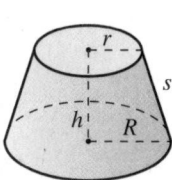

Right Circular Cylinder

$\text{Volume} = \pi r^2 h$

$\text{Lateral Surface Area} = 2\pi r h$

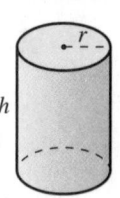

Sphere

$\text{Volume} = \dfrac{4}{3}\pi r^3$

$\text{Surface Area} = 4\pi r^2$

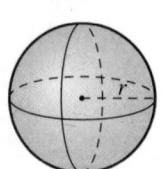